Reece • Urry • Cain • Wasserman • Minorsky • Jackson

Campbell Biology

Custom Edition for University of Alberta

UNIVERSITY OF
ALBERTA

Taken from:
Campbell Biology, Ninth Edition
by Jane B. Reece, Lisa A. Urry, Michael L. Cain, Steven A. Wasserman,
Peter V. Minorsky, and Robert B. Jackson

Cover photo courtesy of Heather Proctor.

Taken from:

Campbell Biology, Ninth Edition
by Jane B. Reece, Lisa A. Urry, Michael L. Cain, Steven A. Wasserman, Peter V. Minorsky, and Robert B. Jackson
Copyright © 2011, 2008, 2005 by Pearson Education, Inc.
Published by Benjamin Cummings
San Francisco, California 94111

Pearson Learning Solutions, 501 Boylston Street, Suite 900, Boston, MA 02116
A Pearson Education Company
www.pearsoned.com

Printed in Canada

1 2 3 4 5 6 7 8 9 10 VOYA 16 15 14 13 12 11

000200010270569291

MHB

ISBN 10: 1-256-28033-X
ISBN 13: 978-1-256-28033-0

Brief Contents

This Table of Contents reflects original material included in this edition that was created by the faculty of the University of Alberta. All other content in this edition is taken from *Campbell Biology,* Ninth Edition, by Jane B. Reece, Lisa A. Urry, Michael L. Cain, Steven A. Wasserman, Peter V. Minorsky, and Robert B. Jackson.

Thanks to Maggie Haag and Cindy Paszkowski for the diligence and hard work they put into this University of Alberta Custom book.

About the Authors

The Ninth Edition author team's contributions reflect their biological expertise as researchers and teaching sensibilities gained from years of experience as instructors at diverse institutions. The team's highly collaborative style continues to be evident in the cohesiveness and consistency of the Ninth Edition.

Jane B. Reece

The head of the Ninth Edition author team, Jane Reece was Neil Campbell's longtime collaborator. She has participated in every edition of *BIOLOGY*. Earlier, Jane taught biology at Middlesex County College and Queensborough Community College. She holds an A.B. in Biology from Harvard University, an M.S. in Microbiology from Rutgers University, and a Ph.D. in Bacteriology from the University of California, Berkeley. Jane's research as a doctoral student and postdoctoral fellow focused on genetic recombination in bacteria. Besides her work on *CAMPBELL BIOLOGY*, she has been a coauthor of *Biology: Concepts & Connections*, *Essential Biology*, and *The World of the Cell*.

Lisa A. Urry

Lisa Urry (Chapter 1 and Units 1–3) is a professor and developmental biologist and recent Chair of the Biology Department at Mills College. After graduating from Tufts University with a double major in Biology and French, Lisa completed her Ph.D. in molecular and developmental biology at Massachusetts Institute of Technology (MIT). She has published a number of research papers, most of them focused on gene expression during embryonic and larval development in sea urchins. Lisa is also deeply committed to promoting opportunities for women in science education and research.

Michael L. Cain

Michael Cain (Units 4 and 5) is an ecologist and evolutionary biologist who is now writing full-time. Michael earned a joint degree in Biology and Math at Bowdoin College, an M.Sc. from Brown University, and a Ph.D. in Ecology and Evolutionary Biology from Cornell University. As a faculty member at New Mexico State University and Rose-Hulman Institute of Technology, he taught a wide range of courses, including introductory biology, ecology, evolution, botany, and conservation biology. Michael is the author of dozens of scientific papers on topics that include foraging behavior in insects and plants, long-distance seed dispersal, and speciation in crickets. In addition to his work on *CAMPBELL BIOLOGY*, Michael is also the lead author of an ecology textbook.

Steven A. Wasserman

Steve Wasserman (Unit 7) is a professor at the University of California, San Diego (UCSD). He earned his A.B. in Biology from Harvard University and his Ph.D. in Biological Sciences from MIT. Through his research on regulatory pathway mechanisms in the fruit fly *Drosophila*, Steve has contributed to the fields of developmental biology, reproduction, and immunity. As a faculty member at the University of Texas Southwestern Medical Center and UCSD, he has taught genetics, development, and physiology to undergraduate, graduate, and medical students. He has also served as the research mentor for more than a dozen doctoral students and more than 50 aspiring scientists at the undergraduate and high school levels. Steve has been the recipient of distinguished scholar awards from both the Markey Charitable Trust and the David and Lucille Packard Foundation. In 2007, he received UCSD's Distinguished Teaching Award for undergraduate teaching.

Peter V. Minorsky

Peter Minorsky (Unit 6) is a professor at Mercy College in New York, where he teaches evolution, ecology, botany, and introductory biology. He received his B.A. in Biology from Vassar College and his Ph.D. in Plant Physiology from Cornell University. He is also the science writer for the journal *Plant Physiology*. After a postdoctoral fellowship at the University of Wisconsin at Madison, Peter taught at Kenyon College, Union College, Western Connecticut State University, and Vassar College. He is an electrophysiologist who studies responses of plants to stress. Peter received the 2008 Award for Teaching Excellence at Mercy College.

Robert B. Jackson

Rob Jackson (Unit 8) is a professor of biology and Nicholas Chair of Environmental Sciences at Duke University. Rob holds a B.S. in Chemical Engineering from Rice University, as well as M.S. degrees in Ecology and Statistics and a Ph.D. in Ecology from Utah State University. Rob directed Duke's Program in Ecology for many years and just finished a term as the Vice President of Science for the Ecological Society of America. Rob has received numerous awards, including a Presidential Early Career Award in Science and Engineering from the National Science Foundation. He also enjoys popular writing, having published a trade book about the environment, *The Earth Remains Forever*, and two books of poetry for children, *Animal Mischief* and *Weekend Mischief*.

Neil A. Campbell

Neil Campbell combined the investigative nature of a research scientist with the soul of an experienced and caring teacher. He earned his M.A. in Zoology from UCLA and his Ph.D. in Plant Biology from the University of California, Riverside, where he received the Distinguished Alumnus Award in 2001. Neil published numerous research articles on desert and coastal plants and how the sensitive plant (*Mimosa*) and other legumes move their leaves. His 30 years of teaching in diverse environments included general biology courses at Cornell University, Pomona College, and San Bernardino Valley College, where he received the college's first Outstanding Professor Award in 1986. Neil was a visiting scholar in the Department of Botany and Plant Sciences at the University of California, Riverside. In addition to his authorship of this book, he coauthored *Biology: Concepts & Connections* and *Essential Biology* with Jane Reece. For the Ninth Edition of this book, we honor Neil's contributions to biology education by adopting the title CAMPBELL BIOLOGY.

Preface

Biology is an enormous subject, one that can seem overwhelming to students and scientists alike. Moreover, discoveries are being made at an unprecedented pace—from new kinds of small RNA molecules to the Neanderthal genome, from new biofuels to communities of organisms thriving beneath vast glaciers, from emerging infectious diseases to cancer vaccines. As a result, a general biology course faces a daunting challenge: to keep students from suffocating under an avalanche of information. CAMPBELL BIOLOGY addresses this challenge by providing a strong foundation for understanding both current knowledge and new developments in the context of underlying biological concepts.

Key Concepts and Unifying Themes

In each chapter of this textbook, a framework of three to six carefully chosen **Key Concepts** provide context for supporting details, helping students distinguish the "forest" from the "trees." The numbered Key Concepts are presented at the beginning of the chapter and then serve as headings for each chapter section. *Concept Check Questions* at the end of each section provide a hierarchical framework for self-assessment that builds students' confidence and then challenges them to push the limits of their understanding with several types of critical thinking questions. The *Summary of Key Concepts* at the end of the chapter refocuses students on the main points. CAMPBELL BIOLOGY also helps students organize and make sense of what they learn on a grander scale by emphasizing **evolution and other unifying themes** that pervade biology. These themes are introduced in Chapter 1 and integrated throughout the book.

New to This Edition: An Emphasis on Making Connections

In addition to Key Concepts and themes, we've created new features for the Ninth Edition that help students see the big picture by *making connections*. These include the following:

New Make Connections Questions: Making connections across chapters

New **Make Connections Questions** help students see how different areas of biology tie together, helping them overcome the tendency to compartmentalize information. Each question challenges students to move beyond memorization and gain a deeper understanding of biological principles by asking them to relate chapter content to material they learned earlier in the course. For example, we ask students to connect

- DNA replication (Chapter 16, see p. 319) to the cell cycle (Chapter 12);
- Soil formation to the properties of water (Chapter 3); and
- Aquatic biomes (Chapter 52, see p. 1163) to osmoregulation (Chapter 44).

At least three Make Connections Questions appear in each chapter. In addition, online *Make Connections Tutorials* in MasteringBiology® (see p. xiii) connect content from two different chapters using figures from the book.

Expanded Evolution Coverage: Making connections to evolution in every chapter

Evolution is the core theme of biology, and in this edition it is more evident than ever. At least one **Evolution section in every chapter** focuses on evolutionary aspects of the chapter material, highlighted by a new Evolution banner. See, for example, the new discussions of enzyme evolution (p. 157), coevolution of flowers and pollinators (p. 806), and evolution of hormone function in animals (pp. 988–989).

New Impact Figures: Making connections between scientific advances and the real world

Our new **Impact Figures** motivate students by highlighting the dramatic impact of recent discoveries in biology. These figures feature high-interest topics such as induced pluripotent stem cells and regenerative medicine (Chapter 20, p. 417), the discovery of *Tiktaalik* (Chapter 34, p. 710), and the use of forensic ecology to track elephant poaching. The *Why It Matters* section of each figure explains the relevance of the research to students' lives, global problems, or the field of biology itself. Each Impact Figure ends with a suggestion for *Further Reading* and a *What If?* or *Make Connections Question* to develop critical thinking skills.

New Visual Organizers and 3-D Art: Making connections visually

The new **Visual Organizer** format highlights the main parts of a figure, helping students see the key categories at a glance. See, for instance, Figure 17.24 on types of small-scale mutations (p. 345) or Figure 27.3, Gram staining (p. 557). Throughout the book, selected figures have been rendered in a more **3-D art style** while keeping an appropriate balance between realism and teaching effectiveness. Figure 52.3, Exploring Global Climate Patterns (p. 1146), is one example.

Restructured Chapter Reviews: Making connections at a higher level

In the chapter summaries, each concept section now concludes with a new **Summary of Key Concepts Question** that is tied to a major learning goal. Also, this edition increases student awareness of different levels of thinking by organizing the end-of-chapter questions into three levels based on **Bloom's taxonomy**, which classifies types of thinking that are important in learning. Our levels are (1) Knowledge/Comprehension, (2) Application/Analysis, and (3) Synthesis/Evaluation. (These same levels are used in the Campbell Test Bank.) The range of question types helps students develop critical thinking skills and prepare for the kinds of questions they'll encounter on exams. New **Write About a Theme Questions** give students practice writing short, coherent essays that connect the chapter's content to one of the book's themes. (A suggested grading rubric can be found on p. xvii, and sample answers are provided for instructors in the MasteringBiology Instructor Resources area.) A new **MasteringBiology preview section** at the end of each chapter lists *Assignments*—tutorials, activities, and questions that instructors can assign. This section also directs students to the *eText* and *Study Area* for online self study.

New Content: Making connections to advances in science

As in each new edition, the Ninth Edition incorporates **new scientific content** and **organizational improvements**. These are summarized on pp. x–xi, following this Preface.

MasteringBiology®: Making connections outside of class

MasteringBiology, the most widely used online assessment and tutorial program for biology, provides an extensive library of homework assignments that are graded automatically. In addition to BioFlix® Tutorials, other Tutorials, Activities, Reading Quiz Questions in every chapter, and 4,500 Test Bank Questions, MasteringBiology for the Ninth Edition features an **improved user interface** and the following **new Tutorials and Questions**: *Make Connections Tutorials, Student Misconceptions Questions* for every chapter, *Data Analysis Tutorials, Experimental Inquiry Tutorials, Video Tutor Sessions*, and *MasteringBiology: Virtual Labs*. For more information, see pp. xviii–xx and www.masteringbiology.com.

Our Hallmark Features

Besides our Key Concepts and unifying themes, several other features have contributed to the success of *CAMPBELL BIOLOGY*. Because text and illustrations are equally important for learning biology, **integration of figures and text** has been a hallmark of this book since its inception. Our popular *Exploring Figures* on selected topics epitomize this approach: Each is

a learning unit of core content that brings together related illustrations and text. Another example is our *Guided Tour Figures*, which use descriptions in blue type to walk students through complex figures like an instructor would, pointing out key structures, functions, and steps of processes.

To encourage **active learning**, recent editions have incorporated new types of questions: *What If? Questions, Figure Legend Questions*, and *Draw It Questions* that ask students to sketch a structure, annotate a figure, or graph data. In the Ninth Edition, these questions are augmented by the new *Make Connections Questions*. Online, the highly interactive *MasteringBiology tutorials* are sophisticated active-learning tools.

Finally, *CAMPBELL BIOLOGY* features **scientific inquiry**, an essential component of any biology course. Complementing stories of scientific discovery in the text narrative and the unit-opening interviews, *Inquiry Figures* help students understand "how we know what we know" and provide a model of how to think like a scientist. Each one begins with a research question and then describes how researchers designed an experiment, interpreted their results, and drew conclusions. The source article is referenced, and a What If? Question asks students to consider an alternative scenario. Selected Inquiry Figures invite students to read and analyze the original research article in the supplement *Inquiry in Action: Interpreting Scientific Papers* (see p. xxiii). At the end of each chapter, *Scientific Inquiry Questions* give students additional opportunities to practice critical thinking by developing hypotheses, designing experiments, and analyzing real research data. Beyond the book, activities involving scientific inquiry are featured in MasteringBiology and other supplements, both print and electronic (see pp. xx–xxiii).

Our Partnership with Instructors

A core value underlying all our work as authors is our belief in the importance of our partnership with instructors. Our primary way of serving instructors, of course, is providing a textbook, supplements, and media resources that serve their students well. In addition, Benjamin Cummings makes available a rich variety of instructor resources, in both print and electronic form (see p. xxii). In our continuing efforts to improve the book and its supplements, we benefit tremendously from instructor feedback, not only in formal reviews from hundreds of scientists, but also via informal communication, often by e-mail.

The real test of any textbook is how well it helps instructors teach and students learn. We welcome comments from the students and instructors who use *CAMPBELL BIOLOGY*. Please address your suggestions to any of us:

Jane Reece at janereece@cal.berkeley.edu
Lisa Urry (Chapter 1 and Units 1–3) at lurry@mills.edu
Michael Cain (Units 4 and 5) at mcain@bowdoin.edu
Peter Minorsky (Unit 6) at pminorsky@mercy.edu
Steve Wasserman (Unit 7) at stevenw@ucsd.edu
Rob Jackson (Unit 8) at jackson@duke.edu

New Content

This section provides just a few highlights of new content and organizational improvements in *CAMPBELL BIOLOGY*, Ninth Edition.

CHAPTER 1 Introduction: Themes in the Study of Life

We have added a separate new theme on energy flow while retaining a theme on environmental interactions. Concept 1.3, on the scientific method, has been reframed to more accurately reflect the scientific process, with a focus on observations and hypotheses. A new Concept 1.4 discusses the value of technology to society while emphasizing the cooperative nature of science and the value of diversity among scientists.

UNIT ONE The Chemistry of Life

For this edition, the basic chemistry is enlivened by new content connecting it to evolution, ecology, and other areas of biology. Examples of new material include omega-3 fatty acids, the isomeric forms of methamphetamine, arsenic contamination of groundwater, and the basis of mad cow disease. The burgeoning importance of nucleic acids throughout biology has prompted us to expand our coverage of DNA and RNA structures in this first unit. In fact, a general aim for the first two units is to infuse the chapters with more detail about nucleic acids, genes, and related topics. Another enhancement, in this and the next two units, is the inclusion of more computer models of important proteins in contexts where they support students' understanding of molecular function.

UNIT TWO The Cell

For Chapter 6, we developed an Exploring Figure on microscopy, which includes new types of microscopy, and we added micrographs of various cell types to the Exploring Figure on eukaryotic cells. We also expanded our description of chromosome composition, with the goal of preempting some common student misconceptions about chromosomes and DNA. New connections to evolution include an introduction to the endosymbiont theory in Chapter 6 and some interesting evolutionary adaptations of cell membranes in Chapter 7. We've added a new section to Chapter 8 on the evolution of enzymes with new functions, which not only strengthens enzyme coverage but also provides an early introduction to the concept that mutations contribute to molecular evolution. In Chapter 9, we simplified the glycolysis figure and emphasized

pyruvate oxidation as a separate step to help students focus on the main ideas. In keeping with our increased focus on global issues in the Ninth Edition, Chapter 10 has an Impact Figure on biofuels and a discussion of the possible effect of climate change on the distribution of C_3 and C_4 plants.

UNIT THREE Genetics

In Chapters 13–17, we have added material to stimulate student interest—for example, a new Impact Figure on genetic testing for disease-associated mutations. As done throughout the Ninth Edition, we ask students to make connections between chapters so that they avoid the trap of compartmentalizing the information in each chapter. For instance, Chapter 15 discusses the Philadelphia chromosome associated with chronic myelogenous leukemia and asks students to connect this information to what they learned about signaling in the cell cycle in Chapter 12. Also, we encourage students to connect what they learn about DNA replication and chromosome structure in Chapter 16 to the material on chromosome behavior during the cell cycle in Chapter 12. Chapter 16 has a new figure showing a current 3-D model of the DNA replication complex, with the lagging strand looping back through it.

Chapters 18–21 are extensively updated, with the changes dominated by new genomic sequence data and discoveries about the regulation of gene expression. (The introduction to genes, genomes, and gene expression in Units One and Two should help prepare students for these revisions.) Chapter 18 includes a new section on nuclear architecture, which describes the organization of chromatin in the nucleus in relation to gene expression. The roles of various types of RNA molecules in regulation also receive special attention. In the section on cancer, we describe how technical advances can contribute to personalized cancer treatments based on the molecular characteristics of an individual's tumor. Chapter 19 discusses the 2009 H1N1 flu pandemic. Chapter 20 includes advances in techniques for DNA sequencing and for obtaining induced pluripotent stem (iPS) cells. Finally, the heavily revised Chapter 21 describes what has been learned from the sequencing of many genomes, including those of a number of human individuals.

UNIT FOUR Mechanisms of Evolution

For this edition, we have continued to bolster our presentation of the vast evidence for evolution by adding new examples and figures that illustrate key conceptual points throughout the unit. For example, Chapter 22 now presents research data on adaptive evolution in soapberry bugs, fossil findings that shed light on the origins of cetaceans, and an Impact Figure on the rise of methicillin-resistant *Staphylococcus aureus*. Chapter 23 examines gene flow and adaptation in songbird populations. Chapter 24 incorporates several new examples of speciation research, including reproductive isolation in mosquitofish, speciation in shrimp, and hybridization of bear species. Other changes strengthen the storyline of the unit, ensuring that the chapters flow smoothly and build to a clear overall picture of what evolution is and how it works. For instance, new connections between Chapters 24 and 25 illustrate how differences in speciation and extinction rates shape the broad patterns in the history of life. We've also added earlier and more discussion of "tree thinking," the interpretation and application of phylogenetic trees, beginning in Chapter 22.

UNIT FIVE The Evolutionary History of Biological Diversity

One of our goals for the diversity unit was to expand the coverage of the scientific evidence underlying the evolutionary story told in the chapters. So, for example, Chapter 27 now presents new findings on the evolutionary origin of bacterial flagella. In keeping with our increased emphasis on big-picture "tree thinking," we've added an "evogram" on tetrapod evolution in Chapter 34. (An evogram is a diagram illustrating the multiple lines of evidence that support the hypothesis shown in an evolutionary tree.) In addition, to help engage students, we've included new applications and woven more ecological information into our discussions of groups of organisms. Examples include new material on global growth of photosynthetic protists (Chapter 28), endangered molluscs (Chapter 33), and the impact of a pathogenic chytrid fungus on amphibian population declines (Chapters 31 and 34).

UNIT SIX Plant Form and Function

Plant biology is in a transitional phase; some professors prefer strong coverage of classical botany while others seek more in-depth coverage of the molecular biology of plants. In developing the Ninth Edition, we have continued to balance the old and the new to provide students with a basic understanding of plant anatomy and function while highlighting dynamic areas of plant research and the many important connections between plants and other organisms. One major revision goal was to provide more explicit discussion of the evolutionary aspects of plant biology, such as the coevolution of insects and animal pollinators (Chapter 38). Updates include new findings in plant development in Concept 35.5 and new material on the dynamism of plant architecture as it relates to resource acquisition in Chapter 36.

UNIT SEVEN Animal Form and Function

In revising this unit, we strove to introduce physiological systems through a comparative approach that underscores how adaptations are linked to shared physiological challenges. In particular, we have highlighted the interrelationship of the endocrine and nervous systems at multiple points in the unit, helping students appreciate how these two forms of communication link tissues, organs, and individuals. Other revisions aim to keep students focused on fundamental concepts amid the details of complex systems. For example, many figures have been reconceived to emphasize key information, including new figures comparing single and double circulation (Chapter 42) and new Exploring Figures on the vertebrate kidney (Chapter 44). Throughout the unit, new state-of-the-art images and material on current and compelling topics—such as circadian rhythms (Chapter 40), the effects of climate change on animal reproductive cycles (Chapter 46), and advances in understanding brain plasticity and function (Chapter 49)—will help engage students and encourage them to make connections beyond the text.

UNIT EIGHT Ecology

Our revision was informed by the fact that biologists are increasingly asked to apply their knowledge to help solve global problems, such as climate change, that already are profoundly affecting life on Earth. As part of our increased emphasis on global ecology in this edition, we have made significant changes to Unit Eight's organization and content. The organizational changes begin with the introductory chapter of the unit (Chapter 52), which includes a new Key Concept 52.1: "Earth's climate varies by latitude and season and is changing rapidly." Introducing the global nature of climate and its effects on life at the beginning of the chapter provides a logical foundation for the rest of the material.

Focus on the Key Concepts.

Each chapter is organized around a framework of 3 to 6 **Key Concepts** that will help you stay focused on the big picture and give you a context for the supporting details.

52

An Introduction to Ecology and the Biosphere

▲ **Figure 52.1 What threatens this amphibian's survival?**

KEY CONCEPTS

52.1 Earth's climate varies by latitude and season and is changing rapidly
52.2 The structure and distribution of terrestrial biomes are controlled by climate and disturbance
52.3 Aquatic biomes are diverse and dynamic systems that cover most of Earth
52.4 Interactions between organisms and the environment limit the distribution of species

OVERVIEW

Discovering Ecology

When University of Delaware undergraduate Justin Yeager spent his summer abroad in Costa Rica, all he wanted was to see the tropical rain forest and to practice his Spanish. Instead, he rediscovered the variable harlequin toad (*Atelopus varius*), a species thought to be extinct in the mountain slopes of Costa

Rica and Panama where it once lived (**Figure 52.1**). During the 1980s and 1990s, roughly two-thirds of the 82 known species of harlequin toads vanished. Scientists think that a disease-causing chytrid fungus, *Batrachochytrium dendrobatidis* (see Figure 31.26), contributed to many of these extinctions. Why was the fungus suddenly thriving in the rain forest? Cloudier days and warmer nights associated with global warming appear to have created an environment ideal for its success. As of 2009, the species that Yeager found was surviving as a single known population of fewer than 100 individuals.

What environmental factors limit the geographic distribution of harlequin toads? How do variations in their food supply or interactions with other species, such as pathogens, affect the size of their population? Questions like these are the subject of **ecology** (from the Greek *oikos*, home, and *logos*, study), the scientific study of the interactions between organisms and the environment. Ecological interactions occur at a hierarchy of scales that ecologists study, from single organisms to the globe (**Figure 52.2**).

Ecology's roots are in our basic human interest in observing other organisms. Naturalists, including Aristotle and Darwin, have long studied the living world and systematically recorded their observations. However, modern ecology involves more than observation. It is a rigorous experimental science that requires a breadth of biological knowledge. Ecologists generate hypotheses, manipulate environmental variables, and observe the outcome. In this unit, you will encounter many examples of ecological experiments, whose complex challenges have made ecologists innovators in experimental design and statistical inference.

In addition to providing a conceptual framework for understanding the field of ecology, Figure 52.2 provides the organizational framework for our final unit. In this chapter, we first describe Earth's climate and the importance of climate and other physical factors in determining the location of major life zones on land and in the oceans. We then examine how ecologists determine what controls the distribution and abundance of individual species. The next three chapters investigate population, community, and ecosystem ecology in detail, including approaches for restoring degraded ecosystems. The final chapter explores conservation biology and global ecology as we consider how ecologists apply biological knowledge to predict the global consequences of human activities and to conserve Earth's biodiversity.

CONCEPT 52.1

Earth's climate varies by latitude and season and is changing rapidly

The most significant influence on the distribution of organisms on land and in the oceans is **climate**, the long-term, prevailing weather conditions in a given area. Four physical

Before you begin reading the chapter, get oriented by reading the **list of Key Concepts,** which introduces the big ideas covered in the chapter.

Each **Key Concept** serves as the heading for a major section of the chapter.

After reading a concept section, check your ▶ understanding using the **Concept Check Questions** at the end of the section. Work through these questions on your own or in a study group—they're good practice for the kinds of questions you might be asked on an exam.

What If? Questions ask you to apply what you've learned. New **Make Connections Questions** ask you to relate content in the chapter to a concept you learned earlier in the course.

If you can answer these questions (see Appendix A to check your work), you're ready to move on. ▶

CONCEPT CHECK 52.1

1. Explain how the sun's unequal heating of Earth's surface leads to the development of deserts around 30° north and south of the equator.
2. What are some of the differences in microclimate between an unplanted agricultural field and a nearby stream corridor with trees?
3. **WHAT IF?** Changes in Earth's climate at the end of the last ice age happened gradually, taking centuries to thousands of years. If the current global warming happens very quickly, as predicted, how may this rapid climate change affect the ability of long-lived trees to evolve, compared with annual plants, which have much shorter generation times?
4. **MAKE CONNECTIONS** In Concept 10.4 (pp. 199–201), you learned about the important differences between C_3 and C_4 plants. Focusing just on the effects of temperature, would you expect the global distribution of C_4 plants to expand or contract as Earth becomes warmer? Why?

For suggested answers, see Appendix A.

Make connections across biology.

By relating the content of a chapter to material you learned earlier in the course, new **Make Connections Questions** help you develop a deeper understanding of biological principles.

CONCEPT CHECK 41.1

2. **MAKE CONNECTIONS** Review the discussion of enzymes in metabolic reactions in Concept 8.4 (pp. 152–156). Then explain why vitamins are required in very small amounts in the diet.

Enzymes
(Chapter 8)
Animal nutrition
(Chapter 41)

CONCEPT CHECK 16.2

3. **MAKE CONNECTIONS** What is the relationship between DNA replication and the S phase of the cell cycle? See Figure 12.6, page 231.

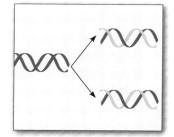

Cell cycle
(Chapter 12)
DNA replication
(Chapter 16)

CONCEPT CHECK 31.2

1. **MAKE CONNECTIONS** Compare Figure 31.5 with Figure 13.6 (p. 252). In terms of haploid versus diploidy, how do the life cycles of fungi and animals differ?

Meiosis
(Chapter 13)
Fungi
(Chapter 31)

New **Make Connections Tutorials**
help you connect biological concepts across chapters in an interactive way.

Make connections to **evolution**, the fundamental theme of biology.

Look for new **Evolution banners** highlighting sections in each chapter that focus on evolutionary aspects of the topic.

The Evolutionary Origins of Mitochondria and Chloroplasts

EVOLUTION Mitochondria and chloroplasts display similarities with bacteria that led to the **endosymbiont theory**, illustrated in Figure 6.16. This theory states that an early ancestor of eukaryotic cells engulfed an oxygen-using nonphotosynthetic prokaryotic cell. Eventually, the engulfed cell formed a relationship with the host cell in which it was enclosed, becoming an *endosymbiont* (a cell living within another cell). Indeed, over the course of evolution, the host cell and its endosymbiont merged into a single organism, a eukaryotic cell with a mitochondrion. At least one of these cells may have then taken up a photosynthetic prokaryote, becoming the ancestor of eukaryotic cells that contain chloroplasts.

This is a widely accepted theory, which we will discuss in more detail in Chapter 25. The model it proposes is consistent ... structural features of mitochondria and chloro... rather than being bounded by a single membrane ... of the endomembrane system, mitochondria ... chloroplasts have two membranes surrounding ... chloroplasts also have an internal system of membra... There is evidence that the ancestral engulfed ... had two outer membranes, which became the ... branes of mitochondria and chloroplasts. Second, ... yotes, mitochondria and chloroplasts contain ribo... well as circular DNA molecules attached to their ... branes. The DNA in these organelles programs the ... of some of their own proteins, which are made on ... ... mes inside the organelles. Third, also consistent ... probable evolutionary origins as cells, mitochondria ... ... oplasts are autonomous (somewhat independent) or... ... at grow and reproduce within the cell.

Practice thinking like a scientist.

New **Impact Figures** demonstrate the ▶
dramatic impact of recent discoveries in biology
and show that biology is constantly changing
as new discoveries add to our understanding.

Inquiry Figures reveal "how we know what
we know" by highlighting how researchers
designed an experiment, interpreted their
results, and drew conclusions.
▼

▼ Figure 56.9
IMPACT

Forensic Ecology and Elephant Poaching

This array of severed tusks is part of an illegal shipment of 6,000 kg of ivory intercepted on its way from Africa to Singapore in 2002. Investigators wondered whether the elephants slaughtered for the ivory—perhaps as many as 6,500—were killed in the area where the shipment originated, primarily Zambia, or instead were killed across Africa, indicating a broader smuggling ring. Samuel Wasser, of the University of Washington, and colleagues amplified specific segments of DNA from the tusks using the polymerase chain reaction (PCR). These segments included stretches of DNA containing short tandem repeats (STRs; see Concept 20.4, pp. 420–421), the number of which varies among different elephant populations. The researchers then compared alleles at seven or more loci with a reference DNA database they had generated for elephants of known geographic origin. Their results showed conclusively that the elephants came from a narrow east-west band centered on Zambia rather than from across Africa.

WHY IT MATTERS The DNA analyses suggested that poaching rates were 30 times higher in Zambia than previously estimated. This news led to improved antipoaching efforts by the Zambian government. Techniques like those used in this study are being employed by conservation biologists to track the harvesting of many endangered species, including whales, sharks, and orchids.

FURTHER READING S. K. Wasser et al., Forensic tools battle ivory poachers, *Scientific American* 399:68–76 (2009); S. K. Wasser et al., Using DNA to track the origin of the largest ivory seizure since the 1989 trade ban, *Proceedings of the National Academy of Sciences USA* 104:4228–4233 (2007).

MAKE CONNECTIONS Figure 26.6 (p. 539) describes another example in which conservation biologists used DNA analyses to compare harvested samples with a reference DNA database. How are these examples similar, and how are they different? What limitations might there be to using such forensic methods in other suspected cases of poaching?

▼ Figure 37.14   **INQUIRY**

**Does the invasive weed garlic mustard disrupt
mutualistic associations between native tree
seedlings and arbuscular mycorrhizal fungi?**

EXPERIMENT Kristina Stinson, of Harvard University, and colleagues investigated the effect of invasive garlic mustard on the growth of native tree seedlings and associated mycorrhizal fungi. In one experiment, they grew seedlings of three North American trees—sugar maple, red maple, and white ash—in four different soils. Two of the soil samples were collected from a location where garlic mustard was growing, and one of these samples was sterilized. The other two soil samples were collected from a location devoid of garlic mustard, and one was then sterilized. After four months of growth, the researchers harvested the shoots and roots and determined the dried biomass. The roots were also analyzed for percent colonization by arbuscular mycorrhizal fungi.

RESULTS Native tree seedlings grew more slowly and were less able to form mycorrhizal associations when grown either in sterilized soil or in unsterilized soil collected from a location that had been invaded by garlic mustard.

CONCLUSION The data support the hypothesis that garlic mustard suppresses growth of native trees by affecting the soil in a way that disrupts mutualistic associations between the trees and arbuscular mycorrhizal fungi.

SOURCE K. A. Stinson et al., Invasive plant suppresses the growth of native tree seedlings by disrupting belowground mutualisms, *PLoS Biol* (Public Library of Science: Biology) 4(5): e140 (2006).

INQUIRY IN ACTION Read and analyze the original paper in *Inquiry in Action: Interpreting Scientific Papers.*

WHAT IF? What effect would applying inorganic phosphate to soil invaded by garlic mustard have on the plant's ability to outcompete native species?

Why It Matters explains the ▶
relevance of the research.

Further Reading directs you ▶
to articles to explore.

A **Make Connections** or ▶
What If? Question
encourages critical thinking.

Some **Inquiry Figures**
invite you to read and
analyze the original research
paper in its complete form.
You can find the journal
article, along with a worksheet
guiding you through it, in
◀ the separate book *Inquiry
in Action: Interpreting
Scientific Papers.*

Mastering BIOLOGY
www.masteringbiology.com

After exploring the featured experiment,
test your analytical skills by answering the
What If? Question. Suggested answers are
provided in Appendix A to help you gauge
your understanding.

New **Experimental Inquiry Tutorials**
give you practice analyzing experimental
design and data and drawing conclusions.

Study the figures as you read the text.

▼ **Figure 5.15 An overview of protein functions.**

Enzymatic proteins

Function: Selective acceleration of chemical reactions
Example: Digestive enzymes catalyze the hydrolysis of bonds in food molecules.

Enzyme

Storage proteins

Function: Storage of amino acids
Examples: Casein, the protein of milk, is the major source of amino acids for baby mammals. Plants have storage proteins in their seeds. Ovalbumin is the protein of egg white, used as an amino acid source for the developing embryo.

Ovalbumin   Amino acids for embryo

Hormonal proteins

Function: Coordination of an organism's activities
Example: Insulin, a hormone secreted by the pancreas, causes other tissues to take up glucose, thus regulating blood sugar concentration.

High blood sugar   Insulin secreted   Normal blood sugar

Contractile and motor proteins

Function: Movement
Examples: Motor proteins are responsible for the undulations of cilia and flagella. Actin and myosin proteins are responsible for the contraction of muscles.

Actin   Myosin
Muscle tissue   100 μm

Defensive proteins

Function: Protection against disease
Example: Antibodies inactivate and help destroy viruses and bacteria.

Antibodies
Virus   Bacterium

Transport proteins

Function: Transport of substances
Examples: Hemoglobin, the iron-containing protein of vertebrate blood, transports oxygen from the lungs to other parts of the body. Other proteins transport molecules across cell membranes.

Transport protein
Cell membrane

Receptor proteins

Function: Response of cell to chemical stimuli
Example: Receptors built into the membrane of a nerve cell detect signaling molecules released by other nerve cells.

Receptor protein
Signaling molecules

Structural proteins

Function: Support
Examples: Keratin is the protein of hair, horns, feathers, and other skin appendages. Insects and spiders use silk fibers to make their cocoons and webs, respectively. Collagen and elastin proteins provide a fibrous framework in animal connective tissues.

Connective tissue   60 μm

◀ New **Visual Organizers** help you to see important categories at a glance.

By integrating text and visuals, **Exploring Figures** help you learn more efficiently.
▼

In selected illustrations, **a three-dimensional art style** helps you visualize biological structures. ▶

Mastering BIOLOGY
www.masteringbiology.com

Many **Tutorials** and **Activities** integrate art from the textbook, providing a unified learning experience.

▼ **Figure 7.22**
Exploring Endocytosis in Animal Cells

Phagocytosis   **Pinocytosis**   **Receptor-Mediated Endocytosis**

EXTRACELLULAR FLUID
Solutes
Pseudopodium
Plasma membrane
Receptor
Ligand
Coat proteins
Coated pit
Coated vesicle

"Food" or other particle
Vesicle
Food vacuole
CYTOPLASM

Receptor-mediated endocytosis enables the cell to acquire bulk quantities of specific substances, even though those substances may not be very concentrated in the extracellular fluid. Embedded in the membrane are proteins with specific receptor sites exposed to the extracellular fluid, to which specific substances (ligands) bind. The receptor proteins then cluster in regions of the membrane called coated pits, which are lined on their cytoplasmic side by a fuzzy layer of coat proteins. Next, each coated pit forms a vesicle containing the ligand molecules. Notice that there are relatively more bound molecules (purple) inside the vesicle, but other molecules (green) are also present. After the ingested material is liberated from the vesicle, the emptied receptors are recycled to the plasma membrane by the same vesicle.

In **phagocytosis**, a cell engulfs a particle by wrapping pseudopodia (singular, *pseudopodium*) around it and packaging it within a membranous sac called a food vacuole. The particle will be digested after the food vacuole fuses with a lysosome containing hydrolytic enzymes (see Figure 6.13a).

In **pinocytosis**, the cell "gulps" droplets of extracellular fluid into tiny vesicles. It is not the fluid itself that is needed by the cell, but the molecules dissolved in the droplets. Because any and all included solutes are taken into the cell, pinocytosis is nonspecific in the substances it transports.

Pseudopodium of amoeba
Bacterium
Food vacuole   1 μm
An amoeba engulfing a bacterium via phagocytosis (TEM).

Plasma membrane
0.5 μm
Pinocytosis vesicles forming (indicated by arrows) in a cell lining a small blood vessel (TEM).

Plasma membrane
Coat proteins
0.25 μm
Top: A coated pit. *Bottom:* A coated vesicle forming during receptor-mediated endocytosis (TEMs).

ANIMATION   *BioFlix*   Visit the Study Area at www.masteringbiology.com for the BioFlix® 3-D Animation on Membrane Transport.

CHAPTER 7   Membrane Structure and Function   **139**

▲
BioFlix® icons direct you to high-impact 3-D animations in the Study Area at www.masteringbiology.com.

Review what you've learned.

Chapter Reviews help you efficiently master the chapter content by focusing on the main points of the chapter and offering opportunities to practice for exams.

Summary Figures present key information in a visual way.

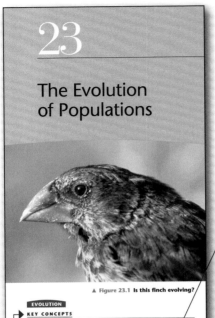

23
The Evolution of Populations

▲ Figure 23.1 **Is this finch evolving?**

EVOLUTION

KEY CONCEPTS

23.1 Genetic variation makes evolution possible
23.2 The Hardy-Weinberg equation can be used to test whether a population is evolving
23.3 Natural selection, genetic drift, and gene flow can alter allele frequencies in a population
23.4 Natural selection is the only mechanism that consistently causes adaptive evolution

OVERVIEW

The Smallest Unit of Evolution

One common misconception about evolution is that individual organisms evolve. It is true that natural selection acts on individuals: Each organism's traits affect its survival and reproductive success compared with other individuals. But the evolutionary impact of natural selection is only apparent in the changes in a *population* of organisms over time.

Key Concepts, which were introduced in the beginning of the chapter and developed in the text, are summarized in the Chapter Review.

New **Summary of Key Concepts Questions** appear at the end of each concept summary. Check your answers using Appendix A.

---

23 CHAPTER REVIEW

SUMMARY OF KEY CONCEPTS

CONCEPT 23.1

Genetic variation makes evolution possible (pp. 469–473)

- **Genetic variation** refers to genetic differences among individuals within a population.
- The nucleotide differences that provide the basis of genetic variation arise by mutation and other processes that produce new alleles and new genes.
- New genetic variants are produced rapidly in organisms with short generation times. In sexually reproducing organisms, most of the genetic differences among individuals result from crossing over, the independent assortment of chromosomes, and fertilization.

? *Why do biologists estimate gene variability and nucleotide variability, and what do these estimates represent?*

CONCEPT 23.2

The Hardy-Weinberg equation can be used to test whether a population is evolving (pp. 473–476)

- A **population**, a localized group of organisms belonging to one species, is united by its **gene pool**, the aggregate of all the alleles in the population.
- The **Hardy-Weinberg principle** states that the allele and genotype frequencies of a population will remain constant if the population is large, mating is random, mutation is negligible, there is no gene flow, and there is no natural selection. For such a population, if p and q represent the frequencies of the only two possible alleles at a particular locus, then p^2 is the frequency of one kind of homozygote, q^2 is the frequency of the other kind of homozygote, and $2pq$ is the frequency of the heterozygous genotype.

? *Is it circular reasoning to calculate p and q from observed genotype frequencies and then use those values of p and q to test if the population is in Hardy-Weinberg equilibrium? Explain your answer. (Hint: Consider a specific case, such as a population with 195 individuals of genotype AA, 10 of genotype Aa, and 195 of genotype aa.)*

CONCEPT 23.3

Natural selection, genetic drift, and gene flow can alter allele frequencies in a population (pp. 476–480)

- In natural selection, individuals that have certain inherited traits tend to survive and reproduce at higher rates than other individuals *because of* those traits.
- In **genetic drift**, chance fluctuations in allele frequencies over generations tend to reduce genetic variation.
- **Gene flow**, the transfer of alleles between populations, tends to reduce genetic differences between populations over time.

? *Would two small, geographically isolated populations in very different environments be likely to evolve in similar ways? Explain.*

CONCEPT 23.4

Natural selection is the only mechanism that consistently causes adaptive evolution (pp. 480–485)

- One organism has greater **relative fitness** than a second organism if it leaves more fertile descendants than the second

organism. The modes of natural selection differ in how selection acts on phenotype (the white arrows in the summary diagram below represent selective pressure on a population).

Original population   Evolved population

Directional selection   Disruptive selection   Stabilizing selection

- Unlike genetic drift and gene flow, natural selection consistently increases the frequencies of alleles that enhance survival and reproduction, thus improving the match between organisms and their environment.
- **Sexual selection** influences evolutionary change in secondary sex characteristics that can give individuals advantages in mating.
- Despite the winnowing effects of selection, populations have considerable genetic variation. Some of this variation represents **neutral variation**; additional variation can be maintained by diploidy and balancing selection.
- There are constraints to evolution: Natural selection can act only on available variation; structures result from modified ancestral anatomy; adaptations are often compromises; and chance, natural selection, and the environment interact.

? *How might secondary sex characteristics differ between males and females in a species in which females compete for mates?*

TEST YOUR UNDERSTANDING

LEVEL 1: KNOWLEDGE/COMPREHENSION

1. Natural selection changes allele frequencies because some _____ survive and reproduce more successfully than others.
   a. alleles   c. gene pools   e. individuals
   b. loci   d. species

2. No two people are genetically identical, except for identical twins. The main source of genetic variation among human individuals is
   a. new mutations that occurred in the preceding generation.
   b. genetic drift due to the small size of the population.
   c. the reshuffling of alleles in sexual reproduction.
   d. geographic variation within the population.
   e. environmental effects.

3. Sparrows with average-sized wings survive severe storms better than those with longer or shorter wings, illustrating
   a. the bottleneck effect.
   b. disruptive selection.
   c. frequency-dependent selection.
   d. neutral variation.
   e. stabilizing selection.

To help you prepare for the various kinds of questions that may appear on a test, the end-of-chapter questions are now organized into three levels based on Bloom's Taxonomy:

Level 1: Knowledge/Comprehension
Level 2: Application/Analysis
Level 3: Synthesis/Evaluation

Evolution Connection Questions in the Chapter Review ask you to think critically about how an aspect of the chapter relates to evolution. ▶

Scientific Inquiry Questions at the end of each chapter give you opportunities to practice scientific thinking by developing hypotheses, designing experiments, and analyzing real research data.

Draw It Exercises in each chapter ask you to put pencil to paper and draw a structure, annotate a figure, or graph experimental data.

LEVEL 2: APPLICATION/ANALYSIS

4. If the nucleotide variability of a locus equals 0%, what is the gene variability and number of alleles at that locus?
   a. gene variability = 0%; number of alleles = 0
   b. gene variability = 0%; number of alleles = 1
   c. gene variability = 0%; number of alleles = 2
   d. gene variability > 0%; number of alleles = 2
   e. Without more information, gene variability and number of alleles cannot be determined.

5. There are 40 individuals in population 1, all with genotype *A1A1*, and there are 25 individuals in population 2, all with genotype *A2A2*. Assume that these populations are located far from each other and that their environmental conditions are very similar. Based on the information given here, the observed genetic variation is most likely an example of
   a. genetic drift.   d. discrete variation.
   b. gene flow.   e. directional selection.
   c. disruptive selection.

6. A fruit fly population has a gene with two alleles, *A1* and *A2*. Tests show that 70% of the gametes produced in the population contain the *A1* allele. If the population is in Hardy-Weinberg equilibrium, what proportion of the flies carry both *A1* and *A2*?
   a. 0.7   b. 0.49   c. 0.21   d. 0.42   e. 0.09

LEVEL 3: SYNTHESIS/EVALUATION

7. **EVOLUTION CONNECTION**
   How is the process of evolution revealed by the imperfections of living organisms?

8. **SCIENTIFIC INQUIRY**
   DRAW IT   Richard Koehn, of the State University of New York, Stony Brook, and Thomas Hilbish, of the University of South Carolina, studied genetic variation in the marine mussel *Mytilus edulis* around Long Island, New York. They measured the frequency of a particular allele (*lap⁹⁴*) for an enzyme involved in regulating the mussel's internal saltwater balance. The researchers presented their data as a series of pie charts linked to sampling sites within Long Island Sound, where the salinity is highly variable, and along the coast of the open ocean, where salinity is constant:

Data from R. K. Koehn and T. J. Hilbish, The adaptive importance of genetic variation, *American Scientist* 75: 134–141 (1987).

(Question 8, continued)
Create a data table for the 11 sampling sites by estimating the frequency of *lap⁹⁴* from the pie charts. (*Hint*: Think of each pie chart as a clock face to help you estimate the proportion of the shaded area.) Then graph the frequencies for sites 1–8 to show how the frequency of this allele changes with increasing salinity in Long Island Sound (from southwest to northeast). How do the data from sites 9–11 compare with the data from the sites within the Sound?
   Construct a hypothesis that explains the patterns you observe in the data and that accounts for the following observations: (1) the *lap⁹⁴* allele helps mussels maintain osmotic balance in water with a high salt concentration but is costly to use in less salty water; and (2) mussels produce larvae that can disperse long distances before they settle on rocks and grow into adults.

9. **WRITE ABOUT A THEME**
   Emergent Properties Heterozygotes at the sickle-cell locus produce both normal and abnormal (sickle-cell) hemoglobin (see Concept 14.4). When hemoglobin molecules are packed into a heterozygote's red blood cells, some cells receive relatively large quantities of abnormal hemoglobin, making these cells prone to sickling. In a short essay (approximately 100–150 words), explain how these molecular and cellular events lead to emergent properties at the individual and population levels of biological organization.

For selected answers, see Appendix A.

MasteringBIOLOGY®   www.masteringbiology.com

1. **MasteringBiology® Assignments**
   Make Connections Tutorial Hardy-Weinberg Principle (Chapter 23) and Inheritance of Alleles (Chapter 14)
   Experimental Inquiry Tutorial Did Natural Selection of Ground Finches Occur When the Environment Changed?
   BioFlix Tutorial Mechanisms of Evolution
   Tutorial Hardy-Weinberg Principle
   Activities Genetic Variation from Sexual Recombination • The Hardy-Weinberg Principle • Causes of Evolutionary Change • Three Modes of Natural Selection
   Questions Student Misconceptions • Reading Quiz • Multiple Choice • End-of-Chapter
2. **eText**
   Read your book online, search, take notes, highlight text, and more.
3. **The Study Area**
   Practice Tests • Cumulative Test • BioFlix 3-D Animations • MP3 Tutor Sessions • Videos • Activities • Investigations • Lab Media • Audio Glossary • Word Study Tools • Art

---

▶ New **Write About a Theme Questions** give you practice writing a short essay that connects the chapter's content to one of the bookwide themes introduced in Chapter 1.

◀ Each chapter now ends with a preview of the **MasteringBiology®** resources that can help you succeed in the course.

Suggested Grading Rubric for "Write About a Theme" Short-Answer Essays			
	Understanding of Theme and Relationship to Topic	**Use of Supporting Examples or Details**	**Appropriate Use of Terminology**	**Quality of Writing**
4	Evidence of full and complete understanding	Examples well chosen, details accurate and applied to theme	Accurate scientific terminology enhances the essay	Excellent organization, sentence structure, and grammar
3	Evidence of good understanding	Examples or details are generally well applied to theme	Terminology is correctly used	Good sentence flow, sentence structure, and grammar
2	Evidence of a basic understanding	Supporting examples and details are adequate	Terminology used is not totally accurate or appropriate	Some organizational and grammatical problems
1	Evidence of limited understanding	Examples and details are minimal	Appropriate terminology is not present	Poorly organized. Grammatical and spelling errors detract from essay
0	Essay shows no understanding of theme	Examples lacking or incorrect	Terminology lacking or incorrect	Essay is very poorly written

◀ This **Writing Rubric** explains criteria on which your writing may be graded. The rubric and tips for writing good short-answer essays can be found in the Study Area at www.masteringbiology.com.

To the Student: How to Effectively

www.masteringbiology.com

The Mastering system empowers you to take charge of your learning—at your convenience, 24/7.

Use the Study Area on your own or in a study group.

BioFlix

▲ **BioFlix® 3-D animations** explore the most difficult biology topics, reinforced with tutorials, quizzes, and more.

▲ **Practice Tests** help you assess your understanding of each chapter, providing feedback for right and wrong answers.

▲ The **Cumulative Test** allows you to build a practice test with questions from multiple chapters.

Access your book online.

◀ The **Pearson eText** gives you access to the text whenever and wherever you can access the Internet. The eText includes powerful interactive and customization functions:

- write notes
- highlight text
- bookmark pages
- zoom
- click hyperlinked words to view definitions
- search
- link to media activities and quizzes

Your professor can also write notes for the class and highlight important material using a new tool that works like an electronic pen on a whiteboard.

Use MasteringBiology®

Get personalized coaching & feedback.

Your instructor may assign self-paced **MasteringBiology® tutorials** that provide individualized coaching with specific hints and feedback on the toughest topics in the course.

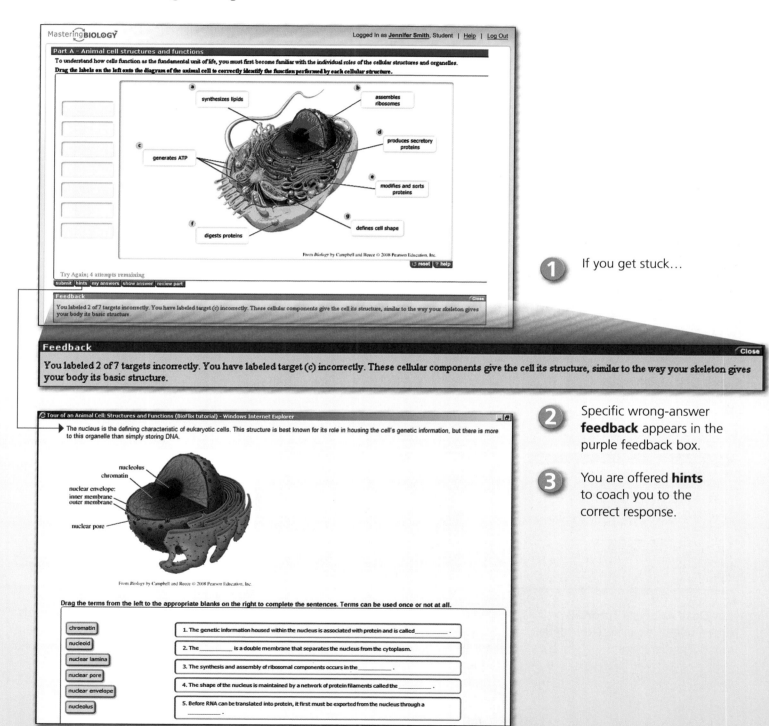

1 If you get stuck…

2 Specific wrong-answer **feedback** appears in the purple feedback box.

3 You are offered **hints** to coach you to the correct response.

MasteringBiology is the most effective and widely used online science tutorial, homework, and assessment system available.

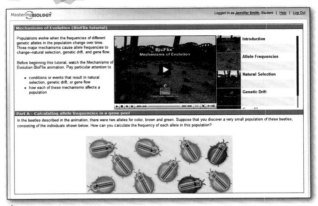

BioFlix® Tutorials use 3-D, movie-quality animations and coaching exercises to help students master tough topics outside of class. Tutorials and animations include:

- A Tour of the Animal Cell
- A Tour of the Plant Cell
- Membrane Transport
- Cellular Respiration
- Photosynthesis
- Mitosis
- Meiosis
- DNA Replication
- Protein Synthesis
- Mechanisms of Evolution

- Water Transport in Plants
- Homeostasis: Regulating Blood Sugar
- Gas Exchange
- How Neurons Work
- How Synapses Work
- Muscle Contraction
- Population Ecology
- The Carbon Cycle

The MasteringBiology **gradebook** provides you with quick results and easy-to-interpret insights into student performance. Every assignment is **automatically graded** and shades of red highlight vulnerable students and challenging assignments.

New **Data Analysis Tutorials** allow students to analyze real data from online databases.

New **Student Misconceptions Questions** provide assignable quizzes for each chapter based on common student misconceptions. Students are provided with feedback, and the instructor is provided with in-class strategies for overcoming these misconceptions.

New **Make Connections Tutorials** help students connect what they are learning in one chapter with material they learned in an earlier chapter.

MasteringBiology®

◄ New **Experimental Inquiry Tutorials,** based on some of biology's most influential experiments, give students practice analyzing experimental design and data, and help students understand how to reach conclusions based on collected data. Topics include:

- What Can You Learn About the Process of Science from Investigating a Cricket's Chirp?
- Which Wavelengths of Light Drive Photosynthesis?
- What Is the Inheritance Pattern of Sex-Linked Traits?
- Does DNA Replication Follow the Conservative, Semiconservative, or Dispersive Model?
- Did Natural Selection of Ground Finches Occur When the Environment Changed?
- What Effect Does Auxin Have on Coleoptile Growth?
- What Role Do Genes Play in Appetite Regulation?
- How Do Calcium Ions Help to Prevent Polyspermy During Egg Fertilization?
- Can a Species' Niche Be Influenced by Interspecific Competition?
- What Factors Influence the Loss of Nutrients from a Forest Ecosystem?

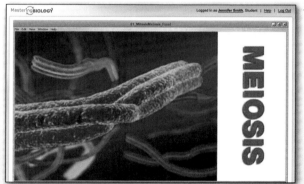

◄ The New **Video Tutor Sessions** walk students through tough topics with clearly explained visuals and demonstrations. Topics include:

- Mitosis and Meiosis
- Sex-Linked Pedigrees
- DNA Structure
- DNA Profiling Techniques
- Biodiversity
- Phylogenetic Trees

◄ The new **MasteringBiology: Virtual Biology Labs** online environment promotes critical thinking skills using virtual experiments and explorations that may be difficult to perform in a wet lab environment due to time, cost, or safety concerns.

- MasteringBiology: Virtual Biology Labs offer unique learning experiences in microscopy, molecular biology, genetics, ecology, and systematics.
- Choose from 20–30 automatically graded, "pre-set" lab activities that are ready to assign to students, or create your own from scratch.
- Each "pre-set" lab provides an assignable lab report with questions that are automatically graded and recorded in the MasteringBiology gradebook.
- Student subscriptions are available standalone or packaged with the CAMPBELL BIOLOGY textbook.

Supplements

For Instructors

Instructor Resource DVD
978-0-321-67786-0 • 0-321-67786-2

Assets for each chapter include:

- All figures, photos, and tables in JPEG and PowerPoint®
- Prepared PowerPoint Presentations for each chapter, with lecture notes, editable figures from the text, and links to animations and videos
- Clicker Questions in PowerPoint
- 250+ Instructor Animations, including 3-D BioFlix®
- Discovery Channel™ Videos
- Test Bank questions in TestGen® software and Microsoft® Word

BioFlix® animations invigorate classroom lectures with 3-minute "movie quality" 3-D graphics (see list on p. xviii).

Customizable PowerPoints provide a jumpstart for each lecture.

Clicker Questions can be used to stimulate effective classroom discussions (for use with or without clickers).

All of the art and photos from the book are provided with customizable labels. More than 1,600 photos from the text and other sources are included.

Printed Test Bank
by Louise Paquin, *McDaniel College*, Michael Dini, *Texas Tech University*, John Lepri, *University of North Carolina, Greensboro*, Jung Choi, *Georgia Institute of Technology*, John Zarnetske, *Hoosick Falls Central School*, and Ronald Balsamo, *Villanova University*
978-0-321-69729-5 • 0-321-69729-4

For the Ninth Edition, the Test Bank authors have increased the number of high-level application and synthesis questions.

Transparency Acetates
978-0-321-69708-0 • 0-321-69708-1

Course Management Systems

Test Bank questions, quizzes, and selected content from the Study Area of MasteringBiology are available in these popular course management systems:

CourseCompass™ (www.pearsonhighered.com)

Blackboard (www.pearsonhighered.com)

Instructor Resources Area in MasteringBiology

This area includes:

- PowerPoint® Lectures
- Clicker Questions
- JPEG Images
- Animations
- Videos
- Lecture Outlines
- Learning Objectives
- Strategies for Overcoming Common Student Misconceptions
- Instructor Guides for Supplements
- Write About a Theme: Tips for Grading Short-Answer Essays
- Suggested Answers for Essay Questions
- Test Bank Files
- Lab Media

For Students

Student Study Guide, Ninth Edition
by Martha R. Taylor
978-0-321-62992-0 • 0-321-62992-2

This popular study guide helps students extract key ideas from the textbook and organize their knowledge of biology. Exercises include concept maps for each chapter, chapter summaries, word roots, chapter tests, and a variety of interactive questions in various formats.

Inquiry in Action: Interpreting Scientific Papers, Second Edition*
by Ruth Buskirk, *University of Texas at Austin*, and Christopher M. Gillen, *Kenyon College*
978-0-321-68336-6 • 0-321-68336-6

Selected Inquiry Figures in the Ninth Edition direct students to read and analyze the complete original research paper. In this supplement, those articles are reprinted and accompanied by questions that help students analyze the article. The Inquiry Figures from the book are reprinted in the supplement.

Practicing Biology: A Student Workbook, Fourth Edition*
by Jean Heitz and Cynthia Giffen, *University of Wisconsin, Madison*
978-0-321-68328-1 • 0-321-68328-5

This workbook offers a variety of activities to suit different learning styles. Activities such as modeling and mapping allow students to visualize and understand biological processes. Other activities focus on basic skills, such as reading and drawing graphs.

Biological Inquiry: A Workbook of Investigative Cases, Third Edition*
by Margaret Waterman, *Southeast Missouri State University*, and Ethel Stanley, *BioQUEST Curriculum Consortium and Beloit College*
978-0-321-68320-5 • 0-321-68320-X

This workbook offers ten investigative cases. A student website is in the Study Area at **www.masteringbiology.com.**

Study Card, Ninth Edition
978-0-321-68322-9 • 0-321-68322-6

This quick-reference card provides an overview of the entire field of biology and helps students see the connections between topics.

Spanish Glossary, Ninth Edition
by Laura P. Zanello, *University of California, Riverside*
978-0-321-68321-2 • 0-321-68321-8

This resource provides definitions in Spanish for all the glossary terms.

Into the Jungle: Great Adventures in the Search for Evolution
by Sean B. Carroll, *University of Wisconsin, Madison*
978-0-321-55671-4 • 0-321-55671-2

These nine short tales vividly depict key discoveries in evolutionary biology and the excitement of the scientific process. Online resources available at www.aw-bc.com/carroll.

Get Ready for Biology
978-0-321-50057-1 • 0-321-50057-1

This engaging workbook helps students brush up on important math and study skills and get up to speed on biological terminology and the basics of chemistry and cell biology.

A Short Guide to Writing About Biology, Seventh Edition
by Jan A. Pechenik, *Tufts University*
978-0-321-66838-7 • 0-321-66838-3

This best-selling writing guide teaches students to think as biologists and to express ideas clearly and concisely through their writing.

An Introduction to Chemistry for Biology Students, Ninth Edition
by George I. Sackheim, *University of Illinois, Chicago*
978-0-8053-9571-6 • 0-8053-9571-7

This text/workbook helps students review and master all the basic facts, concepts, and terminology of chemistry that they need for their life science course.

The Chemistry of Life CD-ROM, Biology Version, Second Edition
by Robert M. Thornton, *University of California, Davis*
978-0-8053-3063-2 • 0-8053-3063-1

This CD-ROM uses animations, interactive simulations, and quizzes with feedback to help students learn or review the chemistry needed to succeed in introductory biology.

For Lab

Investigating Biology Laboratory Manual, Seventh Edition
by Judith G. Morgan, *Emory University*, and M. Eloise Brown Carter, *Oxford College of Emory University*
978-0-321-66821-9 • 0-321-66821-9

The Seventh Edition emphasizes connections to recurring themes in biology, including structure and function, unity and diversity, and the overarching theme of evolution.

Annotated Instructor Edition for Investigating Biology Laboratory Manual, Seventh Edition
by Judith G. Morgan, *Emory University*, and M. Eloise Brown Carter, *Oxford College of Emory University*
978-0-321-67668-9 • 0-321-67668-8

Preparation Guide for Investigating Biology Laboratory Manual, Seventh Edition
by Judith G. Morgan, *Emory University*, and M. Eloise Brown Carter, *Oxford College of Emory University*
978-0-321-67669-6 • 0-321-67669-6

Symbiosis: The Benjamin Cummings Custom Laboratory Program for the Biological Sciences
www.pearsoncustom.com/database/symbiosis/bc.html

MasteringBiology®: Virtual Biology Labs
www.masteringbiology.com
This online environment promotes critical thinking skills using virtual experiments and explorations that may be difficult to perform in a wet lab environment due to time, cost, or safety concerns. Designed to supplement or substitute for existing wet labs, this product offers students unique learning experiences and critical thinking exercises in the areas of microscopy, molecular biology, genetics, ecology, and systematics.

* An Instructor Guide is available for download in the Instructor Resources Area at www.masteringbiology.com.

Featured Figures

Impact Figures

Exploring Figures

Inquiry Figures

* The Inquiry Figure, original research paper, and a worksheet to guide you through the paper are provided in *Inquiry in Action: Interpreting Scientific Papers,* Second Edition.
† See the related Experimental Inquiry Tutorial in MasteringBiology® (www.masteringbiology.com).

Research Method Figures

Interviews

Acknowledgments

The authors wish to express their gratitude to the global community of instructors, researchers, students, and publishing professionals who have contributed to this edition.

As authors of this text, we are mindful of the daunting challenge of keeping up to date in all areas of our rapidly expanding subject. We are grateful to the many scientists who helped shape this edition by discussing their research fields with us, answering specific questions in their areas of expertise, and sharing their ideas about biology education. We are especially grateful to the following, listed alphabetically: John Archibald, John Armour, Kristian Axelsen, Scott Bowling, Barbara Bowman, Andy Cameron, Scott Carroll, Amy Cheng-Vollmer, Michele Clamp, David DeRosier, Doug DeSimone, Binh An Diep, David Ehrhardt, Robert Fowler, Peter Fraser, Matt Friedman, Tom Gingeras, Anita Gondor, Ken Halanych, Jeff Hardin, Catherine Hurlbut, Adam Johnson, Dale Kaiser, Patrick Keeling, Emir Khatipov, Chris Killian, Andrew Knoll, Nikos Kyrpides, Teri Liegler, Zhe-Xi Luo, Kent MacDonald, Nick Matzke, Melissa Michael, Nadia Naffakh, Rolf Ohlsson, Aharon Oren, Tom Owens, Kevin Padian, Nathalie Pardigon, Bruce Pavlik, Kevin J. Peterson, Michael Pollock, Rebekah Rasooly, Andrew Roger, Ole Seehausen, Alastair Simpson, Betty Smocovitis, Frank Solomon, Pam Soltis, Hans Thewissen, Mark Uhen, Vance Vredenburg, Elisabeth Wade, Phil Zamore, and Christine Zardecki. In addition, a total of 168 biologists, listed on pages xxviii–xxix, provided detailed reviews of chapters for this edition, helping us ensure the book's scientific accuracy and improve its pedagogical effectiveness. And finally, we thank Marty Taylor, author of all nine editions of the *Student Study Guide*, for her many contributions to the accuracy, clarity, and consistency of the book.

Thanks also to the other professors and students, from all over the world, who offered suggestions directly to the authors. We alone bear the responsibility for any errors that remain in the text, but the dedication of our consultants, reviewers, and other correspondents makes us confident in the accuracy and effectiveness of this edition.

Interviews with prominent scientists have been a hallmark of CAMPBELL BIOLOGY since its inception, and conducting these interviews was again one of the great pleasures of revising the book. To open the eight units of this edition, we are proud to include interviews with Susan Solomon, Bonnie Bassler, Joan Steitz, Geerat Vermeij, Ford Doolittle, Luis Herrera-Estrella, Toto Olivera, and Camille Parmesan.

The value of CAMPBELL BIOLOGY as a learning tool is greatly enhanced by the supplementary materials that have been created for instructors and students. We recognize that the dedicated authors of these materials are essentially writing mini (and not so mini) books. We much appreciate the hard work and creativity of all the authors listed, with their creations, on pages xxii–xxiii. In addition, we are grateful to Joan Sharp (*Lecture Outlines*, *Learning Objectives*, and *Student Misconceptions*) and Erin Barley and Kathleen Fitzpatrick (*PowerPoint® Lectures*).

The electronic media for this text are invaluable teaching and learning aids. We thank the hardworking and creative authors of the new material for this edition: Tom Owens, Joan Sharp, and Jennifer Yeh (*MasteringBiology®*); Richard Cowlishaw, Tod Duncan, and Stephanie Pandolfi (*Study Area Practice Tests*); and Eric Simon (*VideoTutors*). And we thank Brian White for his work. Also, we are grateful to the many other people—biology instructors, editors, artists, production experts, and narrators—who are listed in the credits for these and other elements of the electronic media that accompany the book. And we thank the reviewers and class testers of BioFlix® and MasteringBiology.

CAMPBELL BIOLOGY, Ninth Edition, results from an unusually strong synergy between a team of scientists and a team of publishing professionals. Our editorial team at Benjamin Cummings again demonstrated unmatched talents, commitment, and pedagogical insights. Our new Acquisitions Editor, Josh Frost, brought publishing savvy, intelligence, and a much appreciated level head to leading the whole team. The clarity and effectiveness of every page owe much to our extraordinary Supervising Editors Pat Burner and Beth Winickoff, who headed the top-notch development team: Developmental Editors John Burner, Matt Lee, and Mary Catherine Hager; and Developmental Artists Hilair Chism, Carla Simmons, Andrew Recher, and Jay McElroy. Our unsurpassed Senior Editorial Manager Ginnie Simione Jutson, Executive Director of Development Deborah Gale, Assistant Editor Logan Triglia, and Editor-in-Chief Beth Wilbur were indispensable in moving the project in the right direction. We also want to thank Robin Heyden for organizing the annual Biology Leadership Conferences and keeping us in touch with the world of AP Biology.

You would not have this beautiful book in your hands today if not for the work of the book production team: Executive Managing Editor Erin Gregg; Managing Editor Michael Early; Senior Production Project Manager Shannon Tozier; Senior Photo Editor Donna Kalal; Photo Researcher Maureen Spuhler; Copy Editor Janet Greenblatt; Art Editor Laura Murray; Proofreaders Joanna Dinsmore and Pete Shanks; Permissions Editors Sue Ewing and Beth Keister; Senior Project Editor Emily Bush, S4Carlisle; Composition Manager Holly Paige, S4Carlisle; Art Production Manager Kristina Seymour, Precision Graphics; Design Director Mark Ong; Designer Gary Hespenheide; and Manufacturing Buyer Michael Penne. We also thank those who worked on the book's supplements: Susan Berge, Nina Lewallen Hufford, Brady Golden, Jane Brundage, James Bruce, and John Hammett. And for creating the wonderful package of electronic media that accompanies the book, we are grateful to Tania Mlawer, Director of Editorial Content for MasteringBiology, and Jonathan Ballard, Deb Greco, Sarah Jensen, Mary Catherine Hager, Alice Fugate, Juliana Tringali, Josh Gentry, Steve Wright, Kristen Sutton, Katie Foley, Karen Sheh, and David Kokorowski, as well as Director of Media Development Lauren Fogel and Director of Media Strategy Stacy Treco.

For their important roles in marketing the book, we thank Christy Lawrence, Lauren Harp, Scott Dustan, Lillian Carr, Jane Campbell, Jessica Perry, Nora Massuda, and Jessica Tree.

We are grateful to Linda Davis, President of Pearson Math and Science, who has shared our commitment to excellence and provided strong support for five editions now. Moreover, we thank Paul Corey, President of Pearson Benjamin Cummings, and Editorial Director Frank Ruggirello for their enthusiasm, encouragement, and support.

The Pearson sales team, which represents CAMPBELL BIOLOGY on campus, is an essential link to the users of the text. They tell us what you like and don't like about the book, communicate the features of the book, and provide prompt service. We thank them for their hard work and professionalism. For representing our book to our international audience, we thank our sales and marketing partners throughout the world. They are all strong allies in biology education.

Finally, we wish to thank our families and friends for their encouragement and patience throughout this long project. Our special thanks to Paul, Dan, Maria, Armelle, and Sean (J.B.R.); Lily, Ross, Lily-too, and Alex (L.A.U.); Debra and Hannah (M.L.C.); Harry, Elga, Aaron, Sophie, Noah, and Gabriele (S.A.W.); Natalie (P.V.M.); and Sally, Robert, David, and Will (R.B.J.). And, as always, thanks to Rochelle, Allison, Jason, and McKay.

Jane Reece, Lisa Urry, Michael Cain,
Steve Wasserman, Peter Minorsky, and Rob Jackson

Reviewers

Ninth Edition Reviewers

Ann Aguanno, *Marymount Manhattan College*
Marc Albrecht, *University of Nebraska*
John Alcock, *Arizona State University*
Eric Alcorn, *Acadia University*
Terry Austin, *Temple College*
Brian Bagatto, *University of Akron*
Virginia Baker, *Chipola College*
Bonnie Baxter, *Westminster College*
Marilee Benore, *University of Michigan, Dearborn*
Catherine Black, *Idaho State University*
William Blaker, *Furman University*
Edward Blumenthal, *Marquette University*
David Bos, *Purdue University*
Scott Bowling, *Auburn University*
Beth Burch, *Huntington University*
Ragan Callaway, *The University of Montana*
Kenneth M. Cameron, *University of Wisconsin, Madison*
Patrick Canary, *Northland Pioneer College*
Cheryl Keller Capone, *Pennsylvania State University*
Karen I. Champ, *Central Florida Community College*
David Champlin, *University of Southern Maine*
Brad Chandler, *Palo Alto College*
Wei-Jen Chang, *Hamilton College*
Jung Choi, *Georgia Institute of Technology*
Steve Christensen, *Brigham Young University, Idaho*
James T. Colbert, *Iowa State University*
William Cushwa, *Clark College*
Shannon Datwyler, *California State University, Sacramento*
Eugene Delay, *University of Vermont*
Daniel DerVartanian, *University of Georgia*
Janet De Souza-Hart, *Massachusetts College of Pharmacy & Health Sciences*
Kathryn A. Durham, *Lorain Community College*
Curt Elderkin, *College of New Jersey*
Mary Ellard-Ivey, *Pacific Lutheran University*
George Ellmore, *Tufts University*
Robert C. Evans, *Rutgers University, Camden*
Sam Fan, *Bradley University*
Paul Farnsworth, *University of New Mexico*
Myriam Alhadeff Feldman, *Cascadia Community College*
Teresa Fischer, *Indian River Community College*
David Fitch, *New York University*
T. Fleming, *Bradley University*
Robert Fowler, *San Jose State University*
Robert Franklin, *College of Charleston*
Art Fredeen, *University of Northern British Columbia*
Matt Friedman, *University of Chicago*
Cynthia M. Galloway, *Texas A&M University, Kingsville*
Simon Gilroy, *University of Wisconsin, Madison*
Jim Goetze, *Laredo Community College*
Lynda Goff, *University of California, Santa Cruz*
Roy Golsteyn, *University of Lethbridge*
Barbara E. Goodman, *University of South Dakota*
David Grise, *Texas A&M University, Corpus Christi*
Devney Hamilton, *Stanford University (student)*
Matthew B. Hamilton, *Georgetown University*
Jeanne M. Harris, *University of Vermont*
Stephanie Harvey, *Georgia Southwestern State University*
Bernard Hauser, *University of Florida*
Andreas Hejnol, *Sars International Centre for Marine Molecular Biology*
Jason Hodin, *Stanford University*
Sara Huang, *Los Angeles Valley College*
Catherine Hurlbut, *Florida State College, Jacksonville*
Diane Husic, *Moravian College*
Thomas Jacobs, *University of Illinois*
Mark Jaffe, *Nova Southeastern University*
Douglas Jensen, *Converse College*
Lance Johnson, *Midland Lutheran College*
Cheryl Jorcyk, *Boise State University*
Caroline Kane, *University of California, Berkeley*
Jennifer Katcher, *Pima Community College*
Eric G. Keeling, *Cary Institute of Ecosystem Studies*
Chris Kennedy, *Simon Fraser University*
Hillar Klandorf, *West Virginia University*
Mark Knauss, *Georgia Highlands College*

Roger Koeppe, *University of Arkansas*
Peter Kourtev, *Central Michigan University*
Eliot Krause, *Seton Hall University*
Steven Kristoff, *Ivy Tech Community College*
William Kroll, *Loyola University*
Rukmani Kuppuswami, *Laredo Community College*
Lee Kurtz, *Georgia Gwinnett College*
Michael P. Labare, *United States Military Academy, West Point*
Ellen Lamb, *University of North Carolina, Greensboro*
William Lamberts, *College of St Benedict and St John's University*
Tali D. Lee, *University of Wisconsin, Eau Claire*
Hugh Lefcort, *Gonzaga University*
Alcinda Lewis, *University of Colorado, Boulder*
Graeme Lindbeck, *Valenica Community College*
Hannah Lui, *University of California, Irvine*
Cindy Malone, *California State University, Northridge*
Julia Marrs, *Barnard College (student)*
Kathleen Marrs, *Indiana University-Purdue University, Indianapolis*
Mike Mayfield, *Ball State University*
Kamau Mbuthia, *Bowling Green State University*
Tanya McGhee, *Craven Community College*
Darcy Medica, *Pennsylvania State University*
Susan Meiers, *Western Illinois University*
Alex Mills, *University of Windsor*
Eli Minkoff, *Bates College*
Subhash Minocha, *University of New Hampshire*
Ivona Mladenovic, *Simon Fraser University*
Courtney Murren, *College of Charleston*
Kimberlyn Nelson, *Pennsylvania State University*
Jacalyn Newman, *University of Pittsburgh*
Kathleen Nolta, *University of Michigan*
Aharon Oren, *The Hebrew University*
Henry R. Owen, *Eastern Illinois University*
Stephanie Pandolfi, *Michigan State University*
Nathalie Pardigon, *Institut Pasteur*
Cindy Paszkowski, *University of Alberta*
Andrew Pease, *Stevenson University*
Nancy Pelaez, *Purdue University*
Irene Perry, *University of Texas of the Permian Basin*
Roger Persell, *Hunter College*
Mark Pilgrim, *College of Coastal Georgia*
Vera M. Piper, *Shenadoah University*
Crima Pogge, *City College of San Francisco*
Michael Pollock, *Mount Royal University*
Roberta Pollock, *Occidental College*
Therese M. Poole, *Georgia State University*
Angela R. Porta, *Kean University*
Robert Powell, *Avila University*
Elena Pravosudova, *University of Nevada, Reno*
Terrell Pritts, *University of Arkansas, Little Rock*
Monica Ranes-Goldberg, *University of California, Berkeley*
Robert S. Rawding, *Gannon University*
Sarah Richart, *Azusa Pacific University*
Kenneth Robinson, *Purdue University*
Heather Roffey, *Marianopolis College*
Patricia Rugaber, *College of Coastal Georgia*
Scott Russell, *University of Oklahoma*
Louis Santiago, *University of California, Riverside*
Tom Sawicki, *Spartanburg Community College*
Thomas W. Schoener, *University of California, Davis*
Patricia Schulte, *University of British Colombia*
Brenda Schumpert, *Valencia Community College*
David Schwartz, *Houston Community College*
Brent Selinger, *University of Lethbridge*
Alison M. Shakarian, *Salve Regina University*
Robin L. Sherman, *Nova Southeastern University*
Sedonia Sipes, *Southern Illinois University, Carbondale*
Joel Stafstrom, *Northern Illinois University*
Alam Stam, *Capital University*
Judy Stone, *Colby College*
Cynthia Surmacz, *Bloomsburg University*
David Tam, *University of North Texas*
Yves Tan, *Cabrillo College*
Emily Taylor, *California Polytechnic State University*
Franklyn Tan Te, *Miami Dade College*
Kent Thomas, *Wichita State University*

Saba Valadkhan, *Center for RNA Molecular Biology*
Sarah VanVickle-Chavez, *Washington University, St. Louis*
William Velhagen, *New York University*
Janice Voltzow, *University of Scranton*
Margaret Voss, *Penn State Erie*
Charles Wade, *C.S. Mott Community College*
Claire Walczak, *Indiana University*
Jerry Waldvogel, *Clemson University*
Robert Lee Wallace, *Ripon College*
Fred Wasserman, *Boston University*
John Weishampel, *University of Central Florida*
Susan Whittemore, *Keene State College*
Janet Wolkenstein, *Hudson Valley Community College*
Grace Wyngaard, *James Madison University*
Paul Yancey, *Whitman College*
Anne D. Yoder, *Duke University*
Nina Zanetti, *Siena College*
Sam Zeveloff, *Weber State University*
Theresa Zucchero, *Methodist University*

Reviewers of Previous Editions

Kenneth Able *(State University of New York, Albany)*
Thomas Adams *(Michigan State University)*
Martin Adamson *(University of British Columbia)*
Dominique Adriaens *(Ghent University)*
Shylaja Akkaraju *(Bronx Community College of CUNY)*
John Alcock *(Arizona State University)*
George R. Aliaga *(Tarrant County College)*
Richard Almon *(State University of New York, Buffalo)*
Bonnie Amos *(Angelo State University)*
Katherine Anderson *(University of California, Berkeley)*
Richard J. Andren *(Montgomery County Community College)*
Estry Ang *(University of Pittsburgh, Greensburg)*
Jeff Appling *(Clemson University)*
J. David Archibald *(San Diego State University)*
David Armstrong *(University of Colorado, Boulder)*
Howard J. Arnott *(University of Texas, Arlington)*
Mary Ashley *(University of Illinois, Chicago)*
Angela S. Aspbury *(Texas State University)*
Robert Atherton *(University of Wyoming)*
Karl Aufderheide *(Texas A&M University)*
Leigh Auleb *(San Francisco State University)*
P. Stephen Baenziger *(University of Nebraska)*
Ellen Baker *(Santa Monica College)*
Katherine Baker *(Millersville University)*
William Barklow *(Framingham State College)*
Susan Barman *(Michigan State University)*
Steven Barnhart *(Santa Rosa Junior College)*
Andrew Barton *(University of Maine Farmington)*
Rebecca A. Bartow *(Western Kentucky University)*
Ron Basmajian *(Merced College)*
David Bass *(University of Central Oklahoma)*
Bonnie Baxter *(Hobart & William Smith)*
Tim Beagley *(Salt Lake Community College)*
Margaret E. Beard *(College of the Holy Cross)*
Tom Beatty *(University of British Columbia)*
Chris Beck *(Emory University)*
Wayne Becker *(University of Wisconsin, Madison)*
Patricia Bedinger *(Colorado State University)*
Jane Beiswenger *(University of Wyoming)*
Anne Bekoff *(University of Colorado, Boulder)*
Marc Bekoff *(University of Colorado, Boulder)*
Tania Beliz *(College of San Mateo)*
Adrianne Bendich *(Hoffman-La Roche, Inc.)*
Barbara Bentley *(State University of New York, Stony Brook)*
Darwin Berg *(University of California, San Diego)*
Werner Bergen *(Michigan State University)*
Gerald Bergstrom *(University of Wisconsin, Milwaukee)*
Anna W. Berkovitz *(Purdue University)*
Dorothy Berner *(Temple University)*
Annalisa Berta *(San Diego State University)*
Paulette Bierzychudek *(Pomona College)*
Charles Biggers *(Memphis State University)*
Kenneth Birnbaum *(New York University)*
Michael W. Black *(California Polytechnic State University, San Luis Obispo)*
Robert Blanchard *(University of New Hampshire)*
Andrew R. Blaustein *(Oregon State University)*
Judy Bluemer *(Morton College)*
Edward Blumenthal *(Marquette University)*
Robert Blystone *(Trinity University)*
Robert Boley *(University of Texas, Arlington)*
Jason E. Bond *(East Carolina University)*

Eric Bonde *(University of Colorado, Boulder)*
Cornelius Bondzi *(Hampton University)*
Richard Boohar *(University of Nebraska, Omaha)*
Carey L. Booth *(Reed College)*
Allan Bornstein *(Southeast Missouri State University)*
Oliver Bossdorf *(State University of New York, Stony Book)*
James L. Botsford *(New Mexico State University)*
Lisa Boucher *(University of Nebraska, Omaha)*
J. Michael Bowes *(Humboldt State University)*
Richard Bowker *(Alma College)*
Robert Bowker *(Glendale Community College, Arizona)*
Barbara Bowman *(Mills College)*
Barry Bowman *(University of California, Santa Cruz)*
Deric Bownds *(University of Wisconsin, Madison)*
Robert Boyd *(Auburn University)*
Sunny Boyd *(University of Notre Dame)*
Jerry Brand *(University of Texas, Austin)*
Edward Braun *(Iowa State University)*
Theodore A. Bremner *(Howard University)*
James Brenneman *(University of Evansville)*
Charles H. Brenner *(Berkeley, California)*
Lawrence Brewer *(University of Kentucky)*
Donald P. Briskin *(University of Illinois, Urbana)*
Paul Broady *(University of Canterbury)*
Chad Brommer *(Emory University)*
Judith L. Bronstein *(University of Arizona)*
Danny Brower *(University of Arizona)*
Carole Browne *(Wake Forest University)*
Mark Browning *(Purdue University)*
David Bruck *(San Jose State University)*
Robb T. Brumfield *(Louisiana State University)*
Herbert Bruneau *(Oklahoma State University)*
Gary Brusca *(Humboldt State University)*
Richard C. Brusca *(University of Arizona, Arizona-Sonora Desert Museum)*
Alan H. Brush *(University of Connecticut, Storrs)*
Howard Buhse *(University of Illinois, Chicago)*
Arthur Buikema *(Virginia Tech)*
Al Burchsted *(College of Staten Island)*
Meg Burke *(University of North Dakota)*
Edwin Burling *(De Anza College)*
William Busa *(Johns Hopkins University)*
Jorge Busciglio *(University of California, Irvine)*
John Bushnell *(University of Colorado)*
Linda Butler *(University of Texas, Austin)*
David Byres *(Florida Community College, Jacksonville)*
Guy A. Caldwell *(University of Alabama)*
Jane Caldwell *(West Virginia University)*
Kim A. Caldwell *(University of Alabama)*
R. Andrew Cameron *(California Institute of Technology)*
Alison Campbell *(University of Waikato)*
Iain Campbell *(University of Pittsburgh)*
W. Zacheus Cande *(University of California, Berkeley)*
Robert E. Cannon *(University of North Carolina, Greensboro)*
Deborah Canington *(University of California, Davis)*
Frank Cantelmo *(St. John's University)*
John Capeheart *(University of Houston, Downtown)*
Gregory Capelli *(College of William and Mary)*
Richard Cardullo *(University of California, Riverside)*
Nina Caris *(Texas A&M University)*
Jeffrey Carmichael *(University of North Dakota)*
Robert Carroll *(East Carolina University)*
Laura L. Carruth *(Georgia State University)*
J. Aaron Cassill *(University of Texas, San Antonio)*
David Champlin *(University of Southern Maine)*
Bruce Chase *(University of Nebraska, Omaha)*
P. Bryant Chase *(Florida State University)*
Doug Cheeseman *(De Anza College)*
Shepley Chen *(University of Illinois, Chicago)*
Giovina Chinchar *(Tougaloo College)*
Joseph P. Chinnici *(Virginia Commonwealth University)*
Jung H. Choi *(Georgia Institute of Technology)*
Geoffrey Church *(Fairfield University)*
Henry Claman *(University of Colorado Health Science Center)*
Anne Clark *(Binghamton University)*
Greg Clark *(University of Texas)*
Patricia J. Clark *(Indiana University-Purdue University, Indianapolis)*
Ross C. Clark *(Eastern Kentucky University)*
Lynwood Clemens *(Michigan State University)*
Janice J. Clymer *(San Diego Mesa College)*
William P. Coffman *(University of Pittsburgh)*
Austin Randy Cohen *(California State University, Northridge)*
J. John Cohen *(University of Colorado Health Science Center)*
Jim Colbert *(Iowa State University)*
Jan Colpaert *(Hasselt University)*

Robert Colvin *(Ohio University)*
Jay Comeaux *(McNeese State University)*
David Cone *(Saint Mary's University)*
Elizabeth Connor *(University of Massachusetts)*
Joanne Conover *(University of Connecticut)*
Gregory Copenhaver *(University of North Carolina, Chapel Hill)*
John Corliss *(University of Maryland)*
James T. Costa *(Western Carolina University)*
Stuart J. Coward *(University of Georgia)*
Charles Creutz *(University of Toledo)*
Bruce Criley *(Illinois Wesleyan University)*
Norma Criley *(Illinois Wesleyan University)*
Joe W. Crim *(University of Georgia)*
Greg Crowther *(University of Washington)*
Karen Curto *(University of Pittsburgh)*
Anne Cusic *(University of Alabama, Birmingham)*
Richard Cyr *(Pennsylvania State University)*
Marymegan Daly *(The Ohio State University)*
W. Marshall Darley *(University of Georgia)*
Cynthia Dassler *(The Ohio State University)*
Marianne Dauwalder *(University of Texas, Austin)*
Larry Davenport *(Samford University)*
Bonnie J. Davis *(San Francisco State University)*
Jerry Davis *(University of Wisconsin, La Crosse)*
Michael A. Davis *(Central Connecticut State University)*
Thomas Davis *(University of New Hampshire)*
John Dearn *(University of Canberra)*
Maria E. de Bellard *(California State University, Northridge)*
Teresa DeGolier *(Bethel College)*
James Dekloe *(University of California, Santa Cruz)*
Patricia A. DeLeon *(University of Delaware)*
Veronique Delesalle *(Gettysburg College)*
T. Delevoryas *(University of Texas, Austin)*
Roger Del Moral *(University of Washington)*
Charles F. Delwiche *(University of Maryland)*
Diane C. DeNagel *(Northwestern University)*
William L. Dentler *(University of Kansas)*
Daniel Dervartanian *(University of Georgia)*
Jean DeSaix *(University of North Carolina, Chapel Hill)*
Biao Ding *(Ohio State University)*
Michael Dini *(Texas Tech University)*
Andrew Dobson *(Princeton University)*
Stanley Dodson *(University of Wisconsin, Madison)*
Mark Drapeau *(University of California, Irvine)*
John Drees *(Temple University School of Medicine)*
Charles Drewes *(Iowa State University)*
Marvin Druger *(Syracuse University)*
Gary Dudley *(University of Georgia)*
Susan Dunford *(University of Cincinnati)*
Betsey Dyer *(Wheaton College)*
Robert Eaton *(University of Colorado)*
Robert S. Edgar *(University of California, Santa Cruz)*
Douglas Eernisse *(California State University, Fullerton)*
Douglas J. Eernisse *(California State University, Fullerton)*
Betty J. Eidemiller *(Lamar University)*
Brad Elder *(Doane College)*
William D. Eldred *(Boston University)*
Michelle Elekonich *(University of Nevada, Las Vegas)*
Mary Ellard-Ivey *(Pacific Lutheran University)*
Norman Ellstrand *(University of California, Riverside)*
Johnny El-Rady *(University of South Florida)*
Dennis Emery *(Iowa State University)*
John Endler *(University of California, Santa Barbara)*
Margaret T. Erskine *(Lansing Community College)*
Gerald Esch *(Wake Forest University)*
Frederick B. Essig *(University of South Florida)*
Mary Eubanks *(Duke University)*
David Evans *(University of Florida)*
Robert C. Evans *(Rutgers University, Camden)*
Sharon Eversman *(Montana State University)*
Olukemi Fadayomi *(Ferris State University)*
Lincoln Fairchild *(Ohio State University)*
Peter Fajer *(Florida State University)*
Bruce Fall *(University of Minnesota)*
Lynn Fancher *(College of DuPage)*
Ellen H. Fanning *(Vanderbilt University)*
Paul Farnsworth *(University of Texas, San Antonio)*
Larry Farrell *(Idaho State University)*
Jerry F. Feldman *(University of California, Santa Cruz)*
Lewis Feldman *(University of California, Berkeley)*
Eugene Fenster *(Longview Community College)*
Russell Fernald *(University of Oregon)*
Rebecca Ferrell *(Metropolitan State College of Denver)*
Kim Finer *(Kent State University)*

Milton Fingerman *(Tulane University)*
Barbara Finney *(Regis College)*
Frank Fish *(West Chester University)*
David Fisher *(University of Hawaii, Manoa)*
Jonathan S. Fisher *(St. Louis University)*
Steven Fisher *(University of California, Santa Barbara)*
Kirk Fitzhugh *(Natural History Museum of Los Angeles County)*
Lloyd Fitzpatrick *(University of North Texas)*
William Fixsen *(Harvard University)*
Abraham Flexer *(Manuscript Consultant, Boulder, Colorado)*
Kerry Foresman *(University of Montana)*
Norma Fowler *(University of Texas, Austin)*
Robert G. Fowler *(San Jose State University)*
David Fox *(University of Tennessee, Knoxville)*
Carl Frankel *(Pennsylvania State University, Hazleton)*
James Franzen *(University of Pittsburgh)*
Bill Freedman *(Dalhousie University)*
Otto Friesen *(University of Virginia)*
Frank Frisch *(Chapman University)*
Virginia Fry *(Monterey Peninsula College)*
Bernard Frye *(University of Texas, Arlington)*
Jed Fuhrman *(University of Southern California)*
Alice Fulton *(University of Iowa)*
Chandler Fulton *(Brandeis University)*
Sara Fultz *(Stanford University)*
Berdell Funke *(North Dakota State University)*
Anne Funkhouser *(University of the Pacific)*
Zofia E. Gagnon *(Marist College)*
Michael Gaines *(University of Miami)*
Arthur W. Galston *(Yale University)*
Stephen Gammie *(University of Wisconsin, Madison)*
Carl Gans *(University of Michigan)*
John Gapter *(University of Northern Colorado)*
Andrea Gargas *(University of Wisconsin, Madison)*
Lauren Garner *(California Polytechnic State University, San Luis Obispo)*
Reginald Garrett *(University of Virginia)*
Patricia Gensel *(University of North Carolina)*
Chris George *(California Polytechnic State University, San Luis Obispo)*
Robert George *(University of Wyoming)*
J. Whitfield Gibbons *(University of Georgia)*
J. Phil Gibson *(Agnes Scott College)*
Frank Gilliam *(Marshall University)*
Simon Gilroy *(Pennsylvania State University)*
Alan D. Gishlick *(Gustavus Adolphus College)*
Todd Gleeson *(University of Colorado)*
Jessica Gleffe *(University of California, Irvine)*
John Glendinning *(Barnard College)*
David Glenn-Lewin *(Wichita State University)*
William Glider *(University of Nebraska)*
Tricia Glidewell *(Marist School)*
Elizabeth A. Godrick *(Boston University)*
Lynda Goff *(University of California, Santa Cruz)*
Elliott Goldstein *(Arizona State University)*
Paul Goldstein *(University of Texas, El Paso)*
Sandra Gollnick *(State University of New York, Buffalo)*
Anne Good *(University of California, Berkeley)*
Judith Goodenough *(University of Massachusetts, Amherst)*
Wayne Goodey *(University of British Columbia)*
Robert Goodman *(University of Wisconsin, Madison)*
Ester Goudsmit *(Oakland University)*
Linda Graham *(University of Wisconsin, Madison)*
Robert Grammer *(Belmont University)*
Joseph Graves *(Arizona State University)*
Phyllis Griffard *(University of Houston, Downtown)*
A. J. F. Griffiths *(University of British Columbia)*
William Grimes *(University of Arizona)*
Mark Gromko *(Bowling Green State University)*
Serine Gropper *(Auburn University)*
Katherine L. Gross *(Ohio State University)*
Gary Gussin *(University of Iowa)*
Mark Guyer *(National Human Genome Research Institute)*
Ruth Levy Guyer *(Bethesda, Maryland)*
R. Wayne Habermehl *(Montgomery County Community College)*
Mac Hadley *(University of Arizona)*
Joel Hagen *(Radford University)*
Jack P. Hailman *(University of Wisconsin)*
Leah Haimo *(University of California, Riverside)*
Ken Halanych *(Auburn University)*
Jody Hall *(Brown University)*
Douglas Hallett, *(Northern Arizona University)*
Rebecca Halyard *(Clayton State College)*
E. William Hamilton *(Washington and Lee University)*
Sam Hammer *(Boston University)*
Penny Hanchey-Bauer *(Colorado State University)*

William F. Hanna (*Massasoit Community College*)
Laszlo Hanzely (*Northern Illinois University*)
Jeff Hardin (*University of Wisconsin, Madison*)
Lisa Harper (*University of California, Berkeley*)
Richard Harrison (*Cornell University*)
Carla Hass (*Pennsylvania State University*)
Chris Haufler (*University of Kansas*)
Bernard A. Hauser (*University of Florida*)
Chris Haynes (*Shelton State Community College*)
Evan B. Hazard (*Bemidji State University, Emeritus*)
H. D. Heath (*California State University, Hayward*)
George Hechtel (*State University of New York, Stony Brook*)
S. Blair Hedges (*Pennsylvania State University*)
Brian Hedlund (*University of Nevada, Las Vegas*)
David Heins (*Tulane University*)
Jean Heitz (*University of Wisconsin, Madison*)
John D. Helmann (*Cornell University*)
Colin Henderson (*University of Montana*)
Susan Hengeveld (*Indiana University*)
Michelle Henricks (*University of California, Los Angeles*)
Caroll Henry (*Chicago State University*)
Frank Heppner (*University of Rhode Island*)
Albert Herrera (*University of Southern California*)
Scott Herrick (*Missouri Western State College*)
Ira Herskowitz (*University of California, San Francisco*)
Paul E. Hertz (*Barnard College*)
David Hibbett (*Clark University*)
R. James Hickey (*Miami University*)
William Hillenius (*College of Charleston*)
Kenneth Hillers (*California Polytechnic State University, San Luis Obispo*)
Ralph Hinegardner (*University of California, Santa Cruz*)
William Hines (*Foothill College*)
Robert Hinrichsen (*Indiana University of Pennsylvania*)
Helmut Hirsch (*State University of New York, Albany*)
Tuan-hua David Ho (*Washington University*)
Carl Hoagstrom (*Ohio Northern University*)
James Hoffman (*University of Vermont*)
A. Scott Holaday (*Texas Tech University*)
N. Michele Holbrook (*Harvard University*)
James Holland (*Indiana State University, Bloomington*)
Charles Holliday (*Lafayette College*)
Lubbock Karl Holte (*Idaho State University*)
Alan R. Holyoak (*Brigham Young University, Idaho*)
Laura Hoopes (*Occidental College*)
Nancy Hopkins (*Massachusetts Institute of Technology*)
Sandra Horikami (*Daytona Beach Community College*)
Kathy Hornberger (*Widener University*)
Pius F. Horner (*San Bernardino Valley College*)
Becky Houck (*University of Portland*)
Margaret Houk (*Ripon College*)
Daniel J. Howard (*New Mexico State University*)
Ronald R. Hoy (*Cornell University*)
Cristin Hulslander (*University of Oregon*)
Donald Humphrey (*Emory University School of Medicine*)
Robert J. Huskey (*University of Virginia*)
Steven Hutcheson (*University of Maryland, College Park*)
Sandra Hsu (*Skyline College*)
Linda L. Hyde (*Gordon College*)
Bradley Hyman (*University of California, Riverside*)
Mark Iked (*San Bernardino Valley College*)
Jeffrey Ihara (*Mira Costa College*)
Cheryl Ingram-Smith (*Clemson University*)
Alice Jacklet (*State University of New York, Albany*)
John Jackson (*North Hennepin Community College*)
John C. Jahoda (*Bridgewater State College*)
Dan Johnson (*East Tennessee State University*)
Lee Johnson (*The Ohio State University*)
Randall Johnson (*University of California, San Diego*)
Stephen Johnson (*William Penn University*)
Wayne Johnson (*Ohio State University*)
Kenneth C. Jones (*California State University, Northridge*)
Russell Jones (*University of California, Berkeley*)
Chad Jordan (*North Carolina State University*)
Alan Journet (*Southeast Missouri State University*)
Walter Judd (*University of Florida*)
Thomas W. Jurik (*Iowa State University*)
Caroline M. Kane (*University of California, Berkeley*)
Thomas C. Kane (*University of Cincinnati*)
Tamos Kapros (*University of Missouri*)
E. L. Karlstrom (*University of Puget Sound*)
Jennifer Katcher (*Pima Community College*)
Laura A. Katz (*Smith College*)
Maureen Kearney (*Field Museum of Natural History*)
Patrick Keeling (*University of British Columbia*)

Elizabeth A. Kellogg (*University of Missouri, St. Louis*)
Norm Kenkel (*University of Manitoba*)
Chris Kennedy (*Simon Fraser University*)
George Khoury (*National Cancer Institute*)
Rebecca T. Kimball (*University of Florida*)
Mark Kirk (*University of Missouri, Columbia*)
Robert Kitchin (*University of Wyoming*)
Attila O. Klein (*Brandeis University*)
Daniel Klionsky (*University of Michigan*)
Jennifer Knight (*University of Colorado*)
Ned Knight (*Linfield College*)
David Kohl (*University of California, Santa Barbara*)
Greg Kopf (*University of Pennsylvania School of Medicine*)
Thomas Koppenheffer (*Trinity University*)
Margareta Krabbe (*Uppsala University*)
Anselm Kratochwil (*Universität Osnabrück*)
Deborah M. Kristan (*California State University, San Marcos*)
William Kroll (*Loyola University, Chicago*)
Janis Kuby (*San Francisco State University*)
Justin P. Kumar (*Indiana University*)
David Kurijaka (*Ohio University*)
Marc-André Lachance (*University of Western Ontario*)
J. A. Lackey (*State University of New York, Oswego*)
Elaine Lai (*Brandeis University*)
Mohamed Lakrim (*Kingsborough Community College*)
Lynn Lamoreux (*Texas A&M University*)
William L'Amoreaux (*College of Staten Island*)
Carmine A. Lanciani (*University of Florida*)
Kenneth Lang (*Humboldt State University*)
Dominic Lannutti (*El Paso Community College*)
Allan Larson (*Washington University*)
John Latto (*University of California, Santa Barbara*)
Diane K. Lavett (*State University of New York, Cortland, and Emory University*)
Charles Leavell (*Fullerton College*)
C. S. Lee (*University of Texas*)
Daewoo Lee (*Ohio University*)
Robert Leonard (*University of California, Riverside*)
Michael R. Leonardo (*Coe College*)
John Lepri (*University of North Carolina, Greensboro*)
Donald Levin (*University of Texas, Austin*)
Mike Levine (*University of California, Berkeley*)
Joseph Levine (*Boston College*)
Bill Lewis (*Shoreline Community College*)
John Lewis (*Loma Linda University*)
Lorraine Lica (*California State University, Hayward*)
Harvey Liftin (*Broward Community College*)
Harvey Lillywhite (*University of Florida, Gainesville*)
Graeme Lindbeck (*Valencia Community College*)
Clark Lindgren (*Grinnell College*)
Diana Lipscomb (*George Washington University*)
Christopher Little (*The University of Texas, Pan American*)
Kevin D. Livingstone (*Trinity University*)
Andrea Lloyd (*Middlebury College*)
Sam Loker (*University of New Mexico*)
Christopher A. Loretz (*State University of New York, Buffalo*)
Jane Lubchenco (*Oregon State University*)
Douglas B. Luckie (*Michigan State University*)
Margaret A. Lynch (*Tufts University*)
Steven Lynch (*Louisiana State University, Shreveport*)
Richard Machemer Jr. (*St. John Fisher College*)
Elizabeth Machunis-Masuoka (*University of Virginia*)
James MacMahon (*Utah State University*)
Christine R. Maher (*University of Southern Maine*)
Linda Maier (*University of Alabama, Huntsville*)
Jose Maldonado (*El Paso Community College*)
Richard Malkin (*University of California, Berkeley*)
Charles Mallery (*University of Miami*)
Keith Malmos (*Valencia Community College, East Campus*)
Cindy Malone (*California State University, Northridge*)
Carol Mapes (*Kutztown University of Pennsylvania*)
William Margolin (*University of Texas Medical School*)
Lynn Margulis (*Boston University*)
Kathleen A. Marrs (*Indiana University-Purdue University, Indianapolis*)
Edith Marsh (*Angelo State University*)
Diane L. Marshall (*University of New Mexico*)
Linda Martin Morris (*University of Washington*)
Karl Mattox (*Miami University of Ohio*)
Joyce Maxwell (*California State University, Northridge*)
Jeffrey D. May (*Marshall University*)
Lee McClenaghan (*San Diego State University*)
Richard McCracken (*Purdue University*)
Andrew McCubbin (*Washington State University*)
Kerry McDonald (*University of Missouri, Columbia*)
Jacqueline McLaughlin (*Pennsylvania State University, Lehigh Valley*)

Neal McReynolds *(Texas A&M International)*
Lisa Marie Meffert *(Rice University)*
Michael Meighan *(University of California, Berkeley)*
Scott Meissner *(Cornell University)*
Paul Melchior *(North Hennepin Community College)*
Phillip Meneely *(Haverford College)*
John Merrill *(Michigan State University)*
Brian Metscher *(University of California, Irvine)*
Ralph Meyer *(University of Cincinnati)*
James Mickle *(North Carolina State University)*
Roger Milkman *(University of Iowa)*
Helen Miller *(Oklahoma State University)*
John Miller *(University of California, Berkeley)*
Kenneth R. Miller *(Brown University)*
John E. Minnich *(University of Wisconsin, Milwaukee)*
Michael J. Misamore *(Texas Christian University)*
Kenneth Mitchell *(Tulane University School of Medicine)*
Alan Molumby *(University of Illinois, Chicago)*
Nicholas Money *(Miami University)*
Russell Monson *(University of Colorado, Boulder)*
Joseph P. Montoya *(Georgia Institute of Technology)*
Frank Moore *(Oregon State University)*
Janice Moore *(Colorado State University)*
Randy Moore *(Wright State University)*
William Moore *(Wayne State University)*
Carl Moos *(Veterans Administration Hospital, Albany, New York)*
Michael Mote *(Temple University)*
Alex Motten *(Duke University)*
Jeanette Mowery *(Madison Area Technical College)*
Deborah Mowshowitz *(Columbia University)*
Rita Moyes *(Texas A&M College Station)*
Darrel L. Murray *(University of Illinois, Chicago)*
John Mutchmor *(Iowa State University)*
Elliot Myerowitz *(California Institute of Technology)*
Gavin Naylor *(Iowa State University)*
John Neess *(University of Wisconsin, Madison)*
Tom Neils *(Grand Rapids Community College)*
Raymond Neubauer *(University of Texas, Austin)*
Todd Newbury *(University of California, Santa Cruz)*
James Newcomb *(New England College)*
Harvey Nichols *(University of Colorado, Boulder)*
Deborah Nickerson *(University of South Florida)*
Bette Nicotri *(University of Washington)*
Caroline Niederman *(Tomball College)*
Maria Nieto *(California State University, Hayward)*
Anders Nilsson *(University of Umeå)*
Greg Nishiyama *(College of the Canyons)*
Charles R. Noback *(College of Physicians and Surgeons, Columbia University)*
Jane Noble-Harvey *(Delaware University)*
Mary C. Nolan *(Irvine Valley College)*
Peter Nonacs *(University of California, Los Angeles)*
Mohamed A. F. Noor *(Duke University)*
Shawn Nordell *(St. Louis University)*
Richard S. Norman *(University of Michigan, Dearborn, Emeritus)*
David O. Norris *(University of Colorado, Boulder)*
Steven Norris *(California State, Channel Islands)*
Gretchen North *(Occidental College)*
Cynthia Norton *(University of Maine, Augusta)*
Steve Norton *(East Carolina University)*
Steve Nowicki *(Duke University)*
Bette H. Nybakken *(Hartnell College)*
Brian O'Conner *(University of Massachusetts, Amherst)*
Gerard O'Donovan *(University of North Texas)*
Eugene Odum *(University of Georgia)*
Mark P. Oemke *(Alma College)*
Linda Ogren *(University of California, Santa Cruz)*
Patricia O'Hern *(Emory University)*
Nathan O. Okia *(Auburn University, Montgomery)*
Jeanette Oliver *(St. Louis Community College, Florissant Valley)*
Gary P. Olivetti *(University of Vermont)*
John Olsen *(Rhodes College)*
Laura J. Olsen *(University of Michigan)*
Sharman O'Neill *(University of California, Davis)*
Wan Ooi *(Houston Community College)*
John Oross *(University of California (Riverside)*
Gay Ostarello *(Diablo Valley College)*
Catherine Ortega *(Fort Lewis College)*
Charissa Osborne *(Butler University)*
Thomas G. Owens *(Cornell University)*
Penny Padgett *(University of North Carolina, Chapel Hill)*
Kevin Padian *(University of California, Berkeley)*
Dianna Padilla *(State University of New York, Stony Brook)*
Anthony T. Paganini *(Michigan State University)*
Barry Palevitz *(University of Georgia)*

Michael A. Palladino *(Monmouth University)*
Daniel Papaj *(University of Arizona)*
Peter Pappas *(County College of Morris)*
Bulah Parker *(North Carolina State University)*
Stanton Parmeter *(Chemeketa Community College)*
Robert Patterson *(San Francisco State University)*
Ronald Patterson *(Michigan State University)*
Crellin Pauling *(San Francisco State University)*
Kay Pauling *(Foothill Community College)*
Daniel Pavuk *(Bowling Green State University)*
Debra Pearce *(Northern Kentucky University)*
Patricia Pearson *(Western Kentucky University)*
Shelley Penrod *(North Harris College)*
Imara Y. Perera *(North Carolina State University)*
Beverly Perry *(Houston Community College)*
David Pfennig *(University of North Carolina, Chapel Hill)*
David S. Pilliod *(California Polytechnic State University, San Luis Obispo)*
J. Chris Pires *(University of Missouri, Columbia)*
Bob Pittman *(Michigan State University)*
James Platt *(University of Denver)*
Martin Poenie *(University of Texas, Austin)*
Scott Poethig *(University of Pennsylvania)*
Jeffrey Pommerville *(Texas A&M University)*
Angela R. Porta *(Kean University)*
Warren Porter *(University of Wisconsin)*
Daniel Potter *(University of California, Davis)*
Donald Potts *(University of California, Santa Cruz)*
Andy Pratt *(University of Canterbury)*
David Pratt *(University of California, Davis)*
Halina Presley *(University of Illinois, Chicago)*
Mary V. Price *(University of California, Riverside)*
Mitch Price *(Pennsylvania State University)*
Rong Sun Pu *(Kean University)*
Rebecca Pyles *(East Tennessee State University)*
Scott Quackenbush *(Florida International University)*
Ralph Quatrano *(Oregon State University)*
Peter Quinby *(University of Pittsburgh)*
Val Raghavan *(Ohio State University)*
Deanna Raineri *(University of Illinois, Champaign-Urbana)*
Talitha Rajah *(Indiana University Southeast)*
Charles Ralph *(Colorado State University)*
Thomas Rand *(Saint Mary's University)*
Robert H. Reaves *(Glendale Community College)*
Kurt Redborg *(Coe College)*
Ahnya Redman *(Pennsylvania State)*
Brian Reeder *(Morehead State University)*
Bruce Reid *(Kean University)*
David Reid *(Blackburn College)*
C. Gary Reiness *(Lewis & Clark College)*
Charles Remington *(Yale University)*
Erin Rempala *(San Diego Mesa College)*
David Reznick *(University of California, Riverside)*
Douglas Rhoads *(University of Arkansas)*
Fred Rhoades *(Western Washington State University)*
Eric Ribbens *(Western Illinois University)*
Christina Richards *(New York University)*
Christopher Riegle *(Irvine Valley College)*
Loren Rieseberg *(University of British Columbia)*
Bruce B. Riley *(Texas A&M University)*
Donna Ritch *(Pennsylvania State University)*
Carol Rivin *(Oregon State University East)*
Laurel Roberts *(University of Pittsburgh)*
Thomas Rodella *(Merced College)*
Rodney Rogers *(Drake University)*
William Roosenburg *(Ohio University)*
Mike Rosenzweig *(Virginia Polytechnic Institute and State University)*
Wayne Rosing *(Middle Tennessee State University)*
Thomas Rost *(University of California, Davis)*
Stephen I. Rothstein *(University of California, Santa Barbara)*
John Ruben *(Oregon State University)*
Albert Ruesink *(Indiana University)*
Neil Sabine *(Indiana University)*
Tyson Sacco *(Cornell University)*
Rowan F. Sage *(University of Toronto)*
Tammy Lynn Sage *(University of Toronto)*
Don Sakaguchi *(Iowa State University)*
Walter Sakai *(Santa Monica College)*
Mark F. Sanders *(University of California, Davis)*
Ted Sargent *(University of Massachusetts, Amherst)*
K. Sathasivan *(University of Texas, Austin)*
Gary Saunders *(University of New Brunswick)*
Thomas R. Sawicki *(Spartanburg Community College)*
Inder Saxena *(University of Texas, Austin)*
Carl Schaefer *(University of Connecticut)*

Detailed Contents

UNIT

4 Mechanisms of Evolution 450

Interview: Geerat J. Vermeij

22 Descent with Modification: A Darwinian View of Life 452

UNIT

5 The Evolutionary History of Biological Diversity 534

Interview: W. Ford Doolittle

26 Phylogeny and the Tree of Life 536

Note to Students: The material included in this book has been specifically selected by your instructors. They have chosen to eliminate some material that is not critical to your course, and in doing so, the price of the book has been adjusted to reflect the content removed. The page and chapter numbers referenced in this custom edition represent their original source.

The Department of Biological Sciences

The Department of Biological Sciences, University of Alberta, is the largest and one of the most diverse departments on campus. It was formed in 1994 from the merger of the Departments of Botany, Entomology, Microbiology, Genetics and Zoology. The department has over 70 professors, 20 adjunct professors, 20 professors emeritus, 70 departmental support staff and a graduate student population of nearly 300. Excellent teaching and research facilities help support a vital teaching and research environment.

Students may pursue the study of biology through seven Honors or Specialization programs within the department and three collaborative programs with other departments. In addition, students in the General Program in the Faculty of Science may choose from the department's rich selection of courses to pursue a major or minor in Biological Sciences.

We invite you to learn more about our department and our programs. This supplement to your textbook has been developed to help you discover what opportunities are available to you as you complete your undergraduate degree. We also hope it will introduce you to some of the people who are conducting fascinating research here in the Department of Biological Sciences, University of Alberta.

Why Study Biology at the University of Alberta?

Diversity of programs: Programs focus on all major areas of biology: ecology, microbiology and biotechnology, molecular biology and genetics, physiology, developmental biology and cell biology, plant biology, systematics and evolution. Three programs offered collaboratively with other departments: bioinformatics, immunology and infection, and paleontology. The Industrial Internship Program (IIP) offers students the opportunity to gain work experience during their undergraduate program.

Diversity of courses: Choose from over 121 undergraduate courses in the department covering subjects such as biology, botany, entomology, genetics, microbiology and zoology. An additional 28 courses are offered in bioinformatics, immunology and infection, marine sciences and paleontology.

Our programs are flexible: Honors and specialization programs offer plenty of space, especially in Years 3 and 4, for options. Courses can be taken in diverse areas within the biological sciences, as well as from other departments (e.g. Cell Biology, Neuroscience, Physiology, Renewable Resources).

Hands-on experience is our priority: More than half of the courses in the Department of Biological Sciences have a laboratory component with either 3 or 6 hours of lab per week in the subjects areas of biology (20 courses), botany (12 courses), entomology (5 courses), genetics (2 courses), microbiology (5 courses), and zoology (17 courses). Labs are also a major component of courses in bioinformatics, immunology and infection, and paleontology. Field experiences are available on and off campus.

Small group seminars: Twenty-five courses offer small-group learning in seminars where students participate in discussions, give presentations and enhance their writing skills.

We have small class sizes too: Half the 300 and 400-level courses have enrolments with 20 or fewer students. Labs are always small, even in the first year.

World-renown faculty: Take lectures or labs from an expert. Seventy-two full-time academic staff teach lectures, labs, seminars and research-oriented courses.

Interact with graduate students: Over 300 graduate students who are pursuing Masters and Doctoral degrees serve as teaching assistants and mentors.

Research opportunities for undergraduates: Courses focusing on undergraduate student research begin as early as 2nd year. Students have the opportunity to take project courses throughout their programs: Biology 299, Biology 398/399 and Biology 498/499. Summer research employment opportunities are also available through NSERC Undergraduate Summer Research Awards, Alberta Innovates—Health Solutions, and through research grants held by individual professors.

Learn in world-class facilities and with world-class collections that are located in the Biological Sciences Building and the Centennial Centre for Interdisciplinary Science: Molecular Biology Service Unit; Advanced Microscopy Facility; Biogeochemical Analytical Laboratory; Low-Level Mercury Analytical Laboratory; Drosophilia Unit; Insect Culture Unit; Biotron Facilities (greenhouses, controlled environment chambers, freshwater and marine holding facilities); Vascular and Cryptogamic Herbaria; Strickland Museum (entomology); Zoology Museum; Paleobotanical Collection; Vertebrate Paleontology Collection; Meanook Biological Research Station; Bamfield Marine Sciences Centre; Geographical Information Systems (GIS) Laboratory and Digital Teaching Resources Laboratory.

Personal attention and advice: Professors act as advisors for all Honors and Specialization programs. The starting point for getting information on all programs is at Student Services, CW 312 Biological Sciences Building.

Undergraduate Student Associations: Most areas of biology have a corresponding undergraduate student association. Student groups sponsor seminars, "Meet the Prof Nights," and social activities. Meet other students that share common interests. Associations include: APES (Animal Biology, Physiology, Ecology and Systematics), Botany, Molecular Genetics, and the Wildlife Society.

Access to Industrial Internships: Participation in the Industrial Internship Program through Biological Sciences requires that a student be registered in one of the department's Honors or Specialization programs.

Access to scholarships: A number of scholarships are available only to students enrolled in Honors or Specialization programs in Biological Sciences.

Teaching and Research

Teaching and research are two key activities at the University of Alberta. In Biological Sciences these activities are tightly linked and undergraduate students benefit from this linkage. Each fact contained in this textbook is ultimately the product of research. Instructors who conduct research understand the process of science and appreciate the interconnectedness of findings from different areas of biology. They are familiar with the latest discoveries and techniques, and are able to evaluate, expand, and explain course content. Get to know faculty members. You will find they really are excited about science. Also, every year, professors in Biological Sciences offer hundreds of interested undergraduate students the opportunity to participate in research through project courses and jobs in the laboratory and field.

Where Are They Now?

Ever ask yourself what you might do with a BSc from the University of Alberta? Here are profiles of some of our graduates.

Linda Campbell

BSc Zoology, MSc Ecology (University of Alberta); PhD (University of Waterloo, 2002)
Current position: Canadian Research Chair in Aquatic Ecosystem Health (Queens University); Voted one of the "Top 40 Under 40" in Canada for 2010.

My research team integrates multiple approaches from diverse fields such as environmental chemistry, aquatic ecology, fish biology and population health. Our ultimate goal is to improve our understanding of the fate and effects of anthropogenic and natural toxicants in aquatic ecosystems.

University of Alberta provided me with a robust education in the fundamentals of ecology which incorporated laboratory, field and library skills. These skills enabled me to develop research projects around the world, ranging from the Rocky Mountains to eastern China. Professors in Biological Sciences were supportive and encouraging, allowing students to strive for high standards.

Brad Stelfox

BSc, PhD Zoology (University of Alberta)
Current positions: Senior Ecologist Forem Technologies; Developer ALCES (A Landscape Cumulative Effects Simulator); Adjunct Professor Department of Biological Sciences, University of Alberta, and the Department of Environmental Design, University of Calgary.

My research and teaching focus on the interface between human land uses and regional landscapes with an emphasis on forest ecosystem management, landscape carbon-pool dynamics, cumulative land-use simulation modeling, climate change scenarios, wildlife management, and fire ecology.

Coming from a farm northwest of Stony Plain, I was so fortunate to be able to study Zoology (now part of Biological Sciences) at the University of Alberta. The caliber of the faculty (professors, teaching assistants, non-academic staff), the diversity of lectures, the friendships, the summer work opportunities, all combined to help shape my interests and commitments, and set the foundation of knowledge that would lead to my career in environmental education and landscape ecology. I will forever be indebted to all who have contributed to this impressive program.

David Krause

BSc Zoology, MSc Zoology (University of Alberta); PhD Geology (University of Michigan)
Current positions: Distinguished Service Professor at Stony Brook University Department of Anatomical Sciences; Founder Malagasy Ankizy Project

The main focus of my research is the evolutionary history, paleobiology, and paleobiogeography of Mesozoic and Early Cenozoic vertebrates, particularly mammals. Almost all of this research is based on strongly field-oriented programs, primarily in the Cretaceous of Madagascar and the Paleocene of the Western Interior of North America. The Malagasy Ankizy Project is dedicated to educating and providing healthcare for poor children in Madagascar.

The possibility of embarking on a paleontological career did not really enter my head until the summer after my first year as a student in the Department of Zoology (now part of Biological Sciences) at the University of Alberta, when a young professor by the name of Richard Fox took me on as a field hand. I was immediately hooked. The opportunity to live and work in the great outdoors coupled with the thrill of discovering animals long extinct seemed like an unbeatable combination. It still does today, but I know full well that I could not have gotten to where I am without a sound training in organismal biology.

Gordon Court

BSc Zoology, MSc Zoology (University of Alberta); PhD Zoology (University of Otago)
Current position: Provincial Wildlife Status Biologist, Fish and Wildlife Division, Alberta Sustainable Resource Development

My research has involved the study of the ecology and ecotoxicology of predatory birds at both ends of the Earth. I began studying peregrine falcons in the Canadian Arctic in the early 1980s and this research continues today through the efforts of others. I still get to be involved but in a less 'hands on' fashion. I also studied persistent organic pollutants in sea-birds (south polar skua and Adelie penguin) in Ross Sea, Antarctica in the early 1990s. I do get back to the Antarctic from time to time, but mostly as a guide/lecturer on Antarctic tour ships. Lately, I've been enjoying the recovery of peregrine falcons in western Canada and the small amount of research that I do today involves documenting the decline in organochlorine pollutants (like DDT) in falcon tissue and watching for the rise (and potential effects) of others, like poly-brominated di-phenyl ethers (fire retardants).

I completed a B.Sc. in the Honors program in Zoology (now Department of Biological Sciences). This program was designed to give the student a broad background in Zoology as a foundation for more specialized work in graduate school. It was intensive and demanding, culminating in a 3-hour oral examination in fourth year. I really never appreciated how good that program was until I started visiting/studying at other universities. I will be forever grateful to the professors and non-academic staff of the Zoology Department who really went the extra-mile to turn out some first-class graduates, many of whom have gone on to very distinguished careers in academia. My career aspirations did not include an academic position, but as a government scientist, I believe I have also benefitted from the strong scientific underpinnings provided by my undergraduate education in Zoology at University of Alberta.

Lindsay Coulter

BSc Animal Biology (University of Alberta)
Current position: David Suzuki's Queen of Green at the David Suzuki Foundation

As David Suzuki's Queen of Green, I provide media commentary on everyday, green living. As a spokesperson I take questions on what it means to live green and clean. I maintain a weekly blog at davidsuzuki.org, a syndicated column in the Metro News and I am the voice of the Suzuki Report which airs on 28 radio stations across B.C. and Alberta.

My childhood love and wonder of nature led me to complete an Animal Biology degree at the University of Alberta. The University of Alberta provided me with a robust education in the fundamentals of ecology which incorporated laboratory, field and library skills. With the help of many supportive professors who turned out to be mentors, I spent 5 years working in the field, mostly in Alberta's boreal forest, identifying birds by song, ear-tagging mice, and radio-collaring weasels. As much as I loved collecting data and contributing to a pool of scientific knowledge, I found my calling in communicating science. My passion for natural history and storytelling has seen me evolve from a "weasel woman" to the "owl lady" to the Queen of Green. From speaking to farmers and ranchers about protecting species at risk to greening Canadian families in time for Earth Day, I will always cherish and lean on my roots in zoology, ecology and conservation.

Michael Deyholos

BSc Genetics (University of Alberta); PhD Biology (McGill University)
Current position: Associate Professor Plant Biotechnology, Biological Sciences, University of Alberta

My lab uses genomics, which allows us to work in a lot of different areas of basic research in plant biology. We apply this to making better crops, including improved hemp and flax fibers as local sources of textiles and as recyclable replacements for fiber glass. We are also trying to use plants as sources of new antibiotics.

A great benefit of the University of Alberta is that so many of our courses have a large laboratory component. I was able to use my undergraduate lab experience to get an internship (Industrial Internship Program, Department of Biological Sciences) at Biomira, a pharmaceutical company. When an opportunity later came up in graduate school to switch to working with plants, I found out that my genetics training from the University of Alberta was equally useful as well.

As one of the instructors in Biology 207, Molecular Genetics and Heredity, I have developed a custom textbook (*An Open Source Molecular Genetics Textbook*, 2010) licensed for non-commercial use by the Creative Commons. The textbook is freely available for the students in Biology 207 through the Biology 207 website http://www.biology.ualberta.ca/courses/biol207/.

John Acorn

BSc Zoology, MSc Entomology (University of Alberta)
Current position: Instructor Renewable Resources, University of Alberta

My work in biology has included hosting two television series ("Acorn, The Nature Nut" and "Twits and Pishers"), writing 16 books, and traveling extensively as a public speaker and field trip leader. I have also had the pleasure of working on original research, primarily involving insect ecology and systematics. I continue to balance research with public communication, and have recently turned my attention to what might best be called the philosophy of environmental science.

As a naturalist since age 5, attending university was a bit of a foregone conclusion for me. My original plan was to pursue a research career in entomology, but once I was exposed to the full breadth of biology I was inspired to explore other areas as well, including the popularization of science, the study of birds, and even paleontology. I continue to have an active interest in recent paleontological developments, especially regarding the vertebrate fossils of Alberta.

Mariam Sai

BSc Specialization Microbiology (University of Alberta)
Current position: Lab Manager, CanBiocin

I have been at CanBiocin for 3 years. CanBiocin was formed as a University of Alberta spin-off company to commercialized novel technologies based on the application of lactic acid bacteria for food safety and animal/human health. As the lab manager my position is quite varied which is what I enjoy about it. Some of my tasks include helping with research, running experiments, designing and implementing lab safety protocols.

In my fourth year of a BSc General program majoring in Biological Sciences, I took Microbiology 265, taught by Dr. Bill Page. That course inspired me to come back to University of Alberta to complete a Specialization degree in Microbiology.

Stephanie Nicol

BSc Immunology & Infection (University of Alberta)
Current position: MSc Student in Department of Medical Microbiology and Immunology, University of Alberta

My research in Dr. Troy Baldwin's laboratory focuses on T cell development in the thymus. T cells, a type of white blood cell, contribute to the immune response against viral or bacterial infections.

Therefore, proper education of these cells is crucial for generating a T cell population that recognizes pathogens as opposed to your own body. This process is important for preventing the development of autoimmune disorders, such as diabetes mellitus or rheumatoid arthritis. It is intriguing research to participate in and I owe it all to the opportunities the University of Alberta's biology program had to offer.

During the first year of my BSc degree, I was uncertain as to what direction I wanted my studies to go, but that all changed with one lecture about the immune system during Biology 107. Afterward I chose to pursue the Immunology and Infection program for the remainder of my degree. Over the next two years I discovered my strengths at the lab bench, which allowed me to participate in the Industrial Internship Program. I was given the fantastic opportunity to be a lab technician for Dycor Technologies Ltd. for one year, gaining valuable work experience while still being a student. Through Biological Sciences I also had the opportunity to do an Honors 499 project during my final year of my degree, which I did in the Baldwin lab, eventually leading me to pursue a graduate degree there afterwards. After completing my BSc Honors in Immunology and Infection, I wished to continue diversifying my education. Prior to beginning graduate studies I also took the Science Journalism course at Bamfield Marine Science Centre through the University of Alberta.

The different programs and opportunities provided by the Department of Biological Sciences allowed me to tailor my Bachelor degree to make it as fulfilling as possible. The experience I gained during my undergraduate education has been invaluable in getting me to where I am today.

Programs

The Department of Biological Sciences, University of Alberta, offers seven distinct programs and three collaborative programs for students registered in either BSc Honors or Specialization. In addition, some programs identify "streams", lists of courses that provide guidance to students wishing to focus even further on specific areas of biology.

All students in Honors and Specialization programs in Biological Sciences take a common core of courses in their first year (see below) which includes Biology 107 and 108. In addition, all Honors and Specialization students take Biology 207 and 208 in the second year. For the most current information on individual program requirements and recommendations, please consult the department website www.biology.ualberta.ca/programs/undergraduate/.

Regardless of their program, students in a BSc Honors or Specialization Program in the Department of Biological Sciences follow a common set of courses in the first year:

Biology 107 (Introduction to Cell Biology); Biology 108 (Introduction to Diversity); Chemistry 101 (Introduction to Chemistry I) and Chemistry 164 (Organic Chemistry) or Chemistry 261 (Organic Chemistry I); Math 113 (Elementary Calculus I) or Math 114 (Elementary Calculus I) or Math 120 (Basic Linear Algebra I); Statistics 151 (Introduction to Applied Statistics I); *6 Arts option (WRS 101 or junior English recommended); and *6 program-specific courses.

Animal Biology

The **Animal Biology** program involves the study of both invertebrate and vertebrate organisms. Students have the opportunity to learn how animals work (form, behavior, and physiology), how they develop (morphogenesis, cell biology, gene expression), how they evolve (genetics, diversity, phy-

logeny) and how they interact with their environment (ecology). While students may choose to study a broad overview of animal biology, the option exists for focusing on one of the program "streams:" Entomology, Marine Biology, Parasitology, or Vertebrate Biology (described on the departmental website www. biology.ualberta.ca). Techniques/skills used in animal biology courses include microscopy, dissections, molecular biology, cell biology, genomics, field work, species identification, and working with collections.

Courses after Biology 107 and 108: Biology 201 (Eukaryotic Cell Biology), Biology 207 (Molecular Genetics and Heredity), Biology 208 (Principles of Ecology), Entomology 220 (Insect Biology), Zoology 224 (Vertebrate Diversity), Zoology 241 (Physiology I: Homeostasis), Zoology 242 (Physiology II: Intercellular Communication), Zoology 250 (Survey of Invertebrates), Biology 299 optional (Research Opportunity Program)

Career options with BSc: Consultant, eco-tourism, pest management, field technologist, laboratory technologist, animal care technologist, interpreter, naturalist, forensic biology, science writer, curatorial technologist, professional school (veterinary, health, law, graduate studies).

Ecology

The **Ecology** program introduces students to the study of the interactions of organisms with their environment. Course offerings provide students with a foundation in plant and animal ecology, studying at the level of individuals, populations, communities and ecosystems, and at a variety of spatial scales. While students may choose to study a broad overview of ecology, the option exists for focusing on one of the program "streams:" Freshwater Biology, Conservation/Wildlife Biology, or Plant Ecology (described at departmental website *www.biology.ualberta.ca*). Techniques/skills used in ecology include sampling methodology, statistics, GIS, modeling, environmental chemistry, molecular biology, and field work.

Courses after Biology 107 and 108: Biology 208 (Principles of Ecology), Biology 207 (Molecular Genetics and Heredity), Botany 205 (Fundamentals of Plant Biology), Entomology 220 (Insect Diversity) or Zoology 250 (Survey of Invertebrates), Microbiology 265 (General Microbiology), Zoology 224 (Vertebrate Diversity) or Zoology 325 (Comparative Vertebrate Anatomy), Biology 299 optional (Research Opportunity Program)

Career options with BSc: Environmental consultant, eco-tourism, pest management, field technologist, laboratory technologist, environmental NGO, environmental law enforcement, interpreter, naturalist, forensic biology, science writer, professional school (law, graduate studies).

Evolutionary Biology

The **Evolutionary Biology** program involves the study of the diversity of organisms including the identification and classification of species, both living and extinct, their evolutionary relationships, adaptations and genetic variations, the ways in which species originate and become extinct, and the mechanisms behind evolutionary change. Students may wish to study a broad overview of evolutionary biology or do a concentration in one of the program "streams": Evolutionary Biology of Vertebrates, Evolution of Development, or Molecular Ecology and Systematics (described on departmental website *www.biology.ualberta.ca*). Techniques/skills used in evolutionary biology include working with a variety of collections, species identification, dissections, microscopy, bioinformatics, and molecular biology.

Courses after Biology 107 and 108: Biology 207 (Molecular Genetics and Heredity), Biology 208 (Principles of Ecology), Biology 321 (Mechanisms of Evolution), Botany 205 (Fundamentals of Plant Biology), Entomology 220 (Insect Diversity), Microbiology 265 (General Microbiology), Zoology 224 (Vertebrate Diversity), Zoology 250 (Survey of Invertebrates), Biology 299 optional (Research Opportunity Program)

Career options with BSc: Curatorial technologist, consultant, forensic science, interpreter, naturalist, environmental assessments, laboratory technologist, field technologists, science writer, professional school (graduate studies).

Microbiology

The **Microbiology** program involves the study of microorganisms including bacteria, archaea, fungi, protozoa and viruses. Courses introduce microbial genetics, cell structure, function and biochemistry, microbial ecology and diversity, and glycobiology. These fundamentals are applied to understanding microbial processes having pathogenic or beneficial effects on human health, animals, plants and the environment, or are exploited in industrial biotechnology. Techniques and skills used in microbiology include aseptic technique, culturing microbes, biochemistry, molecular biology, chemical and enzyme analysis, and data documentation.

Courses after Biology 107 and 108: Biology 201 (Eukaryotic Cell Biology), Biology 207 (Molecular Genetics and Heredity), Biology 208 (Principles of Ecology), Genetics 270 (Foundations of Molecular Genetics), Immunology and Infection 200 (Infection and Immunity), Microbiology 265 (General Microbiology), Biology 299 optional (Research Opportunity Program)

Career options with BSc: Laboratory technologist (research, diagnostics, industry), food and water quality inspector, brewing and food quality control, environmental or bioremediation consultant, wastewater treatment, biotechnology supply sales, government agencies, field technologist, patent officer, science writer, professional school (health, law, graduate studies).

Molecular Biology and Genetics

The Molecular Biology and Genetics program introduces students to the study of heredity and variation in biological systems at the level of molecules that transmit and express genetic information. Courses provide the foundational theory and knowledge for understanding the organization and function of simple and complex genomes, gene expression and regulation, gene manipulation, and genetic control of development. Techniques/skills used in molecular biology and genetics include mutagenesis, recombinant

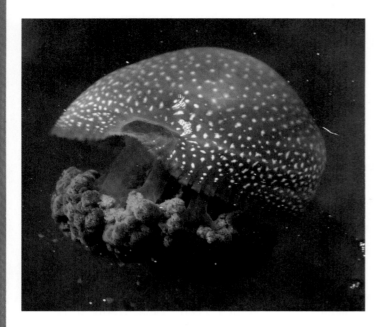

technologies, transgenes, cytogenetics, bioinformatics, evolutionary sequence comparisons, and whole genome sequence analysis.

Courses after Biology 107 and 108: Biology 207 (Molecular Genetics and Heredity) and Genetics 270 (Foundations of Molecular Genetics), as well as Biology 201 (Eukaryotic Cell Biology), Biology 208 (Principles of Ecology), Microbiology 265 (General Microbiology), Biology 299 optional (Research Opportunity Program)

Career options with a BSc: Biotechnologist, scientific writing and/or reviewing, manufacturing and sales of genetic technologies and equipment, medical research, consultant, laboratory technologist, pharmaceuticals, professional schools (health, law, graduate studies).

Physiology, Cell Biology and Developmental Biology

The **Physiology, Cell Biology and Developmental Biology** program studies the processes that occur within all living organisms including the regulation of functions at the subcellular, cell, tissue, organ and whole animal levels, as well as their interactions and integration. Students have the opportunity to study a diverse range of topics such as endocrinology, neurophysiology, developmental biology, immunology, cell signaling, toxicology, and environmental physiology in a wide variety of organisms. Techniques/skills used include microscopy, imaging, molecular biology, biochemistry, cell/tissue culture, electrophysiology, flow cytometry, and spectrometry.

Courses after Biology 107 and 108: Biology 201 (Eukaryotic Cell Biology), Biology 207, Biology 208, Zoology 241 (Animal Physiology: Homeostasis), Zoology 242 (Animal

Physiology: Intercellular Connections), Zoology 303 (Animal Developmental Biology), Zoology 344 (Laboratory Exercises in Animal Physiology, Biology 299 optional (Research Opportunity Program)

Career options with a BSc: Bio-medical technologist, government and industrial consultant, laboratory technologist, pharmaceuticals, professional school (health, law, graduate studies).

Plant Biology

The **Plant Biology** program offers studies of algae, fungi, vasculplants, non-vascular plants such as bryophytes. Courses emphasize diversity, evolution, ecology, physiology, development, genetics and biotechnology. Techniques used in plant biology labs include biochemistry, cell biology, field work, genetics, genomics, microscopy, molecular biology, physiology and working with collections.

Courses after Biology 107 and 108: Biology 207 (Molecular Genetics and Heredity), Biology 208 (Principles of Ecology), Botany 205 (Fundamentals of Botany), Biology 299 optional (Research Opportunity Program

Career options with BSc: Environmental technician, ecologist, laboratory technologist, food or crop inspector, nursery or seed technician, horticulturalist, field technologist, curatorial technologist, interpreter, naturalist, professional or graduate school, consultant, science writer, professional school (graduate school).

Collaborative Programs

Bioinformatics

Bioinformatics is a collaborative program offered by the Department of Biological Sciences and the Department of Computing Science. The goal of the program is to train students to understand, develop and use computational tools and large sets of sequence data to answer questions in biology and medicine. Students take a modified "common first year" in order to include a sequence of computing sciences courses CMPUT 114 (Introduction to Computing Science) and CMPUT115 (Programming with Data Structures) or CMPUT 174 (Introduction to the Foundations of Computation I) and CMPUT175 (Introduction to the Foundations of Computation II). Techniques/skills used in bioinformatics include programming skills, mapping and analyzing DNA and protein sequences, evolutionary sequence comparisons and whole genome sequence analysis.

Courses after Biology 107 and 108: Biology 207 (Molecular Genetics and Heredity), Biology 208 (Principles of Ecology), Computing Science 201 (Practical Programming Methodology), Bioinformatics 301 (Bioinformatics 1).

Career options with a BSc: Programmer, software developer, database manager, biotechnologist, professional school (health and graduate studies).

Immunology and Infection

Immunology and Infection is a collaborative program offered by the Department of Biological Sciences and the Department of Medical Microbiology and Immunology. This is a broadly based program that considers the full range of host responses to pathogens that occur in living organisms. The program has three over-lapping themes: function of the innate and adaptive immune system in a diversity of organisms, the biology of prokaryotic, eukaryotic and viral pathogens, and the biology of host-pathogen interactions. Techniques/skills used in studying immunology and infection are microscopy, molecular biology, cell biology, biochemistry, genomics and proteomics.

Courses after Biology 107 and 108: Biology 201 (Eukaryotic Cell Biology), Biology 207 (Molecular Genetics and Heredity), Biology 208 (Principles of Ecology), Immunology and Infection 200 (Infection and Immunity), Microbiology 265 (General Microbiology)

Career options with a BSc: Laboratory technologist, biotechnology, food inspector, consultant, professional school (health and graduate studies).

Paleontology

The **Paleontology** program is a collaborative program offered by the Department of Biological Sciences and the Department of Earth and Atmospheric Science. The program requires students to gain a broad knowledge of both biological and geological topics including vertebrate and invertebrate paleobiology, evolutionary biology, systematics, functional morphology, sedimentology, stratigraphy and plate tectonics. Techniques/skills used in paleontology are dissection, petrographic sectioning, scanning electron microscopy, species identification, fossil preparation, illustration, 3-D imaging and digital modeling, statistical analyses, biomechanical analyses, and GIS.

Courses after Biology 107 and 108: EAS 100 (Planet Earth), EAS 105(The Dynamic Earth Through Time), EAS 110 Earth Sciences Field School), Biology 207 (Molecular Genetics and Heredity), Biology 208 (Principles of Ecology), EAS 222 (Stratigraphy and Sedimentation), EAS 230 (Introduction to Invertebrate Paleontology), EAS 234 (Geology Field School).

Career options with a BSc: Science writer, scientific illustrator, museum or science centre interpreter, naturalist, consultant, fossil preparation technician, field technologist (petroleum/seismic/construction), curatorial technologist, science education and outreach, micropaleontologist petroleum company, professional school (graduate studies).

Industrial Internship Program

The **Industrial Internship Program** is similar to a co-op program and is available to students enrolled in a Specialization or Honors program in the Department of Biological Sciences. The program formally integrates a student's university education with work experience in co-operating employer organizations. It offers undergraduate students, between the third and fourth year of study, paid work experience in a corporate, industrial or government setting. The internship is for a continuous single-work period of 8, 12, or 16 months. Eligible students must be in good standing in an Honors or Specialization Program in Biological Sciences.

Professional Programs

Pursuing an Honors or Specialization degree in Biological Sciences is an excellent first step towards meeting the course requirements for professional programs in the health and veterinary sciences. For example, the University of Alberta medical school requires that applicants have completed a minimum of 60 credits with 6 credits in biology, 6 in general chemistry, 6 in organic chemistry, 6 in physics, 3 in biochemistry, 3 in statistics, and 6 in English. Except for the 6 credits in physics, these courses are all part of core requirements in programs in Biological Sciences, and physics can be easily added as a science option. Medicine recommends that applicants complete a Bachelors degree, and programs in Biological Sciences offer training in relevant areas connected to human health such as genetics, microbiology, physiology, and immunology. Similar requirements are required for admission to either the University of Calgary Faculty of Veterinary Medicine or Western College of Veterinary Medicine.

Dr. P's Tips for Becoming a Professional Biologist

Are you interested in pursuing a career in the Biological Sciences? Below find some general advice:

- Enroll in an Honors or Specialization program in Biological Sciences. These programs will ensure that you take courses needed for a fundamental education in the area of biology that interests you. You will also be assigned an advisor who is a professional biologist and can answer specific questions about your program and career plans.
- Take courses that offer hands-on experience. These are typically courses with laboratories (or sometimes seminars) that will teach you how to perform laboratory or field procedures, identify organisms, collect and analyze data, and other pertinent skills. Yes, these courses are more work for 3 credits than lecture only courses, but it is worth it.
- Take project courses such as Biology 299, 398, 399, 498 and 499, which actually allow you to participate in research projects and conduct your own research.
- Take courses that will help you to learn to write, use statistics, give presentations, and develop computer skills. Professional biologist need to be able to handle data and communicate their findings effectively.
- Maintain a good Grade Point Average. In the Department of Biological Sciences at U of AB, a GPA of 3.3 is required to enter a graduate program (MSc or PhD). An even higher GPA is needed to get financial support for graduate studies such as a Graduate Teaching Award or an NSERC Post-graduate Scholarship.
- Participate in student activities that allow you to meet people with similar interests in science and biology. These connections and contacts can prove important in the future.
- Talk to the graduate students who work as teaching assistants in your courses. They have diverse backgrounds and can give you advice about course work and jobs based on their own experiences.
- Apply for jobs during the school year, and particularly during the summer, that will allow you to participate in research projects in the laboratory, in collections or facilities, or in fieldwork. These may be through Biological Sciences, other departments on campus, or other organizations (e.g., NGOs, government agencies). The pay may not be phenomenal, but the experience is invaluable.

- It is sometimes difficult for beginning students with limited experience to break into the job market for undergraduate assistants. If you can not find a job, volunteer to help with a lab or field project, or in one of the collections on campus.
- Get to know professors personally. This can lead to a job in the department or finding a supervisor for a project course like BIOL 499. You may even eventually join a professor's lab as a graduate student. Remember, professors have connections in the local and international academic community. Many collaborate with industry and government. Professors can recommend you to colleagues and often know about current job and research opportunities inside and outside academia. They are an important source of reference letters for whatever activities you plan after graduation.

Cindy Paszkowski (aka Dr. P)

AB Biology (Albion College); MSc and PhD Zoology (University of Wisconsin-Madison)
Current positions: Professor and Associate Chair Research, Biological Sciences, University of Alberta

In Grade 3 I stated that I wanted to become a Zoologist, and I did. I joined the University of Alberta in mid-1980's and have taught Biology 108 and a variety of courses in ecology and vertebrate biology. Along with my students and husband, Dr. Bill Tonn (also a professor in Biological Sciences) I have conducted research on freshwater fish, amphibians, and birds all over the province. I have a long involvement with the department's undergraduate programs. As the former Associate Chair Undergraduate, I helped develop the Writing to Learn initiative in Biology 107 and 108 and to promote the use of microscopes in laboratory teaching.

1

Introduction: Themes in the Study of Life

▲ **Figure 1.1 How is the mother-of-pearl plant adapted to its environment?**

KEY CONCEPTS

1.1 The themes of this book make connections across different areas of biology

1.2 The Core Theme: Evolution accounts for the unity and diversity of life

1.3 In studying nature, scientists make observations and then form and test hypotheses

1.4 Science benefits from a cooperative approach and diverse viewpoints

OVERVIEW

Inquiring About Life

The mother-of-pearl plant, or ghost plant (**Figure 1.1** and cover), is native to a single mountain in northeastern Mexico. Its fleshy, succulent leaves and other features allow this plant to store and conserve water. Even when rain falls, the plant's access to water is limited because it grows in crevices

of vertical rock walls, where little soil is present to hold rainwater (**Figure 1.2**). The plant's water-conserving characteristics help it survive and thrive in these nooks and crannies. Similar features are found in many plants that live in dry environments, allowing them to eke out a living where rain is unpredictable.

An organism's adaptations to its environment, such as adaptations for conserving water, are the result of **evolution**, the process of change that has transformed life on Earth from its earliest beginnings to the diversity of organisms living today. Evolution is the fundamental organizing principle of biology and the core theme of this book.

Although biologists know a great deal about life on Earth, many mysteries remain. For instance, what exactly led to the origin of flowering among plants such as the one pictured here? Posing questions about the living world and seeking science-based answers—scientific inquiry—are the central activities of **biology**, the scientific study of life. Biologists' questions can be ambitious. They may ask how a single tiny cell becomes a tree or a dog, how the human mind works, or how the different forms of life in a forest interact. Most people wonder about the organisms living around them, and many interesting questions probably occur to you when you are out-of-doors, surrounded by the natural world. When they do, you are already thinking like a biologist. More than anything else, biology is a quest, an ongoing inquiry about the nature of life.

What is life? Even a small child realizes that a dog or a plant is alive, while a rock or a lawn mower is not. Yet the phenomenon we call life defies a simple, one-sentence definition. We recognize life by what living things do. **Figure 1.3**, on the next page, highlights some of the properties and processes we associate with life.

While limited to a handful of images, Figure 1.3 reminds us that the living world is wondrously varied. How do biologists

▲ **Figure 1.2 The mother-of-pearl plant (*Graptopetalum paraguayense*).** This plant's thick leaves hold water, enabling it to live where soil is scarce. The leaves vary in color, as seen here.

▼ Order. This close-up of a sunflower illustrates the highly ordered structure that characterizes life.

▲ Response to the environment. This Venus flytrap closed its trap rapidly in response to the environmental stimulus of a damselfly landing on the open trap.

▲ Evolutionary adaptation. The appearance of this pygmy sea horse camouflages the animal in its environment. Such adaptations evolve over many generations by the reproductive success of those individuals with heritable traits that are best suited to their environments.

► Reproduction. Organisms (living things) reproduce their own kind. Here, a baby giraffe stands close to its mother.

▲ Regulation. The regulation of blood flow through the blood vessels of this jackrabbit's ears helps maintain a constant body temperature by adjusting heat exchange with the surrounding air.

▲ Energy processing. This hummingbird obtains fuel in the form of nectar from flowers. The hummingbird will use chemical energy stored in its food to power flight and other work.

◄ Growth and development. Inherited information carried by genes controls the pattern of growth and development of organisms, such as this Nile crocodile.

▲ Figure 1.3 Some properties of life.

make sense of this diversity and complexity? This opening chapter sets up a framework for answering this question. The first part of the chapter provides a panoramic view of the biological "landscape," organized around some unifying themes. We then focus on biology's core theme, evolution, with an introduction to the reasoning that led Charles Darwin to his explanatory theory. Next, we look at scientific inquiry—how scientists raise and attempt to answer questions about the natural world. Finally, we address the culture of science and its effects on society.

CONCEPT **1.1**

The themes of this book make connections across different areas of biology

Biology is a subject of enormous scope, and news reports reveal exciting new biological discoveries being made every day. Simply memorizing the factual details of this huge subject is most likely not the best way to develop a coherent view of life. A better approach is to take a more active role by connecting the many things you learn to a set of themes that pervade all of biology. Focusing on a few big ideas—ways of thinking about life that will still hold true decades from now—will help you organize and make sense of all the information you'll encounter as you study biology. To help you, we have selected eight unifying themes to serve as touchstones as you proceed through this book.

Theme: New Properties Emerge at Each Level in the Biological Hierarchy

The study of life extends from the microscopic scale of the molecules and cells that make up organisms to the global scale of the entire living planet. We can divide this enormous range into different levels of biological organization.

Imagine zooming in from space to take a closer and closer look at life on Earth. It is spring in Ontario, Canada, and our destination is a local forest, where we will eventually explore a maple leaf right down to the molecular level. **Figure 1.4**, on the next two pages, narrates this journey into life, with the numbers leading you through the levels of biological organization illustrated by the photographs.

Emergent Properties

If we now zoom back out from the molecular level in Figure 1.4, we can see that novel properties emerge at each step, properties that are not present at the preceding level. These **emergent properties** are due to the arrangement and interactions of parts as complexity increases. For example, although photosynthesis occurs in an intact chloroplast, it will not take place in a disorganized test-tube mixture of chlorophyll and other chloroplast molecules. Photosynthesis requires a specific organization of these molecules in the chloroplast. To take another example, if a blow to the head disrupts the intricate architecture of a human brain, the mind may cease to function properly even though all of the brain tissues are still present. Our thoughts and memories are emergent properties of a complex network of nerve cells. At a much higher level of biological organization—at the ecosystem level—the recycling of chemical elements essential to life, such as carbon, depends on a network of diverse organisms interacting with each other and with the soil, water, and air.

Emergent properties are not unique to life. A box of bicycle parts won't take you anywhere, but if they are arranged in a certain way, you can pedal to your chosen destination. And while the graphite in a pencil "lead" and the diamond in a wedding ring are both pure carbon, they have very different appearances and properties due to the different arrangements of their carbon atoms. Both of these examples point out the importance of arrangement. Compared to such nonliving examples, however, the unrivaled complexity of biological systems makes the emergent properties of life especially challenging to study.

The Power and Limitations of Reductionism

Because the properties of life emerge from complex organization, scientists seeking to understand biological systems confront a dilemma. On the one hand, we cannot fully explain a higher level of order by breaking it down into its parts. A dissected animal no longer functions; a cell reduced to its chemical ingredients is no longer a cell. Disrupting a living system interferes with its functioning. On the other hand, something as complex as an organism or a cell cannot be analyzed without taking it apart.

Reductionism—the approach of reducing complex systems to simpler components that are more manageable to study—is a powerful strategy in biology. For example, by studying the molecular structure of DNA that had been extracted from cells, James Watson and Francis Crick inferred, in 1953, how this molecule could serve as the chemical basis of inheritance. The central role of DNA in cells and organisms became better understood, however, when scientists were able to study the interactions of DNA with other molecules. Biologists must balance the reductionist strategy with the larger-scale, holistic objective of understanding emergent properties—how the parts of cells, organisms, and higher levels of order, such as ecosystems, work together. This is the goal of an approach developed over the last 50 years called systems biology.

Systems Biology

A system is simply a combination of components that function together. A biologist can study a system at any level of organization. A single leaf cell can be considered a system, as can a frog, an ant colony, or a desert ecosytem. To understand how such systems work, it is not enough to have a "parts list," even a complete one. Realizing this, many researchers are now complementing the reductionist approach with new strategies for studying whole systems. This change in perspective is analogous to moving from ground level on a street corner, where you can observe local traffic, to a helicopter high above a city, from which you can see how variables such as time of day, construction projects, accidents, and traffic-signal malfunctions affect traffic throughout the city.

Systems biology is an approach that attempts to model the dynamic behavior of whole biological systems based on a study of the interactions among the system's parts. Successful models enable biologists to predict how a change in one or more variables will affect other components and the whole system. Thus, the systems approach enables us to pose new kinds of questions. How might a drug that lowers blood pressure affect the functioning of organs throughout the human body? How might increasing a crop's water supply affect processes in the plants, such as the storage of molecules essential for human nutrition? How might a gradual increase in atmospheric carbon dioxide alter ecosystems and the entire biosphere? The ultimate aim of systems biology is to answer large-scale questions like the last one.

Exploring Levels of Biological Organization

◄ 1 The Biosphere

As soon as we are near enough to Earth to make out its continents and oceans, we begin to see signs of life—in the green mosaic of the planet's forests, for example. This is our first view of the biosphere, which consists of all life on Earth and all the places where life exists—most regions of land, most bodies of water, the atmosphere to an altitude of several kilometers, and even sediments far below the ocean floor and rocks many kilometers below Earth's surface.

◄ 2 Ecosystems

As we approach Earth's surface for an imaginary landing in Ontario, we can begin to make out a forest with an abundance of trees that lose their leaves in one season and grow new ones in another (deciduous trees). Such a deciduous forest is an example of an ecosystem. Grasslands, deserts, and the ocean's coral reefs are other types of ecosystems. An ecosystem consists of all the living things in a particular area, along with all the nonliving components of the environment with which life interacts, such as soil, water, atmospheric gases, and light. All of Earth's ecosystems combined make up the biosphere.

▶ 3 Communities

The entire array of organisms inhabiting a particular ecosystem is called a biological community. The community in our forest ecosystem includes many kinds of trees and other plants, a diversity of animals, various mushrooms and other fungi, and enormous numbers of diverse microorganisms, which are living forms, such as bacteria, that are too small to see without a microscope. Each of these forms of life is called a *species*.

▶ 4 Populations

A population consists of all the individuals of a species living within the bounds of a specified area. For example, our Ontario forest includes a population of sugar maple trees and a population of white-tailed deer. We can now refine our definition of a community as the set of populations that inhabit a particular area.

▲ 5 Organisms

Individual living things are called organisms. Each of the maple trees and other plants in the forest is an organism, and so is each forest animal—whether deer, squirrel, frog, or beetle. The soil teems with microorganisms such as bacteria.

▼6 Organs and Organ Systems

The structural hierarchy of life continues to unfold as we explore the architecture of the more complex organisms. A maple leaf is an example of an organ, a body part that carries out a particular function in the body. Stems and roots are the other major organs of plants. Examples of human organs are the brain, heart, and kidney. The organs of humans, other complex animals, and plants are organized into organ systems, each a team of organs that cooperate in a larger function. For example, the human digestive system includes such organs as the tongue, stomach, and intestines. Organs consist of multiple tissues.

50 µm

◄7 Tissues

Our next scale change—to see the tissues of a leaf—requires a microscope. Each tissue is made up of a group of cells that work together, performing a specialized function. The leaf shown here has been cut on an angle. The honeycombed tissue in the interior of the leaf (left portion of photo) is the main location of photosynthesis, the process that converts light energy to the chemical energy of sugar and other food. We are viewing the sliced leaf from a perspective that also enables us to see the jigsaw puzzle–like "skin" on the surface of the leaf, a tissue called epidermis (right part of photo). The pores through the epidermis allow the gas carbon dioxide, a raw material for sugar production, to reach the photosynthetic tissue inside the leaf. At this scale, we can also see that each tissue has a distinct cellular structure.

Cell

10 µm

►9 Organelles

Chloroplasts are examples of organelles, the various functional components present in cells. In this image, a very powerful tool called an electron microscope brings a single chloroplast into sharp focus.

Chloroplast

1 µm

◄8 Cells

The cell is life's fundamental unit of structure and function. Some organisms, such as amoebas and most bacteria, are single cells. Other organisms, including plants and animals, are multicellular. Instead of a single cell performing all the functions of life, a multicellular organism has a division of labor among specialized cells. A human body consists of trillions of microscopic cells of many different kinds, such as muscle cells and nerve cells, which are organized into the various specialized tissues. For example, muscle tissue consists of bundles of muscle cells. In the photo at the upper left, we see a more highly magnified view of some cells in a leaf tissue. One cell is only about 40 micrometers (µm) across. It would take about 500 of these cells to reach across a small coin. As tiny as these cells are, you can see that each contains numerous green structures called chloroplasts, which are responsible for photosynthesis.

►10 Molecules

Our last scale change drops us into a chloroplast for a view of life at the molecular level. A molecule is a chemical structure consisting of two or more small chemical units called atoms, which are represented as balls in this computer graphic of a chlorophyll molecule. Chlorophyll is the pigment molecule that makes a maple leaf green. One of the most important molecules on Earth, chlorophyll absorbs sunlight during the first step of photosynthesis. Within each chloroplast, millions of chlorophyll molecules, together with accessory molecules, are organized into the equipment that converts light energy to the chemical energy of food.

Atoms

Chlorophyll molecule

Systems biology is relevant to the study of life at all levels. During the early years of the 20th century, biologists studying how animal bodies function (animal physiology) began integrating data on how multiple organs coordinate processes such as the regulation of sugar concentration in the blood. And in the 1960s, scientists investigating ecosystems pioneered a more mathematically sophisticated systems approach with elaborate models diagramming the network of interactions between organisms and nonliving components of ecosystems, such as salt marshes. More recently, with the sequencing of DNA from many species, systems biology has taken hold at the cellular and molecular levels, as we'll describe later when we discuss DNA.

Theme: Organisms Interact with Other Organisms and the Physical Environment

Turn back again to Figure 1.4, this time focusing on the forest. In an ecosystem, each organism interacts continuously with its environment, which includes both other organisms and physical factors. The leaves of a tree, for example, absorb light from the sun, take in carbon dioxide from the air, and release oxygen to the air (Figure 1.5). Both the organism and the environment are affected by the interactions between them. For example, a plant takes up water and minerals from the soil through its roots, and its roots help form soil by breaking up rocks. On a global scale, plants and other photosynthetic organisms have generated all the oxygen in the air.

A tree also interacts with other organisms, such as soil microorganisms associated with its roots, insects that live in the tree, and animals that eat its leaves and fruit. Interactions between organisms ultimately result in the cycling of nutrients in ecosystems. For example, minerals acquired by a tree will eventually be returned to the soil by other organisms that decompose leaf litter, dead roots, and other organic debris. The minerals are then available to be taken up by plants again.

Like all organisms, we humans interact with our environment. Unfortunately, our interactions sometimes have drastic consequences. For example, since the Industrial Revolution in the 1800s, the burning of fossil fuels (coal, oil, and gas) has been increasing at an ever-accelerating pace. This practice releases gaseous compounds into the atmosphere, including prodigious amounts of carbon dioxide (CO_2). About half the human-generated CO_2 stays in the atmosphere, acting like a layer of glass around the planet that admits radiation that warms the Earth but prevents heat from radiating into outer space. Scientists estimate that the average temperature of the planet has risen 1°C since 1900 due to this "greenhouse effect," and they project an additional rise in average global temperature of at least 3°C over the course of the 21st century.

This global warming, a major aspect of **global climate change**, has already had dire effects on life-forms and their habitats all over planet Earth. Polar bears have lost a significant portion of the ice platform from which they hunt, and there are examples of small rodents and plant species that have shifted their ranges to higher altitudes, as well as bird populations that have altered their migration schedules. Only time will reveal the consequences of these changes. Scientists predict that even if we stopped burning fossil fuels today, it would take several centuries to return to preindustrial CO_2 levels. That scenario is highly improbable, so it is imperative that we learn all we can about the effects of global climate change on Earth and its populations. Acting as the stewards of our planet, we must strive to find ways to address this problem.

Theme: Life Requires Energy Transfer and Transformation

As you saw in Figure 1.5, a tree's leaves absorb sunlight. The input of energy from the sun makes life possible: A fundamental characteristic of living organisms is their use of energy to carry out life's activities. Moving, growing, reproducing, and the other activities of life are work, and work requires energy. In the business of living, organisms often

Sunlight

Leaves absorb light energy from the sun.

Leaves take in carbon dioxide from the air and release oxygen.

CO_2

O_2

Cycling of chemical nutrients

Leaves fall to the ground and are decomposed by organisms that return minerals to the soil.

Water and minerals in the soil are taken up by the tree through its roots.

Animals eat leaves and fruit from the tree.

▲ **Figure 1.5 Interactions of an African acacia tree with other organisms and the physical environment.**

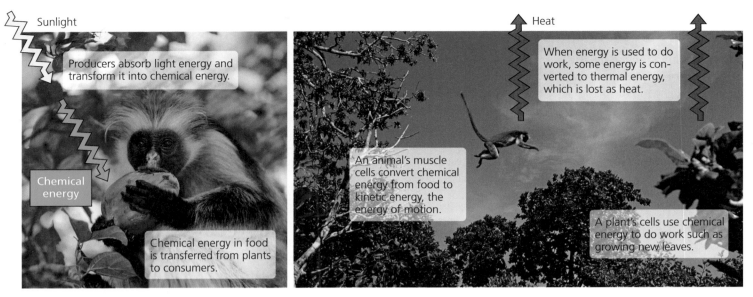

Producers absorb light energy and transform it into chemical energy.

Sunlight

Chemical energy

Chemical energy in food is transferred from plants to consumers.

Heat

When energy is used to do work, some energy is converted to thermal energy, which is lost as heat.

An animal's muscle cells convert chemical energy from food to kinetic energy, the energy of motion.

A plant's cells use chemical energy to do work such as growing new leaves.

(a) Energy flow from sunlight to producers to consumers

(b) Using energy to do work

▲ Figure 1.6 **Energy flow in an ecosystem.** This endangered Red Colobus monkey lives in Tanzania.

transform one form of energy to another. Chlorophyll molecules within the tree's leaves harness the energy of sunlight and use it to drive photosynthesis, converting carbon dioxide and water to sugar and oxygen. The chemical energy in sugar is then passed along by plants and other photosynthetic organisms (producers) to consumers. Consumers are organisms, such as animals, that feed on producers and other consumers **(Figure 1.6a)**.

An animal's muscle cells use sugar as fuel to power movements, converting chemical energy to kinetic energy, the energy of motion **(Figure 1.6b)**. The cells in a leaf use sugar to drive the process of cell proliferation during leaf growth, transforming stored chemical energy into cellular work. In both cases, some of the energy is converted to thermal energy, which dissipates to the surroundings as heat. In contrast to chemical nutrients, which recycle within an ecosystem, energy flows through an ecosystem, usually entering as light and exiting as heat.

Theme: Structure and Function Are Correlated at All Levels of Biological Organization

Another theme evident in Figure 1.4 is the idea that form fits function, which you'll recognize from everyday life. For example, a screwdriver is suited to tighten or loosen screws, a hammer to pound nails. How a device works is correlated with its structure. Applied to biology, this theme is a guide to the anatomy of life at all its structural levels. An example from Figure 1.4 is seen in the leaf: Its thin, flat shape maximizes the amount of sunlight that can be captured by its chloroplasts. Analyzing a biological structure gives us clues about what it does and how it works. Conversely, knowing the function of something provides insight into its construction. An example from the animal kingdom, the wing of a bird, provides additional instances of the structure-function theme **(Figure 1.7)**. In exploring life on its different structural levels, we discover functional beauty at every turn.

(a) A bird's wings have an aerodynamically efficient shape.

(b) Wing bones have a honeycombed internal structure that is strong but lightweight.

▲ Figure 1.7 **Form fits function in a gull's wing. (a)** The shape of a bird's wings and **(b)** the structure of its bones make flight possible.

 How does form fit function in a human hand?

Theme: The Cell Is an Organism's Basic Unit of Structure and Function

In life's structural hierarchy, the cell has a special place as the lowest level of organization that can perform all activities required for life. Moreover, the activities of organisms are all based on the activities of cells. For instance, the movement of your eyes as you read this line is based on activities of muscle and nerve cells. Even a global process such as the recycling of carbon is the cumulative product of cellular activities, including the photosynthesis that occurs in the chloroplasts of leaf cells. Understanding how cells work is a major focus of biological research.

All cells share certain characteristics. For example, every cell is enclosed by a membrane that regulates the passage of materials between the cell and its surroundings. And every cell uses DNA as its genetic information. However, we can distinguish between two main forms of cells: prokaryotic cells and eukaryotic cells. The cells of two groups of microorganisms, called bacteria (singular, *bacterium*) and archaea (singular, *archaean*), are prokaryotic. All other forms of life, including plants and animals, are composed of eukaryotic cells.

A **eukaryotic cell** is subdivided by internal membranes into various membrane-enclosed organelles **(Figure 1.8)**. In most eukaryotic cells, the largest organelle is the nucleus, which contains the cell's DNA. The other organelles are located in the cytoplasm, the entire region between the nucleus and outer membrane of the cell. The chloroplast you saw in Figure 1.4 is an organelle found in eukaryotic cells that carry out photosynthesis. Prokaryotic cells are much simpler and generally smaller than eukaryotic cells, as seen clearly in Figure 1.8. In a **prokaryotic cell**, the DNA is not separated from the rest of the cell by enclosure in a membrane-bounded nucleus. Prokaryotic cells also lack the other kinds of membrane-enclosed organelles that characterize eukaryotic cells. The properties of all organisms, whether prokaryotic or eukaryotic, are based in the structure and function of cells.

Theme: The Continuity of Life Is Based on Heritable Information in the Form of DNA

The division of cells to form new cells is the foundation for all reproduction and for the growth and repair of multicellular organisms. Inside the dividing cell in **Figure 1.9**, you can see structures called chromosomes, which are stained with a blue-glowing dye. The chromosomes have almost all of the cell's genetic material, its **DNA** (short for deoxyribonucleic acid). DNA is the substance of **genes**, the units of inheritance that transmit information from parents to offspring. Your blood group (A, B, AB, or O), for example, is the result of certain genes that you inherited from your parents.

DNA Structure and Function

Each chromosome contains one very long DNA molecule, with hundreds or thousands of genes arranged along its length. The genes encode the information necessary to build other molecules in the cell, most notably proteins. Proteins play structural roles and are also responsible for carrying out cellular work. They thus establish a cell's identity.

The DNA of chromosomes replicates as a cell prepares to divide, and each of the two cellular offspring inherits a complete set of genes, identical to that of the parent cell. Each of us began life as a single cell stocked with DNA inherited from our parents. Replication of that DNA with each round of cell division transmitted copies of the DNA to our trillions of cells. The DNA controls the development and maintenance of the entire organism and, indirectly, everything the organism does **(Figure 1.10)**. The DNA serves as a central database.

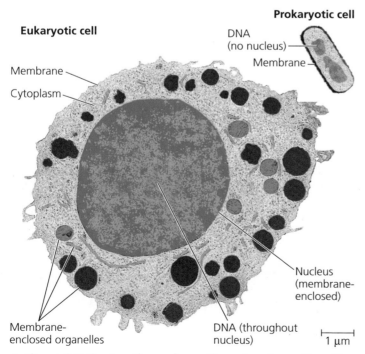

Eukaryotic cell

Prokaryotic cell

DNA (no nucleus)

Membrane

Membrane

Cytoplasm

Membrane-enclosed organelles

DNA (throughout nucleus)

Nucleus (membrane-enclosed)

1 μm

▲ Figure 1.8 **Contrasting eukaryotic and prokaryotic cells in size and complexity.**

25 μm

▲ Figure 1.9 **A lung cell from a newt divides into two smaller cells that will grow and divide again.**

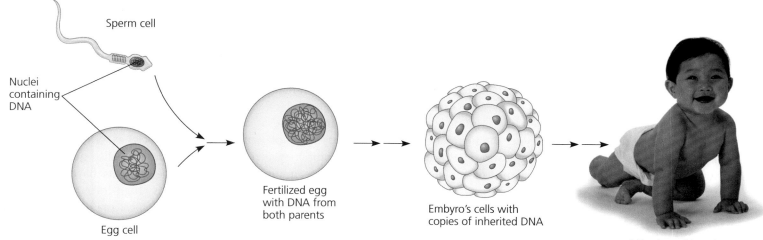

▲ Figure 1.10 **Inherited DNA directs development of an organism.**

Sperm cell

Nuclei containing DNA

Egg cell

Fertilized egg with DNA from both parents

Embyro's cells with copies of inherited DNA

Offspring with traits inherited from both parents

The molecular structure of DNA accounts for its ability to store information. Each DNA molecule is made up of two long chains, called strands, arranged in a double helix. Each chain is made up of four kinds of chemical building blocks called nucleotides, abbreviated A, T, C, and G **(Figure 1.11)**. The way DNA encodes information is analogous to how we arrange the letters of the alphabet into precise sequences with specific meanings. The word *rat*, for example, evokes a rodent; the words *tar* and *art*, which contain the same letters, mean very different things. We can think of nucleotides as a four-letter alphabet of inheritance. Specific sequential arrangements of these four nucleotide letters encode the information in genes, which are typically hundreds or thousands of nucleotides long.

DNA provides the blueprints for making proteins, and proteins are the main players in building and maintaining the cell and carrying out its activities. For instance, the information carried in a bacterial gene may specify a certain protein in a bacterial cell membrane, while the information in a human gene may denote a protein hormone that stimulates growth. Other human proteins include proteins in a muscle cell that drive contraction and the defensive proteins called antibodies. Enzymes, which catalyze (speed up) specific chemical reactions, are mostly proteins and are crucial to all cells.

The DNA of genes controls protein production indirectly, using a related kind of molecule called RNA as an intermediary. The sequence of nucleotides along a gene is transcribed into RNA, which is then translated into a specific protein with a unique shape and function. This entire process, by which the information in a gene directs the production of a cellular product, is called **gene expression**. In translating genes into proteins, all forms of life employ essentially the same genetic code. A particular sequence of nucleotides says the same thing in one organism as it does in another. Differences between organisms reflect differences between their nucleotide sequences rather than between their genetic codes.

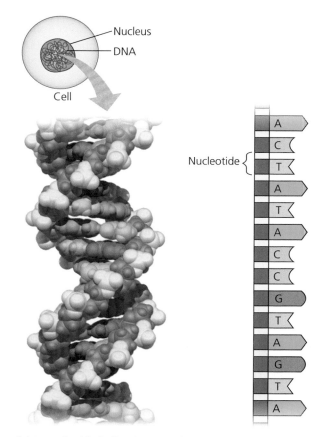

Nucleus

DNA

Cell

Nucleotide

A
C
T
A
T
A
C
C
G
T
A
G
T
A

(a) DNA double helix. This model shows each atom in a segment of DNA. Made up of two long chains of building blocks called nucleotides, a DNA molecule takes the three-dimensional form of a double helix.

(b) Single strand of DNA. These geometric shapes and letters are simple symbols for the nucleotides in a small section of one chain of a DNA molecule. Genetic information is encoded in specific sequences of the four types of nucleotides. (Their names are abbreviated A, T, C, and G.)

▲ Figure 1.11 **DNA: The genetic material.**

Not all RNA molecules in the cell are translated into protein; some RNAs carry out other important tasks. We have known for decades that some types of RNA are actually components of the cellular machinery that manufactures proteins. Recently, scientists have discovered whole new classes of RNA that play other roles in the cell, such as regulating the functioning of protein-coding genes. All these RNAs are specified by genes, and the process of their transcription is also referred to as gene expression. By carrying the instructions for making proteins and RNAs and by replicating with each cell division, DNA ensures faithful inheritance of genetic information from generation to generation.

Genomics: Large-Scale Analysis of DNA Sequences

The entire "library" of genetic instructions that an organism inherits is called its **genome**. A typical human cell has two similar sets of chromosomes, and each set has DNA totaling about 3 billion nucleotide pairs. If the one-letter abbreviations for the nucleotides of one strand were written in letters the size of those you are now reading, the genetic text would fill about 600 books the size of this one. Within this genomic library of nucleotide sequences are genes for about 75,000 kinds of proteins and an as yet unknown number of RNA molecules that do not code for proteins.

Since the early 1990s, the pace at which we can sequence genomes has accelerated at an almost unbelievable rate, enabled by a revolution in technology. The development of new methods and DNA-sequencing machines, such as those shown in **Figure 1.12**, have led the charge. The entire sequence of nucleotides in the human genome is now known, along with the genome sequences of many other organisms, including bacteria, archaea, fungi, plants, and other animals.

The sequencing of the human genome was heralded as a scientific and technological achievement comparable to landing the *Apollo* astronauts on the moon in 1969. But it

▲ **Figure 1.12 Biology as an information science.** Automatic DNA-sequencing machines and abundant computing power make the sequencing of genomes possible. This facility in Walnut Creek, California, is part of the Joint Genome Institute.

was only the beginning of an even bigger research endeavor, an effort to learn how the activities of the myriad proteins encoded by the DNA are coordinated in cells and whole organisms. To make sense of the deluge of data from genome-sequencing projects and the growing catalog of known protein functions, scientists are applying a systems approach at the cellular and molecular levels. Rather than investigating a single gene at a time, these researchers have shifted to studying whole sets of genes of a species as well as comparing genomes between species—an approach called **genomics**.

Three important research developments have made the genomic approach possible. One is "high-throughput" technology, tools that can analyze biological materials very rapidly and produce enormous amounts of data. The automatic DNA-sequencing machines that made the sequencing of the human genome possible are examples of high-throughput devices (see Figure 1.12). The second major development is **bioinformatics**, the use of computational tools to store, organize, and analyze the huge volume of data that result from high-throughput methods. The third key development is the formation of interdisciplinary research teams—melting pots of diverse specialists that may include computer scientists, mathematicians, engineers, chemists, physicists, and, of course, biologists from a variety of fields.

Theme: Feedback Mechanisms Regulate Biological Systems

Just as a coordinated control of traffic flow is necessary for a city to function smoothly, regulation of biological processes is crucial to the operation of living systems. Consider your muscles, for instance. When your muscle cells require more energy during exercise, they increase their consumption of the sugar molecules that serve as fuel. In contrast, when you rest, a different set of chemical reactions converts surplus sugar to storage molecules.

Like most of the cell's chemical processes, those that either decompose or store sugar are accelerated, or catalyzed, by proteins called enzymes. Each type of enzyme catalyzes a specific chemical reaction. In many cases, these reactions are linked into chemical pathways, each step with its own enzyme. How does the cell coordinate its various chemical pathways? In our example of sugar management, how does the cell match fuel supply to demand, regulating its opposing pathways of sugar consumption and storage? The key is the ability of many biological processes to self-regulate by a mechanism called feedback.

In feedback regulation, the output, or product, of a process regulates that very process. The most common form of regulation in living systems is **negative feedback**, in which accumulation of an end product of a process slows that process. For example, the cell's breakdown of sugar generates chemical energy in the form of a substance called ATP. When a cell makes more ATP than it can use, the excess ATP "feeds back"

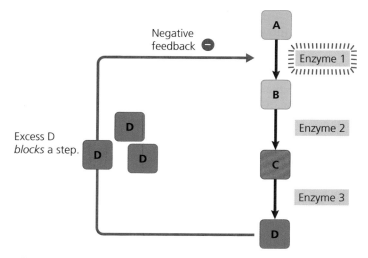

(a) Negative feedback. This three-step chemical pathway converts substance A to substance D. A specific enzyme catalyzes each chemical reaction. Accumulation of the final product (D) inhibits the first enzyme in the sequence, thus slowing down production of more D.

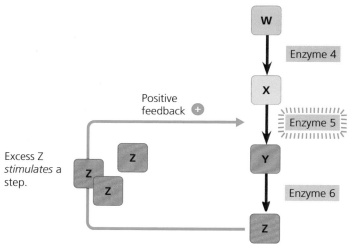

(b) Positive feedback. In a biochemical pathway regulated by positive feedback, a product stimulates an enzyme in the reaction sequence, increasing the rate of production of the product.

▲ **Figure 1.13 Regulation by feedback mechanisms.**

? *What would happen to the feedback system if enzyme 2 were missing?*

and inhibits an enzyme near the beginning of the pathway **(Figure 1.13a)**.

Though less common than processes regulated by negative feedback, there are also many biological processes regulated by **positive feedback**, in which an end product *speeds up* its own production **(Figure 1.13b)**. The clotting of your blood in response to injury is an example. When a blood vessel is damaged, structures in the blood called platelets begin to aggregate at the site. Positive feedback occurs as chemicals released by the platelets attract *more* platelets. The platelet pileup then initiates a complex process that seals the wound with a clot.

Feedback is a regulatory motif common to life at all levels, from the molecular level to ecosystems and the biosphere.

Such regulation is an example of the integration that makes living systems much greater than the sum of their parts.

Evolution, the Overarching Theme of Biology

Having considered all the other themes that run through this book, let's now turn to biology's core theme—evolution. Evolution is the one idea that makes sense of everything we know about living organisms. Life has been evolving on Earth for billions of years, resulting in a vast diversity of past and present organisms. But along with the diversity we find many shared features. For example, while the sea horse, jackrabbit, hummingbird, crocodile, and giraffes in Figure 1.3 look very different, their skeletons are basically similar. The scientific explanation for this unity and diversity—and for the suitability of organisms for their environments—is evolution: the idea that the organisms living on Earth today are the modified descendants of common ancestors. In other words, we can explain traits shared by two organisms with the idea that they have descended from a common ancestor, and we can account for differences with the idea that heritable changes have occurred along the way. Many kinds of evidence support the occurrence of evolution and the theory that describes how it takes place. In the next section, we'll consider the fundamental concept of evolution in greater detail.

CONCEPT CHECK 1.1

1. For each biological level in Figure 1.4, write a sentence that includes the next "lower" level. Example: "A community consists of *populations* of the various species inhabiting a specific area."
2. What theme or themes are exemplified by (a) the sharp spines of a porcupine, (b) the cloning of a plant from a single cell, and (c) a hummingbird using sugar to power its flight?
3. **WHAT IF?** For each theme discussed in this section, give an example not mentioned in the book.

For suggested answers, see Appendix A.

CONCEPT 1.2

The Core Theme: Evolution accounts for the unity and diversity of life

EVOLUTION The list of biological themes discussed in Concept 1.1 is not absolute; some people might find a shorter or longer list more useful. There is consensus among biologists, however, as to the core theme of biology: It is evolution. To quote one of the founders of modern evolutionary theory, Theodosius Dobzhansky, "Nothing in biology makes sense except in the light of evolution."

In addition to encompassing a hierarchy of size scales from molecules to the biosphere, biology extends across the great diversity of species that have ever lived on Earth. To understand Dobzhansky's statement, we need to discuss how biologists think about this vast diversity.

Classifying the Diversity of Life

Diversity is a hallmark of life. Biologists have so far identified and named about 1.8 million species. To date, this diversity of life is known to include at least 100,000 species of fungi, 290,000 plant species, 52,000 vertebrate species (animals with backbones), and 1 million insect species (more than half of all known forms of life)—not to mention the myriad types of single-celled organisms. Researchers identify thousands of additional species each year. Estimates of the total number of species range from about 10 million to over 100 million. Whatever the actual number, the enormous variety of life

gives biology a very broad scope. Biologists face a major challenge in attempting to make sense of this variety.

Grouping Species: The Basic Idea

There is a human tendency to group diverse items according to their similarities and their relationships to each other. For instance, we may speak of "squirrels" and "butterflies," though we recognize that many different species belong to each group. We may even sort groups into broader categories, such as rodents (which include squirrels) and insects (which include butterflies). Taxonomy, the branch of biology that names and classifies species, formalizes this ordering of species into groups of increasing breadth, based on the degree to which they share characteristics (**Figure 1.14**). You will learn more about the details of this taxonomic scheme in Chapter 26. For

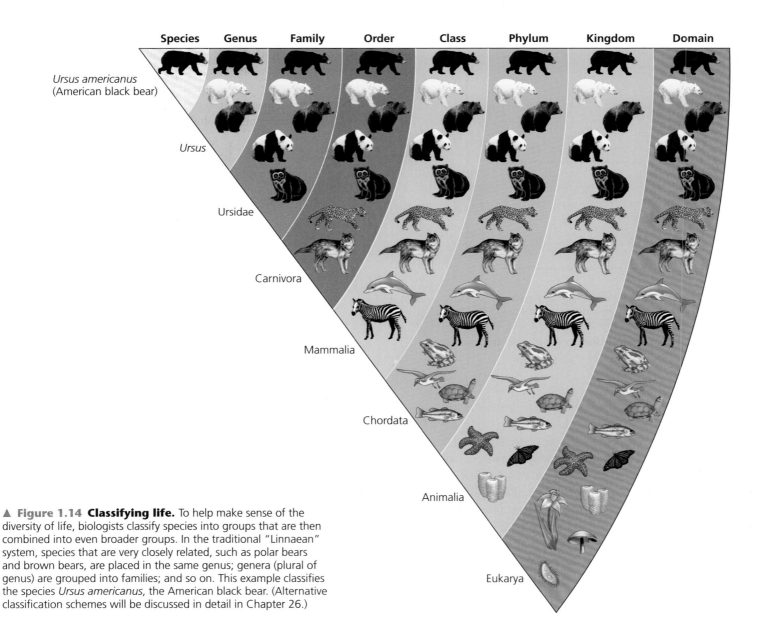

▲ **Figure 1.14 Classifying life.** To help make sense of the diversity of life, biologists classify species into groups that are then combined into even broader groups. In the traditional "Linnaean" system, species that are very closely related, such as polar bears and brown bears, are placed in the same genus; genera (plural of genus) are grouped into families; and so on. This example classifies the species *Ursus americanus*, the American black bear. (Alternative classification schemes will be discussed in detail in Chapter 26.)

now, we will focus on the big picture by considering the broadest units of classification, kingdoms and domains.

The Three Domains of Life

Historically, scientists have classified the diversity of life-forms into kingdoms and finer groupings by careful comparisons of structure, function, and other obvious features. In the last few decades, new methods of assessing species relationships, such as comparisons of DNA sequences, have led to an ongoing reevaluation of the number and boundaries of kingdoms. Researchers have proposed anywhere from six kingdoms to dozens of kingdoms. While debate continues at the kingdom level, there is consensus among biologists that the kingdoms of life can be grouped into three even higher levels of classification called domains. The three domains are named Bacteria, Archaea, and Eukarya (**Figure 1.15**).

The organisms making up two of the three domains—domain **Bacteria** and domain **Archaea**—are all prokaryotic. Most prokaryotes are single-celled and microscopic. Previously, bacteria and archaea were combined in a single kingdom because they shared the prokaryotic form of cell structure. But much evidence now supports the view that bacteria and archaea represent two very distinct branches of prokaryotic life, different in key ways that you'll learn about in Chapter 27. There is also evidence that archaea are at least as closely related to eukaryotic organisms as they are to bacteria.

All the eukaryotes (organisms with eukaryotic cells) are now grouped in domain **Eukarya**. This domain includes three kingdoms of multicellular eukaryotes: kingdoms Plantae,

---

▼ **Figure 1.15** **The three domains of life.**

(a) Domain Bacteria

Bacteria are the most diverse and widespread prokaryotes and are now classified into multiple kingdoms. Each rod-shaped structure in this photo is a bacterial cell.

(b) Domain Archaea

Many of the prokaryotes known as **archaea** live in Earth's extreme environments, such as salty lakes and boiling hot springs. Domain Archaea includes multiple kingdoms. Each round structure in this photo is an archaeal cell.

(c) Domain Eukarya

◄ **Kingdom Animalia** consists of multicellular eukaryotes that ingest other organisms.

▲ **Kingdom Plantae** consists of terrestrial multicellular eukaryotes (land plants) that carry out photosynthesis, the conversion of light energy to the chemical energy in food.

▶ **Kingdom Fungi** is defined in part by the nutritional mode of its members (such as this mushroom), which absorb nutrients from outside their bodies.

▶ **Protists** are mostly unicellular eukaryotes and some relatively simple multicellular relatives. Pictured here is an assortment of protists inhabiting pond water. Scientists are currently debating how to classify protists in a way that accurately reflects their evolutionary relationships.

Fungi, and Animalia. These three kingdoms are distinguished partly by their modes of nutrition. Plants produce their own sugars and other food molecules by photosynthesis. Fungi absorb dissolved nutrients from their surroundings; many decompose dead organisms and organic wastes (such as leaf litter and animal feces) and absorb nutrients from these sources. Animals obtain food by ingestion, which is the eating and digesting of other organisms. Animalia is, of course, the kingdom to which we belong. But neither animals, plants, nor fungi are as numerous or diverse as the single-celled eukaryotes we call protists. Although protists were once placed in a single kingdom, biologists now realize that they do not form a single natural group of species. And recent evidence shows that some protist groups are more closely related to multicellular eukaryotes such as animals and fungi than they are to each other. Thus, the recent taxonomic trend has been to split the protists into several groups.

Unity in the Diversity of Life

As diverse as life is, it also displays remarkable unity. Earlier we mentioned both the similar skeletons of different vertebrate animals and the universal genetic language of DNA (the genetic code). In fact, similarities between organisms are evident at all levels of the biological hierarchy. For example, unity is obvious in many features of cell structure **(Figure 1.16)**.

How can we account for life's dual nature of unity and diversity? The process of evolution, explained next, illuminates both the similarities and differences in the world of life and introduces another dimension of biology: historical time.

Charles Darwin and the Theory of Natural Selection

The history of life, as documented by fossils and other evidence, is the saga of a changing Earth billions of years old, inhabited by an evolving cast of living forms **(Figure 1.17)**. This evolutionary view of life came into sharp focus in November 1859, when Charles Robert Darwin published one of the most important and influential books ever written. Entitled *On the Origin of Species by Means of Natural Selection*, Darwin's book was an immediate bestseller and soon made "Darwinism," as it was dubbed at the time, almost synonymous with the concept of evolution **(Figure 1.18)**.

The Origin of Species articulated two main points. The first point was that contemporary species arose from a succession of ancestors, an idea that Darwin supported with a large amount of evidence. (We will discuss the evidence for evolution in detail in Chapter 22.) Darwin called this evolutionary history of species "descent with modification." It was an insightful phrase, as it captured the duality of life's unity and diversity—unity in the kinship among species that descended

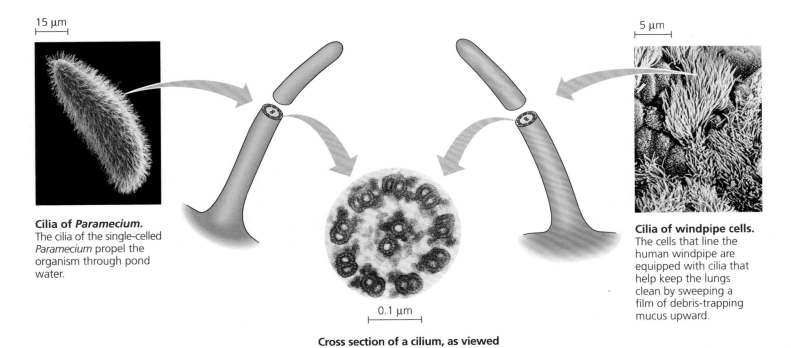

Cilia of *Paramecium*.
The cilia of the single-celled *Paramecium* propel the organism through pond water.

15 μm

Cross section of a cilium, as viewed with an electron microscope

0.1 μm

Cilia of windpipe cells.
The cells that line the human windpipe are equipped with cilia that help keep the lungs clean by sweeping a film of debris-trapping mucus upward.

5 μm

▲ **Figure 1.16 An example of unity underlying the diversity of life: the architecture of cilia in eukaryotes.** Cilia (singular, *cilium*) are extensions of cells that function in locomotion. They occur in eukaryotes as diverse as *Paramecium* and humans. Even organisms so different share a common architecture for their cilia, which have an elaborate system of tubules that is striking in cross-sectional views.

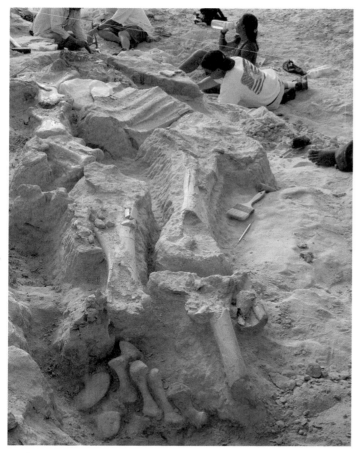

▲ **Figure 1.17 Digging into the past.** Paleontologists carefully excavate the hind leg of a long-necked dinosaur (*Rapetosaurus krausei*) from rocks in Madagascar.

from common ancestors, diversity in the modifications that evolved as species branched from their common ancestors (Figure 1.19). Darwin's second main point was a proposed mechanism for descent with modification. He called this evolutionary mechanism "natural selection."

Darwin synthesized his theory of natural selection from observations that by themselves were neither new nor

profound. Others had the pieces of the puzzle, but Darwin saw how they fit together. He started with the following three observations from nature: First, individuals in a population vary in their traits, many of which seem to be heritable (passed on from parents to offspring). Second, a population can produce far more offspring than can survive to produce offspring of their own. With more individuals than the environment is able to support, competition is inevitable. Third, species generally suit their environments—in other words, they

▲ **Figure 1.18 Charles Darwin as a young man.**

are adapted to their environments. For instance, a common adaptation among birds with tough seeds as their major food source is that they have especially strong beaks.

Darwin made inferences from these observations to arrive at his theory of evolution. He reasoned that individuals with inherited traits that are best suited to the local environment are more likely to survive and reproduce than less suited individuals. Over many generations, a higher and higher proportion of individuals in a population will have the advantageous traits. Evolution occurs as the unequal reproductive success of individuals ultimately leads to adaptation to their environment, as long as the environment remains the same.

Darwin called this mechanism of evolutionary adaptation **natural selection** because the natural environment "selects" for the propagation of certain traits among naturally occurring variant traits in the population. The example

◀ **Figure 1.19 Unity and diversity in the orchid family.** These three orchids are variations on a common floral theme. For example, each of these flowers has a liplike petal that helps attract pollinating insects and provides a landing platform for the pollinators.

① Population with varied inherited traits

② Elimination of individuals with certain traits

③ Reproduction of survivors

④ Increasing frequency of traits that enhance survival and reproductive success

▲ **Figure 1.20 Natural selection.** This imaginary beetle population has colonized a locale where the soil has been blackened by a recent brush fire. Initially, the population varies extensively in the inherited coloration of the individuals, from very light gray to charcoal. For hungry birds that prey on the beetles, it is easiest to spot the beetles that are lightest in color.

in **Figure 1.20** illustrates the ability of natural selection to "edit" a population's heritable variations in color. We see the products of natural selection in the exquisite adaptations of various organisms to the special circumstances of their way of life and their environment. The wings of the bat shown in **Figure 1.21** are an excellent example of adaptation.

The Tree of Life

Take another look at the skeletal architecture of the bat's wings in Figure 1.21. These forelimbs, though adapted for flight, actually have all the same bones, joints, nerves, and blood vessels found in other limbs as diverse as the human arm, the horse's foreleg, and the whale's flipper. Indeed, all mammalian forelimbs are anatomical variations of a common architecture, much as the flowers in Figure 1.19 are variations on an underlying "orchid" theme. Such examples of kinship connect life's unity in diversity to the Darwinian

concept of descent with modification. In this view, the unity of mammalian limb anatomy reflects inheritance of that structure from a common ancestor—the "prototype" mammal from which all other mammals descended. The diversity of mammalian forelimbs results from modification by natural selection operating over millions of generations in different environmental contexts. Fossils and other evidence corroborate anatomical unity in supporting this view of mammalian descent from a common ancestor.

Darwin proposed that natural selection, by its cumulative effects over long periods of time, could cause an ancestral species to give rise to two or more descendant species. This could occur, for example, if one population fragmented into several subpopulations isolated in different environments. In these separate arenas of natural selection, one species could gradually radiate into multiple species as the geographically isolated populations adapted over many generations to different sets of environmental factors.

The "family tree" of 14 finches in **Figure 1.22** illustrates a famous example of adaptive radiation of new species from a common ancestor. Darwin collected specimens of these birds during his 1835 visit to the remote Galápagos Islands, 900 kilometers (km) off the Pacific coast of South America. These relatively young, volcanic islands are home to many species of plants and animals found nowhere else in the world, though most Galápagos organisms are clearly related to species on the South American mainland. After volcanism built the Galápagos several million years ago, finches probably diversified on the various islands from an ancestral finch species that by chance reached the archipelago from elsewhere. (Once thought to have originated on the mainland of South America like many Galápagos organisms, the ancestral finches are now thought to have come from the West Indies—islands of the Caribbean that were once much closer to the Galápagos than they are now.)

▲ **Figure 1.21 Evolutionary adaptation.** Bats, the only mammals capable of active flight, have wings with webbing between extended "fingers." In the Darwinian view of life, such adaptations are refined over time by natural selection.

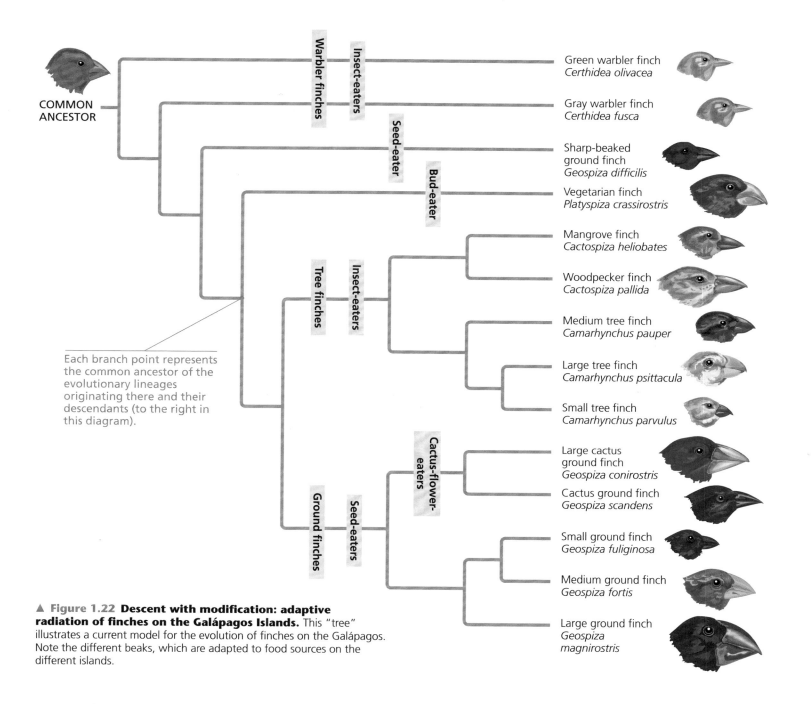

COMMON ANCESTOR

Warbler finches — Insect-eaters
- Green warbler finch *Certhidea olivacea*
- Gray warbler finch *Certhidea fusca*

Seed-eater
- Sharp-beaked ground finch *Geospiza difficilis*

Bud-eater
- Vegetarian finch *Platyspiza crassirostris*

Tree finches — Insect-eaters
- Mangrove finch *Cactospiza heliobates*
- Woodpecker finch *Cactospiza pallida*
- Medium tree finch *Camarhynchus pauper*
- Large tree finch *Camarhynchus psittacula*
- Small tree finch *Camarhynchus parvulus*

Ground finches — Seed-eaters — Cactus-flower-eaters
- Large cactus ground finch *Geospiza conirostris*
- Cactus ground finch *Geospiza scandens*
- Small ground finch *Geospiza fuliginosa*
- Medium ground finch *Geospiza fortis*
- Large ground finch *Geospiza magnirostris*

Each branch point represents the common ancestor of the evolutionary lineages originating there and their descendants (to the right in this diagram).

▲ Figure 1.22 **Descent with modification: adaptive radiation of finches on the Galápagos Islands.** This "tree" illustrates a current model for the evolution of finches on the Galápagos. Note the different beaks, which are adapted to food sources on the different islands.

Years after Darwin's collection of Galápagos finches, researchers began to sort out the relationships among the finch species, first from anatomical and geographic data and more recently with the help of DNA sequence comparisons.

Biologists' diagrams of evolutionary relationships generally take treelike forms, though today biologists usually turn the trees sideways as in Figure 1.22. Tree diagrams make sense: Just as an individual has a genealogy that can be diagrammed as a family tree, each species is one twig of a branching tree of life extending back in time through ancestral species more and more remote. Species that are very similar, such as the Galápagos finches, share a common ancestor at a relatively recent branch point on the tree of life. But through an ancestor that lived much farther back in time, finches are related to sparrows, hawks, penguins, and all other birds. And birds, mammals, and all other vertebrates share a common ancestor even more ancient. We find evidence of still broader relationships in such similarities as the identical construction of all eukaryotic cilia (see Figure 1.16). Trace life back far enough, and there are only fossils of the primeval prokaryotes that inhabited Earth over 3.5 billion years ago. We can recognize their vestiges in our own cells—in the universal genetic code, for example. All of life is connected through its long evolutionary history.

CONCEPT CHECK **1.2**

1. How is a mailing address analogous to biology's hierarchical taxonomic system?
2. Explain why "editing" is an appropriate metaphor for how natural selection acts on a population's heritable variation.
3. **WHAT IF?** The three domains you learned about in Concept 1.2 can be represented in the tree of life as the three main branches, with three subbranches on the eukaryotic branch being the kingdoms Plantae, Fungi, and Animalia. What if fungi and animals are more closely related to each other than either of these kingdoms is to plants—as recent evidence strongly suggests? Draw a simple branching pattern that symbolizes the proposed relationship between these three eukaryotic kingdoms.

For suggested answers, see Appendix A.

CONCEPT **1.3**

In studying nature, scientists make observations and then form and test hypotheses

The word *science* is derived from a Latin verb meaning "to know." **Science** is a way of knowing—an approach to understanding the natural world. It developed out of our curiosity about ourselves, other life-forms, our planet, and the universe. Striving to understand seems to be one of our basic urges.

At the heart of science is **inquiry**, a search for information and explanation, often focusing on specific questions. Inquiry drove Darwin to seek answers in nature for how species adapt to their environments. And today inquiry drives the genomic analyses that are helping us understand biological unity and diversity at the molecular level. In fact, the inquisitive mind is the engine that drives all progress in biology.

There is no formula for successful scientific inquiry, no single scientific method with a rule book that researchers must rigidly follow. As in all quests, science includes elements of challenge, adventure, and luck, along with careful planning, reasoning, creativity, cooperation, competition, patience, and the persistence to overcome setbacks. Such diverse elements of inquiry make science far less structured than most people realize. That said, it is possible to distill certain characteristics that help to distinguish science from other ways of describing and explaining nature.

Scientists attempt to understand how natural phenomena work using a process of inquiry that includes making observations, forming logical hypotheses, and testing them. The process is necessarily repetitive: In testing a hypothesis, more observations may force formation of a new hypothesis or revision of the original one, and further testing. In this way,

scientists circle closer and closer to their best estimation of the laws governing nature.

Making Observations

In the course of their work, scientists describe natural structures and processes as accurately as possible through careful observation and analysis of data. The observations are often valuable in their own right. For example, a series of detailed observations have shaped our understanding of cell structure, and another set of observations are currently expanding our databases of genomes of diverse species.

Types of Data

Observation is the use of the senses to gather information, either directly or indirectly with the help of tools such as microscopes that extend our senses. Recorded observations are called **data**. Put another way, data are items of information on which scientific inquiry is based.

The term *data* implies numbers to many people. But some data are *qualitative*, often in the form of recorded descriptions rather than numerical measurements. For example, Jane Goodall spent decades recording her observations of chimpanzee behavior during field research in a Tanzanian jungle **(Figure 1.23)**. She also documented her observations with photographs and movies. Along with these qualitative data, Goodall also enriched the field of animal behavior with volumes of *quantitative* data, which are generally recorded as

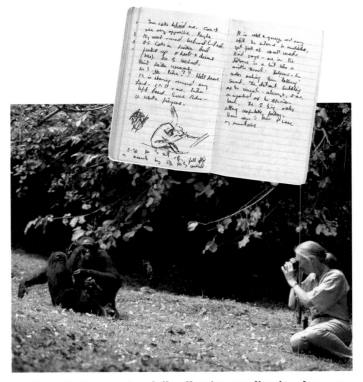

▲ **Figure 1.23 Jane Goodall collecting qualitative data on chimpanzee behavior.** Goodall recorded her observations in field notebooks, often with sketches of the animals' behavior.

measurements. Skim through any of the scientific journals in your college library, and you'll see many examples of quantitative data organized into tables and graphs.

Inductive Reasoning

Collecting and analyzing observations can lead to important conclusions based on a type of logic called **inductive reasoning**. Through induction, we derive generalizations from a large number of specific observations. "The sun always rises in the east" is an example. And so is "All organisms are made of cells." The latter generalization, part of the so-called cell theory, was based on two centuries of microscopic observations by biologists of cells in diverse biological specimens. Careful observations and data analyses, along with the generalizations reached by induction, are fundamental to our understanding of nature.

Forming and Testing Hypotheses

Observations and inductive reasoning stimulate us to seek natural causes and explanations for those observations. What *caused* the diversification of finches on the Galápagos Islands? What *causes* the roots of a plant seedling to grow downward and the leaf-bearing shoot to grow upward? What *explains* the generalization that the sun always rises in the east? In science, such inquiry usually involves the proposing and testing of hypothetical explanations—that is, hypotheses.

The Role of Hypotheses in Inquiry

In science, a **hypothesis** is a tentative answer to a well-framed question—an explanation on trial. It is usually a rational accounting for a set of observations, based on the available data and guided by inductive reasoning. A scientific hypothesis leads to predictions that can be tested by making additional observations or by performing experiments.

We all use hypotheses in solving everyday problems. Let's say, for example, that your flashlight fails during a camp-out. That's an observation. The question is obvious: Why doesn't the flashlight work? Two reasonable hypotheses based on your experience are that (1) the batteries in the flashlight are dead or (2) the bulb is burnt out. Each of these alternative hypotheses leads to predictions you can test with experiments. For example, the dead-battery hypothesis predicts that replacing the batteries will fix the problem. **Figure 1.24** diagrams this campground inquiry. Of course, we rarely dissect our thought processes this way when we are solving a problem using hypotheses, predictions, and experiments. But the hypothesis-based nature of science clearly has its origins in the human tendency to figure things out by trial and error.

Deductive Reasoning and Hypothesis Testing

A type of logic called deduction is built into the use of hypotheses in science. Deduction contrasts with induction,

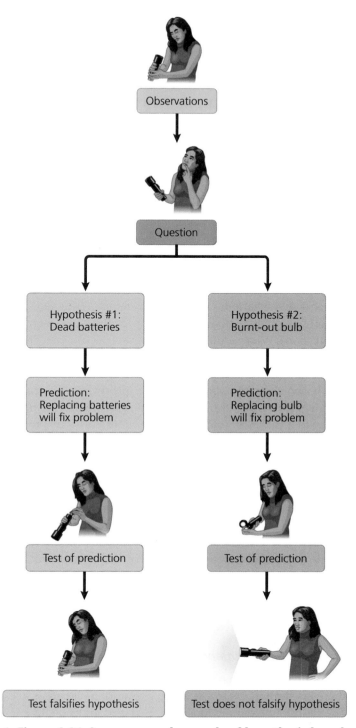

▲ **Figure 1.24 A campground example of hypothesis-based inquiry.**

which, remember, is reasoning from a set of specific observations to reach a general conclusion—a process that feeds into hypothesis formation. **Deductive reasoning** is generally used after the hypothesis has been developed and involves logic that flows in the opposite direction, from the general to the specific. From general premises, we extrapolate to the specific results we should expect if the premises are true. If all organisms are made of cells (premise 1), and humans are organisms (premise 2), then humans are composed of cells (deductive prediction about a specific case).

When using hypotheses in the scientific process, deductions usually take the form of predictions of experimental or observational results that will be found if a particular hypothesis (premise) is correct. We then test the hypothesis by carrying out the experiments or observations to see whether or not the results are as predicted. This deductive testing takes the form of "If . . . then" logic. In the case of the flashlight example: *If* the dead-battery hypothesis is correct and you replace the batteries with new ones, *then* the flashlight should work.

The flashlight inquiry demonstrates a key point about the use of hypotheses in science: that the initial observations may give rise to multiple hypotheses. The ideal is to design experiments to test all these candidate explanations. In addition to the two explanations tested in Figure 1.24, for instance, another of the many possible alternative hypotheses is that *both* the batteries *and* the bulb are bad. What does this hypothesis predict about the outcome of the experiments in Figure 1.24? What additional experiment would you design to test this hypothesis of multiple malfunctions?

We can mine the flashlight scenario for yet another important lesson about the scientific inquiry process. The burnt-out bulb hypothesis stands out as the most likely explanation, but notice that the testing supports that hypothesis *not* by proving that it is correct, but rather by not eliminating it through falsification (proving it false). Perhaps the first bulb was simply loose, so it wasn't making electrical contact, and the new bulb was inserted correctly. We could attempt to falsify the burnt-out bulb hypothesis by trying another experiment—removing the original bulb and carefully reinstalling it. If the flashlight still doesn't work, the burnt-out bulb hypothesis can stand. But no amount of experimental testing can *prove* a hypothesis beyond a shadow of doubt, because it is impossible to test *all* alternative hypotheses. A hypothesis gains credibility by surviving multiple attempts to falsify it while alternative hypotheses are eliminated (falsified) by testing.

Questions That Can and Cannot Be Addressed by Science

Scientific inquiry is a powerful way to learn about nature, but there are limitations to the kinds of questions it can answer. The flashlight example illustrates two important qualities of scientific hypotheses. First, a hypothesis must be *testable*; there must be some way to check the validity of the idea. Second, a hypothesis must be *falsifiable*; there must be some observation or experiment that could reveal if such an idea is actually *not* true. The hypothesis that dead batteries are the sole cause of the broken flashlight could be falsified by replacing the old batteries with new ones and finding that the flashlight still doesn't work.

Not all hypotheses meet the criteria of science: You wouldn't be able to devise a test to falsify the hypothesis that invisible campground ghosts are fooling with your flashlight! Because science requires natural explanations for natural phenomena, it can neither support nor falsify hypotheses that angels, ghosts, or spirits, whether benevolent or evil, cause storms, rainbows, illnesses, and cures. Such supernatural explanations are simply outside the bounds of science, as are religious matters, which are issues of personal faith.

The Flexibility of the Scientific Method

The flashlight example of Figure 1.24 traces an idealized process of inquiry called *the scientific method*. We can recognize the elements of this process in most of the research articles published by scientists, but rarely in such structured form. Very few scientific inquiries adhere rigidly to the sequence of steps prescribed by the "textbook" scientific method. For example, a scientist may start to design an experiment, but then backtrack upon realizing that more preliminary observations are necessary. In other cases, puzzling observations simply don't prompt well-defined questions until other research places those observations in a new context. For example, Darwin collected specimens of the Galápagos finches, but it wasn't until years later, as the idea of natural selection began to gel, that biologists began asking key questions about the history of those birds.

Moreover, scientists sometimes redirect their research when they realize they have been asking the wrong question. For example, in the early 20th century, much research on schizophrenia and manic-depressive disorder (now called bipolar disorder) got sidetracked by focusing too much on the question of how life experiences might cause these serious maladies. Research on the causes and potential treatments became more productive when it was refocused on questions of how certain chemical imbalances in the brain contribute to mental illness. To be fair, we acknowledge that such twists and turns in scientific inquiry become more evident with the advantage of historical perspective.

It is important for you to get some experience with the power of the scientific method—by using it for some of the laboratory inquiries in your biology course, for example. But it is also important to avoid stereotyping science as a lockstep adherence to this method.

A Case Study in Scientific Inquiry: Investigating Mimicry in Snake Populations

Now that we have highlighted the key features of scientific inquiry—making observations and forming and testing hypotheses—you should be able to recognize these features in a case study of actual scientific research.

The story begins with a set of observations and inductive generalizations. Many poisonous animals are brightly colored, often with distinctive patterns that stand out against the background. This is called *warning coloration* because it apparently signals "dangerous species" to potential predators. But there are also mimics. These imposters look like poisonous species but are actually harmless. A question that follows from these observations is: What is the function of such mimicry? A reasonable hypothesis is that the "deception" is an evolutionary adaptation that reduces the harmless animal's risk of being eaten because predators mistake it for the poisonous species. This hypothesis was first formulated by British scientist Henry Bates in 1862.

As obvious as this hypothesis may seem, it has been relatively difficult to test, especially with field experiments. But in 2001, biologists David and Karin Pfennig, of the University of North Carolina, along with William Harcombe, an undergraduate, designed a simple but elegant set of field experiments to test Bates's mimicry hypothesis.

The team investigated a case of mimicry among snakes that live in North and South Carolina **(Figure 1.25)**. A venomous snake called the eastern coral snake has warning coloration: bold, alternating rings of red, yellow (or white), and black. (The word *venomous* is used when a poisonous species delivers their poison actively, by stinging, stabbing, or biting.) Predators rarely attack these coral snakes. It is unlikely that the predators learn this avoidance behavior by trial and error, as a first encounter with a coral snake is usually deadly. In areas where coral snakes live, natural selection has apparently increased the frequency of predators that have inherited an instinctive avoidance of the coral snake's coloration. A nonvenomous snake named the scarlet kingsnake mimics the ringed coloration of the coral snake.

Both types of snakes live in the Carolinas, but the kingsnakes' geographic range also extends into regions where no coral snakes are found (see Figure 1.25). The geographic distribution of the snakes made it possible to test the key prediction of the mimicry hypothesis. Avoiding snakes with warning coloration is an adaptation we expect to be present only in predator populations that evolved in areas where the venomous coral snakes are present. Therefore, mimicry should help protect kingsnakes from predators *only in regions where coral snakes also live*. The mimicry hypothesis predicts that predators adapted to the warning coloration of coral snakes will attack kingsnakes less frequently than will predators in areas where coral snakes are absent.

Field Experiments with Artificial Snakes

To test the prediction, Harcombe made hundreds of artificial snakes out of wire covered with plasticine. He fashioned two versions of fake snakes: an *experimental group* with the red, black, and white ring pattern of kingsnakes and a *control group* of plain brown artificial snakes as a basis of comparison **(Figure 1.26)**.

The researchers placed equal numbers of the two types of artificial snakes in field sites throughout North and South

Scarlet kingsnake (nonvenomous)

Key
Range of scarlet kingsnake only
Overlapping ranges of scarlet kingsnake and eastern coral snake

Eastern coral snake (venomous)

Scarlet kingsnake (nonvenomous)

▲ **Figure 1.25 The geographic ranges of a venomous snake and its mimic.** The scarlet kingsnake (*Lampropeltis triangulum*) mimics the warning coloration of the venomous eastern coral snake (*Micrurus fulvius*).

(a) Artificial kingsnake

(b) Brown artificial snake that has been attacked

▲ **Figure 1.26 Artificial snakes used in field experiments to test the mimicry hypothesis.** A bear has chewed on the brown artificial snake in **(b)**.

Carolina, including the region where coral snakes are absent. After four weeks, the scientists retrieved the fake snakes and recorded how many had been attacked by looking for bite or claw marks. The most common predators were foxes, coyotes, and raccoons, but black bears also attacked some of the artificial snakes (see Figure 1.26b).

The data fit the key prediction of the mimicry hypothesis. Compared to the brown artificial snakes, the ringed artificial snakes were attacked by predators less frequently only in field sites within the geographic range of the venomous coral snakes. **Figure 1.27** summarizes the field experiments that the researchers carried out. This figure also introduces a format we will use throughout the book for other examples of biological inquiry.

Experimental Controls and Repeatability

The snake mimicry experiment is an example of a **controlled experiment**, one that is designed to compare an experimental group (the artificial kingsnakes, in this case) with a control group (the brown artificial snakes). Ideally, the experimental and control groups differ only in the one factor the experiment is designed to test—in our example, the effect of the snakes' coloration on the behavior of predators. Without the control group, the researchers would not have been able to rule out other factors as causes of the more frequent attacks on the artificial kingsnakes—such as different numbers of predators or different temperatures in the different test areas. The clever experimental design left coloration as the only factor that could account for the low predation rate on the artificial kingsnakes placed within the range of coral snakes. It was not the absolute number of attacks on the artificial kingsnakes that counted, but the difference between that number and the number of attacks on the brown snakes.

A common misconception is that the term *controlled experiment* means that scientists control the experimental environment to keep everything constant except the one variable being tested. But that's impossible in field research and not realistic even in highly regulated laboratory environments. Researchers usually "control" unwanted variables not by *eliminating* them through environmental regulation, but by *canceling out* their effects by using control groups.

Another hallmark of science is that the observations and experimental results must be repeatable. Observations that can't be verified may be interesting or even entertaining, but they cannot count as evidence in scientific inquiry. The headlines of supermarket tabloids would have you believe that humans are occasionally born with the head of a dog and that some of your classmates are extraterrestrials. The unconfirmed eyewitness accounts and the computer-rigged photos are amusing but unconvincing. In science, evidence from observations and experiments is only convincing if it stands up to the criterion of repeatability. The scientists who investigated snake mimicry in the Carolinas obtained similar data when they

---

▼ **Figure 1.27**   **INQUIRY**

Does the presence of venomous coral snakes affect predation rates on their mimics, kingsnakes?

EXPERIMENT David Pfennig and his colleagues made artificial snakes to test a prediction of the mimicry hypothesis: that kingsnakes benefit from mimicking the warning coloration of venomous coral snakes only in regions where coral snakes are present. The researchers placed equal numbers of artificial kingsnakes (experimental group) and brown artificial snakes (control group) at 14 field sites, half in the area the two snakes cohabit and half in the area where coral snakes are absent. The researchers recovered the artificial snakes after four weeks and tabulated predation data based on teeth and claw marks on the snakes.

RESULTS In field sites where coral snakes are absent, most attacks were on artificial kingsnakes. Where coral snakes were present, most attacks were on brown artificial snakes.

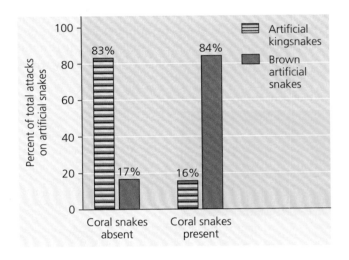

CONCLUSION The field experiments support the mimicry hypothesis by not falsifying the prediction, which was that mimicking coral snakes is effective only in areas where coral snakes are present. The experiments also tested an alternative hypothesis: that predators generally avoid all snakes with brightly colored rings. That hypothesis was falsified by the data showing that in areas without coral snakes, the ringed coloration failed to repel predators. (The fake kingsnakes may have been attacked more often in those areas because their bright pattern made them easier to spot than the brown fakes.)

SOURCE D. W. Pfennig, W. R. Harcombe, and K. S. Pfennig, Frequency-dependent Batesian mimicry, *Nature* 410:323 (2001).

INQUIRY IN ACTION Read and analyze the original paper in *Inquiry in Action: Interpreting Scientific Papers.*

(MB) See the related Experimental Inquiry Tutorial in MasteringBiology.

WHAT IF? What experimental results would you predict if predators throughout the Carolinas avoided all snakes with brightly colored ring patterns?

repeated their experiments with different species of coral snakes and kingsnakes in Arizona. And *you* should be able to obtain similar results if you were to repeat the snake experiments.

Theories in Science

"It's just a theory!" Our everyday use of the term *theory* often implies an untested speculation. But the term *theory* has a different meaning in science. What is a scientific theory, and how is it different from a hypothesis or from mere speculation?

First, a scientific **theory** is much broader in scope than a hypothesis. *This* is a hypothesis: "Mimicking the coloration of venomous snakes is an adaptation that protects nonvenomous snakes from predators." But *this* is a theory: "Evolutionary adaptations arise by natural selection." Darwin's theory of natural selection accounts for an enormous diversity of adaptations, including mimicry.

Second, a theory is general enough to spin off many new, specific hypotheses that can be tested. For example, two researchers at Princeton University, Peter and Rosemary Grant, were motivated by the theory of natural selection to test the specific hypothesis that the beaks of Galápagos finches evolve in response to changes in the types of available food. (Their results supported their hypothesis; see p. 469.)

And third, compared to any one hypothesis, a theory is generally supported by a much greater body of evidence. Those theories that become widely adopted in science (such as the theory of natural selection) explain a great diversity of observations and are supported by a vast accumulation of evidence. In fact, scrutiny of theories continues through testing of the specific, falsifiable hypotheses they spawn.

In spite of the body of evidence supporting a widely accepted theory, scientists must sometimes modify or even reject theories when new research methods produce results that don't fit. For example, the theory of biological diversity that lumped bacteria and archaea together as a kingdom of prokaryotes began to erode when new methods for comparing cells and molecules made it possible to test some of the hypothetical relationships between organisms that were based on the theory. If there is "truth" in science, it is conditional, based on the preponderance of available evidence.

CONCEPT CHECK 1.3

1. Contrast inductive reasoning with deductive reasoning.
2. In the snake mimicry experiment, what is the variable?
3. Why is natural selection called a theory?
4. **WHAT IF?** Suppose you extended the snake mimicry experiment to an area of Virginia where neither type of snake is known to live. What results would you predict at your field site?

For suggested answers, see Appendix A.

CONCEPT 1.4

Science benefits from a cooperative approach and diverse viewpoints

Movies and cartoons sometimes portray scientists as loners working in isolated labs. In reality, science is an intensely social activity. Most scientists work in teams, which often include both graduate and undergraduate students **(Figure 1.28)**. And to succeed in science, it helps to be a good communicator. Research results have no impact until shared with a community of peers through seminars, publications, and websites.

Building on the Work of Others

The great scientist Sir Isaac Newton once said: "To explain all nature is too difficult a task for any one man or even for any one age. 'Tis much better to do a little with certainty, and leave the rest for others that come after you. . . ." Anyone who becomes a scientist, driven by curiosity about how nature works, is sure to benefit greatly from the rich storehouse of discoveries by others who have come before.

Scientists working in the same research field often check one another's claims by attempting to confirm observations or repeat experiments. If experimental results cannot be repeated by scientific colleagues, this failure may reflect some underlying weakness in the original claim, which will then have to be revised. In this sense, science polices itself. Integrity and adherence to high professional standards in reporting results are central to the scientific endeavor. After all, the validity of experimental data is key to designing further lines of inquiry.

It is not unusual for several scientists to converge on the same research question. Some scientists enjoy the challenge of being first with an important discovery or key experiment, while others derive more satisfaction from cooperating with fellow scientists working on the same problem.

▲ **Figure 1.28 Science as a social process.** In laboratory meetings, lab members help each other interpret data, troubleshoot experiments, and plan future lines of inquiry.

Cooperation is facilitated when scientists use the same organism. Often it is a widely used **model organism**—a species that is easy to grow in the lab and lends itself particularly well to the questions being investigated. Because all organisms are evolutionarily related, lessons learned from a model organism are often widely applicable. For example, genetic studies of the fruit fly *Drosophila melanogaster* have taught us a lot about how genes work in other species, including humans. Some other popular model organisms are the mustard plant *Arabidopsis thaliana*, the soil worm *Caenorhabditis elegans*, the zebrafish *Danio rerio*, the mouse *Mus musculus*, and the bacterium *Escherichia coli*. As you read through this book, note the many contributions that these and other model organisms have made to the study of life.

Biologists may come at interesting questions from different angles. Some biologists focus on ecosystems, while others study natural phenomena at the level of organisms or cells. This book is divided into units that look at biology from different levels. Yet any given problem can be addressed from many perspectives, which in fact complement each other.

As a beginning biology student, you can benefit from making connections between the different levels of biology. You can begin to develop this skill by noticing when certain topics crop up again and again in different units. One such topic is sickle-cell disease, a well-understood genetic condition that is prevalent among native inhabitants of Africa and other warm regions and their descendants. Another topic viewed at different levels in this book is global climate change, mentioned earlier in this chapter. Sickle-cell disease and global climate change will appear in several units of the book, each time addressed at a new level. We hope these recurring topics will help you integrate the material you're learning and enhance your enjoyment of biology by helping you keep the "big picture" in mind.

Science, Technology, and Society

The biology community is part of society at large, embedded in the cultural milieu of the times. Some philosophers of science argue that scientists are so influenced by cultural and political values that science is no more objective than other ways of understanding nature. At the other extreme are people who speak of scientific theories as though they were natural laws instead of human interpretations of nature. The reality of science is probably somewhere in between—rarely perfectly objective, but continuously vetted through the expectation that observations and experiments be repeatable and hypotheses be testable and falsifiable.

The relationship of science to society becomes clearer when we add technology to the picture. Though science and technology sometimes employ similar inquiry patterns, their basic goals differ. The goal of science is to understand natural phenomena. In contrast, **technology** generally *applies* scientific knowledge for some specific purpose. Biologists and

▲ **Figure 1.29 DNA technology and crime scene investigation.** In 2008, forensic analysis of DNA samples from a crime scene led to the release of Charles Chatman from prison after he had served nearly 27 years for a rape he didn't commit. The photo shows Judge John Creuzot hugging Mr. Chatman after his conviction was overturned. The details of forensic analysis of DNA will be described in Chapter 20.

other scientists usually speak of "discoveries," while engineers and other technologists more usually speak of "inventions." And the beneficiaries of those inventions include scientists, who put new technology to work in their research. Thus, science and technology are interdependent.

The potent combination of science and technology can have dramatic effects on society. Sometimes, the applications of basic research that turn out to be the most beneficial come out of the blue, from completely unanticipated observations in the course of scientific exploration. For example, discovery of the structure of DNA by Watson and Crick 60 years ago and subsequent achievements in DNA science led to the technologies of DNA manipulation that are transforming applied fields such as medicine, agriculture, and forensics **(Figure 1.29)**. Perhaps Watson and Crick envisioned that their discovery would someday lead to important applications, but it is unlikely that they could have predicted exactly what all those applications would be.

The directions that technology takes depend less on the curiosity that drives basic science than on the current needs and wants of people and on the social environment of the times. Debates about technology center more on "*should* we do it" than "*can* we do it." With advances in technology come difficult choices. For example, under what circumstances is it acceptable to use DNA technology to find out if particular people have genes for hereditary diseases? Should such tests always be voluntary, or are there circumstances when genetic testing should be mandatory? Should insurance companies or employers have access to the information, as they do for many other types of personal health data? These questions are becoming much more urgent as the sequencing of individual genomes becomes quicker and cheaper.

Such ethical issues have as much to do with politics, economics, and cultural values as with science and technology. All citizens—not only professional scientists—have a responsibility to be informed about how science works and about the potential benefits and risks of technology. The relationship between science, technology, and society increases the significance and value of any biology course.

The Value of Diverse Viewpoints in Science

Many of the technological innovations with the most profound impact on human society originated in settlements along trade routes, where a rich mix of different cultures ignited new ideas. For example, the printing press, which helped spread knowledge to all social classes and ultimately led to the book in your hands, was invented by the German Johannes Gutenberg around 1440. This invention relied on several innovations from China, including paper and ink. Paper traveled along trade routes from China to Baghdad, where technology was developed for its mass production. This technology then migrated to Europe, as did water-based ink from China, which was modified by Gutenberg to become oil-based ink. We have the cross-fertilization of diverse cultures to thank for the printing press, and the same can be said for other important inventions.

Along similar lines, science stands to gain much from embracing a diversity of backgrounds and viewpoints among its practitioners. But just how diverse a population are scientists in relation to gender, race, ethnicity, and other attributes?

The scientific community reflects the cultural standards and behaviors of society at large. It is therefore not surprising that until recently, women and certain minorities have faced huge obstacles in their pursuit to become professional scientists in many countries around the world. Over the past 50 years, changing attitudes about career choices have increased the proportion of women in biology and some other sciences, so that now women constitute roughly half of undergraduate biology majors and biology Ph.D. students. The pace has been slow at higher levels in the profession, however, and women and many racial and ethnic groups are still significantly underrepresented in many branches of science. This lack of diversity hampers the progress of science. The more voices that are heard at the table, the more robust, valuable, and productive the scientific interchange will be. The authors of this textbook welcome all students to the community of biologists, wishing you the joys and satisfactions of this very exciting and satisfying field of science—biology.

CONCEPT CHECK 1.4

1. How does science differ from technology?
2. **WHAT IF?** The gene that causes sickle-cell disease is present in a higher percentage of residents of sub-Saharan Africa than it is among those of African descent living in the United States. The presence of this gene provides some protection from malaria, a serious disease that is widespread in sub-Saharan Africa. Discuss an evolutionary process that could account for the different percentages among residents of the two regions.

For suggested answers, see Appendix A.

1 CHAPTER REVIEW

SUMMARY OF KEY CONCEPTS

CONCEPT 1.1

The themes of this book make connections across different areas of biology (pp. 2–11)

- **Theme: New properties emerge at each level in the biological hierarchy**
  The hierarchy of life unfolds as follows: biosphere > ecosystem > community > population > organism > organ system > organ > tissue > cell > organelle > molecule > atom. With each step upward from atoms, new properties emerge as a result of interactions among components at the lower levels. In an approach called reductionism, complex systems are broken down to simpler components that are more manageable to study. In **systems biology**, scientists attempt to model the dynamic behavior of whole biological systems based on a study of the interactions among the system's parts.

- **Theme: Organisms interact with other organisms and the physical environment**
  Plants take up nutrients from the soil and chemicals from the air and use energy from the sun. Interactions between plants and other organisms result in cycling of chemical nutrients within an ecosystem. One harmful outcome of human interactions with the environment has been global climate change, caused by burning of fossil fuels and increasing atmospheric CO_2.

- **Theme: Life requires energy transfer and transformation**
  Energy flows through an ecosystem. All organisms must perform work, which requires energy. Energy from sunlight is converted to chemical energy by producers, which is then passed on to consumers.

- **Theme: Structure and function are correlated at all levels of biological organization**
  The form of a biological structure suits its function and vice versa.

- **Theme: The cell is an organism's basic unit of structure and function**
  The cell is the lowest level of organization that can perform all activities required for life. Cells are either prokaryotic or eukaryotic. **Eukaryotic cells** contain membrane-enclosed organelles, including a DNA-containing nucleus. **Prokaryotic cells** lack such organelles.

- **Theme: The continuity of life is based on heritable information in the form of DNA**
  Genetic information is encoded in the nucleotide sequences of **DNA**. It is DNA that transmits heritable information from parents to offspring. DNA sequences program a cell's protein production by being transcribed into RNA and then translated into specific proteins, a process called **gene expression**. Gene expression also results in RNAs that are not translated into protein but serve other important functions. **Genomics** is the large-scale analysis of the DNA sequences within a species as well as the comparison of sequences between species.

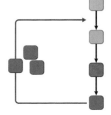

- **Theme: Feedback mechanisms regulate biological systems**
  In **negative feedback**, accumulation of an end product slows the process that makes that product. In **positive feedback**, the end product stimulates the production of more product. Feedback is a type of regulation common to life at all levels, from molecules to ecosystems.

- **Evolution, the Overarching Theme of Biology**
  Evolution accounts for the unity and diversity of life and also for the match of organisms to their environments.

? *Why is evolution considered the core theme of biology?*

CONCEPT 1.2

The Core Theme: Evolution accounts for the unity and diversity of life (pp. 11–18)

- Biologists classify species according to a system of broader and broader groups. Domain **Bacteria** and domain **Archaea** consist of prokaryotes. Domain **Eukarya**, the eukaryotes, includes various groups of protists and the kingdoms Plantae, Fungi, and Animalia. As diverse as life is, there is also evidence of remarkable unity, which is revealed in the similarities between different kinds of organisms.

- Darwin proposed **natural selection** as the mechanism for evolutionary adaptation of populations to their environments.

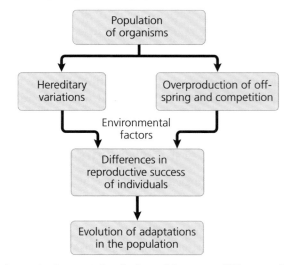

- Each species is one twig of a branching tree of life extending back in time through ancestral species more and more remote. All of life is connected through its long evolutionary history.

? *How could natural selection have led to the evolution of adaptations such as the thick, water-conserving leaves of the mother-of-pearl plant on the cover of this book?*

CONCEPT 1.3

In studying nature, scientists make observations and then form and test hypotheses (pp. 18–23)

- In scientific **inquiry**, scientists make observations (collect **data**) and use **inductive reasoning** to draw a general conclusion, which can be developed into a testable **hypothesis**. **Deductive reasoning** makes predictions that can be used to test hypotheses: If a hypothesis is correct, and we test it, then we can expect the predictions to come true. Hypotheses must be testable and falsifiable; science can address neither the possibility of supernatural phenomena nor the validity of religious beliefs.
- **Controlled experiments**, such as the study investigating mimicry in snake populations, are designed to demonstrate the effect of one variable by testing control groups and experimental groups that differ in only that one variable.
- A scientific **theory** is broad in scope, generates new hypotheses, and is supported by a large body of evidence.

? *What are the roles of inductive and deductive reasoning in the process of scientific inquiry?*

CONCEPT 1.4

Science benefits from a cooperative approach and diverse viewpoints (pp. 23–25)

- Science is a social activity. The work of each scientist builds on the work of others that have come before. Scientists must be able to repeat each other's results, so integrity is key. Biologists approach questions at different levels; their approaches complement each other.
- **Technology** is a method or device that applies scientific knowledge for some specific purpose that affects society. The ultimate impact of basic research is not always immediately obvious.
- Diversity among scientists promotes progress in science.

? *Explain why different approaches and diverse backgrounds among scientists are important.*

LEVEL 1: KNOWLEDGE/COMPREHENSION

1. All the organisms on your campus make up
   - a. an ecosystem.
   - b. a community.
   - c. a population.
   - d. an experimental group.
   - e. a taxonomic domain.

2. Which of the following is a correct sequence of levels in life's hierarchy, proceeding downward from an individual animal?
   - a. brain, organ system, nerve cell, nervous tissue
   - b. organ system, nervous tissue, brain
   - c. organism, organ system, tissue, cell, organ
   - d. nervous system, brain, nervous tissue, nerve cell
   - e. organ system, tissue, molecule, cell

3. Which of the following is *not* an observation or inference on which Darwin's theory of natural selection is based?
   - a. Poorly adapted individuals never produce offspring.
   - b. There is heritable variation among individuals.
   - c. Because of overproduction of offspring, there is competition for limited resources.
   - d. Individuals whose inherited characteristics best fit them to the environment will generally produce more offspring.
   - e. A population can become adapted to its environment over time.

4. Systems biology is mainly an attempt to
   - a. analyze genomes from different species.
   - b. simplify complex problems by reducing the system into smaller, less complex units.
   - c. understand the behavior of entire biological systems.
   - d. build high-throughput machines for the rapid acquisition of biological data.
   - e. speed up the technological application of scientific knowledge.

5. Protists and bacteria are grouped into different domains because
   - a. protists eat bacteria.
   - b. bacteria are not made of cells.
   - c. protists have a membrane-bounded nucleus, which bacterial cells lack.
   - d. bacteria decompose protists.
   - e. protists are photosynthetic.

6. Which of the following best demonstrates the unity among all organisms?
   - a. matching DNA nucleotide sequences
   - b. descent with modification
   - c. the structure and function of DNA
   - d. natural selection
   - e. emergent properties

7. A controlled experiment is one that
   - a. proceeds slowly enough that a scientist can make careful records of the results.
   - b. tests experimental and control groups in parallel.
   - c. is repeated many times to make sure the results are accurate.
   - d. keeps all variables constant.
   - e. is supervised by an experienced scientist.

8. Which of the following statements best distinguishes hypotheses from theories in science?
   - a. Theories are hypotheses that have been proved.
   - b. Hypotheses are guesses; theories are correct answers.
   - c. Hypotheses usually are relatively narrow in scope; theories have broad explanatory power.
   - d. Hypotheses and theories are essentially the same thing.
   - e. Theories are proved true; hypotheses are often falsified.

LEVEL 2: APPLICATION/ANALYSIS

9. Which of the following is an example of qualitative data?
   - a. The temperature decreased from 20°C to 15°C.
   - b. The plant's height is 25 centimeters (cm).
   - c. The fish swam in a zigzag motion.
   - d. The six pairs of robins hatched an average of three chicks.
   - e. The contents of the stomach are mixed every 20 seconds.

10. Which of the following best describes the logic of scientific inquiry?
    - a. If I generate a testable hypothesis, tests and observations will support it.
    - b. If my prediction is correct, it will lead to a testable hypothesis.
    - c. If my observations are accurate, they will support my hypothesis.
    - d. If my hypothesis is correct, I can expect certain test results.
    - e. If my experiments are set up right, they will lead to a testable hypothesis.

11. **DRAW IT** With rough sketches, draw a biological hierarchy similar to the one in Figure 1.4 but using a coral reef as the ecosystem, a fish as the organism, its stomach as the organ, and DNA as the molecule. Include all levels in the hierarchy.

LEVEL 3: SYNTHESIS/EVALUATION

12. **EVOLUTION CONNECTION**
    A typical prokaryotic cell has about 3,000 genes in its DNA, while a human cell has about 20,500 genes. About 1,000 of these genes are present in both types of cells. Based on your understanding of evolution, explain how such different organisms could have this same subset of genes. What sorts of functions might these shared genes have?

13. **SCIENTIFIC INQUIRY**
    Based on the results of the snake mimicry case study, suggest another hypothesis researchers might use to extend the investigation.

14. **WRITE ABOUT A THEME**
    Evolution In a short essay (100–150 words), discuss Darwin's view of how natural selection resulted in both unity and diversity of life on Earth. Include in your discussion some of his evidence. (See p. xv for a suggested grading rubric. The rubric and tips for writing good essays can also be found in the Study Area of MasteringBiology.)

For selected answers, see Appendix A.

Mastering BIOLOGY® www.masteringbiology.com

1. MasteringBiology® Assignments
Experimental Inquiry Tutorial What Can You Learn About the Process of Science from Investigating a Cricket's Chirp?
Tutorial The Scientific Method
Activities The Levels of Life Card Game • Form Fits Function: Cells • Heritable Information: DNA • Introduction to Experimental Design • GraphIt!: An Introduction to Graphing
Questions Student Misconceptions • Reading Quiz • Multiple Choice • End-of-Chapter

2. eText
Read your book online, search, take notes, highlight text, and more.

3. The Study Area
Practice Tests • Cumulative Test • *BioFlix* 3-D Animations • MP3 Tutor Sessions • Videos • Activities • Investigations • Lab Media • Audio Glossary • Word Study Tools • Art

The Chemistry of Life

An Interview with
Susan Solomon

Although Susan Solomon is not a biologist, her research as an atmospheric chemist has profound implications for life on Earth. Since earning degrees from the Illinois Institute of Technology and the University of California, Berkeley, Dr. Solomon has been a leader in determining the cause of the Antarctic ozone hole and in producing the 2007 report of the United Nations Intergovernmental Panel on Climate Change (IPCC), which concluded that

warming of Earth's climate is unequivocal. These activities have given her a public role in communicating science to policymakers and society at large. In recognition of her scientific accomplishments, she has been awarded the U.S. National Medal of Science, the Blue Planet Prize, and, with Al Gore and the other IPCC members, the Nobel Peace Prize. A member of the U.S. National Academy of Sciences, the European Academy of Sciences, the Academy of Sciences of France, and the Royal Society of the United Kingdom, she works for the National Oceanic and Atmospheric Administration in Boulder, Colorado.

How is Earth's atmosphere important to life?
Life on Earth today could not have evolved without an atmosphere. We all know that we and many other organisms require oxygen (O_2) from the atmosphere, and plants use carbon dioxide (CO_2) to grow. The atmosphere also contains a form of oxygen called ozone that has three oxygen atoms (O_3) instead of two. Organisms would never have been able to leave the ocean and survive on land without the development of an ozone layer in the upper atmosphere. Ozone has the important property of absorbing ultraviolet (UV) light, which would otherwise cause DNA damage. Damage from UV can lead to skin cancer and cataracts; it can also harm many crops and even phytoplankton [small photosynthetic aquatic organisms].

Early in your career, you led an expedition to make measurements of the atmosphere in Antarctica. Tell us about that.
In 1985, the British Antarctic Survey reported a surprising discovery: that the springtime ozone at their station in Antarctica had fallen by 30–50% since the late 1970s, resulting in an "ozone hole"! Peo-

ple had begun to be worried about whether the ozone layer might be vulnerable to changes caused by human activity, but only very minor changes had been expected. In 1986, I had the chance to lead a new Antarctic expedition to help confirm the British data and to study the problem further. We didn't just measure ozone; we measured about a dozen other atmospheric molecules that allowed us to tell *why* the ozone was being destroyed.

What did you find out?
It turns out that the ozone chemistry in Antarctica is extremely different from what it is anywhere else. That's because Antarctica is very cold—it really is the coldest place on Earth. It's so cold that clouds form in its upper stratosphere, about 10–30 kilometers above sea level, and those clouds help convert chemicals from chlorofluorocarbons (CFCs) to ozone-damaging substances.

CFCs are synthetic compounds, made only by humans. They were used back then for a variety of purposes—for example, in refrigeration, as solvents, and as propellants for sprays. Many tons of CFCs were emitted every year. I came up with the idea that the reason an ozone hole developed in Antarctica had to do with chemical reactions that happen between a gas and a surface and that the surface in this case was the small particles that make up those stratospheric clouds. Our data supported this hypothesis. The reactions on those particles make the CFCs hundreds of times more damaging than they would be otherwise. The absence of such clouds in most other parts of the world is why we don't have ozone holes elsewhere, although stratospheric clouds form occasionally in the Arctic and there is significant ozone loss there. Scientists had been concerned since the mid-1970s that human use of CFCs might cause some ozone depletion, but they had expected a loss of only about 3–5% in 100 years.

How do CFCs destroy ozone?
When CFCs arrive at the stratosphere, which typically takes a few years, high-energy radiation up there can break them down, releasing chlorine atoms. The chlorine atoms destroy the ozone catalytically, which means that the atoms don't get used up in the process. So even if only a small amount of CFC is broken down, the tiny bit of chlorine produced can destroy an enormous amount of ozone.

In the U.N. Montreal Protocol of 1987, the nations of the world agreed to stop producing CFCs. However, the CFCs in the atmosphere disappear only very slowly; typically they hang around for 50 to 100 years. What that means is that the CFCs we've already put in the atmosphere will continue to produce an ozone hole for many decades to come, even though we're not using these substances any more. Global emissions are very near zero now, and we're beginning to see the ozone hole slowly diminish. But it will probably not go away completely until around 2060.

While the ozone hole remains, it continues to cause damage. For example, there is evidence that the phytoplankton in the Antarctic Ocean are being affected by increased UV, and the phytoplankton are the base of the main Antarctic food chain: They feed the krill, which feed the fish, which feed the penguins, seals, and whales.

Let's talk about an effect that other atmospheric changes are having—climate change.
There's no question that the planet is getting warmer. We know that, on average, our planet is about 1.4°F (0.8°C) warmer than it was 100 years ago, and this past decade has been the warmest decade in at least the last 100 years. We also know that glaciers worldwide are retreating and that sea level is rising. There's a breadth of scientific data, acquired by different techniques, that tells us that global warming really is unequivocal.

The warming has to do with the greenhouse effect, right?
We're lucky that this planet has a greenhouse effect, because if it didn't, we would be very cold indeed! Our planet is heated by the sun, and much of the infrared radiation (heat) that would otherwise

be released back into space is trapped by "greenhouse gases" in the atmosphere. This makes the planet about 30°C hotter than it would be otherwise. But of course anything can be bad if you have too much of it, and what we're doing now is increasing the greenhouse effect of our atmosphere beyond its natural state. If we keep emitting the greenhouse gases that are causing the warming, then we will see some very significant warming in the coming century.

The main greenhouse gas we're adding to the atmosphere is CO_2, from burning fossil fuel and to a lesser extent deforestation. We have increased the atmospheric concentration of CO_2 by about 30% compared to any value that has been found for the last 800,000 years. This has been determined by digging up ice cores in Antarctica and measuring the gases in the air bubbles trapped in the ice. So we know that we have perturbed the atmosphere in a way that the planet hasn't seen in at least 800,000 years.

The CFCs we discussed earlier are actually the third most important greenhouse gas at present, after CO_2 and methane. Pound for pound, CFCs are much more potent as greenhouse gases than CO_2. The phase-out of CFCs since the signing of the Montreal Protocol has not only avoided a lot of ozone destruction that would otherwise have happened, but has also reduced our input of gases that cause climate change.

How is life on Earth being affected by climate change?
There are some things that we can already begin to see and talk about, but there's an enormous amount that we still don't know. We do know that the oceans are getting more acidic because CO_2 is taken up by the ocean and converted to carbonic acid, which can affect the ability of shellfish to make their shells. Other ocean life is also likely to be harmed by the increased acidity, such as the organisms of coral reefs. But there's also emerging evidence that some other marine organisms may do better— lobsters, perhaps.

As a westerner I'm extremely concerned about the greatly increased population of pine beetles in the western United States. These beetles are killing pine trees in unprecedented numbers. There's good evidence that a contributing factor to this explosion of pine beetles is global warming. I think we're going to see more of this kind of thing. Also, it is clear that bird migration is already being affected by global warming. Whether global warming will lead to extinction of some animals is an important question. The signature extinction issue is the polar bear; as the sea ice of the Arctic decreases, the polar bear could become extinct. We don't really know yet how much biological adaptation is possible in the time available. We'll probably find out that there are some winner species out there and some loser species. In agriculture, many crops are sensitive to increasing temperatures. One of the relevant findings about corn is that for every degree of warming, about 10% of crop production is lost—a big change.

Does less precipitation always go along with higher temperatures?
In some places there will probably be less precipitation and in other places more. There's a band of subtropical and tropical regions where we are pretty confident that it will get drier—for example, Mexico, the Mediterranean region, parts of Australia. In the higher latitudes, places like Canada and Norway will likely get wetter. In between, it's harder to predict.

Tell us about the IPCC and your work on it.
The IPCC is fundamentally a mechanism for the communication of information about climate change from the science community to the policy community. It was set up in 1988 when people were beginning to recognize that climate change was a real possibility. Policymakers decided that they needed to get reliable scientific information so they could begin to talk about what to do, if anything. Every six or seven years, scientists are asked by their governments to get together and assess what we know and don't know on the basis of the published scientific literature.

I have been involved in the IPCC since 1992, and in 2001 I was elected by the panel, representing over 100 governments, to co-chair the scientific assessment team. In a process lasting several years, we generated a detailed report summarizing the state of climate science. Our report was then reviewed by dozens of governments and more than 600 scientists. The report itself and every one of their 30,000 comments are available on the Internet. We refined and refined the draft in consideration of those comments and finalized the document in 2007.

What were the main conclusions of your 2007 report?
The first conclusion, based on many independent lines of evidence, was that the Earth is warming. There's no doubt we are now living on a planet that is warmer than a century ago. The second main conclusion was that most—more than half—of the warming is very likely due to increases in greenhouse gases, primarily CO_2. We did a careful analysis of the uncertainties: When we say "very likely," we mean that there's a 90% chance or greater that most of the warming is due to emissions of greenhouse gases by human activity.

What have you learned about working at the interface of science and policy?
It's one of the most difficult things a scientist can do. Science normally takes us into a laboratory or out into the field or into scholarly discussions with colleagues. Getting involved with policy is quite different: It takes us out of the lab and makes us much more aware of the strong emotions around many issues. In that sense, it's a bit daunting. But it's uplifting to see how valuable science can be in helping society make more informed choices. Scientists can help make sure that whatever it is we choose to do as a society we're doing knowingly, not in ignorance. I appreciate all the reasons why people ask tough questions about the science. How much do we know? What really are the uncertainties? Yes, there's a lot at stake here, all the more reason why there has to be really good science going into it.

"There's a breadth of scientific data, acquired by different techniques, that tells us that global warming really is unequivocal."

Susan Solomon (right) with Jane Reece

2

The Chemical Context of Life

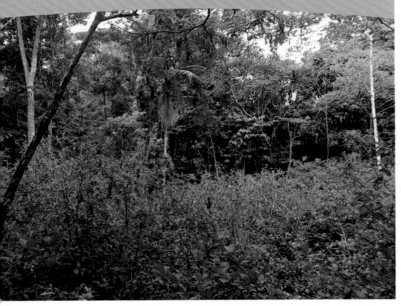

▲ Figure 2.1 **Who tends this "garden"?**

KEY CONCEPTS

2.1 Matter consists of chemical elements in pure form and in combinations called compounds

2.2 An element's properties depend on the structure of its atoms

2.3 The formation and function of molecules depend on chemical bonding between atoms

2.4 Chemical reactions make and break chemical bonds

OVERVIEW

A Chemical Connection to Biology

The Amazon rain forest in South America is a showcase for the diversity of life on Earth. Colorful birds, insects, and other animals live in a densely-packed environment of trees, shrubs, vines, and wildflowers, and an excursion along a waterway or a forest path typically reveals a lush variety of plant life. Visitors traveling near the Amazon's headwaters in Peru are therefore surprised to come across tracts of forest like that seen in the foreground of the photo in **Figure 2.1**. This patch is almost completely dominated by a single plant species—a small flowering tree called *Duroia hirsuta*. Travelers may wonder if the plot of land is planted and maintained by local people, but the indigenous people are as mystified as the visitors. They call these stands of *Duroia* trees "devil's gardens," from a legend attributing them to an evil forest spirit.

Seeking a scientific explanation, a research team at Stanford University recently solved the "devil's garden" mystery. **Figure 2.2** describes their main experiment. The researchers showed that the "farmers" who create and maintain these gardens are actually ants that live in the hollow stems of the *Duroia* trees. The ants do not plant the *Duroia* trees, but they prevent other plant species from growing in the garden by injecting intruders with a poisonous chemical. In this way, the ants create space for the growth of the *Duroia* trees that serve as their home. With the ability to maintain and expand its habitat, a single colony of devil's garden ants can live for hundreds of years.

The chemical used by the ants to weed their garden turns out to be formic acid. This substance is produced by many species of ants and in fact got its name from the Latin word for ant, *formica*. For many ant species, the formic acid probably serves as a disinfectant that protects the ants against microbial parasites. The devil's garden ant is the first ant species found to use formic acid as an herbicide, an important addition to the list of functions mediated by chemicals in the insect world. Scientists have long known that chemicals play a major role in insect communication, attraction of mates, and defense against predators.

Research on devil's gardens is only one example of the relevance of chemistry to the study of life. Unlike a list of college courses, nature is not neatly packaged into the individual natural sciences—biology, chemistry, physics, and so forth. Biologists specialize in the study of life, but organisms and their environments are natural systems to which the concepts of chemistry and physics apply. Biology is a multidisciplinary science.

This unit of chapters introduces some basic concepts of chemistry that apply to the study of life. We will make many connections to the themes introduced in Chapter 1. One of these themes is the organization of life into a hierarchy of structural levels, with additional properties emerging at each successive level. In this unit, we will see how emergent properties are apparent at the lowest levels of biological organization—such as the ordering of atoms into molecules and the interactions of those molecules within cells. Somewhere in the transition from molecules to cells, we will cross the blurry boundary between nonlife and life. This chapter focuses on the chemical components that make up all matter.

▼ Figure 2.2

INQUIRY

What creates "devil's gardens" in the rain forest?

EXPERIMENT Working under Deborah Gordon and with Michael Greene, graduate student Megan Frederickson sought the cause of "devil's gardens," stands of a single species of tree, *Duroia hirsuta*. One hypothesis was that ants living in these trees, *Myrmelachista schumanni*, produce a poisonous chemical that kills trees of other species; another was that the *Duroia* trees themselves kill competing trees, perhaps by means of a chemical.

To test these hypotheses, Frederickson did field experiments in Peru. Two saplings of a local nonhost tree species, *Cedrela odorata*, were planted inside each of ten devil's gardens. At the base of one sapling, a sticky insect barrier was applied; the other was unprotected. Two more *Cedrela* saplings, with and without barriers, were planted about 50 meters outside each garden.

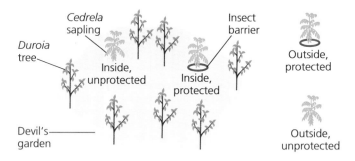

The researchers observed ant activity on the *Cedrela* leaves and measured areas of dead leaf tissue after one day. They also chemically analyzed contents of the ants' poison glands.

RESULTS The ants made injections from the tips of their abdomens into leaves of unprotected saplings in their gardens (see photo). Within one day, these leaves developed dead areas (see graph). The protected saplings were uninjured, as were the saplings planted outside the gardens. Formic acid was the only chemical detected in the poison glands of the ants.

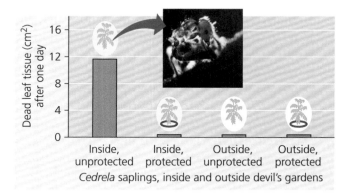

Cedrela saplings, inside and outside devil's gardens

CONCLUSION Ants of the species *Myrmelachista schumanni* kill nonhost trees by injecting the leaves with formic acid, thus creating hospitable habitats (devil's gardens) for the ant colony.

SOURCE M. E. Frederickson, M. J. Greene, and D. M. Gordon, "Devil's gardens" bedevilled by ants, *Nature* 437:495–496 (2005).

INQUIRY IN ACTION Read and analyze the original paper in *Inquiry in Action: Interpreting Scientific Papers*.

WHAT IF? What would be the results if the unprotected saplings' inability to grow in the devil's gardens was caused by a chemical released by the *Duroia* trees rather than by the ants?

CONCEPT **2.1**

Matter consists of chemical elements in pure form and in combinations called compounds

Organisms are composed of **matter**, which is defined as anything that takes up space and has mass.* Matter exists in many diverse forms. Rocks, metals, oils, gases, and humans are just a few examples of what seems an endless assortment of matter.

Elements and Compounds

Matter is made up of elements. An **element** is a substance that cannot be broken down to other substances by chemical reactions. Today, chemists recognize 92 elements occurring in nature; gold, copper, carbon, and oxygen are examples. Each element has a symbol, usually the first letter or two of its name. Some symbols are derived from Latin or German; for instance, the symbol for sodium is Na, from the Latin word *natrium*.

A **compound** is a substance consisting of two or more different elements combined in a fixed ratio. Table salt, for example, is sodium chloride (NaCl), a compound composed of the elements sodium (Na) and chlorine (Cl) in a 1:1 ratio. Pure sodium is a metal, and pure chlorine is a poisonous gas. When chemically combined, however, sodium and chlorine form an edible compound. Water (H_2O), another compound, consists of the elements hydrogen (H) and oxygen (O) in a 2:1 ratio. These are simple examples of organized matter having emergent properties: A compound has characteristics different from those of its elements (**Figure 2.3**).

Sodium   **Chlorine**   **Sodium chloride**

▲ **Figure 2.3 The emergent properties of a compound.** The metal sodium combines with the poisonous gas chlorine, forming the edible compound sodium chloride, or table salt.

---

*Sometimes we substitute the term weight for mass, although the two are not identical. Mass is the amount of matter in an object, whereas the weight of an object is how strongly that mass is pulled by gravity. The weight of an astronaut walking on the moon is approximately 1/6 the astronaut's weight on Earth, but his or her mass is the same. However, as long as we are earthbound, the weight of an object is a measure of its mass; in everyday language, therefore, we tend to use the terms interchangeably.

The Elements of Life

Of the 92 natural elements, about 20–25% are **essential elements** that an organism needs to live a healthy life and reproduce. The essential elements are similar among organisms, but there is some variation—for example, humans need 25 elements, but plants need only 17.

Just four elements—oxygen (O), carbon (C), hydrogen (H), and nitrogen (N)—make up 96% of living matter. Calcium (Ca), phosphorus (P), potassium (K), sulfur (S), and a few other elements account for most of the remaining 4% of an organism's mass. **Trace elements** are required by an organism in only minute quantities. Some trace elements, such as iron (Fe), are needed by all forms of life; others are required only by certain species. For example, in vertebrates (animals with backbones), the element iodine (I) is an essential ingredient of a hormone produced by the thyroid gland. A daily intake of only 0.15 milligram (mg) of iodine is adequate for normal activity of the human thyroid. An iodine deficiency in the diet causes the thyroid gland to grow to abnormal size, a condition called goiter. Where it is available, eating seafood or iodized salt reduces the incidence of goiter. All the elements needed by the human body are listed in Table 2.1.

Some naturally occurring elements are toxic to organisms. In humans, for instance, the element arsenic has been linked to numerous diseases and can be lethal. In some areas of the world, arsenic occurs naturally and can make its way into the groundwater. As a result of using water from drilled wells in southern Asia, millions of people have been inadvertently exposed to arsenic-laden water. Efforts are under way to reduce arsenic levels in their water supply.

▲ **Figure 2.4 Serpentine plant community.** The plants in the large photo are growing on serpentine soil, which contains elements that are usually toxic to plants. The insets show a close-up of serpentine rock and one of the plants, a Tiburon Mariposa lily.

Case Study:
Evolution of Tolerance to Toxic Elements

EVOLUTION Some species have become adapted to environments containing elements that are usually toxic. A compelling example is found in serpentine plant communities. Serpentine is a jade-like mineral that contains toxic elements such as chromium, nickel, and cobalt. Although most plants cannot survive in soil that forms from serpentine rock, a small number of plant species have adaptations that allow them to do so (Figure 2.4). Presumably, variants of ancestral, nonserpentine species arose that could survive in serpentine soils, and subsequent natural selection resulted in the distinctive array of species we see in these areas today.

CONCEPT CHECK 2.1

1. **MAKE CONNECTIONS** Review the discussion of emergent properties in Chapter 1 (p. 3). Explain how table salt has emergent properties.
2. Is a trace element an essential element? Explain.
3. In humans, iron is a trace element required for the proper functioning of hemoglobin, the molecule that carries oxygen in red blood cells. What might be the effects of an iron deficiency?
4. **MAKE CONNECTIONS** Review the discussion of natural selection in Chapter 1 (pp. 14–16) and explain how natural selection might have played a role in the evolution of species that are tolerant of serpentine soils.

For suggested answers, see Appendix A.

Table 2.1 Elements in the Human Body		
Element	**Symbol**	**Percentage of Body Mass (including water)**
Oxygen	O	65.0%
Carbon	C	18.5%
Hydrogen	H	9.5%
Nitrogen	N	3.3%
Calcium	Ca	1.5%
Phosphorus	P	1.0%
Potassium	K	0.4%
Sulfur	S	0.3%
Sodium	Na	0.2%
Chlorine	Cl	0.2%
Magnesium	Mg	0.1%

(Oxygen through Nitrogen: 96.3%; Calcium through Magnesium: 3.7%)

Trace elements (less than 0.01% of mass): Boron (B), chromium (Cr), cobalt (Co), copper (Cu), fluorine (F), iodine (I), iron (Fe), manganese (Mn), molybdenum (Mo), selenium (Se), silicon (Si), tin (Sn), vanadium (V), zinc (Zn)

CONCEPT 2.2

An element's properties depend on the structure of its atoms

Each element consists of a certain type of atom that is different from the atoms of any other element. An **atom** is the smallest unit of matter that still retains the properties of an element. Atoms are so small that it would take about a million of them to stretch across the period printed at the end of this sentence. We symbolize atoms with the same abbreviation used for the element that is made up of those atoms. For example, the symbol C stands for both the element carbon and a single carbon atom.

Subatomic Particles

Although the atom is the smallest unit having the properties of an element, these tiny bits of matter are composed of even smaller parts, called *subatomic particles*. Physicists have split the atom into more than a hundred types of particles, but only three kinds of particles are relevant here: **neutrons**, **protons**, and **electrons**. Protons and electrons are electrically charged. Each proton has one unit of positive charge, and each electron has one unit of negative charge. A neutron, as its name implies, is electrically neutral.

Protons and neutrons are packed together tightly in a dense core, or **atomic nucleus**, at the center of an atom; protons give the nucleus a positive charge. The electrons form a sort of cloud of negative charge around the nucleus, and it is the attraction between opposite charges that keeps the electrons in the vicinity of the nucleus. **Figure 2.5** shows two commonly used models of the structure of the helium atom as an example.

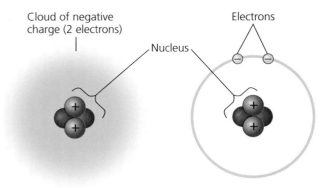

Cloud of negative charge (2 electrons)

Nucleus

Electrons

(a) This model represents the two electrons as a cloud of negative charge.

(b) In this more simplified model, the electrons are shown as two small yellow spheres on a circle around the nucleus.

▲ **Figure 2.5 Simplified models of a helium (He) atom.** The helium nucleus consists of 2 neutrons (brown) and 2 protons (pink). Two electrons (yellow) exist outside the nucleus. These models are not to scale; they greatly overestimate the size of the nucleus in relation to the electron cloud.

The neutron and proton are almost identical in mass, each about 1.7×10^{-24} gram (g). Grams and other conventional units are not very useful for describing the mass of objects so minuscule. Thus, for atoms and subatomic particles (and for molecules, too), we use a unit of measurement called the **dalton**, in honor of John Dalton, the British scientist who helped develop atomic theory around 1800. (The dalton is the same as the *atomic mass unit*, or *amu*, a unit you may have encountered elsewhere.) Neutrons and protons have masses close to 1 dalton. Because the mass of an electron is only about 1/2,000 that of a neutron or proton, we can ignore electrons when computing the total mass of an atom.

Atomic Number and Atomic Mass

Atoms of the various elements differ in their number of subatomic particles. All atoms of a particular element have the same number of protons in their nuclei. This number of protons, which is unique to that element, is called the **atomic number** and is written as a subscript to the left of the symbol for the element. The abbreviation $_2$He, for example, tells us that an atom of the element helium has 2 protons in its nucleus. Unless otherwise indicated, an atom is neutral in electrical charge, which means that its protons must be balanced by an equal number of electrons. Therefore, the atomic number tells us the number of protons and also the number of electrons in an electrically neutral atom.

We can deduce the number of neutrons from a second quantity, the **mass number**, which is the sum of protons plus neutrons in the nucleus of an atom. The mass number is written as a superscript to the left of an element's symbol. For example, we can use this shorthand to write an atom of helium as $_2^4$He. Because the atomic number indicates how many protons there are, we can determine the number of neutrons by subtracting the atomic number from the mass number: The helium atom, $_2^4$He, has 2 neutrons. For sodium (Na):

Mass number = number of protons + neutrons
           = 23 for sodium

$_{11}^{23}$Na

Atomic number = number of protons
           = number of electrons in a neutral atom
           = 11 for sodium

Number of neutrons = mass number – atomic number
           = 23 – 11 = 12 for sodium

The simplest atom is hydrogen, $_1^1$H, which has no neutrons; it consists of a single proton with a single electron.

As mentioned earlier, the contribution of electrons to mass is negligible. Therefore, almost all of an atom's mass is concentrated in its nucleus. Because neutrons and protons each have a mass very close to 1 dalton, the mass number is an approximation of the total mass of an atom, called its **atomic mass**. So we might say that the atomic mass of sodium ($_{11}^{23}$Na) is 23 daltons, although more precisely it is 22.9898 daltons.

Isotopes

All atoms of a given element have the same number of protons, but some atoms have more neutrons than other atoms of the same element and therefore have greater mass. These different atomic forms of the same element are called **isotopes** of the element. In nature, an element occurs as a mixture of its isotopes. For example, consider the three isotopes of the element carbon, which has the atomic number 6. The most common isotope is carbon-12, $^{12}_{6}C$, which accounts for about 99% of the carbon in nature. The isotope $^{12}_{6}C$ has 6 neutrons. Most of the remaining 1% of carbon consists of atoms of the isotope $^{13}_{6}C$, with 7 neutrons. A third, even rarer isotope, $^{14}_{6}C$, has 8 neutrons. Notice that all three isotopes of carbon have 6 protons; otherwise, they would not be carbon. Although the isotopes of an element have slightly different masses, they behave identically in chemical reactions. (The number usually given as the atomic mass of an element, such as 22.9898 daltons for sodium, is actually an average of the atomic masses of all the element's naturally occurring isotopes.)

Both ^{12}C and ^{13}C are stable isotopes, meaning that their nuclei do not have a tendency to lose particles. The isotope ^{14}C, however, is unstable, or radioactive. A **radioactive isotope** is one in which the nucleus decays spontaneously, giving off particles and energy. When the decay leads to a change in the number of protons, it transforms the atom to an atom of a different element. For example, when a radioactive carbon atom decays, it becomes an atom of nitrogen.

Radioactive isotopes have many useful applications in biology. In Chapter 25, you will learn how researchers use measurements of radioactivity in fossils to date these relics of past life. As shown in **Figure 2.6**, radioactive isotopes are also useful as tracers to follow atoms through metabolism, the chemical processes of an organism. Cells use the radioactive atoms as they would use nonradioactive isotopes of the same element, but the radioactive tracers can be readily detected.

Radioactive tracers are important diagnostic tools in medicine. For example, certain kidney disorders can be diagnosed by injecting small doses of substances containing radioactive isotopes into the blood and then measuring the amount of tracer excreted in the urine. Radioactive tracers are also used in combination with sophisticated imaging instruments. PET scanners, for instance, can monitor chemical processes, such as those involved in cancerous growth, as they actually occur in the body (**Figure 2.7**).

Although radioactive isotopes are very useful in biological research and medicine, radiation from decaying isotopes also poses a hazard to life by damaging cellular molecules. The severity of this damage depends on the type and amount of radiation an organism absorbs. One of the most serious environmental threats is radioactive fallout from nuclear accidents. The doses of most isotopes used in medical diagnosis, however, are relatively safe.

▼ **Figure 2.6**

RESEARCH METHOD

Radioactive Tracers

APPLICATION Scientists use radioactive isotopes to label certain chemical compounds, creating tracers that allow them to follow a metabolic process or locate the compound within an organism. In this example, radioactive tracers are utilized to determine the effect of temperature on the rate at which cells make copies of their DNA.

TECHNIQUE

Compounds including radioactive tracer (bright blue)

Human cells

Incubators

10°C 15°C 20°C 25°C 30°C 35°C 40°C 45°C 50°C

❶ Compounds used by cells to make DNA are added to human cells. One ingredient is labeled with ^3H, a radioactive isotope of hydrogen. Nine dishes of cells are incubated at different temperatures. The cells make new DNA, incorporating the radioactive tracer.

❷ Cells from each incubator are placed in tubes; their DNA is isolated; and unused labeled compounds are removed.

10° 15° 20° 25° 30° 35° 40° 45° 50°

DNA (old and new)

❸ A solution called scintillation fluid is added to the samples, which are then placed in a scintillation counter. As the ^3H in the newly made DNA decays, it emits radiation that excites chemicals in the scintillation fluid, causing them to give off light. Flashes of light are recorded by the scintillation counter.

RESULTS The frequency of flashes, which is recorded as counts per minute, is proportional to the amount of the radioactive tracer present, indicating the amount of new DNA. In this experiment, when the counts per minute are plotted against temperature, it is clear that temperature affects the rate of DNA synthesis; the most DNA was made at 35°C.

Optimum temperature for DNA synthesis

Counts per minute (× 1,000)

30
20
10
0

10 20 30 40 50
Temperature (°C)

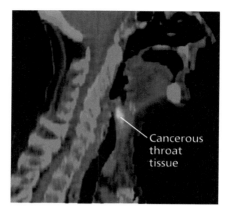

◀ **Figure 2.7 A PET scan, a medical use for radioactive isotopes.** PET, an acronym for positron-emission tomography, detects locations of intense chemical activity in the body. The bright yellow spot marks an area with an elevated level of radioactively labeled glucose, which in turn indicates high metabolic activity, a hallmark of cancerous tissue.

Cancerous throat tissue

(a) A ball bouncing down a flight of stairs provides an analogy for energy levels of electrons, because the ball can come to rest only on each step, not between steps.

Third shell (highest energy level in this model)

Second shell (higher energy level)

First shell (lowest energy level)

Energy absorbed

Energy lost

Atomic nucleus

(b) An electron can move from one shell to another only if the energy it gains or loses is exactly equal to the difference in energy between the energy levels of the two shells. Arrows in this model indicate some of the stepwise changes in potential energy that are possible.

▲ **Figure 2.8 Energy levels of an atom's electrons.** Electrons exist only at fixed levels of potential energy called electron shells.

The Energy Levels of Electrons

The simplified models of the atom in Figure 2.5 greatly exaggerate the size of the nucleus relative to the volume of the whole atom. If an atom of helium were the size of a typical football stadium, the nucleus would be the size of a pencil eraser in the center of the field. Moreover, the electrons would be like two tiny gnats buzzing around the stadium. Atoms are mostly empty space.

When two atoms approach each other during a chemical reaction, their nuclei do not come close enough to interact. Of the three kinds of subatomic particles we have discussed, only electrons are directly involved in the chemical reactions between atoms.

An atom's electrons vary in the amount of energy they possess. **Energy** is defined as the capacity to cause change— for instance, by doing work. **Potential energy** is the energy that matter possesses because of its location or structure. For example, water in a reservoir on a hill has potential energy because of its altitude. When the gates of the reservoir's dam are opened and the water runs downhill, the energy can be used to do work, such as turning generators. Because energy has been expended, the water has less energy at the bottom of the hill than it did in the reservoir. Matter has a natural tendency to move to the lowest possible state of potential energy; in this example, the water runs downhill. To restore the potential energy of a reservoir, work must be done to elevate the water against gravity.

The electrons of an atom have potential energy because of how they are arranged in relation to the nucleus. The negatively charged electrons are attracted to the positively charged nucleus. It takes work to move a given electron farther away from the nucleus, so the more distant an electron is from the nucleus, the greater its potential energy. Unlike the continuous flow of water downhill, changes in the potential energy of electrons can occur only in steps of fixed amounts. An electron having a certain amount of energy is something like a ball on a staircase **(Figure 2.8a)**. The ball can have different amounts of potential energy, depending on which step it is

on, but it cannot spend much time between the steps. Similarly, an electron's potential energy is determined by its energy level. An electron cannot exist between energy levels.

An electron's energy level is correlated with its average distance from the nucleus. Electrons are found in different **electron shells**, each with a characteristic average distance and energy level. In diagrams, shells can be represented by concentric circles **(Figure 2.8b)**. The first shell is closest to the nucleus, and electrons in this shell have the lowest potential energy. Electrons in the second shell have more energy, and electrons in the third shell even more energy. An electron can change the shell it occupies, but only by absorbing or losing an amount of energy equal to the difference in potential energy between its position in the old shell and that in the new shell. When an electron absorbs energy, it moves to a shell farther out from the nucleus. For example, light energy can excite an electron to a higher energy level. (Indeed, this is the first step taken when plants harness the energy of sunlight for photosynthesis, the process that produces food from carbon dioxide and water.) When an electron loses energy, it "falls back" to a shell closer to the nucleus, and the lost energy is usually released to the environment as heat. For example, sunlight excites electrons in the surface of a car to higher energy levels. When the electrons fall back to their original levels, the car's surface heats up. This thermal energy can be transferred to the air or to your hand if you touch the car.

Electron Distribution and Chemical Properties

The chemical behavior of an atom is determined by the distribution of electrons in the atom's electron shells. Beginning with hydrogen, the simplest atom, we can imagine building the atoms of the other elements by adding 1 proton and 1 electron at a time (along with an appropriate number of neutrons). **Figure 2.9**, an abbreviated version of what is called the *periodic table of the elements*, shows this distribution of electrons for the first 18 elements, from hydrogen ($_1$H) to argon ($_{18}$Ar). The elements are arranged in three rows, or periods, corresponding to the number of electron shells in their atoms. The left-to-right sequence of elements in each row corresponds to the sequential addition of electrons and protons.

Hydrogen's 1 electron and helium's 2 electrons are located in the first shell. Electrons, like all matter, tend to exist in the lowest available state of potential energy. In an atom, this state is in the first shell. However, the first shell can hold no more than 2 electrons; thus, hydrogen and helium are the only elements in the first row of the table. An atom with more than 2 electrons must use higher shells because the first shell

is full. The next element, lithium, has 3 electrons. Two of these electrons fill the first shell, while the third electron occupies the second shell. The second shell holds a maximum of 8 electrons. Neon, at the end of the second row, has 8 electrons in the second shell, giving it a total of 10 electrons.

The chemical behavior of an atom depends mostly on the number of electrons in its *outermost* shell. We call those outer electrons **valence electrons** and the outermost electron shell the **valence shell**. In the case of lithium, there is only 1 valence electron, and the second shell is the valence shell. Atoms with the same number of electrons in their valence shells exhibit similar chemical behavior. For example, fluorine (F) and chlorine (Cl) both have 7 valence electrons, and both form compounds when combined with the element sodium (see Figure 2.3). An atom with a completed valence shell is unreactive; that is, it will not interact readily with other atoms. At the far right of the periodic table are helium, neon, and argon, the only three elements shown in Figure 2.9 that have full valence shells. These elements are said to be *inert*, meaning chemically unreactive. All the other atoms in Figure 2.9 are chemically reactive because they have incomplete valence shells.

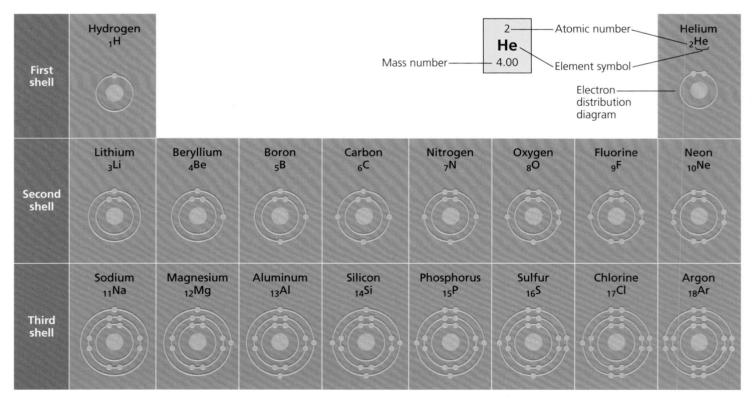

▲ **Figure 2.9 Electron distribution diagrams for the first 18 elements in the periodic table.** In a standard periodic table, information for each element is presented as shown for helium in the inset. In the diagrams in this table, electrons are represented as yellow dots and electron shells as concentric circles. These diagrams are a convenient way to picture the distribution of an atom's electrons among its electron shells, but these simplified models do not accurately represent the shape of the atom or the location of its electrons. The elements are arranged in rows, each representing the filling of an electron shell. As electrons are added, they occupy the lowest available shell.

? *What is the atomic number of magnesium? How many protons and electrons does it have? How many electron shells? How many valence electrons?*

Electron Orbitals

In the early 1900s, the electron shells of an atom were visualized as concentric paths of electrons orbiting the nucleus, somewhat like planets orbiting the sun. It is still convenient to use two-dimensional concentric-circle diagrams, as in Figure 2.9, to symbolize three-dimensional electron

Neon, with two filled shells (10 electrons)
First shell
Second shell

(a) Electron distribution diagram. An electron distribution diagram is shown here for a neon atom, which has a total of 10 electrons. Each concentric circle represents an electron shell, which can be subdivided into electron orbitals.

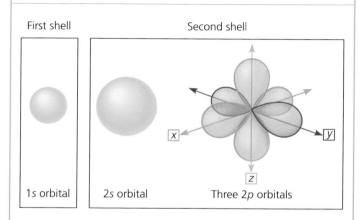

First shell
Second shell

x
y
z

1s orbital   2s orbital   Three 2p orbitals

(b) Separate electron orbitals. The three-dimensional shapes represent electron orbitals—the volumes of space where the electrons of an atom are most likely to be found. Each orbital holds a maximum of 2 electrons. The first electron shell, on the left, has one spherical (s) orbital, designated 1s. The second shell, on the right, has one larger s orbital (designated 2s for the second shell) plus three dumbbell-shaped orbitals called p orbitals (2p for the second shell). The three 2p orbitals lie at right angles to one another along imaginary x-, y-, and z-axes of the atom. Each 2p orbital is outlined here in a different color.

1s, 2s, and 2p orbitals

(c) Superimposed electron orbitals. To reveal the complete picture of the electron orbitals of neon, we superimpose the 1s orbital of the first shell and the 2s and three 2p orbitals of the second shell.

▲ **Figure 2.10 Electron orbitals.**

shells. However, you need to remember that each concentric circle represents only the *average* distance between an electron in that shell and the nucleus. Accordingly, the concentric-circle diagrams do not give a real picture of an atom. In reality, we can never know the exact location of an electron. What we can do instead is describe the space in which an electron spends most of its time. The three-dimensional space where an electron is found 90% of the time is called an **orbital**.

Each electron shell contains electrons at a particular energy level, distributed among a specific number of orbitals of distinctive shapes and orientations. **Figure 2.10** shows the orbitals of neon as an example, with its electron distribution diagram for reference. You can think of an orbital as a component of an electron shell. The first electron shell has only one spherical s orbital (called 1s), but the second shell has four orbitals: one large spherical s orbital (called 2s) and three dumbbell-shaped p orbitals (called 2p orbitals). (The third shell and other higher electron shells also have s and p orbitals, as well as orbitals of more complex shapes.)

No more than 2 electrons can occupy a single orbital. The first electron shell can therefore accommodate up to 2 electrons in its s orbital. The lone electron of a hydrogen atom occupies the 1s orbital, as do the 2 electrons of a helium atom. The four orbitals of the second electron shell can hold up to 8 electrons, 2 in each orbital. Electrons in each of the four orbitals have nearly the same energy, but they move in different volumes of space.

The reactivity of atoms arises from the presence of unpaired electrons in one or more orbitals of their valence shells. As you will see in the next section, atoms interact in a way that completes their valence shells. When they do so, it is the *unpaired* electrons that are involved.

CONCEPT CHECK 2.2

1. A lithium atom has 3 protons and 4 neutrons. What is its atomic mass in daltons?
2. A nitrogen atom has 7 protons, and the most common isotope of nitrogen has 7 neutrons. A radioactive isotope of nitrogen has 8 neutrons. Write the atomic number and mass number of this radioactive nitrogen as a chemical symbol with a subscript and superscript.
3. How many electrons does fluorine have? How many electron shells? Name the orbitals that are occupied. How many electrons are needed to fill the valence shell?
4. **WHAT IF?** In Figure 2.9, if two or more elements are in the same row, what do they have in common? If two or more elements are in the same column, what do they have in common?

For suggested answers, see Appendix A.

CONCEPT 2.3

The formation and function of molecules depend on chemical bonding between atoms

Now that we have looked at the structure of atoms, we can move up the hierarchy of organization and see how atoms combine to form molecules and ionic compounds. Atoms with incomplete valence shells can interact with certain other atoms in such a way that each partner completes its valence shell: The atoms either share or transfer valence electrons. These interactions usually result in atoms staying close together, held by attractions called **chemical bonds**. The strongest kinds of chemical bonds are covalent bonds and ionic bonds.

Covalent Bonds

A **covalent bond** is the sharing of a pair of valence electrons by two atoms. For example, let's consider what happens when two hydrogen atoms approach each other. Recall that hydrogen has 1 valence electron in the first shell, but the shell's capacity is 2 electrons. When the two hydrogen atoms come close enough for their 1s orbitals to overlap, they can share their electrons (**Figure 2.11**). Each hydrogen atom is now associated with 2 electrons in what amounts

to a completed valence shell. Two or more atoms held together by covalent bonds constitute a **molecule**, in this case a hydrogen molecule.

Figure 2.12a shows several ways of representing a hydrogen molecule. Its *molecular formula*, H_2, simply indicates that the molecule consists of two atoms of hydrogen. Electron sharing can be depicted by an electron distribution diagram or by a *Lewis dot structure*, in which element symbols are surrounded by dots that represent the valence electrons (H:H). We can also use a *structural formula*, H—H, where the line represents a **single bond**, a pair of shared electrons. A space-filling model comes closest to representing the actual shape of the molecule.

Oxygen has 6 electrons in its second electron shell and therefore needs 2 more electrons to complete its valence shell. Two oxygen atoms form a molecule by sharing *two* pairs of valence electrons (**Figure 2.12b**). The atoms are thus joined by a **double bond** (O=O).

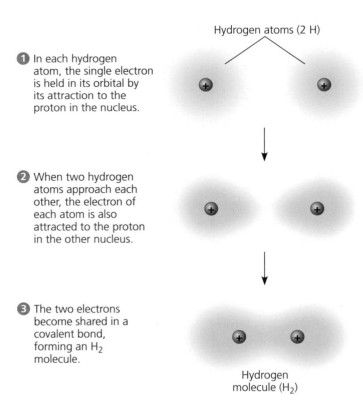

① In each hydrogen atom, the single electron is held in its orbital by its attraction to the proton in the nucleus.

② When two hydrogen atoms approach each other, the electron of each atom is also attracted to the proton in the other nucleus.

③ The two electrons become shared in a covalent bond, forming an H_2 molecule.

Hydrogen atoms (2 H)

Hydrogen molecule (H_2)

▲ **Figure 2.11 Formation of a covalent bond.**

Name and Molecular Formula	Electron Distribution Diagram	Lewis Dot Structure and Structural Formula	Space-Filling Model
(a) Hydrogen (H_2). Two hydrogen atoms share one pair of electrons, forming a single bond.		H:H H—H	
(b) Oxygen (O_2). Two oxygen atoms share two pairs of electrons, forming a double bond.		Ö::Ö O=O	
(c) Water (H_2O). Two hydrogen atoms and one oxygen atom are joined by single bonds, forming a molecule of water.		:Ö:H H O—H | H	
(d) Methane (CH_4). Four hydrogen atoms can satisfy the valence of one carbon atom, forming methane.		H H:C:H H H | H—C—H | H	

▲ **Figure 2.12 Covalent bonding in four molecules.** The number of electrons required to complete an atom's valence shell generally determines how many covalent bonds that atom will form. This figure shows several ways of indicating covalent bonds.

Each atom that can share valence electrons has a bonding capacity corresponding to the number of covalent bonds the atom can form. When the bonds form, they give the atom a full complement of electrons in the valence shell. The bonding capacity of oxygen, for example, is 2. This bonding capacity is called the atom's **valence** and usually equals the number of unpaired electrons required to complete the atom's outermost (valence) shell. See if you can determine the valences of hydrogen, oxygen, nitrogen, and carbon by studying the electron distribution diagrams in Figure 2.9. You can see that the valence of hydrogen is 1; oxygen, 2; nitrogen, 3; and carbon, 4. However, the situation is more complicated for elements in the third row of the periodic table. Phosphorus, for example, can have a valence of 3, as we would predict from the presence of 3 unpaired electrons in its valence shell. In some molecules that are biologically important, however, phosphorus can form three single bonds and one double bond. Therefore, it can also have a valence of 5.

The molecules H_2 and O_2 are pure elements rather than compounds because a compound is a combination of two or more *different* elements. Water, with the molecular formula H_2O, is a compound. Two atoms of hydrogen are needed to satisfy the valence of one oxygen atom. **Figure 2.12c** shows the structure of a water molecule. Water is so important to life that Chapter 3 is devoted entirely to its structure and behavior.

Methane, the main component of natural gas, is a compound with the molecular formula CH_4. It takes four hydrogen atoms, each with a valence of 1, to complement one atom of carbon, with its valence of 4 **(Figure 2.12d)**. We will look at many other compounds of carbon in Chapter 4.

Atoms in a molecule attract shared electrons to varying degrees, depending on the element. The attraction of a particular atom for the electrons of a covalent bond is called its **electronegativity**. The more electronegative an atom is, the more strongly it pulls shared electrons toward itself. In a covalent bond between two atoms of the same element, the electrons are shared equally because the two atoms have the same electronegativity—the tug-of-war is at a standoff. Such a bond is called a **nonpolar covalent bond**. For example, the single bond of H_2 is nonpolar, as is the double bond of O_2. However, when one atom is bonded to a more electronegative atom, the electrons of the bond are not shared equally. This type of bond is called a **polar covalent bond**. Such bonds vary in their polarity, depending on the relative electronegativity of the two atoms. For example, the bonds between the oxygen and hydrogen atoms of a water molecule are quite polar **(Figure 2.13)**.

Because oxygen (O) is more electronegative than hydrogen (H), shared electrons are pulled more toward oxygen.

This results in a partial negative charge on the oxygen and a partial positive charge on the hydrogens.

$\delta-$

O

H   H

$\delta+$ $\delta+$

H_2O

▲ **Figure 2.13 Polar covalent bonds in a water molecule.**

Oxygen is one of the most electronegative of all the elements, attracting shared electrons much more strongly than hydrogen does. In a covalent bond between oxygen and hydrogen, the electrons spend more time near the oxygen nucleus than they do near the hydrogen nucleus. Because electrons have a negative charge and are pulled toward oxygen in a water molecule, the oxygen atom has a partial negative charge (indicated by the Greek letter δ with a minus sign, $\delta-$, or "delta minus"), and each hydrogen atom has a partial positive charge ($\delta+$, or "delta plus"). In contrast, the individual bonds of methane (CH_4) are much less polar because the electronegativities of carbon and hydrogen are similar.

Ionic Bonds

In some cases, two atoms are so unequal in their attraction for valence electrons that the more electronegative atom strips an electron completely away from its partner. This is what happens when an atom of sodium ($_{11}Na$) encounters an atom of chlorine ($_{17}Cl$) **(Figure 2.14)**. A sodium atom has a total of 11 electrons, with its single valence electron in the third electron shell. A chlorine atom has a total of 17 electrons,

① The lone valence electron of a sodium atom is transferred to join the 7 valence electrons of a chlorine atom.

② Each resulting ion has a completed valence shell. An ionic bond can form between the oppositely charged ions.

Na
Sodium atom

Cl
Chlorine atom

Na⁺
Sodium ion
(a cation)

Cl⁻
Chloride ion
(an anion)

Sodium chloride (NaCl)

▲ **Figure 2.14 Electron transfer and ionic bonding.** The attraction between oppositely charged atoms, or ions, is an ionic bond. An ionic bond can form between any two oppositely charged ions, even if they have not been formed by transfer of an electron from one to the other.

with 7 electrons in its valence shell. When these two atoms meet, the lone valence electron of sodium is transferred to the chlorine atom, and both atoms end up with their valence shells complete. (Because sodium no longer has an electron in the third shell, the second shell is now the valence shell.)

The electron transfer between the two atoms moves one unit of negative charge from sodium to chlorine. Sodium, now with 11 protons but only 10 electrons, has a net electrical charge of 1+. A charged atom (or molecule) is called an **ion**. When the charge is positive, the ion is specifically called a **cation**; the sodium atom has become a cation. Conversely, the chlorine atom, having gained an extra electron, now has 17 protons and 18 electrons, giving it a net electrical charge of 1–. It has become a chloride ion—an **anion**, or negatively charged ion. Because of their opposite charges, cations and anions attract each other; this attraction is called an **ionic bond**. The transfer of an electron is not the formation of a bond; rather, it allows a bond to form because it results in two ions of opposite charge. Any two ions of opposite charge can form an ionic bond. The ions do not need to have acquired their charge by an electron transfer with each other.

Compounds formed by ionic bonds are called **ionic compounds**, or **salts**. We know the ionic compound sodium chloride (NaCl) as table salt (**Figure 2.15**). Salts are often found in nature as crystals of various sizes and shapes. Each salt crystal is an aggregate of vast numbers of cations and anions bonded by their electrical attraction and arranged in a three-dimensional lattice. Unlike a covalent compound, which consists of molecules having a definite size and number of atoms, an ionic compound does not consist of molecules. The formula for an ionic compound, such as NaCl, indicates only the ratio of elements in a crystal of the salt. "NaCl" by itself is not a molecule.

Not all salts have equal numbers of cations and anions. For example, the ionic compound magnesium chloride ($MgCl_2$) has two chloride ions for each magnesium ion. Magnesium ($_{12}Mg$) must lose 2 outer electrons if the atom is to have a

complete valence shell, so it tends to become a cation with a net charge of 2+ (Mg^{2+}). One magnesium cation can therefore form ionic bonds with two chloride anions.

The term *ion* also applies to entire molecules that are electrically charged. In the salt ammonium chloride (NH_4Cl), for instance, the anion is a single chloride ion (Cl^-), but the cation is ammonium (NH_4^+), a nitrogen atom with four covalently bonded hydrogen atoms. The whole ammonium ion has an electrical charge of 1+ because it is 1 electron short.

Environment affects the strength of ionic bonds. In a dry salt crystal, the bonds are so strong that it takes a hammer and chisel to break enough of them to crack the crystal in two. If the same salt crystal is dissolved in water, however, the ionic bonds are much weaker because each ion is partially shielded by its interactions with water molecules. Most drugs are manufactured as salts because they are quite stable when dry but can dissociate (come apart) easily in water. In the next chapter, you will learn how water dissolves salts.

Weak Chemical Bonds

In organisms, most of the strongest chemical bonds are covalent bonds, which link atoms to form a cell's molecules. But weaker bonding within and between molecules is also indispensable in the cell, contributing greatly to the emergent properties of life. Many large biological molecules are held in their functional form by weak bonds. In addition, when two molecules in the cell make contact, they may adhere temporarily by weak bonds. The reversibility of weak bonding can be an advantage: Two molecules can come together, respond to one another in some way, and then separate.

Several types of weak chemical bonds are important in organisms. One is the ionic bond as it exists between ions dissociated in water, which we just discussed. Hydrogen bonds and van der Waals interactions are also crucial to life.

Hydrogen Bonds

Among the various kinds of weak chemical bonds, hydrogen bonds are so important in the chemistry of life that they deserve special attention. The partial positive charge on a hydrogen atom that is covalently bonded to an electronegative atom allows the hydrogen to be attracted to a different electronegative atom nearby. This noncovalent attraction between a hydrogen and an electronegative atom is called a **hydrogen bond**. In living cells, the electronegative partners are usually oxygen or nitrogen atoms. Refer to **Figure 2.16** to examine the simple case of hydrogen bonding between water (H_2O) and ammonia (NH_3).

Van der Waals Interactions

Even a molecule with nonpolar covalent bonds may have positively and negatively charged regions. Electrons are not always symmetrically distributed in such a molecule; at any

▲ **Figure 2.15 A sodium chloride (NaCl) crystal.** The sodium ions (Na^+) and chloride ions (Cl^-) are held together by ionic bonds. The formula NaCl tells us that the ratio of Na^+ to Cl^- is 1:1.

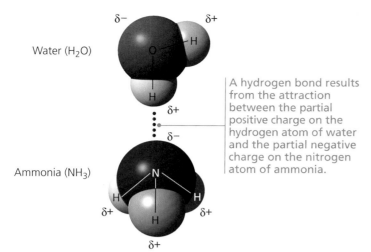

Water (H_2O)

$\delta-$ $\delta+$

A hydrogen bond results from the attraction between the partial positive charge on the hydrogen atom of water and the partial negative charge on the nitrogen atom of ammonia.

$\delta+$

$\delta-$

Ammonia (NH_3)

$\delta+$ $\delta+$

$\delta+$

▲ **Figure 2.16 A hydrogen bond.**
DRAW IT *Draw five water molecules using structural formulas and indicating partial charges, and show how they can make hydrogen bonds with each other.*

instant, they may accumulate by chance in one part of the molecule or another. The results are ever-changing regions of positive and negative charge that enable all atoms and molecules to stick to one another. These **van der Waals interactions** are individually weak and occur only when atoms and molecules are very close together. When many such interactions occur simultaneously, however, they can be powerful: Van der Waals interactions are the reason a gecko lizard (right) can walk straight up a wall! Each gecko toe has hundreds of thousands of tiny hairs, with multiple projections at each hair's tip that increase surface area. Apparently, the van der Waals interactions between the hair tip molecules and the molecules of the wall's surface are so numerous that despite their individual weakness, together they can support the gecko's body weight.

Van der Waals interactions, hydrogen bonds, ionic bonds in water, and other weak bonds may form not only between molecules but also between parts of a large molecule, such as a protein. The cumulative effect of weak bonds is to reinforce the three-dimensional shape of the molecule. You will learn more about the very important biological roles of weak bonds in Chapter 5.

Molecular Shape and Function

A molecule has a characteristic size and shape. The precise shape of a molecule is usually very important to its function in the living cell.

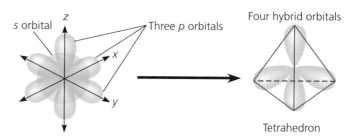

(a) Hybridization of orbitals. The single *s* and three *p* orbitals of a valence shell involved in covalent bonding combine to form four teardrop-shaped hybrid orbitals. These orbitals extend to the four corners of an imaginary tetrahedron (outlined in pink).

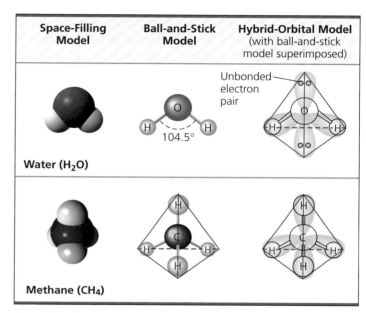

Space-Filling Model	Ball-and-Stick Model	Hybrid-Orbital Model (with ball-and-stick model superimposed)

Water (H_2O)

Unbonded electron pair

104.5°

Methane (CH_4)

(b) Molecular-shape models. Three models representing molecular shape are shown for water and methane. The positions of the hybrid orbitals determine the shapes of the molecules.

▲ **Figure 2.17 Molecular shapes due to hybrid orbitals.**

A molecule consisting of two atoms, such as H_2 or O_2, is always linear, but most molecules with more than two atoms have more complicated shapes. These shapes are determined by the positions of the atoms' orbitals. When an atom forms covalent bonds, the orbitals in its valence shell undergo rearrangement. For atoms with valence electrons in both *s* and *p* orbitals (review Figure 2.10), the single *s* and three *p* orbitals form four new hybrid orbitals shaped like identical teardrops extending from the region of the atomic nucleus **(Figure 2.17a)**. If we connect the larger ends of the teardrops with lines, we have the outline of a geometric shape called a tetrahedron, a pyramid with a triangular base.

For the water molecule (H_2O), two of the hybrid orbitals in the oxygen atom's valence shell are shared with hydrogen atoms **(Figure 2.17b)**. The result is a molecule shaped roughly like a V, with its two covalent bonds spread apart at an angle of 104.5°.

The methane molecule (CH_4) has the shape of a completed tetrahedron because all four hybrid orbitals of the carbon atom are shared with hydrogen atoms (see Figure 2.17b). The carbon nucleus is at the center, with its four covalent bonds radiating to hydrogen nuclei at the corners of the tetrahedron. Larger molecules containing multiple carbon atoms, including many of the molecules that make up living matter, have more complex overall shapes. However, the tetrahedral shape of a carbon atom bonded to four other atoms is often a repeating motif within such molecules.

Molecular shape is crucial in biology because it determines how biological molecules recognize and respond to one another with specificity. Biological molecules often bind temporarily to each other by forming weak bonds, but this can happen only if their shapes are complementary. We can see this specificity in the effects of opiates, drugs derived from opium. Opiates, such as morphine and heroin, relieve pain and alter mood by weakly binding to specific receptor molecules on the surfaces of brain cells. Why would brain cells carry receptors for opiates, compounds that are not made by our bodies? The discovery of endorphins in 1975 answered this question. Endorphins are signaling molecules made by the pituitary gland that bind to the receptors, relieving pain and producing euphoria during times of stress, such as intense exercise. It turns out that opiates have shapes similar to endorphins and mimic them by binding to endorphin receptors in the brain. That is why opiates (such as morphine) and endorphins have similar effects (**Figure 2.18**). The role of molecular shape in brain chemistry illustrates the relationship between structure and function, one of biology's unifying themes.

CONCEPT CHECK 2.3

1. Why does the structure H—C=C—H fail to make sense chemically?
2. What holds the atoms together in a crystal of magnesium chloride ($MgCl_2$)?
3. **WHAT IF?** If you were a pharmaceutical researcher, why would you want to learn the three-dimensional shapes of naturally occurring signaling molecules?

For suggested answers, see Appendix A.

CONCEPT 2.4

Chemical reactions make and break chemical bonds

The making and breaking of chemical bonds, leading to changes in the composition of matter, are called **chemical reactions**. An example is the reaction between hydrogen and oxygen molecules that forms water:

Key

- ■ Carbon
- ▨ Hydrogen
- ■ Nitrogen
- ▨ Sulfur
- ▨ Oxygen

Natural endorphin

Morphine

(a) Structures of endorphin and morphine. The boxed portion of the endorphin molecule (left) binds to receptor molecules on target cells in the brain. The boxed portion of the morphine molecule (right) is a close match.

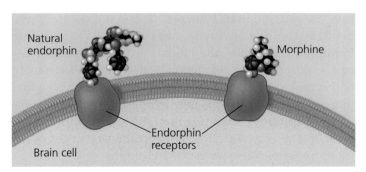

(b) Binding to endorphin receptors. Both endorphin and morphine can bind to endorphin receptors on the surface of a brain cell.

▲ **Figure 2.18 A molecular mimic.** Morphine affects pain perception and emotional state by mimicking the brain's natural endorphins.

$$2\,H_2 \quad + \quad O_2 \quad \longrightarrow \quad 2\,H_2O$$

Reactants   **Reaction**   **Products**

This reaction breaks the covalent bonds of H_2 and O_2 and forms the new bonds of H_2O. When we write a chemical reaction, we use an arrow to indicate the conversion of the starting materials, called the **reactants**, to the **products**. The coefficients indicate the number of molecules involved; for example, the coefficient 2 in front of the H_2 means that

▲ **Figure 2.19 Photosynthesis: a solar-powered rearrangement of matter.** *Elodea*, a freshwater plant, produces sugar by rearranging the atoms of carbon dioxide and water in the chemical process known as photosynthesis, which is powered by sunlight. Much of the sugar is then converted to other food molecules. Oxygen gas (O_2) is a by-product of photosynthesis; notice the bubbles of oxygen escaping from the leaves in the photo.

? *Explain how this photo relates to the reactants and products in the equation for photosynthesis given in the text. (You will learn more about photosynthesis in Chapter 10.)*

the reaction starts with two molecules of hydrogen. Notice that all atoms of the reactants must be accounted for in the products. Matter is conserved in a chemical reaction: Reactions cannot create or destroy matter but can only rearrange it.

Photosynthesis, which takes place within the cells of green plant tissues, is a particularly important example of how chemical reactions rearrange matter. Humans and other animals ultimately depend on photosynthesis for food and oxygen, and this process is at the foundation of almost all ecosystems. The following chemical shorthand summarizes the process of photosynthesis:

$$6\ CO_2 + 6\ H_2O \rightarrow C_6H_{12}O_6 + 6\ O_2$$

The raw materials of photosynthesis are carbon dioxide (CO_2), which is taken from the air, and water (H_2O), which is absorbed from the soil. Within the plant cells, sunlight powers the conversion of these ingredients to a sugar called glucose ($C_6H_{12}O_6$) and oxygen molecules (O_2), a by-product that the plant releases into the surroundings **(Figure 2.19)**. Although photosynthesis is actually a sequence of many chemical reactions, we still end up with the same number and types of atoms that we had when we started. Matter has simply been rearranged, with an input of energy provided by sunlight.

All chemical reactions are reversible, with the products of the forward reaction becoming the reactants for the reverse reaction. For example, hydrogen and nitrogen molecules can combine to form ammonia, but ammonia can also decompose to regenerate hydrogen and nitrogen:

$$3\ H_2 + N_2 \rightleftharpoons 2\ NH_3$$

The two opposite-headed arrows indicate that the reaction is reversible.

One of the factors affecting the rate of a reaction is the concentration of reactants. The greater the concentration of reactant molecules, the more frequently they collide with one another and have an opportunity to react and form products. The same holds true for products. As products accumulate, collisions resulting in the reverse reaction become more frequent. Eventually, the forward and reverse reactions occur at the same rate, and the relative concentrations of products and reactants stop changing. The point at which the reactions offset one another exactly is called **chemical equilibrium**. This is a dynamic equilibrium; reactions are still going on, but with no net effect on the concentrations of reactants and products. Equilibrium does *not* mean that the reactants and products are equal in concentration, but only that their concentrations have stabilized at a particular ratio. The reaction involving ammonia reaches equilibrium when ammonia decomposes as rapidly as it forms. In some chemical reactions, the equilibrium point may lie so far to the right that these reactions go essentially to completion; that is, virtually all the reactants are converted to products.

We will return to the subject of chemical reactions after more detailed study of the various types of molecules that are important to life. In the next chapter, we focus on water, the substance in which all the chemical processes of organisms occur.

CONCEPT CHECK 2.4

1. **MAKE CONNECTIONS** Consider the reaction between hydrogen and oxygen that forms water, shown with ball-and-stick models on page 42. Study Figure 2.12 and draw the Lewis dot structures representing this reaction.
2. Which type of chemical reaction occurs faster at equilibrium, the formation of products from reactants or reactants from products?
3. **WHAT IF?** Write an equation that uses the products of photosynthesis as reactants and the reactants of photosynthesis as products. Add energy as another product. This new equation describes a process that occurs in your cells. Describe this equation in words. How does this equation relate to breathing?

For suggested answers, see Appendix A.

SUMMARY OF KEY CONCEPTS

CONCEPT 2.1

Matter consists of chemical elements in pure form and in combinations called compounds (pp. 31–32)

- **Elements** cannot be broken down chemically to other substances. A **compound** contains two or more different elements in a fixed ratio. Oxygen, carbon, hydrogen, and nitrogen make up approximately 96% of living matter.

> **?** *In what way does the need for iodine or iron in your diet differ from your need for calcium or phosphorus?*

CONCEPT 2.2

An element's properties depend on the structure of its atoms (pp. 33–37)

- An **atom**, the smallest unit of an element, has the following components:

Nucleus

Protons (+ charge) determine element

Neutrons (no charge) determine isotope

Atom

Electrons (– charge) form negative cloud and determine chemical behavior

- An electrically neutral atom has equal numbers of electrons and protons; the number of protons determines the **atomic number**. The **atomic mass** is measured in **daltons** and is roughly equal to the sum of protons plus neutrons. **Isotopes** of an element differ from each other in neutron number and therefore mass. Unstable isotopes give off particles and energy as radioactivity.
- In an atom, electrons occupy specific **electron shells**; the electrons in a shell have a characteristic energy level. Electron distribution in shells determines the chemical behavior of an atom. An atom that has an incomplete outer shell, the **valence shell**, is reactive.
- Electrons exist in **orbitals**, three-dimensional spaces with specific shapes that are components of electron shells.

Electron orbitals

> **DRAW IT** *Draw the electron distribution diagrams for neon ($_{10}$Ne) and argon ($_{18}$Ar). Use these diagrams to explain why these elements are chemically unreactive.*

CONCEPT 2.3

The formation and function of molecules depend on chemical bonding between atoms (pp. 38–42)

- **Chemical bonds** form when atoms interact and complete their valence shells. **Covalent bonds** form when pairs of electrons are shared.

H· + H· ⟶ H:H
Single covalent bond

:Ö· + ·Ö: ⟶ Ö::Ö
Double covalent bond

- **Molecules** consist of two or more covalently bonded atoms. The attraction of an atom for the electrons of a covalent bond is its **electronegativity**. If both atoms are the same, they have the same electronegativity and share a **nonpolar covalent bond**. Electrons of a **polar covalent bond** are pulled closer to the more electronegative atom.
- An **ion** forms when an atom or molecule gains or loses an electron and becomes charged. An **ionic bond** is the attraction between two oppositely charged ions.

Ionic bond

Electron transfer forms ions

Na Sodium atom

Cl Chlorine atom

Na⁺ Sodium ion (a cation)

Cl⁻ Chloride ion (an anion)

- Weak bonds reinforce the shapes of large molecules and help molecules adhere to each other. A **hydrogen bond** is an attraction between a hydrogen atom carrying a partial positive charge ($\delta+$) and an electronegative atom ($\delta-$). **Van der Waals interactions** occur between transiently positive and negative regions of molecules.
- A molecule's shape is determined by the positions of its atoms' valence orbitals. Covalent bonds result in hybrid orbitals, which are responsible for the shapes of H_2O, CH_4, and many more complex biological molecules. Shape is usually the basis for the recognition of one biological molecule by another.

> **?** *In terms of electron sharing between atoms, compare nonpolar covalent bonds, polar covalent bonds, and the formation of ions.*

CONCEPT 2.4

Chemical reactions make and break chemical bonds (pp. 42–43)

- **Chemical reactions** change **reactants** into **products** while conserving matter. All chemical reactions are theoretically reversible. **Chemical equilibrium** is reached when the forward and reverse reaction rates are equal.

> **?** *What would happen to the concentration of products if more reactants were added to a reaction that was in chemical equilibrium? How would this addition affect the equilibrium?*

TEST YOUR UNDERSTANDING

LEVEL 1: KNOWLEDGE/COMPREHENSION

1. In the term *trace element*, the adjective *trace* means that
   a. the element is required in very small amounts.
   b. the element can be used as a label to trace atoms through an organism's metabolism.
   c. the element is very rare on Earth.
   d. the element enhances health but is not essential for the organism's long-term survival.
   e. the element passes rapidly through the organism.

2. Compared with ^{31}P, the radioactive isotope ^{32}P has
   a. a different atomic number.
   b. a different charge.
   c. one more proton.
   d. one more electron.
   e. one more neutron.

3. The reactivity of an atom arises from
   a. the average distance of the outermost electron shell from the nucleus.
   b. the existence of unpaired electrons in the valence shell.
   c. the sum of the potential energies of all the electron shells.
   d. the potential energy of the valence shell.
   e. the energy difference between the s and p orbitals.

4. Which statement is true of all atoms that are anions?
   a. The atom has more electrons than protons.
   b. The atom has more protons than electrons.
   c. The atom has fewer protons than does a neutral atom of the same element.
   d. The atom has more neutrons than protons.
   e. The net charge is 1−.

5. Which of the following statements correctly describes any chemical reaction that has reached equilibrium?
   a. The concentrations of products and reactants are equal.
   b. The reaction is now irreversible.
   c. Both forward and reverse reactions have halted.
   d. The rates of the forward and reverse reactions are equal.
   e. No reactants remain.

LEVEL 2: APPLICATION/ANALYSIS

6. We can represent atoms by listing the number of protons, neutrons, and electrons—for example, $2p^+$, $2n^0$, $2e^-$ for helium. Which of the following represents the ^{18}O isotope of oxygen?
   a. $6p^+$, $8n^0$, $6e^-$
   b. $8p^+$, $10n^0$, $8e^-$
   c. $9p^+$, $9n^0$, $9e^-$
   d. $7p^+$, $2n^0$, $9e^-$
   e. $10p^+$, $8n^0$, $9e^-$

7. The atomic number of sulfur is 16. Sulfur combines with hydrogen by covalent bonding to form a compound, hydrogen sulfide. Based on the number of valence electrons in a sulfur atom, predict the molecular formula of the compound.
   a. HS
   b. HS_2
   c. H_2S
   d. H_3S_2
   e. H_4S

8. What coefficients must be placed in the following blanks so that all atoms are accounted for in the products?

   $C_6H_{12}O_6 \rightarrow$ _____ $C_2H_6O +$ _____ CO_2

   a. 1; 2
   b. 3; 1
   c. 1; 3
   d. 1; 1
   e. 2; 2

9. Draw Lewis dot structures for each hypothetical molecule shown below, using the correct number of valence electrons for each atom. Determine which molecule makes sense because each atom has a complete valence shell and each bond has the correct number of electrons. Explain what makes the other molecules nonsensical, considering the number of bonds each type of atom can make.

   (a) O=C—H

   (b)
   ```
        H  H
        |  |
   H—O—C—C=O
           |
           H
   ```

   (c)
   ```
       H       H
       |       |
   H—C—H—C=O
       |
       H
   ```

   (d)
   ```
       O
       ‖
   H—N=H
   ```

LEVEL 3: SYNTHESIS/EVALUATION

10. EVOLUTION CONNECTION

The percentages of naturally occurring elements making up the human body (see Table 2.1) are similar to the percentages of these elements found in other organisms. How could you account for this similarity among organisms?

11. SCIENTIFIC INQUIRY

Female silkworm moths (*Bombyx mori*) attract males by emitting chemical signals that spread through the air. A male hundreds of meters away can detect these molecules and fly toward their source. The sensory organs responsible for this behavior are the comblike antennae visible in the photograph shown here. Each filament of an antenna is equipped with thousands of receptor cells that detect the sex attractant. Based on what you learned in this chapter, propose a hypothesis to account for the ability of the male moth to detect a specific molecule in the presence of many other molecules in the air. What predictions does your hypothesis make? Design an experiment to test one of these predictions.

12. WRITE ABOUT A THEME

Emergent Properties While waiting at an airport, Neil Campbell once overheard this claim: "It's paranoid and ignorant to worry about industry or agriculture contaminating the environment with their chemical wastes. After all, this stuff is just made of the same atoms that were already present in our environment." Drawing on your knowledge of electron distribution, bonding, and the theme of emergent properties (pp. 3–5), write a short essay (100–150 words) countering this argument.

For selected answers, see Appendix A.

MasteringBIOLOGY® www.masteringbiology.com

1. MasteringBiology® Assignments

Tutorials The Anatomy of Atoms • Atomic Number and Mass Number
Activities Structure of the Atomic Nucleus • Electron Arrangement • Covalent Bonds • Nonpolar and Polar Molecules • Ionic Bonds • Hydrogen Bonds
Questions Student Misconceptions • Reading Quiz • Multiple Choice • End-of-Chapter

2. eText

Read your book online, search, take notes, highlight text, and more.

3. The Study Area

Practice Tests • Cumulative Test • *BioFlix* 3-D Animations • MP3 Tutor Sessions • Videos • Activities • Investigations • Lab Media • Audio Glossary • Word Study Tools • Art

3

Water and Life

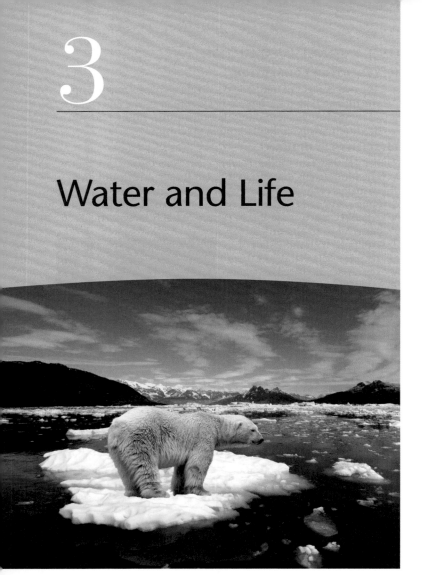

▲ **Figure 3.1 How does the habitat of a polar bear depend on the chemistry of water?**

KEY CONCEPTS

3.1 Polar covalent bonds in water molecules result in hydrogen bonding

3.2 Four emergent properties of water contribute to Earth's suitability for life

3.3 Acidic and basic conditions affect living organisms

OVERVIEW

The Molecule That Supports All of Life

As astronomers study newly discovered planets orbiting distant stars, they hope to find evidence of water on these far-off celestial bodies, for water is the substance that makes possible life as we know it here on Earth. All organisms familiar to us are made mostly of water and live in an environment dominated by water. Water is the biological medium here on Earth, and possibly on other planets as well.

Three-quarters of Earth's surface is covered by water. Although most of this water is in liquid form, water is also present on Earth as a solid (ice) and a gas (water vapor). Water is the only common substance to exist in the natural environment in all three physical states of matter. Furthermore, the solid state of water floats on the liquid, a rare property emerging from the chemistry of the water molecule. Ice can thus provide a hunting platform for the polar bear in **Figure 3.1**.

The abundance of water is a major reason Earth is habitable. In a classic book called *The Fitness of the Environment*, ecologist Lawrence Henderson highlighted the importance of water to life. While acknowledging that life adapts to its environment through natural selection, Henderson emphasized that for life to exist at all, the environment must first be suitable.

Life on Earth began in water and evolved there for 3 billion years before spreading onto land. Modern life, even terrestrial (land-dwelling) life, remains tied to water. All living organisms require water more than any other substance. Human beings, for example, can survive for quite a few weeks without food, but only a week or so without water. Molecules of water participate in many chemical reactions necessary to sustain life. Most cells are surrounded by water, and cells themselves are about 70–95% water.

What properties of the simple water molecule make it so indispensable to life on Earth? In this chapter, you will learn how the structure of a water molecule allows it to interact with other molecules, including other water molecules. This ability leads to water's unique emergent properties that help make Earth suitable for life.

CONCEPT 3.1

Polar covalent bonds in water molecules result in hydrogen bonding

Water is so common that it is easy to overlook the fact that it is an exceptional substance with many extraordinary qualities. Following the theme of emergent properties, we can trace water's unique behavior to the structure and interactions of its molecules.

Studied on its own, the water molecule is deceptively simple. It is shaped like a wide V, with its two hydrogen atoms joined to the oxygen atom by single covalent bonds. Oxygen is more electronegative than hydrogen, so the electrons of the covalent bonds spend more time closer to oxygen than to hydrogen; these are **polar covalent bonds** (see Figure 2.13). This unequal sharing of electrons and water's V-like shape make it a **polar molecule**, meaning that its overall charge is unevenly distributed: The oxygen region of the molecule has a partial negative charge ($\delta-$), and each hydrogen has a partial positive charge ($\delta+$).

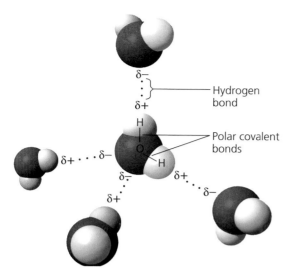

▲ **Figure 3.2 Hydrogen bonds between water molecules.**
The charged regions in a water molecule are due to its polar covalent bonds. Oppositely charged regions of neighboring water molecules are attracted to each other, forming hydrogen bonds. Each molecule can hydrogen-bond to multiple partners, and these associations are constantly changing.

DRAW IT *Draw partial charges on all the atoms of the water molecule on the far left above, and draw two more water molecules hydrogen-bonded to it.*

The properties of water arise from attractions between oppositely charged atoms of different water molecules: The slightly positive hydrogen of one molecule is attracted to the slightly negative oxygen of a nearby molecule. The two molecules are thus held together by a hydrogen bond **(Figure 3.2)**. When water is in its liquid form, its hydrogen bonds are very fragile, each about 1/20 as strong as a covalent bond. The hydrogen bonds form, break, and re-form with great frequency. Each lasts only a few trillionths of a second, but the molecules are constantly forming new hydrogen bonds with a succession of partners. Therefore, at any instant, a substantial percentage of all the water molecules are hydrogen-bonded to their neighbors. The extraordinary qualities of water are emergent properties resulting in large part from the hydrogen bonding that organizes water molecules into a higher level of structural order.

CONCEPT CHECK 3.1

1. **MAKE CONNECTIONS** What is electronegativity, and how does it affect interactions between water molecules? Review p. 39 and Figure 2.13.
2. Why is it unlikely that two neighboring water molecules would be arranged like this?

$$O \overset{\displaystyle H\ H}{\underset{\displaystyle H\ H}{\diagdown\diagup}} O$$

3. **WHAT IF?** What would be the effect on the properties of the water molecule if oxygen and hydrogen had equal electronegativity?

For suggested answers, see Appendix A.

CONCEPT 3.2

Four emergent properties of water contribute to Earth's suitability for life

We will examine four emergent properties of water that contribute to Earth's suitability as an environment for life: cohesive behavior, ability to moderate temperature, expansion upon freezing, and versatility as a solvent.

Cohesion of Water Molecules

Water molecules stay close to each other as a result of hydrogen bonding. Although the arrangement of molecules in a sample of liquid water is constantly changing, at any given moment many of the molecules are linked by multiple hydrogen bonds. These linkages make water more structured than most other liquids. Collectively, the hydrogen bonds hold the substance together, a phenomenon called **cohesion**.

Cohesion due to hydrogen bonding contributes to the transport of water and dissolved nutrients against gravity in plants **(Figure 3.3)**. Water from the roots reaches the leaves through a network of water-conducting cells. As water evaporates from a

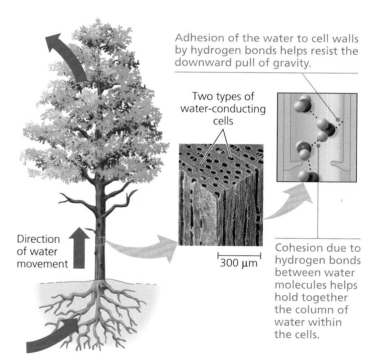

Adhesion of the water to cell walls by hydrogen bonds helps resist the downward pull of gravity.

Two types of water-conducting cells

Direction of water movement

300 μm

Cohesion due to hydrogen bonds between water molecules helps hold together the column of water within the cells.

▲ **Figure 3.3 Water transport in plants.** Evaporation from leaves pulls water upward from the roots through water-conducting cells. Because of the properties of cohesion and adhesion, the tallest trees can transport water more than 100 m upward—approximately one-quarter the height of the Empire State Building in New York City.

ANIMATION ***BioFlix*** Visit the Study Area at **www.masteringbiology.com** for the BioFlix® 3-D Animation on Water Transport in Plants.

▲ **Figure 3.4 Walking on water.** The high surface tension of water, resulting from the collective strength of its hydrogen bonds, allows this raft spider to walk on the surface of a pond.

leaf, hydrogen bonds cause water molecules leaving the veins to tug on molecules farther down, and the upward pull is transmitted through the water-conducting cells all the way to the roots. **Adhesion**, the clinging of one substance to another, also plays a role. Adhesion of water to cell walls by hydrogen bonds helps counter the downward pull of gravity (see Figure 3.3).

Related to cohesion is **surface tension**, a measure of how difficult it is to stretch or break the surface of a liquid. Water has a greater surface tension than most other liquids. At the interface between water and air is an ordered arrangement of water molecules, hydrogen-bonded to one another and to the water below. This makes the water behave as though coated with an invisible film. You can observe the surface tension of water by slightly overfilling a drinking glass; the water will stand above the rim. In a more biological example, some animals can stand, walk, or run on water without breaking the surface (**Figure 3.4**).

Moderation of Temperature by Water

Water moderates air temperature by absorbing heat from air that is warmer and releasing the stored heat to air that is cooler. Water is effective as a heat bank because it can absorb or release a relatively large amount of heat with only a slight change in its own temperature. To understand this capability of water, we must first look briefly at heat and temperature.

Heat and Temperature

Anything that moves has **kinetic energy**, the energy of motion. Atoms and molecules have kinetic energy because they are always moving, although not necessarily in any particular direction. The faster a molecule moves, the greater its kinetic energy. **Heat** is a form of energy. For a given body of matter, the amount of heat is a measure of the matter's *total* kinetic energy due to motion of its molecules; thus, heat depends in part on the matter's volume. Although heat is related to temperature, they are not the same thing. **Temperature** is a

measure of heat intensity that represents the *average* kinetic energy of the molecules, regardless of volume. When water is heated in a coffeemaker, the average speed of the molecules increases, and the thermometer records this as a rise in temperature of the liquid. The amount of heat also increases in this case. Note, however, that although the pot of coffee has a much higher temperature than, say, the water in a swimming pool, the swimming pool contains more heat because of its much greater volume.

Whenever two objects of different temperature are brought together, heat passes from the warmer to the cooler object until the two are the same temperature. Molecules in the cooler object speed up at the expense of the kinetic energy of the warmer object. An ice cube cools a drink not by adding coldness to the liquid, but by absorbing heat from the liquid as the ice itself melts.

In general, we will use the **Celsius scale** to indicate temperature. (Celsius degrees are abbreviated °C; Appendix C shows how to convert between Celsius and Fahrenheit.) At sea level, water freezes at 0°C and boils at 100°C. The temperature of the human body averages 37°C, and comfortable room temperature is about 20–25°C.

One convenient unit of heat used in this book is the **calorie (cal)**. A calorie is the amount of heat it takes to raise the temperature of 1 g of water by 1°C. Conversely, a calorie is also the amount of heat that 1 g of water releases when it cools by 1°C. A **kilocalorie (kcal)**, 1,000 cal, is the quantity of heat required to raise the temperature of 1 kilogram (kg) of water by 1°C. (The "calories" on food packages are actually kilocalories.) Another energy unit used in this book is the **joule (J)**. One joule equals 0.239 cal; one calorie equals 4.184 J.

Water's High Specific Heat

The ability of water to stabilize temperature stems from its relatively high specific heat. The **specific heat** of a substance is defined as the amount of heat that must be absorbed or lost for 1 g of that substance to change its temperature by 1°C. We already know water's specific heat because we have defined a calorie as the amount of heat that causes 1 g of water to change its temperature by 1°C. Therefore, the specific heat of water is 1 calorie per gram and per degree Celsius, abbreviated as 1 cal/g·°C. Compared with most other substances, water has an unusually high specific heat. For example, ethyl alcohol, the type of alcohol in alcoholic beverages, has a specific heat of 0.6 cal/g·°C; that is, only 0.6 cal is required to raise the temperature of 1 g of ethyl alcohol by 1°C.

Because of the high specific heat of water relative to other materials, water will change its temperature less when it absorbs or loses a given amount of heat. The reason you can burn your fingers by touching the side of an iron pot on the stove when the water in the pot is still lukewarm is that the specific heat of water is ten times greater than that of iron.

▲ **Figure 3.5 Effect of a large body of water on climate.** By absorbing or releasing heat, oceans moderate coastal climates. In this example from an August day in Southern California, the relatively cool ocean reduces coastal air temperatures by absorbing heat.

In other words, the same amount of heat will raise the temperature of 1 g of the iron much faster than it will raise the temperature of 1 g of the water. Specific heat can be thought of as a measure of how well a substance resists changing its temperature when it absorbs or releases heat. Water resists changing its temperature; when it does change its temperature, it absorbs or loses a relatively large quantity of heat for each degree of change.

We can trace water's high specific heat, like many of its other properties, to hydrogen bonding. Heat must be absorbed in order to break hydrogen bonds; by the same token, heat is released when hydrogen bonds form. A calorie of heat causes a relatively small change in the temperature of water because much of the heat is used to disrupt hydrogen bonds before the water molecules can begin moving faster. And when the temperature of water drops slightly, many additional hydrogen bonds form, releasing a considerable amount of energy in the form of heat.

What is the relevance of water's high specific heat to life on Earth? A large body of water can absorb and store a huge amount of heat from the sun in the daytime and during summer while warming up only a few degrees. At night and during winter, the gradually cooling water can warm the air. This is the reason coastal areas generally have milder climates than inland regions (**Figure 3.5**). The high specific heat of water also tends to stabilize ocean temperatures, creating a favorable environment for marine life. Thus, because of its high specific heat, the water that covers most of Earth keeps temperature fluctuations on land and in water within limits that permit life. Also, because organisms are made primarily of water, they are better able to resist changes in their own temperature than if they were made of a liquid with a lower specific heat.

Evaporative Cooling

Molecules of any liquid stay close together because they are attracted to one another. Molecules moving fast enough to overcome these attractions can depart the liquid and enter the air as a gas. This transformation from a liquid to a gas is called vaporization, or *evaporation*. Recall that the speed of molecular movement varies and that temperature is the *average* kinetic energy of molecules. Even at low temperatures, the speediest molecules can escape into the air. Some evaporation occurs at any temperature; a glass of water at room temperature, for example, will eventually evaporate completely. If a liquid is heated, the average kinetic energy of molecules increases and the liquid evaporates more rapidly.

Heat of vaporization is the quantity of heat a liquid must absorb for 1 g of it to be converted from the liquid to the gaseous state. For the same reason that water has a high specific heat, it also has a high heat of vaporization relative to most other liquids. To evaporate 1 g of water at 25°C, about 580 cal of heat is needed—nearly double the amount needed to vaporize a gram of alcohol or ammonia. Water's high heat of vaporization is another emergent property resulting from the strength of its hydrogen bonds, which must be broken before the molecules can make their exodus from the liquid.

The high amount of energy required to vaporize water has a wide range of effects. On a global scale, for example, it helps moderate Earth's climate. A considerable amount of solar heat absorbed by tropical seas is consumed during the evaporation of surface water. Then, as moist tropical air circulates poleward, it releases heat as it condenses and forms rain. On an organismal level, water's high heat of vaporization accounts for the severity of steam burns. These burns are caused by the heat energy released when steam condenses into liquid on the skin.

As a liquid evaporates, the surface of the liquid that remains behind cools down. This **evaporative cooling** occurs because the "hottest" molecules, those with the greatest kinetic energy, are the most likely to leave as gas. It is as if the hundred fastest runners at a college transferred to another school; the average speed of the remaining students would decline.

Evaporative cooling of water contributes to the stability of temperature in lakes and ponds and also provides a mechanism that prevents terrestrial organisms from overheating. For example, evaporation of water from the leaves of a plant helps keep the tissues in the leaves from becoming too warm in the sunlight. Evaporation of sweat from human skin dissipates body heat and helps prevent overheating on a hot day or when excess heat is generated by strenuous activity. High humidity on a hot day increases discomfort because the high concentration of water vapor in the air inhibits the evaporation of sweat from the body.

Floating of Ice on Liquid Water

Water is one of the few substances that are less dense as a solid than as a liquid. In other words, ice floats on liquid water. While other materials contract and become denser when they solidify, water expands. The cause of this exotic behavior is, once again, hydrogen bonding. At temperatures above

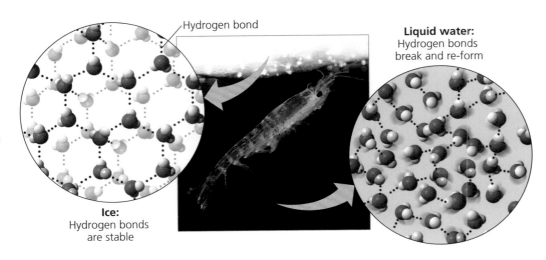

▶ **Figure 3.6 Ice: crystalline structure and floating barrier.** In ice, each molecule is hydrogen-bonded to four neighbors in a three-dimensional crystal. Because the crystal is spacious, ice has fewer molecules than an equal volume of liquid water. In other words, ice is less dense than liquid water. Floating ice becomes a barrier that protects the liquid water below from the colder air. The marine organism shown here is a type of shrimp called krill; it was photographed beneath floating ice in the Southern Ocean near Antarctica.

WHAT IF? *If water did not form hydrogen bonds, what would happen to the shrimp's environment?*

Hydrogen bond

Ice: Hydrogen bonds are stable

Liquid water: Hydrogen bonds break and re-form

4°C, water behaves like other liquids, expanding as it warms and contracting as it cools. As the temperature falls from 4°C to 0°C, water begins to freeze because more and more of its molecules are moving too slowly to break hydrogen bonds. At 0°C, the molecules become locked into a crystalline lattice, each water molecule hydrogen-bonded to four partners **(Figure 3.6).** The hydrogen bonds keep the molecules at "arm's length," far enough apart to make ice about 10% less dense (10% fewer molecules for the same volume) than liquid water at 4°C. When ice absorbs enough heat for its temperature to rise above 0°C, hydrogen bonds between molecules are disrupted. As the crystal collapses, the ice melts, and molecules are free to slip closer together. Water reaches its greatest density at 4°C and then begins to expand as the molecules move faster. Even in liquid water, many of the molecules are connected by hydrogen bonds, though only transiently: The hydrogen bonds are constantly breaking and re-forming.

The ability of ice to float due to its lower density is an important factor in the suitability of the environment for life. If ice sank, then eventually all ponds, lakes, and even oceans would freeze solid, making life as we know it impossible on Earth. During summer, only the upper few inches of the ocean would thaw. Instead, when a deep body of water cools, the floating ice insulates the liquid water below, preventing it from freezing and allowing life to exist under the frozen surface, as shown in the photo in Figure 3.6. Besides insulating the water below, ice also provides solid habitat for some animals, such as polar bears and seals (see Figure 3.1).

Along with many other scientists, Susan Solomon, the interviewee for this unit (see pp. 28-29), is worried that these bodies of ice are at risk of disappearing. Global warming, which is caused by carbon dioxide and other "greenhouse" gases in the atmosphere, is having a profound effect on icy environments around the globe. In the Arctic, the average air temperature has risen 1.4°C just since 1961. This temperature increase has affected the seasonal balance between Arctic sea ice and liquid water, causing ice to form later in the year, to melt earlier, and to cover a smaller area. The alarming rate at which glaciers and

Arctic sea ice are disappearing is posing an extreme challenge to animals that depend on ice for their survival.

Water: The Solvent of Life

A sugar cube placed in a glass of water will dissolve. The glass will then contain a uniform mixture of sugar and water; the concentration of dissolved sugar will be the same everywhere in the mixture. A liquid that is a completely homogeneous mixture of two or more substances is called a **solution.** The dissolving agent of a solution is the **solvent,** and the substance that is dissolved is the **solute.** In this case, water is the solvent and sugar is the solute. An **aqueous solution** is one in which water is the solvent.

The medieval alchemists tried to find a universal solvent, one that would dissolve anything. They learned that nothing works better than water. Yet, water is not a universal solvent; if it were, it would dissolve any container in which it was stored, including our cells. Water is a very versatile solvent, however, a quality we can trace to the polarity of the water molecule.

Suppose, for example, that a spoonful of table salt, the ionic compound sodium chloride (NaCl), is placed in water **(Figure 3.7).** At the surface of each grain, or crystal, of salt, the sodium and chloride ions are exposed to the solvent. These ions and the water molecules have a mutual affinity owing to the attraction between opposite charges. The oxygen regions of the water molecules are negatively charged and are attracted to sodium cations. The hydrogen regions are positively charged and are attracted to chloride anions. As a result, water molecules surround the individual sodium and chloride ions, separating and shielding them from one another. The sphere of water molecules around each dissolved ion is called a **hydration shell.** Working inward from the surface of each salt crystal, water eventually dissolves all the ions. The result is a solution of two solutes, sodium cations and chloride anions, homogeneously mixed with water, the solvent. Other ionic compounds also dissolve in water. Seawater, for instance, contains a great variety of dissolved ions, as do living cells.

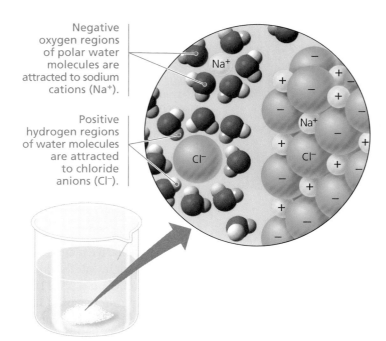

Negative oxygen regions of polar water molecules are attracted to sodium cations (Na^+).

Positive hydrogen regions of water molecules are attracted to chloride anions (Cl^-).

▲ **Figure 3.7 Table salt dissolving in water.** A sphere of water molecules, called a hydration shell, surrounds each solute ion.

WHAT IF? *What would happen if you heated this solution for a long time?*

A compound does not need to be ionic to dissolve in water; many compounds made up of nonionic polar molecules, such as sugars, are also water-soluble. Such compounds dissolve when water molecules surround each of the solute molecules, forming hydrogen bonds with them. Even molecules as large as proteins can dissolve in water if they have ionic and polar regions on their surface **(Figure 3.8)**. Many different kinds of polar compounds are dissolved (along with ions) in the water of such biological fluids as blood, the sap of plants, and the liquid within all cells. Water is the solvent of life.

This oxygen is attracted to a slight positive charge on the lysozyme molecule.

This hydrogen is attracted to a slight negative charge on the lysozyme molecule.

▲ **Figure 3.8 A water-soluble protein.** Human lysozyme is a protein found in tears and saliva that has antibacterial action. This model shows the lysozyme molecule (purple) in an aqueous environment. Ionic and polar regions on the protein's surface attract water molecules.

Hydrophilic and Hydrophobic Substances

Any substance that has an affinity for water is said to be **hydrophilic** (from the Greek *hydro*, water, and *philios*, loving). In some cases, substances can be hydrophilic without actually dissolving. For example, some molecules in cells are so large that they do not dissolve. Instead, they remain suspended in the aqueous liquid of the cell. Such a mixture is an example of a **colloid**, a stable suspension of fine particles in a liquid. Another example of a hydrophilic substance that does not dissolve is cotton, a plant product. Cotton consists of giant molecules of cellulose, a compound with numerous regions of partial positive and partial negative charges that can form hydrogen bonds with water. Water adheres to the cellulose fibers. Thus, a cotton towel does a great job of drying the body, yet it does not dissolve in the washing machine. Cellulose is also present in the walls of water-conducting cells in a plant; you read earlier how the adhesion of water to these hydrophilic walls allows water transport to occur.

There are, of course, substances that do not have an affinity for water. Substances that are nonionic and nonpolar (or otherwise cannot form hydrogen bonds) actually seem to repel water; these substances are said to be **hydrophobic** (from the Greek *phobos*, fearing). An example from the kitchen is vegetable oil, which, as you know, does not mix stably with water-based substances such as vinegar. The hydrophobic behavior of the oil molecules results from a prevalence of relatively nonpolar covalent bonds, in this case bonds between carbon and hydrogen, which share electrons almost equally. Hydrophobic molecules related to oils are major ingredients of cell membranes. (Imagine what would happen to a cell if its membrane dissolved!)

Solute Concentration in Aqueous Solutions

Biological chemistry is "wet" chemistry. Most of the chemical reactions in organisms involve solutes dissolved in water. To understand such reactions, we must know how many atoms and molecules are involved and be able to calculate the concentration of solutes in an aqueous solution (the number of solute molecules in a volume of solution).

When carrying out experiments, we use mass to calculate the number of molecules. We know the mass of each atom in a given molecule, so we can calculate the **molecular mass**, which is simply the sum of the masses of all the atoms in a molecule. As an example, let's calculate the molecular mass of table sugar (sucrose), which has the molecular formula $C_{12}H_{22}O_{11}$. In round numbers of daltons, the mass of a carbon atom is 12, the mass of a hydrogen atom is 1, and the mass of an oxygen atom is 16. Thus, sucrose has a molecular mass of $(12 \times 12) + (22 \times 1) + (11 \times 16) = 342$ daltons. Of course, weighing out small numbers of molecules is not practical. For this reason, we usually measure substances in units called moles. Just as a dozen always means 12 objects, a **mole (mol)** represents an exact number of objects: 6.02×10^{23}, which is called Avogadro's number. Because of the way in which Avogadro's number and the unit *dalton* were originally defined, there are 6.02×10^{23} daltons in 1 g. This is significant because once we determine the molecular mass of a molecule such as sucrose, we can use the same number (342), but with the unit *gram*, to represent the mass of 6.02×10^{23} molecules of sucrose, or 1 mol of sucrose (this is sometimes called the *molar mass*). To obtain 1 mol of sucrose in the lab, therefore, we weigh out 342 g.

The practical advantage of measuring a quantity of chemicals in moles is that a mole of one substance has exactly the same number of molecules as a mole of any other substance. If the molecular mass of substance A is 342 daltons and that of substance B is 10 daltons, then 342 g of A will have the same number of molecules as 10 g of B. A mole of ethyl alcohol (C_2H_6O) also contains 6.02×10^{23} molecules, but its mass is only 46 g because the mass of a molecule of ethyl alcohol is less than that of a molecule of sucrose. Measuring in moles makes it convenient for scientists working in the laboratory to combine substances in fixed ratios of molecules.

How would we make a liter (L) of solution consisting of 1 mol of sucrose dissolved in water? We would measure out 342 g of sucrose and then gradually add water, while stirring, until the sugar was completely dissolved. We would then add enough water to bring the total volume of the solution up to 1 L. At that point, we would have a 1-molar (1 M) solution of sucrose. **Molarity**—the number of moles of solute per liter of solution—is the unit of concentration most often used by biologists for aqueous solutions.

Water's capacity as a versatile solvent complements the other properties discussed in this chapter. Since these remarkable properties allow water to support life on Earth so well, scientists who seek life elsewhere in the universe look for water as a sign that a planet might sustain life.

Possible Evolution of Life on Other Planets with Water

EVOLUTION Humans have probably always gazed skyward, wondering whether other living beings exist beyond Earth. And if life has arisen on other planets, into what form or forms has it evolved? Biologists who look for life elsewhere in the universe (known as *astrobiologists*) have concentrated their search on planets that might have water. To date, more than 200 planets have been found outside our solar system, and there is evidence for the presence of water vapor on one or two of them. In our own solar system, Mars has been most compelling to astrobiologists as a focus of study.

Like Earth, Mars has an ice cap at both poles. And in the decades since the age of space exploration began, scientists have found intriguing signs that water may exist elsewhere on Mars. Finally, in 2008, the robotic spacecraft *Phoenix* landed on Mars and began to sample its surface. Years of debate were

◀ **Figure 3.9 Subsurface ice and morning frost on Mars.** This photograph was taken by the Mars lander *Phoenix* in 2008. The trench was scraped by a robotic arm, uncovering ice (white in rectangle near bottom) below the surface material. Frost also appears as a white coating in several places in the upper half of the image. This photograph was colorized by NASA to highlight the ice.

resolved by the images sent back from *Phoenix*: Ice is definitely present just under Mars's surface, and enough water vapor is in the Martian atmosphere for frost to form **(Figure 3.9)**. This exciting finding has reinvigorated the search for signs of life, past or present, on Mars and other planets. If any life-forms or fossils are found, their study will shed light on the process of evolution from an entirely new perspective.

CONCEPT CHECK 3.2

1. Describe how properties of water contribute to the upward movement of water in a tree.
2. Explain the saying "It's not the heat; it's the humidity."
3. How can the freezing of water crack boulders?
4. The concentration of the appetite-regulating hormone ghrelin is about $1.3 \times 10^{-10} M$ in a fasting person. How many molecules of ghrelin are in 1 L of blood?
5. **WHAT IF?** A water strider (which can walk on water) has legs that are coated with a hydrophobic substance. What might be the benefit? What would happen if the substance were hydrophilic?

For suggested answers, see Appendix A.

CONCEPT 3.3

Acidic and basic conditions affect living organisms

Occasionally, a hydrogen atom participating in a hydrogen bond between two water molecules shifts from one molecule to the other. When this happens, the hydrogen atom leaves its electron behind, and what is actually transferred is a **hydrogen ion** (H^+), a single proton with a charge of 1+. The water molecule that lost a proton is now a **hydroxide ion** (OH^-), which has a charge of 1−. The proton binds to the other water molecule, making that molecule a **hydronium ion** (H_3O^+). We can picture the chemical reaction as shown at the top of the next page.

2 H₂O   Hydronium ion (H₃O⁺)   Hydroxide ion (OH⁻)

By convention, H^+ (the hydrogen ion) is used to represent H_3O^+ (the hydronium ion), and we follow that practice here. Keep in mind, though, that H^+ does not exist on its own in an aqueous solution. It is always associated with another water molecule in the form of H_3O^+.

As indicated by the double arrows, this is a reversible reaction that reaches a state of dynamic equilibrium when water molecules dissociate at the same rate that they are being re-formed from H^+ and OH^-. At this equilibrium point, the concentration of water molecules greatly exceeds the concentrations of H^+ and OH^-. In pure water, only one water molecule in every 554 million is dissociated; the concentration of each ion in pure water is $10^{-7}\,M$ (at 25°C). This means there is only one ten-millionth of a mole of hydrogen ions per liter of pure water and an equal number of hydroxide ions.

Although the dissociation of water is reversible and statistically rare, it is exceedingly important in the chemistry of life. H^+ and OH^- are very reactive. Changes in their concentrations can drastically affect a cell's proteins and other complex molecules. As we have seen, the concentrations of H^+ and OH^- are equal in pure water, but adding certain kinds of solutes, called acids and bases, disrupts this balance. Biologists use something called the pH scale to describe how acidic or basic (the opposite of acidic) a solution is. In the remainder of this chapter, you will learn about acids, bases, and pH and why changes in pH can adversely affect organisms.

Acids and Bases

What would cause an aqueous solution to have an imbalance in H^+ and OH^- concentrations? When acids dissolve in water, they donate additional H^+ to the solution. An **acid** is a substance that increases the hydrogen ion concentration of a solution. For example, when hydrochloric acid (HCl) is added to water, hydrogen ions dissociate from chloride ions:

$$HCl \rightarrow H^+ + Cl^-$$

This source of H^+ (dissociation of water is the other source) results in an acidic solution—one having more H^+ than OH^-.

A substance that reduces the hydrogen ion concentration of a solution is called a **base**. Some bases reduce the H^+ concentration directly by accepting hydrogen ions. Ammonia (NH_3), for instance, acts as a base when the unshared electron pair in nitrogen's valence shell attracts a hydrogen ion from the solution, resulting in an ammonium ion (NH_4^+):

$$NH_3 + H^+ \rightleftharpoons NH_4^+$$

Other bases reduce the H^+ concentration indirectly by dissociating to form hydroxide ions, which combine with hydrogen ions and form water. One such base is sodium hydroxide (NaOH), which in water dissociates into its ions:

$$NaOH \rightarrow Na^+ + OH^-$$

In either case, the base reduces the H^+ concentration. Solutions with a higher concentration of OH^- than H^+ are known as basic solutions. A solution in which the H^+ and OH^- concentrations are equal is said to be neutral.

Notice that single arrows were used in the reactions for HCl and NaOH. These compounds dissociate completely when mixed with water, so hydrochloric acid is called a strong acid and sodium hydroxide a strong base. In contrast, ammonia is a relatively weak base. The double arrows in the reaction for ammonia indicate that the binding and release of hydrogen ions are reversible reactions, although at equilibrium there will be a fixed ratio of NH_4^+ to NH_3.

There are also weak acids, which reversibly release and accept back hydrogen ions. An example is carbonic acid:

$$H_2CO_3 \rightleftharpoons HCO_3^- + H^+$$

Carbonic acid   Bicarbonate ion   Hydrogen ion

Here the equilibrium so favors the reaction in the left direction that when carbonic acid is added to pure water, only 1% of the molecules are dissociated at any particular time. Still, that is enough to shift the balance of H^+ and OH^- from neutrality.

The pH Scale

In any aqueous solution at 25°C, the *product* of the H^+ and OH^- concentrations is constant at 10^{-14}. This can be written

$$[H^+][OH^-] = 10^{-14}$$

In such an equation, brackets indicate molar concentration. In a neutral solution at room temperature (25°C), $[H^+] = 10^{-7}$ and $[OH^-] = 10^{-7}$, so in this case, 10^{-14} is the product of $10^{-7} \times 10^{-7}$. If enough acid is added to a solution to increase $[H^+]$ to $10^{-5}\,M$, then $[OH^-]$ will decline by an equivalent amount to $10^{-9}\,M$ (note that $10^{-5} \times 10^{-9} = 10^{-14}$). This constant relationship expresses the behavior of acids and bases in an aqueous solution. An acid not only adds hydrogen ions to a solution, but also removes hydroxide ions because of the tendency for H^+ to combine with OH^-, forming water. A base has the opposite effect, increasing OH^- concentration but also reducing H^+ concentration by the formation of water. If enough of a base is added to raise the OH^- concentration to $10^{-4}\,M$, it will cause the H^+ concentration to drop to $10^{-10}\,M$. Whenever we know the concentration of either H^+ or OH^- in an aqueous solution, we can deduce the concentration of the other ion.

Because the H^+ and OH^- concentrations of solutions can vary by a factor of 100 trillion or more, scientists have

pH Scale

pH	
0	
1	Battery acid
2	Gastric juice, lemon juice
3	Vinegar, wine, cola
4	Tomato juice
	Beer
5	Black coffee
	Rainwater
6	Urine
	Saliva
7	**Pure water**
	Human blood, tears
8	Seawater
	Inside of small intestine
9	
10	
	Milk of magnesia
11	
	Household ammonia
12	
13	Household bleach
	Oven cleaner
14	

Acidic solution
H^+ H^+ H^+ OH^- H^+ OH^- H^+ H^+ H^+ H^+

Neutral solution
OH^- OH^- H^+ H^+ OH^- OH^- OH^- H^+ H^+ H^+

Basic solution
OH^- OH^- OH^- H^+ OH^- OH^- OH^- OH^- H^+ OH^-

Increasingly **Acidic** $[H^+] > [OH^-]$

Neutral $[H^+] = [OH^-]$

Increasingly **Basic** $[H^+] < [OH^-]$

▲ **Figure 3.10 The pH scale and pH values of some aqueous solutions.**

developed a way to express this variation more conveniently than in moles per liter. The pH scale **(Figure 3.10)** compresses the range of H^+ and OH^- concentrations by employing logarithms. The **pH** of a solution is defined as the negative logarithm (base 10) of the hydrogen ion concentration:

$$pH = -\log [H^+]$$

For a neutral aqueous solution, $[H^+]$ is 10^{-7} M, giving us

$$-\log 10^{-7} = -(-7) = 7$$

Notice that pH *declines* as H^+ concentration *increases*. Notice, too, that although the pH scale is based on H^+ concentration, it also implies OH^- concentration. A solution of pH 10 has a hydrogen ion concentration of 10^{-10} M and a hydroxide ion concentration of 10^{-4} M.

The pH of a neutral aqueous solution at 25°C is 7, the midpoint of the pH scale. A pH value less than 7 denotes an acidic solution; the lower the number, the more acidic the solution. The pH for basic solutions is above 7. Most biological fluids are within the range pH 6–8. There are a few exceptions, however,

including the strongly acidic digestive juice of the human stomach, which has a pH of about 2.

Remember that each pH unit represents a tenfold difference in H^+ and OH^- concentrations. It is this mathematical feature that makes the pH scale so compact. A solution of pH 3 is not twice as acidic as a solution of pH 6, but a thousand times ($10 \times 10 \times 10$) more acidic. When the pH of a solution changes slightly, the actual concentrations of H^+ and OH^- in the solution change substantially.

Buffers

The internal pH of most living cells is close to 7. Even a slight change in pH can be harmful, because the chemical processes of the cell are very sensitive to the concentrations of hydrogen and hydroxide ions. The pH of human blood is very close to 7.4, or slightly basic. A person cannot survive for more than a few minutes if the blood pH drops to 7 or rises to 7.8, and a chemical system exists in the blood that maintains a stable pH. If you add 0.01 mol of a strong acid to a liter of pure water, the pH drops from 7.0 to 2.0. If the same amount of acid is added to a liter of blood, however, the pH decrease is only from 7.4 to 7.3. Why does the addition of acid have so much less of an effect on the pH of blood than it does on the pH of water?

The presence of substances called buffers allows biological fluids to maintain a relatively constant pH despite the addition of acids or bases. A **buffer** is a substance that minimizes changes in the concentrations of H^+ and OH^- in a solution. It does so by accepting hydrogen ions from the solution when they are in excess and donating hydrogen ions to the solution when they have been depleted. Most buffer solutions contain a weak acid and its corresponding base, which combine reversibly with hydrogen ions.

There are several buffers that contribute to pH stability in human blood and many other biological solutions. One of these is carbonic acid (H_2CO_3), formed when CO_2 reacts with water in blood plasma. As mentioned earlier, carbonic acid dissociates to yield a bicarbonate ion (HCO_3^-) and a hydrogen ion (H^+):

	Response to a rise in pH		
H_2CO_3	⇌	HCO_3^- +	H^+
H^+ donor (acid)	Response to a drop in pH	H^+ acceptor (base)	Hydrogen ion

The chemical equilibrium between carbonic acid and bicarbonate acts as a pH regulator, the reaction shifting left or right as other processes in the solution add or remove hydrogen ions. If the H^+ concentration in blood begins to fall (that is, if pH rises), the reaction proceeds to the right and more carbonic acid dissociates, replenishing hydrogen ions. But when H^+ concentration in blood begins to rise (when pH drops), the reaction proceeds to the left, with HCO_3^- (the base) removing the hydrogen ions from the solution and forming H_2CO_3. Thus, the carbonic acid–bicarbonate buffering system consists of an acid and a base in equilibrium with each other. Most other buffers are also acid-base pairs.

Acidification: A Threat to Water Quality

Among the many threats to water quality posed by human activities is the burning of fossil fuels, which releases gaseous compounds into the atmosphere. When certain of these compounds react with water, the water becomes more acidic, altering the delicate balance of conditions for life on Earth.

Carbon dioxide is the main product of fossil fuel combustion. About 25% of human-generated CO_2 is absorbed by the oceans. In spite of the huge volume of water in the oceans, scientists worry that the absorption of so much CO_2 will harm marine ecosystems.

Recent data have shown that such fears are well founded. When CO_2 dissolves in seawater, it reacts with water to form carbonic acid, which lowers ocean pH, a process known as **ocean acidification**. Based on measurements of CO_2 levels in air bubbles trapped in ice over thousands of years, scientists calculate that the pH of the oceans is 0.1 pH unit lower now than at any time in the past 420,000 years. Recent studies predict that it will drop another 0.3–0.5 pH unit by the end of this century.

As seawater acidifies, the extra hydrogen ions combine with carbonate ions (CO_3^{2-}) to form bicarbonate ions (HCO_3^-), thereby reducing the carbonate concentration **(Figure 3.11)**.

Some carbon dioxide (CO_2) in the atmosphere dissolves in the ocean, where it reacts with water to form carbonic acid (H_2CO_3).

$$CO_2 + H_2O \rightarrow H_2CO_3$$

Carbonic acid dissociates into hydrogen ions (H^+) and bicarbonate ions (HCO_3^-).

$$H_2CO_3 \rightarrow H^+ + HCO_3^-$$

The added H^+ combines with carbonate ions (CO_3^{2-}), forming more HCO_3^-.

$$H^+ + CO_3^{2-} \rightarrow HCO_3^-$$

$$CO_3^{2-} + Ca^{2+} \rightarrow CaCO_3$$

Less CO_3^{2-} is available for calcification — the formation of calcium carbonate ($CaCO_3$)— by marine organisms such as corals.

▲ **Figure 3.11 Atmospheric CO_2 from human activities and its fate in the ocean.**

▼ Figure 3.12

IMPACT

The Threat of Ocean Acidification to Coral Reef Ecosystems

Recently, scientists have sounded the alarm about the effects of ocean acidification, the process in which oceans become more acidic due to increased atmospheric carbon dioxide levels (see Figure 3.11). They predict that the resulting decrease in the concentration of carbonate ion (CO_3^{2-}) will take a serious toll on coral reef calcification. Taking many studies into account, and including the effects of ocean warming as well, one group of scientists defined three scenarios for coral reefs during this century, depending on whether the concentration of atmospheric CO_2 (a) stays at today's level, (b) increases at the current rate, or (c) increases more rapidly. The photographs below show coral reefs resembling those predicted under each scenario.

(a) (b) (c)

The healthy coral reef in (a) supports a highly diverse group of species and bears little resemblance to the damaged coral reef in (c).

WHY IT MATTERS The disappearance of coral reef ecosystems would be a tragic loss of biological diversity. In addition, coral reefs provide shoreline protection, a feeding ground for many commercial fishery species, and a popular tourist draw, so coastal human communities would suffer from greater wave damage, collapsed fisheries, and reduced tourism.

FURTHER READING O. Hoegh-Guldberg et al., Coral reefs under rapid climate change and ocean acidification, *Science* 318:1737–1742 (2007). S. C. Doney, The dangers of ocean acidification, *Scientific American*, March 2006, 58–65.

WHAT IF? Would lowering the ocean's carbonate concentration have any effect, even indirectly, on organisms that don't form $CaCO_3$? Explain.

Scientists predict that ocean acidification will cause the carbonate concentration to decrease by 40% by the year 2100. This is of great concern because carbonate is required for calcification, the production of calcium carbonate ($CaCO_3$) by many marine organisms, including reef-building corals and animals that build shells. Coral reefs are sensitive ecosystems that act as havens for a great diversity of marine life **(Figure 3.12)**.

The burning of fossil fuels is also a major source of sulfur oxides and nitrogen oxides. These compounds react with water in the air to form strong acids, which fall to Earth with rain or snow. **Acid precipitation** refers to rain, snow, or fog with a pH lower (more acidic) than 5.2. (Uncontaminated rain has a pH of about 5.6, which is slightly acidic due to the formation of carbonic acid from CO_2 and water.) Acid precipitation can damage life in lakes and streams, and it adversely affects plants on land by changing soil chemistry. To address this problem, the U.S. Congress amended the Clean Air Act in 1990, and the mandated improvements in industrial technologies have been largely responsible for improving the health of most North American lakes and forests.

If there is any reason for optimism about the future quality of water resources on our planet, it is that we have made progress in learning about the delicate chemical balances in oceans, lakes, and rivers. Continued progress can come only from the actions of informed individuals, like yourselves, who are concerned about environmental quality. This requires understanding the crucial role that water plays in the suitability of the environment for continued life on Earth.

3 CHAPTER REVIEW

SUMMARY OF KEY CONCEPTS

CONCEPT 3.1

Polar covalent bonds in water molecules result in hydrogen bonding (pp. 46–47)

- A hydrogen bond forms when the slightly negatively charged oxygen of one water molecule is attracted to the slightly positively charged hydrogen of a nearby water molecule. Hydrogen bonding between water molecules is the basis for water's properties.

> **DRAW IT** Label a hydrogen bond and a polar covalent bond in this figure. How many hydrogen bonds can each water molecule make?

CONCEPT 3.2

Four emergent properties of water contribute to Earth's suitability for life (pp. 47–52)

- Hydrogen bonding keeps water molecules close to each other, and this **cohesion** helps pull water upward in the microscopic water-conducting cells of plants. Hydrogen bonding is also responsible for water's **surface tension**.
- Water has a high **specific heat**: Heat is absorbed when hydrogen bonds break and is released when hydrogen bonds form. This helps keep temperatures relatively steady, within limits that permit life. **Evaporative cooling** is based on water's high **heat of vaporization**. The evaporative loss of the most energetic water molecules cools a surface.
- Ice floats because it is less dense than liquid water. This allows life to exist under the frozen surfaces of lakes and polar seas.

Ice: stable hydrogen bonds   **Liquid water:** transient hydrogen bonds

- Water is an unusually versatile **solvent** because its polar molecules are attracted to charged and polar substances capable of forming hydrogen bonds. **Hydrophilic** substances have an affinity for water; **hydrophobic** substances do not. **Molarity**, the number of moles of **solute** per liter of **solution**, is used as a measure of solute concentration in solutions. A **mole** is a certain number of molecules of a substance. The mass of a mole of a substance in grams is the same as the **molecular mass** in daltons.
- The emergent properties of water support life on Earth and may contribute to the potential for life to have evolved on other planets.

> **?** *Describe how different types of solutes dissolve in water. Explain the difference between a solution and a colloid.*

CONCEPT 3.3

Acidic and basic conditions affect living organisms (pp. 52–56)

- A water molecule can transfer an H^+ to another water molecule to form H_3O^+ (represented simply by H^+) and OH^-.
- The concentration of H^+ is expressed as **pH**; $pH = -\log [H^+]$. **Buffers** in biological fluids resist changes in pH. A buffer consists of an acid-base pair that combines reversibly with hydrogen ions.
- The burning of fossil fuels increases the amount of CO_2 in the atmosphere. Some CO_2 dissolves in the oceans, causing **ocean acidification**, which has potentially grave consequences for coral reefs. The burning of fossil fuels also releases oxides of sulfur and nitrogen, leading to **acid precipitation**.

> **?** *Explain how increasing amounts of CO_2 dissolving in the ocean leads to ocean acidification. How does this change in pH affect carbonate ion concentration and the rate of calcification?*

LEVEL 1: KNOWLEDGE/COMPREHENSION

1. Many mammals control their body temperature by sweating. Which property of water is most directly responsible for the ability of sweat to lower body temperature?
   a. water's change in density when it condenses
   b. water's ability to dissolve molecules in the air
   c. the release of heat by the formation of hydrogen bonds
   d. the absorption of heat by the breaking of hydrogen bonds
   e. water's high surface tension

2. The bonds that are broken when water vaporizes are
   a. ionic bonds.
   b. hydrogen bonds between water molecules.
   c. covalent bonds between atoms within water molecules.
   d. polar covalent bonds.
   e. nonpolar covalent bonds.

3. Which of the following is a hydrophobic material?
   a. paper   d. sugar
   b. table salt   e. pasta
   c. wax

4. We can be sure that a mole of table sugar and a mole of vitamin C are equal in their
   a. mass in daltons.   d. number of atoms.
   b. mass in grams.   e. number of molecules.
   c. volume.

5. Measurements show that the pH of a particular lake is 4.0. What is the hydrogen ion concentration of the lake?
   a. $4.0\ M$ b. $10^{-10}\ M$ c. $10^{-4}\ M$ d. $10^{4}\ M$ e. 4%

6. What is the *hydroxide* ion concentration of the lake described in question 5?
   a. $10^{-10}\ M$ b. $10^{-4}\ M$ c. $10^{-7}\ M$ d. $10^{-14}M$ e. $10\ M$

LEVEL 2: APPLICATION/ANALYSIS

7. A slice of pizza has 500 kcal. If we could burn the pizza and use all the heat to warm a 50-L container of cold water, what would be the approximate increase in the temperature of the water? (*Note:* A liter of cold water weighs about 1 kg.)
   a. 50°C   b. 5°C   c. 1°C   d. 100°C   e. 10°C

8. How many grams of acetic acid ($C_2H_4O_2$) would you use to make 10 L of a 0.1 M aqueous solution of acetic acid? (*Note:* The atomic masses, in daltons, are approximately 12 for carbon, 1 for hydrogen, and 16 for oxygen.)
   a. 10 g   b. 0.1 g   c. 6.0 g   d. 60 g   e. 0.6 g

9. **DRAW IT**   Draw the hydration shells that form around a potassium ion and a chloride ion when potassium chloride (KCl) dissolves in water. Label the positive, negative, and partial charges on the atoms.

10. **MAKE CONNECTIONS**   What do global warming (see Chapter 1, p. 6) and ocean acidification have in common?

LEVEL 3: SYNTHESIS/EVALUATION

11. In agricultural areas, farmers pay close attention to the weather forecast. Right before a predicted overnight freeze, farmers spray water on crops to protect the plants. Use the properties of water to explain how this method works. Be sure to mention why hydrogen bonds are responsible for this phenomenon.

12. **EVOLUTION CONNECTION**
    This chapter explains how the emergent properties of water contribute to the suitability of the environment for life. Until fairly recently, scientists assumed that other physical requirements for life included a moderate range of temperature, pH, atmospheric pressure, and salinity, as well as low levels of toxic chemicals. That view has changed with the discovery of organisms known as extremophiles, which have been found flourishing in hot, acidic sulfur springs, around hydrothermal vents deep in the ocean, and in soils with high levels of toxic metals. Why would astrobiologists be interested in studying extremophiles? What does the existence of life in such extreme environments say about the possibility of life on other planets?

13. **SCIENTIFIC INQUIRY**
    Design a controlled experiment to test the hypothesis that acid precipitation inhibits the growth of *Elodea,* a common freshwater plant (see Figure 2.19, p. 43).

14. **SCIENTIFIC INQUIRY**
    In a study reported in 2000, C. Langdon and colleagues used an artificial coral reef system to test the effect of carbonate concentration on the rate of calcification by reef organisms. The graph on the right presents one set of their results. Describe what these data show. How do these results relate to the ocean acidification that is associated with increasing atmospheric CO_2 levels?

15. **SCIENCE, TECHNOLOGY, AND SOCIETY**
    Agriculture, industry, and the growing populations of cities all compete, through political influence, for water. If you were in charge of water resources in an arid region, what would your priorities be for allocating the limited water supply for various uses? How would you try to build consensus among the different special-interest groups?

16. **WRITE ABOUT A THEME**
    Emergent Properties Several emergent properties of water contribute to the suitability of the environment for life. In a short essay (100–150 words), describe how the ability of water to function as a versatile solvent arises from the structure of water molecules.

For selected answers, see Appendix A.

MasteringBIOLOGY®   www.masteringbiology.com

1. MasteringBiology® Assignments
Tutorials Hydrogen Bonding and Water • The pH Scale
Activities The Polarity of Water • Cohesion of Water • Dissociation of Water Molecules • Acids, Bases, and pH
Questions Student Misconceptions • Reading Quiz • Multiple Choice • End-of-Chapter

2. eText
Read your book online, search, take notes, highlight text, and more.

3. The Study Area
Practice Tests • Cumulative Test • *BioFlix* 3-D Animations • MP3 Tutor Sessions • Videos • Activities • Investigations • Lab Media • Audio Glossary • Word Study Tools • Art

4

Carbon and the Molecular Diversity of Life

▲ **Figure 4.1 What properties make carbon the basis of all life?**

KEY CONCEPTS

4.1 Organic chemistry is the study of carbon compounds

4.2 Carbon atoms can form diverse molecules by bonding to four other atoms

4.3 A few chemical groups are key to the functioning of biological molecules

OVERVIEW

Carbon: The Backbone of Life

Water is the universal medium for life on Earth, but living organisms, such as the plants and Roosevelt elk in **Figure 4.1**, are made up of chemicals based mostly on the element carbon. Carbon enters the biosphere through the action of plants. Plants use solar energy to transform atmospheric CO_2 into the molecules of life, which are then taken in by plant-eating animals.

Of all chemical elements, carbon is unparalleled in its ability to form molecules that are large, complex, and varied,

making possible the diversity of organisms that have evolved on Earth. Proteins, DNA, carbohydrates, and other molecules that distinguish living matter from inanimate material are all composed of carbon atoms bonded to one another and to atoms of other elements. Hydrogen (H), oxygen (O), nitrogen (N), sulfur (S), and phosphorus (P) are other common ingredients of these compounds, but it is the element carbon (C) that accounts for the enormous variety of biological molecules.

Large biological molecules, such as proteins, are the main focus of Chapter 5. In this chapter, we investigate the properties of smaller molecules. We will use these small molecules to illustrate concepts of molecular architecture that will help explain why carbon is so important to life, at the same time highlighting the theme that emergent properties arise from the organization of matter in living organisms.

CONCEPT **4.1**

Organic chemistry is the study of carbon compounds

For historical reasons, compounds containing carbon are said to be organic, and the branch of chemistry that specializes in the study of carbon compounds is called **organic chemistry**. Organic compounds range from simple molecules, such as methane (CH_4), to colossal ones, such as proteins, with thousands of atoms. Most organic compounds contain hydrogen atoms in addition to carbon atoms.

The overall percentages of the major elements of life—C, H, O, N, S, and P—are quite uniform from one organism to another. Because of carbon's versatility, however, this limited assortment of atomic building blocks can be used to build an inexhaustible variety of organic molecules. Different species of organisms, and different individuals within a species, are distinguished by variations in their organic molecules.

Since the dawn of human history, people have used other organisms as sources of valued substances—from foods and medicines to fabrics. The science of organic chemistry originated in attempts to purify and improve the yield of such products. By the early 1800s, chemists had learned to make many simple compounds in the laboratory by combining elements under the right conditions. Artificial synthesis of the complex molecules extracted from living matter seemed impossible, however. At that time, the Swedish chemist Jöns Jakob Berzelius made the distinction between organic compounds, those thought to arise only in living organisms, and inorganic compounds, those found only in the nonliving world. *Vitalism*, the belief in a life force outside the jurisdiction of physical and chemical laws, provided the foundation for the new discipline of organic chemistry.

Chemists began to chip away at the support for vitalism when they finally learned to synthesize organic compounds in the laboratory. In 1828, Friedrich Wöhler, a German chemist who had studied with Berzelius, tried to make an "inorganic" salt, ammonium cyanate, by mixing solutions of ammonium ions (NH_4^+) and cyanate ions (CNO^-). Wöhler was astonished to find that instead he had made urea, an organic compound present in the urine of animals. Wöhler challenged the vitalists when he wrote, "I must tell you that I can prepare urea without requiring a kidney or an animal, either man or dog." However, one of the ingredients used in the synthesis, the cyanate, had been extracted from animal blood, and the vitalists were not swayed by Wöhler's discovery. A few years later, however, Hermann Kolbe, a student of Wöhler's, made the organic compound acetic acid from inorganic substances that could be prepared directly from pure elements. Vitalism crumbled completely after several decades of laboratory synthesis of increasingly complex organic compounds.

Organic Molecules and the Origin of Life on Earth

EVOLUTION In 1953, Stanley Miller, a graduate student of Harold Urey's at the University of Chicago, helped bring the abiotic (nonliving) synthesis of organic compounds into the context of evolution. Study **Figure 4.2** to learn about his classic experiment. From his results, Miller concluded that complex organic molecules could arise spontaneously under conditions thought to have existed on the early Earth. Miller also performed experiments designed to mimic volcanic conditions, with roughly similar results. In 2008, a former graduate student of Miller's discovered some samples from these experiments. Reanalyzing them using modern equipment, he identified additional organic compounds that had not been found by Miller. Although the jury is still out, these experiments support the idea that abiotic synthesis of organic compounds, perhaps near volcanoes, could have been an early stage in the origin of life (see Chapter 25).

The pioneers of organic chemistry helped shift the mainstream of biological thought from vitalism to *mechanism*, the view that physical and chemical laws govern all natural phenomena, including the processes of life. Organic chemistry was redefined as the study of carbon compounds, regardless of origin. Organisms produce most of the naturally occurring organic compounds, and these molecules represent a diversity and range of complexity unrivaled by inorganic compounds. However, the rules of chemistry apply to all molecules. The foundation of organic chemistry is not some intangible life force, but the unique chemical versatility of the element carbon.

CONCEPT CHECK 4.1

1. Why was Wöhler astonished to find he had made urea?
2. **WHAT IF?** When Miller tried his experiment without the electrical discharge, no organic compounds were found. What might explain this result?

For suggested answers, see Appendix A.

▼ **Figure 4.2**   **INQUIRY**

Can organic molecules form under conditions believed to simulate those on the early Earth?

EXPERIMENT In 1953, Stanley Miller set up a closed system to mimic conditions thought to have existed on the early Earth. A flask of water simulated the primeval sea. The water was heated so that some vaporized and moved into a second, higher flask containing the "atmosphere"—a mixture of gases. Sparks were discharged in the synthetic atmosphere to mimic lightning.

2 The "atmosphere" contained a mixture of hydrogen gas (H_2), methane (CH_4), ammonia (NH_3), and water vapor.

3 Sparks were discharged to mimic lightning.

"Atmosphere"

CH_4

Water vapor

Electrode

1 The water mixture in the "sea" flask was heated; vapor entered the "atmosphere" flask.

NH_3 H_2

Condenser

Cooled "rain" containing organic molecules

Cold water

H_2O "sea"

Sample for chemical analysis

5 As material cycled through the apparatus, Miller periodically collected samples for analysis.

4 A condenser cooled the atmosphere, raining water and any dissolved molecules down into the sea flask.

RESULTS Miller identified a variety of organic molecules that are common in organisms. These included simple compounds, such as formaldehyde (CH_2O) and hydrogen cyanide (HCN), and more complex molecules, such as amino acids and long chains of carbon and hydrogen known as hydrocarbons.

CONCLUSION Organic molecules, a first step in the origin of life, may have been synthesized abiotically on the early Earth. (We will explore this hypothesis in more detail in Chapter 25.)

SOURCE S. L. Miller, A production of amino acids under possible primitive Earth conditions, *Science* 117:528–529 (1953).

WHAT IF? If Miller had increased the concentration of NH_3 in his experiment, how might the relative amounts of the products HCN and CH_2O have differed?

CONCEPT 4.2

Carbon atoms can form diverse molecules by bonding to four other atoms

The key to an atom's chemical characteristics is its electron configuration. This configuration determines the kinds and number of bonds an atom will form with other atoms.

The Formation of Bonds with Carbon

Carbon has 6 electrons, with 2 in the first electron shell and 4 in the second shell; thus, it has 4 valence electrons in a shell that holds 8 electrons. A carbon atom usually completes its valence shell by sharing its 4 electrons with other atoms so that 8 electrons are present. Each pair of shared electrons constitutes a covalent bond (see Figure 2.12d). In organic molecules, carbon usually forms single or double covalent bonds. Each carbon atom acts as an intersection point from which a molecule can branch off in as many as four directions. This ability is one facet of carbon's versatility that makes large, complex molecules possible.

When a carbon atom forms four single covalent bonds, the arrangement of its four hybrid orbitals causes the bonds to angle toward the corners of an imaginary tetrahedron (see Figure 2.17b). The bond angles in methane (CH_4) are 109.5° (**Figure 4.3a**), and they are roughly the same in any group of atoms where carbon has four single bonds. For example,

ethane (C_2H_6) is shaped like two overlapping tetrahedrons (**Figure 4.3b**). In molecules with more carbons, every grouping of a carbon bonded to four other atoms has a tetrahedral shape. But when two carbon atoms are joined by a double bond, as in ethene (C_2H_4), the atoms joined to those carbons are in the same plane as the carbons (**Figure 4.3c**). We find it convenient to write molecules as structural formulas, as if the molecules being represented are two-dimensional, but keep in mind that molecules are three-dimensional and that the shape of a molecule often determines its function.

The electron configuration of carbon gives it covalent compatibility with many different elements. **Figure 4.4** shows the valences of carbon and its most frequent partners—hydrogen, oxygen, and nitrogen. These are the four major atomic components of organic molecules. These valences are the basis for the rules of covalent bonding in organic chemistry—the building code for the architecture of organic molecules.

Let's consider how the rules of covalent bonding apply to carbon atoms with partners other than hydrogen. We'll look at two examples, the simple molecules carbon dioxide and urea.

In the carbon dioxide molecule (CO_2), a single carbon atom is joined to two atoms of oxygen by double covalent bonds. The structural formula for CO_2 is shown here:

$$O=C=O$$

Each line in a structural formula represents a pair of shared electrons. Thus, the two double bonds in CO_2 have the same number of shared electrons as four single bonds. The arrangement completes the valence shells of all atoms in the molecule.

Name and Comment	Molecular Formula	Structural Formula	Ball-and-Stick Model (molecular shape in pink)	Space-Filling Model
(a) Methane. When a carbon atom has four single bonds to other atoms, the molecule is tetrahedral.	CH_4			
(b) Ethane. A molecule may have more than one tetrahedral group of single-bonded atoms. (Ethane consists of two such groups.)	C_2H_6			
(c) Ethene (ethylene). When two carbon atoms are joined by a double bond, all atoms attached to those carbons are in the same plane; the molecule is flat.	C_2H_4			

▲ **Figure 4.3 The shapes of three simple organic molecules.**

Hydrogen
(valence = 1)

Oxygen
(valence = 2)

Nitrogen
(valence = 3)

Carbon
(valence = 4)

▲ **Figure 4.4 Valences of the major elements of organic molecules.** Valence is the number of covalent bonds an atom can form. It is generally equal to the number of electrons required to complete the valence (outermost) shell (see Figure 2.9). All the electrons are shown for each atom in the electron distribution diagrams (top). Only the valence shell electrons are shown in the Lewis dot structures (bottom). Note that carbon can form four bonds.

MAKE CONNECTIONS *Refer to Figure 2.9 (p. 36) and draw the Lewis dot structures for sodium, phosphorus, sulfur, and chlorine.*

Because CO_2 is a very simple molecule and lacks hydrogen, it is often considered inorganic, even though it contains carbon. Whether we call CO_2 organic or inorganic, however, it is clearly important to the living world as the source of carbon for all organic molecules in organisms.

Urea, $CO(NH_2)_2$, is the organic compound found in urine that Wöhler synthesized in the early 1800s. Again, each atom has the required number of covalent bonds. In this case, one carbon atom participates in both single and double bonds.

Urea and carbon dioxide are molecules with only one carbon atom. But as Figure 4.3 shows, a carbon atom can also use one or more valence electrons to form covalent bonds to other carbon atoms, linking the atoms into chains of seemingly infinite variety.

Molecular Diversity Arising from Carbon Skeleton Variation

Carbon chains form the skeletons of most organic molecules. The skeletons vary in length and may be straight, branched, or arranged in closed rings **(Figure 4.5)**. Some carbon skeletons have double bonds, which vary in number and location. Such variation in carbon skeletons is one important source of the molecular complexity and diversity that characterize living matter. In addition, atoms of other elements can be bonded to the skeletons at available sites.

Hydrocarbons

All of the molecules shown in Figures 4.3 and 4.5 are **hydrocarbons**, organic molecules consisting of only carbon and hydrogen. Atoms of hydrogen are attached to the carbon skeleton wherever electrons are available for covalent bonding. Hydrocarbons are the major components of petroleum, which is called a fossil fuel because it consists of the partially decomposed remains of organisms that lived millions of years ago.

▼ **Figure 4.5 Four ways that carbon skeletons can vary.**

(a) Length

Ethane

Propane

Carbon skeletons vary in length.

(b) Branching

Butane

2-Methylpropane
(commonly called isobutane)

Skeletons may be unbranched or branched.

(c) Double bond position

1-Butene

2-Butene

The skeleton may have double bonds, which can vary in location.

(d) Presence of rings

Cyclohexane

Benzene

Some carbon skeletons are arranged in rings. In the abbreviated structural formula for each compound (at the right), each corner represents a carbon and its attached hydrogens.

Although hydrocarbons are not prevalent in most living organisms, many of a cell's organic molecules have regions consisting of only carbon and hydrogen. For example, the molecules known as fats have long hydrocarbon tails attached to a nonhydrocarbon component **(Figure 4.6**, on the next page). Neither petroleum nor fat dissolves in water; both are hydrophobic compounds because the great majority of their bonds are relatively nonpolar carbon-to-hydrogen linkages. Another characteristic of hydrocarbons is that they can undergo reactions that release a relatively large amount of energy. The gasoline that fuels a car consists of hydrocarbons, and the hydrocarbon tails of fats serve as stored fuel for animals.

— Nucleus

— Fat droplets

10 μm

(a) Part of a human adipose cell   (b) A fat molecule

▲ **Figure 4.6 The role of hydrocarbons in fats.** **(a)** Mammalian adipose cells stockpile fat molecules as a fuel reserve. This colorized TEM shows part of a human adipose cell with many fat droplets, each containing a large number of fat molecules. **(b)** A fat molecule consists of a small, nonhydrocarbon component joined to three hydrocarbon tails that account for the hydrophobic behavior of fats. The tails can be broken down to provide energy. (Black = carbon; gray = hydrogen; red = oxygen.)

MAKE CONNECTIONS *How do the tails account for the hydrophobic nature of fats? (See Concept 3.2, p. 51.)*

Isomers

Variation in the architecture of organic molecules can be seen in **isomers**, compounds that have the same numbers of atoms of the same elements but different structures and hence different properties. We will examine three types of isomers: structural isomers, *cis-trans* isomers, and enantiomers.

Structural isomers differ in the covalent arrangements of their atoms. Compare, for example, the two five-carbon compounds in **Figure 4.7a**. Both have the molecular formula C_5H_{12}, but they differ in the covalent arrangement of their carbon skeletons. The skeleton is straight in one compound but branched in the other. The number of possible isomers increases tremendously as carbon skeletons increase in size. There are only three forms of C_5H_{12} (two of which are shown in Figure 4.7a), but there are 18 variations of C_8H_{18} and 366,319 possible structural isomers of $C_{20}H_{42}$. Structural isomers may also differ in the location of double bonds.

In *cis-trans* **isomers** (formerly called *geometric isomers*), carbons have covalent bonds to the same atoms, but these atoms differ in their spatial arrangements due to the inflexibility of double bonds. Single bonds allow the atoms they join to rotate freely about the bond axis without changing the compound. In contrast, double bonds do not permit such rotation. If a double bond joins two carbon atoms, and each C also has two different atoms (or groups of atoms) attached to it, then two distinct *cis-trans* isomers are possible. Consider a simple molecule with two double-bonded carbons, each of which has an H and an X attached to it **(Figure 4.7b)**. The arrangement with both Xs on the same side of the double bond is called a *cis isomer*, and that with the Xs on opposite sides is called a *trans* isomer. The subtle difference in shape between such isomers can dramatically affect the biological activities of organic molecules. For example, the biochem-

▼ **Figure 4.7 Three types of isomers, compounds with the same molecular formula but different structures.**

(a) Structural isomers

Structural isomers differ in covalent partners, as shown in this example of two isomers of C_5H_{12}: pentane (left) and 2-methyl butane (right).

(b) *Cis-trans* isomers

cis isomer: The two Xs are on the same side.

trans isomer: The two Xs are on opposite sides.

Cis-trans isomers differ in arrangement about a double bond. In these diagrams, X represents an atom or group of atoms attached to a double-bonded carbon.

(c) Enantiomers

L isomer

D isomer

Enantiomers differ in spatial arrangement around an asymmetric carbon, resulting in molecules that are mirror images, like left and right hands. The two isomers are designated the L and D isomers from the Latin for "left" and "right" (*levo* and *dextro*). Enantiomers cannot be superimposed on each other.

DRAW IT *There are three structural isomers of C_5H_{12}; draw the one not shown in (a).*

istry of vision involves a light-induced change of rhodopsin, a chemical compound in the eye, from the *cis* isomer to the *trans* isomer. Another example involves *trans* fats, which are discussed in Chapter 5.

Enantiomers are isomers that are mirror images of each other and that differ in shape due to the presence of an *asymmetric carbon*, one that is attached to four different atoms or groups of atoms. (See the middle carbon in the ball-and-stick models shown in **Figure 4.7c**.) The four groups can be arranged in space around the asymmetric carbon in two different ways that are mirror images. Enantiomers are, in a way, left-handed and right-handed versions of the molecule. Just as your right hand won't fit into a left-handed glove, a "right-handed" molecule won't fit into the same space as the "left-handed" version.

▲ **Figure 4.8 The pharmacological importance of enantiomers.** Ibuprofen and albuterol are examples of drugs whose enantiomers have different effects. (*S* and *R* are letters used in one system to distinguish between enantiomers.) Ibuprofen reduces inflammation and pain. It is commonly sold as a mixture of the two enantiomers. The *S* enantiomer is 100 times more effective than the other. Albuterol is used to relax bronchial muscles, improving airflow in asthma patients. Only *R*-albuterol is synthesized and sold as a drug; the *S* form counteracts the active *R* form.

Usually, only one isomer is biologically active because only that form can bind to specific molecules in an organism.

The concept of enantiomers is important in the pharmaceutical industry because the two enantiomers of a drug may not be equally effective, as is the case for both ibuprofen and the asthma medication albuterol (**Figure 4.8**). Methamphetamine also occurs in two enantiomers that have very different effects. One enantiomer is the highly addictive stimulant drug known as "crank," sold illegally in the street drug trade. The other has a much weaker effect and is even found as an ingredient in an over-the-counter vapor inhaler for treatment of nasal congestion! The differing effects of enantiomers in the body demonstrate that organisms are sensitive to even the most subtle variations in molecular architecture. Once again, we see that molecules have emergent properties that depend on the specific arrangement of their atoms.

CONCEPT CHECK 4.2

1. **DRAW IT** Draw a structural formula for C_2H_4.
2. Which molecules in Figure 4.5 are isomers? For each pair, identify the type of isomer.
3. How are gasoline and fat chemically similar?
4. **WHAT IF?** Can propane (C_3H_8) form isomers?

For suggested answers, see Appendix A.

CONCEPT 4.3

A few chemical groups are key to the functioning of biological molecules

The distinctive properties of an organic molecule depend not only on the arrangement of its carbon skeleton but also on the chemical groups attached to that skeleton. We can think of hydrocarbons, the simplest organic molecules, as the underlying framework for more complex organic molecules. A number of chemical groups can replace one or more of the hydrogens bonded to the carbon skeleton of the hydrocarbon. (Some groups include atoms of the carbon skeleton, as we will see.) These groups may participate in chemical reactions or may contribute to function indirectly by their effects on molecular shape. The number and arrangement of the groups help give each molecule its unique properties.

The Chemical Groups Most Important in the Processes of Life

Consider the differences between estradiol (a type of estrogen) and testosterone. These compounds are female and male sex hormones, respectively, in humans and other vertebrates. Both are steroids, organic molecules with a common carbon skeleton in the form of four fused rings. These sex hormones differ only in the chemical groups attached to the rings (shown here in abbreviated form); the distinctions in molecular architecture are shaded in blue:

The different actions of these two molecules on many targets throughout the body help produce the contrasting anatomical and physiological features of male and female vertebrates. Thus, even our sexuality has its biological basis in variations of molecular architecture.

In the example of sex hormones, different chemical groups contribute to function by affecting the molecule's shape. In other cases, the chemical groups affect molecular function by being directly involved in chemical reactions; these important chemical groups are known as **functional groups**. Each functional group participates in chemical reactions in a characteristic way from one organic molecule to another.

The seven chemical groups most important in biological processes are the hydroxyl, carbonyl, carboxyl, amino, sulfhydryl, phosphate, and methyl groups. The first six groups can act as functional groups; they are also hydrophilic and thus increase the solubility of organic compounds in water. The methyl group is not reactive, but instead often serves as a recognizable tag on biological molecules. Before reading further, study **Figure 4.9** on the next two pages to familiarize yourself with these biologically important chemical groups.

Exploring Some Biologically Important Chemical Groups

CHEMICAL GROUP	Hydroxyl	Carbonyl	Carboxyl
STRUCTURE	 (may be written HO—) In a **hydroxyl group** (—OH), a hydrogen atom is bonded to an oxygen atom, which in turn is bonded to the carbon skeleton of the organic molecule. (Do not confuse this functional group with the hydroxide ion, OH⁻.)	 The **carbonyl group** (>CO) consists of a carbon atom joined to an oxygen atom by a double bond.	 When an oxygen atom is double-bonded to a carbon atom that is also bonded to an —OH group, the entire assembly of atoms is called a **carboxyl group** (—COOH).
NAME OF COMPOUND	**Alcohols** (Their specific names usually end in *-ol*.)	**Ketones** if the carbonyl group is within a carbon skeleton **Aldehydes** if the carbonyl group is at the end of the carbon skeleton	**Carboxylic acids**, or organic acids
EXAMPLE	 **Ethanol**, the alcohol present in alcoholic beverages	 **Acetone**, the simplest ketone **Propanal**, an aldehyde	 **Acetic acid**, which gives vinegar its sour taste
FUNCTIONAL PROPERTIES	• Is polar as a result of the electrons spending more time near the electronegative oxygen atom. • Can form hydrogen bonds with water molecules, helping dissolve organic compounds such as sugars. (Sugars are shown in Figure 5.3.)	• A ketone and an aldehyde may be structural isomers with different properties, as is the case for acetone and propanal. • Ketone and aldehyde groups are also found in sugars, giving rise to two major groups of sugars: ketoses (containing ketone groups) and aldoses (containing aldehyde groups).	• Acts as an acid; can donate an H⁺ because the covalent bond between oxygen and hydrogen is so polar: Nonionized Ionized • Found in cells in the ionized form with a charge of 1− and called a carboxylate ion.

Amino	Sulfhydryl	Phosphate	Methyl

(may be written HS —)

The **amino group** (—NH₂) consists of a nitrogen atom bonded to two hydrogen atoms and to the carbon skeleton.

The **sulfhydryl group** (—SH) consists of a sulfur atom bonded to an atom of hydrogen; it resembles a hydroxyl group in shape.

In the **phosphate group** shown here, a phosphorus atom is bonded to four oxygen atoms; one oxygen is bonded to the carbon skeleton; two oxygens carry negative charges (—OPO_3^{2-}). In this text, Ⓟ represents an attached phosphate group.

A **methyl group** (—CH₃) consists of a carbon bonded to three hydrogen atoms. The carbon of a methyl group may be attached to a carbon or to a different atom.

Amines

Thiols

Organic phosphates

Methylated compounds

Glycine, a compound that is both an amine and a carboxylic acid because it has both an amino group and a carboxyl group; compounds with both groups are called **amino acids**

Cysteine, an important sulfur-containing amino acid

Glycerol phosphate, which takes part in many important chemical reactions in cells; glycerol phosphate also provides the backbone for phospholipids, the most prevalent molecules in cell membranes

5-Methyl cytidine, a component of DNA that has been modified by addition of a methyl group

- Acts as a base; can pick up an H⁺ from the surrounding solution (water, in living organisms):

  H⁺ + —N(H)(H) ⇌ —⁺N—H(H)(H)

  Nonionized   Ionized

- Found in cells in the ionized form with a charge of 1+.

- Two sulfhydryl groups can react, forming a covalent bond. This "cross-linking" helps stabilize protein structure (see Figure 5.20, Tertiary Structure).
- Cross-linking of cysteines in hair proteins maintains the curliness or straightness of hair. Straight hair can be "permanently" curled by shaping it around curlers and then breaking and re-forming the cross-linking bonds.

- Contributes negative charge to the molecule of which it is a part (2− when at the end of a molecule, as above; 1− when located internally in a chain of phosphates).
- Molecules containing phosphate groups have the potential to react with water, releasing energy.

- Addition of a methyl group to DNA, or to molecules bound to DNA, affects the expression of genes.
- Arrangement of methyl groups in male and female sex hormones affects their shape and function (see p. 63).

MAKE CONNECTIONS *Given the information in this figure and what you know about the electronegativity of oxygen (see Concept 2.3, p. 39), predict which of the following molecules would be the stronger acid (see Concept 3.3, p. 53). Explain your answer.*

a.
H—C(H)(H)—C(H)(H)—C(=O)(OH)

b.
H—C(H)(H)—C(=O)—C(=O)(OH)

ATP: An Important Source of Energy for Cellular Processes

The "Phosphate" column in Figure 4.9 shows a simple example of an organic phosphate molecule. A more complicated organic phosphate, **adenosine triphosphate**, or **ATP**, is worth mentioning here because its function in the cell is so important. ATP consists of an organic molecule called adenosine attached to a string of three phosphate groups:

Where three phosphates are present in series, as in ATP, one phosphate may be split off as a result of a reaction with water. This inorganic phosphate ion, $HOPO_3^{2-}$, is often abbreviated $\textcircled{P}_i$ in this book. Having lost one phosphate, ATP becomes adenosine *di*phosphate, or ADP. Although ATP is sometimes said to store energy, it is more accurate to think of it as storing the potential to react with water. This reaction releases energy that can be used by the cell. You will learn about this in more detail in Chapter 8.

CONCEPT CHECK 4.3

1. What does the term *amino acid* signify about the structure of such a molecule?
2. What chemical change occurs to ATP when it reacts with water and releases energy?
3. **WHAT IF?** Suppose you had an organic molecule such as cysteine (see Figure 4.9, sulfhydryl group example), and you chemically removed the —NH_2 group and replaced it with —COOH. Draw the structural formula for this molecule and speculate about its chemical properties. Is the central carbon asymmetric before the change? After?

For suggested answers, see Appendix A.

The Chemical Elements of Life: *A Review*

Living matter, as you have learned, consists mainly of carbon, oxygen, hydrogen, and nitrogen, with smaller amounts of sulfur and phosphorus. These elements all form strong covalent bonds, an essential characteristic in the architecture of complex organic molecules. Of all these elements, carbon is the virtuoso of the covalent bond. The versatility of carbon makes possible the great diversity of organic molecules, each with particular properties that emerge from the unique arrangement of its carbon skeleton and the chemical groups appended to that skeleton. At the foundation of all biological diversity lies this variation at the molecular level.

4 CHAPTER REVIEW

SUMMARY OF KEY CONCEPTS

CONCEPT 4.1

Organic chemistry is the study of carbon compounds (pp. 58–59)

- Living matter is made mostly of carbon, oxygen, hydrogen, and nitrogen, with some sulfur and phosphorus. Biological diversity has its molecular basis in carbon's ability to form a huge number of molecules with particular shapes and chemical properties.
- Organic compounds were once thought to arise only within living organisms, but this idea (vitalism) was disproved when chemists were able to synthesize organic compounds in the laboratory.

> **?** *How did Stanley Miller's experiments extend the idea of mechanism to the origin of life?*

CONCEPT 4.2

Carbon atoms can form diverse molecules by bonding to four other atoms (pp. 60–63)

- Carbon, with a valence of 4, can bond to various other atoms, including O, H, and N. Carbon can also bond to other carbon atoms, forming the carbon skeletons of organic compounds.

These skeletons vary in length and shape and have bonding sites for atoms of other elements. **Hydrocarbons** consist only of carbon and hydrogen.

- **Isomers** are compounds with the same molecular formula but different structures and properties. Three types of isomers are **structural isomers**, *cis-trans* **isomers**, and **enantiomers**.

> **?** *Refer back to Figure 4.9. What type of isomers are acetone and propanal? How many asymmetric carbons are present in acetic acid, glycine, and glycerol phosphate? Can these three molecules exist as forms that are enantiomers?*

CONCEPT 4.3

A few chemical groups are key to the functioning of biological molecules (pp. 63–66)

- Chemical groups attached to the carbon skeletons of organic molecules participate in chemical reactions (**functional groups**) or contribute to function by affecting molecular shape (see Figure 4.9).
- **ATP (adenosine triphosphate)** consists of adenosine attached to three phosphate groups. ATP can react with water, forming inorganic phosphate and ADP (adenosine diphosphate). This reaction releases energy that can be used by the cell (see the equation at the top of the next page).

Reacts
with H_2O

(P)–(P)–(P)–[Adenosine] ⟶ (P)$_i$ + (P)–(P)–[Adenosine] + Energy

ATP   Inorganic   ADP
                 phosphate

[?] *In what ways does a methyl group differ chemically from the other six important chemical groups shown in Figure 4.9?*

TEST YOUR UNDERSTANDING

LEVEL 1: KNOWLEDGE/COMPREHENSION

1. Organic chemistry is currently defined as
   a. the study of compounds made only by living cells.
   b. the study of carbon compounds.
   c. the study of vital forces.
   d. the study of natural (as opposed to synthetic) compounds.
   e. the study of hydrocarbons.

2. Which functional group is *not* present in this molecule?
   a. carboxyl
   b. sulfhydryl
   c. hydroxyl
   d. amino

3. **MAKE CONNECTIONS** Which chemical group is most likely to be responsible for an organic molecule behaving as a base (see Concept 3.3, p. 53)?
   a. hydroxyl   c. carboxyl   e. phosphate
   b. carbonyl   d. amino

LEVEL 2: APPLICATION/ANALYSIS

4. Which of the following hydrocarbons has a double bond in its carbon skeleton?
   a. C_3H_8 b. C_2H_6 c. CH_4 d. C_2H_4 e. C_2H_2

5. Choose the term that correctly describes the relationship between these two sugar molecules:
   a. structural isomers
   b. *cis-trans* isomers
   c. enantiomers
   d. isotopes

6. Identify the asymmetric carbon in this molecule:

7. Which action could produce a carbonyl group?
   a. the replacement of the —OH of a carboxyl group with hydrogen
   b. the addition of a thiol to a hydroxyl
   c. the addition of a hydroxyl to a phosphate
   d. the replacement of the nitrogen of an amine with oxygen
   e. the addition of a sulfhydryl to a carboxyl

8. Which of the molecules shown in question 5 has an asymmetric carbon? Which carbon is asymmetric?

LEVEL 3: SYNTHESIS/EVALUATION

9. **EVOLUTION CONNECTION**
   DRAW IT Some scientists think that life elsewhere in the universe might be based on the element silicon, rather than on carbon, as on Earth. Look at the electron distribution diagram for silicon in Figure 2.9 and draw the Lewis dot structure for silicon. What properties does silicon share with carbon that would make silicon-based life more likely than, say, neon-based life or aluminum-based life?

10. **SCIENTIFIC INQUIRY**
    Thalidomide achieved notoriety 50 years ago because of a wave of birth defects among children born to women who took this drug during pregnancy as a treatment for morning sickness. Thalidomide is a mixture of two enantiomers; one reduces morning sickness, but the other causes severe birth defects. (Although the beneficial enantiomer can be synthesized and given to patients, it is converted in the body to the harmful enantiomer.) The U.S. Food and Drug Administration (FDA) withheld approval of thalidomide in 1960. Since then, however, the FDA has approved this drug for the treatment of conditions associated with Hansen's disease (leprosy) and newly diagnosed multiple myeloma, a blood and bone marrow cancer. In clinical trials, thalidomide also shows promise as a treatment for AIDS, tuberculosis, inflammatory diseases, and some other types of cancer. Assuming that molecules related to thalidomide could be synthesized in the laboratory, describe in a broad way the type of experiments you would do to improve the benefits of this drug and minimize its harmful effects.

11. **WRITE ABOUT A THEME**
    Structure and Function In 1918, an epidemic of sleeping sickness caused an unusual rigid paralysis in some survivors, similar to symptoms of advanced Parkinson's disease. Years later, L-dopa (below, left), a chemical used to treat Parkinson's disease, was given to some of these patients, as dramatized in the movie *Awakenings*, starring Robin Williams. L-dopa was remarkably effective at eliminating the paralysis, at least temporarily. However, its enantiomer, D-dopa (right), was subsequently shown to have no effect at all, as is the case for Parkinson's disease. In a short essay (100–150 words), discuss how the effectiveness of one enantiomer and not the other illustrates the theme of structure and function.

L-dopa   D-dopa

For selected answers, see Appendix A.

MasteringBIOLOGY   www.masteringbiology.com

1. MasteringBiology® Assignments
   Tutorial Carbon Bonding and Functional Groups
   Activities Diversity of Carbon-Based Molecules • Isomers • Functional Groups
   Questions Student Misconceptions • Reading Quiz • Multiple Choice • End-of-Chapter

2. eText
   Read your book online, search, take notes, highlight text, and more.

3. The Study Area
   Practice Tests • Cumulative Test • *BioFlix* 3-D Animations • MP3 Tutor Sessions • Videos • Activities • Investigations • Lab Media • Audio Glossary • Word Study Tools • Art

5

The Structure and Function of Large Biological Molecules

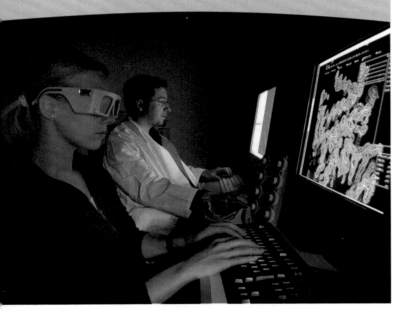

▲ **Figure 5.1 Why do scientists study the structures of macromolecules?**

KEY CONCEPTS

5.1 Macromolecules are polymers, built from monomers
5.2 Carbohydrates serve as fuel and building material
5.3 Lipids are a diverse group of hydrophobic molecules
5.4 Proteins include a diversity of structures, resulting in a wide range of functions
5.5 Nucleic acids store, transmit, and help express hereditary information

OVERVIEW

The Molecules of Life

Given the rich complexity of life on Earth, we might expect organisms to have an enormous diversity of molecules. Remarkably, however, the critically important large molecules of all living things—from bacteria to elephants—fall into just four main classes: carbohydrates, lipids, proteins, and nucleic

acids. On the molecular scale, members of three of these classes—carbohydrates, proteins, and nucleic acids—are huge and are therefore called **macromolecules**. For example, a protein may consist of thousands of atoms that form a molecular colossus with a mass well over 100,000 daltons. Considering the size and complexity of macromolecules, it is noteworthy that biochemists have determined the detailed structure of so many of them. The scientist in the foreground of **Figure 5.1** is using 3-D glasses to help her visualize the structure of the protein displayed on her screen.

The architecture of a large biological molecule helps explain how that molecule works. Like water and simple organic molecules, large biological molecules exhibit unique emergent properties arising from the orderly arrangement of their atoms. In this chapter, we'll first consider how macromolecules are built. Then we'll examine the structure and function of all four classes of large biological molecules: carbohydrates, lipids, proteins, and nucleic acids.

CONCEPT 5.1

Macromolecules are polymers, built from monomers

The macromolecules in three of the four classes of life's organic compounds—carbohydrates, proteins, and nucleic acids—are chain-like molecules called polymers (from the Greek *polys*, many, and *meros*, part). A **polymer** is a long molecule consisting of many similar or identical building blocks linked by covalent bonds, much as a train consists of a chain of cars. The repeating units that serve as the building blocks of a polymer are smaller molecules called **monomers** (from the Greek *monos*, single). Some of the molecules that serve as monomers also have other functions of their own.

The Synthesis and Breakdown of Polymers

Although each class of polymer is made up of a different type of monomer, the chemical mechanisms by which cells make and break down polymers are basically the same in all cases. In cells, these processes are facilitated by **enzymes**, specialized macromolecules that speed up chemical reactions. Monomers are connected by a reaction in which two molecules are covalently bonded to each other, with the loss of a water molecule; this is known as a **dehydration reaction** (Figure 5.2a). When a bond forms between two monomers, each monomer contributes part of the water molecule that is released during the reaction: One monomer provides a hydroxyl group (—OH), while the other provides a hydrogen (—H). This reaction is repeated as monomers are added to the chain one by one, making a polymer.

Polymers are disassembled to monomers by **hydrolysis**, a process that is essentially the reverse of the dehydration reac-

(a) Dehydration reaction: synthesizing a polymer

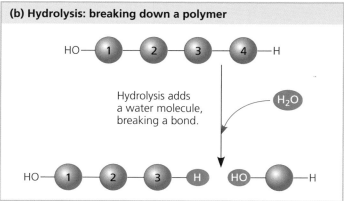

(b) Hydrolysis: breaking down a polymer

tion **(Figure 5.2b)**. Hydrolysis means to break using water (from the Greek *hydro*, water, and *lysis*, break). The bond between the monomers is broken by the addition of a water molecule, with the hydrogen from the water attaching to one monomer and the hydroxyl group attaching to the adjacent monomer. An example of hydrolysis working within our bodies is the process of digestion. The bulk of the organic material in our food is in the form of polymers that are much too large to enter our cells. Within the digestive tract, various enzymes attack the polymers, speeding up hydrolysis. The released monomers are then absorbed into the bloodstream for distribution to all body cells. Those cells can then use dehydration reactions to assemble the monomers into new, different polymers that can perform specific functions required by the cell.

The Diversity of Polymers

Each cell has thousands of different macromolecules; the collection varies from one type of cell to another even in the same organism. The inherent differences between human siblings reflect small variations in polymers, particularly DNA and proteins. Molecular differences between unrelated individuals are more extensive and those between species greater still. The diversity of macromolecules in the living world is vast, and the possible variety is effectively limitless.

What is the basis for such diversity in life's polymers? These molecules are constructed from only 40 to 50 common monomers and some others that occur rarely. Building a huge variety of polymers from such a limited number of monomers is analogous to constructing hundreds of thousands of words from only 26 letters of the alphabet. The key is arrangement—the particular linear sequence that the units follow. However, this analogy falls far short of describing the great diversity of macromolecules because most biological polymers have many more monomers than the number of letters in the longest word. Proteins, for example, are built from 20 kinds of amino acids arranged in chains that are typically hundreds of amino acids long. The molecular logic of life is simple but elegant: Small molecules common to all organisms are ordered into unique macromolecules.

Despite this immense diversity, molecular structure and function can still be grouped roughly by class. Let's examine each of the four major classes of large biological molecules. For each class, the large molecules have emergent properties not found in their individual building blocks.

CONCEPT CHECK 5.1

1. What are the four main classes of large biological molecules? Which class does not consist of polymers?
2. How many molecules of water are needed to completely hydrolyze a polymer that is ten monomers long?
3. **WHAT IF?** Suppose you eat a serving of fish. What reactions must occur for the amino acid monomers in the protein of the fish to be converted to new proteins in your body?

For suggested answers, see Appendix A.

CONCEPT 5.2

Carbohydrates serve as fuel and building material

Carbohydrates include both sugars and polymers of sugars. The simplest carbohydrates are the monosaccharides, or simple sugars; these are the monomers from which more complex carbohydrates are constructed. Disaccharides are double sugars, consisting of two monosaccharides joined by a covalent bond. Carbohydrates also include macromolecules called polysaccharides, polymers composed of many sugar building blocks.

Sugars

Monosaccharides (from the Greek *monos*, single, and *sacchar*, sugar) generally have molecular formulas that are some multiple of the unit CH_2O. Glucose ($C_6H_{12}O_6$), the most common monosaccharide, is of central importance in the chemistry

Aldoses (Aldehyde Sugars) Carbonyl group at end of carbon skeleton	Ketoses (Ketone Sugars) Carbonyl group within carbon skeleton
Trioses: 3-carbon sugars ($C_3H_6O_3$)	
Glyceraldehyde An initial breakdown product of glucose	**Dihydroxyacetone** An initial breakdown product of glucose
Pentoses: 5-carbon sugars ($C_5H_{10}O_5$)	
Ribose A component of RNA	**Ribulose** An intermediate in photosynthesis
Hexoses: 6-carbon sugars ($C_6H_{12}O_6$)	
Glucose **Galactose** Energy sources for organisms	**Fructose** An energy source for organisms

▲ **Figure 5.3 The structure and classification of some monosaccharides.** Sugars vary in the location of their carbonyl groups (orange), the length of their carbon skeletons, and the spatial arrangement around asymmetric carbons (compare, for example, the purple portions of glucose and galactose).

MAKE CONNECTIONS *In the 1970s, a process was developed that converts the glucose in corn syrup to its sweeter isomer, fructose. High-fructose corn syrup, a common ingredient in soft drinks and processed food, is a mixture of glucose and fructose. What type of isomers are glucose and fructose? See Figure 4.7, p. 62.*

of life. In the structure of glucose, we can see the trademarks of a sugar: The molecule has a carbonyl group (C=O) and multiple hydroxyl groups (—OH) **(Figure 5.3)**. Depending on the location of the carbonyl group, a sugar is either an aldose (aldehyde sugar) or a ketose (ketone sugar). Glucose, for example, is an aldose; fructose, an isomer of glucose, is a ketose. (Most names for sugars end in *-ose.*) Another criterion for classifying sugars is the size of the carbon skeleton, which ranges from three to seven carbons long. Glucose, fructose, and other sugars that have six carbons are called hexoses. Trioses (three-carbon sugars) and pentoses (five-carbon sugars) are also common.

Still another source of diversity for simple sugars is in the spatial arrangement of their parts around asymmetric carbons. (Recall that an asymmetric carbon is a carbon attached to four different atoms or groups of atoms.) Glucose and galactose, for example, differ only in the placement of parts around one asymmetric carbon (see the purple boxes in Figure 5.3). What seems like a small difference is significant enough to give the two sugars distinctive shapes and behaviors.

Although it is convenient to draw glucose with a linear carbon skeleton, this representation is not completely accurate. In aqueous solutions, glucose molecules, as well as most other five- and six-carbon sugars, form rings **(Figure 5.4)**.

Monosaccharides, particularly glucose, are major nutrients for cells. In the process known as cellular respiration, cells extract energy in a series of reactions starting with glucose molecules. Simple-sugar molecules are not only a major fuel for cellular work, but their carbon skeletons also serve as raw material for the synthesis of other types of small organic molecules, such as amino acids and fatty acids. Sugar molecules that are not immediately used in these ways are generally incorporated as monomers into disaccharides or polysaccharides.

A **disaccharide** consists of two monosaccharides joined by a **glycosidic linkage**, a covalent bond formed between two monosaccharides by a dehydration reaction. For example, maltose is a disaccharide formed by the linking of two molecules of glucose **(Figure 5.5a)**. Also known as malt sugar, maltose is an ingredient used in brewing beer. The most prevalent disaccharide is sucrose, which is table sugar. Its two monomers are glucose and fructose **(Figure 5.5b)**. Plants generally transport carbohydrates from leaves to roots and other nonphotosynthetic organs in the form of sucrose. Lactose, the sugar present in milk, is another disaccharide, in this case a glucose molecule joined to a galactose molecule.

Polysaccharides

Polysaccharides are macromolecules, polymers with a few hundred to a few thousand monosaccharides joined by glycosidic linkages. Some polysaccharides serve as storage material, hydrolyzed as needed to provide sugar for cells. Other polysaccharides serve as building material for structures that

(a) **Linear and ring forms.** Chemical equilibrium between the linear and ring structures greatly favors the formation of rings. The carbons of the sugar are numbered 1 to 6, as shown. To form the glucose ring, carbon 1 bonds to the oxygen attached to carbon 5.

(b) **Abbreviated ring structure.** Each corner represents a carbon. The ring's thicker edge indicates that you are looking at the ring edge-on; the components attached to the ring lie above or below the plane of the ring.

▲ **Figure 5.4 Linear and ring forms of glucose.**

DRAW IT   *Start with the linear form of fructose (see Figure 5.3) and draw the formation of the fructose ring in two steps. First, number the carbons starting at the top of the linear structure. Then attach carbon 5 via its oxygen to carbon 2. Compare the number of carbons in the fructose and glucose rings.*

(a) **Dehydration reaction in the synthesis of maltose.** The bonding of two glucose units forms maltose. The glycosidic linkage joins the number 1 carbon of one glucose to the number 4 carbon of the second glucose. Joining the glucose monomers in a different way would result in a different disaccharide.

(b) **Dehydration reaction in the synthesis of sucrose.** Sucrose is a disaccharide formed from glucose and fructose. Notice that fructose, though a hexose like glucose, forms a five-sided ring.

▲ **Figure 5.5 Examples of disaccharide synthesis.**

DRAW IT   *Referring to Figure 5.4, number the carbons in each sugar in this figure. Show how the numbering is consistent with the name of the glycosidic linkage in each disaccharide.*

protect the cell or the whole organism. The architecture and function of a polysaccharide are determined by its sugar monomers and by the positions of its glycosidic linkages.

Storage Polysaccharides

Both plants and animals store sugars for later use in the form of storage polysaccharides. Plants store **starch**, a polymer of glucose monomers, as granules within cellular structures known as plastids, which include chloroplasts. Synthesizing starch enables the plant to stockpile surplus glucose. Because glucose is a major cellular fuel, starch represents stored en-

ergy. The sugar can later be withdrawn from this carbohydrate "bank" by hydrolysis, which breaks the bonds between the glucose monomers. Most animals, including humans, also have enzymes that can hydrolyze plant starch, making glucose available as a nutrient for cells. Potato tubers and grains—the fruits of wheat, maize (corn), rice, and other grasses—are the major sources of starch in the human diet.

Most of the glucose monomers in starch are joined by 1–4 linkages (number 1 carbon to number 4 carbon), like the glucose units in maltose (see Figure 5.5a). The simplest form of starch, amylose, is unbranched. Amylopectin, a more complex

(a) Starch: a plant polysaccharide. This micrograph shows part of a plant cell with a chloroplast, the cellular organelle where glucose is made and then stored as starch granules. Amylose (unbranched) and amylopectin (branched) are two forms of starch.

Chloroplast   Starch granules

Amylopectin

Amylose

1 μm

(b) Glycogen: an animal polysaccharide. Animal cells stockpile glycogen as dense clusters of granules within liver and muscle cells, as shown in this micrograph of part of a liver cell. Mitochondria are cellular organelles that help break down glucose released from glycogen. Note that glycogen is more branched than amylopectin starch.

Mitochondria   Glycogen granules

Glycogen

0.5 μm

▲ **Figure 5.6 Storage polysaccharides of plants and animals.** These examples, starch and glycogen, are composed entirely of glucose monomers, represented here by hexagons. Because of the angle of the 1–4 linkages, the polymer chains tend to form helices in unbranched regions.

starch, is a branched polymer with 1–6 linkages at the branch points. Both of these starches are shown in **Figure 5.6a**.

Animals store a polysaccharide called **glycogen**, a polymer of glucose that is like amylopectin but more extensively branched (**Figure 5.6b**). Humans and other vertebrates store glycogen mainly in liver and muscle cells. Hydrolysis of glycogen in these cells releases glucose when the demand for sugar increases. This stored fuel cannot sustain an animal for long, however. In humans, for example, glycogen stores are depleted in about a day unless they are replenished by consumption of food. This is an issue of concern in low-carbohydrate diets.

Structural Polysaccharides

Organisms build strong materials from structural polysaccharides. For example, the polysaccharide called **cellulose** is a major component of the tough walls that enclose plant cells. On a global scale, plants produce almost 10^{14} kg (100 billion tons) of cellulose per year; it is the most abundant organic compound on Earth. Like starch, cellulose is a polymer of glucose, but the glycosidic linkages in these two polymers differ. The difference is based on the fact that there are actually two slightly different ring structures for glucose (**Figure 5.7a**). When glucose forms a ring, the hydroxyl group attached to the number 1 carbon is positioned either below or above the plane of the ring. These two ring forms for glucose are called alpha (α) and beta (β), respectively. In starch, all the glucose monomers are in the α configuration (**Figure 5.7b**), the arrangement we saw in Figures 5.4 and 5.5. In contrast, the glucose monomers of cellulose are all in the β configuration, making every glucose monomer "upside down" with respect to its neighbors (**Figure 5.7c**).

The differing glycosidic linkages in starch and cellulose give the two molecules distinct three-dimensional shapes. Whereas certain starch molecules are largely helical, a cellulose molecule is straight. Cellulose is never branched, and some hydroxyl groups on its glucose monomers are free to hydrogen-bond with the hydroxyls of other cellulose molecules lying parallel to it. In plant cell walls, parallel cellulose molecules held together in this way are grouped into units called microfibrils (**Figure 5.8**). These cable-like microfibrils are a strong building material for plants and an important substance for humans because cellulose is the major constituent of paper and the only component of cotton.

Enzymes that digest starch by hydrolyzing its α linkages are unable to hydrolyze the β linkages of cellulose because of the distinctly different shapes of these two molecules. In fact, few organisms possess enzymes that can digest cellulose. Animals, including humans, do not; the cellulose in our food passes through the digestive tract and is eliminated with the feces. Along the way, the cellulose abrades the wall of the digestive tract and stimulates the lining to secrete mucus, which aids in the smooth passage of food through the tract. Thus, although cellulose is not a nutrient for humans, it is an important part of a healthful diet. Most fresh fruits, vegetables, and whole grains are rich in cellulose. On food packages, "insoluble fiber" refers mainly to cellulose.

(a) **α and β glucose ring structures.** These two interconvertible forms of glucose differ in the placement of the hydroxyl group (highlighted in blue) attached to the number 1 carbon.

α Glucose

β Glucose

(b) **Starch: 1–4 linkage of α glucose monomers.** All monomers are in the same orientation. Compare the positions of the —OH groups highlighted in yellow with those in cellulose (c).

(c) **Cellulose: 1–4 linkage of β glucose monomers.** In cellulose, every β glucose monomer is upside down with respect to its neighbors.

▲ Figure 5.7 **Starch and cellulose structures.**

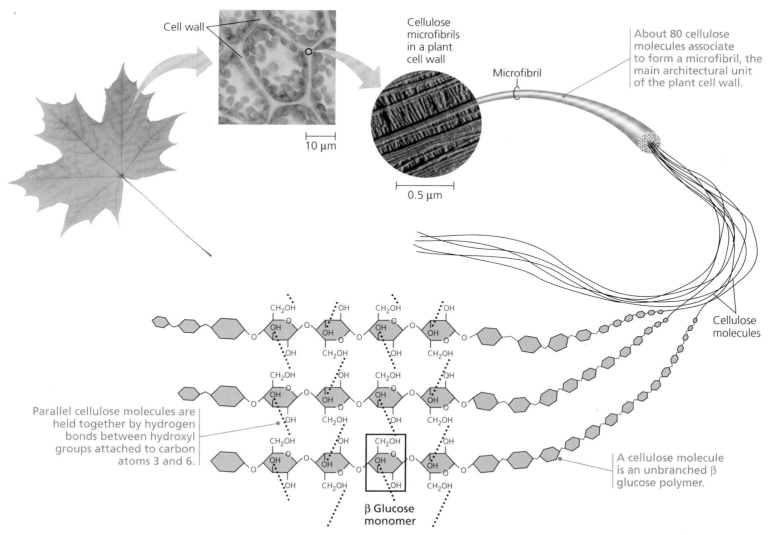

Cell wall

Cellulose microfibrils in a plant cell wall

Microfibril

About 80 cellulose molecules associate to form a microfibril, the main architectural unit of the plant cell wall.

10 μm

0.5 μm

Cellulose molecules

Parallel cellulose molecules are held together by hydrogen bonds between hydroxyl groups attached to carbon atoms 3 and 6.

A cellulose molecule is an unbranched β glucose polymer.

β Glucose monomer

▲ Figure 5.8 **The arrangement of cellulose in plant cell walls.**

Some microorganisms can digest cellulose, breaking it down into glucose monomers. A cow harbors cellulose-digesting prokaryotes and protists in its stomach. These microbes hydrolyze the cellulose of hay and grass and convert the glucose to other compounds that nourish the cow. Similarly, a termite, which is unable to digest cellulose by itself, has prokaryotes or protists living in its gut that can make a meal of wood. Some fungi can also digest cellulose, thereby helping recycle chemical elements within Earth's ecosystems.

Another important structural polysaccharide is **chitin**, the carbohydrate used by arthropods (insects, spiders, crustaceans, and related animals) to build their exoskeletons (**Figure 5.9**). An exoskeleton is a hard case that surrounds the soft parts of an animal. Pure chitin is leathery and flexible, but it becomes hardened when encrusted with calcium carbonate, a salt. Chitin is also found in many fungi, which use this polysaccharide rather than cellulose as the building material for their cell walls. Chitin is similar to cellulose, with β linkages, except that the glucose monomer of chitin has a nitrogen-containing appendage (see Figure 5.9, top right).

◀ The structure of the chitin monomer

◀ Chitin forms the exoskeleton of arthropods. This cicada is molting, shedding its old exoskeleton and emerging in adult form.

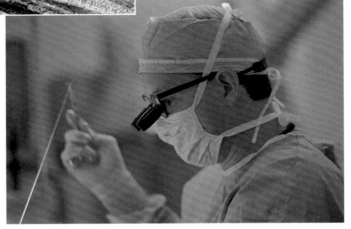

▲ Chitin is used to make a strong and flexible surgical thread that decomposes after the wound or incision heals.

▲ **Figure 5.9 Chitin, a structural polysaccharide.**

CONCEPT **5.3**

Lipids are a diverse group of hydrophobic molecules

Lipids are the one class of large biological molecules that does not include true polymers, and they are generally not big enough to be considered macromolecules. The compounds called **lipids** are grouped together because they share one important trait: They mix poorly, if at all, with water. The hydrophobic behavior of lipids is based on their molecular structure. Although they may have some polar bonds associated with oxygen, lipids consist mostly of hydrocarbon regions. Lipids are varied in form and function. They include waxes and certain pigments, but we will focus on the most biologically important types of lipids: fats, phospholipids, and steroids.

Fats

Although fats are not polymers, they are large molecules assembled from smaller molecules by dehydration reactions. A **fat** is constructed from two kinds of smaller molecules: glycerol and fatty acids (**Figure 5.10a**). Glycerol is an alcohol; each of its three carbons bears a hydroxyl group. A **fatty acid** has a long carbon skeleton, usually 16 or 18 carbon atoms in length. The carbon at one end of the skeleton is part of a carboxyl group, the functional group that gives these molecules the name fatty *acid*. The rest of the skeleton consists of a hydrocarbon chain. The relatively nonpolar C—H bonds in the hydrocarbon chains of fatty acids are the reason fats are hydrophobic. Fats separate from water because the water molecules hydrogen-bond to one another and exclude the fats. This is the reason that vegetable oil (a liquid fat) separates from the aqueous vinegar solution in a bottle of salad dressing.

In making a fat, three fatty acid molecules are each joined to glycerol by an ester linkage, a bond between a hydroxyl group and a carboxyl group. The resulting fat, also called a **triacylglycerol**, thus consists of three fatty acids linked to one glycerol molecule. (Still another name for a fat is *triglyc-*

Glycerol

Fatty acid
(in this case, palmitic acid)

(a) One of three dehydration reactions in the synthesis of a fat

Ester linkage

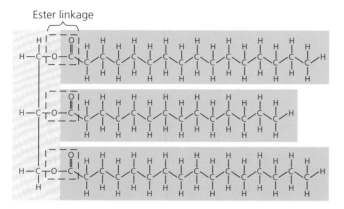

(b) Fat molecule (triacylglycerol)

▲ **Figure 5.10 The synthesis and structure of a fat, or triacylglycerol.** The molecular building blocks of a fat are one molecule of glycerol and three molecules of fatty acids. **(a)** One water molecule is removed for each fatty acid joined to the glycerol. **(b)** A fat molecule with three fatty acid units, two of them identical. The carbons of the fatty acids are arranged zigzag to suggest the actual orientations of the four single bonds extending from each carbon (see Figure 4.3a).

eride, a word often found in the list of ingredients on packaged foods.) The fatty acids in a fat can be the same, or they can be of two or three different kinds, as in **Figure 5.10b**.

The terms *saturated fats* and *unsaturated fats* are commonly used in the context of nutrition (**Figure 5.11**). These terms refer to the structure of the hydrocarbon chains of the fatty acids. If there are no double bonds between carbon atoms composing a chain, then as many hydrogen atoms as possible are bonded to the carbon skeleton. Such a structure is said to be *saturated* with hydrogen, and the resulting fatty acid therefore called a **saturated fatty acid** (**Figure 5.11a**). An **unsaturated fatty acid** has one or more double bonds, with one fewer hydrogen atom on each double-bonded carbon. Nearly all double bonds in naturally occurring fatty acids are *cis* double bonds, which cause a kink in the hydrocarbon chain wherever they occur (**Figure 5.11b**). (See Figure 4.7 to remind yourself about *cis* and *trans* double bonds.)

A fat made from saturated fatty acids is called a saturated fat. Most animal fats are saturated: The hydrocarbon chains of their fatty acids—the "tails" of the fat molecules—lack double bonds, and their flexibility allows the fat molecules to pack together tightly. Saturated animal fats—such as lard and butter—are solid at room temperature. In contrast, the fats of plants

▼ **Figure 5.11 Saturated and unsaturated fats and fatty acids.**

(a) Saturated fat

At room temperature, the molecules of a saturated fat, such as the fat in butter, are packed closely together, forming a solid.

Structural formula of a saturated fat molecule (Each hydrocarbon chain is represented as a zigzag line, where each bend represents a carbon atom and hydrogens are not shown.)

Space-filling model of stearic acid, a saturated fatty acid (red = oxygen, black = carbon, gray = hydrogen)

(b) Unsaturated fat

At room temperature, the molecules of an unsaturated fat such as olive oil cannot pack together closely enough to solidify because of the kinks in some of their fatty acid hydrocarbon chains.

Structural formula of an unsaturated fat molecule

Space-filling model of oleic acid, an unsaturated fatty acid

Cis double bond causes bending.

and fishes are generally unsaturated, meaning that they are built of one or more types of unsaturated fatty acids. Usually liquid at room temperature, plant and fish fats are referred to as oils—olive oil and cod liver oil are examples. The kinks where the *cis* double bonds are located prevent the molecules from packing together closely enough to solidify at room temperature. The phrase "hydrogenated vegetable oils" on food labels means that unsaturated fats have been synthetically converted to saturated fats by adding hydrogen. Peanut butter, margarine, and many other products are hydrogenated to prevent lipids from separating out in liquid (oil) form.

A diet rich in saturated fats is one of several factors that may contribute to the cardiovascular disease known as atherosclerosis. In this condition, deposits called plaques develop within the walls of blood vessels, causing inward bulges that impede blood flow and reduce the resilience of the vessels. Recent studies have shown that the process of hydrogenating vegetable oils produces not only saturated fats but also unsaturated fats with *trans* double bonds. These **trans fats** may contribute more than saturated fats to atherosclerosis (see Chapter 42) and other problems. Because trans fats are especially common in baked goods and processed foods, the U.S. Department of Agriculture requires nutritional labels to include information on trans fat content. Some U.S. cities and at least one country—Denmark—have even banned the use of trans fats in restaurants.

Certain unsaturated fatty acids must be supplied in the human diet because they cannot be synthesized in the body. These essential fatty acids include the omega-3 fatty acids, which are required for normal growth in children and appear to protect against cardiovascular disease in adults. Fatty fish and certain nuts and vegetable oils are rich in omega-3 fatty acids (so named because they have a double bond at the third carbon-carbon bond from the end of the hydrocarbon chain).

The major function of fats is energy storage. The hydrocarbon chains of fats are similar to gasoline molecules and just as rich in energy. A gram of fat stores more than twice as much energy as a gram of a polysaccharide, such as starch. Because plants are relatively immobile, they can function with bulky energy storage in the form of starch. (Vegetable oils are gener-

ally obtained from seeds, where more compact storage is an asset to the plant.) Animals, however, must carry their energy stores with them, so there is an advantage to having a more compact reservoir of fuel—fat. Humans and other mammals stock their long-term food reserves in adipose cells (see Figure 4.6a), which swell and shrink as fat is deposited and withdrawn from storage. In addition to storing energy, adipose tissue also cushions such vital organs as the kidneys, and a layer of fat beneath the skin insulates the body. This subcutaneous layer is especially thick in whales, seals, and most other marine mammals, protecting them from cold ocean water.

Phospholipids

Cells could not exist without another type of lipid—**phospholipids** **(Figure 5.12)**. Phospholipids are essential for cells because they make up cell membranes. Their structure provides a classic example of how form fits function at the molecular level. As shown in Figure 5.12, a phospholipid is similar to a fat molecule but has only two fatty acids attached to glycerol rather than three. The third hydroxyl group of glycerol is joined to a phosphate group, which has a negative electrical charge in the cell. Additional small molecules, which are usually charged or polar, can be linked to the phosphate group to form a variety of phospholipids.

The two ends of phospholipids show different behavior toward water. The hydrocarbon tails are hydrophobic and are excluded from water. However, the phosphate group and its attachments form a hydrophilic head that has an affinity for water. When phospholipids are added to water, they self-assemble into double-layered structures called "bilayers," shielding their hydrophobic portions from water **(Figure 5.13)**.

◀ **Figure 5.12 The structure of a phospholipid.** A phospholipid has a hydrophilic (polar) head and two hydrophobic (nonpolar) tails. Phospholipid diversity is based on differences in the two fatty acids and in the groups attached to the phosphate group of the head. This particular phospholipid, called a phosphatidylcholine, has an attached choline group. The kink in one of its tails is due to a *cis* double bond. Shown here are **(a)** the structural formula, **(b)** the space-filling model (yellow = phosphorus, blue = nitrogen), and **(c)** the symbol for a phospholipid that will appear throughout this book. (In most figures, this symbol will be used to represent a phospholipid with either saturated or unsaturated tails.)

DRAW IT *Draw an oval around the hydrophilic head of the space-filling model.*

Hydrophilic head

Choline

Phosphate

Glycerol

Fatty acids

Hydrophobic tails

(a) Structural formula

(b) Space-filling model

Hydrophilic head

Hydrophobic tails

(c) Phospholipid symbol

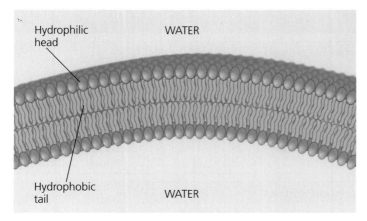

▲ **Figure 5.13 Bilayer structure formed by self-assembly of phospholipids in an aqueous environment.** The phospholipid bilayer shown here is the main fabric of biological membranes. Note that the hydrophilic heads of the phospholipids are in contact with water in this structure, whereas the hydrophobic tails are in contact with each other and remote from water.

At the surface of a cell, phospholipids are arranged in a similar bilayer. The hydrophilic heads of the molecules are on the outside of the bilayer, in contact with the aqueous solutions inside and outside of the cell. The hydrophobic tails point toward the interior of the bilayer, away from the water. The phospholipid bilayer forms a boundary between the cell and its external environment; in fact, cells could not exist without phospholipids.

Steroids

Steroids are lipids characterized by a carbon skeleton consisting of four fused rings. Different steroids, such as cholesterol and the vertebrate sex hormones, are distinguished by the particular chemical groups attached to this ensemble of rings (**Figure 5.14**). **Cholesterol** is a crucial molecule in animals. It is a common component of animal cell membranes and is also the precursor from which other steroids are synthesized. In vertebrates, cholesterol is synthesized in the liver

▲ **Figure 5.14 Cholesterol, a steroid.** Cholesterol is the molecule from which other steroids, including the sex hormones, are synthesized. Steroids vary in the chemical groups attached to their four interconnected rings (shown in gold).

MAKE CONNECTIONS *Compare cholesterol with the sex hormones shown in Concept 4.3 on p. 63. Circle the chemical groups that cholesterol has in common with estradiol; put a square around the chemical groups that cholesterol has in common with testosterone.*

and obtained from the diet. A high level of cholesterol in the blood may contribute to atherosclerosis. In fact, both saturated fats and trans fats exert their negative impact on health by affecting cholesterol levels.

CONCEPT CHECK 5.3

1. Compare the structure of a fat (triglyceride) with that of a phospholipid.
2. Why are human sex hormones considered lipids?
3. **WHAT IF?** Suppose a membrane surrounded an oil droplet, as it does in the cells of plant seeds. Describe and explain the form it might take.

For suggested answers, see Appendix A.

CONCEPT 5.4

Proteins include a diversity of structures, resulting in a wide range of functions

Nearly every dynamic function of a living being depends on proteins. In fact, the importance of proteins is underscored by their name, which comes from the Greek word *proteios*, meaning "first," or "primary." Proteins account for more than 50% of the dry mass of most cells, and they are instrumental in almost everything organisms do. Some proteins speed up chemical reactions, while others play a role in defense, storage, transport, cellular communication, movement, or structural support. **Figure 5.15**, on the next page, shows examples of proteins with these functions, which you'll learn more about in later chapters.

Life would not be possible without enzymes, most of which are proteins. Enzymatic proteins regulate metabolism by acting as **catalysts**, chemical agents that selectively speed up chemical reactions without being consumed by the reaction. Because an enzyme can perform its function over and over again, these molecules can be thought of as workhorses that keep cells running by carrying out the processes of life.

A human has tens of thousands of different proteins, each with a specific structure and function; proteins, in fact, are the most structurally sophisticated molecules known. Consistent with their diverse functions, they vary extensively in structure, each type of protein having a unique three-dimensional shape.

Polypeptides

Diverse as proteins are, they are all unbranched polymers constructed from the same set of 20 amino acids. Polymers of amino acids are called **polypeptides**. A **protein** is a biologically functional molecule that consists of one or more polypeptides, each folded and coiled into a specific three-dimensional structure.

▼ **Figure 5.15 An overview of protein functions.**

Enzymatic proteins

Function: Selective acceleration of chemical reactions

Example: Digestive enzymes catalyze the hydrolysis of bonds in food molecules.

Defensive proteins

Function: Protection against disease

Example: Antibodies inactivate and help destroy viruses and bacteria.

Antibodies
Virus
Bacterium

Storage proteins

Function: Storage of amino acids

Examples: Casein, the protein of milk, is the major source of amino acids for baby mammals. Plants have storage proteins in their seeds. Ovalbumin is the protein of egg white, used as an amino acid source for the developing embryo.

Ovalbumin
Amino acids for embryo

Transport proteins

Function: Transport of substances

Examples: Hemoglobin, the iron-containing protein of vertebrate blood, transports oxygen from the lungs to other parts of the body. Other proteins transport molecules across cell membranes.

Transport protein
Cell membrane

Hormonal proteins

Function: Coordination of an organism's activities

Example: Insulin, a hormone secreted by the pancreas, causes other tissues to take up glucose, thus regulating blood sugar concentration.

High blood sugar
Insulin secreted
Normal blood sugar

Receptor proteins

Function: Response of cell to chemical stimuli

Example: Receptors built into the membrane of a nerve cell detect signaling molecules released by other nerve cells.

Receptor protein
Signaling molecules

Contractile and motor proteins

Function: Movement

Examples: Motor proteins are responsible for the undulations of cilia and flagella. Actin and myosin proteins are responsible for the contraction of muscles.

Actin   Myosin
Muscle tissue   100 μm

Structural proteins

Function: Support

Examples: Keratin is the protein of hair, horns, feathers, and other skin appendages. Insects and spiders use silk fibers to make their cocoons and webs, respectively. Collagen and elastin proteins provide a fibrous framework in animal connective tissues.

Collagen
Connective tissue   60 μm

Amino Acid Monomers

All amino acids share a common structure. An **amino acid** is an organic molecule possessing both an amino group and a carboxyl group (see Figure 4.9). The illustration at the right shows the general formula for an amino acid. At the center of the amino acid is an asymmetric carbon atom called the *alpha (α) carbon*. Its four different partners are an amino group, a car-

Side chain (R group)
R
α carbon
Amino group
Carboxyl group

boxyl group, a hydrogen atom, and a variable group symbolized by R. The R group, also called the side chain, differs with each amino acid.

Figure 5.16 shows the 20 amino acids that cells use to build their thousands of proteins. Here the amino groups and carboxyl groups are all depicted in ionized form, the way they usually exist at the pH found in a cell. The side chain (R group) may be as simple as a hydrogen atom, as in the amino acid glycine, or it may be a carbon skeleton with various functional groups attached, as in glutamine.

▼ **Figure 5.16 The 20 amino acids of proteins.** The amino acids are grouped here according to the properties of their side chains (R groups) and shown in their prevailing ionic forms at pH 7.2, the pH within a cell. The three-letter and one-letter abbreviations for the amino acids are in parentheses. All amino acids used in proteins are L enantiomers, the form shown here (see Figure 4.7).

Nonpolar side chains; hydrophobic

Glycine
(Gly or G)

Alanine
(Ala or A)

Valine
(Val or V)

Leucine
(Leu or L)

Isoleucine
(Ile or I)

Methionine
(Met or M)

Phenylalanine
(Phe or F)

Tryptophan
(Trp or W)

Proline
(Pro or P)

Polar side chains; hydrophilic

Serine
(Ser or S)

Threonine
(Thr or T)

Cysteine
(Cys or C)

Tyrosine
(Tyr or Y)

Asparagine
(Asn or N)

Glutamine
(Gln or Q)

Electrically charged side chains; hydrophilic

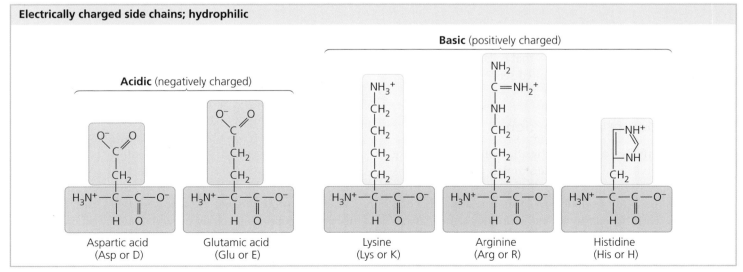

Basic (positively charged)

Acidic (negatively charged)

Aspartic acid
(Asp or D)

Glutamic acid
(Glu or E)

Lysine
(Lys or K)

Arginine
(Arg or R)

Histidine
(His or H)

The physical and chemical properties of the side chain determine the unique characteristics of a particular amino acid, thus affecting its functional role in a polypeptide. In Figure 5.16, the amino acids are grouped according to the properties of their side chains. One group consists of amino acids with nonpolar side chains, which are hydrophobic. Another group consists of amino acids with polar side chains, which are hydrophilic. Acidic amino acids are those with side chains that are generally negative in charge owing to the presence of a carboxyl group, which is usually dissociated (ionized) at cellular pH. Basic amino acids have amino groups in their side chains that are generally positive in charge. (Notice that *all* amino acids have carboxyl groups and amino groups; the terms *acidic* and *basic* in this context refer only to groups on the side chains.) Because they are charged, acidic and basic side chains are also hydrophilic.

Amino Acid Polymers

Now that we have examined amino acids, let's see how they are linked to form polymers (**Figure 5.17**). When two amino acids are positioned so that the carboxyl group of one is adjacent to the amino group of the other, they can become joined by a dehydration reaction, with the removal of a water molecule. The resulting covalent bond is called a **peptide bond**. Repeated over and over, this process yields a polypeptide, a polymer of many amino acids linked by peptide bonds.

The repeating sequence of atoms highlighted in purple in Figure 5.17 is called the polypeptide backbone. Extending from this backbone are the different side chains (R groups) of the amino acids. Polypeptides range in length from a few amino acids to a thousand or more. Each specific polypeptide has a unique linear sequence of amino acids. Note that one end of the polypeptide chain has a free amino group, while the opposite end has a free carboxyl group. Thus, a polypeptide of any length has a single amino end (N-terminus) and a single carboxyl end (C-terminus). In a polypeptide of any significant size, the side chains far outnumber the terminal groups, so the chemical nature of the molecule as a whole is determined by the kind and sequence of the side chains. The immense variety of polypeptides in nature illustrates an important concept introduced earlier—that cells can make many different polymers by linking a limited set of monomers into diverse sequences.

Protein Structure and Function

The specific activities of proteins result from their intricate three-dimensional architecture, the simplest level of which is the sequence of their amino acids. The pioneer in determining the amino acid sequence of proteins was Frederick Sanger, who, with his colleagues at Cambridge University in England, worked on the hormone insulin in the late 1940s and early 1950s. He used agents that break polypeptides at

▲ **Figure 5.17 Making a polypeptide chain.** Peptide bonds are formed by dehydration reactions, which link the carboxyl group of one amino acid to the amino group of the next. The peptide bonds are formed one at a time, starting with the amino acid at the amino end (N-terminus). The polypeptide has a repetitive backbone (purple) to which the amino acid side chains (yellow and green) are attached.

DRAW IT *Circle and label the carboxyl and amino groups that will form the new peptide bond.*

specific places, followed by chemical methods to determine the amino acid sequence in these small fragments. Sanger and his co-workers were able, after years of effort, to reconstruct the complete amino acid sequence of insulin. Since then, most of the steps involved in sequencing a polypeptide have been automated.

Once we have learned the amino acid sequence of a polypeptide, what can it tell us about the three-dimensional structure (commonly referred to simply as the "structure") of the protein and its function? The term *polypeptide* is not synonymous with the term *protein*. Even for a protein consisting of a single polypeptide, the relationship is somewhat analogous to that between a long strand of yarn and a sweater of particular size and shape that can be knit from the yarn. A functional protein is not *just* a polypeptide chain, but one or more polypeptides precisely twisted, folded, and coiled into a molecule of unique shape (**Figure 5.18**). And it is the amino acid sequence of each polypeptide that determines what

(a) A **ribbon model** shows how the single polypeptide chain folds and coils to form the functional protein. (The yellow lines represent disulfide bridges that stabilize the protein's shape; see Figure 5.20.)

(b) A **space-filling model** shows more clearly the globular shape seen in many proteins, as well as the specific three-dimensional structure unique to lysozyme.

▲ **Figure 5.18 Structure of a protein, the enzyme lysozyme.** Present in our sweat, tears, and saliva, lysozyme is an enzyme that helps prevent infection by binding to and destroying specific molecules on the surface of many kinds of bacteria. The groove is the part of the protein that recognizes and binds to the target molecules on bacterial walls.

three-dimensional structure the protein will have under normal cellular conditions.

When a cell synthesizes a polypeptide, the chain generally folds spontaneously, assuming the functional structure for that protein. This folding is driven and reinforced by the formation of a variety of bonds between parts of the chain, which in turn depends on the sequence of amino acids. Many proteins are roughly spherical (*globular proteins*), while others are shaped like long fibers (*fibrous proteins*). Even within these broad categories, countless variations exist.

A protein's specific structure determines how it works. In almost every case, the function of a protein depends on its ability to recognize and bind to some other molecule. In an especially striking example of the marriage of form and function, **Figure 5.19** shows the exact match of shape between an antibody (a protein in the body) and the particular foreign substance on a flu virus that the antibody binds to and marks for destruction. In Chapter 43, you'll learn more about how the immune system generates antibodies that match the shapes of specific foreign molecules so well. Also, you may recall from Chapter 2 that natural signaling molecules called endorphins bind to specific receptor proteins on the surface of brain cells in humans, producing euphoria and relieving pain. Morphine, heroin, and other opiate drugs are able to mimic endorphins because they all share a similar shape with endorphins and can thus fit into and bind to endorphin receptors in the brain. This fit is very specific, something like a lock and key (see Figure 2.18). Thus, the function of a protein—for instance, the ability of a receptor protein to bind to a particular pain-relieving signaling molecule—is an emergent property resulting from exquisite molecular order.

Antibody protein   Protein from flu virus

▲ **Figure 5.19 An antibody binding to a protein from a flu virus.** A technique called X-ray crystallography was used to generate a computer model of an antibody protein (blue and orange, left) bound to a flu virus protein (green and yellow, right). Computer software was then used to back the images away from each other, revealing the exact complementarity of shape between the two protein surfaces.

Four Levels of Protein Structure

With the goal of understanding the function of a protein, learning about its structure is often productive. In spite of their great diversity, all proteins share three superimposed levels of structure, known as primary, secondary, and tertiary structure. A fourth level, quaternary structure, arises when a protein consists of two or more polypeptide chains. **Figure 5.20**, on the following two pages, describes these four levels of protein structure. Be sure to study this figure thoroughly before going on to the next section.

Exploring Levels of Protein Structure

Primary Structure

Linear chain of amino acids

Amino acids

^+H_3N — Gly Pro Thr Gly Thr Gly Glu Ser Lys Cys
Amino end

1   5   10

Pro
Leu
Met
15 Val

30   25   20
His Val Ala Val Asn Ile Ala Pro Ser Gly Arg Val Ala Asp Leu Val Lys

Val
Phe
Arg
Lys 35   40   45   50
Ala Ala Asp Asp Thr Trp Glu Pro Phe Ala Ser Gly Lys Thr Ser Glu Ser

Gly
Glu
55 Leu
His
70   65   60
Ile Glu Val Lys Tyr Ile Gly Glu Val Phe Glu Glu Glu Thr Thr Leu Gly
Asp
Thr 75
Lys
Ser 80   85   90
Tyr Trp Lys Ala Leu Gly Ile Ser Pro Phe His Glu His Ala Glu Val Val
Phe
95 Thr
Ala
115   110   105   100   Asn
Ser Tyr Pro Ser Leu Leu Ala Ala Ile Thr Tyr Arg Arg Pro Gly Ser Asp
Tyr
Ser
Thr
Thr 120   125
Ala Val Val Thr Asn Pro Lys Glu — C — Carboxyl end
                                    (with O and O⁻)

Primary structure of transthyretin

The **primary structure** of a protein is a linked series of amino acids with a unique sequence. As an example, let's consider transthyretin, a globular blood protein that transports vitamin A and one of the thyroid hormones throughout the body. Transthyretin is made up of four identical polypeptide chains, each composed of 127 amino acids. Shown here is one of these chains unraveled for a closer look at its primary structure. Each of the 127 positions along the chain is occupied by one of the 20 amino acids, indicated here by its three-letter abbreviation.

The primary structure is like the order of letters in a very long word. If left to chance, there would be 20^{127} different ways of making a polypeptide chain 127 amino acids long. However, the precise primary structure of a protein is determined not by the random linking of amino acids, but by inherited genetic information. The primary structure in turn dictates secondary and tertiary structure, due to the chemical nature of the backbone and the side chains (R groups) of the amino acids positioned along the chain.

Secondary Structure

Regions stabilized by hydrogen bonds between atoms of the polypeptide backbone

α helix

Hydrogen bond

β pleated sheet

β strand, shown as a flat arrow pointing toward the carboxyl end

Hydrogen bond

Most proteins have segments of their polypeptide chains repeatedly coiled or folded in patterns that contribute to the protein's overall shape. These coils and folds, collectively referred to as **secondary structure**, are the result of hydrogen bonds between the repeating constituents of the polypeptide backbone (not the amino acid side chains). Within the backbone, the oxygen atoms have a partial negative charge, and the hydrogen atoms attached to the nitrogens have a partial positive charge (see Figure 2.16); therefore, hydrogen bonds can form between these atoms. Individually, these hydrogen bonds are weak, but because they are repeated many times over a relatively long region of the polypeptide chain, they can support a particular shape for that part of the protein.

One such secondary structure is the **α helix**, a delicate coil held together by hydrogen bonding between every fourth amino acid, shown above. Although each transthyretin polypeptide has only one α helix region (see tertiary structure on the next page), other globular proteins have multiple stretches of α helix separated by nonhelical regions (see hemoglobin on the next page). Some fibrous proteins, such as α-keratin, the structural protein of hair, have the α helix formation over most of their length.

The other main type of secondary structure is the **β pleated sheet**. As shown above, in this structure two or more strands of the polypeptide chain lying side by side (called β strands) are connected by hydrogen bonds between parts of the two parallel polypeptide backbones. β pleated sheets make up the core of many globular proteins, as is the case for transthyretin (see tertiary structure on the next page), and dominate some fibrous proteins, including the silk protein of a spider's web. The teamwork of so many hydrogen bonds makes each spider silk fiber stronger than a steel strand of the same weight.

▼ Spiders secrete silk fibers made of a structural protein containing β pleated sheets, which allow the spider web to stretch and recoil.

Tertiary Structure

Three-dimensional shape stabilized by interactions between side chains

Transthyretin polypeptide

Quaternary Structure

Association of multiple polypeptides, forming a functional protein

Transthyretin protein (four identical polypeptides)

Superimposed on the patterns of secondary structure is a protein's tertiary structure, shown above in a ribbon model of the transthyretin polypeptide. While secondary structure involves interactions between backbone constituents, **tertiary structure** is the overall shape of a polypeptide resulting from interactions between the side chains (R groups) of the various amino acids. One type of interaction that contributes to tertiary structure is—somewhat misleadingly—called a **hydrophobic interaction**. As a polypeptide folds into its functional shape, amino acids with hydrophobic (nonpolar) side chains usually end up in clusters at the core of the protein, out of contact with water. Thus, a "hydrophobic interaction" is actually caused by the exclusion of nonpolar substances by water molecules. Once nonpolar amino acid side chains are close together, van der Waals interactions help hold them together. Meanwhile, hydrogen bonds between polar side chains and ionic bonds between positively and negatively charged side chains also help stabilize tertiary structure. These are all weak interactions in the aqueous cellular environment, but their cumulative effect helps give the protein a unique shape.

Covalent bonds called **disulfide bridges** may further reinforce the shape of a protein. Disulfide bridges form where two cysteine monomers, which have sulfhydryl groups (—SH) on their side chains (see Figure 4.9), are brought close together by the folding of the protein. The sulfur of one cysteine bonds to the sulfur of the second, and the disulfide bridge (—S—S—) rivets parts of the protein together (see yellow lines in Figure 5.18a). All of these different kinds of interactions can contribute to the tertiary structure of a protein, as shown here in a small part of a hypothetical protein:

Some proteins consist of two or more polypeptide chains aggregated into one functional macromolecule. **Quaternary structure** is the overall protein structure that results from the aggregation of these polypeptide subunits. For example, shown above is the complete globular transthyretin protein, made up of its four polypeptides.

Another example is collagen, shown below, which is a fibrous protein that has three identical helical polypeptides intertwined into a larger triple helix, giving the long fibers great strength. This suits collagen fibers to their function as the girders of connective tissue in skin, bone, tendons, ligaments, and other body parts. (Collagen accounts for 40% of the protein in a human body.)

Collagen

Hemoglobin, the oxygen-binding protein of red blood cells shown below, is another example of a globular protein with quaternary structure. It consists of four polypeptide subunits, two of one kind (α) and two of another kind (β). Both α and β subunits consist primarily of α-helical secondary structure. Each subunit has a nonpolypeptide component, called heme, with an iron atom that binds oxygen.

Hydrogen bond

Hydrophobic interactions and van der Waals interactions

Disulfide bridge

Ionic bond

Polypeptide backbone

Heme

Iron

β subunit

α subunit

α subunit

β subunit

Hemoglobin

	Primary Structure	Secondary and Tertiary Structures	Quaternary Structure	Function	Red Blood Cell Shape
Normal hemoglobin	1 Val 2 His 3 Leu 4 Thr 5 Pro 6 Glu 7 Glu	β subunit	Normal hemoglobin α β α β	Molecules do not associate with one another; each carries oxygen.	Normal red blood cells are full of individual hemoglobin molecules, each carrying oxygen. 10 μm
Sickle-cell hemoglobin	1 Val 2 His 3 Leu 4 Thr 5 Pro 6 Val 7 Glu	Exposed hydrophobic region β subunit	Sickle-cell hemoglobin α β α β	Molecules interact with one another and crystallize into a fiber; capacity to carry oxygen is greatly reduced.	Fibers of abnormal hemoglobin deform red blood cell into sickle shape. 10 μm

▲ **Figure 5.21 A single amino acid substitution in a protein causes sickle-cell disease.**

MAKE CONNECTIONS *Considering the chemical characteristics of the amino acids valine and glutamic acid (see Figure 5.16), propose a possible explanation for the dramatic effect on protein function that occurs when valine is substituted for glutamic acid.*

Sickle-Cell Disease: A Change in Primary Structure

Even a slight change in primary structure can affect a protein's shape and ability to function. For instance, **sickle-cell disease**, an inherited blood disorder, is caused by the substitution of one amino acid (valine) for the normal one (glutamic acid) at a particular position in the primary structure of hemoglobin, the protein that carries oxygen in red blood cells. Normal red blood cells are disk-shaped, but in sickle-cell disease, the abnormal hemoglobin molecules tend to crystallize, deforming some of the cells into a sickle shape **(Figure 5.21)**. A person with the disease has periodic "sickle-cell crises" when the angular cells clog tiny blood vessels, impeding blood flow. The toll taken on such patients is a dramatic example of how a simple change in protein structure can have devastating effects on protein function.

What Determines Protein Structure?

You've learned that a unique shape endows each protein with a specific function. But what are the key factors determining protein structure? You already know most of the answer: A polypeptide chain of a given amino acid sequence can spontaneously arrange itself into a three-dimensional shape determined and maintained by the interactions responsible for secondary and tertiary structure. This folding normally occurs as the protein is being synthesized in the crowded environment within a cell, aided by other proteins. However, protein structure also depends on the physical and chemical conditions of the protein's environment. If the pH, salt concentration, temperature, or other aspects of its environment are altered, the weak chemical bonds and interactions within a protein may be destroyed, causing the protein to unravel and lose its native shape, a change called **denaturation (Figure 5.22)**. Because it is misshapen, the denatured protein is biologically inactive.

Most proteins become denatured if they are transferred from an aqueous environment to a nonpolar solvent, such as

Normal protein — Denaturation → Denatured protein

Denatured protein — Renaturation → Normal protein

▲ **Figure 5.22 Denaturation and renaturation of a protein.** High temperatures or various chemical treatments will denature a protein, causing it to lose its shape and hence its ability to function. If the denatured protein remains dissolved, it can often renature when the chemical and physical aspects of its environment are restored to normal.

ether or chloroform; the polypeptide chain refolds so that its hydrophobic regions face outward toward the solvent. Other denaturation agents include chemicals that disrupt the hydrogen bonds, ionic bonds, and disulfide bridges that maintain a protein's shape. Denaturation can also result from excessive heat, which agitates the polypeptide chain enough to overpower the weak interactions that stabilize the structure. The white of an egg becomes opaque during cooking because the denatured proteins are insoluble and solidify. This also explains why excessively high fevers can be fatal: Proteins in the blood can denature at very high body temperatures.

When a protein in a test-tube solution has been denatured by heat or chemicals, it can sometimes return to its functional shape when the denaturing agent is removed. We can conclude that the information for building specific shape is intrinsic to the protein's primary structure. The sequence of amino acids determines the protein's shape—where an α helix can form, where β pleated sheets can exist, where disulfide bridges are located, where ionic bonds can form, and so on. But how does protein folding occur in the cell?

Protein Folding in the Cell

Biochemists now know the amino acid sequence for more than 10 million proteins and the three-dimensional shape for more than 20,000. Researchers have tried to correlate the primary structure of many proteins with their three-dimensional structure to discover the rules of protein folding. Unfortunately, however, the protein-folding process is not that simple. Most proteins probably go through several intermediate structures on their way to a stable shape, and looking at the mature structure does not reveal the stages of folding required to achieve that form. However, biochemists have developed methods for tracking a protein through such stages.

Crucial to the folding process are **chaperonins** (also called chaperone proteins), protein molecules that assist in the proper folding of other proteins (**Figure 5.23**). Chaperonins do not specify the final structure of a polypeptide. Instead, they keep the new polypeptide segregated from "bad influences" in the cytoplasmic environment while it folds spontaneously. The chaperonin shown in Figure 5.23, from the bacterium *E. coli*, is a giant multiprotein complex shaped like a hollow cylinder. The cavity provides a shelter for folding polypeptides. In the past decade, researchers have discovered molecular systems that interact with chaperonins and check whether proper folding has occurred. Such systems either refold the misfolded proteins correctly or mark them for destruction.

Misfolding of polypeptides is a serious problem in cells. Many diseases, such as Alzheimer's, Parkinson's, and mad cow disease, are associated with an accumulation of misfolded proteins. In fact, misfolded versions of the transthyretin protein featured in Figure 5.20 have been implicated in several diseases, including one form of senile dementia.

Even when scientists have a correctly folded protein in hand, determining its exact three-dimensional structure is not simple, for a single protein molecule has thousands of atoms. The first 3-D structures were worked out in 1959 for hemoglobin and a related protein. The method that made these feats possible was **X-ray crystallography**, which has since been used to determine the 3-D structure of many other proteins. In a recent example, Roger Kornberg and his colleagues at Stanford University used this method to elucidate the structure of RNA polymerase, an enzyme that plays a crucial role in the expression of genes (**Figure 5.24**, on the next page). Another method for analyzing protein structure is nuclear magnetic resonance (NMR) spectroscopy, which does not require protein crystallization. A still newer approach employs bioinformatics (see Chapter 1) to predict the 3-D structure of polypeptides from their amino acid sequence. X-ray crystallography, NMR spectroscopy, and bioinformatics are complementary approaches to understanding protein structure and function.

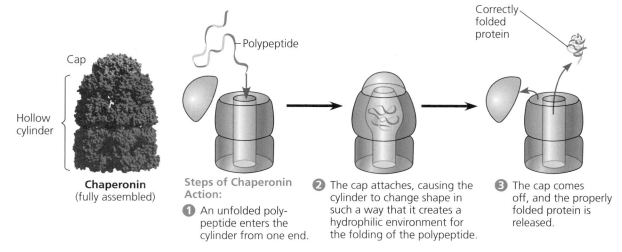

▶ **Figure 5.23 A chaperonin in action.** The computer graphic (left) shows a large chaperonin protein complex from the bacterium *E. coli*. It has an interior space that provides a shelter for the proper folding of newly made polypeptides. The complex consists of two proteins: One protein is a hollow cylinder; the other is a cap that can fit on either end.

Cap

Hollow cylinder

Chaperonin (fully assembled)

Polypeptide

Steps of Chaperonin Action:

❶ An unfolded polypeptide enters the cylinder from one end.

❷ The cap attaches, causing the cylinder to change shape in such a way that it creates a hydrophilic environment for the folding of the polypeptide.

Correctly folded protein

❸ The cap comes off, and the properly folded protein is released.

INQUIRY

What can the 3-D shape of the enzyme RNA polymerase II tell us about its function?

EXPERIMENT In 2006, Roger Kornberg was awarded the Nobel Prize in Chemistry for using X-ray crystallography to determine the 3-D shape of RNA polymerase II, which binds to the DNA double helix and synthesizes RNA. After crystallizing a complex of all three components, Kornberg and his colleagues aimed an X-ray beam through the crystal. The atoms of the crystal diffracted (bent) the X-rays into an orderly array that a digital detector recorded as a pattern of spots called an X-ray diffraction pattern.

RESULTS Using data from X-ray diffraction patterns, as well as the amino acid sequence determined by chemical methods, Kornberg and colleagues built a 3-D model of the complex with the help of computer software.

CONCLUSION By analyzing their model, the researchers developed a hypothesis about the functions of different regions of RNA polymerase II. For example, the region above the DNA may act as a clamp that holds the nucleic acids in place. (You'll learn more about this enzyme in Chapter 17.)

SOURCE A. L. Gnatt et al., Structural basis of transcription: an RNA polymerase II elongation complex at 3.3Å, *Science* 292:1876–1882 (2001).

WHAT IF? If you were an author of the paper and were describing the model, what type of protein structure would you call the small polypeptide spirals in RNA polymerase II?

CONCEPT CHECK 5.4

1. Why does a denatured protein no longer function normally?
2. What parts of a polypeptide participate in the bonds that hold together secondary structure? Tertiary structure?
3. **WHAT IF?** Where would you expect a polypeptide region that is rich in the amino acids valine, leucine, and isoleucine to be located in the folded polypeptide? Explain.

For suggested answers, see Appendix A.

CONCEPT 5.5

Nucleic acids store, transmit, and help express hereditary information

If the primary structure of polypeptides determines a protein's shape, what determines primary structure? The amino acid sequence of a polypeptide is programmed by a discrete unit of inheritance known as a **gene**. Genes consist of DNA, which belongs to the class of compounds called nucleic acids. **Nucleic acids** are polymers made of monomers called *nucleotides*.

The Roles of Nucleic Acids

The two types of nucleic acids, **deoxyribonucleic acid (DNA)** and **ribonucleic acid (RNA)**, enable living organisms to reproduce their complex components from one generation to the next. Unique among molecules, DNA provides directions for its own replication. DNA also directs RNA synthesis and, through RNA, controls protein synthesis **(Figure 5.25)**.

DNA is the genetic material that organisms inherit from their parents. Each chromosome contains one long DNA molecule, usually carrying several hundred or more genes. When a cell reproduces itself by dividing, its DNA molecules are copied and passed along from one generation of cells to the next. Encoded in the structure of DNA is the information that

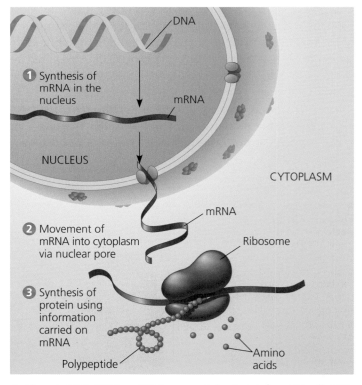

▲ **Figure 5.25 DNA → RNA → protein.** In a eukaryotic cell, DNA in the nucleus programs protein production in the cytoplasm by dictating synthesis of messenger RNA (mRNA). (The cell nucleus is actually much larger relative to the other elements of this figure.)

programs all the cell's activities. The DNA, however, is not directly involved in running the operations of the cell, any more than computer software by itself can print a bank statement or read the bar code on a box of cereal. Just as a printer is needed to print out a statement and a scanner is needed to read a bar code, proteins are required to implement genetic programs. The molecular hardware of the cell—the tools for biological functions—consists mostly of proteins. For example, the oxygen carrier in red blood cells is the protein hemoglobin, not the DNA that specifies its structure.

How does RNA, the other type of nucleic acid, fit into gene expression, the flow of genetic information from DNA to proteins? Each gene along a DNA molecule directs synthesis of a type of RNA called *messenger RNA* (*mRNA*). The mRNA molecule interacts with the cell's protein-synthesizing machinery to direct production of a polypeptide, which folds into all or part of a protein. We can summarize the flow of genetic information as DNA → RNA → protein (see Figure 5.25). The sites of protein synthesis are tiny structures called ribosomes. In a eukaryotic cell, ribosomes are in the cytoplasm, but DNA resides in the nucleus. Messenger RNA conveys genetic instructions for building proteins from the nucleus to the cytoplasm. Prokaryotic cells lack nuclei but still use mRNA to convey a

message from the DNA to ribosomes and other cellular equipment that translate the coded information into amino acid sequences. In recent years, the spotlight has been turned on other, previously unknown types of RNA that play many other roles in the cell. As is so often true in biology, the story is still being written! You'll hear more about the newly discovered functions of RNA molecules in Chapter 18.

The Components of Nucleic Acids

Nucleic acids are macromolecules that exist as polymers called **polynucleotides (Figure 5.26a)**. As indicated by the name, each polynucleotide consists of monomers called **nucleotides**. A nucleotide, in general, is composed of three parts: a nitrogen-containing (nitrogenous) base, a five-carbon sugar (a pentose), and one or more phosphate groups **(Figure 5.26b)**. In a polynucleotide, each monomer has only one phosphate group. The portion of a nucleotide without any phosphate groups is called a *nucleoside*.

To build a nucleotide, let's first consider the nitrogenous bases **(Figure 5.26c)**. Each nitrogenous base has one or two rings that include nitrogen atoms. (They are called nitrogenous *bases* because the nitrogen atoms tend to take up H$^+$

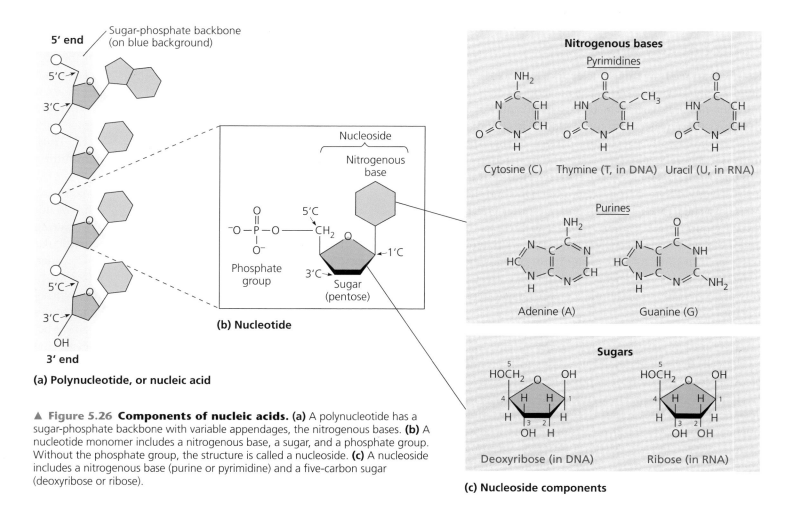

▲ **Figure 5.26 Components of nucleic acids. (a)** A polynucleotide has a sugar-phosphate backbone with variable appendages, the nitrogenous bases. **(b)** A nucleotide monomer includes a nitrogenous base, a sugar, and a phosphate group. Without the phosphate group, the structure is called a nucleoside. **(c)** A nucleoside includes a nitrogenous base (purine or pyrimidine) and a five-carbon sugar (deoxyribose or ribose).

(a) Polynucleotide, or nucleic acid

(b) Nucleotide

(c) Nucleoside components

from solution, thus acting as bases.) There are two families of nitrogenous bases: pyrimidines and purines. A **pyrimidine** has one six-membered ring of carbon and nitrogen atoms. The members of the pyrimidine family are cytosine (C), thymine (T), and uracil (U). **Purines** are larger, with a six-membered ring fused to a five-membered ring. The purines are adenine (A) and guanine (G). The specific pyrimidines and purines differ in the chemical groups attached to the rings. Adenine, guanine, and cytosine are found in both DNA and RNA; thymine is found only in DNA and uracil only in RNA.

Now let's add a sugar to the nitrogenous base. In DNA the sugar is **deoxyribose**; in RNA it is **ribose** (see Figure 5.26c). The only difference between these two sugars is that deoxyribose lacks an oxygen atom on the second carbon in the ring; hence the name *deoxy*ribose. To distinguish the numbers of the sugar carbons from those used for the ring atoms of the attached nitrogenous base, the sugar carbon numbers of a nucleoside or nucleotide have a prime (′) after them. Thus, the second carbon in the sugar ring is the 2′ ("2 prime") carbon, and the carbon that sticks up from the ring is called the 5′ carbon.

So far, we have built a nucleoside (nitrogenous base plus sugar). To complete the construction of a nucleotide, we attach a phosphate group to the 5′ carbon of the sugar (see Figure 5.26b). The molecule is now a nucleoside monophosphate, better known as a nucleotide.

Nucleotide Polymers

Now we can see how these nucleotides are linked together to build a polynucleotide. Adjacent nucleotides are joined by a phosphodiester linkage, which consists of a phosphate group that links the sugars of two nucleotides. This bonding results in a backbone with a repeating pattern of sugar-phosphate units (see Figure 5.26a). (Note that the nitrogenous bases are not part of the backbone.) The two free ends of the polymer are distinctly different from each other. One end has a phosphate attached to a 5′ carbon, and the other end has a hydroxyl group on a 3′ carbon; we refer to these as the 5′ end and the 3′ end, respectively. We can say that a polynucleotide has a built-in directionality along its sugar-phosphate backbone, from 5′ to 3′, somewhat like a one-way street. All along this sugar-phosphate backbone are appendages consisting of the nitrogenous bases.

The sequence of bases along a DNA (or mRNA) polymer is unique for each gene and provides very specific information to the cell. Because genes are hundreds to thousands of nucleotides long, the number of possible base sequences is effectively limitless. A gene's meaning to the cell is encoded in its specific sequence of the four DNA bases. For example, the sequence 5′-AGGTAACTT-3′ means one thing, whereas the sequence 5′-CGCTTTAAC-3′ has a different meaning. (Entire genes, of course, are much longer.) The linear order of bases in a gene specifies the amino acid sequence—the primary structure—of a protein, which in turn specifies that protein's three-dimensional structure and its function in the cell.

The Structures of DNA and RNA Molecules

RNA molecules usually exist as single polynucleotide chains like the one shown in Figure 5.26a. In contrast, DNA molecules have two polynucleotides, or "strands," that spiral around an imaginary axis, forming a **double helix (Figure 5.27a)**. The two sugar-phosphate backbones run in opposite 5′ → 3′ directions from each other; this arrangement is referred to as **antiparallel**, somewhat like a divided highway. The sugar-phosphate backbones are on the outside of the helix, and the nitrogenous bases are paired in the interior of the helix. The two strands are held together by hydrogen bonds between the paired bases (see Figure 5.27a). Most DNA molecules are very long, with thousands or even millions of base pairs. One long DNA double helix includes many genes, each one a particular segment of the molecule.

Only certain bases in the double helix are compatible with each other. Adenine (A) always pairs with thymine (T), and guanine (G) always pairs with cytosine (C). If we were to read the sequence of bases along one strand of the double helix, we would know the sequence of bases along the other strand. If a stretch of one strand has the base sequence 5′-AGGTCCG-3′, then the base-pairing rules tell us that the same stretch of the other strand must have the sequence 3′-TCCAGGC-5′. The two strands of the double helix are *complementary*, each the predictable counterpart of the other. It is this feature of DNA that makes it possible to generate two identical copies of each DNA molecule in a cell that is preparing to divide. When the cell divides, the copies are distributed to the daughter cells, making them genetically identical to the parent cell. Thus, the structure of DNA accounts for its function of transmitting genetic information whenever a cell reproduces.

Complementary base pairing can also occur between parts of two RNA molecules or even between two stretches of nucleotides in the *same* RNA molecule. In fact, base pairing within an RNA molecule allows it to take on the particular three-dimensional shape necessary for its function. Consider, for example, the type of RNA called *transfer RNA* (tRNA), which brings amino acids to the ribosome during the synthesis of a polypeptide. A tRNA molecule is about 80 nucleotides in length. Its functional shape results from base pairing between nucleotides where complementary stretches of the molecule run antiparallel to each other **(Figure 5.27b)**.

Note that in RNA, adenine (A) pairs with uracil (U); thymine (T) is not present in RNA. Another difference between RNA and DNA is that DNA almost always exists as a double helix, whereas RNA molecules are more variable in shape. This variability arises because the extent and location of complementary base pairing within an RNA molecule differs in different types of RNA, as you will see in Chapter 17.

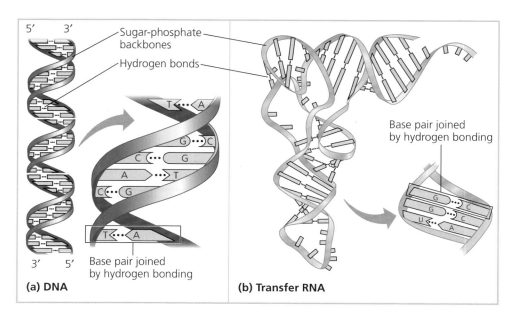

► **Figure 5.27 The structures of DNA and tRNA molecules. (a)** The DNA molecule is usually a double helix, with the sugar-phosphate backbones of the antiparallel polynucleotide strands (symbolized here by blue ribbons) on the outside of the helix. Holding the two strands together are pairs of nitrogenous bases attached to each other by hydrogen bonds. As illustrated here with symbolic shapes for the bases, adenine (A) can pair only with thymine (T), and guanine (G) can pair only with cytosine (C). Each DNA strand in this figure is the structural equivalent of the polynucleotide diagrammed in Figure 5.26a. **(b)** A tRNA molecule has a roughly L-shaped structure, with complementary base pairing of antiparallel stretches of RNA. In RNA, A pairs with U.

DNA and Proteins as Tape Measures of Evolution

EVOLUTION We are accustomed to thinking of shared traits, such as hair and milk production in mammals, as evidence of shared ancestors. Because we now understand that DNA carries heritable information in the form of genes, we can see that genes and their products (proteins) document the hereditary background of an organism. The linear sequences of nucleotides in DNA molecules are passed from parents to offspring; these sequences determine the amino acid sequences of proteins. Siblings have greater similarity in their DNA and proteins than do unrelated individuals of the same species. If the evolutionary view of life is valid, we should be able to extend this concept of "molecular genealogy" to relationships between species: We should expect two species that appear to be closely related based on fossil and anatomical evidence to also share a greater proportion of their DNA and protein sequences than do more distantly related species. In fact, that is the case. An example is the comparison of the β polypeptide chain of human hemoglobin with the corresponding hemoglobin polypeptide in other vertebrates. In this chain of 146 amino acids, humans and gorillas differ in just 1 amino acid, while humans and frogs differ in 67 amino acids. Molecular biology has added a new tape measure to the toolkit biologists use to assess evolutionary kinship.

The Theme of Emergent Properties in the Chemistry of Life: *A Review*

Recall that life is organized along a hierarchy of structural levels (see Figure 1.4). With each increasing level of order, new properties emerge. In Chapters 2–5, we have dissected the chemistry of life. But we have also begun to develop a more integrated view of life, exploring how properties emerge with increasing order.

We have seen that water's behavior results from the interactions of its molecules, each an ordered arrangement of hydrogen and oxygen atoms. We reduced the complexity and diversity of organic compounds to carbon skeletons and appended chemical groups. We saw that macromolecules are assembled from small organic molecules, taking on new properties. By completing our overview with an introduction to macromolecules and lipids, we have built a bridge to Unit Two, where we will study cell structure and function. We will keep a balance between the need to reduce life to simpler processes and the ultimate satisfaction of viewing those processes in their integrated context.

CONCEPT CHECK 5.5

1. **DRAW IT** Go to Figure 5.26a and, for the top three nucleotides, number all the carbons in the sugars, circle the nitrogenous bases, and star the phosphates.
2. **DRAW IT** In a DNA double helix, a region along one DNA strand has this sequence of nitrogenous bases: 5'-TAGGCCT-3'. Copy this sequence, and write down its complementary strand, clearly indicating the 5' and 3' ends of the complementary strand.
3. **WHAT IF?** (a) Suppose a substitution occurred in one DNA strand of the double helix in question 2, resulting in

   5'-TAAGCCT-3'
   3'-ATCCGGA-5'

   Copy these two strands, and circle and label the mismatched bases. (b) If the modified top strand is used by the cell to construct a complementary strand, what would that matching strand be?

For suggested answers, see Appendix A.

SUMMARY OF KEY CONCEPTS

CONCEPT 5.1

Macromolecules are polymers, built from monomers (pp. 68–69)
- Carbohydrates, proteins, and nucleic acids are **polymers**, chains of **monomers**. The components of lipids vary.

Monomers form larger molecules by **dehydration reactions**, in which water molecules are released. Polymers can disassemble by the reverse process, **hydrolysis**. An immense variety of polymers can be built from a small set of monomers.

? *What is the fundamental basis for the differences between carbohydrates, proteins, and nucleic acids?*

Large Biological Molecules	Components	Examples	Functions
CONCEPT 5.2 **Carbohydrates serve as fuel and building material (pp. 69–74)** **?** *Compare the composition, structure, and function of starch and cellulose. What role do starch and cellulose play in the human body?*	Monosaccharide monomer	**Monosaccharides:** glucose, fructose **Disaccharides:** lactose, sucrose	Fuel; carbon sources that can be converted to other molecules or combined into polymers
		Polysaccharides: • Cellulose (plants) • Starch (plants) • Glycogen (animals) • Chitin (animals and fungi)	• Strengthens plant cell walls • Stores glucose for energy • Stores glucose for energy • Strengthens exoskeletons and fungal cell walls
CONCEPT 5.3 **Lipids are a diverse group of hydrophobic molecules (pp. 74–77)** **?** *Why are lipids not considered to be macromolecules or polymers?*	Glycerol / 3 fatty acids	**Triacylglycerols** (fats or oils): glycerol + 3 fatty acids	Important energy source
	Head with (P) / 2 fatty acids	**Phospholipids:** phosphate group + 2 fatty acids	Lipid bilayers of membranes Hydrophobic tails Hydrophilic heads
	Steroid backbone	**Steroids:** four fused rings with attached chemical groups	• Component of cell membranes (cholesterol) • Signaling molecules that travel through the body (hormones)
CONCEPT 5.4 **Proteins include a diversity of structures, resulting in a wide range of functions (pp. 77–86)** **?** *Proteins are the most structurally and functionally diverse class of biological molecules. Explain the basis for this diversity.*	Amino acid monomer (20 types)	• Enzymes • Structural proteins • Storage proteins • Transport proteins • Hormones • Receptor proteins • Motor proteins • Defensive proteins	• Catalyze chemical reactions • Provide structural support • Store amino acids • Transport substances • Coordinate organismal responses • Receive signals from outside cell • Function in cell movement • Protect against disease
CONCEPT 5.5 **Nucleic acids store, transmit, and help express hereditary information (pp. 86–89)** **?** *What role does complementary base pairing play in the functions of nucleic acids?*	Nitrogenous base / Phosphate group (P)–CH₂ / Sugar	**DNA:** • Sugar = deoxyribose • Nitrogenous bases = C, G, A, T • Usually double-stranded	Stores hereditary information
		RNA: • Sugar = ribose • Nitrogenous bases = C, G, A, U • Usually single-stranded	Various functions during gene expression, including carrying instructions from DNA to ribosomes

TEST YOUR UNDERSTANDING

LEVEL 1: KNOWLEDGE/COMPREHENSION

1. Which of the following categories includes all others in the list?
   a. monosaccharide
   b. disaccharide
   c. starch
   d. carbohydrate
   e. polysaccharide

2. The enzyme amylase can break glycosidic linkages between glucose monomers only if the monomers are in the α form. Which of the following could amylase break down?
   a. glycogen, starch, and amylopectin
   b. glycogen and cellulose
   c. cellulose and chitin
   d. starch and chitin
   e. starch, amylopectin, and cellulose

3. Which of the following statements concerning *unsaturated* fats is true?
   a. They are more common in animals than in plants.
   b. They have double bonds in the carbon chains of their fatty acids.
   c. They generally solidify at room temperature.
   d. They contain more hydrogen than do saturated fats having the same number of carbon atoms.
   e. They have fewer fatty acid molecules per fat molecule.

4. The structural level of a protein *least* affected by a disruption in hydrogen bonding is the
   a. primary level.
   b. secondary level.
   c. tertiary level
   d. quaternary level.
   e. All structural levels are equally affected.

5. Enzymes that break down DNA catalyze the hydrolysis of the covalent bonds that join nucleotides together. What would happen to DNA molecules treated with these enzymes?
   a. The two strands of the double helix would separate.
   b. The phosphodiester linkages of the polynucleotide backbone would be broken.
   c. The purines would be separated from the deoxyribose sugars.
   d. The pyrimidines would be separated from the deoxyribose sugars.
   e. All bases would be separated from the deoxyribose sugars.

LEVEL 2: APPLICATION/ANALYSIS

6. The molecular formula for glucose is $C_6H_{12}O_6$. What would be the molecular formula for a polymer made by linking ten glucose molecules together by dehydration reactions?
   a. $C_{60}H_{120}O_{60}$
   b. $C_6H_{12}O_6$
   c. $C_{60}H_{102}O_{51}$
   d. $C_{60}H_{100}O_{50}$
   e. $C_{60}H_{111}O_{51}$

7. Which of the following pairs of base sequences could form a short stretch of a normal double helix of DNA?
   a. 5'-purine-pyrimidine-purine-pyrimidine-3' with 3'-purine-pyrimidine-purine-pyrimidine-5'
   b. 5'-AGCT-3' with 5'-TCGA-3'
   c. 5'-GCGC-3' with 5'-TATA-3'
   d. 5'-ATGC-3' with 5'-GCAT-3'
   e. All of these pairs are correct.

8. Construct a table that organizes the following terms, and label the columns and rows.

phosphodiester linkages	polypeptides	monosaccharides
peptide bonds	triacylglycerols	nucleotides
glycosidic linkages	polynucleotides	amino acids
ester linkages	polysaccharides	fatty acids

9. Copy the polynucleotide strand in Figure 5.26a and label the bases G, T, C, and T, starting from the 5' end. Assuming this is a DNA polynucleotide, now draw the complementary strand, using the same symbols for phosphates (circles), sugars (pentagons), and bases. Label the bases. Draw arrows showing the 5' → 3' direction of each strand. Use the arrows to make sure the second strand is antiparallel to the first. *Hint*: After you draw the first strand vertically, turn the paper upside down; it is easier to draw the second strand from the 5' toward the 3' direction as you go from top to bottom.

LEVEL 3: SYNTHESIS/EVALUATION

10. **EVOLUTION CONNECTION**
    Comparisons of amino acid sequences can shed light on the evolutionary divergence of related species. If you were comparing two living species, would you expect all proteins to show the same degree of divergence? Why or why not?

11. **SCIENTIFIC INQUIRY**
    Suppose you are a research assistant in a lab studying DNA-binding proteins. You have been given the amino acid sequences of all the proteins encoded by the genome of a certain species and have been asked to find candidate proteins that could bind DNA. What type of amino acids would you expect to see in such proteins? Why?

12. **SCIENCE, TECHNOLOGY, AND SOCIETY**
    Some amateur and professional athletes take anabolic steroids to help them "bulk up" or build strength. The health risks of this practice are extensively documented. Apart from health considerations, how do you feel about the use of chemicals to enhance athletic performance? Is an athlete who takes anabolic steroids cheating, or is such use part of the preparation required to succeed in competition? Explain.

13. **WRITE ABOUT A THEME**

    Structure and Function Proteins, which have diverse functions in a cell, are all polymers of the same subunits—amino acids. Write a short essay (100–150 words) that discusses how the structure of amino acids allows this one type of polymer to perform so many functions.

For selected answers, see Appendix A.

1. MasteringBiology® Assignments
Tutorials Types of Carbohydrates • Amino Acid Functional Groups • Levels of Structure in Proteins • Nucleic Acid Building Blocks • The Double Helix
Activities Condensation and Hydrolysis Reactions • Making and Breaking Polymers • Carbohydrate Structure and Function • Carbohydrates • Lipids • Protein Functions • Protein Structure • Nucleic Acid Structure • Structure of RNA and DNA
Questions Student Misconceptions • Reading Quiz • Multiple Choice • End-of-Chapter

2. eText
Read your book online, search, take notes, highlight text, and more.

3. The Study Area
Practice Tests • Cumulative Test • *BioFlix* 3-D Animations • MP3 Tutor Sessions • Videos • Activities • Investigations • Lab Media • Audio Glossary • Word Study Tools • Art

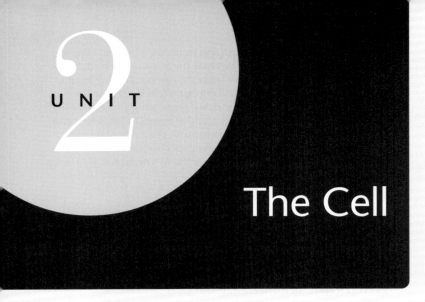

UNIT 2

The Cell

An Interview with

Bonnie L. Bassler

Bonnie Bassler loves her life as a biologist scrutinizing the secret lives of bacteria. For the past 20 years or so, Bonnie and her lab (her "gang," as she calls them) have made momentous discoveries about how bacterial cells use chemicals to communicate with each other in a process called quorum sensing. Dr. Bassler has a B.S. in Biochemistry from the University of California at Davis and a Ph.D. in Biochemistry from The Johns Hopkins University. Among her many awards and honors, she has received a MacArthur Foundation Fellowship and is a member of the National Academy of Sciences. She is the 2010–2011 President of the American Society for Microbiology, the largest specialized life science organization in the world. At Princeton University since 1994, she is currently the Squibb Professor in Molecular Biology and an Investigator of the Howard Hughes Medical Institute.

How did you get started in science?

I've always been interested in nature and animals, and in puzzles and mystery books—I really like figuring things out. As an undergraduate at UC Davis, I worked in a lab on a bacterial project while taking courses in both biochemistry and genetics. Then, as a graduate student at Johns Hopkins, I learned a lot of biochemistry while studying marine bacteria. The bacteria belong to the genus *Vibrio*, and I was working on chemotaxis, movement by cells toward food or away from noxious chemicals in the environment.

What are the advantages of using bacteria for research in cell biology?

Bacteria have been the foundation of molecular biology for the last 100 years because they're accessible. They grow fast, they form clones of identical cells, and they're amenable to biochemical and genetic analyses. Most of what we initially learned about molecular biology—about genes and proteins and other biomolecules—came from work done on bacteria. Because of evolutionary history, the most basic and ancient life processes that happen in bacteria also happen in humans and other higher organisms. Humans have more

bells and whistles, more proteins, more sophistication, more complexity. But if you want to understand the basic components of a process, very often you can use bacteria to do that. Also, working with bacteria fits my personality. I prefer having 10 billion bacterial offspring the day after an experiment to having to wait weeks or months for a small number of baby mice. Every morning there's a surprise waiting for me in the incubator!

What is quorum sensing, and how did you first hear about it?

When I was finishing my graduate work, I heard a talk by Mike Silverman, a scientist with the Agouron Institute in San Diego, about how bacteria "talk" to each other, "count" their own numbers, and coordinate their behavior. Mike had been working on a light-producing (bioluminescent) marine bacterium called *Vibrio fischeri* that lives symbiotically inside a variety of marine animals. The animal provides nutrients for the bacteria, which live in an enclosed space within the animal's body. In return, the bacteria provide light that benefits the animal—by scaring away predators or attracting prey or a mate. But if only a small number of bacteria are present, they do not make light—producing light would waste energy because the light wouldn't be visible. The word "quorum" means "the number needed to do something," and bacteria can sense whether there is a quorum or not and act accordingly.

The way quorum sensing works is that bacteria release certain signaling chemicals into the environment. As the bacterial cells increase in number, the molecules reach a concentration at which many of them bind to receptor proteins on the surface of or inside the bacteria. The signaling molecule fits together with the receptor like a key in a lock. In the case of the surface receptors, each receptor molecule has a part on the outside of the cell and a part on the inside. The signaling chemical binds to the outer part of the receptor, "tickling" the protein so that it makes something happen inside the cell. For instance, in *Vibrio fischeri*, binding of signaling molecules ultimately turns on genes that code for enzymes that make light. Mike had worked out this mechanism of how cells of *Vibrio fischeri* turn on light in synchrony.

It's important to understand that back then, we just didn't think about bacteria like that—we thought bacteria ignored each other and did their own thing as solitary cells. I was totally fascinated. I thought, "He's either crazy or he's brilliant—but I just have to work on that." I went up to the podium after his talk and begged him to let me be his postdoc. Finally he said yes, even though he was a geneticist and I was a biochemist! He took a chance on me.

How does a genetic approach differ from a biochemical one?

Geneticists make lots of mutant organisms, then think up clever strategies to find the ones with mutations in the genes they're interested in. In the case of quorum sensing in bioluminescent bacteria, you look for cells that remain dark. If you have mutated genes involved in quorum sensing, you would expect the bacteria not to make light because light emission depends on the cells communicating with each other. Eventually, you would hope to identify the components that function in normal light-emitting bacteria but not in the mutants. Biochemists, on the other hand, start by isolating molecules and studying their properties directly. Genetics and biochemistry are complementary approaches. I'm glad I know both because the combination is more effective than either approach by itself.

What did you learn about quorum sensing as a postdoc?

In Mike's lab, I worked on another species of bioluminescent *Vibrio* called *Vibrio harveyi*. Because these bacteria are free-living in the ocean, we thought their quorum-sensing molecular circuitry might be more complicated than that of *Vibrio fischeri*. What I found was that *Vibrio harveyi* has two parallel systems for quorum sensing, one that senses cells of the same species and one that counts bacteria of other species. Fast-forwarding a decade or so, this second system seems to be present in *many* bacteria, and the second signaling molecule appears to be universal. So, apparently bacteria can measure the ratios of these two signals, and they're saying, "How many of us and how many of you are there?" Then they do different things, depending on who is in the majority. And this isn't just restricted to bioluminescence. Other bacterial behaviors are also controlled by quorum sensing, such as forming an organized thin layer (called a biofilm) on your teeth or coordinating a virulent infection.

Tell us more about biofilms.

We used to think that most bacteria lived as individual cells suspended in liquid environments. But we now understand that in the wild, they live attached to surfaces in biofilms, and they secrete carbohydrates and other molecules that form a protective slime on the biofilm surface. Most of us have noticed the biofilm coating our teeth every morning. Believe it or not, there are about 600 bacterial species in that biofilm just trying to make a living, getting nutrients from us, but the side effect is that we get cavities. And when someone has a lung infection or an implant or heart valve that harbors an infection, the bacteria are growing as a biofilm in the lungs or on the introduced device. So we now understand why these infections are so hard to treat: It's because the slime on the biofilm is providing a protective shield that antibiotics can't penetrate.

What questions are you and your lab asking now?

My group is interested in how information outside an organism gets inside so that the organism does the right thing at the right time. We work on bacteria because they're simple, but we hope that we will have insights for people working on higher organisms. And we're curious about how collective behaviors first evolved on Earth. How did multicellularity come about? We know that the first organisms were bacteria, but how did they begin to do things together? How did groups of cells in your body come to act like a liver or a heart? We're very interested in how the flow of information through networks facilitates multicellularity.

Are there applications for the basic research you do?

When you're asking fundamental questions, you hope that surprises, things you never thought of, will come out of it. Now that we know that bacteria talk to each other and perform group activities, the question is whether we could interfere with these conversations for therapeutic purposes. Could we make molecules that keep bacteria from "talking" or "hearing"? Maybe these would be new antibiotics. Biofilms are a terrible problem in medicine and dental health, and now that we are starting to know the molecular basis for their formation, maybe we can learn how to prevent them from forming.

Bacteria get a lot of bad press for the negative things they do. On the other hand, bacteria also do many miraculous things that keep us alive; they are working for us every instant of our lives. You are covered with a bacterial biofilm that acts as invisible body armor—these good bacteria occupy all the spaces on your skin, preventing invading bacteria from attaching. Throughout your gut you have a huge mass of bacteria, and they're making vitamins for you and helping you digest your food. So all biofilms aren't bad—and for the good biofilms, what if we could find a molecule to make quorum sensing better? Rather than an antibiotic, this would be a probiotic.

Where do you think this field is going?

I think we'll be turning our attention to the possibility of communication between organisms from different kingdoms and different domains. Bacteria have been around for over 4 billion years and have probably been living with multicellular eukaryotic hosts for hundreds of millions of years. So why wouldn't these hosts have evolved strategies to listen in, say, to the conversation being carried out by a group of pathogenic bacteria? Does our immune system "hear" bacterial signaling molecules? Do hosts actively prevent quorum sensing among pathogenic bacteria? Do they tune in and help the good bacteria? I think this is going to be a dialogue, not a monologue.

What do you enjoy most about your life as a scientist?

I love what I work on. I figured out as a postdoc how much fun this life in science is—that it is not about me against other scientists or who is going to discover something first. Instead, it's me against this bacterium, and we are in it head-to-head for the rest of our lives, in a contest of wills between bacteria trying to keep their secrets and me trying to discover them. Also, the basic question of how groups work together fascinates me. I work with a fantastic group of students and we share everything—everybody gives everybody everything, and then we all get more. That's quorum sensing! Both my molecular and nonmolecular lives involve getting the group to do more than the individual. I love that parallelism! My gang of students show me their data, and it's my job to help them figure out the science and get on with their careers. I'm so lucky—having 24 hands and 12 brains is so much better than two hands and one brain. The science is always changing, and trying to keep up with these young and tireless people is hugely challenging and rewarding.

What is your advice to an undergraduate who is considering a career in biology?

For undergraduates who are considering a life in science, my advice is to work on something that you are passionate about. Don't be limited by thinking that bench science is the only thing a scientist can do. There are so many potential careers for a biologist. You could work on Capitol Hill as a scientific advisor or policymaker. You could teach. You could be a lawyer. You could be a writer who helps the public understand science. You could work on science education at the kindergarten level. Figure out your particular combination of personality traits and what you really love doing as a scientist; then make that niche for yourself and bring science to that career. The sky's the limit for biologists because biology is the science of the 21st century and it touches every part of our lives.

"The sky's the limit for biologists because biology is the science of the 21st century and it touches every part of our lives."

Bonnie Bassler (left) with Lisa Urry (center) and Jane Reece

6

A Tour of the Cell

▲ **Figure 6.1 How do your brain cells help you learn about biology?**

KEY CONCEPTS

6.1 Biologists use microscopes and the tools of biochemistry to study cells

6.2 Eukaryotic cells have internal membranes that compartmentalize their functions

6.3 The eukaryotic cell's genetic instructions are housed in the nucleus and carried out by the ribosomes

6.4 The endomembrane system regulates protein traffic and performs metabolic functions in the cell

6.5 Mitochondria and chloroplasts change energy from one form to another

6.6 The cytoskeleton is a network of fibers that organizes structures and activities in the cell

6.7 Extracellular components and connections between cells help coordinate cellular activities

The Fundamental Units of Life

Given the scope of biology, you may wonder sometimes how you will ever learn all the material in this course! The answer involves cells, which are as fundamental to the living systems of biology as the atom is to chemistry. The contraction of muscle cells moves your eyes as you read this sentence. The words on the page are translated into signals that nerve cells carry to your brain. **Figure 6.1** shows extensions from one nerve cell (purple) making contact with another nerve cell (orange) in the brain. As you study, your goal is to make connections like these that solidify memories and permit learning to occur.

All organisms are made of cells. In the hierarchy of biological organization, the cell is the simplest collection of matter that can be alive. Indeed, many forms of life exist as single-celled organisms. More complex organisms, including plants and animals, are multicellular; their bodies are cooperatives of many kinds of specialized cells that could not survive for long on their own. Even when cells are arranged into higher levels of organization, such as tissues and organs, the cell remains the organism's basic unit of structure and function.

All cells are related by their descent from earlier cells. However, they have been modified in many different ways during the long evolutionary history of life on Earth. But although cells can differ substantially from one another, they share common features. In this chapter, we'll first examine the tools and techniques that allow us to understand cells, then tour the cell and become acquainted with its components.

CONCEPT 6.1

Biologists use microscopes and the tools of biochemistry to study cells

How can cell biologists investigate the inner workings of a cell, usually too small to be seen by the unaided eye? Before we tour the cell, it will be helpful to learn how cells are studied.

Microscopy

The development of instruments that extend the human senses has gone hand in hand with the advance of science. The discovery and early study of cells progressed with the invention of microscopes in 1590 and their refinement during the 1600s. Cell walls were first seen by Robert Hooke in 1665 as he looked through a microscope at dead cells from the bark of an oak tree. But it took the wonderfully crafted lenses of Antoni van Leeuwenhoek to visualize living cells. Imagine Hooke's awe when he visited van Leeuwenhoek in 1674 and the world of microorganisms—what his host called "very little animalcules"—was revealed to him.

The microscopes first used by Renaissance scientists, as well as the microscopes you are likely to use in the laboratory, are all light microscopes. In a **light microscope (LM)**, visible light is passed through the specimen and then through glass lenses. The lenses refract (bend) the light in such a way that the image of the specimen is magnified as it is projected into the eye or into a camera.

Three important parameters in microscopy are magnification, resolution, and contrast. *Magnification* is the ratio of an object's image size to its real size. Light microscopes can magnify effectively to about 1,000 times the actual size of the specimen; at greater magnifications, additional details cannot be seen clearly. *Resolution* is a measure of the clarity of the image; it is the minimum distance two points can be separated and still be distinguished as two points. For example, what appears to the unaided eye as one star in the sky may be resolved as twin stars with a telescope, which has a higher resolving ability than the eye. Similarly, using standard techniques, the light microscope cannot resolve detail finer than about 0.2 micrometer (μm), or 200 nanometers (nm), regardless of the magnification (**Figure 6.2**). The third parameter, *contrast*, accentuates differences in parts of the sample. Improvements in light microscopy have included new methods for enhancing contrast, such as staining or labeling cell components to stand out visually. **Figure 6.3**, on the next page, shows different types of microscopy; study this figure as you read the rest of this section.

Until recently, the resolution barrier prevented cell biologists from using standard light microscopy to study **organelles**, the membrane-enclosed structures within eukaryotic cells. To see these structures in any detail required the development of a new instrument. In the 1950s, the electron microscope was introduced to biology. Rather than light, the **electron microscope (EM)** focuses a beam of electrons through the specimen or onto its surface. Resolution is inversely related to the wavelength of the radiation a microscope uses for imaging, and electron beams have much shorter wavelengths than visible light. Modern electron microscopes can theoretically achieve a resolution of about 0.002 nm, though in practice they usually cannot resolve structures smaller than about 2 nm across. Still, this is a hundredfold improvement over the standard light microscope.

The **scanning electron microscope (SEM)** is especially useful for detailed study of the topography of a specimen (see Figure 6.3). The electron beam scans the surface of the sample, usually coated with a thin film of gold. The beam excites electrons on the surface, and these secondary electrons are detected by a device that translates the pattern of electrons into an electronic signal to a video screen. The result is an image of the specimen's surface that appears three-dimensional.

The **transmission electron microscope (TEM)** is used to study the internal structure of cells (see Figure 6.3). The TEM aims an electron beam through a very thin section of the specimen, similar to the way a light microscope transmits light through a slide. The specimen has been stained with

1 centimeter (cm) = 10^{-2} meter (m) = 0.4 inch
1 millimeter (mm) = 10^{-3} m
1 micrometer (μm) = 10^{-3} mm = 10^{-6} m
1 nanometer (nm) = 10^{-3} μm = 10^{-9} m

▲ **Figure 6.2 The size range of cells.** Most cells are between 1 and 100 μm in diameter (yellow region of chart) and are therefore visible only under a microscope. Notice that the scale along the left side is logarithmic to accommodate the range of sizes shown. Starting at the top of the scale with 10 m and going down, each reference measurement marks a tenfold decrease in diameter or length. For a complete table of the metric system, see Appendix C.

atoms of heavy metals, which attach to certain cellular structures, thus enhancing the electron density of some parts of the cell more than others. The electrons passing through the specimen are scattered more in the denser regions, so fewer are transmitted. The image displays the pattern of transmitted electrons. Instead of using glass lenses, the TEM uses electromagnets as lenses to bend the paths of the electrons, ultimately focusing the image onto a monitor for viewing.

Electron microscopes have revealed many organelles and other subcellular structures that were impossible to resolve with the light microscope. But the light microscope offers advantages, especially in studying living cells. A disadvantage of

▼ Figure 6.3

Exploring Microscopy

Light Microscopy (LM)

Brightfield (unstained specimen). Light passes directly through the specimen. Unless the cell is naturally pigmented or artificially stained, the image has little contrast. (The first four light micrographs show human cheek epithelial cells; the scale bar pertains to all four micrographs.)

Brightfield (stained specimen). Staining with various dyes enhances contrast. Most staining procedures require that cells be fixed (preserved).

Phase-contrast. Variations in density within the specimen are amplified to enhance contrast in unstained cells, which is especially useful for examining living, unpigmented cells.

Differential-interference-contrast (Nomarski). As in phase-contrast microscopy, optical modifications are used to exaggerate differences in density, making the image appear almost 3-D.

Fluorescence. The locations of specific molecules in the cell can be revealed by labeling the molecules with fluorescent dyes or antibodies; some cells have molecules that fluoresce on their own. Fluorescent substances absorb ultraviolet radiation and emit visible light. In this fluorescently labeled uterine cell, nuclear material is blue, organelles called mitochondria are orange, and the cell's "skeleton" is green.

Confocal. The top image is a standard fluorescence micrograph of fluorescently labeled nervous tissue (nerve cells are green, support cells are orange, and regions of overlap are yellow); below it is a confocal image of the same tissue. Using a laser, this "optical sectioning" technique eliminates out-of-focus light from a thick sample, creating a single plane of fluorescence in the image. By capturing sharp images at many different planes, a 3-D reconstruction can be created. The standard image is blurry because out-of-focus light is not excluded.

Deconvolution. The top of this split image is a compilation of standard fluorescence micrographs through the depth of a white blood cell. Below is an image of the same cell reconstructed from many blurry images at different planes, each of which was processed using deconvolution software. This process digitally removes out-of-focus light and reassigns it to its source, creating a much sharper 3-D image.

Super-resolution. On the top is a confocal image of part of a nerve cell, using a fluorescent label that binds to a molecule clustered in small sacs in the cell (vesicles) that are 40 nm in diameter. The greenish-yellow spots are blurry because 40 nm is below the 200-nm limit of resolution for standard light microscopy. Below is an image of the same part of the cell, seen using a new "super-resolution" technique. Sophisticated equipment is used to light up individual fluorescent molecules and record their position. Combining information from many molecules in different places "breaks" the limit of resolution, resulting in the sharp greenish-yellow dots seen here. (Each dot is a 40-nm vesicle.)

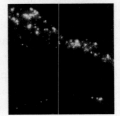

Electron Microscopy (EM)

Scanning electron microscopy (SEM). Micrographs taken with a scanning electron microscope show a 3-D image of the surface of a specimen. This SEM shows the surface of a cell from a trachea (windpipe) covered with cilia. Beating of the cilia helps move inhaled debris upward toward the throat. The SEM and TEM shown here have been artificially colorized. (Electron micrographs are black and white, but are often artificially colorized to highlight particular structures.)

Abbreviations used in this book:
LM = Light Micrograph
SEM = Scanning Electron Micrograph
TEM = Transmission Electron Micrograph

Longitudinal section of cilium Cross section of cilium

Cilia

Transmission electron microscopy (TEM). A transmission electron microscope profiles a thin section of a specimen. Here we see a section through a tracheal cell, revealing its internal structure. In preparing the TEM, some cilia were cut along their lengths, creating longitudinal sections, while other cilia were cut straight across, creating cross sections.

electron microscopy is that the methods used to prepare the specimen kill the cells. For all microscopy techniques, in fact, specimen preparation can introduce artifacts, structural features seen in micrographs that do not exist in the living cell.

In the past several decades, light microscopy has been revitalized by major technical advances (see Figure 6.3). Labeling individual cellular molecules or structures with fluorescent markers has made it possible to see such structures with increasing detail. In addition, both confocal and deconvolution microscopy have sharpened images of three-dimensional tissues and cells. Finally, over the past ten years, a group of new techniques and labeling molecules have allowed researchers to "break" the resolution barrier and distinguish subcellular structures as small as 10–20 nm across. As this "super-resolution microscopy" becomes more widespread, the images we'll see of living cells may well be as awe-inspiring to us as van Leeuwenhoek's were to Robert Hooke 350 years ago.

Microscopes are the most important tools of *cytology*, the study of cell structure. To understand the function of each structure, however, required the integration of cytology and *biochemistry*, the study of the chemical processes (metabolism) of cells.

Cell Fractionation

A useful technique for studying cell structure and function is **cell fractionation**, which takes cells apart and separates major organelles and other subcellular structures from one another (**Figure 6.4**). The instrument used is the centrifuge, which spins test tubes holding mixtures of disrupted cells at a series of increasing speeds. At each speed, the resulting force causes a fraction of the cell components to settle to the bottom of the tube, forming a pellet. At lower speeds, the pellet consists of larger components, and higher speeds yield a pellet with smaller components.

Cell fractionation enables researchers to prepare specific cell components in bulk and identify their functions, a task not usually possible with intact cells. For example, on one of the cell fractions, biochemical tests showed the presence of enzymes involved in cellular respiration, while electron microscopy revealed large numbers of the organelles called mitochondria. Together, these data helped biologists determine that mitochondria are the sites of cellular respiration. Biochemistry and cytology thus complement each other in correlating cell function with structure.

CONCEPT CHECK 6.1

1. How do stains used for light microscopy compare with those used for electron microscopy?
2. **WHAT IF?** Which type of microscope would you use to study (a) the changes in shape of a living white blood cell and (b) the details of surface texture of a hair?

For suggested answers, see Appendix A.

▼ Figure 6.4 **RESEARCH METHOD**

Cell Fractionation

APPLICATION Cell fractionation is used to isolate (fractionate) cell components based on size and density.

TECHNIQUE Cells are homogenized in a blender to break them up. The resulting mixture (homogenate) is centrifuged. The supernatant (liquid) is poured into another tube and centrifuged at a higher speed for a longer time. This process is repeated several times. This "differential centrifugation" results in a series of pellets, each containing different cell components.

Homogenization

Tissue cells

Homogenate

Centrifuged at 1,000 *g* (1,000 times the force of gravity) for 10 min

Centrifugation

Supernatant poured into next tube

Differential centrifugation

20,000 *g* 20 min

Pellet rich in nuclei and cellular debris

80,000 *g* 60 min

150,000 *g* 3 hr

Pellet rich in mitochondria (and chloroplasts if cells are from a plant)

Pellet rich in "microsomes" (pieces of plasma membranes and cells' internal membranes)

Pellet rich in ribosomes

RESULTS In early experiments, researchers used microscopy to identify the organelles in each pellet and biochemical methods to determine their metabolic functions. These identifications established a baseline for this method, enabling today's researchers to know which cell fraction they should collect in order to isolate and study particular organelles.

CONCEPT 6.2

Eukaryotic cells have internal membranes that compartmentalize their functions

Cells—the basic structural and functional units of every organism—are of two distinct types: prokaryotic and eukaryotic. Organisms of the domains Bacteria and Archaea consist of prokaryotic cells. Protists, fungi, animals, and plants all consist of eukaryotic cells.

Comparing Prokaryotic and Eukaryotic Cells

All cells share certain basic features: They are all bounded by a selective barrier, called the *plasma membrane*. Inside all cells is a semifluid, jellylike substance called **cytosol**, in which subcellular components are suspended. All cells contain *chromosomes*, which carry genes in the form of DNA. And all cells have *ribosomes*, tiny complexes that make proteins according to instructions from the genes.

A major difference between prokaryotic and eukaryotic cells is the location of their DNA. In a **eukaryotic cell**, most of the DNA is in an organelle called the *nucleus*, which is bounded by a double membrane (see Figure 6.8, on pp. 100–101). In a **prokaryotic cell**, the DNA is concentrated in a region that is not membrane-enclosed, called the **nucleoid (Figure 6.5)**. The word *eukaryotic* means "true nucleus" (from the Greek *eu*, true, and *karyon*, kernel, here referring to the nucleus), and

the word *prokaryotic* means "before nucleus" (from the Greek *pro*, before), reflecting the fact that prokaryotic cells evolved before eukaryotic cells.

The interior of either type of cell is called the **cytoplasm**; in eukaryotic cells, this term refers only to the region between the nucleus and the plasma membrane. Within the cytoplasm of a eukaryotic cell, suspended in cytosol, are a variety of organelles of specialized form and function. These membrane-bounded structures are absent in prokaryotic cells. Thus, the presence or absence of a true nucleus is just one aspect of the disparity in structural complexity between the two types of cells.

Eukaryotic cells are generally much larger than prokaryotic cells (see Figure 6.2). Size is a general feature of cell structure that relates to function. The logistics of carrying out cellular metabolism sets limits on cell size. At the lower limit, the smallest cells known are bacteria called mycoplasmas, which have diameters between 0.1 and 1.0 μm. These are perhaps the smallest packages with enough DNA to program metabolism and enough enzymes and other cellular equipment to carry out the activities necessary for a cell to sustain itself and reproduce. Typical bacteria are 1–5 μm in diameter, about ten times the size of mycoplasmas. Eukaryotic cells are typically 10–100 μm in diameter.

Metabolic requirements also impose theoretical upper limits on the size that is practical for a single cell. At the boundary of every cell, the **plasma membrane** functions as a selective barrier that allows passage of enough oxygen, nutrients, and wastes to service the entire cell **(Figure 6.6)**. For each square micrometer of membrane, only a limited amount of a particular

▲ **Figure 6.5 A prokaryotic cell.** Lacking a true nucleus and the other membrane-enclosed organelles of the eukaryotic cell, the prokaryotic cell is much simpler in structure. Prokaryotes include bacteria and archaea; the general cell structure of the two domains is essentially the same.

(a) TEM of a plasma membrane. The plasma membrane, here in a red blood cell, appears as a pair of dark bands separated by a light band.

Outside of cell

Inside of cell

0.1 μm

Carbohydrate side chains

Hydrophilic region

Hydrophobic region

Hydrophilic region

Phospholipid

Proteins

(b) Structure of the plasma membrane

▲ **Figure 6.6 The plasma membrane.** The plasma membrane and the membranes of organelles consist of a double layer (bilayer) of phospholipids with various proteins attached to or embedded in it. The hydrophobic parts, including phospholipid tails and interior portions of membrane proteins, are found in the interior of the membrane. The hydrophilic parts, including phospholipid heads, exterior portions of proteins, and channels of proteins, are in contact with the aqueous solution. Carbohydrate side chains may be attached to proteins or lipids on the outer surface of the plasma membrane.

MAKE CONNECTIONS *Review Figure 5.12 (p. 76) and describe the characteristics of a phospholipid that allow it to function as the major component in the plasma membrane.*

substance can cross per second, so the ratio of surface area to volume is critical. As a cell (or any other object) increases in size, its volume grows proportionately more than its surface area. (Area is proportional to a linear dimension squared, whereas volume is proportional to the linear dimension cubed.) Thus, a smaller object has a greater ratio of surface area to volume **(Figure 6.7).**

The need for a surface area sufficiently large to accommodate the volume helps explain the microscopic size of most cells and the narrow, elongated shapes of others, such as nerve cells. Larger organisms do not generally have *larger* cells than smaller organisms—they simply have *more* cells (see Figure 6.7). A sufficiently high ratio of surface area to volume is especially important in cells that exchange a lot of material with their surroundings, such as intestinal cells. Such cells may have many long, thin projections from their surface called *microvilli*, which increase surface area without an appreciable increase in volume.

The evolutionary relationships between prokaryotic and eukaryotic cells will be discussed later in this chapter, and prokaryotic cells will be described in detail in Chapter 27. Most of the discussion of cell structure that follows in this chapter applies to eukaryotic cells.

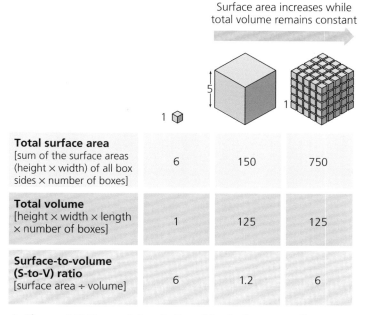

Surface area increases while total volume remains constant

	1	5	1
Total surface area [sum of the surface areas (height × width) of all box sides × number of boxes]	6	150	750
Total volume [height × width × length × number of boxes]	1	125	125
Surface-to-volume (S-to-V) ratio [surface area ÷ volume]	6	1.2	6

▲ **Figure 6.7 Geometric relationships between surface area and volume.** In this diagram, cells are represented as boxes. Using arbitrary units of length, we can calculate the cell's surface area (in square units, or units^2), volume (in cubic units, or units^3), and ratio of surface area to volume. A high surface-to-volume ratio facilitates the exchange of materials between a cell and its environment.

A Panoramic View of the Eukaryotic Cell

In addition to the plasma membrane at its outer surface, a eukaryotic cell has extensive and elaborately arranged internal membranes that divide the cell into compartments—the organelles mentioned earlier. The cell's compartments provide different local environments that facilitate specific metabolic functions, so incompatible processes can go on simultaneously inside a single cell. The plasma membrane and organelle membranes also participate directly in the cell's metabolism, because many enzymes are built right into the membranes.

Because membranes are so fundamental to the organization of the cell, Chapter 7 will discuss them in detail. The basic fabric of most biological membranes is a double layer of phospholipids and other lipids. Embedded in this lipid bilayer or attached to its surfaces are diverse proteins (see Figure 6.6). However, each type of membrane has a unique composition of lipids and proteins suited to that membrane's specific functions. For example, enzymes embedded in the membranes of the organelles called mitochondria function in cellular respiration.

Before continuing with this chapter, examine the eukaryotic cells in **Figure 6.8**, on the next two pages. The generalized diagrams of an animal cell and a plant cell introduce the various organelles and highlight the key differences between animal and plant cells. The micrographs at the bottom of the figure give you a glimpse of cells from different types of eukaryotic organisms.

Exploring Eukaryotic Cells

Animal Cell (cutaway view of generalized cell)

Flagellum: motility structure present in some animal cells, composed of a cluster of microtubules within an extension of the plasma membrane

ENDOPLASMIC RETICULUM (ER): network of membranous sacs and tubes; active in membrane synthesis and other synthetic and metabolic processes; has rough (ribosome-studded) and smooth regions

Rough ER   Smooth ER

Nuclear envelope: double membrane enclosing the nucleus; perforated by pores; continuous with ER

Nucleolus: nonmembranous structure involved in production of ribosomes; a nucleus has one or more nucleoli

Chromatin: material consisting of DNA and proteins; visible in a dividing cell as individual condensed chromosomes

} NUCLEUS

Centrosome: region where the cell's microtubules are initiated; contains a pair of centrioles

Plasma membrane: membrane enclosing the cell

CYTOSKELETON: reinforces cell's shape; functions in cell movement; components are made of protein. Includes:

Microfilaments

Intermediate filaments

Microtubules

Ribosomes (small brown dots): complexes that make proteins; free in cytosol or bound to rough ER or nuclear envelope

Microvilli: projections that increase the cell's surface area

Golgi apparatus: organelle active in synthesis, modification, sorting, and secretion of cell products

Peroxisome: organelle with various specialized metabolic functions; produces hydrogen peroxide as a by-product, then converts it to water

Mitochondrion: organelle where cellular respiration occurs and most ATP is generated

Lysosome: digestive organelle where macromolecules are hydrolyzed

In animal cells but not plant cells:
Lysosomes
Centrosomes, with centrioles
Flagella (but present in some plant sperm)

Animal Cells

Cell

Nucleus

Nucleolus

Human cells from lining of uterus (colorized TEM)

Fungal Cells

Parent cell

Buds

Yeast cells: reproducing by budding (above, colorized SEM) and a single cell (right, colorized TEM)

1 µm

Cell wall

Vacuole

Nucleus

Mitochondrion

Plant Cell (cutaway view of generalized cell)

NUCLEUS
- Nuclear envelope
- Nucleolus
- Chromatin

Rough endoplasmic reticulum

Smooth endoplasmic reticulum

Golgi apparatus

Ribosomes (small brown dots)

Central vacuole: prominent organelle in older plant cells; functions include storage, breakdown of waste products, hydrolysis of macromolecules; enlargement of vacuole is a major mechanism of plant growth

CYTOSKELETON
- Microfilaments
- Intermediate filaments
- Microtubules

Mitochondrion

Peroxisome

Plasma membrane

Cell wall: outer layer that maintains cell's shape and protects cell from mechanical damage; made of cellulose, other polysaccharides, and protein

Wall of adjacent cell

Plasmodesmata: cytoplasmic channels through cell walls that connect the cytoplasms of adjacent cells

Chloroplast: photosynthetic organelle; converts energy of sunlight to chemical energy stored in sugar molecules

In plant cells but not animal cells:
Chloroplasts
Central vacuole
Cell wall
Plasmodesmata

ANIMATION **BioFlix** Visit the Study Area at **www.masteringbiology.com** for the BioFlix® 3-D Animations Tour of an Animal Cell and Tour of a Plant Cell.

Plant Cells

5 μm

- Cell
- Cell wall
- Chloroplast
- Mitochondrion
- Nucleus
- Nucleolus

Cells from duckweed (*Spirodela oligorrhiza*), a floating plant (colorized TEM)

Protistan Cells

8 μm

Unicellular green alga *Chlamydomonas* (above, colorized SEM; right, colorized TEM)

1 μm

- Flagella
- Nucleus
- Nucleolus
- Vacuole
- Chloroplast
- Cell wall

1. After carefully reviewing Figure 6.8, briefly describe the structure and function of the nucleus, the mitochondrion, the chloroplast, and the endoplasmic reticulum.

2. **WHAT IF?** Imagine an elongated cell (such as a nerve cell) that measures $125 \times 1 \times 1$ arbitrary units. Predict how its surface-to-volume ratio would compare with those in Figure 6.7. Then calculate the ratio and check your prediction.

For suggested answers, see Appendix A.

CONCEPT 6.3

The eukaryotic cell's genetic instructions are housed in the nucleus and carried out by the ribosomes

On the first stop of our detailed tour of the cell, let's look at two cellular components involved in the genetic control of the cell: the nucleus, which houses most of the cell's DNA, and the ribosomes, which use information from the DNA to make proteins.

The Nucleus: Information Central

The **nucleus** contains most of the genes in the eukaryotic cell. (Some genes are located in mitochondria and chloroplasts.) It is generally the most conspicuous organelle in a eukaryotic cell, averaging about 5 μm in diameter. The **nuclear envelope** encloses the nucleus **(Figure 6.9)**, separating its contents from the cytoplasm.

The nuclear envelope is a *double* membrane. The two membranes, each a lipid bilayer with associated proteins, are separated by a space of 20–40 nm. The envelope is perforated by pore structures that are about 100 nm in diameter. At the lip of each pore, the inner and outer membranes of the nuclear envelope are continuous. An intricate protein structure called a *pore complex* lines each pore and plays an important role in the cell by regulating the entry and exit of proteins and RNAs, as well as large complexes of macromolecules. Except at the pores, the nuclear side of the envelope is lined by the **nuclear lamina**, a netlike array of protein filaments that maintains the shape of the nucleus by mechanically supporting the nuclear envelope. There is also much evidence for a *nuclear matrix*, a framework of protein fibers extending throughout the nuclear interior. The nuclear lamina and matrix may help organize the genetic material so it functions efficiently.

Within the nucleus, the DNA is organized into discrete units called **chromosomes**, structures that carry the genetic information. Each chromosome contains one long DNA molecule associated with many proteins. Some of the proteins help coil the DNA molecule of each chromosome, reducing its length and allowing it to fit into the nucleus. The complex of DNA and proteins making up chromosomes is called **chromatin**. When a cell is not dividing, stained chromatin appears as a diffuse mass in micrographs, and the chromosomes cannot be distinguished from one another, even though discrete chromosomes are present. As a cell prepares to divide, however, the chromosomes coil (condense) further, becoming thick enough to be distinguished as separate structures. Each eukaryotic species has a characteristic number of chromosomes. For example, a typical human cell has 46 chromosomes in its nucleus; the exceptions are the sex cells (eggs and sperm), which have only 23 chromosomes in humans. A fruit fly cell has 8 chromosomes in most cells and 4 in the sex cells.

A prominent structure within the nondividing nucleus is the **nucleolus** (plural, *nucleoli*), which appears through the electron microscope as a mass of densely stained granules and fibers adjoining part of the chromatin. Here a type of RNA called *ribosomal RNA* (rRNA) is synthesized from instructions in the DNA. Also in the nucleolus, proteins imported from the cytoplasm are assembled with rRNA into large and small subunits of ribosomes. These subunits then exit the nucleus through the nuclear pores to the cytoplasm, where a large and a small subunit can assemble into a ribosome. Sometimes there are two or more nucleoli; the number depends on the species and the stage in the cell's reproductive cycle.

As we saw in Figure 5.25, the nucleus directs protein synthesis by synthesizing messenger RNA (mRNA) according to instructions provided by the DNA. The mRNA is then transported to the cytoplasm via the nuclear pores. Once an mRNA molecule reaches the cytoplasm, ribosomes translate the mRNA's genetic message into the primary structure of a specific polypeptide. This process of transcribing and translating genetic information is described in detail in Chapter 17.

Ribosomes: Protein Factories

Ribosomes, which are complexes made of ribosomal RNA and protein, are the cellular components that carry out protein synthesis **(Figure 6.10)**. Cells that have high rates of protein synthesis have particularly large numbers of ribosomes. For example, a human pancreas cell has a few million ribosomes. Not surprisingly, cells active in protein synthesis also have prominent nucleoli.

Ribosomes build proteins in two cytoplasmic locales. At any given time, *free ribosomes* are suspended in the cytosol, while *bound ribosomes* are attached to the outside of the endoplasmic reticulum or nuclear envelope (see Figure 6.10). Bound and free ribosomes are structurally identical, and ribosomes can alternate between the two roles. Most of the proteins made on free ribosomes function within the cytosol; examples are enzymes that catalyze the first steps of sugar breakdown. Bound ribosomes generally make proteins that are destined for insertion into membranes, for packaging

1 µm

▲ **Surface of nuclear envelope.** TEM of a specimen prepared by a technique known as freeze-fracture.

Nucleus

Nucleolus

Chromatin

Nuclear envelope:
Inner membrane
Outer membrane

Nuclear pore

Nucleus

Rough ER

Pore complex

Ribosome

◄ **Close-up of nuclear envelope**

0.25 µm

▲ **Pore complexes (TEM).** Each pore is ringed by protein particles.

1 µm

▲ **Chromatin.** Part of a chromosome from a non-dividing cell shows two states of coiling of the DNA (blue) and protein (purple) complex. The thicker form is sometimes also organized into long loops.

◄ **Nuclear lamina (TEM).** The netlike lamina lines the inner surface of the nuclear envelope.

▲ **Figure 6.9 The nucleus and its envelope.** Within the nucleus are the chromosomes, which appear as a mass of chromatin (DNA and associated proteins), and one or more nucleoli (singular, *nucleolus*),

which function in ribosome synthesis. The nuclear envelope, which consists of two membranes separated by a narrow space, is perforated with pores and lined by the nuclear lamina.

MAKE CONNECTIONS *Since the chromosomes contain the genetic material and reside in the nucleus, how does the rest of the cell get access to the information they carry? See Figure 5.25, page 86.*

▶ **Figure 6.10 Ribosomes.** This electron micrograph of part of a pancreas cell shows many ribosomes, both free (in the cytosol) and bound (to the endoplasmic reticulum). The simplified diagram of a ribosome shows its two subunits.

DRAW IT *After you have read the section on ribosomes, circle a ribosome in the micrograph that might be making a protein that will be secreted.*

0.25 µm

Ribosomes

ER

Free ribosomes in cytosol

Endoplasmic reticulum (ER)

Ribosomes bound to ER

Large subunit

Small subunit

TEM showing ER and ribosomes

Diagram of a ribosome

within certain organelles such as lysosomes (see Figure 6.8), or for export from the cell (secretion). Cells that specialize in protein secretion—for instance, the cells of the pancreas that secrete digestive enzymes—frequently have a high proportion of bound ribosomes. You will learn more about ribosome structure and function in Chapter 17.

CONCEPT CHECK 6.3

1. What role do ribosomes play in carrying out genetic instructions?
2. Describe the molecular composition of nucleoli and explain their function.
3. **WHAT IF?** As a cell begins the process of dividing, its chromatin becomes more and more condensed. Does the number of chromosomes change during this process? Explain.

For suggested answers, see Appendix A.

CONCEPT 6.4

The endomembrane system regulates protein traffic and performs metabolic functions in the cell

Many of the different membranes of the eukaryotic cell are part of the **endomembrane system**, which includes the nuclear envelope, the endoplasmic reticulum, the Golgi apparatus, lysosomes, various kinds of vesicles and vacuoles, and the plasma membrane. This system carries out a variety of tasks in the cell, including synthesis of proteins, transport of proteins into membranes and organelles or out of the cell, metabolism and movement of lipids, and detoxification of poisons. The membranes of this system are related either through direct physical continuity or by the transfer of membrane segments as tiny **vesicles** (sacs made of membrane). Despite these relationships, the various membranes are not identical in structure and function. Moreover, the thickness, molecular composition, and types of chemical reactions carried out in a given membrane are not fixed, but may be modified several times during the membrane's life. Having already discussed the nuclear envelope, we will now focus on the endoplasmic reticulum and the other endomembranes to which the endoplasmic reticulum gives rise.

The Endoplasmic Reticulum: Biosynthetic Factory

The **endoplasmic reticulum (ER)** is such an extensive network of membranes that it accounts for more than half the total membrane in many eukaryotic cells. (The word *endoplasmic* means "within the cytoplasm," and *reticulum* is

Latin for "little net.") The ER consists of a network of membranous tubules and sacs called cisternae (from the Latin *cisterna*, a reservoir for a liquid). The ER membrane separates the internal compartment of the ER, called the ER lumen (cavity) or cisternal space, from the cytosol. And because the ER membrane is continuous with the nuclear envelope, the space between the two membranes of the envelope is continuous with the lumen of the ER (**Figure 6.11**).

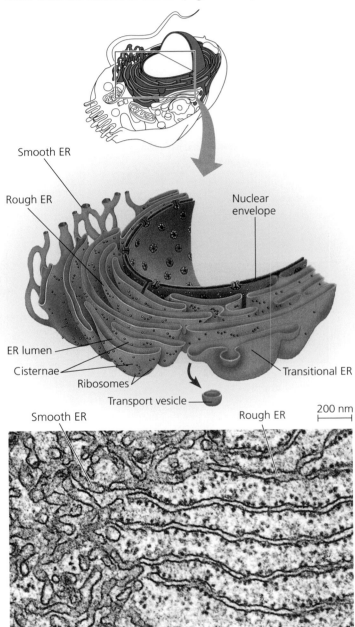

Smooth ER

Rough ER

Nuclear envelope

ER lumen

Cisternae

Ribosomes

Transitional ER

Transport vesicle

Smooth ER

Rough ER

200 nm

▲ **Figure 6.11 Endoplasmic reticulum (ER).** A membranous system of interconnected tubules and flattened sacs called cisternae, the ER is also continuous with the nuclear envelope. (The drawing is a cutaway view.) The membrane of the ER encloses a continuous compartment called the ER lumen (or cisternal space). Rough ER, which is studded on its outer surface with ribosomes, can be distinguished from smooth ER in the electron micrograph (TEM). Transport vesicles bud off from a region of the rough ER called transitional ER and travel to the Golgi apparatus and other destinations.

There are two distinct, though connected, regions of the ER that differ in structure and function: smooth ER and rough ER. **Smooth ER** is so named because its outer surface lacks ribosomes. **Rough ER** is studded with ribosomes on the outer surface of the membrane and thus appears rough through the electron microscope. As already mentioned, ribosomes are also attached to the cytoplasmic side of the nuclear envelope's outer membrane, which is continuous with rough ER.

Functions of Smooth ER

The smooth ER functions in diverse metabolic processes, which vary with cell type. These processes include synthesis of lipids, metabolism of carbohydrates, detoxification of drugs and poisons, and storage of calcium ions.

Enzymes of the smooth ER are important in the synthesis of lipids, including oils, phospholipids, and steroids. Among the steroids produced by the smooth ER in animal cells are the sex hormones of vertebrates and the various steroid hormones secreted by the adrenal glands. The cells that synthesize and secrete these hormones—in the testes and ovaries, for example—are rich in smooth ER, a structural feature that fits the function of these cells.

Other enzymes of the smooth ER help detoxify drugs and poisons, especially in liver cells. Detoxification usually involves adding hydroxyl groups to drug molecules, making them more soluble and easier to flush from the body. The sedative phenobarbital and other barbiturates are examples of drugs metabolized in this manner by smooth ER in liver cells. In fact, barbiturates, alcohol, and many other drugs induce the proliferation of smooth ER and its associated detoxification enzymes, thus increasing the rate of detoxification. This, in turn, increases tolerance to the drugs, meaning that higher doses are required to achieve a particular effect, such as sedation. Also, because some of the detoxification enzymes have relatively broad action, the proliferation of smooth ER in response to one drug can increase tolerance to other drugs as well. Barbiturate abuse, for example, can decrease the effectiveness of certain antibiotics and other useful drugs.

The smooth ER also stores calcium ions. In muscle cells, for example, the smooth ER membrane pumps calcium ions from the cytosol into the ER lumen. When a muscle cell is stimulated by a nerve impulse, calcium ions rush back across the ER membrane into the cytosol and trigger contraction of the muscle cell. In other cell types, calcium ion release from the smooth ER triggers different responses, such as secretion of vesicles carrying newly synthesized proteins.

Functions of Rough ER

Many types of cells secrete proteins produced by ribosomes attached to rough ER. For example, certain pancreatic cells synthesize the protein insulin in the ER and secrete this hormone into the bloodstream. As a polypeptide chain grows from a bound ribosome, the chain is threaded into the ER lumen through a pore formed by a protein complex in the ER membrane. As the new polypeptide enters the ER lumen, it folds into its native shape. Most secretory proteins are **glycoproteins**, proteins that have carbohydrates covalently bonded to them. The carbohydrates are attached to the proteins in the ER by enzymes built into the ER membrane.

After secretory proteins are formed, the ER membrane keeps them separate from proteins that are produced by free ribosomes and that will remain in the cytosol. Secretory proteins depart from the ER wrapped in the membranes of vesicles that bud like bubbles from a specialized region called transitional ER (see Figure 6.11). Vesicles in transit from one part of the cell to another are called **transport vesicles**; we will discuss their fate shortly.

In addition to making secretory proteins, rough ER is a membrane factory for the cell; it grows in place by adding membrane proteins and phospholipids to its own membrane. As polypeptides destined to be membrane proteins grow from the ribosomes, they are inserted into the ER membrane itself and anchored there by their hydrophobic portions. Like the smooth ER, the rough ER also makes membrane phospholipids; enzymes built into the ER membrane assemble phospholipids from precursors in the cytosol. The ER membrane expands and portions of it are transferred in the form of transport vesicles to other components of the endomembrane system.

The Golgi Apparatus: Shipping and Receiving Center

After leaving the ER, many transport vesicles travel to the **Golgi apparatus**. We can think of the Golgi as a warehouse for receiving, sorting, shipping, and even some manufacturing. Here, products of the ER, such as proteins, are modified and stored and then sent to other destinations. Not surprisingly, the Golgi apparatus is especially extensive in cells specialized for secretion.

The Golgi apparatus consists of flattened membranous sacs—cisternae—looking like a stack of pita bread (**Figure 6.12**, on the next page). A cell may have many, even hundreds, of these stacks. The membrane of each cisterna in a stack separates its internal space from the cytosol. Vesicles concentrated in the vicinity of the Golgi apparatus are engaged in the transfer of material between parts of the Golgi and other structures.

A Golgi stack has a distinct structural directionality, with the membranes of cisternae on opposite sides of the stack differing in thickness and molecular composition. The two sides of a Golgi stack are referred to as the *cis* face and the *trans* face; these act, respectively, as the receiving and shipping departments of the Golgi apparatus. The *cis* face is usually located near the ER. Transport vesicles move material from the ER to the Golgi apparatus. A vesicle that buds from the ER can add its membrane and the contents of its lumen to the *cis* face by fusing with a Golgi membrane. The *trans* face gives rise to vesicles that pinch off and travel to other sites.

▼ **Figure 6.12 The Golgi apparatus.** The Golgi apparatus consists of stacks of flattened sacs, or cisternae, which, unlike ER cisternae, are not physically connected. (The drawing is a cutaway view.) A Golgi stack receives and dispatches transport vesicles and the products they contain. A Golgi stack has a structural and functional directionality, with a *cis* face that receives vesicles containing ER products and a *trans* face that dispatches vesicles. The cisternal maturation model proposes that the Golgi cisternae themselves "mature," moving from the *cis* to the *trans* face while carrying some proteins along. In addition, some vesicles recycle enzymes that had been carried forward in moving cisternae, transporting them "backward" to a less mature region where their functions are needed.

Golgi apparatus

cis face ("receiving" side of Golgi apparatus)

6 Vesicles also transport certain proteins back to ER, their site of function.

1 Vesicles move from ER to Golgi.

2 Vesicles coalesce to form new *cis* Golgi cisternae.

Cisternae

3 Cisternal maturation: Golgi cisternae move in a *cis*-to-*trans* direction.

4 Vesicles form and leave Golgi, carrying specific products to other locations or to the plasma membrane for secretion.

5 Vesicles transport some proteins backward to less mature Golgi cisternae, where they function.

trans face ("shipping" side of Golgi apparatus)

0.1 μm

TEM of Golgi apparatus

Products of the endoplasmic reticulum are usually modified during their transit from the *cis* region to the *trans* region of the Golgi apparatus. For example, glycoproteins formed in the ER have their carbohydrates modified, first in the ER itself, then as they pass through the Golgi. The Golgi removes some sugar monomers and substitutes others, producing a large variety of carbohydrates. Membrane phospholipids may also be altered in the Golgi.

In addition to its finishing work, the Golgi apparatus also manufactures some macromolecules. Many polysaccharides secreted by cells are Golgi products. For example, pectins and certain other noncellulose polysaccharides are made in the Golgi of plant cells and then incorporated along with cellulose into their cell walls. Like secretory proteins, nonprotein Golgi products that will be secreted depart from the *trans* face of the Golgi inside transport vesicles that eventually fuse with the plasma membrane.

The Golgi manufactures and refines its products in stages, with different cisternae containing unique teams of enzymes. Until recently, biologists viewed the Golgi as a static structure, with products in various stages of processing transferred from one cisterna to the next by vesicles. While this may occur, recent research has given rise to a new model of the Golgi as a more dynamic structure. According to the *cisternal maturation model*, the cisternae of the Golgi actually progress forward from the *cis* to the *trans* face, carrying and modifying their cargo as they move. Figure 6.12 shows the details of this model.

Before a Golgi stack dispatches its products by budding vesicles from the *trans* face, it sorts these products and targets them for various parts of the cell. Molecular identification tags, such as phosphate groups added to the Golgi products, aid in sorting by acting like ZIP codes on mailing labels. Finally, transport vesicles budded from the Golgi may have external molecules on their membranes that recognize "docking sites" on the surface of specific organelles or on the plasma membrane, thus targeting the vesicles appropriately.

Lysosomes: Digestive Compartments

A **lysosome** is a membranous sac of hydrolytic enzymes that an animal cell uses to digest (hydrolyze) macromolecules. Lysosomal enzymes work best in the acidic environment found in lysosomes. If a lysosome breaks open or leaks its contents, the released enzymes are not very active because the cytosol has a neutral pH. However, excessive leakage from a large number of lysosomes can destroy a cell by self-digestion.

Hydrolytic enzymes and lysosomal membrane are made by rough ER and then transferred to the Golgi apparatus for further processing. At least some lysosomes probably arise by budding from the *trans* face of the Golgi apparatus (see Figure 6.12). How are the proteins of the inner surface of the lysosomal membrane and the digestive enzymes themselves spared from destruction? Apparently, the three-dimensional shapes of these proteins protect vulnerable bonds from enzymatic attack.

Lysosomes carry out intracellular digestion in a variety of circumstances. Amoebas and many other protists eat by engulfing smaller organisms or food particles, a process called **phagocytosis** (from the Greek *phagein*, to eat, and *kytos*, vessel, referring here to the cell). The *food vacuole* formed in this way then fuses with a lysosome, whose enzymes digest the food (**Figure 6.13a**, bottom). Digestion products, including simple sugars, amino acids, and other monomers, pass into the cytosol and become nutrients for the cell. Some human cells also carry out phagocytosis. Among them are macrophages, a type of white blood cell that helps defend the body by engulfing and destroying bacteria and other invaders (see Figure 6.13a, top, and Figure 6.33).

Lysosomes also use their hydrolytic enzymes to recycle the cell's own organic material, a process called *autophagy*. During autophagy, a damaged organelle or small amount of cytosol becomes surrounded by a double membrane (of unknown origin), and a lysosome fuses with the outer membrane of this vesicle (**Figure 6.13b**). The lysosomal enzymes dismantle the enclosed material, and the organic monomers are returned to the cytosol for reuse. With the help of lysosomes, the cell continually renews itself. A human liver cell, for example, recycles half of its macromolecules each week.

The cells of people with inherited lysosomal storage diseases lack a functioning hydrolytic enzyme normally present in lysosomes. The lysosomes become engorged with indigestible substrates, which begin to interfere with other cellular activities. In Tay-Sachs disease, for example, a lipid-digesting enzyme is missing or inactive, and the brain becomes impaired by an accumulation of lipids in the cells. Fortunately, lysosomal storage diseases are rare in the general population.

Vacuoles: Diverse Maintenance Compartments

Vacuoles are large vesicles derived from the endoplasmic reticulum and Golgi apparatus. Thus, vacuoles are an integral part of a cell's endomembrane system. Like all cellular membranes, the vacuolar membrane is selective in transporting solutes; as a result, the solution inside a vacuole differs in composition from the cytosol.

(a) Phagocytosis: lysosome digesting food

(b) Autophagy: lysosome breaking down damaged organelles

▲ **Figure 6.13 Lysosomes.** Lysosomes digest (hydrolyze) materials taken into the cell and recycle intracellular materials. **(a)** *Top*: In this macrophage (a type of white blood cell) from a rat, the lysosomes are very dark because of a stain that reacts with one of the products of digestion within the lysosome (TEM).

Macrophages ingest bacteria and viruses and destroy them using lysosomes. *Bottom*: This diagram shows one lysosome fusing with a food vacuole during the process of phagocytosis by a protist. **(b)** *Top*: In the cytoplasm of this rat liver cell is a vesicle containing two disabled organelles; the vesicle will fuse with a lysosome in the process of autophagy (TEM). *Bottom*: This diagram shows fusion of such a vesicle with a lysosome. This type of vesicle has a double membrane of unknown origin. The outer membrane fuses with the lysosome, and the inner membrane is degraded along with the damaged organelles.

Vacuoles perform a variety of functions in different kinds of cells. **Food vacuoles**, formed by phagocytosis, have already been mentioned (see Figure 6.13a). Many freshwater protists have **contractile vacuoles** that pump excess water out of the cell, thereby maintaining a suitable concentration of ions and molecules inside the cell (see Figure 7.16). In plants and fungi, certain vacuoles carry out enzymatic hydrolysis, a function shared by lysosomes in animal cells. (In fact, some biologists consider these hydrolytic vacuoles to be a type of lysosome.) In plants, smaller vacuoles can hold reserves of important organic compounds, such as the proteins stockpiled in the storage cells in seeds. Vacuoles may also help protect the plant against herbivores by storing compounds that are poisonous or unpalatable to animals. Some plant vacuoles contain pigments, such as the red and blue pigments of petals that help attract pollinating insects to flowers.

Mature plant cells generally contain a large **central vacuole** (**Figure 6.14**), which develops by the coalescence of smaller vacuoles. The solution inside the central vacuole, called cell sap, is the plant cell's main repository of inorganic ions, including potassium and chloride. The central vacuole plays a major role in the growth of plant cells, which enlarge as the vacuole absorbs water, enabling the cell to become larger with a minimal investment in new cytoplasm. The cytosol often occupies only a thin layer between the central vacuole and the plasma membrane, so the ratio of plasma membrane surface to cytosolic volume is sufficient, even for a large plant cell.

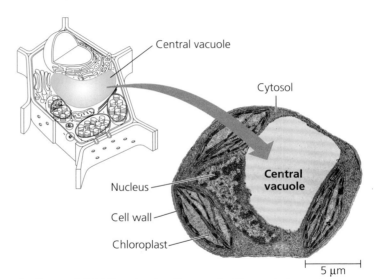

▲ **Figure 6.14 The plant cell vacuole.** The central vacuole is usually the largest compartment in a plant cell; the rest of the cytoplasm is often confined to a narrow zone between the vacuolar membrane and the plasma membrane (TEM).

The Endomembrane System: *A Review*

Figure 6.15 reviews the endomembrane system, showing the flow of membrane lipids and proteins through the various organelles. As the membrane moves from the ER to the Golgi and then elsewhere, its molecular composition and metabolic functions are modified, along with those of its contents. The

❶ Nuclear envelope is connected to rough ER, which is also continuous with smooth ER.

❷ Membranes and proteins produced by the ER flow in the form of transport vesicles to the Golgi.

❸ Golgi pinches off transport vesicles and other vesicles that give rise to lysosomes, other types of specialized vesicles, and vacuoles.

❹ Lysosome is available for fusion with another vesicle for digestion.

❺ Transport vesicle carries proteins to plasma membrane for secretion.

❻ Plasma membrane expands by fusion of vesicles; proteins are secreted from cell.

▲ **Figure 6.15 Review: relationships among organelles of the endomembrane system.** The red arrows show some of the migration pathways for membranes and the materials they enclose.

endomembrane system is a complex and dynamic player in the cell's compartmental organization.

We'll continue our tour of the cell with some organelles that are not closely related to the endomembrane system but play crucial roles in the energy transformations carried out by cells.

CONCEPT CHECK 6.4

1. Describe the structural and functional distinctions between rough and smooth ER.
2. Describe how transport vesicles integrate the endomembrane system.
3. **WHAT IF?** Imagine a protein that functions in the ER but requires modification in the Golgi apparatus before it can achieve that function. Describe the protein's path through the cell, starting with the mRNA molecule that specifies the protein.

For suggested answers, see Appendix A.

CONCEPT 6.5

Mitochondria and chloroplasts change energy from one form to another

Organisms transform the energy they acquire from their surroundings. In eukaryotic cells, mitochondria and chloroplasts are the organelles that convert energy to forms that cells can use for work. **Mitochondria** (singular, *mitochondrion*) are the sites of cellular respiration, the metabolic process that uses oxygen to generate ATP by extracting energy from sugars, fats, and other fuels. **Chloroplasts**, found in plants and algae, are the sites of photosynthesis. These organelles convert solar energy to chemical energy by absorbing sunlight and using it to drive the synthesis of organic compounds such as sugars from carbon dioxide and water.

In addition to having related functions, mitochondria and chloroplasts share a similar evolutionary origin, something we'll discuss briefly before describing their structure. In this section, we will also consider the peroxisome, an oxidative organelle. The evolutionary origin of the peroxisome, as well as its relation to other organelles, is still under debate.

The Evolutionary Origins of Mitochondria and Chloroplasts

EVOLUTION Mitochondria and chloroplasts display similarities with bacteria that led to the **endosymbiont theory**, illustrated in **Figure 6.16**. This theory states that an early ancestor of eukaryotic cells engulfed an oxygen-using nonphotosynthetic prokaryotic cell. Eventually, the engulfed cell formed a relationship with the host cell in which it was enclosed, becoming an *endosymbiont* (a cell living within an-

▲ **Figure 6.16 The endosymbiont theory of the origin of mitochondria and chloroplasts in eukaryotic cells.** According to this theory, the proposed ancestors of mitochondria were oxygen-using nonphotosynthetic prokaryotes, while the proposed ancestors of chloroplasts were photosynthetic prokaryotes. The large arrows represent change over evolutionary time; the small arrows inside the cells show the process of the endosymbiont becoming an organelle.

other cell). Indeed, over the course of evolution, the host cell and its endosymbiont merged into a single organism, a eukaryotic cell with a mitochondrion. At least one of these cells may have then taken up a photosynthetic prokaryote, becoming the ancestor of eukaryotic cells that contain chloroplasts.

This is a widely accepted theory, which we will discuss in more detail in Chapter 25. The model it proposes is consistent with many structural features of mitochondria and chloroplasts. First, rather than being bounded by a single membrane like organelles of the endomembrane system, mitochondria and typical chloroplasts have two membranes surrounding them. (Chloroplasts also have an internal system of membranous sacs.) There is evidence that the ancestral engulfed prokaryotes had two outer membranes, which became the double membranes of mitochondria and chloroplasts. Second, like prokaryotes, mitochondria and chloroplasts contain ribosomes, as well as circular DNA molecules attached to their inner membranes. The DNA in these organelles programs the synthesis of some of their own proteins, which are made on the ribosomes inside the organelles. Third, also consistent with their probable evolutionary origins as cells, mitochondria and chloroplasts are autonomous (somewhat independent) organelles that grow and reproduce within the cell.

In Chapters 9 and 10, we will focus on how mitochondria and chloroplasts function as energy transformers. Here we are concerned mainly with their structures and their roles.

Mitochondria: Chemical Energy Conversion

Mitochondria are found in nearly all eukaryotic cells, including those of plants, animals, fungi, and most protists. Some cells have a single large mitochondrion, but more often a cell has hundreds or even thousands of mitochondria; the number correlates with the cell's level of metabolic activity. For example, cells that move or contract have proportionally more mitochondria per volume than less active cells.

The mitochondrion is enclosed by two membranes, each a phospholipid bilayer with a unique collection of embedded proteins **(Figure 6.17)**. The outer membrane is smooth, but the inner membrane is convoluted, with infoldings called **cristae**. The inner membrane divides the mitochondrion into two internal compartments. The first is the intermembrane space, the narrow region between the inner and outer membranes. The second compartment, the **mitochondrial matrix**, is enclosed by the inner membrane. The matrix contains many different enzymes as well as the mitochondrial DNA and ribosomes. Enzymes in the matrix catalyze some of the steps of cellular respiration. Other proteins that function in respiration, including the enzyme that makes ATP, are built into the inner membrane. As highly folded surfaces, the cristae give the inner mitochondrial membrane a large surface area, thus enhancing the productivity of cellular respiration. This is another example of structure fitting function.

Mitochondria are generally in the range of 1–10 μm long. Time-lapse films of living cells reveal mitochondria moving around, changing their shapes, and fusing or dividing in two, unlike the static structures seen in electron micrographs of dead cells. These observations helped cell biologists understand that mitochondria in a living cell form a branched tubular network, seen in a whole cell in Figure 6.17.

Chloroplasts: Capture of Light Energy

Chloroplasts contain the green pigment chlorophyll, along with enzymes and other molecules that function in the photosynthetic production of sugar. These lens-shaped organelles, about 3–6 μm in length, are found in leaves and other green organs of plants and in algae **(Figure 6.18** and Figure 6.27c).

The contents of a chloroplast are partitioned from the cytosol by an envelope consisting of two membranes separated by a very narrow intermembrane space. Inside the chloroplast is another membranous system in the form of flattened, interconnected sacs called **thylakoids**. In some regions, thylakoids are stacked like poker chips; each stack is called a **granum** (plural, *grana*). The fluid outside the thylakoids is the **stroma**, which contains the chloroplast DNA and ribosomes as well as many enzymes. The membranes of the chloroplast divide the chloroplast space into three compartments: the intermembrane space, the stroma, and the thylakoid space. In Chapter 10, you will learn how this compartmental organization enables the chloroplast to convert light energy to chemical energy during photosynthesis.

As with mitochondria, the static and rigid appearance of chloroplasts in micrographs or schematic diagrams is not true

Mitochondrion

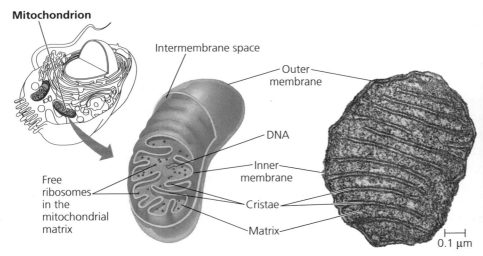

(a) Diagram and TEM of mitochondrion

(b) Network of mitochondria in a protist cell (LM)

▲ **Figure 6.17 The mitochondrion, site of cellular respiration. (a)** The inner and outer membranes of the mitochondrion are evident in the drawing and electron micrograph (TEM). The cristae are infoldings of the inner membrane, which increase its surface area. The cutaway drawing shows the two compartments bounded by the membranes: the intermembrane space and the mitochondrial matrix. Many respiratory enzymes are found in the inner membrane and the matrix. Free ribosomes are also present in the matrix. The DNA molecules are usually circular and are attached to the inner mitochondrial membrane. **(b)** The light micrograph shows an entire unicellular protist (*Euglena gracilis*) at a much lower magnification than the TEM. The mitochondrial matrix has been stained green. The mitochondria form a branched tubular network. The nuclear DNA is stained red, and the molecules of mitochondrial DNA appear as bright yellow spots.

▼ **Figure 6.18 The chloroplast, site of photosynthesis. (a)** Many plants have disk-shaped choloroplasts, as shown here. A typical chloroplast has three compartments: the intermembrane space, the stroma, and the thylakoid space. Free ribosomes are present in the stroma, as are copies of chloroplast DNA molecules. **(b)** This fluorescence micrograph shows a cell of the green alga *Spirogyra crassa*, which is named for its spiral chloroplasts. Under natural light the chloroplasts appear green, but under ultraviolet light they naturally fluoresce red, as shown here.

(a) Diagram and TEM of chloroplast

(b) Chloroplasts in an algal cell

to their dynamic behavior in the living cell. Their shape is changeable, and they grow and occasionally pinch in two, reproducing themselves. They are mobile and, with mitochondria and other organelles, move around the cell along tracks of the cytoskeleton, a structural network we will consider later in this chapter.

The chloroplast is a specialized member of a family of closely related plant organelles called **plastids**. One type of plastid, the *amyloplast*, is a colorless organelle that stores starch (amylose), particularly in roots and tubers. Another is the *chromoplast*, which has pigments that give fruits and flowers their orange and yellow hues.

Peroxisomes: Oxidation

The **peroxisome** is a specialized metabolic compartment bounded by a single membrane **(Figure 6.19)**. Peroxisomes contain enzymes that remove hydrogen atoms from various substrates and transfer them to oxygen (O_2), thus producing hydrogen peroxide (H_2O_2) as a by-product (from which the organelle derives its name). These reactions have many different functions. Some peroxisomes use oxygen to break fatty acids down into smaller molecules that are transported to mitochondria and used as fuel for cellular respiration. Peroxisomes in the liver detoxify alcohol and other harmful compounds by transferring hydrogen from the poisons to oxygen. The H_2O_2 formed by peroxisomes is itself toxic, but the organelle also contains an enzyme that converts H_2O_2 to water. This is an excellent example of how the cell's compartmental structure is crucial to its functions: The enzymes that produce hydrogen peroxide and those that dispose of this toxic compound are sequestered away from other cellular components that could be damaged.

Specialized peroxisomes called *glyoxysomes* are found in the fat-storing tissues of plant seeds. These organelles contain

enzymes that initiate the conversion of fatty acids to sugar, which the emerging seedling uses as a source of energy and carbon until it can produce its own sugar by photosynthesis.

How peroxisomes are related to other organelles is still an open question. They grow larger by incorporating proteins made in the cytosol and ER, as well as lipids made in the ER and within the peroxisome itself. Peroxisomes may increase in number by splitting in two when they reach a certain size, sparking the suggestion of an endosymbiotic evolutionary origin, but others argue against this scenario. The debate continues.

▲ **Figure 6.19 A peroxisome.** Peroxisomes are roughly spherical and often have a granular or crystalline core that is thought to be a dense collection of enzyme molecules. This peroxisome is in a leaf cell (TEM). Notice its proximity to two chloroplasts and a mitochondrion. These organelles cooperate with peroxisomes in certain metabolic functions.

1. Describe two common characteristics of chloroplasts and mitochondria. Consider both function and membrane structure.
2. Do plant cells have mitochondria? Explain.
3. **WHAT IF?** A classmate proposes that mitochondria and chloroplasts should be classified in the endomembrane system. Argue against the proposal.

For suggested answers, see Appendix A.

CONCEPT 6.6

The cytoskeleton is a network of fibers that organizes structures and activities in the cell

In the early days of electron microscopy, biologists thought that the organelles of a eukaryotic cell floated freely in the cytosol. But improvements in both light microscopy and electron microscopy have revealed the **cytoskeleton**, a network of fibers extending throughout the cytoplasm (**Figure 6.20**). The cytoskeleton, which plays a major role in organizing the structures and activities of the cell, is composed of three types of molecular structures: microtubules, microfilaments, and intermediate filaments.

Roles of the Cytoskeleton: Support and Motility

The most obvious function of the cytoskeleton is to give mechanical support to the cell and maintain its shape. This is especially important for animal cells, which lack walls. The remarkable strength and resilience of the cytoskeleton as a whole is based on its architecture. Like a dome tent, the cytoskeleton is stabilized by a balance between opposing forces exerted by its elements. And just as the skeleton of an animal helps fix the positions of other body parts, the cytoskeleton provides anchorage for many organelles and even cytosolic enzyme molecules. The cytoskeleton is more dynamic than an animal skeleton, however. It can be quickly dismantled in one part of the cell and reassembled in a new location, changing the shape of the cell.

Several types of cell motility (movement) also involve the cytoskeleton. The term *cell motility* encompasses both changes in cell location and more limited movements of parts of the cell. Cell motility generally requires the interaction of the cytoskeleton with **motor proteins**. Examples of such cell motility abound. Cytoskeletal elements and motor proteins work together with plasma membrane molecules to allow whole cells to move along fibers outside the cell. Motor proteins bring about the bending of cilia and flagella by gripping microtubules within those organelles and sliding them against each other. A similar mechanism involving microfilaments causes muscle cells to contract. Inside the cell, vesicles and other organelles often use motor protein "feet" to "walk" to their destinations along a track provided by the cytoskeleton. For example, this is how vesicles containing neurotransmitter molecules migrate to the tips of axons, the long extensions of nerve cells that release these molecules as chemical signals to adjacent nerve cells (**Figure 6.21**). The vesicles that bud off

▲ **Figure 6.20 The cytoskeleton.** As shown in this fluorescence micrograph, the cytoskeleton extends throughout the cell. The cytoskeletal elements have been tagged with different fluorescent molecules: green for microtubules and red for microfilaments. A third component of the cytoskeleton, intermediate filaments, is not evident here. (The DNA in the nucleus is blue.)

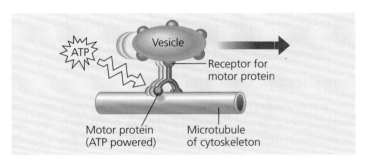

(a) Motor proteins that attach to receptors on vesicles can "walk" the vesicles along microtubules or, in some cases, microfilaments.

(b) In this SEM of a squid giant axon (a nerve cell extension), two vesicles containing neurotransmitters migrate toward the tip of the axon via the mechanism shown in (a).

▲ **Figure 6.21 Motor proteins and the cytoskeleton.**

Table 6.1 The Structure and Function of the Cytoskeleton

Property	Microtubules (Tubulin Polymers)	Microfilaments (Actin Filaments)	Intermediate Filaments
Structure	Hollow tubes; wall consists of 13 columns of tubulin molecules	Two intertwined strands of actin, each a polymer of actin subunits	Fibrous proteins supercoiled into thicker cables
Diameter	25 nm with 15-nm lumen	7 nm	8–12 nm
Protein subunits	Tubulin, a dimer consisting of α-tubulin and β-tubulin	Actin	One of several different proteins (such as keratins), depending on cell type
Main functions	Maintenance of cell shape (compression-resisting "girders")	Maintenance of cell shape (tension-bearing elements)	Maintenance of cell shape (tension-bearing elements)
	Cell motility (as in cilia or flagella)	Changes in cell shape	Anchorage of nucleus and certain other organelles
	Chromosome movements in cell division	Muscle contraction	Formation of nuclear lamina
	Organelle movements	Cytoplasmic streaming	
		Cell motility (as in pseudopodia)	
		Cell division (cleavage furrow formation)	

Fluorescence micrographs of fibroblasts, a favorite cell type for cell biology studies. In each, the structure of interest has been tagged with fluorescent molecules. In the first and third micrographs, the DNA in the nucleus has also been tagged (blue or orange).

from the ER travel to the Golgi along cytoskeletal tracks. The cytoskeleton also manipulates the plasma membrane, making it bend inward to form food vacuoles or other phagocytic vesicles. And the streaming of cytoplasm that circulates materials within many large plant cells is yet another kind of cellular movement brought about by the cytoskeleton.

Components of the Cytoskeleton

Now let's look more closely at the three main types of fibers that make up the cytoskeleton: *Microtubules* are the thickest of the three types; *microfilaments* (also called actin filaments)

are the thinnest; and *intermediate filaments* are fibers with diameters in a middle range (Table 6.1).

Microtubules

All eukaryotic cells have **microtubules**, hollow rods measuring about 25 nm in diameter and from 200 nm to 25 μm in length. The wall of the hollow tube is constructed from a globular protein called tubulin. Each tubulin protein is a *dimer*, a molecule made up of two subunits. A tubulin dimer consists of two slightly different polypeptides, α-tubulin and β-tubulin. Microtubules grow in length by adding tubulin dimers; they can also be disassembled and their tubulin used to build microtubules elsewhere in the cell. Because of the orientation of tubulin dimers, the two ends of a microtubule are slightly different. One end can accumulate or release tubulin dimers at a much higher rate than the other, thus growing and shrinking significantly during cellular activities. (This is called the "plus end," not because it can only add tubulin proteins but because it's the end where both "on" and "off" rates are much higher.)

Microtubules shape and support the cell and also serve as tracks along which organelles equipped with motor proteins can move. In addition to the example in Figure 6.21, microtubules guide secretory vesicles from the Golgi apparatus to the plasma membrane. Microtubules are also involved in the separation of chromosomes during cell division, which will be discussed in Chapter 12.

Centrosomes and Centrioles In animal cells, microtubules grow out from a **centrosome**, a region that is often located near the nucleus and is considered a "microtubule-organizing center." These microtubules function as compression-resisting girders of the cytoskeleton. Within the centrosome is a pair of **centrioles**, each composed of nine sets of triplet microtubules arranged in a ring **(Figure 6.22)**. Before an animal cell divides, the centrioles replicate. Although centrosomes with centrioles may help organize microtubule assembly in animal cells, they are not essential for this function in all eukaryotes; fungi and almost all plant cells lack centrosomes with centrioles but have well-organized microtubules. Apparently, other microtubule-organizing centers play the role of centrosomes in these cells.

Cilia and Flagella In eukaryotes, a specialized arrangement of microtubules is responsible for the beating of **flagella** (singular, *flagellum*) and **cilia** (singular, *cilium*), microtubule-containing extensions that project from some cells. (The bacterial flagellum, shown in Figure 6.5, has a completely different structure.) Many unicellular eukaryotes are propelled through water by cilia or flagella that act as locomotor appendages, and the sperm of animals, algae, and some plants have flagella. When cilia or flagella extend from cells that are held in place as part of a tissue layer, they can move fluid over the surface of the tissue. For example, the ciliated lining of the trachea (windpipe) sweeps mucus containing trapped debris out of the lungs (see the EMs in Figure 6.3). In a woman's reproductive tract, the cilia lining the oviducts help move an egg toward the uterus.

Motile cilia usually occur in large numbers on the cell surface. They are about 0.25 μm in diameter and about 2–20 μm long. Flagella are the same diameter but longer, 10–200 μm. Also, flagella are usually limited to just one or a few per cell.

Flagella and cilia differ in their beating patterns **(Figure 6.23)**. A flagellum has an undulating motion that generates force in the same direction as the flagellum's axis, like the tail of a fish. In contrast, cilia work more like oars, with alternating power and

Centrosome

Microtubule

Centrioles

0.25 μm

Longitudinal section of one centriole   Microtubules   Cross section of the other centriole

▲ **Figure 6.22 Centrosome containing a pair of centrioles.** Most animal cells have a centrosome, a region near the nucleus where the cell's microtubules are initiated. Within the centrosome is a pair of centrioles, each about 250 nm (0.25 μm) in diameter. The two centrioles are at right angles to each other, and each is made up of nine sets of three microtubules. The blue portions of the drawing represent nontubulin proteins that connect the microtubule triplets (TEM).

? *How many microtubules are in a centrosome? In the drawing, circle and label one microtubule and describe its structure. Circle and label a triplet.*

recovery strokes generating force in a direction perpendicular to the cilium's axis, much as the oars of a racing crew boat extend outward at a right angle to the boat's forward movement.

A cilium may also act as a signal-receiving "antenna" for the cell. Cilia that have this function are generally nonmotile, and there is only one per cell. (In fact, in vertebrate animals, it appears that almost all cells have such a cilium, which is called a *primary cilium*.) Membrane proteins on this kind of cilium transmit molecular signals from the cell's environment to its interior, triggering signaling pathways that may lead to changes in the cell's activities. Cilium-based signaling appears to be crucial to brain function and to embryonic development.

Though different in length, number per cell, and beating pattern, motile cilia and flagella share a common structure. Each motile cilium and flagellum has a group of microtubules sheathed in an extension of the plasma membrane **(Figure 6.24)**. Nine doublets of microtubules are arranged in a ring; in the center of the ring are two single microtubules.

▶ **Figure 6.23**
A comparison of the beating of flagella and motile cilia.

(a) Motion of flagella. A flagellum usually undulates, its snakelike motion driving a cell in the same direction as the axis of the flagellum. Propulsion of a human sperm cell is an example of flagellate locomotion (LM).

Direction of swimming

5 μm

(b) Motion of cilia. Cilia have a back-and-forth motion. The rapid power stroke moves the cell in a direction perpendicular to the axis of the cilium. Then, during the slower recovery stroke, the cilium bends and sweeps sideways, closer to the cell surface. A dense nap of cilia, beating at a rate of about 40 to 60 strokes a second, covers this *Colpidium*, a freshwater protist (colorized SEM).

Direction of organism's movement

Power stroke   Recovery stroke

15 μm

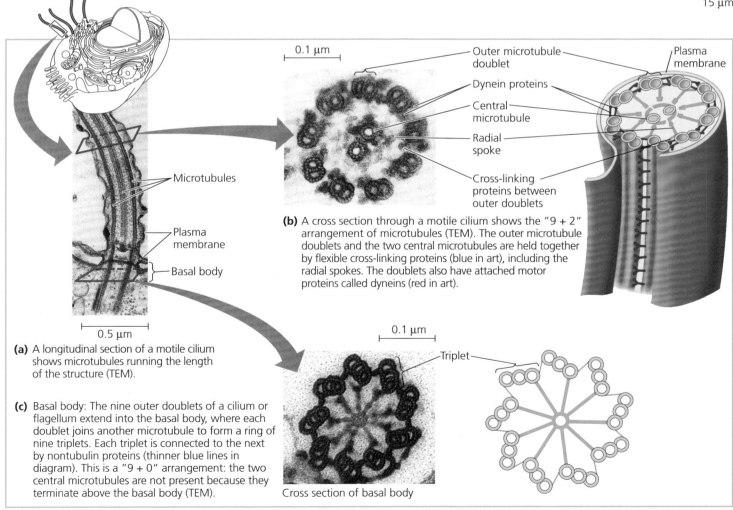

Microtubules

Plasma membrane

Basal body

0.5 μm

(a) A longitudinal section of a motile cilium shows microtubules running the length of the structure (TEM).

(c) Basal body: The nine outer doublets of a cilium or flagellum extend into the basal body, where each doublet joins another microtubule to form a ring of nine triplets. Each triplet is connected to the next by nontubulin proteins (thinner blue lines in diagram). This is a "9 + 0" arrangement: the two central microtubules are not present because they terminate above the basal body (TEM).

0.1 μm

Outer microtubule doublet

Dynein proteins

Central microtubule

Radial spoke

Cross-linking proteins between outer doublets

Plasma membrane

(b) A cross section through a motile cilium shows the "9 + 2" arrangement of microtubules (TEM). The outer microtubule doublets and the two central microtubules are held together by flexible cross-linking proteins (blue in art), including the radial spokes. The doublets also have attached motor proteins called dyneins (red in art).

0.1 μm

Triplet

Cross section of basal body

▲ **Figure 6.24 Structure of a flagellum or motile cilium.**

DRAW IT *In (a), circle the central pair of microtubules. Show where they terminate, and explain why they aren't seen in the cross section of the basal body in (c).*

This arrangement, referred to as the "9 + 2" pattern, is found in nearly all eukaryotic flagella and motile cilia. (Nonmotile primary cilia have a "9 + 0" pattern, lacking the central pair of microtubules.) The microtubule assembly of a cilium or flagellum is anchored in the cell by a **basal body**, which is structurally very similar to a centriole, with microtubule triplets in a "9 + 0" pattern. In fact, in many animals (including humans), the basal body of the fertilizing sperm's flagellum enters the egg and becomes a centriole.

In flagella and motile cilia, flexible cross-linking proteins, evenly spaced along the length of the cilium or flagellum, connect the outer doublets to each other and to the two central microtubules. Each outer doublet also has pairs of protruding proteins spaced along its length and reaching toward the neighboring doublet; these are large motor proteins called **dyneins**, each composed of several polypeptides. Dyneins are responsible for the bending movements of the organelle. A dynein molecule performs a complex cycle of movements caused by changes in the shape of the protein, with ATP providing the energy for these changes (Figure 6.25).

The mechanics of dynein-based bending involve a process that resembles walking. A typical dynein protein has two "feet" that "walk" along the microtubule of the adjacent doublet, one foot maintaining contact while the other releases and reattaches one step farther along the microtubule. Without any restraints on the movement of the microtubule doublets, one doublet would continue to "walk" along and slide past the surface of the other, elongating the cilium or flagellum rather than bending it (see Figure 6.25a). For lateral movement of a cilium or flagellum, the dynein "walking" must have something to pull against, as when the muscles in your leg pull against your bones to move your knee. In cilia and flagella, the microtubule doublets seem to be held in place by the cross-linking proteins just inside the outer doublets and by the radial spokes and other structural elements. Thus, neighboring doublets cannot slide past each other very far. Instead, the forces exerted by dynein "walking" cause the doublets to curve, bending the cilium or flagellum (see Figure 6.25b and c).

Microfilaments (Actin Filaments)

Microfilaments are solid rods about 7 nm in diameter. They are also called actin filaments because they are built from molecules of **actin**, a globular protein. A microfilament is a twisted double chain of actin subunits (see Table 6.1). Besides occurring as linear filaments, microfilaments can form structural networks when certain proteins bind along the side of an actin filament and allow a new filament to extend as a branch. Like microtubules, microfilaments seem to be present in all eukaryotic cells.

In contrast to the compression-resisting role of microtubules, the structural role of microfilaments in the cytoskeleton is to bear tension (pulling forces). A three-dimensional network formed by microfilaments just inside the plasma

(a) Effect of unrestrained dynein movement. If a cilium or flagellum had no cross-linking proteins, the two feet of each dynein along one doublet (powered by ATP) would alternately grip and release the adjacent doublet. This "walking" motion would push the adjacent doublet up. Instead of bending, the doublets would slide past each other.

(b) Effect of cross-linking proteins. In a cilium or flagellum, two adjacent doublets cannot slide far because they are physically restrained by proteins, so they bend. (Only two of the nine outer doublets in Figure 6.24b are shown here.)

(c) Wavelike motion. Synchronized cycles of movement of many dyneins probably cause a bend to begin at the base of the cilium or flagellum and move outward toward the tip. Many successive bends, such as the ones shown here to the left and right, result in a wavelike motion. In this diagram, the two central microtubules and the cross-linking proteins are not shown.

▲ **Figure 6.25 How dynein "walking" moves flagella and cilia.**

Microvillus

Plasma membrane

Microfilaments (actin filaments)

Intermediate filaments

0.25 μm

▲ **Figure 6.26 A structural role of microfilaments.** The surface area of this nutrient-absorbing intestinal cell is increased by its many microvilli (singular, *microvillus*), cellular extensions reinforced by bundles of microfilaments. These actin filaments are anchored to a network of intermediate filaments (TEM).

Muscle cell

0.5 μm

Actin filament

Myosin filament

Myosin head

(a) Myosin motors in muscle cell contraction. The "walking" of myosin projections (the so-called heads) drives the parallel myosin and actin filaments past each other so that the actin filaments approach each other in the middle (red arrows). This shortens the muscle cell. Muscle contraction involves the shortening of many muscle cells at the same time (TEM).

Cortex (outer cytoplasm): gel with actin network

100 μm

Inner cytoplasm: sol with actin subunits

Extending pseudopodium

(b) Amoeboid movement. Interaction of actin filaments with myosin causes contraction of the cell, pulling the cell's trailing end (at left) forward (to the right) (LM).

Chloroplast

30 μm

(c) Cytoplasmic streaming in plant cells. A layer of cytoplasm cycles around the cell, moving over a carpet of parallel actin filaments. Myosin motors attached to organelles in the fluid cytosol may drive the streaming by interacting with the actin (LM).

▲ **Figure 6.27 Microfilaments and motility.** In these three examples, interactions between actin filaments and motor proteins bring about cell movement.

membrane (*cortical microfilaments*) helps support the cell's shape (see Figure 6.8). This network gives the outer cytoplasmic layer of a cell, called the **cortex**, the semisolid consistency of a gel, in contrast with the more fluid (*sol*) state of the interior cytoplasm. In animal cells specialized for transporting materials across the plasma membrane, such as intestinal cells, bundles of microfilaments make up the core of microvilli, delicate projections that increase the cell's surface area **(Figure 6.26)**.

Microfilaments are well known for their role in cell motility, particularly as part of the contractile apparatus of muscle cells. Thousands of actin filaments are arranged parallel to one another along the length of a muscle cell, interdigitated with thicker filaments made of a protein called **myosin** **(Figure 6.27a)**. Like dynein when it interacts with microtubules, myosin acts as a motor protein by means of projections that "walk" along the actin filaments. Contraction of the muscle cell results from the actin and myosin filaments sliding past one another in this way, shortening the cell. In other kinds of cells, actin filaments are associated with myosin in miniature and less elaborate versions of the arrangement in muscle cells. These actin-myosin aggregates are responsible for

localized contractions of cells. For example, a contracting belt of microfilaments forms a cleavage furrow that pinches a dividing animal cell into two daughter cells.

Localized contraction brought about by actin and myosin also plays a role in amoeboid movement **(Figure 6.27b)**. A cell such as an amoeba crawls along a surface by extending cellular extensions called **pseudopodia** (from the Greek *pseudes*, false, and *pod*, foot), and moving toward them. Pseudopodia extend by assembly of actin subunits into microfilament networks that convert cytoplasm from a sol to a gel inside these cell projections. Cell surface proteins on the pseudopodium make strong attachments to the "road." Next, the interaction of microfilaments with myosin near the cell's trailing end causes contraction of that region, loosening its cell-surface attachments and pulling it forward toward the pseudopodia. Amoebae lacking myosin can still form pseudopodia, but forward movement is greatly slowed. Amoebas are not the only cells that move by crawling; so do many cells in the animal body, including some white blood cells.

In plant cells, both actin-myosin interactions and sol-gel transformations brought about by actin may be involved in **cytoplasmic streaming**, a circular flow of cytoplasm within cells **(Figure 6.27c)**. This movement, which is especially common in large plant cells, speeds the distribution of materials within the cell.

Intermediate Filaments

Intermediate filaments are named for their diameter, which, at 8–12 nm, is larger than the diameter of microfilaments but smaller than that of microtubules (see Table 6.1, p. 113). Specialized for bearing tension (like microfilaments), intermediate filaments are a diverse class of cytoskeletal elements. Each type is constructed from a particular molecular subunit belonging to a family of proteins whose members include the keratins. Microtubules and microfilaments, in contrast, are consistent in diameter and composition in all eukaryotic cells.

Intermediate filaments are more permanent fixtures of cells than are microfilaments and microtubules, which are often disassembled and reassembled in various parts of a cell. Even after cells die, intermediate filament networks often persist; for example, the outer layer of our skin consists of dead skin cells full of keratin proteins. Chemical treatments that remove microfilaments and microtubules from the cytoplasm of living cells leave a web of intermediate filaments that retains its original shape. Such experiments suggest that intermediate filaments are especially sturdy and that they play an important role in reinforcing the shape of a cell and fixing the position of certain organelles. For instance, the nucleus typically sits within a cage made of intermediate filaments, fixed in location by branches of the filaments that extend into the cytoplasm. Other intermediate filaments make up the nuclear lamina, which lines the interior of the nuclear envelope (see Figure 6.9). By supporting a cell's shape, intermediate filaments help the cell carry out its specific function. For example, the long extensions (axons) of nerve cells that transmit impulses are strengthened by intermediate filaments. Thus, the various kinds of intermediate filaments may function together as the permanent framework of the entire cell.

CONCEPT 6.7

Extracellular components and connections between cells help coordinate cellular activities

Having crisscrossed the cell to explore its interior components, we complete our tour of the cell by returning to the surface of this microscopic world, where there are additional structures with important functions. The plasma membrane is usually regarded as the boundary of the living cell, but most cells synthesize and secrete materials that are extracellular, or external to the plasma membrane. Although these materials and the structures they form are outside the cell, their study is important to cell biology because they are involved in a great many cellular functions.

Cell Walls of Plants

The **cell wall** is an extracellular structure of plant cells that distinguishes them from animal cells (see Figure 6.8). The wall protects the plant cell, maintains its shape, and prevents excessive uptake of water. On the level of the whole plant, the strong walls of specialized cells hold the plant up against the force of gravity. Prokaryotes, fungi, and some protists also have cell walls, as you saw in Figures 6.5 and 6.8, but we will postpone discussion of them until Unit Five.

Plant cell walls are much thicker than the plasma membrane, ranging from 0.1 µm to several micrometers. The exact chemical composition of the wall varies from species to species and even from one cell type to another in the same plant, but the basic design of the wall is consistent. Microfibrils made of the polysaccharide cellulose (see Figure 5.8) are synthesized by an enzyme called cellulose synthase and secreted to the extracellular space, where they become embedded in a matrix of other polysaccharides and proteins. This combination of materials, strong fibers in a "ground substance" (matrix), is the same basic architectural design found in steel-reinforced concrete and in fiberglass.

A young plant cell first secretes a relatively thin and flexible wall called the **primary cell wall** **(Figure 6.28)**. In actively

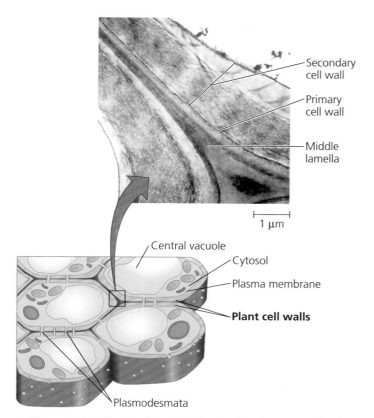

▲ **Figure 6.28 Plant cell walls.** The drawing shows several cells, each with a large vacuole, a nucleus, and several chloroplasts and mitochondria. The transmission electron micrograph shows the cell walls where two cells come together. The multilayered partition between plant cells consists of adjoining walls individually secreted by the cells.

growing cells, the cellulose fibrils are oriented at right angles to the direction of cell expansion. Researchers investigated the role of microtubules in orienting these cellulose fibrils (Figure 6.29). Their observations strongly support the idea that microtubules in the cell cortex guide cellulose synthase as it synthesizes and deposits cellulose fibrils. By orienting cellulose deposition, microtubules thus affect the growth pattern of the cells.

Between primary walls of adjacent cells is the **middle lamella**, a thin layer rich in sticky polysaccharides called pectins. The middle lamella glues adjacent cells together (see Figure 6.28). (Pectin is used as a thickening agent in jams and jellies.) When the cell matures and stops growing, it strengthens its wall. Some plant cells do this simply by secreting hardening substances into the primary wall. Other cells add a **secondary cell wall** between the plasma membrane and the primary wall. The secondary wall, often deposited in several laminated layers, has a strong and durable matrix that affords the cell protection and support. Wood, for example, consists mainly of secondary walls. Plant cell walls are usually perforated by channels between adjacent cells called plasmodesmata (see Figure 6.28), which will be discussed shortly.

▼ **Figure 6.29**

INQUIRY

What role do microtubules play in orienting deposition of cellulose in cell walls?

EXPERIMENT Previous experiments on preserved plant tissues had shown alignment of microtubules in the cell cortex with cellulose fibrils in the cell wall. Also, drugs that disrupted microtubules were observed to cause disoriented cellulose fibrils. To further investigate the possible role of cortical microtubules in guiding cellulose fibril deposition, David Ehrhardt and colleagues at Stanford University used a type of confocal microscopy to study cell wall deposition in living cells. In these cells, they labeled both cellulose synthase and microtubules with fluorescent markers and observed them over time.

RESULTS Each fluorescence image below represents a combination of 30 images taken over a 5-minute period to detect the movement of cellulose synthase and microtubules. These two coincided highly over time. The labeling molecules caused cellulose synthase to fluoresce green and the microtubules to fluoresce red. The arrowheads indicate prominent areas where the two are seen to align.

10 µm

Distribution of cellulose synthase over time

Distribution of microtubules over time

CONCLUSION The organization of microtubules appears to directly guide the path of cellulose synthase as it lays down cellulose, thus determining the orientation of cellulose fibrils.

SOURCE A. R. Paradez et al., Visualization of cellulose synthase demonstrates functional association with microtubules, *Science* 312:1491–1495 (2006).

WHAT IF? In a second experiment, the researchers exposed the plant cells to blue light, previously shown to cause reorientation of microtubules. What events would you predict would follow blue light exposure?

The Extracellular Matrix (ECM) of Animal Cells

Although animal cells lack walls akin to those of plant cells, they do have an elaborate **extracellular matrix (ECM)**. The main ingredients of the ECM are glycoproteins and other carbohydrate-containing molecules secreted by the cells. (Recall that glycoproteins are proteins with covalently bonded carbohydrate, usually short chains of sugars.) The most abundant glycoprotein in the ECM of most animal cells is **collagen**, which forms strong fibers outside the cells (see Figure 5.20). In fact, collagen accounts for about 40% of the total protein in the human body. The collagen fibers are embedded in a network woven out of **proteoglycans** secreted

Collagen fibers are embedded in a web of proteoglycan complexes.

Fibronectin attaches the ECM to integrins embedded in the plasma membrane.

Plasma membrane

EXTRACELLULAR FLUID

Micro-filaments

CYTOPLASM

A **proteoglycan complex** consists of hundreds of proteoglycan molecules attached noncovalently to a single long polysaccharide molecule.

Integrins, membrane proteins with two subunits, bind to the ECM on one side and to associated proteins attached to microfilaments on the other. This linkage can transmit signals between the cell's external environment and its interior and can result in changes in cell behavior.

Polysaccharide molecule

Carbo-hydrates

Core protein

Proteoglycan molecule

Proteoglycan complex

▲ **Figure 6.30 Extracellular matrix (ECM) of an animal cell.** The molecular composition and structure of the ECM vary from one cell type to another. In this example, three different types of glycoproteins are present: proteoglycans, collagen, and fibronectin.

by cells (**Figure 6.30**). A proteoglycan molecule consists of a small core protein with many carbohydrate chains covalently attached, so that it may be up to 95% carbohydrate. Large proteoglycan complexes can form when hundreds of proteoglycan molecules become noncovalently attached to a single long polysaccharide molecule, as shown in Figure 6.30. Some cells are attached to the ECM by still other ECM glycoproteins, such as **fibronectin**. Fibronectin and other ECM proteins bind to cell-surface receptor proteins called **integrins** that are built into the plasma membrane. Integrins span the membrane and bind on their cytoplasmic side to associated proteins attached to microfilaments of the cytoskeleton. The name *integrin* is based on the word *integrate*: Integrins are in a position to transmit signals between the ECM and the cytoskeleton and thus to integrate changes occurring outside and inside the cell.

Current research on fibronectin, other ECM molecules, and integrins is revealing the influential role of the extracellular matrix in the lives of cells. By communicating with a cell through integrins, the ECM can regulate a cell's behavior. For example, some cells in a developing embryo migrate along specific pathways by matching the orientation of their microfilaments to the "grain" of fibers in the extracellular matrix. Researchers have also learned that the extracellular matrix around a cell can influence the activity of genes in the nucleus. Information about the ECM probably reaches the nucleus by a combination of mechanical and chemical signaling pathways. Mechanical signaling involves fibronectin, integrins, and microfilaments of the cytoskeleton. Changes in the cytoskeleton may in turn trigger chemical signaling

pathways inside the cell, leading to changes in the set of proteins being made by the cell and therefore changes in the cell's function. In this way, the extracellular matrix of a particular tissue may help coordinate the behavior of all the cells of that tissue. Direct connections between cells also function in this coordination, as we discuss next.

Cell Junctions

Cells in an animal or plant are organized into tissues, organs, and organ systems. Neighboring cells often adhere, interact, and communicate via sites of direct physical contact.

Plasmodesmata in Plant Cells

It might seem that the nonliving cell walls of plants would isolate plant cells from one another. But in fact, as shown in **Figure 6.31**, cell walls are perforated with **plasmodesmata** (singular, *plasmodesma*; from the Greek *desmos*, to bind),

Cell walls

Interior of cell

Interior of cell

0.5 μm

Plasmodesmata   Plasma membranes

▲ **Figure 6.31 Plasmodesmata between plant cells.** The cytoplasm of one plant cell is continuous with the cytoplasm of its neighbors via plasmodesmata, cytoplasmic channels through the cell walls (TEM).

membrane-lined channels filled with cytoplasm. Cytosol passes through the plasmodesmata and joins the internal chemical environments of adjacent cells. These connections unify most of the plant into one living continuum. The plasma membranes of adjacent cells line the channel of each plasmodesma and thus are continuous. Water and small solutes can pass freely from cell to cell, and recent experiments have shown that in some circumstances, certain proteins and RNA molecules can also do this (see Concept 36.6). The macromolecules transported to neighboring cells appear to reach the plasmodesmata by moving along fibers of the cytoskeleton.

Tight Junctions, Desmosomes, and Gap Junctions in Animal Cells

In animals, there are three main types of cell junctions: *tight junctions*, *desmosomes*, and *gap junctions*. (Gap junctions are most like the plasmodesmata of plants, although gap junction pores are not lined with membrane.) All three types of cell junctions are especially common in epithelial tissue, which lines the external and internal surfaces of the body. **Figure 6.32** uses epithelial cells of the intestinal lining to illustrate these junctions.

▼ **Figure 6.32**

Exploring Cell Junctions in Animal Tissues

Tight junctions prevent fluid from moving across a layer of cells

Tight junction

Tight junction

Intermediate filaments

Desmosome

Gap junction

Ions or small molecules

Space between cells

Plasma membranes of adjacent cells

Extracellular matrix

Tight Junctions

At **tight junctions**, the plasma membranes of neighboring cells are very tightly pressed against each other, bound together by specific proteins (purple). Forming continuous seals around the cells, tight junctions prevent leakage of extracellular fluid across a layer of epithelial cells. For example, tight junctions between skin cells make us watertight by preventing leakage between cells in our sweat glands.

TEM   0.5 μm

Desmosomes

Desmosomes (also called *anchoring junctions*) function like rivets, fastening cells together into strong sheets. Intermediate filaments made of sturdy keratin proteins anchor desmosomes in the cytoplasm. Desmosomes attach muscle cells to each other in a muscle. Some "muscle tears" involve the rupture of desmosomes.

TEM   1 μm

Gap Junctions

Gap junctions (also called *communicating junctions*) provide cytoplasmic channels from one cell to an adjacent cell and in this way are similar in their function to the plasmodesmata in plants. Gap junctions consist of membrane proteins that surround a pore through which ions, sugars, amino acids, and other small molecules may pass. Gap junctions are necessary for communication between cells in many types of tissues, such as heart muscle, and in animal embryos.

TEM   0.1 μm

1. In what way are the cells of plants and animals structurally different from single-celled eukaryotes?
2. **WHAT IF?** If the plant cell wall or the animal extracellular matrix were impermeable, what effect would this have on cell function?
3. **MAKE CONNECTIONS** The polypeptide chain that makes up a tight junction weaves back and forth through the membrane four times, with two extracellular loops, and one loop plus short C-terminal and N-terminal tails in the cytoplasm. Looking at Figure 5.16 (p. 79), what would you predict about the amino acid sequence of the tight-junction protein?

For suggested answers, see Appendix A.

▲ **Figure 6.33 The emergence of cellular functions.** The ability of this macrophage (brown) to recognize, apprehend, and destroy bacteria (yellow) is a coordinated activity of the whole cell. Its cytoskeleton, lysosomes, and plasma membrane are among the components that function in phagocytosis (colorized SEM).

The Cell: A Living Unit Greater Than the Sum of Its Parts

From our panoramic view of the cell's compartmental organization to our close-up inspection of each organelle's architecture, this tour of the cell has provided many opportunities to correlate structure with function. (This would be a good time to review cell structure by returning to Figure 6.8, on pp. 100 and 101.) But even as we dissect the cell, remember that none of its components works alone. As an example of cellular integration, consider the microscopic scene in **Figure 6.33**. The large cell is a macrophage (see Figure 6.13a). It helps defend the mammalian body against infections by ingesting bacteria (the smaller cells) into phagocytic vesicles. The macrophage crawls along a surface and reaches out to the bacteria with thin pseudopodia (called filopodia). Actin filaments interact with other elements of the cytoskeleton in these movements. After the macrophage engulfs the bacteria, they are destroyed by lysosomes. The elaborate endomembrane system produces the lysosomes. The digestive enzymes of the lysosomes and the proteins of the cytoskeleton are all made on ribosomes. And the synthesis of these proteins is programmed by genetic messages dispatched from the DNA in the nucleus. All these processes require energy, which mitochondria supply in the form of ATP. Cellular functions arise from cellular order: The cell is a living unit greater than the sum of its parts.

6 CHAPTER REVIEW

SUMMARY OF KEY CONCEPTS

CONCEPT 6.1

Biologists use microscopes and the tools of biochemistry to study cells (pp. 94–97)

- Improvements in microscopy that affect the parameters of magnification, resolution, and contrast have catalyzed progress in the study of cell structure. **Light microscopy** (LM) and **electron microscopy** (EM), as well as other types, remain important tools.
- Cell biologists can obtain pellets enriched in particular cellular components by centrifuging disrupted cells at sequential speeds, a process known as **cell fractionation**. Larger cellular components are in the pellet after lower-speed centrifugation, and smaller components are in the pellet after higher-speed centrifugation.

? *How do microscopy and biochemistry complement each other to reveal cell structure and function?*

CONCEPT 6.2

Eukaryotic cells have internal membranes that compartmentalize their functions (pp. 98–102)

- All cells are bounded by a **plasma membrane**.
- **Prokaryotic cells** lack nuclei and other membrane-enclosed **organelles**, while **eukaryotic cells** have internal membranes that compartmentalize cellular functions.
- The surface-to-volume ratio is an important parameter affecting cell size and shape.
- Plant and animal cells have most of the same organelles: a nucleus, endoplasmic reticulum, Golgi apparatus, and mitochondria. Some organelles are found only in plant or in animal cells. Chloroplasts are present only in cells of photosynthetic eukaryotes.

? *Explain how the compartmental organization of a eukaryotic cell contributes to its biochemical functioning.*

	Cell Component	Structure	Function
CONCEPT 6.3 The eukaryotic cell's genetic instructions are housed in the nucleus and carried out by the ribosomes (pp. 102–104) **?** *Describe the relationship between the nucleus and ribosomes.*	Nucleus (ER)	Surrounded by nuclear envelope (double membrane) perforated by nuclear pores; nuclear envelope continuous with endoplasmic reticulum (ER)	Houses chromosomes, which are made of chromatin (DNA and proteins); contains nucleoli, where ribosomal subunits are made; pores regulate entry and exit of materials
	Ribosome	Two subunits made of ribosomal RNA and proteins; can be free in cytosol or bound to ER	Protein synthesis
CONCEPT 6.4 The endomembrane system regulates protein traffic and performs metabolic functions in the cell (pp. 104–109) **?** *Describe the key role played by transport vesicles in the endomembrane system.*	Endoplasmic reticulum (Nuclear envelope)	Extensive network of membrane-bounded tubules and sacs; membrane separates lumen from cytosol; continuous with nuclear envelope	Smooth ER: synthesis of lipids, metabolism of carbohydrates, Ca^{2+} storage, detoxification of drugs and poisons Rough ER: aids in synthesis of secretory and other proteins from bound ribosomes; adds carbohydrates to proteins to make glycoproteins; produces new membrane
	Golgi apparatus	Stacks of flattened membranous sacs; has polarity (*cis* and *trans* faces)	Modification of proteins, carbohydrates on proteins, and phospholipids; synthesis of many polysaccharides; sorting of Golgi products, which are then released in vesicles
	Lysosome	Membranous sac of hydrolytic enzymes (in animal cells)	Breakdown of ingested substances, cell macromolecules, and damaged organelles for recycling
	Vacuole	Large membrane-bounded vesicle	Digestion, storage, waste disposal, water balance, cell growth, and protection
CONCEPT 6.5 Mitochondria and chloroplasts change energy from one form to another (pp. 109–112) **?** *What is the endosymbiont theory?*	Mitochondrion	Bounded by double membrane; inner membrane has infoldings (cristae)	Cellular respiration
	Chloroplast	Typically two membranes around fluid stroma, which contains thylakoids stacked into grana (in cells of photosynthetic eukaryotes, including plants)	Photosynthesis
	Peroxisome	Specialized metabolic compartment bounded by a single membrane	Contains enzymes that transfer hydrogen atoms from substrates to oxygen, producing hydrogen peroxide (H_2O_2) as a by-product; H_2O_2 is converted to water by another enzyme

CONCEPT 6.6

The cytoskeleton is a network of fibers that organizes structures and activities in the cell (pp. 112–118)

- The **cytoskeleton** functions in structural support for the cell and in motility and signal transmission.
- **Microtubules** shape the cell, guide organelle movement, and separate chromosomes in dividing cells. **Cilia** and **flagella** are motile appendages containing microtubules. Primary cilia also play sensory and signaling roles. **Microfilaments** are thin rods functioning in muscle contraction, amoeboid movement, **cytoplasmic streaming**, and microvillus support. **Intermediate filaments** support cell shape and fix organelles in place.

? *Describe the role of motor proteins inside the eukaryotic cell and in whole-cell movement.*

CONCEPT 6.7

Extracellular components and connections between cells help coordinate cellular activities (pp. 118–122)

- Plant **cell walls** are made of cellulose fibers embedded in other polysaccharides and proteins. Cellulose deposition is oriented along microtubules.
- Animal cells secrete glycoproteins that form the **extracellular matrix (ECM)**, which functions in support, adhesion, movement, and regulation.
- Cell junctions connect neighboring cells in plants and animals. Plants have **plasmodesmata** that pass through adjoining cell walls. Animal cells have **tight junctions**, **desmosomes**, and **gap junctions**.

? *Compare the composition and functions of a plant cell wall and the extracellular matrix of an animal cell.*

TEST YOUR UNDERSTANDING

LEVEL 1: KNOWLEDGE/COMPREHENSION

1. Which structure is *not* part of the endomembrane system?
   - a. nuclear envelope
   - b. chloroplast
   - c. Golgi apparatus
   - d. plasma membrane
   - e. ER

2. Which structure is common to plant *and* animal cells?
   - a. chloroplast
   - b. wall made of cellulose
   - c. central vacuole
   - d. mitochondrion
   - e. centriole

3. Which of the following is present in a prokaryotic cell?
   - a. mitochondrion
   - b. ribosome
   - c. nuclear envelope
   - d. chloroplast
   - e. ER

4. Which structure-function pair is *mismatched*?
   - a. nucleolus; production of ribosomal subunits
   - b. lysosome; intracellular digestion
   - c. ribosome; protein synthesis
   - d. Golgi; protein trafficking
   - e. microtubule; muscle contraction

LEVEL 2: APPLICATION/ANALYSIS

5. Cyanide binds to at least one molecule involved in producing ATP. If a cell is exposed to cyanide, most of the cyanide will be found within the
   - a. mitochondria.
   - b. ribosomes.
   - c. peroxisomes.
   - d. lysosomes.
   - e. endoplasmic reticulum.

6. What is the most likely pathway taken by a newly synthesized protein that will be secreted by a cell?
   - a. ER → Golgi → nucleus
   - b. Golgi → ER → lysosome
   - c. nucleus → ER → Golgi
   - d. ER → Golgi → vesicles that fuse with plasma membrane
   - e. ER → lysosomes → vesicles that fuse with plasma membrane

7. Which cell would be best for studying lysosomes?
   - a. muscle cell
   - b. nerve cell
   - c. phagocytic white blood cell
   - d. leaf cell of a plant
   - e. bacterial cell

8. **DRAW IT** From memory, draw two eukaryotic cells, labeling the structures listed here and showing any physical connections between the internal structures of each cell: nucleus, rough ER, smooth ER, mitochondrion, centrosome, chloroplast, vacuole, lysosome, microtubule, cell wall, ECM, microfilament, Golgi apparatus, intermediate filament, plasma membrane, peroxisome, ribosome, nucleolus, nuclear pore, vesicle, flagellum, microvilli, plasmodesma.

LEVEL 3: SYNTHESIS/EVALUATION

9. **EVOLUTION CONNECTION**
   Which aspects of cell structure best reveal evolutionary unity? What are some examples of specialized modifications?

10. **SCIENTIFIC INQUIRY**
    Imagine protein X, destined to span the plasma membrane. Assume that the mRNA carrying the genetic message for protein X has already been translated by ribosomes in a cell culture. If you fractionate the cells (see Figure 6.4), in which fraction would you find protein X? Explain by describing its transit through the cell.

11. **WRITE ABOUT A THEME**
    Emergent Properties Considering some of the characteristics that define life and drawing on your new knowledge of cellular structures and functions, write a short essay (100–150 words) that discusses this statement: Life is an emergent property that appears at the level of the cell. (Review pp. 3–5 in Chapter 1.)

For selected answers, see Appendix A.

MasteringBIOLOGY®   www.masteringbiology.com

1. MasteringBiology® Assignments
BioFlix **Tutorials** Tour of an Animal Cell: The Endomembrane System • Structures and Functions; Tour of a Plant Cell: Structures and Functions
Tutorials Connections Between Cells
Activities Metric System Review • Prokaryotic Cell Structure and Function • Discovery Channel Video: Cells • Role of the Nucleus and Ribosomes in Protein Synthesis • Transport into the Nucleus • A Pulse Chase Experiment • The Endomembrane System • Cilia and Flagella • Cell Junctions • Review: Animal Cell Structure and Function
Questions Student Misconceptions • Reading Quiz • Multiple Choice • End-of-Chapter

2. eText
Read your book online, search, take notes, highlight text, and more.

3. The Study Area
Practice Tests • Cumulative Test • *BioFlix* 3-D Animations • MP3 Tutor Sessions • Videos • Activities • Investigations • Lab Media • Audio Glossary • Word Study Tools • Art

7

Membrane Structure and Function

▲ **Figure 7.1 How do cell membrane proteins help regulate chemical traffic?**

OVERVIEW

Life at the Edge

The plasma membrane is the edge of life, the boundary that separates the living cell from its surroundings. A remarkable film only about 8 nm thick—it would take over 8,000 plasma membranes to equal the thickness of this page—the plasma membrane controls traffic into and out of the cell it surrounds. Like all biological membranes, the plasma membrane exhibits **selective permeability**; that is, it allows some substances to cross it more easily than others. One of the earliest episodes in the evolution of life may have been the formation of a membrane that enclosed a solution different from the surrounding solution while still permitting the uptake of nutrients and elimination of waste products. The ability of the cell to discriminate in its chemical exchanges with its environment is fundamental to life, and it is the plasma membrane and its component molecules that make this selectivity possible.

In this chapter, you will learn how cellular membranes control the passage of substances. The image in **Figure 7.1** shows the elegant structure of a eukaryotic plasma membrane protein that plays a crucial role in nerve cell signaling. This protein provides a channel for a stream of potassium ions (K^+) to exit a nerve cell at a precise moment after nerve stimulation, restoring the cell's ability to fire again. (The orange ball in the center represents one potassium ion moving through the channel.) In this way, the plasma membrane and its proteins not only act as an outer boundary but also enable the cell to carry out its functions. The same applies to the many varieties of internal membranes that partition the eukaryotic cell: The molecular makeup of each membrane allows compartmentalized specialization in cells. To understand how membranes work, we'll begin by examining their architecture.

CONCEPT 7.1

Cellular membranes are fluid mosaics of lipids and proteins

Lipids and proteins are the staple ingredients of membranes, although carbohydrates are also important. The most abundant lipids in most membranes are phospholipids. The ability of phospholipids to form membranes is inherent in their molecular structure. A phospholipid is an **amphipathic** molecule, meaning it has both a hydrophilic region and a hydrophobic region (see Figure 5.12). Other types of membrane lipids are also amphipathic. Furthermore, most of the proteins within membranes have both hydrophobic and hydrophilic regions.

How are phospholipids and proteins arranged in the membranes of cells? In the **fluid mosaic model**, the membrane is a fluid structure with a "mosaic" of various proteins embedded in or attached to a double layer (bilayer) of phospholipids. Scientists propose models as hypotheses, ways of organizing and explaining existing information. Let's explore how the fluid mosaic model was developed.

Membrane Models: *Scientific Inquiry*

Scientists began building molecular models of the membrane decades before membranes were first seen with the electron microscope (in the 1950s). In 1915, membranes isolated from red blood cells were chemically analyzed and found to be composed of lipids and proteins. Ten years later, two Dutch scientists reasoned that cell membranes must be phospholipid bilayers. Such a double layer of molecules could exist as a stable boundary between two aqueous compartments because the molecular arrangement shelters the hydrophobic tails of the phospholipids from water while exposing the hydrophilic heads to water (**Figure 7.2**).

If a phospholipid bilayer was the main fabric of a membrane, where were the proteins located? Although the heads of phospholipids are hydrophilic, the surface of a pure phospholipid bilayer adheres less strongly to water than does the surface of a biological membrane. Given this difference, Hugh Davson and James Danielli suggested in 1935 that the membrane might be coated on both sides with hydrophilic proteins. They proposed a sandwich model: a phospholipid bilayer between two layers of proteins.

When researchers first used electron microscopes to study cells in the 1950s, the pictures seemed to support the Davson-Danielli model. By the late 1960s, however, many cell biologists recognized two problems with the model. First, inspection of a variety of membranes revealed that membranes with different functions differ in structure and chemical composition. A second, more serious problem became apparent once membrane proteins were better characterized. Unlike proteins dissolved in the cytosol, membrane proteins are not very soluble in water because they are amphipathic. If such proteins were layered on the surface of the membrane, their hydrophobic parts would be in aqueous surroundings.

Taking these observations into account, S. J. Singer and G. Nicolson proposed in 1972 that membrane proteins reside in the phospholipid bilayer with their hydrophilic regions protruding (**Figure 7.3**). This molecular arrangement would maximize contact of hydrophilic regions of proteins and

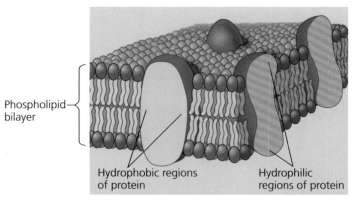
Phospholipid bilayer

Hydrophobic regions of protein

Hydrophilic regions of protein

▲ Figure 7.3 **The original fluid mosaic model for membranes.**

phospholipids with water in the cytosol and extracellular fluid, while providing their hydrophobic parts with a nonaqueous environment. In this fluid mosaic model, the membrane is a mosaic of protein molecules bobbing in a fluid bilayer of phospholipids.

A method of preparing cells for electron microscopy called freeze-fracture has demonstrated visually that proteins are indeed embedded in the phospholipid bilayer of the membrane (**Figure 7.4**). Freeze-fracture splits a membrane along the middle of the bilayer, somewhat like pulling apart a chunky peanut butter sandwich. When the membrane layers are viewed in the electron microscope, the interior of the

▼ Figure 7.4　**RESEARCH METHOD**

Freeze-fracture

APPLICATION A cell membrane can be split into its two layers, revealing the structure of the membrane's interior.

TECHNIQUE A cell is frozen and fractured with a knife. The fracture plane often follows the hydrophobic interior of a membrane, splitting the phospholipid bilayer into two separated layers. Each membrane protein goes wholly with one of the layers.

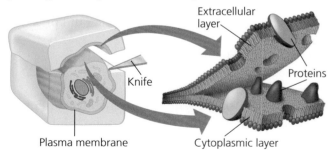
Extracellular layer

Knife

Proteins

Plasma membrane

Cytoplasmic layer

RESULTS These SEMs show membrane proteins (the "bumps") in the two layers, demonstrating that proteins are embedded in the phospholipid bilayer.

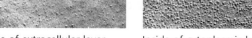
Inside of extracellular layer

Inside of cytoplasmic layer

▼ Figure 7.2 **Phospholipid bilayer (cross section).**

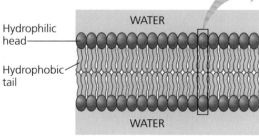

WATER

Hydrophilic head

Hydrophobic tail

WATER

MAKE CONNECTIONS *Consulting Figure 5.12 (p. 76), circle the hydrophilic and hydrophobic portions of the enlarged phospholipids on the right. Explain what each portion contacts when the phospholipids are in the plasma membrane.*

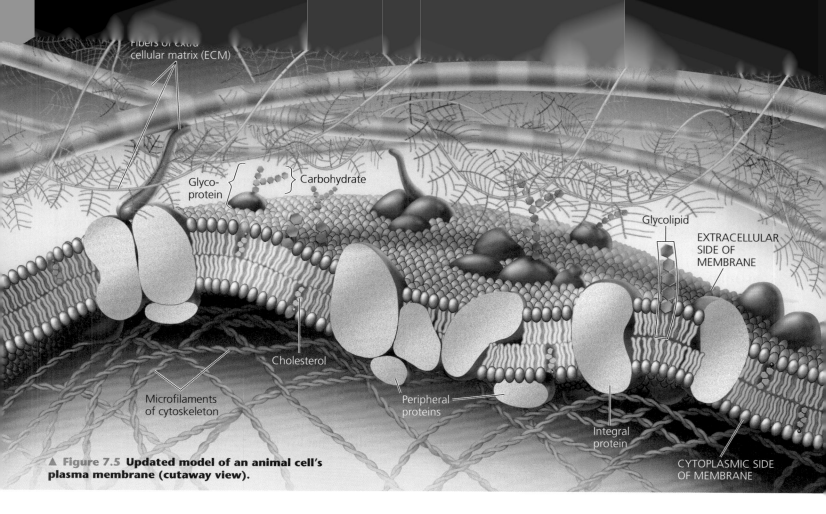

Fibers of extra cellular matrix (ECM)

Glyco-protein

Carbohydrate

Glycolipid

EXTRACELLULAR SIDE OF MEMBRANE

Cholesterol

Microfilaments of cytoskeleton

Peripheral proteins

Integral protein

CYTOPLASMIC SIDE OF MEMBRANE

▲ **Figure 7.5 Updated model of an animal cell's plasma membrane (cutaway view).**

bilayer appears cobblestoned, with protein particles interspersed in a smooth matrix, in agreement with the fluid mosaic model. Some proteins remain attached to one layer or the other, like the peanut chunks in the sandwich.

Because models are hypotheses, replacing one model of membrane structure with another does not imply that the original model was worthless. The acceptance or rejection of a model depends on how well it fits observations and explains experimental results. New findings may make a model obsolete; even then, it may not be totally scrapped, but revised to incorporate the new observations. The fluid mosaic model is continually being refined. For example, groups of proteins are often found associated in long-lasting, specialized patches, where they carry out common functions. The lipids themselves appear to form defined regions as well. Also, the membrane may be much more packed with proteins than imagined in the classic fluid mosaic model—compare the updated model in **Figure 7.5** with the original model in Figure 7.3. Let's now take a closer look at membrane structure.

The Fluidity of Membranes

Membranes are not static sheets of molecules locked rigidly in place. A membrane is held together primarily by hydrophobic interactions, which are much weaker than covalent bonds (see Figure 5.20). Most of the lipids and some of

the proteins can shift about laterally—that is, in the plane of the membrane, like partygoers elbowing their way through a crowded room **(Figure 7.6)**. It is quite rare, however, for a molecule to flip-flop transversely across the membrane, switching from one phospholipid layer to the other; to do so, the hydrophilic part of the molecule must cross the hydrophobic interior of the membrane.

The lateral movement of phospholipids within the membrane is rapid. Adjacent phospholipids switch positions about 10^7 times per second, which means that a phospholipid can travel about 2 μm—the length of many bacterial cells—in 1 second. Proteins are much larger than lipids and move more slowly, but some membrane proteins do drift, as shown in a classic experiment described in **Figure 7.7**, on the next page.

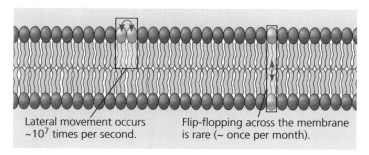

Lateral movement occurs ~10^7 times per second.

Flip-flopping across the membrane is rare (~ once per month).

▲ Figure 7.6 **The movement of phospholipids.**

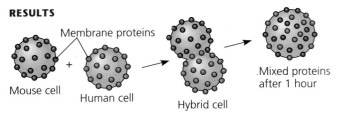

Figure 7.7

INQUIRY

Do membrane proteins move?

EXPERIMENT Larry Frye and Michael Edidin, at Johns Hopkins University, labeled the plasma membrane proteins of a mouse cell and a human cell with two different markers and fused the cells. Using a microscope, they observed the markers on the hybrid cell.

RESULTS

Membrane proteins

Mouse cell + Human cell → Hybrid cell → Mixed proteins after 1 hour

CONCLUSION The mixing of the mouse and human membrane proteins indicates that at least some membrane proteins move sideways within the plane of the plasma membrane.

SOURCE L. D. Frye and M. Edidin, The rapid intermixing of cell surface antigens after formation of mouse-human heterokaryons, *Journal of Cell Science* 7:319 (1970).

WHAT IF? Suppose the proteins did not mix in the hybrid cell, even many hours after fusion. Would you be able to conclude that proteins don't move within the membrane? What other explanation could there be?

And some membrane proteins seem to move in a highly directed manner, perhaps driven along cytoskeletal fibers by motor proteins connected to the membrane proteins' cytoplasmic regions. However, many other membrane proteins seem to be held immobile by their attachment to the cytoskeleton or to the extracellular matrix (see Figure 7.5).

A membrane remains fluid as temperature decreases until finally the phospholipids settle into a closely packed arrangement and the membrane solidifies, much as bacon grease forms lard when it cools. The temperature at which a membrane solidifies depends on the types of lipids it is made of. The membrane remains fluid to a lower temperature if it is rich in phospholipids with unsaturated hydrocarbon tails (see Figures 5.11 and 5.12). Because of kinks in the tails where double bonds are located, unsaturated hydrocarbon tails cannot pack together as closely as saturated hydrocarbon tails, and this makes the membrane more fluid (**Figure 7.8a**).

The steroid cholesterol, which is wedged between phospholipid molecules in the plasma membranes of animal cells, has different effects on membrane fluidity at different temperatures (**Figure 7.8b**). At relatively high temperatures—at 37°C, the body temperature of humans, for example—cholesterol makes the membrane less fluid by restraining phospholipid movement. However, because cholesterol also hinders the close packing of phospholipids, it lowers the temperature required for the membrane to solidify. Thus, cholesterol can be thought of as a "fluidity buffer" for the membrane, resisting changes in membrane fluidity that can be caused by changes in temperature.

Membranes must be fluid to work properly; they are usually about as fluid as salad oil. When a membrane solidifies, its permeability changes, and enzymatic proteins in the membrane may become inactive if their activity requires them to be able to move within the membrane. However, membranes that are too fluid cannot support protein function either. Therefore, extreme environments pose a challenge for life, resulting in evolutionary adaptations that include differences in membrane lipid composition.

Evolution of Differences in Membrane Lipid Composition

EVOLUTION Variations in the cell membrane lipid compositions of many species appear to be evolutionary adaptations that maintain the appropriate membrane fluidity under specific environmental conditions. For instance, fishes that live in extreme cold have membranes with a high proportion of unsaturated hydrocarbon tails, enabling their membranes to remain fluid (see Figure 7.8a). At the other extreme, some bacteria and archaea thrive at temperatures greater than 90°C (194°F) in thermal hot springs and geysers. Their membranes include unusual lipids that may prevent excessive fluidity at such high temperatures.

The ability to change the lipid composition of cell membranes in response to changing temperatures has evolved in organisms that live where temperatures vary. In many plants that tolerate extreme cold, such as winter wheat, the percentage of unsaturated phospholipids increases in autumn, an adjustment that keeps the membranes from solidifying during winter. Certain bacteria and archaea can also change the proportion of unsaturated phospholipids in their cell membranes, depending on the temperature at which they are growing. Overall, natural selection has apparently favored organisms whose mix of membrane lipids ensures an appropriate level of membrane fluidity for their environment.

 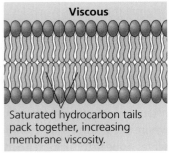

Fluid — Unsaturated hydrocarbon tails (kinked) prevent packing, enhancing membrane fluidity.

Viscous — Saturated hydrocarbon tails pack together, increasing membrane viscosity.

(a) Unsaturated versus saturated hydrocarbon tails.

(b) Cholesterol within the animal cell membrane. Cholesterol reduces membrane fluidity at moderate temperatures by reducing phospholipid movement, but at low temperatures it hinders solidification by disrupting the regular packing of phospholipids.

Cholesterol

▲ **Figure 7.8 Factors that affect membrane fluidity.**

Membrane Proteins and Their Functions

Now we come to the *mosaic* aspect of the fluid mosaic model. Somewhat like a tile mosaic, a membrane is a collage of different proteins, often clustered together in groups, embedded in the fluid matrix of the lipid bilayer (see Figure 7.5). More than 50 kinds of proteins have been found so far in the plasma membrane of red blood cells, for example. Phospholipids form the main fabric of the membrane, but proteins determine most of the membrane's functions. Different types of cells contain different sets of membrane proteins, and the various membranes within a cell each have a unique collection of proteins.

Notice in Figure 7.5 that there are two major populations of membrane proteins: integral proteins and peripheral proteins. **Integral proteins** penetrate the hydrophobic interior of the lipid bilayer. The majority are *transmembrane proteins*, which span the membrane; other integral proteins extend only partway into the hydrophobic interior. The hydrophobic regions of an integral protein consist of one or more stretches of nonpolar amino acids (see Figure 5.16), usually coiled into α helices **(Figure 7.9)**. The hydrophilic parts of the molecule are exposed to the aqueous solutions on either side of the membrane. Some proteins also have a hydrophilic channel through their center that allows passage of hydrophilic substances (see Figure 7.1). **Peripheral proteins** are not embedded in the lipid bilayer at all; they are appendages loosely bound to the surface of the membrane, often to exposed parts of integral proteins (see Figure 7.5).

On the cytoplasmic side of the plasma membrane, some membrane proteins are held in place by attachment to the cytoskeleton. And on the extracellular side, certain membrane proteins are attached to fibers of the extracellular matrix (see Figure 6.30; *integrins* are one type of integral protein). These attachments combine to give animal cells a stronger framework than the plasma membrane alone could provide.

Figure 7.10 gives an overview of six major functions performed by proteins of the plasma membrane. A single cell

◀ **Figure 7.9 The structure of a transmembrane protein.** Bacteriorhodopsin (a bacterial transport protein) has a distinct orientation in the membrane, with its N-terminus outside the cell and its C-terminus inside. This ribbon model highlights the α-helical secondary structure of the hydrophobic parts, which lie mostly within the hydrophobic interior of the membrane. The protein includes seven transmembrane helices. The nonhelical hydrophilic segments are in contact with the aqueous solutions on the extracellular and cytoplasmic sides of the membrane.

(a) Transport. *Left:* A protein that spans the membrane may provide a hydrophilic channel across the membrane that is selective for a particular solute. *Right:* Other transport proteins shuttle a substance from one side to the other by changing shape (see Figure 7.17). Some of these proteins hydrolyze ATP as an energy source to actively pump substances across the membrane.

(b) Enzymatic activity. A protein built into the membrane may be an enzyme with its active site exposed to substances in the adjacent solution. In some cases, several enzymes in a membrane are organized as a team that carries out sequential steps of a metabolic pathway.

(c) Signal transduction. A membrane protein (receptor) may have a binding site with a specific shape that fits the shape of a chemical messenger, such as a hormone. The external messenger (signaling molecule) may cause the protein to change shape, allowing it to relay the message to the inside of the cell, usually by binding to a cytoplasmic protein (see Figure 11.6).

(d) Cell-cell recognition. Some glycoproteins serve as identification tags that are specifically recognized by membrane proteins of other cells. This type of cell-cell binding is usually short-lived compared to that shown in (e).

(e) Intercellular joining. Membrane proteins of adjacent cells may hook together in various kinds of junctions, such as gap junctions or tight junctions (see Figure 6.32). This type of binding is more long-lasting than that shown in (d).

(f) Attachment to the cytoskeleton and extracellular matrix (ECM). Microfilaments or other elements of the cytoskeleton may be noncovalently bound to membrane proteins, a function that helps maintain cell shape and stabilizes the location of certain membrane proteins. Proteins that can bind to ECM molecules can coordinate extracellular and intracellular changes (see Figure 6.30).

▲ **Figure 7.10 Some functions of membrane proteins.** In many cases, a single protein performs multiple tasks.

? *Some transmembrane proteins can bind to a particular ECM molecule and, when bound, transmit a signal into the cell. Use the proteins shown here to explain how this might occur.*

IMPACT

Blocking HIV Entry into Cells as a Treatment for HIV Infections

Despite multiple exposures to HIV, a small number of people do not develop AIDS and show no evidence of HIV-infected cells. Comparing their genes with the genes of infected individuals, researchers discovered that resistant individuals have an unusual form of a gene that codes for an immune cell-surface protein called CCR5. Further work showed that HIV binds to a main protein receptor (CD4) on an immune cell, but most types of HIV also need to bind to CCR5 as a "co-receptor" to actually infect the cell (below, left). An absence of CCR5 on the cells of resistant individuals, due to the gene alteration, prevents the virus from entering the cells (below, right).

HIV can infect a cell that has CCR5 on its surface, as in most people.

HIV cannot infect a cell lacking CCR5 on its surface, as in resistant individuals.

WHY IT MATTERS Researchers have been searching for drugs to block cell-surface receptors involved in HIV infection. The main receptor protein, CD4, performs many important functions for cells, so interfering with it could cause dangerous side effects. Discovery of the CCR5 co-receptor provided a safer target for development of drugs that mask CCR5 and block HIV entry. One such drug, maraviroc (brand name Selzentry), was approved for treatment of HIV infection in 2007.

FURTHER READING T. Kenakin, New bull's-eyes for drugs, *Scientific American* 293(4):50–57 (2005).

MAKE CONNECTIONS Study Figures 2.18 (p. 42) and 5.19 (p. 81), both of which show pairs of molecules binding to each other. What would you predict about CCR5 that would allow HIV to bind to it? How could a drug molecule interfere with this binding?

may have membrane proteins carrying out several of these functions, and a single membrane protein may have multiple functions. In this way, the membrane is a functional mosaic as well as a structural one.

Proteins on the surface of a cell are important in the medical field because some proteins can help outside agents invade the cell. For example, cell-surface proteins help the human immunodeficiency virus (HIV) infect immune system cells, leading to acquired immune deficiency syndrome (AIDS). (You'll read more about HIV in Chapter 19.) Learning about the proteins that HIV binds to on immune cells has been central to developing a treatment for HIV infection (**Figure 7.11**).

The Role of Membrane Carbohydrates in Cell-Cell Recognition

Cell-cell recognition, a cell's ability to distinguish one type of neighboring cell from another, is crucial to the functioning of an organism. It is important, for example, in the sorting of cells into tissues and organs in an animal embryo. It is also the basis for the rejection of foreign cells by the immune system, an important line of defense in vertebrate animals. Cells recognize other cells by binding to molecules, often containing carbohydrates, on the extracellular surface of the plasma membrane (see Figure 7.10d).

Membrane carbohydrates are usually short, branched chains of fewer than 15 sugar units. Some are covalently bonded to lipids, forming molecules called **glycolipids**. (Recall that *glyco* refers to the presence of carbohydrate.) However, most are covalently bonded to proteins, which are thereby **glycoproteins** (see Figure 7.5).

The carbohydrates on the extracellular side of the plasma membrane vary from species to species, among individuals of the same species, and even from one cell type to another in a single individual. The diversity of the molecules and their location on the cell's surface enable membrane carbohydrates to function as markers that distinguish one cell from another. For example, the four human blood types designated A, B, AB, and O reflect variation in the carbohydrate part of glycoproteins on the surface of red blood cells.

Synthesis and Sidedness of Membranes

Membranes have distinct inside and outside faces. The two lipid layers may differ in specific lipid composition, and each protein has directional orientation in the membrane (see Figure 7.9). **Figure 7.12** shows how membrane sidedness arises: The asymmetrical arrangement of proteins, lipids, and their associated carbohydrates in the plasma membrane is determined as the membrane is being built by the endoplasmic reticulum (ER) and Golgi apparatus.

CONCEPT CHECK 7.1

1. The carbohydrates attached to some proteins and lipids of the plasma membrane are added as the membrane is made and refined in the ER and Golgi apparatus. The new membrane then forms transport vesicles that travel to the cell surface. On which side of the vesicle membrane are the carbohydrates?

2. **WHAT IF?** The soil immediately around hot springs is much warmer than that in neighboring regions. Two closely related species of native grasses are found, one in the warmer region and one in the cooler region. If you analyzed their membrane lipid compositions, what would you expect to find? Explain.

For suggested answers, see Appendix A.

1 Membrane proteins and lipids are synthesized in the endoplasmic reticulum (ER). Carbohydrates (green) are added to the transmembrane proteins (purple dumbbells), making them glycoproteins. The carbohydrate portions may then be modified.

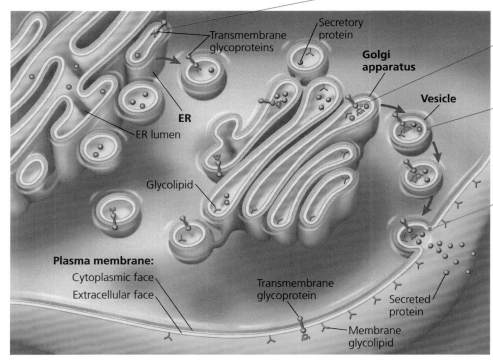

2 Inside the Golgi apparatus, the glycoproteins undergo further carbohydrate modification, and lipids acquire carbohydrates, becoming glycolipids.

3 The glycoproteins, glycolipids, and secretory proteins (purple spheres) are transported in vesicles to the plasma membrane.

4 As vesicles fuse with the plasma membrane, the outside face of the vesicle becomes continuous with the inside (cytoplasmic) face of the plasma membrane. This releases the secretory proteins from the cell, a process called *exocytosis*, and positions the carbohydrates of membrane glycoproteins and glycolipids on the outside (extracellular) face of the plasma membrane.

DRAW IT *Draw an integral membrane protein extending from partway through the ER membrane into the ER lumen. Next, draw the protein where it would be located in a series of numbered steps ending at the plasma membrane. Would the protein contact the cytoplasm or the extracellular fluid?*

CONCEPT 7.2

Membrane structure results in selective permeability

The biological membrane is an exquisite example of a supramolecular structure—many molecules ordered into a higher level of organization—with emergent properties beyond those of the individual molecules. The remainder of this chapter focuses on one of the most important of those properties: the ability to regulate transport across cellular boundaries, a function essential to the cell's existence. We will see once again that form fits function: The fluid mosaic model helps explain how membranes regulate the cell's molecular traffic.

A steady traffic of small molecules and ions moves across the plasma membrane in both directions. Consider the chemical exchanges between a muscle cell and the extracellular fluid that bathes it. Sugars, amino acids, and other nutrients enter the cell, and metabolic waste products leave it. The cell takes in O_2 for use in cellular respiration and expels CO_2. Also, the cell regulates its concentrations of inorganic ions, such as Na^+, K^+, Ca^{2+}, and Cl^-, by shuttling them one way or the other across the plasma membrane. In spite of heavy traffic through them, cell membranes are selectively permeable, and substances do not cross the barrier indiscriminately. The cell is able to take up some small molecules and ions and exclude others. Also, substances that move through the membrane do so at different rates.

The Permeability of the Lipid Bilayer

Nonpolar molecules, such as hydrocarbons, carbon dioxide, and oxygen, are hydrophobic and can therefore dissolve in the lipid bilayer of the membrane and cross it easily, without the aid of membrane proteins. However, the hydrophobic interior of the membrane impedes the direct passage of ions and polar molecules, which are hydrophilic, through the membrane. Polar molecules such as glucose and other sugars pass only slowly through a lipid bilayer, and even water, an extremely small polar molecule, does not cross very rapidly. A charged atom or molecule and its surrounding shell of water (see Figure 3.7) find the hydrophobic interior of the membrane even more difficult to penetrate. Furthermore, the lipid bilayer is only one aspect of the gatekeeper system responsible for the selective permeability of a cell. Proteins built into the membrane play key roles in regulating transport.

Transport Proteins

Cell membranes *are* permeable to specific ions and a variety of polar molecules. These hydrophilic substances can avoid contact with the lipid bilayer by passing through **transport proteins** that span the membrane.

Some transport proteins, called *channel proteins*, function by having a hydrophilic channel that certain molecules or atomic ions use as a tunnel through the membrane (see Figure 7.10a, left). For example, the passage of water molecules through the membrane in certain cells is greatly facilitated by channel proteins known as **aquaporins**. Each aquaporin allows entry of up to *3 billion* (3×10^9) water molecules per second, passing single file through its central channel, which fits ten at a time. Without aquaporins, only a tiny fraction of these water molecules would pass through the same area of the cell membrane in a second, so the channel protein brings about a tremendous increase in rate. Other transport proteins, called *carrier proteins*, hold onto their passengers and change shape in a way that shuttles them across the membrane (see Figure 7.10a, right). A transport protein is specific for the substance it translocates (moves), allowing only a certain substance (or a small group of related substances) to cross the membrane. For example, a specific carrier protein in the plasma membrane of red blood cells transports glucose across the membrane 50,000 times faster than glucose can pass through on its own. This "glucose transporter" is so selective that it even rejects fructose, a structural isomer of glucose.

Thus, the selective permeability of a membrane depends on both the discriminating barrier of the lipid bilayer and the specific transport proteins built into the membrane. But what establishes the *direction* of traffic across a membrane? At a given time, what determines whether a particular substance will enter the cell or leave the cell? And what mechanisms actually drive molecules across membranes? We will address these questions next as we explore two modes of membrane traffic: passive transport and active transport.

CONCEPT CHECK 7.2

1. Two molecules that can cross a lipid bilayer without help from membrane proteins are O_2 and CO_2. What property allows this to occur?
2. Why is a transport protein needed to move water molecules rapidly and in large quantities across a membrane?
3. **MAKE CONNECTIONS** Aquaporins exclude passage of hydronium ions (H_3O^+; see pp. 52–53). Recent research on fat metabolism has shown that some aquaporins allow passage of glycerol, a three-carbon alcohol (see Figure 5.10, p. 75), as well as H_2O. Since H_3O^+ is much closer in size to water than is glycerol, what do you suppose is the basis of this selectivity?

For suggested answers, see Appendix A.

CONCEPT 7.3

Passive transport is diffusion of a substance across a membrane with no energy investment

Molecules have a type of energy called thermal energy (heat), due to their constant motion. One result of this motion is **diffusion**, the movement of molecules of any substance so that they spread out evenly into the available space. Each molecule moves randomly, yet diffusion of a *population* of molecules may be directional. To understand this process, let's imagine a synthetic membrane separating pure water from a solution of a dye in water. Study **Figure 7.13a** carefully to appreciate how diffusion would result in both solutions having equal concentrations of the dye molecules. Once that point is reached, there will be a dynamic equilibrium, with as many dye molecules crossing the membrane each second in one direction as in the other.

We can now state a simple rule of diffusion: In the absence of other forces, a substance will diffuse from where it is more concentrated to where it is less concentrated. Put another way, any substance will diffuse down its **concentration gradient**, the region along which the density of a chemical substance increases or decreases (in this case, decreases). No work must be done to make this happen; diffusion is a spontaneous process, needing no input of energy. Note that each substance diffuses down its *own* concentration gradient, unaffected by the concentration gradients of other substances **(Figure 7.13b)**.

(a) Diffusion of one solute. The membrane has pores large enough for molecules of dye to pass through. Random movement of dye molecules will cause some to pass through the pores; this will happen more often on the side with more dye molecules. The dye diffuses from where it is more concentrated to where it is less concentrated (called diffusing down a concentration gradient). This leads to a dynamic equilibrium: The solute molecules continue to cross the membrane, but at equal rates in both directions.

(b) Diffusion of two solutes. Solutions of two different dyes are separated by a membrane that is permeable to both. Each dye diffuses down its own concentration gradient. There will be a net diffusion of the purple dye toward the left, even though the *total* solute concentration was initially greater on the left side.

▲ **Figure 7.13 The diffusion of solutes across a synthetic membrane.** Each of the large arrows under the diagrams shows the net diffusion of the dye molecules of that color.

Much of the traffic across cell membranes occurs by diffusion. When a substance is more concentrated on one side of a membrane than on the other, there is a tendency for the substance to diffuse across the membrane down its concentration gradient (assuming that the membrane is permeable to that substance). One important example is the uptake of oxygen by a cell performing cellular respiration. Dissolved oxygen diffuses into the cell across the plasma membrane. As long as cellular respiration consumes the O_2 as it enters, diffusion into the cell will continue because the concentration gradient favors movement in that direction.

The diffusion of a substance across a biological membrane is called **passive transport** because the cell does not have to expend energy to make it happen. The concentration gradient itself represents potential energy (see Chapter 2, p. 35) and drives diffusion. Remember, however, that membranes are selectively permeable and therefore have different effects on the rates of diffusion of various molecules. In the case of water, aquaporins allow water to diffuse very rapidly across the membranes of certain cells. As we'll see next, the movement of water across the plasma membrane has important consequences for cells.

Effects of Osmosis on Water Balance

To see how two solutions with different solute concentrations interact, picture a U-shaped glass tube with a selectively permeable artificial membrane separating two sugar solutions **(Figure 7.14)**. Pores in this synthetic membrane are too small for sugar molecules to pass through but large enough for water molecules. How does this affect the *water* concentration? It seems logical that the solution with the higher concentration of solute would have the lower concentration of water and that water would diffuse into it from the other side for that reason. However, for a dilute solution like most biological fluids, solutes do not affect the water concentration significantly. Instead, tight clustering of water molecules around the hydrophilic solute molecules makes some of the water unavailable to cross the membrane. It is the difference in *free* water concentration that is important. In the end, the effect is the same: Water diffuses across the membrane from the region of lower solute concentration (higher free water concentration) to that of higher solute concentration (lower free water concentration) until the solute concentrations on both sides of the membrane are equal. The diffusion of free water across a selectively permeable membrane, whether artificial or cellular, is called **osmosis**. The movement of water across cell membranes and the balance of water between the cell and its environment are crucial to organisms. Let's now apply to living cells what we have learned about osmosis in artificial systems.

Water Balance of Cells Without Walls

To explain the behavior of a cell in a solution, we must consider both solute concentration and membrane permeability.

▲ **Figure 7.14 Osmosis.** Two sugar solutions of different concentrations are separated by a membrane that the solvent (water) can pass through but the solute (sugar) cannot. Water molecules move randomly and may cross in either direction, but overall, water diffuses from the solution with less concentrated solute to that with more concentrated solute. This diffusion of water, or osmosis, equalizes the sugar concentrations on both sides.

WHAT IF? *If an orange dye capable of passing through the membrane was added to the left side of the tube above, how would it be distributed at the end of the experiment? (See Figure 7.13.) Would the final solution levels in the tube be affected?*

Both factors are taken into account in the concept of **tonicity**, the ability of a surrounding solution to cause a cell to gain or lose water. The tonicity of a solution depends in part on its concentration of solutes that cannot cross the membrane (nonpenetrating solutes) relative to that inside the cell. If there is a higher concentration of nonpenetrating solutes in the surrounding solution, water will tend to leave the cell, and vice versa.

If a cell without a wall, such as an animal cell, is immersed in an environment that is **isotonic** to the cell (*iso* means "same"), there will be no *net* movement of water across the plasma membrane. Water diffuses across the membrane, but at the same rate in both directions. In an isotonic environment, the volume of an animal cell is stable **(Figure 7.15a**, on the next page).

Now let's transfer the cell to a solution that is **hypertonic** to the cell (*hyper* means "more," in this case referring to nonpenetrating solutes). The cell will lose water, shrivel, and probably die. This is one way an increase in the salinity (saltiness) of a lake can kill animals there; if the lake water becomes hypertonic to the animals' cells, the cells might shrivel and

(a) Animal cell. An animal cell fares best in an isotonic environment unless it has special adaptations that offset the osmotic uptake or loss of water.

Hypotonic solution

H_2O

Lysed

Isotonic solution

H_2O → H_2O

Normal

Hypertonic solution

H_2O

Shriveled

(b) Plant cell. Plant cells are turgid (firm) and generally healthiest in a hypotonic environment, where the uptake of water is eventually balanced by the wall pushing back on the cell.

H_2O Cell wall

Turgid (normal)

H_2O → H_2O

Flaccid

H_2O

Plasmolyzed

▲ **Figure 7.15 The water balance of living cells.** How living cells react to changes in the solute concentration of their environment depends on whether or not they have cell walls. **(a)** Animal cells, such as this red blood cell, do not have cell walls. **(b)** Plant cells do. (Arrows indicate net water movement after the cells were first placed in these solutions.)

die. However, taking up too much water can be just as hazardous to an animal cell as losing water. If we place the cell in a solution that is **hypotonic** to the cell (*hypo* means "less"), water will enter the cell faster than it leaves, and the cell will swell and lyse (burst) like an overfilled water balloon.

A cell without rigid walls can tolerate neither excessive uptake nor excessive loss of water. This problem of water balance is automatically solved if such a cell lives in isotonic surroundings. Seawater is isotonic to many marine invertebrates. The cells of most terrestrial (land-dwelling) animals are bathed in an extracellular fluid that is isotonic to the cells. In hypertonic or hypotonic environments, however, organisms that lack rigid cell walls must have other adaptations for **osmoregulation**, the control of solute concentrations and water balance. For example, the unicellular protist *Paramecium caudatum* lives in pond water, which is hypotonic to the cell. *P. caudatum* has a plasma membrane that is much less permeable to water than the membranes of most other cells, but this only slows the uptake of water, which continually enters the cell. The *P. caudatum*

Contractile vacuole

50 μm

▲ **Figure 7.16 The contractile vacuole of *Paramecium caudatum*.** The vacuole collects fluid from a system of canals in the cytoplasm. When full, the vacuole and canals contract, expelling fluid from the cell (LM).

cell doesn't burst because it is also equipped with a contractile vacuole, an organelle that functions as a bilge pump to force water out of the cell as fast as it enters by osmosis **(Figure 7.16)**. We will examine other evolutionary adaptations for osmoregulation in Chapter 44.

Water Balance of Cells with Walls

The cells of plants, prokaryotes, fungi, and some protists are surrounded by walls (see Figure 6.28). When such a cell is immersed in a hypotonic solution—bathed in rainwater, for example—the wall helps maintain the cell's water balance. Consider a plant cell. Like an animal cell, the plant cell swells as water enters by osmosis **(Figure 7.15b)**. However, the relatively inelastic wall will expand only so much before it exerts a back pressure on the cell, called *turgor pressure*, that opposes further water uptake. At this point, the cell is **turgid** (very firm), which is the healthy state for most plant cells. Plants that are not woody, such as most houseplants, depend for mechanical support on cells kept turgid by a surrounding hypotonic solution. If a plant's cells and their surroundings are isotonic, there is no net tendency for water to enter, and the cells become **flaccid** (limp).

However, a wall is of no advantage if the cell is immersed in a hypertonic environment. In this case, a plant cell, like an animal cell, will lose water to its surroundings and shrink. As the plant cell shrivels, its plasma membrane pulls away from the wall. This phenomenon, called **plasmolysis**, causes the plant to wilt and can lead to plant death. The walled cells of bacteria and fungi also plasmolyze in hypertonic environments.

Facilitated Diffusion: Passive Transport Aided by Proteins

Let's look more closely at how water and certain hydrophilic solutes cross a membrane. As mentioned earlier, many polar molecules and ions impeded by the lipid bilayer of the membrane diffuse passively with the help of transport proteins that span the membrane. This phenomenon is called **facilitated diffusion**. Cell biologists are still trying to learn exactly how various transport proteins facilitate diffusion. Most transport proteins are very specific: They transport some substances but not others.

As described earlier, the two types of transport proteins are channel proteins and carrier proteins. Channel proteins simply provide corridors that allow specific molecules or ions to cross the membrane **(Figure 7.17a)**. The hydrophilic passageways

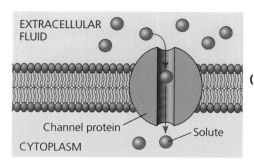

EXTRACELLULAR
FLUID

Channel protein

CYTOPLASM

Solute

(a) A channel protein (purple) has a channel through which water molecules or a specific solute can pass.

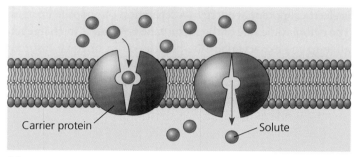

Carrier protein

Solute

(b) A carrier protein alternates between two shapes, moving a solute across the membrane during the shape change.

▲ **Figure 7.17 Two types of transport proteins that carry out facilitated diffusion.** In both cases, the protein can transport the solute in either direction, but the net movement is down the concentration gradient of the solute.

provided by these proteins can allow water molecules or small ions to diffuse very quickly from one side of the membrane to the other. Aquaporins, the water channel proteins, facilitate the massive amounts of diffusion that occur in plant cells and in animal cells such as red blood cells (see Figure 7.15). Certain kidney cells also have a high number of aquaporins, allowing them to reclaim water from urine before it is excreted. If the kidneys did not perform this function, you would excrete about 180 L of urine per day—and have to drink an equal volume of water!

Channel proteins that transport ions are called **ion channels**. Many ion channels function as **gated channels**, which open or close in response to a stimulus. For some gated channels, the stimulus is electrical. The ion channel shown in Figure 7.1, for example, opens in response to an electrical stimulus, allowing potassium ions to leave the cell. Other gated channels open or close when a specific substance other than the one to be transported binds to the channel. Both types of gated channels are important in the functioning of the nervous system.

Carrier proteins, such as the glucose transporter mentioned earlier, seem to undergo a subtle change in shape that somehow translocates the solute-binding site across the membrane **(Figure 7.17b)**. Such a change in shape may be triggered by the binding and release of the transported molecule. Like ion channels, carrier proteins involved in facilitated diffusion result in the net movement of a substance

down its concentration gradient. No energy input is thus required: This is passive transport.

In certain inherited diseases, specific transport systems are either defective or missing altogether. An example is cystinuria, a human disease characterized by the absence of a carrier protein that transports cysteine and some other amino acids across the membranes of kidney cells. Kidney cells normally reabsorb these amino acids from the urine and return them to the blood, but an individual afflicted with cystinuria develops painful stones from amino acids that accumulate and crystallize in the kidneys.

CONCEPT CHECK 7.3

1. How do you think a cell performing cellular respiration rids itself of the resulting CO_2?
2. In the supermarket, produce is often sprayed with water. Explain why this makes vegetables look crisp.
3. **WHAT IF?** If a *Paramecium caudatum* swims from a hypotonic to an isotonic environment, will its contractile vacuole become more active or less? Why?

For suggested answers, see Appendix A.

CONCEPT 7.4

Active transport uses energy to move solutes against their gradients

Despite the help of transport proteins, facilitated diffusion is considered passive transport because the solute is moving down its concentration gradient, a process that requires no energy. Facilitated diffusion speeds transport of a solute by providing efficient passage through the membrane, but it does not alter the direction of transport. Some transport proteins, however, can move solutes against their concentration gradients, across the plasma membrane from the side where they are less concentrated (whether inside or outside) to the side where they are more concentrated.

The Need for Energy in Active Transport

To pump a solute across a membrane against its gradient requires work; the cell must expend energy. Therefore, this type of membrane traffic is called **active transport**. The transport proteins that move solutes against their concentration gradients are all carrier proteins rather than channel proteins. This makes sense because when channel proteins are open, they merely allow solutes to diffuse down their concentration gradients rather than picking them up and transporting them against their gradients.

Active transport enables a cell to maintain internal concentrations of small solutes that differ from concentrations in its environment. For example, compared with its surroundings,

① Cytoplasmic Na⁺ binds to the sodium-potassium pump. The affinity for Na⁺ is high when the protein has this shape.

② Na⁺ binding stimulates phosphorylation by ATP.

③ Phosphorylation leads to a change in protein shape, reducing its affinity for Na⁺, which is released outside.

④ The new shape has a high affinity for K⁺, which binds on the extracellular side and triggers release of the phosphate group.

⑤ Loss of the phosphate group restores the protein's original shape, which has a lower affinity for K⁺.

⑥ K⁺ is released; affinity for Na⁺ is high again, and the cycle repeats.

▲ **Figure 7.18 The sodium-potassium pump: a specific case of active transport.** This transport system pumps ions against steep concentration gradients: Sodium ion concentration ([Na⁺]) is high outside the cell and low inside, while potassium ion concentration ([K⁺]) is low outside the cell and high inside. The pump oscillates between two shapes in a cycle that moves 3 Na⁺ out of the cell for every 2 K⁺ pumped into the cell. The two shapes have different affinities for Na⁺ and K⁺. ATP powers the shape change by transferring a phosphate group to the transport protein (phosphorylating the protein).

an animal cell has a much higher concentration of potassium ions (K⁺) and a much lower concentration of sodium ions (Na⁺). The plasma membrane helps maintain these steep gradients by pumping Na⁺ out of the cell and K⁺ into the cell.

As in other types of cellular work, ATP supplies the energy for most active transport. One way ATP can power active transport is by transferring its terminal phosphate group

directly to the transport protein. This can induce the protein to change its shape in a manner that translocates a solute bound to the protein across the membrane. One transport system that works this way is the **sodium-potassium pump**, which exchanges Na⁺ for K⁺ across the plasma membrane of animal cells (**Figure 7.18**). The distinction between passive transport and active transport is reviewed in **Figure 7.19**.

How Ion Pumps Maintain Membrane Potential

All cells have voltages across their plasma membranes. Voltage is electrical potential energy—a separation of opposite charges. The cytoplasmic side of the membrane is negative in charge relative to the extracellular side because of an unequal distribution of anions and cations on the two sides. The voltage across a membrane, called a **membrane potential**, ranges from about −50 to −200 millivolts (mV). (The minus sign indicates that the inside of the cell is negative relative to the outside.)

The membrane potential acts like a battery, an energy source that affects the traffic of all charged substances across the membrane. Because the inside of the cell is negative compared with the outside, the membrane potential favors the passive transport of cations into the cell and anions out of the cell. Thus, *two* forces drive the diffusion of ions across a membrane: a chemical force (the ion's concentration gradient) and an electrical force (the effect of the membrane potential on

▼ **Figure 7.19 Review: passive and active transport.**

Passive transport. Substances diffuse spontaneously down their concentration gradients, crossing a membrane with no expenditure of energy by the cell. The rate of diffusion can be greatly increased by transport proteins in the membrane.

Active transport. Some transport proteins act as pumps, moving substances across a membrane against their concentration (or electrochemical) gradients. Energy for this work is usually supplied by ATP.

Diffusion. Hydrophobic molecules and (at a slow rate) very small uncharged polar molecules can diffuse through the lipid bilayer.

Facilitated diffusion. Many hydrophilic substances diffuse through membranes with the assistance of transport proteins, either channel proteins (left) or carrier proteins (right).

? *For each solute in the right panel, describe its direction of movement, and state whether it is going with or against its concentration gradient.*

the ion's movement). This combination of forces acting on an ion is called the **electrochemical gradient.**

In the case of ions, then, we must refine our concept of passive transport: An ion diffuses not simply down its *concentration* gradient but, more exactly, down its *electrochemical* gradient. For example, the concentration of Na^+ inside a resting nerve cell is much lower than outside it. When the cell is stimulated, gated channels open that facilitate Na^+ diffusion. Sodium ions then "fall" down their electrochemical gradient, driven by the concentration gradient of Na^+ and by the attraction of these cations to the negative side (inside) of the membrane. In this example, both electrical and chemical contributions to the electrochemical gradient act in the same direction across the membrane, but this is not always so. In cases where electrical forces due to the membrane potential oppose the simple diffusion of an ion down its concentration gradient, active transport may be necessary. You'll learn about the importance of electrochemical gradients and membrane potentials in the transmission of nerve impulses.

Some membrane proteins that actively transport ions contribute to the membrane potential. An example is the sodium-potassium pump. Notice in Figure 7.18 that the pump does not translocate Na^+ and K^+ one for one, but pumps three sodium ions out of the cell for every two potassium ions it pumps into the cell. With each "crank" of the pump, there is a net transfer of one positive charge from the cytoplasm to the extracellular fluid, a process that stores energy as voltage. A transport protein that generates voltage across a membrane is called an **electrogenic pump**. The sodium-potassium pump appears to be the major electrogenic pump of animal cells. The main electrogenic pump of plants, fungi, and bacteria is a **proton pump**, which actively transports protons (hydrogen ions, H^+) out of the cell. The pumping of H^+ transfers positive charge from the cytoplasm to the extracellular solution **(Figure 7.20)**. By generating voltage across membranes, electrogenic pumps help store energy that can be tapped for cellular work. One important use of proton gradients in the cell is for ATP synthesis during cellular respiration, as you will see in Chapter 9. Another is a type of membrane traffic called cotransport.

Cotransport: Coupled Transport by a Membrane Protein

A single ATP-powered pump that transports a specific solute can indirectly drive the active transport of several other solutes in a mechanism called **cotransport**. A substance that has been pumped across a membrane can do work as it moves back across the membrane by diffusion, analogous to water that has been pumped uphill and performs work as it flows back down. Another transport protein, a cotransporter separate from the pump, can couple the "downhill" diffusion of this substance to the "uphill" transport of a second substance against its own concentration (or electrochemical) gradient. For example, a plant cell uses the gradient of H^+ generated by its proton pumps to drive the active transport of amino acids, sugars, and several other nutrients into the cell. One transport protein couples the return of H^+ to the transport of sucrose into the cell **(Figure 7.21)**. This protein can translocate sucrose into the cell against a concentration gradient, but only if the sucrose molecule travels in the company of a hydrogen ion. The hydrogen ion uses the transport protein as an avenue to diffuse down the electrochemical gradient maintained by the proton pump. Plants use sucrose-H^+ cotransport to load sucrose produced by photosynthesis into cells in the veins of leaves. The vascular tissue of the plant can then distribute the sugar to nonphotosynthetic organs, such as roots.

What we know about cotransport proteins in animal cells has helped us find more effective treatments for diarrhea, a serious problem in developing countries. Normally, sodium in waste is reabsorbed in the colon, maintaining constant levels in the body, but diarrhea expels waste so rapidly that reabsorption is not possible, and sodium levels fall precipitously.

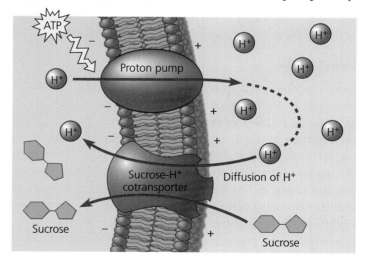

▲ Figure 7.21 **Cotransport: active transport driven by a concentration gradient.** A carrier protein, such as this sucrose-H^+ cotransporter in a plant cell, is able to use the diffusion of H^+ down its electrochemical gradient into the cell to drive the uptake of sucrose. The H^+ gradient is maintained by an ATP-driven proton pump that concentrates H^+ outside the cell, thus storing potential energy that can be used for active transport, in this case of sucrose. Thus, ATP indirectly provides the energy necessary for cotransport. (The cell wall is not shown.)

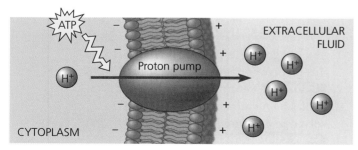

▲ Figure 7.20 **A proton pump.** Proton pumps are electrogenic pumps that store energy by generating voltage (charge separation) across membranes. A proton pump translocates positive charge in the form of hydrogen ions. The voltage and H^+ concentration gradient represent a dual energy source that can drive other processes, such as the uptake of nutrients. Most proton pumps are powered by ATP.

To treat this life-threatening condition, patients are given a solution to drink containing high concentrations of salt (NaCl) and glucose. The solutes are taken up by sodium-glucose cotransporters on the surface of intestinal cells and passed through the cells into the blood. This simple treatment has lowered infant mortality worldwide.

CONCEPT CHECK 7.4

1. Sodium-potassium pumps help nerve cells establish a voltage across their plasma membranes. Do these pumps use ATP or produce ATP? Explain.
2. Explain why the sodium-potassium pump in Figure 7.18 would not be considered a cotransporter.
3. **MAKE CONNECTIONS** Review the characteristics of the lysosome in Concept 6.4 (pp. 106–107). Given the internal environment of a lysosome, what transport protein might you expect to see in its membrane?

For suggested answers, see Appendix A.

CONCEPT 7.5

Bulk transport across the plasma membrane occurs by exocytosis and endocytosis

Water and small solutes enter and leave the cell by diffusing through the lipid bilayer of the plasma membrane or by being pumped or moved across the membrane by transport proteins. However, large molecules, such as proteins and polysaccharides, as well as larger particles, generally cross the membrane in bulk by mechanisms that involve packaging in vesicles. Like active transport, these processes require energy.

Exocytosis

As we described in Chapter 6, the cell secretes certain biological molecules by the fusion of vesicles with the plasma membrane; this process is called **exocytosis**. A transport vesicle that has budded from the Golgi apparatus moves along microtubules of the cytoskeleton to the plasma membrane. When the vesicle membrane and plasma membrane come into contact, specific proteins rearrange the lipid molecules of the two bilayers so that the two membranes fuse. The contents of the vesicle then spill to the outside of the cell, and the vesicle membrane becomes part of the plasma membrane (see Figure 7.12, step 4).

Many secretory cells use exocytosis to export products. For example, the cells in the pancreas that make insulin secrete it into the extracellular fluid by exocytosis. In another example, neurons (nerve cells) use exocytosis to release neurotransmitters that signal other neurons or muscle cells. When plant cells are making walls, exocytosis delivers proteins and carbohydrates from Golgi vesicles to the outside of the cell.

Endocytosis

In **endocytosis**, the cell takes in biological molecules and particulate matter by forming new vesicles from the plasma membrane. Although the proteins involved in the processes are different, the events of endocytosis look like the reverse of exocytosis. A small area of the plasma membrane sinks inward to form a pocket. As the pocket deepens, it pinches in, forming a vesicle containing material that had been outside the cell. Study **Figure 7.22** carefully to understand the three types of endocytosis: phagocytosis ("cellular eating"), pinocytosis ("cellular drinking"), and receptor-mediated endocytosis.

Human cells use receptor-mediated endocytosis to take in cholesterol for membrane synthesis and the synthesis of other steroids. Cholesterol travels in the blood in particles called low-density lipoproteins (LDLs), each a complex of lipids and a protein. LDLs bind to LDL receptors on plasma membranes and then enter the cells by endocytosis. (LDLs thus act as **ligands**, a term for any molecule that binds specifically to a receptor site on another molecule.) In humans with familial hypercholesterolemia, an inherited disease characterized by a very high level of cholesterol in the blood, LDLs cannot enter cells because the LDL receptor proteins are defective or missing. Consequently, cholesterol accumulates in the blood, where it contributes to early atherosclerosis, the buildup of lipid deposits within the walls of blood vessels. This buildup causes the walls to bulge inward, thereby narrowing the vessels and impeding blood flow.

Vesicles not only transport substances between the cell and its surroundings but also provide a mechanism for rejuvenating or remodeling the plasma membrane. Endocytosis and exocytosis occur continually in most eukaryotic cells, yet the amount of plasma membrane in a nongrowing cell remains fairly constant. Apparently, the addition of membrane by one process offsets the loss of membrane by the other.

Energy and cellular work have figured prominently in our study of membranes. We have seen, for example, that active transport is powered by ATP. In the next three chapters, you will learn more about how cells acquire chemical energy to do the work of life.

CONCEPT CHECK 7.5

1. As a cell grows, its plasma membrane expands. Does this involve endocytosis or exocytosis? Explain.
2. **DRAW IT** Return to Figure 7.12, and circle a patch of plasma membrane that is coming from a vesicle involved in exocytosis.
3. **MAKE CONNECTIONS** In Concept 6.7 (pp. 119–120), you learned that animal cells make an extracellular matrix (ECM). Describe the cellular pathway of synthesis and deposition of an ECM glycoprotein.

For suggested answers, see Appendix A.

Exploring Endocytosis in Animal Cells

Phagocytosis

EXTRACELLULAR FLUID

Solutes

Pseudopodium

"Food" or other particle

Food vacuole

CYTOPLASM

In **phagocytosis,** a cell engulfs a particle by wrapping pseudopodia (singular, *pseudopodium*) around it and packaging it within a membranous sac called a food vacuole. The particle will be digested after the food vacuole fuses with a lysosome containing hydrolytic enzymes (see Figure 6.13a).

Pseudopodium of amoeba

Bacterium

Food vacuole

1 μm

An amoeba engulfing a bacterium via phagocytosis (TEM).

Pinocytosis

Plasma membrane

Vesicle

In **pinocytosis,** the cell "gulps" droplets of extracellular fluid into tiny vesicles. It is not the fluid itself that is needed by the cell, but the molecules dissolved in the droplets. Because any and all included solutes are taken into the cell, pinocytosis is nonspecific in the substances it transports.

0.5 μm

Pinocytosis vesicles forming (indicated by arrows) in a cell lining a small blood vessel (TEM).

ANIMATION   ***BioFlix*** Visit the Study Area at **www.masteringbiology.com** for the BioFlix® 3-D Animation on Membrane Transport.

Receptor-Mediated Endocytosis

Receptor

Ligand

Coat proteins

Coated pit

Coated vesicle

Receptor-mediated endocytosis enables the cell to acquire bulk quantities of specific substances, even though those substances may not be very concentrated in the extracellular fluid. Embedded in the membrane are proteins with specific receptor sites exposed to the extracellular fluid, to which specific substances (ligands) bind. The receptor proteins then cluster in regions of the membrane called coated pits, which are lined on their cytoplasmic side by a fuzzy layer of coat proteins. Next, each coated pit forms a vesicle containing the ligand molecules. Notice that there are relatively more bound molecules (purple) inside the vesicle, but other molecules (green) are also present. After the ingested material is liberated from the vesicle, the emptied receptors are recycled to the plasma membrane by the same vesicle.

Plasma membrane

Coat proteins

0.25 μm

Top: A coated pit. *Bottom:* A coated vesicle forming during receptor-mediated endocytosis (TEMs).

SUMMARY OF KEY CONCEPTS

CONCEPT 7.1

Cellular membranes are fluid mosaics of lipids and proteins (pp. 125–131)

- The Davson-Danielli sandwich model of the membrane has been replaced by the **fluid mosaic model**, in which **amphipathic** proteins are embedded in the phospholipid bilayer. Proteins with related functions often cluster in patches.
- Phospholipids and some proteins move laterally within the membrane. The unsaturated hydrocarbon tails of some phospholipids keep membranes fluid at lower temperatures, while cholesterol helps membranes resist changes in fluidity caused by temperature changes. Differences in membrane lipid composition, as well as the ability to change lipid composition, are evolutionary adaptations that ensure membrane fluidity.
- **Integral proteins** are embedded in the lipid bilayer; **peripheral proteins** are attached to the membrane surface. The functions of membrane proteins include transport, enzymatic activity, signal transduction, cell-cell recognition, intercellular joining, and attachment to the cytoskeleton and extracellular matrix. Short chains of sugars linked to proteins (in **glycoproteins**) and lipids (in **glycolipids**) on the exterior side of the plasma membrane interact with surface molecules of other cells.
- Membrane proteins and lipids are synthesized in the ER and modified in the ER and Golgi apparatus. The inside and outside faces of membranes differ in molecular composition.

? *In what ways are membranes crucial to life?*

CONCEPT 7.2

Membrane structure results in selective permeability (pp. 131–132)

- A cell must exchange molecules and ions with its surroundings, a process controlled by the **selective permeability** of the plasma membrane. Hydrophobic substances are soluble in lipid and pass through membranes rapidly, whereas polar molecules and ions generally require specific **transport proteins** to cross the membrane.

? *How do **aquaporins** affect the permeability of a membrane?*

CONCEPT 7.3

Passive transport is diffusion of a substance across a membrane with no energy investment (pp. 132–135)

- **Diffusion** is the spontaneous movement of a substance down its **concentration gradient**. Water diffuses out through the permeable membrane of a cell (**osmosis**) if the solution outside has a higher solute concentration (**hypertonic**) than the cytosol; water enters the cell if the solution has a lower solute concentration (**hypotonic**). If the concentrations are equal (**isotonic**), no net osmosis occurs. Cell survival depends on balancing water uptake and loss. Cells lacking walls (as in animals and some protists) are isotonic with their environments or have adaptations for **osmoregulation**. Plants, prokaryotes, fungi, and some protists have relatively inelastic cell walls, so the cells don't burst in a hypotonic environment.
- In a type of **passive transport** called **facilitated diffusion**, a transport protein speeds the movement of water or a solute across a membrane down its concentration gradient. **Ion channels**, some of which are **gated channels**, facilitate the diffusion of ions across a membrane. Carrier proteins can undergo changes in shape that translocate bound solutes across the membrane.

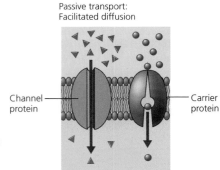

Passive transport:
Facilitated diffusion

Channel protein · Carrier protein

? *What happens to a cell placed in a hypertonic solution? Describe the free water concentration inside and out.*

CONCEPT 7.4

Active transport uses energy to move solutes against their gradients (pp. 135–138)

- Specific membrane proteins use energy, usually in the form of ATP, to do the work of **active transport**. The **sodium-potassium pump** is an example.
- Ions can have both a concentration (chemical) gradient and an electrical gradient (voltage). These gradients combine in the **electrochemical gradient**, which determines the net direction of ionic diffusion. **Electrogenic pumps**, such as the sodium-potassium pump and **proton pumps**, are transport proteins that contribute to electrochemical gradients.
- **Cotransport** of two solutes occurs when a membrane protein enables the "downhill" diffusion of one solute to drive the "uphill" transport of the other.

Active transport

? *ATP is not directly involved in the functioning of a cotransporter. Why, then, is cotransport considered active transport?*

CONCEPT 7.5

Bulk transport across the plasma membrane occurs by exocytosis and endocytosis (p. 138)

- In **exocytosis**, transport vesicles migrate to the plasma membrane, fuse with it, and release their contents. In **endocytosis**, molecules enter cells within vesicles that pinch inward from the plasma membrane. The three types of endocytosis are **phagocytosis**, **pinocytosis**, and **receptor-mediated endocytosis**.

? *Which type of endocytosis involves ligands? What does this type of transport enable a cell to do?*

TEST YOUR UNDERSTANDING

LEVEL 1: KNOWLEDGE/COMPREHENSION

1. In what way do the membranes of a eukaryotic cell vary?
   a. Phospholipids are found only in certain membranes.
   b. Certain proteins are unique to each membrane.

c. Only certain membranes of the cell are selectively permeable.

d. Only certain membranes are constructed from amphipathic molecules.

e. Some membranes have hydrophobic surfaces exposed to the cytoplasm, while others have hydrophilic surfaces facing the cytoplasm.

2. According to the fluid mosaic model of membrane structure, proteins of the membrane are mostly
   a. spread in a continuous layer over the inner and outer surfaces of the membrane.
   b. confined to the hydrophobic interior of the membrane.
   c. embedded in a lipid bilayer.
   d. randomly oriented in the membrane, with no fixed inside-outside polarity.
   e. free to depart from the fluid membrane and dissolve in the surrounding solution.

3. Which of the following factors would tend to increase membrane fluidity?
   a. a greater proportion of unsaturated phospholipids
   b. a greater proportion of saturated phospholipids
   c. a lower temperature
   d. a relatively high protein content in the membrane
   e. a greater proportion of relatively large glycolipids compared with lipids having smaller molecular masses

LEVEL 2: APPLICATION/ANALYSIS

4. Which of the following processes includes all others?
   a. osmosis
   b. diffusion of a solute across a membrane
   c. facilitated diffusion
   d. passive transport
   e. transport of an ion down its electrochemical gradient

5. Based on Figure 7.21, which of these experimental treatments would increase the rate of sucrose transport into the cell?
   a. decreasing extracellular sucrose concentration
   b. decreasing extracellular pH
   c. decreasing cytoplasmic pH
   d. adding an inhibitor that blocks the regeneration of ATP
   e. adding a substance that makes the membrane more permeable to hydrogen ions

6. **DRAW IT** An artificial "cell" consisting of an aqueous solution enclosed in a selectively permeable membrane is immersed in a beaker containing a different solution, the "environment," as shown below. The membrane is permeable to water and to the simple sugars glucose and fructose but impermeable to the disaccharide sucrose.

   a. Draw solid arrows to indicate the net movement of solutes into and/or out of the cell.

   b. Is the solution outside the cell isotonic, hypotonic, or hypertonic?

"Cell"
0.03 M sucrose
0.02 M glucose

"Environment"
0.01 M sucrose
0.01 M glucose
0.01 M fructose

   c. Draw a dashed arrow to show the net osmosis, if any.
   d. Will the artificial cell become more flaccid, more turgid, or stay the same?
   e. Eventually, will the two solutions have the same or different solute concentrations?

LEVEL 3: SYNTHESIS/EVALUATION

7. **EVOLUTION CONNECTION**
   Paramecium and other protists that live in hypotonic environments have cell membranes that limit water uptake, while those living in isotonic environments have membranes that are more permeable to water. What water regulation adaptations might have evolved in protists in hypertonic habitats such as Great Salt Lake? In habitats with changing salt concentration?

8. **SCIENTIFIC INQUIRY**
   An experiment is designed to study the mechanism of sucrose uptake by plant cells. Cells are immersed in a sucrose solution, and the pH of the solution is monitored. Samples of the cells are taken at intervals, and their sucrose concentration is measured. After a decrease in the pH of the solution to a steady, slightly acidic level, sucrose uptake begins. Propose a hypothesis for these results. What do you think would happen if an inhibitor of ATP regeneration by the cell were added to the beaker once the pH is at a steady level? Explain.

9. **SCIENCE, TECHNOLOGY, AND SOCIETY**
   Extensive irrigation in arid regions causes salts to accumulate in the soil. (When water evaporates, salts that were dissolved in the water are left behind in the soil.) Based on what you learned about water balance in plant cells, explain why increased soil salinity (saltiness) might be harmful to crops. Suggest ways to minimize damage. What costs are attached to your solutions?

10. **WRITE ABOUT A THEME**

    Environmental Interactions A human pancreatic cell obtains O_2, fuel molecules such as glucose, and building materials such as amino acids and cholesterol from its environment, and it releases CO_2 as a waste product of cellular respiration. In response to hormonal signals, the cell secretes digestive enzymes. It also regulates its ion concentrations by exchange with its environment. Based on what you have just learned about the structure and function of cellular membranes, write a short essay (100–150 words) that describes how such a cell accomplishes these interactions with its environment.

For selected answers, see Appendix A.

Mastering BIOLOGY www.masteringbiology.com

1. MasteringBiology® Assignments
Make Connections Tutorial Plasma Membranes (Chapter 7) and Phospholipid Structure (Chapter 5)
BioFlix Tutorials Membrane Transport: Diffusion and Passive Transport • The Sodium-Potassium Pump • Cotransport • Bulk Transport
Tutorial Osmosis
Activities Membrane Structure • Selective Permeability of Membranes • Diffusion • Diffusion and Osmosis • Facilitated Diffusion • Membrane Transport Proteins • Osmosis and Water Balance in Cells • Active Transport • Exocytosis and Endocytosis
Questions Student Misconceptions • Reading Quiz • Multiple Choice • End-of-Chapter

2. eText
Read your book online, search, take notes, highlight text, and more.

3. The Study Area
Practice Tests • Cumulative Test • **BioFlix** 3-D Animations • MP3 Tutor Sessions • Videos • Activities • Investigations • Lab Media • Audio Glossary • Word Study Tools • Art

8

An Introduction to Metabolism

▲ **Figure 8.1 What causes these two squid to glow?**

KEY CONCEPTS

8.1 An organism's metabolism transforms matter and energy, subject to the laws of thermodynamics

8.2 The free-energy change of a reaction tells us whether or not the reaction occurs spontaneously

8.3 ATP powers cellular work by coupling exergonic reactions to endergonic reactions

8.4 Enzymes speed up metabolic reactions by lowering energy barriers

8.5 Regulation of enzyme activity helps control metabolism

OVERVIEW

The Energy of Life

The living cell is a chemical factory in miniature, where thousands of reactions occur within a microscopic space. Sugars can be converted to amino acids that are linked together into proteins when needed, and when food is digested, pro-

teins are dismantled into amino acids that can be converted to sugars. Small molecules are assembled into polymers, which may be hydrolyzed later as the needs of the cell change. In multicellular organisms, many cells export chemical products that are used in other parts of the organism. The process called cellular respiration drives the cellular economy by extracting the energy stored in sugars and other fuels. Cells apply this energy to perform various types of work, such as the transport of solutes across the plasma membrane, which we discussed in Chapter 7. In a more exotic example, cells of the two firefly squid (*Watasenia scintillans*) shown mating in **Figure 8.1** convert the energy stored in certain organic molecules to light, a process called bioluminescence. (The light pattern aids in mate recognition and protection from predators lurking below.) Bioluminescence and other metabolic activities carried out by a cell are precisely coordinated and controlled. In its complexity, its efficiency, and its responsiveness to subtle changes, the cell is peerless as a chemical factory. The concepts of metabolism that you learn in this chapter will help you understand how matter and energy flow during life's processes and how that flow is regulated.

CONCEPT 8.1

An organism's metabolism transforms matter and energy, subject to the laws of thermodynamics

The totality of an organism's chemical reactions is called **metabolism** (from the Greek *metabole*, change). Metabolism is an emergent property of life that arises from orderly interactions between molecules.

Organization of the Chemistry of Life into Metabolic Pathways

We can picture a cell's metabolism as an elaborate road map of the thousands of chemical reactions that occur in a cell, arranged as intersecting metabolic pathways. A **metabolic pathway** begins with a specific molecule, which is then altered in a series of defined steps, resulting in a certain product. Each step of the pathway is catalyzed by a specific enzyme:

Analogous to the red, yellow, and green stoplights that control the flow of automobile traffic, mechanisms that regulate enzymes balance metabolic supply and demand.

Metabolism as a whole manages the material and energy resources of the cell. Some metabolic pathways release energy by breaking down complex molecules to simpler compounds. These degradative processes are called **catabolic pathways**, or breakdown pathways. A major pathway of catabolism is cellular respiration, in which the sugar glucose and other organic fuels are broken down in the presence of oxygen to carbon dioxide and water. (Pathways can have more than one starting molecule and/or product.) Energy that was stored in the organic molecules becomes available to do the work of the cell, such as ciliary beating or membrane transport. **Anabolic pathways**, in contrast, consume energy to build complicated molecules from simpler ones; they are sometimes called biosynthetic pathways. Examples of anabolism are the synthesis of an amino acid from simpler molecules and the synthesis of a protein from amino acids. Catabolic and anabolic pathways are the "downhill" and "uphill" avenues of the metabolic landscape. Energy released from the downhill reactions of catabolic pathways can be stored and then used to drive the uphill reactions of anabolic pathways.

In this chapter, we will focus on mechanisms common to metabolic pathways. Because energy is fundamental to all metabolic processes, a basic knowledge of energy is necessary to understand how the living cell works. Although we will use some nonliving examples to study energy, the concepts demonstrated by these examples also apply to **bioenergetics**, the study of how energy flows through living organisms.

Forms of Energy

Energy is the capacity to cause change. In everyday life, energy is important because some forms of energy can be used to do work—that is, to move matter against opposing forces, such as gravity and friction. Put another way, energy is the ability to rearrange a collection of matter. For example, you expend energy to turn the pages of this book, and your cells expend energy in transporting certain substances across membranes. Energy exists in various forms, and the work of life depends on the ability of cells to transform energy from one form to another.

Energy can be associated with the relative motion of objects; this energy is called **kinetic energy**. Moving objects can perform work by imparting motion to other matter: A pool player uses the motion of the cue stick to push the cue ball, which in turn moves the other balls; water gushing through a dam turns turbines; and the contraction of leg muscles pushes bicycle pedals. **Heat**, or **thermal energy**, is kinetic energy associated with the random movement of atoms or molecules. Light is also a type of energy that can be harnessed to perform work, such as powering photosynthesis in green plants.

An object not presently moving may still possess energy. Energy that is not kinetic is called **potential energy**; it is energy that matter possesses because of its location or struc-

ture. Water behind a dam, for instance, possesses energy because of its altitude above sea level. Molecules possess energy because of the arrangement of electrons in the bonds between their atoms. **Chemical energy** is a term used by biologists to refer to the potential energy available for release in a chemical reaction. Recall that catabolic pathways release energy by breaking down complex molecules. Biologists say that these complex molecules, such as glucose, are high in chemical energy. During a catabolic reaction, some bonds are broken and others formed, releasing energy and resulting in lower-energy breakdown products. This transformation also occurs, for example, in the engine of a car when the hydrocarbons of gasoline react explosively with oxygen, releasing the energy that pushes the pistons and producing exhaust. Although less explosive, a similar reaction of food molecules with oxygen provides chemical energy in biological systems, producing carbon dioxide and water as waste products. Biochemical pathways, carried out in the context of cellular structures, enable cells to release chemical energy from food molecules and use the energy to power life processes.

How is energy converted from one form to another? Consider the divers in **Figure 8.2**. The young woman climbing the ladder to the diving platform is releasing chemical energy from the food she ate for lunch and using some of that energy to perform the work of climbing. The kinetic energy of muscle movement is thus being transformed into potential energy due to her increasing height above the water. The young man diving is converting his potential energy to kinetic energy, which is then transferred to the water as he enters it. A small amount of energy is lost as heat due to friction.

A diver has more potential energy on the platform than in the water.

Diving converts potential energy to kinetic energy.

Climbing up converts the kinetic energy of muscle movement to potential energy.

A diver has less potential energy in the water than on the platform.

▲ **Figure 8.2 Transformations between potential and kinetic energy.**

Now let's go back one step and consider the original source of the organic food molecules that provided the necessary chemical energy for the diver to climb the steps. This chemical energy was itself derived from light energy by plants during photosynthesis. Organisms are energy transformers.

The Laws of Energy Transformation

The study of the energy transformations that occur in a collection of matter is called **thermodynamics**. Scientists use the word *system* to denote the matter under study; they refer to the rest of the universe—everything outside the system—as the *surroundings*. An *isolated system*, such as that approximated by liquid in a thermos bottle, is unable to exchange either energy or matter with its surroundings. In an *open system*, energy and matter can be transferred between the system and its surroundings. Organisms are open systems. They absorb energy—for instance, light energy or chemical energy in the form of organic molecules—and release heat and metabolic waste products, such as carbon dioxide, to the surroundings. Two laws of thermodynamics govern energy transformations in organisms and all other collections of matter.

The First Law of Thermodynamics

According to the **first law of thermodynamics**, the energy of the universe is constant: *Energy can be transferred and transformed, but it cannot be created or destroyed.* The first law is also known as the *principle of conservation of energy*. The electric company does not make energy, but merely converts it to a form that is convenient for us to use. By converting sunlight to chemical energy, a plant acts as an energy transformer, not an energy producer.

The brown bear in **Figure 8.3a** will convert the chemical energy of the organic molecules in its food to kinetic and other forms of energy as it carries out biological processes. What happens to this energy after it has performed work? The second law of thermodynamics helps to answer this question.

The Second Law of Thermodynamics

If energy cannot be destroyed, why can't organisms simply recycle their energy over and over again? It turns out that during every energy transfer or transformation, some energy becomes unavailable to do work. In most energy transformations, more usable forms of energy are at least partly converted to heat, which is the energy associated with the random motion of atoms or molecules. Only a small fraction of the chemical energy from the food in Figure 8.3a is transformed into the motion of the brown bear shown in **Figure 8.3b**; most is lost as heat, which dissipates rapidly through the surroundings.

In the process of carrying out chemical reactions that perform various kinds of work, living cells unavoidably convert other forms of energy to heat. A system can put heat to work only when there is a temperature difference that results in the heat flowing from a warmer location to a cooler one. If temperature is uniform, as it is in a living cell, then the only use for heat energy generated during a chemical reaction is to warm a body of matter, such as the organism. (This can make a room crowded with people uncomfortably warm, as each person is carrying out a multitude of chemical reactions!)

A logical consequence of the loss of usable energy during energy transfer or transformation is that each such event makes the universe more disordered. Scientists use a quantity called **entropy** as a measure of disorder, or randomness.

(a) **First law of thermodynamics:** Energy can be transferred or transformed but neither created nor destroyed. For example, chemical reactions in this brown bear (*Ursus arctos*) will convert the chemical (potential) energy in the fish into the kinetic energy of running, shown in (b).

(b) **Second law of thermodynamics:** Every energy transfer or transformation increases the disorder (entropy) of the universe. For example, as it runs, disorder is increased around the bear by the release of heat and small molecules that are the by-products of metabolism. A brown bear can run at speeds up to 35 miles per hour (56 km/hr)—as fast as a racehorse.

▲ **Figure 8.3 The two laws of thermodynamics.**

The more randomly arranged a collection of matter is, the greater its entropy. We can now state the **second law of thermodynamics**: *Every energy transfer or transformation increases the entropy of the universe.* Although order can increase locally, there is an unstoppable trend toward randomization of the universe as a whole.

In many cases, increased entropy is evident in the physical disintegration of a system's organized structure. For example, you can observe increasing entropy in the gradual decay of an unmaintained building. Much of the increasing entropy of the universe is less apparent, however, because it appears as increasing amounts of heat and less ordered forms of matter. As the bear in Figure 8.3b converts chemical energy to kinetic energy, it is also increasing the disorder of its surroundings by producing heat and small molecules, such as the CO_2 it exhales, that are the breakdown products of food.

The concept of entropy helps us understand why certain processes occur without any input of energy. It turns out that for a process to occur on its own, without outside help, it must increase the entropy of the universe. A process that can occur without an input of energy is called a **spontaneous process**. Note that as we're using it here, the word *spontaneous* does not imply that such a process would occur quickly; rather, the word signifies that the process is energetically favorable. (In fact, it may be helpful for you to think of the phrase "energetically favorable" when you read the formal term "spontaneous.") Some spontaneous processes, such as an explosion, may be virtually instantaneous, while others, such as the rusting of an old car over time, are much slower. A process that cannot occur on its own is said to be nonspontaneous; it will happen only if energy is added to the system. We know from experience that certain events occur spontaneously and others do not. For instance, we know that water flows downhill spontaneously but moves uphill only with an input of energy, such as when a machine pumps the water against gravity. This understanding gives us another way to state the second law: *For a process to occur spontaneously, it must increase the entropy of the universe.*

Biological Order and Disorder

Living systems increase the entropy of their surroundings, as predicted by thermodynamic law. It is true that cells create ordered structures from less organized starting materials. For example, simpler molecules are ordered into the more complex structure of an amino acid, and amino acids are ordered into polypeptide chains. At the organismal level as well, complex and beautifully ordered structures result from biological processes that use simpler starting materials **(Figure 8.4)**. However, an organism also takes in organized forms of matter and energy from the surroundings and replaces them with less ordered forms. For example, an animal obtains starch, proteins, and other complex molecules from the food it eats. As catabolic pathways break these molecules down,

▲ **Figure 8.4 Order as a characteristic of life.** Order is evident in the detailed structures of the sea urchin skeleton and the succulent plant shown here. As open systems, organisms can increase their order as long as the order of their surroundings decreases.

the animal releases carbon dioxide and water—small molecules that possess less chemical energy than the food did. The depletion of chemical energy is accounted for by heat generated during metabolism. On a larger scale, energy flows into most ecosystems in the form of light and exits in the form of heat (see Figure 1.6).

During the early history of life, complex organisms evolved from simpler ancestors. For example, we can trace the ancestry of the plant kingdom from much simpler organisms called green algae to more complex flowering plants. However, this increase in organization over time in no way violates the second law. The entropy of a particular system, such as an organism, may actually decrease as long as the total entropy of the *universe*—the system plus its surroundings—increases. Thus, organisms are islands of low entropy in an increasingly random universe. The evolution of biological order is perfectly consistent with the laws of thermodynamics.

CONCEPT CHECK 8.1

1. **MAKE CONNECTIONS** How does the second law of thermodynamics help explain the diffusion of a substance across a membrane? See Figure 7.13 on page 132.
2. Describe the forms of energy found in an apple as it grows on a tree, then falls, then is digested by someone who eats it.
3. **WHAT IF?** If you place a teaspoon of sugar in the bottom of a glass of water, it will dissolve completely over time. Left longer, eventually the water will disappear and the sugar crystals will reappear. Explain these observations in terms of entropy.

For suggested answers, see Appendix A.

The free-energy change of a reaction tells us whether or not the reaction occurs spontaneously

The laws of thermodynamics that we've just discussed apply to the universe as a whole. As biologists, we want to understand the chemical reactions of life—for example, which reactions occur spontaneously and which ones require some input of energy from outside. But how can we know this without assessing the energy and entropy changes in the entire universe for each separate reaction?

Free-Energy Change, ΔG

Recall that the universe is really equivalent to "the system" plus "the surroundings." In 1878, J. Willard Gibbs, a professor at Yale, defined a very useful function called the Gibbs free energy of a system (without considering its surroundings), symbolized by the letter G. We'll refer to the Gibbs free energy simply as free energy. **Free energy** is the portion of a system's energy that can perform work when temperature and pressure are uniform throughout the system, as in a living cell. Let's consider how we determine the free-energy change that occurs when a system changes—for example, during a chemical reaction.

The change in free energy, ΔG, can be calculated for a chemical reaction by applying the following equation:

$$\Delta G = \Delta H - T\Delta S$$

This equation uses only properties of the system (the reaction) itself: ΔH symbolizes the change in the system's *enthalpy* (in biological systems, equivalent to total energy); ΔS is the change in the system's entropy; and T is the absolute temperature in Kelvin (K) units (K = °C + 273; see Appendix C).

Once we know the value of ΔG for a process, we can use it to predict whether the process will be spontaneous (that is, whether it is energetically favorable and will occur without an input of energy). More than a century of experiments has shown that only processes with a negative ΔG are spontaneous. For ΔG to be negative, either ΔH must be negative (the system gives up enthalpy and H decreases) or $T\Delta S$ must be positive (the system gives up order and S increases), or both: When ΔH and $T\Delta S$ are tallied, ΔG has a negative value ($\Delta G < 0$) for all spontaneous processes. In other words, every spontaneous process decreases the system's free energy, and processes that have a positive or zero ΔG are never spontaneous.

This information is immensely interesting to biologists, for it gives us the power to predict which kinds of change can happen without help. Such spontaneous changes can be harnessed to perform work. This principle is very important in the study of metabolism, where a major goal is to determine which reactions can supply energy for cellular work.

Free Energy, Stability, and Equilibrium

As we saw in the previous section, when a process occurs spontaneously in a system, we can be sure that ΔG is negative. Another way to think of ΔG is to realize that it represents the difference between the free energy of the final state and the free energy of the initial state:

$$\Delta G = G_{\text{final state}} - G_{\text{initial state}}$$

Thus, ΔG can be negative only when the process involves a loss of free energy during the change from initial state to final state. Because it has less free energy, the system in its final state is less likely to change and is therefore more stable than it was previously.

We can think of free energy as a measure of a system's instability—its tendency to change to a more stable state. Unstable systems (higher G) tend to change in such a way that they become more stable (lower G). For example, a diver on top of a platform is less stable (more likely to fall) than when floating in the water; a drop of concentrated dye is less stable (more likely to disperse) than when the dye is spread randomly through the liquid; and a glucose molecule is less stable (more likely to break down) than the simpler molecules into which it can be split **(Figure 8.5)**. Unless something prevents it, each of these systems will move toward greater stability: The diver falls, the solution becomes uniformly colored, and the glucose molecule is broken down.

Another term that describes a state of maximum stability is *equilibrium*, which you learned about in Chapter 2 in connection with chemical reactions. There is an important relationship between free energy and equilibrium, including chemical equilibrium. Recall that most chemical reactions are reversible and proceed to a point at which the forward and backward reactions occur at the same rate. The reaction is then said to be at chemical equilibrium, and there is no further net change in the relative concentration of products and reactants.

As a reaction proceeds toward equilibrium, the free energy of the mixture of reactants and products decreases. Free energy increases when a reaction is somehow pushed away from equilibrium, perhaps by removing some of the products (and thus changing their concentration relative to that of the reactants). For a system at equilibrium, G is at its lowest possible value in that system. We can think of the equilibrium state as a free-energy valley. Any change from the equilibrium position will have a positive ΔG and will not be spontaneous. For this reason, systems never spontaneously move away from equilibrium. Because a system at equilibrium cannot spontaneously change, it can do no work. *A process is spontaneous and can perform work only when it is moving toward equilibrium.*

- More free energy (higher G)
- Less stable
- Greater work capacity

In a **spontaneous change**
- The free energy of the system decreases ($\Delta G < 0$)
- The system becomes more stable
- The released free energy can be harnessed to do work

- Less free energy (lower G)
- More stable
- Less work capacity

(a) **Gravitational motion.** Objects move spontaneously from a higher altitude to a lower one.

(b) **Diffusion.** Molecules in a drop of dye diffuse until they are randomly dispersed.

(c) **Chemical reaction.** In a cell, a glucose molecule is broken down into simpler molecules.

▲ **Figure 8.5 The relationship of free energy to stability, work capacity, and spontaneous change.** Unstable systems (top) are rich in free energy, G. They have a tendency to change spontaneously to a more stable state (bottom), and it is possible to harness this "downhill" change to perform work.

Free Energy and Metabolism

We can now apply the free-energy concept more specifically to the chemistry of life's processes.

Exergonic and Endergonic Reactions in Metabolism

Based on their free-energy changes, chemical reactions can be classified as either exergonic ("energy outward") or endergonic ("energy inward"). An **exergonic reaction** proceeds with a net release of free energy **(Figure 8.6a)**. Because the chemical mixture loses free energy (G decreases), ΔG is negative for an exergonic reaction. Using ΔG as a standard for spontaneity, exergonic reactions are those that occur spontaneously. (Remember, the word *spontaneous* implies that it is energetically favorable, not that it will occur rapidly.) The magnitude of ΔG for an exergonic reaction represents the maximum amount of work the reaction can perform.* The greater the decrease in free energy, the greater the amount of work that can be done.

We can use the overall reaction for cellular respiration as an example:

$$C_6H_{12}O_6 + 6\ O_2 \rightarrow 6\ CO_2 + 6\ H_2O$$
$$\Delta G = -686\ \text{kcal/mol}\ (-2{,}870\ \text{kJ/mol})$$

*The word *maximum* qualifies this statement, because some of the free energy is released as heat and cannot do work. Therefore, ΔG represents a theoretical upper limit of available energy.

▼ **Figure 8.6 Free energy changes (ΔG) in exergonic and endergonic reactions.**

(a) Exergonic reaction: energy released, spontaneous

Reactants

Free energy

Energy

Products

Amount of energy released ($\Delta G < 0$)

Progress of the reaction →

(b) Endergonic reaction: energy required, nonspontaneous

Products

Free energy

Energy

Reactants

Amount of energy required ($\Delta G > 0$)

Progress of the reaction →

For each mole (180 g) of glucose broken down by respiration under what are called "standard conditions" (1 M of each reactant and product, 25°C, pH 7), 686 kcal (2,870 kJ) of energy are made available for work. Because energy must be conserved, the chemical products of respiration store 686 kcal less free energy per mole than the reactants. The products are, in a sense, the spent exhaust of a process that tapped the free energy stored in the bonds of the sugar molecules.

It is important to realize that the breaking of bonds does not release energy; on the contrary, as you will soon see, it requires energy. The phrase "energy stored in bonds" is shorthand for the potential energy that can be released when new bonds are formed after the original bonds break, as long as the products are of lower free energy than the reactants.

An **endergonic reaction** is one that absorbs free energy from its surroundings (**Figure 8.6b**). Because this kind of reaction essentially *stores* free energy in molecules (G increases), ΔG is positive. Such reactions are nonspontaneous, and the magnitude of ΔG is the quantity of energy required to drive the reaction. If a chemical process is exergonic (downhill), releasing energy in one direction, then the reverse process must be endergonic (uphill), using energy. A reversible process cannot be downhill in both directions. If $\Delta G = -686$ kcal/mol for respiration, which converts glucose and oxygen to carbon dioxide and water, then the reverse process—the conversion of carbon dioxide and water to glucose and oxygen—must be strongly endergonic, with $\Delta G = +686$ kcal/mol. Such a reaction would never happen by itself.

How, then, do plants make the sugar that organisms use for energy? Plants get the required energy—686 kcal to make a mole of glucose—from the environment by capturing light and converting its energy to chemical energy. Next, in a long series of exergonic steps, they gradually spend that chemical energy to assemble glucose molecules.

Equilibrium and Metabolism

Reactions in an isolated system eventually reach equilibrium and can then do no work, as illustrated by the isolated hydroelectric system in **Figure 8.7a**. The chemical reactions of metabolism are reversible, and they, too, would reach equilibrium if they occurred in the isolation of a test tube. Because systems at equilibrium are at a minimum of G and can do no work, a cell that has reached metabolic equilibrium is dead! The fact that metabolism as a whole is never at equilibrium is one of the defining features of life.

Like most systems, a living cell is not in equilibrium. The constant flow of materials in and out of the cell keeps the metabolic pathways from ever reaching equilibrium, and the cell continues to do work throughout its life. This principle is illustrated by the open (and more realistic) hydroelectric system in **Figure 8.7b**. However, unlike this simple single-step system, a catabolic pathway in a cell releases free energy in a series of re-

(a) An isolated hydroelectric system. Water flowing downhill turns a turbine that drives a generator providing electricity to a lightbulb, but only until the system reaches equilibrium.

(b) An open hydroelectric system. Flowing water keeps driving the generator because intake and outflow of water keep the system from reaching equilibrium.

(c) A multistep open hydroelectric system. Cellular respiration is analogous to this system: Glucose is broken down in a series of exergonic reactions that power the work of the cell. The product of each reaction becomes the reactant for the next, so no reaction reaches equilibrium.

▲ **Figure 8.7 Equilibrium and work in isolated and open systems.**

actions. An example is cellular respiration, illustrated by analogy in **Figure 8.7c**. Some of the reversible reactions of respiration are constantly "pulled" in one direction—that is, they are kept out of equilibrium. The key to maintaining this lack of equilibrium is that the product of a reaction does not accumulate but instead becomes a reactant in the next step; finally, waste products are expelled from the cell. The overall sequence of reactions is kept going by the huge free-energy difference between glucose and oxygen at the top of the energy "hill" and carbon dioxide and water at the "downhill" end. As long as our cells have a steady supply of glucose or other fuels and oxygen and are able to expel waste products to the surroundings, their metabolic pathways never reach equilibrium and can continue to do the work of life.

We see once again how important it is to think of organisms as open systems. Sunlight provides a daily source of free energy for an ecosystem's plants and other photosynthetic organisms. Animals and other nonphotosynthetic organisms in an ecosystem must have a source of free energy in the form of the organic products of photosynthesis. Now that we have applied the free-energy concept to metabolism, we are ready to see how a cell actually performs the work of life.

CONCEPT CHECK 8.2

1. Cellular respiration uses glucose and oxygen, which have high levels of free energy, and releases CO_2 and water, which have low levels of free energy. Is cellular respiration spontaneous or not? Is it exergonic or endergonic? What happens to the energy released from glucose?
2. **MAKE CONNECTIONS** As you saw in Figure 7.20 on page 137, a key process in metabolism is the transport of hydrogen ions (H^+) across a membrane to create a concentration gradient. Other processes can result in an equal concentration of H^+ on each side. Which situation allows the H^+ to perform work in this system? How is the answer consistent with what is shown in regard to energy in Figure 7.20?
3. **WHAT IF?** Some night-time partygoers wear glow-in-the-dark necklaces. The necklaces start glowing once they are "activated," which usually involves snapping the necklace in a way that allows two chemicals to react and emit light in the form of chemiluminescence. Is the chemical reaction exergonic or endergonic? Explain your answer.

For suggested answers, see Appendix A.

CONCEPT 8.3

ATP powers cellular work by coupling exergonic reactions to endergonic reactions

A cell does three main kinds of work:

- *Chemical work*, the pushing of endergonic reactions that would not occur spontaneously, such as the synthesis of polymers from monomers (chemical work will be discussed further here and in Chapters 9 and 10)
- *Transport work*, the pumping of substances across membranes against the direction of spontaneous movement (see Chapter 7)
- *Mechanical work*, such as the beating of cilia (see Chapter 6), the contraction of muscle cells, and the movement of chromosomes during cellular reproduction

A key feature in the way cells manage their energy resources to do this work is **energy coupling**, the use of an exergonic process to drive an endergonic one. ATP is responsible for mediating most energy coupling in cells, and in most cases it acts as the immediate source of energy that powers cellular work.

The Structure and Hydrolysis of ATP

ATP (adenosine triphosphate) was introduced in Chapter 4 when we discussed the phosphate group as a functional group. ATP contains the sugar ribose, with the nitrogenous base adenine and a chain of three phosphate groups bonded to it **(Figure 8.8a)**. In addition to its role in energy coupling, ATP is also one of the nucleoside triphosphates used to make RNA (see Figure 5.26).

The bonds between the phosphate groups of ATP can be broken by hydrolysis. When the terminal phosphate bond is broken by addition of a water molecule, a molecule of inorganic phosphate ($HOPO_3^{2-}$, abbreviated $℗_i$ throughout this book) leaves the ATP, which becomes adenosine diphosphate,

(a) The structure of ATP. In the cell, most hydroxyl groups of phosphates are ionized ($—O^-$).

(b) The hydrolysis of ATP. The reaction of ATP and water yields inorganic phosphate ($℗_i$) and ADP and releases energy.

▲ **Figure 8.8 The structure and hydrolysis of adenosine triphosphate (ATP).**

or ADP (Figure 8.8b). The reaction is exergonic and releases 7.3 kcal of energy per mole of ATP hydrolyzed:

$$ATP + H_2O \rightarrow ADP + \textcircled{P}_i$$
$$\Delta G = -7.3 \text{ kcal/mol} (-30.5 \text{ kJ/mol})$$

This is the free-energy change measured under standard conditions. In the cell, conditions do not conform to standard conditions, primarily because reactant and product concentrations differ from 1 M. For example, when ATP hydrolysis occurs under cellular conditions, the actual ΔG is about −13 kcal/mol, 78% greater than the energy released by ATP hydrolysis under standard conditions.

Because their hydrolysis releases energy, the phosphate bonds of ATP are sometimes referred to as high-energy phosphate bonds, but the term is misleading. The phosphate bonds of ATP are not unusually strong bonds, as "high-energy" may imply; rather, the reactants (ATP and water) themselves have high energy relative to the energy of the products (ADP and $\textcircled{P}_i$). The release of energy during the hydrolysis of ATP comes from the chemical change to a state of lower free energy, not from the phosphate bonds themselves.

ATP is useful to the cell because the energy it releases on losing a phosphate group is somewhat greater than the energy most other molecules could deliver. But why does this hydrolysis release so much energy? If we reexamine the ATP molecule in Figure 8.8a, we can see that all three phosphate groups are negatively charged. These like charges are crowded together, and their mutual repulsion contributes to the instability of this region of the ATP molecule. The triphosphate tail of ATP is the chemical equivalent of a compressed spring.

How the Hydrolysis of ATP Performs Work

When ATP is hydrolyzed in a test tube, the release of free energy merely heats the surrounding water. In an organism, this same generation of heat can sometimes be beneficial. For instance, the process of shivering uses ATP hydrolysis during muscle contraction to generate heat and warm the body. In most cases in the cell, however, the generation of heat alone would be an inefficient (and potentially dangerous) use of a valuable energy resource. Instead, the cell's proteins harness the energy released during ATP hydrolysis in several ways to perform the three types of cellular work—chemical, transport, and mechanical.

For example, with the help of specific enzymes, the cell is able to use the energy released by ATP hydrolysis directly to drive chemical reactions that, by themselves, are endergonic. If the ΔG of an endergonic reaction is less than the amount of energy released by ATP hydrolysis, then the two reactions can be coupled so that, overall, the coupled reactions are exergonic (Figure 8.9). This usually involves the transfer of a phosphate

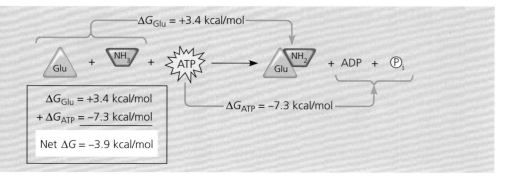

(a) Glutamic acid conversion to glutamine. Glutamine synthesis from glutamic acid (Glu) by itself is endergonic (ΔG is positive), so it is not spontaneous.

Glu + NH₃ → Glu NH₂ $\Delta G_{Glu} = +3.4$ kcal/mol
Glutamic acid   Ammonia   Glutamine

(b) Conversion reaction coupled with ATP hydrolysis. In the cell, glutamine synthesis occurs in two steps, coupled by a phosphorylated intermediate. ① ATP phosphorylates glutamic acid, making it less stable. ② Ammonia displaces the phosphate group, forming glutamine.

Glu + ATP → ① Glu—P + ADP → ② Glu NH₂ + ADP + $\textcircled{P}_i$
Glutamic acid   Phosphorylated intermediate   Glutamine

(c) Free-energy change for coupled reaction. ΔG for the glutamic acid conversion to glutamine (+3.4 kcal/mol) plus ΔG for ATP hydrolysis (–7.3 kcal/mol) gives the free-energy change for the overall reaction (–3.9 kcal/mol). Because the overall process is exergonic (net ΔG is negative), it occurs spontaneously.

$\Delta G_{Glu} = +3.4$ kcal/mol

Glu + NH₃ + ATP → Glu NH₂ + ADP + $\textcircled{P}_i$

$\Delta G_{ATP} = -7.3$ kcal/mol

$\Delta G_{Glu} = +3.4$ kcal/mol
$+ \Delta G_{ATP} = -7.3$ kcal/mol
Net $\Delta G = -3.9$ kcal/mol

▲ **Figure 8.9 How ATP drives chemical work: Energy coupling using ATP hydrolysis.** In this example, the exergonic process of ATP hydrolysis is used to drive an endergonic process—the cellular synthesis of the amino acid glutamine from glutamic acid and ammonia.

Transport protein   Solute

(a) **Transport work:** ATP phosphorylates transport proteins.

Vesicle   Cytoskeletal track

Motor protein   Protein and
                  vesicle moved

(b) **Mechanical work:** ATP binds noncovalently to motor proteins
and then is hydrolyzed.

▲ **Figure 8.10 How ATP drives transport and mechanical work.** ATP hydrolysis causes changes in the shapes and binding affinities of proteins. This can occur either **(a)** directly, by phosphorylation, as shown for a membrane protein carrying out active transport of a solute (see also Figure 7.18), or **(b)** indirectly, via noncovalent binding of ATP and its hydrolytic products, as is the case for motor proteins that move vesicles (and other organelles) along cytoskeletal "tracks" in the cell (see also Figure 6.21).

group from ATP to some other molecule, such as the reactant. The recipient with the phosphate group covalently bonded to it is then called a **phosphorylated intermediate**. The key to coupling exergonic and endergonic reactions is the formation of this phosphorylated intermediate, which is more reactive (less stable) than the original unphosphorylated molecule.

Transport and mechanical work in the cell are also nearly always powered by the hydrolysis of ATP. In these cases, ATP hydrolysis leads to a change in a protein's shape and often its ability to bind another molecule. Sometimes this occurs via a phosphorylated intermediate, as seen for the transport protein in **Figure 8.10a**. In most instances of mechanical work involving motor proteins "walking" along cytoskeletal elements **(Figure 8.10b)**, a cycle occurs in which ATP is first bound noncovalently to the motor protein. Next, ATP is hydrolyzed, releasing ADP and P_i. Another ATP molecule can then bind. At each stage, the motor protein changes its shape and ability to bind the cytoskeleton, resulting in movement of the protein along the cytoskeletal track.

The Regeneration of ATP

An organism at work uses ATP continuously, but ATP is a renewable resource that can be regenerated by the addition of phosphate to ADP **(Figure 8.11)**. The free energy required to

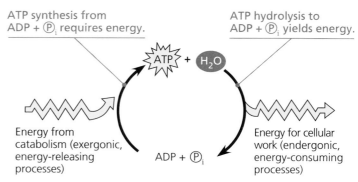

ATP synthesis from
ADP + P_i requires energy.

ATP hydrolysis to
ADP + P_i yields energy.

Energy from
catabolism (exergonic,
energy-releasing
processes)

Energy for cellular
work (endergonic,
energy-consuming
processes)

▲ **Figure 8.11 The ATP cycle.** Energy released by breakdown reactions (catabolism) in the cell is used to phosphorylate ADP, regenerating ATP. Chemical potential energy stored in ATP drives most cellular work.

phosphorylate ADP comes from exergonic breakdown reactions (catabolism) in the cell. This shuttling of inorganic phosphate and energy is called the ATP cycle, and it couples the cell's energy-yielding (exergonic) processes to the energy-consuming (endergonic) ones. The ATP cycle proceeds at an astonishing pace. For example, a working muscle cell recycles its entire pool of ATP in less than a minute. That turnover represents 10 million molecules of ATP consumed and regenerated per second per cell. If ATP could not be regenerated by the phosphorylation of ADP, humans would use up nearly their body weight in ATP each day.

Because both directions of a reversible process cannot be downhill, the regeneration of ATP from ADP and P_i is necessarily endergonic:

$$ADP + P_i \rightarrow ATP + H_2O$$
$$\Delta G = +7.3 \text{ kcal/mol } (+30.5 \text{ kJ/mol}) \text{ (standard conditions)}$$

Since ATP formation from ADP and P_i is not spontaneous, free energy must be spent to make it occur. Catabolic (exergonic) pathways, especially cellular respiration, provide the energy for the endergonic process of making ATP. Plants also use light energy to produce ATP. Thus, the ATP cycle is a revolving door through which energy passes during its transfer from catabolic to anabolic pathways.

CONCEPT CHECK 8.3

1. How does ATP typically transfer energy from exergonic to endergonic reactions in the cell?
2. Which of the following combinations has more free energy: glutamic acid + ammonia + ATP, or glutamine + ADP + P_i? Explain your answer.
3. **MAKE CONNECTIONS** Considering what you learned in Concepts 7.3 and 7.4 (pp. 134–136), does Figure 8.10a show passive or active transport? Explain.

For suggested answers, see Appendix A.

CONCEPT 8.4

Enzymes speed up metabolic reactions by lowering energy barriers

The laws of thermodynamics tell us what will and will not happen under given conditions but say nothing about the rate of these processes. A spontaneous chemical reaction occurs without any requirement for outside energy, but it may occur so slowly that it is imperceptible. For example, even though the hydrolysis of sucrose (table sugar) to glucose and fructose is exergonic, occurring spontaneously with a release of free energy ($\Delta G = -7$ kcal/mol), a solution of sucrose dissolved in sterile water will sit for years at room temperature with no appreciable hydrolysis. However, if we add a small amount of the enzyme sucrase to the solution, then all the sucrose may be hydrolyzed within seconds, as shown below:

| Sucrose | Glucose | Fructose |
| ($C_{12}H_{22}O_{11}$) | ($C_6H_{12}O_6$) | ($C_6H_{12}O_6$) |

How does the enzyme do this?

An **enzyme** is a macromolecule that acts as a **catalyst**, a chemical agent that speeds up a reaction without being consumed by the reaction. (In this chapter, we are focusing on enzymes that are proteins. RNA enzymes, also called ribozymes, are discussed in Chapters 17 and 25.) Without regulation by enzymes, chemical traffic through the pathways of metabolism would become terribly congested because many chemical reactions would take such a long time. In the next two sections, we will see what prevents a spontaneous reaction from occurring faster and how an enzyme changes the situation.

The Activation Energy Barrier

Every chemical reaction between molecules involves both bond breaking and bond forming. For example, the hydrolysis of sucrose involves breaking the bond between glucose and fructose and one of the bonds of a water molecule and then forming two new bonds, as shown above. Changing one molecule into another generally involves contorting the starting molecule into a highly unstable state before the reaction can proceed. This contortion can be compared to the bending of a metal key ring when you pry it open to add a new key. The key ring is highly unstable in its opened form but returns to a stable state once the key is threaded all the way onto the ring. To reach the contorted state where bonds can change, reactant molecules must absorb energy from their surroundings. When the new bonds of the product molecules form, energy

is released as heat, and the molecules return to stable shapes with lower energy than the contorted state.

The initial investment of energy for starting a reaction—the energy required to contort the reactant molecules so the bonds can break—is known as the *free energy of activation*, or **activation energy**, abbreviated E_A in this book. We can think of activation energy as the amount of energy needed to push the reactants to the top of an energy barrier, or uphill, so that the "downhill" part of the reaction can begin. Activation energy is often supplied in the form of thermal energy (heat) that the reactant molecules absorb from the surroundings. The absorption of thermal energy accelerates the reactant molecules, so they collide more often and more forcefully. It also agitates the atoms within the molecules, making the breakage of bonds more likely. When the molecules have absorbed enough energy for the bonds to break, the reactants are in an unstable condition known as the *transition state*.

Figure 8.12 graphs the energy changes for a hypothetical exergonic reaction that swaps portions of two reactant molecules:

$$AB + CD \rightarrow AC + BD$$
$$\text{Reactants} \quad \text{Products}$$

The activation of the reactants is represented by the uphill portion of the graph, in which the free-energy content of the

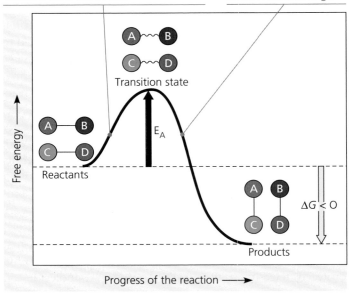

The reactants AB and CD must absorb enough energy from the surroundings to reach the unstable transition state, where bonds can break.

After bonds have broken, new bonds form, releasing energy to the surroundings.

▲ **Figure 8.12 Energy profile of an exergonic reaction.** The "molecules" are hypothetical, with A, B, C, and D representing portions of the molecules. Thermodynamically, this is an exergonic reaction, with a negative ΔG, and the reaction occurs spontaneously. However, the activation energy (E_A) provides a barrier that determines the rate of the reaction.

DRAW IT *Graph the progress of an endergonic reaction in which EF and GH form products EG and FH, assuming that the reactants must pass through a transition state.*

reactant molecules is increasing. At the summit, when energy equivalent to E_A has been absorbed, the reactants are in the transition state: They are activated, and their bonds can be broken. As the atoms then settle into their new, more stable bonding arrangements, energy is released to the surroundings. This corresponds to the downhill part of the curve, which shows the loss of free energy by the molecules. The overall decrease in free energy means that E_A is repaid with interest, as the formation of new bonds releases more energy than was invested in the breaking of old bonds..

The reaction shown in Figure 8.12 is exergonic and occurs spontaneously ($\Delta G < 0$). However, the activation energy provides a barrier that determines the rate of the reaction. The reactants must absorb enough energy to reach the top of the activation energy barrier before the reaction can occur. For some reactions, E_A is modest enough that even at room temperature there is sufficient thermal energy for many of the reactant molecules to reach the transition state in a short time. In most cases, however, E_A is so high and the transition state is reached so rarely that the reaction will hardly proceed at all. In these cases, the reaction will occur at a noticeable rate only if the reactants are heated. For example, the reaction of gasoline and oxygen is exergonic and will occur spontaneously, but energy is required for the molecules to reach the transition state and react. Only when the spark plugs fire in an automobile engine can there be the explosive release of energy that pushes the pistons. Without a spark, a mixture of gasoline hydrocarbons and oxygen will not react because the E_A barrier is too high.

How Enzymes Lower the E_A Barrier

Proteins, DNA, and other complex molecules of the cell are rich in free energy and have the potential to decompose spontaneously; that is, the laws of thermodynamics favor their breakdown. These molecules persist only because at temperatures typical for cells, few molecules can make it over the hump of activation energy. However, the barriers for selected reactions must occasionally be surmounted for cells to carry out the processes needed for life. Heat speeds a reaction by allowing reactants to attain the transition state more often, but this solution would be inappropriate for biological systems. First, high temperature denatures proteins and kills cells. Second, heat would speed up *all* reactions, not just those that are needed. Instead of heat, organisms use catalysis to speed up reactions.

An enzyme catalyzes a reaction by lowering the E_A barrier (Figure 8.13), enabling the reactant molecules to absorb enough energy to reach the transition state even at moderate temperatures. An enzyme cannot change the ΔG for a reaction; it cannot make an endergonic reaction exergonic. Enzymes can only hasten reactions that would eventually occur anyway, but this function makes it possible for the cell to have a dynamic

▲ Figure 8.13 **The effect of an enzyme on activation energy.** Without affecting the free-energy change (ΔG) for a reaction, an enzyme speeds the reaction by reducing its activation energy (E_A).

metabolism, routing chemicals smoothly through the cell's metabolic pathways. And because enzymes are very specific for the reactions they catalyze, they determine which chemical processes will be going on in the cell at any particular time.

Substrate Specificity of Enzymes

The reactant an enzyme acts on is referred to as the enzyme's **substrate**. The enzyme binds to its substrate (or substrates, when there are two or more reactants), forming an **enzyme-substrate complex**. While enzyme and substrate are joined, the catalytic action of the enzyme converts the substrate to the product (or products) of the reaction. The overall process can be summarized as follows:

$$\text{Enzyme} + \text{Substrate(s)} \rightleftharpoons \text{Enzyme-substrate complex} \rightleftharpoons \text{Enzyme} + \text{Product(s)}$$

For example, the enzyme sucrase (most enzyme names end in -*ase*) catalyzes the hydrolysis of the disaccharide sucrose into its two monosaccharides, glucose and fructose (see p. 152):

$$\text{Sucrase} + \text{Sucrose} + H_2O \rightleftharpoons \text{Sucrase-sucrose-}H_2O \text{ complex} \rightleftharpoons \text{Sucrase} + \text{Glucose} + \text{Fructose}$$

The reaction catalyzed by each enzyme is very specific; an enzyme can recognize its specific substrate even among closely related compounds. For instance, sucrase will act only on sucrose and will not bind to other disaccharides, such as maltose. What accounts for this molecular recognition? Recall that most enzymes are proteins, and proteins are macromolecules with unique three-dimensional configurations. The specificity of an enzyme results from its shape, which is a consequence of its amino acid sequence.

Only a restricted region of the enzyme molecule actually binds to the substrate. This region, called the **active site**, is typically a pocket or groove on the surface of the enzyme where catalysis occurs (**Figure 8.14a**). Usually, the active site is formed by only a few of the enzyme's amino acids, with the rest of the protein molecule providing a framework that determines the configuration of the active site. The specificity of an enzyme is attributed to a compatible fit between the shape of its active site and the shape of the substrate.

An enzyme is not a stiff structure locked into a given shape. In fact, recent work by biochemists has shown clearly that enzymes (and other proteins as well) seem to "dance" between subtly different shapes in a dynamic equilibrium, with slight differences in free energy for each "pose." The shape that best fits the substrate isn't necessarily the one with the lowest energy, but during the very short time the enzyme takes on this shape, its active site can bind to the substrate. It has been known for more than 50 years that the active site itself is also not a rigid receptacle for the substrate. As the substrate enters the active site, the enzyme changes shape slightly due to interactions between the substrate's chemical groups and chemical groups on the side chains of the amino acids that form the active site. This shape change makes the active site fit even more snugly around the substrate (**Figure 8.14b**). This **induced fit** is like a clasping handshake. Induced fit brings chemical groups of the active site into positions that enhance their ability to catalyze the chemical reaction.

Catalysis in the Enzyme's Active Site

In most enzymatic reactions, the substrate is held in the active site by so-called weak interactions, such as hydrogen bonds and ionic bonds. R groups of a few of the amino acids that make up the active site catalyze the conversion of substrate to product, and the product departs from the active site. The enzyme is then free to take another substrate molecule into its active site. The entire cycle happens so fast that a single enzyme molecule typically acts on about a thousand substrate molecules per second. Some enzymes are much faster. Enzymes, like other catalysts, emerge from the reaction in their original form. Therefore, very small amounts of enzyme can have a huge metabolic impact by functioning over and over again in catalytic cycles. **Figure 8.15** shows a catalytic cycle involving two substrates and two products.

Enzyme

Enzyme-substrate complex

(a) In this computer graphic model, the active site of this enzyme (hexokinase, shown in blue) forms a groove on its surface. Its substrate is glucose (red).

(b) When the substrate enters the active site, it forms weak bonds with the enzyme, inducing a change in the shape of the protein. This change allows additional weak bonds to form, causing the active site to enfold the substrate and hold it in place.

▲ **Figure 8.14 Induced fit between an enzyme and its substrate.**

Most metabolic reactions are reversible, and an enzyme can catalyze either the forward or the reverse reaction, depending on which direction has a negative ΔG. This in turn depends mainly on the relative concentrations of reactants and products. The net effect is always in the direction of equilibrium.

Enzymes use a variety of mechanisms that lower activation energy and speed up a reaction (see Figure 8.15, step ❸). First, in reactions involving two or more reactants, the active site provides a template on which the substrates can come together in the proper orientation for a reaction to occur between them. Second, as the active site of an enzyme clutches the bound substrates, the enzyme may stretch the substrate molecules toward their transition-state form, stressing and bending critical chemical bonds that must be broken during the reaction. Because E_A is proportional to the difficulty of breaking the bonds, distorting the substrate helps it approach the transition state and thus reduces the amount of free energy that must be absorbed to achieve that state.

Third, the active site may also provide a microenvironment that is more conducive to a particular type of reaction than the solution itself would be without the enzyme. For example, if the active site has amino acids with acidic R groups, the active site may be a pocket of low pH in an otherwise neutral cell. In such cases, an acidic amino acid may facilitate H^+ transfer to the substrate as a key step in catalyzing the reaction.

A fourth mechanism of catalysis is the direct participation of the active site in the chemical reaction. Sometimes this process even involves brief covalent bonding between the substrate and the side chain of an amino acid of the enzyme. Subsequent steps of the reaction restore the side chains to their original states, so that the active site is the same after the reaction as it was before.

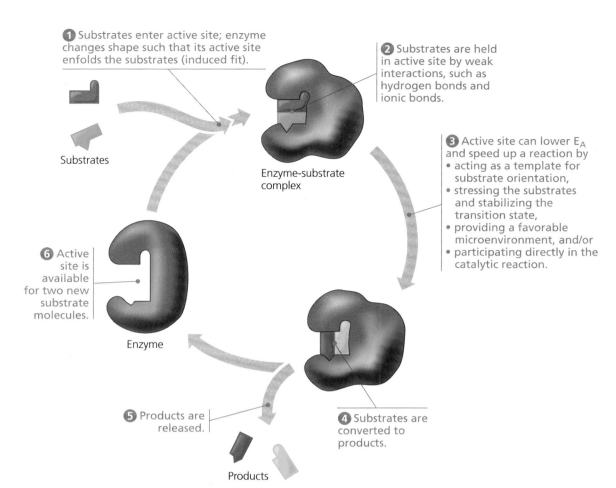

① Substrates enter active site; enzyme changes shape such that its active site enfolds the substrates (induced fit).

Substrates

Enzyme-substrate complex

② Substrates are held in active site by weak interactions, such as hydrogen bonds and ionic bonds.

③ Active site can lower E_A and speed up a reaction by
• acting as a template for substrate orientation,
• stressing the substrates and stabilizing the transition state,
• providing a favorable microenvironment, and/or
• participating directly in the catalytic reaction.

⑥ Active site is available for two new substrate molecules.

Enzyme

⑤ Products are released.

④ Substrates are converted to products.

Products

◀ **Figure 8.15 The active site and catalytic cycle of an enzyme.** An enzyme can convert one or more reactant molecules to one or more product molecules. The enzyme shown here converts two substrate molecules to two product molecules.

The rate at which a particular amount of enzyme converts substrate to product is partly a function of the initial concentration of the substrate: The more substrate molecules that are available, the more frequently they access the active sites of the enzyme molecules. However, there is a limit to how fast the reaction can be pushed by adding more substrate to a fixed concentration of enzyme. At some point, the concentration of substrate will be high enough that all enzyme molecules have their active sites engaged. As soon as the product exits an active site, another substrate molecule enters. At this substrate concentration, the enzyme is said to be *saturated*, and the rate of the reaction is determined by the speed at which the active site converts substrate to product. When an enzyme population is saturated, the only way to increase the rate of product formation is to add more enzyme. Cells often increase the rate of a reaction by producing more enzyme molecules.

Effects of Local Conditions on Enzyme Activity

The activity of an enzyme—how efficiently the enzyme functions—is affected by general environmental factors, such as temperature and pH. It can also be affected by chemicals that specifically influence that enzyme. In fact, researchers have learned much about enzyme function by employing such chemicals.

Effects of Temperature and pH

Recall from Chapter 5 that the three-dimensional structures of proteins are sensitive to their environment. As a consequence, each enzyme works better under some conditions than under other conditions, because these *optimal conditions* favor the most active shape for the enzyme molecule.

Temperature and pH are environmental factors important in the activity of an enzyme. Up to a point, the rate of an enzymatic reaction increases with increasing temperature, partly because substrates collide with active sites more frequently when the molecules move rapidly. Above that temperature, however, the speed of the enzymatic reaction drops sharply. The thermal agitation of the enzyme molecule disrupts the hydrogen bonds, ionic bonds, and other weak interactions that stabilize the active shape of the enzyme, and the protein molecule eventually denatures. Each enzyme has an optimal temperature at which its reaction rate is greatest. Without denaturing the enzyme, this temperature allows the greatest number of molecular collisions and the fastest conversion of the reactants to product molecules. Most human enzymes have optimal temperatures of about 35–40°C (close to human body temperature). The thermophilic bacteria that live in hot springs contain enzymes with optimal temperatures of 70°C or higher (**Figure 8.16a** on the next page).

(a) Optimal temperature for two enzymes

(b) Optimal pH for two enzymes

▲ **Figure 8.16 Environmental factors affecting enzyme activity.** Each enzyme has an optimal **(a)** temperature and **(b)** pH that favor the most active shape of the protein molecule.

DRAW IT *Given that a mature lysosome has an internal pH of around 4.5, draw a curve in (b) showing what you would predict for a lysosomal enzyme, labeling its optimal pH.*

Just as each enzyme has an optimal temperature, it also has a pH at which it is most active. The optimal pH values for most enzymes fall in the range of pH 6–8, but there are exceptions. For example, pepsin, a digestive enzyme in the human stomach, works best at pH 2. Such an acidic environment denatures most enzymes, but pepsin is adapted to maintain its functional three-dimensional structure in the acidic environment of the stomach. In contrast, trypsin, a digestive enzyme residing in the alkaline environment of the human intestine, has an optimal pH of 8 and would be denatured in the stomach **(Figure 8.16b)**.

Cofactors

Many enzymes require nonprotein helpers for catalytic activity. These adjuncts, called **cofactors**, may be bound tightly to the enzyme as permanent residents, or they may bind loosely and reversibly along with the substrate. The cofactors of some enzymes are inorganic, such as the metal atoms zinc, iron, and copper in ionic form. If the cofactor is an organic molecule, it is more specifically called a **coenzyme**. Most vitamins are important in nutrition because they act as coenzymes or raw materials from which coenzymes are made. Cofactors function in various ways, but in all cases where they

are used, they perform a crucial chemical function in catalysis. You'll encounter examples of cofactors later in the book.

Enzyme Inhibitors

Certain chemicals selectively inhibit the action of specific enzymes, and we have learned a lot about enzyme function by studying the effects of these molecules. If the inhibitor attaches to the enzyme by covalent bonds, inhibition is usually irreversible.

Many enzyme inhibitors, however, bind to the enzyme by weak interactions, in which case inhibition is reversible. Some reversible inhibitors resemble the normal substrate molecule and compete for admission into the active site **(Figure 8.17a and b)**. These mimics, called **competitive inhibitors**, reduce

▼ **Figure 8.17 Inhibition of enzyme activity.**

(a) Normal binding

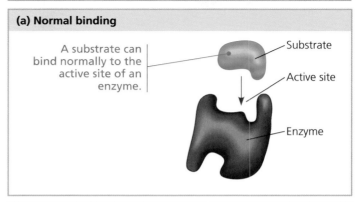

A substrate can bind normally to the active site of an enzyme.

Substrate
Active site
Enzyme

(b) Competitive inhibition

A competitive inhibitor mimics the substrate, competing for the active site.

Competitive inhibitor

(c) Noncompetitive inhibition

A noncompetitive inhibitor binds to the enzyme away from the active site, altering the shape of the enzyme so that even if the substrate can bind, the active site functions less effectively.

Noncompetitive inhibitor

the productivity of enzymes by blocking substrates from entering active sites. This kind of inhibition can be overcome by increasing the concentration of substrate so that as active sites become available, more substrate molecules than inhibitor molecules are around to gain entry to the sites.

In contrast, **noncompetitive inhibitors** do not directly compete with the substrate to bind to the enzyme at the active site **(Figure 8.17c)**. Instead, they impede enzymatic reactions by binding to another part of the enzyme. This interaction causes the enzyme molecule to change its shape in such a way that the active site becomes less effective at catalyzing the conversion of substrate to product.

Toxins and poisons are often irreversible enzyme inhibitors. An example is sarin, a nerve gas that caused the death of several people and injury to many others when it was released by terrorists in the Tokyo subway in 1995. This small molecule binds covalently to the R group on the amino acid serine, which is found in the active site of acetylcholinesterase, an enzyme important in the nervous system. Other examples include the pesticides DDT and parathion, inhibitors of key enzymes in the nervous system. Finally, many antibiotics are inhibitors of specific enzymes in bacteria. For instance, penicillin blocks the active site of an enzyme that many bacteria use to make their cell walls.

Citing enzyme inhibitors that are metabolic poisons may give the impression that enzyme inhibition is generally abnormal and harmful. In fact, molecules naturally present in the cell often regulate enzyme activity by acting as inhibitors. Such regulation—selective inhibition—is essential to the control of cellular metabolism, as we will discuss in Concept 8.5.

The Evolution of Enzymes

EVOLUTION Thus far, biochemists have discovered and named more than 4,000 different enzymes in various species, and this list probably represents the tip of the proverbial iceberg. How did this grand profusion of enzymes arise? Recall that most enzymes are proteins, and proteins are encoded by genes. A permanent change in a gene, known as a *mutation*, can result in a protein with one or more changed amino acids. In the case of an enzyme, if the changed amino acids are in the active site or some other crucial region, the altered enzyme might have a novel activity or might bind to a different substrate. Under environmental conditions where the new function benefits the organism, natural selection would tend to favor the mutated form of the gene, causing it to persist in the population. This simplified model is generally accepted as the main way in which the multitude of different enzymes arose over the past few billion years of life's history.

Data supporting this model have been collected by researchers using a lab procedure that mimics evolution in natural populations. One group tested whether the function of an enzyme called β-galactosidase could change over time in populations of the bacterium *Escherichia coli* (*E. coli*). β-galactosidase

Two changed amino acids were found near the active site.

Active site

Two changed amino acids were found in the active site.

Two changed amino acids were found on the surface.

▲ **Figure 8.18 Mimicking evolution of an enzyme with a new function.** After seven rounds of mutation and selection in a lab, the enzyme β-galactosidase evolved into an enzyme specialized for breaking down a sugar different from lactose. This ribbon model shows one subunit of the altered enzyme; six amino acids were different.

breaks down the disaccharide lactose into the simple sugars glucose and galactose. Using molecular techniques, the researchers introduced random mutations into *E. coli* genes and then tested the bacteria for their ability to break down a slightly different disaccharide (one that has the sugar fucose in place of galactose). They selected the mutant bacteria that could do this best and exposed them to another round of mutation and selection. After seven rounds, the "evolved" enzyme bound the new substrate several hundred times more strongly, and broke it down 10 to 20 times more quickly, than did the original enzyme.

The researchers found that six amino acids had changed in the enzyme altered in this experiment. Two of these changed amino acids were in the active site, two were nearby, and two were on the surface of the protein **(Figure 8.18)**. This experiment and others like it strengthen the notion that a few changes can indeed alter enzyme function.

CONCEPT CHECK 8.4

1. Many spontaneous reactions occur very slowly. Why don't all spontaneous reactions occur instantly?
2. Why do enzymes act only on very specific substrates?
3. **WHAT IF?** Malonate is an inhibitor of the enzyme succinate dehydrogenase. How would you determine whether malonate is a competitive or noncompetitive inhibitor?
4. **MAKE CONNECTIONS** In nature, what conditions could lead to natural selection favoring bacteria with enzymes that could break down the fucose-containing disaccharide discussed above? See the discussion of natural selection in Concept 1.2, pages 14–16.

For suggested answers, see Appendix A.

CONCEPT 8.5

Regulation of enzyme activity helps control metabolism

Chemical chaos would result if all of a cell's metabolic pathways were operating simultaneously. Intrinsic to life's processes is a cell's ability to tightly regulate its metabolic pathways by controlling when and where its various enzymes are active. It does this either by switching on and off the genes that encode specific enzymes (as we will discuss in Unit Three) or, as we discuss here, by regulating the activity of enzymes once they are made.

Allosteric Regulation of Enzymes

In many cases, the molecules that naturally regulate enzyme activity in a cell behave something like reversible noncompetitive inhibitors (see Figure 8.17c): These regulatory molecules change an enzyme's shape and the functioning of its active site by binding to a site elsewhere on the molecule, via noncovalent interactions. **Allosteric regulation** is the term used to describe any case in which a protein's function at one site is affected by the binding of a regulatory molecule to a separate site. It may result in either inhibition or stimulation of an enzyme's activity.

Allosteric Activation and Inhibition

Most enzymes known to be allosterically regulated are constructed from two or more subunits, each composed of a polypeptide chain with its own active site. The entire complex oscillates between two different shapes, one catalytically active and the other inactive (**Figure 8.19a**). In the simplest kind of allosteric regulation, an activating or inhibiting regulatory molecule binds to a regulatory site (sometimes called an allosteric site), often located where subunits join. The binding of an *activator* to a regulatory site stabilizes the shape that has functional active sites, whereas the binding of an *inhibitor* stabilizes the inactive form of the enzyme. The subunits of an allosteric enzyme fit together in such a way that a shape change in one subunit is transmitted to all others. Through this interaction of subunits, a single activator or inhibitor molecule that binds to one regulatory site will affect the active sites of all subunits.

Fluctuating concentrations of regulators can cause a sophisticated pattern of response in the activity of cellular enzymes. The products of ATP hydrolysis (ADP and $\circled{P}_i$), for example, play a complex role in balancing the flow of traffic between anabolic and catabolic pathways by their effects on key enzymes. ATP binds to several catabolic enzymes allosterically, lowering their affinity for substrate and thus inhibiting their activity. ADP, however, functions as an activator of the same enzymes. This is logical because catabolism functions

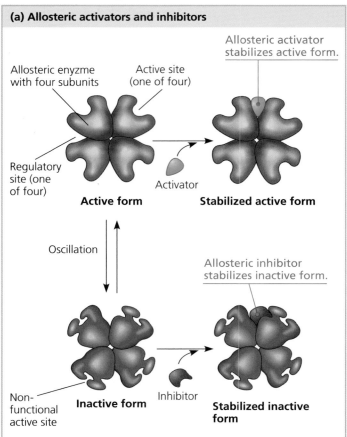

▼ **Figure 8.19 Allosteric regulation of enzyme activity.**

(a) Allosteric activators and inhibitors

Allosteric enzyme with four subunits

Active site (one of four)

Regulatory site (one of four)

Activator

Active form

Allosteric activator stabilizes active form.

Stabilized active form

Oscillation

Allosteric inhibitor stabilizes inactive form.

Non-functional active site

Inactive form

Inhibitor

Stabilized inactive form

At low concentrations, activators and inhibitors dissociate from the enzyme. The enzyme can then oscillate again.

(b) Cooperativity: another type of allosteric activation

Binding of one substrate molecule to active site of one subunit locks all subunits in active conformation.

Substrate

Inactive form

Stabilized active form

The inactive form shown on the left oscillates with the active form when the active form is not stabilized by substrate.

in regenerating ATP. If ATP production lags behind its use, ADP accumulates and activates the enzymes that speed up catabolism, producing more ATP. If the supply of ATP exceeds demand, then catabolism slows down as ATP molecules accumulate and bind to the same enzymes, inhibiting them. (You'll see specific examples of this type of regulation when you learn about cellular respiration in the next chapter.) ATP, ADP, and other related molecules also affect key enzymes in anabolic pathways. In this way, allosteric enzymes control the rates of important reactions in both sorts of metabolic pathways.

In another kind of allosteric activation, a *substrate* molecule binding to one active site in a multisubunit enzyme triggers a shape change in all the subunits, thereby increasing catalytic activity at the other active sites (**Figure 8.19b**). Called **cooperativity**, this mechanism amplifies the response of enzymes to substrates: One substrate molecule primes an enzyme to act on additional substrate molecules more readily. Cooperativity is considered "allosteric" regulation because binding of the substrate to one active site affects catalysis in another active site.

Although the vertebrate oxygen transport protein hemoglobin is not an enzyme, classic studies of cooperative binding in this protein have elucidated the principle of cooperativity. Hemoglobin is made up of four subunits, each of which has an oxygen-binding site (see Figure 5.20). The binding of an oxygen molecule to one binding site increases the affinity for oxygen of the remaining binding sites. Thus, where oxygen is at high levels, such as in the lungs or gills, hemoglobin's affinity for oxygen increases as more binding sites are filled. In oxygen-deprived tissues, however, the release of each oxygen molecule decreases the oxygen affinity of the other binding sites, resulting in the release of oxygen where it is most needed. Cooperativity works similarly in multisubunit enzymes that have been studied.

Identification of Allosteric Regulators

Although allosteric regulation is probably quite widespread, relatively few of the many known metabolic enzymes have been shown to be regulated in this way. Allosteric regulatory molecules are hard to characterize, in part because they tend to bind the enzyme at low affinity and are therefore hard to isolate. Recently, however, pharmaceutical companies have turned their attention to allosteric regulators. These molecules are attractive drug candidates for enzyme regulation because they exhibit higher specificity for particular enzymes than do inhibitors that bind to the active site. (An active site may be similar to the active site in another, related enzyme, whereas allosteric regulatory sites appear to be quite distinct between enzymes.)

Figure 8.20 describes a search for allosteric regulators, carried out as a collaboration between researchers at the University of California at San Francisco and a company called Sunesis Pharmaceuticals. The study was designed to find allosteric inhibitors of *caspases*, protein-digesting enzymes that play an active role in inflammation and cell death. By specifically regulating these enzymes, we may be able to better manage inappropriate inflammatory responses, such as those commonly seen in vascular and neurodegenerative diseases.

▼ **Figure 8.20**

INQUIRY

Are there allosteric inhibitors of caspase enzymes?

EXPERIMENT In an effort to identify allosteric inhibitors of caspases, Justin Scheer and co-workers screened close to 8,000 compounds for their ability to bind to a possible allosteric binding site in caspase 1 and inhibit the enzyme's activity. Each compound was designed to form a disulfide bond with a cysteine near the site in order to stabilize the low-affinity interaction that is expected of an allosteric inhibitor. As the caspases are known to exist in both active and inactive forms, the researchers hypothesized that this linkage might lock the enzyme in the inactive form.

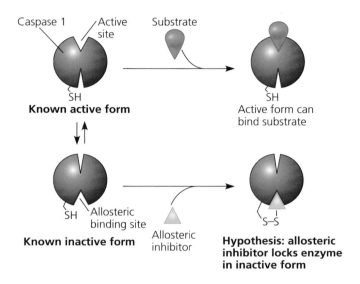

To test this model, X-ray diffraction analysis was used to determine the structure of caspase 1 when bound to one of the inhibitors and to compare it with the active and inactive structures.

RESULTS Fourteen compounds were identified that could bind to the proposed allosteric site (red) of caspase 1 and block enzymatic activity. The enzyme's shape when one such inhibitor was bound resembled the inactive caspase 1 more than the active form.

CONCLUSION That particular inhibitory compound apparently locks the enzyme in its inactive form, as expected for a true allosteric regulator. The data therefore support the existence of an allosteric inhibitory site on caspase 1 that can be used to control enzymatic activity.

SOURCE J. M. Scheer et al., A common allosteric site and mechanism in caspases, *Proceedings of the National Academy of Sciences* 103: 7595–7600 (2006).

WHAT IF? As a control, the researchers broke the disulfide linkage between one of the inhibitors and the caspase. Assuming that the experimental solution contains no other inhibitors, how would you expect the caspase 1 activity to be affected?

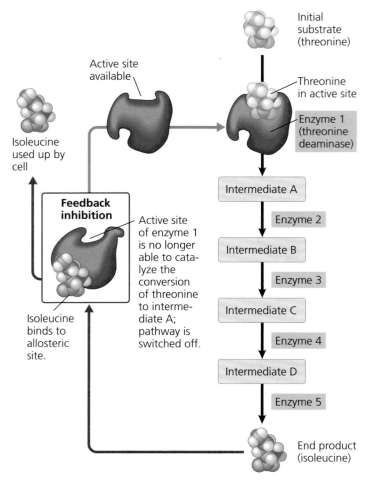

▲ **Figure 8.21 Feedback inhibition in isoleucine synthesis.**

Initial substrate (threonine)

Active site available

Threonine in active site

Enzyme 1 (threonine deaminase)

Isoleucine used up by cell

Feedback inhibition

Active site of enzyme 1 is no longer able to catalyze the conversion of threonine to intermediate A; pathway is switched off.

Isoleucine binds to allosteric site.

Intermediate A

Enzyme 2

Intermediate B

Enzyme 3

Intermediate C

Enzyme 4

Intermediate D

Enzyme 5

End product (isoleucine)

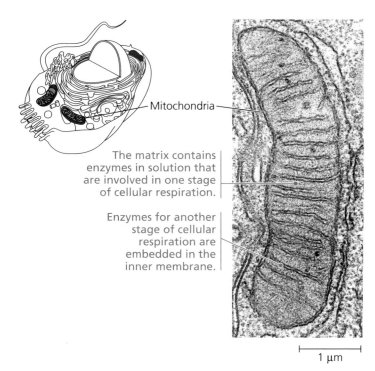

Mitochondria

The matrix contains enzymes in solution that are involved in one stage of cellular respiration.

Enzymes for another stage of cellular respiration are embedded in the inner membrane.

1 μm

▲ **Figure 8.22 Organelles and structural order in metabolism.** Organelles such as the mitochondrion (TEM) contain enzymes that carry out specific functions, in this case cellular respiration.

Feedback Inhibition

When ATP allosterically inhibits an enzyme in an ATP-generating pathway, as we discussed earlier, the result is feedback inhibition, a common mode of metabolic control. In **feedback inhibition**, a metabolic pathway is switched off by the inhibitory binding of its end product to an enzyme that acts early in the pathway. **Figure 8.21** shows an example of this control mechanism operating on an anabolic pathway. Certain cells use this five-step pathway to synthesize the amino acid isoleucine from threonine, another amino acid. As isoleucine accumulates, it slows down its own synthesis by allosterically inhibiting the enzyme for the first step of the pathway. Feedback inhibition thereby prevents the cell from wasting chemical resources by making more isoleucine than is necessary.

Specific Localization of Enzymes Within the Cell

The cell is not just a bag of chemicals with thousands of different kinds of enzymes and substrates in a random mix. The cell is compartmentalized, and cellular structures help bring order to metabolic pathways. In some cases, a team of enzymes for several steps of a metabolic pathway are assembled into a multienzyme complex. The arrangement facilitates the

sequence of reactions, with the product from the first enzyme becoming the substrate for an adjacent enzyme in the complex, and so on, until the end product is released. Some enzymes and enzyme complexes have fixed locations within the cell and act as structural components of particular membranes. Others are in solution within particular membrane-enclosed eukaryotic organelles, each with its own internal chemical environment. For example, in eukaryotic cells, the enzymes for cellular respiration reside in specific locations within mitochondria **(Figure 8.22)**.

In this chapter, you have learned that metabolism, the intersecting set of chemical pathways characteristic of life, is a choreographed interplay of thousands of different kinds of cellular molecules. In the next chapter, we explore cellular respiration, the major catabolic pathway that breaks down organic molecules, releasing energy for the crucial processes of life.

CONCEPT CHECK 8.5

1. How do an activator and an inhibitor have different effects on an allosterically regulated enzyme?
2. **WHAT IF?** Imagine you are a pharmacological researcher who wants to design a drug that inhibits a particular enzyme. Upon reading the scientific literature, you find that the enzyme's active site is similar to that of several other enzymes. What might be a good approach to developing your inhibitor drug?

For suggested answers, see Appendix A.

8 CHAPTER REVIEW

SUMMARY OF KEY CONCEPTS

CONCEPT 8.1

An organism's metabolism transforms matter and energy, subject to the laws of thermodynamics (pp. 142–145)

- **Metabolism** is the collection of chemical reactions that occur in an organism. **Enzymes** catalyze reactions in intersecting **metabolic pathways**, which may be **catabolic** (breaking down molecules, releasing energy) or **anabolic** (building molecules, consuming energy).
- **Energy** is the capacity to cause change; some forms of energy do work by moving matter. **Kinetic energy** is associated with motion and includes **thermal energy (heat)** associated with random motion of atoms or molecules. **Potential energy** is related to the location or structure of matter and includes **chemical energy** possessed by a molecule due to its structure.
- **The first law of thermodynamics**, conservation of energy, states that energy cannot be created or destroyed, only transferred or transformed. The **second law of thermodynamics** states that **spontaneous processes**, those requiring no outside input of energy, increase the **entropy** (disorder) of the universe.

> **?** *Explain how the highly ordered structure of a cell does not conflict with the second law of thermodynamics.*

CONCEPT 8.2

The free-energy change of a reaction tells us whether or not the reaction occurs spontaneously (pp. 146–149)

- A living system's **free energy** is energy that can do work under cellular conditions. The change in free energy (ΔG) during a biological process is related directly to enthalpy change (ΔH) and to the change in entropy (ΔS): $\Delta G = \Delta H - T\Delta S$. Organisms live at the expense of free energy. During a spontaneous change, free energy decreases and the stability of a system increases. At maximum stability, the system is at equilibrium and can do no work.
- In an **exergonic** (spontaneous) chemical reaction, the products have less free energy than the reactants ($-\Delta G$). **Endergonic** (nonspontaneous) reactions require an input of energy ($+\Delta G$). The addition of starting materials and the removal of end products prevent metabolism from reaching equilibrium.

> **?** *Explain the meaning of each component in the equation for the change in free energy of a spontaneous chemical reaction. Why are spontaneous reactions important in the metabolism of a cell?*

CONCEPT 8.3

ATP powers cellular work by coupling exergonic reactions to endergonic reactions (pp. 149–151)

- **ATP** is the cell's energy shuttle. Hydrolysis of its terminal phosphate yields ADP and phosphate and releases free energy.
- Through **energy coupling**, the exergonic process of ATP hydrolysis drives endergonic reactions by transfer of a phosphate group to specific reactants, forming a **phosphorylated intermediate** that is more reactive. ATP hydrolysis (sometimes with protein phosphorylation) also causes changes in the shape and binding affinities of transport and motor proteins.
- Catabolic pathways drive regeneration of ATP from ADP + $(P)_i$.

> **?** *Describe the ATP cycle: How is ATP used and regenerated in a cell?*

CONCEPT 8.4

Enzymes speed up metabolic reactions by lowering energy barriers (pp. 152–157)

- In a chemical reaction, the energy necessary to break the bonds of the reactants is the **activation energy**, E_A.
- **Enzymes** lower the E_A barrier:

- Each type of enzyme has a unique **active site** that combines specifically with its **substrate(s)**, the reactant molecule(s) on which it acts. The enzyme changes shape slightly when it binds the substrate(s) (**induced fit**).
- The active site can lower an E_A barrier by orienting substrates correctly, straining their bonds, providing a favorable microenvironment, or even covalently bonding with the substrate.
- Each enzyme has an optimal temperature and pH. Inhibitors reduce enzyme function. A **competitive inhibitor** binds to the active site, whereas a **noncompetitive inhibitor** binds to a different site on the enzyme.
- Natural selection, acting on organisms with mutant genes encoding altered enzymes, is a major evolutionary force responsible for the diverse array of enzymes found in organisms.

> **?** *How do both activation energy barriers and enzymes help maintain the structural and metabolic order of life?*

CONCEPT 8.5

Regulation of enzyme activity helps control metabolism (pp. 158–160)

- Many enzymes are subject to **allosteric regulation**: Regulatory molecules, either activators or inhibitors, bind to specific regulatory sites, affecting the shape and function of the enzyme. In **cooperativity**, binding of one substrate molecule can stimulate binding or activity at other active sites. In **feedback inhibition**, the end product of a metabolic pathway allosterically inhibits the enzyme for a previous step in the pathway.
- Some enzymes are grouped into complexes, some are incorporated into membranes, and some are contained inside organelles, increasing the efficiency of metabolic processes.

> **?** *What roles do allosteric regulation and feedback inhibition play in the metabolism of a cell?*

TEST YOUR UNDERSTANDING

LEVEL 1: KNOWLEDGE/COMPREHENSION

1. Choose the pair of terms that correctly completes this sentence: Catabolism is to anabolism as _____ is to _____.
   a. exergonic; spontaneous
   b. exergonic; endergonic
   c. free energy; entropy
   d. work; energy
   e. entropy; enthalpy

2. Most cells cannot harness heat to perform work because
   a. heat is not a form of energy.
   b. cells do not have much heat; they are relatively cool.
   c. temperature is usually uniform throughout a cell.
   d. heat can never be used to do work.
   e. heat must remain constant during work.

3. Which of the following metabolic processes can occur without a net influx of energy from some other process?
   a. $ADP + \text{(P)}_i \rightarrow ATP + H_2O$
   b. $C_6H_{12}O_6 + 6\ O_2 \rightarrow 6\ CO_2 + 6\ H_2O$
   c. $6\ CO_2 + 6\ H_2O \rightarrow C_6H_{12}O_6 + 6\ O_2$
   d. amino acids $\rightarrow$ protein
   e. glucose + fructose $\rightarrow$ sucrose

4. If an enzyme in solution is saturated with substrate, the most effective way to obtain a faster yield of products is to
   a. add more of the enzyme.
   b. heat the solution to 90°C.
   c. add more substrate.
   d. add an allosteric inhibitor.
   e. add a noncompetitive inhibitor.

5. Some bacteria are metabolically active in hot springs because
   a. they are able to maintain a lower internal temperature.
   b. high temperatures make catalysis unnecessary.
   c. their enzymes have high optimal temperatures.
   d. their enzymes are completely insensitive to temperature.
   e. they use molecules other than proteins or RNAs as their main catalysts.

LEVEL 2: APPLICATION/ANALYSIS

6. If an enzyme is added to a solution where its substrate and product are in equilibrium, what will occur?
   a. Additional product will be formed.
   b. Additional substrate will be formed.
   c. The reaction will change from endergonic to exergonic.
   d. The free energy of the system will change.
   e. Nothing; the reaction will stay at equilibrium.

LEVEL 3: SYNTHESIS/EVALUATION

7. **DRAW IT** Using a series of arrows, draw the branched metabolic reaction pathway described by the following statements, and then answer the question at the end. Use red arrows and minus signs to indicate inhibition.

   L can form either M or N.
   M can form O.
   O can form either P or R.
   P can form Q.
   R can form S.
   O inhibits the reaction of L to form M.
   Q inhibits the reaction of O to form P.
   S inhibits the reaction of O to form R.

   Which reaction would prevail if both Q and S were present in the cell in high concentrations?
   a. L → M
   b. M → O
   c. L → N
   d. O → P
   e. R → S

8. **EVOLUTION CONNECTION**
   A recent revival of the antievolutionary "intelligent design" argument holds that biochemical pathways are too complex to have evolved, because all intermediate steps in a given pathway must be present to produce the final product. Critique this argument. How could you use the diversity of metabolic pathways that produce the same or similar products to support your case?

9. **SCIENTIFIC INQUIRY**
   DRAW IT A researcher has developed an assay to measure the activity of an important enzyme present in liver cells growing in culture. She adds the enzyme's substrate to a dish of cells and then measures the appearance of reaction products. The results are graphed as the amount of product on the y-axis versus time on the x-axis. The researcher notes four sections of the graph. For a short period of time, no products appear (section A). Then (section B) the reaction rate is quite high (the slope of the line is steep). Next, the reaction gradually slows down (section C). Finally, the graph line becomes flat (section D). Draw and label the graph, and propose a model to explain the molecular events occurring at each stage of this reaction profile.

10. **SCIENCE, TECHNOLOGY, AND SOCIETY**
    Organophosphates (organic compounds containing phosphate groups) are commonly used as insecticides to improve crop yield. Organophosphates typically interfere with nerve signal transmission by inhibiting the enzymes that degrade transmitter molecules. They affect humans and other vertebrates as well as insects. Thus, the use of organophosphate pesticides poses some health risks. On the other hand, these molecules break down rapidly upon exposure to air and sunlight. As a consumer, what level of risk are you willing to accept in exchange for an abundant and affordable food supply?

11. **WRITE ABOUT A THEME**
    Energy Transfer Life requires energy. In a short essay (100–150 words), describe the basic principles of bioenergetics in an animal cell. How is the flow and transformation of energy different in a photosynthesizing cell? Include the role of ATP and enzymes in your discussion.

For selected answers, see Appendix A.

MasteringBIOLOGY®   www.masteringbiology.com

1. MasteringBiology® Assignments
Tutorials ATP and Energy • How Enzymes Function • Enzyme and Substrate Concentrations • Factors That Affect Reaction Rate • Enzyme Inhibition • Regulating Enzyme Action
Activities Energy Transformations • The Structure of ATP • Chemical Reactions and ATP • How Enzymes Work
Questions Student Misconceptions • Reading Quiz • Multiple Choice • End-of-Chapter

2. eText
Read your book online, search, take notes, highlight text, and more.

3. The Study Area
Practice Tests • Cumulative Test • *BioFlix* 3-D Animations • MP3 Tutor Sessions • Videos • Activities • Investigations • Lab Media • Audio Glossary • Word Study Tools • Art

9

Cellular Respiration and Fermentation

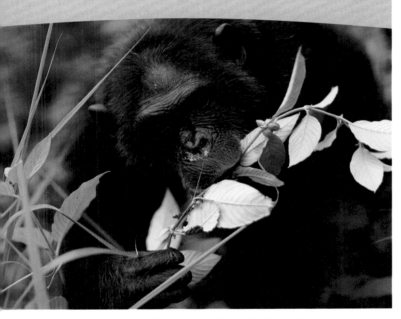

▲ **Figure 9.1 How do these leaves power the work of life for this chimpanzee?**

KEY CONCEPTS

9.1 Catabolic pathways yield energy by oxidizing organic fuels

9.2 Glycolysis harvests chemical energy by oxidizing glucose to pyruvate

9.3 After pyruvate is oxidized, the citric acid cycle completes the energy-yielding oxidation of organic molecules

9.4 During oxidative phosphorylation, chemiosmosis couples electron transport to ATP synthesis

9.5 Fermentation and anaerobic respiration enable cells to produce ATP without the use of oxygen

9.6 Glycolysis and the citric acid cycle connect to many other metabolic pathways

Life Is Work

Living cells require transfusions of energy from outside sources to perform their many tasks—for example, assembling polymers, pumping substances across membranes, moving, and reproducing. The chimpanzee in **Figure 9.1** obtains energy for its cells by eating plants; some animals feed on other organisms that eat plants. The energy stored in the organic molecules of food ultimately comes from the sun. Energy flows into an ecosystem as sunlight and exits as heat; in contrast, the chemical elements essential to life are recycled (**Figure 9.2**). Photosynthesis generates oxygen and organic molecules used by the mitochondria of eukaryotes (including plants and algae) as fuel for cellular respiration. Respiration breaks this fuel down, generating ATP. The waste products of this type of respiration, carbon dioxide and water, are the raw materials for photosynthesis. In this chapter, we consider how cells harvest the chemical energy stored in organic molecules and use it to generate ATP, the molecule that drives most cellular work. After presenting some basics about respiration, we will focus on three key pathways of respiration: glycolysis, the citric acid cycle, and oxidative phosphorylation. We'll also consider fermentation, a somewhat simpler pathway coupled to glycolysis that has deep evolutionary roots.

▲ **Figure 9.2 Energy flow and chemical recycling in ecosystems.** Energy flows into an ecosystem as sunlight and ultimately leaves as heat, while the chemical elements essential to life are recycled.

ANIMATION *BioFlix* Visit the Study Area at **www.masteringbiology.com** for the BioFlix® 3-D Animation on The Carbon Cycle.

CONCEPT 9.1

Catabolic pathways yield energy by oxidizing organic fuels

As you learned in Chapter 8, metabolic pathways that release stored energy by breaking down complex molecules are called catabolic pathways. Electron transfer plays a major role in these pathways. In this section, we consider these processes, which are central to cellular respiration.

Catabolic Pathways and Production of ATP

Organic compounds possess potential energy as a result of the arrangement of electrons in the bonds between their atoms. Compounds that can participate in exergonic reactions can act as fuels. With the help of enzymes, a cell systematically degrades complex organic molecules that are rich in potential energy to simpler waste products that have less energy. Some of the energy taken out of chemical storage can be used to do work; the rest is dissipated as heat.

One catabolic process, **fermentation**, is a partial degradation of sugars or other organic fuel that occurs without the use of oxygen. However, the most prevalent and efficient catabolic pathway is **aerobic respiration**, in which oxygen is consumed as a reactant along with the organic fuel (*aerobic* is from the Greek *aer*, air, and *bios*, life). The cells of most eukaryotic and many prokaryotic organisms can carry out aerobic respiration. Some prokaryotes use substances other than oxygen as reactants in a similar process that harvests chemical energy without oxygen; this process is called *anaerobic respiration* (the prefix *an-* means "without"). Technically, the term **cellular respiration** includes both aerobic and anaerobic processes. However, it originated as a synonym for aerobic respiration because of the relationship of that process to organismal respiration, in which an animal breathes in oxygen. Thus, *cellular respiration* is often used to refer to the aerobic process, a practice we follow in most of this chapter.

Although very different in mechanism, aerobic respiration is in principle similar to the combustion of gasoline in an automobile engine after oxygen is mixed with the fuel (hydrocarbons). Food provides the fuel for respiration, and the exhaust is carbon dioxide and water. The overall process can be summarized as follows:

$$\text{Organic compounds} + \text{Oxygen} \rightarrow \text{Carbon dioxide} + \text{Water} + \text{Energy}$$

Although carbohydrates, fats, and proteins can all be processed and consumed as fuel, it is helpful to learn the steps of cellular respiration by tracking the degradation of the sugar glucose ($C_6H_{12}O_6$):

$$C_6H_{12}O_6 + 6\,O_2 \rightarrow 6\,CO_2 + 6\,H_2O + \text{Energy (ATP + heat)}$$

Glucose is the fuel that cells most often use; we will discuss other organic molecules contained in foods later in the chapter.

This breakdown of glucose is exergonic, having a free-energy change of −686 kcal (2,870 kJ) per mole of glucose decomposed ($\Delta G = -686$ kcal/mol). Recall that a negative ΔG indicates that the products of the chemical process store less energy than the reactants and that the reaction can happen spontaneously—in other words, without an input of energy.

Catabolic pathways do not directly move flagella, pump solutes across membranes, polymerize monomers, or perform other cellular work. Catabolism is linked to work by a chemical drive shaft—ATP, which you learned about in Chapter 8. To keep working, the cell must regenerate its supply of ATP from ADP and P_i (see Figure 8.11). To understand how cellular respiration accomplishes this, let's examine the fundamental chemical processes known as oxidation and reduction.

Redox Reactions: Oxidation and Reduction

How do the catabolic pathways that decompose glucose and other organic fuels yield energy? The answer is based on the transfer of electrons during the chemical reactions. The relocation of electrons releases energy stored in organic molecules, and this energy ultimately is used to synthesize ATP.

The Principle of Redox

In many chemical reactions, there is a transfer of one or more electrons (e^-) from one reactant to another. These electron transfers are called oxidation-reduction reactions, or **redox reactions** for short. In a redox reaction, the loss of electrons from one substance is called **oxidation**, and the addition of electrons to another substance is known as **reduction**. (Note that *adding* electrons is called *reduction*; negatively charged electrons added to an atom *reduce* the amount of positive charge of that atom.) To take a simple, nonbiological example, consider the reaction between the elements sodium (Na) and chlorine (Cl) that forms table salt:

$$\underset{\underset{\text{(gains electron)}}{\xleftarrow{\hspace{2cm}}\text{becomes reduced}}}{\overset{\overset{\text{becomes oxidized}}{\text{(loses electron)}}{\xrightarrow{\hspace{2cm}}}}{\text{Na} + \text{Cl} \longrightarrow \text{Na}^+ + \text{Cl}^-}}$$

We could generalize a redox reaction this way:

$$\underset{\xleftarrow{\hspace{1.5cm}}\text{becomes reduced}}{\overset{\overset{\text{becomes oxidized}}{\xrightarrow{\hspace{1.5cm}}}}{Xe^- + Y \longrightarrow X + Ye^-}}$$

In the generalized reaction, substance Xe^-, the electron donor, is called the **reducing agent**; it reduces Y, which accepts the donated electron. Substance Y, the electron acceptor, is the **oxidizing agent**; it oxidizes Xe^- by removing its electron. Because an electron transfer requires both a donor and an acceptor, oxidation and reduction always go together.

Not all redox reactions involve the complete transfer of electrons from one substance to another; some change the degree of electron sharing in covalent bonds. The reaction between methane and oxygen, shown in **Figure 9.3**, is an ex-

Reactants

Products

becomes oxidized

$$CH_4 \quad + \quad 2 O_2 \quad \longrightarrow \quad CO_2 \quad + \quad Energy \quad + \quad 2 H_2O$$

becomes reduced

Methane (reducing agent)

Oxygen (oxidizing agent)

Carbon dioxide

Water

▲ **Figure 9.3 Methane combustion as an energy-yielding redox reaction.** The reaction releases energy to the surroundings because the electrons lose potential energy when they end up being shared unequally, spending more time near electronegative atoms such as oxygen.

ample. As explained in Chapter 2, the covalent electrons in methane are shared nearly equally between the bonded atoms because carbon and hydrogen have about the same affinity for valence electrons; they are about equally electronegative. But when methane reacts with oxygen, forming carbon dioxide, electrons end up shared less equally between the carbon atom and its new covalent partners, the oxygen atoms, which are very electronegative. In effect, the carbon atom has partially "lost" its shared electrons; thus, methane has been oxidized.

Now let's examine the fate of the reactant O_2. The two atoms of the oxygen molecule (O_2) share their electrons equally. But when oxygen reacts with the hydrogen from methane, forming water, the electrons of the covalent bonds spend more time near the oxygen (see Figure 9.3). In effect, each oxygen atom has partially "gained" electrons, so the oxygen molecule has been reduced. Because oxygen is so electronegative, it is one of the most potent of all oxidizing agents.

Energy must be added to pull an electron away from an atom, just as energy is required to push a ball uphill. The more electronegative the atom (the stronger its pull on electrons), the more energy is required to take an electron away from it. An electron loses potential energy when it shifts from a less electronegative atom toward a more electronegative one, just as a ball loses potential energy when it rolls downhill. A redox reaction that moves electrons closer to oxygen, such as the burning (oxidation) of methane, therefore releases chemical energy that can be put to work.

Oxidation of Organic Fuel Molecules During Cellular Respiration

The oxidation of methane by oxygen is the main combustion reaction that occurs at the burner of a gas stove. The combustion of gasoline in an automobile engine is also a redox reaction; the energy released pushes the pistons. But the energy-yielding redox process of greatest interest to biologists is respiration: the oxidation of glucose and other molecules in food. Examine again the summary equation for cellular respiration, but this time think of it as a redox process:

becomes oxidized

$$C_6H_{12}O_6 \quad + \quad 6 O_2 \quad \longrightarrow \quad 6 CO_2 \quad + \quad 6 H_2O \quad + \quad Energy$$

becomes reduced

As in the combustion of methane or gasoline, the fuel (glucose) is oxidized and oxygen is reduced. The electrons lose potential energy along the way, and energy is released.

In general, organic molecules that have an abundance of hydrogen are excellent fuels because their bonds are a source of "hilltop" electrons, whose energy may be released as these electrons "fall" down an energy gradient when they are transferred to oxygen. The summary equation for respiration indicates that hydrogen is transferred from glucose to oxygen. But the important point, not visible in the summary equation, is that the energy state of the electron changes as hydrogen (with its electron) is transferred to oxygen. In respiration, the oxidation of glucose transfers electrons to a lower energy state, liberating energy that becomes available for ATP synthesis.

The main energy-yielding foods, carbohydrates and fats, are reservoirs of electrons associated with hydrogen. Only the barrier of activation energy holds back the flood of electrons to a lower energy state (see Figure 8.12). Without this barrier, a food substance like glucose would combine almost instantaneously with O_2. If we supply the activation energy by igniting glucose, it burns in air, releasing 686 kcal (2,870 kJ) of heat per mole of glucose (about 180 g). Body temperature is not high enough to initiate burning, of course. Instead, if you swallow some glucose, enzymes in your cells will lower the barrier of activation energy, allowing the sugar to be oxidized in a series of steps.

Stepwise Energy Harvest via NAD^+ and the Electron Transport Chain

If energy is released from a fuel all at once, it cannot be harnessed efficiently for constructive work. For example, if a gasoline tank explodes, it cannot drive a car very far. Cellular respiration does not oxidize glucose in a single explosive step either. Rather, glucose and other organic fuels are broken down in a series of steps, each one catalyzed by an enzyme. At key steps, electrons are stripped from the glucose. As is often the case in oxidation reactions, each electron travels with a proton—thus, as a hydrogen atom. The hydrogen atoms are not transferred directly to oxygen, but instead are usually passed first to an electron carrier, a coenzyme called **NAD^+** (nicotinamide adenine dinucleotide, a derivative of the vitamin niacin). NAD^+ is well suited as an electron carrier because it can cycle easily between oxidized (NAD^+) and reduced (NADH) states. As an electron acceptor, NAD^+ functions as an oxidizing agent during respiration.

How does NAD^+ trap electrons from glucose and other organic molecules? Enzymes called dehydrogenases remove a

NAD+

Nicotinamide
(oxidized form)

Dehydrogenase

Reduction of NAD+

Oxidation of NADH

+ 2[H]
(from food)

NADH

Nicotinamide
(reduced form)

+ H+

◄ **Figure 9.4 NAD$^+$ as an electron shuttle.** The full name for NAD$^+$, nicotinamide adenine dinucleotide, describes its structure: The molecule consists of two nucleotides joined together at their phosphate groups (shown in yellow). (Nicotinamide is a nitrogenous base, although not one that is present in DNA or RNA; see Figure 5.26.) The enzymatic transfer of 2 electrons and 1 proton (H$^+$) from an organic molecule in food to NAD$^+$ reduces the NAD$^+$ to NADH; the second proton (H$^+$) is released. Most of the electrons removed from food are transferred initially to NAD$^+$.

pair of hydrogen atoms (2 electrons and 2 protons) from the substrate (glucose, in this example), thereby oxidizing it. The enzyme delivers the 2 electrons along with 1 proton to its coenzyme, NAD$^+$ **(Figure 9.4)**. The other proton is released as a hydrogen ion (H$^+$) into the surrounding solution:

$$H-\overset{|}{\underset{|}{C}}-OH + NAD^+ \xrightarrow{\text{Dehydrogenase}} \overset{|}{C}=O + NADH + H^+$$

By receiving 2 negatively charged electrons but only 1 positively charged proton, NAD$^+$ has its charge neutralized when it is reduced to NADH. The name NADH shows the hydrogen that has been received in the reaction. NAD$^+$ is the most versatile electron acceptor in cellular respiration and functions in several of the redox steps during the breakdown of glucose.

Electrons lose very little of their potential energy when they are transferred from glucose to NAD$^+$. Each NADH molecule formed during respiration represents stored energy that can be tapped to make ATP when the electrons complete their "fall" down an energy gradient from NADH to oxygen.

How do electrons that are extracted from glucose and stored as potential energy in NADH finally reach oxygen? It will help to compare the redox chemistry of cellular respiration to a much simpler reaction: the reaction between hydrogen and oxygen to form water **(Figure 9.5a)**. Mix H$_2$ and O$_2$, provide a spark for activation energy, and the

gases combine explosively. In fact, combustion of liquid H$_2$ and O$_2$ is harnessed to power the main engines of the space shuttle after it is launched, boosting it into orbit. The explosion represents a release of energy as the electrons of hydrogen "fall" closer to the electronegative oxygen atoms. Cellular respiration also brings hydrogen and oxygen together to form water, but there are two important differences. First, in cellular respiration, the hydrogen that reacts with oxygen is derived from organic molecules rather than H$_2$. Second, instead of occurring in one explosive reaction, respiration uses an

(a) Uncontrolled reaction

(b) Cellular respiration

▲ **Figure 9.5 An introduction to electron transport chains. (a)** The one-step exergonic reaction of hydrogen with oxygen to form water releases a large amount of energy in the form of heat and light: an explosion. **(b)** In cellular respiration, the same reaction occurs in stages: An electron transport chain breaks the "fall" of electrons in this reaction into a series of smaller steps and stores some of the released energy in a form that can be used to make ATP. (The rest of the energy is released as heat.)

electron transport chain to break the fall of electrons to oxygen into several energy-releasing steps (**Figure 9.5b**). An **electron transport chain** consists of a number of molecules, mostly proteins, built into the inner membrane of the mitochondria of eukaryotic cells and the plasma membrane of aerobically respiring prokaryotes. Electrons removed from glucose are shuttled by NADH to the "top," higher-energy end of the chain. At the "bottom," lower-energy end, O_2 captures these electrons along with hydrogen nuclei (H^+), forming water.

Electron transfer from NADH to oxygen is an exergonic reaction with a free-energy change of -53 kcal/mol (-222 kJ/mol). Instead of this energy being released and wasted in a single explosive step, electrons cascade down the chain from one carrier molecule to the next in a series of redox reactions, losing a small amount of energy with each step until they finally reach oxygen, the terminal electron acceptor, which has a very great affinity for electrons. Each "downhill" carrier is more electronegative than, and thus capable of oxidizing, its "uphill" neighbor, with oxygen at the bottom of the chain. Therefore, the electrons removed from glucose by NAD^+ fall down an energy gradient in the electron transport chain to a far more stable location in the electronegative oxygen atom. Put another way, oxygen pulls electrons down the chain in an energy-yielding tumble analogous to gravity pulling objects downhill.

In summary, during cellular respiration, most electrons travel the following "downhill" route: glucose → NADH → electron transport chain → oxygen. Later in this chapter, you will learn more about how the cell uses the energy released from this exergonic electron fall to regenerate its supply of ATP. For now, having covered the basic redox mechanisms of cellular respiration, let's look at the entire process by which energy is harvested from organic fuels.

The Stages of Cellular Respiration: *A Preview*

The harvesting of energy from glucose by cellular respiration is a cumulative function of three metabolic stages:

1. Glycolysis (color-coded teal throughout the chapter)
2. Pyruvate oxidation and the citric acid cycle (color-coded salmon)
3. Oxidative phosphorylation: electron transport and chemiosmosis (color-coded violet)

Biochemists usually reserve the term *cellular respiration* for stages 2 and 3. We include glycolysis, however, because most respiring cells deriving energy from glucose use glycolysis to produce the starting material for the citric acid cycle.

As diagrammed in **Figure 9.6**, glycolysis and pyruvate oxidation followed by the citric acid cycle are the catabolic pathways that break down glucose and other organic fuels. **Glycolysis**, which occurs in the cytosol, begins the degradation process by breaking glucose into two molecules of a compound called pyruvate. In eukaryotes, pyruvate enters the mitochondrion and is oxidized to a compound called acetyl CoA, which enters the **citric acid cycle**. There, the breakdown of glucose to carbon dioxide is completed. (In prokaryotes, these processes take place in the cytosol.) Thus, the carbon dioxide produced by respiration represents fragments of oxidized organic molecules.

Some of the steps of glycolysis and the citric acid cycle are redox reactions in which dehydrogenases transfer electrons from substrates to NAD^+, forming NADH. In the third stage of respiration, the electron transport chain accepts electrons from the breakdown products of the first two stages (most often via NADH) and passes these electrons from one molecule to another. At the end of the chain, the electrons are combined with molecular oxygen and hydrogen ions (H^+), forming water (see

▶ **Figure 9.6 An overview of cellular respiration.** During glycolysis, each glucose molecule is broken down into two molecules of the compound pyruvate. In eukaryotic cells, as shown here, the pyruvate enters the mitochondrion. There it is oxidized to acetyl CoA, which is further oxidized to CO_2 in the citric acid cycle. NADH and a similar electron carrier, a coenzyme called $FADH_2$, transfer electrons derived from glucose to electron transport chains, which are built into the inner mitochondrial membrane. (In prokaryotes, the electron transport chains are located in the plasma membrane.) During oxidative phosphorylation, electron transport chains convert the chemical energy to a form used for ATP synthesis in the process called chemiosmosis.

 BioFlix Visit the Study Area at **www.masteringbiology.com** for the BioFlix® 3-D Animation on Cellular Respiration.

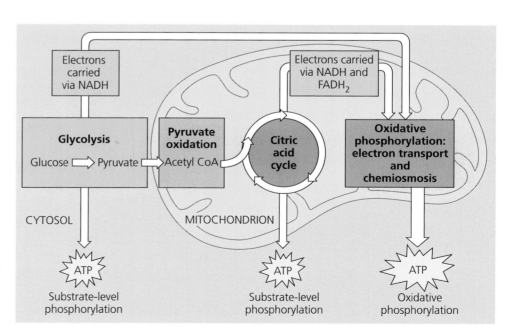

Figure 9.5b). The energy released at each step of the chain is stored in a form the mitochondrion (or prokaryotic cell) can use to make ATP from ADP. This mode of ATP synthesis is called **oxidative phosphorylation** because it is powered by the redox reactions of the electron transport chain.

In eukaryotic cells, the inner membrane of the mitochondrion is the site of electron transport and chemiosmosis, the processes that together constitute oxidative phosphorylation. (In prokaryotes, these processes take place in the plasma membrane.) Oxidative phosphorylation accounts for almost 90% of the ATP generated by respiration. A smaller amount of ATP is formed directly in a few reactions of glycolysis and the citric acid cycle by a mechanism called **substrate-level phosphorylation (Figure 9.7)**. This mode of ATP synthesis occurs when an enzyme transfers a phosphate group from a substrate molecule to ADP, rather than adding an inorganic phosphate to ADP as in oxidative phosphorylation. "Substrate molecule" here refers to an organic molecule generated as an intermediate during the catabolism of glucose.

For each molecule of glucose degraded to carbon dioxide and water by respiration, the cell makes up to about 32 molecules of ATP, each with 7.3 kcal/mol of free energy. Respiration cashes in the large denomination of energy banked in a single molecule of glucose (686 kcal/mol) for the small change of many molecules of ATP, which is more practical for the cell to spend on its work.

This preview has introduced you to how glycolysis, the citric acid cycle, and oxidative phosphorylation fit into the process of cellular respiration. We are now ready to take a closer look at each of these three stages of respiration.

CONCEPT CHECK 9.1

1. Compare and contrast aerobic and anaerobic respiration.
2. **WHAT IF?** If the following redox reaction occurred, which compound would be oxidized? Which reduced?

$$C_4H_6O_5 + NAD^+ \longrightarrow C_4H_4O_5 + NADH + H^+$$

For suggested answers, see Appendix A.

▲ **Figure 9.7 Substrate-level phosphorylation.** Some ATP is made by direct transfer of a phosphate group from an organic substrate to ADP by an enzyme. (For examples in glycolysis, see Figure 9.9, steps 7 and 10.)

MAKE CONNECTIONS *Review Figure 8.8 on page 149. Do you think the potential energy is higher for the reactants or the products in the reaction shown above? Explain.*

CONCEPT 9.2

Glycolysis harvests chemical energy by oxidizing glucose to pyruvate

The word *glycolysis* means "sugar splitting," and that is exactly what happens during this pathway. Glucose, a six-carbon sugar, is split into two three-carbon sugars. These smaller sugars are then oxidized and their remaining atoms rearranged to form two molecules of pyruvate. (Pyruvate is the ionized form of pyruvic acid.)

As summarized in **Figure 9.8**, glycolysis can be divided into two phases: energy investment and energy payoff. During the energy investment phase, the cell actually spends ATP. This investment is repaid with interest during the energy payoff phase, when ATP is produced by substrate-level phosphorylation and NAD^+ is reduced to NADH by electrons released from the oxidation of glucose. The net energy yield from glycolysis, per glucose molecule, is 2 ATP plus 2 NADH. The ten steps of the glycolytic pathway are shown in **Figure 9.9**.

All of the carbon originally present in glucose is accounted for in the two molecules of pyruvate; no carbon is released as CO_2 during glycolysis. Glycolysis occurs whether or not O_2 is present. However, if O_2 *is* present, the chemical energy stored in pyruvate and NADH can be extracted by pyruvate oxidation, the citric acid cycle, and oxidative phosphorylation.

▲ **Figure 9.8 The energy input and output of glycolysis.**

▼ **Figure 9.9 A closer look at glycolysis.** The orientation diagram on the left relates glycolysis to the entire process of respiration. Note that glycolysis is a source of ATP and NADH.

WHAT IF? *What would happen if you removed the dihydroxyacetone phosphate generated in step ❹ as fast as it was produced?*

Glycolysis: Energy Investment Phase

Glucose

Hexokinase transfers a phosphate group from ATP to glucose, making it more chemically reactive. The charge on the phosphate also traps the sugar in the cell.

Glucose 6-phosphate

Glucose 6-phosphate is converted to its isomer, fructose 6-phosphate.

Fructose 6-phosphate

Phosphofructokinase transfers a phosphate group from ATP to the opposite end of the sugar, investing a second molecule of ATP. This is a key step for regulation of glycolysis.

Fructose 1,6-bisphosphate

Aldolase cleaves the sugar molecule into two different three-carbon sugars (isomers).

Dihydroxyacetone phosphate

Glyceraldehyde 3-phosphate

To step 6

Isomerase catalyzes the reversible conversion between the two isomers. This reaction never reaches equilibrium: Glyceraldehyde 3-phosphate is used as the substrate of the next reaction (step 6) as fast as it forms.

The energy payoff phase occurs after glucose is split into two three-carbon sugars. Thus, the coefficient 2 precedes all molecules in this phase.

Glycolysis: Energy Payoff Phase

1,3-Bisphospho-glycerate

This enzyme catalyzes two sequential reactions. First, the sugar is oxidized by the transfer of electrons to NAD+, forming NADH. Second, the energy released from this exergonic redox reaction is used to attach a phosphate group to the oxidized substrate, making a product of very high potential energy.

3-Phospho-glycerate

The phosphate group added in the previous step is transferred to ADP (substrate-level phosphorylation) in an exergonic reaction. The carbonyl group of a sugar has been oxidized to the carboxyl group (—COO⁻) of an organic acid (3-phosphoglycerate).

2-Phospho-glycerate

This enzyme relocates the remaining phosphate group.

Phosphoenol-pyruvate (PEP)

Enolase causes a double bond to form in the substrate by extracting a water molecule, yielding phosphoenolpyruvate (PEP), a compound with a very high potential energy.

Pyruvate

The phosphate group is transferred from PEP to ADP (a second example of substrate-level phosphorylation), forming pyruvate.

CONCEPT CHECK 9.2

1. During the redox reaction in glycolysis (step 6 in Figure 9.9), which molecule acts as the oxidizing agent? The reducing agent?

2. **MAKE CONNECTIONS** Step 3 in Figure 9.9 is a major point of regulation of glycolysis. The enzyme phosphofructokinase is allosterically regulated by ATP and re-lated molecules (see Concept 8.5, p. 158). Considering the overall result of glycolysis, would you expect ATP to inhibit or stimulate activity of this enzyme? (*Hint:* Make sure you consider the role of ATP as an allosteric regulator, not as a substrate of the enzyme.)

For suggested answers, see Appendix A.

After pyruvate is oxidized, the citric acid cycle completes the energy-yielding oxidation of organic molecules

Glycolysis releases less than a quarter of the chemical energy in glucose that can be released by cells; most of the energy remains stockpiled in the two molecules of pyruvate. If molecular oxygen is present, the pyruvate enters a mitochondrion (in eukaryotic cells), where the oxidation of glucose is completed. (In prokaryotic cells, this process occurs in the cytosol.)

Oxidation of Pyruvate to Acetyl CoA

Upon entering the mitochondrion via active transport, pyruvate is first converted to a compound called acetyl coenzyme A, or **acetyl CoA (Figure 9.10)**. This step, linking glycolysis and the citric acid cycle, is carried out by a multienzyme complex that catalyzes three reactions: ❶ Pyruvate's carboxyl group (—COO^-), which is already fully oxidized and thus has little chemical energy, is removed and given off as a molecule of CO_2. (This is the first step in which CO_2 is released during respiration.) ❷ The remaining two-carbon fragment is oxidized, forming acetate (CH_3COO^-, the ionized form of acetic acid). The extracted electrons are transferred to NAD^+,

▲ **Figure 9.10 Oxidation of pyruvate to acetyl CoA, the step before the citric acid cycle.** Pyruvate is a charged molecule, so in eukaryotic cells it must enter the mitochondrion via active transport, with the help of a transport protein. Next, a complex of several enzymes (the pyruvate dehydrogenase complex) catalyzes the three numbered steps, which are described in the text. The acetyl group of acetyl CoA will enter the citric acid cycle. The CO_2 molecule will diffuse out of the cell. By convention, coenzyme A is abbreviated S-CoA when it is attached to a molecule, emphasizing the sulfur atom (S).

storing energy in the form of NADH. ❸ Finally, coenzyme A (CoA), a sulfur-containing compound derived from a B vitamin, is attached via its sulfur atom to the acetate, forming acetyl CoA, which has a high potential energy; in other words, the reaction of acetyl CoA to yield lower-energy products is highly exergonic. This molecule will now feed its acetyl group into the citric acid cycle for further oxidation.

The Citric Acid Cycle

The citric acid cycle is also called the tricarboxylic acid cycle or the Krebs cycle, the latter honoring Hans Krebs, the German-British scientist who was largely responsible for working out the pathway in the 1930s. The cycle functions as a metabolic furnace that oxidizes organic fuel derived from pyruvate. **Figure 9.11** summarizes the inputs and outputs as pyruvate is broken down to three CO_2 molecules, including the molecule of CO_2 released during the conversion of pyruvate to acetyl CoA. The cycle generates 1 ATP per turn by

▲ **Figure 9.11 An overview of pyruvate oxidation and the citric acid cycle.** The inputs and outputs per pyruvate molecule are shown. To calculate on a per-glucose basis, multiply by 2, because each glucose molecule is split during glycolysis into two pyruvate molecules.

substrate-level phosphorylation, but most of the chemical energy is transferred to NAD^+ and a related electron carrier, the coenzyme FAD (flavin adenine dinucleotide, derived from riboflavin, a B vitamin), during the redox reactions. The reduced coenzymes, NADH and $FADH_2$, shuttle their cargo of high-energy electrons into the electron transport chain.

Now let's look at the citric acid cycle in more detail. The cycle has eight steps, each catalyzed by a specific enzyme. You can see in **Figure 9.12** that for each turn of the citric acid cycle, two carbons (red) enter in the relatively reduced form of an acetyl group (step 1), and two different carbons (blue) leave in the completely oxidized form of CO_2 molecules

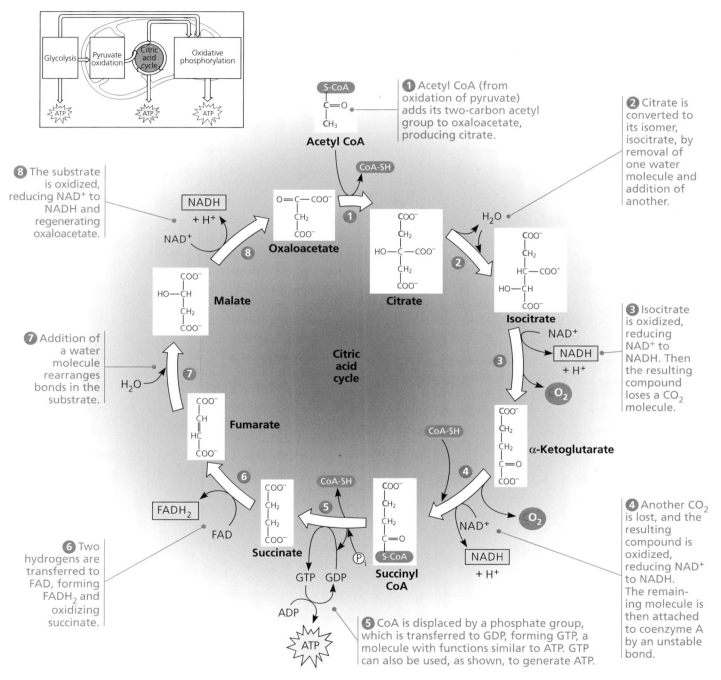

1 Acetyl CoA (from oxidation of pyruvate) adds its two-carbon acetyl group to oxaloacetate, producing citrate.

2 Citrate is converted to its isomer, isocitrate, by removal of one water molecule and addition of another.

3 Isocitrate is oxidized, reducing NAD^+ to NADH. Then the resulting compound loses a CO_2 molecule.

4 Another CO_2 is lost, and the resulting compound is oxidized, reducing NAD^+ to NADH. The remaining molecule is then attached to coenzyme A by an unstable bond.

5 CoA is displaced by a phosphate group, which is transferred to GDP, forming GTP, a molecule with functions similar to ATP. GTP can also be used, as shown, to generate ATP.

6 Two hydrogens are transferred to FAD, forming $FADH_2$ and oxidizing succinate.

7 Addition of a water molecule rearranges bonds in the substrate.

8 The substrate is oxidized, reducing NAD^+ to NADH and regenerating oxaloacetate.

▲ **Figure 9.12 A closer look at the citric acid cycle.** In the chemical structures, red type traces the fate of the two carbon atoms that enter the cycle via acetyl CoA (step 1), and blue type indicates the two carbons that exit the cycle as CO_2 in steps 3 and 4. (The red labeling goes only through step 5 because the succinate molecule is symmetrical; the two ends cannot be distinguished from each other.) Notice that the carbon atoms that enter the cycle from acetyl CoA do not leave the cycle in the same turn. They remain in the cycle, occupying a different location in the molecules on their next turn, after another acetyl group is added. As a consequence, the oxaloacetate that is regenerated at step 8 is composed of different carbon atoms each time around. In eukaryotic cells, all the citric acid cycle enzymes are located in the mitochondrial matrix except for the enzyme that catalyzes step 6, which resides in the inner mitochondrial membrane. Carboxylic acids are represented in their ionized forms, as —COO^-, because the ionized forms prevail at the pH within the mitochondrion. For example, citrate is the ionized form of citric acid.

(steps 3 and 4). The acetyl group of acetyl CoA joins the cycle by combining with the compound oxaloacetate, forming citrate (step 1). (Citrate is the ionized form of citric acid, for which the cycle is named.) The next seven steps decompose the citrate back to oxaloacetate. It is this regeneration of oxaloacetate that makes this process a *cycle*.

Now let's tally the energy-rich molecules produced by the citric acid cycle. For each acetyl group entering the cycle, 3 NAD^+ are reduced to NADH (steps 3, 4, and 8). In step 6, electrons are transferred not to NAD^+, but to FAD, which accepts 2 electrons and 2 protons to become $FADH_2$. In many animal tissue cells, step 5 produces a guanosine triphosphate (GTP) molecule by substrate-level phosphorylation, as shown in Figure 9.12. GTP is a molecule similar to ATP in its structure and cellular function. This GTP may be used to make an ATP molecule (as shown) or directly power work in the cell. In the cells of plants, bacteria, and some animal tissues, step 5 forms an ATP molecule directly by substrate-level phosphorylation. The output from step 5 represents the only ATP generated directly by the citric acid cycle.

Most of the ATP produced by respiration results from oxidative phosphorylation, when the NADH and $FADH_2$ produced by the citric acid cycle relay the electrons extracted from food to the electron transport chain. In the process, they supply the necessary energy for the phosphorylation of ADP to ATP. We will explore this process in the next section.

CONCEPT CHECK 9.3

1. Name the molecules that conserve most of the energy from the citric acid cycle's redox reactions. How is this energy converted to a form that can be used to make ATP?
2. What processes in your cells produce the CO_2 that you exhale?
3. **WHAT IF?** The conversions shown in Figure 9.10 and step 4 of Figure 9.12 are each catalyzed by a large multienzyme complex. What similarities are there in the reactions that occur in these two cases?

For suggested answers, see Appendix A.

CONCEPT 9.4

During oxidative phosphorylation, chemiosmosis couples electron transport to ATP synthesis

Our main objective in this chapter is to learn how cells harvest the energy of glucose and other nutrients in food to make ATP. But the metabolic components of respiration we have dissected so far, glycolysis and the citric acid cycle, produce only 4 ATP molecules per glucose molecule, all by substrate-level phosphorylation: 2 net ATP from glycolysis and 2 ATP from the citric acid cycle. At this point, molecules of NADH (and $FADH_2$) account for most of the energy extracted from the glucose. These electron escorts link glycolysis and the citric acid cycle to the machinery of oxidative phosphorylation, which uses energy released by the electron transport chain to power ATP synthesis. In this section, you will learn first how the electron transport chain works and then how electron flow down the chain is coupled to ATP synthesis.

The Pathway of Electron Transport

The electron transport chain is a collection of molecules embedded in the inner membrane of the mitochondrion in eukaryotic cells. (In prokaryotes, these molecules reside in the plasma membrane.) The folding of the inner membrane to form cristae increases its surface area, providing space for thousands of copies of the chain in each mitochondrion. (Once again, we see that structure fits function.) Most components of the chain are proteins, which exist in multiprotein complexes numbered I through IV. Tightly bound to these proteins are *prosthetic groups*, nonprotein components essential for the catalytic functions of certain enzymes.

Figure 9.13 shows the sequence of electron carriers in the electron transport chain and the drop in free energy as electrons travel down the chain. During electron transport along the chain, electron carriers alternate between reduced and oxidized states as they accept and donate electrons. Each component of the chain becomes reduced when it accepts electrons from its "uphill" neighbor, which has a lower affinity for electrons (is less electronegative). It then returns to its oxidized form as it passes electrons to its "downhill," more electronegative neighbor.

Now let's take a closer look at the electron transport chain in Figure 9.13. We'll first describe the passage of electrons through complex I in some detail, as an illustration of the general principles involved in electron transport. Electrons removed from glucose by NAD^+, during glycolysis and the citric acid cycle, are transferred from NADH to the first molecule of the electron transport chain in complex I. This molecule is a flavoprotein, so named because it has a prosthetic group called flavin mononucleotide (FMN). In the next redox reaction, the flavoprotein returns to its oxidized form as it passes electrons to an iron-sulfur protein (Fe·S in complex I), one of a family of proteins with both iron and sulfur tightly bound. The iron-sulfur protein then passes the electrons to a compound called ubiquinone (Q in Figure 9.13). This electron carrier is a small hydrophobic molecule, the only member of the electron transport chain that is not a protein. Ubiquinone is individually mobile within the membrane rather than residing in a particular complex. (Another name for ubiquinone is coenzyme Q, or CoQ; you may have seen it sold as a nutritional supplement.)

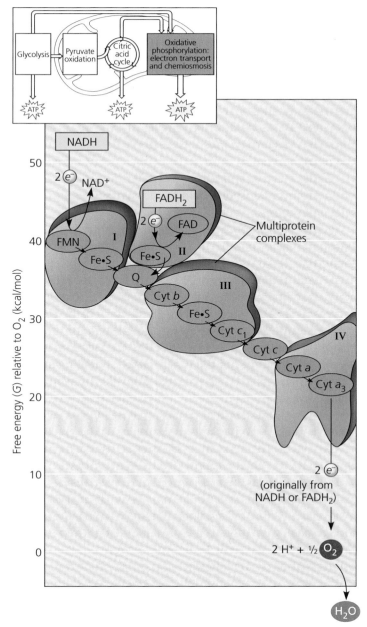

Free energy (G) relative to O_2 (kcal/mol)

NADH

$2\,e^-$ NAD$^+$

FMN   I

FADH$_2$

$2\,e^-$ FAD

Fe•S   Fe•S   II

Multiprotein complexes

Q

Cyt b   III

Fe•S

Cyt c$_1$

Cyt c   IV

Cyt a

Cyt a$_3$

$2\,e^-$
(originally from NADH or FADH$_2$)

$2\,H^+ + \frac{1}{2}\,O_2$

H_2O

▲ **Figure 9.13 Free-energy change during electron transport.** The overall energy drop (ΔG) for electrons traveling from NADH to oxygen is 53 kcal/mol, but this "fall" is broken up into a series of smaller steps by the electron transport chain. (An oxygen atom is represented here as $\frac{1}{2}\,O_2$ to emphasize that the electron transport chain reduces molecular oxygen, O_2, not individual oxygen atoms.)

Most of the remaining electron carriers between ubiquinone and oxygen are proteins called **cytochromes**. Their prosthetic group, called a heme group, has an iron atom that accepts and donates electrons. (It is similar to the heme group in hemoglobin, the protein of red blood cells, except that the iron in hemoglobin carries oxygen, not electrons.) The electron transport chain has several types of cytochromes,

each a different protein with a slightly different electron-carrying heme group. The last cytochrome of the chain, cyt a_3, passes its electrons to oxygen, which is *very* electronegative. Each oxygen atom also picks up a pair of hydrogen ions from the aqueous solution, forming water.

Another source of electrons for the transport chain is FADH$_2$, the other reduced product of the citric acid cycle. Notice in Figure 9.13 that FADH$_2$ adds its electrons to the electron transport chain from within complex II, at a lower energy level than NADH does. Consequently, although NADH and FADH$_2$ each donate an equivalent number of electrons (2) for oxygen reduction, the electron transport chain provides about one-third less energy for ATP synthesis when the electron donor is FADH$_2$ rather than NADH. We'll see why in the next section.

The electron transport chain makes no ATP directly. Instead, it eases the fall of electrons from food to oxygen, breaking a large free-energy drop into a series of smaller steps that release energy in manageable amounts. How does the mitochondrion (or the prokaryotic plasma membrane) couple this electron transport and energy release to ATP synthesis? The answer is a mechanism called chemiosmosis.

Chemiosmosis: The Energy-Coupling Mechanism

Populating the inner membrane of the mitochondrion or the prokaryotic plasma membrane are many copies of a protein complex called **ATP synthase**, the enzyme that actually makes ATP from ADP and inorganic phosphate. ATP synthase works like an ion pump running in reverse. Recall from Chapter 7 that ion pumps usually use ATP as an energy source to transport ions against their gradients. In fact, the proton pump shown in Figure 7.20 is an ATP synthase. As we mentioned in Chapter 8, enzymes can catalyze a reaction in either direction, depending on the ΔG for the reaction, which is affected by the local concentrations of reactants and products. Rather than hydrolyzing ATP to pump protons against their concentration gradient, under the conditions of cellular respiration ATP synthase uses the energy of an existing ion gradient to power ATP synthesis. The power source for the ATP synthase is a difference in the concentration of H$^+$ on opposite sides of the inner mitochondrial membrane. (We can also think of this gradient as a difference in pH, since pH is a measure of H$^+$ concentration.) This process, in which energy stored in the form of a hydrogen ion gradient across a membrane is used to drive cellular work such as the synthesis of ATP, is called **chemiosmosis** (from the Greek *osmos*, push). We have previously used the word *osmosis* in discussing water transport, but here it refers to the flow of H$^+$ across a membrane.

From studying the structure of ATP synthase, scientists have learned how the flow of H$^+$ through this large enzyme powers ATP generation. ATP synthase is a multisubunit complex with four main parts, each made up of multiple polypeptides. Protons move one by one into binding sites on one of the parts (the rotor), causing it to spin in a way that catalyzes ATP production from ADP and inorganic phosphate (**Figure 9.14**). The flow of protons thus behaves somewhat like a rushing stream that turns a waterwheel. ATP synthase is the smallest molecular rotary motor known in nature.

How does the inner mitochondrial membrane or the prokaryotic plasma membrane generate and maintain the H^+ gradient that drives ATP synthesis by the ATP synthase protein complex? Establishing the H^+ gradient is a major function of the electron transport chain, which is shown in

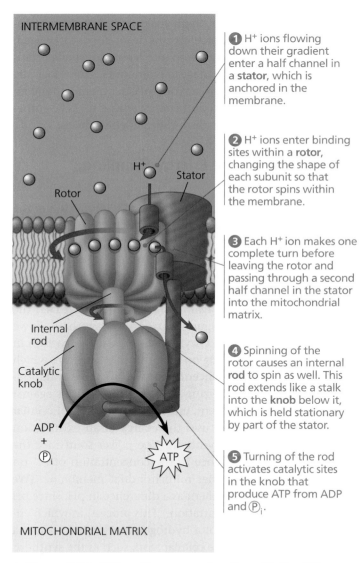

❶ H^+ ions flowing down their gradient enter a half channel in a **stator**, which is anchored in the membrane.

❷ H^+ ions enter binding sites within a **rotor**, changing the shape of each subunit so that the rotor spins within the membrane.

❸ Each H^+ ion makes one complete turn before leaving the rotor and passing through a second half channel in the stator into the mitochondrial matrix.

❹ Spinning of the rotor causes an internal **rod** to spin as well. This rod extends like a stalk into the **knob** below it, which is held stationary by part of the stator.

❺ Turning of the rod activates catalytic sites in the knob that produce ATP from ADP and P_i.

▲ **Figure 9.14 ATP synthase, a molecular mill.** The ATP synthase protein complex functions as a mill, powered by the flow of hydrogen ions. Multiple copies of this complex reside in mitochondrial and chloroplast membranes of eukaryotes and in the plasma membranes of prokaryotes. Each of the four parts of ATP synthase consists of a number of polypeptide subunits.

its mitochondrial location in **Figure 9.15**. The chain is an energy converter that uses the exergonic flow of electrons from NADH and $FADH_2$ to pump H^+ across the membrane, from the mitochondrial matrix into the intermembrane space. The H^+ has a tendency to move back across the membrane, diffusing down its gradient. And the ATP synthases are the only sites that provide a route through the membrane for H^+. As we described previously, the passage of H^+ through ATP synthase uses the exergonic flow of H^+ to drive the phosphorylation of ADP. Thus, the energy stored in an H^+ gradient across a membrane couples the redox reactions of the electron transport chain to ATP synthesis, an example of chemiosmosis.

At this point, you may be wondering how the electron transport chain pumps hydrogen ions. Researchers have found that certain members of the electron transport chain accept and release protons (H^+) along with electrons. (The aqueous solutions inside and surrounding the cell are a ready source of H^+.) At certain steps along the chain, electron transfers cause H^+ to be taken up and released into the surrounding solution. In eukaryotic cells, the electron carriers are spatially arranged in the inner mitochondrial membrane in such a way that H^+ is accepted from the mitochondrial matrix and deposited in the intermembrane space (see Figure 9.15). The H^+ gradient that results is referred to as a **proton-motive force**, emphasizing the capacity of the gradient to perform work. The force drives H^+ back across the membrane through the H^+ channels provided by ATP synthases.

In general terms, *chemiosmosis is an energy-coupling mechanism that uses energy stored in the form of an H^+ gradient across a membrane to drive cellular work.* In mitochondria, the energy for gradient formation comes from exergonic redox reactions, and ATP synthesis is the work performed. But chemiosmosis also occurs elsewhere and in other variations. Chloroplasts use chemiosmosis to generate ATP during photosynthesis; in these organelles, light (rather than chemical energy) drives both electron flow down an electron transport chain and the resulting H^+ gradient formation. Prokaryotes, as already mentioned, generate H^+ gradients across their plasma membranes. They then tap the proton-motive force not only to make ATP inside the cell but also to rotate their flagella and to pump nutrients and waste products across the membrane. Because of its central importance to energy conversions in prokaryotes and eukaryotes, chemiosmosis has helped unify the study of bioenergetics. Peter Mitchell was awarded the Nobel Prize in 1978 for originally proposing the chemiosmotic model.

An Accounting of ATP Production by Cellular Respiration

In the last few sections, we have looked rather closely at the key processes of cellular respiration. Now let's take a step

Figure 9.15 **Chemiosmosis couples the electron transport chain to ATP synthesis.** ① NADH and FADH$_2$ shuttle high-energy electrons extracted from food during glycolysis and the citric acid cycle into an electron transport chain built into the inner mitochondrial membrane. The gold arrows trace the transport of electrons, which finally pass to oxygen at the "downhill" end of the chain, forming water. As Figure 9.13 showed, most of the electron carriers of the chain are grouped into four complexes. Two mobile carriers, ubiquinone (Q) and cytochrome c (Cyt c), move rapidly, ferrying electrons between the large complexes. As complexes I, III, and IV accept and then donate electrons, they pump protons from the mitochondrial matrix into the intermembrane space. (In prokaryotes, protons are pumped outside the plasma membrane.) Note that FADH$_2$ deposits its electrons via complex II and so results in fewer protons being pumped into the intermembrane space than occurs with NADH. Chemical energy originally harvested from food is transformed into a proton-motive force, a gradient of H$^+$ across the membrane. ② During chemiosmosis, the protons flow back down their gradient via ATP synthase, which is built into the membrane nearby. The ATP synthase harnesses the proton-motive force to phosphorylate ADP, forming ATP. Together, electron transport and chemiosmosis make up oxidative phosphorylation.

WHAT IF? *If complex IV were nonfunctional, could chemiosmosis produce any ATP, and if so, how would the rate of synthesis differ?*

back and remind ourselves of its overall function: harvesting the energy of glucose for ATP synthesis.

During respiration, most energy flows in this sequence: glucose → NADH → electron transport chain → proton-motive force → ATP. We can do some bookkeeping to calculate the ATP profit when cellular respiration oxidizes a molecule of glucose to six molecules of carbon dioxide. The three main departments of this metabolic enterprise are glycolysis, the citric acid cycle, and the electron transport chain, which drives oxidative phosphorylation. **Figure 9.16**, on the next page, gives a detailed accounting of the ATP yield per glucose molecule oxidized. The tally adds the 4 ATP produced directly by substrate-level phosphorylation during glycolysis and the citric acid cycle to the many more molecules of ATP generated by oxidative phosphorylation. Each NADH that transfers a pair of electrons from glucose to the electron transport chain contributes enough to the proton-motive force to generate a maximum of about 3 ATP.

Why are the numbers in Figure 9.16 inexact? There are three reasons we cannot state an exact number of ATP molecules generated by the breakdown of one molecule of glucose. First, phosphorylation and the redox reactions are not directly coupled to each other, so the ratio of the number of

▲ **Figure 9.16 ATP yield per molecule of glucose at each stage of cellular respiration.**

? *Explain exactly how the numbers "26 or 28" were calculated.*

NADH molecules to the number of ATP molecules is not a whole number. We know that 1 NADH results in 10 H^+ being transported out across the inner mitochondrial membrane, but the exact number of H^+ that must reenter the mitochondrial matrix via ATP synthase to generate 1 ATP has long been debated. Based on experimental data, however, most biochemists now agree that the most accurate number is 4 H^+. Therefore, a single molecule of NADH generates enough proton-motive force for the synthesis of 2.5 ATP. The citric acid cycle also supplies electrons to the electron transport chain via $FADH_2$, but since its electrons enter later in the chain, each molecule of this electron carrier is responsible for transport of only enough H^+ for the synthesis of 1.5 ATP. These numbers also take into account the slight energetic cost of moving the ATP formed in the mitochondrion out into the cytosol, where it will be used.

Second, the ATP yield varies slightly depending on the type of shuttle used to transport electrons from the cytosol into the mitochondrion. The mitochondrial inner membrane is impermeable to NADH, so NADH in the cytosol is segregated from the machinery of oxidative phosphorylation. The 2 electrons of NADH captured in glycolysis must be conveyed into the mitochondrion by one of several electron shuttle systems. Depending on the kind of shuttle in a particular cell type, the electrons are passed either to NAD^+ or to FAD in the mitochondrial matrix (see Figure 9.16). If the electrons are passed to FAD, as in brain cells, only about 1.5 ATP can result from each NADH that was originally generated in the cytosol. If the

electrons are passed to mitochondrial NAD^+, as in liver cells and heart cells, the yield is about 2.5 ATP per NADH.

A third variable that reduces the yield of ATP is the use of the proton-motive force generated by the redox reactions of respiration to drive other kinds of work. For example, the proton-motive force powers the mitochondrion's uptake of pyruvate from the cytosol. However, if *all* the proton-motive force generated by the electron transport chain were used to drive ATP synthesis, one glucose molecule could generate a maximum of 28 ATP produced by oxidative phosphorylation plus 4 ATP (net) from substrate-level phosphorylation to give a total yield of about 32 ATP (or only about 30 ATP if the less efficient shuttle were functioning).

We can now roughly estimate the efficiency of respiration—that is, the percentage of chemical energy in glucose that has been transferred to ATP. Recall that the complete oxidation of a mole of glucose releases 686 kcal of energy under standard conditions ($\Delta G = -686$ kcal/mol). Phosphorylation of ADP to form ATP stores at least 7.3 kcal per mole of ATP. Therefore, the efficiency of respiration is 7.3 kcal per mole of ATP times 32 moles of ATP per mole of glucose divided by 686 kcal per mole of glucose, which equals 0.34. Thus, about 34% of the potential chemical energy in glucose has been transferred to ATP; the actual percentage is probably higher because ΔG is lower under cellular conditions. Cellular respiration is remarkably efficient in its energy conversion. By comparison, the most efficient automobile converts only about 25% of the energy stored in gasoline to energy that moves the car.

The rest of the energy stored in glucose is lost as heat. We humans use some of this heat to maintain our relatively high body temperature (37°C), and we dissipate the rest through sweating and other cooling mechanisms.

Under certain conditions, it may be beneficial to reduce the efficiency of cellular respiration. A remarkable adaptation is shown by hibernating mammals, which overwinter in a state of inactivity and lowered metabolism. Although their internal body temperature is lower than normal, it still must be kept significantly higher than the external air temperature. One type of tissue, called brown fat, is made up of cells packed full of mitochondria. The inner mitochondrial membrane contains a channel protein called the uncoupling protein, which allows protons to flow back down their concentration gradient without generating ATP. Activation of these proteins in hibernating mammals results in ongoing oxidation of stored fuel stores (fats), generating heat without any ATP production. In the absence of such an adaptation, the ATP level would build up to a point that cellular respiration would be shut down due to regulatory mechanisms to be discussed later.

CONCEPT CHECK 9.4

1. What effect would an absence of O_2 have on the process shown in Figure 9.15?
2. **WHAT IF?** In the absence of O_2, as in question 1, what do you think would happen if you decreased the pH of the intermembrane space of the mitochondrion? Explain your answer.
3. **MAKE CONNECTIONS** In Concept 7.1 (pp. 127–128), you learned that membranes must be fluid to function properly. How does the operation of the electron transport chain support that assertion?

For suggested answers, see Appendix A.

CONCEPT 9.5

Fermentation and anaerobic respiration enable cells to produce ATP without the use of oxygen

Because most of the ATP generated by cellular respiration is due to the work of oxidative phosphorylation, our estimate of ATP yield from aerobic respiration is contingent on an adequate supply of oxygen to the cell. Without the electronegative oxygen to pull electrons down the transport chain, oxidative phosphorylation eventually ceases. However, there are two general mechanisms by which certain cells can oxidize organic fuel and generate ATP *without* the use of oxygen: anaerobic respiration and fermentation. The distinction between these two is that an electron transport chain is used in anaerobic respiration but not in fermentation. (The electron transport chain is also called the respiratory chain because of its role in both types of cellular respiration.)

We have already mentioned anaerobic respiration, which takes place in certain prokaryotic organisms that live in environments without oxygen. These organisms have an electron transport chain but do not use oxygen as a final electron acceptor at the end of the chain. Oxygen performs this function very well because it is extremely electronegative, but other, less electronegative substances can also serve as final electron acceptors. Some "sulfate-reducing" marine bacteria, for instance, use the sulfate ion (SO_4^{2-}) at the end of their respiratory chain. Operation of the chain builds up a proton-motive force used to produce ATP, but H_2S (hydrogen sulfide) is produced as a by-product rather than water. The rotten-egg odor you may have smelled while walking through a salt marsh or a mudflat signals the presence of sulfate-reducing bacteria.

Fermentation is a way of harvesting chemical energy without using either oxygen or any electron transport chain—in other words, without cellular respiration. How can food be oxidized without cellular respiration? Remember, oxidation simply refers to the loss of electrons to an electron acceptor, so it does not need to involve oxygen. Glycolysis oxidizes glucose to two molecules of pyruvate. The oxidizing agent of glycolysis is NAD^+, and neither oxygen nor any electron transfer chain is involved. Overall, glycolysis is exergonic, and some of the energy made available is used to produce 2 ATP (net) by substrate-level phosphorylation. If oxygen *is* present, then additional ATP is made by oxidative phosphorylation when NADH passes electrons removed from glucose to the electron transport chain. But glycolysis generates 2 ATP whether oxygen is present or not—that is, whether conditions are aerobic or anaerobic.

As an alternative to respiratory oxidation of organic nutrients, fermentation is an extension of glycolysis that allows continuous generation of ATP by the substrate-level phosphorylation of glycolysis. For this to occur, there must be a sufficient supply of NAD^+ to accept electrons during the oxidation step of glycolysis. Without some mechanism to recycle NAD^+ from NADH, glycolysis would soon deplete the cell's pool of NAD^+ by reducing it all to NADH and would shut itself down for lack of an oxidizing agent. Under aerobic conditions, NAD^+ is recycled from NADH by the transfer of electrons to the electron transport chain. An anaerobic alternative is to transfer electrons from NADH to pyruvate, the end product of glycolysis.

Types of Fermentation

Fermentation consists of glycolysis plus reactions that regenerate NAD^+ by transferring electrons from NADH to pyruvate or derivatives of pyruvate. The NAD^+ can then be reused to oxidize sugar by glycolysis, which nets two molecules of ATP by substrate-level phosphorylation. There are many types of fermentation, differing in the end products formed from pyruvate. Two common types are alcohol fermentation and lactic acid fermentation.

In **alcohol fermentation** (Figure 9.17a), pyruvate is converted to ethanol (ethyl alcohol) in two steps. The first step releases carbon dioxide from the pyruvate, which is converted to the two-carbon compound acetaldehyde. In the second step, acetaldehyde is reduced by NADH to ethanol. This regenerates the supply of NAD^+ needed for the continuation of glycolysis. Many bacteria carry out alcohol fermentation under anaerobic conditions. Yeast (a fungus) also carries out alcohol fermentation. For thousands of years, humans

have used yeast in brewing, winemaking, and baking. The CO_2 bubbles generated by baker's yeast during alcohol fermentation allow bread to rise.

During **lactic acid fermentation** (Figure 9.17b), pyruvate is reduced directly by NADH to form lactate as an end product, with no release of CO_2. (Lactate is the ionized form of lactic acid.) Lactic acid fermentation by certain fungi and bacteria is used in the dairy industry to make cheese and yogurt.

Human muscle cells make ATP by lactic acid fermentation when oxygen is scarce. This occurs during the early stages of strenuous exercise, when sugar catabolism for ATP production outpaces the muscle's supply of oxygen from the blood. Under these conditions, the cells switch from aerobic respiration to fermentation. The lactate that accumulates was previously thought to cause muscle fatigue and pain, but recent research suggests instead that increased levels of potassium ions (K^+) may be to blame, while lactate appears to enhance muscle performance. In any case, the excess lactate is gradually carried away by the blood to the liver, where it is converted back to pyruvate by liver cells. Because oxygen is available, this pyruvate can then enter the mitochondria in liver cells and complete cellular respiration.

Comparing Fermentation with Anaerobic and Aerobic Respiration

Fermentation, anaerobic respiration, and aerobic respiration are three alternative cellular pathways for producing ATP by harvesting the chemical energy of food. All three use glycolysis to oxidize glucose and other organic fuels to pyruvate, with a net production of 2 ATP by substrate-level phosphorylation. And in all three pathways, NAD^+ is the oxidizing agent that accepts electrons from food during glycolysis.

A key difference among the three pathways is the contrasting mechanisms for oxidizing NADH back to NAD^+, which is required to sustain glycolysis. In fermentation, the final electron acceptor is an organic molecule such as pyruvate (lactic acid fermentation) or acetaldehyde (alcohol fermentation). In cellular respiration, by contrast, electrons carried by NADH are transferred to an electron transport chain, where they move stepwise down a series of redox reactions to a final electron acceptor. In aerobic respiration, the final electron acceptor is oxygen; in anaerobic respiration, the final acceptor is another molecule that is electronegative (although invariably less so than oxygen). Passage of electrons from NADH to the electron transport chain not only regenerates the NAD^+ required for glycolysis but pays an ATP bonus when the stepwise electron transport from this NADH to oxygen drives oxidative phosphorylation. An even bigger ATP payoff comes from the oxidation of pyruvate in the mitochondrion, which is unique to respiration. Without an electron transport chain, the energy still stored in pyruvate is unavailable to most cells. Thus, cellular respiration harvests much more energy from

(a) Alcohol fermentation

(b) Lactic acid fermentation

▲ **Figure 9.17 Fermentation.** In the absence of oxygen, many cells use fermentation to produce ATP by substrate-level phosphorylation. Pyruvate, the end product of glycolysis, serves as an electron acceptor for oxidizing NADH back to NAD^+, which can then be reused in glycolysis. Two of the common end products formed from fermentation are **(a)** ethanol and **(b)** lactate, the ionized form of lactic acid.

each sugar molecule than fermentation can. In fact, aerobic respiration yields up to 16 times as much ATP per glucose molecule as does fermentation—up to 32 molecules of ATP for respiration, compared with 2 molecules of ATP produced by substrate-level phosphorylation in fermentation.

Some organisms, called **obligate anaerobes**, carry out only fermentation or anaerobic respiration. In fact, these organisms cannot survive in the presence of oxygen, some forms of which can actually be toxic if protective systems are not present in the cell. A few cell types, such as cells of the vertebrate brain, can carry out only aerobic oxidation of pyruvate, not fermentation. Other organisms, including yeasts and many bacteria, can make enough ATP to survive using either fermentation or respiration. Such species are called **facultative anaerobes**. On the cellular level, our muscle cells behave as facultative anaerobes. In such cells, pyruvate is a fork in the metabolic road that leads to two alternative catabolic routes (**Figure 9.18**). Under aerobic conditions, pyruvate can be converted to acetyl CoA, and oxidation continues in the citric acid cycle via aerobic respiration. Under anaerobic conditions, lactic acid fermentation occurs: Pyruvate is diverted from the citric acid cycle, serving instead as an electron acceptor to recycle NAD^+. To make the same amount of ATP, a facultative anaerobe has to consume sugar at a much faster rate when fermenting than when respiring.

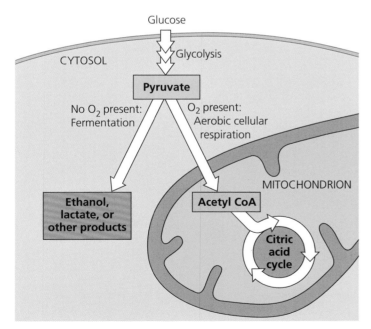

▲ **Figure 9.18 Pyruvate as a key juncture in catabolism.**
Glycolysis is common to fermentation and cellular respiration. The end product of glycolysis, pyruvate, represents a fork in the catabolic pathways of glucose oxidation. In a facultative anaerobe or a muscle cell, which are capable of both aerobic cellular respiration and fermentation, pyruvate is committed to one of those two pathways, usually depending on whether or not oxygen is present.

The Evolutionary Significance of Glycolysis

EVOLUTION The role of glycolysis in both fermentation and respiration has an evolutionary basis. Ancient prokaryotes are thought to have used glycolysis to make ATP long before oxygen was present in Earth's atmosphere. The oldest known fossils of bacteria date back 3.5 billion years, but appreciable quantities of oxygen probably did not begin to accumulate in the atmosphere until about 2.7 billion years ago. Cyanobacteria produced this O_2 as a by-product of photosynthesis. Therefore, early prokaryotes may have generated ATP exclusively from glycolysis. The fact that glycolysis is today the most widespread metabolic pathway among Earth's organisms suggests that it evolved very early in the history of life. The cytosolic location of glycolysis also implies great antiquity; the pathway does not require any of the membrane-bounded organelles of the eukaryotic cell, which evolved approximately 1 billion years after the prokaryotic cell. Glycolysis is a metabolic heirloom from early cells that continues to function in fermentation and as the first stage in the breakdown of organic molecules by respiration.

CONCEPT CHECK 9.5

1. Consider the NADH formed during glycolysis. What is the final acceptor for its electrons during fermentation? What is the final acceptor for its electrons during aerobic respiration?
2. **WHAT IF?** A glucose-fed yeast cell is moved from an aerobic environment to an anaerobic one. How would its rate of glucose consumption change if ATP were to be generated at the same rate?

For suggested answers, see Appendix A.

CONCEPT 9.6

Glycolysis and the citric acid cycle connect to many other metabolic pathways

So far, we have treated the oxidative breakdown of glucose in isolation from the cell's overall metabolic economy. In this section, you will learn that glycolysis and the citric acid cycle are major intersections of the cell's catabolic and anabolic (biosynthetic) pathways.

The Versatility of Catabolism

Throughout this chapter, we have used glucose as the fuel for cellular respiration. But free glucose molecules are not common in the diets of humans and other animals. We obtain most of our calories in the form of fats, proteins, sucrose and other disaccharides, and starch, a polysaccharide. All these

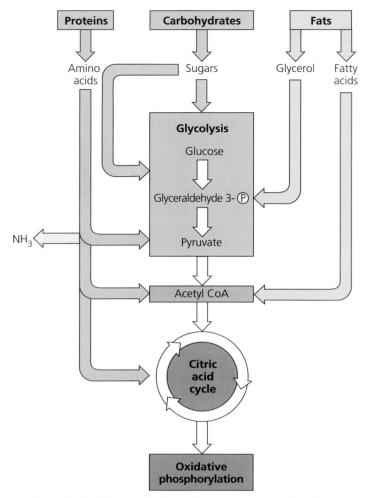

Proteins **Carbohydrates** **Fats**

Amino acids | Sugars | Glycerol | Fatty acids

Glycolysis

Glucose

↓

Glyceraldehyde 3-Ⓟ

↓

Pyruvate

NH₃

Acetyl CoA

Citric acid cycle

Oxidative phosphorylation

▲ **Figure 9.19 The catabolism of various molecules from food.** Carbohydrates, fats, and proteins can all be used as fuel for cellular respiration. Monomers of these molecules enter glycolysis or the citric acid cycle at various points. Glycolysis and the citric acid cycle are catabolic funnels through which electrons from all kinds of organic molecules flow on their exergonic fall to oxygen.

organic molecules in food can be used by cellular respiration to make ATP (**Figure 9.19**).

Glycolysis can accept a wide range of carbohydrates for catabolism. In the digestive tract, starch is hydrolyzed to glucose, which can then be broken down in the cells by glycolysis and the citric acid cycle. Similarly, glycogen, the polysaccharide that humans and many other animals store in their liver and muscle cells, can be hydrolyzed to glucose between meals as fuel for respiration. The digestion of disaccharides, including sucrose, provides glucose and other monosaccharides as fuel for respiration.

Proteins can also be used for fuel, but first they must be digested to their constituent amino acids. Many of the amino acids are used by the organism to build new proteins. Amino acids present in excess are converted by enzymes to intermediates of glycolysis and the citric acid cycle. Before amino acids can feed into glycolysis or the citric acid cycle, their amino groups must be removed, a process called *deamination*. The nitrogenous refuse is excreted from the animal in the form of ammonia (NH₃), urea, or other waste products.

Catabolism can also harvest energy stored in fats obtained either from food or from storage cells in the body. After fats are digested to glycerol and fatty acids, the glycerol is converted to glyceraldehyde 3-phosphate, an intermediate of glycolysis. Most of the energy of a fat is stored in the fatty acids. A metabolic sequence called **beta oxidation** breaks the fatty acids down to two-carbon fragments, which enter the citric acid cycle as acetyl CoA. NADH and FADH₂ are also generated during beta oxidation; they can enter the electron transport chain, leading to further ATP production. Fats make excellent fuel, in large part due to their chemical structure and the high energy level of their electrons (equally shared between carbon and hydrogen) compared to those of carbohydrates. A gram of fat oxidized by respiration produces more than twice as much ATP as a gram of carbohydrate. Unfortunately, this also means that a person trying to lose weight must work hard to use up fat stored in the body because so many calories are stockpiled in each gram of fat.

Biosynthesis (Anabolic Pathways)

Cells need substance as well as energy. Not all the organic molecules of food are destined to be oxidized as fuel to make ATP. In addition to calories, food must also provide the carbon skeletons that cells require to make their own molecules. Some organic monomers obtained from digestion can be used directly. For example, as previously mentioned, amino acids from the hydrolysis of proteins in food can be incorporated into the organism's own proteins. Often, however, the body needs specific molecules that are not present as such in food. Compounds formed as intermediates of glycolysis and the citric acid cycle can be diverted into anabolic pathways as precursors from which the cell can synthesize the molecules it requires. For example, humans can make about half of the 20 amino acids in proteins by modifying compounds siphoned away from the citric acid cycle; the rest are "essential amino acids" that must be obtained in the diet. Also, glucose can be made from pyruvate, and fatty acids can be synthesized from acetyl CoA. Of course, these anabolic, or biosynthetic, pathways do not generate ATP, but instead consume it.

In addition, glycolysis and the citric acid cycle function as metabolic interchanges that enable our cells to convert some kinds of molecules to others as we need them. For example, an intermediate compound generated during glycolysis, dihydroxyacetone phosphate (see Figure 9.9, step 5), can be converted to one of the major precursors of fats. If we eat more food than we need, we store fat even if our diet is fat-free. Metabolism is remarkably versatile and adaptable.

Regulation of Cellular Respiration via Feedback Mechanisms

Basic principles of supply and demand regulate the metabolic economy. The cell does not waste energy making more of a particular substance than it needs. If there is a glut of a certain amino acid, for example, the anabolic pathway that synthesizes that amino acid from an intermediate of the citric acid cycle is switched off. The most common mechanism for this control is feedback inhibition: The end product of the anabolic pathway inhibits the enzyme that catalyzes an early step of the pathway (see Figure 8.21). This prevents the needless diversion of key metabolic intermediates from uses that are more urgent.

The cell also controls its catabolism. If the cell is working hard and its ATP concentration begins to drop, respiration speeds up. When there is plenty of ATP to meet demand, respiration slows down, sparing valuable organic molecules for other functions. Again, control is based mainly on regulating the activity of enzymes at strategic points in the catabolic pathway. As shown in **Figure 9.20**, one important switch is phosphofructokinase, the enzyme that catalyzes step 3 of glycolysis (see Figure 9.9). That is the first step that commits the substrate irreversibly to the glycolytic pathway. By controlling the rate of this step, the cell can speed up or slow down the entire catabolic process. Phosphofructokinase can thus be considered the pacemaker of respiration.

Phosphofructokinase is an allosteric enzyme with receptor sites for specific inhibitors and activators. It is inhibited by ATP and stimulated by AMP (adenosine monophosphate), which the cell derives from ADP. As ATP accumulates, inhibition of the enzyme slows down glycolysis. The enzyme becomes active again as cellular work converts ATP to ADP (and AMP) faster than ATP is being regenerated. Phosphofructokinase is also sensitive to citrate, the first product of the citric acid cycle. If citrate accumulates in mitochondria, some of it passes into the cytosol and inhibits phosphofructokinase. This mechanism helps synchronize the rates of glycolysis and the citric acid cycle. As citrate accumulates, glycolysis slows down, and the supply of acetyl groups to the citric acid cycle decreases. If citrate consumption increases, either because of a demand for more ATP or because anabolic pathways are draining off intermediates of the citric acid cycle, glycolysis accelerates and meets the demand. Metabolic balance is augmented by the control of enzymes that catalyze other key steps of glycolysis and the citric acid cycle. Cells are thrifty, expedient, and responsive in their metabolism.

Cellular respiration and metabolic pathways play a role of central importance in organisms. Examine Figure 9.2 again to put cellular respiration into the broader context of energy flow and chemical cycling in ecosystems. The energy that keeps us alive is *released*, not *produced*, by cellular respiration. We are tapping energy that was stored in food by photosynthesis. In the next chapter, you will learn how photosynthesis captures light and converts it to chemical energy.

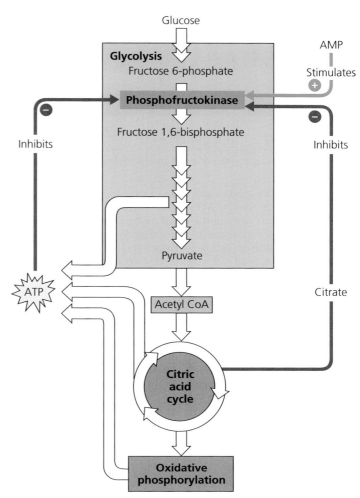

▲ **Figure 9.20 The control of cellular respiration.** Allosteric enzymes at certain points in the respiratory pathway respond to inhibitors and activators that help set the pace of glycolysis and the citric acid cycle. Phosphofructokinase, which catalyzes an early step in glycolysis (see Figure 9.9), is one such enzyme. It is stimulated by AMP (derived from ADP) but is inhibited by ATP and by citrate. This feedback regulation adjusts the rate of respiration as the cell's catabolic and anabolic demands change.

CONCEPT CHECK 9.6

1. **MAKE CONNECTIONS** Compare the structure of a fat (see Figure 5.10, p. 75) with that of a carbohydrate (see Figure 5.3, p. 70). What features of their structures make fat a much better fuel?

2. Under what circumstances might your body synthesize fat molecules?

3. **MAKE CONNECTIONS** Return to Figure 5.6b on page 72 and look at the arrangement of glycogen and mitochondria in the micrograph. What is the connection between glycogen and mitochondria?

4. **WHAT IF?** What will happen in a muscle cell that has used up its supply of oxygen and ATP? (Review Figures 9.18 and 9.20.)

5. **WHAT IF?** During intense exercise, can a muscle cell use fat as a concentrated source of chemical energy? Explain. (Review Figures 9.18 and 9.19.)

For suggested answers, see Appendix A.

SUMMARY OF KEY CONCEPTS

CONCEPT 9.1

Catabolic pathways yield energy by oxidizing organic fuels (pp. 164–168)

- Cells break down glucose and other organic fuels to yield chemical energy in the form of ATP. **Fermentation** is a partial degradation of glucose without the use of oxygen. **Cellular respiration** is a more complete breakdown of glucose; in **aerobic respiration**, oxygen is used as a reactant. The cell taps the energy stored in food molecules through **redox reactions**, in which one substance partially or totally shifts electrons to another. **Oxidation** is the loss of electrons from one substance, while **reduction** is the addition of electrons to the other.
- During aerobic respiration, glucose ($C_6H_{12}O_6$) is oxidized to CO_2, and O_2 is reduced to H_2O. Electrons lose potential energy during their transfer from glucose or other organic compounds to oxygen. Electrons are usually passed first to **NAD⁺**, reducing it to NADH, and then from NADH to an **electron transport chain**, which conducts them to O_2 in energy-releasing steps. The energy is used to make ATP.
- Aerobic respiration occurs in three stages: (1) **glycolysis**, (2) pyruvate oxidation and the **citric acid cycle**, and (3) **oxidative phosphorylation** (electron transport and chemiosmosis).

> **?** *Describe the difference between the two processes in cellular respiration that produce ATP: oxidative phosphorylation and substrate-level phosphorylation.*

CONCEPT 9.2

Glycolysis harvests chemical energy by oxidizing glucose to pyruvate (pp. 168–169)

Inputs		Outputs
Glucose	Glycolysis →	2 Pyruvate + 2 ATP + 2 NADH

> **?** *What is the source of energy for the formation of ATP and NADH in glycolysis?*

CONCEPT 9.3

After pyruvate is oxidized, the citric acid cycle completes the energy-yielding oxidation of organic molecules (pp. 170–172)

- In eukaryotic cells, pyruvate enters the mitochondrion and is oxidized to **acetyl CoA**, which is further oxidized in the citric acid cycle.

Inputs: 2 Pyruvate → 2 Acetyl CoA, 2 Oxaloacetate — Citric acid cycle — Outputs: 2 ATP, 8 NADH, 6 CO_2, 2 FADH₂

> **?** *What molecular products indicate the complete oxidation of glucose during cellular respiration?*

CONCEPT 9.4

During oxidative phosphorylation, chemiosmosis couples electron transport to ATP synthesis (pp. 172–177)

- NADH and FADH₂ transfer electrons to the electron transport chain. Electrons move down the chain, losing energy in several energy-releasing steps. Finally, electrons are passed to O_2, reducing it to H_2O.

- At certain steps along the electron transport chain, electron transfer causes protein complexes to move H⁺ from the mitochondrial matrix (in eukaryotes) to the intermembrane space, storing energy as a **proton-motive force** (H⁺ gradient). As H⁺ diffuses back into the matrix through **ATP synthase**, its passage drives the phosphorylation of ADP, a process called **chemiosmosis**.

- About 34% of the energy stored in a glucose molecule is transferred to ATP during cellular respiration, producing a maximum of about 32 ATP.

> **?** *Briefly explain the mechanism by which ATP synthase produces ATP. List three locations in which ATP synthases are found.*

CONCEPT 9.5

Fermentation and anaerobic respiration enable cells to produce ATP without the use of oxygen (pp. 177–179)

- Glycolysis nets 2 ATP by substrate-level phosphorylation, whether oxygen is present or not. Under anaerobic conditions, either anaerobic respiration or fermentation can take place. In anaerobic respiration, an electron transport chain is present with a final electron acceptor other than oxygen. In fermentation, the electrons from NADH are passed to pyruvate or a derivative of pyruvate, regenerating the NAD⁺ required to oxidize more glucose. Two common types of fermentation are **alcohol fermentation** and **lactic acid fermentation**.
- Fermentation and anaerobic or aerobic respiration all use glycolysis to oxidize glucose, but they differ in their final electron acceptor and whether an electron transport chain is used (respiration) or not (fermentation). Respiration yields more ATP;

aerobic respiration, with O_2 as the final electron acceptor, yields about 16 times as much ATP as does fermentation.

- Glycolysis occurs in nearly all organisms and is thought to have evolved in ancient prokaryotes before there was O_2 in the atmosphere.

? *Which process yields more ATP, fermentation or anaerobic respiration? Explain.*

CONCEPT 9.6

Glycolysis and the citric acid cycle connect to many other metabolic pathways (pp. 179–181)

- Catabolic pathways funnel electrons from many kinds of organic molecules into cellular respiration. Many carbohydrates can enter glycolysis, most often after conversion to glucose. Amino acids of proteins must be deaminated before being oxidized. The fatty acids of fats undergo **beta oxidation** to two-carbon fragments and then enter the citric acid cycle as acetyl CoA. Anabolic pathways can use small molecules from food directly or build other substances using intermediates of glycolysis or the citric acid cycle.
- Cellular respiration is controlled by allosteric enzymes at key points in glycolysis and the citric acid cycle.

? *Describe how the catabolic pathways of glycolysis and the citric acid cycle intersect with anabolic pathways in the metabolism of a cell.*

TEST YOUR UNDERSTANDING

LEVEL 1: KNOWLEDGE/COMPREHENSION

1. The *immediate* energy source that drives ATP synthesis by ATP synthase during oxidative phosphorylation is the
   a. oxidation of glucose and other organic compounds.
   b. flow of electrons down the electron transport chain.
   c. affinity of oxygen for electrons.
   d. H^+ concentration across the membrane holding ATP synthase.
   e. transfer of phosphate to ADP.

2. Which metabolic pathway is common to both fermentation and cellular respiration of a glucose molecule?
   a. the citric acid cycle
   b. the electron transport chain
   c. glycolysis
   d. synthesis of acetyl CoA from pyruvate
   e. reduction of pyruvate to lactate

3. In mitochondria, exergonic redox reactions
   a. are the source of energy driving prokaryotic ATP synthesis.
   b. are directly coupled to substrate-level phosphorylation.
   c. provide the energy that establishes the proton gradient.
   d. reduce carbon atoms to carbon dioxide.
   e. are coupled via phosphorylated intermediates to endergonic processes.

4. The final electron acceptor of the electron transport chain that functions in aerobic oxidative phosphorylation is
   a. oxygen. b. water. c. NAD^+. d. pyruvate. e. ADP.

LEVEL 2: APPLICATION/ANALYSIS

5. What is the oxidizing agent in the following reaction?
   Pyruvate + NADH + H^+ → Lactate + NAD^+
   a. oxygen b. NADH c. NAD^+ d. lactate e. pyruvate

6. When electrons flow along the electron transport chains of mitochondria, which of the following changes occurs?
   a. The pH of the matrix increases.
   b. ATP synthase pumps protons by active transport.

c. The electrons gain free energy.
   d. The cytochromes phosphorylate ADP to form ATP.
   e. NAD^+ is oxidized.

7. Most CO_2 from catabolism is released during
   a. glycolysis.
   b. the citric acid cycle.
   c. lactate fermentation.
   d. electron transport.
   e. oxidative phosphorylation.

LEVEL 3: SYNTHESIS/EVALUATION

8. **DRAW IT** The graph here shows the pH difference across the inner mitochondrial membrane over time in an actively respiring cell. At the time indicated by the vertical arrow, a metabolic poison is added that specifically and completely inhibits all function of mitochondrial ATP synthase. Draw what you would expect to see for the rest of the graphed line.

9. **EVOLUTION CONNECTION**
   ATP synthases are found in the prokaryotic plasma membrane and in mitochondria and chloroplasts. What does this suggest about the evolutionary relationship of these eukaryotic organelles to prokaryotes? How might the amino acid sequences of the ATP synthases from the different sources support or refute your hypothesis?

10. **SCIENTIFIC INQUIRY**
    In the 1930s, some physicians prescribed low doses of a compound called dinitrophenol (DNP) to help patients lose weight. This unsafe method was abandoned after some patients died. DNP uncouples the chemiosmotic machinery by making the lipid bilayer of the inner mitochondrial membrane leaky to H^+. Explain how this could cause weight loss and death.

11. **WRITE ABOUT A THEME**
    Emergent Properties In a short essay (100–150 words), explain how oxidative phosphorylation—the production of ATP using energy derived from the redox reactions of a spatially organized electron transport chain followed by chemiosmosis—is an example of how new properties emerge at each level of the biological hierarchy.

For selected answers, see Appendix A.

MasteringBIOLOGY® www.masteringbiology.com

1. MasteringBiology® Assignments
BioFlix **Tutorials** Cellular Respiration: Inputs and Outputs • Glycolysis • Acetyl CoA Formation and the Citric Acid Cycle • Oxidative Phosphorylation • Summary
Tutorial Pathways for Pyruvate
Activities Build a Chemical Cycling System • Overview of Cellular Respiration • Redox Reactions • Glycolysis • The Citric Acid Cycle • Electron Transport • Fermentation • Glucose Metabolism • Discovery Channel Video: Space Plants
Questions Student Misconceptions • Reading Quiz • Multiple Choice • End-of-Chapter

2. eText
Read your book online, search, take notes, highlight text, and more.

3. The Study Area
Practice Tests • Cumulative Test • *BioFlix* 3-D Animations • MP3 Tutor Sessions • Videos • Activities • Investigations • Lab Media • Audio Glossary • Word Study Tools • Art

10

Photosynthesis

▲ **Figure 10.1 How can sunlight, seen here as a spectrum of colors in a rainbow, power the synthesis of organic substances?**

KEY CONCEPTS

10.1 Photosynthesis converts light energy to the chemical energy of food

10.2 The light reactions convert solar energy to the chemical energy of ATP and NADPH

10.3 The Calvin cycle uses the chemical energy of ATP and NADPH to reduce CO_2 to sugar

10.4 Alternative mechanisms of carbon fixation have evolved in hot, arid climates

The Process That Feeds the Biosphere

Life on Earth is solar powered. The chloroplasts of plants capture light energy that has traveled 150 million kilometers from the sun and convert it to chemical energy that is stored in sugar and other organic molecules. This conversion process is called **photosynthesis**. Let's begin by placing photosynthesis in its ecological context.

Photosynthesis nourishes almost the entire living world directly or indirectly. An organism acquires the organic compounds it uses for energy and carbon skeletons by one of two major modes: autotrophic nutrition or heterotrophic nutrition. **Autotrophs** are "self-feeders" (*auto-* means "self," and *trophos* means "feeder"); they sustain themselves without eating anything derived from other living beings. Autotrophs produce their organic molecules from CO_2 and other inorganic raw materials obtained from the environment. They are the ultimate sources of organic compounds for all nonautotrophic organisms, and for this reason, biologists refer to autotrophs as the *producers* of the biosphere.

Almost all plants are autotrophs; the only nutrients they require are water and minerals from the soil and carbon dioxide from the air. Specifically, plants are *photo*autotrophs, organisms that use light as a source of energy to synthesize organic substances **(Figure 10.1)**. Photosynthesis also occurs in algae, certain other protists, and some prokaryotes **(Figure 10.2)**. In this chapter, we will touch on these other groups in passing, but our emphasis will be on plants. Variations in autotrophic nutrition that occur in prokaryotes and algae will be described in Chapters 27 and 28.

Heterotrophs obtain their organic material by the second major mode of nutrition. Unable to make their own food, they live on compounds produced by other organisms (*hetero-* means "other"). Heterotrophs are the biosphere's *consumers*. The most obvious form of this "other-feeding" occurs when an animal eats plants or other animals. But heterotrophic nutrition may be more subtle. Some heterotrophs consume the remains of dead organisms by decomposing and feeding on organic litter such as carcasses, feces, and fallen leaves; they are known as decomposers. Most fungi and many types of prokaryotes get their nourishment this way. Almost all heterotrophs, including humans, are completely dependent, either directly or indirectly, on photoautotrophs for food—and also for oxygen, a by-product of photosynthesis.

The Earth's supply of fossil fuels was formed from remains of organisms that died hundreds of millions of years ago. In a sense, then, fossil fuels represent stores of the sun's energy from the distant past. Because these resources are being used at a much higher rate than they are replenished, researchers

(a) Plants

(b) Multicellular alga

(c) Unicellular protists
10 μm

(d) Cyanobacteria
40 μm

(e) Purple sulfur bacteria
1 μm

▲ **Figure 10.2 Photoautotrophs.** These organisms use light energy to drive the synthesis of organic molecules from carbon dioxide and (in most cases) water. They feed themselves and the entire living world. **(a)** On land, plants are the predominant producers of food. In aquatic environments, photoautotrophs include unicellular and **(b)** multicellular algae, such as this kelp; **(c)** some non-algal unicellular protists, such as *Euglena*; **(d)** the prokaryotes called cyanobacteria; and **(e)** other photosynthetic prokaryotes, such as these purple sulfur bacteria, which produce sulfur (the yellow globules within the cells) (c–e, LMss).

▼ **Figure 10.3**

IMPACT

Alternative Fuels from Plants and Algae

Biofuels from crops such as corn, soybeans, and cassava have been proposed as a supplement or even replacement for fossil fuels. To produce "bioethanol," the starch made naturally by the plants is simply converted to glucose and then fermented to ethanol by microorganisms. Alternatively, a simple chemical process can yield "biodiesel" from plant oils. Either product can be mixed with gasoline or used alone to power vehicles. Some species of unicellular algae are especially prolific oil producers, and they can be easily cultured in containers such as the tubular plastic bags shown below.

WHY IT MATTERS The rate of fossil fuel use by humans far outpaces its formation in the earth: Fossil fuels are a nonrenewable source of energy. Tapping the power of sunlight by using products of photosynthesis to generate energy is a sustainable alternative if cost-effective techniques can be developed. It is generally agreed that using algae is preferable to growing crops for this purpose because this use of cropland diminishes the food supply and drives up food prices.

FURTHER READING A. L. Haag, Algae bloom again, *Nature* 447:520–521 (2007).

WHAT IF? The main product of fossil fuel combustion is CO_2, and this combustion is the source of the increase in atmospheric CO_2 concentration. Scientists have proposed strategically situating containers of these algae near industrial plants, as shown above, or near highly congested city streets. Why does this arrangement make sense?

are exploring methods of capitalizing on the photosynthetic process to provide alternative fuels **(Figure 10.3)**.

In this chapter, you will learn how photosynthesis works. After a discussion of the general principles of photosynthesis, we will consider the two stages of photosynthesis: the light reactions, in which solar energy is captured and transformed into chemical energy; and the Calvin cycle, in which the chemical energy is used to make organic molecules of food. Finally, we will consider a few aspects of photosynthesis from an evolutionary perspective.

CONCEPT 10.1

Photosynthesis converts light energy to the chemical energy of food

The remarkable ability of an organism to harness light energy and use it to drive the synthesis of organic compounds emerges from structural organization in the cell: Photosynthetic enzymes and other molecules are grouped together in a biological membrane, enabling the necessary series of chemical reactions to be carried out efficiently. The process of photosynthesis most likely originated in a group of bacteria that had infolded regions of the plasma membrane containing clusters of such molecules. In existing photosynthetic bacteria, infolded photosynthetic membranes function similarly to the internal membranes of the chloroplast, a eukaryotic organelle. According to the endosymbiont theory, the original chloroplast was a photosynthetic prokaryote that lived inside an ancestor of eukaryotic cells. (You learned about this theory in Chapter 6 and it will be described more fully in Chapter 25.) Chloroplasts are present in a variety of photosynthesizing organisms (see Figure 10.2), but here we will focus on plants.

Chloroplasts: The Sites of Photosynthesis in Plants

All green parts of a plant, including green stems and unripened fruit, have chloroplasts, but the leaves are the major sites of photosynthesis in most plants **(Figure 10.4)**. There are about half a million chloroplasts in a chunk of leaf with a top surface area of 1 mm². Chloroplasts are found mainly in the cells of the **mesophyll**, the tissue in the interior of the leaf. Carbon dioxide enters the leaf, and oxygen exits, by way of microscopic pores called **stomata** (singular, *stoma*; from the Greek, meaning "mouth"). Water absorbed by the roots is delivered to the leaves in veins. Leaves also use veins to export sugar to roots and other nonphotosynthetic parts of the plant.

A typical mesophyll cell has about 30–40 chloroplasts, each organelle measuring about 2–4 μm by 4–7 μm. A chloroplast has an envelope of two membranes surrounding a dense fluid called the **stroma**. Suspended within the stroma is a third membrane system, made up of sacs called **thylakoids**, which segregates the stroma from the *thylakoid space* inside these sacs. In some places, thylakoid sacs are stacked in columns called *grana* (singular, *granum*). **Chlorophyll**, the green pigment that gives leaves their color, resides in the thylakoid membranes of the chloroplast. (The internal photosynthetic membranes of some prokaryotes are also called thylakoid membranes; see Figure 27.7b.) It is the light energy absorbed

▲ **Figure 10.4 Zooming in on the location of photosynthesis in a plant.** Leaves are the major organs of photosynthesis in plants. These pictures take you into a leaf, then into a cell, and finally into a chloroplast, the organelle where photosynthesis occurs (middle, LM; bottom, TEM).

by chlorophyll that drives the synthesis of organic molecules in the chloroplast. Now that we have looked at the sites of photosynthesis in plants, we are ready to look more closely at the process of photosynthesis.

Tracking Atoms Through Photosynthesis: *Scientific Inquiry*

Scientists have tried for centuries to piece together the process by which plants make food. Although some of the steps are still not completely understood, the overall photosynthetic equation has been known since the 1800s: In the presence of light, the green parts of plants produce organic compounds and oxygen from carbon dioxide and water. Using molecular formulas, we can summarize the complex series of chemical reactions in photosynthesis with this chemical equation:

$$6 CO_2 + 12 H_2O + \text{Light energy} \rightarrow C_6H_{12}O_6 + 6 O_2 + 6 H_2O$$

We use glucose ($C_6H_{12}O_6$) here to simplify the relationship between photosynthesis and respiration, but the direct product of photosynthesis is actually a three-carbon sugar that can be used to make glucose. Water appears on both sides of the equation because 12 molecules are consumed and 6 molecules are newly formed during photosynthesis. We can simplify the equation by indicating only the net consumption of water:

$$6 CO_2 + 6 H_2O + \text{Light energy} \rightarrow C_6H_{12}O_6 + 6 O_2$$

Writing the equation in this form, we can see that the overall chemical change during photosynthesis is the reverse of the one that occurs during cellular respiration. Both of these metabolic processes occur in plant cells. However, as you will soon learn, chloroplasts do not synthesize sugars by simply reversing the steps of respiration.

Now let's divide the photosynthetic equation by 6 to put it in its simplest possible form:

$$CO_2 + H_2O \rightarrow [CH_2O] + O_2$$

Here, the brackets indicate that CH_2O is not an actual sugar but represents the general formula for a carbohydrate. In other words, we are imagining the synthesis of a sugar molecule one carbon at a time. Six repetitions would theoretically produce a glucose molecule. Let's now use this simplified formula to see how researchers tracked the elements C, H, and O from the reactants of photosynthesis to the products.

The Splitting of Water

One of the first clues to the mechanism of photosynthesis came from the discovery that the O_2 given off by plants is derived from H_2O and not from CO_2. The chloroplast splits water into hydrogen and oxygen. Before this discovery, the prevailing hypothesis was that photosynthesis split carbon dioxide ($CO_2 \rightarrow C + O_2$) and then added water to the carbon

($C + H_2O \rightarrow [CH_2O]$). This hypothesis predicted that the O_2 released during photosynthesis came from CO_2. This idea was challenged in the 1930s by C. B. van Niel, of Stanford University. Van Niel was investigating photosynthesis in bacteria that make their carbohydrate from CO_2 but do not release O_2. He concluded that, at least in these bacteria, CO_2 is not split into carbon and oxygen. One group of bacteria used hydrogen sulfide (H_2S) rather than water for photosynthesis, forming yellow globules of sulfur as a waste product (these globules are visible in Figure 10.2e). Here is the chemical equation for photosynthesis in these sulfur bacteria:

$$CO_2 + 2 H_2S \rightarrow [CH_2O] + H_2O + 2 S$$

Van Niel reasoned that the bacteria split H_2S and used the hydrogen atoms to make sugar. He then generalized that idea, proposing that all photosynthetic organisms require a hydrogen source but that the source varies:

Sulfur bacteria: $CO_2 + 2 H_2S \rightarrow [CH_2O] + H_2O + 2 S$
Plants: $CO_2 + 2 H_2O \rightarrow [CH_2O] + H_2O + O_2$
General: $CO_2 + 2 H_2X \rightarrow [CH_2O] + H_2O + 2 X$

Thus, van Niel hypothesized that plants split H_2O as a source of electrons from hydrogen atoms, releasing O_2 as a by-product.

Nearly 20 years later, scientists confirmed van Niel's hypothesis by using oxygen-18 (^{18}O), a heavy isotope, as a tracer to follow the fate of oxygen atoms during photosynthesis. The experiments showed that the O_2 from plants was labeled with ^{18}O *only* if water was the source of the tracer (experiment 1). If the ^{18}O was introduced to the plant in the form of CO_2, the label did not turn up in the released O_2 (experiment 2). In the following summary, red denotes labeled atoms of oxygen (^{18}O):

Experiment 1: $CO_2 + 2 H_2O \rightarrow [CH_2O] + H_2O + O_2$
Experiment 2: $CO_2 + 2 H_2O \rightarrow [CH_2O] + H_2O + O_2$

A significant result of the shuffling of atoms during photosynthesis is the extraction of hydrogen from water and its incorporation into sugar. The waste product of photosynthesis, O_2, is released to the atmosphere. **Figure 10.5** shows the fates of all atoms in photosynthesis.

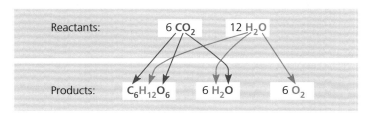

▲ **Figure 10.5 Tracking atoms through photosynthesis.** The atoms from CO_2 are shown in magenta, and the atoms from H_2O are shown in blue.

Photosynthesis as a Redox Process

Let's briefly compare photosynthesis with cellular respiration. Both processes involve redox reactions. During cellular respiration, energy is released from sugar when electrons associated with hydrogen are transported by carriers to oxygen, forming water as a by-product (see p. 164). The electrons lose potential energy as they "fall" down the electron transport chain toward electronegative oxygen, and the mitochondrion harnesses that energy to synthesize ATP (see Figure 9.15). Photosynthesis reverses the direction of electron flow. Water is split, and electrons are transferred along with hydrogen ions from the water to carbon dioxide, reducing it to sugar.

$$\underset{\text{becomes oxidized}}{\underbrace{\text{Energy} + 6\,CO_2 + \overbrace{6\,H_2O \longrightarrow C_6H_{12}O_6}^{\text{becomes reduced}} + 6\,O_2}}$$

Because the electrons increase in potential energy as they move from water to sugar, this process requires energy—in other words is endergonic. This energy boost is provided by light.

The Two Stages of Photosynthesis: *A Preview*

The equation for photosynthesis is a deceptively simple summary of a very complex process. Actually, photosynthesis is not a single process, but two processes, each with multiple steps. These two stages of photosynthesis are known as the **light reactions** (the *photo* part of photosynthesis) and the **Calvin cycle** (the *synthesis* part) **(Figure 10.6)**.

The light reactions are the steps of photosynthesis that convert solar energy to chemical energy. Water is split, providing a source of electrons and protons (hydrogen ions, H^+) and giving off O_2 as a by-product. Light absorbed by chlorophyll drives a transfer of the electrons and hydrogen ions from water to an acceptor called **NADP$^+$** (nicotinamide adenine dinucleotide phosphate), where they are temporarily stored. The electron acceptor NADP$^+$ is first cousin to NAD$^+$, which functions as an electron carrier in cellular respiration; the two molecules differ only by the presence of an extra phosphate group in the NADP$^+$ molecule. The light reactions use solar power to reduce NADP$^+$ to NADPH by adding a pair of electrons along with an H^+. The light reactions also generate ATP, using chemiosmosis to power the addition of a phosphate group to ADP, a process called **photophosphorylation**. Thus, light energy is initially converted to chemical energy in the form of two compounds: NADPH, a source of electrons as "reducing power" that can be passed along to an electron acceptor, reducing it, and ATP, the versatile energy currency of cells. Notice that the light reactions produce no sugar; that happens in the second stage of photosynthesis, the Calvin cycle.

The Calvin cycle is named for Melvin Calvin, who, along with his colleagues, began to elucidate its steps in the late 1940s. The cycle begins by incorporating CO_2 from the air

▶ **Figure 10.6 An overview of photosynthesis: cooperation of the light reactions and the Calvin cycle.** In the chloroplast, the thylakoid membranes are the sites of the light reactions, whereas the Calvin cycle occurs in the stroma. The light reactions use solar energy to make ATP and NADPH, which supply chemical energy and reducing power, respectively, to the Calvin cycle. The Calvin cycle incorporates CO_2 into organic molecules, which are converted to sugar. (Recall that most simple sugars have formulas that are some multiple of CH_2O.)

ANIMATION **BioFlix** Visit the Study Area at **www.masteringbiology.com** for the BioFlix® 3-D Animation on Photosynthesis.

into organic molecules already present in the chloroplast. This initial incorporation of carbon into organic compounds is known as **carbon fixation**. The Calvin cycle then reduces the fixed carbon to carbohydrate by the addition of electrons. The reducing power is provided by NADPH, which acquired its cargo of electrons in the light reactions. To convert CO_2 to carbohydrate, the Calvin cycle also requires chemical energy in the form of ATP, which is also generated by the light reactions. Thus, it is the Calvin cycle that makes sugar, but it can do so only with the help of the NADPH and ATP produced by the light reactions. The metabolic steps of the Calvin cycle are sometimes referred to as the dark reactions, or light-independent reactions, because none of the steps requires light *directly*. Nevertheless, the Calvin cycle in most plants occurs during daylight, for only then can the light reactions provide the NADPH and ATP that the Calvin cycle requires. In essence, the chloroplast uses light energy to make sugar by coordinating the two stages of photosynthesis.

As Figure 10.6 indicates, the thylakoids of the chloroplast are the sites of the light reactions, while the Calvin cycle occurs in the stroma. On the outside of the thylakoids, molecules of $NADP^+$ and ADP pick up electrons and phosphate, respectively, and NADPH and ATP are then released to the stroma, where they play crucial roles in the Calvin cycle. The two stages of photosynthesis are treated in this figure as metabolic modules that take in ingredients and crank out products. In the next two sections, we'll look more closely at how the two stages work, beginning with the light reactions.

CONCEPT CHECK 10.1

1. How do the reactant molecules of photosynthesis reach the chloroplasts in leaves?
2. How did the use of an oxygen isotope help elucidate the chemistry of photosynthesis?
3. **WHAT IF?** The Calvin cycle requires ATP and NADPH, products of the light reactions. If a classmate asserted that the light reactions don't depend on the Calvin cycle and, with continual light, could just keep on producing ATP and NADPH, how would you respond?

For suggested answers, see Appendix A.

CONCEPT 10.2

The light reactions convert solar energy to the chemical energy of ATP and NADPH

Chloroplasts are chemical factories powered by the sun. Their thylakoids transform light energy into the chemical energy of ATP and NADPH. To understand this conversion better, we need to know about some important properties of light.

The Nature of Sunlight

Light is a form of energy known as electromagnetic energy, also called electromagnetic radiation. Electromagnetic energy travels in rhythmic waves analogous to those created by dropping a pebble into a pond. Electromagnetic waves, however, are disturbances of electric and magnetic fields rather than disturbances of a material medium such as water.

The distance between the crests of electromagnetic waves is called the **wavelength**. Wavelengths range from less than a nanometer (for gamma rays) to more than a kilometer (for radio waves). This entire range of radiation is known as the **electromagnetic spectrum** (Figure 10.7). The segment most important to life is the narrow band from about 380 nm to 750 nm in wavelength. This radiation is known as **visible light** because it can be detected as various colors by the human eye.

The model of light as waves explains many of light's properties, but in certain respects light behaves as though it consists of discrete particles, called **photons**. Photons are not tangible objects, but they act like objects in that each of them has a fixed quantity of energy. The amount of energy is inversely related to the wavelength of the light: the shorter the wavelength, the greater the energy of each photon of that light. Thus, a photon of violet light packs nearly twice as much energy as a photon of red light.

Although the sun radiates the full spectrum of electromagnetic energy, the atmosphere acts like a selective window, allowing visible light to pass through while screening out a substantial fraction of other radiation. The part of the spectrum we can see—visible light—is also the radiation that drives photosynthesis.

▲ **Figure 10.7 The electromagnetic spectrum.** White light is a mixture of all wavelengths of visible light. A prism can sort white light into its component colors by bending light of different wavelengths at different angles. (Droplets of water in the atmosphere can act as prisms, forming a rainbow; see Figure 10.1.) Visible light drives photosynthesis.

Photosynthetic Pigments: The Light Receptors

When light meets matter, it may be reflected, transmitted, or absorbed. Substances that absorb visible light are known as *pigments*. Different pigments absorb light of different wavelengths, and the wavelengths that are absorbed disappear. If a pigment is illuminated with white light, the color we see is the color most reflected or transmitted by the pigment. (If a pigment absorbs all wavelengths, it appears black.) We see green when we look at a leaf because chlorophyll absorbs violet-blue and red light while transmitting and reflecting green light (Figure 10.8). The ability of a pigment to absorb various wavelengths of light can be measured with an instrument called a **spectrophotometer**. This machine directs beams of light of different wavelengths through a solution of the pigment and measures the fraction of the light transmitted at each wavelength. A graph plotting a pigment's light absorption versus wavelength is called an **absorption spectrum** (Figure 10.9).

The absorption spectra of chloroplast pigments provide clues to the relative effectiveness of different wavelengths for driving photosynthesis, since light can perform work in chloroplasts only if it is absorbed. Figure 10.10a shows the absorption spectra of three types of pigments in chloroplasts: **chlorophyll *a***, which participates directly in the light reactions; the accessory pigment *chlorophyll b*; and a group of accessory pigments called carotenoids. The spectrum of chlorophyll *a* suggests that violet-blue and red light work best for photosynthesis, since they are absorbed, while green is the least effective

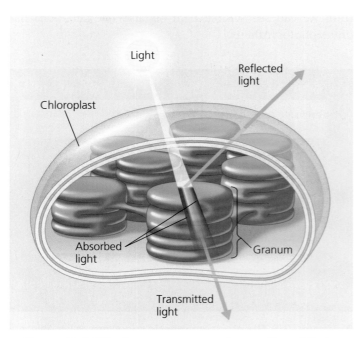

▲ **Figure 10.8 Why leaves are green: interaction of light with chloroplasts.** The chlorophyll molecules of chloroplasts absorb violet-blue and red light (the colors most effective in driving photosynthesis) and reflect or transmit green light. This is why leaves appear green.

▼ **Figure 10.9** | **RESEARCH METHOD**

Determining an Absorption Spectrum

APPLICATION An absorption spectrum is a visual representation of how well a particular pigment absorbs different wavelengths of visible light. Absorption spectra of various chloroplast pigments help scientists decipher each pigment's role in a plant.

TECHNIQUE A spectrophotometer measures the relative amounts of light of different wavelengths absorbed and transmitted by a pigment solution.

1 White light is separated into colors (wavelengths) by a prism.

2 One by one, the different colors of light are passed through the sample (chlorophyll in this example). Green light and blue light are shown here.

3 The transmitted light strikes a photoelectric tube, which converts the light energy to electricity.

4 The electric current is measured by a galvanometer. The meter indicates the fraction of light transmitted through the sample, from which we can determine the amount of light absorbed.

RESULTS See Figure 10.10a for absorption spectra of three types of chloroplast pigments.

---

color. This is confirmed by an **action spectrum** for photosynthesis (Figure 10.10b), which profiles the relative effectiveness of different wavelengths of radiation in driving the process. An action spectrum is prepared by illuminating chloroplasts with light of different colors and then plotting wavelength against some measure of photosynthetic rate, such as CO_2 consumption or O_2 release. The action spectrum for photosynthesis was first demonstrated by Theodor W. Engelmann, a German botanist, in 1883. Before equipment for measuring O_2 levels had even been invented, Engelmann performed a

▼ Figure 10.10

INQUIRY

Which wavelengths of light are most effective in driving photosynthesis?

EXPERIMENT Absorption and action spectra, along with a classic experiment by Theodor W. Engelmann, reveal which wavelengths of light are photosynthetically important.

RESULTS

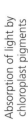

(a) Absorption spectra. The three curves show the wavelengths of light best absorbed by three types of chloroplast pigments.

(b) Action spectrum. This graph plots the rate of photosynthesis versus wavelength. The resulting action spectrum resembles the absorption spectrum for chlorophyll *a* but does not match exactly (see part a). This is partly due to the absorption of light by accessory pigments such as chlorophyll *b* and carotenoids.

(c) Engelmann's experiment. In 1883, Theodor W. Engelmann illuminated a filamentous alga with light that had been passed through a prism, exposing different segments of the alga to different wavelengths. He used aerobic bacteria, which concentrate near an oxygen source, to determine which segments of the alga were releasing the most O_2 and thus photosynthesizing most. Bacteria congregated in greatest numbers around the parts of the alga illuminated with violet-blue or red light.

CONCLUSION Light in the violet-blue and red portions of the spectrum is most effective in driving photosynthesis.

SOURCE T. W. Engelmann, *Bacterium photometricum. Ein Betrag zur vergleichenden Physiologie des Licht- und farbensinnes, Archiv. für Physiologie* 30:95–124 (1883).

(MB) See the related Experimental Inquiry Tutorial in MasteringBiology.

WHAT IF? If Engelmann had used a filter that allowed only red light to pass through, how would the results have differed?

---

clever experiment in which he used bacteria to measure rates of photosynthesis in filamentous algae **(Figure 10.10c)**. His results are a striking match to the modern action spectrum shown in Figure 10.10b.

Notice by comparing Figures 10.10a and 10.10b that the action spectrum for photosynthesis does not exactly match the absorption spectrum of chlorophyll *a*. The absorption spectrum of chlorophyll *a* alone underestimates the effectiveness of certain wavelengths in driving photosynthesis. This is partly because accessory pigments with different absorption spectra are also photosynthetically important in chloroplasts and broaden the spectrum of colors that can be used for photosynthesis. **Figure 10.11** shows the structure of chlorophyll *a* compared with that of **chlorophyll *b***. A slight structural difference between them is enough to cause the two pigments to absorb at slightly different wavelengths in the red and blue parts of the spectrum (see Figure 10.10a). As a result, chlorophyll *a* is blue green and chlorophyll *b* is olive green.

Other accessory pigments include **carotenoids**, hydrocarbons that are various shades of yellow and orange because they absorb violet and blue-green light (see Figure 10.10a). Carotenoids may broaden the spectrum of colors that can drive photosynthesis. However, a more important function of at least some carotenoids seems to be *photoprotection*: These

Porphyrin ring: light-absorbing "head" of molecule; note magnesium atom at center

Hydrocarbon tail: interacts with hydrophobic regions of proteins inside thylakoid membranes of chloroplasts; H atoms not shown

▲ **Figure 10.11 Structure of chlorophyll molecules in chloroplasts of plants.** Chlorophyll *a* and chlorophyll *b* differ only in one of the functional groups bonded to the porphyrin ring. (Also see the space-filling model of chlorophyll in Figure 1.4, p. 5.)

compounds absorb and dissipate excessive light energy that would otherwise damage chlorophyll or interact with oxygen, forming reactive oxidative molecules that are dangerous to the cell. Interestingly, carotenoids similar to the photoprotective ones in chloroplasts have a photoprotective role in the human eye. These and related molecules, often found in health food products, are valued as "phytochemicals" (from the Greek *phyton*, plant), compounds with antioxidant properties. Plants can synthesize all the antioxidants they require, but humans and other animals must obtain some of them from their diets.

Excitation of Chlorophyll by Light

What exactly happens when chlorophyll and other pigments absorb light? The colors corresponding to the absorbed wavelengths disappear from the spectrum of the transmitted and reflected light, but energy cannot disappear. When a molecule absorbs a photon of light, one of the molecule's electrons is elevated to an orbital where it has more potential energy. When the electron is in its normal orbital, the pigment molecule is said to be in its ground state. Absorption of a photon boosts an electron to an orbital of higher energy, and the pigment molecule is then said to be in an excited state. The only photons absorbed are those whose energy is exactly equal to the energy difference between the ground state and an excited state, and this energy difference varies from one kind of molecule to another. Thus, a particular compound absorbs only photons corresponding to specific wavelengths, which is why each pigment has a unique absorption spectrum.

Once absorption of a photon raises an electron from the ground state to an excited state, the electron cannot remain there long. The excited state, like all high-energy states, is unstable. Generally, when isolated pigment molecules absorb light, their excited electrons drop back down to the ground-state orbital in a billionth of a second, releasing their excess energy as heat. This conversion of light energy to heat is what makes the top of an automobile so hot on a sunny day. (White cars are coolest because their paint reflects all wavelengths of visible light, although it may absorb ultraviolet and other invisible radiation.) In isolation, some pigments, including chlorophyll, emit light as well as heat after absorbing photons. As excited electrons fall back to the ground state, photons are given off. This afterglow is called fluorescence. If a solution of chlorophyll isolated from chloroplasts is illuminated, it will fluoresce in the red-orange part of the spectrum and also give off heat (**Figure 10.12**).

A Photosystem: A Reaction-Center Complex Associated with Light-Harvesting Complexes

Chlorophyll molecules excited by the absorption of light energy produce very different results in an intact chloroplast than they do in isolation (see Figure 10.12). In their native environment of the thylakoid membrane, chlorophyll molecules are organized along with other small organic molecules and proteins into complexes called photosystems.

A **photosystem** is composed of a **reaction-center complex** surrounded by several light-harvesting complexes (**Figure 10.13**). The reaction-center complex is an organized association of proteins holding a special pair of chlorophyll *a* molecules. Each **light-harvesting complex** consists of various pigment molecules (which may include chlorophyll *a*, chlorophyll *b*, and carotenoids) bound to proteins. The number and variety of pigment molecules enable a photosystem to harvest light over a larger surface area and a larger portion of the spectrum than could any single pigment molecule alone. Together, these light-harvesting complexes act as an antenna for the reaction-center complex. When a pigment molecule

▶ **Figure 10.12 Excitation of isolated chlorophyll by light. (a)** Absorption of a photon causes a transition of the chlorophyll molecule from its ground state to its excited state. The photon boosts an electron to an orbital where it has more potential energy. If the illuminated molecule exists in isolation, its excited electron immediately drops back down to the ground-state orbital, and its excess energy is given off as heat and fluorescence (light). **(b)** A chlorophyll solution excited with ultraviolet light fluoresces with a red-orange glow.

WHAT IF? *If a leaf containing a similar concentration of chlorophyll as the solution was exposed to the same ultraviolet light, no fluorescence would be seen. Explain the difference in fluorescence emission between the solution and the leaf.*

(a) Excitation of isolated chlorophyll molecule

(b) Fluorescence

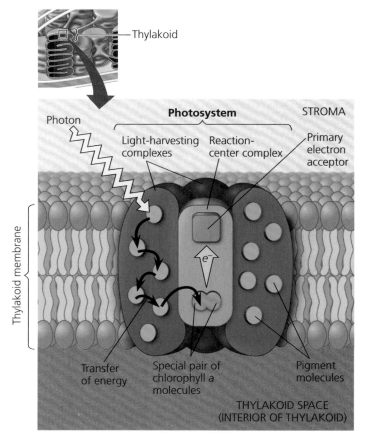

Thylakoid

Photosystem   STROMA

Photon

Light-harvesting complexes

Reaction-center complex

Primary electron acceptor

Thylakoid membrane

e⁻

Transfer of energy

Special pair of chlorophyll *a* molecules

Pigment molecules

THYLAKOID SPACE (INTERIOR OF THYLAKOID)

(a) How a photosystem harvests light. When a photon strikes a pigment molecule in a light-harvesting complex, the energy is passed from molecule to molecule until it reaches the reaction-center complex. Here, an excited electron from the special pair of chlorophyll *a* molecules is transferred to the primary electron acceptor.

Chlorophyll   STROMA

Thylakoid membrane

Protein subunits

THYLAKOID SPACE

(b) Structure of photosystem II. This computer model of photosystem II, based on X-ray crystallography, shows two photosystem complexes side by side. Chlorophyll molecules (small green ball-and-stick models) are interspersed with protein subunits (cylinders and ribbons). For simplicity, photosystem II will be shown as a single complex in the rest of the chapter.

▲ **Figure 10.13 The structure and function of a photosystem.**

absorbs a photon, the energy is transferred from pigment molecule to pigment molecule within a light-harvesting complex, somewhat like a human "wave" at a sports arena, until it is passed into the reaction-center complex. The reaction-center complex also contains a molecule capable of accepting

electrons and becoming reduced; this is called the **primary electron acceptor**. The pair of chlorophyll *a* molecules in the reaction-center complex are special because their molecular environment—their location and the other molecules with which they are associated—enables them to use the energy from light not only to boost one of their electrons to a higher energy level, but also to transfer it to a different molecule— the primary electron acceptor.

The solar-powered transfer of an electron from the reaction-center chlorophyll *a* pair to the primary electron acceptor is the first step of the light reactions. As soon as the chlorophyll electron is excited to a higher energy level, the primary electron acceptor captures it; this is a redox reaction. In the flask shown in Figure 10.12, isolated chlorophyll fluoresces because there is no electron acceptor, so electrons of photoexcited chlorophyll drop right back to the ground state. In the structured environment of a chloroplast, however, an electron acceptor is readily available, and the potential energy represented by the excited electron is not dissipated as light and heat. Thus, each photosystem—a reaction-center complex surrounded by light-harvesting complexes—functions in the chloroplast as a unit. It converts light energy to chemical energy, which will ultimately be used for the synthesis of sugar.

The thylakoid membrane is populated by two types of photosystems that cooperate in the light reactions of photosynthesis. They are called **photosystem II (PS II)** and **photosystem I (PS I)**. (They were named in order of their discovery, but photosystem II functions first in the light reactions.) Each has a characteristic reaction-center complex—a particular kind of primary electron acceptor next to a special pair of chlorophyll *a* molecules associated with specific proteins. The reaction-center chlorophyll *a* of photosystem II is known as P680 because this pigment is best at absorbing light having a wavelength of 680 nm (in the red part of the spectrum). The chlorophyll *a* at the reaction-center complex of photosystem I is called P700 because it most effectively absorbs light of wavelength 700 nm (in the far-red part of the spectrum). These two pigments, P680 and P700, are nearly identical chlorophyll *a* molecules. However, their association with different proteins in the thylakoid membrane affects the electron distribution in the two pigments and accounts for the slight differences in their light-absorbing properties. Now let's see how the two photosystems work together in using light energy to generate ATP and NADPH, the two main products of the light reactions.

Linear Electron Flow

Light drives the synthesis of ATP and NADPH by energizing the two photosystems embedded in the thylakoid membranes of chloroplasts. The key to this energy transformation is a flow of electrons through the photosystems and other molecular components built into the thylakoid membrane. This is called

**Photosystem II
(PS II)**

**Photosystem I
(PS I)**

linear electron flow, and it occurs during the light reactions of photosynthesis, as shown in **Figure 10.14**. The following steps correspond to the numbered steps in the figure.

1 A photon of light strikes a pigment molecule in a light-harvesting complex of PS II, boosting one of its electrons to a higher energy level. As this electron falls back to its ground state, an electron in a nearby pigment molecule is simultaneously raised to an excited state. The process continues, with the energy being relayed to other pigment molecules until it reaches the P680 pair of chlorophyll *a* molecules in the PS II reaction-center complex. It excites an electron in this pair of chlorophylls to a higher energy state.

2 This electron is transferred from the excited P680 to the primary electron acceptor. We can refer to the resulting form of P680, missing an electron, as P680⁺.

3 An enzyme catalyzes the splitting of a water molecule into two electrons, two hydrogen ions (H^+), and an oxygen atom. The electrons are supplied one by one to the P680⁺ pair, each electron replacing one transferred to the primary electron acceptor. (P680⁺ is the strongest biological oxidizing agent known; its electron "hole" must be filled. This greatly facilitates the transfer of electrons from the

split water molecule.) The H^+ are released into the thylakoid lumen. The oxygen atom immediately combines with an oxygen atom generated by the splitting of another water molecule, forming O_2.

4 Each photoexcited electron passes from the primary electron acceptor of PS II to PS I via an electron transport chain, the components of which are similar to those of the electron transport chain that functions in cellular respiration. The electron transport chain between PS II and PS I is made up of the electron carrier plastoquinone (Pq), a cytochrome complex, and a protein called plastocyanin (Pc).

5 The exergonic "fall" of electrons to a lower energy level provides energy for the synthesis of ATP. As electrons pass through the cytochrome complex, H^+ are pumped into the thylakoid lumen, contributing to the proton gradient that is subsequently used in chemiosmosis.

6 Meanwhile, light energy has been transferred via light-harvesting complex pigments to the PS I reaction-center complex, exciting an electron of the P700 pair of chlorophyll *a* molecules located there. The photoexcited electron was then transferred to PS I's primary electron acceptor, creating an electron "hole" in the P700—which we now can call P700$^+$. In other words, P700$^+$ can now act as an electron acceptor, accepting an electron that reaches the bottom of the electron transport chain from PS II.

7 Photoexcited electrons are passed in a series of redox reactions from the primary electron acceptor of PS I down a second electron transport chain through the protein ferredoxin (Fd). (This chain does not create a proton gradient and thus does not produce ATP.)

8 The enzyme NADP$^+$ reductase catalyzes the transfer of electrons from Fd to NADP$^+$. Two electrons are required for its reduction to NADPH. This molecule is at a higher energy level than water, and its electrons are more readily available for the reactions of the Calvin cycle than were those of water. This process also removes an H$^+$ from the stroma.

As complicated as the scheme shown in Figure 10.14 is, do not lose track of its functions. The light reactions use solar power to generate ATP and NADPH, which provide chemical energy and reducing power, respectively, to the carbohydrate-synthesizing reactions of the Calvin cycle. The energy changes of electrons during their linear flow through the light reactions are shown in a mechanical analogy in **Figure 10.15**.

Cyclic Electron Flow

In certain cases, photoexcited electrons can take an alternative path called **cyclic electron flow**, which uses photosystem I but not photosystem II. You can see in **Figure 10.16** that cyclic flow is a short circuit: The electrons cycle back from ferredoxin (Fd) to the cytochrome complex and from there continue on to a P700 chlorophyll in the PS I reaction-center complex. There is no production of NADPH and no release of oxygen. Cyclic flow does, however, generate ATP.

Several of the currently existing groups of photosynthetic bacteria are known to have photosystem I but not photosystem II; for these species, which include the purple sulfur bacteria (see Figure 10.2e), cyclic electron flow is the sole means of generating ATP in photosynthesis. Evolutionary biologists hypothesize that these bacterial groups are descendants of

▲ **Figure 10.15 A mechanical analogy for linear electron flow during the light reactions.**

the bacteria in which photosynthesis first evolved, in a form similar to cyclic electron flow.

Cyclic electron flow can also occur in photosynthetic species that possess both photosystems; this includes some prokaryotes, such as the cyanobacteria shown in Figure 10.2d, as well as the eukaryotic photosynthetic species that have been tested so far. Although the process is probably in part an "evolutionary leftover," it clearly plays at least one beneficial role for these organisms. Mutant plants that are not able to carry out cyclic electron flow are capable of growing well in low light, but do not grow well where light is intense. This is evidence for the idea that cyclic electron flow may be photoprotective. Later you'll learn more about cyclic electron flow as it relates to a particular adaptation of photosynthesis (C$_4$ plants; see Concept 10.4).

Whether ATP synthesis is driven by linear or cyclic electron flow, the actual mechanism is the same. Before we move on to consider the Calvin cycle, let's review chemiosmosis, the process that uses membranes to couple redox reactions to ATP production.

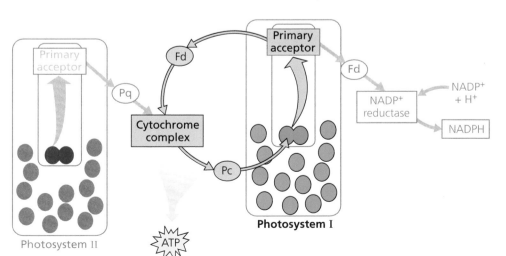

◀ **Figure 10.16 Cyclic electron flow.** Photoexcited electrons from PS I are occasionally shunted back from ferredoxin (Fd) to chlorophyll via the cytochrome complex and plastocyanin (Pc). This electron shunt supplements the supply of ATP (via chemiosmosis) but produces no NADPH. The "shadow" of linear electron flow is included in the diagram for comparison with the cyclic route. The two ferredoxin molecules shown in this diagram are actually one and the same—the final electron carrier in the electron transport chain of PS I.

? *Look at Figure 10.15, and explain how you would alter it to show a mechanical analogy for cyclic electron flow.*

A Comparison of Chemiosmosis in Chloroplasts and Mitochondria

Chloroplasts and mitochondria generate ATP by the same basic mechanism: chemiosmosis. An electron transport chain assembled in a membrane pumps protons across the membrane as electrons are passed through a series of carriers that are progressively more electronegative. In this way, electron transport chains transform redox energy to a proton-motive force, potential energy stored in the form of an H^+ gradient across a membrane. Built into the same membrane is an ATP synthase complex that couples the diffusion of hydrogen ions down their gradient to the phosphorylation of ADP. Some of the electron carriers, including the iron-containing proteins called cytochromes, are very similar in chloroplasts and mitochondria. The ATP synthase complexes of the two organelles are also very much alike. But there are noteworthy differences between oxidative phosphorylation in mitochondria and photophosphorylation in chloroplasts. In mitochondria, the high-energy electrons dropped down the transport chain are extracted from organic molecules (which are thus oxidized), while in chloroplasts, the source of electrons is water. Chloroplasts do not need molecules from food to make ATP; their photosystems capture light energy and use it to drive the electrons from water to the top of the transport chain. In other words, mitochondria use chemiosmosis to transfer chemical energy from food molecules to ATP, whereas chloroplasts transform light energy into chemical energy in ATP.

Although the spatial organization of chemiosmosis differs slightly between chloroplasts and mitochondria, it is easy to see similarities in the two (**Figure 10.17**). The inner membrane of the mitochondrion pumps protons from the mitochondrial matrix out to the intermembrane space, which then serves as a reservoir of hydrogen ions. The thylakoid membrane of the chloroplast pumps protons from the stroma into the thylakoid space (interior of the thylakoid), which functions as the H^+ reservoir. If you imagine the cristae of mitochondria pinching off from the inner membrane, this may help you see how the thylakoid space and the intermembrane space are comparable spaces in the two organelles, while the mitochondrial matrix is analogous to the stroma of the chloroplast. In the mitochondrion, protons diffuse down their concentration gradient from the intermembrane space through ATP synthase to the matrix, driving ATP synthesis. In the chloroplast, ATP is synthesized as the hydrogen ions diffuse from the thylakoid space back to the stroma through ATP synthase complexes, whose catalytic knobs are on the stroma side of the membrane. Thus, ATP forms in the stroma, where it is used to help drive sugar synthesis during the Calvin cycle (**Figure 10.18**).

The proton (H^+) gradient, or pH gradient, across the thylakoid membrane is substantial. When chloroplasts in an

Key ■ Higher [H^+] ▢ Lower [H^+]

Mitochondrion **Chloroplast**

MITOCHONDRION STRUCTURE CHLOROPLAST STRUCTURE

Intermembrane space H^+ Diffusion Thylakoid space

Inner membrane Electron transport chain Thylakoid membrane

ATP synthase

Matrix Stroma

ADP + P$_i$ ATP

H^+

▲ **Figure 10.17 Comparison of chemiosmosis in mitochondria and chloroplasts.** In both kinds of organelles, electron transport chains pump protons (H^+) across a membrane from a region of low H^+ concentration (light gray in this diagram) to one of high H^+ concentration (dark gray). The protons then diffuse back across the membrane through ATP synthase, driving the synthesis of ATP.

experimental setting are illuminated, the pH in the thylakoid space drops to about 5 (the H^+ concentration increases), and the pH in the stroma increases to about 8 (the H^+ concentration decreases). This gradient of three pH units corresponds to a thousandfold difference in H^+ concentration. If in the laboratory the lights are turned off, the pH gradient is abolished, but it can quickly be restored by turning the lights back on. Experiments such as this provided strong evidence in support of the chemiosmotic model.

Based on studies in several laboratories, Figure 10.18 shows a current model for the organization of the light-reaction "machinery" within the thylakoid membrane. Each of the molecules and molecular complexes in the figure is present in numerous copies in each thylakoid. Notice that NADPH, like ATP, is produced on the side of the membrane facing the stroma, where the Calvin cycle reactions take place.

Let's summarize the light reactions. Electron flow pushes electrons from water, where they are at a low state of potential energy, ultimately to NADPH, where they are stored at a high state of potential energy. The light-driven electron current also generates ATP. Thus, the equipment of the thylakoid membrane converts light energy to chemical energy stored in ATP and NADPH. (Oxygen is a by-product.) Let's now see how the Calvin cycle uses the products of the light reactions to synthesize sugar from CO_2.

▲ Figure 10.18 The light reactions and chemiosmosis: the organization of the thylakoid membrane. This diagram shows a current model for the organization of the thylakoid membrane. The gold arrows track the linear electron flow outlined in Figure 10.14. As electrons pass from carrier to carrier in redox reactions, hydrogen ions removed from the stroma are deposited in the thylakoid space, storing energy as a proton-motive force (H^+ gradient). At least three steps in the light reactions contribute to the proton gradient: **1** Water is split by photosystem II on the side of the membrane facing the thylakoid space; **2** as plastoquinone (Pq), a mobile carrier, transfers electrons to the cytochrome complex, four protons are translocated across the membrane into the thylakoid space; and **3** a hydrogen ion is removed from the stroma when it is taken up by $NADP^+$. Notice that in step 2, hydrogen ions are being pumped from the stroma into the thylakoid space, as in Figure 10.17. The diffusion of H^+ from the thylakoid space back to the stroma (along the H^+ concentration gradient) powers the ATP synthase. These light-driven reactions store chemical energy in NADPH and ATP, which shuttle the energy to the carbohydrate-producing Calvin cycle.

CONCEPT CHECK 10.2

1. What color of light is *least* effective in driving photosynthesis? Explain.
2. Compared to a solution of isolated chlorophyll, why do intact chloroplasts release less heat and fluorescence when illuminated?
3. In the light reactions, what is the initial electron donor? Where do the electrons finally end up?
4. **WHAT IF?** In an experiment, isolated chloroplasts placed in an illuminated solution with the appropriate chemicals can carry out ATP synthesis. Predict what would happen to the rate of synthesis if a compound is added to the solution that makes membranes freely permeable to hydrogen ions.

For suggested answers, see Appendix A.

CONCEPT 10.3

The Calvin cycle uses the chemical energy of ATP and NADPH to reduce CO₂ to sugar

The Calvin cycle is similar to the citric acid cycle in that a starting material is regenerated after molecules enter and leave the cycle. However, while the citric acid cycle is catabolic, oxidizing acetyl CoA and using the energy to synthesize ATP, the Calvin cycle is anabolic, building carbohydrates from smaller molecules and consuming energy. Carbon

enters the Calvin cycle in the form of CO_2 and leaves in the form of sugar. The cycle spends ATP as an energy source and consumes NADPH as reducing power for adding high-energy electrons to make the sugar.

As we mentioned previously, the carbohydrate produced directly from the Calvin cycle is actually not glucose, but a three-carbon sugar; the name of this sugar is **glyceraldehyde 3-phosphate (G3P)**. For the net synthesis of one molecule of G3P, the cycle must take place three times, fixing three molecules of CO_2. (Recall that carbon fixation refers to the initial incorporation of CO_2 into organic material.) As we trace the steps of the cycle, keep in mind that we are following three molecules of CO_2 through the reactions. **Figure 10.19** divides

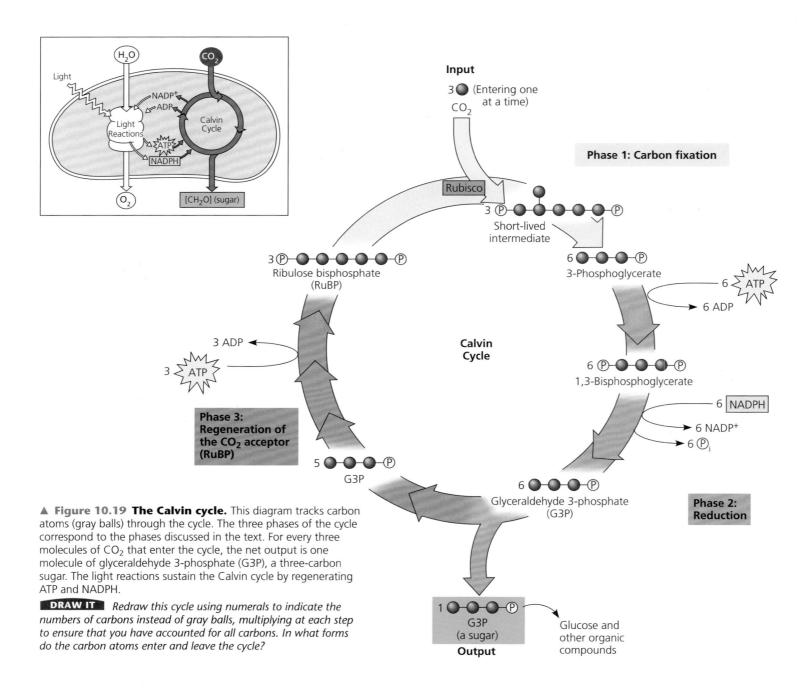

▲ **Figure 10.19 The Calvin cycle.** This diagram tracks carbon atoms (gray balls) through the cycle. The three phases of the cycle correspond to the phases discussed in the text. For every three molecules of CO_2 that enter the cycle, the net output is one molecule of glyceraldehyde 3-phosphate (G3P), a three-carbon sugar. The light reactions sustain the Calvin cycle by regenerating ATP and NADPH.

DRAW IT *Redraw this cycle using numerals to indicate the numbers of carbons instead of gray balls, multiplying at each step to ensure that you have accounted for all carbons. In what forms do the carbon atoms enter and leave the cycle?*

the Calvin cycle into three phases: carbon fixation, reduction, and regeneration of the CO_2 acceptor.

Phase 1: Carbon fixation. The Calvin cycle incorporates each CO_2 molecule, one at a time, by attaching it to a five-carbon sugar named ribulose bisphosphate (abbreviated RuBP). The enzyme that catalyzes this first step is RuBP carboxylase, or **rubisco**. (This is the most abundant protein in chloroplasts and is also thought to be the most abundant protein on Earth.) The product of the reaction is a six-carbon intermediate so unstable that it immediately splits in half, forming two molecules of 3-phosphoglycerate (for each CO_2 fixed).

Phase 2: Reduction. Each molecule of 3-phosphoglycerate receives an additional phosphate group from ATP, becoming 1,3-bisphosphoglycerate. Next, a pair of electrons donated from NADPH reduces 1,3-bisphosphoglycerate, which also loses a phosphate group, becoming G3P. Specifically, the electrons from NADPH reduce a carboxyl group on 1,3-bisphosphoglycerate to the aldehyde group of G3P, which stores more potential energy. G3P is a sugar—the same three-carbon sugar formed in glycolysis by the splitting of glucose (see Figure 9.9). Notice in Figure 10.19 that for every *three* molecules of CO_2 that enter the cycle, there are *six* molecules of G3P formed. But only one molecule of this three-carbon sugar can be counted as a net gain of carbohydrate. The cycle began with 15 carbons' worth of carbohydrate in the form of three molecules of the five-carbon sugar RuBP. Now there are 18 carbons' worth of carbohydrate in the form of six molecules of G3P. One molecule exits the cycle to be used by the plant cell, but the other five molecules must be recycled to regenerate the three molecules of RuBP.

Phase 3: Regeneration of the CO_2 acceptor (RuBP). In a complex series of reactions, the carbon skeletons of five molecules of G3P are rearranged by the last steps of the Calvin cycle into three molecules of RuBP. To accomplish this, the cycle spends three more molecules of ATP. The RuBP is now prepared to receive CO_2 again, and the cycle continues.

For the net synthesis of one G3P molecule, the Calvin cycle consumes a total of nine molecules of ATP and six molecules of NADPH. The light reactions regenerate the ATP and NADPH. The G3P spun off from the Calvin cycle becomes the starting material for metabolic pathways that synthesize other organic compounds, including glucose and other carbohydrates. Neither the light reactions nor the Calvin cycle alone can make sugar from CO_2. Photosynthesis is an emergent property of the intact chloroplast, which integrates the two stages of photosynthesis.

CONCEPT CHECK 10.3

1. To synthesize one glucose molecule, the Calvin cycle uses _____ molecules of CO_2, _____ molecules of ATP, and _____ molecules of NADPH.
2. Explain why the large numbers of ATP and NADPH molecules used during the Calvin cycle are consistent with the high value of glucose as an energy source.
3. **WHAT IF?** Explain why a poison that inhibits an enzyme of the Calvin cycle will also inhibit the light reactions.
4. **MAKE CONNECTIONS** Review Figures 9.9 (p. 169) and 10.19. Discuss the roles of intermediate and product played by glyceraldehyde 3-phosphate (G3P) in the two processes shown in these figures.

For suggested answers, see Appendix A.

CONCEPT **10.4**

Alternative mechanisms of carbon fixation have evolved in hot, arid climates

EVOLUTION Ever since plants first moved onto land about 475 million years ago, they have been adapting to the problems of terrestrial life, particularly the problem of dehydration. In Chapters 29 and 36, we will consider anatomical adaptations that help plants conserve water, while in this chapter we are concerned with metabolic adaptations. The solutions often involve trade-offs. An important example is the compromise between photosynthesis and the prevention of excessive water loss from the plant. The CO_2 required for photosynthesis enters a leaf via stomata, the pores on the leaf surface (see Figure 10.4). However, stomata are also the main avenues of transpiration, the evaporative loss of water from leaves. On a hot, dry day, most plants close their stomata, a response that conserves water. This response also reduces photosynthetic yield by limiting access to CO_2. With stomata even partially closed, CO_2 concentrations begin to decrease in the air spaces within the leaf, and the concentration of O_2 released from the light reactions begins to increase. These conditions within the leaf favor an apparently wasteful process called photorespiration.

Photorespiration: An Evolutionary Relic?

In most plants, initial fixation of carbon occurs via rubisco, the Calvin cycle enzyme that adds CO_2 to ribulose bisphosphate. Such plants are called **C_3 plants** because the first organic product of carbon fixation is a three-carbon compound,

3-phosphoglycerate (see Figure 10.19). Rice, wheat, and soybeans are C_3 plants that are important in agriculture. When their stomata partially close on hot, dry days, C_3 plants produce less sugar because the declining level of CO_2 in the leaf starves the Calvin cycle. In addition, rubisco can bind O_2 in place of CO_2. As CO_2 becomes scarce within the air spaces of the leaf, rubisco adds O_2 to the Calvin cycle instead of CO_2. The product splits, and a two-carbon compound leaves the chloroplast. Peroxisomes and mitochondria rearrange and split this compound, releasing CO_2. The process is called **photorespiration** because it occurs in the light (*photo*) and consumes O_2 while producing CO_2 (*respiration*). However, unlike normal cellular respiration, photorespiration generates no ATP; in fact, photorespiration consumes ATP. And unlike photosynthesis, photorespiration produces no sugar. In fact, photorespiration *decreases* photosynthetic output by siphoning organic material from the Calvin cycle and releasing CO_2 that would otherwise be fixed.

How can we explain the existence of a metabolic process that seems to be counterproductive for the plant? According to one hypothesis, photorespiration is evolutionary baggage—a metabolic relic from a much earlier time when the atmosphere had less O_2 and more CO_2 than it does today. In the ancient atmosphere that prevailed when rubisco first evolved, the inability of the enzyme's active site to exclude O_2 would have made little difference. The hypothesis suggests that modern rubisco retains some of its chance affinity for O_2, which is now so concentrated in the atmosphere that a certain amount of photorespiration is inevitable.

We now know that, at least in some cases, photorespiration plays a protective role in plants. Plants that are impaired in their ability to carry out photorespiration (due to defective genes) are more susceptible to damage induced by excess light. Researchers consider this clear evidence that photorespiration acts to neutralize the otherwise damaging products of the light reactions, which build up when a low CO_2 concentration limits the progress of the Calvin cycle. Whether there are other benefits of photorespiration is still unknown. In many types of plants—including a significant number of crop plants—photorespiration drains away as much as 50% of the carbon fixed by the Calvin cycle. As heterotrophs that depend on carbon fixation in chloroplasts for our food, we naturally view photorespiration as wasteful. Indeed, if photorespiration could be reduced in certain plant species without otherwise affecting photosynthetic productivity, crop yields and food supplies might increase.

In some plant species, alternate modes of carbon fixation have evolved that minimize photorespiration and optimize the Calvin cycle—even in hot, arid climates. The two most important of these photosynthetic adaptations are C_4 photosynthesis and crassulacean acid metabolism (CAM).

C_4 Plants

The **C_4 plants** are so named because they preface the Calvin cycle with an alternate mode of carbon fixation that forms a four-carbon compound as its first product. Several thousand species in at least 19 plant families use the C_4 pathway. Among the C_4 plants important to agriculture are sugarcane and corn, members of the grass family.

A unique leaf anatomy is correlated with the mechanism of C_4 photosynthesis (**Figure 10.20**; compare with Figure 10.4). In C_4 plants, there are two distinct types of photosynthetic cells: bundle-sheath cells and mesophyll cells. **Bundle-sheath cells** are arranged into tightly packed sheaths around the veins of the leaf. Between the bundle sheath and the leaf surface are the more loosely arranged mesophyll cells. The Calvin cycle is confined to the chloroplasts of the bundle-sheath cells. However, the Calvin cycle is preceded by incorporation of CO_2 into organic compounds in the mesophyll cells. See the numbered steps in Figure 10.20, which are also described here:

❶ The first step is carried out by an enzyme present only in mesophyll cells called **PEP carboxylase**. This enzyme adds CO_2 to phosphoenolpyruvate (PEP), forming the four-carbon product oxaloacetate. PEP carboxylase has a much higher affinity for CO_2 than does rubisco and no affinity for O_2. Therefore, PEP carboxylase can fix carbon efficiently when rubisco cannot—that is, when it is hot and dry and stomata are partially closed, causing CO_2 concentration in the leaf to fall and O_2 concentration to rise.

❷ After the C_4 plant fixes carbon from CO_2, the mesophyll cells export their four-carbon products (malate in the example shown in Figure 10.20) to bundle-sheath cells through plasmodesmata (see Figure 6.31).

❸ Within the bundle-sheath cells, the four-carbon compounds release CO_2, which is reassimilated into organic material by rubisco and the Calvin cycle. The same reaction regenerates pyruvate, which is transported to mesophyll cells. There, ATP is used to convert pyruvate to PEP, allowing the reaction cycle to continue; this ATP can be thought of as the "price" of concentrating CO_2 in the bundle-sheath cells. To generate this extra ATP, bundle-sheath cells carry out cyclic electron flow, the process described earlier in this chapter (see Figure 10.16). In fact, these cells contain PS I but no PS II, so cyclic electron flow is their only photosynthetic mode of generating ATP.

In effect, the mesophyll cells of a C_4 plant pump CO_2 into the bundle sheath, keeping the CO_2 concentration in the bundle-sheath cells high enough for rubisco to bind carbon

Mesophyll cell

PEP carboxylase

CO_2

The C_4 pathway

Oxaloacetate (4C)   PEP (3C)

ADP

ATP

Malate (4C)

Pyruvate (3C)

Bundle-sheath cell

CO_2

Calvin Cycle

Sugar

Vascular tissue

❶ In mesophyll cells, the enzyme PEP carboxylase adds carbon dioxide to PEP.

❷ A four-carbon compound conveys the atoms of the CO_2 into a bundle-sheath cell via plasmodesmata.

❸ In bundle-sheath cells, CO_2 is released and enters the Calvin cycle.

Photosynthetic cells of C_4 plant leaf — Mesophyll cell, Bundle-sheath cell

Vein (vascular tissue)

C_4 leaf anatomy

Stoma

▲ **Figure 10.20 C_4 leaf anatomy and the C_4 pathway.** The structure and biochemical functions of the leaves of C_4 plants are an evolutionary adaptation to hot, dry climates. This adaptation maintains a CO_2 concentration in the bundle sheath that favors photosynthesis over photorespiration.

dioxide rather than oxygen. The cyclic series of reactions involving PEP carboxylase and the regeneration of PEP can be thought of as a CO_2-concentrating pump that is powered by ATP. In this way, C_4 photosynthesis minimizes photorespiration and enhances sugar production. This adaptation is especially advantageous in hot regions with intense sunlight, where stomata partially close during the day, and it is in such environments that C_4 plants evolved and thrive today.

Since the Industrial Revolution began in the 1800s, human activities such as the burning of fossil fuels have drastically increased the concentration of CO_2 in the atmosphere. The resulting global climate change, including an increase in average temperatures around the planet, may have far-reaching effects on plant species. Scientists are concerned that increasing CO_2 concentration and temperature may affect C_3 and C_4 plants differently, thus changing the relative abundance of these species in a given plant community.

Which type of plant would stand to gain more from increasing CO_2 levels? Recall that in C_3 plants, the binding of O_2 rather than CO_2 by rubisco leads to photorespiration, lowering the efficiency of photosynthesis. C_4 plants overcome this problem by concentrating CO_2 in the bundle-sheath cells

at the cost of ATP. Rising CO_2 levels should benefit C_3 plants by lowering the amount of photorespiration that occurs. At the same time, rising temperatures have the opposite effect, increasing photorespiration. (Other factors such as water availability may also come into play.) In contrast, many C_4 plants could be largely unaffected by increasing CO_2 levels or temperature. In different regions, the particular combination of these two factors is likely to alter the balance of C_3 and C_4 plants in varying ways. The effects of such a widespread and variable change in community structure are unpredictable and thus a cause of legitimate concern.

CAM Plants

A second photosynthetic adaptation to arid conditions has evolved in many succulent (water-storing) plants, numerous cacti, pineapples, and representatives of several other plant families. These plants open their stomata during the night and close them during the day, just the reverse of how other plants behave. Closing stomata during the day helps desert plants conserve water, but it also prevents CO_2 from entering the leaves. During the night, when their stomata are open, these plants take up CO_2 and incorporate it into a variety

► **Figure 10.21 C$_4$ and CAM photosynthesis compared.** Both adaptations are characterized by preliminary incorporation of CO$_2$ into organic acids, followed by transfer of CO$_2$ to the Calvin cycle. The C$_4$ and CAM pathways are two evolutionary solutions to the problem of maintaining photosynthesis with stomata partially or completely closed on hot, dry days.

Sugarcane

Pineapple

C$_4$

CAM

Mesophyll cell

Organic acid

❶ CO$_2$ incorporated into four-carbon organic acids (carbon fixation)

Organic acid

Night

CO$_2$

CO$_2$

Bundle-sheath cell

Calvin Cycle

❷ CO$_2$ released by organic acids to the Calvin cycle

Calvin Cycle

Day

Sugar

Sugar

(a) Spatial separation of steps.
In C$_4$ plants, carbon fixation and the Calvin cycle occur in different types of cells.

(b) Temporal separation of steps.
In CAM plants, carbon fixation and the Calvin cycle occur in the same cells at different times.

of organic acids. This mode of carbon fixation is called **crassulacean acid metabolism**, or **CAM**, after the plant family Crassulaceae, the succulents in which the process was first discovered. The mesophyll cells of **CAM plants** store the organic acids they make during the night in their vacuoles until morning, when the stomata close. During the day, when the light reactions can supply ATP and NADPH for the Calvin cycle, CO$_2$ is released from the organic acids made the night before to become incorporated into sugar in the chloroplasts.

Notice in **Figure 10.21** that the CAM pathway is similar to the C$_4$ pathway in that carbon dioxide is first incorporated into organic intermediates before it enters the Calvin cycle. The difference is that in C$_4$ plants, the initial steps of carbon fixation are separated structurally from the Calvin cycle, whereas in CAM plants, the two steps occur at separate times but within the same cell. (Keep in mind that CAM, C$_4$, and C$_3$ plants all eventually use the Calvin cycle to make sugar from carbon dioxide.)

CONCEPT CHECK 10.4

1. Explain why photorespiration lowers photosynthetic output for plants.
2. The presence of only PS I, not PS II, in the bundle-sheath cells of C$_4$ plants has an effect on O$_2$ concentration. What is that effect, and how might that benefit the plant?
3. **MAKE CONNECTIONS** Refer to the discussion of ocean acidification in Concept 3.3 (p. 55). Ocean acidification and changes in the distribution of C$_3$ and C$_4$ plants may seem to be two very different problems, but what do they have in common? Explain.
4. **WHAT IF?** How would you expect the relative abundance of C$_3$ versus C$_4$ and CAM species to change in a geographic region whose climate becomes much hotter and drier, with no change in CO$_2$ concentration?

For suggested answers, see Appendix A.

The Importance of Photosynthesis: *A Review*

In this chapter, we have followed photosynthesis from photons to food. The light reactions capture solar energy and use it to make ATP and transfer electrons from water to $NADP^+$, forming NADPH. The Calvin cycle uses the ATP and NADPH to produce sugar from carbon dioxide. The energy that enters the chloroplasts as sunlight becomes stored as chemical energy in organic compounds. See **Figure 10.22** for a review of the entire process.

What are the fates of photosynthetic products? The sugar made in the chloroplasts supplies the entire plant with chemical energy and carbon skeletons for the synthesis of all the major organic molecules of plant cells. About 50% of the organic material made by photosynthesis is consumed as fuel for cellular respiration in the mitochondria of the plant cells. Sometimes there is a loss of photosynthetic products to photorespiration.

Technically, green cells are the only autotrophic parts of the plant. The rest of the plant depends on organic molecules exported from leaves via veins. In most plants, carbohydrate is transported out of the leaves in the form of sucrose, a disaccharide. After arriving at nonphotosynthetic cells, the sucrose provides raw material for cellular respiration and a multitude of anabolic pathways that synthesize proteins, lipids, and other products. A considerable amount of sugar in the form of glucose is linked together to make the polysaccharide cellulose, especially in plant cells that are still growing and maturing. Cellulose, the main ingredient of cell walls, is the most abundant organic molecule in the plant—and probably on the surface of the planet.

Most plants manage to make more organic material each day than they need to use as respiratory fuel and precursors for biosynthesis. They stockpile the extra sugar by synthesizing starch, storing some in the chloroplasts themselves and some in storage cells of roots, tubers, seeds, and fruits. In accounting for the consumption of the food molecules produced by photosynthesis, let's not forget that most plants lose leaves, roots, stems, fruits, and sometimes their entire bodies to heterotrophs, including humans.

On a global scale, photosynthesis is the process responsible for the presence of oxygen in our atmosphere. Furthermore, in terms of food production, the collective productivity of the minuscule chloroplasts is prodigious: Photosynthesis makes an estimated 160 billion metric tons of carbohydrate per year (a metric ton is 1,000 kg, about 1.1 tons). That's organic matter equivalent in mass to a stack of about 60 trillion copies of this textbook—17 stacks of books reaching from Earth to the sun! No other chemical process on the planet can match the output of photosynthesis. And as we mentioned earlier, researchers are seeking ways to capitalize on photosynthetic production to produce alternative fuels. No process is more important than photosynthesis to the welfare of life on Earth.

▶ **Figure 10.22 A review of photosynthesis.** This diagram outlines the main reactants and products of the light reactions and the Calvin cycle as they occur in the chloroplasts of plant cells. The entire ordered operation depends on the structural integrity of the chloroplast and its membranes. Enzymes in the chloroplast and cytosol convert glyceraldehyde 3-phosphate (G3P), the direct product of the Calvin cycle, to many other organic compounds.

MAKE CONNECTIONS *Return to the micrograph in Figure 5.6a, on page 72. Label and describe where the light reactions and the Calvin cycle take place. Also explain where the starch granules in the micrograph came from.*

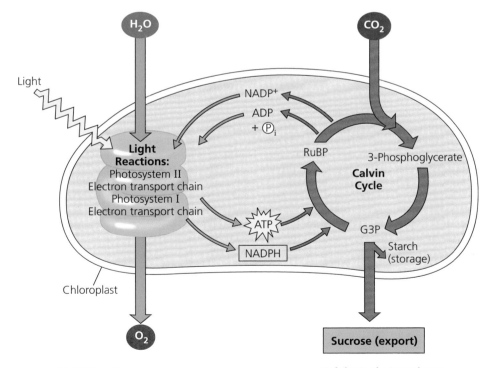

Light Reactions:
- Are carried out by molecules in the thylakoid membranes
- Convert light energy to the chemical energy of ATP and NADPH
- Split H_2O and release O_2 to the atmosphere

Calvin Cycle Reactions:
- Take place in the stroma
- Use ATP and NADPH to convert CO_2 to the sugar G3P
- Return ADP, inorganic phosphate, and $NADP^+$ to the light reactions

SUMMARY OF KEY CONCEPTS

CONCEPT 10.1

Photosynthesis converts light energy to the chemical energy of food (pp. 186–189)

- In **autotrophic** eukaryotes, photosynthesis occurs in **chloroplasts**, organelles containing **thylakoids**. Stacks of thylakoids form grana. **Photosynthesis** is summarized as

$$6\ CO_2 + 12\ H_2O + Light\ energy \rightarrow C_6H_{12}O_6 + 6\ O_2 + 6\ H_2O.$$

Chloroplasts split water into hydrogen and oxygen, incorporating the electrons of hydrogen into sugar molecules. Photosynthesis is a redox process: H_2O is oxidized, and CO_2 is reduced. The **light reactions** in the thylakoid membranes split water, releasing O_2, producing ATP, and forming **NADPH**. The **Calvin cycle** in the **stroma** forms sugar from CO_2, using ATP for energy and NADPH for reducing power.

? *Compare and describe the roles of CO_2 and H_2O in respiration and photosynthesis.*

CONCEPT 10.2

The light reactions convert solar energy to the chemical energy of ATP and NADPH (pp. 189–197)

- Light is a form of electromagnetic energy. The colors we see as **visible light** include those **wavelengths** that drive photosynthesis. A pigment absorbs light of specific wavelengths; **chlorophyll *a*** is the main photosynthetic pigment in plants. Other accessory pigments absorb different wavelengths of light and pass the energy on to chlorophyll *a*.
- A pigment goes from a ground state to an excited state when a **photon** of light boosts one of the pigment's electrons to a higher-energy orbital. This excited state is unstable. Electrons from isolated pigments tend to fall back to the ground state, giving off heat and/or light.
- A **photosystem** is composed of a **reaction-center complex** surrounded by **light-harvesting complexes** that funnel the energy of photons to the reaction-center complex. When a special pair of reaction-center chlorophyll *a* molecules absorbs energy, one of its electrons is boosted to a higher energy level and transferred to the **primary electron acceptor**. **Photosystem II** contains P680 chlorophyll *a* molecules in the reaction-center complex; **photosystem I** contains P700 molecules.
- **Linear electron flow** during the light reactions uses both photosystems and produces NADPH, ATP, and oxygen:

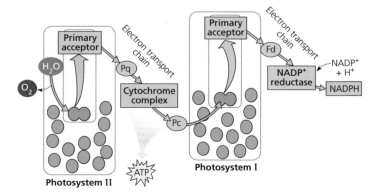

- **Cyclic electron flow** employs only photosystem I, producing ATP but no NADPH or O_2.
- During chemiosmosis in both mitochondria and chloroplasts, electron transport chains generate an H^+ gradient across a membrane. ATP synthase uses this proton-motive force to make ATP.

? *The absorption spectrum of chlorophyll *a* differs from the action spectrum of photosynthesis. Explain this observation.*

CONCEPT 10.3

The Calvin cycle uses the chemical energy of ATP and NADPH to reduce CO_2 to sugar (pp. 198–199)

- The Calvin cycle occurs in the stroma, using electrons from NADPH and energy from ATP. One molecule of **G3P** exits the cycle per three CO_2 molecules fixed and is converted to glucose and other organic molecules.

DRAW IT *On the diagram above, draw where ATP and NADPH are used and where rubisco functions. Describe these steps.*

CONCEPT 10.4

Alternative mechanisms of carbon fixation have evolved in hot, arid climates (pp. 199–202)

- On dry, hot days, **C_3 plants** close their stomata, conserving water. Oxygen from the light reactions builds up. In **photorespiration**, O_2 substitutes for CO_2 in the active site of rubisco. This process consumes organic fuel and releases CO_2 without producing ATP or carbohydrate. Photorespiration may be an evolutionary relic, and it may play a photoprotective role.
- **C_4 plants** minimize the cost of photorespiration by incorporating CO_2 into four-carbon compounds in mesophyll cells. These compounds are exported to **bundle-sheath cells**, where they release carbon dioxide for use in the Calvin cycle.
- **CAM plants** open their stomata at night, incorporating CO_2 into organic acids, which are stored in mesophyll cells. During the day, the stomata close, and the CO_2 is released from the organic acids for use in the Calvin cycle.
- Organic compounds produced by photosynthesis provide the energy and building material for ecosystems.

? *Why are C_4 and CAM photosynthesis more energetically expensive than C_3 photosynthesis? What climate conditions would favor C_4 and CAM plants?*

TEST YOUR UNDERSTANDING

LEVEL 1: KNOWLEDGE/COMPREHENSION

1. The light reactions of photosynthesis supply the Calvin cycle with
   a. light energy.
   b. CO_2 and ATP.
   c. H_2O and NADPH.
   d. ATP and NADPH.
   e. sugar and O_2.

2. Which of the following sequences correctly represents the flow of electrons during photosynthesis?
   a. NADPH → O_2 → CO_2
   b. H_2O → NADPH → Calvin cycle
   c. NADPH → chlorophyll → Calvin cycle
   d. H_2O → photosystem I → photosystem II
   e. NADPH → electron transport chain → O_2

3. How is photosynthesis similar in C_4 plants and CAM plants?
   a. In both cases, only photosystem I is used.
   b. Both types of plants make sugar without the Calvin cycle.
   c. In both cases, rubisco is not used to fix carbon initially.
   d. Both types of plants make most of their sugar in the dark.
   e. In both cases, thylakoids are not involved in photosynthesis.

4. Which of the following statements is a correct distinction between autotrophs and heterotrophs?
   a. Only heterotrophs require chemical compounds from the environment.
   b. Cellular respiration is unique to heterotrophs.
   c. Only heterotrophs have mitochondria.
   d. Autotrophs, but not heterotrophs, can nourish themselves beginning with CO_2 and other nutrients that are inorganic.
   e. Only heterotrophs require oxygen.

5. Which of the following does *not* occur during the Calvin cycle?
   a. carbon fixation
   b. oxidation of NADPH
   c. release of oxygen
   d. regeneration of the CO_2 acceptor
   e. consumption of ATP

LEVEL 2: APPLICATION/ANALYSIS

6. In mechanism, photophosphorylation is most similar to
   a. substrate-level phosphorylation in glycolysis.
   b. oxidative phosphorylation in cellular respiration.
   c. the Calvin cycle.
   d. carbon fixation.
   e. reduction of $NADP^+$.

7. Which process is most directly driven by light energy?
   a. creation of a pH gradient by pumping protons across the thylakoid membrane
   b. carbon fixation in the stroma
   c. reduction of $NADP^+$ molecules
   d. removal of electrons from chlorophyll molecules
   e. ATP synthesis

LEVEL 3: SYNTHESIS/EVALUATION

8. **EVOLUTION CONNECTION**
   Photorespiration can decrease soybeans' photosynthetic output by about 50%. Would you expect this figure to be higher or lower in wild relatives of soybeans? Why?

9. **SCIENTIFIC INQUIRY**
   MAKE CONNECTIONS **DRAW IT** The following diagram represents an experiment with isolated thylakoids. The thylakoids were first made acidic by soaking them in a solution at pH 4. After the thylakoid space reached pH 4, the thylakoids were transferred to a basic solution at pH 8. The thylakoids then made ATP in the dark. (See Concept 3.3, pp. 53–54, to review pH).

Draw an enlargement of part of the thylakoid membrane in the beaker with the solution at pH 8. Draw ATP synthase. Label the areas of high H^+ concentration and low H^+ concentration. Show the direction protons flow through the enzyme, and show the reaction where ATP is synthesized. Would ATP end up in the thylakoid or outside of it? Explain why the thylakoids in the experiment were able to make ATP in the dark.

10. **SCIENCE, TECHNOLOGY, AND SOCIETY**
    Scientific evidence indicates that the CO_2 added to the air by the burning of wood and fossil fuels is contributing to global warming, a rise in global temperature. Tropical rain forests are estimated to be responsible for approximately 20% of global photosynthesis, yet the consumption of large amounts of CO_2 by living trees is thought to make little or no *net* contribution to reduction of global warming. Why might this be? (*Hint*: What processes in both living and dead trees produce CO_2?)

11. **WRITE ABOUT A THEME**
    Energy Transfer Life is solar powered. Almost all the producers of the biosphere depend on energy from the sun to produce the organic molecules that supply the energy and carbon skeletons needed for life. In a short essay (100–150 words), describe how the process of photosynthesis in the chloroplasts of plants transforms the energy of sunlight into the chemical energy of sugar molecules.

For selected answers, see Appendix A.

 www.masteringbiology.com

1. MasteringBiology® Assignments
Experimental Inquiry Tutorial Which Wavelengths of Light Drive Photosynthesis?
BioFlix Tutorials Photosynthesis: Inputs, Outputs, and Chloroplast Structure • The Light Reactions • The Calvin Cycle
Tutorial Energy Flow in Plants—Concept Map
Activities Overview of Photosynthesis • The Sites of Photosynthesis • Chemiosmosis • Light Energy and Pigments • Photosynthesis • The Light Reactions • The Calvin Cycle • Photosynthesis in Dry Climates
Questions Student Misconceptions • Reading Quiz • Multiple Choice • End-of-Chapter

2. eText
Read your book online, search, take notes, highlight text, and more.

3. The Study Area
Practice Tests • Cumulative Test • **BioFlix** 3-D Animations • MP3 Tutor Sessions • Videos • Activities • Investigations • Lab Media • Audio Glossary • Word Study Tools • Art

12

The Cell Cycle

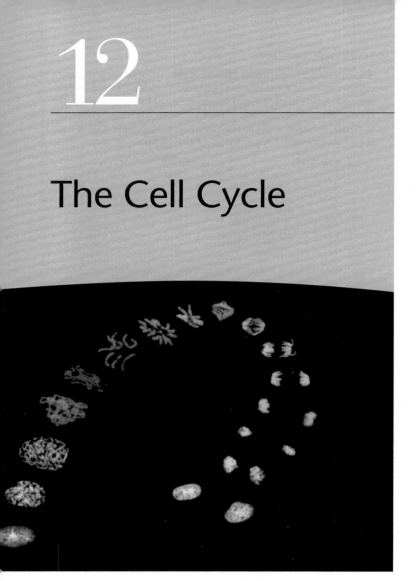

▲ **Figure 12.1 How do a cell's chromosomes change during cell division?**

KEY CONCEPTS

12.1 Most cell division results in genetically identical daughter cells

12.2 The mitotic phase alternates with interphase in the cell cycle

12.3 The eukaryotic cell cycle is regulated by a molecular control system

OVERVIEW

The Key Roles of Cell Division

The ability of organisms to produce more of their own kind is the one characteristic that best distinguishes living things from nonliving matter. This unique capacity to procreate, like all biological functions, has a cellular basis. Rudolf Virchow, a German physician, put it this way in 1855: "Where a cell exists, there must have been a preexisting cell, just as the animal arises only from an animal and the plant

only from a plant." He summarized this concept with the Latin axiom *"Omnis cellula e cellula,"* meaning "Every cell from a cell." The continuity of life is based on the reproduction of cells, or **cell division**. The series of fluorescence micrographs in **Figure 12.1** follows an animal cell's chromosomes, from lower left to lower right, as one cell divides into two.

Cell division plays several important roles in life. The division of one prokaryotic cell reproduces an entire organism. The same is true of a unicellular eukaryote (**Figure 12.2a**). Cell division also enables multicellular eukaryotes to develop from a single cell, like the fertilized egg that gave rise to the two-celled embryo in **Figure 12.2b**. And after such an organism is fully grown, cell division continues to function in renewal and repair, replacing cells that die from normal wear and tear or accidents. For example, dividing cells in your bone marrow continuously make new blood cells (**Figure 12.2c**).

The cell division process is an integral part of the **cell cycle**, the life of a cell from the time it is first formed from a dividing parent cell until its own division into two daughter cells. (Our use of the words *daughter* or *sister* in relation to cells is not meant to imply gender.) Passing identical genetic material to cellular offspring is a crucial function of cell division. In this chapter, you will learn how this process occurs. After studying the cellular mechanics of cell division in eukaryotes and bacteria, you will learn about the molecular control system that regulates progress through the eukaryotic cell cycle and what happens when the control system malfunctions. Because a breakdown in cell cycle control plays a major role in cancer development, this aspect of cell biology is an active area of research.

◄ **(a) Reproduction.** An amoeba, a single-celled eukaryote, is dividing into two cells. Each new cell will be an individual organism (LM).

► **(b) Growth and development.** This micrograph shows a sand dollar embryo shortly after the fertilized egg divided, forming two cells (LM).

◄ **(c) Tissue renewal.** These dividing bone marrow cells will give rise to new blood cells (LM).

▲ **Figure 12.2 The functions of cell division.**

CONCEPT 12.1

Most cell division results in genetically identical daughter cells

The reproduction of an assembly as complex as a cell cannot occur by a mere pinching in half; a cell is not like a soap bubble that simply enlarges and splits in two. In both prokaryotes and eukaryotes, most cell division involves the distribution of identical genetic material—DNA—to two daughter cells. (The exception is meiosis, the special type of eukaryotic cell division that can produce sperm and eggs.) What is most remarkable about cell division is the fidelity with which the DNA is passed along from one generation of cells to the next. A dividing cell duplicates its DNA, allocates the two copies to opposite ends of the cell, and only then splits into daughter cells. After we describe the distribution of DNA during cell division in animal and plant cells, we'll consider the process in other eukaryotes as well as in bacteria.

Cellular Organization of the Genetic Material

A cell's endowment of DNA, its genetic information, is called its **genome**. Although a prokaryotic genome is often a single DNA molecule, eukaryotic genomes usually consist of a number of DNA molecules. The overall length of DNA in a eukaryotic cell is enormous. A typical human cell, for example, has about 2 m of DNA—a length about 250,000 times greater than the cell's diameter. Yet before the cell can divide to form genetically identical daughter cells, all of this DNA must be copied, or replicated, and then the two copies must be separated so that each daughter cell ends up with a complete genome.

The replication and distribution of so much DNA is manageable because the DNA molecules are packaged into structures called **chromosomes**, so named because they take up certain dyes used in microscopy (from the Greek *chroma*, color, and *soma*, body) **(Figure 12.3)**. Each eukaryotic chromosome consists of one very long, linear DNA molecule associated with many proteins (see Figure 6.9). The DNA molecule carries several hundred to a few thousand genes, the units of information that specify an organism's inherited traits. The associated proteins maintain the structure of the chromosome and help control the activity of the genes. Together, the entire complex of DNA and proteins that is the building material of chromosomes is referred to as **chromatin**. As you will soon see, the chromatin of a chromosome varies in its degree of condensation during the process of cell division.

Every eukaryotic species has a characteristic number of chromosomes in each cell nucleus. For example, the nuclei of human **somatic cells** (all body cells except the reproductive cells) each contain 46 chromosomes, made up of two sets of 23, one set inherited from each parent. Reproductive cells, or **gametes**—sperm and eggs—have half as many chromosomes as somatic cells, or one set of 23 chromosomes in humans. The

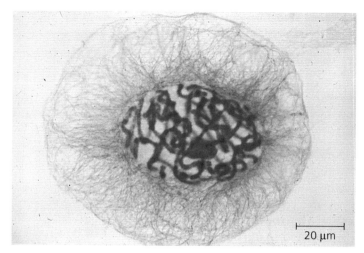

▲ **Figure 12.3 Eukaryotic chromosomes.** Chromosomes (stained purple) are visible within the nucleus of this cell from an African blood lily. The thinner red threads in the surrounding cytoplasm are the cytoskeleton. The cell is preparing to divide (LM).

number of chromosomes in somatic cells varies widely among species: 18 in cabbage plants, 48 in chimpanzees, 56 in elephants, 90 in hedgehogs, and 148 in one species of alga. We'll now consider how these chromosomes behave during cell division.

Distribution of Chromosomes During Eukaryotic Cell Division

When a cell is not dividing, and even as it replicates its DNA in preparation for cell division, each chromosome is in the form of a long, thin chromatin fiber. After DNA replication, however, the chromosomes condense as a part of cell division: Each chromatin fiber becomes densely coiled and folded, making the chromosomes much shorter and so thick that we can see them with a light microscope.

Each duplicated chromosome has two **sister chromatids**, which are joined copies of the original chromosome **(Figure 12.4)**. The two chromatids, each containing an identical DNA molecule, are initially attached all along their lengths by protein complexes called *cohesins*; this attachment is known as *sister chromatid cohesion*. Each sister chromatid has a **centromere**, a region containing specific DNA sequences

Sister chromatids

Centromere   0.5 μm

▲ **Figure 12.4 A highly condensed, duplicated human chromosome (SEM).**

DRAW IT *Circle one sister chromatid of the chromosome in this micrograph.*

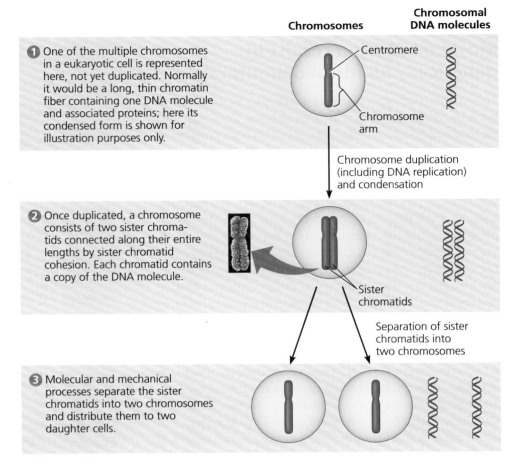

► Figure 12.5 **Chromosome duplication and distribution during cell division.**

? *How many chromatid arms does the chromosome in* ❷ *have?*

Chromosomes   **Chromosomal DNA molecules**

❶ One of the multiple chromosomes in a eukaryotic cell is represented here, not yet duplicated. Normally it would be a long, thin chromatin fiber containing one DNA molecule and associated proteins; here its condensed form is shown for illustration purposes only.

Centromere

Chromosome arm

Chromosome duplication (including DNA replication) and condensation

❷ Once duplicated, a chromosome consists of two sister chromatids connected along their entire lengths by sister chromatid cohesion. Each chromatid contains a copy of the DNA molecule.

Sister chromatids

Separation of sister chromatids into two chromosomes

❸ Molecular and mechanical processes separate the sister chromatids into two chromosomes and distribute them to two daughter cells.

where the chromatid is attached most closely to its sister chromatid. This attachment is mediated by proteins bound to the centromeric DNA sequences and gives the condensed, duplicated chromosome a narrow "waist." The part of a chromatid on either side of the centromere is referred to as an *arm* of the chromatid. (An uncondensed, unduplicated chromosome has a single centromere and two arms.)

Later in the cell division process, the two sister chromatids of each duplicated chromosome separate and move into two new nuclei, one forming at each end of the cell. Once the sister chromatids separate, they are no longer called sister chromatids but are considered individual chromosomes. Thus, each new nucleus receives a collection of chromosomes identical to that of the parent cell **(Figure 12.5)**. **Mitosis**, the division of the genetic material in the nucleus, is usually followed immediately by **cytokinesis**, the division of the cytoplasm. One cell has become two, each the genetic equivalent of the parent cell.

What happens to the chromosome number as we follow the human life cycle through the generations? You inherited 46 chromosomes, one set of 23 from each parent. They were combined in the nucleus of a single cell when a sperm from your father united with an egg from your mother, forming a fertilized egg, or zygote. Mitosis and cytokinesis produced the 200 trillion somatic cells that now make up your body, and the same processes continue to generate new cells to replace dead and damaged ones. In contrast, you produce gametes—eggs or sperm—by a variation of cell division called *meiosis*, which yields nonidentical daughter cells that have only one set of chromosomes, half as many chromosomes as the parent cell. Meiosis in humans occurs only in the gonads (ovaries or testes). In each generation, meiosis reduces the chromosome number from 46 (two sets of chromosomes) to 23 (one set). Fertilization fuses two gametes together and returns the chromosome number to 46, and mitosis conserves that number in every somatic cell nucleus of the new individual. In Chapter 13, we will examine the role of meiosis in reproduction and inheritance in more detail. In the remainder of this chapter, we focus on mitosis and the rest of the cell cycle in eukaryotes.

CONCEPT CHECK 12.1

1. How many chromatids are in a duplicated chromosome?
2. **WHAT IF?** A chicken has 78 chromosomes in its somatic cells. How many chromosomes did the chicken inherit from each parent? How many chromosomes are in each of the chicken's gametes? How many chromosomes will be in each somatic cell of the chicken's offspring?

For suggested answers, see Appendix A.

CONCEPT 12.2

The mitotic phase alternates with interphase in the cell cycle

In 1882, a German anatomist named Walther Flemming developed dyes that allowed him to observe, for the first time, the behavior of chromosomes during mitosis and cytokinesis. (In fact, Flemming coined the terms *mitosis* and *chromatin*.) During the period between one cell division and the next, it appeared to Flemming that the cell was simply growing larger. But we now know that many critical events occur during this stage in the life of a cell.

Phases of the Cell Cycle

Mitosis is just one part of the cell cycle (Figure 12.6). In fact, the **mitotic (M) phase**, which includes both mitosis and cytokinesis, is usually the shortest part of the cell cycle. Mitotic cell division alternates with a much longer stage called **interphase**, which often accounts for about 90% of the cycle. During interphase, a cell that is about to divide grows and copies its chromosomes in preparation for cell division. Interphase can be divided into subphases: the G_1 **phase** ("first gap"), the **S phase** ("synthesis"), and the G_2 **phase** ("second gap"). During all three subphases, a cell that will eventually divide grows by producing proteins and cytoplasmic organelles such as mitochondria and endoplasmic reticulum. However, chromosomes are duplicated only during the S phase. (We will discuss synthesis of DNA in Chapter 16.) Thus, a cell grows (G_1), continues to grow as it copies its chromosomes (S), grows more as it completes preparations for cell division (G_2), and divides (M). The daughter cells may then repeat the cycle.

A particular human cell might undergo one division in 24 hours. Of this time, the M phase would occupy less than 1 hour, while the S phase might occupy about 10–12 hours, or about half the cycle. The rest of the time would be apportioned between the G_1 and G_2 phases. The G_2 phase usually takes 4–6 hours; in our example, G_1 would occupy about 5–6 hours. G_1 is the most variable in length in different types of cells. Some cells in a multicellular organism divide very infrequently or not at all. These cells spend their time in G_1 (or a related phase called G_0) doing their job in the organism—a nerve cell carries impulses, for example.

Mitosis is conventionally broken down into five stages: **prophase**, **prometaphase**, **metaphase**, **anaphase**, and

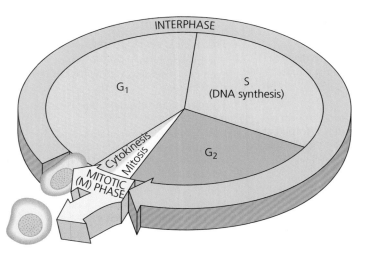

▲ **Figure 12.6 The cell cycle.** In a dividing cell, the mitotic (M) phase alternates with interphase, a growth period. The first part of interphase (G_1) is followed by the S phase, when the chromosomes duplicate; G_2 is the last part of interphase. In the M phase, mitosis distributes the daughter chromosomes to daughter nuclei, and cytokinesis divides the cytoplasm, producing two daughter cells. The relative durations of G_1, S, and G_2 may vary.

telophase. Overlapping with the latter stages of mitosis, cytokinesis completes the mitotic phase. **Figure 12.7**, on the next two pages, describes these stages in an animal cell. Study this figure thoroughly before progressing to the next two sections, which examine mitosis and cytokinesis more closely.

The Mitotic Spindle: *A Closer Look*

Many of the events of mitosis depend on the **mitotic spindle**, which begins to form in the cytoplasm during prophase. This structure consists of fibers made of microtubules and associated proteins. While the mitotic spindle assembles, the other microtubules of the cytoskeleton partially disassemble, providing the material used to construct the spindle. The spindle microtubules elongate (polymerize) by incorporating more subunits of the protein tubulin (see Table 6.1) and shorten (depolymerize) by losing subunits.

In animal cells, the assembly of spindle microtubules starts at the **centrosome**, a subcellular region containing material that functions throughout the cell cycle to organize the cell's microtubules. (It is also called the *microtubule-organizing center*.) A pair of centrioles is located at the center of the centrosome, but they are not essential for cell division: If the centrioles are destroyed with a laser microbeam, a spindle nevertheless forms during mitosis. In fact, centrioles are not even present in plant cells, which do form mitotic spindles.

During interphase in animal cells, the single centrosome duplicates, forming two centrosomes, which remain together near the nucleus. The two centrosomes move apart during prophase and prometaphase of mitosis as spindle microtubules grow out from them. By the end of prometaphase, the two centrosomes, one at each pole of the spindle, are at opposite ends of the cell. An **aster**, a radial array of short microtubules, extends from each centrosome. The spindle includes the centrosomes, the spindle microtubules, and the asters.

Each of the two sister chromatids of a duplicated chromosome has a **kinetochore**, a structure of proteins associated with specific sections of chromosomal DNA at each centromere. The chromosome's two kinetochores face in opposite directions. During prometaphase, some of the spindle microtubules attach to the kinetochores; these are called kinetochore microtubules. (The number of microtubules attached to a kinetochore varies among species, from one microtubule in yeast cells to 40 or so in some mammalian cells.) When one of a chromosome's kinetochores is "captured" by microtubules, the chromosome begins to move toward the pole from which those microtubules extend. However, this movement is checked as soon as microtubules from the opposite pole attach to the other kinetochore. What happens next is like a tug-of-war that ends in a draw. The chromosome moves first in one direction, then the other, back and forth, finally settling midway between the two ends of the cell. At metaphase, the centromeres of all the duplicated chromosomes are on a plane midway between the spindle's

Exploring Mitosis in an Animal Cell

G₂ of Interphase

Centrosomes (with centriole pairs)

Chromatin (duplicated)

Nucleolus

Nuclear envelope

Plasma membrane

Prophase

Early mitotic spindle

Aster

Centromere

Chromosome, consisting of two sister chromatids

Prometaphase

Fragments of nuclear envelope

Nonkinetochore microtubules

Kinetochore

Kinetochore microtubule

G₂ of Interphase

- A nuclear envelope encloses the nucleus.
- The nucleus contains one or more nucleoli (singular, *nucleolus*).
- Two centrosomes have formed by duplication of a single centrosome. Centrosomes are regions in animal cells that organize the microtubules of the spindle. Each centrosome contains two centrioles.
- Chromosomes, duplicated during S phase, cannot be seen individually because they have not yet condensed.

The light micrographs show dividing lung cells from a newt, which has 22 chromosomes in its somatic cells. Chromosomes appear blue, microtubules green, and intermediate filaments red. For simplicity, the drawings show only 6 chromosomes.

Prophase

- The chromatin fibers become more tightly coiled, condensing into discrete chromosomes observable with a light microscope.
- The nucleoli disappear.
- Each duplicated chromosome appears as two identical sister chromatids joined at their centromeres and, in some species, all along their arms by cohesins (sister chromatid cohesion).
- The mitotic spindle (named for its shape) begins to form. It is composed of the centrosomes and the microtubules that extend from them. The radial arrays of shorter microtubules that extend from the centrosomes are called asters ("stars").
- The centrosomes move away from each other, propelled partly by the lengthening microtubules between them.

Prometaphase

- The nuclear envelope fragments.
- The microtubules extending from each centrosome can now invade the nuclear area.
- The chromosomes have become even more condensed.
- Each of the two chromatids of each chromosome now has a kinetochore, a specialized protein structure at the centromere.
- Some of the microtubules attach to the kinetochores, becoming "kinetochore microtubules," which jerk the chromosomes back and forth.
- Nonkinetochore microtubules interact with those from the opposite pole of the spindle.

? *How many molecules of DNA are in the prometaphase drawing? How many molecules per chromosome? How many double helices are there per chromosome? Per chromatid?*

10 μm

Metaphase

Anaphase

Telophase and Cytokinesis

Metaphase plate

Spindle

Centrosome at one spindle pole

Daughter chromosomes

Cleavage furrow

Nucleolus forming

Nuclear envelope forming

Metaphase

- The centrosomes are now at opposite poles of the cell.
- The chromosomes convene at the *metaphase plate*, a plane that is equidistant between the spindle's two poles. The chromosomes' centromeres lie at the metaphase plate.
- For each chromosome, the kinetochores of the sister chromatids are attached to kinetochore microtubules coming from opposite poles.

Anaphase

- Anaphase is the shortest stage of mitosis, often lasting only a few minutes.
- Anaphase begins when the cohesin proteins are cleaved. This allows the two sister chromatids of each pair to part suddenly. Each chromatid thus becomes a full-fledged chromosome.
- The two liberated daughter chromosomes begin moving toward opposite ends of the cell as their kinetochore microtubules shorten. Because these microtubules are attached at the centromere region, the chromosomes move centromere first (at about 1 μm/min).
- The cell elongates as the nonkinetochore microtubules lengthen.
- By the end of anaphase, the two ends of the cell have equivalent—and complete—collections of chromosomes.

Telophase

- Two daughter nuclei form in the cell. Nuclear envelopes arise from the fragments of the parent cell's nuclear envelope and other portions of the endomembrane system.
- Nucleoli reappear.
- The chromosomes become less condensed.
- Any remaining spindle microtubules are depolymerized.
- Mitosis, the division of one nucleus into two genetically identical nuclei, is now complete.

Cytokinesis

- The division of the cytoplasm is usually well under way by late telophase, so the two daughter cells appear shortly after the end of mitosis.
- In animal cells, cytokinesis involves the formation of a cleavage furrow, which pinches the cell in two.

ANIMATION **BioFlix** Visit the Study Area at **www.masteringbiology.com** for the BioFlix® 3-D Animation on Mitosis.

two poles. This plane is called the **metaphase plate**, which is an imaginary rather than an actual cellular structure (**Figure 12.8**). Meanwhile, microtubules that do not attach to kinetochores have been elongating, and by metaphase they overlap and interact with other nonkinetochore microtubules from the opposite pole of the spindle. (These are sometimes called "polar" microtubules.) By metaphase, the microtubules of the asters have also grown and are in contact with the plasma membrane. The spindle is now complete.

▲ **Figure 12.8 The mitotic spindle at metaphase.** The kinetochores of each chromosome's two sister chromatids face in opposite directions. Here, each kinetochore is attached to a *cluster* of kinetochore microtubules extending from the nearest centrosome. Nonkinetochore microtubules overlap at the metaphase plate (TEMs).

DRAW IT *On the lower micrograph, draw a line indicating the position of the metaphase plate. Circle an aster. Draw arrows indicating the directions of chromosome movement once anaphase begins.*

The structure of the completed spindle correlates well with its function during anaphase. Anaphase commences suddenly when the cohesins holding together the sister chromatids of each chromosome are cleaved by an enzyme called *separase*. Once the chromatids become separate, full-fledged chromosomes, they move toward opposite ends of the cell.

How do the kinetochore microtubules function in this poleward movement of chromosomes? Apparently, two mechanisms are in play, both involving motor proteins. (To review how motor proteins move an object along a microtubule, see Figure 6.21.) A clever experiment carried out in 1987 suggested that motor proteins on the kinetochores "walk" the chromosomes along the microtubules, which depolymerize at their kinetochore ends after the motor proteins have passed (**Figure 12.9**). (This is referred to as the "Pacman" mechanism because of its resemblance to the arcade game character that moves by eating all the dots in its path.) However, other researchers, working with different cell types or cells from other species, have shown that chromosomes are "reeled in" by motor proteins at the spindle poles and that the microtubules depolymerize after they pass by these motor proteins. The general consensus now is that both mechanisms are used and that their relative contributions vary among cell types.

In a dividing animal cell, the nonkinetochore microtubules are responsible for elongating the whole cell during anaphase. Nonkinetochore microtubules from opposite poles overlap each other extensively during metaphase (see Figure 12.8). During anaphase, the region of overlap is reduced as motor proteins attached to the microtubules walk them away from one another, using energy from ATP. As the microtubules push apart from each other, their spindle poles are pushed apart, elongating the cell. At the same time, the microtubules lengthen somewhat by the addition of tubulin subunits to their overlapping ends. As a result, the microtubules continue to overlap.

At the end of anaphase, duplicate groups of chromosomes have arrived at opposite ends of the elongated parent cell. Nuclei re-form during telophase. Cytokinesis generally begins during anaphase or telophase, and the spindle eventually disassembles by depolymerization of microtubules.

Cytokinesis: *A Closer Look*

In animal cells, cytokinesis occurs by a process known as **cleavage**. The first sign of cleavage is the appearance of a **cleavage furrow**, a shallow groove in the cell surface near the old metaphase plate (**Figure 12.10a**). On the cytoplasmic side of the furrow is a contractile ring of actin microfilaments associated with molecules of the protein myosin. The actin microfilaments interact with the myosin molecules, causing the ring to contract. The contraction of the dividing cell's ring of microfilaments is like the pulling of a drawstring. The cleavage furrow deepens until the parent cell is pinched in two, producing two completely separated cells, each with its own nucleus and share of cytosol, organelles, and other subcellular structures.

▼ Figure 12.9 INQUIRY

At which end do kinetochore microtubules shorten during anaphase?

EXPERIMENT Gary Borisy and colleagues at the University of Wisconsin wanted to determine whether kinetochore microtubules depolymerize at the kinetochore end or the pole end as chromosomes move toward the poles during mitosis. First they labeled the microtubules of a pig kidney cell in early anaphase with a yellow fluorescent dye.

Then they marked a region of the kinetochore microtubules between one spindle pole and the chromosomes by using a laser to eliminate the fluorescence from that region, while leaving the microtubules intact (see below). As anaphase proceeded, they monitored the changes in microtubule length on either side of the mark.

RESULTS As the chromosomes moved poleward, the microtubule segments on the kinetochore side of the mark shortened, while those on the spindle pole side stayed the same length.

CONCLUSION During anaphase in this cell type, chromosome movement is correlated with kinetochore microtubules shortening at their kinetochore ends and not at their spindle pole ends. This experiment supports the hypothesis that during anaphase, a chromosome is walked along a microtubule as the microtubule depolymerizes at its kinetochore end, releasing tubulin subunits.

SOURCE G. J. Gorbsky, P. J. Sammak, and G. G. Borisy, Chromosomes move poleward in anaphase along stationary microtubules that coordinately disassemble from their kinetochore ends, *Journal of Cell Biology* 104:9–18 (1987).

WHAT IF? If this experiment had been done on a cell type in which "reeling in" at the poles was the main cause of chromosome movement, how would the mark have moved relative to the poles? How would the microtubule lengths have changed?

▼ Figure 12.10 Cytokinesis in animal and plant cells.

(a) Cleavage of an animal cell (SEM)

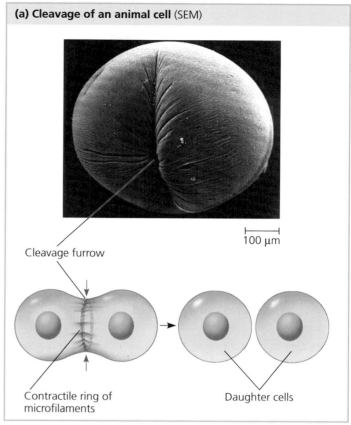

(b) Cell plate formation in a plant cell (TEM)

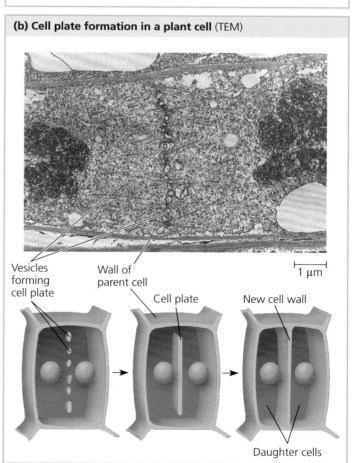

Nucleus Nucleolus Chromatin condensing Chromosomes Cell plate 10 µm

❶ Prophase. The chromatin is condensing and the nucleolus is beginning to disappear. Although not yet visible in the micrograph, the mitotic spindle is starting to form.

❷ Prometaphase. Discrete chromosomes are now visible; each consists of two aligned, identical sister chromatids. Later in prometaphase, the nuclear envelope will fragment.

❸ Metaphase. The spindle is complete, and the chromosomes, attached to microtubules at their kinetochores, are all at the metaphase plate.

❹ Anaphase. The chromatids of each chromosome have separated, and the daughter chromosomes are moving to the ends of the cell as their kinetochore microtubules shorten.

❺ Telophase. Daughter nuclei are forming. Meanwhile, cytokinesis has started: The cell plate, which will divide the cytoplasm in two, is growing toward the perimeter of the parent cell.

▲ **Figure 12.11 Mitosis in a plant cell.** These light micrographs show mitosis in cells of an onion root.

Cytokinesis in plant cells, which have cell walls, is markedly different. There is no cleavage furrow. Instead, during telophase, vesicles derived from the Golgi apparatus move along microtubules to the middle of the cell, where they coalesce, producing a **cell plate (Figure 12.10b)**. Cell wall materials carried in the vesicles collect in the cell plate as it grows. The cell plate enlarges until its surrounding membrane fuses with the plasma membrane along the perimeter of the cell. Two daughter cells result, each with its own plasma membrane. Meanwhile, a new cell wall arising from the contents of the cell plate has formed between the daughter cells.

Figure 12.11 is a series of micrographs of a dividing plant cell. Examining this figure will help you review mitosis and cytokinesis.

Binary Fission in Bacteria

Prokaryotes (bacteria and archaea) can undergo a type of reproduction in which the cell grows to roughly double its size and then divides to form two cells. The term **binary fission**, meaning "division in half," refers to this process and to the asexual reproduction of single-celled eukaryotes, such as the amoeba in Figure 12.2a. However, the process in eukaryotes involves mitosis, while that in prokaryotes does not.

In bacteria, most genes are carried on a single *bacterial chromosome* that consists of a circular DNA molecule and associated proteins. Although bacteria are smaller and simpler than eukaryotic cells, the challenge of replicating their genomes in an orderly fashion and distributing the copies equally to two daughter cells is still formidable. The chromosome of the bacterium *Escherichia coli*, for example, when it is fully stretched out, is about 500 times as long as the cell. For

such a long chromosome to fit within the cell requires that it be highly coiled and folded.

In *E. coli*, the process of cell division is initiated when the DNA of the bacterial chromosome begins to replicate at a specific place on the chromosome called the **origin of replication**, producing two origins. As the chromosome continues to replicate, one origin moves rapidly toward the opposite end of the cell **(Figure 12.12)**. While the chromosome is replicating, the cell elongates. When replication is complete and the bacterium has reached about twice its initial size, its plasma membrane pinches inward, dividing the parent *E. coli* cell into two daughter cells. In this way, each cell inherits a complete genome.

Using the techniques of modern DNA technology to tag the origins of replication with molecules that glow green in fluorescence microscopy (see Figure 6.3), researchers have directly observed the movement of bacterial chromosomes. This movement is reminiscent of the poleward movements of the centromere regions of eukaryotic chromosomes during anaphase of mitosis, but bacteria don't have visible mitotic spindles or even microtubules. In most bacterial species studied, the two origins of replication end up at opposite ends of the cell or in some other very specific location, possibly anchored there by one or more proteins. How bacterial chromosomes move and how their specific location is established and maintained are still not fully understood. However, several proteins have been identified that play important roles: One resembling eukaryotic actin apparently functions in bacterial chromosome movement during cell division, and another that is related to tubulin seems to help pinch the plasma membrane inward, separating the two bacterial daughter cells.

UNIVERSITY OF ALBERTA FACULTY BIO

Tracy Raivio BSc in Genetics (University of Alberta); PhD in Microbiology and Infectious Diseases (University of Calgary)

Current Position: Associate Professor, Department of Biological Sciences

I am involved in teaching Genetics 270 (Foundations of Molecular Genetics) and Genetics 304 (Gene Expression and its Regulation).

I am interested in understanding how bacteria sense and respond to changes in their environment. This is particularly important for single-celled microbes, as they may experience many dramatically different locales during their lifetimes and must adapt rapidly to avoid death. My research group uses genetic, molecular biological, biochemical, and genomic techniques, together with animal models to identify, characterize, and determine the cellular role of bacterial signaling and adaptive proteins. We are particularly interested in bacterial two-component regulatory proteins, which are used by almost all microbes to sense discrete environmental changes and trigger appropriate physiological changes, but are absent from animals. These regulators are of particular interest because of their broad distribution in microbes and the potential to develop novel antimicrobial compounds that target them.

My research group focuses on one model stress response in the Gram-negative bacterium *Escherichia coli*, called the Cpx envelope stress response. This signaling pathway utilizes a sensor protein to detect threats to the bacterial envelope and then conveys this information to a regulatory protein that causes changes in gene expression to mediate adaptation. Most recently, we have shown that induction of this stress response leads to the inhibition of envelope localized virulence determinants that are necessary to cause disease. Our work has further shown that Cpx-dependent adaptations affect many cellular processes, including cell wall construction, translation, and other regulatory pathways. We are currently working towards understanding how these processes lead to adaptation to envelope stress and what the molecular mechanism is for detecting envelope stress signals. This work suggests the exciting possibility that the Cpx response could be targeted for development of antimicrobial treatments for human disease.

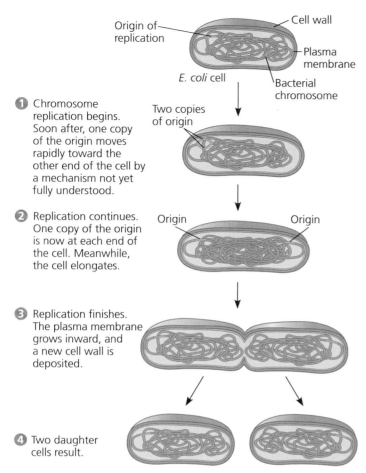

① Chromosome replication begins. Soon after, one copy of the origin moves rapidly toward the other end of the cell by a mechanism not yet fully understood.

② Replication continues. One copy of the origin is now at each end of the cell. Meanwhile, the cell elongates.

③ Replication finishes. The plasma membrane grows inward, and a new cell wall is deposited.

④ Two daughter cells result.

▲ **Figure 12.12 Bacterial cell division by binary fission.** The bacterium *E. coli*, shown here, has a single, circular chromosome.

The Evolution of Mitosis

EVOLUTION Given that prokaryotes preceded eukaryotes on Earth by more than a billion years, we might hypothesize that mitosis evolved from simpler prokaryotic mechanisms of cell reproduction. The fact that some of the proteins involved in bacterial binary fission are related to eukaryotic proteins that function in mitosis supports that hypothesis.

As eukaryotes evolved, along with their larger genomes and nuclear envelopes, the ancestral process of binary fission, seen today in bacteria, somehow gave rise to mitosis. **Figure 12.13** shows some variations on cell division in different groups of organisms. These processes may be similar to mechanisms used by ancestral species and thus may resemble steps in the evolution of mitosis from a binary fission-like process presumably carried out by very early bacteria. Possible intermediate stages are suggested by two unusual types of nuclear division found today in certain unicellular eukaryotes—dinoflagellates, diatoms, and some yeasts. These two modes of nuclear division are thought to be cases where ancestral mechanisms have remained relatively unchanged over evolutionary time. In both types, the nuclear envelope remains intact, in contrast to what happens in most eukaryotic cells.

(a) Bacteria. During binary fission in bacteria, the origins of the daughter chromosomes move to opposite ends of the cell. The mechanism is not fully understood, but proteins may anchor the daughter chromosomes to specific sites on the plasma membrane.

(b) Dinoflagellates. In unicellular protists called dinoflagellates, the chromosomes attach to the nuclear envelope, which remains intact during cell division. Microtubules pass through the nucleus inside cytoplasmic tunnels, reinforcing the spatial orientation of the nucleus, which then divides in a process reminiscent of bacterial binary fission.

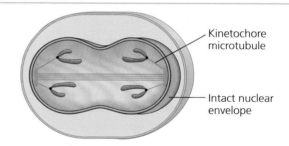

(c) Diatoms and some yeasts. In two other groups of unicellular protists, diatoms and some yeasts, the nuclear envelope also remains intact during cell division. In these organisms, the microtubules form a spindle *within* the nucleus. Microtubules separate the chromosomes, and the nucleus splits into two daughter nuclei.

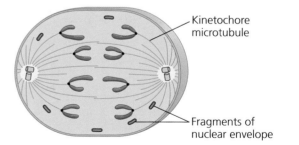

(d) Most eukaryotes. In most other eukaryotes, including plants and animals, the spindle forms outside the nucleus, and the nuclear envelope breaks down during mitosis. Microtubules separate the chromosomes, and two nuclear envelopes then form.

▲ **Figure 12.13 Mechanisms of cell division in several groups of organisms.** Some unicellular eukaryotes existing today have mechanisms of cell division that may resemble intermediate steps in the evolution of mitosis. Except for (a), these schematic diagrams do not show cell walls.

1. How many chromosomes are shown in the diagram in Figure 12.8? Are they duplicated? How many chromatids are shown?
2. Compare cytokinesis in animal cells and plant cells.
3. What is the function of nonkinetochore microtubules?
4. Compare the roles of tubulin and actin during eukaryotic cell division with the roles of tubulin-like and actin-like proteins during bacterial binary fission.
5. **MAKE CONNECTIONS** What other functions do actin and tubulin carry out? Name the proteins they interact with to do so. (Review Figures 6.21a and 6.27a.)
6. **WHAT IF?** During which stages of the cell cycle does a chromosome consist of two identical chromatids?

For suggested answers, see Appendix A.

CONCEPT 12.3

The eukaryotic cell cycle is regulated by a molecular control system

The timing and rate of cell division in different parts of a plant or animal are crucial to normal growth, development, and maintenance. The frequency of cell division varies with the type of cell. For example, human skin cells divide frequently throughout life, whereas liver cells maintain the ability to divide but keep it in reserve until an appropriate need arises— say, to repair a wound. Some of the most specialized cells, such as fully formed nerve cells and muscle cells, do not divide at all in a mature human. These cell cycle differences result from regulation at the molecular level. The mechanisms of this regulation are of intense interest, not only for understanding the life cycles of normal cells but also for understanding how cancer cells manage to escape the usual controls.

Evidence for Cytoplasmic Signals

What controls the cell cycle? One reasonable hypothesis might be that each event in the cell cycle merely leads to the next, as in a simple metabolic pathway. According to this hypothesis, the replication of chromosomes in the S phase, for example, might cause cell growth during the G_2 phase, which might in turn lead inevitably to the onset of mitosis. However, this hypothesis, which proposes a pathway that is not subject to either internal or external regulation, turns out to be incorrect.

In the early 1970s, a variety of experiments led to an alternative hypothesis: that the cell cycle is driven by specific signaling molecules present in the cytoplasm. Some of the first strong evidence for this hypothesis came from experiments with mammalian cells grown in culture. In these experiments, two cells in different phases of the cell cycle were fused to form

▼ Figure 12.14 INQUIRY

Do molecular signals in the cytoplasm regulate the cell cycle?

EXPERIMENT Researchers at the University of Colorado wondered whether a cell's progression through the cell cycle is controlled by cytoplasmic molecules. To investigate this, they selected cultured mammalian cells that were at different phases of the cell cycle and induced them to fuse. Two such experiments are shown here.

CONCLUSION The results of fusing a G_1 cell with a cell in the S or M phase of the cell cycle suggest that molecules present in the cytoplasm during the S or M phase control the progression to those phases.

SOURCE R. T. Johnson and P. N. Rao, Mammalian cell fusion: Induction of premature chromosome condensation in interphase nuclei, *Nature* 226:717–722 (1970).

WHAT IF? If the progression of phases did not depend on cytoplasmic molecules and each phase began when the previous one was complete, how would the results have differed?

a single cell with two nuclei. If one of the original cells was in the S phase and the other was in G_1, the G_1 nucleus immediately entered the S phase, as though stimulated by signaling molecules present in the cytoplasm of the first cell. Similarly, if a cell undergoing mitosis (M phase) was fused with another cell in any stage of its cell cycle, even G_1, the second nucleus immediately entered mitosis, with condensation of the chromatin and formation of a mitotic spindle (**Figure 12.14**).

The Cell Cycle Control System

The experiment shown in Figure 12.14 and other experiments on animal cells and yeasts demonstrated that the sequential events of the cell cycle are directed by a distinct **cell cycle control system**, a cyclically operating set of molecules in the cell that both triggers and coordinates key events

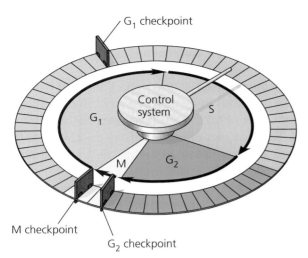

G₁ checkpoint

Control system

S

G₁

G₂

M

M checkpoint

G₂ checkpoint

▲ **Figure 12.15 Mechanical analogy for the cell cycle control system.** In this diagram of the cell cycle, the flat "stepping stones" around the perimeter represent sequential events. Like the control device of an automatic washer, the cell cycle control system proceeds on its own, driven by a built-in clock. However, the system is subject to internal and external regulation at various checkpoints, of which three are shown (red).

G₁ checkpoint

G₀

G₁

G₁

(a) If a cell receives a go-ahead signal at the G₁ checkpoint, the cell continues on in the cell cycle.

(b) If a cell does not receive a go-ahead signal at the G₁ checkpoint, the cell exits the cell cycle and goes into G₀, a nondividing state.

▲ **Figure 12.16 The G₁ checkpoint.**

WHAT IF? *What might be the result if the cell ignored the checkpoint and progressed through the cell cycle?*

in the cell cycle. The cell cycle control system has been compared to the control device of an automatic washing machine **(Figure 12.15)**. Like the washer's timing device, the cell cycle control system proceeds on its own, according to a built-in clock. However, just as a washer's cycle is subject to both internal control (such as the sensor that detects when the tub is filled with water) and external adjustment (such as activation of the start mechanism), the cell cycle is regulated at certain checkpoints by both internal and external signals.

A **checkpoint** in the cell cycle is a control point where stop and go-ahead signals can regulate the cycle. Animal cells generally have built-in stop signals that halt the cell cycle at checkpoints until overridden by go-ahead signals. Many signals registered at checkpoints come from cellular surveillance mechanisms inside the cell. These signals report whether crucial cellular processes that should have occurred by that point have in fact been completed correctly and thus whether or not the cell cycle should proceed. Checkpoints also register signals from outside the cell, as we will discuss later. Three major checkpoints are found in the G₁, G₂, and M phases (see Figure 12.15).

For many cells, the G₁ checkpoint—dubbed the "restriction point" in mammalian cells—seems to be the most important. If a cell receives a go-ahead signal at the G₁ checkpoint, it will usually complete the G₁, S, G₂, and M phases and divide. If it does not receive a go-ahead signal at that point, it will exit the cycle, switching into a nondividing state called the **G₀ phase** **(Figure 12.16)**. Most cells of the human body are actually in the G₀ phase. As mentioned earlier, mature nerve cells and muscle cells never divide. Other cells, such as liver cells, can be "called back" from the G₀ phase to the cell cycle by external cues, such as growth factors released during injury.

To understand how cell cycle checkpoints work, we first need to see what kinds of molecules make up the cell cycle control system (the molecular basis for the cell cycle clock) and how a cell progresses through the cycle. Then we will consider the internal and external checkpoint signals that can make the clock pause or continue.

The Cell Cycle Clock: Cyclins and Cyclin-Dependent Kinases

Rhythmic fluctuations in the abundance and activity of cell cycle control molecules pace the sequential events of the cell cycle. These regulatory molecules are mainly proteins of two types: protein kinases and cyclins. Protein kinases are enzymes that activate or inactivate other proteins by phosphorylating them. Particular protein kinases give the go-ahead signals at the G₁ and G₂ checkpoints.

Many of the kinases that drive the cell cycle are actually present at a constant concentration in the growing cell, but much of the time they are in an inactive form. To be active, such a kinase must be attached to a **cyclin**, a protein that gets its name from its cyclically fluctuating concentration in the cell. Because of this requirement, these kinases are called **cyclin-dependent kinases**, or **Cdks**. The activity of a Cdk rises and falls with changes in the concentration of its cyclin partner. **Figure 12.17a**, on the next page, shows the fluctuating activity of **MPF**, the cyclin-Cdk complex that was discovered first (in frog eggs). Note that the peaks of MPF activity correspond to the peaks of cyclin concentration. The cyclin level rises during the S and G₂ phases and then falls abruptly during M phase.

The initials MPF stand for "maturation-promoting factor," but we can think of MPF as "M-phase-promoting factor" because it triggers the cell's passage past the G₂ checkpoint into

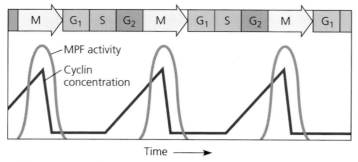

(a) **Fluctuation of MPF activity and cyclin concentration during the cell cycle**

❶ Synthesis of cyclin begins in late S phase and continues through G₂. Because cyclin is protected from degradation during this stage, it accumulates.

❺ During G₁, the degradation of cyclin continues, and the Cdk component of MPF is recycled.

❹ During anaphase, the cyclin component of MPF is degraded, terminating the M phase. The cell enters the G₁ phase.

❸ MPF promotes mitosis by phosphorylating various proteins. MPF's activity peaks during metaphase.

❷ Cyclin combines with Cdk, producing MPF. When enough MPF molecules accumulate, the cell passes the G₂ checkpoint and begins mitosis.

(b) **Molecular mechanisms that help regulate the cell cycle**

▲ **Figure 12.17 Molecular control of the cell cycle at the G₂ checkpoint.** The steps of the cell cycle are timed by rhythmic fluctuations in the activity of cyclin-dependent kinases (Cdks). Here we focus on a cyclin-Cdk complex in animal cells called MPF, which acts at the G₂ checkpoint as a go-ahead signal, triggering the events of mitosis.

? *Explain how the events in the diagram in (b) are related to the "Time" axis of the graph in (a).*

M phase (**Figure 12.17b**). When cyclins that accumulate during G₂ associate with Cdk molecules, the resulting MPF complex phosphorylates a variety of proteins, initiating mitosis. MPF acts both directly as a kinase and indirectly by activating other kinases. For example, MPF causes phosphorylation of various proteins of the nuclear lamina (see Figure 6.9), which promotes

fragmentation of the nuclear envelope during prometaphase of mitosis. There is also evidence that MPF contributes to molecular events required for chromosome condensation and spindle formation during prophase.

During anaphase, MPF helps switch itself off by initiating a process that leads to the destruction of its own cyclin. The noncyclin part of MPF, the Cdk, persists in the cell, inactive until it becomes part of MPF again by associating with new cyclin molecules synthesized during the S and G₂ phases of the next round of the cycle.

Cell behavior at the G₁ checkpoint is also regulated by the activity of cyclin-Cdk protein complexes. Animal cells appear to have at least three Cdk proteins and several different cyclins that operate at this checkpoint. The fluctuating activities of different cyclin-Cdk complexes are of major importance in controlling all the stages of the cell cycle.

Stop and Go Signs: Internal and External Signals at the Checkpoints

Research scientists are currently working out the pathways that link signals originating inside and outside the cell with the responses by cyclin-dependent kinases and other proteins. An example of an internal signal occurs at the third important checkpoint, the M phase checkpoint. Anaphase, the separation of sister chromatids, does not begin until all the chromosomes are properly attached to the spindle at the metaphase plate. Researchers have learned that as long as some kinetochores are unattached to spindle microtubules, the sister chromatids remain together, delaying anaphase. Only when the kinetochores of all the chromosomes are properly attached to the spindle does the appropriate regulatory protein complex become activated. (In this case, the regulatory molecule is not a cyclin-Cdk complex but, instead, a different complex made up of several proteins.) Once activated, the complex sets off a chain of molecular events that activates the enzyme separase, which cleaves the cohesins, allowing the sister chromatids to separate. This mechanism ensures that daughter cells do not end up with missing or extra chromosomes.

Studies using animal cells in culture have led to the identification of many external factors, both chemical and physical, that can influence cell division. For example, cells fail to divide if an essential nutrient is lacking in the culture medium. (This is analogous to trying to run an automatic washing machine without the water supply hooked up; an internal sensor won't allow the machine to continue past the point where water is needed.) And even if all other conditions are favorable, most types of mammalian cells divide in culture only if the growth medium includes specific growth factors. A **growth factor** is a protein released by certain cells that stimulates other cells to divide. Researchers have discovered more than 50 growth factors. Different cell types respond specifically to different growth factors or combinations of growth factors.

① A sample of human connective tissue is cut up into small pieces.

Scalpels

Petri dish

◀ **Figure 12.18 The effect of platelet-derived growth factor (PDGF) on cell division.**

② Enzymes are used to digest the extracellular matrix in the tissue pieces, resulting in a suspension of free fibroblasts.

③ Cells are transferred to culture vessels containing a basic growth medium consisting of glucose, amino acids, salts, and antibiotics (to prevent bacterial growth).

④ PDGF is added to half the vessels. The culture vessels are incubated at 37°C for 24 hours.

Without PDGF

In the basic growth medium without PDGF (the control), the cells fail to divide.

With PDGF

In the basic growth medium plus PDGF, the cells proliferate. The SEM shows cultured fibroblasts.

MAKE CONNECTIONS

PDGF signals cells by binding to a cell-surface receptor tyrosine kinase. If you added a chemical that blocked phosphorylation, how would the results differ?

10 µm

Cells anchor to dish surface and divide (anchorage dependence).

When cells have formed a complete single layer, they stop dividing (density-dependent inhibition).

If some cells are scraped away, the remaining cells divide to fill the gap and then stop once they contact each other (density-dependent inhibition).

20 µm

(a) Normal mammalian cells. Contact with neighboring cells and the availability of nutrients, growth factors, and a substratum for attachment limit cell density to a single layer.

20 µm

(b) Cancer cells. Cancer cells usually continue to divide well beyond a single layer, forming a clump of overlapping cells. They do not exhibit anchorage dependence or density-dependent inhibition.

▲ **Figure 12.19 Density-dependent inhibition and anchorage dependence of cell division.** Individual cells are shown disproportionately large in the drawings.

Consider, for example, *platelet-derived growth factor (PDGF)*, which is made by blood cell fragments called platelets. The experiment illustrated in **Figure 12.18** demonstrates that PDGF is required for the division of cultured fibroblasts, a type of connective tissue cell. Fibroblasts have PDGF receptors on their plasma membranes. The binding of PDGF molecules to these receptors (which are receptor tyrosine kinases) triggers a signal transduction pathway that allows the cells to pass the G_1 checkpoint and divide. PDGF stimulates fibroblast division not only in the artificial conditions of cell culture, but also in an animal's body. When an injury occurs, platelets release PDGF in the vicinity. The resulting proliferation of fibroblasts helps heal the wound.

The effect of an external physical factor on cell division is clearly seen in **density-dependent inhibition**, a phenomenon in which crowded cells stop dividing **(Figure 12.19a)**. As first observed many years ago, cultured cells normally divide until they form a single layer of cells on the inner surface of the culture container, at which point the cells stop dividing. If some cells are removed, those bordering the open space begin dividing again and continue until the vacancy is filled. Follow-up studies revealed that the binding of a cell-surface protein to its counterpart on an adjoining cell sends a growth-inhibiting signal to both cells, preventing them from moving forward in the cell cycle, even in the presence of growth factors.

Most animal cells also exhibit **anchorage dependence** (see Figure 12.19a). To divide, they must be attached to a substratum, such as the inside of a culture jar or the extracellular matrix of a tissue. Experiments suggest that like cell density, anchorage is signaled to the cell cycle control system via pathways involving plasma membrane proteins and elements of the cytoskeleton linked to them.

Density-dependent inhibition and anchorage dependence appear to function in the body's tissues as well as in cell culture, checking the growth of cells at some optimal density and location. Cancer cells, which we discuss next, exhibit neither density-dependent inhibition nor anchorage dependence (Figure 12.19b).

Loss of Cell Cycle Controls in Cancer Cells

Cancer cells do not heed the normal signals that regulate the cell cycle. They divide excessively and invade other tissues. If unchecked, they can kill the organism.

Cancer cells in culture do not stop dividing when growth factors are depleted. A logical hypothesis is that cancer cells do not need growth factors in their culture medium to grow and divide. They may make a required growth factor themselves, or they may have an abnormality in the signaling pathway that conveys the growth factor's signal to the cell cycle control system even in the absence of that factor. Another possibility is an abnormal cell cycle control system. In all of these scenarios, the underlying basis of the abnormality is almost always a change in one or more genes that alters the function of their protein products, resulting in faulty cell cycle control. You will learn more in Chapter 18 about the genetic bases of these changes and how these conditions may lead to cancer.

There are other important differences between normal cells and cancer cells that reflect derangements of the cell cycle. If and when they stop dividing, cancer cells do so at random points in the cycle, rather than at the normal checkpoints. Moreover, cancer cells can go on dividing indefinitely

in culture if they are given a continual supply of nutrients; in essence, they are "immortal." A striking example is a cell line that has been reproducing in culture since 1951. Cells of this line are called HeLa cells because their original source was a tumor removed from a woman named Henrietta Lacks. By contrast, nearly all normal mammalian cells growing in culture divide only about 20 to 50 times before they stop dividing, age, and die. (We'll see a possible reason for this phenomenon when we discuss DNA replication in Chapter 16.) Finally, cancer cells evade the normal controls that trigger a cell to undergo apoptosis when something is wrong—for example, when an irreparable mistake has occurred during DNA replication preceding mitosis.

The abnormal behavior of cancer cells can be catastrophic when it occurs in the body. The problem begins when a single cell in a tissue undergoes **transformation**, the process that converts a normal cell to a cancer cell. The body's immune system normally recognizes a transformed cell as an insurgent and destroys it. However, if the cell evades destruction, it may proliferate and form a tumor, a mass of abnormal cells within otherwise normal tissue. The abnormal cells may remain at the original site if they have too few genetic and cellular changes to survive at another site. In that case, the tumor is called a **benign tumor**. Most benign tumors do not cause serious problems and can be completely removed by surgery. In contrast, a **malignant tumor** includes cells whose genetic and cellular changes enable them to spread to new tissues and impair the functions of one or more organs. An individual with a malignant tumor is said to have cancer; **Figure 12.20** shows the development of breast cancer.

The changes that have occurred in cells of malignant tumors show up in many ways besides excessive proliferation. These cells may have unusual numbers of chromosomes,

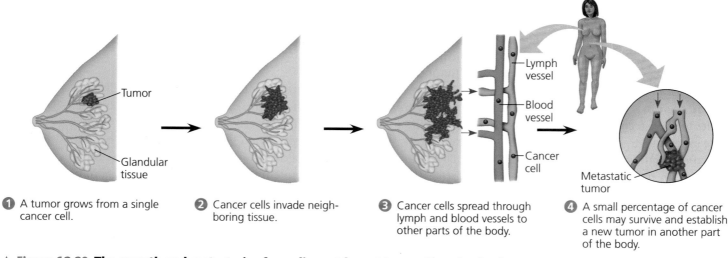

① A tumor grows from a single cancer cell.

② Cancer cells invade neighboring tissue.

③ Cancer cells spread through lymph and blood vessels to other parts of the body.

④ A small percentage of cancer cells may survive and establish a new tumor in another part of the body.

▲ **Figure 12.20 The growth and metastasis of a malignant breast tumor.** The cells of malignant (cancerous) tumors grow in an uncontrolled way and can spread to neighboring tissues and, via lymph and blood vessels, to other parts of the body. The spread of cancer cells beyond their original site is called metastasis.

though whether this is a cause or an effect of transformation is a current topic of debate. Their metabolism may be disabled, and they may cease to function in any constructive way. Abnormal changes on the cell surface cause cancer cells to lose attachments to neighboring cells and the extracellular matrix, allowing them to spread into nearby tissues. Cancer cells may also secrete signaling molecules that cause blood vessels to grow toward the tumor. A few tumor cells may separate from the original tumor, enter blood vessels and lymph vessels, and travel to other parts of the body. There, they may proliferate and form a new tumor. This spread of cancer cells to locations distant from their original site is called **metastasis** (see Figure 12.20).

A tumor that appears to be localized may be treated with high-energy radiation, which damages DNA in cancer cells much more than it does in normal cells, apparently because the majority of cancer cells have lost the ability to repair such damage. To treat known or suspected metastatic tumors, chemotherapy is used, in which drugs that are toxic to actively dividing cells are administered through the circulatory system. As you might expect, chemotherapeutic drugs interfere with specific steps in the cell cycle. For example, the drug Taxol freezes the mitotic spindle by preventing microtubule depolymerization, which stops actively dividing cells from proceeding past metaphase. The side effects of chemotherapy are due to the drugs' effects on normal cells that divide often. For example, nausea results from chemotherapy's effects on intestinal cells, hair loss from effects on hair follicle cells, and susceptibility to infection from effects on immune system cells.

Over the past several decades, researchers have produced a flood of valuable information about cell-signaling pathways and how their malfunction contributes to the development of cancer through effects on the cell cycle. Coupled with new molecular techniques, such as the ability to rapidly sequence the DNA of cells in a particular tumor, medical treatments for cancer are beginning to become more "personalized" to a particular patient's tumor. Breast cancer provides a good example. Basic research on the processes described in this chapter has augmented our understanding of the molecular events underlying development of breast cancer. Proteins functioning in cell signaling pathways that affect the cell cycle are often found to be altered in breast cancer cells. Analyzing the level and sequences of such proteins has allowed physicians to better tailor the treatment to the cancers of some individuals, as shown in **Figure 12.21**.

One of the big lessons we've learned about the development of cancer, though, is how very complex the process is. There are many areas that remain to be explored. Perhaps the reason we have so many unanswered questions about cancer cells is that there is still so much to learn about how normal cells function. The cell, life's basic unit of structure and function, holds enough secrets to engage researchers well into the future.

▼ Figure 12.21

IMPACT

Advances in Treatment of Breast Cancer

Cancer cells, such as the breast cancer cell shown below, are analyzed by DNA sequencing and other molecular techniques to look for alterations in the level or sequence of specific proteins associated with cancer. For example, the cells of roughly 20–25% of breast cancer tumors show abnormally high amounts of a cell-surface receptor tyrosine kinase called HER2, and many show an increase in the number of estrogen receptor (ER) molecules, intracellular receptors that can trigger cell division. Based on lab findings, a physician can prescribe chemotherapy with a molecule that blocks the function of the specific protein (Herceptin for HER2 and tamoxifen for ERs). Treatment using these agents, when appropriate, has led to increased survival rates and fewer cancer recurrences.

WHY IT MATTERS Approximately one out of every eight women will develop breast cancer, the most common cancer among women. Worldwide, the incidence of breast cancer has been increasing annually. However, the mortality rate from this disease is falling in the United States and elsewhere, probably a result of earlier detection and improved treatment. Furthermore, what we are learning from the study of breast cancer also enhances our understanding of the development and treatment of other types of cancer.

FURTHER READING F. J. Esteva and G. N. Hortobagyi, Gaining ground on breast cancer, *Scientific American* 298:58–65 (2008).

CONCEPT CHECK 12.3

1. In Figure 12.14, why do the nuclei resulting from experiment 2 contain different amounts of DNA?
2. How does MPF allow a cell to pass the G_2 phase checkpoint and enter mitosis? (See Figure 12.17.)
3. What phase are most of your body cells in?
4. Compare and contrast a benign tumor and a malignant tumor.
5. **WHAT IF?** What would happen if you performed the experiment in Figure 12.18 with cancer cells?

For suggested answers, see Appendix A.

SUMMARY OF KEY CONCEPTS

- Unicellular organisms reproduce by **cell division**; multicellular organisms depend on cell division for their development from a fertilized egg and for growth and repair. Cell division is part of the **cell cycle**, an ordered sequence of events in the life of a cell from its origin until it divides into daughter cells.

CONCEPT 12.1

Most cell division results in genetically identical daughter cells (pp. 229–230)

- The genetic material (DNA) of a cell—its **genome**—is partitioned among **chromosomes**. Each eukaryotic chromosome consists of one DNA molecule associated with many proteins that maintain chromosome structure and help control the activity of genes. Together, the complex of DNA and associated proteins is called **chromatin**. The chromatin of a chromosome exists in different states of condensation at different times. In animals, **gametes** have one set of chromosomes and **somatic cells** have two sets.
- Cells replicate their genetic material before they divide, ensuring that each daughter cell can receive a copy of the DNA. In preparation for cell division, chromosomes are duplicated, each one then consisting of two identical **sister chromatids** joined along their lengths by sister chromatid cohesion and held most tightly together at a constricted region at the **centromeres** of the chromatids. When this cohesion is broken, the chromatids separate during cell division, becoming the chromosomes of the new daughter cells. Eukaryotic cell division consists of **mitosis** (division of the nucleus) and **cytokinesis** (division of the cytoplasm).

? *Differentiate between these terms: chromosome, chromatin, and chromatid.*

CONCEPT 12.2

The mitotic phase alternates with interphase in the cell cycle (pp. 230–238)

- Between divisions, a cell is in **interphase**: the G_1, **S**, and G_2 phases. The cell grows throughout interphase, but DNA is replicated only during the synthesis (S) phase. Mitosis and cytokinesis make up the **mitotic (M) phase** of the cell cycle.

- The **mitotic spindle** is an apparatus of microtubules that controls chromosome movement during mitosis. In animal cells, the spindle arises from the **centrosomes** and includes spindle microtubules and **asters**. Some spindle microtubules attach to the **kinetochores** of chromosomes and move the chromosomes to the **metaphase plate**. In anaphase, sister chromatids separate, and motor proteins move them along the kinetochore microtubules toward opposite ends of the cell. Meanwhile, motor proteins push nonkinetochore microtubules from opposite poles away from each other, elongating the cell. In telophase, genetically identical daughter nuclei form at opposite ends of the cell.
- Mitosis is usually followed by cytokinesis. Animal cells carry out cytokinesis by **cleavage**, and plant cells form a **cell plate**.
- During **binary fission** in bacteria, the chromosome replicates and the two daughter chromosomes actively move apart. Some of the proteins involved in bacterial binary fission are related to eukaryotic actin and tubulin.
- Since prokaryotes preceded eukaryotes by more than a billion years, it is likely that mitosis evolved from prokaryotic cell division. Certain unicellular eukaryotes exhibit mechanisms of cell division that may be similar to those of ancestors of existing eukaryotes. Such mechanisms might have been intermediate steps in the evolution of mitosis from bacterial binary fission.

? *In which of the three subphases of interphase and the stages of mitosis do chromosomes exist as single DNA molecules?*

CONCEPT 12.3

The eukaryotic cell cycle is regulated by a molecular control system (pp. 238–243)

- Signaling molecules present in the cytoplasm regulate progress through the cell cycle.
- The **cell cycle control system** is molecularly based. Cyclic changes in regulatory proteins work as a cell cycle clock. The key molecules are **cyclins** and **cyclin-dependent kinases (Cdks)**. The clock has specific **checkpoints** where the cell cycle stops until a go-ahead signal is received. Cell culture has enabled researchers to study the molecular details of cell division. Both internal signals and external signals control the cell cycle checkpoints via signal transduction pathways. Most cells exhibit **density-dependent inhibition** of cell division as well as **anchorage dependence**.
- Cancer cells elude normal cell cycle regulation and divide out of control, forming tumors. **Malignant tumors** invade surrounding tissues and can undergo **metastasis**, exporting cancer cells to other parts of the body, where they may form secondary tumors. Recent advances in understanding the cell cycle and cell signaling, as well as techniques for sequencing DNA, have allowed improvements in cancer treatment.

? *Explain the significance of the G_1, G_2, and M checkpoints and the go-ahead signals involved in the cell cycle control system.*

TEST YOUR UNDERSTANDING

LEVEL 1: KNOWLEDGE/COMPREHENSION

1. Through a microscope, you can see a cell plate beginning to develop across the middle of a cell and nuclei forming on either side of the cell plate. This cell is most likely
   a. an animal cell in the process of cytokinesis.
   b. a plant cell in the process of cytokinesis.

c. an animal cell in the S phase of the cell cycle.
d. a bacterial cell dividing.
e. a plant cell in metaphase.

2. Vinblastine is a standard chemotherapeutic drug used to treat cancer. Because it interferes with the assembly of microtubules, its effectiveness must be related to
a. disruption of mitotic spindle formation.
b. inhibition of regulatory protein phosphorylation.
c. suppression of cyclin production.
d. myosin denaturation and inhibition of cleavage furrow formation.
e. inhibition of DNA synthesis.

3. One difference between cancer cells and normal cells is that cancer cells
a. are unable to synthesize DNA.
b. are arrested at the S phase of the cell cycle.
c. continue to divide even when they are tightly packed together.
d. cannot function properly because they are affected by density-dependent inhibition.
e. are always in the M phase of the cell cycle.

4. The decline of MPF activity at the end of mitosis is due to
a. the destruction of the protein kinase Cdk.
b. decreased synthesis of Cdk.
c. the degradation of cyclin.
d. the accumulation of cyclin.
e. synthesis of DNA.

5. In the cells of some organisms, mitosis occurs without cytokinesis. This will result in
a. cells with more than one nucleus.
b. cells that are unusually small.
c. cells lacking nuclei.
d. destruction of chromosomes.
e. cell cycles lacking an S phase.

6. Which of the following does *not* occur during mitosis?
a. condensation of the chromosomes
b. replication of the DNA
c. separation of sister chromatids
d. spindle formation
e. separation of the spindle poles

LEVEL 2: APPLICATION/ANALYSIS

7. In the light micrograph below of dividing cells near the tip of an onion root, identify a cell in each of the following stages: prophase, prometaphase, metaphase, anaphase, and telophase. Describe the major events occurring at each stage.

8. A particular cell has half as much DNA as some other cells in a mitotically active tissue. The cell in question is most likely in
a. G_1.   c. prophase.   e. anaphase.
b. G_2.   d. metaphase.

9. The drug cytochalasin B blocks the function of actin. Which of the following aspects of the animal cell cycle would be most disrupted by cytochalasin B?
a. spindle formation
b. spindle attachment to kinetochores
c. DNA synthesis
d. cell elongation during anaphase
e. cleavage furrow formation and cytokinesis

10. **DRAW IT** Draw one eukaryotic chromosome as it would appear during interphase, during each of the stages of mitosis, and during cytokinesis. Also draw and label the nuclear envelope and any microtubules attached to the chromosome(s).

LEVEL 3: SYNTHESIS/EVALUATION

11. EVOLUTION CONNECTION
The result of mitosis is that the daughter cells end up with the same number of chromosomes that the parent cell had. Another way to maintain the number of chromosomes would be to carry out cell division first and then duplicate the chromosomes in each daughter cell. Do you think this would be an equally good way of organizing the cell cycle? Why do you suppose that evolution has not led to this alternative?

12. SCIENTIFIC INQUIRY
Although both ends of a microtubule can gain or lose subunits, one end (called the plus end) polymerizes and depolymerizes at a higher rate than the other end (the minus end). For spindle microtubules, the plus ends are in the center of the spindle, and the minus ends are at the poles. Motor proteins that move along microtubules specialize in walking either toward the plus end or toward the minus end; the two types are called plus end–directed and minus end–directed motor proteins, respectively. Given what you know about chromosome movement and spindle changes during anaphase, predict which type of motor proteins would be present on (a) kinetochore microtubules and (b) nonkinetochore microtubules.

13. WRITE ABOUT A THEME
The Genetic Basis of Life The continuity of life is based on heritable information in the form of DNA. In a short essay (100–150 words), explain how the process of mitosis faithfully parcels out exact copies of this heritable information in the production of genetically identical daughter cells.

For selected answers, see Appendix A.

MasteringBIOLOGY®   www.masteringbiology.com

1. MasteringBiology® Assignments
BioFlix **Tutorials** Mitosis: Mitosis and the Cell Cycle • Mechanism of Mitosis • Comparing Cell Division in Animals, Plants, and Bacteria
Activities The Cell Cycle • Mitosis and Cytokinesis Animation • The Phases of Mitosis • Four Phases of the Cell Cycle • Causes of Cancer
Questions Student Misconceptions • Reading Quiz • Multiple Choice • End-of-Chapter

2. eText
Read your book online, search, take notes, highlight text, and more.

3. The Study Area
Practice Tests • Cumulative Test • *BioFlix* 3-D Animations • MP3 Tutor Sessions • Videos · Activities • Investigations • Lab Media • Audio Glossary • Word Study Tools • Art

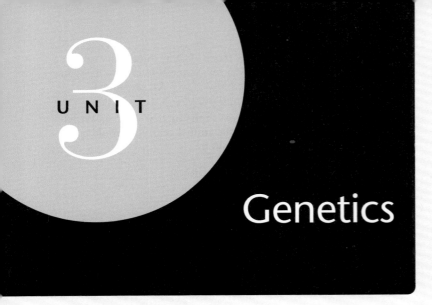

UNIT 3

Genetics

An Interview with
Joan A. Steitz

RNA is Joan Steitz's favorite molecule, and her research into its structures and functions has made contributions of enormous importance to our understanding of genetics at the molecular level. Raised in Minnesota, Dr. Steitz has a B.S. in Chemistry from Antioch College and a Ph.D. in Biochemistry and Molecular Biology from Harvard, where she worked in the laboratory of James D. Watson. Among her many awards and honors are the National Medal of Science, the Gairdner International Award, and 12 honorary doctorates. She is a member of the National Academy of Sciences and the Institute of Medicine. A teacher and researcher at Yale University since 1970, she is now Sterling Professor of Molecular Biophysics and Biochemistry and an Investigator of the Howard Hughes Medical Institute.

How did you get started in molecular genetics?
I first learned about the structure of DNA in my third year of college, during a co-op job at MIT. I was enthralled with the idea that DNA might be the molecular basis for all of the genetics—red hair, wrinkled peas, and so forth—that I had learned about in high school. After that, I worked in a molecular biology lab in Germany as a student abroad. Nevertheless, I decided to go to medical school.

I didn't apply to a Ph.D. program because I'd never seen a woman heading up a research lab, and it didn't enter my mind that I could do that. But I did know some women physicians, so I applied to medical school and was admitted to Harvard. However, the summer before I was supposed to enter, I ended up working in the lab of cell biologist Joe Gall, then at the University of Minnesota. For the first time, I had my own project, and I loved it. By August 1st, I decided that I didn't care if I would never be the head of a lab; I just wanted to do research. Luckily, I was able to switch from the medical school to a graduate program at Harvard.

How did you end up as a graduate student of Jim Watson?
I was interested in the question of whether all cellular organelles have DNA, like mitochondria do. So I first approached a cell biolo-gist, a famous microscopist who nevertheless reserved a bench in the corner of his lab for biochemistry. He conceded that his lab might be suitable, then gave me an unencouraging look and said, "But you're a woman. What are you going to do when you get married and have kids?" I barely made it out of his office before bursting into tears. Then I went to my second-choice thesis advisor, Jim Watson. I had done very well in his course, and he accepted me into his lab. So I became his first female graduate student, something I didn't discover until months later.

What was it like being in Watson's lab?
The Watson lab was a very exciting place at that time, in 1964. We knew that genes in DNA were transcribed into complementary RNA (a process called transcription) and that RNA called messenger RNA (mRNA) was translated into protein by ribosomes (translation). Besides mRNA, the only kinds of cellular RNA that were known were transfer RNA (tRNA) and ribosomal RNA (rRNA), although it was also known that some viruses had RNA instead of DNA as their genomes. But when I started grad school, we didn't yet know the genetic code—how the nucleotide sequence in mRNA corresponds to the amino acid sequence in protein—or much of anything about how transcription or translation occurred.

Jim would go off to meetings, and when he came back, everybody would crowd around him in the hall to find out what was new. Imagine the excitement when we heard, at an international biochemistry congress I actually attended, that the genetic code had been figured out! Or when someone in our lab discovered that a special kind of tRNA initiated protein synthesis. Things were happening very, very rapidly! The atmosphere was fiercely competitive but paradoxically collegial—the three or four labs that were working on the mechanisms of transcription and translation were all in contact with each other.

What was your research as a graduate student?
I worked on a newly discovered virus, R17, that infects the bacterium *E. coli*. Like other simple viruses, R17 is just a small amount of nucleic acid inside a protein coat. Throughout that era, molecular biologists fervently believed that unless you worked on something really simple, you would never figure out the molecular basis of life. So a virus that had only three genes (later found to be four) was the perfect thing to study.

The nucleic acid of R17, its genome, is RNA. This RNA gets into bacterial cells, and about an hour later out come 10,000 copies of the virus. So lots of things are happening in those cells. I studied a viral protein called the A-protein. For my thesis, I characterized the A-protein and what happened if there were mutations in its gene: You got virus particles that looked normal in the electron microscope but couldn't infect a bacterium. It turned out that the A-protein was needed for the virus to attach to the cell.

What did you do after graduate school?
I was married by then, and my husband had arranged to do a post-doc at the Medical Research Council (MRC) at Cambridge University, a mecca for structural and molecular biology. Jim Watson had written to Francis Crick asking him to find a place for me, but when I arrived at Cambridge, Francis suggested I do library research. Eventually, however, I found a bit of bench space for a lab project.

Fred Sanger's lab was nearby, and he was just working out his method for sequencing RNA. There was a lot of interchange with the people in Fred's lab, and they were very interested in the sequence of the R17 genome. Since it was very small, it was a really good molecule to work on. Previously, a paper had been published describing a method for isolating the particular stretches of mRNA bound to a functioning ribosome: You treated the mRNA-ribosome complex with ribonuclease, an enzyme that breaks down unprotected RNA, and you ended up with the part of the mRNA that had been bound and therefore protected by the ribosome, about 30 nucleotides long. The project I took on was to make ribosomes bind to R17 RNA (which functions as mRNA in normal virus infection) under conditions where they start but do not elongate proteins, and then isolate the ribosome-bound RNA segments. I would then determine the sequence of the parts of this RNA where translation started. Other people had considered and rejected this project. They were all male postdocs with wives and children who knew that in two years they would have to interview for tenure-track jobs, and this project had little chance of quick success. But since I thought I couldn't aim higher than a research position in somebody else's lab, I felt free to take on a risky project. (So, being a woman determined the two most important decisions of my early scientific career: ending up in Watson's lab and choosing my project at Cambridge.)

I determined the RNA nucleotide sequences at the beginning of the three R17 genes known at the time. These sequences included AUG, already known to be the "start codon" in mRNA (the first nucleotide triplet translated). And the sequences that followed AUG fit what was already known about the protein sequences, according to the genetic code. We also established that there were spaces between genes in the viral genome. And we figured out that sometimes the virus RNA folded into secondary structures that were important in regulating how many ribosomes would get on at a particular start site. This work at Cambridge—and better academic opportunities for women in the United States—led to my faculty position at Yale.

When you arrived at Yale, what was your first big discovery?
I found out how ribosomes locate the regions on mRNA where they attach and start translation. At Cambridge I had worked out the three 30-nucleotide sequences where ribosomes bind to R17 RNA, but it still wasn't clear how ribosomes honed in on these sequences out of the virus's 3,500 nucleotides. One idea was that a stretch of mRNA rich in purines, just upstream of where translation actually starts, would base-pair with the 3' end of the rRNA molecule in the small ribosomal subunit of bacteria. So I went to work testing that hypothesis. I soon had direct evidence that there actually is a physical interaction between the end of the "16S" rRNA molecule and the regions of mRNA that are bound by ribosomes. So this RNA-RNA base pairing, along with RNA-RNA base pairing between tRNA and mRNA, is the basis of polypeptide initiation.

You then turned to eukaryotic mRNA. What is different about mRNA production in eukaryotic cells, compared with bacteria?
The main difference comes from the fact that the genes of humans and other eukaryotes have interruptions in them, stretches of nucleic acid that are not translated. These interruptions, called *introns*, have to be removed from the RNA transcript before it is translated. But we didn't know this when I got interested in the subject. At that time, all we knew was that only 5–10% of the RNA transcribed from eukaryotic genes got out of the nucleus as mRNA. I was intrigued by this mystery and decided to switch from prokaryotes to eukaryotes to try to study it. Then, when introns were discovered, the reason for the loss of RNA became clear—though not how the extra RNA was removed. To make mRNA, somehow the introns have to be precisely removed and the coding bits have to be glued back together—a process called RNA splicing.

What have you learned since then about RNA splicing?
The most important molecular players are small RNA molecules that base-pair with sequences at the ends of RNA introns. This base pairing initiates the assembly of a ribosome-sized machine called a *spliceosome* made of RNA-protein subunits called snRNPs (pronounced "snurps") and other proteins. A spliceosome removes introns and joins together the protein-coding pieces. So RNA-RNA base pairing is the basis of the whole splicing process, just like it's the basis of the initiation of translation. Now there is more and more evidence that the RNAs are the catalytic components of the spliceosome, with the proteins playing supporting roles.

Does your research have any medical relevance?
We learned early on that people with lupus, an autoimmune disease, make antibodies to snRNPs, the RNA-protein subunits of spliceosomes. This discovery has been useful for the diagnosis of a number of autoimmune diseases and even for the prognosis of individual patients—although it hasn't led to cures. What we do in my lab, however, is very basic research. Somebody's got to figure out the basics in order for somebody else to figure out how to apply it.

What's going on now in the RNA field?
Lots of new classes of small RNA molecules have been discovered that, like rRNA, tRNA, and the RNAs in snRNPs, do not themselves code for protein. All these RNAs are important in getting information out of the DNA and into the functioning proteins of the cell. For instance, tiny RNAs called microRNAs, which associate with particular proteins, are involved in regulating translation. Again, it's RNA-RNA base pairing that determines the specificity. The theme of my research over my entire career has been finding out how RNAs interact with other RNAs to provide specificity along the pathway of gene expression. Proteins play important auxiliary roles, but it's basically been one RNA interacting with another RNA. I started working on RNA while I was a student, and it has continued to be my favorite molecule! There's enough to learn to last for many more lifetimes.

What do the discoveries about RNA suggest about the early stages of life on Earth?
Most biologists think that RNA was the first and most important genetic material, probably serving the first cells as both genome and the means by which the information in the genome directed cellular functions. Over time, cells have replaced the RNA genome with DNA, and many of the other RNA molecules with proteins. But the crucial processes of gene expression and its regulation are still dependent on various RNAs—4 billion years after life first arose!

"I started working on RNA while I was a student, and it has continued to be my favorite molecule!"

Joan Steitz (center) with Lisa Urry (right) and Jane Reece

13

Meiosis and Sexual Life Cycles

▲ **Figure 13.1 What accounts for family resemblance?**

KEY CONCEPTS

13.1 Offspring acquire genes from parents by inheriting chromosomes

13.2 Fertilization and meiosis alternate in sexual life cycles

13.3 Meiosis reduces the number of chromosome sets from diploid to haploid

13.4 Genetic variation produced in sexual life cycles contributes to evolution

OVERVIEW

Variations on a Theme

Most people who send out birth announcements mention the sex of the baby, but they don't feel the need to specify that their offspring is a human being! One of the characteristics of life is the ability of organisms to reproduce their own kind—elephants produce little elephants, and oak trees gen-

erate oak saplings. Exceptions to this rule show up only as sensational but highly suspect stories in tabloid newspapers.

Another rule often taken for granted is that offspring resemble their parents more than they do unrelated individuals. If you examine the family members shown in **Figure 13.1**—actress Sissy Spacek and her husband Jack Fisk with daughters Madison and Schuyler Fisk—you can pick out some similar features among them. The transmission of traits from one generation to the next is called inheritance, or **heredity** (from the Latin *heres*, heir). However, sons and daughters are not identical copies of either parent or of their siblings. Along with inherited similarity, there is also **variation**. Farmers have exploited the principles of heredity and variation for thousands of years, breeding plants and animals for desired traits. But what are the biological mechanisms leading to the hereditary similarity and variation that we call a "family resemblance"? The answer to this question eluded biologists until the advance of genetics in the 20th century.

Genetics is the scientific study of heredity and hereditary variation. In this unit, you will learn about genetics at multiple levels, from organisms to cells to molecules. On the practical side, you will see how genetics continues to revolutionize medicine and agriculture, and you will be asked to consider some social and ethical questions raised by our ability to manipulate DNA, the genetic material. At the end of the unit, you will be able to stand back and consider the whole genome, an organism's entire complement of DNA. Rapid acquisition and analysis of the genome sequences of many species, including our own, have taught us a great deal about evolution on the molecular level—in other words, evolution of the genome itself. In fact, genetic methods and discoveries are catalyzing progress in all areas of biology, from cell biology to physiology, developmental biology, behavior, and even ecology.

We begin our study of genetics in this chapter by examining how chromosomes pass from parents to offspring in sexually reproducing organisms. The processes of meiosis (a special type of cell division) and fertilization (the fusion of sperm and egg) maintain a species' chromosome count during the sexual life cycle. We will describe the cellular mechanics of meiosis and explain how this process differs from mitosis. Finally, we will consider how both meiosis and fertilization contribute to genetic variation, such as the variation obvious in the family shown in Figure 13.1.

CONCEPT 13.1

Offspring acquire genes from parents by inheriting chromosomes

Family friends may tell you that you have your mother's freckles or your father's eyes. Of course, parents do not, in any literal sense, give their children freckles, eyes, hair, or any other traits. What, then, *is* actually inherited?

Inheritance of Genes

Parents endow their offspring with coded information in the form of hereditary units called **genes**. The genes we inherit from our mothers and fathers are our genetic link to our parents, and they account for family resemblances such as shared eye color or freckles. Our genes program the specific traits that emerge as we develop from fertilized eggs into adults.

The genetic program is written in the language of DNA, the polymer of four different nucleotides you learned about in Chapters 1 and 5. Inherited information is passed on in the form of each gene's specific sequence of DNA nucleotides, much as printed information is communicated in the form of meaningful sequences of letters. In both cases, the language is symbolic. Just as your brain translates the word *apple* into a mental image of the fruit, cells translate genes into freckles and other features. Most genes program cells to synthesize specific enzymes and other proteins, whose cumulative action produces an organism's inherited traits. The programming of these traits in the form of DNA is one of the unifying themes of biology.

The transmission of hereditary traits has its molecular basis in the precise replication of DNA, which produces copies of genes that can be passed from parents to offspring. In animals and plants, reproductive cells called **gametes** are the vehicles that transmit genes from one generation to the next. During fertilization, male and female gametes (sperm and eggs) unite, thereby passing on genes of both parents to their offspring.

Except for small amounts of DNA in mitochondria and chloroplasts, the DNA of a eukaryotic cell is packaged into chromosomes within the nucleus. Every species has a characteristic number of chromosomes. For example, humans have 46 chromosomes in their **somatic cells**—all cells of the body except the gametes and their precursors. Each chromosome consists of a single long DNA molecule elaborately coiled in association with various proteins. One chromosome includes several hundred to a few thousand genes, each of which is a specific sequence of nucleotides within the DNA molecule. A gene's specific location along the length of a chromosome is called the gene's **locus** (plural, *loci*; from the Latin, meaning "place"). Our genetic endowment consists of the genes that are part of the chromosomes we inherited from our parents.

Comparison of Asexual and Sexual Reproduction

Only organisms that reproduce asexually have offspring that are exact genetic copies of themselves. In **asexual reproduction**, a single individual is the sole parent and passes copies of all its genes to its offspring without the fusion of gametes. For example, single-celled eukaryotic organisms can reproduce asexually by mitotic cell division, in which DNA is copied and allocated equally to two daughter cells. The genomes of the offspring are virtually exact copies of the parent's genome. Some multicellular organisms are also capable of reproducing

(a) Hydra **(b) Redwoods**

▲ **Figure 13.2 Asexual reproduction in two multicellular organisms. (a)** This relatively simple animal, a hydra, reproduces by budding. The bud, a localized mass of mitotically dividing cells, develops into a small hydra, which detaches from the parent (LM). **(b)** All the trees in this circle of redwoods arose asexually from a single parent tree, whose stump is in the center of the circle.

asexually (**Figure 13.2**). Because the cells of the offspring are derived by mitosis in the parent, the "chip off the old block" is usually genetically identical to its parent. An individual that reproduces asexually gives rise to a **clone**, a group of genetically identical individuals. Genetic differences occasionally arise in asexually reproducing organisms as a result of changes in the DNA called mutations, which we will discuss in Chapter 17.

In **sexual reproduction**, two parents give rise to offspring that have unique combinations of genes inherited from the two parents. In contrast to a clone, offspring of sexual reproduction vary genetically from their siblings and both parents: They are variations on a common theme of family resemblance, not exact replicas. Genetic variation like that shown in Figure 13.1 is an important consequence of sexual reproduction. What mechanisms generate this genetic variation? The key is the behavior of chromosomes during the sexual life cycle.

CONCEPT CHECK 13.1

1. Explain what causes the traits of parents (such as hair color) to show up in their offspring.
2. How do asexually reproducing organisms produce offspring that are genetically identical to each other and to their parents?
3. **WHAT IF?** A horticulturalist breeds orchids, trying to obtain a plant with a unique combination of desirable traits. After many years, she finally succeeds. To produce more plants like this one, should she cross-breed it with another plant or clone it? Why?

For suggested answers, see Appendix A.

CONCEPT 13.2

Fertilization and meiosis alternate in sexual life cycles

A **life cycle** is the generation-to-generation sequence of stages in the reproductive history of an organism, from conception to production of its own offspring. In this section, we use humans as an example to track the behavior of chromosomes through the sexual life cycle. We begin by considering the chromosome count in human somatic cells and gametes. We will then explore how the behavior of chromosomes relates to the human life cycle and other types of sexual life cycles.

Sets of Chromosomes in Human Cells

In humans, each somatic cell has 46 chromosomes. During mitosis, the chromosomes become condensed enough to be visible under a light microscope. At this point, they can be distinguished from one another by their size, the positions of their centromeres, and the pattern of colored bands produced by certain stains.

Careful examination of a micrograph of the 46 human chromosomes from a single cell in mitosis reveals that there are two chromosomes of each of 23 types. This becomes clear when images of the chromosomes are arranged in pairs, starting with the longest chromosomes. The resulting ordered display is called a **karyotype** (Figure 13.3). The two chromosomes composing a pair have the same length, centromere position, and staining pattern: These are called **homologous chromosomes**, or homologs. Both chromosomes of each pair carry genes controlling the same inherited characters. For example, if a gene for eye color is situated at a particular locus on a certain chromosome, then the homolog of that chromosome will also have a version of the same gene specifying eye color at the equivalent locus.

The two distinct chromosomes referred to as X and Y are an important exception to the general pattern of homologous chromosomes in human somatic cells. Human females have a homologous pair of X chromosomes (XX), but males have one X and one Y chromosome (XY). Only small parts of the X and Y are homologous. Most of the genes carried on the X chromosome do not have counterparts on the tiny Y, and the Y chromosome has genes lacking on the X. Because they determine an individual's sex, the X and Y chromosomes are called **sex chromosomes**. The other chromosomes are called **autosomes**.

The occurrence of pairs of homologous chromosomes in each human somatic cell is a consequence of our sexual origins. We inherit one chromosome of each pair from each parent. Thus, the 46 chromosomes in our somatic cells are actually two sets of 23 chromosomes—a maternal set (from our mother) and a paternal set (from our father). The number of chromosomes in

RESEARCH METHOD

Preparing a Karyotype

APPLICATION A karyotype is a display of condensed chromosomes arranged in pairs. Karyotyping can be used to screen for defective chromosomes or abnormal numbers of chromosomes associated with certain congenital disorders, such as Down syndrome.

TECHNIQUE Karyotypes are prepared from isolated somatic cells, which are treated with a drug to stimulate mitosis and then grown in culture for several days. Cells arrested in metaphase, when chromosomes are most highly condensed, are stained and then viewed with a microscope equipped with a digital camera. A photograph of the chromosomes is displayed on a computer monitor, and the images of the chromosomes are arranged into pairs according to their appearance.

Pair of homologous duplicated chromosomes

Centromere

Sister chromatids

Metaphase chromosome

5 μm

RESULTS This karyotype shows the chromosomes from a normal human male. The size of the chromosome, position of the centromere, and pattern of stained bands help identify specific chromosomes. Although difficult to discern in the karyotype, each metaphase chromosome consists of two closely attached sister chromatids (see the diagram of a pair of homologous duplicated chromosomes).

a single set is represented by *n*. Any cell with two chromosome sets is called a **diploid cell** and has a diploid number of chromosomes, abbreviated $2n$. For humans, the diploid number is 46 ($2n = 46$), the number of chromosomes in our somatic cells. In a cell in which DNA synthesis has occurred, all the chromosomes are duplicated, and therefore each consists of two identical sister chromatids, associated closely at the centromere and along the arms. **Figure 13.4** helps clarify the various terms that we use to describe duplicated chromosomes in a diploid cell. Study this figure so that you understand the differences between homologous chromosomes, sister chromatids, nonsister chromatids, and chromosome sets.

Unlike somatic cells, gametes contain a single set of chromosomes. Such cells are called **haploid cells**, and each has a haploid number of chromosomes (*n*). For humans, the haploid number is 23 ($n = 23$). The set of 23 consists of the 22 autosomes plus a single sex chromosome. An unfertilized egg contains an X chromosome, but a sperm may contain an X or a Y chromosome.

Note that each sexually reproducing species has a characteristic diploid number and haploid number. For example, the fruit fly, *Drosophila melanogaster*, has a diploid number ($2n$) of 8 and a haploid number (*n*) of 4, while dogs have a diploid number of 78 and a haploid number of 39.

Now that you have learned the concepts of diploid and haploid numbers of chromosomes, let's consider chromosome behavior during sexual life cycles. We'll use the human life cycle as an example.

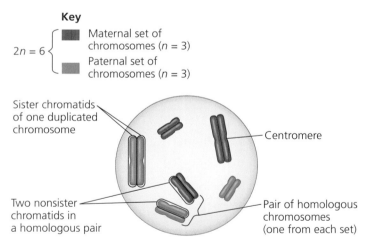

▲ Figure 13.4 Describing chromosomes. A cell from an organism with a diploid number of 6 ($2n = 6$) is depicted here following chromosome duplication and condensation. Each of the six duplicated chromosomes consists of two sister chromatids associated closely along their lengths. Each homologous pair is composed of one chromosome from the maternal set (red) and one from the paternal set (blue). Each set is made up of three chromosomes in this example. Nonsister chromatids are any two chromatids in a pair of homologous chromosomes that are not sister chromatids—in other words, one maternal and one paternal chromatid.

? *What is the haploid number of this cell? Is a "set" of chromosomes haploid or diploid?*

Behavior of Chromosome Sets in the Human Life Cycle

The human life cycle begins when a haploid sperm from the father fuses with a haploid egg from the mother. This union of gametes, culminating in fusion of their nuclei, is called **fertilization**. The resulting fertilized egg, or **zygote**, is diploid because it contains two haploid sets of chromosomes bearing genes representing the maternal and paternal family lines. As a human develops into a sexually mature adult, mitosis of the zygote and its descendant cells generates all the somatic cells of the body. Both chromosome sets in the zygote and all the genes they carry are passed with precision to the somatic cells.

The only cells of the human body not produced by mitosis are the gametes, which develop from specialized cells called *germ cells* in the gonads—ovaries in females and testes in males **(Figure 13.5)**. Imagine what would happen if human gametes were made by mitosis: They would be diploid like the somatic cells. At the next round of fertilization, when two gametes fused, the normal chromosome number of 46 would

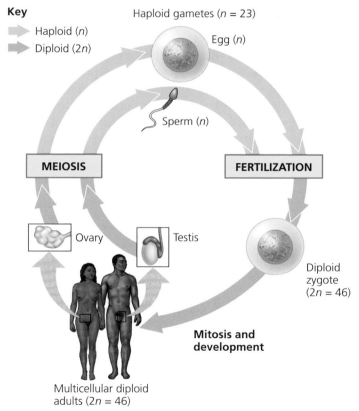

▲ Figure 13.5 The human life cycle. In each generation, the number of chromosome sets doubles at fertilization but is halved during meiosis. For humans, the number of chromosomes in a haploid cell is 23, consisting of one set ($n = 23$); the number of chromosomes in the diploid zygote and all somatic cells arising from it is 46, consisting of two sets ($2n = 46$).

This figure introduces a color code that will be used for other life cycles later in this book. The aqua arrows identify haploid stages of a life cycle, and the tan arrows identify diploid stages.

double to 92, and each subsequent generation would double the number of chromosomes yet again. This does not happen, however, because in sexually reproducing organisms, gamete formation involves a type of cell division called **meiosis**. This type of cell division reduces the number of sets of chromosomes from two to one in the gametes, counterbalancing the doubling that occurs at fertilization. In animals, meiosis occurs only in germ cells, which are in the ovaries or testes. As a result of meiosis, each human sperm and egg is haploid ($n = 23$). Fertilization restores the diploid condition by combining two haploid sets of chromosomes, and the human life cycle is repeated, generation after generation (see Figure 13.5). You will learn more about the production of sperm and eggs in Chapter 46.

In general, the steps of the human life cycle are typical of many sexually reproducing animals. Indeed, the processes of fertilization and meiosis are the hallmarks of sexual reproduction in plants, fungi, and protists as well as in animals. Fertilization and meiosis alternate in sexual life cycles, maintaining a constant number of chromosomes in each species from one generation to the next.

The Variety of Sexual Life Cycles

Although the alternation of meiosis and fertilization is common to all organisms that reproduce sexually, the timing of these two events in the life cycle varies, depending on the species. These variations can be grouped into three main types of life cycles. In the type that occurs in humans and most other animals, gametes are the only haploid cells. Meiosis occurs in germ cells during the production of gametes,

which undergo no further cell division prior to fertilization. After fertilization, the diploid zygote divides by mitosis, producing a multicellular organism that is diploid (**Figure 13.6a**).

Plants and some species of algae exhibit a second type of life cycle called **alternation of generations**. This type includes both diploid and haploid stages that are multicellular. The multicellular diploid stage is called the *sporophyte*. Meiosis in the sporophyte produces haploid cells called *spores*. Unlike a gamete, a haploid spore doesn't fuse with another cell but divides mitotically, generating a multicellular haploid stage called the *gametophyte*. Cells of the gametophyte give rise to gametes by mitosis. Fusion of two haploid gametes at fertilization results in a diploid zygote, which develops into the next sporophyte generation. Therefore, in this type of life cycle, the sporophyte generation produces a gametophyte as its offspring, and the gametophyte generation produces the next sporophyte generation (**Figure 13.6b**). Clearly, the term *alternation of generations* is a fitting name for this type of life cycle.

A third type of life cycle occurs in most fungi and some protists, including some algae. After gametes fuse and form a diploid zygote, meiosis occurs without a multicellular diploid offspring developing. Meiosis produces not gametes but haploid cells that then divide by mitosis and give rise to either unicellular descendants or a haploid multicellular adult organism. Subsequently, the haploid organism carries out further mitoses, producing the cells that develop into gametes. The only diploid stage found in these species is the single-celled zygote (**Figure 13.6c**).

Note that *either* haploid or diploid cells can divide by mitosis, depending on the type of life cycle. Only diploid cells,

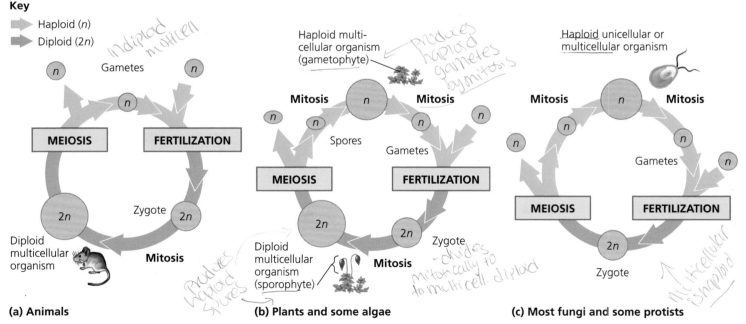

▲ **Figure 13.6 Three types of sexual life cycles.** The common feature of all three cycles is the alternation of meiosis and fertilization, key events that contribute to genetic variation among offspring. The cycles differ in the timing of these two key events.

however, can undergo meiosis because haploid cells have a single set of chromosomes that cannot be further reduced. Though the three types of sexual life cycles differ in the timing of meiosis and fertilization, they share a fundamental result: genetic variation among offspring. A closer look at meiosis will reveal the sources of this variation.

CONCEPT CHECK 13.2

1. **MAKE CONNECTIONS** In Figure 13.4, how many DNA molecules (double helices) are present (see Figure 12.5)?
2. How does the alternation of meiosis and fertilization in the life cycles of sexually reproducing organisms maintain the normal chromosome count for each species?
3. Each sperm of a pea plant contains seven chromosomes. What are the haploid and diploid numbers for this species?
4. **WHAT IF?** A certain eukaryote lives as a unicellular organism, but during environmental stress, it produces gametes. The gametes fuse, and the resulting zygote undergoes meiosis, generating new single cells. What type of organism could this be?

For suggested answers, see Appendix A.

CONCEPT 13.3

Meiosis reduces the number of chromosome sets from diploid to haploid

Many of the steps of meiosis closely resemble corresponding steps in mitosis. Meiosis, like mitosis, is preceded by the duplication of chromosomes. However, this single duplication is followed by not one but two consecutive cell divisions, called **meiosis I** and **meiosis II**. These two divisions result in four daughter cells (rather than the two daughter cells of mitosis), each with only half as many chromosomes as the parent cell.

The Stages of Meiosis

The overview of meiosis in **Figure 13.7** shows, for a single pair of homologous chromosomes in a diploid cell, that both members of the pair are duplicated and the copies sorted into four haploid daughter cells. Recall that sister chromatids are two copies of *one* chromosome, closely associated all along their lengths; this association is called *sister chromatid cohesion*. Together, the sister chromatids make up one duplicated chromosome (see Figure 13.4). In contrast, the two chromosomes of a homologous pair are individual chromosomes that were inherited from different parents. Homologs appear alike in the microscope, but they may have different versions of genes, each called an *allele*, at corresponding loci (for example, an allele for freckles on one chromosome and an

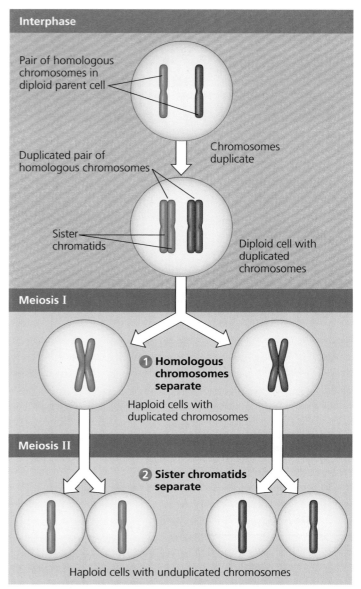

▲ **Figure 13.7 Overview of meiosis: how meiosis reduces chromosome number.** After the chromosomes duplicate in interphase, the diploid cell divides *twice*, yielding four haploid daughter cells. This overview tracks just one pair of homologous chromosomes, which for the sake of simplicity are drawn in the condensed state throughout. (They would not normally be condensed during interphase.) The red chromosome was inherited from the female parent, the blue chromosome from the male parent.

DRAW IT *Redraw the cells in this figure using a simple double helix to represent each DNA molecule.*

allele for the absence of freckles at the same locus on the homolog). Homologs are not associated with each other in any obvious way except during meiosis, as you will soon see.

Figure 13.8, on the next two pages, describes in detail the stages of the two divisions of meiosis for an animal cell whose diploid number is 6. Meiosis halves the total number of chromosomes in a very specific way, reducing the number of sets from two to one, with each daughter cell receiving one set of chromosomes. Study Figure 13.8 thoroughly before going on.

Exploring Meiosis in an Animal Cell

MEIOSIS I: Separates homologous chromosomes

Prophase I	Metaphase I	Anaphase I	Telophase I and Cytokinesis

Centrosome (with centriole pair)

Sister chromatids

Chiasmata

Spindle

Homologous chromosomes

Fragments of nuclear envelope

Duplicated homologous chromosomes (red and blue) pair and exchange segments; 2n = 6 in this example.

Centromere (with kinetochore)

Metaphase plate

Microtubule attached to kinetochore

Chromosomes line up by homologous pairs.

Sister chromatids remain attached

Homologous chromosomes separate

Each pair of homologous chromosomes separates.

Cleavage furrow

Two haploid cells form; each chromosome still consists of two sister chromatids.

Prophase I

During early prophase I, before the stage shown above:

- Chromosomes begin to condense, and homologs loosely pair along their lengths, aligned gene by gene.

- Paired homologs become physically connected to each other along their lengths by a zipper-like protein structure, the *synaptonemal complex;* this state is called **synapsis.**

- **Crossing over,** a genetic rearrangement between nonsister chromatids involving the exchange of corresponding segments of DNA molecules, begins during pairing and synaptonemal complex formation, and is completed while homologs are in synapsis.

At the stage shown above:

- Synapsis has ended with the disassembly of the synaptonemal complex in mid-prophase, and the

chromosomes in each pair have moved apart slightly.

- Each homologous pair has one or more X-shaped regions called **chiasmata** (singular, *chiasma*). A chiasma exists at the point where a crossover has occurred. It appears as a cross because sister chromatid cohesion still holds the two original sister chromatids together, even in regions beyond the crossover point, where one chromatid is now part of the other homolog.

- Centrosome movement, spindle formation, and nuclear envelope breakdown occur as in mitosis.

Later in prophase I, after the stage shown above:

- Microtubules from one pole or the other attach to the two kinetochores, protein structures at the centromeres of the two homologs. The homologous pairs then move toward the metaphase plate.

Metaphase I

- Pairs of homologous chromosomes are now arranged at the metaphase plate, with one chromosome in each pair facing each pole.

- Both chromatids of one homolog are attached to kinetochore microtubules from one pole; those of the other homolog are attached to microtubules from the opposite pole.

Anaphase I

- Breakdown of proteins responsible for sister chromatid cohesion along chromatid arms allows homologs to separate.

- The homologs move toward opposite poles, guided by the spindle apparatus.

- Sister chromatid cohesion persists at the centromere, causing chromatids to move as a unit toward the same pole.

Telophase I and Cytokinesis

- At the beginning of telophase I, each half of the cell has a complete haploid set of duplicated chromosomes. Each chromosome is composed of two sister chromatids; one or both chromatids include regions of nonsister chromatid DNA.

- Cytokinesis (division of the cytoplasm) usually occurs simultaneously with telophase I, forming two haploid daughter cells.

- In animal cells like these, a cleavage furrow forms. (In plant cells, a cell plate forms.)

- In some species, chromosomes decondense and nuclear envelopes form.

- No chromosome duplication occurs between meiosis I and meiosis II.

MEIOSIS II: Separates sister chromatids

Prophase II	Metaphase II	Anaphase II	Telophase II and Cytokinesis

During another round of cell division, the sister chromatids finally separate; four haploid daughter cells result, containing unduplicated chromosomes.

Sister chromatids separate

Haploid daughter cells forming

Prophase II

- A spindle apparatus forms.
- In late prophase II (not shown here), chromosomes, each still composed of two chromatids associated at the centromere, move toward the metaphase II plate.

Metaphase II

- The chromosomes are positioned at the metaphase plate as in mitosis.
- Because of crossing over in meiosis I, the two sister chromatids of each chromosome are *not* genetically identical.
- The kinetochores of sister chromatids are attached to microtubules extending from opposite poles.

Anaphase II

- Breakdown of proteins holding the sister chromatids together at the centromere allows the chromatids to separate. The chromatids move toward opposite poles as individual chromosomes.

Telophase II and Cytokinesis

- Nuclei form, the chromosomes begin decondensing, and cytokinesis occurs.
- The meiotic division of one parent cell produces four daughter cells, each with a haploid set of (unduplicated) chromosomes.
- The four daughter cells are genetically distinct from one another and from the parent cell.

MAKE CONNECTIONS *Look at Figure 12.7 and imagine the two daughter cells undergoing another round of mitosis, yielding four cells. Compare the number of chromosomes in each of those four cells, after mitosis, with the number in each cell in Figure 13.8, after meiosis. What is it about the process of meiosis that accounts for this difference, even though meiosis also includes two cell divisions?*

ANIMATION

BioFlix Visit the Study Area at **www.masteringbiology.com** for the BioFlix® 3-D Animation on Meiosis.

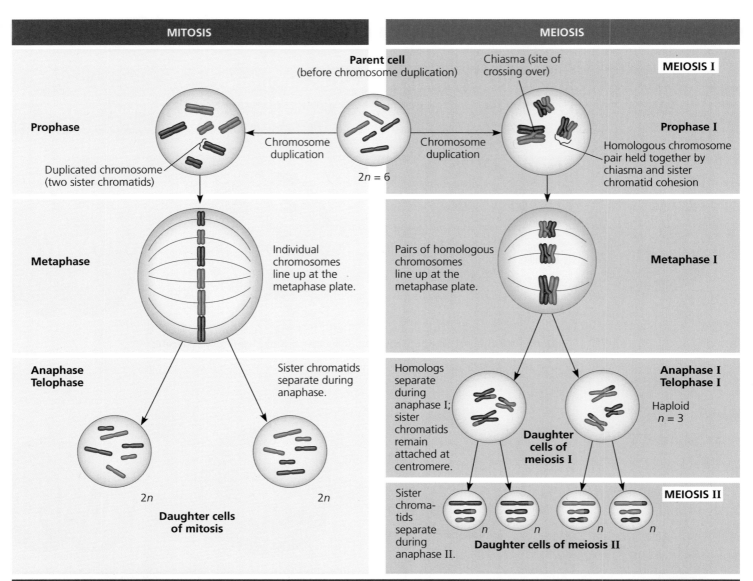

	MITOSIS	MEIOSIS	

Parent cell
(before chromosome duplication)

Chiasma (site of crossing over)

MEIOSIS I

Prophase

Duplicated chromosome (two sister chromatids)

Chromosome duplication

$2n = 6$

Chromosome duplication

Prophase I

Homologous chromosome pair held together by chiasma and sister chromatid cohesion

Metaphase

Individual chromosomes line up at the metaphase plate.

Pairs of homologous chromosomes line up at the metaphase plate.

Metaphase I

**Anaphase
Telophase**

Sister chromatids separate during anaphase.

Homologs separate during anaphase I; sister chromatids remain attached at centromere.

**Anaphase I
Telophase I**

Haploid
$n = 3$

Daughter cells of meiosis I

$2n$ $2n$

Daughter cells of mitosis

Sister chromatids separate during anaphase II.

MEIOSIS II

n n n n

Daughter cells of meiosis II

SUMMARY

Property	Mitosis	Meiosis
DNA replication	Occurs during interphase before mitosis begins	Occurs during interphase before meiosis I begins
Number of divisions	One, including prophase, metaphase, anaphase, and telophase	Two, each including prophase, metaphase, anaphase, and telophase
Synapsis of homologous chromosomes	Does not occur	Occurs during prophase I along with crossing over between nonsister chromatids; resulting chiasmata hold pairs together due to sister chromatid cohesion
Number of daughter cells and genetic composition	Two, each diploid ($2n$) and genetically identical to the parent cell	Four, each haploid (n), containing half as many chromosomes as the parent cell; genetically different from the parent cell and from each other
Role in the animal body	Enables multicellular adult to arise from zygote; produces cells for growth, repair, and, in some species, asexual reproduction	Produces gametes; reduces number of chromosomes by half and introduces genetic variability among the gametes

▲ **Figure 13.9 A comparison of mitosis and meiosis in diploid cells.**

DRAW IT *Could any other combinations of chromosomes be generated during meiosis II from the specific cells shown in telophase I? Explain. (Hint: Draw the cells as they would appear in metaphase II.)*

A Comparison of Mitosis and Meiosis

Figure 13.9 summarizes the key differences between meiosis and mitosis in diploid cells. Basically, meiosis reduces the number of chromosome sets from two (diploid) to one (haploid), whereas mitosis conserves the number of chromosome sets. Therefore, meiosis produces cells that differ genetically from their parent cell and from each other, whereas mitosis produces daughter cells that are genetically identical to their parent cell and to each other.

Three events unique to meiosis occur during meiosis I:

1. **Synapsis and crossing over.** During prophase I, duplicated homologs pair up, and the formation of the synaptonemal complex between them holds them in synapsis. Crossing over also occurs during prophase I. Synapsis and crossing over normally do not occur during prophase of mitosis.

2. **Homologous pairs at the metaphase plate.** At metaphase I of meiosis, chromosomes are positioned at the metaphase plate as pairs of homologs, rather than individual chromosomes, as in metaphase of mitosis.

3. **Separation of homologs.** At anaphase I of meiosis, the duplicated chromosomes of each homologous pair move toward opposite poles, but the sister chromatids of each duplicated chromosome remain attached. In anaphase of mitosis, by contrast, sister chromatids separate.

How do sister chromatids stay together through meiosis I but separate from each other in meiosis II and mitosis? Sister chromatids are attached along their lengths by protein complexes called *cohesins*. In mitosis, this attachment lasts until the end of metaphase, when enzymes cleave the cohesins, freeing the sister chromatids to move to opposite poles of the cell. In meiosis, sister chromatid cohesion is released in two steps, one at the start of anaphase I and one at anaphase II. In metaphase I, homologs are held together by cohesion between sister chromatid arms in regions beyond points of crossing over, where stretches of sister chromatids now belong to different chromosomes. As shown in Figure 13.8, the combination of crossing over and sister chromatid cohesion along the arms results in the formation of a chiasma. Chiasmata hold homologs together as the spindle forms for the first meiotic division. At the onset of anaphase I, the release of cohesion along sister chromatid arms allows homologs to separate. At anaphase II, the release of sister chromatid cohesion at the centromeres allows the sister chromatids to separate. Thus, sister chromatid cohesion and crossing over, acting together, play an essential role in the lining up of chromosomes by homologous pairs at metaphase I.

Meiosis I is called the *reductional division* because it halves the number of chromosome sets per cell—a reduction from two sets (the diploid state) to one set (the haploid state). During the second meiotic division, meiosis II (sometimes called the *equational division*), the sister chromatids separate, pro-

ducing haploid daughter cells. The mechanism for separating sister chromatids is virtually identical in meiosis II and mitosis. The molecular basis of chromosome behavior during meiosis continues to be a focus of intense research.

CONCEPT CHECK 13.3

1. **MAKE CONNECTIONS** How are the chromosomes in a cell at metaphase of mitosis similar to and different from the chromosomes in a cell at metaphase of meiosis II? (Compare Figures 12.7 and 13.8.)

2. **WHAT IF?** Given that the synaptonemal complex disappears by the end of prophase, how would the two homologs be associated if crossing over did not occur? What effect might this ultimately have on gamete formation?

For suggested answers, see Appendix A.

CONCEPT 13.4

Genetic variation produced in sexual life cycles contributes to evolution

How do we account for the genetic variation illustrated in Figure 13.1? As you will learn in more detail in later chapters, mutations are the original source of genetic diversity. These changes in an organism's DNA create the different versions of genes known as *alleles*. Once these differences arise, reshuffling of the alleles during sexual reproduction produces the variation that results in each member of a sexually reproducing population having a unique combination of traits.

Origins of Genetic Variation Among Offspring

In species that reproduce sexually, the behavior of chromosomes during meiosis and fertilization is responsible for most of the variation that arises in each generation. Let's examine three mechanisms that contribute to the genetic variation arising from sexual reproduction: independent assortment of chromosomes, crossing over, and random fertilization.

Independent Assortment of Chromosomes

One aspect of sexual reproduction that generates genetic variation is the random orientation of pairs of homologous chromosomes at metaphase of meiosis I. At metaphase I, the homologous pairs, each consisting of one maternal and one paternal chromosome, are situated at the metaphase plate. (Note that the terms *maternal* and *paternal* refer, respectively, to the mother and father of the individual whose cells are undergoing meiosis.) Each pair may orient with either its maternal or paternal homolog closer to a given pole—its orientation is as random as the flip of a coin. Thus, there is a 50% chance that a particular daughter cell of meiosis I will get the maternal chromosome of a certain homologous pair and a 50% chance that it will get the paternal chromosome.

Because each pair of homologous chromosomes is positioned independently of the other pairs at metaphase I, the first meiotic division results in each pair sorting its maternal and paternal homologs into daughter cells independently of every other pair. This is called *independent assortment*. Each daughter cell represents one outcome of all possible combinations of maternal and paternal chromosomes. As shown in **Figure 13.10**, the number of combinations possible for daughter cells formed by meiosis of a diploid cell with $n = 2$ (two pairs of homologous chromosomes) is four: two possible arrangements for the first pair times two possible arrangements for the second pair. Note that only two of the four combinations of daughter cells shown in the figure would result from meiosis of a *single* diploid cell, because a single parent cell would have one or the other possible chromosomal arrangement at metaphase I, but not both. However, the population of daughter cells resulting from meiosis of a large number of diploid cells contains all four types in approximately equal numbers. In the case of $n = 3$, eight combinations of chromosomes are possible for daughter cells. More generally, the number of possible combinations when chromosomes sort independently during meiosis is 2^n, where n is the haploid number of the organism.

In the case of humans ($n = 23$), the number of possible combinations of maternal and paternal chromosomes in the resulting gametes is 2^{23}, or about 8.4 million. Each gamete that you produce in your lifetime contains one of roughly 8.4 million possible combinations of chromosomes.

Crossing Over

As a consequence of the independent assortment of chromosomes during meiosis, each of us produces a collection of gametes differing greatly in their combinations of the chromosomes we inherited from our two parents. Figure 13.10 suggests that each chromosome in a gamete is exclusively maternal or paternal in origin. In fact, this is *not* the case, because crossing over produces **recombinant chromosomes**, individual chromosomes that carry genes (DNA) derived

from two different parents **(Figure 13.11)**. In meiosis in humans, an average of one to three crossover events occur per chromosome pair, depending on the size of the chromosomes and the position of their centromeres.

Crossing over begins very early in prophase I as homologous chromosomes pair loosely along their lengths. Each gene on one homolog is aligned precisely with the corresponding gene on the other homolog. In a single crossover event, the DNA of two *nonsister* chromatids—one maternal and one paternal chromatid of a homologous pair—is broken by specific proteins at precisely corresponding points, and the two segments beyond the crossover point are each joined to the other chromatid. Thus, a paternal chromatid is joined to a piece of maternal chromatid beyond the crossover point, and vice versa. In this way, crossing over produces chromosomes with new combinations of maternal and paternal alleles (see Figure 13.11).

At metaphase II, chromosomes that contain one or more recombinant chromatids can be oriented in two alternative, nonequivalent ways with respect to other chromosomes, because their sister chromatids are no longer identical. The different possible arrangements of nonidentical sister chromatids during meiosis II further increase the number of genetic types of daughter cells that can result from meiosis.

You will learn more about crossing over in Chapter 15. The important point for now is that crossing over, by combining DNA inherited from two parents into a single chromosome, is an important source of genetic variation in sexual life cycles.

Random Fertilization

The random nature of fertilization adds to the genetic variation arising from meiosis. In humans, each male and female gamete represents one of about 8.4 million (2^{23}) possible chromosome combinations due to independent assortment. The fusion of a male gamete with a female gamete during

▶ **Figure 13.10 The independent assortment of homologous chromosomes in meiosis.**

Possibility 1

Possibility 2

Two equally probable arrangements of chromosomes at metaphase I

Metaphase II

Daughter cells

Combination 1   Combination 2

Combination 3   Combination 4

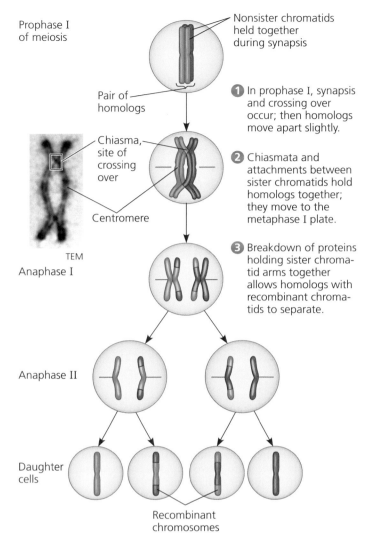

Prophase I
of meiosis

Nonsister chromatids
held together
during synapsis

Pair of
homologs

Chiasma,
site of
crossing
over

Centromere

TEM

Anaphase I

Anaphase II

Daughter
cells

Recombinant
chromosomes

1 In prophase I, synapsis
and crossing over
occur; then homologs
move apart slightly.

2 Chiasmata and
attachments between
sister chromatids hold
homologs together;
they move to the
metaphase I plate.

3 Breakdown of proteins
holding sister chroma-
tid arms together
allows homologs with
recombinant chroma-
tids to separate.

▲ **Figure 13.11 The results of crossing over during meiosis.**

fertilization will produce a zygote with any of about 70 tril-lion ($2^{23} \times 2^{23}$) diploid combinations. If we factor in the vari-ation brought about by crossing over, the number of possibilities is truly astronomical. It may sound trite, but you really *are* unique.

The Evolutionary Significance of Genetic Variation Within Populations

EVOLUTION Now that you've learned how new combina-tions of genes arise among offspring in a sexually reproducing population, let's see how the genetic variation in a population relates to evolution. Darwin recognized that a population evolves through the differential reproductive success of its variant members. On average, those individuals best suited to the local environment leave the most offspring, thereby trans-mitting their genes. Thus, natural selection results in the ac-cumulation of genetic variations favored by the environment. As the environment changes, the population may survive if,

in each generation, at least some of its members can cope ef-fectively with the new conditions. Mutations are the original source of different alleles, which are then mixed and matched during meiosis. New and different combinations of alleles may work better than those that previously prevailed. The ability of sexual reproduction to generate genetic diversity is one of the most commonly proposed explanations for the evolutionary persistence of this process.

On the other hand, in a stable environment, asexual repro-duction would seem to be more advantageous, because it en-sures perpetuation of successful combinations of alleles. Furthermore, asexual reproduction is less expensive; its energy costs to the organism are lower than those of sexual reproduc-tion, for reasons that will be discussed in Chapter 46.

In spite of these apparent disadvantages, sexual reproduc-tion is almost universal among animals as far as we know. While a few species are capable of reproducing asexually under unusual circumstances, animals that always reproduce asexually are quite rare. The best-established example, to date, is a group of microscopic animals called bdelloid rotifers (the "b" in "bdelloid" is silent), shown in **Figure 13.12**. This group includes about 400 species that live in a great variety of envi-ronments around the world. They inhabit streams, lake bot-toms, puddles, lichens, tree bark, and masses of decaying vegetation. Recent studies have provided convincing evi-dence that these animals reproduce only asexually and proba-bly haven't engaged in sex in the 40 million years since their evolutionary origins!

Does the discovery of the evolutionarily successful, asexu-ally reproducing bdelloid rotifer cast doubt on the advantage of genetic variation arising from sexual reproduction? On the contrary, this group may be considered an exception that proves the rule. In studies of bdelloid rotifers, biologists have found mechanisms other than sexual reproduction that in-crease genetic diversity in these organisms. For example, they live in environments that can dry up for long periods of time, during which they can enter a state of suspended animation. In this state, their cell membranes may crack in places, allow-ing entry of DNA from other rotifers and even other species. Evidence sug-gests that this DNA can be-come incorporated into the genome of the rotifer, lead-ing to increased genetic diversity. (You'll learn more about this process, called *horizontal gene transfer*, in Chapter 26.) Taken as a whole, these studies sup-port the idea that genetic variation is evolutionarily advantageous and that a

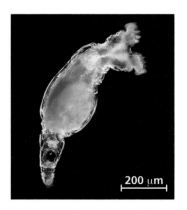

200 µm

▲ **Figure 13.12 A bdelloid rotifer, an animal that reproduces only asexually.**

different mechanism to generate genetic variation has evolved in bdelloid rotifers.

In this chapter, we have seen how sexual reproduction greatly increases the genetic variation present in a population. Although Darwin realized that heritable variation is what makes evolution possible, he could not explain why offspring resemble—but are not identical to—their parents. Ironically, Gregor Mendel, a contemporary of Darwin, published a theory of inheritance that helps explain genetic variation, but his discoveries had no impact on biologists until 1900, more than 15 years after Darwin (1809–1882) and Mendel (1822–1884) had died. In the next chapter, you will learn how Mendel discovered the basic rules governing the inheritance of specific traits.

13 CHAPTER REVIEW

SUMMARY OF KEY CONCEPTS

CONCEPT 13.1

Offspring acquire genes from parents by inheriting chromosomes (pp. 248–249)

- Each **gene** in an organism's DNA exists at a specific **locus** on a certain chromosome. We inherit one set of chromosomes from our mother and one set from our father.
- In **asexual reproduction**, a single parent produces genetically identical offspring by mitosis. **Sexual reproduction** combines sets of genes from two different parents, leading to genetically diverse offspring.

> ? *Explain why human offspring resemble their parents but are not identical to them.*

CONCEPT 13.2

Fertilization and meiosis alternate in sexual life cycles (pp. 250–253)

- As seen in a **karyotype**, normal human **somatic cells** are **diploid**. They have 46 chromosomes made up of two sets of 23—one set from each parent. In human diploid cells, there are 22 **homologous** pairs of **autosomes**, each with a maternal and a paternal homolog. The 23rd pair, the **sex chromosomes**, determines whether the person is female (XX) or male (XY).
- At sexual maturity in the human **life cycle**, ovaries and testes (the gonads) produce **haploid gametes** by **meiosis**, each gamete containing a single set of 23 chromosomes ($n = 23$). During **fertilization**, an egg and sperm unite, forming a diploid ($2n = 46$) single-celled **zygote**, which develops into a multicellular organism by mitosis.
- Sexual life cycles differ in the timing of meiosis relative to fertilization and in the point(s) of the cycle at which a multicellular organism is produced by mitosis.

> ? *Compare the life cycles of animals and plants, mentioning their similarities and differences.*

CONCEPT 13.3

Meiosis reduces the number of chromosome sets from diploid to haploid (pp. 253–257)

- The two cell divisions of meiosis, **meiosis I** and **meiosis II**, produce four haploid daughter cells. The number of chromosome sets is reduced from two (diploid) to one (haploid) during meiosis I, the reductional division.
- Meiosis is distinguished from mitosis by three events of meiosis I:

Prophase I: Each homologous pair undergoes **synapsis** and **crossing over** between nonsister chromatids with the subsequent appearance of **chiasmata**.

Metaphase I: Chromosomes line up as homologous pairs on the metaphase plate.

Anaphase I: Homologs separate from each other; sister chromatids remain joined at the centromere.

Meiosis II separates the sister chromatids.

- The combination of sister chromatid cohesion and crossing over leads to chiasmata, which hold homologs together until anaphase I. Cohesins are cleaved along the chromatid arms at anaphase I, allowing the homologs to separate, and at the centromeres in anaphase II, allowing sister chromatids to separate.

> ? *During prophase I, homologous chromosomes pair up and undergo synapsis and crossing over. Explain why this cannot also occur during prophase II.*

CONCEPT 13.4

Genetic variation produced in sexual life cycles contributes to evolution (pp. 257–260)

- Three events in sexual reproduction contribute to genetic variation in a population: independent assortment of chromosomes during meiosis, crossing over during meiosis I, and random fertilization of egg cells by sperm. Crossing over involves breakage and rejoining of the DNA of nonsister chromatids in a homologous pair, resulting in recombinant chromatids that will become **recombinant chromosomes**.

- Genetic variation is the raw material for evolution by natural selection. Mutations are the original source of this variation; the production of new combinations of variant genes in sexual reproduction generates additional genetic diversity. Animals that reproduce only asexually are quite rare, underscoring the apparently great advantage of genetic diversity.

? *Explain how three processes unique to meiosis generate a great deal of genetic variation.*

TEST YOUR UNDERSTANDING

LEVEL 1: KNOWLEDGE/COMPREHENSION

1. A human cell containing 22 autosomes and a Y chromosome is
   a. a sperm.
   b. an egg.
   c. a zygote.
   d. a somatic cell of a male.
   e. a somatic cell of a female.

2. Which life cycle stage is found in plants but not animals?
   a. gamete
   b. zygote
   c. multicellular diploid
   d. multicellular haploid
   e. unicellular diploid

3. Homologous chromosomes move toward opposite poles of a dividing cell during
   a. mitosis.   d. fertilization.
   b. meiosis I.   e. binary fission.
   c. meiosis II.

LEVEL 2: APPLICATION/ANALYSIS

4. Meiosis II is similar to mitosis in that
   a. sister chromatids separate during anaphase.
   b. DNA replicates before the division.
   c. the daughter cells are diploid.
   d. homologous chromosomes synapse.
   e. the chromosome number is reduced.

5. If the DNA content of a diploid cell in the G_1 phase of the cell cycle is x, then the DNA content of the same cell at metaphase of meiosis I would be
   a. $0.25x$.   d. $2x$.
   b. $0.5x$.   e. $4x$.
   c. x.

6. If we continued to follow the cell lineage from question 5, then the DNA content of a single cell at metaphase of meiosis II would be
   a. $0.25x$.   d. $2x$.
   b. $0.5x$.   e. $4x$.
   c. x.

7. How many different combinations of maternal and paternal chromosomes can be packaged in gametes made by an organism with a diploid number of 8 ($2n = 8$)?
   a. 2   d. 16
   b. 4   e. 32
   c. 8

8. **DRAW IT** The diagram at right shows a cell in meiosis.
   (a) Copy the drawing to a separate sheet of paper and label appropriate structures with these terms, drawing lines or brackets as needed: chromosome (label as duplicated or unduplicated), centromere, kinetochore, sister chromatids, nonsister chromatids, homologous pair, homologs, chiasma, sister chromatid cohesion.

   (b) Describe the makeup of a haploid set and a diploid set.
   (c) Identify the stage of meiosis shown.

LEVEL 3: SYNTHESIS/EVALUATION

9. How can you tell the cell in question 8 is undergoing meiosis, not mitosis?

10. **EVOLUTION CONNECTION**
    Many species can reproduce either asexually or sexually. What might be the evolutionary significance of the switch from asexual to sexual reproduction that occurs in some organisms when the environment becomes unfavorable?

11. **SCIENTIFIC INQUIRY**
    The diagram above represents a meiotic cell in a certain individual. A previous study has shown that the freckles gene is located at the locus marked F, and the hair-color gene is located at the locus marked H, both on the long chromosome. The individual from whom this cell was taken has inherited different alleles for each gene ("freckles" and "black hair" from one parent, and "no freckles" and "blond hair" from the other). Predict allele combinations in the gametes resulting from this meiotic event. (It will help if you draw out the rest of meiosis, labeling alleles by name.) List other possible combinations of these alleles in this individual's gametes.

12. **WRITE ABOUT A THEME**
    The Genetic Basis of Life The continuity of life is based on heritable information in the form of DNA. In a short essay (100–150 words), explain how chromosome behavior during sexual reproduction in animals ensures perpetuation of parental traits in offspring and, at the same time, genetic variation among offspring.

For selected answers, see Appendix A.

MasteringBIOLOGY www.masteringbiology.com

1. MasteringBiology® Assignments
Video Tutor Session Mitosis and Meiosis
  BioFlix Tutorials Meiosis: Genes, Chromosomes, and Sexual Reproduction • The Mechanism • Determinants of Heredity and Genetic Variation
Activities Asexual and Sexual Life Cycles • Meiosis • Meiosis Animation • Origins of Genetic Variation
Questions Student Misconceptions • Reading Quiz • Multiple Choice • End-of-Chapter

2. eText
Read your book online, search, take notes, highlight text, and more.

3. The Study Area
Practice Tests • Cumulative Test • **BioFlix** 3-D Animations • MP3 Tutor Sessions • Videos • Activities • Investigations • Lab Media • Audio Glossary • Word Study Tools • Art

14

Mendel and the Gene Idea

▲ **Figure 14.1 What principles of inheritance did Gregor Mendel discover by breeding garden pea plants?**

KEY CONCEPTS

14.1 Mendel used the scientific approach to identify two laws of inheritance

14.2 The laws of probability govern Mendelian inheritance

14.3 Inheritance patterns are often more complex than predicted by simple Mendelian genetics

14.4 Many human traits follow Mendelian patterns of inheritance

OVERVIEW

Drawing from the Deck of Genes

If you spotted a woman with bright purple hair walking down the street, you would probably deduce that she hadn't inherited her striking hair color from either parent. Consciously or not, you have transformed a lifetime of observations of hair color and other features into a list of possible variations that occur naturally among people. Brown, blue, green, or gray eyes; black, brown, blond, or red hair—these are just a few examples of heritable variations that we may observe among individuals in a population. What are the genetic principles that account for the transmission of such traits from parents to offspring in humans and other organisms?

The explanation of heredity most widely in favor during the 1800s was the "blending" hypothesis, the idea that genetic material contributed by the two parents mixes in a manner analogous to the way blue and yellow paints blend to make green. This hypothesis predicts that over many generations, a freely mating population will give rise to a uniform population of individuals. However, our everyday observations and the results of breeding experiments with animals and plants contradict that prediction. The blending hypothesis also fails to explain other phenomena of inheritance, such as traits reappearing after skipping a generation.

An alternative to the blending model is a "particulate" hypothesis of inheritance: the gene idea. According to this model, parents pass on discrete heritable units—genes—that retain their separate identities in offspring. An organism's collection of genes is more like a deck of cards than a pail of paint. Like playing cards, genes can be shuffled and passed along, generation after generation, in undiluted form.

Modern genetics had its genesis in an abbey garden, where a monk named Gregor Mendel documented a particulate mechanism for inheritance. **Figure 14.1** shows Mendel (back row, holding a sprig of fuchsia) with his fellow monks. Mendel developed his theory of inheritance several decades before chromosomes were observed under the microscope and the significance of their behavior was understood. In this chapter, we will step into Mendel's garden to re-create his experiments and explain how he arrived at his theory of inheritance. We will also explore inheritance patterns more complex than those observed by Mendel in garden peas. Finally, we will see how the Mendelian model applies to the inheritance of human variations, including hereditary disorders such as sickle-cell disease.

CONCEPT 14.1

Mendel used the scientific approach to identify two laws of inheritance

Mendel discovered the basic principles of heredity by breeding garden peas in carefully planned experiments. As we retrace his work, you will recognize the key elements of the scientific process that were introduced in Chapter 1.

Mendel's Experimental, Quantitative Approach

Mendel grew up on his parents' small farm in a region of Austria that is now part of the Czech Republic. In this agricultural area, Mendel and the other children received agricultural training in school along with their basic education. As an adolescent, Mendel overcame financial hardship and illness to excel in high school and, later, at the Olmutz Philosophical Institute.

In 1843, at the age of 21, Mendel entered an Augustinian monastery, a reasonable choice at that time for someone who valued the life of the mind. He considered becoming a teacher but failed the necessary examination. In 1851, he left the monastery to pursue two years of study in physics and chemistry at the University of Vienna. These were very important years for Mendel's development as a scientist, in large part due to the strong influence of two professors. One was the physicist Christian Doppler, who encouraged his students to learn science through experimentation and trained Mendel to use mathematics to help explain natural phenomena. The other was a botanist named Franz Unger, who aroused Mendel's interest in the causes of variation in plants. The instruction Mendel received from these two mentors later played a critical role in his experiments with garden peas.

After attending the university, Mendel returned to the monastery and was assigned to teach at a local school, where several other instructors were enthusiastic about scientific research. In addition, his fellow monks shared a long-standing fascination with the breeding of plants. The monastery therefore provided fertile soil in more ways than one for Mendel's scientific endeavors. Around 1857, Mendel began breeding garden peas in the abbey garden to study inheritance. Although the question of heredity had long been a focus of curiosity at the monastery, Mendel's fresh approach allowed him to deduce principles that had remained elusive to others.

One reason Mendel probably chose to work with peas is that they are available in many varieties. For example, one variety has purple flowers, while another variety has white flowers. A heritable feature that varies among individuals, such as flower color, is called a **character**. Each variant for a character, such as purple or white color for flowers, is called a **trait**.

Other advantages of using peas are their short generation time and the large number of offspring from each mating. Furthermore, Mendel could strictly control mating between plants. The reproductive organs of a pea plant are in its flowers, and each pea flower has both pollen-producing organs (stamens) and an egg-bearing organ (carpel).* In nature, pea plants usually self-fertilize: Pollen grains from the stamens land on the carpel of the same flower, and sperm released from the pollen grains fertilize eggs present in the carpel. To achieve cross-pollination (fertilization between different plants), Mendel removed the immature stamens of a plant before they produced pollen and then dusted pollen from another plant onto the

---

*As you learned in Figure 13.6b, meiosis in plants produces spores, not gametes. In flowering plants like the pea, each spore develops into a microscopic haploid gametophyte that contains only a few cells and is located on the parent plant. The gametophyte produces sperm, in pollen grains, and eggs, in the carpel. For simplicity, we will not include the gametophyte stage in our discussion of fertilization in plants.

▼ **Figure 14.2** **RESEARCH METHOD**

Crossing Pea Plants

APPLICATION By crossing (mating) two true-breeding varieties of an organism, scientists can study patterns of inheritance. In this example, Mendel crossed pea plants that varied in flower color.

TECHNIQUE

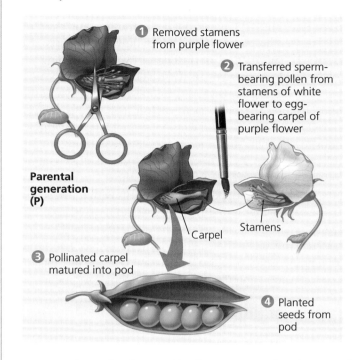

1. Removed stamens from purple flower
2. Transferred sperm-bearing pollen from stamens of white flower to egg-bearing carpel of purple flower

Parental generation (P)

Carpel Stamens

3. Pollinated carpel matured into pod

4. Planted seeds from pod

RESULTS When pollen from a white flower was transferred to a purple flower, the first-generation hybrids all had purple flowers. The result was the same for the reciprocal cross, which involved the transfer of pollen from purple flowers to white flowers.

First filial generation offspring (F$_1$)

5. Examined offspring: all purple flowers

---

altered flowers (**Figure 14.2**). Each resulting zygote then developed into a plant embryo encased in a seed (pea). Mendel could thus always be sure of the parentage of new seeds.

Mendel chose to track only those characters that occurred in two distinct, alternative forms. For example, his plants had either purple flowers or white flowers; there were no colors intermediate between these two varieties. Had Mendel focused instead on characters that varied in a continuum among individuals—seed weight, for example—he would not have discovered the particulate nature of inheritance. (You'll learn why later.)

Mendel also made sure that he started his experiments with varieties that, over many generations of self-pollination, had produced only the same variety as the parent plant. Such plants are said to be **true-breeding**. For example, a plant with purple flowers is true-breeding if the seeds produced by self-pollination in successive generations all give rise to plants that also have purple flowers.

In a typical breeding experiment, Mendel cross-pollinated two contrasting, true-breeding pea varieties—for example, purple-flowered plants and white-flowered plants (see Figure 14.2). This mating, or *crossing*, of two true-breeding varieties is called **hybridization**. The true-breeding parents are referred to as the **P generation** (parental generation), and their hybrid offspring are the F_1 **generation** (first filial generation, the word *filial* from the Latin word for "son"). Allowing these F_1 hybrids to self-pollinate (or to cross-pollinate with other F_1 hybrids) produces an F_2 **generation** (second filial generation). Mendel usually followed traits for at least the P, F_1, and F_2 generations. Had Mendel stopped his experiments with the F_1 generation, the basic patterns of inheritance would have escaped him. Mendel's quantitative analysis of the F_2 plants from thousands of genetic crosses like these allowed him to deduce two fundamental principles of heredity, which have come to be called the law of segregation and the law of independent assortment.

The Law of Segregation

If the blending model of inheritance were correct, the F_1 hybrids from a cross between purple-flowered and white-flowered pea plants would have pale purple flowers, a trait intermediate between those of the P generation. Notice in Figure 14.2 that the experiment produced a very different result: All the F_1 offspring had flowers just as purple as the purple-flowered parents. What happened to the white-flowered plants' genetic contribution to the hybrids? If it were lost, then the F_1 plants could produce only purple-flowered offspring in the F_2 generation. But when Mendel allowed the F_1 plants to self-pollinate and planted their seeds, the white-flower trait reappeared in the F_2 generation.

Mendel used very large sample sizes and kept accurate records of his results: 705 of the F_2 plants had purple flowers, and 224 had white flowers. These data fit a ratio of approximately three purple to one white **(Figure 14.3)**. Mendel reasoned that the heritable factor for white flowers did not disappear in the F_1 plants, but was somehow hidden, or masked, when the purple-flower factor was present. In Mendel's terminology, purple flower color is a *dominant* trait, and white flower color is a *recessive* trait. The reappearance of white-flowered plants in the F_2 generation was evidence that the heritable factor causing white flowers had not been diluted or destroyed by coexisting with the purple-flower factor in the F_1 hybrids.

Mendel observed the same pattern of inheritance in six other characters, each represented by two distinctly different

traits **(Table 14.1)**. For example, when Mendel crossed a true-breeding variety that produced smooth, round pea seeds with one that produced wrinkled seeds, all the F_1 hybrids produced round seeds; this is the dominant trait for seed shape. In the F_2 generation, approximately 75% of the seeds were round and 25% were wrinkled—a 3:1 ratio, as in Figure 14.3. Now let's see how Mendel deduced the law of

▼ **Figure 14.3**

INQUIRY

When F_1 hybrid pea plants self- or cross-pollinate, which traits appear in the F_2 generation?

EXPERIMENT Around 1860, in a monastery garden in Brünn, Austria, Gregor Mendel used the character of flower color in pea plants to follow traits through two generations. He crossed true-breeding purple-flowered plants and white-flowered plants (crosses are symbolized by ✕). The resulting F_1 hybrids were allowed to self-pollinate or were cross-pollinated with other F_1 hybrids. The F_2 generation plants were then observed for flower color.

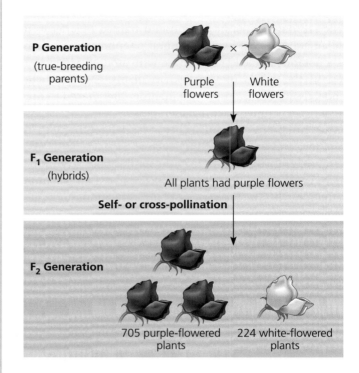

P Generation
(true-breeding parents)

Purple flowers   ✕   White flowers

F_1 Generation
(hybrids)

All plants had purple flowers

Self- or cross-pollination

F_2 Generation

705 purple-flowered plants   224 white-flowered plants

RESULTS Both purple-flowered and white-flowered plants appeared in the F_2 generation, in a ratio of approximately 3:1.

CONCLUSION The "heritable factor" for the recessive trait (white flowers) had not been destroyed, deleted, or "blended" in the F_1 generation but was merely masked by the presence of the factor for purple flowers, which is the dominant trait.

SOURCE G. Mendel, Experiments in plant hybridization, *Proceedings of the Natural History Society of Brünn* 4:3–47 (1866).

WHAT IF? If you mated two purple-flowered plants from the P generation, what ratio of traits would you expect to observe in the offspring? Explain.

Table 14.1 The Results of Mendel's F₁ Crosses for Seven Characters in Pea Plants				
Character	**Dominant Trait** ×	**Recessive Trait**	**F₂ Generation Dominant: Recessive**	**Ratio**
Flower color	Purple	White	705:224	3.15:1
Flower position	Axial	Terminal	651:207	3.14:1
Seed color	Yellow	Green	6,022:2,001	3.01:1
Seed shape	Round	Wrinkled	5,474:1,850	2.96:1
Pod shape	Inflated	Constricted	882:299	2.95:1
Pod color	Green	Yellow	428:152	2.82:1
Stem length	Tall	Dwarf	787:277	2.84:1

▲ **Figure 14.4 Alleles, alternative versions of a gene.** A somatic cell has two copies of each chromosome (forming a homologous pair) and thus two copies of each gene; the alleles may be identical or different. This figure depicts a pair of homologous chromosomes in an F₁ hybrid pea plant. The paternally inherited chromosome (blue), which was present in the sperm within a pollen grain, has an allele for purple flowers, and the maternally inherited chromosome (red), which was present in an egg within a carpel, has an allele for white flowers.

segregation from his experimental results. In the discussion that follows, we will use modern terms instead of some of the terms used by Mendel. (For example, we'll use "gene" instead of Mendel's "heritable factor.")

Mendel's Model

Mendel developed a model to explain the 3:1 inheritance pattern that he consistently observed among the F₂ offspring in his pea experiments. We describe four related concepts making up this model, the fourth of which is the law of segregation.

First, *alternative versions of genes account for variations in inherited characters.* The gene for flower color in pea plants, for example, exists in two versions, one for purple flowers and the other for white flowers. These alternative versions of a gene are

called **alleles** (**Figure 14.4**). Today, we can relate this concept to chromosomes and DNA. As noted in Chapter 13, each gene is a sequence of nucleotides at a specific place, or locus, along a particular chromosome. The DNA at that locus, however, can vary slightly in its nucleotide sequence and hence in its information content. The purple-flower allele and the white-flower allele are two DNA sequence variations possible at the flower-color locus on one of a pea plant's chromosomes.

Second, *for each character, an organism inherits two copies of a gene, one from each parent.* (These are also called alleles of that gene.) Remarkably, Mendel made this deduction without knowing about the role, or even the existence, of chromosomes. Recall from Chapter 13 that each somatic cell in a diploid organism has two sets of chromosomes, one set inherited from each parent. Thus, a genetic locus is actually represented twice in a diploid cell, once on each homolog of a specific pair of chromosomes. The two alleles at a particular locus may be identical, as in the true-breeding plants of Mendel's P generation. Or the alleles may differ, as in the F₁ hybrids (see Figure 14.4).

Third, *if the two alleles at a locus differ, then one, the* **dominant allele**, *determines the organism's appearance; the other, the* **recessive allele**, *has no noticeable effect on the organism's appearance.* Accordingly, Mendel's F₁ plants had purple flowers because the allele for that trait is dominant and the allele for white flowers is recessive.

The fourth and final part of Mendel's model, the **law of segregation**, states that *the two alleles for a heritable character segregate (separate from each other) during gamete formation and end up in different gametes.* Thus, an egg or a sperm gets only one of the two alleles that are present in the somatic cells of the organism making the gamete. In terms of chromosomes, this segregation corresponds to the distribution of the two members of a pair of homologous chromosomes to different gametes in meiosis (see Figure 13.7). Note that if an organism has identical alleles for a particular character—that is, the organism is true-breeding for that character—then that allele is present in all gametes. But if different alleles are present, as in the F_1 hybrids, then 50% of the gametes receive the dominant allele and 50% receive the recessive allele.

Does Mendel's segregation model account for the 3:1 ratio he observed in the F_2 generation of his numerous crosses? For the flower-color character, the model predicts that the two different alleles present in an F_1 individual will segregate into gametes such that half the gametes will have the purple-flower allele and half will have the white-flower allele. During self-pollination, gametes of each class unite randomly. An egg with a purple-flower allele has an equal chance of being fertilized by a sperm with a purple-flower allele or one with a white-flower allele. Since the same is true for an egg with a white-flower allele, there are four equally likely combinations of sperm and egg. **Figure 14.5** illustrates these combinations using a **Punnett square**, a handy diagrammatic device for predicting the allele composition of offspring from a cross between individuals of known genetic makeup. Notice that we use a capital letter to symbolize a dominant allele and a lowercase letter for a recessive allele. In our example, P is the purple-flower allele, and p is the white-flower allele; the gene itself is sometimes referred to as the P/p gene.

In the F_2 offspring, what color will the flowers be? One-fourth of the plants have inherited two purple-flower alleles; clearly, these plants will have purple flowers. One-half of the F_2 offspring have inherited one purple-flower allele and one white-flower allele; these plants will also have purple flowers, the dominant trait. Finally, one-fourth of the F_2 plants have inherited two white-flower alleles and will express the recessive trait. Thus, Mendel's model accounts for the 3:1 ratio of traits that he observed in the F_2 generation.

Useful Genetic Vocabulary

An organism that has a pair of identical alleles for a character is said to be **homozygous** for the gene controlling that character. In the parental generation in Figure 14.5, the purple pea plant is homozygous for the dominant allele (PP), while the white plant is homozygous for the recessive allele (pp). Homozygous plants "breed true" because all of their gametes contain the same allele—either P or p in this example. If we cross dominant homozygotes with recessive homozygotes, every offspring will have two different alleles—Pp in the case of the F_1 hybrids of our flower-color experiment (see Figure 14.5). An organism that has two different alleles for a gene is said to be **heterozygous** for that gene. Unlike homozygotes, heterozygotes produce gametes with different alleles, so they are not true-breeding. For example, P- and p-containing gametes are both produced by our F_1 hybrids. Self-pollination of the F_1 hybrids thus produces both purple-flowered and white-flowered offspring.

Because of the different effects of dominant and recessive alleles, an organism's traits do not always reveal its genetic composition. Therefore, we distinguish between an organism's appearance or observable traits, called its **phenotype**, and its genetic makeup, its **genotype**. In the case of flower color in pea plants, PP and Pp plants have the same phenotype (purple) but different genotypes. **Figure 14.6** reviews these terms. Note that "phenotype" refers to physiological traits as well as traits that relate directly to appearance.

Each true-breeding plant of the parental generation has identical alleles, PP or pp.

Gametes (circles) each contain only one allele for the flower-color gene. In this case, every gamete produced by one parent has the same allele.

P Generation

Appearance: Purple flowers White flowers
Genetic makeup: PP pp

Gametes: P p

Union of parental gametes produces F_1 hybrids having a Pp combination. Because the purple-flower allele is dominant, all these hybrids have purple flowers.

When the hybrid plants produce gametes, the two alleles segregate. Half of the gametes receive the P allele and the other half the p allele.

F_1 Generation

Appearance: Purple flowers
Genetic makeup: Pp

Gametes: $\frac{1}{2}$ P $\frac{1}{2}$ p

This box, a Punnett square, shows all possible combinations of alleles in offspring that result from an $F_1 \times F_1$ ($Pp \times Pp$) cross. Each square represents an equally probable product of fertilization. For example, the bottom left box shows the genetic combination resulting from a p egg fertilized by a P sperm.

Random combination of the gametes results in the 3:1 ratio that Mendel observed in the F_2 generation.

F_2 Generation

Sperm from F_1 (Pp) plant
P p

Eggs from F_1 (Pp) plant
P: PP Pp
p: Pp pp

3 : 1

▲ **Figure 14.5 Mendel's law of segregation.** This diagram shows the genetic makeup of the generations in Figure 14.3. It illustrates Mendel's model for inheritance of the alleles of a single gene. Each plant has two alleles for the gene controlling flower color, one allele inherited from each of the plant's parents. To construct a Punnett square that predicts the F_2 generation offspring, we list all the possible gametes from one parent (here, the F_1 female) along the left side of the square and all the possible gametes from the other parent (here, the F_1 male) along the top. The boxes represent the offspring resulting from all the possible unions of male and female gametes.

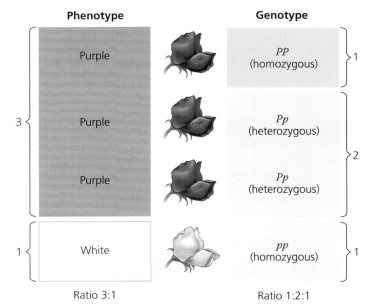

Phenotype			Genotype	

Purple — *PP* (homozygous) — 1

Purple — *Pp* (heterozygous)

3 { Purple — *Pp* (heterozygous) } 2

1 { White — *pp* (homozygous) } 1

Ratio 3:1   Ratio 1:2:1

▲ **Figure 14.6 Phenotype versus genotype.** Grouping F₂ offspring from a cross for flower color according to phenotype results in the typical 3:1 phenotypic ratio. In terms of genotype, however, there are actually two categories of purple-flowered plants, *PP* (homozygous) and *Pp* (heterozygous), giving a 1:2:1 genotypic ratio.

For example, there is a pea variety that lacks the normal ability to self-pollinate. This physiological variation (non-self-pollination) is a phenotypic trait.

The Testcross

Suppose we have a "mystery" pea plant that has purple flowers. We cannot tell from its flower color if this plant is homozygous (*PP*) or heterozygous (*Pp*) because both genotypes result in the same purple phenotype. To determine the genotype, we can cross this plant with a white-flowered plant (*pp*), which will make only gametes with the recessive allele (*p*). The allele in the gamete contributed by the mystery plant will therefore determine the appearance of the offspring (**Figure 14.7**). If all the offspring of the cross have purple flowers, then the purple-flowered mystery plant must be homozygous for the dominant allele, because a *PP* × *pp* cross produces all *Pp* offspring. But if both the purple and the white phenotypes appear among the offspring, then the purple-flowered parent must be heterozygous. The offspring of a *Pp* × *pp* cross will be expected to have a 1:1 phenotypic ratio. Breeding an organism of unknown genotype with a recessive homozygote is called a **testcross** because it can reveal the genotype of that organism. The testcross was devised by Mendel and continues to be an important tool of geneticists.

The Law of Independent Assortment

Mendel derived the law of segregation from experiments in which he followed only a *single* character, such as flower color. All the F₁ progeny produced in his crosses of true-breeding parents were **monohybrids**, meaning that they were

The Testcross

APPLICATION An organism that exhibits a dominant trait, such as purple flowers in pea plants, can be either homozygous for the dominant allele or heterozygous. To determine the organism's genotype, geneticists can perform a testcross.

TECHNIQUE In a testcross, the individual with the unknown genotype is crossed with a homozygous individual expressing the recessive trait (white flowers in this example), and Punnett squares are used to predict the possible outcomes.

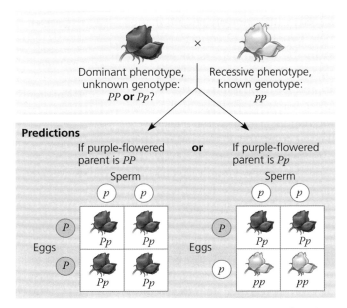

Dominant phenotype, unknown genotype: *PP* or *Pp*? × Recessive phenotype, known genotype: *pp*

Predictions

If purple-flowered parent is *PP*   or   If purple-flowered parent is *Pp*

RESULTS Matching the results to either prediction identifies the unknown parental genotype (either *PP* or *Pp* in this example). In this testcross, we transferred pollen from a white-flowered plant to the carpels of a purple-flowered plant; the opposite (reciprocal) cross would have led to the same results.

All offspring purple   or   ½ offspring purple and ½ offspring white

heterozygous for the one particular character being followed in the cross. We refer to a cross between such heterozygotes as a **monohybrid cross**.

Mendel identified his second law of inheritance by following *two* characters at the same time, such as seed color and seed shape. Seeds (peas) may be either yellow or green. They also may be either round (smooth) or wrinkled. From single-character crosses, Mendel knew that the allele for yellow seeds is dominant (*Y*), and the allele for green seeds is recessive (*y*). For the seed-shape character, the allele for round is dominant (*R*), and the allele for wrinkled is recessive (*r*).

Imagine crossing two true-breeding pea varieties that differ in *both* of these characters—a cross between a plant with yellow-round seeds (*YYRR*) and a plant with green-wrinkled seeds (*yyrr*).

The F₁ plants will be **dihybrids**, individuals heterozygous for the two characters being followed in the cross (*YyRr*). But are these two characters transmitted from parents to offspring as a package? That is, will the *Y* and *R* alleles always stay together, generation after generation? Or are seed color and seed shape inherited independently? **Figure 14.8** shows how a **dihybrid cross**, a cross between F₁ dihybrids, can determine which of these two hypotheses is correct.

The F₁ plants, of genotype *YyRr*, exhibit both dominant phenotypes, yellow seeds with round shapes, no matter which hypothesis is correct. The key step in the experiment is to see what happens when F₁ plants self-pollinate and produce F₂ offspring. If the hybrids must transmit their alleles in the same combinations in which the alleles were inherited from the P generation, then the F₁ hybrids will produce only two classes of gametes: *YR* and *yr*. This "dependent assortment" hypothesis predicts that the phenotypic ratio of the F₂ generation will be 3:1, just as in a monohybrid cross (see Figure 14.8, left side).

The alternative hypothesis is that the two pairs of alleles segregate independently of each other. In other words, genes are packaged into gametes in all possible allelic combinations, as long as each gamete has one allele for each gene. In our example, an F₁ plant will produce four classes of gametes in equal quantities: *YR*, *Yr*, *yR*, and *yr*. If sperm of the four classes fertilize eggs of the four classes, there will be 16 (4 × 4) equally probable ways in which the alleles can combine in the F₂ generation, as shown in Figure 14.8, right side. These combinations result in four phenotypic categories with a ratio of 9:3:3:1 (nine yellow-round to three green-round to three yellow-wrinkled to one green-wrinkled). When Mendel did the experiment and classified the F₂ offspring, his results were close to the predicted 9:3:3:1 phenotypic ratio, supporting the hypothesis that the alleles for one gene—controlling seed color or seed shape, in this example—are sorted into gametes independently of the alleles of other genes.

Mendel tested his seven pea characters in various dihybrid combinations

and always observed a 9:3:3:1 phenotypic ratio in the F₂ generation. However, notice in Figure 14.8 that there is a 3:1 phenotypic ratio for each one of the two characters if you consider them separately: three yellow to one green, and three round to one wrinkled. As far as a single character is concerned, the alleles segregate as if this were a monohybrid cross. The results of

▼ **Figure 14.8**

INQUIRY

Do the alleles for one character assort into gametes dependently or independently of the alleles for a different character?

EXPERIMENT Gregor Mendel followed the characters of seed color and seed shape through the F₂ generation. He crossed a true-breeding plant with yellow-round seeds with a true-breeding plant with green-wrinkled seeds, producing dihybrid F₁ plants. Self-pollination of the F₁ dihybrids produced the F₂ generation. The two hypotheses (dependent and independent assortment) predict different phenotypic ratios.

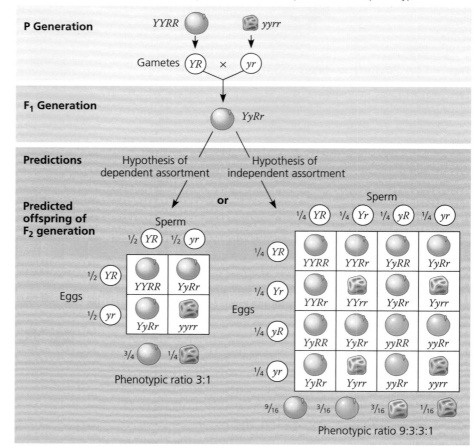

RESULTS

315 ⬤   108 ⬤   101 ▨   32 ▨   Phenotypic ratio approximately 9:3:3:1

CONCLUSION Only the hypothesis of independent assortment predicts the appearance of two of the observed phenotypes: green-round seeds and yellow-wrinkled seeds (see the right-hand Punnett square). The alleles for seed color and seed shape sort into gametes independently of each other.

SOURCE G. Mendel, Experiments in plant hybridization, *Proceedings of the Natural History Society of Brünn* 4:3–47 (1866).

WHAT IF? Suppose Mendel had transferred pollen from an F₁ plant to the carpel of a plant that was homozygous recessive for both genes. Set up the cross and draw Punnett squares that predict the offspring for both hypotheses. Would this cross have supported the hypothesis of independent assortment equally well?

Mendel's dihybrid experiments are the basis for what we now call the **law of independent assortment**, which states that *each pair of alleles segregates independently of each other pair of alleles during gamete formation.*

This law applies only to genes (allele pairs) located on different chromosomes—that is, on chromosomes that are not homologous—or very far apart on the same chromosome. (The latter case will be explained in Chapter 15, along with the more complex inheritance patterns of genes located near each other, which tend to be inherited together.) All the pea characters Mendel chose for analysis were controlled by genes on different chromosomes (or far apart on one chromosome); this situation greatly simplified interpretation of his multicharacter pea crosses. All the examples we consider in the rest of this chapter involve genes located on different chromosomes.

CONCEPT CHECK 14.1

1. **DRAW IT** Pea plants heterozygous for flower position and stem length (*AaTt*) are allowed to self-pollinate, and 400 of the resulting seeds are planted. Draw a Punnett square for this cross. How many offspring would be predicted to have terminal flowers and be dwarf? (See Table 14.1.)
2. **WHAT IF?** List all gametes that could be made by a pea plant heterozygous for seed color, seed shape, and pod shape (*YyRrIi*; see Table 14.1). How large a Punnett square would you need to draw to predict the offspring of a self-pollination of this "trihybrid"?
3. **MAKE CONNECTIONS** In some pea plant crosses, the plants are self-pollinated. Refer back to Concept 13.1 (pp. 248–249) and explain whether self-pollination is considered asexual or sexual reproduction.

For suggested answers, see Appendix A.

CONCEPT 14.2
The laws of probability govern Mendelian inheritance

Mendel's laws of segregation and independent assortment reflect the same rules of probability that apply to tossing coins, rolling dice, and drawing cards from a deck. The probability scale ranges from 0 to 1. An event that is certain to occur has a probability of 1, while an event that is certain *not* to occur has a probability of 0. With a coin that has heads on both sides, the probability of tossing heads is 1, and the probability of tossing tails is 0. With a normal coin, the chance of tossing heads is ½, and the chance of tossing tails is ½. The probability of drawing the ace of spades from a 52-card deck is $\frac{1}{52}$. The probabilities of all possible outcomes for an event must add up to 1. With a deck of cards, the chance of picking a card other than the ace of spades is $\frac{51}{52}$.

Tossing a coin illustrates an important lesson about probability. For every toss, the probability of heads is ½. The outcome of any particular toss is unaffected by what has happened on previous trials. We refer to phenomena such as coin tosses as independent events. Each toss of a coin, whether done sequentially with one coin or simultaneously with many, is independent of every other toss. And like two separate coin tosses, the alleles of one gene segregate into gametes independently of another gene's alleles (the law of independent assortment). Two basic rules of probability can help us predict the outcome of the fusion of such gametes in simple monohybrid crosses and more complicated crosses.

The Multiplication and Addition Rules Applied to Monohybrid Crosses

How do we determine the probability that two or more independent events will occur together in some specific combination? For example, what is the chance that two coins tossed simultaneously will both land heads up? The **multiplication rule** states that to determine this probability, we multiply the probability of one event (one coin coming up heads) by the probability of the other event (the other coin coming up heads). By the multiplication rule, then, the probability that both coins will land heads up is ½ × ½ = ¼.

We can apply the same reasoning to an F_1 monohybrid cross. With seed shape in pea plants as the heritable character, the genotype of F_1 plants is *Rr*. Segregation in a heterozygous plant is like flipping a coin in terms of calculating the probability of each outcome: Each egg produced has a ½ chance of carrying the dominant allele (*R*) and a ½ chance of carrying the recessive allele (*r*). The same odds apply to each sperm cell produced. For a particular F_2 plant to have wrinkled seeds, the recessive trait, both the egg and the sperm that come together must carry the *r* allele. The probability that an *r* allele will be present in both gametes at fertilization is found by multiplying ½ (the probability that the egg will have an *r*) × ½ (the probability that the sperm will have an *r*). Thus, the multiplication rule tells us that the probability of an F_2 plant having wrinkled seeds (*rr*) is ¼ (**Figure 14.9**, on the next page). Likewise, the probability of an F_2 plant carrying both dominant alleles for seed shape (*RR*) is ¼.

To figure out the probability that an F_2 plant from a monohybrid cross will be heterozygous rather than homozygous, we need to invoke a second rule. Notice in Figure 14.9 that the dominant allele can come from the egg and the recessive allele from the sperm, or vice versa. That is, F_1 gametes can combine to produce *Rr* offspring in two *mutually exclusive* ways: For any particular heterozygous F_2 plant, the dominant allele can come from the egg *or* the sperm, but not from both. According to the **addition rule**, the probability that any one of two or more mutually exclusive events will occur is calculated by adding their individual probabilities. As we have just seen, the multiplication rule gives us the individual

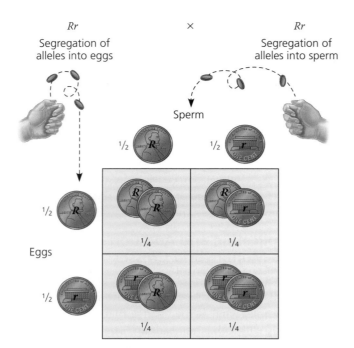

Rr × Rr
Segregation of alleles into eggs   Segregation of alleles into sperm

Sperm

$\frac{1}{2}$ R $\frac{1}{2}$ r

Eggs

$\frac{1}{2}$ R | RR $\frac{1}{4}$ | Rr $\frac{1}{4}$

$\frac{1}{2}$ r | Rr $\frac{1}{4}$ | rr $\frac{1}{4}$

▲ **Figure 14.9 Segregation of alleles and fertilization as chance events.** When a heterozygote (Rr) forms gametes, whether a particular gamete ends up with an R or an r is like the toss of a coin. We can determine the probability for any genotype among the offspring of two heterozygotes by multiplying together the individual probabilities of an egg and sperm having a particular allele (R or r in this example).

probabilities that we will now add together. The probability for one possible way of obtaining an F_2 heterozygote—the dominant allele from the egg and the recessive allele from the sperm—is ¼. The probability for the other possible way—the recessive allele from the egg and the dominant allele from the sperm—is also ¼ (see Figure 14.9). Using the rule of addition, then, we can calculate the probability of an F_2 heterozygote as ¼ + ¼ = ½.

Solving Complex Genetics Problems with the Rules of Probability

We can also apply the rules of probability to predict the outcome of crosses involving multiple characters. Recall that each allelic pair segregates independently during gamete formation (the law of independent assortment). Thus, a dihybrid or other multicharacter cross is equivalent to two or more independent monohybrid crosses occurring simultaneously. By applying what we have learned about monohybrid crosses, we can determine the probability of specific genotypes occurring in the F_2 generation without having to construct unwieldy Punnett squares.

Consider the dihybrid cross between $YyRr$ heterozygotes shown in Figure 14.8. We will focus first on the seed-color character. For a monohybrid cross of Yy plants, we can use a simple Punnett square to determine that the probabilities of the offspring genotypes are ¼ for YY, ½ for Yy, and ¼ for yy. We can draw a second Punnett square to determine that the same

probabilities apply to the offspring genotypes for seed shape: ¼ RR, ½ Rr, and ¼ rr. Knowing these probabilities, we can simply use the multiplication rule to determine the probability of each of the genotypes in the F_2 generation. To give two examples, the calculations for finding the probabilities of two of the possible F_2 genotypes ($YYRR$ and $YyRR$) are shown below:

Probability of $YYRR$ = ¼ (probability of YY) × ¼ (RR) = $\frac{1}{16}$

Probability of $YyRR$ = ½ (Yy) × ¼ (RR) = ⅛

The $YYRR$ genotype corresponds to the upper left box in the larger Punnett square in Figure 14.8 (one box = $\frac{1}{16}$). Looking closely at the larger Punnett square in Figure 14.8, you will see that 2 of the 16 boxes (⅛) correspond to the $YyRR$ genotype.

Now let's see how we can combine the multiplication and addition rules to solve even more complex problems in Mendelian genetics. Imagine a cross of two pea varieties in which we track the inheritance of three characters. Let's cross a trihybrid with purple flowers and yellow, round seeds (heterozygous for all three genes) with a plant with purple flowers and green, wrinkled seeds (heterozygous for flower color but homozygous recessive for the other two characters). Using Mendelian symbols, our cross is $PpYyRr$ × $Ppyyrr$. What fraction of offspring from this cross are predicted to exhibit the recessive phenotypes for *at least two* of the three characters?

To answer this question, we can start by listing all genotypes that fulfill this condition: $ppyyRr$, $ppYyrr$, $Ppyyrr$, $PPyyrr$, and $ppyyrr$. (Because the condition is *at least two* recessive traits, it includes the last genotype, which shows all three recessive traits.) Next, we calculate the probability for each of these genotypes resulting from our $PpYyRr$ × $Ppyyrr$ cross by multiplying together the individual probabilities for the allele pairs, just as we did in our dihybrid example. Note that in a cross involving heterozygous and homozygous allele pairs (for example, Yy × yy), the probability of heterozygous offspring is ½ and the probability of homozygous offspring is ½. Finally, we use the addition rule to add the probabilities for all the different genotypes that fulfill the condition of at least two recessive traits, as shown below:

$ppyyRr$	¼ (probability of pp) × ½ (yy) × ½ (Rr)	= $\frac{1}{16}$
$ppYyrr$	¼ × ½ × ½	= $\frac{1}{16}$
$Ppyyrr$	½ × ½ × ½	= $\frac{2}{16}$
$PPyyrr$	¼ × ½ × ½	= $\frac{1}{16}$
$ppyyrr$	¼ × ½ × ½	= $\frac{1}{16}$
Chance of *at least two* recessive traits		= $\frac{6}{16}$ or ⅜

In time, you'll be able to solve genetics problems faster by using the rules of probability than by filling in Punnett squares.

We cannot predict with certainty the exact numbers of progeny of different genotypes resulting from a genetic cross. But the rules of probability give us the *chance* of various outcomes. Usually, the larger the sample size, the closer the results will conform to our predictions. The reason Mendel counted so many offspring from his crosses is that he understood this statistical feature of inheritance and had a keen sense of the rules of chance.

CONCEPT CHECK 14.2

1. For any gene with a dominant allele *A* and recessive allele *a*, what proportions of the offspring from an *AA* × *Aa* cross are expected to be homozygous dominant, homozygous recessive, and heterozygous?

2. Two organisms, with genotypes *BbDD* and *BBDd*, are mated. Assuming independent assortment of the *B/b* and *D/d* genes, write the genotypes of all possible offspring from this cross and use the rules of probability to calculate the chance of each genotype occurring.

3. **WHAT IF?** Three characters (flower color, seed color, and pod shape) are considered in a cross between two pea plants (*PpYyIi* × *ppYyii*). What fraction of offspring are predicted to be homozygous recessive for at least two of the three characters?

For suggested answers, see Appendix A.

CONCEPT 14.3

Inheritance patterns are often more complex than predicted by simple Mendelian genetics

In the 20th century, geneticists extended Mendelian principles not only to diverse organisms, but also to patterns of inheritance more complex than those described by Mendel. For the work that led to his two laws of inheritance, Mendel chose pea plant characters that turn out to have a relatively simple genetic basis: Each character is determined by one gene, for which there are only two alleles, one completely dominant and the other completely recessive. (There is one exception: Mendel's pod-shape character is actually determined by two genes.) Not all heritable characters are determined so simply, and the relationship between genotype and phenotype is rarely so straightforward. Mendel himself realized that he could not explain the more complicated patterns he observed in crosses involving other pea characters or other plant species. This does not diminish the utility of Mendelian genetics (also called Mendelism), however, because the basic principles of segregation and independent assortment apply even to more complex patterns of inheritance. In this section, we will extend Mendelian genetics to hereditary patterns that were not reported by Mendel.

Extending Mendelian Genetics for a Single Gene

The inheritance of characters determined by a single gene deviates from simple Mendelian patterns when alleles are not completely dominant or recessive, when a particular gene has more than two alleles, or when a single gene produces multiple phenotypes. We will describe examples of each of these situations in this section.

Degrees of Dominance

Alleles can show different degrees of dominance and recessiveness in relation to each other. In Mendel's classic pea crosses, the F_1 offspring always looked like one of the two parental varieties because one allele in a pair showed **complete dominance** over the other. In such situations, the phenotypes of the heterozygote and the dominant homozygote are indistinguishable.

For some genes, however, neither allele is completely dominant, and the F_1 hybrids have a phenotype somewhere between those of the two parental varieties. This phenomenon, called **incomplete dominance**, is seen when red snapdragons are crossed with white snapdragons: All the F_1 hybrids have pink flowers **(Figure 14.10)**. This third, intermediate phenotype results from flowers of the heterozygotes having

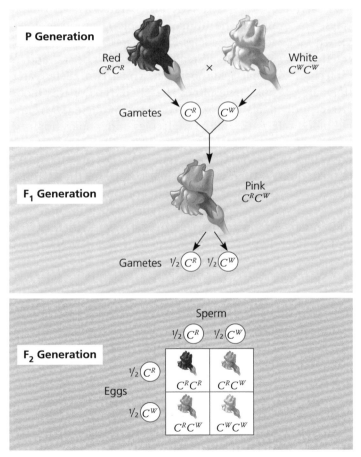

▲ **Figure 14.10 Incomplete dominance in snapdragon color.** When red snapdragons are crossed with white ones, the F_1 hybrids have pink flowers. Segregation of alleles into gametes of the F_1 plants results in an F_2 generation with a 1:2:1 ratio for both genotype and phenotype. Neither allele is dominant, so rather than using upper- and lowercase letters, we use the letter *C* with a superscript to indicate an allele for flower color: C^R for red and C^W for white.

? *Suppose a classmate argues that this figure supports the blending hypothesis for inheritance. What might your classmate say, and how would you respond?*

less red pigment than the red homozygotes. (This is unlike the case of Mendel's pea plants, where the *Pp* heterozygotes make enough pigment for the flowers to be purple, indistinguishable from those of *PP* plants.)

At first glance, incomplete dominance of either allele seems to provide evidence for the blending hypothesis of inheritance, which would predict that the red or white trait could never be retrieved from the pink hybrids. In fact, interbreeding F_1 hybrids produces F_2 offspring with a phenotypic ratio of one red to two pink to one white. (Because heterozygotes have a separate phenotype, the genotypic and phenotypic ratios for the F_2 generation are the same, 1:2:1.) The segregation of the red-flower and white-flower alleles in the gametes produced by the pink-flowered plants confirms that the alleles for flower color are heritable factors that maintain their identity in the hybrids; that is, inheritance is particulate.

Another variation on dominance relationships between alleles is called **codominance**; in this variation, the two alleles each affect the phenotype in separate, distinguishable ways. For example, the human MN blood group is determined by codominant alleles for two specific molecules located on the surface of red blood cells, the M and N molecules. A single gene locus, at which two allelic variations are possible, determines the phenotype of this blood group. Individuals homozygous for the *M* allele (*MM*) have red blood cells with only M molecules; individuals homozygous for the *N* allele (*NN*) have red blood cells with only N molecules. But *both* M and N molecules are present on the red blood cells of individuals heterozygous for the *M* and *N* alleles (*MN*). Note that the MN phenotype is *not* intermediate between the M and N phenotypes, which distinguishes codominance from incomplete dominance. Rather, *both* M and N phenotypes are exhibited by heterozygotes, since both molecules are present.

The Relationship Between Dominance and Phenotype We've now seen that the relative effects of two alleles range from complete dominance of one allele, through incomplete dominance of either allele, to codominance of both alleles. It is important to understand that an allele is called *dominant* because it is seen in the phenotype, not because it somehow subdues a recessive allele. Alleles are simply variations in a gene's nucleotide sequence. When a dominant allele coexists with a recessive allele in a heterozygote, they do not actually interact at all. It is in the pathway from genotype to phenotype that dominance and recessiveness come into play.

To illustrate the relationship between dominance and phenotype, we can use one of the characters Mendel studied—round versus wrinkled pea seed shape. The dominant allele (round) codes for an enzyme that helps convert an unbranched form of starch to a branched form in the seed. The recessive allele (wrinkled) codes for a defective form of this enzyme, leading to an accumulation of unbranched starch,

which causes excess water to enter the seed by osmosis. Later, when the seed dries, it wrinkles. If a dominant allele is present, no excess water enters the seed and it does not wrinkle when it dries. One dominant allele results in enough of the enzyme to synthesize adequate amounts of branched starch, which means that dominant homozygotes and heterozygotes have the same phenotype: round seeds.

A closer look at the relationship between dominance and phenotype reveals an intriguing fact: For any character, the observed dominant/recessive relationship of alleles depends on the level at which we examine phenotype. **Tay-Sachs disease**, an inherited disorder in humans, provides an example. The brain cells of a child with Tay-Sachs disease cannot metabolize certain lipids because a crucial enzyme does not work properly. As these lipids accumulate in brain cells, the child begins to suffer seizures, blindness, and degeneration of motor and mental performance and dies within a few years.

Only children who inherit two copies of the Tay-Sachs allele (homozygotes) have the disease. Thus, at the *organismal* level, the Tay-Sachs allele qualifies as recessive. However, the activity level of the lipid-metabolizing enzyme in heterozygotes is intermediate between that in individuals homozygous for the normal allele and that in individuals with Tay-Sachs disease. The intermediate phenotype observed at the *biochemical* level is characteristic of incomplete dominance of either allele. Fortunately, the heterozygote condition does not lead to disease symptoms, apparently because half the normal enzyme activity is sufficient to prevent lipid accumulation in the brain. Extending our analysis to yet another level, we find that heterozygous individuals produce equal numbers of normal and dysfunctional enzyme molecules. Thus, at the *molecular* level, the normal allele and the Tay-Sachs allele are codominant. As you can see, whether alleles appear to be completely dominant, incompletely dominant, or codominant depends on the level at which the phenotype is analyzed.

Frequency of Dominant Alleles Although you might assume that the dominant allele for a particular character would be more common in a population than the recessive allele, this is not a given. For example, about one baby out of 400 in the United States is born with extra fingers or toes, a condition known as polydactyly. Some cases are caused by the presence of a dominant allele. The low frequency of polydactyly indicates that the recessive allele, which results in five digits per appendage, is far more prevalent than the dominant allele in the population. In Chapter 23, you will learn how relative frequencies of alleles in a population are affected by natural selection.

Multiple Alleles

Only two alleles exist for the pea characters that Mendel studied, but most genes exist in more than two allelic forms. The ABO blood groups in humans, for instance, are determined by three alleles of a single gene: I^A, I^B, and *i*. A person's blood

<table>
<tr><td colspan="4">(a) The three alleles for the ABO blood groups and their carbohydrates. Each allele codes for an enzyme that may add a specific carbohydrate (designated by the superscript on the allele and shown as a triangle or circle) to red blood cells.</td></tr>
</table>

Allele	I^A	I^B	i
Carbohydrate	A △	B ○	none

<table>
<tr><td colspan="5">(b) Blood group genotypes and phenotypes. There are six possible genotypes, resulting in four different phenotypes.</td></tr>
</table>

Genotype	I^AI^A or I^Ai	I^BI^B or I^Bi	I^AI^B	ii
Red blood cell appearance				
Phenotype (blood group)	A	B	AB	O

▲ **Figure 14.11 Multiple alleles for the ABO blood groups.** The four blood groups result from different combinations of three alleles.

❓ *Based on the surface carbohydrate phenotype in (b), what are the dominance relationships among the alleles?*

group (phenotype) may be one of four types: A, B, AB, or O. These letters refer to two carbohydrates—A and B—that may be found on the surface of red blood cells. A person's blood cells may have carbohydrate A (type A blood), carbohydrate B (type B), both (type AB), or neither (type O), as shown schematically in **Figure 14.11**. Matching compatible blood groups is critical for safe blood transfusions.

Pleiotropy

So far, we have treated Mendelian inheritance as though each gene affects only one phenotypic character. Most genes, however, have multiple phenotypic effects, a property called **pleiotropy** (from the Greek *pleion*, more). In humans, for example, pleiotropic alleles are responsible for the multiple symptoms associated with certain hereditary diseases, such as cystic fibrosis and sickle-cell disease, discussed later in this chapter. In the garden pea, the gene that determines flower color also affects the color of the coating on the outer surface of the seed, which can be gray or white. Given the intricate molecular and cellular interactions responsible for an organism's development and physiology, it isn't surprising that a single gene can affect a number of characteristics in an organism.

Extending Mendelian Genetics for Two or More Genes

Dominance relationships, multiple alleles, and pleiotropy all have to do with the effects of the alleles of a single gene. We now consider two situations in which two or more genes are involved in determining a particular phenotype.

Epistasis

In **epistasis** (from the Greek for "standing upon"), the phenotypic expression of a gene at one locus alters that of a gene at a second locus. An example will help clarify this concept. In Labrador retrievers (commonly called "Labs"), black coat color is dominant to brown. Let's designate *B* and *b* as the two alleles for this character. For a Lab to have brown fur, its genotype must be *bb*; these dogs are called chocolate Labs. But there is more to the story. A second gene determines whether or not pigment will be deposited in the hair. The dominant allele, symbolized by *E*, results in the deposition of either black or brown pigment, depending on the genotype at the first locus. But if the Lab is homozygous recessive for the second locus (*ee*), then the coat is yellow, regardless of the genotype at the black/brown locus. In this case, the gene for pigment deposition (*E/e*) is said to be epistatic to the gene that codes for black or brown pigment (*B/b*).

What happens if we mate black Labs that are heterozygous for both genes (*BbEe*)? Although the two genes affect the same phenotypic character (coat color), they follow the law of independent assortment. Thus, our breeding experiment represents an F_1 dihybrid cross, like those that produced a 9:3:3:1 ratio in Mendel's experiments. We can use a Punnett square to represent the genotypes of the F_2 offspring **(Figure 14.12)**. As a result

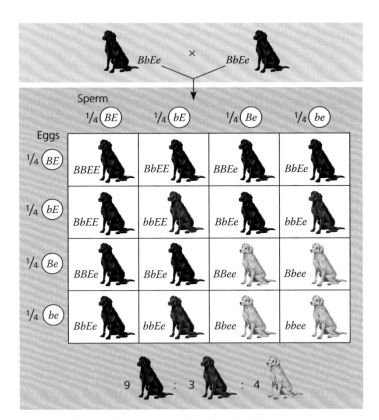

▲ **Figure 14.12 An example of epistasis.** This Punnett square illustrates the genotypes and phenotypes predicted for offspring of matings between two black Labrador retrievers of genotype *BbEe*. The *E/e* gene, which is epistatic to the *B/b* gene coding for hair pigment, controls whether or not pigment of any color will be deposited in the hair.

of epistasis, the phenotypic ratio among the F$_2$ offspring is nine black to three chocolate (brown) to four yellow. Other types of epistatic interactions produce different ratios, but all are modified versions of 9:3:3:1.

Polygenic Inheritance

Mendel studied characters that could be classified on an either-or basis, such as purple versus white flower color. But for many characters, such as human skin color and height, an either-or classification is impossible because the characters vary in the population in gradations along a continuum. These are called **quantitative characters**. Quantitative variation usually indicates **polygenic inheritance**, an additive effect of two or more genes on a single phenotypic character (the converse of pleiotropy, where a single gene affects several phenotypic characters).

There is evidence, for instance, that skin pigmentation in humans is controlled by at least three separately inherited genes (probably more, but we will simplify). Let's consider three genes, with a dark-skin allele for each gene (*A*, *B*, or *C*) contributing one "unit" of darkness (also a simplification) to the phenotype and being incompletely dominant to the other allele (*a*, *b*, or *c*). An *AABBCC* person would be very dark, while an *aabbcc* individual would be very light. An *AaBbCc* person would have skin of an intermediate shade. Because the alleles have a cumulative effect, the genotypes *AaBbCc* and *AABbcc* would make the same genetic contribution (three units) to skin darkness. As shown in **Figure 14.13**, there are seven skin-color phenotypes that could result from a mating between *AaBbCc* heterozygotes. In a large number of such matings, the majority of offspring would be expected to have intermediate phenotypes (skin color in the middle range). Environmental factors, such as exposure to the sun, also affect the skin-color phenotype.

Nature and Nurture: The Environmental Impact on Phenotype

Another departure from simple Mendelian genetics arises when the phenotype for a character depends on environment as well as genotype. A single tree, locked into its inherited genotype, has leaves that vary in size, shape, and greenness, depending on their exposure to wind and sun. For humans, nutrition influences height, exercise alters build, sun-tanning darkens the skin, and experience improves performance on intelligence tests. Even identical twins, who are genetic equals, accumulate phenotypic differences as a result of their unique experiences.

Whether human characteristics are more influenced by genes or the environment—nature versus nurture—is a very old and hotly contested debate that we will not attempt to settle here. We can say, however, that a genotype generally is not associated with a rigidly defined phenotype, but rather with a range of phenotypic possibilities due to environmental influences. This phenotypic range is called the **norm of reaction** for a genotype **(Figure 14.14)**. For some characters, such as the

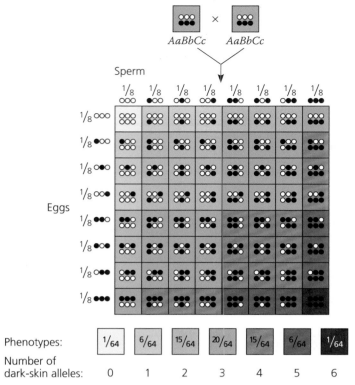

▲ **Figure 14.13 A simplified model for polygenic inheritance of skin color.** According to this model, three separately inherited genes affect the darkness of skin. The heterozygous individuals (*AaBbCc*) represented by the two rectangles at the top of this figure each carry three dark-skin alleles (black circles, which represent *A*, *B*, or *C*) and three light-skin alleles (white circles, which represent *a*, *b*, or *c*). The Punnett square shows all the possible genetic combinations in gametes and in offspring of a large number of hypothetical matings between these heterozygotes. The results are summarized by the phenotypic ratios under the Punnett square.

DRAW IT *Make a bar graph of the results, with skin color (number of dark-skin alleles) along the x-axis and fraction of offspring along the y-axis. Draw a rough curve corresponding to the results and discuss what it shows about the relative proportions of different phenotypes among the offspring.*

▲ **Figure 14.14 The effect of environment on phenotype.** The outcome of a genotype lies within its norm of reaction, a phenotypic range that depends on the environment in which the genotype is expressed. For example, hydrangea flowers of the same genetic variety range in color from blue-violet to pink, with the shade and intensity of color depending on the acidity and aluminum content of the soil.

ABO blood group system, the norm of reaction has no breadth whatsoever; that is, a given genotype mandates a very specific phenotype. Other characteristics, such as a person's blood count of red and white cells, vary quite a bit, depending on such factors as the altitude, the customary level of physical activity, and the presence of infectious agents.

Generally, norms of reaction are broadest for polygenic characters. Environment contributes to the quantitative nature of these characters, as we have seen in the continuous variation of skin color. Geneticists refer to such characters as **multifactorial**, meaning that many factors, both genetic and environmental, collectively influence phenotype.

Integrating a Mendelian View of Heredity and Variation

We have now broadened our view of Mendelian inheritance by exploring degrees of dominance as well as multiple alleles, pleiotropy, epistasis, polygenic inheritance, and the phenotypic impact of the environment. How can we integrate these refinements into a comprehensive theory of Mendelian genetics? The key is to make the transition from the reductionist emphasis on single genes and phenotypic characters to the emergent properties of the organism as a whole, one of the themes of this book.

The term *phenotype* can refer not only to specific characters, such as flower color and blood group, but also to an organism in its entirety—*all* aspects of its physical appearance, internal anatomy, physiology, and behavior. Similarly, the term *genotype* can refer to an organism's entire genetic makeup, not just its alleles for a single genetic locus. In most cases, a gene's impact on phenotype is affected by other genes and by the environment. In this integrated view of heredity and variation, an organism's phenotype reflects its overall genotype and unique environmental history.

Considering all that can occur in the pathway from genotype to phenotype, it is indeed impressive that Mendel could uncover the fundamental principles governing the transmission of individual genes from parents to offspring. Mendel's two laws, segregation and independent assortment, explain heritable variations in terms of alternative forms of genes (hereditary "particles," now known as the alleles of genes) that are passed along, generation after generation, according to simple rules of probability. This theory of inheritance is equally valid for peas, flies, fishes, birds, and human beings—indeed, for any organism with a sexual life cycle. Furthermore, by extending the principles of segregation and independent assortment to help explain such hereditary patterns as epistasis and quantitative characters, we begin to see how broadly Mendelism applies. From Mendel's abbey garden came a theory of particulate inheritance that anchors modern genetics. In the last section of this chapter, we will apply Mendelian genetics to human inheritance, with emphasis on the transmission of hereditary diseases.

CONCEPT 14.4

Many human traits follow Mendelian patterns of inheritance

Peas are convenient subjects for genetic research, but humans are not. The human generation span is long—about 20 years—and human parents produce many fewer offspring than peas and most other species. Even more important, it wouldn't be ethical to ask pairs of humans to breed so that the phenotypes of their offspring could be analyzed! In spite of these constraints, the study of human genetics continues, spurred on by our desire to understand our own inheritance. New molecular biological techniques have led to many breakthrough discoveries, as we will see in Chapter 20, but basic Mendelism endures as the foundation of human genetics.

Pedigree Analysis

Unable to manipulate the mating patterns of people, geneticists must analyze the results of matings that have already occurred. They do so by collecting information about a family's history for a particular trait and assembling this information into a family tree describing the traits of parents and children across the generations—the family **pedigree**.

Figure 14.15a, on the next page, shows a three-generation pedigree that traces the occurrence of a pointed contour of the hairline on the forehead. This trait, called a widow's peak, is due to a dominant allele, *W*. Because the widow's-peak allele is dominant, all individuals who lack a widow's peak must be homozygous recessive (*ww*). The two grandparents with widow's peaks must have the *Ww* genotype, since some of their offspring are homozygous recessive. The offspring in the second generation who *do* have widow's peaks must also be heterozygous, because they are the products of *Ww* × *ww* matings. The third generation in this pedigree consists of two sisters. The one

Key

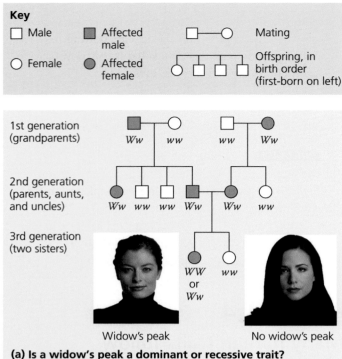

□ Male	■ Affected male
○ Female	● Affected female

□—○ Mating

Offspring, in birth order (first-born on left)

1st generation (grandparents)
Ww   ww   ww   Ww

2nd generation (parents, aunts, and uncles)
Ww ww ww Ww   Ww ww

3rd generation (two sisters)
WW or Ww   ww

Widow's peak   No widow's peak

(a) Is a widow's peak a dominant or recessive trait?
Tips for pedigree analysis: Notice in the third generation that the second-born daughter lacks a widow's peak, although both of her parents had the trait. Such a pattern of inheritance supports the hypothesis that the trait is due to a dominant allele. If the trait were due to a *recessive* allele, and both parents had the recessive phenotype, then *all* of their offspring would also have the recessive phenotype.

1st generation (grandparents)
Ff   Ff   ff   Ff

2nd generation (parents, aunts, and uncles)
FF or Ff ff ff Ff   Ff ff

3rd generation (two sisters)
ff   FF or Ff

Attached earlobe   Free earlobe

(b) Is an attached earlobe a dominant or recessive trait?
Tips for pedigree analysis: Notice that the first-born daughter in the third generation has attached earlobes, although both of her parents lack that trait (they have free earlobes). Such a pattern is easily explained if the attached-lobe phenotype is due to a recessive allele. If it were due to a *dominant* allele, then at least one parent would also have had the trait.

▲ **Figure 14.15 Pedigree analysis.** Each of these pedigrees traces a trait through three generations of the same family. The two traits have different inheritance patterns, as seen by analysis of the pedigrees.

who has a widow's peak could be either homozygous (*WW*) or heterozygous (*Ww*), given what we know about the genotypes of her parents (both *Ww*).

Figure 14.15b is a pedigree of the same family, but this time we focus on a recessive trait, attached earlobes. We'll use *f* for the recessive allele and *F* for the dominant allele, which results in free earlobes. As you work your way through the pedigree, notice once again that you can apply what you have learned about Mendelian inheritance to understand the genotypes shown for the family members.

An important application of a pedigree is to help us calculate the probability that a future child will have a particular genotype and phenotype. Suppose that the couple represented in the second generation of Figure 14.15 decides to have one more child. What is the probability that the child will have a widow's peak? This is equivalent to a Mendelian F_1 monohybrid cross (*Ww × Ww*), and thus the probability that a child will inherit a dominant allele and have a widow's peak is ¾ (¼ *WW* + ½ *Ww*). What is the probability that the child will have attached earlobes? Again, we can treat this as a monohybrid cross (*Ff × Ff*), but this time we want to know the chance that the offspring will be homozygous recessive (*ff*). That probability is ¼. Finally, what is the chance that the child will have a widow's peak *and* attached earlobes? Assuming that the genes for these two characters are on different chromosomes, the two pairs of alleles will assort independently in this dihybrid cross (*WwFf × WwFf*). Thus, we can use the multiplication rule: ¾ (chance of widow's peak) × ¼ (chance of attached earlobes) = ³⁄₁₆ (chance of widow's peak and attached earlobes).

Pedigrees are a more serious matter when the alleles in question cause disabling or deadly diseases instead of innocuous human variations such as hairline or earlobe configuration. However, for disorders inherited as simple Mendelian traits, the same techniques of pedigree analysis apply.

Recessively Inherited Disorders

Thousands of genetic disorders are known to be inherited as simple recessive traits. These disorders range in severity from relatively mild, such as albinism (lack of pigmentation, which results in susceptibility to skin cancers and vision problems), to life-threatening, such as cystic fibrosis.

The Behavior of Recessive Alleles

How can we account for the behavior of alleles that cause recessively inherited disorders? Recall that genes code for proteins of specific function. An allele that causes a genetic disorder (let's call it allele *a*) codes for either a malfunctioning protein or no protein at all. In the case of disorders classified as recessive, heterozygotes (*Aa*) are typically normal in phenotype because one copy of the normal allele (*A*) produces a sufficient amount of the specific protein. Thus, a recessively inherited disorder shows up only in the homozygous individuals (*aa*)

▲ **Figure 14.16 Albinism: a recessive trait.** One of the two sisters shown here has normal coloration; the other is albino. Most recessive homozygotes are born to parents who are carriers of the disorder but themselves have a normal phenotype, the case shown in the Punnett square.

? *What is the probability that the sister with normal coloration is a carrier of the albinism allele?*

who inherit one recessive allele from each parent. Although phenotypically normal with regard to the disorder, heterozygotes may transmit the recessive allele to their offspring and thus are called **carriers**. Figure 14.16 illustrates these ideas using albinism as an example.

Most people who have recessive disorders are born to parents who are carriers of the disorder but have a normal phenotype, as is the case shown in the Punnett square in Figure 14.16. A mating between two carriers corresponds to a Mendelian F_1 monohybrid cross, so the predicted genotypic ratio for the offspring is 1 AA : 2 Aa : 1 aa. Thus, each child has a ¼ chance of inheriting a double dose of the recessive allele; in the case of albinism, such a child will be albino. From the genotypic ratio, we also can see that out of three offspring with the *normal* phenotype (one AA plus two Aa), two are predicted to be heterozygous carriers, a ⅔ chance. Recessive homozygotes could also result from $Aa \times aa$ and $aa \times aa$ matings, but if the disorder is lethal before reproductive age or results in sterility (neither of which is true for albinism), no aa individuals will reproduce. Even if recessive homozygotes are able to reproduce, such individuals will still account for a much smaller percentage of the population than heterozygous carriers (for reasons we will examine in Chapter 23).

In general, genetic disorders are not evenly distributed among all groups of people. For example, the incidence of Tay-Sachs disease, which we described earlier in this chapter, is disproportionately high among Ashkenazic Jews, Jewish people whose ancestors lived in central Europe. In that population, Tay-Sachs disease occurs in one out of 3,600 births, an incidence about 100 times greater than that among non-Jews or Mediterranean (Sephardic) Jews. This uneven distribution results from the different genetic histories of the world's peoples during less technological times, when populations were more geographically (and hence genetically) isolated.

When a disease-causing recessive allele is rare, it is relatively unlikely that two carriers of the same harmful allele will meet and mate. However, if the man and woman are close relatives (for example, siblings or first cousins), the probability of passing on recessive traits increases greatly. These are called consanguineous ("same blood") matings, and they are indicated in pedigrees by double lines. Because people with recent common ancestors are more likely to carry the same recessive alleles than are unrelated people, it is more likely that a mating of close relatives will produce offspring homozygous for recessive traits—including harmful ones. Such effects can be observed in many types of domesticated and zoo animals that have become inbred.

There is debate among geneticists about the extent to which human consanguinity increases the risk of inherited diseases. Many deleterious alleles have such severe effects that a homozygous embryo spontaneously aborts long before birth. Still, most societies and cultures have laws or taboos forbidding marriages between close relatives. These rules may have evolved out of empirical observation that in most populations, stillbirths and birth defects are more common when parents are closely related. Social and economic factors have also influenced the development of customs and laws against consanguineous marriages.

Cystic Fibrosis

The most common lethal genetic disease in the United States is **cystic fibrosis**, which strikes one out of every 2,500 people of European descent but is much rarer in other groups. Among people of European descent, one out of 25 (4%) are carriers of the cystic fibrosis allele. The normal allele for this gene codes for a membrane protein that functions in the transport of chloride ions between certain cells and the extracellular fluid. These chloride transport channels are defective or absent in the plasma membranes of children who inherit two recessive alleles for cystic fibrosis. The result is an abnormally high concentration of extracellular chloride, which causes the mucus that coats certain cells to become thicker and stickier than normal. The mucus builds up in the pancreas, lungs, digestive tract, and other organs, leading to multiple (pleiotropic) effects, including poor absorption of nutrients from the intestines, chronic bronchitis, and recurrent bacterial infections.

If untreated, most children with cystic fibrosis die before their 5th birthday. But daily doses of antibiotics to prevent infection, gentle pounding on the chest to clear mucus from clogged airways, and other preventive treatments can prolong life. In the United States, more than half of those with cystic fibrosis now survive into their late 20s or even 30s and beyond.

Sickle-Cell Disease:
A Genetic Disorder with Evolutionary Implications

EVOLUTION The most common inherited disorder among people of African descent is **sickle-cell disease**, which affects one out of 400 African-Americans. Sickle-cell disease is caused by the substitution of a single amino acid in the hemoglobin protein of red blood cells; in homozygous individuals, all hemoglobin is of the sickle-cell (abnormal) variety. When the oxygen content of an affected individual's blood is low (at high altitudes or under physical stress, for instance), the sickle-cell hemoglobin molecules aggregate into long rods that deform the red cells into a sickle shape (see Figure 5.21). Sickled cells may clump and clog small blood vessels, often leading to other symptoms throughout the body, including physical weakness, pain, organ damage, and even paralysis. Regular blood transfusions can ward off brain damage in children with sickle-cell disease, and new drugs can help prevent or treat other problems, but there is no cure.

Although two sickle-cell alleles are necessary for an individual to manifest full-blown sickle-cell disease, the presence of one sickle-cell allele can affect the phenotype. Thus, at the organismal level, the normal allele is incompletely dominant to the sickle-cell allele. Heterozygotes (carriers), said to have *sickle-cell trait*, are usually healthy, but they may suffer some sickle-cell symptoms during prolonged periods of reduced blood oxygen. At the molecular level, the two alleles are codominant; both normal and abnormal (sickle-cell) hemoglobins are made in heterozygotes.

About one out of ten African-Americans have sickle-cell trait, an unusually high frequency of heterozygotes for an allele with severe detrimental effects in homozygotes. Why haven't evolutionary processes resulted in the disappearance of this allele among this population? One explanation is that having a single copy of the sickle-cell allele reduces the frequency and severity of malaria attacks, especially among young children. The malaria parasite spends part of its life cycle in red blood cells (see Figure 28.10), and the presence of even heterozygous amounts of sickle-cell hemoglobin results in lower parasite densities and hence reduced malaria symptoms. Thus, in tropical Africa, where infection with the malaria parasite is common, the sickle-cell allele confers an advantage to heterozygotes even though it is harmful in the homozygous state. (The balance between these two effects will be discussed in Chapter 23, p. 484.) The relatively high frequency of African-Americans with sickle-cell trait is a vestige of their African roots.

Dominantly Inherited Disorders

Although many harmful alleles are recessive, a number of human disorders are due to dominant alleles. One example is *achondroplasia*, a form of dwarfism that occurs in one of every 25,000 people. Heterozygous individuals have the dwarf phenotype **(Figure 14.17)**. Therefore, all people who are not achondroplastic dwarfs—99.99% of the population—are homozygous for the recessive allele. Like the presence of extra fingers or toes mentioned earlier, achondroplasia is a trait for which the recessive allele is much more prevalent than the corresponding dominant allele.

▲ **Figure 14.17 Achondroplasia: a dominant trait.** Dr. Michael C. Ain has achondroplasia, a form of dwarfism caused by a dominant allele. This has inspired his work: He is a specialist in the repair of bone defects caused by achondroplasia and other disorders. The dominant allele (*D*) might have arisen as a mutation in the egg or sperm of a parent or could have been inherited from an affected parent, as shown for an affected father in the Punnett square.

Dominant alleles that cause a lethal disease are much less common than recessive alleles that have lethal effects. All lethal alleles arise by mutations (changes to the DNA) in cells that produce sperm or eggs; presumably, such mutations are equally likely to be recessive or dominant. A lethal recessive allele can be passed from one generation to the next by heterozygous carriers because the carriers themselves have normal phenotypes. A lethal dominant allele, however, often causes the death of afflicted individuals before they can mature and reproduce, so the allele is not passed on to future generations.

Huntington's Disease: A Late-Onset Lethal Disease

The timing of onset of a disease significantly affects its inheritance. A lethal dominant allele is able to be passed on if it causes death at a relatively advanced age. By the time symptoms are evident, the individual with the allele may have already transmitted it to his or her children. For example, **Huntington's disease**, a degenerative disease of the nervous system, is caused by a lethal dominant allele that has no obvious phenotypic effect until the individual is about 35 to 45 years old. Once the deterioration of the nervous system begins, it is irreversible and inevitably fatal. As with other dominant traits, a child born to a parent with the Huntington's disease allele has a 50% chance of inheriting the allele and the disorder (see the Punnett square in Figure 14.17). In the United States, this devastating disease afflicts about one in 10,000 people.

At one time, the onset of symptoms was the only way to know if a person had inherited the Huntington's allele, but this is no longer the case. By analyzing DNA samples from a large family with a high incidence of the disorder, geneticists tracked the Huntington's allele to a locus near the tip of chromosome 4, and the gene was sequenced in 1993. This information led to the development of a test that could detect the presence of the Huntington's allele in an individual's genome. (The methods that make such tests possible are discussed in Chapter 20.) The availability of this test poses an agonizing dilemma for those with a family history of Huntington's disease. Some individuals may want to be tested for this disease before planning a family, whereas others may decide it would be too stressful to find out. Clearly, this is a highly personal decision.

Multifactorial Disorders

The hereditary diseases we have discussed so far are sometimes described as simple Mendelian disorders because they result from abnormality of one or both alleles at a single genetic locus. Many more people are susceptible to diseases that have a multifactorial basis—a genetic component plus a significant environmental influence. Heart disease, diabetes, cancer, alcoholism, certain mental illnesses such as schizophrenia and bipolar disorder, and many other diseases are multifactorial. In many cases, the hereditary component is polygenic. For example, many genes affect cardiovascular health, making some of us more prone than others to heart attacks and strokes. No matter what our genotype, however, our lifestyle has a tremendous effect on phenotype for cardiovascular health and other multifactorial characters. Exercise, a healthful diet, abstinence from smoking, and an ability to handle stressful situations all reduce our risk of heart disease and some types of cancer.

At present, so little is understood about the genetic contributions to most multifactorial diseases that the best public health strategy is to educate people about the importance of environmental factors and to promote healthful behavior.

Genetic Testing and Counseling

Avoiding simple Mendelian disorders is possible when the risk of a particular genetic disorder can be assessed before a child is conceived or during the early stages of the pregnancy. Many hospitals have genetic counselors who can provide information to prospective parents concerned about a family history for a specific disease.

Counseling Based on Mendelian Genetics and Probability Rules

Consider the case of a hypothetical couple, John and Carol. Each had a brother who died from the same recessively inherited lethal disease. Before conceiving their first child, John and Carol seek genetic counseling to determine the risk of having a child with the disease. From the information about their brothers, we know that both parents of John and both parents of Carol must have been carriers of the recessive allele. Thus, John and Carol are both products of $Aa \times Aa$ crosses, where a symbolizes the allele that causes this particular disease. We also know that John and Carol are not homozygous recessive

(*aa*), because they do not have the disease. Therefore, their genotypes are either *AA* or *Aa*.

Given a genotypic ratio of 1 *AA* : 2 *Aa* : 1 *aa* for offspring of an $Aa \times Aa$ cross, John and Carol each have a ⅔ chance of being carriers (*Aa*). According to the rule of multiplication, the overall probability of their firstborn having the disorder is ⅔ (the chance that John is a carrier) times ⅔ (the chance that Carol is a carrier) times ¼ (the chance of two carriers having a child with the disease), which equals ⅑. Suppose that Carol and John decide to have a child—after all, there is an ⁸⁄₉ chance that their baby will not have the disorder. If, despite these odds, their child is born with the disease, then we would know that *both* John and Carol are, in fact, carriers (*Aa* genotype). If both John and Carol are carriers, there is a ¼ chance that any subsequent child this couple has will have the disease. The probability is higher for subsequent children because the diagnosis of the disease in the first child established that both parents are carriers, not because the genotype of the first child affects in any way that of future children.

When we use Mendel's laws to predict possible outcomes of matings, it is important to remember that each child represents an independent event in the sense that its genotype is unaffected by the genotypes of older siblings. Suppose that John and Carol have three more children, and *all three* have the hypothetical hereditary disease. There is only one chance in 64 (¼ × ¼ × ¼) that such an outcome will occur. Despite this run of misfortune, the chance that still another child of this couple will have the disease remains ¼.

Tests for Identifying Carriers

Most children with recessive disorders are born to parents with normal phenotypes. The key to accurately assessing the genetic risk for a particular disease is therefore to find out whether the prospective parents are heterozygous carriers of the recessive allele. For an increasing number of heritable disorders, tests are available that can distinguish individuals of normal phenotype who are dominant homozygotes from those who are heterozygous carriers (**Figure 14.18**, on the next page). There are now tests that can identify carriers of the alleles for Tay-Sachs disease, sickle-cell disease, and the most common form of cystic fibrosis.

These tests for identifying carriers enable people with family histories of genetic disorders to make informed decisions about having children, but raise other issues. Could carriers be denied health or life insurance or lose the jobs providing those benefits, even though they themselves are healthy? The Genetic Information Nondiscrimination Act, signed into law in the United States in 2008, allays these concerns by prohibiting discrimination in employment or insurance coverage based on genetic test results. A question that remains is whether sufficient genetic counseling is available to help large numbers of individuals understand their genetic test results. Even when test results are clearly understood, affected individuals may still face difficult decisions. Advances in biotechnology offer

IMPACT

Genetic Testing

Since the sequencing of the human genome was completed in 2003, there has been a virtual explosion in the number and kinds of DNA-based genetic tests. As of 2010, genetic testing for over 2,000 different disease-causing alleles is available.

WHY IT MATTERS For prospective parents with a family history of a recessive or late-onset dominant disorder, deciding whether to have children can be a difficult decision. Genetic testing can eliminate some of the uncertainty and allow better predictions of the probabilities and risks involved.

FURTHER READING Designing rules for designer babies, *Scientific American* 300:29 (2009).

WHAT IF? If one parent tests positive and the other tests negative for a recessive allele associated with a disorder, what is the probability that their first child will have the disorder? That their first child will be a carrier? That, if their first child is a carrier, the second will also be a carrier?

the potential to reduce human suffering, but along with them come ethical issues that require conscientious deliberation.

Fetal Testing

Suppose a couple expecting a child learns that they are both carriers of the Tay-Sachs allele. In the 14th–16th week of pregnancy, tests performed along with a technique called **amniocentesis** can determine whether the developing fetus has Tay-Sachs disease (**Figure 14.19a**). In this procedure, a physician inserts a needle into the uterus and extracts about 10 mL of amniotic fluid, the liquid that bathes the fetus. Some genetic disorders can be detected from the presence of certain molecules in the amniotic fluid itself. Tests for other disorders, including Tay-Sachs disease, are performed on the DNA of cells cultured in the laboratory, descendants of fetal cells sloughed off into the amniotic fluid. A karyotype of these cultured cells can also identify certain chromosomal defects (see Figure 13.3).

In an alternative technique called **chorionic villus sampling (CVS)**, a physician inserts a narrow tube through the cervix into the uterus and suctions out a tiny sample of tissue from the placenta, the organ that transmits nutrients and fetal wastes between the fetus and the mother (**Figure 14.19b**). The cells of the chorionic villi of the placenta, the portion sampled, are derived from the fetus and have the same genotype and DNA sequence as the new individual. These cells are proliferating rapidly enough to allow karyotyping to be carried out immediately. This rapid analysis represents an advantage over amniocentesis, in which the cells must be cultured for several weeks before karyotyping. Another advantage of CVS is that it can be performed as early as the 8th–10th week of pregnancy.

Recently, medical scientists have developed methods for isolating fetal cells, or even fetal DNA, that have escaped into the mother's blood. Although very few are present, the cells can be cultured and tested, and the fetal DNA can also be analyzed.

Imaging techniques allow a physician to examine a fetus directly for major anatomical abnormalities that might not show up in genetic tests. In the *ultrasound* technique, reflected sound waves are used to produce an image of the fetus by a simple noninvasive procedure. In *fetoscopy*, a needle-thin tube containing a viewing scope and fiber optics (to transmit light) is inserted into the uterus.

Ultrasound and isolation of fetal cells or DNA from maternal blood pose no known risk to either mother or fetus, while the other procedures can cause complications in a small percentage of cases. Amniocentesis or CVS for diagnostic testing is generally offered to women over age 35, due to their increased risk of bearing a child with Down syndrome, and may also be offered to younger women if there are known concerns. If the fetal tests reveal a serious disorder, the parents face the difficult choice of either terminating the pregnancy or preparing to care for a child with a genetic disorder.

Newborn Screening

Some genetic disorders can be detected at birth by simple biochemical tests that are now routinely performed in most hospitals in the United States. One common screening program is for phenylketonuria (PKU), a recessively inherited disorder that occurs in about one out of every 10,000–15,000 births in the United States. Children with this disease cannot properly metabolize the amino acid phenylalanine. This compound and its by-product, phenylpyruvate, can accumulate to toxic levels in the blood, causing severe intellectual disability (mental retardation). However, if PKU is detected in the newborn, a special diet low in phenylalanine will usually allow normal development. (Among many other substances, this diet excludes the artificial sweetener aspartame, which contains phenylalanine.) Unfortunately, few other genetic disorders are treatable at present.

Fetal and newborn screening for serious inherited diseases, tests for identifying carriers, and genetic counseling all rely on the Mendelian model of inheritance. We owe the "gene idea"—the concept of heritable factors transmitted according

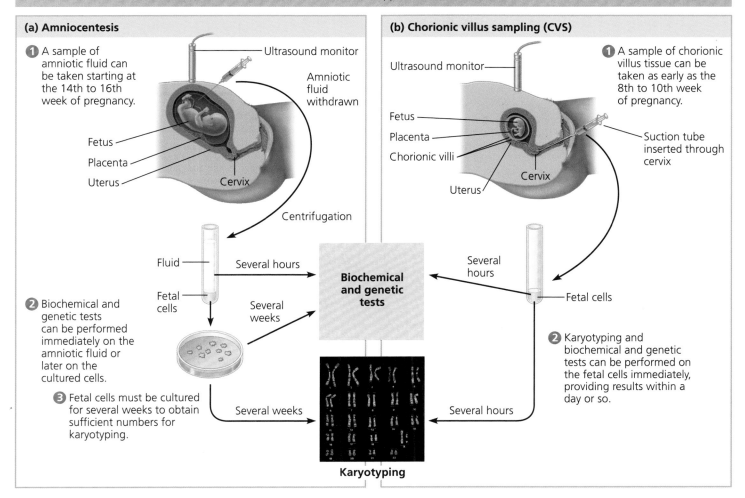

▼ **Figure 14.19 Testing a fetus for genetic disorders.** Biochemical tests may detect substances associated with particular disorders, and genetic testing can detect many genetic abnormalities. Karyotyping shows whether the chromosomes of the fetus are normal in number and appearance.

(a) Amniocentesis

1 A sample of amniotic fluid can be taken starting at the 14th to 16th week of pregnancy.

Ultrasound monitor

Amniotic fluid withdrawn

Fetus

Placenta

Uterus

Cervix

Centrifugation

Fluid

Several hours

Fetal cells

Several weeks

2 Biochemical and genetic tests can be performed immediately on the amniotic fluid or later on the cultured cells.

3 Fetal cells must be cultured for several weeks to obtain sufficient numbers for karyotyping.

Several weeks

Biochemical and genetic tests

Karyotyping

(b) Chorionic villus sampling (CVS)

Ultrasound monitor

1 A sample of chorionic villus tissue can be taken as early as the 8th to 10th week of pregnancy.

Fetus

Placenta

Chorionic villi

Cervix

Uterus

Suction tube inserted through cervix

Several hours

Fetal cells

2 Karyotyping and biochemical and genetic tests can be performed on the fetal cells immediately, providing results within a day or so.

Several hours

to simple rules of chance—to the elegant quantitative experiments of Gregor Mendel. The importance of his discoveries was overlooked by most biologists until early in the 20th century, decades after he reported his findings. In the next chapter, you will learn how Mendel's laws have their physical basis in the behavior of chromosomes during sexual life cycles and how the synthesis of Mendelism and a chromosome theory of inheritance catalyzed progress in genetics.

CONCEPT CHECK 14.4

1. Beth and Tom each have a sibling with cystic fibrosis, but neither Beth nor Tom nor any of their parents have the disease. Calculate the probability that if this couple has a child, the child will have cystic fibrosis. What would be the probability if a test revealed that Tom is a carrier but Beth is not? Explain your answers.

2. **MAKE CONNECTIONS** Review Figures 5.16, 5.20, and 5.21 (pp. 79 and 82–84). Explain how the change of a single amino acid in hemoglobin leads to the aggregation of hemoglobin into long rods.

3. Joan was born with six toes on each foot, a dominant trait called polydactyly. Two of her five siblings and her mother, but not her father, also have extra digits. What is Joan's genotype for the number-of-digits character? Explain your answer. Use D and d to symbolize the alleles for this character.

4. **MAKE CONNECTIONS** In Table 14.1 (p. 265), note the phenotypic ratio of the dominant to recessive trait in the F_2 generation for the monohybrid cross involving flower color. Then determine the phenotypic ratio for the offspring of the second-generation couple in Figure 14.15b. What accounts for the difference in the two ratios?

For suggested answers, see Appendix A.

14 CHAPTER REVIEW

SUMMARY OF KEY CONCEPTS

CONCEPT 14.1

Mendel used the scientific approach to identify two laws of inheritance (pp. 262–269)

- In the 1860s, Gregor Mendel formulated a theory of inheritance based on experiments with garden peas, proposing that parents pass on to their offspring discrete genes that retain their identity through generations. This theory includes two "laws."
- The **law of segregation** states that genes have alternative forms, or **alleles**. In a diploid organism, the two alleles of a gene segregate (separate) during meiosis and gamete formation; each sperm or egg carries only one allele of each pair. This law explains the 3:1 ratio of F_2 phenotypes observed when **monohybrids** self-pollinate. Each organism inherits one allele for each gene from each parent. In **heterozygotes**, the two alleles are different, and expression of one (the **dominant allele**) masks the phenotypic effect of the other (the **recessive allele**). **Homozygotes** have identical alleles of a given gene and are **true-breeding**.
- The **law of independent assortment** states that the pair of alleles for a given gene segregates into gametes independently of the pair of alleles for any other gene. In a cross between **dihybrids** (individuals heterozygous for two genes), the offspring have four phenotypes in a 9:3:3:1 ratio.

> ? When Mendel crossed true-breeding purple- and white-flowered pea plants, the white-flowered trait disappeared from the F_1 generation but reappeared in the F_2 generation. Use genetic terms to explain why that happened.

CONCEPT 14.2

The laws of probability govern Mendelian inheritance (pp. 269–271)

- The **multiplication rule** states that the probability of two or more events occurring together is equal to the product of the individual probabilities of the independent single events. The **addition rule** states that the probability of an event that can occur in two or more independent, mutually exclusive ways is the sum of the individual probabilities.
- The rules of probability can be used to solve complex genetics problems. A dihybrid or other multicharacter cross is equivalent to two or more independent monohybrid crosses occurring simultaneously. In calculating the chances of the various offspring genotypes from such crosses, each character is first considered separately and then the individual probabilities are multiplied.

> **DRAW IT** Redraw the Punnett square on the right side of Figure 14.8 as two smaller monohybrid Punnett squares, one for each gene. Below each square, list the fractions of each phenotype produced. Use the rule of multiplication to compute the overall fraction of each possible dihybrid phenotype. What is the phenotypic ratio?

CONCEPT 14.3

Inheritance patterns are often more complex than predicted by simple Mendelian genetics (pp. 271–275)

- Extensions of Mendelian genetics for a single gene:

Relationship among alleles of a single gene	Description	Example
Complete dominance of one allele	Heterozygous phenotype same as that of homozygous dominant	PP Pp
Incomplete dominance of either allele	Heterozygous phenotype intermediate between the two homozygous phenotypes	C^RC^R C^RC^W C^WC^W
Codominance	Both phenotypes expressed in heterozygotes	I^AI^B
Multiple alleles	In the whole population, some genes have more than two alleles	ABO blood group alleles I^A, I^B, i
Pleiotropy	One gene is able to affect multiple phenotypic characters	Sickle-cell disease

- Extensions of Mendelian genetics for two or more genes:

Relationship among two or more genes	Description	Example
Epistasis	The phenotypic expression of one gene affects that of another	$BbEe \times BbEe$ ... 9 : 3 : 4
Polygenic inheritance	A single phenotypic character is affected by two or more genes	$AaBbCc \times AaBbCc$

- The expression of a genotype can be affected by environmental influences, the "nurture" in nature versus nurture. The phenotypic range of a particular genotype is called its **norm of reaction**.

Polygenic characters that are also influenced by the environment are called **multifactorial** characters.
- An organism's overall phenotype, including its physical appearance, internal anatomy, physiology, and behavior, reflects its overall genotype and unique environmental history. Even in more complex inheritance patterns, Mendel's fundamental laws of segregation and independent assortment still apply.

> **?** *Which of the following are demonstrated by the inheritance patterns of the ABO blood group alleles: complete dominance, incomplete dominance, codominance, multiple alleles, pleiotropy, epistasis, and/or polygenic inheritance? Explain how, for each of your answers.*

CONCEPT 14.4

Many human traits follow Mendelian patterns of inheritance (pp. 275–281)

- Analysis of family **pedigrees** can be used to deduce the possible genotypes of individuals and make predictions about future offspring. Predictions are statistical probabilities rather than certainties.
- Many genetic disorders are inherited as simple recessive traits. Most affected (homozygous recessive) individuals are children of phenotypically normal, heterozygous **carriers**.

- Lethal dominant alleles are eliminated from the population if affected people die before reproducing. Nonlethal dominant alleles and lethal ones that strike relatively late in life can be inherited in a Mendelian way.
- Many human diseases are multifactorial—that is, they have both genetic and environmental components and do not follow simple Mendelian inheritance patterns.
- Using family histories, genetic counselors help couples determine the probability that their children will have genetic disorders. Genetic testing of prospective parents to reveal whether they are carriers of recessive alleles associated with specific disorders has become widely available. **Amniocentesis** and **chorionic villus sampling** can indicate whether a suspected genetic disorder is present in a fetus. Other genetic tests can be performed after birth.

> **?** *Both members of a couple know that they are carriers of the cystic fibrosis allele. None of their three children has cystic fibrosis, but any one of them might be a carrier. They would like to have a fourth child but are worried that it would very likely have the disease, since the first three do not. What would you tell the couple? Would it remove some more uncertainty in their prediction if they could find out from genetic tests whether the three children are carriers?*

TIPS FOR GENETICS PROBLEMS

1. Write down symbols for the alleles. (These may be given in the problem.) When represented by single letters, the dominant allele is uppercase and the recessive is lowercase.

2. Write down the possible genotypes, as determined by the phenotype.
   a. If the phenotype is that of the dominant trait (for example, purple flowers), then the genotype is either homozygous dominant or heterozygous (*PP* or *Pp*, in this example).
   b. If the phenotype is that of the recessive trait, the genotype must be homozygous recessive (for example, *pp*).
   c. If the problem says "true-breeding," the genotype is homozygous.

3. Determine what the problem is asking for. If asked to do a cross, write it out in the form [Genotype] × [Genotype], using the alleles you've decided on.

4. To figure out the outcome of a cross, set up a Punnett square.
   a. Put the gametes of one parent at the top and those of the other on the left. To determine the allele(s) in each gamete for a given genotype, set up a systematic way to list all the possibilities. (Remember, each gamete has one allele of each gene.) Note that there are 2^n possible types of gametes, where n is the number of gene loci that are heterozygous. For example, an individual with genotype *AaBbCc* would produce $2^3 = 8$ types of gametes. Write the genotypes of the gametes in circles above the columns and to the left of the rows.
   b. Fill in the Punnett square as if each possible sperm were fertilizing each possible egg, making all of the possible offspring. In a cross of *AaBbCc* × *AaBbCc*, for example, the Punnett square would have 8 columns and 8 rows, so there are 64 different offspring; you would know the genotype of each and thus the phenotype. Count genotypes and phenotypes to obtain the genotypic and phenotypic ratios. Because the Punnett square is so large, this method is not the most efficient. Instead, see tip 5.

5. You can use the rules of probability if the Punnett square would be too big. (For example, see the question at the end of the summary for Concept 14.2 and question 7 on the next page.) You can consider each gene separately (see pp. 270–271).

6. If, instead, the problem gives you the phenotypic ratios of offspring, but not the genotypes of the parents in a given cross, the phenotypes can help you deduce the parents' unknown genotypes.
   a. For example, if ½ of the offspring have the recessive phenotype and ½ the dominant, you know that the cross was between a heterozygote and a homozygous recessive.
   b. If the ratio is 3:1, the cross was between two heterozygotes.
   c. If two genes are involved and you see a 9:3:3:1 ratio in the offspring, you know that each parent is heterozygous for both genes. Caution: Don't assume that the reported numbers will exactly equal the predicted ratios. For example, if there are 13 offspring with the dominant trait and 11 with the recessive, assume that the ratio is one dominant to one recessive.

7. For pedigree problems, use the tips in Figure 14.15 and below to determine what kind of trait is involved.
   a. If parents without the trait have offspring with the trait, the trait must be recessive and the parents both carriers.
   b. If the trait is seen in every generation, it is most likely dominant (see the next possibility, though).
   c. If both parents have the trait, then in order for it to be recessive, all offspring must show the trait.
   d. To determine the likely genotype of a certain individual in a pedigree, first label the genotypes of all the family members you can. Even if some of the genotypes are incomplete, label what you do know. For example, if an individual has the dominant phenotype, the genotype must be *AA* or *Aa*; you can write this as *A_*. Try different possibilities to see which fits the results. Use the rules of probability to calculate the probability of each possible genotype being the correct one.

LEVEL 1: KNOWLEDGE/COMPREHENSION

1. Match each term on the left with a statement on the right.

Term	Statement
__ Gene	a. Has no effect on phenotype in a heterozygote
__ Allele	
__ Character	b. A variant for a character
__ Trait	c. Having two identical alleles for a gene
__ Dominant allele	d. A cross between individuals heterozygous for a single character
__ Recessive allele	
__ Genotype	e. An alternative version of a gene
__ Phenotype	f. Having two different alleles for a gene
__ Homozygous	g. A heritable feature that varies among individuals
__ Heterozygous	
__ Testcross	h. An organism's appearance or observable traits
__ Monohybrid cross	i. A cross between an individual with an unknown genotype and a homozygous recessive individual
	j. Determines phenotype in a heterozygote
	k. The genetic makeup of an individual
	l. A heritable unit that determines a character; can exist in different forms

2. **DRAW IT** Two pea plants heterozygous for the characters of pod color and pod shape are crossed. Draw a Punnett square to determine the phenotypic ratios of the offspring.

3. In some plants, a true-breeding, red-flowered strain gives all pink flowers when crossed with a white-flowered strain: $C^R C^R$ (red) × $C^W C^W$ (white) → $C^R C^W$ (pink). If flower position (axial or terminal) is inherited as it is in peas (see Table 14.1), what will be the ratios of genotypes and phenotypes of the F_1 generation resulting from the following cross: axial-red (true-breeding) × terminal-white? What will be the ratios in the F_2 generation?

4. A man with type A blood marries a woman with type B blood. Their child has type O blood. What are the genotypes of these three individuals? What genotypes, and in what frequencies, would you expect in future offspring from this marriage?

5. A man has six fingers on each hand and six toes on each foot. His wife and their daughter have the normal number of digits. Remember that extra digits is a dominant trait. What fraction of this couple's children would be expected to have extra digits?

6. **DRAW IT** A pea plant heterozygous for inflated pods (*Ii*) is crossed with a plant homozygous for constricted pods (*ii*). Draw a Punnett square for this cross. Assume that pollen comes from the *ii* plant.

LEVEL 2: APPLICATION/ANALYSIS

7. Flower position, stem length, and seed shape are three characters that Mendel studied. Each is controlled by an independently assorting gene and has dominant and recessive expression as follows:

Character	Dominant	Recessive
Flower position	Axial (*A*)	Terminal (*a*)
Stem length	Tall (*T*)	Dwarf (*t*)
Seed shape	Round (*R*)	Wrinkled (*r*)

If a plant that is heterozygous for all three characters is allowed to self-fertilize, what proportion of the offspring would you expect to be as follows? (*Note*: Use the rules of probability instead of a huge Punnett square.)

(a) homozygous for the three dominant traits
(b) homozygous for the three recessive traits
(c) heterozygous for all three characters
(d) homozygous for axial and tall, heterozygous for seed shape

8. A black guinea pig crossed with an albino guinea pig produces 12 black offspring. When the albino is crossed with a second black one, 7 blacks and 5 albinos are obtained. What is the best explanation for this genetic outcome? Write genotypes for the parents, gametes, and offspring.

9. In sesame plants, the one-pod condition (*P*) is dominant to the three-pod condition (*p*), and normal leaf (*L*) is dominant to wrinkled leaf (*l*). Pod type and leaf type are inherited independently. Determine the genotypes for the two parents for all possible matings producing the following offspring:

(a) 318 one-pod, normal leaf and 98 one-pod, wrinkled leaf
(b) 323 three-pod, normal leaf and 106 three-pod, wrinkled leaf
(c) 401 one-pod, normal leaf
(d) 150 one-pod, normal leaf, 147 one-pod, wrinkled leaf, 51 three-pod, normal leaf, and 48 three-pod, wrinkled leaf
(e) 223 one-pod, normal leaf, 72 one-pod, wrinkled leaf, 76 three-pod, normal leaf, and 27 three-pod, wrinkled leaf

10. Phenylketonuria (PKU) is an inherited disease caused by a recessive allele. If a woman and her husband, who are both carriers, have three children, what is the probability of each of the following?

(a) All three children are of normal phenotype.
(b) One or more of the three children have the disease.
(c) All three children have the disease.
(d) At least one child is phenotypically normal.
(*Note*: It will help to remember that the probabilities of all possible outcomes always add up to 1.)

11. The genotype of F_1 individuals in a tetrahybrid cross is *AaBbCcDd*. Assuming independent assortment of these four genes, what are the probabilities that F_2 offspring will have the following genotypes?

(a) *aabbccdd*
(b) *AaBbCcDd*
(c) *AABBCCDD*
(d) *AaBBccDd*
(e) *AaBBCCdd*

12. What is the probability that each of the following pairs of parents will produce the indicated offspring? (Assume independent assortment of all gene pairs.)

(a) *AABBCC* × *aabbcc* → *AaBbCc*
(b) *AABbCc* × *AaBbCc* → *AAbbCC*
(c) *AaBbCc* × *AaBbCc* → *AaBbCc*
(d) *aaBbCC* × *AABbcc* → *AaBbCc*

13. Karen and Steve each have a sibling with sickle-cell disease. Neither Karen nor Steve nor any of their parents have the disease, and none of them have been tested to see if they have the sickle-cell trait. Based on this incomplete information, calculate the probability that if this couple has a child, the child will have sickle-cell disease.

14. In 1981, a stray black cat with unusual rounded, curled-back ears was adopted by a family in California. Hundreds of descendants of the cat have since been born, and cat fanciers hope to develop the curl cat into a show breed. Suppose you

owned the first curl cat and wanted to develop a true-breeding variety. How would you determine whether the curl allele is dominant or recessive? How would you obtain true-breeding curl cats? How could you be sure they are true-breeding?

15. Imagine that a newly discovered, recessively inherited disease is expressed only in individuals with type O blood, although the disease and blood group are independently inherited. A normal man with type A blood and a normal woman with type B blood have already had one child with the disease. The woman is now pregnant for a second time. What is the probability that the second child will also have the disease? Assume that both parents are heterozygous for the gene that causes the disease.

16. In tigers, a recessive allele causes an absence of fur pigmentation (a white tiger) and a cross-eyed condition. If two phenotypically normal tigers that are heterozygous at this locus are mated, what percentage of their offspring will be cross-eyed? What percentage of cross-eyed tigers will be white?

17. In maize (corn) plants, a dominant allele *I* inhibits kernel color, while the recessive allele *i* permits color when homozygous. At a different locus, the dominant allele *P* causes purple kernel color, while the homozygous recessive genotype *pp* causes red kernels. If plants heterozygous at both loci are crossed, what will be the phenotypic ratio of the offspring?

18. The pedigree below traces the inheritance of alkaptonuria, a biochemical disorder. Affected individuals, indicated here by the colored circles and squares, are unable to metabolize a substance called alkapton, which colors the urine and stains body tissues. Does alkaptonuria appear to be caused by a dominant allele or by a recessive allele? Fill in the genotypes of the individuals whose genotypes can be deduced. What genotypes are possible for each of the other individuals?

19. Imagine that you are a genetic counselor, and a couple planning to start a family comes to you for information. Charles was married once before, and he and his first wife had a child with cystic fibrosis. The brother of his current wife, Elaine, died of cystic fibrosis. What is the probability that Charles and Elaine will have a baby with cystic fibrosis? (Neither Charles, Elaine, nor their parents have cystic fibrosis.)

20. In mice, black fur (*B*) is dominant to white (*b*). At a different locus, a dominant allele (*A*) produces a band of yellow just below the tip of each hair in mice with black fur. This gives a frosted appearance known as agouti. Expression of the recessive allele (*a*) results in a solid coat color. If mice that are heterozygous at both loci are crossed, what is the expected phenotypic ratio of their offspring?

LEVEL 3: SYNTHESIS/EVALUATION

21. EVOLUTION CONNECTION
Over the past half century, there has been a trend in the United States and other developed countries for people to marry and start families later in life than did their parents and grandparents. What effects might this trend have on the incidence (frequency) of late-acting dominant lethal alleles in the population?

22. SCIENTIFIC INQUIRY
You are handed a mystery pea plant with tall stems and axial flowers and asked to determine its genotype as quickly as possible. You know that the allele for tall stems (*T*) is dominant to that for dwarf stems (*t*) and that the allele for axial flowers (*A*) is dominant to that for terminal flowers (*a*).

(a) What are *all* the possible genotypes for your mystery plant?

(b) Describe the *one* cross you would do, out in your garden, to determine the exact genotype of your mystery plant.

(c) While waiting for the results of your cross, you predict the results for each possible genotype listed in part a. How do you do this? Why is this not called "performing a cross"?

(d) Explain how the results of your cross and your predictions will help you learn the genotype of your mystery plant.

23. SCIENCE, TECHNOLOGY, AND SOCIETY
Imagine that one of your parents has Huntington's disease. What is the probability that you, too, will someday manifest the disease? There is no cure for Huntington's. Would you want to be tested for the Huntington's allele? Why or why not?

24. WRITE ABOUT A THEME
The Genetic Basis of Life The continuity of life is based on heritable information in the form of DNA. In a short essay (100–150 words), explain how the passage of genes from parents to offspring, in the form of particular alleles, ensures perpetuation of parental traits in offspring and, at the same time, genetic variation among offspring. Use genetic terms in your explanation.

For selected answers, see Appendix A.

 www.masteringbiology.com

1. MasteringBiology® Assignments
Tutorials Determining Genotype: Pea Pod Color • Inheritance of Fur Color in Mice • Pedigree Analysis: Galactosemia
Activities Monohybrid Cross • Dihybrid Cross • Mendel's Experiments • The Principle of Independent Assortment • Gregor's Garden • Incomplete Dominance
Questions Student Misconceptions • Reading Quiz • Multiple Choice • End-of-Chapter
2. eText
Read your book online, search, take notes, highlight text, and more.
3. The Study Area
Practice Tests • Cumulative Test • *BioFlix* 3-D Animations • MP3 Tutor Sessions • Videos • Activities • Investigations • Lab Media • Audio Glossary • Word Study Tools • Art

15

The Chromosomal Basis of Inheritance

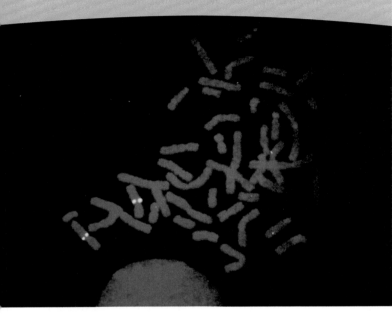

▲ **Figure 15.1 Where are Mendel's hereditary factors located in the cell?**

KEY CONCEPTS

15.1 Mendelian inheritance has its physical basis in the behavior of chromosomes

15.2 Sex-linked genes exhibit unique patterns of inheritance

15.3 Linked genes tend to be inherited together because they are located near each other on the same chromosome

15.4 Alterations of chromosome number or structure cause some genetic disorders

15.5 Some inheritance patterns are exceptions to standard Mendelian inheritance

Locating Genes Along Chromosomes

Gregor Mendel's "hereditary factors" were purely an abstract concept when he proposed their existence in 1860. At that time, no cellular structures were known that could house these imaginary units. Even after chromosomes were first observed, many biologists remained skeptical about Mendel's laws of segregation and independent assortment until there was sufficient evidence that these principles of heredity had a physical basis in chromosomal behavior.

Today, we know that genes—Mendel's "factors"—are located along chromosomes. We can see the location of a particular gene by tagging chromosomes with a fluorescent dye that highlights that gene. For example, the four yellow dots in **Figure 15.1** mark the locus of a specific gene on the sister chromatids of a homologous pair of replicated human chromosomes. This chapter extends what you learned in the past two chapters: We describe the chromosomal basis for the transmission of genes from parents to offspring, along with some important exceptions to the standard mode of inheritance.

CONCEPT 15.1

Mendelian inheritance has its physical basis in the behavior of chromosomes

Using improved techniques of microscopy, cytologists worked out the process of mitosis in 1875 and meiosis in the 1890s. Cytology and genetics converged when biologists began to see parallels between the behavior of chromosomes and the behavior of Mendel's proposed hereditary factors during sexual life cycles: Chromosomes and genes are both present in pairs in diploid cells; homologous chromosomes separate and alleles segregate during the process of meiosis; and fertilization restores the paired condition for both chromosomes and genes. Around 1902, Walter S. Sutton, Theodor Boveri, and others independently noted these parallels, and the **chromosome theory of inheritance** began to take form. According to this theory, Mendelian genes have specific loci (positions) along chromosomes, and it is the chromosomes that undergo segregation and independent assortment.

Figure 15.2 shows that the behavior of homologous chromosomes during meiosis can account for the segregation of the alleles at each genetic locus to different gametes. The figure also shows that the behavior of nonhomologous chromosomes can account for the independent assortment of the alleles for two or more genes located on different chromosomes. By carefully studying this figure, which traces the same dihybrid pea cross you learned about in Figure 14.8, you can see how the behavior of chromosomes during meiosis in the F_1 generation and subsequent random fertilization give rise to the F_2 phenotypic ratio observed by Mendel.

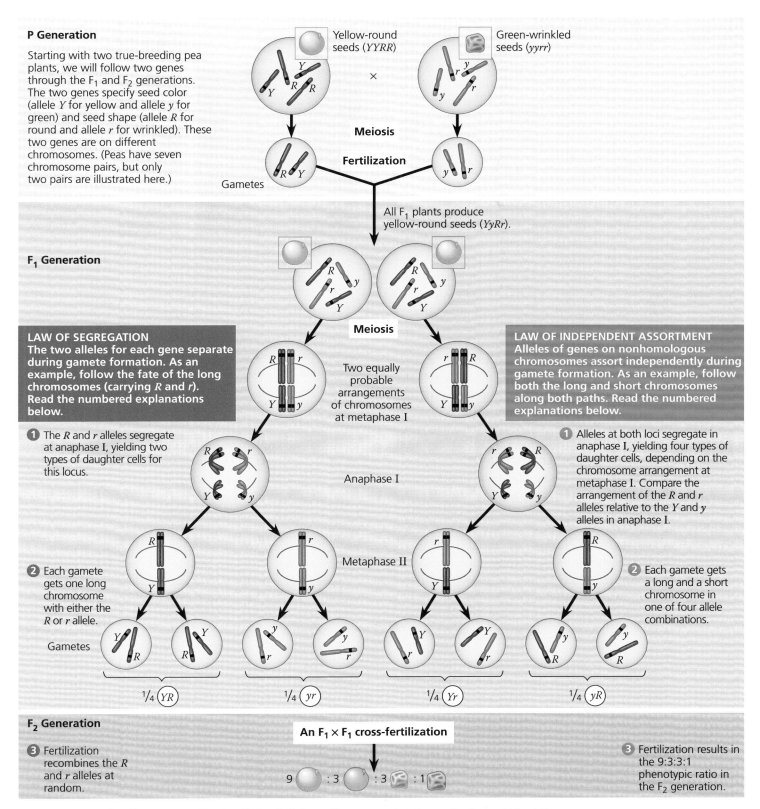

P Generation

Starting with two true-breeding pea plants, we will follow two genes through the F₁ and F₂ generations. The two genes specify seed color (allele *Y* for yellow and allele *y* for green) and seed shape (allele *R* for round and allele *r* for wrinkled). These two genes are on different chromosomes. (Peas have seven chromosome pairs, but only two pairs are illustrated here.)

Yellow-round seeds (*YYRR*)

Green-wrinkled seeds (*yyrr*)

×

Meiosis

Fertilization

Gametes

All F₁ plants produce yellow-round seeds (*YyRr*).

F₁ Generation

Meiosis

LAW OF SEGREGATION
The two alleles for each gene separate during gamete formation. As an example, follow the fate of the long chromosomes (carrying *R* and *r*). Read the numbered explanations below.

Two equally probable arrangements of chromosomes at metaphase I

LAW OF INDEPENDENT ASSORTMENT
Alleles of genes on nonhomologous chromosomes assort independently during gamete formation. As an example, follow both the long and short chromosomes along both paths. Read the numbered explanations below.

1 The *R* and *r* alleles segregate at anaphase I, yielding two types of daughter cells for this locus.

Anaphase I

1 Alleles at both loci segregate in anaphase I, yielding four types of daughter cells, depending on the chromosome arrangement at metaphase I. Compare the arrangement of the *R* and *r* alleles relative to the *Y* and *y* alleles in anaphase I.

Metaphase II

2 Each gamete gets one long chromosome with either the *R* or *r* allele.

Gametes

2 Each gamete gets a long and a short chromosome in one of four allele combinations.

¹/₄ *YR*   ¹/₄ *yr*   ¹/₄ *Yr*   ¹/₄ *yR*

F₂ Generation

3 Fertilization recombines the *R* and *r* alleles at random.

An F₁ × F₁ cross-fertilization

9 ⬤ : 3 ⬤ : 3 ⬛ : 1 ⬛

3 Fertilization results in the 9:3:3:1 phenotypic ratio in the F₂ generation.

▲ **Figure 15.2 The chromosomal basis of Mendel's laws.** Here we correlate the results of one of Mendel's dihybrid crosses (see Figure 14.8) with the behavior of chromosomes during meiosis (see Figure 13.8). The arrangement of chromosomes at metaphase I of meiosis and their movement during anaphase I account for the segregation and independent assortment of the alleles for seed color and shape. Each cell that undergoes meiosis in an F₁ plant produces two kinds of gametes. If we count the results for all cells, however, each F₁ plant produces equal numbers of all four kinds of gametes because the alternative chromosome arrangements at metaphase I are equally likely.

? *If you crossed an F₁ plant with a plant that was homozygous recessive for both genes (yyrr), how would the phenotypic ratio of the offspring compare with the 9:3:3:1 ratio seen here?*

Morgan's Experimental Evidence: Scientific Inquiry

The first solid evidence associating a specific gene with a specific chromosome came early in the 20th century from the work of Thomas Hunt Morgan, an experimental embryologist at Columbia University. Although Morgan was initially skeptical about both Mendelism and the chromosome theory, his early experiments provided convincing evidence that chromosomes are indeed the location of Mendel's heritable factors.

Morgan's Choice of Experimental Organism

Many times in the history of biology, important discoveries have come to those insightful or lucky enough to choose an experimental organism suitable for the research problem being tackled. Mendel chose the garden pea because a number of distinct varieties were available. For his work, Morgan selected a species of fruit fly, *Drosophila melanogaster*, a common insect that feeds on the fungi growing on fruit. Fruit flies are prolific breeders; a single mating will produce hundreds of offspring, and a new generation can be bred every two weeks. Morgan's laboratory began using this convenient organism for genetic studies in 1907 and soon became known as "the fly room."

Another advantage of the fruit fly is that it has only four pairs of chromosomes, which are easily distinguishable with a light microscope. There are three pairs of autosomes and one pair of sex chromosomes. Female fruit flies have a pair of homologous X chromosomes, and males have one X chromosome and one Y chromosome.

While Mendel could readily obtain different pea varieties from seed suppliers, Morgan was probably the first person to want different varieties of the fruit fly. He faced the tedious task of carrying out many matings and then microscopically inspecting large numbers of offspring in search of naturally occurring variant individuals. After many months of this, he lamented, "Two years' work wasted. I have been breeding those flies for all that time and I've got nothing out of it." Morgan persisted, however, and was finally rewarded with the discovery of a single male fly with white eyes instead of the usual red. The phenotype for a character most commonly observed in natural populations, such as red eyes in *Drosophila*, is called the **wild type** (Figure 15.3). Traits that are alternatives to the wild type, such as white eyes in *Drosophila*, are called *mutant phenotypes* because they are due to alleles assumed to have originated as changes, or mutations, in the wild-type allele.

Morgan and his students invented a notation for symbolizing alleles in *Drosophila* that is still widely used for fruit flies. For a given character in flies, the gene takes its symbol from the first mutant (non–wild type) discovered. Thus, the allele for white eyes in *Drosophila* is symbolized by *w*. A superscript + identifies the allele for the wild-type trait—w^+ for the allele for red eyes, for example. Over the years, a variety

▲ **Figure 15.3 Morgan's first mutant.** Wild-type *Drosophila* flies have red eyes (left). Among his flies, Morgan discovered a mutant male with white eyes (right). This variation made it possible for Morgan to trace a gene for eye color to a specific chromosome (LMs).

of gene notation systems have been developed for different organisms. For example, human genes are usually written in all capitals, such as *HD* for the allele for Huntington's disease.

Correlating Behavior of a Gene's Alleles with Behavior of a Chromosome Pair

Morgan mated his white-eyed male fly with a red-eyed female. All the F_1 offspring had red eyes, suggesting that the wild-type allele is dominant. When Morgan bred the F_1 flies to each other, he observed the classical 3:1 phenotypic ratio among the F_2 offspring. However, there was a surprising additional result: The white-eye trait showed up only in males. All the F_2 females had red eyes, while half the males had red eyes and half had white eyes. Therefore, Morgan concluded that somehow a fly's eye color was linked to its sex. (If the eye-color gene were unrelated to sex, he would have expected half of the white-eyed flies to be male and half female.)

Recall that a female fly has two X chromosomes (XX), while a male fly has an X and a Y (XY). The correlation between the trait of white eye color and the male sex of the affected F_2 flies suggested to Morgan that the gene involved in his white-eyed mutant was located exclusively on the X chromosome, with no corresponding allele present on the Y chromosome. His reasoning can be followed in **Figure 15.4**. For a male, a single copy of the mutant allele would confer white eyes; since a male has only one X chromosome, there can be no wild-type allele (w^+) present to mask the recessive allele. On the other hand, a female could have white eyes only if both her X chromosomes carried the recessive mutant allele (*w*). This was impossible for the F_2 females in Morgan's experiment because all the F_1 fathers had red eyes.

Morgan's finding of the correlation between a particular trait and an individual's sex provided support for the chromosome theory of inheritance: namely, that a specific gene is

▼ Figure 15.4

INQUIRY

In a cross between a wild-type female fruit fly and a mutant white-eyed male, what color eyes will the F₁ and F₂ offspring have?

EXPERIMENT Thomas Hunt Morgan wanted to analyze the behavior of two alleles of a fruit fly eye-color gene. In crosses similar to those done by Mendel with pea plants, Morgan and his colleagues mated a wild-type (red-eyed) female with a mutant white-eyed male.

Morgan then bred an F₁ red-eyed female to an F₁ red-eyed male to produce the F₂ generation.

RESULTS The F₂ generation showed a typical Mendelian ratio of 3 red-eyed flies : 1 white-eyed fly. However, no females displayed the white-eye trait; all white-eyed flies were males.

CONCLUSION All F₁ offspring had red eyes, so the mutant white-eye trait (*w*) must be recessive to the wild-type red-eye trait (*w⁺*). Since the recessive trait—white eyes—was expressed only in males in the F₂ generation, Morgan deduced that this eye-color gene is located on the X chromosome and that there is no corresponding locus on the Y chromosome.

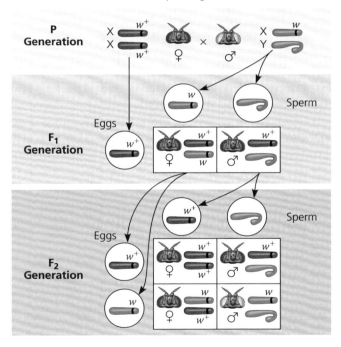

SOURCE: T. H. Morgan, Sex-limited inheritance in *Drosophila, Science* 32:120–122 (1910).

See the related Experimental Inquiry Tutorial in MasteringBiology.

WHAT IF? Suppose this eye-color gene were located on an autosome. Predict the phenotypes (including gender) of the F₂ flies in this hypothetical cross. (*Hint*: Draw a Punnett square.)

---

carried on a specific chromosome (in this case, an eye-color gene on the X chromosome). In addition, Morgan's work indicated that genes located on a sex chromosome exhibit unique inheritance patterns, which we will discuss in the next section. Recognizing the importance of Morgan's early work, many bright students were attracted to his fly room.

CONCEPT CHECK 15.1

1. Which one of Mendel's laws relates to the inheritance of alleles for a single character? Which law relates to the inheritance of alleles for two characters in a dihybrid cross?
2. **MAKE CONNECTIONS** Review the description of meiosis in Figure 13.8 (pp. 254–255) and Mendel's two laws in Concept 14.1 (pp. 264–269). What is the physical basis for each of Mendel's laws?
3. **WHAT IF?** Propose a possible reason that the first naturally occurring mutant fruit fly Morgan saw involved a gene on a sex chromosome.

For suggested answers, see Appendix A.

CONCEPT 15.2

Sex-linked genes exhibit unique patterns of inheritance

As you just learned, Morgan's discovery of a trait (white eyes) that correlated with the sex of flies was a key episode in the development of the chromosome theory of inheritance. Because the identity of the sex chromosomes in an individual could be inferred by observing the sex of the fly, the behavior of the two members of the pair of sex chromosomes could be correlated with the behavior of the two alleles of the eye-color gene. In this section, we consider the role of sex chromosomes in inheritance in more detail. We begin by reviewing the chromosomal basis of sex determination in humans and some other animals.

The Chromosomal Basis of Sex

Whether we are male or female is one of our more obvious phenotypic characters. Although the anatomical and physiological differences between women and men are numerous, the chromosomal basis for determining sex is rather simple. In humans and other mammals, there are two varieties of sex chromosomes, designated X and Y. The Y chromosome is much smaller than the X chromosome **(Figure 15.5)**. A person who inherits two

▲ **Figure 15.5 Human sex chromosomes.**

X chromosomes, one from each parent, usually develops as a female. A male develops from a zygote containing one X chromosome and one Y chromosome (**Figure 15.6a**). Short segments at either end of the Y chromosome are the only regions that are homologous with corresponding regions of the X.

(a) The X-Y system. In mammals, the sex of an offspring depends on whether the sperm cell contains an X chromosome or a Y.

(b) The X-0 system. In grasshoppers, cockroaches, and some other insects, there is only one type of sex chromosome, the X. Females are XX; males have only one sex chromosome (X0). Sex of the offspring is determined by whether the sperm cell contains an X chromosome or no sex chromosome.

(c) The Z-W system. In birds, some fishes, and some insects, the sex chromosomes present in the egg (not the sperm) determine the sex of offspring. The sex chromosomes are designated Z and W. Females are ZW and males are ZZ.

(d) The haplo-diploid system. There are no sex chromosomes in most species of bees and ants. Females develop from fertilized eggs and are thus diploid. Males develop from unfertilized eggs and are haploid; they have no fathers.

▲ **Figure 15.6 Some chromosomal systems of sex determination.** Numerals indicate the number of autosomes in the species pictured. In *Drosophila*, males are XY, but sex depends on the ratio between the number of X chromosomes and the number of autosome sets, not simply on the presence of a Y chromosome.

These homologous regions allow the X and Y chromosomes in males to pair and behave like homologous chromosomes during meiosis in the testes.

In mammalian testes and ovaries, the two sex chromosomes segregate during meiosis, and each gamete receives one. Each egg contains one X chromosome. In contrast, sperm fall into two categories: Half the sperm cells a male produces contain an X chromosome, and half contain a Y chromosome. We can trace the sex of each offspring to the events of conception: If a sperm cell bearing an X chromosome happens to fertilize an egg, the zygote is XX, a female; if a sperm cell containing a Y chromosome fertilizes an egg, the zygote is XY, a male (see Figure 15.6a). Thus, sex determination is a matter of chance—a fifty-fifty chance. Note that the mammalian X-Y system isn't the only chromosomal system for determining sex. **Figure 15.6b–d** illustrates three other systems.

In humans, the anatomical signs of sex begin to emerge when the embryo is about 2 months old. Before then, the rudiments of the gonads are generic—they can develop into either testes or ovaries, depending on whether or not a Y chromosome is present. In 1990, a British research team identified a gene on the Y chromosome required for the development of testes. They named the gene *SRY*, for s̲ex-determining r̲egion of Y̲. In the absence of *SRY*, the gonads develop into ovaries. The biochemical, physiological, and anatomical features that distinguish males and females are complex, and many genes are involved in their development. In fact, *SRY* codes for a protein that regulates other genes.

Researchers have sequenced the human Y chromosome and have identified 78 genes that code for about 25 proteins (some genes are duplicates). About half of these genes are expressed only in the testis, and some are required for normal testicular functioning and the production of normal sperm. A gene located on either sex chromosome is called a **sex-linked gene**; those located on the Y chromosome are called *Y-linked genes*. The Y chromosome is passed along virtually intact from a father to all his sons. Because there are so few Y-linked genes, very few disorders are transferred from father to son on the Y chromosome. A rare example is that in the absence of certain Y-linked genes, an XY individual is male but does not produce normal sperm.

The human X chromosome contains approximately 1,100 genes, which are called **X-linked genes**. The fact that males and females inherit a different number of X chromosomes leads to a pattern of inheritance different from that produced by genes located on autosomes.

Inheritance of X-Linked Genes

While most Y-linked genes help determine sex, the X chromosomes have genes for many characters unrelated to sex. X-linked genes in humans follow the same pattern of inheritance that Morgan observed for the eye-color locus he studied in *Drosophila* (see Figure 15.4). Fathers pass X-linked

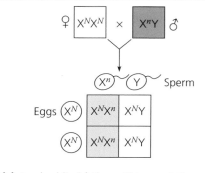

(a) A color-blind father will transmit the mutant allele to all daughters but to no sons. When the mother is a dominant homozygote, the daughters will have the normal phenotype but will be carriers of the mutation.

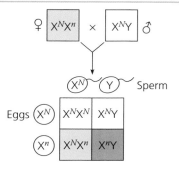

(b) If a carrier mates with a male who has normal color vision, there is a 50% chance that each daughter will be a carrier like her mother and a 50% chance that each son will have the disorder.

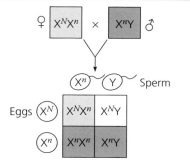

(c) If a carrier mates with a color-blind male, there is a 50% chance that each child born to them will have the disorder, regardless of sex. Daughters who have normal color vision will be carriers, whereas males who have normal color vision will be free of the recessive allele.

▲ **Figure 15.7 The transmission of X-linked recessive traits.** In this diagram, color blindness is used as an example. The superscript N represents the dominant allele for normal color vision carried on the X chromosome, and the superscript n represents the recessive allele, which has a mutation causing color blindness. White boxes indicate unaffected individuals, light orange boxes indicate carriers, and dark orange boxes indicate color-blind individuals.

? *If a color-blind woman married a man who had normal color vision, what would be the probable phenotypes of their children?*

alleles to all of their daughters but to none of their sons. In contrast, mothers can pass X-linked alleles to both sons and daughters, as shown in **Figure 15.7**.

If an X-linked trait is due to a recessive allele, a female will express the phenotype only if she is homozygous for that allele. Because males have only one locus, the terms *homozygous* and *heterozygous* lack meaning for describing their X-linked genes; the term *hemizygous* is used in such cases. Any male receiving the recessive allele from his mother will express the trait. For this reason, far more males than females have X-linked recessive disorders. However, even though the chance of a female inheriting a double dose of the mutant allele is much less than the probability of a male inheriting a single dose, there *are* females with X-linked disorders. For instance, color blindness is a mild disorder almost always inherited as an X-linked trait. A color-blind daughter may be born to a color-blind father whose mate is a carrier (see Figure 15.7c). Because the X-linked allele for color blindness is relatively rare, though, the probability that such a man and woman will mate is low.

A number of human X-linked disorders are much more serious than color blindness. An example is **Duchenne muscular dystrophy**, which affects about one out of every 3,500 males born in the United States. The disease is characterized by a progressive weakening of the muscles and loss of coordination. Affected individuals rarely live past their early 20s. Researchers have traced the disorder to the absence of a key muscle protein called dystrophin and have mapped the gene for this protein to a specific locus on the X chromosome.

Hemophilia is an X-linked recessive disorder defined by the absence of one or more of the proteins required for blood clotting. When a person with hemophilia is injured, bleeding is prolonged because a firm clot is slow to form. Small cuts in the skin are usually not a problem, but bleeding in the muscles or joints can be painful and can lead to serious damage. In the 1800s, hemophilia was widespread among the royal families of Europe. Queen Victoria of England is known to have passed the allele to several of her descendants. Subsequent intermarriage with royal family members of other nations, such as Spain and Russia, further spread this X-linked trait, and its incidence is well documented in royal pedigrees. Today, people with hemophilia are treated as needed with intravenous injections of the protein that is missing.

X Inactivation in Female Mammals

Female mammals, including humans, inherit two X chromosomes—twice the number inherited by males—so you may wonder whether females make twice as much as males of the proteins encoded by X-linked genes. In fact, most of one X chromosome in each cell in female mammals becomes inactivated during early embryonic development. As a result, the cells of females and males have the same effective dose (one copy) of most X-linked genes. The inactive X in each cell of a female condenses into a compact object called a **Barr body** (discovered by Canadian anatomist Murray Barr), which lies along the inside of the nuclear envelope. Most of the genes of the X chromosome that forms the Barr body are not expressed. In the ovaries, Barr-body chromosomes are reactivated in the cells that give rise to eggs, so every female gamete has an active X.

British geneticist Mary Lyon demonstrated that the selection of which X chromosome will form the Barr body occurs randomly and independently in each embryonic cell present at the time of X inactivation. As a consequence, females consist

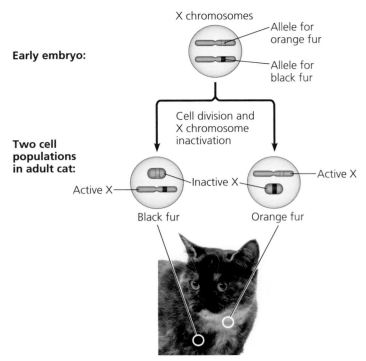

Early embryo:

X chromosomes

Allele for orange fur

Allele for black fur

Cell division and X chromosome inactivation

Two cell populations in adult cat:

Active X — Inactive X — Active X

Black fur   Orange fur

▲ **Figure 15.8 X inactivation and the tortoiseshell cat.** The tortoiseshell gene is on the X chromosome, and the tortoiseshell phenotype requires the presence of two different alleles, one for orange fur and one for black fur. Normally, only females can have both alleles, because only they have two X chromosomes. If a female cat is heterozygous for the tortoiseshell gene, she is tortoiseshell. Orange patches are formed by populations of cells in which the X chromosome with the orange allele is active; black patches have cells in which the X chromosome with the black allele is active. ("Calico" cats also have white areas, which are determined by yet another gene.)

of a *mosaic* of two types of cells: those with the active X derived from the father and those with the active X derived from the mother. After an X chromosome is inactivated in a particular cell, all mitotic descendants of that cell have the same inactive X. Thus, if a female is heterozygous for a sex-linked trait, about half her cells will express one allele, while the others will express the alternate allele. **Figure 15.8** shows how this mosaicism results in the mottled coloration of a tortoiseshell cat. In humans, mosaicism can be observed in a recessive X-linked mutation that prevents the development of sweat glands. A woman who is heterozygous for this trait has patches of normal skin and patches of skin lacking sweat glands.

Inactivation of an X chromosome involves modification of the DNA and the histone proteins bound to it, including attachment of methyl groups ($-CH_3$) to one of the nitrogenous bases of DNA nucleotides. (The regulatory role of DNA methylation is discussed further in Chapter 18.) A particular region of each X chromosome contains several genes involved in the inactivation process. The two regions, one on each X chromosome, associate briefly with each other in each cell at an early stage of embryonic development. Then one of the genes, called *XIST* (for *X-inactive specific*

transcript) becomes active *only* on the chromosome that will become the Barr body. Multiple copies of the RNA product of this gene apparently attach to the X chromosome on which they are made, eventually almost covering it. Interaction of this RNA with the chromosome seems to initiate X inactivation, and the RNA products of other genes nearby on the X chromosome help to regulate the process.

CONCEPT CHECK 15.2

1. A white-eyed female *Drosophila* is mated with a red-eyed (wild-type) male, the reciprocal cross of the one shown in Figure 15.4. What phenotypes and genotypes do you predict for the offspring?
2. Neither Tim nor Rhoda has Duchenne muscular dystrophy, but their firstborn son does have it. What is the probability that a second child of this couple will have the disease? What is the probability if the second child is a boy? A girl?
3. **MAKE CONNECTIONS** Consider what you learned about dominant and recessive alleles in Concept 14.1 (p. 265). If a disorder were caused by a dominant X-linked allele, how would the inheritance pattern differ from what we see for recessive X-linked disorders?

For suggested answers, see Appendix A.

CONCEPT 15.3

Linked genes tend to be inherited together because they are located near each other on the same chromosome

The number of genes in a cell is far greater than the number of chromosomes; in fact, each chromosome has hundreds or thousands of genes. (The Y chromosome is an exception.) Genes located near each other on the same chromosome tend to be inherited together in genetic crosses; such genes are said to be genetically linked and are called **linked genes**. (Note the distinction between the terms *sex-linked gene*, referring to a single gene on a sex chromosome, and *linked genes*, referring to two or more genes on the same chromosome that tend to be inherited together.) When geneticists follow linked genes in breeding experiments, the results deviate from those expected from Mendel's law of independent assortment.

How Linkage Affects Inheritance

To see how linkage between genes affects the inheritance of two different characters, let's examine another of Morgan's *Drosophila* experiments. In this case, the characters are body color and wing size, each with two different phenotypes.

Wild-type flies have gray bodies and normal-sized wings. In addition to these flies, Morgan had managed to obtain, through breeding, doubly mutant flies with black bodies and wings much smaller than normal, called vestigial wings. The mutant alleles are recessive to the wild-type alleles, and neither gene is on a sex chromosome. In his investigation of these two genes, Morgan carried out the crosses shown in Figure 15.9. The first was a P generation cross to generate F_1 dihybrid flies, and the second was a testcross.

The resulting flies had a much higher proportion of the combinations of traits seen in the P generation flies (called parental phenotypes) than would be expected if the two genes assorted independently. Morgan thus concluded that body color and wing size are usually inherited together in

▼ **Figure 15.9**

INQUIRY

How does linkage between two genes affect inheritance of characters?

EXPERIMENT Morgan wanted to know whether the genes for body color and wing size were genetically linked, and if so, how this affected their inheritance. The alleles for body color are b^+ (gray) and b (black), and those for wing size are vg^+ (normal) and vg (vestigial).

Morgan mated true-breeding P (parental) generation flies—wild-type flies with black, vestigial-winged flies—to produce heterozygous F_1 dihybrids ($b^+ b \ vg^+ vg$), all of which are wild-type in appearance.

He then mated wild-type F_1 dihybrid females with black, vestigial-winged males. This testcross will reveal the genotype of the eggs made by the dihybrid female.

The male's sperm contributes only recessive alleles, so the phenotype of the offspring reflects the genotype of the female's eggs.

Note: Although only females (with pointed abdomens) are shown, half the offspring in each class would be males (with rounded abdomens).

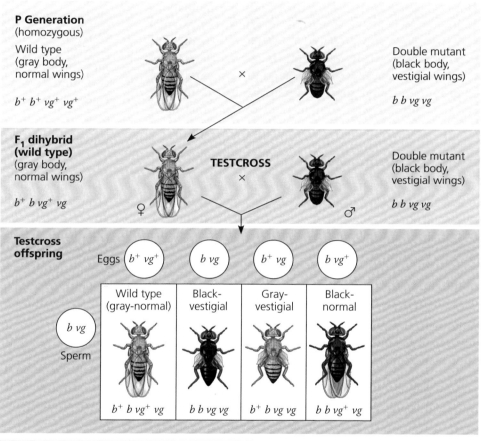

PREDICTED RATIOS

If genes are located on different chromosomes:	1	:	1	:	1	:	1

If genes are located on the same chromosome *and* parental alleles are always inherited together:	1	:	1	:	0	:	0

RESULTS 965 : 944 : 206 : 185

CONCLUSION Since most offspring had a parental (P generation) phenotype, Morgan concluded that the genes for body color and wing size are genetically linked on the same chromosome. However, the production of a relatively small number of offspring with nonparental phenotypes indicated that some mechanism occasionally breaks the linkage between specific alleles of genes on the same chromosome.

SOURCE: T. H. Morgan and C. J. Lynch, The linkage of two factors in *Drosophila* that are not sex-linked, *Biological Bulletin* 23:174–182 (1912).

WHAT IF? If the parental (P generation) flies had been true-breeding for gray body with vestigial wings and black body with normal wings, which phenotypic class(es) would be largest among the testcross offspring?

specific (parental) combinations because the genes for these characters are near each other on the same chromosome:

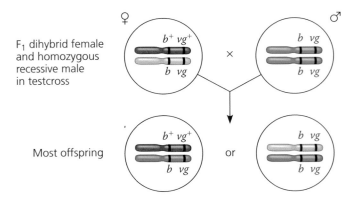

F₁ dihybrid female and homozygous recessive male in testcross

Most offspring   or

However, as Figure 15.9 shows, both of the combinations of traits not seen in the P generation (called nonparental phenotypes) were also produced in Morgan's experiments, suggesting that the body-color and wing-size alleles are not always linked genetically. To understand this conclusion, we need to further explore **genetic recombination**, the production of offspring with combinations of traits that differ from those found in either parent.

Genetic Recombination and Linkage

In Chapter 13, you learned that meiosis and random fertilization generate genetic variation among offspring of sexually reproducing organisms. Here we will examine the chromosomal basis of recombination in relation to the genetic findings of Mendel and Morgan.

Recombination of Unlinked Genes: Independent Assortment of Chromosomes

Mendel learned from crosses in which he followed two characters that some offspring have combinations of traits that do not match those of either parent. For example, we can represent the cross between a pea plant with yellow-round seeds that is heterozygous for both seed color and seed shape (a dihybrid, *YyRr*) and a plant with green-wrinkled seeds (homozygous for both recessive alleles, *yyrr*) by the following Punnett square:

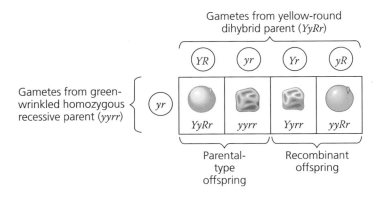

Gametes from yellow-round dihybrid parent (*YyRr*)

Gametes from green-wrinkled homozygous recessive parent (*yyrr*)

Parental-type offspring   Recombinant offspring

Notice in this Punnett square that one-half of the offspring are expected to inherit a phenotype that matches either of the parental (P generation) phenotypes. These offspring are called **parental types**. But two nonparental phenotypes are also found among the offspring. Because these offspring have new combinations of seed shape and color, they are called **recombinant types**, or **recombinants** for short. When 50% of all offspring are recombinants, as in this example, geneticists say that there is a 50% frequency of recombination. The predicted phenotypic ratios among the offspring are similar to what Mendel actually found in *YyRr* × *yyrr* crosses (a type of testcross because it reveals the genotype of the gametes made by the dihybrid *YyRr* plant).

A 50% frequency of recombination in such testcrosses is observed for any two genes that are located on different chromosomes and thus cannot be linked. The physical basis of recombination between unlinked genes is the random orientation of homologous chromosomes at metaphase I of meiosis, which leads to the independent assortment of the two unlinked genes (see Figure 13.10 and the question in the Figure 15.2 legend).

Recombination of Linked Genes: Crossing Over

Now let's return to Morgan's fly room to see how we can explain the results of the *Drosophila* testcross illustrated in Figure 15.9. Recall that most of the offspring from the testcross for body color and wing size had parental phenotypes. That suggested that the two genes were on the same chromosome, since the occurrence of parental types with a frequency greater than 50% indicates that the genes are linked. About 17% of offspring, however, were recombinants.

Faced with these results, Morgan proposed that some process must occasionally break the physical connection between specific alleles of genes on the same chromosome. Subsequent experiments demonstrated that this process, now called **crossing over**, accounts for the recombination of linked genes. In crossing over, which occurs while replicated homologous chromosomes are paired during prophase of meiosis I, a set of proteins orchestrates an exchange of corresponding segments of one maternal and one paternal chromatid (see Figure 13.11). In effect, end portions of two nonsister chromatids trade places each time a crossover occurs.

Figure 15.10 shows how crossing over in a dihybrid female fly resulted in recombinant eggs and ultimately recombinant offspring in Morgan's testcross. Most of the eggs had a chromosome with either the *b⁺ vg⁺* or *b vg* parental genotype for body color and wing size, but some eggs had a recombinant chromosome (*b⁺ vg* or *b vg⁺*). Fertilization of these various classes of eggs by homozygous recessive sperm (*b vg*) produced an offspring population in which 17% exhibited a nonparental, recombinant phenotype, reflecting combinations of alleles not seen before in either P generation parent.

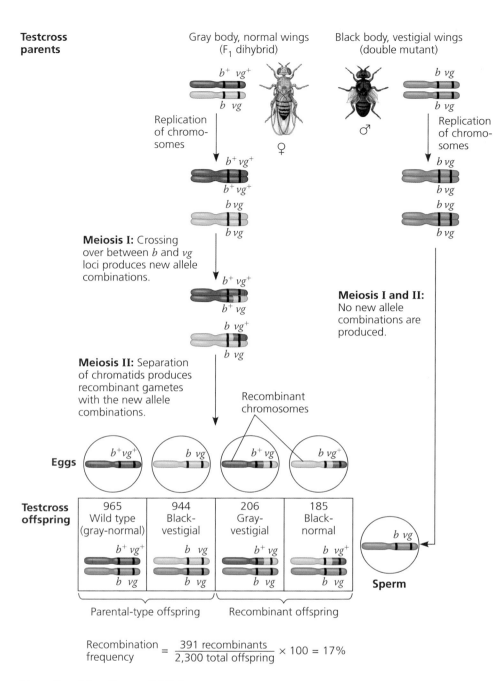

Testcross parents

Gray body, normal wings (F₁ dihybrid)

$b^+ \; vg^+$
$b \;\; vg$

Black body, vestigial wings (double mutant)

$b \;\; vg$
$b \;\; vg$

Replication of chromosomes

$b^+ \; vg^+$
$b^+ \; vg^+$
$b \;\; vg$
$b \;\; vg$

Replication of chromosomes

$b \;\; vg$
$b \;\; vg$
$b \;\; vg$
$b \;\; vg$

Meiosis I: Crossing over between *b* and *vg* loci produces new allele combinations.

$b^+ \; vg^+$
$b^+ \; vg$
$b \;\; vg^+$
$b \;\; vg$

Meiosis II: Separation of chromatids produces recombinant gametes with the new allele combinations.

Meiosis I and II: No new allele combinations are produced.

Recombinant chromosomes

Eggs

$b^+ vg^+$ | $b \; vg$ | $b^+ \; vg$ | $b \; vg^+$

Testcross offspring

965 Wild type (gray-normal)	944 Black-vestigial	206 Gray-vestigial	185 Black-normal
$b^+ \; vg^+$	$b \;\; vg$	$b^+ \; vg$	$b \;\; vg^+$
$b \;\; vg$	$b \;\; vg$	$b \;\; vg$	$b \;\; vg$

Sperm

$b \; vg$

Parental-type offspring — Recombinant offspring

$$\text{Recombination frequency} = \frac{391 \text{ recombinants}}{2,300 \text{ total offspring}} \times 100 = 17\%$$

◀ **Figure 15.10 Chromosomal basis for recombination of linked genes.** In these diagrams re-creating the testcross in Figure 15.9, we track chromosomes as well as genes. The maternal chromosomes are color-coded red and pink to distinguish one homolog from the other before any meiotic crossing over has taken place. Because crossing over between the *b* and *vg* loci occurs in some, but not all, egg-producing cells, more eggs with parental-type chromosomes than with recombinant ones are produced in the mating females. Fertilization of the eggs by sperm of genotype *b vg* gives rise to some recombinant offspring. The recombination frequency is the percentage of recombinant flies in the total pool of offspring.

DRAW IT *Suppose, as in the question at the bottom of Figure 15.9, the parental (P generation) flies were true-breeding for gray body with vestigial wings and black body with normal wings. Draw the chromosomes in each of the four possible kinds of eggs from an F₁ female, and label each chromosome as "parental" or "recombinant."*

New Combinations of Alleles: Variation for Natural Selection

EVOLUTION In Chapter 13, you learned how the physical behavior of chromosomes during meiosis contributes to the generation of variation in offspring. Each pair of homologous chromosomes lines up independently of other pairs during metaphase I, and crossing over prior to that, during prophase I, can mix and match parts of maternal and paternal homologs. Chapter 14 described Mendel's elegant experiments showing that the behavior of the abstract entities known as genes (or, more concretely, alleles of genes) also leads to variation in offspring. Now, putting these different ideas together, you can see that the recombinant chromosomes resulting from crossing over may bring alleles together in new combinations, and the

subsequent events of meiosis distribute to gametes the recombinant chromosomes in a multitude of combinations, such as the new variants seen in Figures 15.9 and 15.10. Random fertilization then increases even further the number of variant allele combinations that can be created.

This abundance of genetic variation provides the raw material on which natural selection works. If the traits conferred by particular combinations of alleles are better suited for a given environment, organisms possessing those genotypes will be expected to thrive and leave more offspring, ensuring the continuation of their genetic complement. In the next generation, of course, the alleles will be shuffled anew. Ultimately, the interplay between environment and genotype will determine which genetic combinations persist over time.

Mapping the Distance Between Genes Using Recombination Data: *Scientific Inquiry*

The discovery of linked genes and recombination due to crossing over led one of Morgan's students, Alfred H. Sturtevant, to a method for constructing a **genetic map**, an ordered list of the genetic loci along a particular chromosome.

Sturtevant hypothesized that the percentage of recombinant offspring, the *recombination frequency*, calculated from experiments like the one in Figures 15.9 and 15.10, depends on the distance between genes on a chromosome. He assumed that crossing over is a random event, with the chance of crossing over approximately equal at all points along a chromosome. Based on these assumptions, Sturtevant predicted that *the farther apart two genes are, the higher the probability that a crossover will occur between them and therefore the higher the recombination frequency*. His reasoning was simple: The greater the distance between two genes, the more points there are between them where crossing over can occur. Using recombination data from various fruit fly crosses, Sturtevant proceeded to assign relative positions to genes on the same chromosomes—that is, to *map* genes.

A genetic map based on recombination frequencies is called a **linkage map**. **Figure 15.11** shows Sturtevant's linkage map of three genes: the body-color (*b*) and wing-size (*vg*) genes depicted in Figure 15.10 and a third gene, called cinnabar (*cn*). Cinnabar is one of many *Drosophila* genes affecting eye color. Cinnabar eyes, a mutant phenotype, are a brighter red than the wild-type color. The recombination frequency between *cn* and *b* is 9%; that between *cn* and *vg*, 9.5%; and that between *b* and *vg*, 17%. In other words, crossovers between *cn* and *b* and between *cn* and *vg* are about half as frequent as crossovers between *b* and *vg*. Only a map that locates *cn* about midway between *b* and *vg* is consistent with these data, as you can prove to yourself by drawing alternative maps. Sturtevant expressed the distances between genes in **map units**, defining one map unit as equivalent to a 1% recombination frequency.

In practice, the interpretation of recombination data is more complicated than this example suggests. Some genes on a chromosome are so far from each other that a crossover between them is virtually certain. The observed frequency of recombination in crosses involving two such genes can have a maximum value of 50%, a result indistinguishable from that for genes on different chromosomes. In this case, the physical connection between genes on the same chromosome is not reflected in the results of genetic crosses. Despite being on the same chromosome and thus being *physically connected*, the genes are *genetically unlinked*; alleles of such genes assort independently, as if they were on different chromosomes. In fact, at least two of the genes for pea characters that Mendel studied are now known to be on the same chromosome, but the distance between them is so great that linkage is not observed in genetic crosses. Consequently, the two genes behaved as if they were on different chromosomes in Mendel's experiments.

▼ **Figure 15.11** **RESEARCH METHOD**

Constructing a Linkage Map

APPLICATION A linkage map shows the relative locations of genes along a chromosome.

TECHNIQUE A linkage map is based on the assumption that the probability of a crossover between two genetic loci is proportional to the distance separating the loci. The recombination frequencies used to construct a linkage map for a particular chromosome are obtained from experimental crosses, such as the cross depicted in Figures 15.9 and 15.10. The distances between genes are expressed as map units, with one map unit equivalent to a 1% recombination frequency. Genes are arranged on the chromosome in the order that best fits the data.

RESULTS In this example, the observed recombination frequencies between three *Drosophila* gene pairs (*b–cn* 9%, *cn–vg* 9.5%, and *b–vg* 17%) best fit a linear order in which *cn* is positioned about halfway between the other two genes:

The *b–vg* recombination frequency (17%) is slightly less than the sum of the *b–cn* and *cn–vg* frequencies (9 + 9.5 = 18.5%) because of the few times that one crossover occurs between *b* and *cn* and another crossover occurs between *cn* and *vg*. The second crossover would "cancel out" the first, reducing the observed *b–vg* recombination frequency while contributing to the frequency between each of the closer pairs of genes. The value of 18.5% (18.5 map units) is closer to the actual distance between the genes, so a geneticist would add the smaller distances in constructing a map.

Genes located far apart on a chromosome are mapped by adding the recombination frequencies from crosses involving closer pairs of genes lying between the two distant genes.

Using recombination data, Sturtevant and his colleagues were able to map numerous *Drosophila* genes in linear arrays. They found that the genes clustered into four groups of linked genes (*linkage groups*). Light microscopy had revealed four pairs of chromosomes in *Drosophila*, so the linkage map provided additional evidence that genes are located on chromosomes. Each chromosome has a linear array of specific genes, each gene with its own locus (**Figure 15.12**).

Because a linkage map is based strictly on recombination frequencies, it gives only an approximate picture of a chromosome. The frequency of crossing over is not actually uniform over the length of a chromosome, as Sturtevant assumed, and therefore map units do not correspond to actual physical distances (in nanometers, for instance). A linkage map does portray the order of genes along a chromosome, but it does not accurately portray the precise locations of those genes. Other methods enable geneticists to construct **cytogenetic maps** of chromosomes, which locate genes with respect to chromosomal

Mutant phenotypes

| Short aristae | Black body | Cinnabar eyes | Vestigial wings | Brown eyes |

0   48.5   57.5   67.0   104.5

| Long aristae (appendages on head) | Gray body | Red eyes | Normal wings | Red eyes |

Wild-type phenotypes

▲ **Figure 15.12 A partial genetic (linkage) map of a *Drosophila* chromosome.** This simplified map shows just a few of the genes that have been mapped on *Drosophila* chromosome II. The number at each gene locus indicates the number of map units between that locus and the locus for arista length (left). Notice that more than one gene can affect a given phenotypic characteristic, such as eye color. Also, note that in contrast to the homologous autosomes (II–IV), the X and Y sex chromosomes (I) have distinct shapes.

features, such as stained bands, that can be seen in the microscope. The ultimate maps, which we will discuss in Chapter 21, display the physical distances between gene loci in DNA nucleotides. Comparing a linkage map with such a physical map or with a cytogenetic map of the same chromosome, we find that the linear order of genes is identical in all the maps, but the spacing between genes is not.

CONCEPT CHECK 15.3

1. When two genes are located on the same chromosome, what is the physical basis for the production of recombinant offspring in a testcross between a dihybrid parent and a double-mutant (recessive) parent?
2. For each type of offspring of the testcross in Figure 15.9, explain the relationship between its phenotype and the alleles contributed by the female parent.
3. **WHAT IF?** Genes *A*, *B*, and *C* are located on the same chromosome. Testcrosses show that the recombination frequency between *A* and *B* is 28% and between *A* and *C* is 12%. Can you determine the linear order of these genes? Explain.

For suggested answers, see Appendix A.

CONCEPT **15.4**

Alterations of chromosome number or structure cause some genetic disorders

As you have learned so far in this chapter, the phenotype of an organism can be affected by small-scale changes involving individual genes. Random mutations are the source of all new alleles, which can lead to new phenotypic traits.

Large-scale chromosomal changes can also affect an organism's phenotype. Physical and chemical disturbances, as well as errors during meiosis, can damage chromosomes in major ways or alter their number in a cell. Large-scale chromosomal alterations in humans and other mammals often lead to spontaneous abortion (miscarriage) of a fetus, and individuals born with these types of genetic defects commonly exhibit various developmental disorders. Plants may tolerate such genetic defects better than animals do.

Abnormal Chromosome Number

Ideally, the meiotic spindle distributes chromosomes to daughter cells without error. But there is an occasional mishap, called a **nondisjunction**, in which the members of a pair of homologous chromosomes do not move apart properly during meiosis I or sister chromatids fail to separate during meiosis II **(Figure 15.13)**. In these cases, one gamete

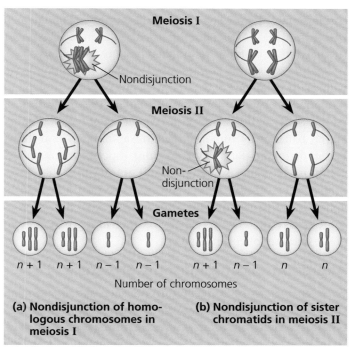

▲ **Figure 15.13 Meiotic nondisjunction.** Gametes with an abnormal chromosome number can arise by nondisjunction in either meiosis I or meiosis II. For simplicity, the figure does not show the spores formed by meiosis in plants. Ultimately, spores form gametes that have the defects shown. (See Figure 13.6.)

CHAPTER 15 The Chromosomal Basis of Inheritance **297**

receives two of the same type of chromosome and another gamete receives no copy. The other chromosomes are usually distributed normally.

If either of the aberrant gametes unites with a normal one at fertilization, the zygote will also have an abnormal number of a particular chromosome, a condition known as **aneuploidy**. (Aneuploidy may involve more than one chromosome.) Fertilization involving a gamete that has no copy of a particular chromosome will lead to a missing chromosome in the zygote (so that the cell has $2n - 1$ chromosomes); the aneuploid zygote is said to be **monosomic** for that chromosome. If a chromosome is present in triplicate in the zygote (so that the cell has $2n + 1$ chromosomes), the aneuploid cell is **trisomic** for that chromosome. Mitosis will subsequently transmit the anomaly to all embryonic cells. If the organism survives, it usually has a set of traits caused by the abnormal dose of the genes associated with the extra or missing chromosome. Down syndrome is an example of trisomy in humans that will be discussed later. Nondisjunction can also occur during mitosis. If such an error takes place early in embryonic development, then the aneuploid condition is passed along by mitosis to a large number of cells and is likely to have a substantial effect on the organism.

Some organisms have more than two complete chromosome sets in all somatic cells. The general term for this chromosomal alteration is **polyploidy**; the specific terms *triploidy* ($3n$) and *tetraploidy* ($4n$) indicate three or four chromosomal sets, respectively. One way a triploid cell may arise is by the fertilization of an abnormal diploid egg produced by nondisjunction of all its chromosomes. Tetraploidy could result from the failure of a $2n$ zygote to divide after replicating its chromosomes. Subsequent normal mitotic divisions would then produce a $4n$ embryo.

Polyploidy is fairly common in the plant kingdom. As we will see in Chapter 24, the spontaneous origin of polyploid individuals plays an important role in the evolution of plants. Many of the plant species we eat are polyploid; for example, bananas are triploid, wheat hexaploid ($6n$), and strawberries octoploid ($8n$). Polyploid animal species are much less common, although some are found among fishes and amphibians. In general, polyploids are more nearly normal in appearance than aneuploids. One extra (or missing) chromosome apparently disrupts genetic balance more than does an entire extra set of chromosomes.

Alterations of Chromosome Structure

Errors in meiosis or damaging agents such as radiation can cause breakage of a chromosome, which can lead to four types of changes in chromosome structure **(Figure 15.14)**. A **deletion** occurs when a chromosomal fragment is lost. The affected chromosome is then missing certain genes. (If the centromere is deleted, the entire chromosome will be lost.) The "deleted" fragment may become attached as an extra segment to a sister chromatid, producing a **duplication**.

▼ **Figure 15.14 Alterations of chromosome structure.** Red arrows indicate breakage points. Dark purple highlights the chromosomal parts affected by the rearrangements.

(a) Deletion

A **deletion** removes a chromosomal segment.

(b) Duplication

A **duplication** repeats a segment.

(c) Inversion

An **inversion** reverses a segment within a chromosome.

(d) Translocation

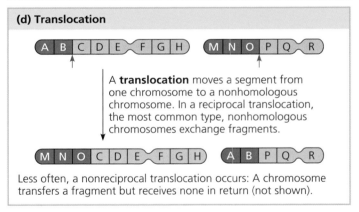

A **translocation** moves a segment from one chromosome to a nonhomologous chromosome. In a reciprocal translocation, the most common type, nonhomologous chromosomes exchange fragments.

Less often, a nonreciprocal translocation occurs: A chromosome transfers a fragment but receives none in return (not shown).

Alternatively, a detached fragment could attach to a nonsister chromatid of a homologous chromosome. In that case, though, the "duplicated" segments might not be identical because the homologs could carry different alleles of certain genes. A chromosomal fragment may also reattach to the original chromosome but in the reverse orientation, producing an **inversion**. A fourth possible result of chromosomal breakage is for the fragment to join a nonhomologous chromosome, a rearrangement called a **translocation**.

Deletions and duplications are especially likely to occur during meiosis. In crossing over, nonsister chromatids sometimes exchange unequal-sized segments of DNA, so that one partner gives up more genes than it receives. The products of such an unequal crossover are one chromosome with a deletion and one chromosome with a duplication.

A diploid embryo that is homozygous for a large deletion (or has a single X chromosome with a large deletion, in a male) is usually missing a number of essential genes, a condition that is ordinarily lethal. Duplications and translocations also tend to be harmful. In reciprocal translocations, in which segments are exchanged between nonhomologous chromosomes, and in inversions, the balance of genes is not abnormal—all genes are present in their normal doses. Nevertheless, translocations and inversions can alter phenotype because a gene's expression can be influenced by its location among neighboring genes; such events sometimes have devastating effects.

Human Disorders Due to Chromosomal Alterations

Alterations of chromosome number and structure are associated with a number of serious human disorders. As described earlier, nondisjunction in meiosis results in aneuploidy in gametes and any resulting zygotes. Although the frequency of aneuploid zygotes may be quite high in humans, most of these chromosomal alterations are so disastrous to development that the affected embryos are spontaneously aborted long before birth. However, some types of aneuploidy appear to upset the genetic balance less than others, with the result that individuals with certain aneuploid conditions can survive to birth and beyond. These individuals have a set of traits—a *syndrome*—characteristic of the type of aneuploidy. Genetic disorders caused by aneuploidy can be diagnosed before birth by fetal testing (see Figure 14.19).

Down Syndrome (Trisomy 21)

One aneuploid condition, **Down syndrome**, affects approximately one out of every 700 children born in the United States (Figure 15.15). Down syndrome is usually the result of an extra chromosome 21, so that each body cell has a total of 47 chromosomes. Because the cells are trisomic for chromosome 21, Down syndrome is often called *trisomy 21*. Down syndrome includes characteristic facial features, short stature, correctable heart defects, and developmental delays. Individuals with Down syndrome have an increased chance of developing leukemia and Alzheimer's disease but have a lower rate of high blood pressure, atherosclerosis (hardening of the arteries), stroke, and many types of solid tumors. Although people with Down syndrome, on average, have a life span shorter than normal, most, with proper medical treatment, live to middle age and beyond. Many live independently or at home with their families, are employed, and are valuable contributors to their communities. Almost all males and about half of females with Down syndrome are sexually underdeveloped and sterile.

The frequency of Down syndrome increases with the age of the mother. While the disorder occurs in just 0.04% of children born to women under age 30, the risk climbs to 0.92% for

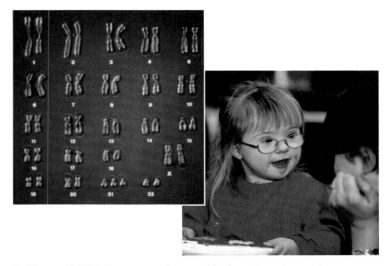

▲ **Figure 15.15 Down syndrome.** The karyotype shows trisomy 21, the most common cause of Down syndrome. The child exhibits the facial features characteristic of this disorder.

mothers at age 40 and is even higher for older mothers. The correlation of Down syndrome with maternal age has not yet been explained. Most cases result from nondisjunction during meiosis I, and some research points to an age-dependent abnormality in a meiosis checkpoint that normally delays anaphase until all the kinetochores are attached to the spindle (like the M phase checkpoint of the mitotic cell cycle; see Chapter 12). Trisomies of some other chromosomes also increase in incidence with maternal age, although infants with other autosomal trisomies rarely survive for long. Due to its low risk and its potential for providing useful information, prenatal screening for trisomies in the embryo is now offered to all pregnant women. In 2008, the Prenatally and Postnatally Diagnosed Conditions Awareness Act was signed into law in the United States. This law stipulates that medical practitioners give accurate, up-to-date information about any prenatal or postnatal diagnosis received by parents and that they connect parents with appropriate support services.

Aneuploidy of Sex Chromosomes

Nondisjunction of sex chromosomes produces a variety of aneuploid conditions. Most of these conditions appear to upset the genetic balance less than aneuploid conditions involving autosomes. This may be because the Y chromosome carries relatively few genes and because extra copies of the X chromosome become inactivated as Barr bodies in somatic cells.

An extra X chromosome in a male, producing XXY, occurs approximately once in every 500 to 1,000 live male births. People with this disorder, called *Klinefelter syndrome*, have male sex organs, but the testes are abnormally small and the man is sterile. Even though the extra X is inactivated, some breast enlargement and other female body characteristics are common. Affected individuals may have subnormal intelligence. About 1 of every 1,000 males is born with an extra Y chromosome (XYY). These males undergo normal sexual development and do not exhibit any well-defined syndrome, but they tend to be somewhat taller than average.

Females with trisomy X (XXX), which occurs once in approximately 1,000 live female births, are healthy and have no unusual physical features other than being slightly taller than average. Triple-X females are at risk for learning disabilities but are fertile. Monosomy X, called *Turner syndrome*, occurs about once in every 2,500 female births and is the only known viable monosomy in humans. Although these X0 individuals are phenotypically female, they are sterile because their sex organs do not mature. When provided with estrogen replacement therapy, girls with Turner syndrome do develop secondary sex characteristics. Most have normal intelligence.

Disorders Caused by Structurally Altered Chromosomes

Many deletions in human chromosomes, even in a heterozygous state, cause severe problems. One such syndrome, known as *cri du chat* ("cry of the cat"), results from a specific deletion in chromosome 5. A child born with this deletion is severely intellectually disabled, has a small head with unusual facial features, and has a cry that sounds like the mewing of a distressed cat. Such individuals usually die in infancy or early childhood.

Chromosomal translocations have been implicated in certain cancers, including *chronic myelogenous leukemia (CML)*. This disease occurs when a reciprocal translocation happens during mitosis of cells that will become white blood cells. In these cells, the exchange of a large portion of chromosome 22 with a small fragment from a tip of chromosome 9 produces a much shortened, easily recognized chromosome 22, called the *Philadelphia chromosome* (**Figure 15.16**). Such an exchange causes cancer by activating a gene that leads to uncontrolled cell cycle progression. The mechanism of gene activation will be discussed in Chapter 18.

Normal chromosome 9

Normal chromosome 22

Reciprocal translocation

Translocated chromosome 9

Translocated chromosome 22
(Philadelphia chromosome)

▲ **Figure 15.16 Translocation associated with chronic myelogenous leukemia (CML).** The cancerous cells in nearly all CML patients contain an abnormally short chromosome 22, the so-called Philadelphia chromosome, and an abnormally long chromosome 9. These altered chromosomes result from the reciprocal translocation shown here, which presumably occurred in a single white blood cell precursor undergoing mitosis and was then passed along to all descendant cells.

CONCEPT 15.5

Some inheritance patterns are exceptions to standard Mendelian inheritance

In the previous section, you learned about deviations from the usual patterns of chromosomal inheritance due to abnormal events in meiosis and mitosis. We conclude this chapter by describing two normally occurring exceptions to Mendelian genetics, one involving genes located in the nucleus and the other involving genes located outside the nucleus. In both cases, the sex of the parent contributing an allele is a factor in the pattern of inheritance.

Genomic Imprinting

Throughout our discussions of Mendelian genetics and the chromosomal basis of inheritance, we have assumed that a given allele will have the same effect whether it was inherited from the mother or the father. This is probably a safe assumption most of the time. For example, when Mendel crossed purple-flowered pea plants with white-flowered pea plants, he observed the same results regardless of whether the purple-flowered parent supplied the eggs or the sperm. In recent years, however, geneticists have identified two to three dozen traits in mammals that depend on which parent passed along the alleles for those traits. Such variation in phenotype depending on whether an allele is inherited from the male or female parent is called **genomic imprinting**. (Note that unlike sex-linked genes, most imprinted genes are on autosomes.)

Genomic imprinting occurs during gamete formation and results in the silencing of a particular allele of certain genes. Because these genes are imprinted differently in sperm and eggs, a zygote expresses only one allele of an imprinted gene, that inherited from either the female or the male parent. The imprints are then transmitted to all body cells during development. In each generation, the old imprints are "erased" in gamete-producing cells, and the chromosomes of the developing gametes are newly imprinted according to the sex of the individual forming the gametes. In a given species, the imprinted genes are always imprinted in the same way. For instance, a gene imprinted for maternal allele expression is always imprinted this way, generation after generation.

Consider, for example, the mouse gene for insulin-like growth factor 2 (*Igf2*), one of the first imprinted genes to be identified. Although this growth factor is required for normal prenatal growth, only the paternal allele is expressed (Figure 15.17a). Evidence that the *Igf2* gene is imprinted came initially from crosses between normal-sized (wild-type) mice and dwarf (mutant) mice homozygous for a recessive mutation in the *Igf2* gene. The phenotypes of heterozygous offspring (with one normal allele and one mutant) differed, depending on whether the mutant allele came from the mother or the father (Figure 15.17b).

What exactly is a genomic imprint? In many cases, it seems to consist of methyl (—CH$_3$) groups that are added to cytosine nucleotides of one of the alleles. Such methylation may silence the allele, an effect consistent with evidence that heavily methylated genes are usually inactive (see Chapter 18). However, for a few genes, methylation has been shown to *activate* expression of the allele. This is the case for the *Igf2* gene: Methylation of certain cytosines on the paternal chromosome leads to expression of the paternal *Igf2* allele. The apparent inconsistency as to whether methylation activates or silences alleles was resolved in part when researchers found that DNA methylation operates indirectly by recruiting enzymes that modify DNA-associated proteins (histones), leading to condensation of the local DNA. Depending on the original function of the condensed DNA in regulating allele expression, the result is either silencing or activation of a given allele.

Genomic imprinting is thought to affect only a small fraction of the genes in mammalian genomes, but most of the known imprinted genes are critical for embryonic development. In experiments with mice, for example, embryos engineered to inherit both copies of certain chromosomes from the same parent usually die before birth, whether that parent is male or female. A few years ago, however, scientists in Japan combined the genetic material from two eggs in a zygote while allowing expression of the *Igf2* gene from only one of the egg nuclei. The zygote developed into an apparently healthy mouse. Normal development seems to require that embryonic cells have exactly one active copy—not zero, not two—of certain genes. The association of aberrant imprinting

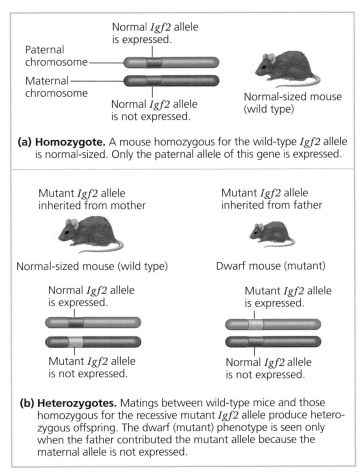

(a) Homozygote. A mouse homozygous for the wild-type *Igf2* allele is normal-sized. Only the paternal allele of this gene is expressed.

(b) Heterozygotes. Matings between wild-type mice and those homozygous for the recessive mutant *Igf2* allele produce heterozygous offspring. The dwarf (mutant) phenotype is seen only when the father contributed the mutant allele because the maternal allele is not expressed.

▲ **Figure 15.17 Genomic imprinting of the mouse *Igf2* gene.**

with abnormal development and certain cancers has stimulated numerous studies of how different genes are imprinted.

Inheritance of Organelle Genes

Although our focus in this chapter has been on the chromosomal basis of inheritance, we end with an important amendment: Not all of a eukaryotic cell's genes are located on nuclear chromosomes, or even in the nucleus; some genes are located in organelles in the cytoplasm. Because they are outside the nucleus, these genes are sometimes called *extranuclear genes* or *cytoplasmic genes*. Mitochondria, as well as chloroplasts and other plastids in plants, contain small circular DNA molecules that carry a number of genes. These organelles reproduce themselves and transmit their genes to daughter organelles. Organelle genes are not distributed to offspring according to the same rules that direct the distribution of nuclear chromosomes during meiosis, so they do not display Mendelian inheritance.

The first hint that extranuclear genes exist came from studies by the German scientist Karl Correns on the inheritance of yellow or white patches on the leaves of an otherwise green plant. In 1909, he observed that the coloration of the offspring was determined only by the maternal parent (the

◀ **Figure 15.18 Variegated leaves from English holly (*Ilex aquifolium*).** Variegated (striped or spotted) leaves result from mutations in pigment genes located in plastids, which generally are inherited from the maternal parent.

source of eggs) and not by the paternal parent (the source of sperm). Subsequent research showed that such coloration patterns, or variegation, are due to mutations in plastid genes that control pigmentation (**Figure 15.18**). In most plants, a zygote receives all its plastids from the cytoplasm of the egg and none from the sperm, which contributes little more than a haploid set of chromosomes. An egg may contain plastids with different alleles for a pigmentation gene. As the zygote develops, plastids containing wild-type or mutant pigmentation genes are distributed randomly to daughter cells. The pattern of leaf coloration exhibited by a plant depends on the ratio of wild-type to mutant plastids in its various tissues.

Similar maternal inheritance is also the rule for mitochondrial genes in most animals and plants, because almost all the mitochondria passed on to a zygote come from the cytoplasm of the egg. The products of most mitochondrial genes help make up the protein complexes of the electron transport chain and ATP synthase (see Chapter 9). Defects in one or more of these proteins, therefore, reduce the amount of ATP the cell can make and have been shown to cause a number of rare human disorders. Because the parts of the body most susceptible to energy deprivation are the nervous system and the muscles, most mitochondrial diseases primarily affect these systems. For example, *mitochondrial myopathy* causes weakness, intolerance of exercise, and muscle deterioration. Another mitochondrial disorder is *Leber's hereditary optic neuropathy*, which can produce sudden blindness in people as young as their 20s or 30s. The four mutations found thus far to cause this disorder affect oxidative phosphorylation during cellular respiration, a crucial function for the cell.

In addition to the rare diseases clearly caused by defects in mitochondrial DNA, mitochondrial mutations inherited from a person's mother may contribute to at least some cases of diabetes and heart disease, as well as to other disorders that commonly debilitate the elderly, such as Alzheimer's disease. In the course of a lifetime, new mutations gradually accumulate in our mitochondrial DNA, and some researchers think that these mutations play a role in the normal aging process.

Wherever genes are located in the cell—in the nucleus or in cytoplasmic organelles—their inheritance depends on the precise replication of DNA, the genetic material. In the next chapter, you will learn how this molecular reproduction occurs.

CONCEPT CHECK 15.5

1. Gene dosage, the number of active copies of a gene, is important to proper development. Identify and describe two processes that establish the proper dosage of certain genes.
2. Reciprocal crosses between two primrose varieties, A and B, produced the following results: A female × B male → offspring with all green (nonvariegated) leaves; B female × A male → offspring with spotted (variegated) leaves. Explain these results.
3. **WHAT IF?** Mitochondrial genes are critical to the energy metabolism of cells, but mitochondrial disorders caused by mutations in these genes are generally not lethal. Why not?

For suggested answers, see Appendix A.

---

15 CHAPTER REVIEW

SUMMARY OF KEY CONCEPTS

CONCEPT 15.1

Mendelian inheritance has its physical basis in the behavior of chromosomes (pp. 286–289)

- The **chromosome theory of inheritance** states that genes are located on chromosomes and that the behavior of chromosomes during meiosis accounts for Mendel's laws of segregation and independent assortment.
- Morgan's discovery that transmission of the X chromosome in *Drosophila* correlates with inheritance of an eye-color trait was the first solid evidence indicating that a specific gene is associated with a specific chromosome.

? *What characteristic of the sex chromosomes allowed Morgan to correlate their behavior with that of the alleles of the eye-color gene?*

CONCEPT 15.2

Sex-linked genes exhibit unique patterns of inheritance (pp. 289–292)

- Sex is an inherited phenotypic character usually determined by which sex chromosomes are present. Humans and other mammals have an X-Y system in which sex is determined by whether a Y chromosome is present. Other systems are found in birds, fishes, and insects.
- The sex chromosomes carry **sex-linked genes** for some traits that are unrelated to sex characteristics. For instance, recessive alleles causing color blindness are **X-linked** (carried on the X chromosome). Fathers transmit this and other X-linked alleles to all daughters but to no sons. Any male who inherits such an allele from his mother will express the trait.
- In mammalian females, one of the two X chromosomes in each cell is randomly inactivated during early embryonic development,

becoming highly condensed into a **Barr body**. The descendant cells inherit the same inactivated X chromosome. If a female is heterozygous for a particular gene located on the X chromosome, she will be mosaic for that character, with about half her cells expressing the maternal allele and about half expressing the paternal allele.

? *Why are males affected much more often than females by X-linked disorders?*

CONCEPT 15.3

Linked genes tend to be inherited together because they are located near each other on the same chromosome (pp. 292–297)

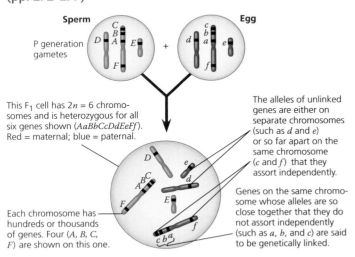

Sperm ← → Egg
P generation gametes

This F₁ cell has $2n = 6$ chromosomes and is heterozygous for all six genes shown ($AaBbCcDdEeFf$). Red = maternal; blue = paternal.

The alleles of unlinked genes are either on separate chromosomes (such as d and e) or so far apart on the same chromosome (c and f) that they assort independently.

Each chromosome has hundreds or thousands of genes. Four (A, B, C, F) are shown on this one.

Genes on the same chromosome whose alleles are so close together that they do not assort independently (such as a, b, and c) are said to be genetically linked.

- Among offspring from an F₁ testcross, **parental types** have the same combination of traits as those in the P generation parents. **Recombinant types** (**recombinants**) exhibit new combinations of traits not seen in either P generation parent. Because of the independent assortment of chromosomes, unlinked genes exhibit a 50% frequency of recombination in the gametes. For genetically **linked genes**, **crossing over** between nonsister chromatids during meiosis I accounts for the observed recombinants, always less than 50% of the total.
- The order of genes on a chromosome and the relative distances between them can be deduced from recombination frequencies observed in genetic crosses. These data allow construction of a **linkage map** (a type of **genetic map**). The farther apart genes are, the more likely their allele combinations will be recombined during crossing over.

? *Why are specific alleles of two genes that are farther apart more likely to show recombination than those of two closer genes?*

CONCEPT 15.4

Alterations of chromosome number or structure cause some genetic disorders (pp. 297–300)

- **Aneuploidy**, an abnormal chromosome number, can result from **nondisjunction** during meiosis. When a normal gamete unites with one containing two copies or no copies of a particular chromosome, the resulting zygote and its descendant cells either have one extra copy of that chromosome (**trisomy**, $2n + 1$) or are missing a copy (**monosomy**, $2n - 1$). **Polyploidy** (more than two complete sets of chromosomes) can result from complete nondisjunction during gamete formation.
- Chromosome breakage can result in alterations of chromosome structure: **deletions**, **duplications**, **inversions**, and **translocations**. Translocations can be reciprocal or nonreciprocal.

- Changes in the number of chromosomes per cell or in the structure of individual chromosomes can affect the phenotype and, in some cases, lead to human disorders. Such alterations cause **Down syndrome** (usually due to trisomy of chromosome 21), certain cancers associated with chromosomal translocations, and various other human disorders.

? *Why are inversions and reciprocal translocations less likely to be lethal than are aneuploidy, duplications, deletions, and nonreciprocal translocations?*

CONCEPT 15.5

Some inheritance patterns are exceptions to standard Mendelian inheritance (pp. 300–302)

- In mammals, the phenotypic effects of a small number of particular genes depend on which allele is inherited from each parent, a phenomenon called **genomic imprinting**. Imprints are formed during gamete production, with the result that one allele (either maternal or paternal) is not expressed in offspring.
- The inheritance of traits controlled by the genes present in mitochondria and plastids depends solely on the maternal parent because the zygote's cytoplasm containing these organelles comes from the egg. Some diseases affecting the nervous and muscular systems are caused by defects in mitochondrial genes that prevent cells from making enough ATP.

? *Explain how genomic imprinting and inheritance of mitochondrial and chloroplast DNA are exceptions to standard Mendelian inheritance.*

TEST YOUR UNDERSTANDING

LEVEL 1: KNOWLEDGE/COMPREHENSION

1. A man with hemophilia (a recessive, sex-linked condition) has a daughter of normal phenotype. She marries a man who is normal for the trait. What is the probability that a daughter of this mating will be a hemophiliac? That a son will be a hemophiliac? If the couple has four sons, what is the probability that all four will be born with hemophilia?

2. Pseudohypertrophic muscular dystrophy is an inherited disorder that causes gradual deterioration of the muscles. It is seen almost exclusively in boys born to apparently normal parents and usually results in death in the early teens. Is this disorder caused by a dominant or a recessive allele? Is its inheritance sex-linked or autosomal? How do you know? Explain why this disorder is almost never seen in girls.

3. A wild-type fruit fly (heterozygous for gray body color and normal wings) is mated with a black fly with vestigial wings. The offspring have the following phenotypic distribution: wild-type, 778; black-vestigial, 785; black-normal, 158; gray-vestigial, 162. What is the recombination frequency between these genes for body color and wing size?

4. What pattern of inheritance would lead a geneticist to suspect that an inherited disorder of cell metabolism is due to a defective mitochondrial gene?

5. A space probe discovers a planet inhabited by creatures that reproduce with the same hereditary patterns seen in humans. Three phenotypic characters are height (T = tall, t = dwarf), head appendages (A = antennae, a = no antennae), and nose morphology (S = upturned snout, s = downturned snout). Since the creatures are not "intelligent," Earth scientists are able to do some controlled breeding experiments using various heterozygotes in testcrosses. For tall heterozygotes with antennae, the offspring are

tall-antennae, 46; dwarf-antennae, 7; dwarf-no antennae, 42; tall-no antennae, 5. For heterozygotes with antennae and an up-turned snout, the offspring are antennae-upturned snout, 47; antennae-downturned snout, 2; no antennae-downturned snout, 48; no antennae-upturned snout, 3. Calculate the recombination frequencies for both experiments.

LEVEL 2: APPLICATION/ANALYSIS

6. Using the information from problem 5, scientists do a further testcross using a heterozygote for height and nose morphology. The offspring are: tall-upturned snout, 40; dwarf-upturned snout, 9; dwarf-downturned snout, 42; tall-downturned snout, 9. Calculate the recombination frequency from these data; then use your answer from problem 5 to determine the correct sequence of the three linked genes.

7. Red-green color blindness is caused by a sex-linked recessive allele. A color-blind man marries a woman with normal vision whose father was color-blind. What is the probability that they will have a color-blind daughter? What is the probability that their first son will be color-blind? (Note the different wording in the two questions.)

8. A wild-type fruit fly (heterozygous for gray body color and red eyes) is mated with a black fruit fly with purple eyes. The offspring are wild-type, 721; black-purple, 751; gray-purple, 49; black-red, 45. What is the recombination frequency between these genes for body color and eye color? Using information from problem 3, what fruit flies (genotypes and phenotypes) would you mate to determine the sequence of the body-color, wing-size, and eye-color genes on the chromosome?

9. **DRAW IT** A fruit fly that is true-breeding for gray body with vestigial wings (b^+ b^+ vg vg) is mated with one that is true-breeding for black body with normal wings (b b vg^+ vg^+).
   (a) Draw the chromosomes for the P generation flies, using red for the gray fly and pink for the black one. Show the position of each allele.
   (b) Draw the chromosomes and label the alleles of an F_1 fly.
   (c) Suppose an F_1 female is testcrossed. Draw the chromosomes of the resulting offspring in a Punnett square.
   (d) Knowing that the distance between these two genes is 17 map units, predict the phenotypic ratios of these offspring.

10. Women born with an extra X chromosome (XXX) are generally healthy and indistinguishable in appearance from normal XX women. What is a likely explanation for this finding? How could you test this explanation?

11. Determine the sequence of genes along a chromosome based on the following recombination frequencies: A–B, 8 map units; A–C, 28 map units; A–D, 25 map units; B–C, 20 map units; B–D, 33 map units.

12. Assume that genes A and B are on the same chromosome and are 50 map units apart. An animal heterozygous at both loci is crossed with one that is homozygous recessive at both loci. What percentage of the offspring will show recombinant phenotypes resulting from crossovers? Without knowing these genes are on the same chromosome, how would you interpret the results of this cross?

13. Two genes of a flower, one controlling blue (B) versus white (b) petals and the other controlling round (R) versus oval (r) stamens, are linked and are 10 map units apart. You cross a homozygous blue-oval plant with a homozygous white-round plant. The resulting F_1 progeny are crossed with homozygous white-oval plants, and 1,000 F_2 progeny are obtained. How many F_2 plants of each of the four phenotypes do you expect?

14. You design *Drosophila* crosses to provide recombination data for gene *a*, which is located on the chromosome shown in Figure 15.12. Gene *a* has recombination frequencies of 14% with the vestigial-wing locus and 26% with the brown-eye locus. Approximately where is *a* located along the chromosome?

LEVEL 3: SYNTHESIS/EVALUATION

15. Banana plants, which are triploid, are seedless and therefore sterile. Propose a possible explanation.

16. **EVOLUTION CONNECTION**
   You have seen that crossing over, or recombination, is thought to be evolutionarily advantageous because it continually shuffles genetic alleles into novel combinations, allowing evolutionary processes to occur. Until recently, it was thought that the genes on the Y chromosome might degenerate because they lack homologous genes on the X chromosome with which to recombine. However, when the Y chromosome was sequenced, eight large regions were found to be internally homologous to each other, and quite a few of the 78 genes represent duplicates. (Y chromosome researcher David Page has called it a "hall of mirrors.") What might be a benefit of these regions?

17. **SCIENTIFIC INQUIRY**
   Butterflies have an X-Y sex determination system that is different from that of flies or humans. Female butterflies may be either XY or XO, while butterflies with two or more X chromosomes are males. This photograph shows a tiger swallowtail *gynandromorph*, an individual that is half male (left side) and half female (right side). Given that the first division of the zygote divides the embryo into the future right and left halves of the butterfly, propose a hypothesis that explains how nondisjunction during the first mitosis might have produced this unusual-looking butterfly.

18. **WRITE ABOUT A THEME**
   The Genetic Basis of Life The continuity of life is based on heritable information in the form of DNA. In a short essay (100–150 words), relate the structure and behavior of chromosomes to inheritance in both asexually and sexually reproducing species.

For selected answers, see Appendix A.

Mastering**BIOLOGY®**   www.masteringbiology.com

1. MasteringBiology® Assignments
Make Connections Tutorial Chromosomal Inheritance (Chapter 15) and Independent Assortment (Chapter 14)
Experimental Inquiry Tutorial What Is the Inheritance Pattern of Sex-Linked Traits?
Video Tutor Session Sex-Linked Pedigrees
Tutorials Sex Linkage • Linked Genes and Linkage Mapping • Chromosomal Mutations
Activities Sex-Linked Genes • Linked Genes and Crossing Over • Mistakes in Meiosis • Polyploid Plants
Questions Student Misconceptions • Reading Quiz • Multiple Choice • End-of-Chapter

2. eText
Read your book online, search, take notes, highlight text, and more.

3. The Study Area
Practice Tests • Cumulative Test • *BioFlix* 3-D Animations • MP3 Tutor Sessions • Videos • Activities • Investigations • Lab Media • Audio Glossary • Word Study Tools • Art

16

The Molecular Basis of Inheritance

▲ Figure 16.1 **How was the structure of DNA determined?**

KEY CONCEPTS

16.1 DNA is the genetic material

16.2 Many proteins work together in DNA replication and repair

16.3 A chromosome consists of a DNA molecule packed together with proteins

OVERVIEW

Life's Operating Instructions

In April 1953, James Watson and Francis Crick shook the scientific world with an elegant double-helical model for the structure of deoxyribonucleic acid, or DNA. **Figure 16.1** shows Watson (left) and Crick admiring their DNA model, which they built from tin and wire. Over the past 60 years or so, their model has evolved from a novel proposition to an icon of modern biology. Mendel's heritable factors and Morgan's genes on chromosomes are, in fact, composed of DNA. Chemically speaking, your genetic endowment is the DNA

you inherited from your parents. DNA, the substance of inheritance, is the most celebrated molecule of our time.

Of all nature's molecules, nucleic acids are unique in their ability to direct their own replication from monomers. Indeed, the resemblance of offspring to their parents has its basis in the precise replication of DNA and its transmission from one generation to the next. Hereditary information is encoded in the chemical language of DNA and reproduced in all the cells of your body. It is this DNA program that directs the development of your biochemical, anatomical, physiological, and, to some extent, behavioral traits. In this chapter, you will discover how biologists deduced that DNA is the genetic material and how Watson and Crick worked out its structure. You will also learn about **DNA replication**, the process by which a DNA molecule is copied, and how cells repair their DNA. Finally, you will explore how a molecule of DNA is packaged together with proteins in a chromosome.

CONCEPT 16.1

DNA is the genetic material

Today, even schoolchildren have heard of DNA, and scientists routinely manipulate DNA in the laboratory, often to change the heritable traits of cells in their experiments. Early in the 20th century, however, identifying the molecules of inheritance loomed as a major challenge to biologists.

The Search for the Genetic Material: *Scientific Inquiry*

Once T. H. Morgan's group showed that genes exist as parts of chromosomes (described in Chapter 15), the two chemical components of chromosomes—DNA and protein—became the candidates for the genetic material. Until the 1940s, the case for proteins seemed stronger, especially since biochemists had identified them as a class of macromolecules with great heterogeneity and specificity of function, essential requirements for the hereditary material. Moreover, little was known about nucleic acids, whose physical and chemical properties seemed far too uniform to account for the multitude of specific inherited traits exhibited by every organism. This view gradually changed as experiments with microorganisms yielded unexpected results. As with the work of Mendel and Morgan, a key factor in determining the identity of the genetic material was the choice of appropriate experimental organisms. The role of DNA in heredity was first worked out while studying bacteria and the viruses that infect them, which are far simpler than pea plants, fruit flies, or humans. In this section, we will trace the search for the genetic material in some detail as a case study in scientific inquiry.

Evidence That DNA Can Transform Bacteria

The discovery of the genetic role of DNA dates back to 1928. While attempting to develop a vaccine against pneumonia, a British medical officer named Frederick Griffith was studying *Streptococcus pneumoniae*, a bacterium that causes pneumonia in mammals. Griffith had two strains (varieties) of the bacterium, one pathogenic (disease-causing) and one nonpathogenic (harmless). He was surprised to find that when he killed the pathogenic bacteria with heat and then mixed the cell remains with living bacteria of the nonpathogenic strain, some of the living cells became pathogenic (**Figure 16.2**). Furthermore, this newly acquired trait of pathogenicity was

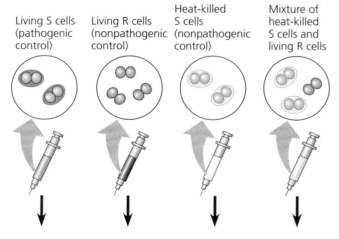

▼ Figure 16.2

INQUIRY

Can a genetic trait be transferred between different bacterial strains?

EXPERIMENT Frederick Griffith studied two strains of the bacterium *Streptococcus pneumoniae*. Bacteria of the S (smooth) strain can cause pneumonia in mice; they are pathogenic because they have an outer capsule that protects them from an animal's defense system. Bacteria of the R (rough) strain lack a capsule and are nonpathogenic. To test for the trait of pathogenicity, Griffith injected mice with the two strains:

Living S cells (pathogenic control)

Living R cells (nonpathogenic control)

Heat-killed S cells (nonpathogenic control)

Mixture of heat-killed S cells and living R cells

RESULTS

Mouse dies   Mouse healthy   Mouse healthy   Mouse dies

In blood sample, living S cells are found that can reproduce, yielding more S cells.

CONCLUSION Griffith concluded that the living R bacteria had been transformed into pathogenic S bacteria by an unknown, heritable substance from the dead S cells that allowed the R cells to make capsules.

SOURCE F. Griffith, The significance of pneumococcal types, *Journal of Hygiene* 27:113–159 (1928).

WHAT IF? How did this experiment rule out the possibility that the R cells could have simply used the capsules of the dead S cells to become pathogenic?

inherited by all the descendants of the transformed bacteria. Clearly, some chemical component of the dead pathogenic cells caused this heritable change, although the identity of the substance was not known. Griffith called the phenomenon **transformation**, now defined as a change in genotype and phenotype due to the assimilation of external DNA by a cell. (This use of the word *transformation* should not be confused with the conversion of a normal animal cell to a cancerous one, discussed near the end of Concept 12.3)

Griffith's work set the stage for a 14-year effort by American bacteriologist Oswald Avery to identify the transforming substance. Avery focused on three main candidates: DNA, RNA (the other nucleic acid in cells), and protein. Avery broke open the heat-killed pathogenic bacteria and extracted the cellular contents. He treated each of three samples with an agent that inactivated one type of molecule, then tested the sample for its ability to transform live nonpathogenic bacteria. Only when DNA was allowed to remain active did transformation occur. In 1944, Avery and his colleagues Maclyn McCarty and Colin MacLeod announced that the transforming agent was DNA. Their discovery was greeted with interest but considerable skepticism, in part because of the lingering belief that proteins were better candidates for the genetic material. Moreover, many biologists were not convinced that the genes of bacteria would be similar in composition and function to those of more complex organisms. But the major reason for the continued doubt was that so little was known about DNA.

Evidence That Viral DNA Can Program Cells

Additional evidence for DNA as the genetic material came from studies of viruses that infect bacteria (**Figure 16.3**). These viruses are called **bacteriophages** (meaning "bacteria-eaters"), or **phages** for short. Viruses are much simpler than

Phage head

Tail sheath

Tail fiber

DNA

100 nm

Bacterial cell

▲ **Figure 16.3 Viruses infecting a bacterial cell.** Phages called T2 attach to the host cell and inject their genetic material through the plasma membrane while the head and tail parts remain on the outer bacterial surface (colorized TEM).

cells. A **virus** is little more than DNA (or sometimes RNA) enclosed by a protective coat, which is often simply protein. To produce more viruses, a virus must infect a cell and take over the cell's metabolic machinery.

Phages have been widely used as tools by researchers in molecular genetics. In 1952, Alfred Hershey and Martha Chase performed experiments showing that DNA is the genetic material of a phage known as T2. This is one of many phages that infect *Escherichia coli* (*E. coli*), a bacterium that normally lives in the intestines of mammals and is a model organism for molecular biologists. At that time, biologists already knew that T2,

like many other phages, was composed almost entirely of DNA and protein. They also knew that the T2 phage could quickly turn an *E. coli* cell into a T2-producing factory that released many copies when the cell ruptured. Somehow, T2 could reprogram its host cell to produce viruses. But which viral component—protein or DNA—was responsible?

Hershey and Chase answered this question by devising an experiment showing that only one of the two components of T2 actually enters the *E. coli* cell during infection (**Figure 16.4**). In their experiment, they used a radioactive isotope of sulfur to tag protein in one batch of T2 and a radioactive isotope of

▼ **Figure 16.4** | **INQUIRY**

Is protein or DNA the genetic material of phage T2?

EXPERIMENT Alfred Hershey and Martha Chase used radioactive sulfur and phosphorus to trace the fates of protein and DNA, respectively, of T2 phages that infected bacterial cells. They wanted to see which of these molecules entered the cells and could reprogram them to make more phages.

❶ Mixed radioactively labeled phages with bacteria. The phages infected the bacterial cells.

❷ Agitated the mixture in a blender to free phage parts outside the bacteria from the cells.

❸ Centrifuged the mixture so that bacteria formed a pellet at the bottom of the test tube; free phages and phage parts, which are lighter, remained suspended in the liquid.

❹ Measured the radioactivity in the pellet and the liquid.

Phage
Radioactive protein
Bacterial cell
DNA
Empty protein shell
Phage DNA
Centrifuge
Radioactivity (phage protein) in liquid
Pellet (bacterial cells and contents)

Batch 1: Phages were grown with radioactive sulfur (^{35}S), which was incorporated into phage protein (pink).

Batch 2: Phages were grown with radioactive phosphorus (^{32}P), which was incorporated into phage DNA (blue).

Radioactive DNA
Centrifuge
Pellet
Radioactivity (phage DNA) in pellet

RESULTS When proteins were labeled (batch 1), radioactivity remained outside the cells; but when DNA was labeled (batch 2), radioactivity was found inside the cells. Bacterial cells with radioactive phage DNA released new phages with some radioactive phosphorus.

CONCLUSION Phage DNA entered bacterial cells, but phage proteins did not. Hershey and Chase concluded that DNA, not protein, functions as the genetic material of phage T2.

SOURCE A. D. Hershey and M. Chase, Independent functions of viral protein and nucleic acid in growth of bacteriophage, *Journal of General Physiology* 36:39–56 (1952).

How would the results have differed if proteins carried the genetic information?

phosphorus to tag DNA in a second batch. Because protein, but not DNA, contains sulfur, radioactive sulfur atoms were incorporated only into the protein of the phage. In a similar way, the atoms of radioactive phosphorus labeled only the DNA, not the protein, because nearly all the phage's phosphorus is in its DNA. In the experiment, separate samples of non-radioactive *E. coli* cells were allowed to be infected by the protein-labeled and DNA-labeled batches of T2. The researchers then tested the two samples shortly after the onset of infection to see which type of molecule—protein or DNA—had entered the bacterial cells and would therefore be capable of reprogramming them.

Hershey and Chase found that the phage DNA entered the host cells but the phage protein did not. Moreover, when these bacteria were returned to a culture medium, the infection ran its course, and the *E. coli* released phages that contained some radioactive phosphorus, further showing that the DNA inside the cell played an ongoing role during the infection process.

Hershey and Chase concluded that the DNA injected by the phage must be the molecule carrying the genetic information that makes the cells produce new viral DNA and proteins. The Hershey-Chase experiment was a landmark study because it provided powerful evidence that nucleic acids, rather than proteins, are the hereditary material, at least for viruses.

Additional Evidence That DNA Is the Genetic Material

Further evidence that DNA is the genetic material came from the laboratory of biochemist Erwin Chargaff. It was already known that DNA is a polymer of nucleotides, each consisting of three components: a nitrogenous (nitrogen-containing) base, a pentose sugar called deoxyribose, and a phosphate group **(Figure 16.5)**. The base can be adenine (A), thymine (T), guanine (G), or cytosine (C). Chargaff analyzed the base composition of DNA from a number of different organisms. In 1950, he reported that the base composition of DNA varies from one species to another. For example, 30.3% of human DNA nucleotides have the base A, whereas DNA from the bacterium *E. coli* has only 26.0% A. This evidence of molecular diversity among species, which had been presumed absent from DNA, made DNA a more credible candidate for the genetic material.

Chargaff also noticed a peculiar regularity in the ratios of nucleotide bases. In the DNA of each species he studied, the number of adenines approximately equaled the number of thymines, and the number of guanines approximately equaled the number of cytosines. In human DNA, for example, the four bases are present in these percentages: A = 30.3% and T = 30.3%; G = 19.5% and C = 19.9%.

These two findings became known as *Chargaff's rules*: (1) the base composition varies between species, and (2) within a species, the number of A and T bases are equal and the number of G and C bases are equal. The basis for these rules remained unexplained until the discovery of the double helix.

Sugar–phosphate backbone   **Nitrogenous bases**

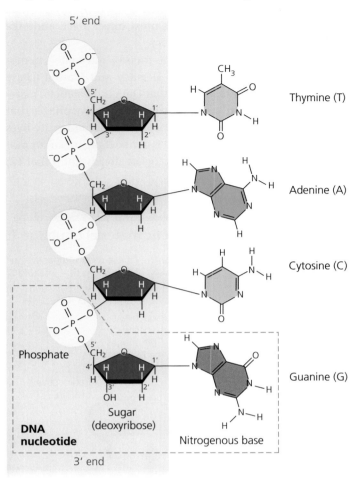

▲ **Figure 16.5 The structure of a DNA strand.** Each DNA nucleotide monomer consists of a nitrogenous base (T, A, C, or G), the sugar deoxyribose (blue), and a phosphate group (yellow). The phosphate group of one nucleotide is attached to the sugar of the next, forming a "backbone" of alternating phosphates and sugars from which the bases project. The polynucleotide strand has directionality, from the 5′ end (with the phosphate group) to the 3′ end (with the —OH group of the sugar). 5′ and 3′ refer to the numbers assigned to the carbons in the sugar ring.

Building a Structural Model of DNA: *Scientific Inquiry*

Once most biologists were convinced that DNA was the genetic material, the challenge was to determine how the structure of DNA could account for its role in inheritance. By the early 1950s, the arrangement of covalent bonds in a nucleic acid polymer was well established (see Figure 16.5), and researchers focused on discovering the three-dimensional structure of DNA. Among the scientists working on the problem were Linus Pauling, at the California Institute of Technology, and Maurice Wilkins and Rosalind Franklin, at King's College in London. First to come up with the correct answer, however, were two scientists who were relatively unknown at the time—the American James Watson and the Englishman Francis Crick.

The brief but celebrated partnership that solved the puzzle of DNA structure began soon after Watson journeyed to Cambridge University, where Crick was studying protein structure with a technique called X-ray crystallography (see Figure 5.24). While visiting the laboratory of Maurice Wilkins, Watson saw an X-ray diffraction image of DNA produced by Wilkins's accomplished colleague Rosalind Franklin (**Figure 16.6a**). Images produced by X-ray crystallography are not actually pictures of molecules. The spots and smudges in **Figure 16.6b** were produced by X-rays that were diffracted (deflected) as they passed through aligned fibers of purified DNA. Watson was familiar with the type of X-ray diffraction pattern that helical molecules produce, and an examination of the photo that Wilkins showed him confirmed that DNA was helical in shape. It also augmented earlier data obtained by Franklin and others suggesting the width of the helix and the spacing of the nitrogenous bases along it. The pattern in this photo implied that the helix was made up of two strands, contrary to a three-stranded model that Linus Pauling had proposed a short time earlier. The presence of two strands accounts for the now-familiar term **double helix** (**Figure 16.7**).

Watson and Crick began building models of a double helix that would conform to the X-ray measurements and what was then known about the chemistry of DNA, including Chargaff's

(a) Rosalind Franklin

(b) Franklin's X-ray diffraction photograph of DNA

▲ **Figure 16.6 Rosalind Franklin and her X-ray diffraction photo of DNA.** Franklin, a very accomplished X-ray crystallographer, conducted critical experiments resulting in the photograph that allowed Watson and Crick to deduce the double-helical structure of DNA.

rule of base equivalences. Having also read an unpublished annual report summarizing Franklin's work, they knew she had concluded that the sugar-phosphate backbones were on the outside of the DNA molecule, contrary to their working model. Franklin's arrangement was appealing because it put the

(a) Key features of DNA structure. The "ribbons" in this diagram represent the sugar-phosphate backbones of the two DNA strands. The helix is "right-handed," curving up to the right. The two strands are held together by hydrogen bonds (dotted lines) between the nitrogenous bases, which are paired in the interior of the double helix.

▲ **Figure 16.7 The double helix.**

(b) Partial chemical structure. For clarity, the two DNA strands are shown untwisted in this partial chemical structure. Strong covalent bonds link the units of each strand, while weaker hydrogen bonds hold one strand to the other. Notice that the strands are antiparallel, meaning that they are oriented in opposite directions.

(c) Space-filling model. The tight stacking of the base pairs is clear in this computer model. Van der Waals interactions between the stacked pairs play a major role in holding the molecule together (see Chapter 2).

relatively hydrophobic nitrogenous bases in the molecule's interior, away from the surrounding aqueous solution, and the negatively charged phosphate groups wouldn't be forced together in the interior. Watson constructed a model with the nitrogenous bases facing the interior of the double helix. In this model, the two sugar-phosphate backbones are **antiparallel**—that is, their subunits run in opposite directions (see Figure 16.7). You can imagine the overall arrangement as a rope ladder with rigid rungs. The side ropes represent the sugar-phosphate backbones, and the rungs represent pairs of nitrogenous bases. Now imagine holding one end of the ladder and twisting the other end, forming a spiral. Franklin's X-ray data indicated that the helix makes one full turn every 3.4 nm along its length. With the bases stacked just 0.34 nm apart, there are ten layers of base pairs, or rungs of the ladder, in each full turn of the helix.

The nitrogenous bases of the double helix are paired in specific combinations: adenine (A) with thymine (T), and guanine (G) with cytosine (C). It was mainly by trial and error that Watson and Crick arrived at this key feature of DNA. At first, Watson imagined that the bases paired like with like—for example, A with A and C with C. But this model did not fit the X-ray data, which suggested that the double helix had a uniform diameter. Why is this requirement inconsistent with like-with-like pairing of bases? Adenine and guanine are purines, nitrogenous bases with two organic rings, while cytosine and thymine are nitrogenous bases called pyrimidines, which have a single ring. Thus, purines (A and G) are about twice as wide as pyrimidines (C and T). A purine-purine pair is too wide and a pyrimidine-pyrimidine pair too narrow to account for the 2-nm diameter of the double helix. Always pairing a purine with a pyrimidine, however, results in a uniform diameter:

Purine + purine: too wide

Pyrimidine + pyrimidine: too narrow

Purine + pyrimidine: width consistent with X-ray data

Watson and Crick reasoned that there must be additional specificity of pairing dictated by the structure of the bases. Each base has chemical side groups that can form hydrogen bonds with its appropriate partner: Adenine can form two hydrogen bonds with thymine and only thymine; guanine forms three hydrogen bonds with cytosine and only cytosine. In shorthand, A pairs with T, and G pairs with C (**Figure 16.8**).

The Watson-Crick model took into account Chargaff's ratios and ultimately explained them. Wherever one strand of a DNA molecule has an A, the partner strand has a T. And a G in one strand is always paired with a C in the complementary strand. Therefore, in the DNA of any organism, the amount of

H
N—H·····O   CH₃

Sugar   Sugar

Adenine (A)   Thymine (T)

H
O·····H—N

Sugar

                        Sugar
H

Guanine (G)   Cytosine (C)

▲ **Figure 16.8 Base pairing in DNA.** The pairs of nitrogenous bases in a DNA double helix are held together by hydrogen bonds, shown here as black dotted lines.

adenine equals the amount of thymine, and the amount of guanine equals the amount of cytosine. Although the base-pairing rules dictate the combinations of nitrogenous bases that form the "rungs" of the double helix, they do not restrict the sequence of nucleotides *along* each DNA strand. The linear sequence of the four bases can be varied in countless ways, and each gene has a unique order, or base sequence.

In April 1953, Watson and Crick surprised the scientific world with a succinct, one-page paper in the journal *Nature*.* The paper reported their molecular model for DNA: the double helix, which has since become the symbol of molecular biology. Watson and Crick, along with Maurice Wilkins, were awarded the Nobel Prize in 1962 for this work. (Sadly, Rosalind Franklin died at the age of 38, in 1958, and was thus ineligible for the prize.) The beauty of the double helix model was that the structure of DNA suggested the basic mechanism of its replication.

CONCEPT CHECK 16.1

1. A fly has the following percentages of nucleotides in its DNA: 27.3% A, 27.6% T, 22.5% G, and 22.5% C. How do these numbers demonstrate Chargaff's rule about base ratios?

2. Given a polynucleotide sequence such as GAATTC, can you tell which is the 5′ end? If not, what further information do you need to identify the ends? (See Figure 16.5.)

3. **WHAT IF?** Griffith did not expect transformation to occur in his experiment. What results was he expecting? Explain.

For suggested answers, see Appendix A.

*J. D. Watson and F. H. C. Crick, Molecular structure of nucleic acids: a structure for deoxyribose nucleic acids, *Nature* 171:737–738 (1953).

CONCEPT 16.2

Many proteins work together in DNA replication and repair

The relationship between structure and function is manifest in the double helix. The idea that there is specific pairing of nitrogenous bases in DNA was the flash of inspiration that led Watson and Crick to the double helix. At the same time, they saw the functional significance of the base-pairing rules. They ended their classic paper with this wry statement: "It has not escaped our notice that the specific pairing we have postulated immediately suggests a possible copying mechanism for the genetic material." In this section, you will learn about the basic principle of DNA replication, as well as some important details of the process.

The Basic Principle: Base Pairing to a Template Strand

In a second paper, Watson and Crick stated their hypothesis for how DNA replicates:

> Now our model for deoxyribonucleic acid is, in effect, a pair of templates, each of which is complementary to the other. We imagine that prior to duplication the hydrogen bonds are broken, and the two chains unwind and separate. Each chain then acts as a template for the formation onto itself of a new companion chain, so that eventually we shall have two pairs of chains, where we only had one before. Moreover, the sequence of the pairs of bases will have been duplicated exactly.*

---

*F. H. C. Crick and J. D. Watson, The complementary structure of deoxyribonucleic acid, *Proceedings of the Royal Society of London A* 223:80 (1954).

Figure 16.9 illustrates Watson and Crick's basic idea. To make it easier to follow, we show only a short section of double helix in untwisted form. Notice that if you cover one of the two DNA strands of Figure 16.9a, you can still determine its linear sequence of nucleotides by referring to the uncovered strand and applying the base-pairing rules. The two strands are complementary; each stores the information necessary to reconstruct the other. When a cell copies a DNA molecule, each strand serves as a template for ordering nucleotides into a new, complementary strand. Nucleotides line up along the template strand according to the base-pairing rules and are linked to form the new strands. Where there was one double-stranded DNA molecule at the beginning of the process, there are soon two, each an exact replica of the "parental" molecule. The copying mechanism is analogous to using a photographic negative to make a positive image, which can in turn be used to make another negative, and so on.

This model of DNA replication remained untested for several years following publication of the DNA structure. The requisite experiments were simple in concept but difficult to perform. Watson and Crick's model predicts that when a double helix replicates, each of the two daughter molecules will have one old strand, from the parental molecule, and one newly made strand. This **semiconservative model** can be distinguished from a conservative model of replication, in which the two parental strands somehow come back together after the process (that is, the parental molecule is conserved). In yet a third model, called the dispersive model, all four strands of DNA following replication have a mixture of old and new DNA. These three models are shown in

(a) The parental molecule has two complementary strands of DNA. Each base is paired by hydrogen bonding with its specific partner, A with T and G with C.

(b) The first step in replication is separation of the two DNA strands. Each parental strand can now serve as a template that determines the order of nucleotides along a new, complementary strand.

(c) The complementary nucleotides line up and are connected to form the sugar-phosphate backbones of the new strands. Each "daughter" DNA molecule consists of one parental strand (dark blue) and one new strand (light blue).

▲ **Figure 16.9 A model for DNA replication: the basic concept.** In this simplified illustration, a short segment of DNA has been untwisted into a structure that resembles a ladder. The side rails of the ladder are the sugar-phosphate backbones of the two DNA strands; the rungs are the pairs of nitrogenous bases. Simple shapes symbolize the four kinds of bases. Dark blue represents DNA strands present in the parental molecule; light blue represents newly synthesized DNA.

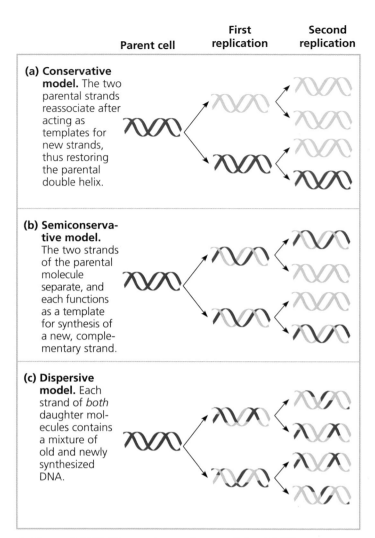

	Parent cell	First replication	Second replication

(a) Conservative model. The two parental strands reassociate after acting as templates for new strands, thus restoring the parental double helix.

(b) Semiconservative model. The two strands of the parental molecule separate, and each functions as a template for synthesis of a new, complementary strand.

(c) Dispersive model. Each strand of *both* daughter molecules contains a mixture of old and newly synthesized DNA.

▲ **Figure 16.10 Three alternative models of DNA replication.** Each short segment of double helix symbolizes the DNA within a cell. Beginning with a parent cell, we follow the DNA for two more generations of cells—two rounds of DNA replication. Newly made DNA is light blue.

Figure 16.10. Although mechanisms for conservative or dispersive DNA replication are not easy to devise, these models remained possibilities until they could be ruled out. After two years of preliminary work in the late 1950s, Matthew Meselson and Franklin Stahl devised a clever experiment that distinguished between the three models, described in detail in **Figure 16.11.** Their experiment supported the semiconservative model of DNA replication, as predicted by Watson and Crick, and is widely acknowledged among biologists to be a classic example of elegant experimental design.

The basic principle of DNA replication is conceptually simple. However, the actual process involves some complicated biochemical gymnastics, as we will now see.

DNA Replication: *A Closer Look*

The bacterium *E. coli* has a single chromosome of about 4.6 million nucleotide pairs. In a favorable environment, an *E. coli* cell

▼ **Figure 16.11**

INQUIRY

Does DNA replication follow the conservative, semiconservative, or dispersive model?

EXPERIMENT At the California Institute of Technology, Matthew Meselson and Franklin Stahl cultured *E. coli* for several generations in a medium containing nucleotide precursors labeled with a heavy isotope of nitrogen, ^{15}N. They then transferred the bacteria to a medium with only ^{14}N, a lighter isotope. A sample was taken after DNA replicated once; another sample was taken after DNA replicated again. They extracted DNA from the bacteria in the samples and then centrifuged each DNA sample to separate DNA of different densities.

❶ Bacteria cultured in medium with ^{15}N (heavy isotope)

❷ Bacteria transferred to medium with ^{14}N (lighter isotope)

RESULTS

❸ DNA sample centrifuged after first replication

❹ DNA sample centrifuged after second replication

Less dense

More dense

CONCLUSION Meselson and Stahl compared their results to those predicted by each of the three models in Figure 16.10, as shown below. The first replication in the ^{14}N medium produced a band of hybrid (^{15}N-^{14}N) DNA. This result eliminated the conservative model. The second replication produced both light and hybrid DNA, a result that refuted the dispersive model and supported the semiconservative model. They therefore concluded that DNA replication is semiconservative.

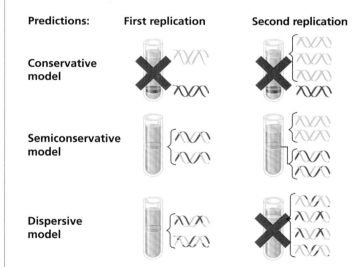

Predictions:	First replication	Second replication
Conservative model		
Semiconservative model		
Dispersive model		

SOURCE M. Meselson and F. W. Stahl, The replication of DNA in *Escherichia coli*, *Proceedings of the National Academy of Sciences USA* 44:671–682 (1958).

INQUIRY IN ACTION Read and analyze the original paper in *Inquiry in Action: Interpreting Scientific Papers.*

See the related Experimental Inquiry Tutorial in MasteringBiology.

WHAT IF? If Meselson and Stahl had first grown the cells in ^{14}N-containing medium and then moved them into ^{15}N-containing medium before taking samples, what would have been the result?

can copy all this DNA and divide to form two genetically identical daughter cells in less than an hour. Each of *your* cells has 46 DNA molecules in its nucleus, one long double-helical molecule per chromosome. In all, that represents about 6 billion nucleotide pairs, or over a thousand times more DNA than is found in a bacterial cell. If we were to print the one-letter symbols for these bases (A, G, C, and T) the size of the type you are now reading, the 6 billion nucleotide pairs of information in a diploid human cell would fill about 1,200 books as thick as this text. Yet it takes one of your cells just a few hours to copy all of this DNA. This replication of an enormous amount of genetic information is achieved with very few errors—only about one per 10 billion nucleotides. The copying of DNA is remarkable in its speed and accuracy.

More than a dozen enzymes and other proteins participate in DNA replication. Much more is known about how this "replication machine" works in bacteria (such as *E. coli*) than

in eukaryotes, and we will describe the basic steps of the process for *E. coli*, except where otherwise noted. What scientists have learned about eukaryotic DNA replication suggests, however, that most of the process is fundamentally similar for prokaryotes and eukaryotes.

Getting Started

The replication of a DNA molecule begins at particular sites called **origins of replication**, short stretches of DNA having a specific sequence of nucleotides. The *E. coli* chromosome, like many other bacterial chromosomes, is circular and has a single origin. Proteins that initiate DNA replication recognize this sequence and attach to the DNA, separating the two strands and opening up a replication "bubble." Replication of DNA then proceeds in both directions until the entire molecule is copied **(Figure 16.12a)**. In contrast to a bacterial chromosome, a eukaryotic chromosome may have hundreds

▼ **Figure 16.12 Origins of replication in *E. coli* and eukaryotes.** The red arrows indicate the movement of the replication forks and thus the overall directions of DNA replication within each bubble.

(a) Origin of replication in an *E. coli* cell

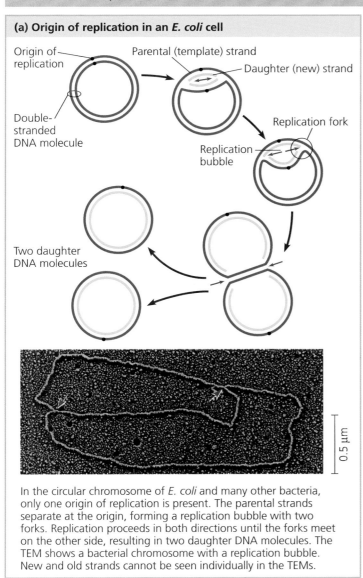

In the circular chromosome of *E. coli* and many other bacteria, only one origin of replication is present. The parental strands separate at the origin, forming a replication bubble with two forks. Replication proceeds in both directions until the forks meet on the other side, resulting in two daughter DNA molecules. The TEM shows a bacterial chromosome with a replication bubble. New and old strands cannot be seen individually in the TEMs.

(b) Origins of replication in a eukaryotic cell

In each linear chromosome of eukaryotes, DNA replication begins when replication bubbles form at many sites along the giant DNA molecule. The bubbles expand as replication proceeds in both directions. Eventually, the bubbles fuse and synthesis of the daughter strands is complete. The TEM shows three replication bubbles along the DNA of a cultured Chinese hamster cell.

DRAW IT *In the TEM in (b), add arrows for the third bubble.*

or even a few thousand replication origins. Multiple replication bubbles form and eventually fuse, thus speeding up the copying of the very long DNA molecules (**Figure 16.12b**). As in bacteria, eukaryotic DNA replication proceeds in both directions from each origin.

At each end of a replication bubble is a **replication fork**, a Y-shaped region where the parental strands of DNA are being unwound. Several kinds of proteins participate in the unwinding (**Figure 16.13**). **Helicases** are enzymes that untwist the double helix at the replication forks, separating the two parental strands and making them available as template strands. After the parental strands separate, **single-strand binding proteins** bind to the unpaired DNA strands, keeping them from re-pairing. The untwisting of the double helix causes tighter twisting and strain ahead of the replication fork. **Topoisomerase** helps relieve this strain by breaking, swiveling, and rejoining DNA strands.

The unwound sections of parental DNA strands are now available to serve as templates for the synthesis of new complementary DNA strands. However, the enzymes that synthesize DNA cannot *initiate* the synthesis of a polynucleotide; they can only add nucleotides to the end of an already existing chain that is base-paired with the template strand. The initial nucleotide chain that is produced during DNA synthesis is actually a short stretch of RNA, not DNA. This RNA chain is called a **primer** and is synthesized by the enzyme **primase** (see Figure 16.13). Primase starts a complementary RNA chain from a single RNA nucleotide,

adding RNA nucleotides one at a time, using the parental DNA strand as a template. The completed primer, generally 5–10 nucleotides long, is thus base-paired to the template strand. The new DNA strand will start from the 3′ end of the RNA primer.

Synthesizing a New DNA Strand

Enzymes called **DNA polymerases** catalyze the synthesis of new DNA by adding nucleotides to a preexisting chain. In *E. coli*, there are several different DNA polymerases, but two appear to play the major roles in DNA replication: DNA polymerase III and DNA polymerase I. The situation in eukaryotes is more complicated, with at least 11 different DNA polymerases discovered so far; however, the general principles are the same.

Most DNA polymerases require a primer and a DNA template strand, along which complementary DNA nucleotides line up. In *E. coli*, DNA polymerase III (abbreviated DNA pol III) adds a DNA nucleotide to the RNA primer and then continues adding DNA nucleotides, complementary to the parental DNA template strand, to the growing end of the new DNA strand. The rate of elongation is about 500 nucleotides per second in bacteria and 50 per second in human cells.

Each nucleotide added to a growing DNA strand comes from a nucleoside triphosphate, which is a nucleoside (a sugar and a base) with three phosphate groups. You have already encountered such a molecule—ATP (adenosine triphosphate; see Figure 8.8). The only difference between the ATP of energy metabolism and dATP, the nucleoside triphosphate that supplies an adenine nucleotide to DNA, is the sugar component, which is deoxyribose in the building block of DNA but ribose in ATP. Like ATP, the nucleoside triphosphates used for DNA synthesis are chemically reactive, partly because their triphosphate tails have an unstable cluster of negative charge. As each monomer joins the growing end of a DNA strand, two phosphate groups are lost as a molecule of pyrophosphate ($\text{P}—\text{P}_i$). Subsequent hydrolysis of the pyrophosphate to two molecules of inorganic phosphate (P_i) is a coupled exergonic reaction that helps drive the polymerization reaction (**Figure 16.14**).

Antiparallel Elongation

As we have noted previously, the two ends of a DNA strand are different, giving each strand directionality, like a one-way street (see Figure 16.5). In addition, the two strands of DNA in a double helix are antiparallel, meaning that they are oriented in opposite directions to each other, like a divided highway (see Figure 16.14). Clearly, the two new strands formed during DNA replication must also be antiparallel to their template strands.

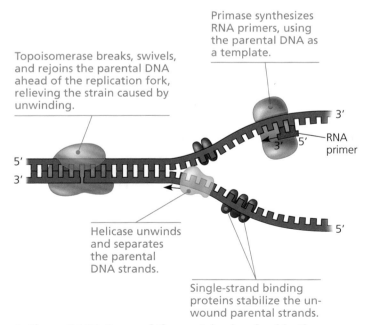

Topoisomerase breaks, swivels, and rejoins the parental DNA ahead of the replication fork, relieving the strain caused by unwinding.

Primase synthesizes RNA primers, using the parental DNA as a template.

RNA primer

Helicase unwinds and separates the parental DNA strands.

Single-strand binding proteins stabilize the unwound parental strands.

▲ **Figure 16.13 Some of the proteins involved in the initiation of DNA replication.** The same proteins function at both replication forks in a replication bubble. For simplicity, only the left-hand fork is shown, and the DNA bases are drawn much larger in relation to the proteins than they are in reality.

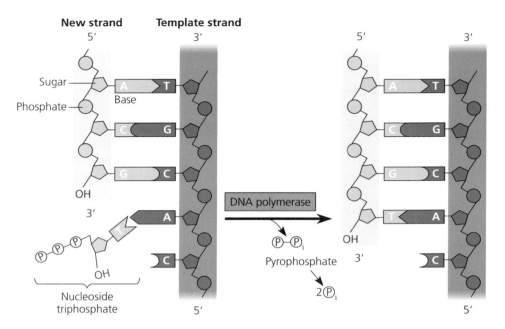

◄ **Figure 16.14 Incorporation of a nucleotide into a DNA strand.** DNA polymerase catalyzes the addition of a nucleoside triphosphate to the 3' end of a growing DNA strand, with the release of two phosphates.

? *Use this diagram to explain what we mean when we say that each DNA strand has directionality.*

How does the antiparallel arrangement of the double helix affect replication? Because of their structure, DNA polymerases can add nucleotides only to the free 3' end of a primer or growing DNA strand, never to the 5' end (see Figure 16.14). Thus, a new DNA strand can elongate only in the 5' → 3' direction. With this in mind, let's examine one of the two replication forks in a bubble **(Figure 16.15)**. Along one template strand, DNA polymerase III can synthesize a complementary strand continuously by elongating the new DNA in the mandatory 5' → 3' direction. DNA pol III remains in the replication fork on that template strand and continuously adds nucleotides to the new complementary strand as the fork progresses. The DNA strand made by this mechanism is called the **leading strand**. Only one primer is required for DNA pol III to synthesize the leading strand (see Figure 16.15).

To elongate the other new strand of DNA in the mandatory 5' → 3' direction, DNA pol III must work along the other template strand in the direction *away from* the replication fork. The DNA strand elongating in this direction is called the **lagging strand**.* In contrast to the leading strand, which elongates continuously, the lagging strand is synthesized discontinuously, as a series of segments. These segments of the lagging strand are called **Okazaki fragments**, after the Japanese scientist who discovered them. The fragments are about 1,000–2,000 nucleotides long in *E. coli* and 100–200 nucleotides long in eukaryotes.

---

*Synthesis of the leading strand and synthesis of the lagging strand occur concurrently and at the same rate. The lagging strand is so named because its synthesis is delayed slightly relative to synthesis of the leading strand; each new fragment of the lagging strand cannot be started until enough template has been exposed at the replication fork.

Overview

① After RNA primer is made, DNA pol III starts to synthesize the leading strand.

② The leading strand is elongated continuously in the 5'→ 3' direction as the fork progresses.

▲ **Figure 16.15 Synthesis of the leading strand during DNA replication.** This diagram focuses on the left replication fork shown in the overview box. DNA polymerase III (DNA pol III), shaped like a cupped hand, is shown closely associated with a protein called the "sliding clamp" that encircles the newly synthesized double helix like a doughnut. The sliding clamp moves DNA pol III along the DNA template strand.

Overview

Origin of replication

Leading strand

Lagging strand

Lagging strand

Leading strand

2 1

← Overall directions → of replication

1 Primase joins RNA nucleotides into a primer.

Template strand

3′

5′ 3′

5′

2 DNA pol III adds DNA nucleotides to the primer, forming Okazaki fragment 1.

RNA primer for fragment 1

3′

5′ 1 3′

5′

3 After reaching the next RNA primer to the right, DNA pol III detaches.

3′

5′

Okazaki fragment 1

1

3′ 5′

RNA primer for fragment 2

Okazaki fragment 2

5′ 3′

4 Fragment 2 is primed. Then DNA pol III adds DNA nucleotides, detaching when it reaches the fragment 1 primer.

2

1 3′ 5′

5′ 3′

5 DNA pol I replaces the RNA with DNA, adding to the 3′ end of fragment 2.

2

1 3′ 5′

6 DNA ligase forms a bond between the newest DNA and the DNA of fragment 1.

5′ 3′

7 The lagging strand in this region is now complete.

2

1 3′ 5′

← Overall direction of replication

▲ **Figure 16.16 Synthesis of the lagging strand.**

Figure 16.16 illustrates the steps in the synthesis of the lagging strand at one fork. Whereas only one primer is required on the leading strand, each Okazaki fragment on the lagging strand must be primed separately (steps **1** and **4**). After DNA pol III forms an Okazaki fragment (steps **2**–**4**), another DNA polymerase, DNA polymerase I (DNA pol I), replaces the RNA nucleotides of the adjacent primer with DNA nucleotides (step **5**). But DNA pol I cannot join the final nucleotide of this replacement DNA segment to the first DNA nucleotide of the adjacent Okazaki fragment. Another enzyme, **DNA ligase**, accomplishes this task, joining the sugar-phosphate backbones of all the Okazaki fragments into a continuous DNA strand (step **6**).

Figure 16.17 summarizes DNA replication. Please study it carefully before proceeding.

The DNA Replication Complex

It is traditional—and convenient—to represent DNA polymerase molecules as locomotives moving along a DNA "railroad track," but such a model is inaccurate in two important ways. First, the various proteins that participate in DNA replication actually form a single large complex, a "DNA replication machine." Many protein-protein interactions facilitate the efficiency of this complex. For example, by interacting with other proteins at the fork, primase apparently acts as a molecular brake, slowing progress of the replication fork and coordinating the placement of primers and the rates of replication on the leading and lagging strands. Second, the DNA replication complex may not move along the DNA; rather, the DNA may move through the complex during the replication process. In eukaryotic cells, multiple copies of the complex, perhaps grouped into "factories," may be anchored to the nuclear matrix, a framework of fibers extending through the interior of the nucleus. Recent studies support a model in which two DNA polymerase molecules, one on each template strand, "reel in" the parental DNA and extrude newly made daughter DNA molecules. Additional evidence suggests that the lagging strand is looped back through the complex **(Figure 16.18).**

Proofreading and Repairing DNA

We cannot attribute the accuracy of DNA replication solely to the specificity of base pairing. Although errors in the completed DNA molecule amount to only one in 10^{10} (10 billion) nucleotides, initial pairing errors between incoming nucleotides and those in the template strand are 100,000 times more common—an error rate of one in 10^5 nucleotides. During DNA replication, DNA polymerases proofread each nucleotide against its template as soon as it is added to the growing strand. Upon finding an incorrectly paired nucleotide, the polymerase removes the nucleotide and then resumes synthesis. (This action is similar to fixing a typing error by deleting the wrong letter and then entering the correct letter.)

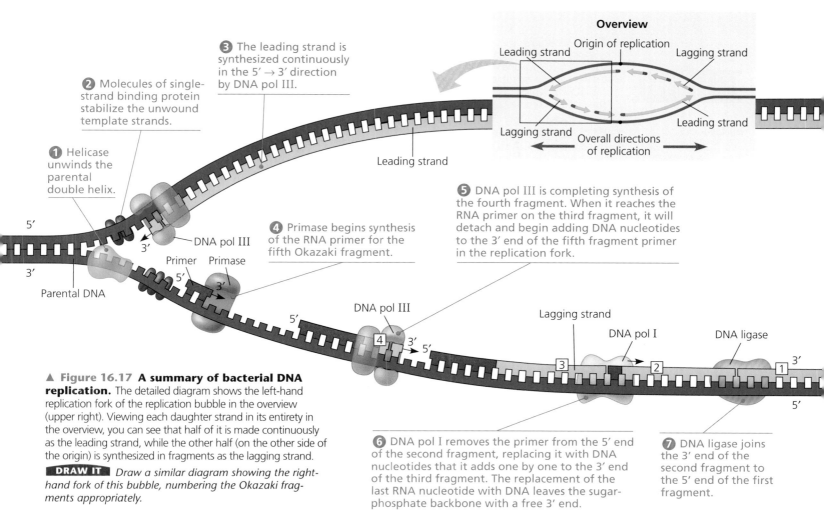

❸ The leading strand is synthesized continuously in the 5' → 3' direction by DNA pol III.

❷ Molecules of single-strand binding protein stabilize the unwound template strands.

❶ Helicase unwinds the parental double helix.

Overview

Leading strand   Origin of replication   Lagging strand

Lagging strand   Overall directions of replication   Leading strand

Leading strand

DNA pol III

Primer   Primase

Parental DNA

❹ Primase begins synthesis of the RNA primer for the fifth Okazaki fragment.

❺ DNA pol III is completing synthesis of the fourth fragment. When it reaches the RNA primer on the third fragment, it will detach and begin adding DNA nucleotides to the 3' end of the fifth fragment primer in the replication fork.

DNA pol III

Lagging strand

DNA pol I   DNA ligase

▲ **Figure 16.17 A summary of bacterial DNA replication.** The detailed diagram shows the left-hand replication fork of the replication bubble in the overview (upper right). Viewing each daughter strand in its entirety in the overview, you can see that half of it is made continuously as the leading strand, while the other half (on the other side of the origin) is synthesized in fragments as the lagging strand.

DRAW IT *Draw a similar diagram showing the right-hand fork of this bubble, numbering the Okazaki fragments appropriately.*

❻ DNA pol I removes the primer from the 5' end of the second fragment, replacing it with DNA nucleotides that it adds one by one to the 3' end of the third fragment. The replacement of the last RNA nucleotide with DNA leaves the sugar-phosphate backbone with a free 3' end.

❼ DNA ligase joins the 3' end of the second fragment to the 5' end of the first fragment.

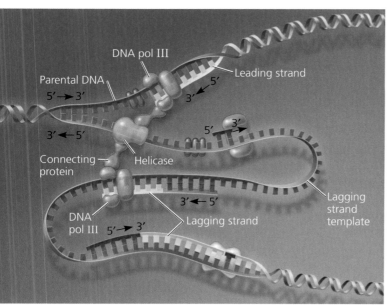

▲ **Figure 16.18 A current model of the DNA replication complex.** Two DNA polymerase III molecules work together in a complex, one on each template strand. The lagging strand template DNA loops through the complex.

BioFlix Visit the Study Area at **www.masteringbiology.com** for the BioFlix® 3-D Animation on DNA Replication.

Mismatched nucleotides sometimes evade proofreading by a DNA polymerase. In **mismatch repair**, other enzymes remove and replace incorrectly paired nucleotides that have resulted from replication errors. Researchers spotlighted the importance of such repair enzymes when they found that a hereditary defect in one of them is associated with a form of colon cancer. Apparently, this defect allows cancer-causing errors to accumulate in the DNA faster than normal.

Incorrectly paired or altered nucleotides can also arise after replication. In fact, maintenance of the genetic information encoded in DNA requires frequent repair of various kinds of damage to existing DNA. DNA molecules are constantly subjected to potentially harmful chemical and physical agents, such as cigarette smoke and X-rays, as we'll discuss in Chapter 17. In addition, DNA bases often undergo spontaneous chemical changes under normal cellular conditions. However, these changes in DNA are usually corrected before they become permanent changes—*mutations*—perpetuated through successive replications. Each cell continuously monitors and repairs its genetic material. Because repair of damaged DNA is so important to the survival of an organism, it is no surprise that many different DNA repair enzymes have evolved. Almost 100 are known in *E. coli*, and about 130 have been identified so far in humans.

1 Teams of enzymes detect and repair damaged DNA, such as this thymine dimer (often caused by ultraviolet radiation), which distorts the DNA molecule.

Nuclease

2 A nuclease enzyme cuts the damaged DNA strand at two points, and the damaged section is removed.

DNA polymerase

3 Repair synthesis by a DNA polymerase fills in the missing nucleotides.

DNA ligase

4 DNA ligase seals the free end of the new DNA to the old DNA, making the strand complete.

▲ **Figure 16.19 Nucleotide excision repair of DNA damage.**

Most cellular systems for repairing incorrectly paired nucleotides, whether they are due to DNA damage or to replication errors, use a mechanism that takes advantage of the base-paired structure of DNA. In many cases, a segment of the strand containing the damage is cut out (excised) by a DNA-cutting enzyme—a **nuclease**—and the resulting gap is then filled in with nucleotides, using the undamaged strand as a template. The enzymes involved in filling the gap are a DNA polymerase and DNA ligase. One such DNA repair system is called **nucleotide excision repair** (**Figure 16.19**).

An important function of the DNA repair enzymes in our skin cells is to repair genetic damage caused by the ultraviolet rays of sunlight. One type of damage, shown in Figure 16.19, is the covalent linking of thymine bases that are adjacent on a DNA strand. Such *thymine dimers* cause the DNA to buckle and interfere with DNA replication. The importance of repairing this kind of damage is underscored by the disorder xeroderma pigmentosum, which in most cases is caused by an inherited defect in a nucleotide excision repair enzyme. Individuals with this disorder are hypersensitive to sunlight; mutations in their skin cells caused by ultraviolet light are left uncorrected, resulting in skin cancer.

Evolutionary Significance of Altered DNA Nucleotides

EVOLUTION Faithful replication of the genome and repair of DNA damage are important for the functioning of the

organism and for passing on a complete, accurate genome to the next generation. The error rate after proofreading and repair is extremely low, but rare mistakes do slip through. Once a mismatched nucleotide pair is replicated, the sequence change is permanent in the daughter molecule that has the incorrect nucleotide as well as in any subsequent copies. As you know, a permanent change in the DNA sequence is called a mutation.

As you'll learn in Chapter 17, mutations can change the phenotype of an organism. And if they occur in germ cells (which give rise to gametes), mutations can be passed on from generation to generation. The vast majority of such changes are harmful, but a very small percentage can be beneficial. In either case, mutations are the source of the variation on which natural selection operates during evolution and are ultimately responsible for the appearance of new species. (You'll learn more about this process in Unit Four.) The balance between complete fidelity of DNA replication or repair and a low mutation rate has, over long periods of time, allowed the evolution of the rich diversity of species we see on Earth today.

Replicating the Ends of DNA Molecules

In spite of the impressive capabilities of DNA polymerases, there is a small portion of the cell's DNA that DNA polymerases can neither replicate nor repair. For linear DNA, such as the DNA of eukaryotic chromosomes, the fact that a DNA polymerase can add nucleotides only to the 3′ end of a preexisting polynucleotide leads to what might appear to be a problem. The usual replication machinery provides no way to complete the 5′ ends of daughter DNA strands. Even if an Okazaki fragment can be started with an RNA primer bound to the very end of the template strand, once that primer is removed, it cannot be replaced with DNA because there is no 3′ end available for nucleotide addition (**Figure 16.20**). As a result, repeated rounds of replication produce shorter and shorter DNA molecules with uneven ("staggered") ends.

Most prokaryotes have a circular chromosome, with no ends, so the shortening of DNA does not occur. But what protects the genes of linear eukaryotic chromosomes from being eroded away during successive rounds of DNA replication? It turns out that eukaryotic chromosomal DNA molecules have special nucleotide sequences called **telomeres** at their ends (**Figure 16.21**). Telomeres do not contain genes; instead, the DNA typically consists of multiple repetitions of one short nucleotide sequence. In each human telomere, for example, the six-nucleotide sequence TTAGGG is repeated between 100 and 1,000 times. Telomeric DNA acts as a kind of buffer zone that protects the organism's genes. In addition, specific proteins associated with telomeric DNA prevent the staggered ends of the daughter molecule from activating the cell's systems for monitoring DNA damage. (Staggered ends of a DNA molecule, which often result from double-strand breaks, can trigger signal transduction pathways leading to cell cycle arrest or cell death.)

▲ **Figure 16.20 Shortening of the ends of linear DNA molecules.** Here we follow the end of one strand of a DNA molecule through two rounds of replication. After the first round, the new lagging strand is shorter than its template. After a second round, both the leading and lagging strands have become shorter than the original parental DNA. Although not shown here, the other ends of these DNA molecules also become shorter.

▲ **Figure 16.21 Telomeres.** Eukaryotes have repetitive, noncoding sequences called telomeres at the ends of their DNA. Telomeres are stained orange in these mouse chromosomes (LM).

Telomeres provide their protective function by postponing the erosion of genes located near the ends of DNA molecules. As shown in Figure 16.20, telomeres become shorter during every round of replication. As we would expect, telomeric DNA tends to be shorter in dividing somatic cells of older individuals and in cultured cells that have divided many times. It has been proposed that shortening of telomeres is somehow connected to the aging process of certain tissues and even to aging of the organism as a whole.

But what about cells whose genome must persist virtually unchanged from an organism to its offspring over many generations? If the chromosomes of germ cells became shorter in every cell cycle, essential genes would eventually be missing from the gametes they produce. However, this does not occur: An enzyme called **telomerase** catalyzes the lengthening of telomeres in eukaryotic germ cells, thus restoring their original length and compensating for the shortening that occurs during DNA replication. Telomerase is not active in most human somatic cells, but its activity in germ cells results in telomeres of maximum length in the zygote.

Normal shortening of telomeres may protect organisms from cancer by limiting the number of divisions that somatic cells can undergo. Cells from large tumors often have unusually short telomeres, as we would expect for cells that have undergone many cell divisions. Further shortening would presumably lead to self-destruction of the tumor cells. Intriguingly, researchers have found telomerase activity in cancerous somatic cells, suggesting that its ability to stabilize telomere length may allow these cancer cells to persist. Many cancer cells do seem capable of unlimited cell division, as do immortal strains of cultured cells (see Chapter 12). If telomerase is indeed an important factor in many cancers, it may provide a useful target for both cancer diagnosis and chemotherapy.

Thus far in this chapter, you have learned about the structure and replication of a DNA molecule. In the next section, we'll take a step back and examine how DNA is packaged into chromosomes, the structures that carry the genetic information.

CONCEPT CHECK 16.2

1. What role does complementary base pairing play in the replication of DNA?
2. Make a table listing the functions of seven proteins involved in DNA replication in *E. coli*.
3. **MAKE CONNECTIONS** What is the relationship between DNA replication and the S phase of the cell cycle? See Figure 12.6, page 231.
4. **WHAT IF?** If the DNA pol I in a given cell were nonfunctional, how would that affect the synthesis of a *leading* strand? In the overview box in Figure 16.17, point out where DNA pol I would normally function on the top leading strand.

For suggested answers, see Appendix A.

A chromosome consists of a DNA molecule packed together with proteins

The main component of the genome in most bacteria is one double-stranded, circular DNA molecule that is associated with a small amount of protein. Although we refer to this structure as the *bacterial chromosome*, it is very different from a eukaryotic chromosome, which consists of one linear DNA molecule associated with a large amount of protein. In *E. coli*, the chromosomal DNA consists of about 4.6 million nucleotide pairs, representing about 4,400 genes. This is 100 times more DNA than is found in a typical virus, but only about one-thousandth as much DNA as in a human somatic cell. Still, that is a lot of DNA to be packaged in such a small container.

Stretched out, the DNA of an *E. coli* cell would measure about a millimeter in length, 500 times longer than the cell.

▼ Figure 16.22

Exploring Chromatin Packing in a Eukaryotic Chromosome

This series of diagrams and transmission electron micrographs depicts a current model for the progressive levels of DNA coiling and folding. The illustration zooms out from a single molecule of DNA to a metaphase chromosome, which is large enough to be seen with a light microscope.

DNA double helix (2 nm in diameter)

Histones

Nucleosome (10 nm in diameter)

Histone tail

H1

DNA, the double helix

Shown here is a ribbon model of DNA, with each ribbon representing one of the sugar-phosphate backbones. As you will recall from Figure 16.7, the phosphate groups along the backbone contribute a negative charge along the outside of each strand. The TEM shows a molecule of naked DNA; the double helix alone is 2 nm across.

Histones

Proteins called **histones** are responsible for the first level of DNA packing in chromatin. Although each histone is small—containing only about 100 amino acids—the total mass of histone in chromatin approximately equals the mass of DNA. More than a fifth of a histone's amino acids are positively charged (lysine or arginine) and therefore bind tightly to the negatively charged DNA.

Four types of histones are most common in chromatin: H2A, H2B, H3, and H4. The histones are very similar among eukaryotes; for example, all but two of the amino acids in cow H4 are identical to those in pea H4. The apparent conservation of histone genes during evolution probably reflects the important role of histones in organizing DNA within cells.

The four main types of histones are critical to the next level of DNA packing. (A fifth type of histone, called H1, is involved in a further stage of packing.)

Nucleosomes, or "beads on a string" (10-nm fiber)

In electron micrographs, unfolded chromatin is 10 nm in diameter (the *10-nm fiber*). Such chromatin resembles beads on a string (see the TEM). Each "bead" is a **nucleosome**, the basic unit of DNA packing; the "string" between beads is called *linker DNA*.

A nucleosome consists of DNA wound twice around a protein core composed of two molecules each of the four main histone types. The amino end (N-terminus) of each histone (the *histone tail*) extends outward from the nucleosome.

In the cell cycle, the histones leave the DNA only briefly during DNA replication. Generally, they do the same during transcription, another process that requires access to the DNA by the cell's molecular machinery. Chapter 18 will discuss some recent findings about the role of histone tails and nucleosomes in the regulation of gene expression.

Within a bacterium, however, certain proteins cause the chromosome to coil and "supercoil," densely packing it so that it fills only part of the cell. Unlike the nucleus of a eukaryotic cell, this dense region of DNA in a bacterium, called the **nucleoid**, is not bounded by membrane (see Figure 6.5).

Eukaryotic chromosomes each contain a single linear DNA double helix that, in humans, averages about 1.5×10^8 nucleotide pairs. This is an enormous amount of DNA relative to a chromosome's condensed length. If completely stretched out, such a DNA molecule would be about 4 cm long, thousands of times the diameter of a cell nucleus—and that's not even considering the DNA of the other 45 human chromosomes!

In the cell, eukaryotic DNA is precisely combined with a large amount of protein. Together, this complex of DNA and protein, called **chromatin**, fits into the nucleus through an elaborate, multilevel system of packing. Our current view of the successive levels of DNA packing in a chromosome is outlined in **Figure 16.22**. Study this figure carefully before reading further.

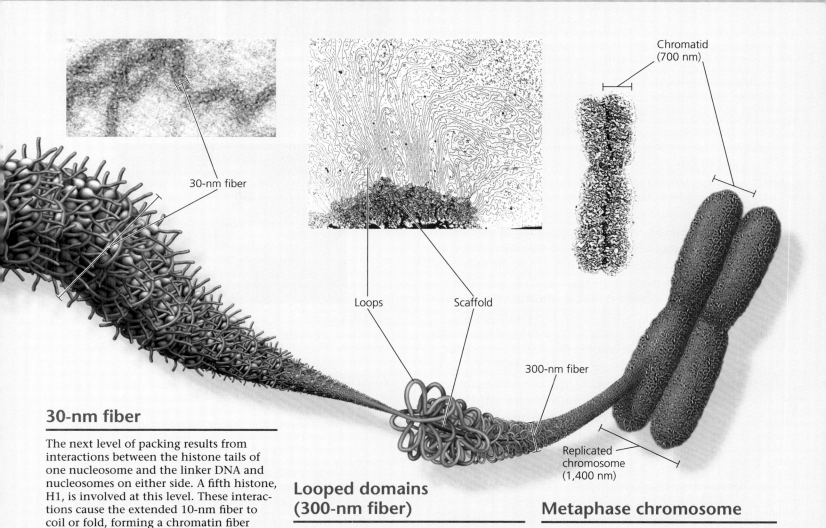

30-nm fiber

The next level of packing results from interactions between the histone tails of one nucleosome and the linker DNA and nucleosomes on either side. A fifth histone, H1, is involved at this level. These interactions cause the extended 10-nm fiber to coil or fold, forming a chromatin fiber roughly 30 nm in thickness, the *30-nm fiber*. Although the 30-nm fiber is quite prevalent in the interphase nucleus, the packing arrangement of nucleosomes in this form of chromatin is still a matter of some debate.

Looped domains (300-nm fiber)

The 30-nm fiber, in turn, forms loops called *looped domains* attached to a chromosome scaffold made of proteins, thus making up a *300-nm fiber*. The scaffold is rich in one type of topoisomerase, and H1 molecules also appear to be present.

Metaphase chromosome

In a mitotic chromosome, the looped domains themselves coil and fold in a manner not yet fully understood, further compacting all the chromatin to produce the characteristic metaphase chromosome shown in the micrograph above. The width of one chromatid is 700 nm. Particular genes always end up located at the same places in metaphase chromosomes, indicating that the packing steps are highly specific and precise.

Chromatin undergoes striking changes in its degree of packing during the course of the cell cycle (see Figure 12.7). In interphase cells stained for light microscopy, the chromatin usually appears as a diffuse mass within the nucleus, suggesting that the chromatin is highly extended. As a cell prepares for mitosis, its chromatin coils and folds up (condenses), eventually forming a characteristic number of short, thick metaphase chromosomes that are distinguishable from each other with the light microscope.

Though interphase chromatin is generally much less condensed than the chromatin of mitotic chromosomes, it shows several of the same levels of higher-order packing. Some of the chromatin comprising a chromosome seems to be present as a 10-nm fiber, but much is compacted into a 30-nm fiber, which in some regions is further folded into looped domains. Early on, biologists assumed that interphase chromatin was a tangled mass in the nucleus, like a bowl of spaghetti, but this is far from the case. Although an interphase chromosome lacks an obvious scaffold, its looped domains appear to be attached to the nuclear lamina, on the inside of the nuclear envelope, and perhaps also to fibers of the nuclear matrix. These attachments may help organize regions of chromatin where genes are active. The chromatin of each chromosome occupies a specific restricted area within the interphase nucleus, and the chromatin fibers of different chromosomes do not become entangled (**Figure 16.23**).

Even during interphase, the centromeres and telomeres of chromosomes, as well as other chromosomal regions in some cells, exist in a highly condensed state similar to that seen in a metaphase chromosome. This type of interphase chromatin, visible as irregular clumps with a light microscope, is called **heterochromatin**, to distinguish it from the less compacted, more dispersed **euchromatin** ("true chromatin"). Because of its compaction, heterochromatic DNA is largely inaccessible to the machinery in the cell responsible for transcribing the genetic information coded in the DNA, a crucial early step in gene expression. In contrast, the looser packing of euchromatin makes its DNA accessible to this machinery, so the genes present in euchromatin can be transcribed. The chromosome is a dynamic structure that is condensed, loosened, modified, and remodeled as necessary for various cell processes, including mitosis, meiosis, and gene activity. Chemical modifications of histones affect the state of chromatin condensation and also have multiple effects on gene activity, as you will see in Chapter 18.

In this chapter, you have learned how DNA molecules are arranged in chromosomes and how DNA replication provides the copies of genes that parents pass to offspring. However, it is not enough that genes be copied and transmitted; the information they carry must be used by the cell. In other words, genes must also be "expressed." In the next chapter, we will examine how the cell expresses the genetic information encoded in DNA.

▼ Figure 16.23

IMPACT

Painting Chromosomes

Using techniques you'll learn about in Chapter 20, researchers have been able to treat human chromosomes with special molecular tags, such that each chromosome pair can be seen as a different color. Below on the left is a spread of chromosomes treated in this way; on the right they are organized into a karyotype.

WHY IT MATTERS The ability to visually distinguish among chromosomes has allowed researchers to see how the chromosomes are arranged in the interphase nucleus. As you can see in the interphase nucleus below, each chromosome appears to occupy a specific territory during interphase. In general, the two homologs of a pair are not located together.

FURTHER READING M. R. Speicher and N. P. Carter, The new cytogenetics: blurring the boundaries with molecular biology, *Nature Reviews Genetics* 6:782–792 (2005); J. L. Marx, New methods for expanding the chromosomal paint kit, *Science* 273:430 (1996).

MAKE CONNECTIONS If you arrested a human cell in metaphase I of meiosis and applied this technique, what would you observe? How would this differ from what you would see in metaphase of mitosis? Review Figure 13.8 (pp. 254–255) and Figure 12.7 (pp. 232–233).

CONCEPT CHECK 16.3

1. Describe the structure of a nucleosome, the basic unit of DNA packing in eukaryotic cells.
2. What two properties, one structural and one functional, distinguish heterochromatin from euchromatin?
3. **MAKE CONNECTIONS** Interphase chromosomes appear to be attached to the nuclear lamina and perhaps also the nuclear matrix. Describe these two structures. See page 102 and Figure 6.9 on page 103.

For suggested answers, see Appendix A.

SUMMARY OF KEY CONCEPTS

CONCEPT 16.1

DNA is the genetic material (pp. 305–310)

- Experiments with bacteria and with **phages** provided the first strong evidence that the genetic material is DNA.
- Watson and Crick deduced that DNA is a **double helix** and built a structural model. Two **antiparallel** sugar-phosphate chains wind around the outside of the molecule; the nitrogenous bases project into the interior, where they hydrogen-bond in specific pairs, A with T, G with C.

Sugar-phosphate backbone

Nitrogenous bases

Hydrogen bond

? *What does it mean when we say that the two DNA strands in the double helix are antiparallel? What would an end of the double helix look like if the strands were parallel?*

CONCEPT 16.2

Many proteins work together in DNA replication and repair (pp. 311–319)

- The Meselson-Stahl experiment showed that **DNA replication** is **semiconservative**: The parental molecule unwinds, and each strand then serves as a template for the synthesis of a new strand according to base-pairing rules.
- DNA replication at one **replication fork** is summarized here:

DNA pol III synthesizes **leading strand** continuously

Parental DNA

DNA pol III starts DNA synthesis at 3' end of primer, continues in 5' → 3' direction

Origin of replication

Helicase

Primase synthesizes a short RNA **primer**

Lagging strand synthesized in short **Okazaki fragments**, later joined by **DNA ligase**

DNA pol I replaces the RNA primer with DNA nucleotides

- DNA polymerases proofread new DNA, replacing incorrect nucleotides. In **mismatch repair**, enzymes correct errors that persist. **Nucleotide excision repair** is a general process by which **nucleases** cut out and replace damaged stretches of DNA.
- The ends of eukaryotic chromosomal DNA get shorter with each round of replication. The presence of **telomeres**, repetitive sequences at the ends of linear DNA molecules, postpones the erosion of genes. **Telomerase** catalyzes the lengthening of telomeres in germ cells.

? *Compare DNA replication on the leading and lagging strands, including both similarities and differences.*

CONCEPT 16.3

A chromosome consists of a DNA molecule packed together with proteins (pp. 320–322)

- The bacterial chromosome is usually a circular DNA molecule with some associated proteins, making up the **nucleoid** of the cell. Eukaryotic **chromatin** making up a chromosome is composed of DNA, **histones**, and other proteins. The histones bind to each other and to the DNA to form **nucleosomes**, the most basic units of DNA packing. Histone tails extend outward from each bead-like nucleosome core. Additional coiling and folding leads ultimately to the highly condensed chromatin of the metaphase chromosome. In interphase cells, most chromatin is less compacted (**euchromatin**), but some remains highly condensed (**heterochromatin**). Euchromatin, but not heterochromatin, is generally accessible for transcription of genes.

? *Describe the levels of chromatin packing you'd expect to see in an interphase nucleus.*

TEST YOUR UNDERSTANDING

LEVEL 1: KNOWLEDGE/COMPREHENSION

1. In his work with pneumonia-causing bacteria and mice, Griffith found that
   a. the protein coat from pathogenic cells was able to transform nonpathogenic cells.
   b. heat-killed pathogenic cells caused pneumonia.
   c. some substance from pathogenic cells was transferred to nonpathogenic cells, making them pathogenic.
   d. the polysaccharide coat of bacteria caused pneumonia.
   e. bacteriophages injected DNA into bacteria.

2. What is the basis for the difference in how the leading and lagging strands of DNA molecules are synthesized?
   a. The origins of replication occur only at the 5' end.
   b. Helicases and single-strand binding proteins work at the 5' end.
   c. DNA polymerase can join new nucleotides only to the 3' end of a growing strand.
   d. DNA ligase works only in the 3' → 5' direction.
   e. Polymerase can work on only one strand at a time.

3. In analyzing the number of different bases in a DNA sample, which result would be consistent with the base-pairing rules?
   a. $A = G$
   b. $A + G = C + T$
   c. $A + T = G + T$
   d. $A = C$
   e. $G = T$

4. The elongation of the leading strand during DNA synthesis
   a. progresses away from the replication fork.
   b. occurs in the 3' → 5' direction.
   c. produces Okazaki fragments.
   d. depends on the action of DNA polymerase.
   e. does not require a template strand.

5. In a nucleosome, the DNA is wrapped around
   a. polymerase molecules.
   b. ribosomes.
   c. histones.
   d. a thymine dimer.
   e. satellite DNA.

LEVEL 2: APPLICATION/ANALYSIS

6. *E. coli* cells grown on ^{15}N medium are transferred to ^{14}N medium and allowed to grow for two more generations (two rounds of DNA replication). DNA extracted from these cells is centrifuged. What density distribution of DNA would you expect in this experiment?
   a. one high-density and one low-density band
   b. one intermediate-density band
   c. one high-density and one intermediate-density band
   d. one low-density and one intermediate-density band
   e. one low-density band

7. A biochemist isolates, purifies, and combines in a test tube a variety of molecules needed for DNA replication. When she adds some DNA to the mixture, replication occurs, but each DNA molecule consists of a normal strand paired with numerous segments of DNA a few hundred nucleotides long. What has she probably left out of the mixture?
   a. DNA polymerase
   b. DNA ligase
   c. nucleotides
   d. Okazaki fragments
   e. primase

8. The spontaneous loss of amino groups from adenine in DNA results in hypoxanthine, an uncommon base, opposite thymine. What combination of proteins could repair such damage?
   a. nuclease, DNA polymerase, DNA ligase
   b. telomerase, primase, DNA polymerase
   c. telomerase, helicase, single-strand binding protein
   d. DNA ligase, replication fork proteins, adenylyl cyclase
   e. nuclease, telomerase, primase

9. **MAKE CONNECTIONS** Although the proteins that cause the *E. coli* chromosome to coil are not histones, what property would you expect them to share with histones, given their ability to bind to DNA (see Figure 5.16, p. 79)?

LEVEL 3: SYNTHESIS/EVALUATION

10. The table below shows the base composition of DNA in several species. Explain how these data demonstrate Chargaff's rules.

Source	Adenine	Guanine	Cytosine	Thymine
E. coli	24.7%	26.0%	25.7%	23.6%
Wheat	28.1	21.8	22.7	27.4
Sea urchin	32.8	17.7	17.3	32.1
Salmon	29.7	20.8	20.4	29.1
Human	30.4	19.6	19.9	30.1
Ox	29.0	21.2	21.2	28.7

11. EVOLUTION CONNECTION

Some bacteria may be able to respond to environmental stress by increasing the rate at which mutations occur during cell division. How might this be accomplished? Might there be an evolutionary advantage of this ability? Explain.

12. SCIENTIFIC INQUIRY

 DRAW IT Model building can be an important part of the scientific process. The illustration shown above is a computer-generated model of a DNA replication complex. The parental and newly synthesized DNA strands are color-coded differently, as are each of the following three proteins: DNA pol III, the sliding clamp, and single-strand binding protein. Use what you've learned in this chapter to clarify this model by labeling each DNA strand and each protein and indicating the overall direction of DNA replication.

13. WRITE ABOUT A THEME

The Genetic Basis of Life; Structure and Function The continuity of life is based on heritable information in the form of DNA, and structure and function are correlated at all levels of biological organization. In a short essay (100–150 words), describe how the structure of DNA is correlated with its role as the molecular basis of inheritance.

For selected answers, see Appendix A.

MasteringBIOLOGY®   www.masteringbiology.com

1. MasteringBiology® Assignments
Experimental Inquiry Tutorial Does DNA Replication Follow the Conservative, Semiconservative, or Dispersive Model?
Video Tutor Session DNA Structure
BioFlix Tutorials DNA Replication: DNA Structure and Replication Machinery • Synthesis of the Leading and Lagging Strands
Tutorial DNA Replication
Activities The Hershey-Chase Experiment • DNA and RNA Structure • DNA Double Helix • DNA Replication: An Overview • DNA Replication: A Closer Look • DNA Replication: A Review • DNA Synthesis • DNA Packing
Questions Student Misconceptions • Reading Quiz • Multiple Choice • End-of-Chapter

2. eText
Read your book online, search, take notes, highlight text, and more.

3. The Study Area
Practice Tests • Cumulative Test • *BioFlix* 3-D Animations • MP3 Tutor Sessions • Videos • Activities • Investigations • Lab Media • Audio Glossary • Word Study Tools • Art

17

From Gene to Protein

▲ Figure 17.1 **How does a single faulty gene result in the dramatic appearance of an albino deer?**

KEY CONCEPTS

17.1 Genes specify proteins via transcription and translation

17.2 Transcription is the DNA-directed synthesis of RNA: *a closer look*

17.3 Eukaryotic cells modify RNA after transcription

17.4 Translation is the RNA-directed synthesis of a polypeptide: *a closer look*

17.5 Mutations of one or a few nucleotides can affect protein structure and function

17.6 While gene expression differs among the domains of life, the concept of a gene is universal

The Flow of Genetic Information

In 2006, a young albino deer seen frolicking with several brown deer in the mountains of eastern Germany elicited a public outcry (Figure 17.1). A local hunting organization announced that the albino deer suffered from a "genetic disorder" and should be shot. Some argued that the deer should merely be prevented from mating with other deer to safeguard the population's gene pool. Others favored relocating the albino deer to a nature reserve because they worried that it might be more noticeable to predators if left in the wild. A German rock star even held a benefit concert to raise funds for the relocation. What led to the striking phenotype of this deer, the cause of this lively debate?

You learned in Chapter 14 that inherited traits are determined by genes and that the trait of albinism is caused by a recessive allele of a pigmentation gene. The information content of genes is in the form of specific sequences of nucleotides along strands of DNA, the genetic material. But how does this information determine an organism's traits? Put another way, what does a gene actually say? And how is its message translated by cells into a specific trait, such as brown hair, type A blood, or, in the case of an albino deer, a total lack of pigment? The albino deer has a faulty version of a key protein, an enzyme required for pigment synthesis, and this protein is faulty because the gene that codes for it contains incorrect information.

This example illustrates the main point of this chapter: The DNA inherited by an organism leads to specific traits by dictating the synthesis of proteins and of RNA molecules involved in protein synthesis. In other words, proteins are the link between genotype and phenotype. **Gene expression** is the process by which DNA directs the synthesis of proteins (or, in some cases, just RNAs). The expression of genes that code for proteins includes two stages: transcription and translation. This chapter describes the flow of information from gene to protein in detail and explains how genetic mutations affect organisms through their proteins. Understanding the processes of gene expression, which are similar in all three domains of life, will allow us to revisit the concept of the gene in more detail at the end of the chapter.

CONCEPT 17.1

Genes specify proteins via transcription and translation

Before going into the details of how genes direct protein synthesis, let's step back and examine how the fundamental relationship between genes and proteins was discovered.

Evidence from the Study of Metabolic Defects

In 1902, British physician Archibald Garrod was the first to suggest that genes dictate phenotypes through enzymes that catalyze specific chemical reactions in the cell. Garrod postulated that the symptoms of an inherited disease reflect a person's inability to make a particular enzyme. He later referred to such diseases as "inborn errors of metabolism." Garrod gave as one example the hereditary condition called alkaptonuria. In this disorder, the urine is black because it contains the chemical alkapton, which darkens upon exposure to air. Garrod reasoned that most people have an enzyme that metabolizes alkapton, whereas people with alkaptonuria have inherited an inability to make that enzyme.

Garrod may have been the first to recognize that Mendel's principles of heredity apply to humans as well as peas. Garrod's realization was ahead of its time, but research several decades later supported his hypothesis that a gene dictates the production of a specific enzyme. Biochemists accumulated much evidence that cells synthesize and degrade most organic molecules via metabolic pathways, in which each chemical reaction in a sequence is catalyzed by a specific enzyme (see p. 142). Such metabolic pathways lead, for instance, to the synthesis of the pigments that give the brown deer in Figure 17.1 their fur color or fruit flies (*Drosophila*) their eye color (see Figure 15.3). In the 1930s, the American biochemist and geneticist George Beadle and his French colleague Boris Ephrussi speculated that in *Drosophila*, each of the various mutations affecting eye color blocks pigment synthesis at a specific step by preventing production of the enzyme that catalyzes that step. But neither the chemical reactions nor the enzymes that catalyze them were known at the time.

Nutritional Mutants in Neurospora: Scientific Inquiry

A breakthrough in demonstrating the relationship between genes and enzymes came a few years later at Stanford University, where Beadle and Edward Tatum began working with a bread mold, *Neurospora crassa*. They bombarded *Neurospora* with X-rays, shown in the 1920s to cause genetic changes, and then looked among the survivors for mutants that differed in their nutritional needs from the wild-type bread mold. Wild-type *Neurospora* has modest food requirements. It can grow in the laboratory on a simple solution of inorganic salts, glucose, and the vitamin biotin, incorporated into agar, a support medium. From this *minimal medium*, the mold cells use their metabolic pathways to produce all the other molecules they need. Beadle and Tatum identified mutants that could not survive on minimal medium, apparently because they were unable to synthesize certain essential molecules from the minimal ingredients. To ensure survival of these nutritional mutants, Beadle and Tatum allowed them to grow on a *complete growth medium*, which consisted of minimal medium supplemented with all 20 amino acids and a few other nutrients. The complete growth medium could support any mutant that couldn't synthesize one of the supplements.

To characterize the metabolic defect in each nutritional mutant, Beadle and Tatum took samples from the mutant growing on complete medium and distributed them to a number of different vials. Each vial contained minimal medium plus a single additional nutrient. The particular supplement that allowed growth indicated the metabolic defect. For example, if the only supplemented vial that supported growth of the mutant was the one fortified with the amino acid arginine, the researchers could conclude that the mutant was defective in the biochemical pathway that wild-type cells use to synthesize arginine.

In fact, such arginine-requiring mutants were obtained and studied by two colleagues of Beadle and Tatum, Adrian Srb and Norman Horowitz, who wanted to investigate the biochemical pathway for arginine synthesis in *Neurospora* (Figure 17.2). Srb and Horowitz pinned down each mutant's defect more specifically, using additional tests to distinguish among three classes of arginine-requiring mutants. Mutants in each class required a different set of compounds along the arginine-synthesizing pathway, which has three steps. These results, and those of many similar experiments done by Beadle and Tatum, suggested that each class was blocked at a different step in this pathway because mutants in that class lacked the enzyme that catalyzes the blocked step.

Because each mutant was defective in a single gene, Beadle and Tatum saw that, taken together, the collected results provided strong support for a working hypothesis they had proposed earlier. The *one gene–one enzyme hypothesis*, as they dubbed it, states that the function of a gene is to dictate the production of a specific enzyme. Further support for this hypothesis came from experiments that identified the specific enzymes lacking in the mutants. Beadle and Tatum shared a Nobel Prize in 1958 for "their discovery that genes act by regulating definite chemical events" (in the words of the Nobel committee).

The Products of Gene Expression: A Developing Story

As researchers learned more about proteins, they made revisions to the one gene–one enzyme hypothesis. First of all, not all proteins are enzymes. Keratin, the structural protein of animal hair, and the hormone insulin are two examples of nonenzyme proteins. Because proteins that are not enzymes are nevertheless gene products, molecular biologists began to think in terms of one gene–one protein. However, many proteins are constructed from two or more different polypeptide chains, and each polypeptide is specified by its own gene. For example, hemoglobin, the oxygen-transporting protein of vertebrate red blood cells, contains two kinds of polypeptides, and thus two genes code for this protein (see Figure 5.20). Beadle and Tatum's idea was therefore restated as the *one gene–one polypeptide hypothesis*. Even this description is not entirely accurate, though. First, many eukaryotic genes can each code for a set of closely related polypeptides via a process called alternative splicing, which you will learn about later in this chapter. Second, quite a few genes code for RNA molecules that have important functions in cells

▼ Figure 17.2

INQUIRY

Do individual genes specify the enzymes that function in a biochemical pathway?

EXPERIMENT Working with the mold *Neurospora crassa*, Adrian Srb and Norman Horowitz, then at Stanford University, used Beadle and Tatum's experimental approach to isolate mutants that required arginine in their growth medium. The researchers showed that these mutants fell into three classes, each defective in a different gene. From other considerations, they suspected that the metabolic pathway of arginine biosynthesis involved a precursor nutrient and the intermediate molecules ornithine and citrulline. Their most famous experiment, shown here, tested both the one gene–one enzyme hypothesis and their postulated arginine-synthesizing pathway. In this experiment, they grew their three classes of mutants under the four different conditions shown in the Results section below. They included minimal medium (MM) as a control because they knew that wild-type cells could grow on MM but mutant cells could not. (See test tubes on the right.)

Growth:
Wild-type
cells growing
and dividing

No growth:
Mutant cells
cannot grow
and divide

Minimal medium

RESULTS The wild-type strain was capable of growth under all experimental conditions, requiring only the minimal medium. The three classes of mutants each had a specific set of growth requirements. For example, class II mutants could not grow when ornithine alone was added but could grow when either citrulline or arginine was added.

		Classes of *Neurospora crassa*			
		Wild type	**Class I mutants**	**Class II mutants**	**Class III mutants**
Condition	Minimal medium (MM) (control)				
	MM + ornithine				
	MM + citrulline				
	MM + arginine (control)				
	Summary of results	Can grow with or without any supplements	Can grow on ornithine, citrulline, or arginine	Can grow only on citrulline or arginine	Require arginine to grow

CONCLUSION From the growth requirements of the mutants, Srb and Horowitz deduced that each class of mutant was unable to carry out one step in the pathway for synthesizing arginine, presumably because it lacked the necessary enzyme. Because each of their mutants was mutated in a single gene, they concluded that each mutated gene must normally dictate the production of one enzyme. Their results supported the one gene–one enzyme hypothesis proposed by Beadle and Tatum and also confirmed that the arginine pathway described in the mammalian liver also operates in *Neurospora*. (Notice in the Results that a mutant can grow only if supplied with a compound made *after* the defective step because this bypasses the defect.)

Gene (codes for enzyme)	Wild type	Class I mutants (mutation in gene *A*)	Class II mutants (mutation in gene *B*)	Class III mutants (mutation in gene *C*)
	Precursor	Precursor	Precursor	Precursor
Gene *A* →	Enzyme A	✗ Enzyme A	Enzyme A	Enzyme A
	Ornithine	Ornithine	Ornithine	Ornithine
Gene *B* →	Enzyme B	Enzyme B	✗ Enzyme B	Enzyme B
	Citrulline	Citrulline	Citrulline	Citrulline
Gene *C* →	Enzyme C	Enzyme C	Enzyme C	✗ Enzyme C
	Arginine	Arginine	Arginine	Arginine

SOURCE A. M. Srb and N. H. Horowitz, The ornithine cycle in *Neurospora* and its genetic control, *Journal of Biological Chemistry* 154:129–139 (1944).

WHAT IF? Suppose the experiment had shown that class I mutants could grow only in MM supplemented by ornithine or arginine and that class II mutants could grow in MM supplemented by citrulline, ornithine, or arginine. What conclusions would the researchers have drawn from those results regarding the biochemical pathway and the defect in class I and class II mutants?

even though they are never translated into protein. For now, we will focus on genes that do code for polypeptides. (Note that it is common to refer to these gene products as proteins—a practice you will encounter in this book—rather than more precisely as polypeptides.)

Basic Principles of Transcription and Translation

Genes provide the instructions for making specific proteins. But a gene does not build a protein directly. The bridge between DNA and protein synthesis is the nucleic acid RNA. You learned in Chapter 5 that RNA is chemically similar to DNA except that it contains ribose instead of deoxyribose as its sugar and has the nitrogenous base uracil rather than thymine (see Figure 5.26). Thus, each nucleotide along a DNA strand has A, G, C, or T as its base, and each nucleotide along an RNA strand has A, G, C, or U as its base. An RNA molecule usually consists of a single strand.

It is customary to describe the flow of information from gene to protein in linguistic terms because both nucleic acids and proteins are polymers with specific sequences of monomers that convey information, much as specific sequences of letters communicate information in a language like English. In DNA or RNA, the monomers are the four types of nucleotides, which differ in their nitrogenous bases. Genes are typically hundreds or thousands of nucleotides long, each gene having a specific sequence of nucleotides. Each polypeptide of a protein also has monomers arranged in a particular linear order (the protein's primary structure), but its monomers are amino acids. Thus, nucleic acids and proteins contain information written in two different chemical languages. Getting from DNA to protein requires two major stages: transcription and translation.

Transcription is the synthesis of RNA using information in the DNA. The two nucleic acids are written in different forms of the same language, and the information is simply transcribed, or "rewritten," from DNA to RNA. Just as a DNA strand provides a template for making a new complementary strand during DNA replication, it also can serve as a template for assembling a complementary sequence of RNA nucleotides. For a protein-coding gene, the resulting RNA molecule is a faithful transcript of the gene's protein-building instructions. This type of RNA molecule is called **messenger RNA (mRNA)** because it carries a genetic message from the DNA to the protein-synthesizing machinery of the cell. (Transcription is the general term for the synthesis of *any* kind of RNA on a DNA template. Later, you will learn about some other types of RNA produced by transcription.)

Translation is the synthesis of a polypeptide using the information in the mRNA. During this stage, there is a change in language: The cell must translate the nucleotide sequence of an mRNA molecule into the amino acid sequence of a polypeptide. The sites of translation are **ribosomes**, complex particles that facilitate the orderly linking of amino acids into polypeptide chains.

Transcription and translation occur in all organisms, both those that lack a membrane-bounded nucleus (bacteria and archaea) and those that have one (eukaryotes). Because most studies of transcription and translation have used bacteria and eukaryotic cells, these are our main focus in this chapter. Our understanding of transcription and translation in archaea lags behind, but in the last section of the chapter we will discuss a few aspects of archaeal gene expression.

The basic mechanics of transcription and translation are similar for bacteria and eukaryotes, but there is an important difference in the flow of genetic information within the cells. Because bacteria do not have nuclei, their DNA is not separated by nuclear membranes from ribosomes and the other protein-synthesizing equipment **(Figure 17.3a)**. As you will see later, this lack of compartmentalization allows translation of an mRNA to begin while its transcription is still in progress. In a eukaryotic cell, by contrast, the nuclear envelope separates transcription from translation in space and time **(Figure 17.3b)**. Transcription occurs in the nucleus, and mRNA is then transported to the cytoplasm, where translation occurs. But before eukaryotic RNA transcripts from protein-coding genes can leave the nucleus, they are modified in various ways to produce the final, functional mRNA. The transcription of a protein-coding eukaryotic gene results in *pre-mRNA*, and further processing yields the finished mRNA. The initial RNA transcript from any gene, including those specifying RNA that is not translated into protein, is more generally called a **primary transcript**.

To summarize: Genes program protein synthesis via genetic messages in the form of messenger RNA. Put another way, cells are governed by a molecular chain of command with a directional flow of genetic information, shown here by arrows:

This concept was dubbed the *central dogma* by Francis Crick in 1956. How has the concept held up over time? In the 1970s, scientists were surprised to discover that some RNA molecules can act as templates for DNA synthesis, a process you'll read about in Chapter 19. However, these exceptions do not invalidate the idea that, in general, genetic information flows from DNA to RNA to protein. In the next section, we discuss how the instructions for assembling amino acids into a specific order are encoded in nucleic acids.

The Genetic Code

When biologists began to suspect that the instructions for protein synthesis were encoded in DNA, they recognized a problem: There are only four nucleotide bases to specify 20 amino acids. Thus, the genetic code cannot be a language like Chinese, where each written symbol corresponds to a word. How many nucleotides, then, correspond to an amino acid?

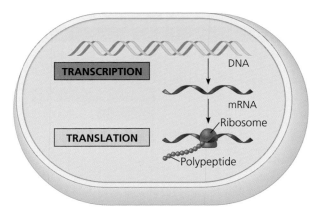

(a) **Bacterial cell.** In a bacterial cell, which lacks a nucleus, mRNA produced by transcription is immediately translated without additional processing.

(b) **Eukaryotic cell.** The nucleus provides a separate compartment for transcription. The original RNA transcript, called pre-mRNA, is processed in various ways before leaving the nucleus as mRNA.

▲ **Figure 17.3 Overview: the roles of transcription and translation in the flow of genetic information.** In a cell, inherited information flows from DNA to RNA to protein. The two main stages of information flow are transcription and translation. A miniature version of part (a) or (b) accompanies several figures later in the chapter as an orientation diagram to help you see where a particular figure fits into the overall scheme.

Codons: Triplets of Nucleotides

If each kind of nucleotide base were translated into an amino acid, only 4 of the 20 amino acids could be specified. Would a language of two-letter code words suffice? The two-nucleotide sequence AG, for example, could specify one amino acid, and GT could specify another. Since there are four possible nucleotide bases in each position, this would give us 16 (that is, 4^2) possible arrangements—still not enough to code for all 20 amino acids.

Triplets of nucleotide bases are the smallest units of uniform length that can code for all the amino acids. If each arrangement of three consecutive nucleotide bases specifies an amino acid, there can be 64 (that is, 4^3) possible code words—more than enough to specify all the amino acids. Experiments have verified that the flow of information from gene to protein is based on a **triplet code**: The genetic instructions for a polypeptide chain are written in the DNA as a series of nonoverlapping, three-nucleotide words. The series of words in a gene is transcribed into a complementary series of nonoverlapping, three-nucleotide words in mRNA, which is then translated into a chain of amino acids (**Figure 17.4**).

During transcription, the gene determines the sequence of nucleotide bases along the length of the RNA molecule that is being synthesized. For each gene, only one of the two DNA strands is transcribed. This strand is called the **template strand** because it provides the pattern, or template, for the sequence of nucleotides in an RNA transcript. For any given gene, the same strand is used as the template every time the gene is transcribed. For other genes on the same DNA molecule, however, the opposite strand may be the one that always functions as the template.

▲ **Figure 17.4 The triplet code.** For each gene, one DNA strand functions as a template for transcription of RNAs, such as mRNA. The base-pairing rules for DNA synthesis also guide transcription, except that uracil (U) takes the place of thymine (T) in RNA. During translation, the mRNA is read as a sequence of nucleotide triplets, called codons. Each codon specifies an amino acid to be added to the growing polypeptide chain. The mRNA is read in the 5' → 3' direction.

? *Compare the sequence of the mRNA to that of the nontemplate DNA strand, in both cases reading from 5' → 3'.*

An mRNA molecule is complementary rather than identical to its DNA template because RNA nucleotides are assembled on the template according to base-pairing rules (see Figure 17.4). The pairs are similar to those that form during DNA replication, except that U, the RNA substitute for T, pairs with A and the mRNA nucleotides contain ribose instead of deoxyribose. Like a new strand of DNA, the RNA molecule is synthesized in an antiparallel direction to the template strand of DNA. (To review what is meant by "antiparallel" and the 5′ and 3′ ends of a nucleic acid chain, see Figure 16.7.) In the example in Figure 17.4, the nucleotide triplet ACC along the DNA (written as 3′-ACC-5′) provides a template for 5′-UGG-3′ in the mRNA molecule. The mRNA nucleotide triplets are called **codons**, and they are customarily written in the 5′ → 3′ direction. In our example, UGG is the codon for the amino acid tryptophan (abbreviated Trp). The term *codon* is also used for the DNA nucleotide triplets along the *nontemplate* strand. These codons are complementary to the template strand and thus identical in sequence to the mRNA, except that they have T instead of U. (For this reason, the nontemplate DNA strand is sometimes called the "coding strand.")

During translation, the sequence of codons along an mRNA molecule is decoded, or translated, into a sequence of amino acids making up a polypeptide chain. The codons are read by the translation machinery in the 5′ → 3′ direction along the mRNA. Each codon specifies which one of the 20 amino acids will be incorporated at the corresponding position along a polypeptide. Because codons are nucleotide triplets, the number of nucleotides making up a genetic message must be three times the number of amino acids in the protein product. For example, it takes 300 nucleotides along an mRNA strand to code for the amino acids in a polypeptide that is 100 amino acids long.

Cracking the Code

Molecular biologists cracked the genetic code of life in the early 1960s when a series of elegant experiments disclosed the amino acid translations of each of the RNA codons. The first codon was deciphered in 1961 by Marshall Nirenberg, of the National Institutes of Health, and his colleagues. Nirenberg synthesized an artificial mRNA by linking identical RNA nucleotides containing uracil as their base. No matter where this message started or stopped, it could contain only one codon in repetition: UUU. Nirenberg added this "poly-U" to a test-tube mixture containing amino acids, ribosomes, and the other components required for protein synthesis. His artificial system translated the poly-U into a polypeptide containing many units of the amino acid phenylalanine (Phe), strung together as a long polyphenylalanine chain. Thus, Nirenberg determined that the mRNA codon UUU specifies the amino acid phenylalanine. Soon, the amino acids specified by the codons AAA, GGG, and CCC were also determined.

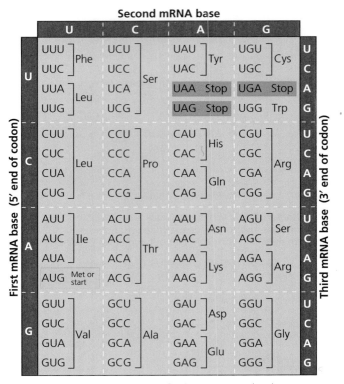

▲ **Figure 17.5 The codon table for mRNA.** The three nucleotide bases of an mRNA codon are designated here as the first, second, and third bases, reading in the 5′ → 3′ direction along the mRNA. (Practice using this table by finding the codons in Figure 17.4.) The codon AUG not only stands for the amino acid methionine (Met) but also functions as a "start" signal for ribosomes to begin translating the mRNA at that point. Three of the 64 codons function as "stop" signals, marking where ribosomes end translation. See Figure 5.16 for a list of the full names of all the amino acids.

Although more elaborate techniques were required to decode mixed triplets such as AUA and CGA, all 64 codons were deciphered by the mid-1960s. As **Figure 17.5** shows, 61 of the 64 triplets code for amino acids. The three codons that do not designate amino acids are "stop" signals, or termination codons, marking the end of translation. Notice that the codon AUG has a dual function: It codes for the amino acid methionine (Met) and also functions as a "start" signal, or initiation codon. Genetic messages usually begin with the mRNA codon AUG, which signals the protein-synthesizing machinery to begin translating the mRNA at that location. (Because AUG also stands for methionine, polypeptide chains begin with methionine when they are synthesized. However, an enzyme may subsequently remove this starter amino acid from the chain.)

Notice in Figure 17.5 that there is redundancy in the genetic code, but no ambiguity. For example, although codons GAA and GAG both specify glutamic acid (redundancy), neither of them ever specifies any other amino acid (no ambiguity). The redundancy in the code is not altogether random. In many cases, codons that are synonyms for a particular amino acid differ only in the third nucleotide base of the triplet. We will consider a possible benefit of this redundancy later in the chapter.

Our ability to extract the intended message from a written language depends on reading the symbols in the correct groupings—that is, in the correct **reading frame**. Consider this statement: "The red dog ate the bug." Group the letters incorrectly by starting at the wrong point, and the result will probably be gibberish: for example, "her edd oga tet heb ug." The reading frame is also important in the molecular language of cells. The short stretch of polypeptide shown in Figure 17.4, for instance, will be made correctly only if the mRNA nucleotides are read from left to right (5′ → 3′) in the groups of three shown in the figure: UGG UUU GGC UCA. Although a genetic message is written with no spaces between the codons, the cell's protein-synthesizing machinery reads the message as a series of nonoverlapping three-letter words. The message is *not* read as a series of overlapping words—UGGUUU, and so on—which would convey a very different message.

Evolution of the Genetic Code

EVOLUTION The genetic code is nearly universal, shared by organisms from the simplest bacteria to the most complex plants and animals. The RNA codon CCG, for instance, is translated as the amino acid proline in all organisms whose genetic code has been examined. In laboratory experiments, genes can be transcribed and translated after being transplanted from one species to another, sometimes with quite striking results, as shown in **Figure 17.6**! Bacteria can be pro-

grammed by the insertion of human genes to synthesize certain human proteins for medical use, such as insulin. Such applications have produced many exciting developments in the area of biotechnology (see Chapter 20).

Exceptions to the universality of the genetic code include translation systems in which a few codons differ from the standard ones. Slight variations in the genetic code exist in certain unicellular eukaryotes and in the organelle genes of some species. Despite these exceptions, the evolutionary significance of the code's *near* universality is clear. A language shared by all living things must have been operating very early in the history of life—early enough to be present in the common ancestor of all present-day organisms. A shared genetic vocabulary is a reminder of the kinship that bonds all life on Earth.

CONCEPT CHECK 17.1

1. **MAKE CONNECTIONS** In a research article about alkaptonuria published in 1902, Garrod suggested that humans inherit two "characters" (alleles) for a particular enzyme and that both parents must contribute a faulty version for the offspring to have the disorder. Today, would this disorder be called dominant or recessive? See Concept 14.4, pages 276–278.
2. What polypeptide product would you expect from a poly-G mRNA that is 30 nucleotides long?
3. **DRAW IT** The template strand of a gene contains the sequence 3′-TTCAGTCGT-5′. Draw the nontemplate sequence and the mRNA sequence, indicating 5′ and 3′ ends of each. Compare the two sequences.
4. **WHAT IF?** **DRAW IT** Imagine that the nontemplate sequence in question 3 was transcribed instead of the template sequence. Draw the mRNA sequence and translate it using Figure 17.5. (Be sure to pay attention to the 5′ and 3′ ends.) Predict how well the protein synthesized from the nontemplate strand would function, if at all.

For suggested answers, see Appendix A.

CONCEPT 17.2

Transcription is the DNA-directed synthesis of RNA: *a closer look*

Now that we have considered the linguistic logic and evolutionary significance of the genetic code, we are ready to reexamine transcription, the first stage of gene expression, in more detail.

Molecular Components of Transcription

Messenger RNA, the carrier of information from DNA to the cell's protein-synthesizing machinery, is transcribed from the template strand of a gene. An enzyme called an **RNA polymerase** pries the two strands of DNA apart and joins

(a) Tobacco plant expressing a firefly gene. The yellow glow is produced by a chemical reaction catalyzed by the protein product of the firefly gene.

(b) Pig expressing a jellyfish gene. Researchers injected the gene for a fluorescent protein into fertilized pig eggs. One of the eggs developed into this fluorescent pig.

▲ **Figure 17.6 Expression of genes from different species.** Because diverse forms of life share a common genetic code, one species can be programmed to produce proteins characteristic of a second species by introducing DNA from the second species into the first.

together RNA nucleotides complementary to the DNA template strand, thus elongating the RNA polynucleotide (**Figure 17.7**). Like the DNA polymerases that function in DNA replication, RNA polymerases can assemble a polynucleotide only in its $5' \rightarrow 3'$ direction. Unlike DNA polymerases, however, RNA polymerases are able to start a chain from scratch; they don't need a primer.

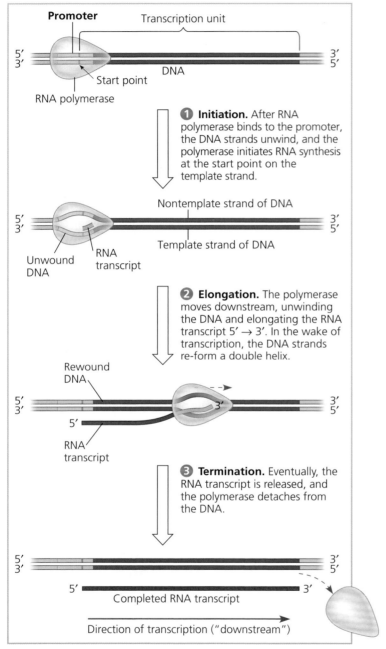

Promoter

Transcription unit

5′
3′

Start point
RNA polymerase

DNA
3′
5′

1 **Initiation.** After RNA polymerase binds to the promoter, the DNA strands unwind, and the polymerase initiates RNA synthesis at the start point on the template strand.

Nontemplate strand of DNA

5′
3′

3′
5′

Template strand of DNA

Unwound DNA

RNA transcript

2 **Elongation.** The polymerase moves downstream, unwinding the DNA and elongating the RNA transcript $5' \rightarrow 3'$. In the wake of transcription, the DNA strands re-form a double helix.

Rewound DNA

5′
3′

3′

3′
5′

5′

RNA transcript

3 **Termination.** Eventually, the RNA transcript is released, and the polymerase detaches from the DNA.

5′
3′

3′
5′

5′

Completed RNA transcript

3′

Direction of transcription ("downstream")

▲ **Figure 17.7 The stages of transcription: initiation, elongation, and termination.** This general depiction of transcription applies to both bacteria and eukaryotes, but the details of termination differ, as described in the text. Also, in a bacterium, the RNA transcript is immediately usable as mRNA; in a eukaryote, the RNA transcript must first undergo processing.

MAKE CONNECTIONS *Compare the use of a template strand during transcription and replication. See Figure 16.17, page 317.*

Specific sequences of nucleotides along the DNA mark where transcription of a gene begins and ends. The DNA sequence where RNA polymerase attaches and initiates transcription is known as the **promoter**; in bacteria, the sequence that signals the end of transcription is called the **terminator**. (The termination mechanism is different in eukaryotes; we'll describe it later.) Molecular biologists refer to the direction of transcription as "downstream" and the other direction as "upstream." These terms are also used to describe the positions of nucleotide sequences within the DNA or RNA. Thus, the promoter sequence in DNA is said to be upstream from the terminator. The stretch of DNA that is transcribed into an RNA molecule is called a **transcription unit**.

Bacteria have a single type of RNA polymerase that synthesizes not only mRNA but also other types of RNA that function in protein synthesis, such as ribosomal RNA. In contrast, eukaryotes have at least three types of RNA polymerase in their nuclei. The one used for mRNA synthesis is called RNA polymerase II. The other RNA polymerases transcribe RNA molecules that are not translated into protein. In the discussion of transcription that follows, we start with the features of mRNA synthesis common to both bacteria and eukaryotes and then describe some key differences.

Synthesis of an RNA Transcript

The three stages of transcription, as shown in Figure 17.7 and described next, are initiation, elongation, and termination of the RNA chain. Study Figure 17.7 to familiarize yourself with the stages and the terms used to describe them.

RNA Polymerase Binding and Initiation of Transcription

The promoter of a gene includes within it the transcription **start point** (the nucleotide where RNA synthesis actually begins) and typically extends several dozen or more nucleotide pairs upstream from the start point. RNA polymerase binds in a precise location and orientation on the promoter, therefore determining where transcription starts and which of the two strands of the DNA helix is used as the template.

Certain sections of a promoter are especially important for binding RNA polymerase. In bacteria, the RNA polymerase itself specifically recognizes and binds to the promoter. In eukaryotes, a collection of proteins called **transcription factors** mediate the binding of RNA polymerase and the initiation of transcription. Only after transcription factors are attached to the promoter does RNA polymerase II bind to it. The whole complex of transcription factors and RNA polymerase II bound to the promoter is called a **transcription initiation complex**. **Figure 17.8** shows the role of transcription factors and a crucial promoter DNA sequence called a **TATA box** in forming the initiation complex at a eukaryotic promoter.

The interaction between eukaryotic RNA polymerase II and transcription factors is an example of the importance of protein-protein interactions in controlling eukaryotic

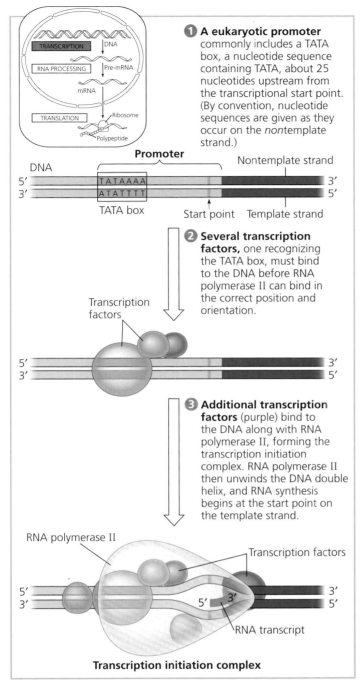

1 **A eukaryotic promoter** commonly includes a TATA box, a nucleotide sequence containing TATA, about 25 nucleotides upstream from the transcriptional start point. (By convention, nucleotide sequences are given as they occur on the *non*template strand.)

2 **Several transcription factors,** one recognizing the TATA box, must bind to the DNA before RNA polymerase II can bind in the correct position and orientation.

3 **Additional transcription factors** (purple) bind to the DNA along with RNA polymerase II, forming the transcription initiation complex. RNA polymerase II then unwinds the DNA double helix, and RNA synthesis begins at the start point on the template strand.

Promoter

DNA

5′ TATAAAA 3′
3′ ATATTTT 5′

TATA box   Start point   Template strand

Nontemplate strand

Transcription factors

RNA polymerase II

Transcription factors

RNA transcript

Transcription initiation complex

▲ **Figure 17.8 The initiation of transcription at a eukaryotic promoter.** In eukaryotic cells, proteins called transcription factors mediate the initiation of transcription by RNA polymerase II.

? *Explain how the interaction of RNA polymerase with the promoter would differ if the figure showed transcription initiation for bacteria.*

transcription. (And as you learned in Figure 16.22, the DNA of a eukaryotic chromosome is complexed with histones and other proteins in the form of chromatin. The roles of these proteins in making the DNA accessible to transcription factors will be discussed in Chapter 18). Once the appropriate transcription factors are firmly attached to the promoter DNA and the polymerase is bound in the correct orientation,

the enzyme unwinds the two DNA strands and starts transcribing the template strand.

Elongation of the RNA Strand

As RNA polymerase moves along the DNA, it continues to untwist the double helix, exposing about 10–20 DNA nucleotides at a time for pairing with RNA nucleotides **(Figure 17.9)**. The enzyme adds nucleotides to the 3′ end of the growing RNA molecule as it continues along the double helix. In the wake of this advancing wave of RNA synthesis, the new RNA molecule peels away from its DNA template, and the DNA double helix re-forms. Transcription progresses at a rate of about 40 nucleotides per second in eukaryotes.

A single gene can be transcribed simultaneously by several molecules of RNA polymerase following each other like trucks in a convoy. A growing strand of RNA trails off from each polymerase, with the length of each new strand reflecting how far along the template the enzyme has traveled from the start point (see the mRNA molecules in Figure 17.25). The congregation of many polymerase molecules simultaneously transcribing a single gene increases the amount of mRNA transcribed from it, which helps the cell make the encoded protein in large amounts.

Termination of Transcription

The mechanism of termination differs between bacteria and eukaryotes. In bacteria, transcription proceeds through a terminator sequence in the DNA. The transcribed terminator (an RNA sequence) functions as the termination signal,

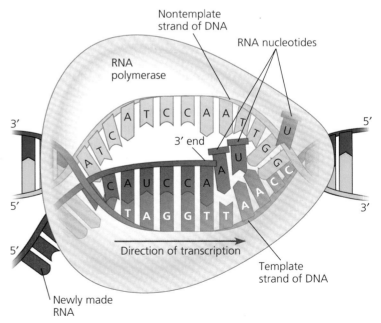

▲ **Figure 17.9 Transcription elongation.** RNA polymerase moves along the DNA template strand, joining complementary RNA nucleotides to the 3′ end of the growing RNA transcript. Behind the polymerase, the new RNA peels away from the template strand, which re-forms a double helix with the nontemplate strand.

causing the polymerase to detach from the DNA and release the transcript, which requires no further modification before translation. In eukaryotes, RNA polymerase II transcribes a sequence on the DNA called the polyadenylation signal sequence, which codes for a polyadenylation signal (AAUAAA) in the pre-mRNA. Then, at a point about 10–35 nucleotides downstream from the AAUAAA signal, proteins associated with the growing RNA transcript cut it free from the polymerase, releasing the pre-mRNA. The pre-mRNA then undergoes processing, the topic of the next section.

CONCEPT CHECK **17.2**

1. **MAKE CONNECTIONS** Compare DNA polymerase and RNA polymerase in terms of how they function, the requirement for a template and primer, the direction of synthesis, and the type of nucleotides used. See Figure 16.17, page 317.
2. What is a promoter, and is it located at the upstream or downstream end of a transcription unit?
3. What enables RNA polymerase to start transcribing a gene at the right place on the DNA in a bacterial cell? In a eukaryotic cell?
4. **WHAT IF?** Suppose X-rays caused a sequence change in the TATA box of a particular gene's promoter. How would that affect transcription of the gene? (See Figure 17.8.)

For suggested answers, see Appendix A.

CONCEPT **17.3**

Eukaryotic cells modify RNA after transcription

Enzymes in the eukaryotic nucleus modify pre-mRNA in specific ways before the genetic messages are dispatched to the cytoplasm. During this **RNA processing**, both ends of the primary transcript are altered. Also, in most cases, certain interior sections of the RNA molecule are cut out and the remaining parts spliced together. These modifications produce an mRNA molecule ready for translation.

Alteration of mRNA Ends

Each end of a pre-mRNA molecule is modified in a particular way (**Figure 17.10**). The 5′ end is synthesized first; it receives a **5′ cap**, a modified form of a guanine (G) nucleotide added onto the 5′ end after transcription of the first 20–40 nucleotides. The 3′ end of the pre-mRNA molecule is also modified before the mRNA exits the nucleus. Recall that the pre-mRNA is released soon after the polyadenylation signal, AAUAAA, is transcribed. At the 3′ end, an enzyme adds 50–250 more adenine (A) nucleotides, forming a **poly-A tail**. The 5′ cap and poly-A tail share several important functions. First, they seem to facilitate the export of the mature mRNA from the nucleus. Second, they help protect the mRNA from degradation by hydrolytic enzymes. And third, they help ribosomes attach to the 5′ end of the mRNA once the mRNA reaches the cytoplasm. Figure 17.10 shows a diagram of a eukaryotic mRNA molecule with cap and tail. The figure also shows the untranslated regions (UTRs) at the 5′ and 3′ ends of the mRNA (referred to as the 5′ UTR and 3′ UTR). The UTRs are parts of the mRNA that will not be translated into protein, but they have other functions, such as ribosome binding.

Split Genes and RNA Splicing

A remarkable stage of RNA processing in the eukaryotic nucleus is the removal of large portions of the RNA molecule that is initially synthesized—a cut-and-paste job called **RNA splicing**, similar to editing a video (**Figure 17.11**). The average length of a transcription unit along a human DNA molecule is about 27,000 nucleotide pairs, so the primary RNA transcript is also that long. However, it takes only 1,200 nucleotides in RNA to code for the average-sized protein of 400 amino acids. (Remember, each amino acid is encoded by a *triplet* of nucleotides.) This means that most eukaryotic genes and their RNA transcripts have long noncoding stretches of nucleotides, regions that are not translated. Even more surprising

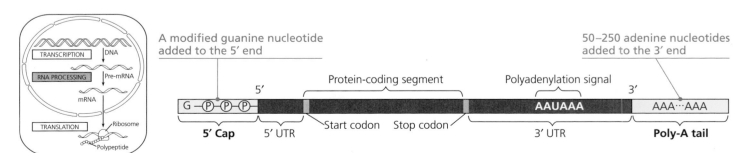

▲ **Figure 17.10 RNA processing: Addition of the 5′ cap and poly-A tail.** Enzymes modify the two ends of a eukaryotic pre-mRNA molecule. The modified ends may promote the export of mRNA from the nucleus, and they help protect the mRNA from degradation. When the mRNA reaches the cytoplasm, the modified ends, in conjunction with certain cytoplasmic proteins, facilitate ribosome attachment. The 5′ cap and poly-A tail are not translated into protein, nor are the regions called the 5′ untranslated region (5′ UTR) and 3′ untranslated region (3′ UTR).

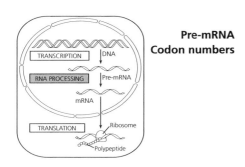

Pre-mRNA
Codon numbers

| 5' Exon | Intron | Exon | Intron | Exon | 3' |

5' Cap ... 1–30 ... 31–104 ... 105–146 ... Poly-A tail

Introns cut out and exons spliced together

mRNA

5' Cap ... 1–146 ... Poly-A tail

5' UTR — Coding segment — 3' UTR

▲ **Figure 17.11 RNA processing: RNA splicing.** The RNA molecule shown here codes for β-globin, one of the polypeptides of hemoglobin. The numbers under the RNA refer to codons; β-globin is 146 amino acids long.

The β-globin gene and its pre-mRNA transcript have three exons, corresponding to sequences that will leave the nucleus as mRNA. (The 5' UTR and 3' UTR are parts of exons because they are included in the mRNA; however, they do not code for protein.) During RNA processing, the introns are cut out and the exons spliced together. In many genes, the introns are much larger than the exons.

is that most of these noncoding sequences are interspersed between coding segments of the gene and thus between coding segments of the pre-mRNA. In other words, the sequence of DNA nucleotides that codes for a eukaryotic polypeptide is usually not continuous; it is split into segments. The noncoding segments of nucleic acid that lie between coding regions are called *in*tervening sequences, or **introns**. The other regions are called **exons**, because they are eventually *ex*pressed, usually by being translated into amino acid sequences. (Exceptions include the UTRs of the exons at the ends of the RNA, which make up part of the mRNA but are not translated into protein. Because of these exceptions, you may find it helpful to think of exons as sequences of RNA that *exit* the nucleus.) The terms *intron* and *exon* are used for both RNA sequences and the DNA sequences that encode them.

In making a primary transcript from a gene, RNA polymerase II transcribes both introns and exons from the DNA, but the mRNA molecule that enters the cytoplasm is an abridged version. The introns are cut out from the molecule and the exons joined together, forming an mRNA molecule with a continuous coding sequence. This is the process of RNA splicing.

How is pre-mRNA splicing carried out? Researchers have learned that the signal for RNA splicing is a short nucleotide sequence at each end of an intron. Joan Steitz, our interviewee for this unit (see pp. 246–247), discovered in 1979 that particles called *small nuclear ribonucleoproteins*, abbreviated *snRNPs* (pronounced "snurps"), recognize these splice sites. As the full name implies, snRNPs are located in the cell nucleus and are composed of RNA and protein molecules. The RNA in a snRNP particle is called a *small nuclear RNA (snRNA)*; each snRNA molecule is about 150 nucleotides long. Several different snRNPs join with additional proteins to form an even larger assembly called a **spliceosome**, which is almost as big as a ribosome. The spliceosome interacts with certain sites along an intron, releasing the intron, which is rapidly degraded, and joining together the two exons that flanked the intron **(Figure 17.12)**. It turns out that snRNAs catalyze these processes, as well as participating in spliceosome assembly and splice site recognition.

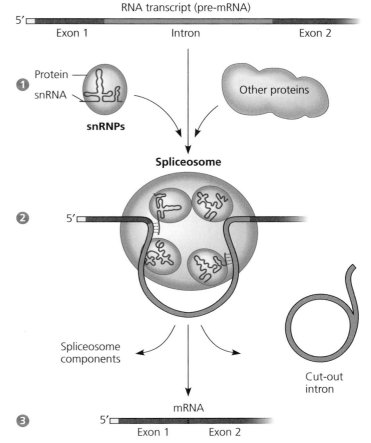

▲ **Figure 17.12 The roles of snRNPs and spliceosomes in pre-mRNA splicing.** The diagram shows only a portion of the pre-mRNA transcript; additional introns and exons lie downstream from the ones pictured here. ❶ Small nuclear ribonucleoproteins (snRNPs) and other proteins form a molecular complex called a spliceosome on a pre-mRNA molecule containing exons and introns. ❷ Within the spliceosome, snRNA base-pairs with nucleotides at specific sites along the intron. ❸ The spliceosome cuts the pre-mRNA, releasing the intron for rapid degradation, and at the same time splices the exons together. The spliceosome then comes apart, releasing mRNA, which now contains only exons.

Ribozymes

The idea of a catalytic role for snRNA arose from the discovery of **ribozymes**, RNA molecules that function as enzymes. In some organisms, RNA splicing can occur without proteins or even additional RNA molecules: The intron RNA functions as a ribozyme and catalyzes its own excision! For example, in the ciliate protist *Tetrahymena*, self-splicing occurs in the production of ribosomal RNA (rRNA), a component of the organism's ribosomes. The pre-rRNA actually removes its own introns. The discovery of ribozymes rendered obsolete the idea that all biological catalysts are proteins.

Three properties of RNA enable some RNA molecules to function as enzymes. First, because RNA is single-stranded, a region of an RNA molecule may base-pair with a complementary region elsewhere in the same molecule, which gives the molecule a particular three-dimensional structure. A specific structure is essential to the catalytic function of ribozymes, just as it is for enzymatic proteins. Second, like certain amino acids in an enzymatic protein, some of the bases in RNA contain functional groups that may participate in catalysis. Third, the ability of RNA to hydrogen-bond with other nucleic acid molecules (either RNA or DNA) adds specificity to its catalytic activity. For example, complementary base pairing between the RNA of the spliceosome and the RNA of a primary RNA transcript precisely locates the region where the ribozyme catalyzes splicing. Later in this chapter, you will see how these properties of RNA also allow it to perform important noncatalytic roles in the cell, such as recognition of the three-nucleotide codons on mRNA.

The Functional and Evolutionary Importance of Introns

EVOLUTION Whether or not RNA splicing and the presence of introns have provided selective advantages during evolutionary history is a matter of some debate. In any case, it is informative to consider their possible adaptive benefits. Specific functions have not been identified for most introns, but at least some contain sequences that regulate gene expression, and many affect gene products.

One important consequence of the presence of introns in genes is that a single gene can encode more than one kind of polypeptide. Many genes are known to give rise to two or more different polypeptides, depending on which segments are treated as exons during RNA processing; this is called **alternative RNA splicing** (see Figure 18.13). For example, sex differences in fruit flies are largely due to differences in how males and females splice the RNA transcribed from certain genes. Results from the Human Genome Project (discussed in Chapter 21) suggest that alternative RNA splicing is one reason humans can get along with about the same number of genes as a nematode (roundworm). Because of alternative splicing, the number of different protein products an organism produces can be much greater than its number of genes.

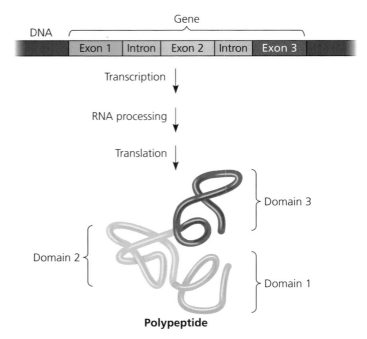

▲ **Figure 17.13 Correspondence between exons and protein domains.**

Proteins often have a modular architecture consisting of discrete structural and functional regions called **domains**. One domain of an enzyme, for example, might include the active site, while another might allow the enzyme to bind to a cellular membrane. In quite a few cases, different exons code for the different domains of a protein **(Figure 17.13)**.

The presence of introns in a gene may facilitate the evolution of new and potentially beneficial proteins as a result of a process known as *exon shuffling*. Introns increase the probability of crossing over between the exons of alleles of a gene—simply by providing more terrain for crossovers without interrupting coding sequences. This might result in new combinations of exons and proteins with altered structure and function. We can also imagine the occasional mixing and matching of exons between completely different (nonallelic) genes. Exon shuffling of either sort could lead to new proteins with novel combinations of functions. While most of the shuffling would result in nonbeneficial changes, occasionally a beneficial variant might arise.

CONCEPT CHECK 17.3

1. How can human cells make 75,000–100,000 different proteins, given that there are about 20,000 human genes?
2. How is RNA splicing similar to editing a video? What would introns correspond to in this analogy?
3. **WHAT IF?** What would be the effect of treating cells with an agent that removed the cap from mRNAs?

For suggested answers, see Appendix A.

CONCEPT 17.4

Translation is the RNA-directed synthesis of a polypeptide:
a closer look

We will now examine in greater detail how genetic information flows from mRNA to protein—the process of translation. As we did for transcription, we'll concentrate on the basic steps of translation that occur in both bacteria and eukaryotes, while pointing out key differences.

Molecular Components of Translation

In the process of translation, a cell "reads" a genetic message and builds a polypeptide accordingly. The message is a series of codons along an mRNA molecule, and the translator is called **transfer RNA (tRNA)**. The function of tRNA is to transfer amino acids from the cytoplasmic pool of amino acids to a growing polypeptide in a ribosome. A cell keeps its cytoplasm stocked with all 20 amino acids, either by synthesizing them from other compounds or by taking them up from the surrounding solution. The ribosome, a structure made of proteins and RNAs, adds each amino acid brought to it by tRNA to the growing end of a polypeptide chain **(Figure 17.14)**.

Translation is simple in principle but complex in its biochemistry and mechanics, especially in the eukaryotic cell. In dissecting translation, we'll concentrate on the slightly less complicated version of the process that occurs in bacteria. We'll begin by looking at the major players in this cellular process and then see how they act together in making a polypeptide.

The Structure and Function of Transfer RNA

The key to translating a genetic message into a specific amino acid sequence is the fact that molecules of tRNA are not all identical, and each type of tRNA molecule translates a particular mRNA codon into a particular amino acid. A tRNA molecule arrives at a ribosome bearing a specific amino acid at one end. At the other end of the tRNA is a nucleotide triplet called an **anticodon**, which base-pairs with a complementary codon on mRNA. For example, consider the mRNA codon GGC, which is translated as the amino acid glycine. The tRNA that base-pairs with this codon by hydrogen bonding has CCG as its anticodon and carries glycine at its other end (see the incoming tRNA approaching the ribosome in Figure 17.14). As an mRNA molecule is moved through a ribosome, glycine will be added to the polypeptide chain whenever the codon GGC is presented for translation. Codon by codon, the genetic message is translated as tRNAs deposit amino acids in the order prescribed, and the ribosome joins the amino acids into a chain. The tRNA molecule is a translator in the sense that it

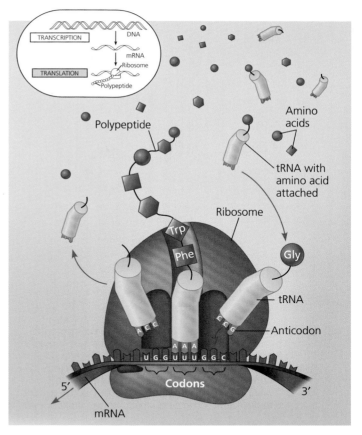

▲ **Figure 17.14 Translation: the basic concept.** As a molecule of mRNA is moved through a ribosome, codons are translated into amino acids, one by one. The interpreters are tRNA molecules, each type with a specific anticodon at one end and a corresponding amino acid at the other end. A tRNA adds its amino acid cargo to a growing polypeptide chain when the anticodon hydrogen-bonds to a complementary codon on the mRNA. The figures that follow show some of the details of translation in a bacterial cell.

 ANIMATION **BioFlix** Visit the Study Area at **www.masteringbiology.com** for the BioFlix® 3-D Animation on Protein Synthesis.

can read a nucleic acid word (the mRNA codon) and interpret it as a protein word (the amino acid).

Like mRNA and other types of cellular RNA, transfer RNA molecules are transcribed from DNA templates. In a eukaryotic cell, tRNA, like mRNA, is made in the nucleus and then travels from the nucleus to the cytoplasm, where translation occurs. In both bacterial and eukaryotic cells, each tRNA molecule is used repeatedly, picking up its designated amino acid in the cytosol, depositing this cargo onto a polypeptide chain at the ribosome, and then leaving the ribosome, ready to pick up another amino acid.

A tRNA molecule consists of a single RNA strand that is only about 80 nucleotides long (compared to hundreds of nucleotides for most mRNA molecules). Because of the presence of complementary stretches of nucleotide bases that can hydrogen-bond to each other, this single strand can fold back upon itself

(a) Two-dimensional structure. The four base-paired regions and three loops are characteristic of all tRNAs, as is the base sequence of the amino acid attachment site at the 3′ end. The anticodon triplet is unique to each tRNA type, as are some sequences in the other two loops. (The asterisks mark bases that have been chemically modified, a characteristic of tRNA. The modified bases contribute to tRNA function in a way that is not yet understood.)

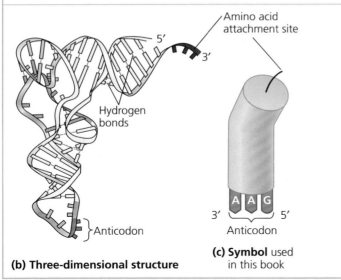

(b) Three-dimensional structure

(c) Symbol used in this book

▲ **Figure 17.15 The structure of transfer RNA (tRNA).** Anticodons are conventionally written 3′ → 5′ to align properly with codons written 5′ → 3′ (see Figure 17.14). For base pairing, RNA strands must be antiparallel, like DNA. For example, anticodon 3′-AAG-5′ pairs with mRNA codon 5′-UUC-3′.

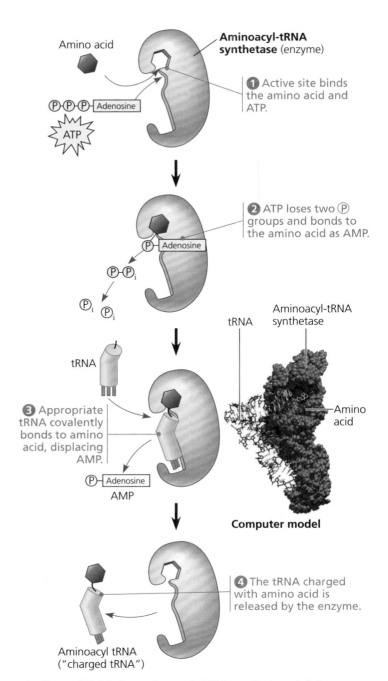

▲ **Figure 17.16 An aminoacyl-tRNA synthetase joining a specific amino acid to a tRNA.** Linkage of the tRNA and amino acid is an endergonic process that occurs at the expense of ATP. The ATP loses two phosphate groups, becoming AMP (adenosine monophosphate).

From the other end of the L-shaped tRNA molecule protrudes its 3′ end, which is the attachment site for an amino acid. Thus, the structure of a tRNA molecule fits its function.

The accurate translation of a genetic message requires two instances of molecular recognition. First, a tRNA that binds to an mRNA codon specifying a particular amino acid must carry that amino acid, and no other, to the ribosome. The correct matching up of tRNA and amino acid is carried out by a family of related enzymes called **aminoacyl-tRNA synthetases** (**Figure 17.16**). The active site of each type of aminoacyl-tRNA

and form a molecule with a three-dimensional structure. Flattened into one plane to clarify this base pairing, a tRNA molecule looks like a cloverleaf (**Figure 17.15a**). The tRNA actually twists and folds into a compact three-dimensional structure that is roughly L-shaped (**Figure 17.15b**). The loop extending from one end of the L includes the anticodon, the particular nucleotide triplet that base-pairs to a specific mRNA codon.

synthetase fits only a specific combination of amino acid and tRNA. (Regions of both the amino acid attachment end and the anticodon end of the tRNA are instrumental in ensuring the specific fit.) There are 20 different synthetases, one for each amino acid; each synthetase is able to bind all the different tRNAs that code for its particular amino acid. The synthetase catalyzes the covalent attachment of the amino acid to its tRNA in a process driven by the hydrolysis of ATP. The resulting aminoacyl tRNA, also called a charged tRNA, is released from the enzyme and is then available to deliver its amino acid to a growing polypeptide chain on a ribosome.

The second instance of molecular recognition is the pairing of the tRNA anticodon with the appropriate mRNA codon. If one tRNA variety existed for each mRNA codon specifying an amino acid, there would be 61 tRNAs (see Figure 17.5). In fact, there are only about 45, signifying that some tRNAs must be able to bind to more than one codon. Such versatility is possible because the rules for base pairing between the third nucleotide base of a codon and the corresponding base of a tRNA anticodon are relaxed compared to those at other codon positions. For example, the nucleotide base U at the 5′ end of a tRNA anticodon can pair with either A or G in the third position (at the 3′ end) of an mRNA codon. The flexible base pairing at this codon position is called **wobble**. Wobble explains why the synonymous codons for a given amino acid most often differ in their third nucleotide base, but not in the other bases. For example, a tRNA with the anticodon 3′-UCU-5′ can base-pair with either the mRNA codon 5′-AGA-3′ or 5′-AGG-3′, both of which code for arginine (see Figure 17.5).

Ribosomes

Ribosomes facilitate the specific coupling of tRNA anticodons with mRNA codons during protein synthesis. A ribosome consists of a large subunit and a small subunit, each made up of proteins and one or more **ribosomal RNAs (rRNAs)** **(Figure 17.17)**. In eukaryotes, the subunits are made in the nucleolus. Ribosomal RNA genes are transcribed, and the RNA is processed and assembled with proteins imported from the cytoplasm. The resulting ribosomal subunits are then exported via nuclear pores to the cytoplasm. In both bacteria and eukaryotes, large and small subunits join to form a functional ribosome only when they attach to an mRNA molecule. About one-third of the mass of a ribosome is made up of proteins; the rest consists of rRNAs, either three molecules (in bacteria) or four (in eukaryotes). Because most cells contain thousands of ribosomes, rRNA is the most abundant type of cellular RNA.

Although the ribosomes of bacteria and eukaryotes are very similar in structure and function, those of eukaryotes are slightly larger and differ somewhat from bacterial ribosomes in their molecular composition. The differences are medically significant. Certain antibiotic drugs can inactivate bacterial ribosomes without inhibiting the ability of eukaryotic ribosomes to make proteins. These drugs, including tetracycline and streptomycin, are used to combat bacterial infections.

(a) Computer model of functioning ribosome. This is a model of a bacterial ribosome, showing its overall shape. The eukaryotic ribosome is roughly similar. A ribosomal subunit is a complex of ribosomal RNA molecules and proteins.

(b) Schematic model showing binding sites. A ribosome has an mRNA binding site and three tRNA binding sites, known as the A, P, and E sites. This schematic ribosome will appear in later diagrams.

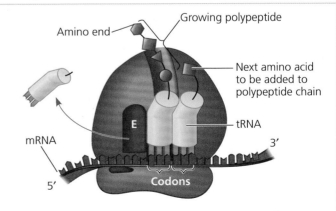

(c) Schematic model with mRNA and tRNA. A tRNA fits into a binding site when its anticodon base-pairs with an mRNA codon. The P site holds the tRNA attached to the growing polypeptide. The A site holds the tRNA carrying the next amino acid to be added to the polypeptide chain. Discharged tRNA leaves from the E site.

▲ **Figure 17.17 The anatomy of a functioning ribosome.**

The structure of a ribosome reflects its function of bringing mRNA together with tRNAs carrying amino acids. In addition to a binding site for mRNA, each ribosome has three binding sites for tRNA, as described in Figure 17.17. The **P site** (**p**eptidyl-tRNA binding site) holds the tRNA carrying the growing polypeptide chain, while the **A site** (**a**minoacyl-tRNA binding site) holds the tRNA carrying the next amino acid to be added to the chain. Discharged tRNAs leave the ribosome from the **E site** (**e**xit site). The ribosome holds the tRNA and mRNA in close proximity and positions the new amino acid for addition to the carboxyl end of the growing polypeptide. It then catalyzes the formation of the peptide bond. As the polypeptide becomes longer, it passes through an *exit tunnel* in the ribosome's large subunit. When the polypeptide is complete, it is released through the exit tunnel.

A lot of evidence strongly supports the hypothesis that rRNA, not protein, is primarily responsible for both the structure and the function of the ribosome. The proteins, which are largely on the exterior, support the shape changes of the rRNA molecules as they carry out catalysis during translation. Ribosomal RNA is the main constituent of the interface between the two subunits and of the A and P sites, and it is the catalyst of peptide bond formation. Thus, a ribosome can be regarded as one colossal ribozyme!

Building a Polypeptide

We can divide translation, the synthesis of a polypeptide chain, into three stages (analogous to those of transcription): initiation, elongation, and termination. All three stages require protein "factors" that aid in the translation process. For certain aspects of chain initiation and elongation, energy is also required. It is provided by the hydrolysis of guanosine triphosphate (GTP), a molecule closely related to ATP.

Ribosome Association and Initiation of Translation

The initiation stage of translation brings together mRNA, a tRNA bearing the first amino acid of the polypeptide, and the two subunits of a ribosome (**Figure 17.18**). First, a small ribosomal subunit binds to both mRNA and a specific initiator tRNA, which carries the amino acid methionine. In bacteria, the small subunit can bind these two in either order; it binds the mRNA at a specific RNA sequence, just upstream of the start codon, AUG. (Joan Steitz, our Unit Three interviewee, discovered the binding site on the mRNA and showed that complementary base pairing between this site and a ribosomal RNA was involved.) In

eukaryotes, the small subunit, with the initiator tRNA already bound, binds to the 5′ cap of the mRNA and then moves, or *scans*, downstream along the mRNA until it reaches the start codon; the initiator tRNA then hydrogen-bonds to the AUG start codon. In either case, the start codon signals the start of translation; this is important because it establishes the codon reading frame for the mRNA.

The union of mRNA, initiator tRNA, and a small ribosomal subunit is followed by the attachment of a large ribosomal subunit, completing the *translation initiation complex*. Proteins called *initiation factors* are required to bring all these components together. The cell also expends energy obtained by hydrolysis of a GTP molecule to form the initiation complex. At the completion of the initiation process, the initiator tRNA sits in the P site of the ribosome, and the vacant A site is ready for the next aminoacyl tRNA. Note that a polypeptide is always synthesized in one direction, from the initial methionine at the amino end, also called the N-terminus, toward the final amino acid at the carboxyl end, also called the C-terminus (see Figure 5.17).

Elongation of the Polypeptide Chain

In the elongation stage of translation, amino acids are added one by one to the previous amino acid at the C-terminus of the growing chain. Each addition involves the participation of several proteins called *elongation factors* and occurs in a three-step cycle described in **Figure 17.19**. Energy expenditure occurs in the first and third steps. Codon recognition requires hydrolysis of one molecule of GTP, which increases the accuracy and efficiency of this step. One more GTP is hydrolyzed to provide energy for the translocation step.

❶ A small ribosomal subunit binds to a molecule of mRNA. In a bacterial cell, the mRNA binding site on this subunit recognizes a specific nucleotide sequence on the mRNA just upstream of the start codon. An initiator tRNA, with the anticodon UAC, base-pairs with the start codon, AUG. This tRNA carries the amino acid methionine (Met).

❷ The arrival of a large ribosomal subunit completes the initiation complex. Proteins called initiation factors (not shown) are required to bring all the translation components together. Hydrolysis of GTP provides the energy for the assembly. The initiator tRNA is in the P site; the A site is available to the tRNA bearing the next amino acid.

▲ **Figure 17.18 The initiation of translation.**

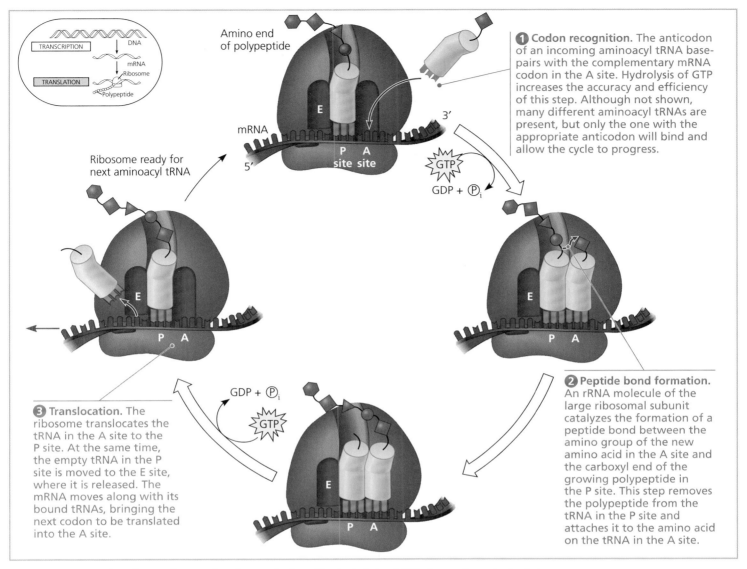

Amino end
of polypeptide

1 **Codon recognition.** The anticodon of an incoming aminoacyl tRNA base-pairs with the complementary mRNA codon in the A site. Hydrolysis of GTP increases the accuracy and efficiency of this step. Although not shown, many different aminoacyl tRNAs are present, but only the one with the appropriate anticodon will bind and allow the cycle to progress.

TRANSCRIPTION — DNA
mRNA
Ribosome
TRANSLATION
Polypeptide

mRNA

Ribosome ready for
next aminoacyl tRNA

E
P   A
site site
5'
3'

GTP
GDP + Ⓟᵢ

E
P   A

2 **Peptide bond formation.** An rRNA molecule of the large ribosomal subunit catalyzes the formation of a peptide bond between the amino group of the new amino acid in the A site and the carboxyl end of the growing polypeptide in the P site. This step removes the polypeptide from the tRNA in the P site and attaches it to the amino acid on the tRNA in the A site.

E
P   A

GDP + Ⓟᵢ
GTP

E
P   A

3 **Translocation.** The ribosome translocates the tRNA in the A site to the P site. At the same time, the empty tRNA in the P site is moved to the E site, where it is released. The mRNA moves along with its bound tRNAs, bringing the next codon to be translated into the A site.

▲ **Figure 17.19** **The elongation cycle of translation.** The hydrolysis of GTP plays an important role in the elongation process. Not shown are the proteins called elongation factors.

The mRNA is moved through the ribosome in one direction only, 5′ end first; this is equivalent to the ribosome moving 5′ → 3′ on the mRNA. The important point is that the ribosome and the mRNA move relative to each other, unidirectionally, codon by codon. The elongation cycle takes less than a tenth of a second in bacteria and is repeated as each amino acid is added to the chain until the polypeptide is completed.

Termination of Translation

The final stage of translation is termination (**Figure 17.20**, on the next page). Elongation continues until a stop codon in the mRNA reaches the A site of the ribosome. The nucleotide base triplets UAG, UAA, and UGA do not code for amino acids but instead act as signals to stop translation. A *release factor*, a protein shaped like an aminoacyl tRNA, binds directly to the stop codon in the A site. The release factor causes the addition of a

water molecule instead of an amino acid to the polypeptide chain. (There are plenty of water molecules available in the aqueous cellular environment.) This reaction breaks (hydrolyzes) the bond between the completed polypeptide and the tRNA in the P site, releasing the polypeptide through the exit tunnel of the ribosome's large subunit. The remainder of the translation assembly then comes apart in a multistep process, aided by other protein factors. Breakdown of the translation assembly requires the hydrolysis of two more GTP molecules.

Polyribosomes

A single ribosome can make an average-sized polypeptide in less than a minute. Typically, however, multiple ribosomes translate an mRNA at the same time; that is, a single mRNA is used to make many copies of a polypeptide simultaneously. Once a ribosome is far enough past the start codon, a second ribosome can attach to the mRNA, eventually resulting in a number

Release factor

Free polypeptide

Stop codon (UAG, UAA, or UGA)

2 GTP

2 GDP + 2 Ⓟ$_i$

❶ When a ribosome reaches a stop codon on mRNA, the A site of the ribosome accepts a "release factor," a protein shaped like a tRNA, instead of an aminoacyl tRNA.

❷ The release factor promotes hydrolysis of the bond between the tRNA in the P site and the last amino acid of the polypeptide, thus freeing the polypeptide from the ribosome.

❸ The two ribosomal subunits and the other components of the assembly dissociate.

▲ **Figure 17.20 The termination of translation.** Like elongation, termination requires GTP hydrolysis as well as additional protein factors, which are not shown here.

of ribosomes trailing along the mRNA. Such strings of ribosomes, called **polyribosomes** (or *polysomes*), can be seen with an electron microscope (**Figure 17.21**). Polyribosomes are found in both bacterial and eukaryotic cells. They enable a cell to make many copies of a polypeptide very quickly.

Completing and Targeting the Functional Protein

The process of translation is often not sufficient to make a functional protein. In this section, you will learn about modifications that polypeptide chains undergo after the translation process as well as some of the mechanisms used to target completed proteins to specific sites in the cell.

Protein Folding and Post-Translational Modifications

During its synthesis, a polypeptide chain begins to coil and fold spontaneously as a consequence of its amino acid sequence (primary structure), forming a protein with a specific shape: a three-dimensional molecule with secondary and tertiary structure (see Figure 5.20). Thus, a gene determines primary structure, and primary structure in turn determines shape. In many cases, a chaperone protein (chaperonin) helps the polypeptide fold correctly (see Figure 5.23).

Additional steps—*post-translational modifications*—may be required before the protein can begin doing its particular job in the cell. Certain amino acids may be chemically modified by the attachment of sugars, lipids, phosphate groups, or other additions. Enzymes may remove one or more amino acids from the leading (amino) end of the polypeptide chain. In some cases, a polypeptide chain may be enzymatically cleaved into two or more pieces. For example, the protein insulin is first synthesized as a single polypeptide chain but becomes active only after an enzyme cuts out a central part of the chain,

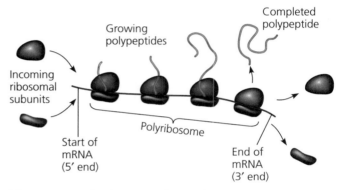

Growing polypeptides

Completed polypeptide

Incoming ribosomal subunits

Start of mRNA (5′ end)

Polyribosome

End of mRNA (3′ end)

(a) An mRNA molecule is generally translated simultaneously by several ribosomes in clusters called polyribosomes.

Ribosomes

mRNA

0.1 μm

(b) This micrograph shows a large polyribosome in a bacterial cell. Growing polypeptides are not visible here (TEM).

▲ **Figure 17.21 Polyribosomes.**

leaving a protein made up of two polypeptide chains connected by disulfide bridges. In other cases, two or more polypeptides that are synthesized separately may come together, becoming the subunits of a protein that has quaternary structure. A familiar example is hemoglobin (see Figure 5.20).

Targeting Polypeptides to Specific Locations

In electron micrographs of eukaryotic cells active in protein synthesis, two populations of ribosomes (and polyribosomes) are evident: free and bound (see Figure 6.10). Free ribosomes are suspended in the cytosol and mostly synthesize proteins that stay in the cytosol and function there. In contrast, bound ribosomes are attached to the cytosolic side of the endoplasmic reticulum (ER) or to the nuclear envelope. Bound ribosomes make proteins of the endomembrane system (the nuclear envelope, ER, Golgi apparatus, lysosomes, vacuoles, and plasma membrane) as well as proteins secreted from the cell, such as insulin. It is important to note that the ribosomes themselves are identical and can switch their status from free to bound.

What determines whether a ribosome is free in the cytosol or bound to rough ER? Polypeptide synthesis always begins in the cytosol as a free ribosome starts to translate an mRNA molecule. There the process continues to completion—*unless* the growing polypeptide itself cues the ribosome to attach to the ER. The polypeptides of proteins destined for the endomembrane system or for secretion are marked by a **signal peptide**, which targets the protein to the ER **(Figure 17.22)**. The signal peptide, a sequence of about 20 amino acids at or near the leading end (N-terminus) of the polypeptide, is recognized as it emerges from the ribosome by a protein-RNA complex called a **signal-recognition particle (SRP)**. This particle functions as an escort that brings the ribosome to a receptor protein built into the ER membrane. The receptor is part of a multiprotein translocation complex. Polypeptide synthesis continues there, and the growing polypeptide snakes across the membrane into the ER lumen via a protein pore. The signal peptide is usually removed by an enzyme. The rest of the completed polypeptide, if it is to be secreted from the cell, is released into solution within the ER lumen (as in Figure 17.22). Alternatively, if the polypeptide is to be a membrane protein, it remains partially embedded in the ER membrane.

Other kinds of signal peptides are used to target polypeptides to mitochondria, chloroplasts, the interior of the nucleus, and other organelles that are not part of the endomembrane system. The critical difference in these cases is that translation is completed in the cytosol before the polypeptide is imported into the organelle. The mechanisms of translocation also vary, but in all cases studied to date, the "postal zip codes" that address proteins for secretion or to cellular locations are signal peptides of some sort. Bacteria also employ signal peptides to target proteins to the plasma membrane for secretion.

❶ Polypeptide synthesis begins on a free ribosome in the cytosol.

❷ An SRP binds to the signal peptide, halting synthesis momentarily.

❸ The SRP binds to a receptor protein in the ER membrane. This receptor is part of a protein complex (a translocation complex) that has a membrane pore and a signal-cleaving enzyme.

❹ The SRP leaves, and polypeptide synthesis resumes, with simultaneous translocation across the membrane. (The signal peptide stays attached to the translocation complex.)

❺ The signal-cleaving enzyme cuts off the signal peptide.

❻ The rest of the completed polypeptide leaves the ribosome and folds into its final conformation.

Ribosome

mRNA

Signal peptide

Signal-recognition particle (SRP)

SRP receptor protein

CYTOSOL

ER LUMEN

Translocation complex

Signal peptide removed

ER membrane

Protein

▲ **Figure 17.22 The signal mechanism for targeting proteins to the ER.** A polypeptide destined for the endomembrane system or for secretion from the cell begins with a signal peptide, a series of amino acids that targets it for the ER. This figure shows the synthesis of a secretory protein and its simultaneous import into the ER. In the ER and then in the Golgi, the protein will be processed further. Finally, a transport vesicle will convey it to the plasma membrane for release from the cell (see Figure 7.12).

CONCEPT CHECK 17.4

1. What two processes ensure that the correct amino acid is added to a growing polypeptide chain?
2. Discuss the ways in which rRNA structure likely contributes to ribosomal function.
3. Describe how a polypeptide to be secreted is transported to the endomembrane system.
4. **WHAT IF?** **DRAW IT** If a tRNA has the anticodon 3'-CGU-5', what two different codons could it bind to? Draw each on an mRNA, labeling all 5' and 3' ends. Add the amino acid carried by this tRNA.

For suggested answers, see Appendix A.

CONCEPT 17.5

Mutations of one or a few nucleotides can affect protein structure and function

Now that you have explored the process of gene expression, you are ready to understand the effects of changes to the genetic information of a cell (or virus). These changes, called **mutations**, are responsible for the huge diversity of genes found among organisms because mutations are the ultimate source of new genes. In Figure 15.14, we considered chromosomal rearrangements that affect long segments of DNA, which can be considered large-scale mutations. Here we examine small-scale mutations of one or a few nucleotide pairs, including **point mutations**, changes in a single nucleotide pair of a gene.

If a point mutation occurs in a gamete or in a cell that gives rise to gametes, it may be transmitted to offspring and to a succession of future generations. If the mutation has an adverse effect on the phenotype of an organism, the mutant condition is referred to as a genetic disorder or hereditary disease. For example, we can trace the genetic basis of sickle-cell disease to the mutation of a single nucleotide pair in the gene that encodes the β-globin polypeptide of hemoglobin. The change of a single nucleotide in the DNA's template strand leads to the production of an abnormal protein (**Figure 17.23**; also see Figure 5.21). In individuals who are homozygous for the mutant allele, the sickling of red blood cells caused by the altered hemoglobin produces the multiple symptoms associated with sickle-cell disease (see Chapter 14). Another disorder caused by a point mutation is a heart condition, familial cardiomyopathy, that is responsible for some incidents of sudden death in young athletes. Point mutations in several genes have been identified, any of which can lead to this disorder.

Types of Small-Scale Mutations

Let's now consider how small-scale mutations affect proteins. Point mutations within a gene can be divided into two general categories: (1) single nucleotide-pair substitutions and (2) nucleotide-pair insertions or deletions. Insertions and deletions can involve one or more nucleotide pairs.

Substitutions

A **nucleotide-pair substitution** is the replacement of one nucleotide and its partner with another pair of nucleotides (**Figure 17.24a**). Some substitutions have no effect on the encoded protein, owing to the redundancy of the genetic code. For example, if 3'-CCG-5' on the template strand mutated to 3'-CCA-5', the mRNA codon that used to be GGC would become GGU, but a glycine would still be inserted at the proper location in the protein (see Figure 17.5). In other words, a change in a nucleotide pair may transform one codon into another that is translated into the same amino acid. Such a change is an example of a **silent mutation**, which has no observable effect on the phenotype. (Silent mutations can occur outside genes as well.) Substitutions that change one amino acid to another one are called **missense mutations**. Such a mutation may have little effect on the protein: The new amino acid may have properties similar to those of the amino acid it replaces, or it may be in a region of the protein where the exact sequence of amino acids is not essential to the protein's function.

▼ **Figure 17.23** **The molecular basis of sickle-cell disease: a point mutation.** The allele that causes sickle-cell disease differs from the wild-type (normal) allele by a single DNA nucleotide pair.

Wild-type hemoglobin

Wild-type hemoglobin DNA

3' CTT 5'
5' GAA 3'

mRNA

5' GAA 3'

Normal hemoglobin

Glu

Sickle-cell hemoglobin

Mutant hemoglobin DNA

3' CAT 5'
5' GTA 3'

mRNA

5' GUA 3'

Sickle-cell hemoglobin

Val

In the DNA, the mutant (sickle-cell) template strand (top) has an A where the wild-type template has a T.

The mutant mRNA has a U instead of an A in one codon.

The mutant hemoglobin has a valine (Val) instead of a glutamic acid (Glu).

▼ **Figure 17.24 Types of small-scale mutations that affect mRNA sequence.** All but one of the types shown here also affect the amino acid sequence of the encoded polypeptide.

Wild type

DNA template strand 3′ T A C T T C A A A C C G A T T 5′
5′ A T G A A G T T T G G C T A A 3′

mRNA 5′ A U G A A G U U U G G C U A A 3′
Protein Met Lys Phe Gly Stop
Amino end Carboxyl end

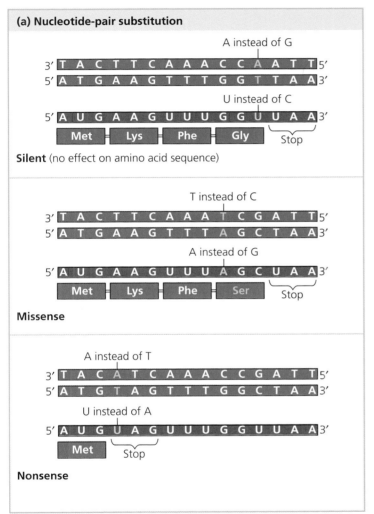

(a) Nucleotide-pair substitution

A instead of G

3′ T A C T T C A A A C C A A T T 5′
5′ A T G A A G T T T G G T T A A 3′

U instead of C

5′ A U G A A G U U U G G U U A A 3′
Met Lys Phe Gly Stop

Silent (no effect on amino acid sequence)

T instead of C

3′ T A C T T C A A A T C G A T T 5′
5′ A T G A A G T T T A G C T A A 3′

A instead of G

5′ A U G A A G U U U A G C U A A 3′
Met Lys Phe Ser Stop

Missense

A instead of T

3′ T A C A T C A A A C C G A T T 5′
5′ A T G T A G T T T G G C T A A 3′

U instead of A

5′ A U G U A G U U U G G U U A A 3′
Met Stop

Nonsense

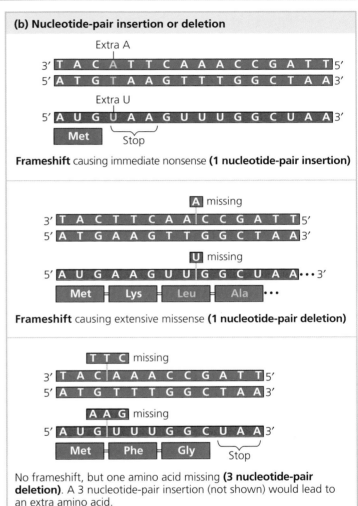

(b) Nucleotide-pair insertion or deletion

Extra A

3′ T A C A T T C A A A C C G A T T 5′
5′ A T G T A A G T T T G G C T A A 3′

Extra U

5′ A U G U A A G U U U G G C U A A 3′
Met Stop

Frameshift causing immediate nonsense **(1 nucleotide-pair insertion)**

A missing

3′ T A C T T C A A C C G A T T 5′
5′ A T G A A G T T G G C T A A 3′

U missing

5′ A U G A A G U U G G C U A A ••• 3′
Met Lys Leu Ala •••

Frameshift causing extensive missense **(1 nucleotide-pair deletion)**

T T C missing

3′ T A C A A A C C G A T T 5′
5′ A T G T T T G G C T A A 3′

A A G missing

5′ A U G U U U G G C U A A 3′
Met Phe Gly Stop

No frameshift, but one amino acid missing **(3 nucleotide-pair deletion)**. A 3 nucleotide-pair insertion (not shown) would lead to an extra amino acid.

However, the nucleotide-pair substitutions of greatest interest are those that cause a major change in a protein. The alteration of a single amino acid in a crucial area of a protein—such as in the part of hemoglobin shown in Figure 17.23 or in the active site of an enzyme as shown in Figure 8.18—will significantly alter protein activity. Occasionally, such a mutation leads to an improved protein or one with novel capabilities, but much more often such mutations are detrimental, leading to a useless or less active protein that impairs cellular function.

Substitution mutations are usually missense mutations; that is, the altered codon still codes for an amino acid and thus makes sense, although not necessarily the *right* sense. But a point mutation can also change a codon for an amino acid into a stop codon. This is called a **nonsense mutation**, and it causes translation to be terminated prematurely; the resulting polypeptide will be shorter than the polypeptide encoded by the normal gene. Nearly all nonsense mutations lead to nonfunctional proteins.

Insertions and Deletions

Insertions and **deletions** are additions or losses of nucleotide pairs in a gene **(Figure 17.24b)**. These mutations have a disastrous effect on the resulting protein more often than substitutions do. Insertion or deletion of nucleotides may alter the reading frame of the genetic message, the triplet grouping of nucleotides on the mRNA that is read during translation. Such a mutation, called a **frameshift mutation**, will occur whenever the number of nucleotides inserted or deleted is not a multiple of three. All the nucleotides that are downstream of the deletion or insertion will be improperly grouped into codons, and the result will be extensive missense, usually ending sooner or later in nonsense and premature termination. Unless the frameshift is very near the end of the gene, the protein is almost certain to be nonfunctional.

Mutagens

Mutations can arise in a number of ways. Errors during DNA replication or recombination can lead to nucleotide-pair substitutions, insertions, or deletions, as well as to mutations affecting longer stretches of DNA. If an incorrect nucleotide is added to a growing chain during replication, for example, the base on that nucleotide will then be mismatched with the nucleotide base on the other strand. In many cases, the error will be corrected by systems you learned about in Chapter 16. Otherwise, the incorrect base will be used as a template in the next round of replication, resulting in a mutation. Such mutations are called *spontaneous mutations*. It is difficult to calculate the rate at which such mutations occur. Rough estimates have been made of the rate of mutation during DNA replication for both *E. coli* and eukaryotes, and the numbers are similar: About one nucleotide in every 10^{10} is altered, and the change is passed on to the next generation of cells.

A number of physical and chemical agents, called **mutagens**, interact with DNA in ways that cause mutations. In the 1920s, Hermann Muller discovered that X-rays caused genetic changes in fruit flies, and he used X-rays to make *Drosophila* mutants for his genetic studies. But he also recognized an alarming implication of his discovery: X-rays and other forms of high-energy radiation pose hazards to the genetic material of people as well as laboratory organisms. Mutagenic radiation, a physical mutagen, includes ultraviolet (UV) light, which can cause disruptive thymine dimers in DNA (see Figure 16.19).

Chemical mutagens fall into several categories. Nucleotide analogs are chemicals that are similar to normal DNA nucleotides but that pair incorrectly during DNA replication. Some other chemical mutagens interfere with correct DNA replication by inserting themselves into the DNA and distorting the double helix. Still other mutagens cause chemical changes in bases that change their pairing properties.

Researchers have developed a variety of methods to test the mutagenic activity of chemicals. A major application of these tests is the preliminary screening of chemicals to identify those that may cause cancer. This approach makes sense because most carcinogens (cancer-causing chemicals) are mutagenic, and conversely, most mutagens are carcinogenic.

CONCEPT 17.6

While gene expression differs among the domains of life, the concept of a gene is universal

Although bacteria and eukaryotes carry out transcription and translation in very similar ways, we have noted certain differences in cellular machinery and in details of the processes in these two domains. The division of organisms into three domains was established about 40 years ago, when archaea were recognized as distinct from bacteria. Like bacteria, archaea are prokaryotes. However, archaea share many aspects of the mechanisms of gene expression with eukaryotes, as well as a few with bacteria.

Comparing Gene Expression in Bacteria, Archaea, and Eukarya

Recent advances in molecular biology have enabled researchers to determine the complete nucleotide sequences of hundreds of genomes, including many genomes from each domain. This wealth of data allows us to compare gene and protein sequences across domains. Foremost among genes of interest are those that encode components of such fundamental biological processes as transcription and translation.

Bacterial and eukaryotic RNA polymerases differ significantly from each other, while the single archaeal RNA polymerase resembles the three eukaryotic ones. Archaea and eukaryotes use a complex set of transcription factors, unlike the smaller set of accessory proteins in bacteria. Transcription is terminated differently in bacteria and eukaryotes. The little that is known about archaeal transcription termination suggests that it is similar to the eukaryotic process.

As far as translation is concerned, archaeal ribosomes are the same size as bacterial ribosomes, but their sensitivities to chemical inhibitors more closely match those of eukaryotic ribosomes. We mentioned earlier that initiation of translation is slightly different in bacteria and eukaryotes. In this respect, the archaeal process is more like that of bacteria.

The most important differences between bacteria and eukaryotes with regard to gene expression arise from the bacterial cell's lack of compartmental organization. Like a one-room workshop, a bacterial cell ensures a streamlined operation. In the absence of a nucleus, it can simultaneously transcribe and translate the same gene (**Figure 17.25**), and the newly made protein can quickly diffuse to its site of function. Most researchers suspect that transcription and translation are coupled like this in archaeal cells as well, since archaea lack a nuclear envelope. In contrast, the eukaryotic cell's nuclear envelope segregates transcription from translation and provides a compartment for extensive RNA processing. This processing stage includes additional steps whose regulation can help coordinate the eukaryotic cell's elaborate activities (see Chapter 18).

Learning more about the proteins and RNAs involved in archaeal transcription and translation will tell us much about the evolution of these processes in all three domains. In spite of the differences in gene expression cataloged here, however, the idea of the gene itself is a unifying concept among all forms of life.

▲ **Figure 17.25 Coupled transcription and translation in bacteria.** In bacterial cells, the translation of mRNA can begin as soon as the leading (5′) end of the mRNA molecule peels away from the DNA template. The micrograph (TEM) shows a strand of *E. coli* DNA being transcribed by RNA polymerase molecules. Attached to each RNA polymerase molecule is a growing strand of mRNA, which is already being translated by ribosomes. The newly synthesized polypeptides are not visible in the micrograph but are shown in the diagram.

? *Which one of the mRNA molecules started transcription first? On that mRNA, which ribosome started translating first?*

What Is a Gene? *Revisiting the Question*

Our definition of a gene has evolved over the past few chapters, as it has through the history of genetics. We began with the Mendelian concept of a gene as a discrete unit of inheritance that affects a phenotypic character (Chapter 14). We saw that Morgan and his colleagues assigned such genes to specific loci on chromosomes (Chapter 15). We went on to view a gene as a region of specific nucleotide sequence along the length of the DNA molecule of a chromosome (Chapter 16). Finally, in this chapter, we have considered a functional definition of a gene as a DNA sequence that codes for a specific polypeptide chain. (**Figure 17.26**, on the next page, summarizes the path from gene to polypeptide in a eukaryotic cell.) All these definitions are useful, depending on the context in which genes are being studied.

Clearly, the statement that a gene codes for a polypeptide is too simple. Most eukaryotic genes contain noncoding segments (such as introns), so large portions of these genes have no corresponding segments in polypeptides. Molecular biologists also often include promoters and certain other regulatory regions of DNA within the boundaries of a gene. These DNA sequences are not transcribed, but they can be considered part of the functional gene because they must be present for transcription to occur. Our definition of a gene must also be broad enough to include the DNA that is transcribed into rRNA, tRNA, and other RNAs that are not translated. These genes have no polypeptide products but play crucial roles in the cell. Thus, we arrive at the following definition: *A gene is a region of DNA that can be expressed to produce a final functional product that is either a polypeptide or an RNA molecule.*

When considering phenotypes, however, it is often useful to start by focusing on genes that code for polypeptides. In this chapter, you have learned in molecular terms how a typical gene is expressed—by transcription into RNA and then translation into a polypeptide that forms a protein of specific structure and function. Proteins, in turn, bring about an organism's observable phenotype.

A given type of cell expresses only a subset of its genes. This is an essential feature in multicellular organisms: You'd be in trouble if the lens cells in your eyes started expressing the genes for hair proteins, which are normally expressed only in hair follicle cells! Gene expression is precisely regulated. We'll explore gene regulation in the next chapter, beginning with the simpler case of bacteria and continuing with eukaryotes.

CONCEPT CHECK 17.6

1. Would the coupling of processes shown in Figure 17.25 be found in a eukaryotic cell? Explain.
2. **WHAT IF?** In eukaryotic cells, mRNAs have been found to have a circular arrangement in which proteins hold the poly-A tail near the 5′ cap. How might this increase translation efficiency?

For suggested answers, see Appendix A.

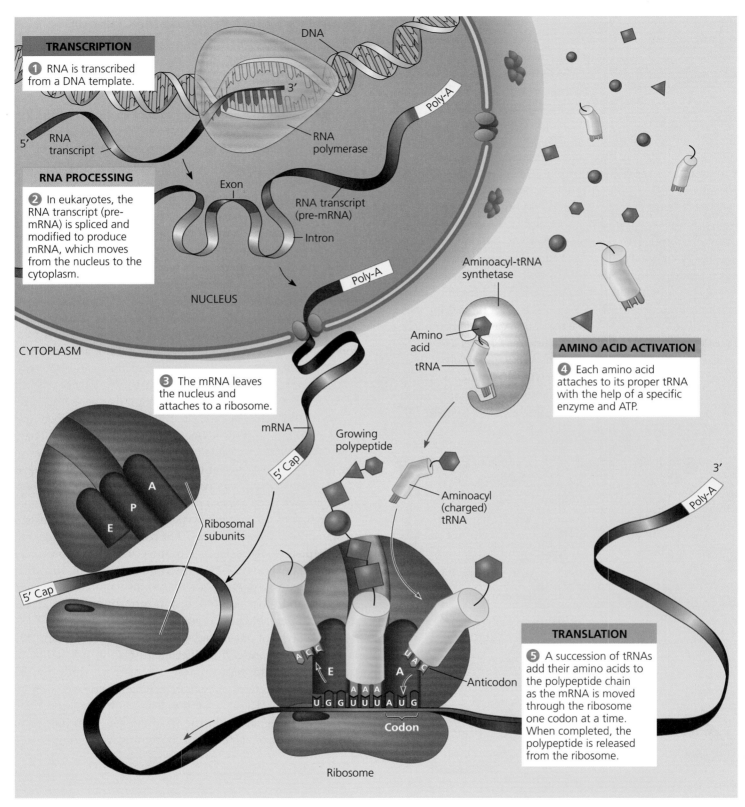

TRANSCRIPTION

1 RNA is transcribed from a DNA template.

DNA

RNA polymerase

5′

RNA transcript

3′

Poly-A

RNA PROCESSING

2 In eukaryotes, the RNA transcript (pre-mRNA) is spliced and modified to produce mRNA, which moves from the nucleus to the cytoplasm.

Exon

RNA transcript (pre-mRNA)

Intron

Poly-A

NUCLEUS

CYTOPLASM

3 The mRNA leaves the nucleus and attaches to a ribosome.

mRNA

5′ Cap

Ribosomal subunits

5′ Cap

E P A

Aminoacyl-tRNA synthetase

Amino acid

tRNA

AMINO ACID ACTIVATION

4 Each amino acid attaches to its proper tRNA with the help of a specific enzyme and ATP.

Growing polypeptide

Aminoacyl (charged) tRNA

3′

Poly-A

Anticodon

TRANSLATION

5 A succession of tRNAs add their amino acids to the polypeptide chain as the mRNA is moved through the ribosome one codon at a time. When completed, the polypeptide is released from the ribosome.

A C C

E

A A A

U A C

A

U G G U U U A U G

Codon

Ribosome

▲ **Figure 17.26 A summary of transcription and translation in a eukaryotic cell.** This diagram shows the path from one gene to one polypeptide. Keep in mind that each gene in the DNA can be transcribed repeatedly into many identical RNA molecules and that each mRNA can be translated repeatedly to yield many identical polypeptide molecules. (Also, remember that the final products of some genes are not polypeptides but RNA molecules, including tRNA and rRNA.) In general, the steps of transcription and translation are similar in bacterial, archaeal, and eukaryotic cells. The major difference is the occurrence of RNA processing in the eukaryotic nucleus. Other significant differences are found in the initiation stages of both transcription and translation and in the termination of transcription.

SUMMARY OF KEY CONCEPTS

CONCEPT 17.1

Genes specify proteins via transcription and translation (pp. 325–331)

- DNA controls metabolism by directing cells to make specific enzymes and other proteins, via the process of **gene expression**. Beadle and Tatum's studies of mutant strains of *Neurospora* led to the one gene–one polypeptide hypothesis. Genes code for polypeptide chains or specify RNA molecules.
- **Transcription** is the synthesis of RNA complementary to a **template strand** of DNA, providing a nucleotide-to-nucleotide transfer of information. **Translation** is the synthesis of a polypeptide whose amino acid sequence is specified by the nucleotide sequence in **mRNA**; this informational transfer thus involves a change of language, from that of nucleotides to that of amino acids.
- Genetic information is encoded as a sequence of nonoverlapping nucleotide triplets, or **codons**. A codon in messenger RNA (mRNA) either is translated into an amino acid (61 of the 64 codons) or serves as a stop signal (3 codons). Codons must be read in the correct **reading frame**.

> **?** *Describe the process of gene expression, by which a gene affects the phenotype of an organism.*

CONCEPT 17.2

Transcription is the DNA-directed synthesis of RNA: *a closer look* **(pp. 331–334)**

- RNA synthesis is catalyzed by **RNA polymerase**, which links together RNA nucleotides complementary to a DNA template strand. This process follows the same base-pairing rules as DNA replication, except that in RNA, uracil substitutes for thymine.

- The three stages of transcription are initiation, elongation, and termination. A **promoter**, often including a **TATA box** in eukaryotes, establishes where RNA synthesis is initiated. **Transcription factors** help eukaryotic RNA polymerase recognize promoter sequences, forming a **transcription initiation complex**. The mechanisms of termination are different in bacteria and eukaryotes.

> **?** *What are the similarities and differences in the initiation of gene transcription in bacteria and eukaryotes?*

CONCEPT 17.3

Eukaryotic cells modify RNA after transcription (pp. 334–336)

- Before leaving the nucleus, eukaryotic mRNA molecules undergo **RNA processing**, which includes RNA splicing, the addition of a modified nucleotide **5' cap** to the 5' end, and the addition of a **poly-A tail** to the 3' end.

- Most eukaryotic genes are split into segments: They have **introns** interspersed among the **exons** (the regions included in the mRNA). In **RNA splicing**, introns are removed and exons joined. RNA splicing is typically carried out by **spliceosomes**, but in some cases, RNA alone catalyzes its own splicing. The catalytic ability of some RNA molecules, called **ribozymes**, derives from the inherent properties of RNA. The presence of introns allows for **alternative RNA splicing**.

> **?** *What function do the 5' cap and the poly-A tail serve on a eukaryotic mRNA?*

CONCEPT 17.4

Translation is the RNA-directed synthesis of a polypeptide: *a closer look* **(pp. 337–344)**

- A cell translates an mRNA message into protein using **transfer RNAs (tRNAs)**. After being bound to a specific amino acid by an **aminoacyl-tRNA synthetase**, a tRNA lines up via its **anticodon** at the complementary codon on mRNA. A **ribosome**, made up of **ribosomal RNAs (rRNAs)** and proteins, facilitates this coupling with binding sites for mRNA and tRNA.

- Ribosomes coordinate the three stages of translation: initiation, elongation, and termination. The formation of peptide bonds between amino acids is catalyzed by rRNA as tRNAs move through the **A** and **P sites** and exit through the **E site**.
- A single mRNA molecule can be translated simultaneously by a number of ribosomes, forming a **polyribosome**.
- After translation, modifications to proteins can affect their three-dimensional shape. Free ribosomes in the cytosol initiate synthesis of all proteins, but proteins destined for the endomembrane system or for secretion are transported into the ER. Such proteins have a **signal peptide** to which a **signal-recognition particle (SRP)** binds, enabling the translating ribosome to bind to the ER.

> **?** *What function do tRNAs serve in the process of translation?*

CONCEPT 17.5

Mutations of one or a few nucleotides can affect protein structure and function (pp. 344–346)

- Small-scale **mutations** include **point mutations**, changes in one DNA nucleotide pair, which may lead to production of nonfunctional proteins. **Nucleotide-pair substitutions** can cause **missense** or **nonsense mutations**. Nucleotide-pair **insertions** or **deletions** may produce **frameshift mutations**.
- Spontaneous mutations can occur during DNA replication, recombination, or repair. Chemical and physical **mutagens** cause DNA damage that can alter genes.

> **?** *What will be the results of chemically modifying one nucleotide base of a gene? What role is played by DNA repair systems in the cell?*

CONCEPT 17.6

While gene expression differs among the domains of life, the concept of a gene is universal (pp. 346–348)

- There are some differences in gene expression among bacteria, archaea, and eukaryotes. Because bacterial cells lack a nuclear envelope, translation can begin while transcription is still in progress. Archaeal cells show similarities to both eukaryotic and bacterial cells in their processes of gene expression. In a eukaryotic cell, the nuclear envelope separates transcription from translation, and extensive RNA processing occurs in the nucleus.
- A gene is a region of DNA whose final functional product is either a polypeptide or an RNA molecule.

? *How does the presence of a nuclear envelope affect gene expression in eukaryotes?*

TEST YOUR UNDERSTANDING

LEVEL 1: KNOWLEDGE/COMPREHENSION

1. In eukaryotic cells, transcription cannot begin until
   a. the two DNA strands have completely separated and exposed the promoter.
   b. several transcription factors have bound to the promoter.
   c. the 5' caps are removed from the mRNA.
   d. the DNA introns are removed from the template.
   e. DNA nucleases have isolated the transcription unit.

2. Which of the following is *not* true of a codon?
   a. It consists of three nucleotides.
   b. It may code for the same amino acid as another codon.
   c. It never codes for more than one amino acid.
   d. It extends from one end of a tRNA molecule.
   e. It is the basic unit of the genetic code.

3. The anticodon of a particular tRNA molecule is
   a. complementary to the corresponding mRNA codon.
   b. complementary to the corresponding triplet in rRNA.
   c. the part of tRNA that bonds to a specific amino acid.
   d. changeable, depending on the amino acid that attaches to the tRNA.
   e. catalytic, making the tRNA a ribozyme.

4. Which of the following is *not* true of RNA processing?
   a. Exons are cut out before mRNA leaves the nucleus.
   b. Nucleotides may be added at both ends of the RNA.
   c. Ribozymes may function in RNA splicing.
   d. RNA splicing can be catalyzed by spliceosomes.
   e. A primary transcript is often much longer than the final RNA molecule that leaves the nucleus.

5. Which component is *not* directly involved in translation?
   a. mRNA   b. DNA   c. tRNA   d. ribosomes   e. GTP

LEVEL 2: APPLICATION/ANALYSIS

6. Using Figure 17.5, identify a 5' → 3' sequence of nucleotides in the DNA template strand for an mRNA coding for the polypeptide sequence Phe-Pro-Lys.
   a. 5'-UUUGGGAAA-3'   d. 5'-CTTCGGGAA-3'
   b. 5'-GAACCCCTT-3'   e. 5'-AAACCCUUU-3'
   c. 5'-AAAACCTTT-3'

7. Which of the following mutations would be *most* likely to have a harmful effect on an organism?
   a. a nucleotide-pair substitution
   b. a deletion of three nucleotides near the middle of a gene
   c. a single nucleotide deletion in the middle of an intron

d. a single nucleotide deletion near the end of the coding sequence
e. a single nucleotide insertion downstream of, and close to, the start of the coding sequence

8. **DRAW IT** Fill in the following table:

Type of RNA	Functions
Messenger RNA (mRNA)	
Transfer RNA (tRNA)	
	Plays catalytic (ribozyme) roles and structural roles in ribosomes
Primary transcript	
Small nuclear RNA (snRNA)	

LEVEL 3: SYNTHESIS/EVALUATION

9. **EVOLUTION CONNECTION** Most amino acids are coded for by a set of similar codons (see Figure 17.5). What evolutionary explanations can you give for this pattern? (*Hint*: There is one explanation relating to ancestry, and some less obvious ones of a "form-fits-function" type.)

10. **SCIENTIFIC INQUIRY**
    Knowing that the genetic code is almost universal, a scientist uses molecular biological methods to insert the human β-globin gene (shown in Figure 17.11) into bacterial cells, hoping the cells will express it and synthesize functional β-globin protein. Instead, the protein produced is nonfunctional and is found to contain many fewer amino acids than does β-globin made by a eukaryotic cell. Explain why.

11. **WRITE ABOUT A THEME**
    Evolution and The Genetic Basis of Life Evolution accounts for the unity and diversity of life, and the continuity of life is based on heritable information in the form of DNA. In a short essay (100–150 words), discuss how the fidelity with which DNA is inherited is related to the processes of evolution. (Review the discussion of proofreading and DNA repair in Concept 16.2, pp. 316–318.)

For selected answers, see Appendix A.

MasteringBIOLOGY   www.masteringbiology.com

1. MasteringBiology® Assignments
Make Connections Tutorial Point Mutations (Chapter 17) and Protein Structure (Chapter 5)
BioFlix Tutorials Protein Synthesis: Overview • Transcription and RNA Processing • Translation and Protein Targeting Pathways
Tutorials The Genetic Code • Following the Instructions in DNA • Types of RNA • Point Mutations
Activities Overview of Protein Synthesis • RNA Synthesis • Transcription • RNA Processing • Synthesizing Proteins • Translation • The Triplet Nature of the Genetic Code
Questions Student Misconceptions • Reading Quiz • Multiple Choice • End-of-Chapter

2. eText
Read your book online, search, take notes, highlight text, and more.

3. The Study Area
Practice Tests • Cumulative Test • BioFlix 3-D Animations • MP3 Tutor Sessions • Videos • Activities • Investigations • Lab Media • Audio Glossary • Word Study Tools • Art

18
Regulation of Gene Expression

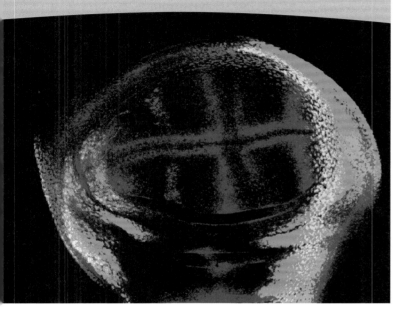

▲ **Figure 18.1 What regulates the precise pattern of gene expression in the developing wing of a fly embryo?**

KEY CONCEPTS

18.1 Bacteria often respond to environmental change by regulating transcription

18.2 Eukaryotic gene expression is regulated at many stages

18.3 Noncoding RNAs play multiple roles in controlling gene expression

18.4 A program of differential gene expression leads to the different cell types in a multicellular organism

18.5 Cancer results from genetic changes that affect cell cycle control

OVERVIEW

Conducting the Genetic Orchestra

It's almost concert time! Dissonance reigns as the orchestra members individually tune their instruments. Then, after a brief hush, the conductor's baton rises, pauses, and begins a series of elaborate movements, directing specific instruments to join in and others to raise or lower their volume at defined moments. Properly balanced and timed, discordant sounds are thus transformed into a beautiful symphony that enraptures the audience.

In a similar way, cells intricately and precisely regulate their gene expression. Both prokaryotes and eukaryotes must alter their patterns of gene expression in response to changes in environmental conditions. Multicellular eukaryotes must also develop and maintain multiple cell types. Each cell type contains the same genome but expresses a different subset of genes, a significant challenge in gene regulation.

An adult fruit fly, for example, develops from a single fertilized egg, passing through a wormlike stage called a larva. At every stage, gene expression is carefully regulated, ensuring that the right genes are expressed only at the correct time and place. In the larva, the adult wing forms in a disk-shaped pocket of several thousand cells, shown in **Figure 18.1**. The tissue in this image has been treated to reveal the mRNA for three genes—labeled red, blue, and green—using techniques covered in Chapter 20. (Red and green together appear yellow.) The intricate pattern of expression for each gene is the same from larva to larva at this stage, and it provides a graphic display of the precision of gene regulation. But what is the molecular basis for this pattern? Why is one particular gene expressed only in the few hundred cells that appear blue in this image and not in the other cells?

In this chapter, we first explore how bacteria regulate expression of their genes in response to different environmental conditions. We then examine how eukaryotes regulate gene expression to maintain different cell types. Gene expression in eukaryotes, as in bacteria, is often regulated at the stage of transcription, but control at other stages is also important. In recent years, researchers have been surprised to discover the many roles played by RNA molecules in regulating eukaryotic gene expression, a topic we cover next. We then consider what happens when a complex program of gene regulation works properly during embryonic development: A single cell—the fertilized egg—becomes a fully functioning organism made up of many different cell types. Finally, we investigate how cancer can result when gene regulation goes awry. Orchestrating proper gene expression by all cells is crucial to the functions of life.

CONCEPT 18.1

Bacteria often respond to environmental change by regulating transcription

Bacterial cells that can conserve resources and energy have a selective advantage over cells that are unable to do so. Thus, natural selection has favored bacteria that express only the genes whose products are needed by the cell.

Consider, for instance, an individual *E. coli* cell living in the erratic environment of a human colon, dependent for its nutrients on the whimsical eating habits of its host. If the environment is lacking in the amino acid tryptophan, which the bacterium needs to survive, the cell responds by activating a metabolic pathway that makes tryptophan from another compound. Later, if the human host eats a tryptophan-rich meal, the bacterial cell stops producing tryptophan, thus saving itself from squandering its resources to produce a substance that is available from the surrounding solution in prefabricated form. This is just one example of how bacteria tune their metabolism to changing environments.

Metabolic control occurs on two levels, as shown for the synthesis of tryptophan in **Figure 18.2**. First, cells can adjust the activity of enzymes already present. This is a fairly fast response, which relies on the sensitivity of many enzymes to chemical cues that increase or decrease their catalytic activity (see Chapter 8). The activity of the first enzyme in the tryptophan synthesis pathway is inhibited by the pathway's end product **(Figure 18.2a)**. Thus, if tryptophan accumulates in a cell, it shuts down the synthesis of more tryptophan by inhibiting enzyme activity. Such *feedback inhibition*, typical of

anabolic (biosynthetic) pathways, allows a cell to adapt to short-term fluctuations in the supply of a substance it needs.

Second, cells can adjust the production level of certain enzymes; that is, they can regulate the expression of the genes encoding the enzymes. If, in our example, the environment provides all the tryptophan the cell needs, the cell stops making the enzymes that catalyze the synthesis of tryptophan **(Figure 18.2b)**. In this case, the control of enzyme production occurs at the level of transcription, the synthesis of messenger RNA coding for these enzymes. More generally, many genes of the bacterial genome are switched on or off by changes in the metabolic status of the cell. One basic mechanism for this control of gene expression in bacteria, described as the *operon model*, was discovered in 1961 by François Jacob and Jacques Monod at the Pasteur Institute in Paris. Let's see what an operon is and how it works, using the control of tryptophan synthesis as our first example.

Operons: The Basic Concept

E. coli synthesizes the amino acid tryptophan from a precursor molecule in the multistep pathway shown in Figure 18.2. Each reaction in the pathway is catalyzed by a specific enzyme, and the five genes that code for the subunits of these enzymes are clustered together on the bacterial chromosome. A single promoter serves all five genes, which together constitute a transcription unit. (Recall from Chapter 17 that a promoter is a site where RNA polymerase can bind to DNA and begin transcription.) Thus, transcription gives rise to one long mRNA molecule that codes for the five polypeptides making up the enzymes in the tryptophan pathway. The cell can translate this one mRNA into five separate polypeptides because the mRNA is punctuated with start and stop codons that signal where the coding sequence for each polypeptide begins and ends.

A key advantage of grouping genes of related function into one transcription unit is that a single "on-off switch" can control the whole cluster of functionally related genes; in other words, these genes are *coordinately controlled*. When an *E. coli* cell must make tryptophan for itself because the nutrient medium lacks this amino acid, all the enzymes for the metabolic pathway are synthesized at one time. The switch is a segment of DNA called an **operator**. Both its location and name suit its function: Positioned within the promoter or, in some cases, between the promoter and the enzyme-coding genes, the operator controls the access of RNA polymerase to the genes. All together, the operator, the promoter, and the genes they control—the entire stretch of DNA required for enzyme production for the tryptophan pathway—constitute an **operon**. The *trp* operon (*trp* for tryptophan) is one of many operons in the *E. coli* genome **(Figure 18.3)**.

If the operator is the operon's switch for controlling transcription, how does this switch work? By itself, the *trp* operon is turned on; that is, RNA polymerase can bind to the promoter and transcribe the genes of the operon. The operon

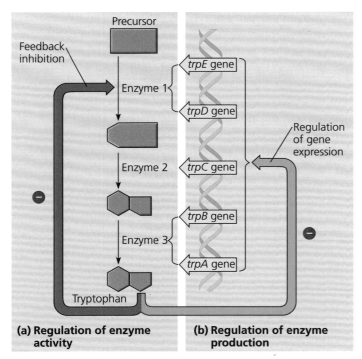

▲ **Figure 18.2 Regulation of a metabolic pathway.** In the pathway for tryptophan synthesis, an abundance of tryptophan can both **(a)** inhibit the activity of the first enzyme in the pathway (feedback inhibition), a rapid response, and **(b)** repress expression of the genes encoding all subunits of the enzymes in the pathway, a longer-term response. Genes *trpE* and *trpD* encode the two subunits of enzyme 1, and genes *trpB* and *trpA* encode the two subunits of enzyme 3. (The genes were named before the order in which they functioned in the pathway was determined.) The ⊖ symbol stands for inhibition.

(a) **Tryptophan absent, repressor inactive, operon on.** RNA polymerase attaches to the DNA at the promoter and transcribes the operon's genes.

(b) **Tryptophan present, repressor active, operon off.** As tryptophan accumulates, it inhibits its own production by activating the repressor protein, which binds to the operator, blocking transcription.

▲ **Figure 18.3 The *trp* operon in *E. coli*: regulated synthesis of repressible enzymes.** Tryptophan is an amino acid produced by an anabolic pathway catalyzed by repressible enzymes. **(a)** The five genes encoding the polypeptide subunits of the enzymes in this pathway (see Figure 18.2) are grouped, along with a promoter, into the *trp* operon. The *trp* operator (the repressor binding site) is located within the *trp* promoter (the RNA polymerase binding site). **(b)** Accumulation of tryptophan, the end product of the pathway, represses transcription of the *trp* operon, thus blocking synthesis of all the enzymes in the pathway and shutting down tryptophan production.

? *Describe what happens to the* trp *operon as the cell uses up its store of tryptophan.*

can be switched off by a protein called the *trp* **repressor**. The repressor binds to the operator and blocks attachment of RNA polymerase to the promoter, preventing transcription of the genes. A repressor protein is specific for the operator of a particular operon. For example, the repressor that switches off the *trp* operon by binding to the *trp* operator has no effect on other operons in the *E. coli* genome.

The *trp* repressor is the protein product of a **regulatory gene** called *trpR*, which is located some distance from the *trp* operon and has its own promoter. Regulatory genes are expressed continuously, although at a low rate, and a few *trp* repressor molecules are always present in *E. coli* cells. Why, then, is the *trp* operon not switched off permanently? First, the binding of repressors to operators is reversible. An operator vacillates between two states: one without the repressor bound and one with the repressor bound. The relative duration of each state depends on the number of active repressor molecules around. Second, the *trp* repressor, like most regulatory proteins, is an allosteric protein, with two alternative

shapes, active and inactive (see Figure 8.20). The *trp* repressor is synthesized in an inactive form with little affinity for the *trp* operator. Only if tryptophan binds to the *trp* repressor at an allosteric site does the repressor protein change to the active form that can attach to the operator, turning the operon off.

Tryptophan functions in this system as a **corepressor**, a small molecule that cooperates with a repressor protein to switch an operon off. As tryptophan accumulates, more tryptophan molecules associate with *trp* repressor molecules, which can then bind to the *trp* operator and shut down production of the tryptophan pathway enzymes. If the cell's tryptophan level drops, transcription of the operon's genes resumes. The *trp* operon is one example of how gene expression can respond to changes in the cell's internal and external environment.

Repressible and Inducible Operons: Two Types of Negative Gene Regulation

The *trp* operon is said to be a *repressible operon* because its transcription is usually on but can be inhibited (repressed) when a specific small molecule (in this case, tryptophan) binds allosterically to a regulatory protein. In contrast, an *inducible operon* is usually off but can be stimulated (induced) when a specific small molecule interacts with a regulatory protein. The classic example of an inducible operon is the *lac* operon (*lac* for lactose), which was the subject of Jacob and Monod's pioneering research.

The disaccharide lactose (milk sugar) is available to *E. coli* in the human colon if the host drinks milk. Lactose metabolism begins with hydrolysis of the disaccharide into its component monosaccharides, glucose and galactose, a reaction catalyzed by the enzyme β-galactosidase. Only a few molecules of this enzyme are present in an *E. coli* cell growing in the absence of lactose. If lactose is added to the bacterium's environment, however, the number of β-galactosidase molecules in the cell increases a thousandfold within about 15 minutes.

The gene for β-galactosidase is part of the *lac* operon, which includes two other genes coding for enzymes that function in lactose utilization. The entire transcription unit is under the command of one main operator and promoter. The regulatory gene, *lacI*, located outside the operon, codes for an allosteric repressor protein that can switch off the *lac* operon by binding to the operator. So far, this sounds just like regulation of the *trp* operon, but there is one important difference. Recall that the *trp* repressor is inactive by itself and requires tryptophan as a corepressor in order to bind to the operator. The *lac* repressor, in contrast, is active by itself, binding to the operator and switching the *lac* operon off. In this case, a specific small molecule, called an **inducer**, *inactivates* the repressor.

For the *lac* operon, the inducer is allolactose, an isomer of lactose formed in small amounts from lactose that enters the cell. In the absence of lactose (and hence allolactose), the *lac* repressor is in its active configuration, and the genes of the *lac* operon are silenced (**Figure 18.4a**). If lactose is added to the cell's surroundings, allolactose binds to the *lac* repressor and alters its conformation, nullifying the repressor's ability to attach to the operator. Without bound repressor, the *lac* operon is transcribed into mRNA for the lactose-utilizing enzymes (**Figure 18.4b**).

In the context of gene regulation, the enzymes of the lactose pathway are referred to as *inducible enzymes* because their synthesis is induced by a chemical signal (allolactose, in this case). Analogously, the enzymes for tryptophan synthesis are said to be repressible. *Repressible enzymes* generally function in anabolic pathways, which synthesize essential end products from raw materials (precursors). By suspending production of an end product when it is already present in sufficient quantity, the cell can allocate its organic precursors and energy

(a) Lactose absent, repressor active, operon off. The *lac* repressor is innately active, and in the absence of lactose it switches off the operon by binding to the operator.

▼ **Figure 18.4 The *lac* operon in *E. coli*: regulated synthesis of inducible enzymes.** *E. coli* uses three enzymes to take up and metabolize lactose. The genes for these three enzymes are clustered in the *lac* operon. One gene, *lacZ*, codes for β-galactosidase, which hydrolyzes lactose to glucose and galactose. The second gene, *lacY*, codes for a permease, the membrane protein that transports lactose into the cell. The third gene, *lacA*, codes for an enzyme called transacetylase, whose function in lactose metabolism is still unclear. The gene for the *lac* repressor, *lacI*, happens to be adjacent to the *lac* operon, an unusual situation. The function of the teal region at the upstream end of the promoter (the left end in these diagrams) will be revealed in Figure 18.5.

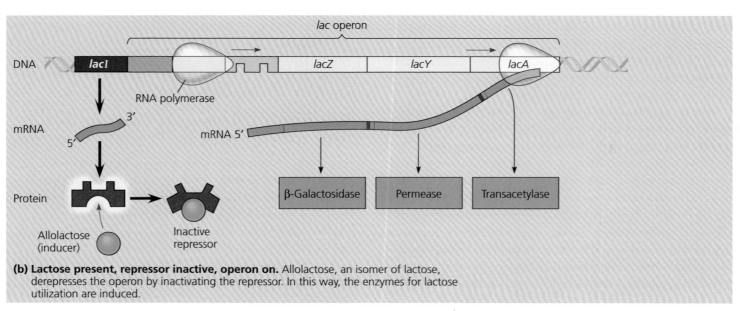

(b) Lactose present, repressor inactive, operon on. Allolactose, an isomer of lactose, derepresses the operon by inactivating the repressor. In this way, the enzymes for lactose utilization are induced.

for other uses. In contrast, inducible enzymes usually function in catabolic pathways, which break down a nutrient to simpler molecules. By producing the appropriate enzymes only when the nutrient is available, the cell avoids wasting energy and precursors making proteins that are not needed.

Regulation of both the *trp* and *lac* operons involves the *negative* control of genes, because the operons are switched off by the active form of the repressor protein. It may be easier to see this for the *trp* operon, but it is also true for the *lac* operon. Allolactose induces enzyme synthesis not by acting directly on the genome, but by freeing the *lac* operon from the negative effect of the repressor. Gene regulation is said to be *positive* only when a regulatory protein interacts directly with the genome to switch transcription on. Let's look at an example of the positive control of genes, again involving the *lac* operon.

Positive Gene Regulation

When glucose and lactose are both present in its environment, *E. coli* preferentially uses glucose. The enzymes for glucose breakdown in glycolysis (see Figure 9.9) are continually present. Only when lactose is present *and* glucose is in short supply does *E. coli* use lactose as an energy source, and only then does it synthesize appreciable quantities of the enzymes for lactose breakdown.

How does the *E. coli* cell sense the glucose concentration and relay this information to the genome? Again, the mechanism depends on the interaction of an allosteric regulatory protein with a small organic molecule, in this case **cyclic AMP (cAMP)**, which accumulates when glucose is scarce. The regulatory protein, called *catabolite activator protein (CAP)*, is an **activator**, a protein that binds to DNA and stimulates transcription of a gene. When cAMP binds to this regulatory protein, CAP assumes its active shape and can attach to a specific site at the upstream end of the *lac* promoter **(Figure 18.5a)**. This attachment increases the affinity of RNA polymerase for the promoter, which is actually rather low even when no repressor is bound to the operator. By facilitating the binding of RNA polymerase to the promoter and thereby increasing the rate of transcription, the attachment of CAP to the promoter directly stimulates gene expression. Therefore, this mechanism qualifies as positive regulation.

If the amount of glucose in the cell increases, the cAMP concentration falls, and without cAMP, CAP detaches from the operon. Because CAP is inactive, RNA polymerase binds less efficiently to the promoter, and transcription of the *lac* operon proceeds at only a low level, even in the presence of lactose **(Figure 18.5b)**. Thus, the *lac* operon is under dual control: negative control by the *lac* repressor and positive control by CAP. The state of the *lac* repressor (with or without bound allolactose) determines whether or not transcription of the *lac* operon's genes occurs at all; the state of CAP (with or without bound cAMP) controls the *rate* of transcription if

the operon is repressor-free. It is as though the operon has both an on-off switch and a volume control.

In addition to regulating the *lac* operon, CAP helps regulate other operons that encode enzymes used in catabolic pathways. All told, it may affect the expression of more than 100 genes in *E. coli*. When glucose is plentiful and CAP is inactive, the synthesis of enzymes that catabolize compounds other than glucose generally slows down. The ability to catabolize other compounds, such as lactose, enables a cell deprived of glucose to survive. The compounds present in the cell at the moment determine which operons are switched on—the result of simple interactions of activator and repressor proteins with the promoters of the genes in question.

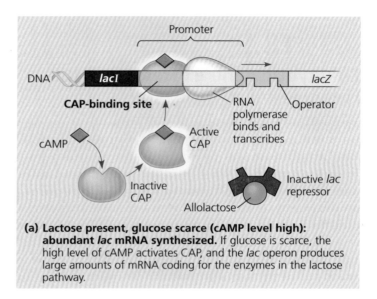

(a) Lactose present, glucose scarce (cAMP level high): abundant *lac* mRNA synthesized. If glucose is scarce, the high level of cAMP activates CAP, and the *lac* operon produces large amounts of mRNA coding for the enzymes in the lactose pathway.

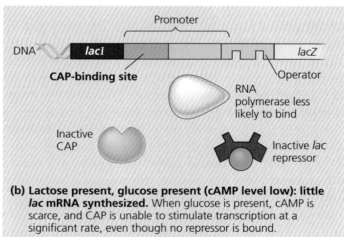

(b) Lactose present, glucose present (cAMP level low): little *lac* mRNA synthesized. When glucose is present, cAMP is scarce, and CAP is unable to stimulate transcription at a significant rate, even though no repressor is bound.

▲ **Figure 18.5 Positive control of the *lac* operon by catabolite activator protein (CAP).** RNA polymerase has high affinity for the *lac* promoter only when catabolite activator protein (CAP) is bound to a DNA site at the upstream end of the promoter. CAP attaches to its DNA site only when associated with cyclic AMP (cAMP), whose concentration in the cell rises when the glucose concentration falls. Thus, when glucose is present, even if lactose also is available, the cell preferentially catabolizes glucose and makes very little of the lactose-utilizing enzymes.

1. How does binding of the *trp* corepressor and the *lac* inducer to their respective repressor proteins alter repressor function and transcription in each case?

2. Describe the binding of RNA polymerase, repressors, and activators to the *lac* operon when both lactose and glucose are scarce. What is the effect of these scarcities on transcription of the *lac* operon?

3. **WHAT IF?** A certain mutation in *E. coli* changes the *lac* operator so that the active repressor cannot bind. How would this affect the cell's production of β-galactosidase?

For suggested answers, see Appendix A.

CONCEPT 18.2

Eukaryotic gene expression is regulated at many stages

All organisms, whether prokaryotes or eukaryotes, must regulate which genes are expressed at any given time. Both unicellular organisms and the cells of multicellular organisms must continually turn genes on and off in response to signals from their external and internal environments. Regulation of gene expression is also essential for cell specialization in multicellular organisms, which are made up of different types of cells, each with a distinct role. To perform its role, each cell type must maintain a specific program of gene expression in which certain genes are expressed and others are not.

Differential Gene Expression

A typical human cell might express about 20% of its protein-coding genes at any given time. Highly differentiated cells, such as muscle or nerve cells, express an even smaller fraction of their genes. Almost all the cells in an organism contain an identical genome. (Cells of the immune system are one exception.) However, the subset of genes expressed in the cells of each type is unique, allowing these cells to carry out their specific function. The differences between cell types, therefore, are due not to different genes being present, but to **differential gene expression**, the expression of different genes by cells with the same genome.

The function of any cell, whether a single-celled eukaryote or a particular cell type in a multicellular organism, depends on the appropriate set of genes being expressed. The transcription factors of a cell must locate the right genes at the right time, a task on a par with finding a needle in a haystack. When gene expression proceeds abnormally, serious imbalances and diseases, including cancer, can arise.

Figure 18.6 summarizes the entire process of gene expression in a eukaryotic cell, highlighting key stages in the expression of a protein-coding gene. Each stage depicted in

▲ **Figure 18.6 Stages in gene expression that can be regulated in eukaryotic cells.** In this diagram, the colored boxes indicate the processes most often regulated; each color indicates the type of molecule that is affected (blue = DNA, orange = RNA, purple = protein). The nuclear envelope separating transcription from translation in eukaryotic cells offers an opportunity for post-transcriptional control in the form of RNA processing that is absent in prokaryotes. In addition, eukaryotes have a greater variety of control mechanisms operating before transcription and after translation. The expression of any given gene, however, does not necessarily involve every stage shown; for example, not every polypeptide is cleaved.

Figure 18.6 is a potential control point at which gene expression can be turned on or off, accelerated, or slowed down.

Only 50 years ago, an understanding of the mechanisms that control gene expression in eukaryotes seemed almost hopelessly out of reach. Since then, new research methods, notably advances in DNA technology (see Chapter 20), have enabled molecular biologists to uncover many of the details of eukaryotic gene regulation. In all organisms, a common control point for gene expression is at transcription; regulation at this stage often occurs in response to signals coming from outside the cell, such as hormones or other signaling molecules. For this reason, the term *gene expression* is often equated with transcription for both bacteria and eukaryotes. While this is most often the case for bacteria, the greater complexity of eukaryotic cell structure and function provides opportunities for regulating gene expression at many additional stages (see Figure 18.6). In the remainder of this section, we'll examine some of the important control points of eukaryotic gene expression more closely.

Regulation of Chromatin Structure

Recall that the DNA of eukaryotic cells is packaged with proteins in an elaborate complex known as chromatin, the basic unit of which is the nucleosome (see Figure 16.22). The structural organization of chromatin not only packs a cell's DNA into a compact form that fits inside the nucleus, but also helps regulate gene expression in several ways. The location of a gene's promoter relative to nucleosomes and to the sites where the DNA attaches to the chromosome scaffold or nuclear lamina can affect whether the gene is transcribed. In addition, genes within heterochromatin, which is highly condensed, are usually not expressed. Lastly, certain chemical modifications to the histone proteins and to the DNA of chromatin can influence both chromatin structure and gene expression. Here we examine the effects of these modifications, which are catalyzed by specific enzymes.

Histone Modifications

There is abundant evidence that chemical modifications to histones, the proteins around which the DNA is wrapped in nucleosomes, play a direct role in the regulation of gene transcription. The N-terminus of each histone molecule in a nucleosome protrudes outward from the nucleosome **(Figure 18.7a)**. These histone tails are accessible to various modifying enzymes that catalyze the addition or removal of specific chemical groups.

In **histone acetylation,** acetyl groups ($—COCH_3$) are attached to lysines in histone tails; deacetylation is the removal of acetyl groups. When the lysines are acetylated, their positive charges are neutralized and the histone tails no longer bind to neighboring nucleosomes **(Figure 18.7b)**. Such binding promotes the folding of chromatin into a more compact structure; when this binding does not occur, chromatin has a looser structure. As a result, transcription proteins have easier

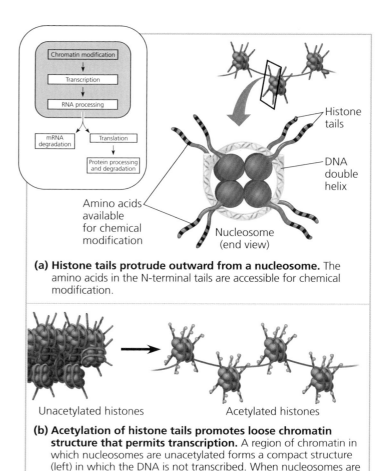

(a) Histone tails protrude outward from a nucleosome. The amino acids in the N-terminal tails are accessible for chemical modification.

(b) Acetylation of histone tails promotes loose chromatin structure that permits transcription. A region of chromatin in which nucleosomes are unacetylated forms a compact structure (left) in which the DNA is not transcribed. When nucleosomes are highly acetylated (right), the chromatin becomes less compact, and the DNA is accessible for transcription.

▲ **Figure 18.7 A simple model of histone tails and the effect of histone acetylation.** In addition to acetylation, histones can undergo several other types of modifications that also help determine the chromatin configuration in a region.

access to genes in an acetylated region. Researchers have shown that some enzymes that acetylate or deacetylate histones are closely associated with or even components of the transcription factors that bind to promoters (see Figure 17.8). These observations suggest that histone acetylation enzymes may promote the initiation of transcription not only by remodeling chromatin structure, but also by binding to and thus "recruiting" components of the transcription machinery.

Other chemical groups, such as methyl and phosphate groups, can be reversibly attached to amino acids in histone tails. Addition of methyl groups ($—CH_3$) to histone tails (histone methylation) can promote condensation of the chromatin, while addition of a phosphate group (phosphorylation) to an amino acid next to a methylated amino acid can have the opposite effect. The recent discovery that modifications to histone tails can affect chromatin structure and gene expression has led to the *histone code hypothesis*. This hypothesis proposes that specific combinations of modifications, as well as the order in which they have occurred, help determine the chromatin configuration, which in turn influences transcription.

DNA Methylation

While some enzymes methylate the tails of histone proteins, a different set of enzymes can methylate certain bases in the DNA itself, usually cytosine. Such **DNA methylation** occurs in most plants, animals, and fungi. Long stretches of inactive DNA, such as that of inactivated mammalian X chromosomes (see Figure 15.8), are generally more methylated than regions of actively transcribed DNA, although there are exceptions. On a smaller scale, individual genes are usually more heavily methylated in cells in which they are not expressed. Removal of the extra methyl groups can turn on some of these genes.

At least in some species, DNA methylation seems to be essential for the long-term inactivation of genes that occurs during normal cell differentiation in the embryo. For instance, experiments have shown that deficient DNA methylation (due to lack of a methylating enzyme) leads to abnormal embryonic development in organisms as different as mice and *Arabidopsis* (a mustard plant). Once methylated, genes usually stay that way through successive cell divisions in a given individual. At DNA sites where one strand is already methylated, enzymes methylate the correct daughter strand after each round of DNA replication. Methylation patterns are thus passed on, and cells forming specialized tissues keep a chemical record of what occurred during embryonic development. A methylation pattern maintained in this way also accounts for *genomic imprinting* in mammals, where methylation permanently regulates expression of either the maternal or paternal allele of particular genes at the start of development (see Figure 15.17).

Epigenetic Inheritance

The chromatin modifications that we have just discussed do not entail a change in the DNA sequence, yet they may be passed along to future generations of cells. Inheritance of traits transmitted by mechanisms not directly involving the nucleotide sequence is called **epigenetic inheritance**. Whereas mutations in the DNA are permanent changes, modifications to the chromatin can be reversed, by processes that are not yet fully understood. The molecular systems for chromatin modification may well interact with each other in a regulated way. In *Drosophila*, for example, experiments have suggested that a particular histone-modifying enzyme recruits a DNA methylation enzyme to one region and that the two enzymes collaborate to silence a particular set of genes. Working in the opposite order, proteins have also been found that first bind to methylated DNA and then recruit histone deacetylation enzymes. Thus, a dual mechanism, involving both DNA methylation and histone deacetylation, can repress transcription.

Researchers are amassing more and more evidence for the importance of epigenetic information in the regulation of gene expression. Epigenetic variations might help explain why one identical twin acquires a genetically based disease, such as schizophrenia, but the other does not, despite their identical genomes. Alterations in normal patterns of DNA methylation are seen in some cancers, where they are associated with inappropriate gene expression. Evidently, enzymes that modify chromatin structure are integral parts of the eukaryotic cell's machinery for regulating transcription.

Regulation of Transcription Initiation

Chromatin-modifying enzymes provide initial control of gene expression by making a region of DNA either more or less able to bind the transcription machinery. Once the chromatin of a gene is optimally modified for expression, the initiation of transcription is the next major step at which gene expression is regulated. As in bacteria, the regulation of transcription initiation in eukaryotes involves proteins that bind to DNA and either facilitate or inhibit binding of RNA polymerase. The process is more complicated in eukaryotes, however. Before looking at how eukaryotic cells control their transcription, let's review the structure of a typical eukaryotic gene and its transcript.

Organization of a Typical Eukaryotic Gene

A eukaryotic gene and the DNA elements (segments) that control it are typically organized as shown in **Figure 18.8**, which extends what you learned about eukaryotic genes in Chapter 17. Recall that a cluster of proteins called a *transcription initiation complex* assembles on the promoter sequence at the "upstream" end of the gene. One of these proteins, RNA polymerase II, then proceeds to transcribe the gene, synthesizing a primary RNA transcript (pre-mRNA). RNA processing includes enzymatic addition of a 5′ cap and a poly-A tail, as well as splicing out of introns, to yield a mature mRNA. Associated with most eukaryotic genes are multiple **control elements**, segments of noncoding DNA that serve as binding sites for the proteins called transcription factors, which in turn regulate transcription. Control elements and the transcription factors they bind are critical to the precise regulation of gene expression seen in different cell types.

The Roles of Transcription Factors

To initiate transcription, eukaryotic RNA polymerase requires the assistance of transcription factors. Some transcription factors, such as those illustrated in Figure 17.8, are essential for the transcription of *all* protein-coding genes; therefore, they are often called *general transcription factors*. Only a few general transcription factors independently bind a DNA sequence, such as the TATA box within the promoter; the others primarily bind proteins, including each other and RNA polymerase II. Protein-protein interactions are crucial to the initiation of eukaryotic transcription. Only when the complete initiation complex has assembled can the polymerase begin to move along the DNA template strand, producing a complementary strand of RNA.

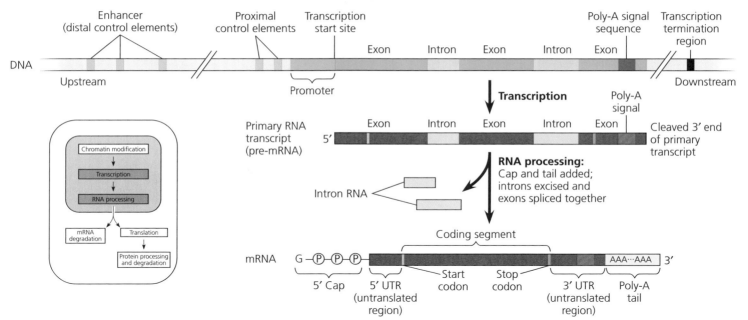

Enhancer
(distal control elements)

Proximal
control elements

Transcription
start site

Poly-A signal
sequence

Transcription
termination
region

DNA

Upstream

Promoter

Exon   Intron   Exon   Intron   Exon

Downstream

Transcription

Poly-A
signal

Primary RNA
transcript
(pre-mRNA)

5′

Exon   Intron   Exon   Intron   Exon

Cleaved 3′ end
of primary
transcript

Chromatin modification

Transcription

RNA processing

mRNA
degradation

Translation

Protein processing
and degradation

RNA processing:
Cap and tail added;
introns excised and
exons spliced together

Intron RNA

Coding segment

mRNA   G–Ⓟ–Ⓟ–Ⓟ   AAA···AAA   3′

5′ Cap   5′ UTR
(untranslated
region)

Start
codon

Stop
codon

3′ UTR
(untranslated
region)

Poly-A
tail

▲ **Figure 18.8 A eukaryotic gene and its transcript.** Each eukaryotic gene has a promoter, a DNA sequence where RNA polymerase binds and starts transcription, proceeding "downstream." A number of control elements (gold) are involved in regulating the initiation of transcription; these are DNA sequences located near (proximal to) or far from (distal to) the promoter. Distal control elements can be grouped together as enhancers, one of which is shown for this gene. A polyadenylation (poly-A) signal sequence in the last exon of the gene is transcribed into an RNA sequence that signals where the transcript is cleaved and the poly-A tail added. Transcription may continue for hundreds of nucleotides beyond the poly-A signal before terminating. RNA processing of the primary transcript into a functional mRNA involves three steps: addition of the 5′ cap, addition of the poly-A tail, and splicing. In the cell, the 5′ cap is added soon after transcription is initiated; splicing and poly-A tail addition may also occur while transcription is still under way (see Figure 17.10).

The interaction of general transcription factors and RNA polymerase II with a promoter usually leads to only a low rate of initiation and production of few RNA transcripts. In eukaryotes, high levels of transcription of particular genes at the appropriate time and place depend on the interaction of control elements with another set of proteins, which can be thought of as *specific transcription factors*.

Enhancers and Specific Transcription Factors As you can see in Figure 18.8, some control elements, named *proximal control elements*, are located close to the promoter. (Although some biologists consider proximal control elements part of the promoter, in this book we do not.) The more distant *distal control elements*, groupings of which are called **enhancers**, may be thousands of nucleotides upstream or downstream of a gene or even within an intron. A given gene may have multiple enhancers, each active at a different time or in a different cell type or location in the organism. Each enhancer, however, is generally associated with only that gene and no other.

In eukaryotes, the rate of gene expression can be strongly increased or decreased by the binding of specific transcription factors, either activators or repressors, to the control elements of enhancers. Hundreds of transcription activators have been discovered in eukaryotes; the structure of one example is shown in **Figure 18.9**. Researchers have identified two common structural elements in a large number of activator proteins: a DNA-binding domain—a part of the protein's three-dimensional structure that binds to DNA—and one or more activation domains. Activation domains bind other regulatory proteins or components of the transcription machinery, facilitating a series of protein-protein interactions that result in transcription of a given gene.

▲ **Figure 18.9 The structure of MyoD, a specific transcription factor that acts as an activator.** The MyoD protein is made up of two subunits (purple and salmon) with extensive regions of α helix. Each subunit has a DNA-binding domain and an activation domain (indicated by brackets for the purple subunit). The activation domain includes binding sites for the other subunit as well as other proteins. MyoD is involved in muscle development in vertebrate embryos and will be discussed further in Concept 18.4.

① Activator proteins bind to distal control elements grouped as an enhancer in the DNA. This enhancer has three binding sites, each called a distal control element.

Activators

DNA

Enhancer

Distal control element

Promoter

Gene

TATA box

② A DNA-bending protein brings the bound activators closer to the promoter. General transcription factors, mediator proteins, and RNA polymerase II are nearby.

DNA-bending protein

General transcription factors

Group of mediator proteins

RNA polymerase II

Chromatin modification

Transcription

RNA processing

mRNA degradation

Translation

Protein processing and degradation

③ The activators bind to certain mediator proteins and general transcription factors, helping them form an active transcription initiation complex on the promoter.

RNA polymerase II

Transcription initiation complex

RNA synthesis

▲ **Figure 18.10 A model for the action of enhancers and transcription activators.** Bending of the DNA by a protein enables enhancers to influence a promoter hundreds or even thousands of nucleotides away. Specific transcription factors called activators bind to the enhancer DNA sequences and then to a group of mediator proteins, which in turn bind to general transcription factors, assembling the transcription initiation complex. These protein-protein interactions facilitate the correct positioning of the complex on the promoter and the initiation of RNA synthesis. Only one enhancer (with three orange control elements) is shown here, but a gene may have several enhancers that act at different times or in different cell types.

Figure 18.10 shows a current model for how binding of activators to an enhancer located far from the promoter can influence transcription. Protein-mediated bending of the DNA is thought to bring the bound activators into contact with a group of *mediator proteins*, which in turn interact with proteins at the promoter. These multiple protein-protein interactions help assemble and position the initiation complex on the promoter. Support for this model includes a study showing that the proteins regulating a mouse globin gene contact both the gene's promoter and an enhancer located about 50,000 nucleotides upstream. Evidently, these two regions in the DNA must come together in a very specific fashion for this interaction to occur.

Specific transcription factors that function as repressors can inhibit gene expression in several different ways. Some repressors bind directly to control element DNA (in enhancers or elsewhere), blocking activator binding or, in some cases, turning off transcription even when activators are bound. Other repressors block the binding of activators to proteins that allow the activators to bind to DNA.

In addition to influencing transcription directly, some activators and repressors act indirectly by affecting chromatin structure. Studies using yeast and mammalian cells show that some activators recruit proteins that acetylate histones near the promoters of specific genes, thus promoting transcription (see Figure 18.7). Similarly, some repressors recruit proteins that deacetylate histones, leading to reduced transcription, a phenomenon referred to as *silencing*. Indeed, recruitment of chromatin-modifying proteins seems to be the most common mechanism of repression in eukaryotes.

Combinatorial Control of Gene Activation In eukaryotes, the precise control of transcription depends largely on the binding of activators to DNA control elements. Considering the great number of genes that must be regulated in a typical animal or plant cell, the number of completely different nucleotide sequences found in control elements is surprisingly small. A dozen or so short nucleotide sequences appear again and again in the control elements for different genes. On average, each enhancer is composed of about ten control elements, each of which can bind only one or two specific transcription factors. It is the particular *combination* of control elements in an enhancer associated with a gene, rather than the presence of a single unique control element, that is important in regulating transcription of the gene.

Even with only a dozen control element sequences available, a very large number of combinations are possible. A particular combination of control elements will be able to activate transcription only when the appropriate activator proteins are present, which may occur at a precise time during development or in a particular cell type. **Figure 18.11** illustrates how the use of different combinations of just a few control elements can allow differential regulation of transcription in two cell types. This can occur because each cell type contains a different group of activator proteins. How these groups came to differ will be explored in Concept 18.4.

Coordinately Controlled Genes in Eukaryotes

How does the eukaryotic cell deal with genes of related function that need to be turned on or off at the same time? Earlier in this chapter, you learned that in bacteria, such coordinately controlled genes are often clustered into an operon, which is regulated by a single promoter and transcribed into a single mRNA molecule. Thus, the genes are expressed together, and the encoded proteins are produced concurrently. With a few minor exceptions, operons that work in this way have *not* been found in eukaryotic cells.

Co-expressed eukaryotic genes, such as genes coding for the enzymes of a metabolic pathway, are typically scattered over different chromosomes. In these cases, coordinate gene expression depends on the association of a specific combination of control elements with every gene of a dispersed group. The presence of these elements can be compared to the raised flags on a few mailboxes out of many, signaling to the mail carrier to check those boxes. Copies of the activators that recognize the control elements bind to them, promoting simultaneous transcription of the genes, no matter where they are in the genome.

(a) Liver cell. The albumin gene is expressed, and the crystallin gene is not.

(b) Lens cell. The crystallin gene is expressed, and the albumin gene is not.

▲ **Figure 18.11 Cell type–specific transcription.** Both liver cells and lens cells have the genes for making the proteins albumin and crystallin, but only liver cells make albumin (a blood protein) and only lens cells make crystallin (the main protein of the lens of the eye). The specific transcription factors made in a cell determine which genes are expressed. In this example, the genes for albumin and crystallin are shown at the top, each with an enhancer made up of three different control elements. Although the enhancers for the two genes share one control element (gray), each enhancer has a unique combination of elements. All the activators required for high-level expression of the albumin gene are present only in liver cells (a), whereas the activators needed for expression of the crystallin gene are present only in lens cells (b). For simplicity, we consider only the role of activators here, although the presence or absence of repressors may also influence transcription in certain cell types.

? *Describe the enhancer for the albumin gene in each cell. How would the nucleotide sequence of this enhancer in the liver cell compare with that in the lens cell?*

Coordinate control of dispersed genes in a eukaryotic cell often occurs in response to chemical signals from outside the cell. A steroid hormone, for example, enters a cell and binds to a specific intracellular receptor protein, forming a hormone-receptor complex that serves as a transcription activator. Every gene whose transcription is stimulated by a particular steroid hormone, regardless of its chromosomal location, has a control element recognized by that hormone-receptor complex. This is how estrogen activates a group of genes that stimulate cell division in uterine cells, preparing the uterus for pregnancy.

Many signaling molecules, such as nonsteroid hormones and growth factors, bind to receptors on a cell's surface and never actually enter the cell. Such molecules can control gene expression indirectly by triggering signal transduction pathways that lead to activation of particular transcription activators or repressors. Coordinate regulation in such pathways is the same as for steroid hormones: Genes with the same control elements are activated by the same chemical signals. Systems for coordinating gene regulation probably arose early in evolutionary history.

Nuclear Architecture and Gene Expression

You saw in Figure 16.23 that each chromosome in the interphase nucleus occupies a distinct territory. The chromosomes are not completely isolated, however. Recently, techniques have been developed that allow researchers to cross-link and identify regions of chromosomes that associate with each other during interphase. These studies reveal that loops of chromatin extend from individual chromosomal territories into specific sites in the nucleus (**Figure 18.12**). Different loops from the same chromosome and loops from other chromosomes may congregate in such sites, some of which are rich in RNA polymerases and other transcription-associated proteins. Like a recreation center that draws members from many different neighborhoods, these so-called *transcription factories* are thought to be areas specialized for a common function.

The old view that the nuclear contents are like a bowl of amorphous chromosomal spaghetti is giving way to a new

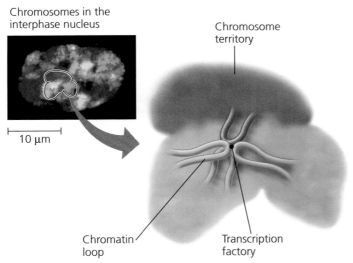

Chromosomes in the interphase nucleus

Chromosome territory

10 μm

Chromatin loop

Transcription factory

▲ **Figure 18.12 Chromosomal interactions in the interphase nucleus.** Although each chromosome has its own territory (see Figure 16.23), loops of chromatin may extend into other sites in the nucleus. Some of these sites are transcription factories that are occupied by multiple chromatin loops from the same chromosome (blue loops) or other chromosomes (red and green loops).

model of a nucleus with a defined architecture and regulated movements of chromatin. Relocation of particular genes from their chromosomal territories to transcription factories may be part of the process of readying genes for transcription. This is an exciting area of current research that raises many fascinating questions for future study.

Mechanisms of Post-Transcriptional Regulation

Transcription alone does not constitute gene expression. The expression of a protein-coding gene is ultimately measured by the amount of functional protein a cell makes, and much happens between the synthesis of the RNA transcript and the activity of the protein in the cell. Researchers are discovering more and more regulatory mechanisms that operate at various stages after transcription (see Figure 18.6). These mechanisms allow a cell to fine-tune gene expression rapidly in response to environmental changes without altering its transcription patterns. Here we discuss how cells can regulate gene expression once a gene has been transcribed.

RNA Processing

RNA processing in the nucleus and the export of mature RNA to the cytoplasm provide several opportunities for regulating gene expression that are not available in prokaryotes. One example of regulation at the RNA-processing level is **alternative RNA splicing**, in which different mRNA molecules are produced from the same primary transcript, depending on which RNA segments are treated as exons and which as introns. Regulatory proteins specific to a cell type control intron-exon choices by binding to regulatory sequences within the primary transcript.

A simple example of alternative RNA splicing is shown in **Figure 18.13** for the troponin T gene, which encodes two different (though related) proteins. Other genes offer possibilities for far greater numbers of products. For instance, researchers have found a *Drosophila* gene with enough alternatively spliced exons to generate about 19,000 membrane proteins that have different extracellular domains. At least 17,500 (94%) of the alternative mRNAs are actually synthesized. Each developing nerve cell in the fly appears to synthesize a unique form of the protein, which acts as an identification badge on the cell surface.

It is clear that alternative RNA splicing can significantly expand the repertoire of a eukaryotic genome. In fact, alternative splicing was proposed as one explanation for the surprisingly low number of human genes counted when the human genome was sequenced about ten years ago. The number of human genes was found to be similar to that of a soil worm (nematode), a mustard plant, or a sea anemone. This discovery prompted questions about what, if not the number of genes, accounts for the more complex morphology (external form) of humans. It turns out that 75–100% of human genes that have multiple exons probably undergo alternative splicing. Thus, the extent of alternative splicing

► **Figure 18.13 Alternative RNA splicing of the troponin T gene.** The primary transcript of this gene can be spliced in more than one way, generating different mRNA molecules. Notice that one mRNA molecule has ended up with exon 3 (green) and the other with exon 4 (purple). These two mRNAs are translated into different but related muscle proteins.

greatly multiplies the number of possible human proteins, which may be better correlated with complexity of form.

mRNA Degradation

The life span of mRNA molecules in the cytoplasm is important in determining the pattern of protein synthesis in a cell. Bacterial mRNA molecules typically are degraded by enzymes within a few minutes of their synthesis. This short life span of mRNAs is one reason bacteria can change their patterns of protein synthesis so quickly in response to environmental changes. In contrast, mRNAs in multicellular eukaryotes typically survive for hours, days, or even weeks. For instance, the mRNAs for the hemoglobin polypeptides (α-globin and β-globin) in developing red blood cells are unusually stable, and these long-lived mRNAs are translated repeatedly in these cells.

Nucleotide sequences that affect how long an mRNA remains intact are often found in the untranslated region (UTR) at the 3' end of the molecule (see Figure 18.8). In one experiment, researchers transferred such a sequence from the short-lived mRNA for a growth factor to the 3' end of a normally stable globin mRNA. The globin mRNA was quickly degraded.

During the past few years, other mechanisms that degrade or block expression of mRNA molecules have come to light. These mechanisms involve an important group of newly discovered RNA molecules that regulate gene expression at several levels, and we will discuss them later in this chapter.

Initiation of Translation

Translation presents another opportunity for regulating gene expression; such regulation occurs most commonly at the initiation stage (see Figure 17.18). For some mRNAs, the initiation of translation can be blocked by regulatory proteins that bind to specific sequences or structures within the untranslated region at the 5' or 3' end (5' or 3' UTR), preventing the attachment of ribosomes. (Recall from Chapter 17 that both the 5' cap and the poly-A tail of an mRNA molecule are important for ribosome binding.) A different mechanism for blocking translation is seen in a variety of mRNAs present in the eggs of many organisms: Initially, these stored mRNAs lack poly-A tails of sufficient length to allow translation initiation. At the appropriate time during embryonic development, however, a cytoplasmic enzyme adds more adenine (A) nucleotides, prompting translation to begin.

Alternatively, translation of *all* the mRNAs in a cell may be regulated simultaneously. In a eukaryotic cell, such "global" control usually involves the activation or inactivation of one or more of the protein factors required to initiate translation. This mechanism plays a role in starting translation of mRNAs that are stored in eggs. Just after fertilization, translation is triggered by the sudden activation of translation initiation factors. The response is a burst of synthesis of the proteins encoded by the stored mRNAs. Some plants and algae store mRNAs during periods of darkness; light then triggers the reactivation of the translational apparatus.

Protein Processing and Degradation

The final opportunities for controlling gene expression occur after translation. Often, eukaryotic polypeptides must be processed to yield functional protein molecules. For instance, cleavage of the initial insulin polypeptide (pro-insulin) forms the active hormone. In addition, many proteins undergo chemical modifications that make them functional. Regulatory proteins are commonly activated or inactivated by the reversible addition of phosphate groups, and proteins destined for the surface of animal cells acquire sugars. Cell-surface proteins and many others must also be transported to target destinations in the cell in order to function. Regulation might occur at any of the steps involved in modifying or transporting a protein.

Finally, the length of time each protein functions in the cell is strictly regulated by means of selective degradation. Many proteins, such as the cyclins involved in regulating the cell cycle, must be relatively short-lived if the cell is to function appropriately (see Figure 12.17). To mark a particular protein for destruction, the cell commonly attaches molecules of a small protein called ubiquitin to the protein. Giant protein complexes called **proteasomes** then recognize the

① Multiple ubiquitin molecules are attached to a protein by enzymes in the cytosol.

② The ubiquitin-tagged protein is recognized by a proteasome, which unfolds the protein and sequesters it within a central cavity.

③ Enzymatic components of the proteasome cut the protein into small peptides, which can be further degraded by other enzymes in the cytosol.

Chromatin modification
Transcription
RNA processing
mRNA degradation
Translation
Protein processing and degradation

Ubiquitin

Protein to be degraded

Ubiquitinated protein

Proteasome

Protein entering a proteasome

Proteasome and ubiquitin to be recycled

Protein fragments (peptides)

▲ **Figure 18.14 Degradation of a protein by a proteasome.** A proteasome, an enormous protein complex shaped like a trash can, chops up unneeded proteins in the cell. In most cases, the proteins attacked by a proteasome have been tagged with short chains of ubiquitin, a small protein. Steps 1 and 3 require ATP. Eukaryotic proteasomes are as massive as ribosomal subunits and are distributed throughout the cell. Their shape somewhat resembles that of chaperone proteins, which protect protein structure rather than destroy it (see Figure 5.23).

ubiquitin-tagged proteins and degrade them (**Figure 18.14**). The importance of proteasomes is underscored by the finding that mutations making specific cell cycle proteins impervious to proteasome degradation can lead to cancer. The 2004 Nobel Prize in Chemistry was awarded to three scientists—two from Israel and one from the United States—who worked out the regulated process of protein degradation.

CONCEPT CHECK 18.2

1. In general, what is the effect of histone acetylation and DNA methylation on gene expression?

2. Compare the roles of general and specific transcription factors in regulating gene expression.

3. Suppose you compared the nucleotide sequences of the distal control elements in the enhancers of three genes that are expressed only in muscle tissue. What would you expect to find? Why?

4. Once mRNA encoding a particular protein reaches the cytoplasm, what are four mechanisms that can regulate the amount of the protein that is active in the cell?

5. **WHAT IF?** Examine Figure 18.11 and suggest a mechanism by which the yellow activator protein comes to be present in the liver cell but not in the lens cell.

For suggested answers, see Appendix A.

CONCEPT 18.3

Noncoding RNAs play multiple roles in controlling gene expression

Genome sequencing has revealed that protein-coding DNA accounts for only 1.5% of the human genome and a similarly small percentage of the genomes of many other multicellular eukaryotes. A very small fraction of the non-protein-coding DNA consists of genes for RNAs such as ribosomal RNA and transfer RNA. Until recently, most of the remaining DNA was assumed to be untranscribed. The idea was that since it didn't specify proteins or the few known types of RNA, such DNA didn't contain meaningful genetic information. However, a flood of recent data has contradicted this idea. For example, an in-depth study of a region comprising 1% of the human genome showed that more than 90% of that region was transcribed. Introns accounted for only a fraction of this transcribed, nontranslated RNA. These and other results suggest that a significant amount of the genome may be transcribed into non-protein-coding RNAs (also called *noncoding RNAs*, or *ncRNAs*), including a variety of small RNAs. While many questions about the functions of these RNAs remain unanswered, researchers are uncovering more evidence of their biological roles every day.

Biologists are excited about these recent discoveries, which hint at a large, diverse population of RNA molecules in the cell that play crucial roles in regulating gene expression—and have gone largely unnoticed until now. Clearly, we must revise our long-standing view that because mRNAs code for proteins, they are the most important RNAs functioning in the cell. This represents a major shift in the thinking of biologists, one that you are witnessing as students entering this field of study. It's as if our exclusive focus on a famous rock star has blinded us to the many backup musicians and songwriters working behind the scenes.

Regulation by both small and large ncRNAs is known to occur at several points in the pathway of gene expression, including mRNA translation and chromatin modification. We will focus mainly on two types of small ncRNAs that have been extensively studied in the past few years; the importance of these RNAs was acknowledged when they were the focus of the 2006 Nobel Prize in Physiology or Medicine.

Effects on mRNAs by MicroRNAs and Small Interfering RNAs

Since 1993, a number of research studies have uncovered small single-stranded RNA molecules, called **microRNAs (miRNAs)**, that are capable of binding to complementary sequences in mRNA molecules. The miRNAs are made from longer RNA precursors that fold back on themselves, forming one or more short double-stranded hairpin structures, each held together by hydrogen bonds **(Figure 18.15)**. After each hairpin is cut away from the precursor, it is trimmed by an enzyme (fittingly called Dicer) into a short double-stranded fragment of about 22 nucleotide pairs. One of the two strands is degraded, while the other strand, which is the miRNA, forms a complex with one or more proteins; the miRNA allows the complex to bind to any mRNA molecule with 7–8 nucleotides of complementary sequence. The miRNA-protein complex then either degrades the target mRNA or blocks its translation. It has been estimated that expression of at least one-half of all human genes may be regulated by miRNAs, a remarkable figure given that the existence of miRNAs was unknown a mere two decades ago.

A growing understanding of the miRNA pathway provided an explanation for a perplexing observation: Researchers had found that injecting double-stranded RNA molecules into a cell somehow turned off expression of a gene with the same sequence as the RNA. They called this experimental phenomenon **RNA interference (RNAi)**. It was later shown to be due to **small interfering RNAs (siRNAs)**, which are similar in size and function to miRNAs. In fact, subsequent research showed that the same cellular machinery generates miRNAs and siRNAs and that both can associate with the same proteins, producing similar results. The distinction between miRNAs and siRNAs is based on the nature of the precursor molecule for each. While an miRNA is usually formed from a single hairpin in a precursor RNA (see Figure 18.15), multiple siRNAs are formed from a much longer, linear, double-stranded RNA molecule.

We mentioned that laboratory investigators had injected double-stranded RNAs into cells, and you may wonder whether such molecules are ever found naturally. As you will learn in Chapter 19, some viruses have double-stranded RNA genomes. Because the cellular RNAi pathway can lead to the destruction of RNAs with sequences complementary to those found in double-stranded RNAs, this pathway may have evolved as a natural defense against infection by such viruses. However, the fact that RNAi can also affect the expression of nonviral cellular genes may reflect a different evolutionary origin for the RNAi pathway. Moreover, many species, including mammals, apparently produce their own long, double-stranded RNA precursors to small RNAs such as siRNAs. Once produced, these RNAs can interfere with gene expression at stages other than translation, as we'll discuss next.

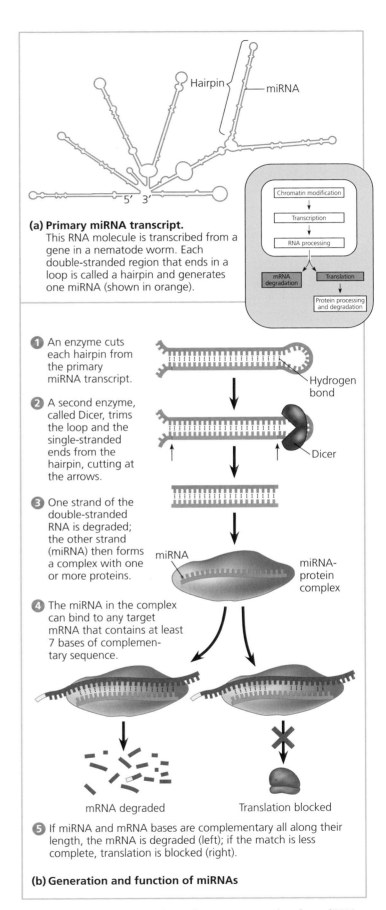

(a) Primary miRNA transcript.
This RNA molecule is transcribed from a gene in a nematode worm. Each double-stranded region that ends in a loop is called a hairpin and generates one miRNA (shown in orange).

1 An enzyme cuts each hairpin from the primary miRNA transcript.

2 A second enzyme, called Dicer, trims the loop and the single-stranded ends from the hairpin, cutting at the arrows.

3 One strand of the double-stranded RNA is degraded; the other strand (miRNA) then forms a complex with one or more proteins.

4 The miRNA in the complex can bind to any target mRNA that contains at least 7 bases of complementary sequence.

mRNA degraded   Translation blocked

5 If miRNA and mRNA bases are complementary all along their length, the mRNA is degraded (left); if the match is less complete, translation is blocked (right).

(b) Generation and function of miRNAs

▲ Figure 18.15 **Regulation of gene expression by miRNAs.**

Chromatin Remodeling and Effects on Transcription by ncRNAs

In addition to affecting mRNAs, small RNAs can cause remodeling of chromatin structure. In some yeasts, siRNAs produced by the yeast cells themselves are required for the formation of heterochromatin at the centromeres of chromosomes. According to one model, an RNA transcript produced from DNA in the centromeric region of the chromosome is copied into double-stranded RNA by a yeast enzyme and then processed into siRNAs. These siRNAs associate with a complex of proteins (different from the one shown in Figure 18.15) and act as a homing device, targeting the complex back to RNA transcripts being made from the centromeric sequences of DNA. Once there, proteins in the complex recruit enzymes that modify the chromatin, turning it into the highly condensed heterochromatin found at the centromere.

A newly discovered class of small ncRNAs called *piwi-associated RNAs* (*piRNAs*) also induce formation of heterochromatin, blocking expression of some parasitic DNA elements in the genome known as transposons. (Transposons are discussed in Chapter 21.) Usually 24–31 nucleotides in length, piRNAs are probably processed from single-stranded RNA precursors. They play an indispensable role in the germ cells of many animal species, where they appear to help re-establish appropriate methylation patterns in the genome during gamete formation.

The cases we have just described involve chromatin remodeling that blocks expression of large regions of the chromosome. Several recent experiments have shown that related RNA-based mechanisms may also block the transcription of specific genes. For instance, some plant miRNAs have sequences that bind to gene promoters and can repress transcription, and piRNAs can block expression of specific genes. And in a twist on the same theme, some cases have even been reported of *activation* of gene expression by miRNAs and piRNAs.

The Evolutionary Significance of Small ncRNAs

EVOLUTION Small ncRNAs can regulate gene expression at multiple steps and in many ways. In general, extra levels of gene regulation might allow evolution of a higher degree of complexity of form. Therefore, the versatility of miRNA regulation has led some biologists to hypothesize that an increase in the number of miRNAs specified by the genome of a given species has allowed morphological complexity to increase over evolutionary time. While this hypothesis is still being debated, it is logical to expand the discussion to include all small ncRNAs. Exciting new techniques for rapidly sequencing genomes are beginning to allow biologists to ask how many genes for ncRNAs are present in the genome of a given species. A survey of different species supports the notion that siRNAs evolved first, followed by miRNAs and later piRNAs, which are found only in animals. And while there

are hundreds of types of miRNAs, there appear to be many thousands of types of piRNAs, allowing the potential for very sophisticated gene regulation by piRNAs.

Given the extensive functions of ncRNAs, it is not surprising that many of the ncRNAs characterized thus far play important roles in embryonic development—the topic we turn to in the next section. Embryonic development is perhaps the ultimate example of precisely regulated gene expression.

CONCEPT CHECK 18.3

1. Compare and contrast miRNAs and siRNAs.
2. **WHAT IF?** If the mRNA being degraded in Figure 18.15 coded for a protein that promotes cell division in a multicellular organism, what would happen if a mutation disabled the gene encoding the miRNA that triggers this degradation?
3. **MAKE CONNECTIONS** In Concept 15.2 (pp. 291–292), you learned about inactivation of one of the X chromosomes in female mammals. Reread those pages, and suggest a model for how the *XIST* noncoding RNA functions to cause Barr body formation.

For suggested answers, see Appendix A.

CONCEPT 18.4

A program of differential gene expression leads to the different cell types in a multicellular organism

In the embryonic development of multicellular organisms, a fertilized egg (a zygote) gives rise to cells of many different types, each with a different structure and corresponding function. Typically, cells are organized into tissues, tissues into organs, organs into organ systems, and organ systems into the whole organism. Thus, any developmental program must produce cells of different types that form higher-level structures arranged in a particular way in three dimensions. The processes that occur during development in plants and animals are detailed in Chapters 35 and 47, respectively. In this chapter, we focus instead on the program of regulation of gene expression that orchestrates development, using a few animal species as examples.

A Genetic Program for Embryonic Development

The photos in **Figure 18.16** illustrate the dramatic difference between a zygote and the organism it becomes. This remarkable transformation results from three interrelated processes: cell division, cell differentiation, and morphogenesis. Through a succession of mitotic cell divisions, the zygote gives rise to a

(a) Fertilized eggs of a frog   **(b) Newly hatched tadpole**

▲ **Figure 18.16 From fertilized egg to animal: What a difference four days makes.** It takes just four days for cell division, differentiation, and morphogenesis to transform each of the fertilized frog eggs shown in (a) into a tadpole like the one in (b).

large number of cells. Cell division alone, however, would merely produce a great ball of identical cells, nothing like a tadpole. During embryonic development, cells not only increase in number, but also undergo cell **differentiation**, the process by which cells become specialized in structure and function. Moreover, the different kinds of cells are not randomly distributed but are organized into tissues and organs in a particular three-dimensional arrangement. The physical processes that give an organism its shape constitute **morphogenesis**, meaning "creation of form."

All three processes have their basis in cellular behavior. Even morphogenesis, the shaping of the organism, can be traced back to changes in the shape, motility, and other characteristics of the cells that make up various regions of the embryo. As you have seen, the activities of a cell depend on the genes it expresses and the proteins it produces. Almost all cells in an organism have the same genome; therefore, differential gene expression results from the genes being regulated differently in each cell type.

In Figure 18.11, you saw a simplified view of how differential gene expression occurs in two cell types, a liver cell and a lens cell. Each of these fully differentiated cells has a particular mix of specific activators that turn on the collection of genes whose products are required in the cell. The fact that both cells arose through a series of mitoses from a common fertilized egg inevitably leads to a question: How do different sets of activators come to be present in the two cells?

It turns out that materials placed into the egg by the mother set up a sequential program of gene regulation that is carried out as cells divide, and this program makes the cells become different from each other in a coordinated fashion. To understand how this works, we will consider two basic developmental processes: First, we'll explore how cells that arise from early embryonic mitoses develop the differences that start each cell along its own differentiation pathway. Second, we'll see how cellular differentiation leads to one particular cell type, using muscle development as an example.

Cytoplasmic Determinants and Inductive Signals

What generates the first differences among cells in an early embryo? And what controls the differentiation of all the various cell types as development proceeds? By this point in the chapter, you can probably deduce the answer: The specific genes expressed in any particular cell of a developing organism determine its path. Two sources of information, used to varying extents in different species, "tell" a cell which genes to express at any given time during embryonic development.

One important source of information early in development is the egg's cytoplasm, which contains both RNA and proteins encoded by the mother's DNA. The cytoplasm of an unfertilized egg is not homogeneous. Messenger RNA, proteins, other substances, and organelles are distributed unevenly in the unfertilized egg, and this unevenness has a profound impact on the development of the future embryo in many species. Maternal substances in the egg that influence the course of early development are called **cytoplasmic determinants** (Figure 18.17a, on the next page). After fertilization, early mitotic divisions distribute the zygote's cytoplasm into separate cells. The nuclei of these cells may thus be exposed to different cytoplasmic determinants, depending on which portions of the zygotic cytoplasm a cell received. The combination of cytoplasmic determinants in a cell helps determine its developmental fate by regulating expression of the cell's genes during the course of cell differentiation.

The other major source of developmental information, which becomes increasingly important as the number of embryonic cells increases, is the environment around a particular cell. Most influential are the signals impinging on an embryonic cell from other embryonic cells in the vicinity, including contact with cell-surface molecules on neighboring cells and the binding of growth factors secreted by neighboring cells. Such signals cause changes in the target cells, a process called **induction** (Figure 18.17b). The molecules conveying these signals within the target cell are cell-surface receptors and other proteins expressed by the embryo's own genes. In general, the signaling molecules send a cell down a specific developmental path by causing changes in its gene expression that eventually result in observable cellular changes. Thus, interactions between embryonic cells help induce differentiation of the many specialized cell types making up a new organism.

Sequential Regulation of Gene Expression During Cellular Differentiation

As the tissues and organs of an embryo develop and their cells differentiate, the cells become noticeably different in structure and function. These observable changes are actually the outcome of a cell's developmental history beginning at the first mitotic division of the zygote, as we have just seen. The

(a) Cytoplasmic determinants in the egg

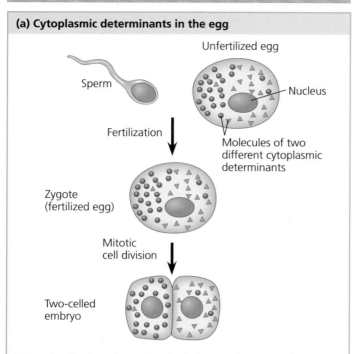

Sperm

Unfertilized egg

Nucleus

Fertilization

Molecules of two different cytoplasmic determinants

Zygote (fertilized egg)

Mitotic cell division

Two-celled embryo

The unfertilized egg has molecules in its cytoplasm, encoded by the mother's genes, that influence development. Many of these cytoplasmic determinants, like the two shown here, are unevenly distributed in the egg. After fertilization and mitotic division, the cell nuclei of the embryo are exposed to different sets of cytoplasmic determinants and, as a result, express different genes.

(b) Induction by nearby cells

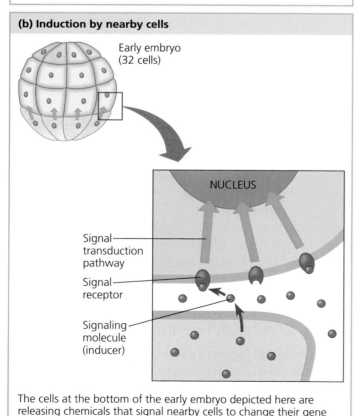

Early embryo (32 cells)

NUCLEUS

Signal transduction pathway

Signal receptor

Signaling molecule (inducer)

The cells at the bottom of the early embryo depicted here are releasing chemicals that signal nearby cells to change their gene expression.

earliest changes that set a cell on a path to specialization are subtle ones, showing up only at the molecular level. Before biologists knew much about the molecular changes occurring in embryos, they coined the term **determination** to refer to the events that lead to the observable differentiation of a cell. Once it has undergone determination, an embryonic cell is irreversibly committed to its final fate. If a committed cell is experimentally placed in another location in the embryo, it will still differentiate into the cell type that is its normal fate.

Today we understand determination in terms of molecular changes. The outcome of determination, observable cell differentiation, is marked by the expression of genes for *tissue-specific proteins*. These proteins are found only in a specific cell type and give the cell its characteristic structure and function. The first evidence of differentiation is the appearance of mRNAs for these proteins. Eventually, differentiation is observable with a microscope as changes in cellular structure. On the molecular level, different sets of genes are sequentially expressed in a regulated manner as new cells arise from division of their precursors. A number of the steps in gene expression may be regulated during differentiation, with transcription among the most important. In the fully differentiated cell, transcription remains the principal regulatory point for maintaining appropriate gene expression.

Differentiated cells are specialists at making tissue-specific proteins. For example, as a result of transcriptional regulation, liver cells specialize in making albumin, and lens cells specialize in making crystallin (see Figure 18.11). Skeletal muscle cells in vertebrates are another instructive example. Each of these cells is a long fiber containing many nuclei within a single plasma membrane. Skeletal muscle cells have high concentrations of muscle-specific versions of the contractile proteins myosin and actin, as well as membrane receptor proteins that detect signals from nerve cells.

Muscle cells develop from embryonic precursor cells that have the potential to develop into a number of cell types, including cartilage cells and fat cells, but particular conditions commit them to becoming muscle cells. Although the committed cells appear unchanged under the microscope, determination has occurred, and they are now *myoblasts*. Eventually, myoblasts start to churn out large amounts of muscle-specific proteins and fuse to form mature, elongated, multinucleate skeletal muscle cells **(Figure 18.18)**.

Researchers have worked out what happens at the molecular level during muscle cell determination by growing myoblasts in culture and analyzing them using molecular biological techniques you will learn about in Chapter 20. In a series of experiments, they isolated different genes, caused each to be expressed in a separate embryonic precursor cell, and then looked for differentiation into myoblasts and muscle cells. In this way, they identified several so-called "master regulatory genes" whose protein products commit the cells to becoming skeletal muscle. Thus, in the case of muscle cells,

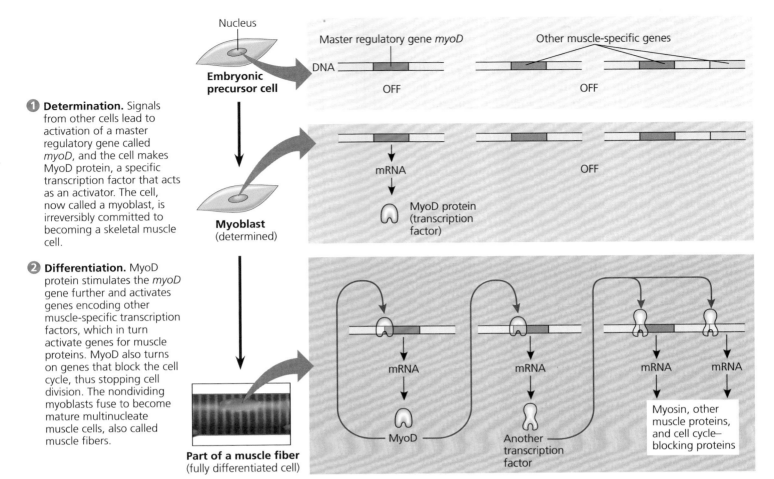

Nucleus

Embryonic precursor cell

Master regulatory gene *myoD*

Other muscle-specific genes

DNA

OFF

OFF

1 **Determination.** Signals from other cells lead to activation of a master regulatory gene called *myoD*, and the cell makes MyoD protein, a specific transcription factor that acts as an activator. The cell, now called a myoblast, is irreversibly committed to becoming a skeletal muscle cell.

Myoblast (determined)

mRNA

OFF

MyoD protein (transcription factor)

2 **Differentiation.** MyoD protein stimulates the *myoD* gene further and activates genes encoding other muscle-specific transcription factors, which in turn activate genes for muscle proteins. MyoD also turns on genes that block the cell cycle, thus stopping cell division. The nondividing myoblasts fuse to become mature multinucleate muscle cells, also called muscle fibers.

Part of a muscle fiber (fully differentiated cell)

mRNA

mRNA

mRNA

mRNA

MyoD

Another transcription factor

Myosin, other muscle proteins, and cell cycle–blocking proteins

▲ **Figure 18.18 Determination and differentiation of muscle cells.** Skeletal muscle cells arise from embryonic cells as a result of changes in gene expression. (In this depiction, the process of gene activation is greatly simplified.)

WHAT IF? *What would happen if a mutation in the* myoD *gene resulted in a MyoD protein that could not activate the* myoD *gene?*

the molecular basis of determination is the expression of one or more of these master regulatory genes.

To understand more about how commitment occurs in muscle cell differentiation, let's focus on the master regulatory gene called *myoD* (see Figure 18.18). This gene encodes MyoD protein, a transcription factor that binds to specific control elements in the enhancers of various target genes and stimulates their expression (see Figure 18.9). Some target genes for MyoD encode still other muscle-specific transcription factors. MyoD also stimulates expression of the *myoD* gene itself, thus perpetuating its effect in maintaining the cell's differentiated state. Presumably, all the genes activated by MyoD have enhancer control elements recognized by MyoD and are thus coordinately controlled. Finally, the secondary transcription factors activate the genes for proteins such as myosin and actin that confer the unique properties of skeletal muscle cells.

The MyoD protein deserves its designation as a master regulatory gene. Researchers have shown that it is even capable of changing some kinds of fully differentiated nonmuscle cells, such as fat cells and liver cells, into muscle cells. Why

doesn't it work on *all* kinds of cells? One likely explanation is that activation of the muscle-specific genes is not solely dependent on MyoD but requires a particular *combination* of regulatory proteins, some of which are lacking in cells that do not respond to MyoD. The determination and differentiation of other kinds of tissues may play out in a similar fashion.

We have now seen how different programs of gene expression that are activated in the fertilized egg can result in differentiated cells and tissues. But for the tissues to function effectively in the organism as a whole, the organism's *body plan*—its overall three-dimensional arrangement—must be established and superimposed on the differentiation process. Next we'll investigate the molecular basis for the establishment of the body plan, using the well-studied *Drosophila* as an example.

Pattern Formation: Setting Up the Body Plan

Cytoplasmic determinants and inductive signals both contribute to the development of a spatial organization in which the tissues and organs of an organism are all in their characteristic places. This process is called **pattern formation**.

Pattern formation in animals begins in the early embryo, when the major axes of an animal are established. Before construction begins on a new building, the locations of the front, back, and sides are determined. In the same way, before the tissues and organs of a bilaterally symmetrical animal appear, the relative positions of the animal's head and tail, right and left sides, and back and front are set up, thus establishing the three major body axes. The molecular cues that control pattern formation, collectively called **positional information**, are provided by cytoplasmic determinants and inductive signals (see Figure 18.17). These cues tell a cell its location relative to the body axes and to neighboring cells and determine how the cell and its progeny will respond to future molecular signals.

During the first half of the 20th century, classical embryologists made detailed anatomical observations of embryonic development in a number of species and performed experiments in which they manipulated embryonic tissues. Although this research laid the groundwork for understanding the mechanisms of development, it did not reveal the specific molecules that guide development or determine how patterns are established.

Then, in the 1940s, scientists began using the genetic approach—the study of mutants—to investigate *Drosophila* development. That approach has had spectacular success. These studies have established that genes control development and have led to an understanding of the key roles that specific molecules play in defining position and directing differentiation. By combining anatomical, genetic, and biochemical approaches to the study of *Drosophila* development, researchers have discovered developmental principles common to many other species, including humans.

The Life Cycle of Drosophila

Fruit flies and other arthropods have a modular construction, an ordered series of segments. These segments make up the body's three major parts: the head, the thorax (the midbody, from which the wings and legs extend), and the abdomen (**Figure 18.19a**). Like other bilaterally symmetrical animals, *Drosophila* has an anterior-posterior (head-to-tail) axis, a dorsal-ventral (back-to-belly) axis, and a right-left axis. In *Drosophila*, cytoplasmic determinants that are localized in the unfertilized egg provide positional information for the placement of anterior-posterior and dorsal-ventral axes even before fertilization. We'll focus here on the molecules involved in establishing the anterior-posterior axis.

The *Drosophila* egg develops in the female's ovary, surrounded by ovarian cells called nurse cells and follicle cells (**Figure 18.19b**, top). These support cells supply the egg with nutrients, mRNAs, and other substances needed for development and make the egg shell. After fertilization and laying of the egg, embryonic development results in the formation of a segmented larva, which goes through three larval stages. Then, in a process much like that by which a caterpillar

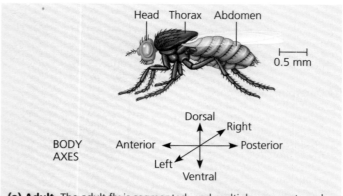

(a) Adult. The adult fly is segmented, and multiple segments make up each of the three main body parts—head, thorax, and abdomen. The body axes are shown by arrows.

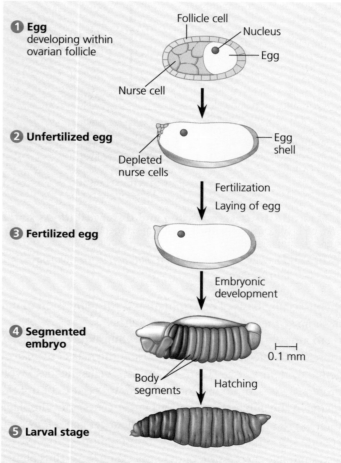

(b) Development from egg to larva. ❶ The yellow egg is surrounded by other cells that form a structure called the follicle within one of the mother's ovaries. ❷ The nurse cells shrink as they supply nutrients and mRNAs to the developing egg, which grows larger. Eventually, the mature egg fills the egg shell that is secreted by the follicle cells. ❸ The egg is fertilized within the mother and then laid. ❹ Embryonic development forms ❺ a larva, which goes through three stages. The third stage forms a cocoon (not shown), within which the larva metamorphoses into the adult shown in (a).

▲ **Figure 18.19 Key developmental events in the life cycle of *Drosophila*.**

becomes a butterfly, the fly larva forms a cocoon in which it metamorphoses into the adult fly pictured in Figure 18.19a.

Genetic Analysis of Early Development: Scientific Inquiry

Edward B. Lewis was a visionary American biologist who, in the 1940s, first showed the value of the genetic approach to studying embryonic development in *Drosophila*. Lewis studied bizarre mutant flies with developmental defects that led to extra wings or legs in the wrong place (**Figure 18.20**). He located the mutations on the fly's genetic map, thus connecting the developmental abnormalities to specific genes. This research supplied the first concrete evidence that genes somehow direct the developmental processes studied by embryologists. The genes Lewis discovered, called **homeotic genes**, control pattern formation in the late embryo, larva, and adult.

Insight into pattern formation during early embryonic development did not come for another 30 years, when two researchers in Germany, Christiane Nüsslein-Volhard and Eric Wieschaus, set out to identify *all* the genes that affect segment formation in *Drosophila*. The project was daunting for three reasons. The first was the sheer number of *Drosophila* genes, now known to total about 13,700. The genes affecting segmentation might be just a few needles in a haystack or might be so numerous and varied that the scientists would be unable to make sense of them. Second, mutations affecting a

Wild type

Eye

Antenna

Mutant

Leg

◀ **Figure 18.20**
Abnormal pattern formation in Drosophila. Mutations in certain regulatory genes, called homeotic genes, cause a misplacement of structures in an animal. These scanning electron micrographs contrast the head of a wild-type fly, bearing a pair of small antennae, with that of a homeotic mutant (a fly with a mutation in a single gene), bearing a pair of legs in place of antennae.

process as fundamental as segmentation would surely be **embryonic lethals**, mutations with phenotypes causing death at the embryonic or larval stage. Because organisms with embryonic lethal mutations never reproduce, they cannot be bred for study. The researchers dealt with this problem by looking for recessive mutations, which can be propagated in heterozygous flies that act as genetic carriers. Third, cytoplasmic determinants in the egg were known to play a role in axis formation, so the researchers knew they would have to study the mother's genes as well as those of the embryo. It is the mother's genes that we will discuss further as we focus on how the anterior-posterior body axis is set up in the developing egg.

Nüsslein-Volhard and Wieschaus began their search for segmentation genes by exposing flies to a mutagenic chemical that affected the flies' gametes. They mated the mutagenized flies and then scanned their descendants for dead embryos or larvae with abnormal segmentation or other defects. For example, to find genes that might set up the anterior-posterior axis, they looked for embryos or larvae with abnormal ends, such as two heads or two tails, predicting that such abnormalities would arise from mutations in maternal genes required for correctly setting up the offspring's head or tail end.

Using this approach, Nüsslein-Volhard and Wieschaus eventually identified about 1,200 genes essential for pattern formation during embryonic development. Of these, about 120 were essential for normal segmentation. Over several years, the researchers were able to group these segmentation genes by general function, to map them, and to clone many of them for further study in the lab. The result was a detailed molecular understanding of the early steps in pattern formation in *Drosophila*.

When the results of Nüsslein-Volhard and Wieschaus were combined with Lewis's earlier work, a coherent picture of *Drosophila* development emerged. In recognition of their discoveries, the three researchers were awarded a Nobel Prize in 1995.

Let's consider further the genes that Nüsslein-Volhard, Wieschaus, and co-workers found for cytoplasmic determinants deposited in the egg by the mother. These genes set up the initial pattern of the embryo by regulating gene expression in broad regions of the early embryo.

Axis Establishment

As we mentioned earlier, cytoplasmic determinants in the egg are the substances that initially establish the axes of the *Drosophila* body. These substances are encoded by genes of the mother, fittingly called maternal effect genes. A **maternal effect gene** is a gene that, when mutant in the mother, results in a mutant phenotype in the offspring, regardless of the offspring's own genotype. In fruit fly development, the mRNA or protein products of maternal effect genes are placed in the egg while it is still in the mother's ovary. When the mother has a mutation in such a gene, she makes a defective gene product (or none at all), and her eggs are defective; when these eggs are fertilized, they fail to develop properly.

Because they control the orientation (polarity) of the egg and consequently of the fly, maternal effect genes are also called **egg-polarity genes**. One group of these genes sets up the anterior-posterior axis of the embryo, while a second group establishes the dorsal-ventral axis. Like mutations in segmentation genes, mutations in maternal effect genes are generally embryonic lethals.

Bicoid: A Morphogen Determining Head Structures To see how maternal effect genes determine the body axes of the offspring, we will focus on one such gene, called *bicoid*, a term meaning "two-tailed." An embryo whose mother has two mutant alleles of the *bicoid* gene lacks the front half of its body and has posterior structures at both ends (**Figure 18.21**). This phenotype suggested to Nüsslein-Volhard and her colleagues that the product of the mother's *bicoid* gene is essential for setting up the anterior end of the fly and might be concentrated at the future anterior end of the embryo. This hypothesis is an example of the *morphogen gradient hypothesis* first proposed by embryologists a century ago; in this hypothesis, gradients of substances called **morphogens** establish an embryo's axes and other features of its form.

DNA technology and other modern biochemical methods enabled the researchers to test whether the *bicoid* product, a protein called Bicoid, is in fact a morphogen that determines the anterior end of the fly. The first question they asked was whether the mRNA and protein products of these genes are located in the egg in a position consistent with the hypothesis.

▲ **Figure 18.21 Effect of the *bicoid* gene on *Drosophila* development.** A wild-type fruit fly larva has a head, three thoracic (T) segments, eight abdominal (A) segments, and a tail. A larva whose mother has two mutant alleles of the *bicoid* gene has two tails and lacks all anterior structures (LMs).

They found that *bicoid* mRNA is highly concentrated at the extreme anterior end of the mature egg, as predicted by the hypothesis (**Figure 18.22**). After the egg is fertilized, the mRNA is translated into protein. The Bicoid protein then diffuses from the anterior end toward the posterior, resulting in a gradient of protein within the early embryo, with the highest concentration at the anterior end. These results are consistent with the hypothesis that Bicoid protein specifies the fly's anterior end. To test the hypothesis more specifically, scientists injected pure *bicoid* mRNA into various regions of early embryos. The protein that resulted from its translation caused anterior structures to form at the injection sites.

▼ **Figure 18.22**

INQUIRY

Is Bicoid a morphogen that determines the anterior end of a fruit fly?

EXPERIMENT Using a genetic approach to study *Drosophila* development, Christiane Nüsslein-Volhard and colleagues at the European Molecular Biology Laboratory in Heidelberg, Germany, analyzed expression of the *bicoid* gene. The researchers hypothesized that *bicoid* normally codes for a morphogen that specifies the head (anterior) end of the embryo. To test this hypothesis, they used molecular techniques to determine where the mRNA and protein encoded by this gene were found in the fertilized egg and early embryo of wild-type flies.

RESULTS *Bicoid* mRNA (dark blue) was confined to the anterior end of the unfertilized egg. Later in development, Bicoid protein (dark orange) was seen to be concentrated in cells at the anterior end of the embryo.

Bicoid mRNA in mature unfertilized egg — Bicoid protein in early embryo

Bicoid mRNA in mature unfertilized egg — Bicoid protein in early embryo

CONCLUSION The location of *bicoid* mRNA and the diffuse gradient of Bicoid protein seen later support the hypothesis that Bicoid protein is a morphogen specifying formation of head-specific structures.

SOURCE: C. Nüsslein-Volhard et al., Determination of anteroposterior polarity in *Drosophila*, *Science* 238:1675–1681 (1987); W. Driever and C. Nüsslein-Volhard, A gradient of *bicoid* protein in *Drosophila* embryos, *Cell* 54:83–93 (1988); T. Berleth et al., The role of localization of *bicoid* RNA in organizing the anterior pattern of the *Drosophila* embryo, *EMBO Journal* 7:1749–1756 (1988).

WHAT IF? If the hypothesis is correct, predict what would happen if you injected *bicoid* mRNA into the anterior end of an egg from a female with a mutation disabling the *bicoid* gene.

The *bicoid* research was groundbreaking for several reasons. First, it led to the identification of a specific protein required for some of the earliest steps in pattern formation. It thus helped us understand how different regions of the egg can give rise to cells that go down different developmental pathways. Second, it increased our understanding of the mother's critical role in the initial phases of embryonic development. Finally, the principle that a gradient of morphogens can determine polarity and position has proved to be a key developmental concept for a number of species, just as early embryologists had thought.

Maternal mRNAs are crucial during development of many species. In *Drosophila*, gradients of specific proteins encoded by maternal mRNAs determine the posterior and anterior ends and establish the dorsal-ventral axis. As the fly embryo grows, it reaches a point when the embryonic program of gene expression takes over, and the maternal mRNAs must be destroyed. (This process involves miRNAs in *Drosophila* and other species.) Later, positional information encoded by the embryo's genes, operating on an ever finer scale, establishes a specific number of correctly oriented segments and triggers the formation of each segment's characteristic structures. When the genes operating in this final step are abnormal, the pattern of the adult is abnormal, as you saw in Figure 18.20.

In this section, we have seen how a carefully orchestrated program of sequential gene regulation controls the transformation of a fertilized egg into a multicellular organism. The program is carefully balanced between turning on the genes for differentiation in the right place and turning off other genes. Even when an organism is fully developed, gene expression is regulated in a similarly fine-tuned manner. In the final section of the chapter, we'll consider how fine this tuning is by looking at how specific changes in expression of one or a few genes can lead to the development of cancer.

CONCEPT CHECK 18.4

1. As you learned in Chapter 12, mitosis gives rise to two daughter cells that are genetically identical to the parent cell. Yet you, the product of many mitotic divisions, are not composed of identical cells. Why?

2. **MAKE CONNECTIONS** Explain how the signaling molecules released by an embryonic cell can induce changes in a neighboring cell without entering the cell.

3. Why are fruit fly maternal effect genes also called egg-polarity genes?

4. **WHAT IF?** In the blowup box in Figure 18.17b, the lower cell is synthesizing signaling molecules, whereas the upper cell is expressing receptors for these molecules. In terms of gene regulation, explain how these cells came to synthesize different molecules.

For suggested answers, see Appendix A.

CONCEPT 18.5

Cancer results from genetic changes that affect cell cycle control

In Chapter 12, we considered cancer as a set of diseases in which cells escape from the control mechanisms that normally limit their growth. Now that we have discussed the molecular basis of gene expression and its regulation, we are ready to look at cancer more closely. The gene regulation systems that go wrong during cancer turn out to be the very same systems that play important roles in embryonic development, the immune response, and many other biological processes. Thus, research into the molecular basis of cancer has both benefited from and informed many other fields of biology.

Types of Genes Associated with Cancer

The genes that normally regulate cell growth and division during the cell cycle include genes for growth factors, their receptors, and the intracellular molecules of signaling pathways. (To review the cell cycle, see Chapter 12.) Mutations that alter any of these genes in somatic cells can lead to cancer. The agent of such change can be random spontaneous mutation. However, it is likely that many cancer-causing mutations result from environmental influences, such as chemical carcinogens, X-rays and other high-energy radiation, and some viruses.

Cancer research led to the discovery of cancer-causing genes called **oncogenes** (from the Greek *onco*, tumor) in certain types of viruses (see Chapter 19). Subsequently, close counterparts of viral oncogenes were found in the genomes of humans and other animals. The normal versions of the cellular genes, called **proto-oncogenes**, code for proteins that stimulate normal cell growth and division.

How might a proto-oncogene—a gene that has an essential function in normal cells—become an oncogene, a cancer-causing gene? In general, an oncogene arises from a genetic change that leads to an increase either in the amount of the proto-oncogene's protein product or in the intrinsic activity of each protein molecule. The genetic changes that convert proto-oncogenes to oncogenes fall into three main categories: movement of DNA within the genome, amplification of a proto-oncogene, and point mutations in a control element or in the proto-oncogene itself (**Figure 18.23**, on the next page).

Cancer cells are frequently found to contain chromosomes that have broken and rejoined incorrectly, translocating fragments from one chromosome to another (see Figure 15.14). Now that you have learned how gene expression is regulated, you can understand the possible consequences of such translocations. If a translocated proto-oncogene ends up near an especially active promoter (or other control element), its transcription may increase, making it an oncogene. The second main type of genetic change, amplification, increases the

▲ **Figure 18.23 Genetic changes that can turn proto-oncogenes into oncogenes.**

number of copies of the proto-oncogene in the cell through repeated gene duplication (discussed in Chapter 21). The third possibility is a point mutation either (1) in the promoter or an enhancer that controls a proto-oncogene, causing an increase in its expression, or (2) in the coding sequence, changing the gene's product to a protein that is more active or more resistant to degradation than the normal protein. All these mechanisms can lead to abnormal stimulation of the cell cycle and put the cell on the path to malignancy.

Tumor-Suppressor Genes

In addition to genes whose products normally promote cell division, cells contain genes whose normal products *inhibit* cell division. Such genes are called **tumor-suppressor genes** because the proteins they encode help prevent uncontrolled cell growth. Any mutation that decreases the normal activity of a tumor-suppressor protein may contribute to the onset of cancer, in effect stimulating growth through the absence of suppression.

The protein products of tumor-suppressor genes have various functions. Some tumor-suppressor proteins repair damaged DNA, a function that prevents the cell from accumulating cancer-causing mutations. Other tumor-suppressor proteins control the adhesion of cells to each other or to the extracellular matrix; proper cell anchorage is crucial in normal tissues—and is often absent in cancers. Still other tumor-suppressor proteins are components of cell-signaling pathways that inhibit the cell cycle.

Interference with Normal Cell-Signaling Pathways

The proteins encoded by many proto-oncogenes and tumor-suppressor genes are components of cell-signaling pathways. Let's take a closer look at how such proteins function in normal

cells and what goes wrong with their function in cancer cells. We will focus on the products of two key genes, the *ras* proto-oncogene and the *p53* tumor-suppressor gene. Mutations in *ras* occur in about 30% of human cancers, and mutations in *p53* in more than 50%.

The Ras protein, encoded by the **_ras_ gene** (named for r̲a̲t s̲arcoma, a connective tissue cancer), is a G protein that relays a signal from a growth factor receptor on the plasma membrane to a cascade of protein kinases. The cellular response at the end of the pathway is the synthesis of a protein that stimulates the cell cycle **(Figure 18.24a)**. Normally, such a pathway will not operate unless triggered by the appropriate growth factor. But certain mutations in the *ras* gene can lead to production of a hyperactive Ras protein that triggers the kinase cascade even in the absence of growth factor, resulting in increased cell division. In fact, hyperactive versions or excess amounts of any of the pathway's components can have the same outcome: excessive cell division.

Figure 18.24b shows a pathway in which a signal leads to the synthesis of a protein that suppresses the cell cycle. In this case, the signal is damage to the cell's DNA, perhaps as the result of exposure to ultraviolet light. Operation of this signaling pathway blocks the cell cycle until the damage has been repaired. Otherwise, the damage might contribute to tumor formation by causing mutations or chromosomal abnormalities. Thus, the genes for the components of the pathway act as tumor-suppressor genes. The **_p53_ gene**, named for the 53,000-dalton molecular weight of its protein product, is a tumor-suppressor gene. The protein it encodes is a specific transcription factor that promotes the synthesis of cell cycle–inhibiting proteins. That is why a mutation that knocks out the *p53* gene, like a mutation that leads to a hyperactive Ras protein, can lead to excessive cell growth and cancer **(Figure 18.24c)**.

(a) Cell cycle–stimulating pathway.
This pathway is triggered by ➊ a growth factor that binds to ➋ its receptor in the plasma membrane. The signal is relayed to ➌ a G protein called Ras. Like all G proteins, Ras is active when GTP is bound to it. Ras passes the signal to ➍ a series of protein kinases. The last kinase activates ➎ a transcription activator that turns on one or more genes for proteins that stimulate the cell cycle. If a mutation makes Ras or any other pathway component abnormally active, excessive cell division and cancer may result.

(b) Cell cycle–inhibiting pathway. In this pathway, ➊ DNA damage is an intracellular signal that is passed via ➋ protein kinases and leads to activation of ➌ p53. Activated p53 promotes transcription of the gene for a protein that inhibits the cell cycle. The resulting suppression of cell division ensures that the damaged DNA is not replicated. If the DNA damage is irreparable, the p53 signal leads to programmed cell death (apoptosis). Mutations causing deficiencies in any pathway component can contribute to the development of cancer.

(c) Effects of mutations. Increased cell division, possibly leading to cancer, can result if the cell cycle is overstimulated, as in (a), or not inhibited when it normally would be, as in (b).

▲ Figure 18.24 **Signaling pathways that regulate cell division.** Both stimulatory and inhibitory pathways regulate the cell cycle, commonly by influencing transcription. Cancer can result from aberrations in such pathways, which may be caused by mutations, either spontaneous or environmentally triggered.

? *Looking at the pathway in (b), explain whether a cancer-causing mutation in a tumor-suppressor gene, such as p53, is more likely to be a recessive or a dominant mutation.*

The *p53* gene has been called the "guardian angel of the genome." Once the gene is activated—for example, by DNA damage—the p53 protein functions as an activator for several other genes. Often it activates a gene called *p21*, whose product halts the cell cycle by binding to cyclin-dependent kinases, allowing time for the cell to repair the DNA. Researchers recently showed that p53 also activates expression of a group of miRNAs, which in turn inhibit the cell cycle. In addition, the p53 protein can turn on genes directly involved in DNA repair. Finally, when DNA damage is irreparable, p53 activates "suicide" genes, whose protein products bring about programmed cell death (apoptosis). Thus, p53 acts in several ways to prevent a cell from passing on mutations due to DNA damage. If mutations do accumulate and the cell survives through many divisions—as is more likely if the *p53* tumor-suppressor gene is defective or missing—cancer may ensue.

The many functions of p53 suggest a complex picture of regulation in normal cells, one that we do not yet fully understand. For the present, the diagram in Figure 18.24 is an accurate view of how mutations can contribute to cancer, but we still don't know exactly how a particular cell becomes a cancer cell. As we discover previously unknown aspects of gene regulation, it is informative to study their role in the onset of cancer. Such studies have shown, for instance, that DNA methylation and histone modification patterns differ in normal and cancer cells and that miRNAs probably participate in cancer development. While we've learned a lot about cancer by studying cell-signaling pathways, there is still a lot left to learn.

The Multistep Model of Cancer Development

More than one somatic mutation is generally needed to produce all the changes characteristic of a full-fledged cancer cell. This may help explain why the incidence of cancer increases greatly with age. If cancer results from an accumulation of mutations and if mutations occur throughout life, then the longer we live, the more likely we are to develop cancer.

The model of a multistep path to cancer is well supported by studies of one of the best-understood types of human cancer, colorectal cancer. About 135,000 new cases of colorectal cancer are diagnosed each year in the United States, and the disease causes 60,000 deaths each year. Like most cancers, colorectal cancer develops gradually (**Figure 18.25**). The first sign is often a polyp, a small, benign growth in the colon lining. The cells of the polyp look normal, although they divide unusually frequently. The tumor grows and may eventually become malignant, invading other tissues. The development of a malignant tumor is paralleled by a gradual accumulation of mutations that convert proto-oncogenes to oncogenes and knock out tumor-suppressor genes. A *ras* oncogene and a mutated *p53* tumor-suppressor gene are often involved.

About half a dozen changes must occur at the DNA level for a cell to become fully cancerous. These changes usually include the appearance of at least one active oncogene and the mutation or loss of several tumor-suppressor genes. Furthermore, since mutant tumor-suppressor alleles are usually recessive, in most cases mutations must knock out *both* alleles in a cell's genome to block tumor suppression. (Most oncogenes, on the other hand, behave as dominant alleles.) The order in which these changes must occur is still under investigation, as is the relative importance of different mutations.

Recently, technical advances in the sequencing of DNA and mRNA have allowed medical researchers to compare the genes expressed by different types of tumors and by the same type in different individuals. These comparisons have led to personalized cancer treatments based on the molecular characteristics of an individual's tumor (see Figure 12.21.)

Inherited Predisposition and Other Factors Contributing to Cancer

The fact that multiple genetic changes are required to produce a cancer cell helps explain the observation that cancers can run in families. An individual inheriting an oncogene or

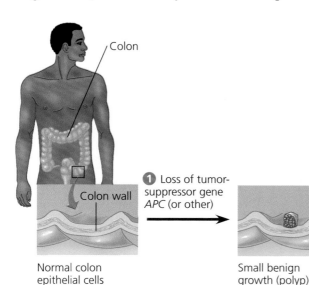

▼ **Figure 18.25 A multistep model for the development of colorectal cancer.** Affecting the colon and/or rectum, this type of cancer is one of the best understood. Changes in a tumor parallel a series of genetic changes, including mutations affecting several tumor-suppressor genes (such as *p53*) and the *ras* proto-oncogene. Mutations of tumor-suppressor genes often entail loss (deletion) of the gene. *APC* stands for "adenomatous polyposis coli," and *DCC* stands for "deleted in colorectal cancer." Other mutation sequences can also lead to colorectal cancer.

Colon

Colon wall

❶ Loss of tumor-suppressor gene *APC* (or other)

❷ Activation of *ras* oncogene

❸ Loss of tumor-suppressor gene *DCC*

❹ Loss of tumor-suppressor gene *p53*

❺ Additional mutations

Normal colon epithelial cells

Small benign growth (polyp)

Larger benign growth (adenoma)

Malignant tumor (carcinoma)

a mutant allele of a tumor-suppressor gene is one step closer to accumulating the necessary mutations for cancer to develop than is an individual without any such mutations.

Geneticists are devoting much effort to identifying inherited cancer alleles so that predisposition to certain cancers can be detected early in life. About 15% of colorectal cancers, for example, involve inherited mutations. Many of these affect the tumor-suppressor gene called *adenomatous polyposis coli*, or *APC* (see Figure 18.25). This gene has multiple functions in the cell, including regulation of cell migration and adhesion. Even in patients with no family history of the disease, the *APC* gene is mutated in 60% of colorectal cancers. In these individuals, new mutations must occur in both *APC* alleles before the gene's function is lost. Since only 15% of colorectal cancers are associated with known inherited mutations, researchers continue in their efforts to identify "markers" that could predict the risk of developing this type of cancer.

There is evidence of a strong inherited predisposition in 5–10% of patients with breast cancer. This is the second most common type of cancer in the United States, striking over 180,000 women (and some men) annually and killing 40,000 each year. In 1990, after 16 years of research, geneticist Mary-Claire King convincingly demonstrated that mutations in one gene—*BRCA1*—were associated with increased susceptibility to breast cancer, a finding that flew in the face of medical opinion at the time. (*BRCA* stands for *breast cancer*.) Mutations in that gene or the related *BRCA2* gene are found in at least half of inherited breast cancers, and tests using DNA sequencing can detect these mutations (**Figure 18.26**). A woman who inherits one mutant *BRCA1* allele has a 60% probability of developing breast cancer before the age of 50, compared with only a 2% probability for an individual homozygous for the normal allele. Both *BRCA1* and *BRCA2* are considered tumor-suppressor genes because their wild-type alleles protect against breast cancer and their mutant alleles are recessive. Apparently, the BRCA1 and BRCA2 proteins both function in the cell's DNA damage repair pathway. More is known about BRCA2, which, in association with another protein, helps repair breaks that occur in both strands of DNA; it is crucial for maintaining undamaged DNA in a cell's nucleus.

Because DNA breakage can contribute to cancer, it makes sense that the risk of cancer can be lowered by minimizing exposure to DNA-damaging agents, such as the ultraviolet radiation in sunlight and chemicals found in cigarette smoke. Novel methods for early diagnosis and treatment of specific cancers are being developed that rely on new techniques for analyzing, and perhaps interfering with, gene expression in tumors. Ultimately, such approaches may lower the death rate from cancer.

The study of genes associated with cancer, inherited or not, increases our basic understanding of how disruption of normal gene regulation can result in this disease. In addition to the mutations and other genetic alterations described in this section, a number of *tumor viruses* can cause cancer in various animals, including humans. In fact, one of the earliest breakthroughs in understanding cancer came in 1911, when Peyton Rous, an American pathologist, discovered a virus that causes cancer in chickens. The Epstein-Barr virus, which causes infectious mononucleosis, has been linked to several types of cancer in humans, notably Burkitt's lymphoma. Papillomaviruses are associated with cancer of the cervix, and a virus called HTLV-1 causes a type of adult leukemia. Worldwide, viruses seem to play a role in about 15% of the cases of human cancer.

Viruses may at first seem very different from mutations as a cause of cancer. However, we now know that viruses can interfere with gene regulation in several ways if they integrate their genetic material into the DNA of a cell. Viral integration may donate an oncogene to the cell, disrupt a tumor-suppressor gene, or convert a proto-oncogene to an oncogene. In addition, some viruses produce proteins that inactivate p53 and other tumor-suppressor proteins, making the cell more prone to becoming cancerous. Viruses are powerful biological agents, and you'll learn more about their function in Chapter 19.

CONCEPT CHECK 18.5

1. **MAKE CONNECTIONS** The p53 protein can activate genes involved in apoptosis, or programmed cell death. Discuss how mutations in genes coding for proteins that function in apoptosis could contribute to cancer.

2. Under what circumstances is cancer considered to have a hereditary component?

3. **WHAT IF?** Explain how the types of mutations that lead to cancer are different for a proto-oncogene and a tumor-suppressor gene, in terms of the effect of the mutation on the activity of the gene product.

For suggested answers, see Appendix A.

▲ **Figure 18.26 Testing for mutations in *BRCA1* and *BRCA2*.** Genetic testing for mutations that increase the risk of breast cancer is available for individuals with a family history of breast cancer. New "high-throughput" sequencing techniques can sequence many DNA samples at once, as shown here.

18 CHAPTER REVIEW

SUMMARY OF KEY CONCEPTS

CONCEPT 18.1

Bacteria often respond to environmental change by regulating transcription (pp. 351–356)

- Cells control metabolism by regulating enzyme activity or the expression of genes coding for enzymes. In bacteria, genes are often clustered into **operons,** with one promoter serving several adjacent genes. An **operator** site on the DNA switches the operon on or off, resulting in coordinate regulation of the genes.

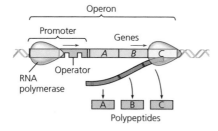

- Both repressible and inducible operons are examples of negative gene regulation. In either type of operon, binding of a specific **repressor** protein to the operator shuts off transcription. (The repressor is encoded by a separate **regulatory gene**.) In a repressible operon, the repressor is active when bound to a **corepressor,** usually the end product of an anabolic pathway.

In an inducible operon, binding of an **inducer** to an innately active repressor inactivates the repressor and turns on transcription. Inducible enzymes usually function in catabolic pathways.

- Some operons are also subject to positive gene regulation via a stimulatory **activator** protein, such as catabolite activator protein (CAP), which, when activated by **cyclic AMP**, binds to a site within the promoter and stimulates transcription.

? *Compare and contrast the roles of the corepressor and the inducer in negative regulation of an operon.*

CONCEPT 18.2

Eukaryotic gene expression is regulated at many stages (pp. 356–364)

? *Describe what must happen for a cell-type-specific gene to be transcribed in a cell of that type.*

CONCEPT 18.3

Noncoding RNAs play multiple roles in controlling gene expression (pp. 364–366)

> *Why are miRNAs called noncoding RNAs? Explain how they participate in gene regulation.*

CONCEPT 18.4

A program of differential gene expression leads to the different cell types in a multicellular organism (pp. 366–373)

- Embryonic cells undergo **differentiation**, becoming specialized in structure and function. **Morphogenesis** encompasses the processes that give shape to the organism and its various parts. Cells differ in structure and function not because they contain different genes but because they express different portions of a common genome.
- **Cytoplasmic determinants** in the unfertilized egg regulate the expression of genes in the zygote that affect the developmental fate of embryonic cells. In the process called **induction**, signaling molecules from embryonic cells cause transcriptional changes in nearby target cells.
- Differentiation is heralded by the appearance of tissue-specific proteins, which enable differentiated cells to carry out their specialized roles.
- In animals, **pattern formation**, the development of a spatial organization of tissues and organs, begins in the early embryo. **Positional information**, the molecular cues that control pattern formation, tells a cell its location relative to the body's axes and to other cells. In *Drosophila*, gradients of **morphogens** encoded by **maternal effect genes** determine the body axes. For example, the gradient of **Bicoid** protein determines the anterior-posterior axis.

> *Describe the two main processes that cause embryonic cells to head down different pathways to their final fates.*

CONCEPT 18.5

Cancer results from genetic changes that affect cell cycle control (pp. 373–377)

- The products of **proto-oncogenes** and **tumor-suppressor genes** control cell division. A DNA change that makes a proto-oncogene excessively active converts it to an **oncogene**, which may promote excessive cell division and cancer. A tumor-suppressor gene encodes a protein that inhibits abnormal cell division. A mutation in such a gene that reduces the activity of its protein product may also lead to excessive cell division and possibly to cancer.
- Many proto-oncogenes and tumor-suppressor genes encode components of growth-stimulating and growth-inhibiting signaling pathways, respectively, and mutations in these genes can interfere with normal cell-signaling pathways. A hyperactive version of a protein in a stimulatory pathway, such as **Ras** (a G protein), functions as an oncogene protein. A defective version of a protein in an inhibitory pathway, such as **p53** (a transcription activator), fails to function as a tumor suppressor.
- In the multistep model of cancer development, normal cells are converted to cancer cells by the accumulation of mutations affecting proto-oncogenes and tumor-suppressor genes. Technical advances in DNA and mRNA sequencing are enabling cancer treatments that are more individually based.
- Individuals who inherit a mutant oncogene or tumor-suppressor allele have a predisposition to develop a particular cancer. Certain viruses promote cancer by integration of viral DNA into a cell's genome.

> *Compare the usual functions of proteins encoded by proto-oncogenes with the functions of proteins encoded by tumor-suppressor genes.*

LEVEL 1: KNOWLEDGE/COMPREHENSION

1. If a particular operon encodes enzymes for making an essential amino acid and is regulated like the *trp* operon, then
   a. the amino acid inactivates the repressor.
   b. the enzymes produced are called inducible enzymes.
   c. the repressor is active in the absence of the amino acid.
   d. the amino acid acts as a corepressor.
   e. the amino acid turns on transcription of the operon.

2. Muscle cells differ from nerve cells mainly because they
   a. express different genes.
   b. contain different genes.
   c. use different genetic codes.
   d. have unique ribosomes.
   e. have different chromosomes.

3. The functioning of enhancers is an example of
   a. transcriptional control of gene expression.
   b. a post-transcriptional mechanism to regulate mRNA.
   c. the stimulation of translation by initiation factors.
   d. post-translational control that activates certain proteins.
   e. a eukaryotic equivalent of prokaryotic promoter functioning.

4. Cell differentiation always involves
   a. the production of tissue-specific proteins, such as muscle actin.
   b. the movement of cells.
   c. the transcription of the *myoD* gene.
   d. the selective loss of certain genes from the genome.
   e. the cell's sensitivity to environmental cues, such as light or heat.

5. Which of the following is an example of post-transcriptional control of gene expression?
   a. the addition of methyl groups to cytosine bases of DNA
   b. the binding of transcription factors to a promoter
   c. the removal of introns and alternative splicing of exons
   d. gene amplification contributing to cancer
   e. the folding of DNA to form heterochromatin

LEVEL 2: APPLICATION/ANALYSIS

6. What would occur if the repressor of an inducible operon were mutated so it could not bind the operator?
   a. irreversible binding of the repressor to the promoter
   b. reduced transcription of the operon's genes
   c. buildup of a substrate for the pathway controlled by the operon
   d. continuous transcription of the operon's genes
   e. overproduction of catabolite activator protein (CAP)

7. Absence of *bicoid* mRNA from a *Drosophila* egg leads to the absence of anterior larval body parts and mirror-image duplication of posterior parts. This is evidence that the product of the *bicoid* gene
   a. is transcribed in the early embryo.
   b. normally leads to formation of tail structures.
   c. normally leads to formation of head structures.
   d. is a protein present in all head structures.
   e. leads to programmed cell death.

8. Which of the following statements about the DNA in one of your brain cells is true?
   a. Most of the DNA codes for protein.
   b. The majority of genes are likely to be transcribed.
   c. Each gene lies immediately adjacent to an enhancer.
   d. Many genes are grouped into operon-like clusters.
   e. It is the same as the DNA in one of your heart cells.

9. Within a cell, the amount of protein made using a given mRNA molecule depends partly on
   a. the degree of DNA methylation.
   b. the rate at which the mRNA is degraded.
   c. the presence of certain transcription factors.
   d. the number of introns present in the mRNA.
   e. the types of ribosomes present in the cytoplasm.

10. Proto-oncogenes can change into oncogenes that cause cancer. Which of the following best explains the presence of these potential time bombs in eukaryotic cells?
    a. Proto-oncogenes first arose from viral infections.
    b. Proto-oncogenes normally help regulate cell division.
    c. Proto-oncogenes are genetic "junk."
    d. Proto-oncogenes are mutant versions of normal genes.
    e. Cells produce proto-oncogenes as they age.

LEVEL 3: SYNTHESIS/EVALUATION

11. **DRAW IT** The diagram below shows five genes, including their enhancers, from the genome of a certain species. Imagine that orange, blue, green, black, red, and purple activator proteins exist that can bind to the appropriately color-coded control elements in the enhancers of these genes.

   a. Draw an X above enhancer elements (of all the genes) that would have activators bound in a cell in which only gene 5 is transcribed. Which colored activators would be present?
   b. Draw a dot above all enhancer elements that would have activators bound in a cell in which the green, blue, and orange activators are present. Which gene(s) would be transcribed?
   c. Imagine that genes 1, 2, and 4 code for nerve-specific proteins, and genes 3 and 5 are skin specific. Which activators would have to be present in each cell type to ensure transcription of the appropriate genes?

12. **EVOLUTION CONNECTION**
    DNA sequences can act as "tape measures of evolution" (see Chapter 5). Scientists analyzing the human genome sequence were surprised to find that some of the regions of the human genome that are most highly conserved (similar to comparable regions in other species) don't code for proteins. Propose a possible explanation for this observation.

13. **SCIENTIFIC INQUIRY**
    Prostate cells usually require testosterone and other androgens to survive. But some prostate cancer cells thrive despite treatments that eliminate androgens. One hypothesis is that estrogen, often considered a female hormone, may be activating genes normally controlled by an androgen in these cancer cells. Describe one or more experiments to test this hypothesis.

14. **SCIENCE, TECHNOLOGY, AND SOCIETY**
    Trace amounts of dioxin were present in Agent Orange, a defoliant sprayed on vegetation during the Vietnam War. Animal tests suggest that dioxin can cause birth defects, cancer, liver and thymus damage, and immune system suppression, sometimes leading to death. But the animal tests are equivocal; a hamster is not affected by a dose that can kill a guinea pig. Dioxin acts somewhat like a steroid hormone, entering a cell and binding to a receptor protein that then attaches to the cell's DNA. How might this mechanism help explain the variety of dioxin's effects on different body systems and in different animals? How might you determine whether a type of illness is related to dioxin exposure? How might you determine whether a particular individual became ill as a result of exposure to dioxin? Which would be more difficult to demonstrate? Why?

15. **WRITE ABOUT A THEME**
    Feedback Regulation In a short essay (100–150 words), discuss how the processes shown in Figure 18.24a and b are examples of feedback mechanisms regulating biological systems.

For selected answers, see Appendix A.

MasteringBIOLOGY® www.masteringbiology.com

1. MasteringBiology® Assignments
Tutorials Regulation of Gene Expression in Bacteria • Regulation of Gene Expression in Eukaryotes • Pattern Formation
Activities The *lac* Operon • The *lac* Operon in *E. coli* • Transcription Initiation in Eukaryotes • Overview: Control of Gene Expression • Control of Transcription • Review: Control of Gene Expression • Early Pattern Formation in *Drosophila* • Role of *bicoid* Gene in *Drosophila* Development
Questions Student Misconceptions • Reading Quiz • Multiple Choice • End-of-Chapter

2. eText
Read your book online, search, take notes, highlight text, and more.

3. The Study Area
Practice Tests • Cumulative Test • *BioFlix* 3-D Animations • MP3 Tutor Sessions • Videos • Activities • Investigations • Lab Media • Audio Glossary • Word Study Tools • Art

UNIVERSITY OF ALBERTA FACULTY BIO

 Katharine Edens Magor BSc and MSc Biochemistry and Biology (Dalhousie); PhD Immunogenetics (Medical U. of South Carolina)

Current Position: Associate Professor, Department of Biological Sciences

Education is a two-way street and I get new ideas from students in my classes and lab. I teach Immunology and Infection (IMIN 200), Research Techniques in Immunology (IMIN 372), and a course on immune systems in 'funny critters' with Brad Magor, Comparative Immunology (IMIN 401).

During my undergraduate program, I took two electives out of interest (Immunology and Virology), which turned out to be important years later. After completing my MSc and a research job, my husband, Brad Magor, and I moved to South Carolina so Brad could pursue his PhD in fish immunology. While in South Carolina, through an unforeseen opportunity, I took on a PhD project on duck antibody genes that had been abandoned by another graduate student. There I got interested in the questions that still inspire my research. Why are ducks exploited as hosts of influenza viruses? Why doesn't influenza harm them? When I started my own research lab at the University of Alberta I knew I wanted to return to these questions. My research looks at diversity and function of immune genes involved in antiviral responses. Recently, I worked with H5N1 bird flu in Robert Webster's lab, the virologist who originally discovered that ducks are the host of influenza.

19

Viruses

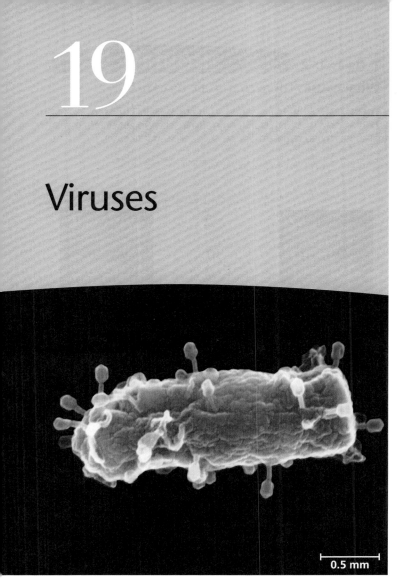

0.5 mm

▲ **Figure 19.1 Are the tiny viruses infecting this _E. coli_ cell alive?**

KEY CONCEPTS

19.1 A virus consists of a nucleic acid surrounded by a protein coat

19.2 Viruses replicate only in host cells

19.3 Viruses, viroids, and prions are formidable pathogens in animals and plants

OVERVIEW

A Borrowed Life

The photo in **Figure 19.1** shows a remarkable event: the attack of a bacterial cell by numerous structures that resemble miniature lollipops. These structures, a type of virus called T4 bacteriophage, are seen infecting the bacterium _Escherichia coli_ in this colorized SEM. By injecting its DNA into the cell, the virus sets in motion a genetic takeover of the bacterium, recruiting cellular machinery to mass-produce many new viruses.

Recall that bacteria and other prokaryotes are cells much smaller and more simply organized than the cells of eukaryotes, such as plants and animals. Viruses are smaller and simpler still. Lacking the structures and metabolic machinery found in a cell, a **virus** is an infectious particle consisting of little more than genes packaged in a protein coat.

Are viruses living or nonliving? Early on, they were considered biological chemicals; in fact, the Latin root for the word _virus_ means "poison." Because viruses are capable of causing a wide variety of diseases and can be spread between organisms, researchers in the late 1800s saw a parallel with bacteria and proposed that viruses were the simplest of living forms. However, viruses cannot reproduce or carry out metabolic activities outside of a host cell. Most biologists studying viruses today would probably agree that they are not alive but exist in a shady area between life-forms and chemicals. The simple phrase used recently by two researchers describes them aptly enough: Viruses lead "a kind of borrowed life."

To a large extent, molecular biology was born in the laboratories of biologists studying viruses that infect bacteria. Experiments with viruses provided important evidence that genes are made of nucleic acids, and they were critical in working out the molecular mechanisms of the fundamental processes of DNA replication, transcription, and translation.

Beyond their value as experimental systems, viruses have unique genetic mechanisms that are interesting in their own right and that also help us understand how viruses cause disease. In addition, the study of viruses has led to the development of techniques that enable scientists to manipulate genes and transfer them from one organism to another. These techniques play an important role in basic research, biotechnology, and medical applications. For instance, viruses are used as agents of gene transfer in gene therapy (see Chapter 20).

In this chapter, we will explore the biology of viruses. We will begin with the structure of these simplest of all genetic systems and then describe the cycles by which they replicate. Next, we will discuss the role of viruses as disease-causing agents, or pathogens, and conclude by considering some even simpler infectious agents, viroids and prions.

CONCEPT 19.1

A virus consists of a nucleic acid surrounded by a protein coat

Scientists were able to detect viruses indirectly long before they were actually able to see them. The story of how viruses were discovered begins near the end of the 19th century.

The Discovery of Viruses: _Scientific Inquiry_

Tobacco mosaic disease stunts the growth of tobacco plants and gives their leaves a mottled, or mosaic, coloration. In 1883, Adolf Mayer, a German scientist, discovered that he could transmit the disease from plant to plant by rubbing sap extracted from diseased leaves onto healthy plants. After an unsuccessful search for an infectious microbe in the sap, Mayer suggested that the disease was caused by unusually small bacteria that were invisible under a microscope. This hypothesis was tested a decade later by Dimitri Ivanowsky, a Russian biologist who passed sap from infected tobacco leaves through a filter designed to remove bacteria. After filtration, the sap still produced mosaic disease.

But Ivanowsky clung to the hypothesis that bacteria caused tobacco mosaic disease. Perhaps, he reasoned, the bacteria were small enough to pass through the filter or made a toxin that could do so. The second possibility was ruled out when the Dutch botanist Martinus Beijerinck carried out a classic series of experiments that showed that the infectious agent in the filtered sap could replicate (Figure 19.2).

In fact, the pathogen replicated only within the host it infected. In further experiments, Beijerinck showed that unlike bacteria used in the lab at that time, the mysterious agent of mosaic disease could not be cultivated on nutrient media in test tubes or petri dishes. Beijerinck imagined a replicating particle much smaller and simpler than a bacterium, and he is generally credited with being the first scientist to voice the concept of a virus. His suspicions were confirmed in 1935 when the American scientist Wendell Stanley crystallized the infectious particle, now known as tobacco mosaic virus (TMV). Subsequently, TMV and many other viruses were actually seen with the help of the electron microscope.

Structure of Viruses

The tiniest viruses are only 20 nm in diameter—smaller than a ribosome. Millions could easily fit on a pinhead. Even the largest known virus, which has a diameter of several hundred nanometers, is barely visible under the light microscope. Stanley's discovery that some viruses could be crystallized was exciting and puzzling news. Not even the simplest of cells can aggregate into regular crystals. But if viruses are not cells, then what are they? Examining the structure of a virus more closely reveals that it is an infectious particle consisting of nucleic acid enclosed in a protein coat and, for some viruses, surrounded by a membranous envelope.

Viral Genomes

We usually think of genes as being made of double-stranded DNA—the conventional double helix—but many viruses defy this convention. Their genomes may consist of double-stranded DNA, single-stranded DNA, double-stranded RNA, or single-stranded RNA, depending on the type of virus. A virus is called a DNA virus or an RNA virus, based on the kind of nucleic acid that makes up its genome. In either case, the genome is usually organized as a single linear or circular molecule of nucleic acid, although the genomes of

▼ Figure 19.2 | **INQUIRY**

What causes tobacco mosaic disease?

EXPERIMENT In the late 1800s, Martinus Beijerinck, of the Technical School in Delft, the Netherlands, investigated the properties of the agent that causes tobacco mosaic disease (then called spot disease).

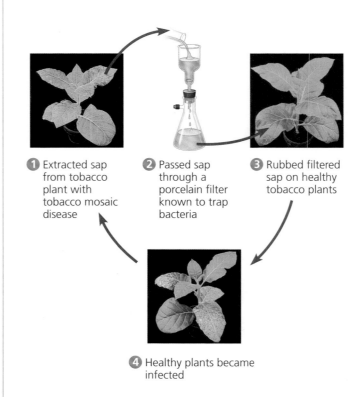

① Extracted sap from tobacco plant with tobacco mosaic disease

② Passed sap through a porcelain filter known to trap bacteria

③ Rubbed filtered sap on healthy tobacco plants

④ Healthy plants became infected

RESULTS When the filtered sap was rubbed on healthy plants, they became infected. Their sap, when extracted and filtered, could then act as the source of infection for another group of plants. Each successive group of plants developed the disease to the same extent as earlier groups.

CONCLUSION The infectious agent was apparently not a bacterium because it could pass through a bacterium-trapping filter. The pathogen must have been replicating in the plants because its ability to cause disease was undiluted after several transfers from plant to plant.

SOURCE M. J. Beijerinck, Concerning a *contagium vivum fluidum* as cause of the spot disease of tobacco leaves, *Verhandelingen der Koninkyke akademie Wettenschappen te Amsterdam* 65:3–21 (1898). Translation published in English as Phytopathological Classics Number 7 (1942), American Phytopathological Society Press, St. Paul, MN.

WHAT IF? If Beijerinck had observed that the infection of each group was weaker than that of the previous group and that ultimately the sap could no longer cause disease, what might he have concluded?

some viruses consist of multiple molecules of nucleic acid. The smallest viruses known have only four genes in their genome, while the largest have several hundred to a thousand. For comparison, bacterial genomes contain about 200 to a few thousand genes.

Capsids and Envelopes

The protein shell enclosing the viral genome is called a **capsid**. Depending on the type of virus, the capsid may be rod-shaped, polyhedral, or more complex in shape (like T4). Capsids are built from a large number of protein subunits called *capsomeres*, but the number of different *kinds* of proteins in a capsid is usually small. Tobacco mosaic virus has a rigid, rod-shaped capsid made from over a thousand molecules of a single type of protein arranged in a helix; rod-shaped viruses are commonly called *helical viruses* for this reason **(Figure 19.3a)**. Adenoviruses, which infect the respiratory tracts of animals, have 252 identical protein molecules arranged in a polyhedral capsid with 20 triangular facets—an icosahedron; thus, these and other similarly shaped viruses are referred to as *icosahedral viruses* **(Figure 19.3b)**.

Some viruses have accessory structures that help them infect their hosts. For instance, a membranous envelope surrounds the capsids of influenza viruses and many other viruses found in animals **(Figure 19.3c)**. These **viral envelopes**, which are derived from the membranes of the host cell, contain host cell phospholipids and membrane proteins. They also contain proteins and glycoproteins of viral origin. (Glycoproteins are proteins with carbohydrates covalently attached.) Some viruses carry a few viral enzyme molecules within their capsids.

Many of the most complex capsids are found among the viruses that infect bacteria, called **bacteriophages**, or simply **phages**. The first phages studied included seven that infect *E. coli*. These seven phages were named type 1 (T1), type 2 (T2), and so forth, in the order of their discovery. The three T-even phages (T2, T4, and T6) turned out to be very similar in structure. Their capsids have elongated icosahedral heads

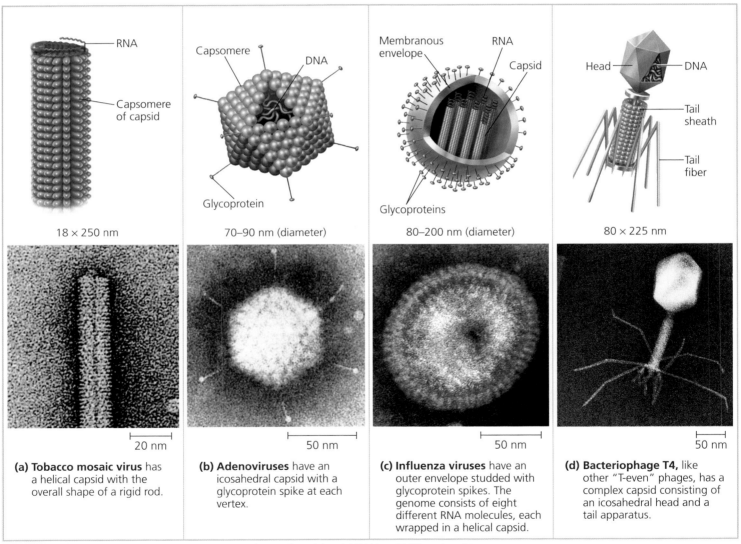

18 × 250 nm   70–90 nm (diameter)   80–200 nm (diameter)   80 × 225 nm

20 nm   50 nm   50 nm   50 nm

(a) Tobacco mosaic virus has a helical capsid with the overall shape of a rigid rod.

(b) Adenoviruses have an icosahedral capsid with a glycoprotein spike at each vertex.

(c) Influenza viruses have an outer envelope studded with glycoprotein spikes. The genome consists of eight different RNA molecules, each wrapped in a helical capsid.

(d) Bacteriophage T4, like other "T-even" phages, has a complex capsid consisting of an icosahedral head and a tail apparatus.

▲ **Figure 19.3 Viral structure.** Viruses are made up of nucleic acid (DNA or RNA) enclosed in a protein coat (the capsid) and sometimes further wrapped in a membranous envelope. The individual protein subunits making up the capsid are called capsomeres. Although diverse in size and shape, viruses have many common structural features. (All micrographs are colorized TEMs.)

enclosing their DNA. Attached to the head is a protein tail piece with fibers by which the phages attach to a bacterium (**Figure 19.3d**). In the next section, we'll examine how these few viral parts function together with cellular components to produce large numbers of viral progeny.

CONCEPT **19.2**

Viruses replicate only in host cells

Viruses lack metabolic enzymes and equipment for making proteins, such as ribosomes. They are obligate intracellular parasites; in other words, they can replicate only within a host cell. It is fair to say that viruses in isolation are merely packaged sets of genes in transit from one host cell to another.

Each particular virus can infect cells of only a limited number of host species, called the **host range** of the virus. This host specificity results from the evolution of recognition systems by the virus. Viruses usually identify host cells by a "lock-and-key" fit between viral surface proteins and specific receptor molecules on the outside of cells. (According to one model, such receptor molecules originally carried out functions that benefited the host cell but were co-opted later by viruses as portals of entry.) Some viruses have broad host ranges. For example, West Nile virus and equine encephalitis virus are distinctly different viruses that can each infect mosquitoes, birds, horses, and humans. Other viruses have host ranges so narrow that they infect only a single species. Measles virus, for instance, can infect only humans. Furthermore, viral infection of multicellular eukaryotes is usually limited to particular tissues. Human cold viruses infect only the cells lining the upper respiratory tract, and the AIDS virus binds to receptors present only on certain types of white blood cells.

General Features of Viral Replicative Cycles

A viral infection begins when a virus binds to a host cell and the viral genome makes its way inside (**Figure 19.4**). The mechanism of genome entry depends on the type of virus and the type of host cell. For example, T-even phages use their elaborate tail apparatus to inject DNA into a bacterium (see Figure 19.3d). Other viruses are taken up by endocytosis or, in the case of

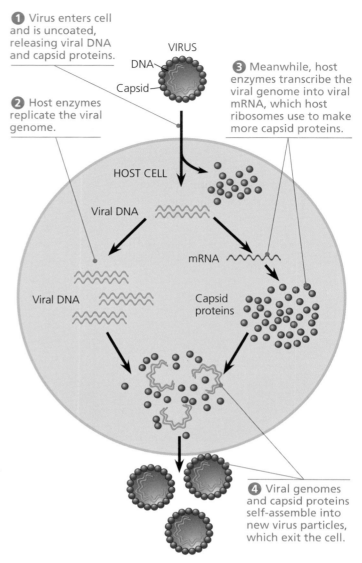

① Virus enters cell and is uncoated, releasing viral DNA and capsid proteins.

② Host enzymes replicate the viral genome.

③ Meanwhile, host enzymes transcribe the viral genome into viral mRNA, which host ribosomes use to make more capsid proteins.

④ Viral genomes and capsid proteins self-assemble into new virus particles, which exit the cell.

VIRUS
DNA
Capsid
HOST CELL
Viral DNA
mRNA
Viral DNA
Capsid proteins

▲ **Figure 19.4 A simplified viral replicative cycle.** A virus is an obligate intracellular parasite that uses the equipment and small molecules of its host cell to replicate. In this simplest of viral cycles, the parasite is a DNA virus with a capsid consisting of a single type of protein.

MAKE CONNECTIONS *Label each of the straight black arrows with one word representing the name of the process that is occurring. Review Figure 17.26 on page 348.*

enveloped viruses, by fusion of the viral envelope with the plasma membrane. Once the viral genome is inside, the proteins it encodes can commandeer the host, reprogramming the cell to copy the viral nucleic acid and manufacture viral proteins. The host provides the nucleotides for making viral nucleic acids, as well as enzymes, ribosomes, tRNAs, amino acids, ATP, and other components needed for making the viral proteins. Many DNA viruses use the DNA polymerases of the host cell to synthesize new genomes along the templates provided by the viral DNA. In contrast, to replicate their genomes, RNA viruses use virally encoded RNA polymerases that can use RNA as a template. (Uninfected cells generally make no enzymes for carrying out this process.)

After the viral nucleic acid molecules and capsomeres are produced, they spontaneously self-assemble into new viruses. In fact, researchers can separate the RNA and capsomeres of TMV and then reassemble complete viruses simply by mixing the components together under the right conditions. The simplest type of viral replicative cycle ends with the exit of hundreds or thousands of viruses from the infected host cell, a process that often damages or destroys the cell. Such cellular damage and death, as well as the body's responses to this destruction, cause many of the symptoms associated with viral infections. The viral progeny that exit a cell have the potential to infect additional cells, spreading the viral infection.

There are many variations on the simplified viral replicative cycle we have just described. We will now take a look at some of these variations in bacterial viruses (phages) and animal viruses; later in the chapter, we will consider plant viruses.

Replicative Cycles of Phages

Phages are the best understood of all viruses, although some of them are also among the most complex. Research on phages led to the discovery that some double-stranded DNA viruses can replicate by two alternative mechanisms: the lytic cycle and the lysogenic cycle.

The Lytic Cycle

A phage replicative cycle that culminates in death of the host cell is known as a **lytic cycle**. The term refers to the last stage of infection, during which the bacterium lyses (breaks open) and releases the phages that were produced within the cell. Each of these phages can then infect a healthy cell, and a few successive lytic cycles can destroy an entire bacterial population in just a few hours. A phage that replicates only by a lytic cycle is a **virulent phage**. **Figure 19.5** illustrates the major steps in the lytic cycle of T4, a typical virulent phage. Study this figure before proceeding.

After reading about the lytic cycle, you may wonder why phages haven't exterminated all bacteria. In fact, phage treatments have been used medically in some countries to help control bacterial infections in humans. Bacteria are not defenseless, however. First, natural selection favors bacterial mutants with receptors that are no longer recognized by a particular type of phage. Second, when phage DNA successfully enters a bacterium, the DNA often is identified as foreign and cut up by cellular enzymes called **restriction enzymes**, which are so named because their activity *restricts* the ability of the phage to infect the bacterium. The bacterial cell's own DNA is methylated in a way that prevents attack

▶ **Figure 19.5 The lytic cycle of phage T4, a virulent phage.** Phage T4 has almost 300 genes, which are transcribed and translated using the host cell's machinery. One of the first phage genes translated after the viral DNA enters the host cell codes for an enzyme that degrades the host cell's DNA (step 2); the phage DNA is protected from breakdown because it contains a modified form of cytosine that is not recognized by the enzyme. The entire lytic cycle, from the phage's first contact with the cell surface to cell lysis, takes only 20–30 minutes at 37°C.

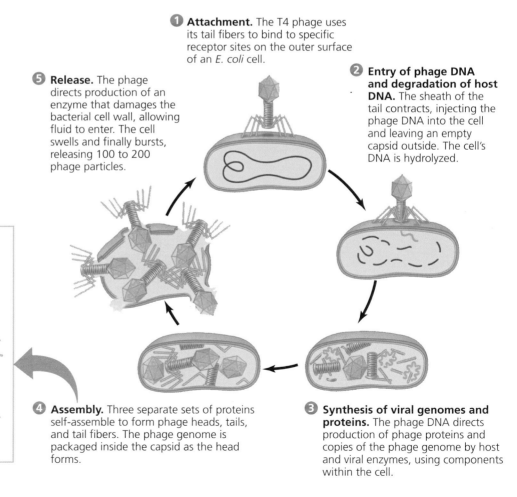

Phage assembly

Head   Tail   Tail fibers

❶ **Attachment.** The T4 phage uses its tail fibers to bind to specific receptor sites on the outer surface of an *E. coli* cell.

❷ **Entry of phage DNA and degradation of host DNA.** The sheath of the tail contracts, injecting the phage DNA into the cell and leaving an empty capsid outside. The cell's DNA is hydrolyzed.

❸ **Synthesis of viral genomes and proteins.** The phage DNA directs production of phage proteins and copies of the phage genome by host and viral enzymes, using components within the cell.

❹ **Assembly.** Three separate sets of proteins self-assemble to form phage heads, tails, and tail fibers. The phage genome is packaged inside the capsid as the head forms.

❺ **Release.** The phage directs production of an enzyme that damages the bacterial cell wall, allowing fluid to enter. The cell swells and finally bursts, releasing 100 to 200 phage particles.

by its own restriction enzymes. But just as natural selection favors bacteria with mutant receptors or effective restriction enzymes, it also favors phage mutants that can bind the altered receptors or are resistant to particular restriction enzymes. Thus, the parasite-host relationship is in constant evolutionary flux.

There is yet a third important reason bacteria have been spared from extinction as a result of phage activity. Instead of lysing their host cells, many phages coexist with them in a state called lysogeny, which we'll now discuss.

The Lysogenic Cycle

In contrast to the lytic cycle, which kills the host cell, the **lysogenic cycle** allows replication of the phage genome without destroying the host. Phages capable of using both modes of replicating within a bacterium are called **temperate phages**. A temperate phage called lambda, written with the Greek letter λ, is widely used in biological research. Phage λ resembles T4, but its tail has only one short tail fiber.

Infection of an *E. coli* cell by phage λ begins when the phage binds to the surface of the cell and injects its linear DNA genome **(Figure 19.6)**. Within the host, the λ DNA molecule forms a circle. What happens next depends on the replicative

mode: lytic cycle or lysogenic cycle. During a lytic cycle, the viral genes immediately turn the host cell into a λ-producing factory, and the cell soon lyses and releases its viral products. During a lysogenic cycle, however, the λ DNA molecule is incorporated into a specific site on the *E. coli* chromosome by viral proteins that break both circular DNA molecules and join them to each other. When integrated into the bacterial chromosome in this way, the viral DNA is known as a **prophage**. One prophage gene codes for a protein that prevents transcription of most of the other prophage genes. Thus, the phage genome is mostly silent within the bacterium. Every time the *E. coli* cell prepares to divide, it replicates the phage DNA along with its own and passes the copies on to daughter cells. A single infected cell can quickly give rise to a large population of bacteria carrying the virus in prophage form. This mechanism enables viruses to propagate without killing the host cells on which they depend.

The term *lysogenic* implies that prophages are capable of generating active phages that lyse their host cells. This occurs when the λ genome is induced to exit the bacterial chromosome and initiate a lytic cycle. An environmental signal, such as a certain chemical or high-energy radiation, usually triggers the switchover from the lysogenic to the lytic mode.

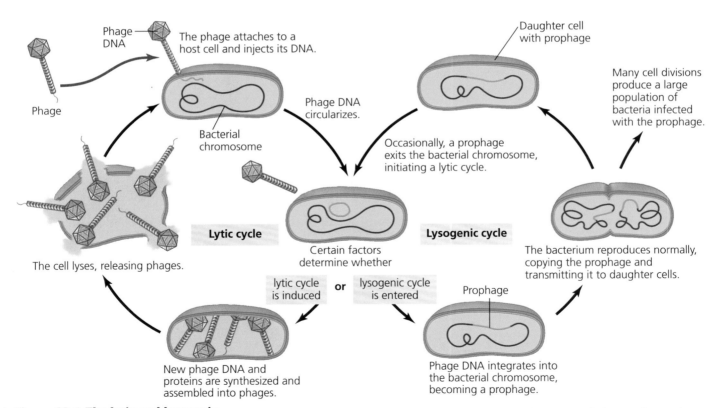

▲ **Figure 19.6 The lytic and lysogenic cycles of phage λ, a temperate phage.** After entering the bacterial cell and circularizing, the λ DNA can immediately initiate the production of a large number of progeny phages (lytic cycle) or integrate into the bacterial chromosome (lysogenic cycle). In most cases, phage λ follows the lytic pathway, which is similar to that detailed in Figure 19.5. However, once a lysogenic cycle begins, the prophage may be carried in the host cell's chromosome for many generations. Phage λ has one main tail fiber, which is short.

Table 19.1 Classes of Animal Viruses

Class/Family	Envelope	Examples That Cause Human Diseases
I. Double-Stranded DNA (dsDNA)		
Adenovirus (see Figure 19.3b)	No	Respiratory viruses; tumor-causing viruses
Papovavirus	No	Papillomavirus (warts, cervical cancer); polyomavirus (tumors)
Herpesvirus	Yes	Herpes simplex I and II (cold sores, genital sores); varicella zoster (shingles, chicken pox); Epstein-Barr virus (mononucleosis, Burkitt's lymphoma)
Poxvirus	Yes	Smallpox virus; cowpox virus
II. Single-Stranded DNA (ssDNA)		
Parvovirus	No	B19 parvovirus (mild rash)
III. Double-Stranded RNA (dsRNA)		
Reovirus	No	Rotavirus (diarrhea); Colorado tick fever virus
IV. Single-Stranded RNA (ssRNA); Serves as mRNA		
Picornavirus	No	Rhinovirus (common cold); poliovirus; hepatitis A virus; other enteric (intestinal) viruses
Coronavirus	Yes	Severe acute respiratory syndrome (SARS)
Flavivirus	Yes	Yellow fever virus; West Nile virus; hepatitis C virus
Togavirus	Yes	Rubella virus; equine encephalitis viruses
V. ssRNA; Template for mRNA Synthesis		
Filovirus	Yes	Ebola virus (hemorrhagic fever)
Orthomyxovirus (see Figures 19.3c and 19.9a)	Yes	Influenza virus
Paramyxovirus	Yes	Measles virus; mumps virus
Rhabdovirus	Yes	Rabies virus
VI. ssRNA; Template for DNA Synthesis		
Retrovirus (see Figure 19.8)	Yes	Human immunodeficiency virus (HIV/AIDS); RNA tumor viruses (leukemia)

In addition to the gene for the transcription-preventing protein, a few other prophage genes may be expressed during lysogeny. Expression of these genes may alter the host's phenotype, a phenomenon that can have important medical significance. For example, the three species of bacteria that cause the human diseases diphtheria, botulism, and scarlet fever would not be so harmful to humans without certain prophage genes that cause the host bacteria to make toxins. And the difference between the *E. coli* strain that resides in our intestines and the O157:H7 strain that has caused several deaths by food poisoning appears to be the presence of prophages in the O157:H7 strain.

Replicative Cycles of Animal Viruses

Everyone has suffered from viral infections, whether cold sores, influenza, or the common cold. Like all viruses, those that cause illness in humans and other animals can replicate only inside host cells. Many variations on the basic scheme of viral infection and replication are represented among the animal viruses. One key variable is the nature of the viral genome: Is it composed of DNA or RNA? Is it double-stranded or single-stranded? The nature of the genome is the basis for the common classification of viruses shown in **Table 19.1**. Single-stranded RNA viruses are further classified into three classes (IV–VI) according to how the RNA genome functions in a host cell.

Whereas few bacteriophages have an envelope or RNA genome, many animal viruses have both. In fact, nearly all animal viruses with RNA genomes have an envelope, as do some with DNA genomes (see Table 19.1). Rather than consider all the mechanisms of viral infection and replication, we will focus on the roles of viral envelopes and on the functioning of RNA as the genetic material of many animal viruses.

Viral Envelopes

An animal virus equipped with an envelope—that is, an outer membrane—uses it to enter the host cell. Protruding from the outer surface of this envelope are viral glycoproteins that bind to specific receptor molecules on the surface of a host cell. **Figure 19.7**, on the next page, outlines the events in the replicative cycle of an enveloped virus with an RNA genome. Ribosomes bound to the endoplasmic reticulum (ER) of the host cell make the protein parts of the envelope glycoproteins; cellular enzymes in the ER and Golgi apparatus then add the sugars. The resulting viral glycoproteins, embedded in host cell–derived membrane, are transported to the cell surface. In a process much like exocytosis, new viral capsids are wrapped in membrane as they bud from the cell. In other words, the viral envelope is derived from the host cell's plasma membrane, although some of the molecules of this membrane are specified by viral genes. The enveloped viruses are now free to infect other cells. This replicative cycle does not necessarily kill the host cell, in contrast to the lytic cycles of phages.

Some viruses have envelopes that are not derived from plasma membrane. Herpesviruses, for example, are temporarily cloaked in membrane derived from the nuclear envelope of the host; they then shed this membrane in the cytoplasm and

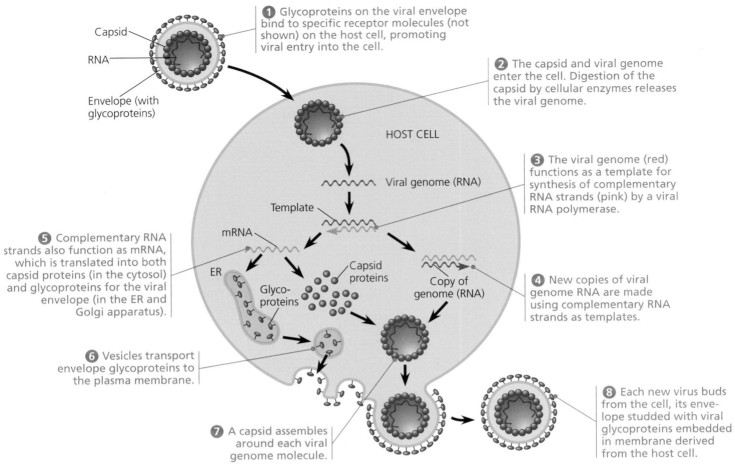

Capsid

RNA

Envelope (with glycoproteins)

1 Glycoproteins on the viral envelope bind to specific receptor molecules (not shown) on the host cell, promoting viral entry into the cell.

2 The capsid and viral genome enter the cell. Digestion of the capsid by cellular enzymes releases the viral genome.

HOST CELL

Viral genome (RNA)

Template

3 The viral genome (red) functions as a template for synthesis of complementary RNA strands (pink) by a viral RNA polymerase.

5 Complementary RNA strands also function as mRNA, which is translated into both capsid proteins (in the cytosol) and glycoproteins for the viral envelope (in the ER and Golgi apparatus).

mRNA

ER

Glyco-proteins

Capsid proteins

Copy of genome (RNA)

4 New copies of viral genome RNA are made using complementary RNA strands as templates.

6 Vesicles transport envelope glycoproteins to the plasma membrane.

7 A capsid assembles around each viral genome molecule.

8 Each new virus buds from the cell, its envelope studded with viral glycoproteins embedded in membrane derived from the host cell.

▲ **Figure 19.7 The replicative cycle of an enveloped RNA virus.** Shown here is a virus with a single-stranded RNA genome that functions as a template for synthesis of mRNA. Some enveloped viruses enter the host cell by fusion of the envelope with the cell's plasma membrane; others enter by endocytosis. For all enveloped RNA viruses, the formation of new envelopes for progeny viruses occurs by the mechanism depicted in this figure.

? *Name a virus that has infected you and has a replicative cycle matching this one. (Hint: See Table 19.1.)*

acquire a new envelope made from membrane of the Golgi apparatus. These viruses have a double-stranded DNA genome and replicate within the host cell nucleus, using a combination of viral and cellular enzymes to replicate and transcribe their DNA. In the case of herpesviruses, copies of the viral DNA can remain behind as mini-chromosomes in the nuclei of certain nerve cells. There they remain latent until some sort of physical or emotional stress triggers a new round of active virus production. The infection of other cells by these new viruses causes the blisters characteristic of herpes, such as cold sores or genital sores. Once someone acquires a herpesvirus infection, flare-ups may recur throughout the person's life.

RNA as Viral Genetic Material

Although some phages and most plant viruses are RNA viruses, the broadest variety of RNA genomes is found among the viruses that infect animals. Among the three types of single-stranded RNA genomes found in animal viruses, the genome of class IV viruses can directly serve as mRNA and thus can be translated into viral protein immediately after infection.

Figure 19.7 shows a virus of class V, in which the RNA genome serves as a *template* for mRNA synthesis. The RNA genome is transcribed into complementary RNA strands, which function both as mRNA and as templates for the synthesis of additional copies of genomic RNA. All viruses that require RNA → RNA synthesis to make mRNA use a viral enzyme capable of carrying out this process; there are no such enzymes in most cells. The viral enzyme is packaged with the genome inside the viral capsid.

The RNA animal viruses with the most complicated replicative cycles are the **retroviruses** (class VI). These viruses are equipped with an enzyme called **reverse transcriptase**, which transcribes an RNA template into DNA, providing an RNA → DNA information flow, the opposite of the usual direction. This unusual phenomenon is the source of the name retroviruses (*retro* means "backward"). Of particular medical importance is **HIV (human immunodeficiency virus)**, the retrovirus that causes **AIDS (acquired immunodeficiency syndrome)**. HIV and other retroviruses are enveloped viruses that contain two identical molecules of single-stranded RNA and two molecules of reverse transcriptase.

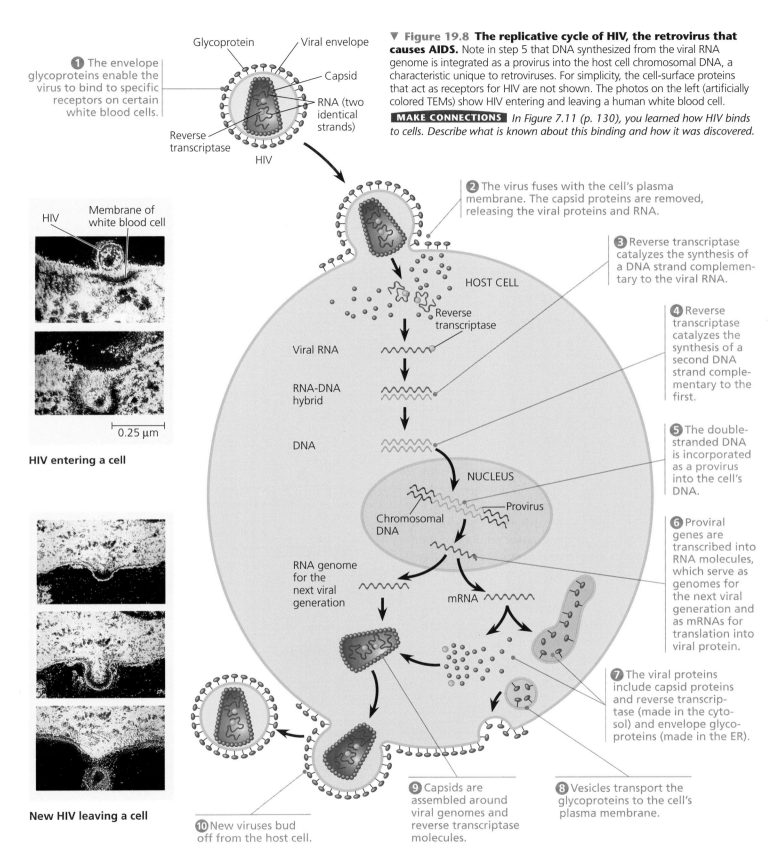

▼ **Figure 19.8 The replicative cycle of HIV, the retrovirus that causes AIDS.** Note in step 5 that DNA synthesized from the viral RNA genome is integrated as a provirus into the host cell chromosomal DNA, a characteristic unique to retroviruses. For simplicity, the cell-surface proteins that act as receptors for HIV are not shown. The photos on the left (artificially colored TEMs) show HIV entering and leaving a human white blood cell.

MAKE CONNECTIONS *In Figure 7.11 (p. 130), you learned how HIV binds to cells. Describe what is known about this binding and how it was discovered.*

Glycoprotein Viral envelope

1 The envelope glycoproteins enable the virus to bind to specific receptors on certain white blood cells.

Capsid

RNA (two identical strands)

Reverse transcriptase

HIV

HIV

Membrane of white blood cell

0.25 μm

HIV entering a cell

New HIV leaving a cell

2 The virus fuses with the cell's plasma membrane. The capsid proteins are removed, releasing the viral proteins and RNA.

HOST CELL

Reverse transcriptase

3 Reverse transcriptase catalyzes the synthesis of a DNA strand complementary to the viral RNA.

Viral RNA

RNA-DNA hybrid

4 Reverse transcriptase catalyzes the synthesis of a second DNA strand complementary to the first.

DNA

5 The double-stranded DNA is incorporated as a provirus into the cell's DNA.

NUCLEUS

Provirus

Chromosomal DNA

6 Proviral genes are transcribed into RNA molecules, which serve as genomes for the next viral generation and as mRNAs for translation into viral protein.

RNA genome for the next viral generation

mRNA

7 The viral proteins include capsid proteins and reverse transcriptase (made in the cytosol) and envelope glycoproteins (made in the ER).

9 Capsids are assembled around viral genomes and reverse transcriptase molecules.

8 Vesicles transport the glycoproteins to the cell's plasma membrane.

10 New viruses bud off from the host cell.

Figure 19.8 traces the HIV replicative cycle, which is typical of a retrovirus. After HIV enters a host cell, its reverse transcriptase molecules are released into the cytoplasm, where they catalyze synthesis of viral DNA. The newly made viral DNA then enters the cell's nucleus and integrates into the DNA of a chromosome. The integrated viral DNA, called a **provirus**, never leaves the host's genome, remaining a permanent resident of the cell. (Recall that a prophage, in contrast, leaves the host's genome at the start of a lytic cycle.) The host's RNA polymerase transcribes the proviral DNA into RNA molecules, which can function both as mRNA for the synthesis of viral proteins and as genomes for the new viruses that will be assembled and released from the cell.

Evolution of Viruses

EVOLUTION We began this chapter by asking whether or not viruses are alive. Viruses do not really fit our definition of living organisms. An isolated virus is biologically inert, unable to replicate its genes or regenerate its own supply of ATP. Yet it has a genetic program written in the universal language of life. Do we think of viruses as nature's most complex associations of molecules or as the simplest forms of life? Either way, we must bend our usual definitions. Although viruses cannot replicate or carry out metabolic activities independently, their use of the genetic code makes it hard to deny their evolutionary connection to the living world.

How did viruses originate? Viruses have been found that infect every form of life—not just bacteria, animals, and plants, but also archaea, fungi, and algae and other protists. Because they depend on cells for their own propagation, it seems likely that viruses are not the descendants of precellular forms of life but evolved—possibly multiple times—*after* the first cells appeared. Most molecular biologists favor the hypothesis that viruses originated from naked bits of cellular nucleic acids that moved from one cell to another, perhaps via injured cell surfaces. The evolution of genes coding for capsid proteins may have facilitated the infection of uninjured cells. Candidates for the original sources of viral genomes include plasmids and transposons. *Plasmids* are small, circular DNA molecules found in bacteria and in the unicellular eukaryotes called yeasts. Plasmids exist apart from the cell's genome, can replicate independently of the genome, and are occasionally transferred between cells. *Transposons* are DNA segments that can move from one location to another within a cell's genome. Thus, plasmids, transposons, and viruses all share an important feature: They are *mobile genetic elements*. We will discuss plasmids in more detail in Chapters 20 and 27, and transposons in Chapter 21.

Consistent with this vision of pieces of DNA shuttling from cell to cell is the observation that a viral genome can have more in common with the genome of its host than with the genomes of viruses that infect other hosts. Indeed, some viral genes are essentially identical to genes of the host. On the other hand, recent sequencing of many viral genomes has shown that the genetic sequences of some viruses are quite similar to those of seemingly distantly related viruses; for example, some animal viruses share similar sequences with plant viruses. This genetic similarity may reflect the persistence of groups of viral genes that were favored by natural selection during the early evolution of viruses and the eukaryotic cells that served as their hosts.

The debate about the origin of viruses has been reinvigorated recently by reports of mimivirus, the largest virus yet discovered. Mimivirus is a double-stranded DNA virus with an icosahedral capsid that is 400 nm in diameter. (The beginning of its name is short for *mi*micking *mi*crobe because the virus is the size of a small bacterium.) Its genome contains 1.2 million bases (about 100 times as many as the influenza virus genome) and an estimated 1,000 genes. Perhaps the most surprising aspect of mimivirus, however, is that some of the genes appear to code for products previously thought to be hallmarks of cellular genomes. These products include proteins involved in translation, DNA repair, protein folding, and polysaccharide synthesis. The researchers who described mimivirus propose that it most likely evolved *before* the first cells and then developed an exploitative relationship with them. Other scientists disagree, maintaining that the virus evolved more recently than cells and has simply been efficient at scavenging genes from its hosts. The question of whether some viruses deserve their own early branch on the tree of life may not be answered for some time.

The ongoing evolutionary relationship between viruses and the genomes of their host cells is an association that makes viruses very useful experimental systems in molecular biology. Knowledge about viruses also allows many practical applications, since viruses have a tremendous impact on all organisms through their ability to cause disease.

CONCEPT CHECK 19.2

1. Compare the effect on the host cell of a lytic (virulent) phage and a lysogenic (temperate) phage.
2. **MAKE CONNECTIONS** The RNA virus in Figure 19.7 has a viral RNA polymerase that functions in step 3 of the virus's replicative cycle. Compare this RNA polymerase to the one in Figure 17.9 (p. 333) in terms of template and overall function.
3. Why is HIV called a retrovirus?
4. **WHAT IF?** If you were a researcher trying to combat HIV infection, what molecular processes could you attempt to block? (See Figure 19.8.)

For suggested answers, see Appendix A.

CONCEPT 19.3

Viruses, viroids, and prions are formidable pathogens in animals and plants

Diseases caused by viral infections afflict humans, agricultural crops, and livestock worldwide. Other smaller, less complex entities known as viroids and prions also cause disease in plants and animals, respectively.

Viral Diseases in Animals

A viral infection can produce symptoms by a number of different routes. Viruses may damage or kill cells by causing the release of hydrolytic enzymes from lysosomes. Some viruses cause infected cells to produce toxins that lead to disease symptoms, and some have molecular components that are toxic, such as envelope proteins. How much damage a virus causes depends partly on the ability of the infected tissue to regenerate by cell division. People usually recover completely from colds because the epithelium of the respiratory tract, which the viruses infect, can efficiently repair itself. In contrast, damage inflicted by poliovirus to mature nerve cells is permanent because these cells do not divide and usually cannot be replaced. Many of the temporary symptoms associated with viral infections, such as fever and aches, actually result from the body's own efforts at defending itself against infection rather than from cell death caused by the virus.

The immune system is a complex and critical part of the body's natural defenses. It is also the basis for the major medical tool for preventing viral infections—vaccines. A **vaccine** is a harmless variant or derivative of a pathogen that stimulates the immune system to mount defenses against the harmful pathogen. Smallpox, a viral disease that was at one time a devastating scourge in many parts of the world, was eradicated by a vaccination program carried out by the World Health Organization (WHO). The very narrow host range of the smallpox virus—it infects only humans—was a critical factor in the success of this program. Similar worldwide vaccination campaigns are currently under way to eradicate polio and measles. Effective vaccines are also available to protect against rubella, mumps, hepatitis B, and a number of other viral diseases.

Although vaccines can prevent certain viral illnesses, medical technology can do little, at present, to cure most viral infections once they occur. The antibiotics that help us recover from bacterial infections are powerless against viruses. Antibiotics kill bacteria by inhibiting enzymes specific to bacteria but have no effect on eukaryotic or virally encoded enzymes. However, the few enzymes that are encoded by viruses have provided targets for other drugs. Most antiviral drugs resemble nucleosides and as a result interfere with viral nucleic acid synthesis. One such drug is acyclovir, which impedes herpesvirus replication by inhibiting the viral polymerase that synthesizes viral DNA. Similarly, azidothymidine (AZT) curbs HIV replication by interfering with the synthesis of DNA by reverse transcriptase. In the past two decades, much effort has gone into developing drugs against HIV. Currently, multidrug treatments, sometimes called "cocktails," have been found to be most effective. Such treatments commonly include a combination of two nucleoside mimics and a protease inhibitor, which interferes with an enzyme required for assembly of the viruses.

Emerging Viruses

Viruses that suddenly become apparent are often referred to as *emerging viruses*. HIV, the AIDS virus, is a classic example: This virus appeared in San Francisco in the early 1980s, seemingly out of nowhere, although later studies uncovered a case in the Belgian Congo in 1959. The deadly Ebola virus, recognized initially in 1976 in central Africa, is one of several emerging viruses that cause *hemorrhagic fever*, an often fatal syndrome (set of symptoms) characterized by fever, vomiting, massive bleeding, and circulatory system collapse. A number of other dangerous emerging viruses cause encephalitis, inflammation of the brain. One example is the West Nile virus, which appeared in North America for the first time in 1999 and has spread to all 48 contiguous states in the United States.

In April 2009, a general outbreak, or **epidemic**, of a flu-like illness appeared in Mexico and the United States. The infectious agent was quickly identifed as an influenza virus related to viruses that cause the seasonal flu (**Figure 19.9a**). This particular virus was named H1N1 for reasons that will be

(a) **2009 pandemic H1N1 influenza A virus.** Viruses (blue) are seen on an infected cell (green) in this colorized SEM.

(b) **2009 pandemic screening.** At a South Korean airport, thermal scans were used to detect passengers with a fever who might have the H1N1 flu.

(c) **1918 flu pandemic.** Many of those infected during the worst flu epidemic in the last 100 years were treated in large makeshift hospitals, such as this one.

▲ **Figure 19.9 Influenza in humans.**

explained shortly. The viral disease spread rapidly, prompting WHO to declare a global epidemic, or **pandemic**, in June 2009. By November, the disease had reached 207 countries, infecting over 600,000 people and killing almost 8,000. Public health agencies responded rapidly with guidelines for shutting down schools and other public places, and vaccine development and screening efforts were accelerated (Figure 19.9b).

How do such viruses burst on the human scene, giving rise to harmful diseases that were previously rare or even unknown? Three processes contribute to the emergence of viral diseases. The first, and perhaps most important, is the mutation of existing viruses. RNA viruses tend to have an unusually high rate of mutation because errors in replicating their RNA genomes are not corrected by proofreading. Some mutations change existing viruses into new genetic varieties (strains) that can cause disease, even in individuals who are immune to the ancestral virus. For instance, seasonal flu epidemics are caused by new strains of influenza virus genetically different enough from earlier strains that people have little immunity to them.

A second process that can lead to the emergence of viral diseases is the dissemination of a viral disease from a small, isolated human population. For instance, AIDS went unnamed and virtually unnoticed for decades before it began to spread around the world. In this case, technological and social factors, including affordable international travel, blood transfusions, sexual promiscuity, and the abuse of intravenous drugs, allowed a previously rare human disease to become a global scourge.

A third source of new viral diseases in humans is the spread of existing viruses from other animals. Scientists estimate that about three-quarters of new human diseases originate in this way. Animals that harbor and can transmit a particular virus but are generally unaffected by it are said to act as a natural reservoir for that virus. For example, the 2009 flu pandemic mentioned earlier was likely passed to humans from pigs; for this reason, it was originally called "swine flu."

In general, flu epidemics provide an instructive example of the effects of viruses moving between species. There are three types of influenza virus: types B and C, which infect only humans and have never caused an epidemic, and type A, which infects a wide range of animals, including birds, pigs, horses, and humans. Influenza A strains have caused four major flu epidemics among humans in the last 100 years. The worst was the first one, the "Spanish flu" pandemic of 1918–1919, which killed about 40 million people, including many World War I soldiers (Figure 19.9c).

Different strains of influenza A are given standardized names; for example, both the strain that caused the 1918 flu and the one that caused the 2009 pandemic flu are called H1N1. The name identifies which forms of two viral surface proteins are present: hemagglutinin (H) and neuraminidase (N). There are 16 different types of hemagglutinin, a protein that helps the flu virus attach to host cells, and 9 types of neuraminidase, an enzyme that helps release new virus particles from infected cells. Waterbirds have been found that carry viruses with all possible combinations of H and N.

A likely scenario for the 1918 pandemic and others is that the virus mutated as it passed from one host species to another. When an animal like a pig or a bird is infected with more than one strain of flu virus, the different strains can undergo genetic recombination if the RNA molecules making up their genomes mix and match during viral assembly. Pigs are thought to have been the breeding ground for the 2009 flu virus, which contains sequences from bird, pig, and human flu viruses. Coupled with mutation, these reassortments can lead to the emergence of a viral strain that is capable of infecting human cells. Humans who have never been exposed to that particular strain before will lack immunity, and the recombinant virus has the potential to be highly pathogenic. If such a flu virus recombines with viruses that circulate widely among humans, it may acquire the ability to spread easily from person to person, dramatically increasing the potential for a major human outbreak.

Although the 2009 H1N1 flu was declared a pandemic, its toll in lives was significantly lower than that of the 1918 flu. Significantly, however, 79% of the confirmed H1N1 cases in 2009 occurred in people under 30 years of age, and the highest mortality rates occurred in people under 64, opposite to patterns seen for seasonal flu. Some scientists hypothesize that the 1918 flu virus was the ancestor of most subsequent H1N1 epidemic-causing viruses, including that responsible for the 2009 pandemic. Older people are likely to have been exposed to earlier H1N1 viruses and have probably built up immunity to them. This could explain why contracting the 2009 H1N1 virus was more deadly for younger people, who were less likely to have been exposed to H1N1 viruses and to have built up immune defenses.

Perhaps a greater long-term threat is the avian flu caused by an H5N1 virus carried by wild and domestic birds. The first documented transmission to humans was in 1997, when 18 people in Hong Kong were infected and 6 subsequently died. While the 2009 H1N1 flu virus spread easily from human to human, reports of human-to-human transmission of the H5N1 avian flu are quite rare. More alarming, however, is the overall mortality rate of the H5N1 virus, which is greater than 50%. Furthermore, the host range of H5N1 is expanding, which provides increasing opportunities for different strains of the virus to reassort their genetic material and for new strains to emerge. If the H5N1 avian flu virus evolves so that it can spread easily from person to person, it could represent a major global health threat akin to that of the 1918 pandemic.

As we have seen, emerging viruses are generally not new; rather, they are existing viruses that mutate, disseminate more widely in the current host species, or spread to new host species. Changes in host behavior or environmental changes can increase the viral traffic responsible for emerging diseases. For example, new roads built through remote areas can allow viruses to spread between previously isolated human populations. Also, the destruction of forests to expand cropland can bring humans into contact with other animals that may host viruses capable of infecting humans.

Viral Diseases in Plants

More than 2,000 types of viral diseases of plants are known, and together they account for an estimated annual loss of $15 billion worldwide due to their destruction of agricultural and horticultural crops. Common signs of viral infection include bleached or brown spots on leaves and fruits, stunted growth, and damaged flowers or roots, all tending to diminish the yield and quality of crops (Figure 19.10).

Plant viruses have the same basic structure and mode of replication as animal viruses. Most plant viruses discovered thus far, including tobacco mosaic virus (TMV), have an RNA genome. Many have a helical capsid, like TMV, while others have an icosahedral capsid (see Figure 19.3).

Viral diseases of plants spread by two major routes. In the first route, called *horizontal transmission*, a plant is infected from an external source of the virus. Because the invading virus must get past the plant's outer protective layer of cells (the epidermis), a plant becomes more susceptible to viral infections if it has been damaged by wind, injury, or herbivores. Herbivores, especially insects, pose a double threat because they can also act as carriers of viruses, transmitting disease from plant to plant. Moreover, farmers and gardeners may transmit plant viruses inadvertently on pruning shears and other tools. The other route of viral infection is *vertical transmission*, in which a plant inherits a viral infection from a parent. Vertical transmission can occur in asexual propagation (for example, through cuttings) or in sexual reproduction via infected seeds.

Once a virus enters a plant cell and begins replicating, viral genomes and associated proteins can spread throughout the plant by means of plasmodesmata, the cytoplasmic connections that penetrate the walls between adjacent plant cells (see Figure 36.20). The passage of viral macromolecules from cell to cell is facilitated by virally encoded proteins that cause enlargement of plasmodesmata. Scientists have not yet devised cures for most viral plant diseases. Consequently, research efforts are focused largely on reducing the transmission of such diseases and on breeding resistant varieties of crop plants.

Viroids and Prions: The Simplest Infectious Agents

As small and simple as viruses are, they dwarf another class of pathogens: **viroids**. These are circular RNA molecules, only a few hundred nucleotides long, that infect plants. Viroids do not encode proteins but can replicate in host plant cells, apparently using host cell enzymes. These small RNA molecules seem to cause errors in the regulatory systems that control plant growth; the typical signs of viroid diseases are abnormal development and stunted growth. One viroid disease, called cadang-cadang, has killed more than 10 million coconut palms in the Philippines.

An important lesson from viroids is that a single molecule can be an infectious agent that spreads a disease. But viroids are nucleic acids, whose ability to be replicated is well known. Even more surprising is the evidence for infectious *proteins*, called **prions**, which appear to cause a number of degenerative brain diseases in various animal species. These diseases include scrapie in sheep; mad cow disease, which has plagued the European beef industry in recent years; and Creutzfeldt-Jakob disease in humans, which has caused the death of some 150 people in Great Britain over the past decade. Prions are most likely transmitted in food, as may occur when people eat prion-laden beef from cattle with mad cow disease. Kuru, another human disease caused by prions, was identified in the early 1900s among the South Fore natives of New Guinea. A kuru epidemic peaked there in the 1960s, puzzling scientists, who at first thought the disease had a genetic basis. Eventually, however, anthropological investigations ferreted out how the disease was spread: ritual cannibalism, a widespread practice among South Fore natives at that time.

Two characteristics of prions are especially alarming. First, prions act very

▶ Figure 19.10 **Viral infection of plants.** Infection with particular viruses causes irregular brown patches on tomatoes (left), black blotching on squash (center), and streaking in tulips due to redistribution of pigment granules (right).

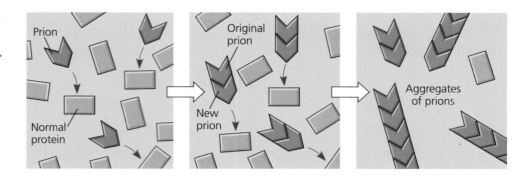

► **Figure 19.11 Model for how prions propagate.** Prions are misfolded versions of normal brain proteins. When a prion contacts a normally folded version of the same protein, it may induce the normal protein to assume the abnormal shape. The resulting chain reaction may continue until high levels of prion aggregation cause cellular malfunction and eventual degeneration of the brain.

slowly, with an incubation period of at least ten years before symptoms develop. The lengthy incubation period prevents sources of infection from being identified until long after the first cases appear, allowing many more infections to occur. Second, prions are virtually indestructible; they are not destroyed or deactivated by heating to normal cooking temperatures. To date, there is no known cure for prion diseases, and the only hope for developing effective treatments lies in understanding the process of infection.

How can a protein, which cannot replicate itself, be a transmissible pathogen? According to the leading model, a prion is a misfolded form of a protein normally present in brain cells. When the prion gets into a cell containing the normal form of the protein, the prion somehow converts normal protein molecules to the misfolded prion versions. Several prions then aggregate into a complex that can convert other normal proteins to prions, which join the chain (**Figure 19.11**). Prion aggregation interferes with normal

cellular functions and causes disease symptoms. This model was greeted with much skepticism when it was first proposed by Stanley Prusiner in the early 1980s, but it is now widely accepted. Prusiner was awarded the Nobel Prize in 1997 for his work on prions.

CONCEPT CHECK 19.3

1. Describe two ways a preexisting virus can become an emerging virus.
2. Contrast horizontal and vertical transmission of viruses in plants.
3. **WHAT IF?** TMV has been isolated from virtually all commercial tobacco products. Why, then, is TMV infection not an additional hazard for smokers?

For suggested answers, see Appendix A.

19 CHAPTER REVIEW

SUMMARY OF KEY CONCEPTS

CONCEPT 19.1

A virus consists of a nucleic acid surrounded by a protein coat (pp. 381–384)

- Researchers discovered viruses in the late 1800s by studying a plant disease, tobacco mosaic disease.
- A **virus** is a small nucleic acid genome enclosed in a protein **capsid** and sometimes a membranous **viral envelope** containing viral proteins that help viruses enter cells. The genome may be single- or double-stranded DNA or RNA.

? *Are viruses generally considered living or nonliving? Explain.*

CONCEPT 19.2

Viruses replicate only in host cells (pp. 384–390)

- Viruses use enzymes, ribosomes, and small molecules of host cells to synthesize progeny viruses during replication. Each type of virus has a characteristic **host range**.

- **Phages** (viruses that infect bacteria) can replicate by two alternative mechanisms: the **lytic cycle** and the **lysogenic cycle**.

The phage attaches to a host cell and injects its DNA.

Lytic cycle
- **Virulent** or **temperate phage**
- Destruction of host DNA
- Production of new phages
- Lysis of host cell causes release of progeny phages

Lysogenic cycle
- **Temperate phage** only
- Genome integrates into bacterial chromosome as **prophage**, which
  (1) is replicated and passed on to daughter cells and
  (2) can be induced to leave the chromosome and initiate a lytic cycle

- Many animal viruses have an envelope. **Retroviruses** (such as **HIV**) use the enzyme **reverse transcriptase** to copy their RNA genome into DNA, which can be integrated into the host genome as a **provirus**.

- Since viruses can replicate only within cells, they probably evolved after the first cells appeared, perhaps as packaged fragments of cellular nucleic acid. The origin of viruses is still being debated.

> **?** *Describe enzymes that are not found in most cells but are necessary for the replication of viruses of certain types.*

CONCEPT 19.3

Viruses, viroids, and prions are formidable pathogens in animals and plants (pp. 390–394)

- Symptoms of viral diseases may be caused by direct viral harm to cells or by the body's immune response. **Vaccines** stimulate the immune system to defend the host against specific viruses.
- Outbreaks of "new" viral diseases in humans are usually caused by existing viruses that expand their host territory. The H1N1 2009 flu virus was a new combination of pig, human, and avian viral genes that caused a pandemic. The H5N1 avian flu virus has the potential to cause a high-mortality flu pandemic.
- Viruses enter plant cells through damaged cell walls (horizontal transmission) or are inherited from a parent (vertical transmission).
- **Viroids** are naked RNA molecules that infect plants and disrupt their growth. **Prions** are slow-acting, virtually indestructible infectious proteins that cause brain diseases in mammals.

> **?** *What aspect of an RNA virus makes it more likely than a DNA virus to become an emerging virus?*

TEST YOUR UNDERSTANDING

LEVEL 1: KNOWLEDGE/COMPREHENSION

1. Which of the following characteristics, structures, or processes is common to both bacteria and viruses?
   a. metabolism
   b. ribosomes
   c. genetic material composed of nucleic acid
   d. cell division
   e. independent existence

2. Emerging viruses arise by
   a. mutation of existing viruses.
   b. the spread of existing viruses to new host species.
   c. the spread of existing viruses more widely within their host species.
   d. all of the above
   e. none of the above

3. To cause a human pandemic, the H5N1 avian flu virus would have to
   a. spread to primates such as chimpanzees.
   b. develop into a virus with a different host range.
   c. become capable of human-to-human transmission.
   d. arise independently in chickens in North and South America.
   e. become much more pathogenic.

LEVEL 2: APPLICATION/ANALYSIS

4. A bacterium is infected with an experimentally constructed bacteriophage composed of the T2 phage protein coat and T4 phage DNA. The new phages produced would have
   a. T2 protein and T4 DNA.
   b. T2 protein and T2 DNA.
   c. a mixture of the DNA and proteins of both phages.
   d. T4 protein and T4 DNA.
   e. T4 protein and T2 DNA.

5. RNA viruses require their own supply of certain enzymes because
   a. host cells rapidly destroy the viruses.
   b. host cells lack enzymes that can replicate the viral genome.
   c. these enzymes translate viral mRNA into proteins.
   d. these enzymes penetrate host cell membranes.
   e. these enzymes cannot be made in host cells.

6. **DRAW IT** Redraw Figure 19.7 to show the replicative cycle of a virus with a single-stranded genome that can function as mRNA (a class IV virus).

LEVEL 3: SYNTHESIS/EVALUATION

7. **EVOLUTION CONNECTION**
   The success of some viruses lies in their ability to evolve rapidly within the host. Such a virus evades the host's defenses by mutating and producing many altered progeny viruses before the body can mount an attack. Thus, the viruses present late in infection differ from those that initially infected the body. Discuss this as an example of evolution in microcosm. Which viral lineages tend to predominate?

8. **SCIENTIFIC INQUIRY**
   When bacteria infect an animal, the number of bacteria in the body increases in an exponential fashion (graph A). After infection by a virulent animal virus with a lytic replicative cycle, there is no evidence of infection for a while. Then the number of viruses rises suddenly and subsequently increases in a series of steps (graph B). Explain the difference in the curves.

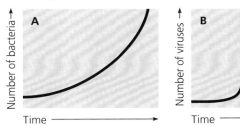

9. **WRITE ABOUT A THEME**
   Structure and Function While viruses are considered by most scientists to be nonliving, they do show some characteristics of life, including the correlation of structure and function. In a short essay (100–150 words), discuss how the structure of a virus correlates with its function.

For selected answers, see Appendix A.

MasteringBIOLOGY® www.masteringbiology.com

1. MasteringBiology® Assignments
Tutorial Viral Replication
Activities Simplified Viral Reproductive Cycle • Phage Lytic Cycle • Phage Lysogenic and Lytic Cycles • Retrovirus (HIV) Reproductive Cycle • The HIV Replicative Cycle • Discovery Channel Video: Emerging Diseases
Questions Student Misconceptions • Reading Quiz • Multiple Choice • End-of-Chapter

2. eText
Read your book online, search, take notes, highlight text, and more.

3. The Study Area
Practice Tests • Cumulative Test • *BioFlix* 3-D Animations • MP3 Tutor Sessions • Videos • Activities • Investigations • Lab Media • Audio Glossary • Word Study Tools • Art

20

Biotechnology

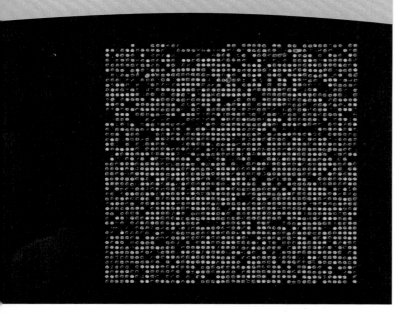

▲ **Figure 20.1 How can this array of spots be used to compare normal and cancerous tissues?**

KEY CONCEPTS

20.1 DNA cloning yields multiple copies of a gene or other DNA segment

20.2 DNA technology allows us to study the sequence, expression, and function of a gene

20.3 Cloning organisms may lead to production of stem cells for research and other applications

20.4 The practical applications of DNA technology affect our lives in many ways

OVERVIEW

The DNA Toolbox

In 2001, a major scientific milestone was announced: Researchers had completed a "first draft" sequence of all 3 billion base pairs of the human genome—only the fourth eukaryotic genome to be sequenced. This news electrified the scientific community. Few among them would have dared to dream that a mere nine years later, genome sequencing would be under way for more than 7,000 species. By 2010, researchers had completed sequencing more than 1,000 bacterial, 80 archaeal, and 100 eukaryotic genomes, with many more in progress.

Ultimately, these achievements are attributable to advances in DNA technology—methods of working with and manipulating DNA—that had their roots in the 1970s. A key accomplishment was the invention of techniques for making **recombinant DNA**, DNA molecules formed when segments of DNA from two different sources—often different species—are combined *in vitro* (in a test tube). This advance gave rise to the development of powerful techniques for analyzing genes and gene expression. How scientists prepare recombinant DNA and use DNA technology to answer fundamental biological questions are one focus of this chapter. In the next chapter (Chapter 21), we'll see how these techniques have allowed the sequencing of whole genomes, and we'll consider what we've learned from these sequences about the evolution of species and of the genome itself.

Another focus of this chapter is how our lives are affected by **biotechnology**, the manipulation of organisms or their components to make useful products. Biotechnology includes such early practices as selective breeding of farm animals and using microorganisms to make wine and cheese. Today, biotechnology also encompasses **genetic engineering**, the direct manipulation of genes for practical purposes. Genetic engineering has launched a revolution in biotechnology, greatly expanding the scope of its potential applications. Tools from the DNA toolbox are now applied in ways that affect everything from agriculture to criminal law to medical research. For instance, on the DNA microarray in **Figure 20.1**, the colored spots represent the relative level of expression of 2,400 human genes in normal and cancerous tissue. Using microarray analysis, researchers can quickly compare gene expression in different samples, such as those tested here. The knowledge gained from such gene expression studies is making a significant contribution to the study of cancer and other diseases.

In this chapter, we'll first describe the main techniques for manipulating DNA and analyzing gene expression and function. Next, we'll explore advances in cloning organisms and producing stem cells, techniques that have both expanded our basic understanding of biology and enhanced our ability to apply this understanding to global problems. Finally, we'll survey the practical applications of biotechnology and consider some of the social and ethical issues that arise as biotechnology becomes more pervasive in our lives.

CONCEPT 20.1

DNA cloning yields multiple copies of a gene or other DNA segment

The molecular biologist studying a particular gene faces a challenge. Naturally occurring DNA molecules are very long, and a single molecule usually carries many genes. Moreover, in many eukaryotic genomes, genes occupy only a small proportion of the chromosomal DNA, the rest being noncoding nucleotide sequences. A single human gene, for example, might constitute only 1/100,000 of a chromosomal DNA molecule. As a further complication, the distinctions between a gene and the surrounding DNA are subtle, consisting only of differences in nucleotide sequence. To work directly with specific genes, scientists have developed methods for preparing well-defined segments of DNA in multiple identical copies, a process called *DNA cloning*.

DNA Cloning and Its Applications: *A Preview*

Most methods for cloning pieces of DNA in the laboratory share certain general features. One common approach uses bacteria, most often *Escherichia coli*. Recall from Figure 16.12 that the *E. coli* chromosome is a large circular molecule of DNA. In addition, *E. coli* and many other bacteria have **plasmids**, small circular DNA molecules that replicate separately from the bacterial chromosome. A plasmid has only a small number of genes; these genes may be useful when the bacterium is in a particular environment but may not be required for survival or reproduction under most conditions.

To clone pieces of DNA in the laboratory, researchers first obtain a plasmid (originally isolated from a bacterial cell and genetically engineered for efficient cloning) and insert DNA from another source ("foreign" DNA) into it **(Figure 20.2)**. The resulting plasmid is now a recombinant DNA molecule. The plasmid is then returned to a bacterial cell, producing a *recombinant bacterium*. This single cell reproduces through repeated cell divisions to form a clone of cells, a population of genetically identical cells. Because the dividing bacteria replicate the recombinant plasmid and pass it on to their descendants, the foreign DNA and any genes it carries are cloned at the same time. The production of multiple copies of a single gene is called **gene cloning**.

Gene cloning is useful for two basic purposes: to make many copies of, or *amplify*, a particular gene and to produce a protein product. Researchers can

isolate copies of a cloned gene from bacteria for use in basic research or to endow an organism with a new metabolic capability, such as pest resistance. For example, a resistance gene present in one crop species might be cloned and transferred into plants of another species. Alternatively, a protein with medical uses, such as human growth hormone, can be harvested in large quantities from cultures of bacteria carrying the cloned gene for the protein.

A single gene is usually a very small part of the total DNA in a cell. For example, a typical gene makes up only about one-millionth of the DNA in a human cell. The ability to

▲ **Figure 20.2 A preview of gene cloning and some uses of cloned genes.** In this simplified diagram of gene cloning, we start with a plasmid (originally isolated from a bacterial cell) and a gene of interest from another organism. Only one plasmid and one copy of the gene of interest are shown at the top of the figure, but the starting materials would include many of each.

amplify such rare DNA fragments is therefore crucial for any application involving a single gene.

Using Restriction Enzymes to Make Recombinant DNA

Gene cloning and genetic engineering rely on the use of enzymes that cut DNA molecules at a limited number of specific locations. These enzymes, called restriction endonucleases, or **restriction enzymes**, were discovered in the late 1960s by biologists doing basic research on bacteria. Restriction enzymes protect the bacterial cell by cutting up foreign DNA from other organisms or phages (see Chapter 19).

Hundreds of different restriction enzymes have been identified and isolated. Each restriction enzyme is very specific, recognizing a particular short DNA sequence, or **restriction site**, and cutting both DNA strands at precise points within this restriction site. The DNA of a bacterial cell is protected from the cell's own restriction enzymes by the addition of methyl groups ($-CH_3$) to adenines or cytosines within the sequences recognized by the enzymes.

The top of **Figure 20.3** illustrates a restriction site recognized by a particular restriction enzyme from *E. coli*. As shown in this example, most restriction sites are symmetrical. That is, the sequence of nucleotides is the same on both strands when read in the $5' \rightarrow 3'$ direction. The most commonly used restriction enzymes recognize sequences containing four to eight nucleotides. Because any sequence this short usually occurs (by chance) many times in a long DNA molecule, a restriction enzyme will make many cuts in a DNA molecule, yielding a set of **restriction fragments**. All copies of a particular DNA molecule always yield the same set of restriction fragments when exposed to the same restriction enzyme. In other words, a restriction enzyme cuts a DNA molecule in a reproducible way. (Later you will learn how the different fragments can be separated and distinguished from each other.)

The most useful restriction enzymes cleave the sugar-phosphate backbones in the two DNA strands in a staggered manner, as indicated in Figure 20.3. The resulting double-stranded restriction fragments have at least one single-stranded end, called a **sticky end**. These short extensions can form hydrogen-bonded base pairs with complementary sticky ends on any other DNA molecules cut with the same enzyme. The associations formed in this way are only temporary but can be made permanent by the enzyme **DNA ligase**. As you saw in Figure 16.16, this enzyme catalyzes the formation of covalent bonds that close up the sugar-phosphate backbones of DNA strands; for example, it joins Okazaki fragments during replication. You can see at the bottom of Figure 20.3 that the ligase-catalyzed joining of DNA from two different sources produces a stable recombinant DNA molecule.

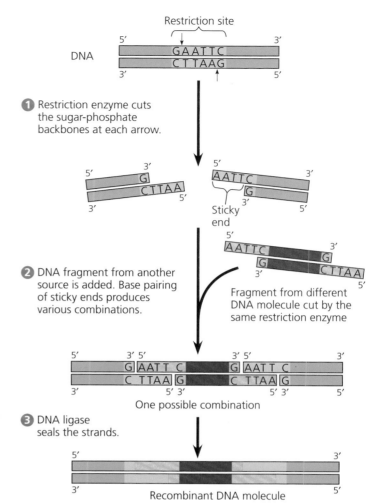

▲ **Figure 20.3 Using a restriction enzyme and DNA ligase to make recombinant DNA.** The restriction enzyme in this example (called *Eco*RI) recognizes a specific six-base-pair sequence, the restriction site, and makes staggered cuts in the sugar-phosphate backbones within this sequence, producing fragments with sticky ends. Any fragments with complementary sticky ends can base-pair, including the two original fragments. If the fragments come from different DNA molecules, the ligated product is recombinant DNA.

DRAW IT *The restriction enzyme* HindIII *recognizes the sequence 5'-AAGCTT-3', cutting between the two 'A's. Draw the double-stranded sequence before and after the enzyme cuts.*

Cloning a Eukaryotic Gene in a Bacterial Plasmid

Now that you've learned about restriction enzymes and DNA ligase, we can see how genes are cloned in plasmids. The original plasmid is called a **cloning vector**, defined as a DNA molecule that can carry foreign DNA into a host cell and replicate there. Bacterial plasmids are widely used as cloning vectors for several reasons: They can be readily obtained from commercial suppliers, manipulated to form recombinant plasmids by insertion of foreign DNA *in vitro*, and then introduced into bacterial cells. Moreover, recombinant bacterial plasmids (and the foreign DNA they carry) multiply rapidly owing to the high reproductive rate of their host cells.

Producing Clones of Cells Carrying Recombinant Plasmids

Let's say we are researchers interested in studying the β-globin gene in a particular species of hummingbird. We start by cloning all the hummingbird genes; later we'll isolate the β-globin gene from all the others, a task very much like finding a needle in a haystack. **Figure 20.4** details one method for cloning hummingbird genes using a bacterial plasmid as the cloning vector.

1 First, we isolate hummingbird genomic DNA from hummingbird cells. We also obtain our chosen vector, a particular bacterial plasmid from *E. coli* cells. The plasmid has been engineered to carry two genes that will later prove useful: *amp^R*, which makes *E. coli* cells resistant to the antibiotic ampicillin, and *lacZ*, which encodes the enzyme β-galactosidase, which hydrolyzes lactose (see p. 354). This enzyme can also hydrolyze a similar synthetic molecule called X-gal to form a blue product. The plasmid contains only one copy of the restriction site recognized by the restriction enzyme used in the next step, and that site is within the *lacZ* gene.

2 Both the plasmid and the hummingbird DNA are cut with the same restriction enzyme, and then **3** the fragments are mixed together, allowing base pairing between their complementary sticky ends. We then add DNA ligase, which covalently bonds the sugar-phosphate backbones of the fragments whose sticky ends have base-paired. Many of the resulting recombinant plasmids contain single hummingbird DNA fragments (three are shown in Figure 20.4), and at least one of them is expected to carry all or part of the β-globin gene. This step will also generate other products, such as plasmids containing multiple hummingbird DNA fragments, a combination of two plasmids, or a rejoined, nonrecombinant version of the original plasmid.

4 The DNA mixture is then added to bacteria that have a mutation in the *lacZ* gene on their own chromosome, making them unable to hydrolyze

RESEARCH METHOD

Cloning Genes in Bacterial Plasmids

APPLICATION Gene cloning is a process that produces many copies of a gene of interest. These copies can be used in sequencing the gene, in producing its encoded protein, or in basic research or other applications.

TECHNIQUE In this example, hummingbird genes are inserted into plasmids from *E. coli*. Only three plasmids and three hummingbird DNA fragments are shown, but millions of copies of the plasmid and a mixture of millions of different hummingbird DNA fragments would be present in the samples.

1 Obtain engineered plasmid DNA and DNA from hummingbird cells. The hummingbird DNA contains the gene of interest.

Bacterial plasmid (cloning vector)
lacZ gene (lactose breakdown)
amp^R gene (ampicillin resistance)
Restriction site
Hummingbird cell

2 Cut both DNA samples with the same restriction enzyme, one that makes a single cut within the *lacZ* gene and many cuts within the hummingbird DNA.

Sticky ends
Gene of interest
Hummingbird DNA fragments

3 Mix the cut plasmids and DNA fragments. Some join by base pairing; add DNA ligase to seal them together. The products include recombinant plasmids and many nonrecombinant plasmids.

Recombinant plasmids
Nonrecombinant plasmid

4 Mix the DNA with bacterial cells that have a mutation in their own *lacZ* gene. Some cells take up a recombinant plasmid or other DNA molecule by transformation.

5 Plate the bacteria on nutrient-containing agar medium supplemented with ampicillin and X-gal, a molecule resembling lactose. Incubate until colonies grow.

Bacteria carrying plasmids

RESULTS Only a cell that took up a plasmid, which has the *amp^R* gene, will reproduce and form a colony. Colonies with nonrecombinant plasmids will be blue because they can hydrolyze X-gal, forming a blue product. Colonies with recombinant plasmids, in which *lacZ* is disrupted, will be white because they cannot hydrolyze X-gal.

Colony carrying nonrecombinant plasmid with intact *lacZ* gene
Colony carrying recombinant plasmid with disrupted *lacZ* gene

WHAT IF? If the medium used in step 5 did not contain ampicillin, what other colonies would grow? What color would they be?

One of many bacterial clones

lactose or X-gal. Under suitable experimental conditions, the cells take up foreign DNA by transformation (see p. 306). Some cells acquire a recombinant plasmid carrying a gene, while others may take up a nonrecombinant plasmid, a fragment of noncoding hummingbird DNA, or nothing at all. The *amp^R* and *lacZ* genes on the plasmid can help us sort out these possibilities.

⑤ First, plating out all the bacteria on solid nutrient medium containing ampicillin allows us to distinguish the cells that have taken up plasmids, whether recombinant or not, from the other cells. Under these conditions, only cells with a plasmid will reproduce because only they have the *amp^R* gene conferring resistance to the ampicillin in the medium. Each reproducing bacterium forms a clone of cells. Once the clone contains between 10^5 and 10^8 cells, it is visible as a mass, or *colony*, on the agar. As cells reproduce, any foreign genes carried by recombinant plasmids are also copied (cloned).

Second, the presence of X-gal in the medium allows us to distinguish colonies with recombinant plasmids from those with nonrecombinant plasmids. Colonies containing nonrecombinant plasmids have the *lacZ* gene intact and will produce functional β-galactosidase. These colonies will be blue because the enzyme hydrolyzes the X-gal in the medium, forming a blue product. In contrast, no functional β-galactosidase is produced in colonies containing recombinant plasmids with foreign DNA inserted into the *lacZ* gene; these colonies will therefore be white.

The procedure to this point will have cloned many different hummingbird DNA fragments, not just the β-globin gene that interests us. In fact, taken together, the white colonies should represent all the DNA sequences from the hummingbird genome, including noncoding regions as well as genes. And because restriction enzymes do not recognize gene boundaries, some genes will be cut and divided up among two or more clones. Shortly, we will discuss the procedure we use to find the colony (cell clone) or colonies carrying the β-globin gene sequences among the many clones carrying other pieces of hummingbird DNA. To understand that procedure, we must first consider how the clones are stored.

Storing Cloned Genes in DNA Libraries

The cloning procedure in Figure 20.4, which starts with a mixture of fragments from the entire genome of an organism, is called a "shotgun" approach;

no single gene is targeted for cloning. Numerous different recombinant plasmids are produced in step 3, and a clone of cells carrying each type of plasmid ends up as a white colony in step 5. The complete set of plasmid-containing cell clones, each carrying copies of a particular segment from the initial genome, is referred to as a **genomic library** (Figure 20.5a). Each "plasmid clone" in the library is like a book containing specific information. Today, scientists often obtain such libraries (or even particular cloned genes) from another researcher, a commercial source, or a sequencing center.

Historically, certain bacteriophages have also been used as cloning vectors for making genomic libraries. Fragments of foreign DNA can be spliced into a trimmed-down version of a phage genome, as into a plasmid, by using a restriction enzyme and DNA ligase. The normal infection process allows production of many new phage particles, each carrying the foreign DNA insert. Today, phages are generally used for making genomic libraries only in special cases.

Another type of vector widely used in library construction is a **bacterial artificial chromosome (BAC)**. In spite of the name, these are simply large plasmids, trimmed down so they contain just the genes necessary to ensure replication. An advantage of using BACs as vectors is that while a standard plasmid can carry a DNA insert no larger than 10,000 base pairs (10 kb), a BAC can carry an insert of 100–300 kb

(a) **Plasmid library.** Shown are three of the thousands of "books" in a plasmid library. Each "book" is a clone of bacterial cells, which contain copies of a particular foreign genome fragment (pink, yellow, black segments) in their recombinant plasmids.

(b) **BAC clone.** Many BAC clones make up a BAC library.

(c) **Storing genome libraries.** Both plasmid and BAC genomic libraries are usually stored in a "multiwell" plastic plate; a 384-well plate is shown here. Each clone occupies one well. (The library of an entire genome would require many such plates.)

▲ **Figure 20.5 Genomic libraries.** A genomic library is a collection of many clones. Each clone carries copies of a particular DNA segment from a foreign genome, integrated into an appropriate DNA vector, such as a plasmid or a bacterial artificial chromosome (BAC). In a complete genomic library, the foreign DNA segments cover the entire genome of an organism. Note that the bacterial chromosomes are not drawn to scale; they are actually about 1,000 times larger than the vectors.

(Figure 20.5b). The very large insert size minimizes the number of clones needed to make up the genomic library, but it also makes them more challenging to work with in the lab, so the insert may later be cut up into smaller pieces that are "subcloned" into plasmid vectors.

Clones are usually stored in multiwelled plastic plates, with one clone per well (Figure 20.5c). This orderly storage of clones, identified by their location in the plate, makes screening for the gene of interest very efficient, as you will see.

In a genomic library, the cloned β-globin gene would include not just exons containing the coding sequence, but also the promoter, untranslated regions, and any introns. Some biologists might be interested in the β-globin protein itself—they might wonder, for instance, if this oxygen-carrying protein is different from its counterpart in other, less metabolically active species. Such researchers can make another kind of DNA library by starting with fully processed mRNA extracted from cells where the gene is expressed (Figure 20.6). The enzyme reverse transcriptase (obtained from retroviruses) is used *in vitro* to make a single-stranded DNA *reverse transcript* of each mRNA molecule. Recall that the 3′ end of the mRNA has a stretch of adenine (A)

1 Reverse transcriptase is added to a test tube containing mRNA isolated from a certain type of cell.

2 Reverse transcriptase makes the first DNA strand using the mRNA as a template and a stretch of dT's as a DNA primer.

3 mRNA is degraded by another enzyme.

4 DNA polymerase synthesizes the second strand, using a primer in the reaction mixture. (Several options exist for primers.)

5 The result is cDNA, which carries the complete coding sequence of the gene but no introns.

▲ **Figure 20.6 Making complementary DNA (cDNA) from eukaryotic genes.** Complementary DNA is DNA made *in vitro* using mRNA as a template for the first strand. Because the mRNA contains only exons, the resulting double-stranded cDNA carries the complete coding sequence of the gene but no introns. Although only one mRNA is shown here, the final collection of cDNAs would reflect all the mRNAs that were present in the cell.

ribonucleotides called a poly-A tail. This feature allows use of a short strand of thymine deoxyribonucleotides (dT's) as a primer for the reverse transcriptase. Following enzymatic degradation of the mRNA, a second DNA strand, complementary to the first, is synthesized by DNA polymerase. The resulting double-stranded DNA is called **complementary DNA (cDNA)**. To create a library, the researchers must now modify the cDNA by adding restriction enzyme recognition sequences at each end. Then the cDNA is inserted into vector DNA in a manner similar to the insertion of genomic DNA fragments. The extracted mRNA is a mixture of all the mRNA molecules in the original cells, transcribed from many different genes. Therefore, the cDNAs that are cloned make up a **cDNA library** containing a collection of genes. However, a cDNA library represents only part of the genome—only the subset of genes that were transcribed in the cells from which the mRNA was isolated.

Genomic and cDNA libraries each have advantages, depending on what is being studied. If you want to clone a gene but don't know what cell type expresses it or cannot obtain enough cells of the appropriate type, a genomic library is almost certain to contain the gene. Also, if you are interested in the regulatory sequences or introns associated with a gene, a genomic library is necessary, since these sequences are absent from mRNAs used in making a cDNA library. On the other hand, to study a specific protein (like β-globin), a cDNA library made from cells expressing the gene (like red blood cells) is ideal. A cDNA library can also be used to study sets of genes expressed in particular cell types, such as brain or liver cells. Finally, by making cDNA from cells of the same type at different times in the life of an organism, researchers can trace changes in patterns of gene expression during development.

Screening a Library for Clones Carrying a Gene of Interest

Now, returning to the results in Figure 20.4, we're ready to screen all the colonies with recombinant plasmids (the white colonies) for a clone of cells containing the hummingbird β-globin gene. We can detect this gene's DNA by its ability to base-pair with a complementary sequence on another nucleic acid molecule, using **nucleic acid hybridization**. The complementary molecule, a short, single-stranded nucleic acid that can be either RNA or DNA, is called a **nucleic acid probe**. If we know at least part of the nucleotide sequence of the gene of interest (perhaps from knowing the amino acid sequence of the protein it encodes or, as in our case, the gene's nucleotide sequence in a closely related species), we can synthesize a probe complementary to it. For example, if part of the sequence on one strand of the desired gene were

5′ ···CTCATCACCGGC··· 3′

then we would synthesize this probe:

3′ GAGTAGTGGCCG 5′

Each probe molecule, which will hydrogen-bond specifically to a complementary sequence in the desired gene, is labeled with a radioactive isotope, a fluorescent tag, or another molecule so we can track it.

Recall that the clones in our hummingbird genomic library have been stored in a multiwell plate (see Figure 20.5c). If we transfer a few cells from each well to a defined location on a membrane made of nylon or nitrocellulose, we can screen a large number of clones simultaneously for the presence of DNA complementary to our DNA probe (**Figure 20.7**).

After we've identified the location of a clone carrying the β-globin gene, we can grow some cells from that colony in liquid culture in a large tank and then easily isolate many copies of the gene for our studies. We can also use the cloned gene as a probe to identify similar or identical genes in DNA from other sources, such as other species of birds.

Expressing Cloned Eukaryotic Genes

Once a particular gene has been cloned in host cells, its protein product can be produced in large amounts for research purposes or valuable practical applications, which we'll explore in Concept 20.4. Cloned genes can be expressed as protein in either bacterial or eukaryotic cells; each option has advantages and disadvantages.

Bacterial Expression Systems

Getting a cloned eukaryotic gene to function in bacterial host cells can be difficult because certain aspects of gene expression are different in eukaryotes and bacteria. To overcome differences in promoters and other DNA control sequences, scientists usually employ an **expression vector**, a cloning vector that contains a highly active bacterial promoter just upstream of a restriction site where the eukaryotic gene can be inserted in the correct reading frame. The bacterial host cell will recognize the promoter and proceed to express the foreign gene now linked to that promoter. Such expression vectors allow the synthesis of many eukaryotic proteins in bacterial cells.

▼ Figure 20.7 ┃ **RESEARCH METHOD**

Detecting a Specific DNA Sequence by Hybridization with a Nucleic Acid Probe

APPLICATION Hybridization with a complementary nucleic acid probe detects a specific DNA sequence within a mixture of DNA molecules. In this example, a collection of bacterial clones from a hummingbird genomic library is screened to identify clones that carry a recombinant plasmid bearing the gene of interest. The library is stored in many multiwell plates, with one clone per well (see Figure 20.5c).

TECHNIQUE Cells from each clone are applied to a special nylon membrane. Each membrane has room for thousands of clones (many more than are shown here), so only a few membranes are needed to hold samples of all the clones in the library. This set of membranes is an *arrayed library* that can be screened for a specific gene using a labeled probe. Here the label is a radioactive nucleotide, but other labels are also commonly linked covalently to the probe nucleotides. These include fluorescent tags or enzymes that can produce either a colored or luminescent product.

① Plate by plate, cells from each well, representing one clone, are transferred to a defined spot on a special nylon membrane. The nylon membrane is treated to break open the cells and denature their DNA; the resulting single-stranded DNA molecules stick to the membrane.

② The membrane is then incubated in a solution of radioactive probe molecules complementary to the gene of interest. Because the DNA immobilized on the membrane is single-stranded, the single-stranded probe can base-pair with any complementary DNA on the membrane. Excess DNA is then rinsed off. (One spot with radioactive probe–DNA hybrids is shown here in orange but would not be distinguishable yet.)

③ The membrane is laid under photographic film, allowing any radioactive areas to expose the film. Black spots on the film correspond to the locations on the membrane of DNA that has hybridized to the probe. Each spot can be traced back to the original well containing the bacterial clone that holds the gene of interest.

RESULTS For a radioactive probe, the location of the black spot on a piece of photographic film identifies the clone containing the gene of interest. (Probes labeled in other ways use other detection systems.) By using probes with different nucleotide sequences in different experiments, researchers can screen the collection of bacterial clones for different genes.

Another problem with expressing cloned eukaryotic genes in bacteria is the presence of noncoding regions (introns) in most eukaryotic genes. Introns can make a eukaryotic gene very long and unwieldy, and they prevent correct expression of the gene by bacterial cells, which do not have RNA-splicing machinery. This problem can be surmounted by using a cDNA form of the gene, which includes only the exons.

Eukaryotic Cloning and Expression Systems

Molecular biologists can avoid eukaryotic-bacterial incompatibility by using eukaryotic cells such as yeasts, rather than bacteria, as hosts for cloning and/or expressing eukaryotic genes of interest. Yeasts, single-celled fungi, offer two advantages: They are as easy to grow as bacteria, and they have plasmids, a rarity among eukaryotes. Scientists have even constructed recombinant plasmids that combine yeast and bacterial DNA and can replicate in either type of cell.

Another reason to use eukaryotic host cells for expressing a cloned eukaryotic gene is that many eukaryotic proteins will not function unless they are modified after translation, for example, by the addition of carbohydrate (glycosylation) or lipid groups. Bacterial cells cannot carry out these modifications, and if the gene product requiring such processing is from a mammal, even yeast cells may not be able to modify the protein correctly. Several cultured cell types have proved successful as host cells for this purpose, including some mammalian cell lines and an insect cell line that can be infected by a virus (called baculovirus) carrying recombinant DNA.

Besides using vectors, scientists have developed a variety of other methods for introducing recombinant DNA into eukaryotic cells. In **electroporation**, a brief electrical pulse applied to a solution containing cells creates temporary holes in their plasma membranes, through which DNA can enter. (This technique is now commonly used for bacteria as well.) Alternatively, scientists can inject DNA directly into single eukaryotic cells using microscopically thin needles. To get DNA into plant cells, the soil bacterium *Agrobacterium* can be used, as well as other methods you will learn about later. If the introduced DNA is incorporated into a cell's genome by genetic recombination, then it may be expressed by the cell.

Cross-Species Gene Expression and Evolutionary Ancestry

EVOLUTION The ability to express eukaryotic proteins in bacteria (even if the proteins aren't glycosylated properly) is quite remarkable when we consider how different eukaryotic and bacterial cells are. Examples abound of genes that are taken from one species and function perfectly well when transferred into another very different species. These observations underscore the shared evolutionary ancestry of species living today.

One example involves a gene called *Pax-6*, which has been found in animals as diverse as vertebrates and fruit flies. The vertebrate *Pax-6* gene product (the PAX-6 protein) triggers a complex program of gene expression resulting in formation of the vertebrate eye, which has a single lens. The fly *Pax-6* gene leads to formation of the compound fly eye, which is quite different from the vertebrate eye. When scientists cloned the mouse *Pax-6* gene and introduced it into a fly embryo, they were surprised to see that it led to formation of a compound fly eye. Conversely, when the fly *Pax-6* gene was transferred into a vertebrate embryo—a frog, in this case—a frog eye formed. Although the genetic programs triggered in vertebrates and flies generate very different eyes, both versions of the *Pax-6* gene can substitute for each other, evidence of their evolution from a gene in a common ancestor.

Simpler examples are seen in Figure 17.6, where a firefly gene is expressed in a tobacco plant, and a jellyfish gene product is seen in a pig. The basic mechanisms of gene expression have ancient evolutionary roots, which is the basis of many recombinant DNA techniques described in this chapter.

Amplifying DNA *in Vitro*: The Polymerase Chain Reaction (PCR)

DNA cloning in cells remains the best method for preparing large quantities of a particular gene or other DNA sequence. However, when the source of DNA is scanty or impure, the **polymerase chain reaction**, or **PCR**, is quicker and more selective. In this technique, any specific target segment within one or many DNA molecules can be quickly amplified in a test tube. With automation, PCR can make billions of copies of a target segment of DNA in a few hours, significantly faster than the days it would take to obtain the same number of copies by screening a DNA library for a clone with the desired gene and letting it replicate within host cells. In fact, PCR is being used increasingly to make enough of a specific DNA fragment to insert it directly into a vector, entirely skipping the steps of making and screening a library. To continue our literary analogy, PCR is like photocopying a few pages rather than checking out a book from the library.

In the PCR procedure, a three-step cycle brings about a chain reaction that produces an exponentially growing population of identical DNA molecules. During each cycle, the reaction mixture is heated to denature (separate) the DNA strands and then cooled to allow annealing (hydrogen bonding) of short, single-stranded DNA primers complementary to sequences on opposite strands at each end of the target sequence; finally, a heat-stable DNA polymerase extends the primers in the $5' \rightarrow 3'$ direction. If a standard DNA polymerase were used, the protein would be denatured along with the DNA during the first heating step and would have to be replaced after each cycle. The key to automating PCR was the discovery of an unusual heat-stable DNA polymerase called Taq polymerase, named after the bacterial species from which it was first isolated. This bacterial species, *Thermus aquaticus*, lives in hot springs, so natural selection has resulted in a heat-stable DNA polymerase that can withstand the heat at the start of each cycle. **Figure 20.8** illustrates the steps in PCR.

Just as impressive as the speed of PCR is its specificity. Only minute amounts of DNA need be present in the starting material, and this DNA can be in a partially degraded state, as long as a few molecules contain the complete target sequence. The key to this high specificity is the primers, which hydrogen-bond *only* to sequences at opposite ends of the target segment. (For high specificity, the primers must be at least 15 or so nucleotides long.) By the end of the third cycle, one-fourth of the molecules are identical to the target segment, with both strands the appropriate length. With each successive cycle, the number of target segment molecules of the correct length doubles, so the number of molecules equals 2^n, where n is the number of cycles. After 30 more cycles, about a billion copies of the target sequence are present!

Despite its speed and specificity, PCR amplification cannot substitute for gene cloning in cells when large amounts of a gene are desired. Occasional errors during PCR replication impose limits on the number of good copies that can be made by this method. When PCR is used to provide the specific DNA fragment for cloning, the resulting clones are sequenced to select clones with error-free inserts. PCR errors also impose limits on the length of DNA fragments that can be copied.

Devised in 1985, PCR has had a major impact on biological research and biotechnology. PCR has been used to amplify DNA from a wide variety of sources: fragments of ancient DNA from a 40,000-year-old frozen woolly mammoth; DNA from fingerprints or from tiny amounts of blood, tissue, or semen found at crime scenes; DNA from single embryonic cells for rapid prenatal diagnosis of genetic disorders; and DNA of viral genes from cells infected with viruses that are difficult to detect, such as HIV. We'll return to applications of PCR later in the chapter.

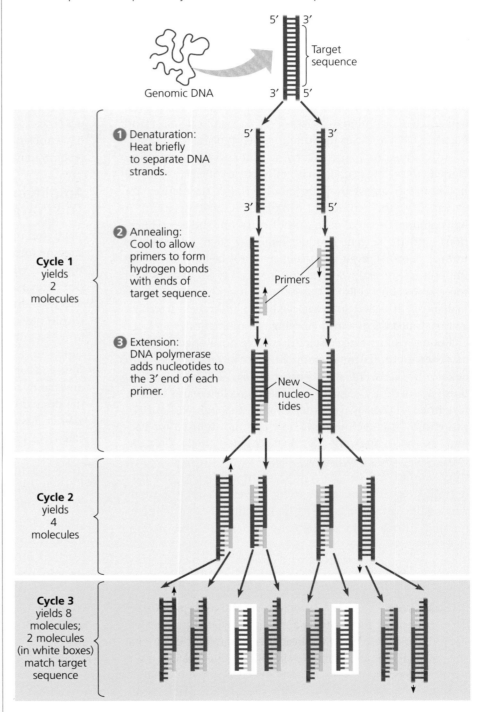

▼ **Figure 20.8**

RESEARCH METHOD

The Polymerase Chain Reaction (PCR)

APPLICATION With PCR, any specific segment—the target sequence—within a DNA sample can be copied many times (amplified), completely *in vitro*.

TECHNIQUE PCR requires double-stranded DNA containing the target sequence, a heat-resistant DNA polymerase, all four nucleotides, and two 15- to 20-nucleotide DNA strands that serve as primers. One primer is complementary to one end of the target sequence on one strand; the second primer is complementary to the other end of the sequence on the other strand.

Genomic DNA

Target sequence

Cycle 1 yields 2 molecules

❶ Denaturation: Heat briefly to separate DNA strands.

❷ Annealing: Cool to allow primers to form hydrogen bonds with ends of target sequence.

Primers

❸ Extension: DNA polymerase adds nucleotides to the 3' end of each primer.

New nucleotides

Cycle 2 yields 4 molecules

Cycle 3 yields 8 molecules; 2 molecules (in white boxes) match target sequence

RESULTS After 3 cycles, two molecules match the target sequence exactly. After 30 more cycles, over 1 billion (10^9) molecules match the target sequence.

1. The restriction site for an enzyme called *Pvu*I is the following sequence:

5'-C G A T C G-3'
3'-G C T A G C-5'

Staggered cuts are made between the T and C on each strand. What type of bonds are being cleaved?

2. **DRAW IT** One strand of a DNA molecule has the following sequence: 5'-CCTTGACGATCGTTACCG-3'. Draw the other strand. Will *Pvu*I cut this molecule? If so, draw the products.

3. What are some potential difficulties in using plasmid vectors and bacterial host cells to produce large quantities of proteins from cloned eukaryotic genes?

4. **MAKE CONNECTIONS** Compare Figure 20.8 with Figure 16.20 (p. 319). How does replication of DNA ends during PCR proceed without shortening the fragments each time?

For suggested answers, see Appendix A.

CONCEPT 20.2

DNA technology allows us to study the sequence, expression, and function of a gene

Once DNA cloning has provided us with large quantities of specific DNA segments, we can tackle some interesting questions about a particular gene and its function. For example, does the sequence of the hummingbird β-globin gene suggest a protein structure that can carry oxygen more efficiently than its counterpart in less metabolically active species? Does a particular human gene differ from person to person, and are certain alleles of that gene associated with a hereditary disorder? Where in the body and when is a given gene expressed? And, ultimately, what role does a certain gene play in an organism?

Before we can begin to address such compelling questions, we must consider a few standard laboratory techniques that are used to analyze the DNA of genes.

Gel Electrophoresis and Southern Blotting

Many approaches for studying DNA molecules involve **gel electrophoresis**. This technique uses a gel made of a polymer, such as the polysaccharide *agarose*. The gel acts as a molecular sieve to separate nucleic acids or proteins on the basis of size, electrical charge, and other physical properties (**Figure 20.9**). Because nucleic acid molecules carry negative charges on their phosphate groups, they all travel toward the positive pole in an

▼ **Figure 20.9**   **RESEARCH METHOD**

Gel Electrophoresis

APPLICATION Gel electrophoresis is used for separating nucleic acids or proteins that differ in size, electrical charge, or other physical properties. DNA molecules are separated by gel electrophoresis in restriction fragment analysis of both cloned genes (see Figure 20.10) and genomic DNA (see Figure 20.11).

TECHNIQUE Gel electrophoresis separates macromolecules on the basis of their rate of movement through an agarose gel in an electric field: The distance a DNA molecule travels is inversely proportional to its length. A mixture of DNA molecules, usually fragments produced by restriction enzyme digestion (cutting) or PCR amplification, is separated into bands. Each band contains thousands of molecules of the same length.

① Each sample, a mixture of DNA molecules, is placed in a separate well near one end of a thin slab of agarose gel. The gel is set into a small plastic support and immersed in an aqueous, buffered solution in a tray with electrodes at each end.

② When the current is turned on, the negatively charged DNA molecules move toward the positive electrode, with shorter molecules moving faster than longer ones. Bands are shown here in blue, but in an actual gel, the bands would not be visible at this time.

RESULTS After the current is turned off, a DNA-binding dye (ethidium bromide) is added. This dye fluoresces pink in ultraviolet light, revealing the separated bands to which it binds. In the gel below, the pink bands correspond to DNA fragments of different lengths separated by electrophoresis. If all the samples were initially cut with the same restriction enzyme, then the different band patterns indicate that they came from different sources.

electric field. As they move, the thicket of agarose fibers impedes longer molecules more than it does shorter ones, separating them by length. Thus, gel electrophoresis separates a mixture of linear DNA molecules into bands, each band consisting of many thousands of DNA molecules of the same length.

One historically useful application of this technique has been *restriction fragment analysis*, which rapidly provides information about DNA sequences. With advances in sequencing technology, the approach taken in labs today is often simply to sequence the DNA sample in question. However, restriction fragment analysis is still done in some cases, and understanding how it is done will give you a better grasp of recombinant DNA technology. In this type of analysis, the DNA fragments produced by restriction enzyme digestion (cutting) of a DNA molecule are separated by gel electrophoresis. When the mixture of restriction fragments undergoes electrophoresis, it yields a band pattern characteristic of the starting molecule and the restriction enzyme used. In fact, the relatively small DNA molecules of viruses and plasmids can be identified simply by their restriction fragment patterns. Because DNA can be recovered undamaged from gels, the procedure also provides a way to prepare pure samples of individual fragments—assuming the bands can be clearly resolved. (Very large DNA molecules, such as those of eukaryotic chromosomes, yield so many fragments that they appear as a smear instead of distinct bands.)

Restriction fragment analysis can be used to compare two different DNA molecules—for example, two alleles of a gene—if the nucleotide difference affects a restriction site. A change in even one base pair of that sequence will prevent a restriction enzyme from cutting there. Variations in DNA sequence among a population are called *polymorphisms* (from the Greek for "many forms"), and this particular type of sequence change is called a **restriction fragment length polymorphism** (**RFLP**, pronounced "Rif-lip"). If one allele contains a RFLP, digestion with the enzyme that recognizes the site will produce a different mixture of fragments for each of the two alleles. Each mixture will give its own band pattern in gel electrophoresis.

For example, sickle-cell disease is caused by mutation of a single nucleotide located within a restriction sequence (a RFLP) in the human β-globin gene (see pp. 277–278 and Figure 17.23). Consequently, while other assays are preferred today, restriction fragment analysis was used for many years to distinguish the normal and sickle-cell alleles of the β-globin gene, as shown in **Figure 20.10**.

The starting materials in Figure 20.10 are samples of the cloned and purified β-globin alleles. But how could this test be done if we didn't have purified alleles to start with? If we wanted to determine whether a person is a heterozygous carrier of the mutant allele for sickle-cell disease, we would directly compare the genomic DNA from that person with DNA from both a person who has sickle-cell disease (and is homozygous for the mutant allele) and a person who is

(a) *Dde*I restriction sites in normal and sickle-cell alleles of the β-globin gene. Shown here are the cloned alleles, separated from the vector DNA but including some DNA next to the coding sequence. The normal allele contains two sites within the coding sequence recognized by the *Dde*I restriction enzyme. The sickle-cell allele lacks one of these sites.

(b) Electrophoresis of restriction fragments from normal and sickle-cell alleles. Samples of each purified allele were cut with the *Dde*I enzyme and then subjected to gel electrophoresis, resulting in three bands for the normal allele and two bands for the sickle-cell allele. (The tiny fragments on the ends of both initial DNA molecules are identical and are not seen here.)

▲ **Figure 20.10 Using restriction fragment analysis to distinguish the normal and sickle-cell alleles of the human β-globin gene.** **(a)** The sickle-cell mutation destroys one of the *Dde*I restriction sites within the gene. **(b)** As a result, digestion with the *Dde*I enzyme generates different sets of fragments from the normal and sickle-cell alleles.

WHAT IF? *Given bacterial clones with recombinant plasmids carrying each of these alleles, how would you isolate the pure DNA samples run on the gel in (b)? (Hint: Study Figures 20.4 and 20.9.)*

homozygous for the normal allele. As we mentioned already, electrophoresis of genomic DNA digested with a restriction enzyme and stained with a DNA-binding dye yields too many bands to distinguish them individually. However, a classic method called **Southern blotting** (developed by British biochemist Edwin Southern), which combines gel electrophoresis and nucleic acid hybridization, allows us to detect just those bands that include parts of the β-globin gene. The principle is the same as in nucleic acid hybridization for screening bacterial clones (see Figure 20.7). In Southern blotting, the probe is usually a radioactively or otherwise labeled single-stranded DNA molecule that is complementary to the gene of interest. **Figure 20.11** outlines the entire procedure and demonstrates how it can differentiate a heterozygote (in this case, for the sickle-cell allele) from an individual homozygous for the normal allele.

The identification of carriers of mutant alleles associated with genetic diseases is only one of the ways Southern blotting has been used. In fact, this technique was a laboratory workhorse for many years. Recently, however, it has been supplanted by more rapid methods, often involving PCR amplification of the specific parts of genomes that may differ.

DNA Sequencing

Once a gene is cloned, its complete nucleotide sequence can be determined. Today, sequencing is automated, carried out by sequencing machines (see Figure 1.12). The first automated procedure was based on a technique called the *dideoxyribonucleotide*

▼ **Figure 20.11** ▌ **RESEARCH METHOD**

Southern Blotting of DNA Fragments

APPLICATION Researchers can detect specific nucleotide sequences within a complex DNA sample with this method. In particular, Southern blotting can be used to compare the restriction fragments produced from different samples of genomic DNA.

TECHNIQUE In this example, we compare genomic DNA samples from three individuals: a homozygote for the normal β-globin allele (I), a homozygote for the mutant sickle-cell allele (II), and a heterozygote (III). As in Figure 20.7, we show a radioactively labeled probe, but other methods of probe labeling and detection are also used.

① **Preparation of restriction fragments.** Each DNA sample is mixed with the same restriction enzyme, in this case *Dde*I. Digestion of each sample yields a mixture of thousands of restriction fragments.

② **Gel electrophoresis.** The restriction fragments in each sample are separated by electrophoresis, forming a characteristic pattern of bands. (In reality, there would be many more bands than shown here, and they would be invisible unless stained.)

③ **DNA transfer (blotting).** With the gel arranged as shown above, capillary action pulls the alkaline solution upward through the gel, denaturing and transferring the DNA to a nitrocellulose membrane. This produces a blot with a pattern of DNA bands exactly like that of the gel.

④ **Hybridization with labeled probe.** The nitrocellulose blot is exposed to a solution containing a probe labeled in some way. In this example, the probe is radioactively labeled, single-stranded DNA complementary to the β-globin gene. Probe molecules attach by base-pairing to any restriction fragments containing a part of the β-globin gene. (The bands would not be visible yet.)

⑤ **Probe detection.** A sheet of photographic film is laid over the blot. The radioactivity in the bound probe exposes the film to form an image corresponding to those bands containing DNA that base-paired with the probe.

RESULTS The band patterns for the three samples are clearly different, so this method can be used to identify heterozygous carriers of the sickle-cell allele (III), as well as those with the disease, who have two mutant alleles (II), and unaffected individuals, who have two normal alleles (I). Band patterns for samples I and II resemble those seen for the purified normal and mutant alleles, respectively, seen in Figure 20.10b. The band pattern for the sample from the heterozygote (III) is a combination of the patterns for the two homozygotes (I and II).

RESEARCH METHOD

Dideoxy Chain Termination Method for Sequencing DNA

APPLICATION The sequence of nucleotides in any cloned DNA fragment of up to 800–1,000 base pairs in length can be determined rapidly with machines that carry out sequencing reactions and separate the labeled reaction products by length.

TECHNIQUE This method synthesizes a set of DNA strands complementary to the original DNA fragment. Each strand starts with the same primer and ends with a dideoxyribonucleotide (ddNTP), a modified nucleotide. Incorporation of a ddNTP terminates a growing DNA strand because it lacks a 3' —OH group, the site for attachment of the next nucleotide (see Figure 16.14). In the set of strands synthesized, each nucleotide position along the original sequence is represented by strands ending at that point with the complementary ddNTP. Because each type of ddNTP is tagged with a distinct fluorescent label, the identity of the ending nucleotides of the new strands, and ultimately the entire original sequence, can be determined.

1 The fragment of DNA to be sequenced is denatured into single strands and incubated in a test tube with the necessary ingredients for DNA synthesis: a primer designed to base-pair with the known 3' end of the template strand, DNA polymerase, the four deoxyribonucleotides, and the four dideoxyribonucleotides, each tagged with a specific fluorescent molecule.

2 Synthesis of each new strand starts at the 3' end of the primer and continues until a dideoxyribonucleotide is inserted, at random, instead of the normal equivalent deoxyribonucleotide. This prevents further elongation of the strand. Eventually, a set of labeled strands of various lengths is generated, with the color of the tag representing the last nucleotide in the sequence.

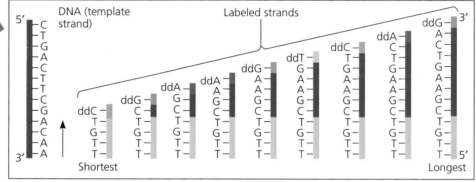

3 The labeled strands in the mixture are separated by passage through a polyacrylamide gel, with shorter strands moving through more quickly. For DNA sequencing, the gel is formed in a capillary tube rather than a slab like that shown in Figure 20.9. The small size of the tube allows a fluorescence detector to sense the color of each fluorescent tag as the strands come through. Strands differing in length by as little as one nucleotide can be distinguished from each other.

RESULTS The color of the fluorescent tag on each strand indicates the identity of the nucleotide at its end. The results can be printed out as a spectrogram, and the sequence, which is complementary to the template strand, can then be read from bottom (shortest strand) to top (longest strand). (Notice that the sequence here begins after the primer.)

(or *dideoxy*) *chain termination method*, for reasons you can see in **Figure 20.12**. This method was developed by British biochemist Frederick Sanger, who received the Nobel Prize in 1980 for this accomplishment. (One of only four people to win two Nobel Prizes, Sanger also won one in 1975 for determining the amino acid sequence of insulin.)

In the last ten years, "next-generation sequencing" techniques have been developed that do not rely on chain termination. Instead, a single template strand is immobilized, and reagents are added that allow so-called *sequencing by synthesis* of a complementary strand, one nucleotide at a time. A chemical trick enables electronic monitors to identify which of the four nucleotides is added, allowing determination of the sequence. Further technical changes have given rise to "third-generation sequencing," with each new technique being faster and less expensive than the previous. In Chapter 21, you'll learn more about how this rapid acceleration of sequencing technology has enhanced our study of genes and whole genomes.

Knowing the sequence of a gene allows researchers to compare it directly with genes in other species, where the function of the gene product may be known. If two genes from different species are quite similar in sequence, it is reasonable to suppose that their gene products perform similar functions. In this way, sequence comparisons provide clues to a gene's function, a topic we'll return to shortly. Another set of clues is provided by experimental approaches that analyze when and where a gene is expressed.

Analyzing Gene Expression

Having cloned a given gene, researchers can make labeled nucleic acid probes that will hybridize with mRNAs transcribed from the gene. The probes can provide information about when or where in the organism the gene is transcribed. Transcription levels are commonly used as a measure of gene expression.

Studying the Expression of Single Genes

Suppose we want to find out how the expression of the β-globin gene changes during the embryonic development of the hummingbird. There are at least two ways to do this.

The first is called **Northern blotting** (a play on words based on this method's close similarity to Southern blotting). In this method, we carry out gel electrophoresis on samples of mRNA from hummingbird embryos at different stages of development, transfer the samples to a nitrocellulose membrane, and then allow the mRNAs on the membrane to hybridize with a labeled probe recognizing β-globin mRNA. If we expose a film to the membrane, the resulting image will look similar to the Southern blot in Figure 20.11, with one band of a given size showing up in each sample. If the mRNA band is seen at a particular stage, we can hypothesize that the protein functions during events taking place at that stage. Like Southern blotting, Northern blotting has been a mainstay over the years, but it is being supplanted in many labs by other techniques.

A method that is quicker and more sensitive than Northern blotting (because it requires less mRNA) and therefore becoming more widely used is the **reverse transcriptase–polymerase chain reaction**, or **RT-PCR** (**Figure 20.13**). Analysis of hummingbird β-globin gene expression with RT-PCR begins similarly to Northern blotting, with the isolation of mRNAs from different developmental stages of hummingbird embryos. Reverse transcriptase is added next to make cDNA, which then serves as a template for PCR amplification using primers from the β-globin gene. When the products are run on a gel, copies of the amplified region will be observed as bands only in samples that originally contained the β-globin mRNA. In the case of hummingbird β-globin, for instance, we might expect to see a band appear at the stage when red blood cells begin forming, with all subsequent stages

▼ **Figure 20.13** **RESEARCH METHOD**

RT-PCR Analysis of the Expression of Single Genes

APPLICATION RT-PCR uses the enzyme reverse transcriptase (RT) in combination with PCR and gel electrophoresis. RT-PCR can be used to compare gene expression between samples—for instance, in different embryonic stages, in different tissues, or in the same type of cell under different conditions.

TECHNIQUE In this example, samples containing mRNAs from six embryonic stages of hummingbird were processed as shown below. (The mRNA from only one stage is shown.)

❶ **cDNA synthesis** is carried out by incubating the mRNAs with reverse transcriptase and other necessary components.

❷ **PCR amplification** of the sample is performed using primers specific to the hummingbird β-globin gene.

❸ **Gel electrophoresis** will reveal amplified DNA products only in samples that contained mRNA transcribed from the β-globin gene.

RESULTS The mRNA for this gene first is expressed at stage 2 and continues to be expressed through stage 6. The size of the amplified fragment (shown by its position on the gel) depends on the distance between the primers that were used.

▲ **Figure 20.14 Determining where genes are expressed by *in situ* hybridization analysis.** This *Drosophila* embryo was incubated in a solution containing probes for five different mRNAs, each probe labeled with a different fluorescently colored tag. The embryo was then viewed using fluorescence microscopy. Each color marks where a specific gene is expressed as mRNA.

showing the same band. RT-PCR can also be carried out with mRNAs collected from different tissues at one time to discover which tissue is producing a specific mRNA.

An alternative way to determine which tissues or cells are expressing certain genes is to track down the location of specific mRNAs using labeled probes in place, or *in situ*, in the intact organism. This technique, called ***in situ* hybridization**, is most often carried out with probes labeled by attachment of fluorescent dyes (see Chapter 6). Different probes can be labeled with different dyes, sometimes with strikingly beautiful results **(Figure 20.14)**.

Studying the Expression of Interacting Groups of Genes

A major goal of biologists is to learn how genes act together to produce and maintain a functioning organism. Now that the entire genomes of a number of organisms have been sequenced, it is possible to study the expression of large groups of genes—a systems approach. Researchers use genome sequences as probes to investigate which genes are transcribed in different situations, such as in different tissues or at different stages of development. They also look for groups of genes that are expressed in a coordinated manner, with the aim of identifying networks of gene expression across an entire genome.

The basic strategy in such global (genome-wide) expression studies is to isolate the mRNAs made in particular cells, use these molecules as templates for making the corresponding cDNAs by reverse transcription, and then employ nucleic acid hybridization to compare this set of cDNAs with a collection of DNA fragments representing all or part of the genome. The results identify the subset of genes in the genome that are being expressed at a given time or under certain conditions. DNA technology makes such studies possible; with automation, they are easily performed on a large scale. Scientists can now measure the expression of thousands of genes at one time.

Genome-wide expression studies are made possible by **DNA microarray assays**. A DNA microarray consists of tiny amounts of a large number of single-stranded DNA fragments representing different genes fixed to a glass slide in a tightly spaced array, or grid (see Figure 20.1). (The microarray is also called a *DNA chip* by analogy to a computer chip.) Ideally, these fragments represent all the genes of an organism. **Figure 20.15** outlines how the DNA fragments on a microarray are tested for hybridization with cDNA molecules that have been prepared from the mRNAs in particular cells of interest and labeled with fluorescent dyes.

Using this technique, researchers have performed DNA microarray assays on more than 90% of the genes of the nematode *Caenorhabditis elegans* during every stage of its life cycle. The results show that expression of nearly 60% of *C. elegans* genes changes dramatically during development and that many genes are expressed in a sex-specific pattern. This study supports the model held by most developmental biologists that embryonic development involves a complex and elaborate program of gene expression, rather than simply the expression of a small number of important genes. This example illustrates the ability of DNA microarrays to reveal general profiles of gene expression over the lifetime of an organism.

In addition to uncovering gene interactions and providing clues to gene function, DNA microarray assays may contribute to a better understanding of diseases and suggest new diagnostic techniques or therapies. For instance, comparing patterns of gene expression in breast cancer tumors and noncancerous breast tissue has already resulted in more informed and effective treatment protocols. Ultimately, information from DNA microarray assays should provide a grander view of how ensembles of genes interact to form an organism and maintain its vital systems.

Determining Gene Function

How do scientists determine the function of a gene identified by the techniques described thus far in the chapter? Perhaps the most common approach is to disable the gene and then observe the consequences in the cell or organism. In one application of this approach, called ***in vitro* mutagenesis**, specific mutations are introduced into a cloned gene, and then the mutated gene is returned to a cell in such a way that it disables ("knocks out") the normal cellular copies of the same gene. If the introduced mutations alter or destroy the function of the gene product, the phenotype of the mutant cell may help reveal the function of the missing normal protein. Using molecular and genetic techniques worked out in the 1980s, researchers can even generate mice with any given gene disabled, in order to study the role of that gene in development and in the adult. Mario Capecchi, Martin Evans, and Oliver Smithies received the Nobel Prize in 2007 for first accomplishing this feat.

RESEARCH METHOD

DNA Microarray Assay of Gene Expression Levels

APPLICATION With this method, researchers can test thousands of genes simultaneously to determine which ones are expressed in a particular tissue, under different environmental conditions, in various disease states, or at different developmental stages. They can also look for coordinated gene expression.

TECHNIQUE

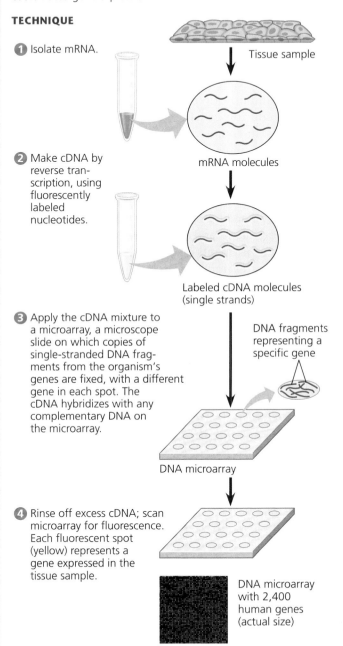

❶ Isolate mRNA.

Tissue sample

mRNA molecules

❷ Make cDNA by reverse transcription, using fluorescently labeled nucleotides.

Labeled cDNA molecules (single strands)

❸ Apply the cDNA mixture to a microarray, a microscope slide on which copies of single-stranded DNA fragments from the organism's genes are fixed, with a different gene in each spot. The cDNA hybridizes with any complementary DNA on the microarray.

DNA fragments representing a specific gene

DNA microarray

❹ Rinse off excess cDNA; scan microarray for fluorescence. Each fluorescent spot (yellow) represents a gene expressed in the tissue sample.

DNA microarray with 2,400 human genes (actual size)

RESULTS The intensity of fluorescence at each spot is a measure of the expression in the tissue sample of the gene represented by that spot. Most often, as in the actual microarray above, two different samples are tested together by labeling the cDNAs prepared from each sample with labels of different colors, often green and red. The resulting color at a spot reveals the relative levels of expression of a particular gene in the two samples: Green indicates expression in one sample, red in the other, yellow in both, and black in neither. (See Figure 20.1 for a larger view.)

A newer method for silencing expression of selected genes exploits the phenomenon of **RNA interference (RNAi)**, described in Chapter 18. This experimental approach uses synthetic double-stranded RNA molecules matching the sequence of a particular gene to trigger breakdown of the gene's messenger RNA or to block its translation. In organisms such as the nematode and the fruit fly, RNAi has already proved valuable for analyzing the functions of genes on a large scale. In one study, RNAi was used to prevent expression of 86% of the genes in early nematode embryos, one gene at a time. Analysis of the phenotypes of the worms that developed from these embryos allowed the researchers to classify most of the genes into a small number of groups by function. This type of analysis, in which the functions of multiple genes are considered in a single study, is sure to become more common as research focuses on the importance of interactions between genes in the system as a whole. This is the basis of systems biology (see Chapter 21).

In humans, ethical considerations prohibit knocking out genes to determine their functions. An alternative approach is to analyze the genomes of large numbers of people with a certain phenotypic condition or disease, such as heart disease or diabetes, to try to find differences they all share compared with people without that condition. These large-scale analyses, called **genome-wide association studies**, do not require complete sequencing of all the genomes in the two groups. Instead, researchers test for *genetic markers*, DNA sequences that vary in the population. In a gene, such sequence variation is the basis of different alleles, as we saw earlier for sickle-cell disease. And just like coding sequences, noncoding DNA at a specific locus on a chromosome may exhibit small nucleotide differences (polymorphisms) among individuals.

Among the most useful of these genetic markers are single base-pair variations in the genomes of the human population. A single base-pair site where variation is found in at least 1% of the population is called a **single nucleotide polymorphism** (**SNP**, pronounced "snip"). A few million SNPs occur in the human genome, about once in 100–300 base pairs of both coding and noncoding DNA sequences. (Roughly 98.5% of our genome doesn't code for protein, as you will learn in Chapter 21.) It isn't necessary to sequence the DNA of multiple individuals to find SNPs; today they can be detected by very sensitive microarray analysis or by PCR.

Once a region is found that has a SNP shared by affected but not unaffected people, researchers focus on that region and sequence it. In the vast majority of cases, the SNP itself does not contribute to the disease, and most SNPs are in noncoding regions. Instead, if the SNP and a disease-causing allele are close enough, scientists can take advantage of the fact that crossing over between the marker and the gene is very unlikely during gamete formation. Therefore, the marker and gene will almost always be inherited together, even though the marker is not

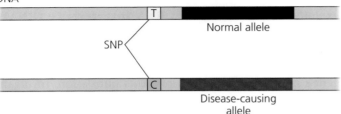

DNA

T

Normal allele

SNP

C

Disease-causing
allele

▲ **Figure 20.16 Single nucleotide polymorphisms (SNPs) as genetic markers for disease-causing alleles.** This diagram depicts homologous segments of DNA from two groups of individuals, those in one group having a particular disease or condition with a genetic basis. Unaffected people have a T at a particular SNP locus, while affected people have a C at that locus. A SNP that varies in this way is likely to be closely linked to one or more alleles of genes that contribute to the disease in question. (Here, only a single strand is shown for each DNA molecule.)

MAKE CONNECTIONS *What does it mean for a SNP to be "closely linked" to a disease-causing allele, and how does this allow the SNP to be used as a genetic marker? (See Concept 15.3, p. 296.)*

part of the gene **(Figure 20.16)**. SNPs have been found that correlate with diabetes, heart disease, and several types of cancer, and the search is on for genes that might be involved.

The techniques and experimental approaches you have learned about thus far have already taught us a great deal about genes and the functions of their products. This research is now being augmented by the development of powerful techniques for cloning whole multicellular organisms. An aim of this work is to obtain special types of cells, called stem cells, that give rise to all the different kinds of tissues. On a basic level, stem cells would allow scientists to use the DNA-based methods previously discussed to study the process of cell differentiation. On a more applied level, recombinant DNA techniques could be used to alter stem cells for the treatment of disease. Methods involving the cloning of organisms and production of stem cells are the subject of the next section.

CONCEPT CHECK 20.2

1. If you isolated DNA from human cells, treated it with a restriction enzyme, and analyzed the sample by gel electrophoresis, what would you see? Explain.
2. Describe the role of complementary base pairing during Southern blotting, DNA sequencing, Northern blotting, RT-PCR, and microarray analysis.
3. Distinguish between a SNP and a RFLP.
4. **WHAT IF?** Consider the microarray in Figure 20.1, a larger image of the one in Figure 20.15. If a sample from normal tissue is labeled with a green fluorescent dye, and a sample from cancerous tissue is labeled red, what can you conclude about a spot that is green? Red? Yellow? Black? Which genes would you be interested in examining further if you were studying cancer? Explain.

For suggested answers, see Appendix A.

CONCEPT 20.3

Cloning organisms may lead to production of stem cells for research and other applications

In parallel with advances in DNA technology, scientists have been developing and refining methods for cloning whole multicellular organisms from single cells. In this context, cloning produces one or more organisms genetically identical to the "parent" that donated the single cell. This is often called *organismal cloning* to differentiate it from gene cloning and, more significantly, from cell cloning—the division of an asexually reproducing cell into a collection of genetically identical cells. (The common theme for all types of cloning is that the product is genetically identical to the parent. In fact, the word *clone* comes from the Greek *klon*, meaning "twig.") The current interest in organismal cloning arises primarily from its potential to generate stem cells, which can in turn generate many different tissues.

The cloning of plants and animals was first attempted over 50 years ago in experiments designed to answer basic biological questions. For example, researchers wondered if all the cells of an organism have the same genes (a concept called *genomic equivalence*) or if cells lose genes during the process of differentiation (see Chapter 18). One way to answer this question is to see whether a differentiated cell can generate a whole organism—in other words, whether cloning an organism is possible. Let's discuss these early experiments before we consider more recent progress in organismal cloning and procedures for producing stem cells.

Cloning Plants: Single-Cell Cultures

The successful cloning of whole plants from single differentiated cells was accomplished during the 1950s by F. C. Steward and his students at Cornell University, who worked with carrot plants **(Figure 20.17)**. They found that differentiated cells taken from the root (the carrot) and incubated in culture medium could grow into normal adult plants, each genetically identical to the parent plant. These results showed that differentiation does not necessarily involve irreversible changes in the DNA. In plants, at least, mature cells can "dedifferentiate" and then give rise to all the specialized cell types of the organism. Any cell with this potential is said to be **totipotent**.

Plant cloning is now used extensively in agriculture. For some plants, such as orchids, cloning is the only commercially practical means of reproducing plants. In other cases, cloning has been used to reproduce a plant with valuable characteristics, such as the ability to resist a plant pathogen. In fact, you yourself may be a plant cloner: If you have ever grown a new plant from a cutting, you have practiced cloning!

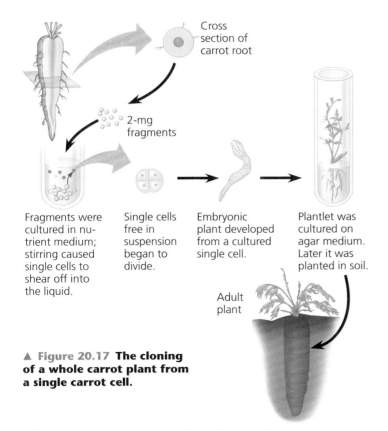

Cross section of carrot root

2-mg fragments

Fragments were cultured in nutrient medium; stirring caused single cells to shear off into the liquid.

Single cells free in suspension began to divide.

Embryonic plant developed from a cultured single cell.

Plantlet was cultured on agar medium. Later it was planted in soil.

Adult plant

▲ **Figure 20.17 The cloning of a whole carrot plant from a single carrot cell.**

Cloning Animals: Nuclear Transplantation

Differentiated cells from animals generally do not divide in culture, much less develop into the multiple cell types of a new organism. Therefore, early researchers had to use a different approach to the question of whether differentiated animal cells can be totipotent. Their approach was to remove the nucleus of an unfertilized or fertilized egg and replace it with the nucleus of a differentiated cell, a procedure called *nuclear transplantation*. If the nucleus from the differentiated donor cell retains its full genetic capability, then it should be able to direct development of the recipient cell into all the tissues and organs of an organism.

Such experiments were conducted on one species of frog (*Rana pipiens*) by Robert Briggs and Thomas King in the 1950s and on another (*Xenopus laevis*) by John Gurdon in the 1970s. These researchers transplanted a nucleus from an embryonic or tadpole cell into an enucleated (nucleus-lacking) egg of the same species. In Gurdon's experiments, the transplanted nucleus was often able to support normal development of the egg into a tadpole (Figure 20.18). However, he found that the potential of a transplanted nucleus to direct normal development was inversely related to the age of the donor: the older the donor nucleus, the lower the percentage of normally developing tadpoles.

From these results, Gurdon concluded that something in the nucleus *does* change as animal cells differentiate. In frogs and most other animals, nuclear potential tends to be restricted more and more as embryonic development and cell differentiation progress.

▼ **Figure 20.18**

INQUIRY

Can the nucleus from a differentiated animal cell direct development of an organism?

EXPERIMENT John Gurdon and colleagues at Oxford University, in England, destroyed the nuclei of frog (*Xenopus laevis*) eggs by exposing the eggs to ultraviolet light. They then transplanted nuclei from cells of frog embryos and tadpoles into the enucleated eggs.

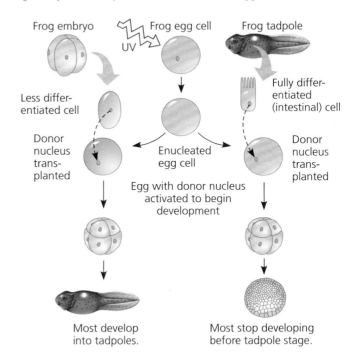

Frog embryo

Frog egg cell

UV

Frog tadpole

Less differentiated cell

Fully differentiated (intestinal) cell

Donor nucleus transplanted

Enucleated egg cell

Donor nucleus transplanted

Egg with donor nucleus activated to begin development

Most develop into tadpoles.

Most stop developing before tadpole stage.

RESULTS When the transplanted nuclei came from an early embryo, whose cells are relatively undifferentiated, most of the recipient eggs developed into tadpoles. But when the nuclei came from the fully differentiated intestinal cells of a tadpole, fewer than 2% of the eggs developed into normal tadpoles, and most of the embryos stopped developing at a much earlier stage.

CONCLUSION The nucleus from a differentiated frog cell can direct development of a tadpole. However, its ability to do so decreases as the donor cell becomes more differentiated, presumably because of changes in the nucleus.

SOURCE J. B. Gurdon et al., The developmental capacity of nuclei transplanted from keratinized cells of adult frogs, *Journal of Embryology and Experimental Morphology* 34:93–112 (1975).

WHAT IF? If each cell in a four-cell embryo was already so specialized that it was not totipotent, what results would you predict for the experiment on the left side of the figure?

Reproductive Cloning of Mammals

In addition to cloning frogs, researchers have long been able to clone mammals by transplanting nuclei or cells from a variety of early embryos. But it was not known whether a nucleus from a fully differentiated cell could be reprogrammed to succeed in acting as a donor nucleus. In 1997, however, researchers at the Roslin Institute in Scotland captured newspaper headlines when they announced the birth of Dolly, a

▼ Figure 20.19 RESEARCH METHOD

Reproductive Cloning of a Mammal by Nuclear Transplantation

APPLICATION This method is used to produce cloned animals whose nuclear genes are identical to those of the animal supplying the nucleus.

TECHNIQUE Shown here is the procedure used to produce Dolly, the first reported case of a mammal cloned using the nucleus of a differentiated cell.

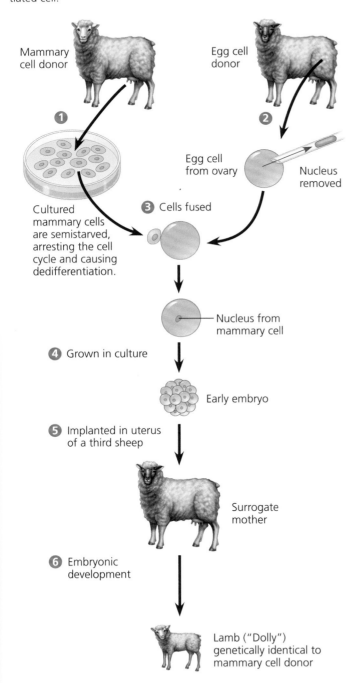

① Mammary cell donor

② Egg cell donor

Egg cell from ovary

Nucleus removed

Cultured mammary cells are semistarved, arresting the cell cycle and causing dedifferentiation.

③ Cells fused

Nucleus from mammary cell

④ Grown in culture

Early embryo

⑤ Implanted in uterus of a third sheep

Surrogate mother

⑥ Embryonic development

Lamb ("Dolly") genetically identical to mammary cell donor

RESULTS The genetic makeup of the cloned animal is identical to that of the animal supplying the nucleus but differs from that of the egg donor and surrogate mother. (The latter two are "Scottish blackface" sheep, with dark faces.)

lamb cloned from an adult sheep by nuclear transplantation from a differentiated cell **(Figure 20.19)**. These researchers achieved the necessary dedifferentiation of donor nuclei by culturing mammary cells in nutrient-poor medium. They then fused these cells with enucleated sheep eggs. The resulting diploid cells divided to form early embryos, which were implanted into surrogate mothers. Out of several hundred implanted embryos, one successfully completed normal development, and Dolly was born.

Later analyses showed that Dolly's chromosomal DNA was indeed identical to that of the nucleus donor. (Her mitochondrial DNA came from the egg donor, as expected.) At the age of 6, Dolly suffered complications from a lung disease usually seen only in much older sheep and was euthanized. Dolly's premature death, as well as her arthritic condition, led to speculation that her cells were in some way not quite as healthy as those of a normal sheep, possibly reflecting incomplete reprogramming of the original transplanted nucleus.

Since 1997, researchers have cloned numerous other mammals, including mice, cats, cows, horses, pigs, dogs, and monkeys. In most cases, their goal has been the production of new individuals; this is known as *reproductive cloning*. We have already learned a lot from such experiments. For example, cloned animals of the same species do *not* always look or behave identically. In a herd of cows cloned from the same line of cultured cells, certain cows are dominant in behavior and others are more submissive. Another example of nonidentity in clones is the first cloned cat, named CC for Carbon Copy **(Figure 20.20)**. She has a calico coat, like her single female parent, but the color and pattern are different because of random X chromosome inactivation, which is a normal occurrence during embryonic development (see Figure 15.8). And identical human twins, which

▲ **Figure 20.20 CC, the first cloned cat, and her single parent.** Rainbow (left) donated the nucleus in a cloning procedure that resulted in CC (right). However, the two cats are not identical: Rainbow is a classic calico cat with orange patches on her fur and has a "reserved personality," while CC has a gray and white coat and is more playful.

are naturally occurring "clones," are always slightly different. Clearly, environmental influences and random phenomena can play a significant role during development.

The successful cloning of so many mammals has heightened speculation about the cloning of humans. Scientists in several labs around the world have tackled the first steps of human cloning. In the most common approach, nuclei from differentiated human cells are transplanted into unfertilized enucleated eggs, and the eggs are stimulated to divide. In 2001, a research group at a biotechnology company in Massachusetts observed a few early cell divisions in such an experiment. A few years later, researchers at Seoul National University, in South Korea, reported cloning embryos to an early stage called the blastocyst stage, but the scientists were later found guilty of research misconduct and data fabrication. This episode sent shock waves through the scientific community. In 2007, the first primate (macaque) embryos were cloned by researchers at the Oregon National Primate Research Center; these clones reached the blastocyst stage. This achievement has moved the field one step closer to human cloning, the prospect of which raises unprecedented ethical issues.

Problems Associated with Animal Cloning

In most nuclear transplantation studies thus far, only a small percentage of cloned embryos develop normally to birth. And like Dolly, many cloned animals exhibit defects. Cloned mice, for instance, are prone to obesity, pneumonia, liver failure, and premature death. Scientists assert that even cloned animals that appear normal are likely to have subtle defects.

In recent years, we have begun to uncover some reasons for the low efficiency of cloning and the high incidence of abnormalities. In the nuclei of fully differentiated cells, a small subset of genes is turned on and expression of the rest is repressed. This regulation often is the result of epigenetic changes in chromatin, such as acetylation of histones or methylation of DNA (see Figure 18.7). During the nuclear transfer procedure, many of these changes must be reversed in the later-stage nucleus from a donor animal for genes to be expressed or repressed appropriately in early stages of development. Researchers have found that the DNA in cells from cloned embryos, like that of differentiated cells, often has more methyl groups than does the DNA in equivalent cells from normal embryos of the same species. This finding suggests that the reprogramming of donor nuclei requires chromatin restructuring, which occurs incompletely during cloning procedures. Because DNA methylation helps regulate gene expression, misplaced methyl groups in the DNA of donor nuclei may interfere with the pattern of gene expression necessary for normal embryonic development. In fact, the success of a cloning attempt may depend in large part on whether or not the chromatin in the donor nucleus can be artificially modified to resemble that of a newly fertilized egg.

Stem Cells of Animals

The major goal of cloning human embryos is not reproduction, but the production of stem cells for treating human diseases. A **stem cell** is a relatively unspecialized cell that can both reproduce itself indefinitely and, under appropriate conditions, differentiate into specialized cells of one or more types. Thus, stem cells are able both to replenish their own population and to generate cells that travel down specific differentiation pathways.

Many early animal embryos contain stem cells capable of giving rise to differentiated embryonic cells of any type. Stem cells can be isolated from early embryos at a stage called the blastula stage or its human equivalent, the blastocyst stage **(Figure 20.21)**. In culture, these *embryonic stem (ES) cells*

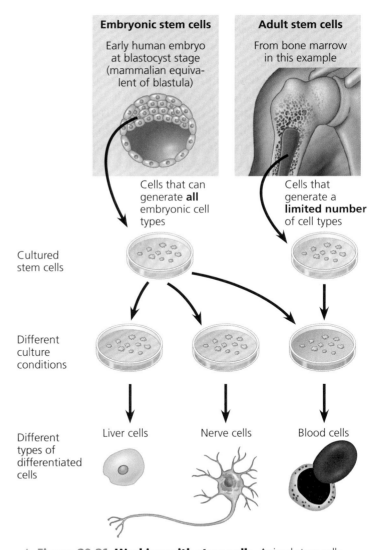

▲ **Figure 20.21 Working with stem cells.** Animal stem cells, which can be isolated from early embryos or adult tissues and grown in culture, are self-perpetuating, relatively undifferentiated cells. Embryonic stem cells are easier to grow than adult stem cells and can theoretically give rise to *all* types of cells in an organism. The range of cell types that can arise from adult stem cells is not yet fully understood.

reproduce indefinitely; and depending on culture conditions, they can be made to differentiate into a wide variety of specialized cells, including even eggs and sperm.

The adult body also has stem cells, which serve to replace nonreproducing specialized cells as needed. In contrast to ES cells, *adult stem cells* are not able to give rise to all cell types in the organism, though they can generate multiple types. For example, one of the several types of stem cells in bone marrow can generate all the different kinds of blood cells (see Figure 20.21), and another can differentiate into bone, cartilage, fat, muscle, and the linings of blood vessels. To the surprise of many, the adult brain has been found to contain stem cells that continue to produce certain kinds of nerve cells there. And recently, researchers have reported finding stem cells in skin, hair, eyes, and dental pulp. Although adult animals have only tiny numbers of stem cells, scientists are learning to identify and isolate these cells from various tissues and, in some cases, to grow them in culture. With the right culture conditions (for instance, the addition of specific growth factors), cultured stem cells from adult animals have been made to differentiate into multiple types of specialized cells, although none are as versatile as ES cells.

Research with embryonic or adult stem cells is a source of valuable data about differentiation and has enormous potential for medical applications. The ultimate aim is to supply cells for the repair of damaged or diseased organs: for example, insulin-producing pancreatic cells for people with type 1 diabetes or certain kinds of brain cells for people with Parkinson's disease or Huntington's disease. Adult stem cells from bone marrow have long been used as a source of immune system cells in patients whose own immune systems are nonfunctional because of genetic disorders or radiation treatments for cancer.

The developmental potential of adult stem cells is limited to certain tissues. ES cells hold more promise than adult stem cells for most medical applications because ES cells are **pluripotent**, capable of differentiating into many different cell types. The only way to obtain ES cells thus far, however, has been to harvest them from human embryos, which raises ethical and political issues.

ES cells are currently obtained from embryos donated by patients undergoing infertility treatment or from long-term cell cultures originally established with cells isolated from donated embryos. If scientists were able to clone human embryos to the blastocyst stage, they might be able to use such clones as the source of ES cells in the future. Furthermore, with a donor nucleus from a person with a particular disease, they might be able to produce ES cells for treatment that match the patient and are thus not rejected by his or her immune system. When the main aim of cloning is to produce ES cells to treat disease, the process is called *therapeutic cloning*. Although most people believe that reproductive cloning of humans is unethical, opinions vary about the morality of therapeutic cloning.

Resolving the debate now seems less imperative because researchers have been able to turn back the clock in fully differentiated cells, reprogramming them to act like ES cells. The accomplishment of this feat, which posed formidable obstacles, was announced in 2007, first by labs using mouse skin cells and then by additional groups using cells from human skin and other organs or tissues. In all these cases, researchers transformed the differentiated cells into ES cells by using retroviruses to introduce extra cloned copies of four "stem cell" master regulatory genes. All the tests that were carried out at the time indicated that the transformed cells, known as *induced pluripotent stem (iPS) cells*, could do everything ES cells can do. More recently, however, several research groups have uncovered differences between iPS and ES cells in gene expression and other cellular functions, such as cell division. At least until these differences are fully understood, the study of ES cells will continue to make important contributions to the development of stem cell therapies. (In fact, ES cells will likely always be a focus of basic research as well.) In the meantime, work is proceeding using the iPS cells in hand.

There are two major potential uses for human iPS cells. First, cells from patients suffering from diseases can be reprogrammed to become iPS cells, which can act as model cells for studying the disease and potential treatments. Human iPS cell lines have already been developed from individuals with type 1 diabetes, Parkinson's disease, and at least a dozen other diseases. Second, in the field of regenerative medicine, a patient's own cells could be reprogrammed into iPS cells and then used to replace nonfunctional tissues (**Figure 20.22**). Developing techniques that direct iPS cells to become specific cell types for this purpose is an area of intense research, one that has already seen some success. The iPS cells created in this way could eventually provide tailor-made "replacement" cells for patients without using any human eggs or embryos, thus circumventing most ethical objections.

CONCEPT CHECK 20.3

1. Based on current knowledge, how would you explain the difference in the percentage of tadpoles that developed from the two kinds of donor nuclei in Figure 20.18?

2. If you were to clone a carrot using the technique shown in Figure 20.17, would all the progeny plants ("clones") look identical? Why or why not?

3. **WHAT IF?** If you were a doctor who wanted to use iPS cells to treat a patient with severe type 1 diabetes, what new technique would have to be developed?

4. **MAKE CONNECTIONS** Compare an individual carrot cell in Figure 20.17 with the fully differentiated muscle cell in Figure 18.18 (p. 369) in terms of their potential to develop into different cell types.

For suggested answers, see Appendix A.

IMPACT

The Impact of Induced Pluripotent Stem (iPS) Cells on Regenerative Medicine

While embryonic stem (ES) cells can generate every cell in an organism, the use of human embryos as their source is controversial. Several research groups have developed similar procedures for reprogramming fully differentiated cells to become induced pluripotent stem (iPS) cells, which act like ES cells. The technique is based on introducing transcription factors that are characteristic of stem cells into differentiated cells, such as skin cells.

WHY IT MATTERS Patients with diseases such as heart disease, diabetes, or Alzheimer's could have their own skin cells reprogrammed to become iPS cells. Once procedures have been developed for converting iPS cells into heart, pancreatic, or nervous system cells, the patients' own iPS cells might be used to treat their disease. This technique has already been used successfully to treat sickle-cell disease in a mouse that had been genetically engineered to have the disease. Shown below is how this therapy could work in humans, once researchers learn how iPS cells can be triggered to differentiate as desired (step 3).

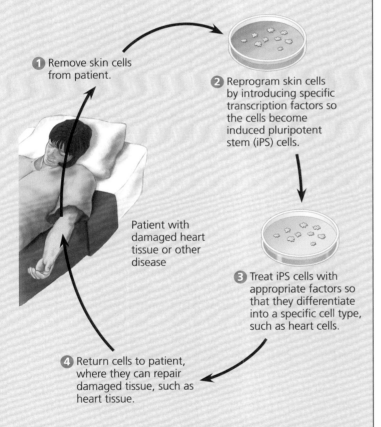

① Remove skin cells from patient.

② Reprogram skin cells by introducing specific transcription factors so the cells become induced pluripotent stem (iPS) cells.

Patient with damaged heart tissue or other disease

③ Treat iPS cells with appropriate factors so that they differentiate into a specific cell type, such as heart cells.

④ Return cells to patient, where they can repair damaged tissue, such as heart tissue.

FURTHER READING G. Vogel and C. Holden, Field leaps forward with new stem cell advances, *Science* 318:1224–1225 (2007); K. Hochedlinger, Your inner healers, *Scientific American* 302:46–53 (2010).

WHAT IF? When organs are transplanted from a donor to a diseased recipient, the recipient's immune system may reject the transplant, a condition with serious and often fatal consequences. Would using converted iPS cells be expected to carry the same risk? Why or why not?

The practical applications of DNA technology affect our lives in many ways

DNA technology is in the news almost every day. Most often, the topic is a new and promising application in medicine, but this is just one of numerous fields benefiting from DNA technology and genetic engineering.

Medical Applications

One important use of DNA technology is the identification of human genes whose mutation plays a role in genetic diseases. These discoveries may lead to ways of diagnosing, treating, and even preventing such conditions. DNA technology is also contributing to our understanding of "nongenetic" diseases, from arthritis to AIDS, since a person's genes influence susceptibility to these diseases. Furthermore, diseases of all sorts involve changes in gene expression within the affected cells and often within the patient's immune system. By using DNA microarray assays or other techniques to compare gene expression in healthy and diseased tissues, as seen in Figure 20.1, researchers hope to find many of the genes that are turned on or off in particular diseases. These genes and their products are potential targets for prevention or therapy.

Diagnosis and Treatment of Diseases

A new chapter in the diagnosis of infectious diseases has been opened by DNA technology, in particular the use of PCR and labeled nucleic acid probes to track down pathogens. For example, because the sequence of the RNA genome of HIV is known, RT-PCR can be used to amplify, and thus detect, HIV RNA in blood or tissue samples (see Figure 20.13). RT-PCR is often the best way to detect an otherwise elusive infective agent.

Medical scientists can now diagnose hundreds of human genetic disorders by using PCR with primers that target the genes associated with these disorders. The amplified DNA product is then sequenced to reveal the presence or absence of the disease-causing mutation. Among the genes for human diseases that have been identified are those for sickle-cell disease, hemophilia, cystic fibrosis, Huntington's disease, and Duchenne muscular dystrophy. Individuals afflicted with such diseases can often be identified before the onset of symptoms, even before birth. PCR can also be used to identify symptomless carriers of potentially harmful recessive alleles, essentially replacing Southern blotting for this purpose.

As you learned earlier, genome-wide association studies have pinpointed SNPs (single nucleotide polymorphisms) that are linked to disease-causing alleles. Individuals can be tested for the presence of a SNP that indicates the presence of the abnormal allele. The presence of particular SNPs is correlated with increased risk for conditions such as heart disease, Alzheimer's, and some types of cancer. Companies that offer individual genetic testing for risk factors like these are looking for the presence of previously identified, linked SNPs. It may be helpful for an individual to learn about their health risks, with the understanding that such genetic tests merely reflect correlations and do not make predictions.

The techniques described in this chapter have also prompted improvements in disease treatments. By analyzing the expression of many genes in breast cancer patients, researchers carrying out one genome-wide association study were able to identify 70 genes whose expression pattern could be correlated with the likelihood that the cancer would recur. Given that low-risk patients have a 96% survival rate over a ten-year period with no treatment, gene expression analysis allows doctors and patients access to valuable information when they are considering treatment options.

Many envision a future of "personalized medicine" where each person's genetic health profile can inform them about diseases or conditions for which they are especially at risk and help them make treatment choices. A genetic profile is currently taken to mean a set of genetic markers such as SNPs, but ultimately it could mean the complete DNA sequence of each individual—once sequencing becomes inexpensive enough.

Human Gene Therapy

Gene therapy—introducing genes into an afflicted individual for therapeutic purposes—holds great potential for treating the relatively small number of disorders traceable to a single defective gene. In theory, a normal allele of the defective gene could be inserted into the somatic cells of the tissue affected by the disorder.

For gene therapy of somatic cells to be permanent, the cells that receive the normal allele must be ones that multiply throughout the patient's life. Bone marrow cells, which include the stem cells that give rise to all the cells of the blood and immune system, are prime candidates. **Figure 20.23** outlines one possible procedure for gene therapy of an individual whose bone marrow cells do not produce a vital enzyme because of a single defective gene. One type of severe combined immunodeficiency (SCID) is caused by just this kind of defect. If the treatment is successful, the patient's bone marrow cells will begin producing the missing protein, and the patient may be cured.

The procedure shown in Figure 20.23 has been used in gene therapy trials for SCID. In a trial begun in France in 2000, ten young children with SCID were treated by the same procedure. Nine of these patients showed significant, definitive improvement after two years, the first indisputable success of gene therapy. However, three of the patients subsequently developed leukemia, a type of blood cell cancer, and one of them died. Two factors may have contributed to the development of leukemia: the insertion of the retroviral

▲ **Figure 20.23 Gene therapy using a retroviral vector.** A retrovirus that has been rendered harmless is used as a vector in this procedure, which exploits the ability of a retrovirus to insert a DNA transcript of its RNA genome into the chromosomal DNA of its host cell (see Figure 19.8). If the foreign gene carried by the retroviral vector is expressed, the cell and its descendants will possess the gene product. Cells that reproduce throughout life, such as bone marrow cells, are ideal candidates for gene therapy.

1. Insert RNA version of normal allele into retrovirus.
2. Let retrovirus infect bone marrow cells that have been removed from the patient and cultured.
3. Viral DNA carrying the normal allele inserts into chromosome.
4. Inject engineered cells into patient.

vector near a gene involved in the proliferation of blood cells and an unknown function of the replacement gene itself. Two other genetic diseases have recently been treated somewhat successfully with gene therapy: one causing progressive blindness and the other leading to degeneration of the nervous system. The successful trials involve very few patients, but are still cause for cautious optimism.

Gene therapy raises many technical issues. For example, how can the activity of the transferred gene be controlled so that cells make appropriate amounts of the gene product at the right time and in the right place? How can we be sure that the insertion of the therapeutic gene does not harm some other necessary cell function? As more is learned about DNA control elements and gene interactions, researchers may be able to answer such questions.

In addition to technical challenges, gene therapy provokes ethical questions. Some critics believe that tampering with human genes in any way is immoral. Other observers see no fundamental difference between the transplantation of genes into somatic cells and the transplantation of organs. You might wonder whether scientists are considering engineering human germ-line cells in the hope of correcting a defect in future generations. At present, no one in the mainstream scientific community is pursuing this goal—it is considered much too risky. Such genetic engineering is routinely done in laboratory mice, though, and the technical problems relating to similar genetic engineering in humans will eventually be solved. Under what circumstances, if any, should we alter the genomes of human germ lines? Would this inevitably lead to the practice of eugenics, a deliberate effort to control the genetic makeup of human populations? While we may not have to resolve these questions right now, considering them is worthwhile because they will probably arise at some point in the future.

Pharmaceutical Products

The pharmaceutical industry derives significant benefit from advances in DNA technology and genetic research, applying them to the development of useful drugs to treat diseases. Pharmaceutical products are synthesized using methods of either organic chemistry or biotechnology, depending on the nature of the product.

Synthesis of Small Molecules for Use as Drugs Determining the sequence and structure of proteins crucial for tumor cell survival has led to the identification of small molecules that combat certain cancers by blocking the function of these proteins. One drug, imatinib (trade name Gleevec), is a small molecule that inhibits a specific receptor tyrosine kinase. The overexpression of this receptor, resulting from a chromosomal translocation, is instrumental in causing chronic myelogenous leukemia (CML; see Figure 15.16). Patients in the early stages of CML who are treated with imatinib have exhibited nearly complete, sustained remission from the cancer. Drugs that work like this have also been used with success to treat a few types of lung and breast cancers. This approach is feasible only for cancers for which the molecular basis is fairly well understood.

Pharmaceutical products that are proteins can be synthesized on a large scale, using cells or whole organisms. Cell cultures are more widely used at present.

Protein Production in Cell Cultures You learned earlier in the chapter about DNA cloning and gene expression systems for producing large quantities of proteins that are present naturally in only minute amounts. The host cells used in such expression systems can even be engineered to secrete a protein as it is made, thereby simplifying the task of purifying it by traditional biochemical methods.

Among the first pharmaceutical products "manufactured" in this way were human insulin and human growth hormone (HGH). Some 2 million people with diabetes in the United

States depend on insulin treatment to control their disease. Human growth hormone has been a boon to children born with a form of dwarfism caused by inadequate amounts of HGH. Another important pharmaceutical product produced by genetic engineering is tissue plasminogen activator (TPA). If administered shortly after a heart attack, TPA helps dissolve blood clots and reduces the risk of subsequent heart attacks.

Protein Production by "Pharm" Animals In some cases, instead of using cell systems to produce large quantities of protein products, pharmaceutical scientists can use whole animals. They can introduce a gene from an animal of one genotype into the genome of another individual, often of a different species. This individual is then called a **transgenic** animal. To do this, they first remove eggs from a female of the recipient species and fertilize them *in vitro*. Meanwhile, they have cloned the desired gene from the donor organism. They then inject the cloned DNA directly into the nuclei of the fertilized eggs. Some of the cells integrate the foreign DNA, the *transgene*, into their genomes and are able to express the foreign gene. The engineered embryos are then surgically implanted in a surrogate mother. If an embryo develops successfully, the result is a transgenic animal that expresses its new, "foreign" gene.

Assuming that the introduced gene encodes a protein desired in large quantities, these transgenic animals can act as pharmaceutical "factories." For example, a transgene for a human blood protein such as antithrombin can be inserted into the genome of a goat in such a way that the transgene's product is secreted in the animal's milk (**Figure 20.24**). The protein is then purified from the milk (which is easier than purification from a cell culture). Researchers have also engineered transgenic chickens that express large amounts of the transgene's product in eggs. Biotechnology companies consider the characteristics of candidate animals in deciding which to use for engineering. For

▲ **Figure 20.24 Goats as "pharm" animals.** This transgenic goat carries a gene for a human blood protein, antithrombin, which she secretes in her milk. Patients with a rare hereditary disorder in which this protein is lacking suffer from formation of blood clots in their blood vessels. Easily purified from the goat's milk, the protein has been approved in the United States and Europe for treating these patients.

example, goats reproduce faster than cows, and it is possible to harvest more protein from goat milk than from the milk of other rapidly reproducing mammals, such as rabbits.

Human proteins produced in transgenic farm animals for use in humans may differ in some ways from the naturally produced human proteins, possibly because of subtle differences in protein modification. Therefore, such proteins must be tested very carefully to ensure that they (or contaminants from the farm animals) will not cause allergic reactions or other adverse effects in patients who receive them.

Forensic Evidence and Genetic Profiles

In violent crimes, body fluids or small pieces of tissue may be left at the scene or on the clothes or other possessions of the victim or assailant. If enough blood, semen, or tissue is available, forensic laboratories can determine the blood type or tissue type by using antibodies to detect specific cell-surface proteins. However, such tests require fairly fresh samples in relatively large amounts. Also, because many people have the same blood or tissue type, this approach can only exclude a suspect; it cannot provide strong evidence of guilt.

DNA testing, on the other hand, can identify the guilty individual with a high degree of certainty, because the DNA sequence of every person is unique (except for identical twins). Genetic markers that vary in the population can be analyzed for a given person to determine that individual's unique set of genetic markers, or **genetic profile**. (This term is preferred over "DNA fingerprint" by forensic scientists, who want to emphasize the heritable aspect of these markers rather than the fact that they produce a pattern on a gel that, like a fingerprint, is visually recognizable.) The FBI started applying DNA technology to forensics in 1988, using RFLP analysis by Southern blotting to detect similarities and differences in DNA samples. This method required much smaller samples of blood or tissue than earlier methods—only about 1,000 cells.

Today, forensic scientists use an even more sensitive method that takes advantage of variations in length of genetic markers called **short tandem repeats (STRs)**. These are tandemly repeated units of two- to five-base sequences in specific regions of the genome. The number of repeats present in these regions is highly variable from person to person (polymorphic), and for one individual, the two alleles of an STR may even differ from each other. For example, one individual may have the sequence ACAT repeated 30 times at one genome locus and 15 times at the same locus on the other homolog, whereas another individual may have 18 repeats at this locus on each homolog. (These two genotypes can be expressed by the two repeat numbers: 30,15 and 18,18.) PCR is used to amplify particular STRs, using sets of primers that are labeled with different-colored fluorescent tags; the length of the region, and thus the number of repeats, can then be determined by electrophoresis. Because Southern blotting is not required, this method is quicker than RFLP analysis. And the PCR step allows use of the method even

when the DNA is in poor condition or available only in minute quantities. A tissue sample containing as few as 20 cells can be sufficient for PCR amplification.

In a murder case, for example, this method can be used to compare DNA samples from the suspect, the victim, and a small amount of blood found at the crime scene. The forensic scientist tests only a few selected portions of the DNA—usually 13 STR markers. However, even this small set of markers can provide a forensically useful genetic profile because the probability that two people (who are not identical twins) would have exactly the same set of STR markers is vanishingly small. The Innocence Project, a nonprofit organization dedicated to overturning wrongful convictions, uses STR analysis of archived samples from crime scenes to revisit old cases. As of 2010, more than 250 innocent people had been released from prison as a result of forensic and legal work by this group **(Figure 20.25)**.

Genetic profiles can also be useful for other purposes. A comparison of the DNA of a mother, her child, and the purported father can conclusively settle a question of paternity. Sometimes paternity is of historical interest: Genetic profiles

(a) In 1984, Earl Washington was convicted and sentenced to death for the 1982 rape and murder of Rebecca Williams. His sentence was commuted to life in prison in 1993 due to new doubts about the evidence. In 2000, STR analysis by forensic scientists associated with The Innocence Project showed conclusively that he was innocent. This photo shows Washington just before his release in 2001, after 17 years in prison.

(b) In STR analysis, selected STR markers in a DNA sample are amplified by PCR, and the PCR products are separated by electrophoresis. The procedure reveals how many repeats are present for each STR locus in the sample. An individual has two alleles per STR locus, each with a certain number of repeats. This table shows the number of repeats for three STR markers in three samples: from semen found on the victim, from Washington, and from another man named Kenneth Tinsley, who was in prison because of an unrelated conviction. These and other STR data (not shown) exonerated Washington and led Tinsley to plead guilty to the murder.

Source of sample	STR marker 1	STR marker 2	STR marker 3
Semen on victim	17,19	13,16	12,12
Earl Washington	16,18	14,15	11,12
Kenneth Tinsley	17,19	13,16	12,12

▲ **Figure 20.25 STR analysis used to release an innocent man from prison.**

provided strong evidence that Thomas Jefferson or one of his close male relatives fathered at least one of the children of his slave Sally Hemings. Genetic profiles can also identify victims of mass casualties. The largest such effort occurred after the attack on the World Trade Center in 2001; more than 10,000 samples of victims' remains were compared with DNA samples from personal items, such as toothbrushes, provided by families. Ultimately, forensic scientists succeeded in identifying almost 3,000 victims using these methods.

Just how reliable is a genetic profile? The greater the number of markers examined in a DNA sample, the more likely it is that the profile is unique to one individual. In forensic cases using STR analysis with 13 markers, the probability of two people having identical DNA profiles is somewhere between one chance in 10 billion and one in several trillion. (For comparison, the world's population in 2009 was about 6.8 billion.) The exact probability depends on the frequency of those markers in the general population. Information on how common various markers are in different ethnic groups is critical because these marker frequencies may vary considerably among ethnic groups and between a particular ethnic group and the population as a whole. With the increasing availability of frequency data, forensic scientists can make extremely accurate statistical calculations. Thus, despite problems that can still arise from insufficient data, human error, or flawed evidence, genetic profiles are now accepted as compelling evidence by legal experts and scientists alike.

Environmental Cleanup

Increasingly, the remarkable ability of certain microorganisms to transform chemicals is being exploited for environmental cleanup. If the growth needs of such microbes make them unsuitable for direct use, scientists can now transfer the genes for their valuable metabolic capabilities into other microorganisms, which can then be used to treat environmental problems. For example, many bacteria can extract heavy metals, such as copper, lead, and nickel, from their environments and incorporate the metals into compounds such as copper sulfate or lead sulfate, which are readily recoverable. Genetically engineered microbes may become important in both mining minerals (especially as ore reserves are depleted) and cleaning up highly toxic mining wastes. Biotechnologists are also trying to engineer microbes that can degrade chlorinated hydrocarbons and other harmful compounds. These microbes could be used in wastewater treatment plants or by manufacturers before the compounds are ever released into the environment.

Agricultural Applications

Scientists are working to learn more about the genomes of agriculturally important plants and animals. For a number of years, they have been using DNA technology in an effort to improve agricultural productivity. The selective breeding of both livestock (animal husbandry) and crops has exploited naturally occurring mutations and genetic recombination for thousands of years.

As we described earlier, DNA technology enables scientists to produce transgenic animals, which speeds up the selective breeding process. The goals of creating a transgenic animal are often the same as the goals of traditional breeding—for instance, to make a sheep with better quality wool, a pig with leaner meat, or a cow that will mature in a shorter time. Scientists might, for example, identify and clone a gene that causes the development of larger muscles (muscles make up most of the meat we eat) in one breed of cattle and transfer it to other cattle or even to sheep. However, problems such as low fertility or increased susceptibility to disease are not uncommon among farm animals carrying genes from other species. Animal health and welfare are important issues to consider when developing transgenic animals.

Agricultural scientists have already endowed a number of crop plants with genes for desirable traits, such as delayed ripening and resistance to spoilage and disease. In one striking way, plants are easier to genetically engineer than most animals. For many plant species, a single tissue cell grown in culture can give rise to an adult plant (see Figure 20.17). Thus, genetic manipulations can be performed on an ordinary somatic cell and the cell then used to generate an organism with new traits.

The most commonly used vector for introducing new genes into plant cells is a plasmid, called the **Ti plasmid**, from the soil bacterium *Agrobacterium tumefaciens*. This plasmid integrates a segment of its DNA, known as T DNA, into the chromosomal DNA of its host plant cells. For vector purposes, researchers work with versions of the plasmid that do not cause disease (unlike the wild-type version) and that have been engineered to carry genes of interest within the borders of the T DNA. **Figure 20.26** (on the next page) outlines one method for using the Ti plasmid to produce transgenic plants.

Genetic engineering is rapidly replacing traditional plant-breeding programs, especially for useful traits, such as herbicide or pest resistance, determined by one or a few genes. Crops engineered with a bacterial gene making the plants resistant to herbicides can grow while weeds are destroyed, and genetically engineered crops that can resist destructive insects reduce the need for chemical insecticides. In India, the insertion of a salinity resistance gene from a coastal mangrove plant into the genomes of several rice varieties has resulted in rice plants that can grow in water three times as salty as seawater. The research foundation that carried out this feat of genetic engineering estimates that one-third of all irrigated land has high salinity owing to overirrigation and intensive use of chemical fertilizers, representing a serious threat to the food supply. Thus, salinity-resistant crop plants would be enormously valuable worldwide.

▼ Figure 20.26 RESEARCH METHOD

Using the Ti Plasmid to Produce Transgenic Plants

APPLICATION Genes conferring useful traits, such as pest resistance, herbicide resistance, delayed ripening, and increased nutritional value, can be transferred from one plant variety or species to another using the Ti plasmid as a vector.

TECHNIQUE

Agrobacterium tumefaciens

❶ The Ti plasmid is isolated from the bacterium *Agrobacterium tumefaciens*. The segment of the plasmid that integrates into the genome of host cells is called T DNA.

Ti plasmid

Site where restriction enzyme cuts

T DNA

DNA with the gene of interest

❷ The foreign gene of interest is inserted into the middle of the T DNA using methods shown in Figure 20.4.

Recombinant Ti plasmid

❸ Recombinant plasmids can be introduced into cultured plant cells by electroporation. Or plasmids can be returned to *Agrobacterium*, which is then applied as a liquid suspension to the leaves of susceptible plants, infecting them. Once a plasmid is taken into a plant cell, its T DNA integrates into the cell's chromosomal DNA.

RESULTS Transformed cells carrying the transgene of interest can regenerate complete plants that exhibit the new trait conferred by the transgene.

Plant with new trait

Safety and Ethical Questions Raised by DNA Technology

Early concerns about potential dangers associated with recombinant DNA technology focused on the possibility that hazardous new pathogens might be created. What might happen, for instance, if cancer cell genes were transferred into bacteria or viruses? To guard against such rogue microbes, scientists developed a set of guidelines that were adopted as formal government regulations in the United States and some other countries. One safety measure is a set of strict laboratory procedures designed to protect researchers from infection by engineered microbes and to prevent the microbes from accidentally leaving the laboratory. In addition, strains of microorganisms to be used in recombinant DNA experiments are genetically crippled to ensure that they cannot survive outside the laboratory. Finally, certain obviously dangerous experiments have been banned.

Today, most public concern about possible hazards centers not on recombinant microbes but on **genetically modified (GM) organisms** used as food. A GM organism is one that has acquired by artificial means one or more genes from another species or even from another variety of the same species. Some salmon, for example, have been genetically modified by addition of a more active salmon growth hormone gene. However, the majority of the GM organisms that contribute to our food supply are not animals, but crop plants.

GM crops are widespread in the United States, Argentina, and Brazil; together these countries account for over 80% of the world's acreage devoted to such crops. In the United States, most corn, soybean, and canola crops are genetically modified, and GM products are not required to be labeled. However, the same foods are an ongoing subject of controversy in Europe, where the GM revolution has met with strong opposition. Many Europeans are concerned about the safety of GM foods and the possible environmental consequences of growing GM plants. Early in 2000, negotiators from 130 countries agreed on a Biosafety Protocol that requires exporters to identify GM organisms present in bulk food shipments and allows importing countries to decide whether the products pose environmental or health risks. (Although the United States declined to sign the agreement, it went into effect anyway because the majority of countries were in favor of it.) Since then, European countries have, on occasion, refused crops from the United States and other countries, leading to trade disputes. Although a small number of GM crops have been grown on European soil, these products have generally failed in local markets, and the future of GM crops in Europe is uncertain.

Advocates of a cautious approach toward GM crops fear that transgenic plants might pass their new genes to close relatives in nearby wild areas. We know that lawn and crop grasses, for example, commonly exchange genes with wild relatives via pollen transfer. If crop plants carrying genes for resistance to herbicides, diseases, or insect pests pollinated wild ones, the offspring might become "super weeds" that are very difficult to control. Another worry concerns possible risks to human health from GM foods. Some people fear that the protein products of transgenes might lead to allergic reactions. Although there is some evidence that this could happen, advocates claim that these proteins could be tested in advance to avoid producing ones that cause allergic reactions.

Today, governments and regulatory agencies throughout the world are grappling with how to facilitate the use of biotechnology in agriculture, industry, and medicine while ensuring that new products and procedures are safe. In the United States, such applications of biotechnology are evaluated for potential risks by various regulatory agencies, including the Food and Drug Administration, the Environmental Protection Agency, the National Institutes of Health, and the Department of Agriculture. Meanwhile, these same agencies and the public must consider the ethical implications of biotechnology.

Advances in biotechnology have allowed us to obtain complete genome sequences for humans and many other species, providing a vast treasure trove of information about genes. We can ask how certain genes differ from species to species, as well as how genes and, ultimately, entire genomes have evolved. (These are the subjects of Chapter 21.) At the same time, the increasing speed and falling cost of sequencing the genomes of

individuals are raising significant ethical questions. Who should have the right to examine someone else's genetic information? How should that information be used? Should a person's genome be a factor in determining eligibility for a job or insurance? Ethical considerations, as well as concerns about potential environmental and health hazards, will likely slow some applications of biotechnology. There is always a danger that too much regulation will stifle basic research and its potential benefits. However, the power of DNA technology and genetic engineering—our ability to profoundly and rapidly alter species that have been evolving for millennia—demands that we proceed with humility and caution.

CONCEPT CHECK 20.4

1. What is the advantage of using stem cells for gene therapy?
2. List at least three different properties that have been acquired by crop plants via genetic engineering.
3. **WHAT IF?** As a physician, you have a patient with symptoms that suggest a hepatitis A infection, but you have not been able to detect viral proteins in the blood. Knowing that hepatitis A is an RNA virus, what lab tests could you perform to support your diagnosis? Explain what the results would mean.

For suggested answers, see Appendix A.

20 CHAPTER REVIEW

SUMMARY OF KEY CONCEPTS

CONCEPT 20.1

DNA cloning yields multiple copies of a gene or other DNA segment (pp. 396–405)

- **Gene cloning** and other techniques, collectively termed DNA technology, can be used to manipulate and analyze DNA and to produce useful new products and organisms.
- In **genetic engineering**, bacterial **restriction enzymes** are used to cut DNA molecules within short, specific nucleotide sequences (**restriction sites**), yielding a set of double-stranded DNA fragments with single-stranded **sticky ends**.

Sticky end

- The sticky ends on **restriction fragments** from one DNA source can base-pair with complementary sticky ends on fragments from other DNA molecules; sealing the base-paired fragments with **DNA ligase** produces **recombinant DNA** molecules.

- Cloning a eukaryotic gene in a bacterial plasmid:

Recombinant DNA plasmids

Cloning vectors include **plasmids** and **bacterial artificial chromosomes (BACs)**. Recombinant plasmids are returned to host cells, each of which divides to form a clone of cells. Collections of clones are stored as **genomic** or **complementary DNA (cDNA) libraries**. Libraries can be screened for a gene of interest using **nucleic acid hybridization** with a **nucleic acid probe**.
- Several technical difficulties hinder the expression of cloned eukaryotic genes in bacterial host cells. The use of cultured

eukaryotic cells (such as yeasts, insect cells, or cultured mammalian cells) as host cells, coupled with appropriate **expression vectors**, helps avoid these problems.

- The **polymerase chain reaction (PCR)** can produce many copies of (amplify) a specific target segment of DNA *in vitro*, using primers that bracket the desired sequence and a heat-resistant DNA polymerase.

 Describe how the process of gene cloning results in a cell clone containing a recombinant plasmid.

CONCEPT 20.2

DNA technology allows us to study the sequence, expression, and function of a gene (pp. 405–412)

- DNA restriction fragments of different lengths can be separated by **gel electrophoresis**. Specific fragments can be identified by **Southern blotting**, using labeled probes that hybridize to the DNA immobilized on a "blot" of the gel. Historically, **restriction fragment length polymorphisms (RFLPs)** were used to screen for some disease-causing alleles, such as the sickle-cell allele.
- Relatively short DNA fragments can be sequenced by the dideoxy chain termination method, which can be performed in automated sequencing machines. The rapid development of faster and cheaper methods is ongoing.
- Expression of a gene can be investigated using hybridization with labeled probes to look for specific mRNAs, either on a gel (**Northern blotting**) or in a whole organism (*in situ* hybridization). Also, RNA can be transcribed into cDNA by reverse transcriptase and the cDNA amplified by PCR with specific primers (**RT-PCR**). **DNA microarrays** allow researchers to compare the expression of many genes at once in different tissues, at different times, or under different conditions.
- For a gene of unknown function, experimental inactivation of the gene and observation of the resulting phenotypic effects can provide clues to its function. In humans, **genome-wide association studies** use **single nucleotide polymorphisms (SNPs)** as genetic markers for alleles that are associated with particular conditions.

 Complementary base pairing is the basis of most procedures used to analyze gene expression. Explain.

CONCEPT 20.3

Cloning organisms may lead to production of stem cells for research and other applications (pp. 412–417)

- Studies showing genomic equivalence (that an organism's cells have the same genome) provided the first examples of organismal cloning.
- Single differentiated cells from mature plants are often **totipotent**: capable of generating all the tissues of a complete new plant.
- Transplantation of the nucleus from a differentiated animal cell into an enucleated egg can sometimes give rise to a new animal.
- Certain embryonic stem (ES) or adult **stem cells** from animal embryos or adult tissues can reproduce and differentiate *in vitro* as well as *in vivo*, offering the potential for medical use. ES cells are **pluripotent** but difficult to acquire. Induced pluripotent stem (iPS) cells resemble ES cells in their capacity to differentiate; they can be generated by reprogramming differentiated cells. iPS cells hold promise for medical research and regenerative medicine.

? *Describe how a researcher could carry out organismal cloning, production of ES cells, and generation of iPS cells, focusing on how the cells are reprogrammed and using mice as an example. (The procedures are basically the same in humans and mice.)*

CONCEPT 20.4

The practical applications of DNA technology affect our lives in many ways (pp. 417–423)

- DNA technology, including the analysis of genetic markers such as SNPs, is increasingly being used in the diagnosis of genetic and other diseases and offers potential for better treatment of genetic disorders (or even permanent cures through **gene therapy**), as well as more informed cancer therapies. Large-scale production of protein hormones and other proteins with therapeutic uses is possible with DNA technology. Some therapeutic proteins are being produced in **transgenic** "pharm" animals.
- Analysis of genetic markers such as **short tandem repeats (STRs)** in DNA isolated from tissue or body fluids found at crime scenes leads to a **genetic profile** that can provide definitive evidence that a suspect is innocent or strong evidence of guilt. Such analysis is also useful in parenthood disputes and in identifying the remains of crime victims.
- Genetically engineered microorganisms can be used to extract minerals from the environment or degrade various types of toxic waste materials.
- The aims of developing transgenic plants and animals are to improve agricultural productivity and food quality.
- The potential benefits of genetic engineering must be carefully weighed against the potential for harm to humans or the environment.

 What factors affect whether a given genetic disease would be a good candidate for successful gene therapy?

TEST YOUR UNDERSTANDING

LEVEL 1: KNOWLEDGE/COMPREHENSION

1. Which of the following tools of recombinant DNA technology is *incorrectly* paired with its use?
   a. restriction enzyme—analysis of RFLPs
   b. DNA ligase—cutting DNA, creating sticky ends of restriction fragments
   c. DNA polymerase—polymerase chain reaction to amplify sections of DNA
   d. reverse transcriptase—production of cDNA from mRNA
   e. electrophoresis—separation of DNA fragments

2. Plants are more readily manipulated by genetic engineering than are animals because
   a. plant genes do not contain introns.
   b. more vectors are available for transferring recombinant DNA into plant cells.
   c. a somatic plant cell can often give rise to a complete plant.
   d. genes can be inserted into plant cells by microinjection.
   e. plant cells have larger nuclei.

3. A paleontologist has recovered a bit of tissue from the 400-year-old preserved skin of an extinct dodo (a bird). To compare a specific region of the DNA from the sample with DNA from living birds, which of the following would be most useful for increasing the amount of dodo DNA available for testing?
   a. RFLP analysis
   b. polymerase chain reaction (PCR)
   c. electroporation
   d. gel electrophoresis
   e. Southern blotting

4. DNA technology has many medical applications. Which of the following is *not* done routinely at present?
   a. production of hormones for treating diabetes and dwarfism
   b. production of microbes that can metabolize toxins
   c. introduction of genetically engineered genes into human gametes
   d. prenatal identification of genetic disease alleles
   e. genetic testing for carriers of harmful alleles

5. In recombinant DNA methods, the term *vector* can refer to
   a. the enzyme that cuts DNA into restriction fragments.
   b. the sticky end of a DNA fragment.
   c. a SNP marker.
   d. a plasmid used to transfer DNA into a living cell.
   e. a DNA probe used to identify a particular gene.

LEVEL 2: APPLICATION/ANALYSIS

6. Which of the following would *not* be true of cDNA produced using human brain tissue as the starting material?
   a. It could be amplified by the polymerase chain reaction.
   b. It could be used to create a complete genomic library.
   c. It was produced from mRNA using reverse transcriptase.
   d. It could be used as a probe to detect genes expressed in the brain.
   e. It lacks the introns of the human genes.

7. Expression of a cloned eukaryotic gene in a bacterial cell involves many challenges. The use of mRNA and reverse transcriptase is part of a strategy to solve the problem of
   a. post-transcriptional processing.
   b. electroporation.
   c. post-translational processing.
   d. nucleic acid hybridization.
   e. restriction fragment ligation.

8. Which of the following sequences in double-stranded DNA is most likely to be recognized as a cutting site for a restriction enzyme?
   a. AAGG   b. AGTC   c. GGCC   d. ACCA   e. AAAA
      TTCC   TCAG   CCGG   TGGT   TTTT

9. **DRAW IT** You are making a genomic library for the aardvark, using a bacterial plasmid as a vector. The green diagram below shows the plasmid, which contains the restriction site for the enzyme used in Figure 20.3. Above the plasmid is a segment of linear aardvark DNA. Diagram your cloning procedure, showing what would happen to these two molecules during each step. Use one color for the aardvark DNA and its bases and another color for those of the plasmid. Label each step and all 5′ and 3′ ends.

5′ TCCATGAATTCTAAAGCGCTTATGAATTCACGGC 3′
3′ AGGTACTTAAGATTTCGCGAATACTTAAGTGCCG 5′

Aardvark DNA

Plasmid

LEVEL 3: SYNTHESIS/EVALUATION

10. **WHAT IF?** Imagine you want to study one of the human crystallins, proteins present in the lens of the eye. To obtain a sufficient amount of the protein of interest, you decide to clone the gene that codes for it. Would you construct a genomic library or a cDNA library? What material would you use as a source of DNA or RNA?

11. **EVOLUTION CONNECTION**
    Ethical considerations aside, if DNA-based technologies became widely used, how might they change the way evolution proceeds, as compared with the natural evolutionary mechanisms of the past 4 billion years?

12. **SCIENTIFIC INQUIRY**
    You hope to study a gene that codes for a neurotransmitter protein produced in human brain cells. You know the amino acid sequence of the protein. Explain how you might (a) identify what genes are expressed in a specific type of brain cell, (b) identify (isolate) the neurotransmitter gene, (c) produce multiple copies of the gene for study, and (d) produce large quantities of the neurotransmitter for evaluation as a potential medication.

13. **SCIENCE, TECHNOLOGY, AND SOCIETY**
    Is there danger of discrimination based on testing for "harmful" genes? What policies can you suggest that would prevent such abuses?

14. **SCIENCE, TECHNOLOGY, AND SOCIETY**
    Government funding of embryonic stem cell research has been a contentious political issue. Why has this debate been so heated? Summarize the arguments for and against embryonic stem cell research, and explain your own position on the issue.

15. **WRITE ABOUT A THEME**
    The Genetic Basis of Life In a short essay (100–150 words), discuss how the genetic basis of life plays a central role in biotechnology.

For selected answers, see Appendix A.

Mastering**BIOLOGY** www.masteringbiology.com

1. MasteringBiology® Assignments
Video Tutor Session DNA Profiling Techniques
Tutorial Restriction Enzymes, Recombinant DNA, and Gene Cloning
Activities Cloning a Gene in Bacteria • Producing Human Growth Hormone • Restriction Enzymes • The Polymerase Chain Reaction • Gel Electrophoresis of DNA • Analyzing DNA Fragments Using Gel Electrophoresis • Discovery Channel Video: Cloning • DNA Fingerprinting • Making Decisions About DNA Technology: Golden Rice • Discovery Channel Videos: DNA Forensics; Transgenics
Questions Student Misconceptions • Reading Quiz • Multiple Choice • End-of-Chapter

2. eText
Read your book online, search, take notes, highlight text, and more.

3. The Study Area
Practice Tests • Cumulative Test • *BioFlix* 3-D Animations • MP3 Tutor Sessions • Videos • Activities • Investigations • Lab Media • Audio Glossary • Word Study Tools • Art

21

Genomes and Their Evolution

▲ **Figure 21.1 What genomic information distinguishes a human from a chimpanzee?**

Reading the Leaves from the Tree of Life

The chimpanzee (*Pan troglodytes*) is our closest living relative on the evolutionary tree of life. The boy in **Figure 21.1** and his chimpanzee companion are intently studying the same leaf, but only one of them is able to talk about it. What accounts for this difference between two primates that share so much of their evolutionary history? With the advent of recent techniques for rapidly sequencing complete genomes, we can now start to address the genetic basis of intriguing questions like this.

The chimpanzee genome was sequenced in 2005, two years after sequencing of the human genome was largely completed. Now that we can compare our genome with that of the chimpanzee base by base, we can tackle the more general issue of what differences in the genetic information account for the distinct characteristics of these two species of primates.

In addition to determining the sequences of the human and chimpanzee genomes, researchers have obtained complete genome sequences for *E. coli* and numerous other prokaryotes, as well as many eukaryotes, including *Zea mays* (corn), *Drosophila melanogaster* (fruit fly), *Mus musculus* (house mouse), and *Macaca mulatta* (rhesus macaque). In 2010, a draft sequence was announced for the genome of *Homo neanderthalensis*, an extinct species closely related to present-day humans. These whole and partial genomes are of great interest in their own right and are also providing important insights into evolution and other biological processes. Broadening the human-chimpanzee comparison to the genomes of other primates and more distantly related animals should reveal the sets of genes that control group-defining characteristics. Beyond that, comparisons with the genomes of bacteria, archaea, fungi, protists, and plants should enlighten us about the long evolutionary history of shared ancient genes and their products.

With the genomes of many species fully sequenced, scientists can study whole sets of genes and their interactions, an approach called **genomics**. The sequencing efforts that feed this approach have generated, and continue to generate, enormous volumes of data. The need to deal with this ever-increasing flood of information has spawned the field of **bioinformatics**, the application of computational methods to the storage and analysis of biological data.

We will begin this chapter by discussing two approaches to genome sequencing and some of the advances in bioinformatics and its applications. We will then summarize what has been learned from the genomes that have been sequenced thus far. Next, we will describe the composition of the human genome as a representative genome of a complex multicellular eukaryote. Finally, we will explore current ideas about how genomes evolve and about how the evolution of developmental mechanisms could have generated the great diversity of life on Earth today.

CONCEPT 21.1

New approaches have accelerated the pace of genome sequencing

Sequencing of the human genome, an ambitious undertaking, officially began as the **Human Genome Project** in 1990. Organized by an international, publicly funded consortium of scientists at universities and research institutes, the project involved 20 large sequencing centers in six countries plus a host of other labs working on small projects.

After sequencing of the human genome was largely completed in 2003, the sequence of each chromosome was carefully analyzed and described in a series of papers, the last of which covered chromosome 1 and was published in 2006. With this refinement, researchers termed the sequencing "virtually complete." To reach these milestones, the project proceeded through three stages that provided progressively more detailed views of the human genome: linkage mapping, physical mapping, and DNA sequencing.

Three-Stage Approach to Genome Sequencing

Even before the Human Genome Project began, earlier research had sketched a rough picture of the organization of the genomes of many organisms. For instance, the karyotyping of many species had revealed their chromosome numbers and banding patterns (see Figure 13.3). And some human genes had already been located on a particular region of a chromosome by fluorescence *in situ* hybridization (FISH), a method in which fluorescently labeled nucleic acid probes are allowed to hybridize to an immobilized array of whole chromosomes (see Figure 15.1). Cytogenetic maps based on this type of information provided the starting point for more detailed mapping of the human genome.

With these cytogenetic maps of the chromosomes in hand, the initial stage in sequencing the human genome was to construct a **linkage map** (a type of genetic map; see Figure 15.11) of several thousand genetic markers spaced throughout the chromosomes (**Figure 21.2**, stage **1**). The order of the markers and the relative distances between them on such a map are based on recombination frequencies. The markers can be genes or any other identifiable sequences in the DNA, such as RFLPs or short tandem repeats (STRs), both discussed in Chapter 20. By 1992, researchers had compiled a human linkage map with some 5,000 markers. Such a map enabled them to locate other markers, including genes, by testing for genetic linkage to the known markers. It was also valuable as a framework for organizing more detailed maps of particular regions. Remember from Chapter 15, however, that absolute distances between genes cannot be determined using this approach.

The next stage was the physical mapping of the human genome. In a **physical map**, the distances between markers

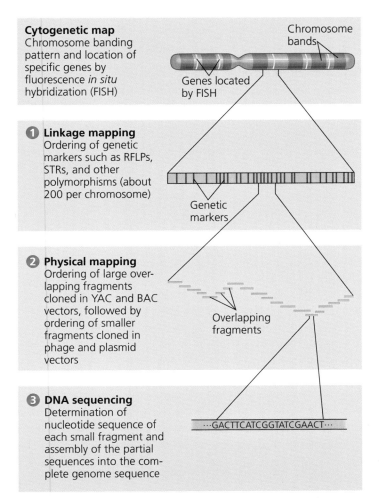

Cytogenetic map
Chromosome banding pattern and location of specific genes by fluorescence *in situ* hybridization (FISH)

Chromosome bands

Genes located by FISH

1 Linkage mapping
Ordering of genetic markers such as RFLPs, STRs, and other polymorphisms (about 200 per chromosome)

Genetic markers

2 Physical mapping
Ordering of large overlapping fragments cloned in YAC and BAC vectors, followed by ordering of smaller fragments cloned in phage and plasmid vectors

Overlapping fragments

3 DNA sequencing
Determination of nucleotide sequence of each small fragment and assembly of the partial sequences into the complete genome sequence

···GACTTCATCGGTATCGAACT···

▲ **Figure 21.2 Three-stage approach to sequencing an entire genome.** Starting with a cytogenetic map of each chromosome, researchers with the Human Genome Project proceeded through three stages to reach the ultimate goal, the virtually complete nucleotide sequence of every chromosome.

are expressed by some physical measure, usually the number of base pairs along the DNA. For whole-genome mapping, a physical map is made by cutting the DNA of each chromosome into a number of restriction fragments and then determining the original order of the fragments in the chromosomal DNA. The key is to make fragments that overlap and then use probes or automated nucleotide sequencing of the ends to find the overlaps (see Figure 21.2, stage **2**). In this way, fragments can be assigned to a sequential order that corresponds to their order in a chromosome.

The DNA fragments used for physical mapping were prepared by DNA cloning. With such a large genome, researchers had to carry out several rounds of DNA cutting, cloning, and physical mapping. In this approach, the first cloning vector was often a yeast artificial chromosome (YAC), which can carry inserted fragments a million base pairs long, or a bacterial artificial chromosome (BAC), which typically carries inserts of 100,000–300,000 base pairs. After such long fragments were put in order, each fragment was cut into smaller pieces, which were cloned in plasmids or phages, ordered in turn, and finally sequenced.

The ultimate goal in mapping any genome is to determine the complete nucleotide sequence of each chromosome (see Figure 21.2, stage ❸). For the human genome, this was accomplished by sequencing machines, using the dideoxy chain termination method described in Figure 20.12. Even with automation, the sequencing of all 3 billion base pairs in a haploid set of human chromosomes presented a formidable challenge. In fact, a major thrust of the Human Genome Project was the development of technology for faster sequencing. Improvements over the years chipped away at each time-consuming step, enabling the rate of sequencing to accelerate impressively: Whereas a productive lab could typically sequence 1,000 base pairs a day in the 1980s, by the year 2000 each research center working on the Human Genome Project was sequencing 1,000 base pairs *per second*, 24 hours a day, seven days a week. Methods like this that can analyze biological materials very rapidly and produce enormous volumes of data are said to be "high-throughput." Sequencing machines are an example of high-throughput devices.

In practice, the three stages shown in Figure 21.2 overlapped in a way that our simplified version does not portray, but they accurately represent the overarching strategy employed in the Human Genome Project. During the project, however, an alternative strategy for genome sequencing emerged that was extremely efficient and became widely adopted.

Whole-Genome Shotgun Approach to Genome Sequencing

In 1992, emboldened by advances in sequencing and computer technology, molecular biologist J. Craig Venter devised an alternative approach to the sequencing of whole genomes. Called the *whole-genome shotgun approach*, it essentially skips the linkage mapping and physical mapping stages and starts directly with the sequencing of DNA fragments from randomly cut DNA. Powerful computer programs then assemble the resulting very large number of overlapping short sequences into a single continuous sequence **(Figure 21.3)**. In 1998, despite the skepticism of many scientists, Venter set up a company (Celera Genomics) and declared his intention to sequence the entire human genome. Five years later, and 13 years after the Human Genome Project began, Celera Genomics and the public consortium jointly announced that sequencing of the human genome was largely complete.

Representatives of the public consortium point out that Celera's accomplishment relied heavily on the consortium's maps and sequence data and that the infrastructure established by their approach was a tremendous aid to Celera's efforts. Venter, on the other hand, has argued for the efficiency and economy of Celera's methods, and indeed, the public consortium made some use of them as well. Evidently, both approaches made valuable contributions.

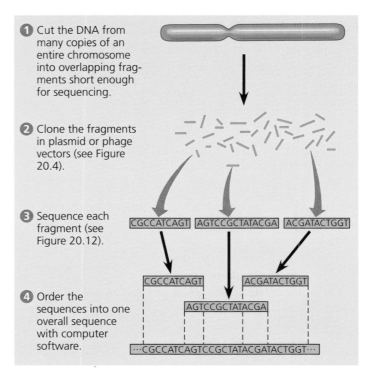

1 Cut the DNA from many copies of an entire chromosome into overlapping fragments short enough for sequencing.

2 Clone the fragments in plasmid or phage vectors (see Figure 20.4).

3 Sequence each fragment (see Figure 20.12).

CGCCATCAGT   AGTCCGCTATACGA   ACGATACTGGT

4 Order the sequences into one overall sequence with computer software.

CGCCATCAGT   ACGATACTGGT
AGTCCGCTATACGA

···CGCCATCAGTCCGCTATACGATACTGGT···

▲ **Figure 21.3 Whole-genome shotgun approach to sequencing.** In this approach, developed by Craig Venter and colleagues at the company he founded, Celera Genomics, random DNA fragments are sequenced and then ordered relative to each other. Compare this approach with the hierarchical, three-stage approach shown in Figure 21.2.

? *The fragments in stage 2 of this figure are depicted as scattered, whereas those in stage 2 of Figure 21.2 are drawn in a much more orderly fashion. How do these depictions reflect the two approaches?*

Today, the whole-genome shotgun approach is widely used. Also, the development of newer sequencing techniques, generally called *sequencing by synthesis* (see Chapter 20), has resulted in massive increases in speed and decreases in the cost of sequencing entire genomes. In these new techniques, many very small fragments (fewer than 100 base pairs) are sequenced at the same time, and computer software rapidly assembles the complete sequence. Because of the sensitivity of these techniques, the fragments can be sequenced directly; the cloning step (stage ❷ in Figure 21.3) is unnecessary. Whereas sequencing the first human genome took 13 years and cost $100 million, James Watson's genome was sequenced during four months in 2007 for about $1 million, and a group of researchers reported in 2010 that they had rapidly sequenced three human genomes for approximately $4,400 each!

These technological advances have also facilitated an approach called **metagenomics** (from the Greek *meta*, beyond), in which DNA from a group of species (a *metagenome*) is collected from an environmental sample and sequenced. Again, computer software accomplishes the task of sorting out the partial sequences and assembling them into specific genomes. So far, this approach has been applied to microbial communities found in environments as diverse as the Sargasso Sea and the human intestine. The ability to sequence the DNA of mixed populations eliminates the need to culture each species separately in the lab, a difficulty that has limited the study of many microbial species.

At first glance, genome sequences of humans and other organisms are simply dry lists of nucleotide bases—millions of A's, T's, C's, and G's in mind-numbing succession. Crucial to making sense of this massive amount of data have been new analytical approaches, which we discuss next.

CONCEPT CHECK 21.1

1. What is the major difference between a linkage map and a physical map of a chromosome?
2. In general, how does the approach to genome mapping used in the Human Genome Project differ from the whole-genome shotgun approach?

For suggested answers, see Appendix A.

CONCEPT 21.2

Scientists use bioinformatics to analyze genomes and their functions

Each of the 20 or so sequencing centers around the world working on the Human Genome Project churned out voluminous amounts of DNA sequence day after day. As the data began to accumulate, the need to coordinate efforts to keep track of all the sequences became clear. Thanks to the foresight of research scientists and government officials involved in the Human Genome Project, its goals included the establishment of banks of data, or databases, and the refining of analytical software. These databases and software programs would then be centralized and made readily accessible on the Internet. Accomplishing this aim has accelerated progress in DNA sequence analysis by making bioinformatics resources available to researchers worldwide and by speeding up the dissemination of information.

Centralized Resources for Analyzing Genome Sequences

Government-funded agencies carried out their mandate to establish databases and provide software with which scientists could analyze the sequence data. For example, in the United States, a joint endeavor between the National Library of Medicine and the National Institutes of Health (NIH) created the National Center for Biotechnology Information (NCBI), which maintains a website (www.ncbi.nlm.nih.gov) with extensive bioinformatics resources. On this site are links to databases, software, and a wealth of information about genomics and related topics. Similar websites have also been established by the European Molecular Biology Laboratory, the DNA Data Bank of Japan, and BGI (formerly known as the Beijing Genome Institute) in Shenzhen, China, three genome centers with which the NCBI collaborates. These large, comprehensive websites are complemented by others maintained by individual or small groups of laboratories. Smaller websites often provide databases and software designed for a narrower purpose, such as studying genetic and genomic changes in one particular type of cancer.

The NCBI database of sequences is called GenBank. As of May 2010, it included the sequences of 119 million fragments of genomic DNA, totaling 114 billion base pairs! GenBank is constantly updated, and the amount of data it contains is estimated to double approximately every 18 months. Any sequence in the database can be retrieved and analyzed using software from the NCBI website or elsewhere.

One software program available on the NCBI website, called BLAST, allows the visitor to compare a DNA sequence with every sequence in GenBank, base by base, to look for similar regions. Another program allows comparison of predicted protein sequences. Yet a third can search any protein sequence for common stretches of amino acids (domains) for which a function is known or suspected, and it can show a three-dimensional model of the domain alongside other relevant information (**Figure 21.4**, on the next page). There is even a software program that can compare a collection of sequences, either nucleic acids or polypeptides, and diagram them in the form of an evolutionary tree based on the sequence relationships. (One such diagram is shown in Figure 21.16.)

Two research institutions, Rutgers University and the University of California, San Diego, also maintain a worldwide Protein Data Bank, a database of all three-dimensional protein structures that have been determined. (The database is accessible at www.wwpdb.org.) These structures can be rotated by the viewer to show all sides of the protein.

There is a vast array of resources available for researchers anywhere in the world to use. Let us now consider the types of questions scientists can address using these resources.

Identifying Protein-Coding Genes and Understanding Their Functions

Using available DNA sequences, geneticists can study genes directly, without having to infer genotype from phenotype as in classical genetics. But this approach, called *reverse genetics*, poses a new challenge: determining the phenotype from the genotype. Given a long DNA sequence from a database such as GenBank, the aim of scientists is to identify all protein-coding genes in the sequence and ultimately their functions. This process is called **gene annotation**.

In the past, gene annotation was carried out laboriously by individual scientists interested in particular genes, but the process has now been largely automated. The usual approach is to use software to scan the stored sequences for transcriptional and translational start and stop signals, for RNA-splicing sites, and for other telltale signs of protein-coding genes. The software also looks for certain short sequences that specify known mRNAs. Thousands of such sequences, called

In this window, a partial amino acid sequence from an unknown muskmelon protein ("Query") is aligned with sequences from other proteins that the computer program found to be similar. Each sequence represents a domain called WD40.

Four hallmarks of the WD40 domain are highlighted in yellow. (Sequence similarity is based on chemical aspects of the amino acids, so the amino acids in each hallmark region are not always identical.)

The Cn3D program displays a three-dimensional ribbon model of cow transducin (the protein highlighted in purple in the Sequence Alignment Viewer). This protein is the only one of those shown for which a structure has been determined. The sequence similarity of the other proteins to cow transducin suggests that their structures are likely to be similar.

This window displays information about the WD40 domain from the Conserved Domain Database.

Cow transducin contains seven WD40 domains, one of which is highlighted here in gray.

The yellow segments correspond to the WD40 hallmarks highlighted in yellow in the window above.

WD40 - Sequence Alignment Viewer

Query	~~~ktGGIRL~RHfksVSAVEWHRk~~gDYLSTlvLreSRAVLIHQlsk~
Cow [transducin]	~nvrvSRELA~GHtgyLSCCRFLDd~~nQIVTs~~Sg~DTTCALWDie~
Mustard weed [transducin]	gtvpvSRMLT~GHrgyVSCCQYVPnedaHLITs~~Sg~DQTCILWDvtt
Corn [GNB protein]	gnmpvSRILT~GHkgyVSCCQYVPdgetRLITS~~Sg~DQTCVLWDvt~
Human [PAFA protein]	~~~ecIRTMH~GHdhnVSSVAIMPng~dHIVSA~~Sr~DKTIKMWEvg~
Nematode [unknown protein #1]	~~~rcVKTLK~GHtnyVFCCCFNPs~~gTLIAS~~GsfDETIRIWCar~
Nematode [unknown protein #2]	~~~rmTKTLK~GHnnyVFCCNFNPq~~sSLVVS~~GsfDESVRIWDvk~
Fission yeast [FWDR protein]	~~~seCISILhGHtdsVLCLTFDS~~~~TLLVS~~GsaDCTVKLWHfs~

CDD Descriptive Items

Name: WD40

WD40 domain, found in a number of eukaryotic proteins that cover a wide variety of functions including adaptor/regulatory modules in signal transduction, pre-mRNA processing and cytoskeleton assembly; typically contains a GH dipeptide 11-24 residues from its N-terminus and the WD dipeptide at its C-terminus and is 40 residues long, hence the name WD40;

WD40 - Cn3D 4.1

▲ **Figure 21.4 Bioinformatics tools available on the Internet.** A website maintained by the National Center for Biotechnology Information allows scientists and the public to access DNA and protein sequences and other stored data. The site includes a link to a protein structure database (Conserved Domain Database, CDD) that can find and describe similar domains in related proteins, as well as software (Cn3D, "See in 3D") that displays three-dimensional models of domains for which the structure has been determined. Some results are shown from a search for regions of proteins similar to an amino acid sequence in a muskmelon protein.

expressed sequence tags, or *ESTs*, have been collected from cDNA sequences and are cataloged in computer databases. This type of analysis identifies sequences that may be previously unknown protein-coding genes.

The identities of about half of the human genes were known before the Human Genome Project began. But what about the others, the previously unknown genes revealed by analysis of DNA sequences? Clues about their identities and functions come from comparing sequences that might be genes with known genes from other organisms, using the software described previously. Due to redundancy in the genetic code, the DNA sequence itself may vary more than the protein sequence does. Thus, scientists interested in proteins often compare the predicted amino acid sequence of a protein to that of other proteins.

Sometimes a newly identified sequence will match, at least partially, the sequence of a gene or protein whose function is well known. For example, part of a new gene may match a known gene that encodes an important signaling pathway protein such as a protein kinase, suggesting that the new gene does, too. Alternatively, the new gene sequence may be similar to a previously encountered sequence whose function is still unknown. Another possibility is that the sequence is entirely unlike anything ever seen before. This was true for about a third of the genes of *E. coli* when its genome was sequenced. In the last case, protein function is usually deduced through a combination of biochemical and functional studies. The biochemical approach aims to determine the three-dimensional structure of the protein as well as other attributes, such as potential binding sites for other molecules. Functional studies usually involve blocking or disabling the gene to see how the phenotype is affected. RNAi, described in Chapter 20, is an example of an experimental technique used to block gene function.

Understanding Genes and Gene Expression at the Systems Level

The impressive computational power provided by the tools of bioinformatics allows the study of whole sets of genes and their interactions, as well as the comparison of genomes from different species. Genomics is a rich source of new insights into fundamental questions about genome organization, regulation of gene expression, growth and development, and evolution.

One informative approach has been taken by a research project called ENCODE (Encyclopedia of DNA Elements), which began in 2003. First, researchers focused intensively on 1% of the human genome and attempted to learn all they could about the functionally important elements in that sequence. They looked for protein-coding genes and genes for noncoding RNAs as well as sequences that regulate DNA replication, gene expression (such as enhancers and promoters), and chromatin modifications. The pilot project was completed in 2007, yielding a wealth of information. One big surprise, discussed in Concept 18.3, was that over 90% of the region was transcribed into RNA, even though less than 2% codes for proteins. The success of this approach has led to two follow-up studies, one extending the analysis to the entire human genome and the other analyzing in a similar fashion the genomes of two model organisms, the soil nematode *Caenorhabditis elegans* and the fruit fly *Drosophila melanogaster*. Because genetic and molecular biological experiments can be performed on these species, testing the activities of potentially functional DNA elements in their genomes will reveal much about how the human genome works.

The success in sequencing genomes and studying entire sets of genes has encouraged scientists to attempt similar systematic study of the full protein sets (*proteomes*) encoded by genomes, an approach called **proteomics**. Proteins, not the genes that encode them, actually carry out most of the activities of the cell. Therefore, we must study when and where proteins are produced in an organism, as well as how they interact in networks, if we are to understand the functioning of cells and organisms.

How Systems Are Studied: An Example

Genomics and proteomics are enabling molecular biologists to approach the study of life from an increasingly global perspective. Using the tools we have described, biologists have begun to compile catalogs of genes and proteins—listings of all the "parts" that contribute to the operation of cells, tissues, and organisms. With such catalogs in hand, researchers have shifted their attention from the individual parts to their functional integration in biological systems. As you may recall, in Chapter 1 we discussed this systems biology approach, which aims to model the dynamic behavior of whole biological systems.

One important use of the systems biology approach is to define gene circuits and protein interaction networks. To map the protein interaction network in the yeast *Saccharomyces cerevisiae*, for instance, researchers used sophisticated techniques to knock out (disable) pairs of genes, one pair at a time, creating doubly mutant cells. They then compared the fitness of each double mutant (based in part on the size of the cell colony it formed) to that predicted from the fitnesses of the two single mutants. The researchers reasoned that if the observed fitness matched the prediction, then the products of the two genes didn't interact with each other, but if the observed fitness was greater or less than predicted, then the gene products interacted in the cell. Computer software then mapped genes based on the similarity of their interactions; a network-like "functional map" of these genetic interactions is displayed in **Figure 21.5**. To process the vast number of protein-protein interactions generated by this experiment and integrate them

▲ **Figure 21.5 The systems biology approach to protein interactions.** This global protein interaction map shows the likely interactions (lines) among about 4,500 gene products (circles) in the yeast *Saccharomyces cerevisiae*. Circles of the same color represent gene products involved in one of the 13 cellular functions listed around the map. The blowup shows additional details of one map region where the gene products (blue circles) carry out amino acid biosynthesis, uptake, and related functions.

into the completed map required powerful computers, mathematical tools, and newly developed software. Thus, the systems biology approach has really been made possible by advances in computer technology and bioinformatics.

Application of Systems Biology to Medicine

The Cancer Genome Atlas is another example of systems biology in which a large group of interacting genes and gene products are analyzed together. This project, under the joint leadership of the National Cancer Institute and the NIH, aims to determine how changes in biological systems lead to cancer. A three-year pilot project beginning in 2007 set out to find all the common mutations in three types of cancer—lung cancer, ovarian cancer, and glioblastoma of the brain—by comparing gene sequences and patterns of gene expression in cancer cells with those in normal cells. Work on glioblastoma has confirmed the role of several suspected genes and identified a few unknown ones, suggesting possible new targets for therapies. The approach has proved so fruitful for these three types of cancer that it has been extended to ten other types, chosen because they are common and often lethal in humans.

Systems biology has tremendous potential in human medicine that is just starting to be explored. Silicon and glass "chips" have been developed that hold a microarray of most of the known human genes (**Figure 21.6**). Such chips are being used to analyze gene expression patterns in patients suffering from various cancers and other diseases, with the eventual aim of tailoring their treatment to their unique genetic makeup and the specifics of their cancers. This approach has had modest success in characterizing subsets of several cancers.

Ultimately, people may carry with their medical records a catalog of their DNA sequence, a sort of genetic bar code, with regions highlighted that predispose them to specific diseases. The use of such sequences for personalized medicine—disease prevention and treatment—has great potential.

Systems biology is a very efficient way to study emergent properties at the molecular level. Recall from Chapter 1 that according to the theme of emergent properties, novel properties arise at each successive level of biological complexity as a result of the arrangement of building blocks at the underlying

◀ **Figure 21.6 A human gene microarray chip.** Tiny spots of DNA arranged in a grid on this silicon wafer represent almost all of the genes in the human genome. Using this chip, researchers can analyze expression patterns for all these genes at the same time.

level. The more we can learn about the arrangement and interactions of the components of genetic systems, the deeper will be our understanding of whole organisms. The rest of this chapter will survey what we've learned from genomic studies thus far.

CONCEPT 21.3

Genomes vary in size, number of genes, and gene density

By early 2010, the sequencing of about 1,200 genomes had been completed and that of over 5,500 genomes and over 200 metagenomes was in progress. In the completely sequenced group, about 1,000 are genomes of bacteria, and 80 are archaeal genomes. Among the 124 eukaryotic species in the group are vertebrates, invertebrates, protists, fungi, and plants. The accumulated genome sequences contain a wealth of information that we are now beginning to mine. What have we learned so far by comparing the genomes that have been sequenced? In this section, we will examine the characteristics of genome size, number of genes, and gene density. Because these characteristics are so broad, we will focus on general trends, for which there are often exceptions.

Genome Size

Comparing the three domains (Bacteria, Archaea, and Eukarya), we find a general difference in genome size between prokaryotes and eukaryotes (**Table 21.1**). While there are some exceptions, most bacterial genomes have between 1 and 6 million base pairs (Mb); the genome of *E. coli*, for instance, has 4.6 Mb. Genomes of archaea are, for the most part, within the size range of bacterial genomes. (Keep in mind, however, that many fewer archaeal genomes have

Table 21.1 Genome Sizes and Estimated Numbers of Genes*

Organism	Haploid Genome Size (Mb)	Number of Genes	Genes per Mb
Bacteria			
Haemophilus influenzae	1.8	1,700	940
Escherichia coli	4.6	4,400	950
Archaea			
Archaeoglobus fulgidus	2.2	2,500	1,130
Methanosarcina barkeri	4.8	3,600	750
Eukaryotes			
Saccharomyces cerevisiae (yeast, a fungus)	12	6,300	525
Caenorhabditis elegans (nematode)	100	20,100	200
Arabidopsis thaliana (mustard family plant)	120	27,000	225
Drosophila melanogaster (fruit fly)	165	13,700	83
Oryza sativa (rice)	430	42,000	98
Zea mays (corn)	2,300	32,000	14
Mus musculus (house mouse)	2,600	22,000	11
Ailuropoda melanoleuca (giant panda)	2,400	21,000	9
Homo sapiens (human)	3,000	<21,000	7
Fritillaria assyriaca (lily family plant)	124,000	ND	ND

*Some values given here are likely to be revised as genome analysis continues. Mb = million base pairs. ND = not determined.

been completely sequenced, so this picture may change.) Eukaryotic genomes tend to be larger: The genome of the single-celled yeast *Saccharomyces cerevisiae* (a fungus) has about 12 Mb, while most animals and plants, which are multicellular, have genomes of at least 100 Mb. There are 165 Mb in the fruit fly genome, while humans have 3,000 Mb, about 500 to 3,000 times as many as a typical bacterium.

Aside from this general difference between prokaryotes and eukaryotes, a comparison of genome sizes among eukaryotes fails to reveal any systematic relationship between genome size and the organism's phenotype. For instance, the genome of *Fritillaria assyriaca*, a flowering plant in the lily family, contains 124 billion base pairs (124,000 Mb), about 40 times the size of the human genome. Even more striking, there is a single-celled amoeba, *Polychaos dubia*, whose genome size has been estimated at 670,000 Mb. (This genome has not yet been sequenced.) On a finer scale, comparing two insect species, the cricket (*Anabrus simplex*) genome turns out to have 11 times as many base pairs as the *Drosophila melanogaster* genome. There

is a wide range of genome sizes within the groups of protists, insects, amphibians, and plants and less of a range within mammals and reptiles.

Number of Genes

The number of genes also varies between prokaryotes and eukaryotes: Bacteria and archaea, in general, have fewer genes than eukaryotes. Free-living bacteria and archaea have from 1,500 to 7,500 genes, while the number of genes in eukaryotes ranges from about 5,000 for unicellular fungi to at least 40,000 for some multicellular eukaryotes (see Table 21.1).

Within the eukaryotes, the number of genes in a species is often lower than expected from simply considering the size of its genome. Looking at Table 21.1, you can see that the genome of the nematode *C. elegans* is 100 Mb in size and contains roughly 20,000 genes. The *Drosophila* genome, in comparison, is much bigger (165 Mb) but has about two-thirds the number of genes—only 13,700 genes.

Considering an example closer to home, we noted that the human genome contains 3,000 Mb, well over ten times the size of either the *Drosophila* or *C. elegans* genome. At the outset of the Human Genome Project, biologists expected somewhere between 50,000 and 100,000 genes to be identified in the completed sequence, based on the number of known human proteins. As the project progressed, the estimate was revised downward several times, and in 2010, the most reliable count placed the number at fewer than 21,000. This relatively low number, similar to the number of genes in the nematode *C. elegans*, has surprised biologists, who had clearly expected many more human genes.

What genetic attributes allow humans (and other vertebrates) to get by with no more genes than nematodes? An important factor is that vertebrate genomes "get more bang for the buck" from their coding sequences because of extensive alternative splicing of RNA transcripts. Recall that this process generates more than one functional protein from a single gene (see Figure 18.13). A typical human gene contains about ten exons, and an estimated 93% or so of these multi-exon genes are spliced in at least two different ways. Some genes are expressed in hundreds of alternatively spliced forms, others in just two. It is not yet possible to catalog all of the different forms, but it is clear that the number of different proteins encoded in the human genome far exceeds the proposed number of genes.

Additional polypeptide diversity could result from post-translational modifications such as cleavage or the addition of carbohydrate groups in different cell types or at different developmental stages. Finally, the discovery of miRNAs and other small RNAs that play regulatory roles have added a new variable to the mix (see Concept 18.3). Some scientists think that this added level of regulation, when present, may contribute to greater organismal complexity for a given number of genes.

Gene Density and Noncoding DNA

In addition to genome size and number of genes, we can compare gene density in different species—in other words, how many genes there are in a given length of DNA. When we compare the genomes of bacteria, archaea, and eukaryotes, we see that eukaryotes generally have larger genomes but fewer genes in a given number of base pairs. Humans have hundreds or thousands of times as many base pairs in their genome as most bacteria, as we already noted, but only 5 to 15 times as many genes; thus, gene density is lower in humans (see Table 21.1). Even unicellular eukaryotes, such as yeasts, have fewer genes per million base pairs than bacteria and archaea. Among the genomes that have been sequenced completely thus far, humans and other mammals have the lowest gene density.

In all bacterial genomes studied so far, most of the DNA consists of genes for protein, tRNA, or rRNA; the small amount remaining consists mainly of nontranscribed regulatory sequences, such as promoters. The sequence of nucleotides along a bacterial protein-coding gene proceeds from start to finish without interruption by noncoding sequences (introns). In eukaryotic genomes, by contrast, most of the DNA neither encodes protein nor is transcribed into RNA molecules of known function, and the DNA includes more complex regulatory sequences. In fact, humans have 10,000 times as much noncoding DNA as bacteria. Some of this DNA in multicellular eukaryotes is present as introns within genes. Indeed, introns account for most of the difference in average length between human genes (27,000 base pairs) and bacterial genes (1,000 base pairs).

In addition to introns, multicellular eukaryotes have a vast amount of non-protein-coding DNA between genes. In the next section, we will describe the composition and arrangement of these great stretches of DNA in the human genome.

CONCEPT CHECK 21.3

1. According to the best current estimate, the human genome contains fewer than 21,000 genes. However, there is evidence that human cells produce many more than 21,000 different polypeptides. What processes might account for this discrepancy?

2. The number of sequenced genomes is constantly being updated. Go to www.genomesonline.org to find the current number of completed genomes for each domain as well as the number of genomes whose sequencing is in progress. (*Hint*: Click on "Enter GOLD," and then click on "Published Complete Genomes" for extra information.)

3. **WHAT IF?** What evolutionary processes might account for prokaryotes having smaller genomes than eukaryotes?

For suggested answers, see Appendix A.

Multicellular eukaryotes have much noncoding DNA and many multigene families

We have spent most of this chapter, and indeed this unit, focusing on genes that code for proteins. Yet the coding regions of these genes and the genes for RNA products such as rRNA, tRNA, and miRNA make up only a small portion of the genomes of most multicellular eukaryotes. The bulk of many eukaryotic genomes consists of DNA sequences that neither code for proteins nor are transcribed to produce RNAs with known functions; this noncoding DNA was often described in the past as "junk DNA." However, much evidence is accumulating that this DNA plays important roles in the cell, an idea supported by its persistence in diverse genomes over many hundreds of generations. For example, comparison of the genomes of humans, rats, and mice has revealed the presence of almost 500 regions of noncoding DNA that are identical in sequence in all three species. This is a higher level of sequence conservation than is seen for protein-coding regions in these species, strongly suggesting that the noncoding regions have important functions. In this section, we examine how genes and noncoding DNA sequences are organized within genomes of multicellular eukaryotes, using the human genome as our main example. Genome organization tells us much about how genomes have evolved and continue to evolve, the next subject we'll consider.

Once the sequencing of the human genome was completed, it became clear that only a tiny part—1.5%—codes for proteins or is transcribed into rRNAs or tRNAs. **Figure 21.7** shows what is known about the makeup of the remaining 98.5%. Gene-related regulatory sequences and introns account, respectively, for 5% and about 20% of the human genome. The rest, located between functional genes, includes some unique noncoding DNA, such as gene fragments and **pseudogenes**, former genes that have accumulated mutations over a long time and no longer produce functional proteins. (The genes that produce small noncoding RNAs are a tiny percentage of the genome, distributed between the 20% introns and the 15% unique noncoding DNA.) Most intergenic DNA, however, is **repetitive DNA**, which consists of sequences that are present in multiple copies in the genome. Somewhat surprisingly, about 75% of this repetitive DNA (44% of the entire human genome) is made up of units called transposable elements and sequences related to them.

Transposable Elements and Related Sequences

Both prokaryotes and eukaryotes have stretches of DNA that can move from one location to another within the genome. These stretches are known as *transposable genetic elements*, or

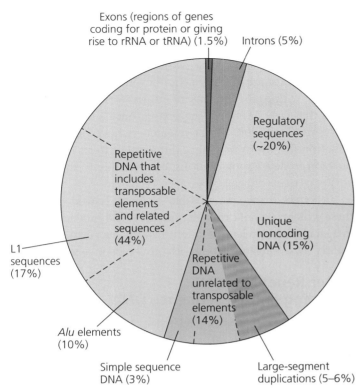

Exons (regions of genes coding for protein or giving rise to rRNA or tRNA) (1.5%)

Introns (5%)

Regulatory sequences (~20%)

Repetitive DNA that includes transposable elements and related sequences (44%)

L1 sequences (17%)

Alu elements (10%)

Unique noncoding DNA (15%)

Repetitive DNA unrelated to transposable elements (14%)

Simple sequence DNA (3%)

Large-segment duplications (5–6%)

▲ **Figure 21.7 Types of DNA sequences in the human genome.** The gene sequences that code for proteins or are transcribed into rRNA or tRNA molecules make up only about 1.5% of the human genome (dark purple in the pie chart), while introns and regulatory sequences associated with genes (light purple) make up about a quarter. The vast majority of the human genome does not code for proteins or give rise to known RNAs, and much of it is repetitive DNA (dark and light green). Because repetitive DNA is the most difficult to sequence and analyze, classification of some portions is tentative, and the percentages given here may shift slightly as genome analysis proceeds. The genes that are transcribed into small noncoding RNAs such as miRNAs, which were recently discovered, are found among unique noncoding DNA sequences and within introns and thus would be included in two segments of this chart.

simply **transposable elements**. During the process called *transposition*, a transposable element moves from one site in a cell's DNA to a different target site by a type of recombination process. Transposable elements are sometimes called "jumping genes," but it should be kept in mind that they never completely detach from the cell's DNA. Instead, the original and new DNA sites are brought together by enzymes and other proteins that bend the DNA.

The first evidence for wandering DNA segments came from American geneticist Barbara McClintock's breeding experiments with Indian corn (maize) in the 1940s and 1950s **(Figure 21.8)**. As she tracked corn plants through multiple generations, McClintock identified changes in the color of corn kernels that made sense only if she postulated the existence of genetic elements capable of moving from other locations in the genome into the genes for kernel color, disrupting the genes so that the kernel color was changed. McClintock's discovery was met with great skepticism and virtually discounted at the time. Her

▲ **Figure 21.8 The effect of transposable elements on corn kernel color.** Barbara McClintock first proposed the idea of mobile genetic elements after observing variegations in corn kernel color (right).

careful work and insightful ideas were finally validated many years later when transposable elements were found in bacteria. In 1983, at the age of 81, McClintock received the Nobel Prize for her pioneering research.

Movement of Transposons and Retrotransposons

Eukaryotic transposable elements are of two types. The first type are **transposons**, which move within a genome by means of a DNA intermediate. Transposons can move by a "cut-and-paste" mechanism, which removes the element from the original site, or by a "copy-and-paste" mechanism, which leaves a copy behind **(Figure 21.9)**. Both mechanisms require an enzyme called *transposase*, which is generally encoded by the transposon.

Most transposable elements in eukaryotic genomes are of the second type, **retrotransposons**, which move by means of an RNA intermediate that is a transcript of the retrotransposon DNA. Retrotransposons always leave a copy at the original site during transposition, since they are initially transcribed

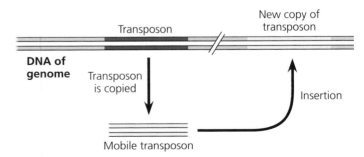

Transposon

New copy of transposon

DNA of genome

Transposon is copied

Insertion

Mobile transposon

▲ **Figure 21.9 Transposon movement.** Movement of transposons by either the cut-and-paste mechanism or the copy-and-paste mechanism (shown here) involves a double-stranded DNA intermediate that is inserted into the genome.

? *How would this figure differ if it showed the cut-and-paste mechanism?*

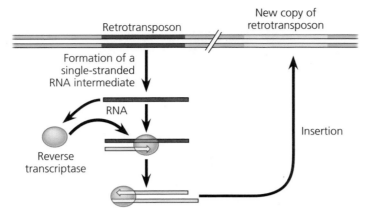

Retrotransposon

New copy of
retrotransposon

Formation of a
single-stranded
RNA intermediate

RNA

Reverse
transcriptase

Insertion

▲ **Figure 21.10 Retrotransposon movement.** Movement begins with formation of a single-stranded RNA intermediate. The remaining steps are essentially identical to part of the retrovirus replicative cycle (see Figure 19.8).

into an RNA intermediate (**Figure 21.10**). To insert at another site, the RNA intermediate is first converted back to DNA by reverse transcriptase, an enzyme encoded by the retrotransposon. (Reverse transcriptase is also encoded by retroviruses, as you learned in Chapter 19. In fact, retroviruses may have evolved from retrotransposons.) Another cellular enzyme catalyzes insertion of the reverse-transcribed DNA at a new site.

Sequences Related to Transposable Elements

Multiple copies of transposable elements and sequences related to them are scattered throughout eukaryotic genomes. A single unit is usually hundreds to thousands of base pairs long, and the dispersed "copies" are similar but usually not identical to each other. Some of these are transposable elements that can move; the enzymes required for this movement may be encoded by any transposable element, including the one that is moving. Others are related sequences that have lost the ability to move altogether. Transposable elements and related sequences make up 25–50% of most mammalian genomes (see Figure 21.7) and even higher percentages in amphibians and many plants. In fact, the very large size of some plant genomes is accounted for not by extra genes, but by extra transposable elements. For example, sequences like these make up 85% of the corn genome!

In humans and other primates, a large portion of transposable element–related DNA consists of a family of similar sequences called *Alu elements*. These sequences alone account for approximately 10% of the human genome. *Alu* elements are about 300 nucleotides long, much shorter than most functional transposable elements, and they do not code for any protein. However, many *Alu* elements are transcribed into RNA; its cellular function, if any, is currently unknown.

An even larger percentage (17%) of the human genome is made up of a type of retrotransposon called *LINE-1*, or *L1*. These sequences are much longer than *Alu* elements—about

6,500 base pairs—and have a low rate of transposition. What might account for this low rate? Recent research has uncovered the presence of sequences within L1 that block the progress of RNA polymerase, which is necessary for transposition. An accompanying genomic analysis found L1 sequences within the introns of nearly 80% of the human genes that were analyzed, suggesting that L1 may help regulate gene expression. Other researchers have proposed that L1 retrotransposons may have differential effects on gene expression in developing neurons, contributing to the great diversity of neuronal cell types.

Although many transposable elements encode proteins, these proteins do not carry out normal cellular functions. Therefore, transposable elements are usually included in the "noncoding" DNA category, along with other repetitive sequences.

Other Repetitive DNA, Including Simple Sequence DNA

Repetitive DNA that is not related to transposable elements probably arises due to mistakes during DNA replication or recombination. Such DNA accounts for about 14% of the human genome (see Figure 21.7). About a third of this (5–6% of the human genome) consists of duplications of long stretches of DNA, with each unit ranging from 10,000 to 300,000 base pairs. The large segments seem to have been copied from one chromosomal location to another site on the same or a different chromosome and probably include some functional genes.

In contrast to scattered copies of long sequences, **simple sequence DNA** contains many copies of tandemly repeated short sequences, as in the following example (showing one DNA strand only):

. . . GTTACGTTACGTTACGTTACGTTACGTTAC . . .

In this case, the repeated unit (GTTAC) consists of 5 nucleotides. Repeated units may contain as many as 500 nucleotides, but often contain fewer than 15 nucleotides, as in this example. When the unit contains 2–5 nucleotides, the series of repeats is called a **short tandem repeat**, or **STR**; we discussed the use of STR analysis in preparing genetic profiles in Chapter 20. The number of copies of the repeated unit can vary from site to site within a given genome. There could be as many as several hundred thousand repetitions of the GTTAC unit at one site, but only half that number at another. STR analysis is performed on sites selected because they have relatively few repeats. The repeat number can vary from person to person, and since humans are diploid, each person has two alleles per site, which can differ. This diversity produces the variation represented in the genetic profiles that result from STR analysis. Altogether, simple sequence DNA makes up 3% of the human genome.

Much of a genome's simple sequence DNA is located at chromosomal telomeres and centromeres, suggesting that this DNA plays a structural role for chromosomes. The DNA at centromeres is essential for the separation of chromatids in cell division (see Chapter 12). Centromeric DNA, along with simple sequence DNA located elsewhere, may also help organize the chromatin within the interphase nucleus. The simple sequence DNA located at telomeres, at the tips of chromosomes, prevents genes from being lost as the DNA shortens with each round of replication (see Chapter 16). Telomeric DNA also binds proteins that protect the ends of a chromosome from degradation and from joining to other chromosomes.

Genes and Multigene Families

We finish our discussion of the various types of DNA sequences in eukaryotic genomes with a closer look at genes. Recall that DNA sequences that code for proteins or give rise to tRNA or rRNA compose a mere 1.5% of the human genome (see Figure 21.7). If we include introns and regulatory sequences associated with genes, the total amount of DNA that is gene-related—coding and noncoding—constitutes about 25% of the human genome. Put another way, only about 6% (1.5% out of 25%) of the length of the average gene is represented in the final gene product.

Like the genes of bacteria, many eukaryotic genes are present as unique sequences, with only one copy per haploid set of chromosomes. But in the human genome and the genomes of many other animals and plants, solitary genes make up less than half of the total gene-related DNA. The rest occur in **multigene families**, collections of two or more identical or very similar genes.

In multigene families that consist of *identical* DNA sequences, those sequences are usually clustered tandemly and, with the notable exception of the genes for histone proteins, have RNAs as their final products. An example is the family of identical DNA sequences that are the genes for the three largest rRNA molecules **(Figure 21.11a)**. These rRNA molecules are transcribed from a single transcription unit that is repeated tandemly hundreds to thousands of times in one or several clusters in the genome of a multicellular eukaryote. The many copies of this rRNA transcription unit help cells to quickly make the millions of ribosomes needed for active protein synthesis. The primary transcript is cleaved to yield the three rRNA molecules, which combine with proteins and one other kind of rRNA (5S rRNA) to form ribosomal subunits.

The classic examples of multigene families of *nonidentical* genes are two related families of genes that encode globins, a group of proteins that include the α and β polypeptide subunits of hemoglobin. One family, located on chromosome 16 in humans, encodes various forms of α-globin; the other, on chromosome 11, encodes forms of β-globin **(Figure 21.11b)**. The different forms of each globin subunit are expressed at different times in development, allowing hemoglobin to function effectively in the changing environment of the developing animal. In humans, for example, the embryonic and fetal forms of hemoglobin have a higher affinity for oxygen

(a) Part of the ribosomal RNA gene family. The TEM at the top shows three of the hundreds of copies of rRNA transcription units in a salamander genome. Each "feather" corresponds to a single unit being transcribed by about 100 molecules of RNA polymerase (dark dots along the DNA), moving left to right (red arrow). The growing RNA transcripts extend from the DNA. In the diagram of a trascription unit below the TEM, the genes for three types of rRNA (blue) are adjacent to regions that are transcribed but later removed (yellow). A single trascript is processed to yield one of each of the three rRNAs (red), key components of the ribosome.

(b) The human α-globin and β-globin gene families. Adult hemoglobin is composed of two α-globin and two β-globin polypeptide subunits, as shown in the molecular model. The genes (dark blue) encoding α- and β-globins are found in two families, organized as shown here. The noncoding DNA separating the functional genes within each family includes pseudogenes (ψ; green), versions of the functional genes that no longer produce functional proteins. Genes and pseudogenes are named with Greek letters. Some genes are expressed only in the embryo or fetus.

▲ **Figure 21.11 Gene families.**

? *In (a), how could you determine the direction of transcription if it wasn't indicated by the red arrow?*

than the adult forms, ensuring the efficient transfer of oxygen from mother to fetus. Also found in the globin gene family clusters are several pseudogenes.

The arrangement of the genes in gene families has given biologists insight into the evolution of genomes. We will consider some of the processes that have shaped the genomes of different species over evolutionary time in the next section.

CONCEPT CHECK 21.4

1. Discuss the characteristics of mammalian genomes that make them larger than prokaryotic genomes.
2. Which of the three mechanisms described in Figures 21.9 and 21.10 result(s) in a copy remaining at the original site as well as appearing in a new location?
3. Contrast the organizations of the rRNA gene family and the globin gene families. For each, explain how the existence of a family of genes benefits the organism.
4. **MAKE CONNECTIONS** Assign each DNA segment at the top of Figure 18.8 (p. 359) to a sector in the pie chart in Figure 21.7.

For suggested answers, see Appendix A.

CONCEPT 21.5
Duplication, rearrangement, and mutation of DNA contribute to genome evolution

EVOLUTION The basis of change at the genomic level is mutation, which underlies much of genome evolution. It seems likely that the earliest forms of life had a minimal number of genes—those necessary for survival and reproduction. If this were indeed the case, one aspect of evolution must have been an increase in the size of the genome, with the extra genetic material providing the raw material for gene diversification. In this section, we will first describe how extra copies of all or part of a genome can arise and then consider subsequent processes that can lead to the evolution of proteins (or RNA products) with slightly different or entirely new functions.

Duplication of Entire Chromosome Sets

An accident in meiosis can result in one or more extra sets of chromosomes, a condition known as polyploidy. Although such accidents would most often be lethal, in rare cases they could facilitate the evolution of genes. In a polyploid organism, one set of genes can provide essential functions for the organism. The genes in the one or more extra sets can diverge by accumulating mutations; these variations may persist if the organism carrying them survives and reproduces. In this way, genes with novel functions can evolve. As long as one copy of an essential gene is expressed, the divergence of another copy can lead to its encoded protein acting in a novel way, thereby changing the organism's phenotype. The outcome of this accumulation of mutations may be the branching off of a new species, as happens often in flowering plants (see Chapter 24). Polyploid animals also exist, but they are much rarer; the tetraploid model organism *Xenopus laevis*, the African clawed frog, is an example.

Alterations of Chromosome Structure

Scientists have long known that sometime in the last 6 million years, when the ancestors of humans and chimpanzees diverged as species, the fusion of two ancestral chromosomes in the human line led to different haploid numbers for humans ($n = 23$) and chimpanzees ($n = 24$). The banding patterns in stained chromosomes suggested that the ancestral versions of current chimp chromosomes 12 and 13 fused end to end, forming chromosome 2 in an ancestor of the human lineage. With the recent explosion in genomic sequence information, we can now compare the chromosomal organizations of many different species on a much finer scale. This information allows us to make inferences about the evolutionary processes that shape chromosomes and may drive speciation. Sequencing and analysis of human chromosome 2 in 2005 provided very strong supporting evidence for the model we have just described (Figure 21.12a).

In another study of broader scope, researchers compared the DNA sequence of each human chromosome with the whole-genome sequence of the mouse. Figure 21.12b shows the results of this comparison for human chromosome 16: Large blocks of genes on this chromosome are found on four mouse chromosomes, indicating that the genes in each block stayed together during the evolution of the mouse and human lineages.

Performing the same comparative analysis between chromosomes of humans and six other mammalian species allowed the researchers to reconstruct the evolutionary history of chromosomal rearrangements in these eight species. They found many duplications and inversions of large portions of chromosomes, the result of mistakes during meiotic recombination in which the DNA broke and was rejoined incorrectly. The rate of these events seems to have accelerated about 100 million years ago, around the time large dinosaurs became extinct and the number of mammalian species increased rapidly. The apparent coincidence is interesting because chromosomal rearrangements are thought to contribute to the generation of new species. Although two individuals with different arrangements could still mate and produce offspring, the offspring would have two nonequivalent sets of chromosomes, making meiosis inefficient or even impossible. Thus, chromosomal rearrangements would lead to two populations that could not successfully mate with each other, a step on the way to their becoming two separate species. (You'll learn more about this in Chapter 24.)

Telomere sequences

Centromere sequences

Telomere-like sequences

Centromere-like sequences

Human chromosome 2

Chimpanzee chromosomes

12

13

(a) Human and chimpanzee chromosomes. The positions of telomere-like and centromere-like sequences on human chromosome 2 (left) match those of telomeres on chimp chromosomes 12 and 13 and the centromere on chimp chromosome 13 (right). This suggests that chromosomes 12 and 13 in a human ancestor fused end to end to form human chromosome 2. The centromere from ancestral chromosome 12 remained functional on human chromosome 2, while the one from ancestral chromosome 13 did not. (Chimp chromosomes 12 and 13 have been renamed 2a and 2b, respectively.)

Human chromosome 16

Mouse chromosomes

7 8 16 17

(b) Human and mouse chromosomes. DNA sequences very similar to large blocks of human chromosome 16 (colored areas in this diagram) are found on mouse chromosomes 7, 8, 16, and 17. This suggests that the DNA sequence in each block has stayed together in the mouse and human lineages since the time they diverged from a common ancestor.

▲ **Figure 21.12 Related chromosome sequences among mammals.**

Somewhat unexpectedly, the same study also unearthed a pattern with medical relevance. Analysis of the chromosomal breakage points associated with the rearrangements showed that they were not randomly distributed; specific sites were used over and over again. A number of these recombination "hot spots" correspond to locations of chromosomal rearrangements within the human genome that are associated with congenital diseases. Researchers are, of course, looking at the other sites as well for their possible association with as yet unidentified diseases.

Duplication and Divergence of Gene-Sized Regions of DNA

Errors during meiosis can also lead to the duplication of chromosomal regions that are smaller than the ones we've just discussed, including segments the length of individual genes. Unequal crossing over during prophase I of meiosis, for instance, can result in one chromosome with a deletion and another with a duplication of a particular gene. As illustrated in **Figure 21.13**, transposable elements can provide homologous sites where nonsister chromatids can cross over, even when other chromatid regions are not correctly aligned.

Also, slippage can occur during DNA replication, such that the template shifts with respect to the new complementary strand, and a part of the template strand is either skipped by the replication machinery or used twice as a template. As a result, a segment of DNA is deleted or duplicated. It is easy to imagine how such errors could occur in regions of repeats. The variable number of repeated units of simple sequence DNA at a given site, used for STR analysis, is probably due to errors like these. Evidence that unequal crossing over and template slippage during DNA replication lead to duplication of genes is found in the existence of multigene families, such as the globin family.

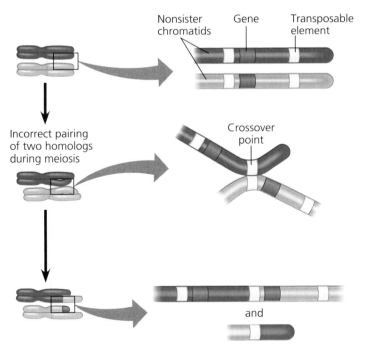

Nonsister chromatids   Gene   Transposable element

Incorrect pairing of two homologs during meiosis

Crossover point

and

▲ **Figure 21.13 Gene duplication due to unequal crossing over.** One mechanism by which a gene (or other DNA segment) can be duplicated is recombination during meiosis between copies of a transposable element flanking the gene. Such recombination between misaligned nonsister chromatids of homologous chromosomes produces one chromatid with two copies of the gene and one chromatid with no copy.

MAKE CONNECTIONS *Examine how crossing over occurs in Figure 13.11 (p. 259). In the middle panel above, draw a line through the portions that result in the upper chromatid in the bottom panel. Use a different color to do the same for the other chromatid.*

Evolution of Genes with Related Functions: The Human Globin Genes

Duplication events can lead to the evolution of genes with related functions, such as those of the α-globin and β-globin gene families (see Figure 21.11b). A comparison of gene sequences within a multigene family can suggest the order in which the genes arose. This approach to re-creating the evolutionary history of the globin genes indicates that they all evolved from one common ancestral globin gene that underwent duplication and divergence into the α-globin and β-globin ancestral genes about 450–500 million years ago (Figure 21.14). Each of these genes was later duplicated several times, and the copies then diverged from each other in sequence, yielding the current family members. In fact, the common ancestral globin gene also gave rise to the oxygen-binding muscle protein myoglobin and to the plant protein leghemoglobin. The latter two proteins function as monomers, and their genes are included in a "globin superfamily."

After the duplication events, the differences between the genes in the globin families undoubtedly arose from mutations that accumulated in the gene copies over many generations. The current model is that the necessary function provided by an α-globin protein, for example, was fulfilled by one gene, while other copies of the α-globin gene accumulated random mutations. Many mutations may have had an adverse effect on the organism and others may have had no effect, but a few mutations must have altered the function of the protein product in a way that was advantageous to the organism at a particular life stage without substantially changing the protein's oxygen-carrying function. Presumably, natural selection acted on these altered genes, maintaining them in the population.

The similarity in the amino acid sequences of the various α-globin and β-globin polypeptides supports this model of gene duplication and mutation (Table 21.2). The amino acid sequences of the β-globins, for instance, are much more similar to each other than to the α-globin sequences. The existence of several pseudogenes among the functional globin genes provides additional evidence for this model (see Figure 21.11b): Random mutations in these "genes" over evolutionary time have destroyed their function.

Evolution of Genes with Novel Functions

In the evolution of the globin gene families, gene duplication and subsequent divergence produced family members whose protein products performed similar functions (oxygen transport). Alternatively, one copy of a duplicated gene can undergo alterations that lead to a completely new function for the protein product. The genes for lysozyme and α-lactalbumin are good examples.

Lysozyme is an enzyme that helps protect animals against bacterial infection by hydrolyzing bacterial cell walls; α-lactalbumin is a nonenzymatic protein that plays a role in milk production in mammals. The two proteins are quite similar in their amino acid sequences and three-dimensional structures. Both genes are found in mammals, whereas only the lysozyme gene is present in birds. These findings suggest that at some time after the lineages leading to mammals and birds had separated, the lysozyme gene was duplicated in the

▲ Figure 21.14 **A model for the evolution of the human α-globin and β-globin gene families from a single ancestral globin gene.**

? *The green elements are pseudogenes. Explain how they could have arisen after gene duplication.*

Table 21.2 **Percentage of Similarity in Amino Acid Sequence Between Human Globin Proteins**

		α-Globins		β-Globins		
		α	ζ	β	γ	ε
α-Globins	α	—	58	42	39	37
	ζ	58	—	34	38	37
β-Globins	β	42	34	—	73	75
	γ	39	38	73	—	80
	ε	37	37	75	80	—

mammalian lineage but not in the avian lineage. Subsequently, one copy of the duplicated lysozyme gene evolved into a gene encoding α-lactalbumin, a protein with a completely different function.

Rearrangements of Parts of Genes: Exon Duplication and Exon Shuffling

Rearrangement of existing DNA sequences within genes has also contributed to genome evolution. The presence of introns in most genes of multicellular eukaryotes may have promoted the evolution of new and potentially useful proteins by facilitating the duplication or repositioning of exons in the genome. Recall from Chapter 17 that an exon often codes for a domain, a distinct structural or functional region of a protein.

We've already seen that unequal crossing over during meiosis can lead to duplication of a gene on one chromosome and its loss from the homologous chromosome (see Figure 21.13). By a similar process, a particular exon within a gene could be duplicated on one chromosome and deleted from the other. The gene with the duplicated exon would code for a protein containing a second copy of the encoded domain. This change in the protein's structure could augment its function by increasing its stability, enhancing its ability to bind a particular ligand, or altering some other property. Quite a few protein-coding genes have multiple copies of related exons, which presumably arose by duplication and then diverged. The gene encoding the extracellular matrix protein collagen is a good example. Collagen is a structural protein with a highly repetitive amino acid sequence, which is reflected in the repetitive pattern of exons in the collagen gene.

Alternatively, we can imagine the occasional mixing and matching of different exons either within a gene or between two different (nonallelic) genes owing to errors in meiotic recombination. This process, termed *exon shuffling*, could lead to new proteins with novel combinations of functions. As an example, let's consider the gene for tissue plasminogen activator (TPA). The TPA protein is an extracellular protein that helps control blood clotting. It has four domains of three types, each encoded by an exon; one exon is present in two copies. Because each type of exon is also found in other proteins, the gene for TPA is thought to have arisen by several instances of exon shuffling and duplication (**Figure 21.15**).

How Transposable Elements Contribute to Genome Evolution

The persistence of transposable elements as a large fraction of some eukaryotic genomes is consistent with the idea that they play an important role in shaping a genome over evolutionary time. These elements can contribute to the evolution of the genome in several ways. They can promote recombination, disrupt cellular genes or control elements, and carry entire genes or individual exons to new locations.

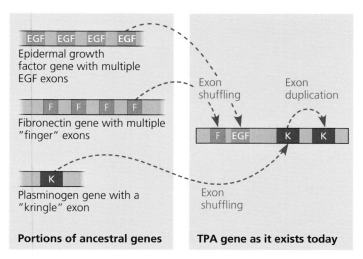

▲ **Figure 21.15 Evolution of a new gene by exon shuffling.** Exon shuffling could have moved exons, each encoding a particular domain, from ancestral forms of the genes for epidermal growth factor, fibronectin, and plasminogen (left) into the evolving gene for tissue plasminogen activator, TPA (right). Duplication of the "kringle" exon from the plasminogen gene after its movement could account for the two copies of this exon in the TPA gene.

? *How could the presence of transposable elements in introns have facilitated the exon shuffling shown here?*

Transposable elements of similar sequence scattered throughout the genome facilitate recombination between different chromosomes by providing homologous regions for crossing over. Most such recombination events are probably detrimental, causing chromosomal translocations and other changes in the genome that may be lethal to the organism. But over the course of evolutionary time, an occasional recombination event of this sort may be advantageous to the organism. (For the change to be heritable, of course, it must happen in a cell that will give rise to a gamete.)

The movement of a transposable element can have a variety of consequences. For instance, if a transposable element "jumps" into the middle of a protein-coding sequence, it will prevent the production of a normal transcript of the gene. If a transposable element inserts within a regulatory sequence, the transposition may lead to increased or decreased production of one or more proteins. Transposition caused both types of effects on the genes coding for pigment-synthesizing enzymes in McClintock's corn kernels. Again, while such changes are usually harmful, in the long run some may prove beneficial by providing a survival advantage.

During transposition, a transposable element may carry along a gene or group of genes to a new position in the genome. This mechanism probably accounts for the location of the α-globin and β-globin gene families on different human chromosomes, as well as the dispersion of the genes of certain other gene families. By a similar tag-along process, an exon from one gene may be inserted into another gene in a mechanism similar to that of exon shuffling during recombination. For example, an exon may be inserted by transposition into the intron of a protein-coding gene. If the inserted exon is retained in the RNA transcript during RNA splicing, the protein that is synthesized will have an additional domain, which may confer a new function on the protein.

All the processes discussed in this section most often produce either harmful effects, which may be lethal, or no effect at all. In a few cases, however, small beneficial heritable changes may occur. Over many generations, the resulting genetic diversity provides valuable raw material for natural selection. Diversification of genes and their products is an important factor in the evolution of new species. Thus, the accumulation of changes in the genome of each species provides a record of its evolutionary history. To read this record, we must be able to identify genomic changes. Comparing the genomes of different species allows us to do that and has increased our understanding of how genomes evolve. You will learn more about these topics in the final section.

CONCEPT 21.6

Comparing genome sequences provides clues to evolution and development

EVOLUTION One researcher has likened the current state of biology to the Age of Exploration in the 15th century after major improvements in navigation and the building of faster ships. In the last 25 years, we have seen rapid advances in genome sequencing and data collection, new techniques for assessing gene activity across the whole genome, and refined approaches for understanding how genes and their products work together in complex systems. We are truly poised on the brink of a new world.

Comparisons of genome sequences from different species reveal much about the evolutionary history of life, from very ancient to more recent. Similarly, comparative studies of the genetic programs that direct embryonic development in different species are beginning to clarify the mechanisms that generated the great diversity of life-forms present today. In this final section of the chapter, we will discuss what has been learned from these two approaches.

Comparing Genomes

The more similar in sequence the genes and genomes of two species are, the more closely related those species are in their evolutionary history. Comparing genomes of closely related species sheds light on more recent evolutionary events, whereas comparing genomes of very distantly related species helps us understand ancient evolutionary history. In either case, learning about characteristics that are shared or divergent between groups enhances our picture of the evolution of life-forms and biological processes. As you learned in Chapter 1, the evolutionary relationships between species can be represented by a diagram in the form of a tree (often turned sideways), where each branch point marks the divergence of two lineages. **Figure 21.16** shows the evolutionary relationships of some groups and species we will be discussing. We will consider comparisons between distantly related species first.

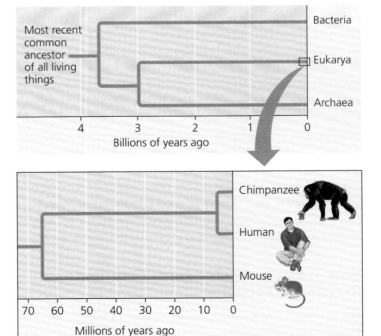

▲ **Figure 21.16 Evolutionary relationships of the three domains of life.** This tree diagram shows the ancient divergence of bacteria, archaea, and eukaryotes. A portion of the eukaryote lineage is expanded in the inset to show the more recent divergence of three mammalian species discussed in this chapter.

Comparing Distantly Related Species

Determining which genes have remained similar—that is, are *highly conserved*—in distantly related species can help clarify evolutionary relationships among species that diverged from each other long ago. Indeed, comparisons of the complete genome sequences of bacteria, archaea, and eukaryotes indicate that these three groups diverged between 2 and 4 billion years ago and strongly support the theory that they are the fundamental domains of life (see Figure 21.16).

In addition to their value in evolutionary biology, comparative genomic studies confirm the relevance of research on model organisms to our understanding of biology in general and human biology in particular. Genes that evolved a very long time ago can still be surprisingly similar in disparate species. As a case in point, several genes in yeast are so similar to certain human disease genes that researchers have deduced the functions of the disease genes by studying their yeast counterparts. This striking similarity underscores the common origin of these two distantly related species.

Comparing Closely Related Species

The genomes of two closely related species are likely to be organized similarly because of their relatively recent divergence. As we mentioned earlier, this allows the fully sequenced genome of one species to be used as a scaffold for assembling the genomic sequences of a closely related species, accelerating mapping of the second genome. For instance, using the human genome sequence as a guide, researchers were able to quickly sequence the chimpanzee genome.

The recent divergence of two closely related species also underlies the small number of gene differences that are found when their genomes are compared. The particular genetic differences can therefore be more easily correlated with phenotypic differences between the two species. An exciting application of this type of analysis is seen as researchers compare the human genome with the genomes of the chimpanzee, mouse, rat, and other mammals. Identifying the genes shared by all of these species but not by nonmammals should give clues about what it takes to make a mammal, while finding the genes shared by chimpanzees and humans but not by rodents should tell us something about primates. And, of course, comparing the human genome with that of the chimpanzee should help us answer the tantalizing question we asked at the beginning of the chapter: What genomic information makes a human or a chimpanzee?

An analysis of the overall composition of the human and chimpanzee genomes, which are thought to have diverged only about 6 million years ago (see Figure 21.16), reveals some general differences. Considering single nucleotide substitutions, the two genomes differ by only 1.2%. When researchers looked at longer stretches of DNA, however, they were surprised to find a further 2.7% difference due to insertions or deletions of larger regions in the genome of one or the other species; many of the insertions were duplications or other repetitive DNA. In fact, a third of the human duplications are not present in the chimpanzee genome, and some of these duplications contain regions associated with human diseases. There are more *Alu* elements in the human genome than in the chimpanzee genome, and the latter contains many copies of a retroviral provirus not present in humans. All of these observations provide clues to the forces that might have swept the two genomes along different paths, but we don't have a complete picture yet. We also don't know how these differences might account for the distinct characteristics of each species.

To discover the basis for the phenotypic differences between the two species, biologists are studying specific genes and types of genes that differ between humans and chimpanzees and comparing them with their counterparts in other mammals. This approach has revealed a number of genes that are apparently changing (evolving) faster in the human than in either the chimpanzee or the mouse. Among them are genes involved in defense against malaria and tuberculosis and at least one gene that regulates brain size. When genes are classified by function, the genes that seem to be evolving the fastest are those that code for transcription factors. This discovery makes sense because transcription factors regulate gene expression and thus play a key role in orchestrating the overall genetic program.

One transcription factor whose gene shows evidence of rapid change in the human lineage is called FOXP2. Several lines of evidence suggest that the *FOXP2* gene functions in vocalization in vertebrates. For one thing, mutations in this gene can produce severe speech and language impairment in humans. Moreover, the *FOXP2* gene is expressed in the brains of zebra finches and canaries at the time when these songbirds are learning their songs. But perhaps the strongest evidence comes from a "knock-out" experiment in which researchers disrupted the *FOXP2* gene in mice and analyzed the resulting phenotype (**Figure 21.17**, on the next page). The homozygous mutant mice had malformed brains and failed to emit normal ultrasonic vocalizations, and mice with one faulty copy of the gene also showed significant problems with vocalization. These results support the idea that the *FOXP2* gene product turns on genes involved in vocalization.

Expanding on this analysis, another research group more recently replaced the *FOXP2* gene in mice with a "humanized" copy coding for the human versions of two amino acids that differ between human and chimp; these are the changes potentially responsible for a human's ability to speak. Although the mice were generally healthy, they had subtly different vocalizations and showed changes in brain cells in circuits associated with speech in human brains.

The *FOXP2* story is an excellent example of how different approaches can complement each other in uncovering biological phenomena of widespread importance. The

INQUIRY

What is the function of a gene (*FOXP2*) that is rapidly evolving in the human lineage?

EXPERIMENT Several lines of evidence support a role for the *FOXP2* gene in the development of speech and language in humans and of vocalization in other vertebrates. In 2005, Joseph Buxbaum and collaborators at the Mount Sinai School of Medicine and several other institutions tested the function of *FOXP2*. They used the mouse, a model organism in which genes can be easily knocked out, as a representative vertebrate that vocalizes: Mice produce ultrasonic squeaks (whistles) to communicate stress. The researchers used genetic engineering to produce mice in which one or both copies of *FOXP2* were disrupted.

Wild type: two normal copies of *FOXP2*	Heterozygote: one copy of *FOXP2* disrupted	Homozygote: both copies of *FOXP2* disrupted

They then compared the phenotypes of these mice. Two of the characters they examined are included here: brain anatomy and vocalization.

Experiment 1: Researchers cut thin sections of brain and stained them with reagents that allow visualization of brain anatomy in a UV fluorescence microscope.

Experiment 2: Researchers separated each newborn pup from its mother and recorded the number of ultrasonic whistles produced by the pup.

RESULTS

Experiment 1: Disruption of both copies of *FOXP2* led to brain abnormalities in which the cells were disorganized. Phenotypic effects on the brain of heterozygotes, with one disrupted copy, were less severe. (Each color reveals a different cell or tissue type.)

Experiment 2: Disruption of both copies of *FOXP2* led to an absence of ultrasonic vocalization in response to stress. The effect on vocalization in the heterozygote was also extreme.

Wild type　Heterozygote　Homozygote

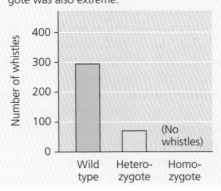

CONCLUSION *FOXP2* plays a significant role in the development of functional communication systems in mice. The results augment evidence from studies of birds and humans, supporting the hypothesis that *FOXP2* may act similarly in diverse organisms.

SOURCE W. Shu et al., Altered ultrasonic vocalization in mice with a disruption in the *Foxp2* gene, *Proceedings of the National Academy of Sciences* 102:9643–9648 (2005).

WHAT IF? Since the results support a role for mouse *FOXP2* in vocalization, you might wonder whether the human FOXP2 protein is a key regulator of speech. If you were given the amino acid sequences of wild-type and mutant human FOXP2 proteins and the wild-type chimpanzee FOXP2 protein, how would you investigate this question? What further clues could you obtain by comparing these sequences to that of the mouse FOXP2 protein?

FOXP2 experiments used mice as a model for humans because it would be unethical (as well as impractical) to carry out such experiments in humans. Mice and humans diverged about 65.5 million years ago (see Figure 21.16) and share about 85% of their genes. This genetic similarity can be exploited in studying human genetic disorders. If researchers know the organ or tissue that is affected by a particular genetic disorder, they can look for genes that are expressed in these locations in mice.

Further research efforts are under way to extend genomic studies to many more microbial species, additional primates, and neglected species from diverse branches of the tree of life.

These studies will advance our understanding of all aspects of biology, including health and ecology as well as evolution.

Comparing Genomes Within a Species

Another exciting consequence of our ability to analyze genomes is our growing understanding of the spectrum of genetic variation in humans. Because the history of the human species is so short—probably about 200,000 years—the amount of DNA variation among humans is small compared to that of many other species. Much of our diversity seems to be in the form of single nucleotide polymorphisms (SNPs, described in Chapter 20), usually detected by DNA sequencing. In the human genome, SNPs occur on average about once in 100–300 base pairs. Scientists have already identified the location of several million SNP sites in the human genome and continue to find more.

In the course of this search, they have also found other variations—including inversions, deletions, and duplications. The most surprising discovery has been the widespread occurrence of *copy-number variants* (*CNVs*), loci where some individuals have one or multiple copies of a particular gene or genetic region, rather than the standard two copies (one on each homolog). CNVs result from regions of the genome being duplicated or deleted inconsistently within the population. A 2010 study of 40 people found more than 8,000 CNVs involving 13% of the genes in the genome, and these CNVs probably represent just a small subset of the total. Since these variants encompass much longer stretches of DNA than the single nucleotides of SNPs, CNVs are more likely to have phenotypic consequences and to play a role in complex diseases and disorders. At the very least, the high incidence of copy-number variation casts doubt on the meaning of the phrase "a normal human genome."

Copy-number variants, SNPs, and variations in repetitive DNA such as short tandem repeats (STRs) will be useful genetic markers for studying human evolution. In 2010, the genomes of two Africans from different communities were sequenced: Archbishop Desmond Tutu, the South African civil rights advocate and a member of the Bantu tribe, the majority population in southern Africa; and !Gubi, a hunter-gatherer from the Khoisan community in Namibia, a minority African population that is probably the human group with the oldest known lineage. The comparison revealed many differences, as you might expect. The analysis was then broadened to compare the protein-coding regions of !Gubi's genome with those of three other Khoisan community members (self-identified Bushmen) living nearby. Remarkably, these four genomes differed more from each other than a European would from an Asian. These data highlight the extensive diversity among African genomes. Extending this approach will help us answer important questions about the differences between human populations and the migratory routes of human populations throughout history.

Comparing Developmental Processes

Biologists in the field of evolutionary developmental biology, or **evo-devo** as it is often called, compare developmental processes of different multicellular organisms. Their aim is to understand how these processes have evolved and how changes in them can modify existing organismal features or lead to new ones. With the advent of molecular techniques and the recent flood of genomic information, we are beginning to realize that the genomes of related species with strikingly different forms may have only minor differences in gene sequence or regulation. Discovering the molecular basis of these differences in turn helps us understand the origins of the myriad diverse forms that cohabit this planet, thus informing our study of evolution.

Widespread Conservation of Developmental Genes Among Animals

In Chapter 18, you learned about the homeotic genes in *Drosophila*, which specify the identity of body segments in the fruit fly (see Figure 18.20). Molecular analysis of the homeotic genes in *Drosophila* has shown that they all include a 180-nucleotide sequence called a **homeobox**, which specifies a 60-amino-acid *homeodomain* in the encoded proteins. An identical or very similar nucleotide sequence has been discovered in the homeotic genes of many invertebrates and vertebrates. The sequences are so similar between humans and fruit flies, in fact, that one researcher has whimsically referred to flies as "little people with wings." The resemblance even extends to the organization of these genes: The vertebrate genes homologous to the homeotic genes of fruit flies have kept the same chromosomal arrangement (**Figure 21.18**, on the next page). Homeobox-containing sequences have also been found in regulatory genes of much more distantly related eukaryotes, including plants and yeasts. From these similarities, we can deduce that the homeobox DNA sequence evolved very early in the history of life and was sufficiently valuable to organisms to have been conserved in animals and plants virtually unchanged for hundreds of millions of years.

Homeotic genes in animals were named *Hox* genes, short for *homeobox*-containing genes, because homeotic genes were the first genes found to have this sequence. Other homeobox-containing genes were later found that do not act as homeotic genes; that is, they do not directly control the identity of body parts. However, most of these genes, in animals at least, are associated with development, suggesting their ancient and fundamental importance in that process. In *Drosophila*, for example, homeoboxes are present not only in the homeotic genes but also in the egg-polarity gene *bicoid* (see Figures 18.21 and 18.22), in several of the segmentation genes, and in a master regulatory gene for eye development.

Researchers have discovered that the homeobox-encoded homeodomain is the part of a protein that binds to DNA

▲ **Figure 21.18 Conservation of homeotic genes in a fruit fly and a mouse.** Homeotic genes that control the form of anterior and posterior structures of the body occur in the same linear sequence on chromosomes in *Drosophila* and mice. Each colored band on the chromosomes shown here represents a homeotic gene. In fruit flies, all homeotic genes are found on one chromosome. The mouse and other mammals have the same or similar sets of genes on four chromosomes. The color code indicates the parts of the embryos in which these genes are expressed and the adult body regions that result. All of these genes are essentially identical in flies and mice, except for those represented by black bands, which are less similar in the two animals.

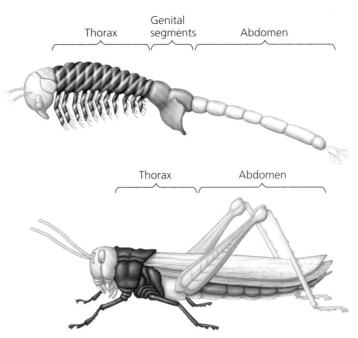

▲ **Figure 21.19 Effect of differences in *Hox* gene expression in crustaceans and insects.** Changes in the expression patterns of *Hox* genes have occurred over evolutionary time. These changes account in part for the different body plans of the brine shrimp *Artemia*, a crustacean (top), and the grasshopper, an insect. Shown here are regions of the adult body color-coded for expression of four *Hox* genes that determine formation of particular body parts during embryonic development. Each color represents a specific *Hox* gene. Colored stripes on the thorax of *Artemia* indicate co-expression of three *Hox* genes.

when the protein functions as a transcriptional regulator. However, the shape of the homeodomain allows it to bind to any DNA segment; its own structure is not specific for a particular sequence. Instead, other, more variable domains in a homeodomain-containing protein determine which genes the protein regulates. Interaction of these variable domains with still other transcription factors helps a homeodomain-containing protein recognize specific enhancers in the DNA. Proteins with homeodomains probably regulate development by coordinating the transcription of batteries of developmental genes, switching them on or off. In embryos of

Drosophila and other animal species, different combinations of homeobox genes are active in different parts of the embryo. This selective expression of regulatory genes, varying over time and space, is central to pattern formation.

Developmental biologists have found that in addition to homeotic genes, many other genes involved in development are highly conserved from species to species. These include numerous genes encoding components of signaling pathways. The extraordinary similarity among particular developmental genes in different animal species raises a question: How can the same genes be involved in the development of animals whose forms are so very different from each other?

Ongoing studies are suggesting answers to this question. In some cases, small changes in regulatory sequences of particular genes cause changes in gene expression patterns that can lead to major changes in body form. For example, the differing patterns of expression of the *Hox* genes along the body axis in insects and crustaceans can explain the variation in number of leg-bearing segments among these segmented animals (**Figure 21.19**). Also, recent research suggests that the same *Hox* gene product may have subtly dissimilar effects in different species, turning on new genes or turning on the same genes at higher or lower levels. In other cases, similar genes direct differing developmental processes in different organisms, resulting in diverse body shapes. Several *Hox* genes,

UNIVERSITY OF ALBERTA FACULTY BIO

Andrew Waskiewicz BA Molecular Biology and Biochemistry (Wesleyan University); PhD Biochemistry (University of Washington)

Current Position: Professor and Canada Research Chair Vertebrate Developmental Genetics, Department of Biological Sciences

I received a BA in Molecular Biology and Biochemistry from Wesleyan University in Connecticut, later completing a PhD in Biochemistry at the University of Washington. In 1996 I started a post-doctoral fellowship at the Fred Hutchinson Center in Zebrafish Developmental Neurobiology. I accepted an Assistant Professor position at the University of Alberta in 2003 and was later appointed a Canada Research Chair in Vertebrate Developmental Genetics. My current teaching is in Zoology 303 (Animal Development Biology), a third year lab course. I also supervise research projects for undergraduate students (e.g., Biology 499).

My lab studies zebrafish development with the goal of understanding human neural disorders, retinal birth defects and glaucoma. We are also pursuing new methods to create zebrafish gene knockouts using zinc finger nucleases. Neuronal disorders represent one of the least understood classes of human disease, owing to the complexity of the vertebrate nervous system. Many neuronal disorders (decreased IQ, deafness and palsies) are attributable to aberrant developmental processes. To gain insight into nerve formation, my laboratory studies zebrafish cranial neuron differentiation with a focus on signaling systems mediated by retinoic acid.

Our zebrafish facility is one of two nodes in the Canadian Zebrafish Genetic Research Centre. The mission of the facility is to help Canadian users perform chemical screens on this model organism. The facility has also developed a number of protocols available as free downloads (free) to interested researchers.

for instance, are expressed in the embryonic and larval stages of the sea urchin, a nonsegmented animal that has a body plan quite different from those of insects and mice. Sea urchin adults make the pincushion-shaped shells you may have seen on the beach (see Figure 8.4). They are among the organisms long used in classical embryological studies (see Chapter 47).

Comparison of Animal and Plant Development

The last common ancestor of animals and plants was probably a single-celled eukaryote that lived hundreds of millions of years ago, so the processes of development must have evolved independently in the two multicellular lineages of organisms. Plants evolved with rigid cell walls, which rule out the morphogenetic movements of cells and tissues that are so important in animals. Instead, morphogenesis in plants relies primarily on differing planes of cell division and on selective cell enlargement. (You will learn about these processes in Chapter 35.) But despite the differences between animals and plants, there are similarities in the molecular mechanisms of development, which are legacies of their shared unicellular origin.

In both animals and plants, development relies on a cascade of transcriptional regulators turning on or turning off genes in a finely tuned series. For example, work on the small flowering plant *Arabidopsis thaliana* has shown that establishing the radial pattern of flower parts, like setting up the head-to-tail axis in *Drosophila*, involves a cascade of transcription factors (see Chapter 35). The genes that direct these processes, however, differ considerably in animals and plants. While quite a few of the master regulatory switches in *Drosophila* are homeobox-containing *Hox* genes, those in *Arabidopsis* belong to a completely different family of genes, called the *Mads-box* genes. And although homeobox-containing genes can be found in plants and *Mads-box* genes in animals, in neither case do they perform the same major roles in development that they do in the other group. Thus, molecular evidence supports the supposition that developmental programs evolved separately in animals and plants.

In this final chapter of the genetics unit, you have learned how studying genomic composition and comparing the genomes of different species can disclose much about how genomes evolve. Further, comparing developmental programs, we can see that the unity of life is reflected in the similarity of molecular and cellular mechanisms used to establish body pattern, although the genes directing development may differ among organisms. The similarities between genomes reflect the common ancestry of life on Earth. But the differences are also crucial, for they have created the huge diversity of organisms that have evolved. In the remainder of the book, we expand our perspective beyond the level of molecules, cells, and genes to explore this diversity on the organismal level.

CONCEPT CHECK 21.6

1. Would you expect the genome of the macaque (a monkey) to be more similar to the mouse genome or the human genome? Why?
2. The DNA sequences called homeoboxes, which help homeotic genes in animals direct development, are common to flies and mice. Given this similarity, explain why these animals are so different.
3. **WHAT IF?** There are three times as many *Alu* elements in the human genome as in the chimpanzee genome. How do you think these extra *Alu* elements arose in the human genome? Propose a role they might have played in the divergence of these two species.

For suggested answers, see Appendix A.

21 CHAPTER REVIEW

SUMMARY OF KEY CONCEPTS

CONCEPT 21.1

New approaches have accelerated the pace of genome sequencing (pp. 427–429)

- The **Human Genome Project** began in 1990, using a three-stage approach. In **linkage mapping**, the order of genes and other inherited markers in the genome and the relative distances between them can be determined from recombination frequencies. Next, **physical mapping** uses overlaps between DNA fragments to order the fragments and determine the distance in base pairs between markers. Finally, the ordered fragments are sequenced, providing the finished genome sequence.
- In the whole-genome shotgun approach, the whole genome is cut into many small, overlapping fragments that are sequenced; computer software then assembles the complete sequence. Correct assembly is made easier when mapping information is also available.

? *Why has the whole-genome shotgun approach been widely adopted for genome-sequencing projects?*

CONCEPT 21.2

Scientists use bioinformatics to analyze genomes and their functions (pp. 429–432)

- Websites on the Internet provide centralized access to genome sequence databases, analytical tools, and genome-related information.
- Computer analysis of genome sequences aids **gene annotation**, the identification of protein-coding sequences and determination of their function. Methods for determining gene function include comparing the sequences of newly discovered genes with those of known genes in other species and observing the phenotypic effects of experimentally inactivating genes of unknown function.
- In systems biology, scientists use the computer-based tools of **bioinformatics** to compare genomes and study sets of genes and proteins as whole systems (**genomics** and **proteomics**). Studies

include large-scale analyses of protein interactions, functional DNA elements, and genes contributing to medical conditions.

> ❓ *What was the most significant finding of the ENCODE pilot project? Why has the project been expanded to include other species?*

CONCEPT 21.3

Genomes vary in size, number of genes, and gene density (pp. 432–434)

	Bacteria	Archaea	Eukarya
Genome size	Most are 1–6 Mb		Most are 10–4,000 Mb, but a few are much larger
Number of genes	1,500–7,500		5,000–40,000
Gene density	Higher than in eukaryotes		Lower than in prokaryotes (Within eukaryotes, lower density is correlated with larger genomes.)
Introns	None in protein-coding genes	Present in some genes	Unicellular eukaryotes: present, but prevalent only in some species Multicellular eukaryotes: present in most genes
Other noncoding DNA	Very little		Can be large amounts; generally more repetitive noncoding DNA in multicellular eukaryotes

> ❓ *Compare genome size, gene number, and gene density (a) in the three domains and (b) among eukaryotes.*

CONCEPT 21.4

Multicellular eukaryotes have much noncoding DNA and many multigene families (pp. 434–438)

- Only 1.5% of the human genome codes for proteins or gives rise to rRNAs or tRNAs; the rest is noncoding DNA, including **pseudogenes** and **repetitive DNA** of unknown function.

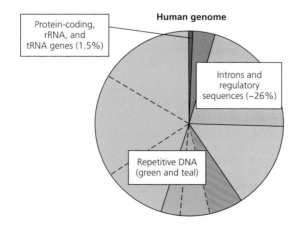

Human genome

Protein-coding, rRNA, and tRNA genes (1.5%)

Introns and regulatory sequences (~26%)

Repetitive DNA (green and teal)

- The most abundant type of repetitive DNA in multicellular eukaryotes consists of **transposable elements** and related sequences. In eukaryotes, there are two types of transposable elements: **transposons**, which move via a DNA intermediate,

and **retrotransposons**, which are more prevalent and move via an RNA intermediate.

- Other repetitive DNA includes short noncoding sequences that are tandemly repeated thousands of times (**simple sequence DNA**, which includes **STRs**); these sequences are especially prominent in centromeres and telomeres, where they probably play structural roles in the chromosome.
- Though many eukaryotic genes are present in one copy per haploid chromosome set, others (most, in some species) are members of a family of related genes, such as the human globin gene families:

α-Globin gene family	β-Globin gene family
Chromosome 16	Chromosome 11

ζ ψ_ζ ψ_{α_2} ψ_{α_1} α_2 α_1 ψ_θ ε $^G\gamma$ $^A\gamma$ ψ_β δ β

> ❓ *Explain how the function of transposable elements might account for their prevalence in human noncoding DNA.*

CONCEPT 21.5

Duplication, rearrangement, and mutation of DNA contribute to genome evolution (pp. 438–442)

- Accidents in cell division can lead to extra copies of all or part of entire chromosome sets, which may then diverge if one set accumulates sequence changes.
- The chromosomal organization of genomes can be compared among species, providing information about evolutionary relationships. Within a given species, rearrangements of chromosomes are thought to contribute to the emergence of new species.
- The genes encoding the various globin proteins evolved from one common ancestral globin gene, which duplicated and diverged into α-globin and β-globin ancestral genes. Subsequent duplication and random mutation gave rise to the present globin genes, all of which code for oxygen-binding proteins. The copies of some duplicated genes have diverged so much that the functions of their encoded proteins (such as lysozyme and α-lactalbumin) are now substantially different.
- Rearrangement of exons within and between genes during evolution has led to genes containing multiple copies of similar exons and/or several different exons derived from other genes.
- Movement of transposable elements or recombination between copies of the same element occasionally generates new sequence combinations that are beneficial to the organism. Such mechanisms can alter the functions of genes or their patterns of expression and regulation.

> ❓ *How could chromosomal rearrangements lead to the emergence of new species?*

CONCEPT 21.6

Comparing genome sequences provides clues to evolution and development (pp. 442–447)

- Comparative studies of genomes from widely divergent and closely related species provide valuable information about ancient and more recent evolutionary history, respectively. Human and chimpanzee sequences show about 4% difference, mostly due to insertions, deletions, and duplications in one lineage. Along with nucleotide variations in specific genes (such as *FOXP2*, a gene affecting speech), these differences may account for the distinct characteristics of the two species. Analysis of single nucleotide polymorphisms (SNPs) and copy-number variants (CNVs) among individuals in a species can also yield information about the evolution of that species.

- Evolutionary developmental (**evo-devo**) biologists have shown that homeotic genes and some other genes associated with animal development contain a **homeobox** region whose sequence is highly conserved among diverse species. Related sequences are present in the genes of plants and yeasts. During embryonic development in both plants and animals, a cascade of transcription regulators turns genes on or off in a carefully regulated sequence. However, the genes that direct analogous developmental processes differ in plants and animals as a result of their remote ancestry.

? *What type of information can be obtained by comparing the genomes of closely related species? Of very distantly related species?*

TEST YOUR UNDERSTANDING

LEVEL 1: KNOWLEDGE/COMPREHENSION

1. Bioinformatics includes all of the following *except*
   a. using computer programs to align DNA sequences.
   b. analyzing protein interactions in a species.
   c. using molecular biology to combine DNA from two different sources in a test tube.
   d. developing computer-based tools for genome analysis.
   e. using mathematical tools to make sense of biological systems.

2. One of the characteristics of retrotransposons is that
   a. they code for an enzyme that synthesizes DNA using an RNA template.
   b. they are found only in animal cells.
   c. they generally move by a cut-and-paste mechanism.
   d. they contribute a significant portion of the genetic variability seen within a population of gametes.
   e. their amplification is dependent on a retrovirus.

3. Homeotic genes
   a. encode transcription factors that control the expression of genes responsible for specific anatomical structures.
   b. are found only in *Drosophila* and other arthropods.
   c. are the only genes that contain the homeobox domain.
   d. encode proteins that form anatomical structures in the fly.
   e. are responsible for patterning during plant development.

LEVEL 2: APPLICATION/ANALYSIS

4. Two eukaryotic proteins have one domain in common but are otherwise very different. Which of the following processes is most likely to have contributed to this similarity?
   a. gene duplication   d. histone modification
   b. RNA splicing   e. random point mutations
   c. exon shuffling

5. **DRAW IT** Below are the amino acid sequences (using the single-letter code; see Figure 5.16) of four short segments of the FOXP2 protein from six species: chimpanzee, orangutan, gorilla, rhesus macaque, mouse, and human. These segments contain all of the amino acid differences between the FOXP2 proteins of these species.

   1. ATETI...PKSSD...TSSTT...NARRD

   2. ATETI...PKSSE...TSSTT...NARRD

   3. ATETI...PKSSD...TSSTT...NARRD

   4. ATETI...PKSSD...TSSNT...S ARRD

   5. ATETI...PKSSD...TSSTT...NARRD

   6. VTETI...PKSSD...TSSTT...NARRD

   Use a highlighter to color any amino acid that varies among the species. (Color that amino acid in all sequences.) Then answer the questions at the top of the next column.

(a) The chimpanzee, gorilla, and rhesus macaque (C, G, R) sequences are identical. Which lines correspond to those sequences?
(b) The human sequence differs from that of the C, G, R species at two amino acids. Which line corresponds to the human sequence? Underline the two differences.
(c) The orangutan sequence differs from the C, G, R sequence at one amino acid (having valine instead of alanine) and from the human sequence at three amino acids. Which line corresponds to the orangutan sequence?
(d) How many amino acid differences are there between the mouse and the C, G, R species? Circle the amino acid(s) that differ(s) in the mouse. How many amino acid differences are there between the mouse and the human? Draw a square around the amino acid(s) that differ(s) in the mouse.
(e) Primates and rodents diverged between 60 and 100 million years ago, and chimpanzees and humans diverged about 6 million years ago. Knowing that, what can you conclude by comparing the amino acid differences between the mouse and the C, G, R species with the differences between the human and the C, G, R species?

LEVEL 3: SYNTHESIS/EVALUATION

6. **EVOLUTION CONNECTION**
   Genes important in the embryonic development of animals, such as homeobox-containing genes, have been relatively well conserved during evolution; that is, they are more similar among different species than are many other genes. Why is this?

7. **SCIENTIFIC INQUIRY**
   The scientists mapping the SNPs in the human genome noticed that groups of SNPs tended to be inherited together, in blocks known as haplotypes, ranging in length from 5,000 to 200,000 base pairs. There are as few as four or five commonly occurring combinations of SNPs per haplotype. Propose an explanation for this observation, integrating what you've learned throughout this chapter and this unit.

8. **WRITE ABOUT A THEME**
   The Genetic Basis of Life The continuity of life is based on heritable information in the form of DNA. In a short essay (100–150 words), explain how mutations in protein-coding genes and regulatory DNA contribute to evolution.

For selected answers, see Appendix A.

1. MasteringBiology® Assignments
Tutorial Shotgun Approach to Whole-Genome Sequencing
Activity The Human Genome Project: Genes on Human Chromosome 17
Questions Student Misconceptions • Reading Quiz • Multiple Choice • End-of-Chapter

2. eText
Read your book online, search, take notes, highlight text, and more.

3. The Study Area
Practice Tests • Cumulative Test • *BioFlix* 3-D Animations • MP3 Tutor Sessions • Videos • Activities • Investigations • Lab Media • Audio Glossary • Word Study Tools • Art

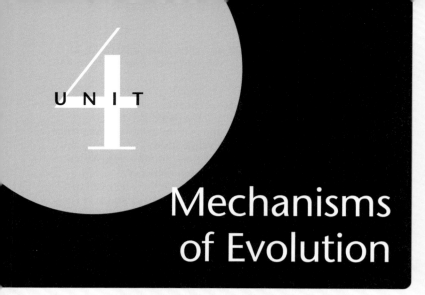

UNIT 4

Mechanisms of Evolution

An Interview with

Geerat J. Vermeij

Born in the Netherlands, Geerat Vermeij (pronounced "ver-may") lost his sight at the age of 3. Undeterred, he went on to earn degrees from Princeton and Yale and is now a Distinguished Professor at the University of California, Davis. A member of the Department of Geology, he nevertheless focuses on biology—the structure, evolution, and ecology of marine molluscs, both living and extinct. He is particularly well known for his work on the

evolutionary "arms race" between long-extinct molluscs and their predators and more generally the roles of organismal interactions in evolution, although his many publications reflect much wider-ranging interests. (One of his books, *Nature: An Economic History*, relates the principles of evolution to the principles of economics; he has also written a memoir, *Privileged Hands: A Scientific Life*.) Dr. Vermeij has received numerous awards, including the MacArthur Award and the Daniel Giraud Elliot Medal from the National Academy of Sciences. His office at UC Davis features a large collection of marine shells and fossils and an extensive library. Jane Reece and Michael Cain spoke with him there.

How did you first become interested in biology?
As far back as I can recall, back to my earliest childhood, I've always liked natural history. When I was a child in the Netherlands, I liked pinecones and seeds and shells on the beach and leaves. I liked the whole ambience of being outside! Also, my parents were very good observers, and they spent a lot of time describing the world to me and letting me touch as much as I possibly could. When I moved to the U.S. at the age of 9, I found myself in a completely different environment. In New Jersey where we lived, there were wild forests full of huge vines, noisy crickets, cicadas, and strange birds, and I found this environment so different from the one I had left behind that I began to ask myself why this was.

When I was in the fourth grade, I had a wonderful teacher who brought shells from Florida to her classroom. And I explored these things and fell in love with them. And again, I wondered why these things were so different from anything I had collected in Holland.

They were beautiful, with lovely shapes and wonderful contrast between the outside surface and the inside. I was smitten. And from then on I knew I was going to do something scientific.

Much of your work focuses on marine molluscs. Please tell us about these animals.
Molluscs include snails, clams, squids, octopuses, and many lesser-known groups. There are something like 100,000 species living, and we know of fossils of tens of thousands of extinct ones, dating all the way back to at least 540 million years ago. Molluscs are a major animal group on the tree of life. Found on land and in fresh water and the sea, they do just about everything you can imagine—they range from top predators (such as squids) to suspension feeders, herbivores, detritus feeders, and parasites. Originally, all molluscs had some kind of mantle covering the major organs of the body. They probably started off as pretty simple creatures without shells, but shells soon evolved. Most living molluscs have shells, though some have lost their shell in the course of evolution.

How do you identify the shells you are studying?
Entirely by touch. You know, shells differ in size, shape, and texture, all of which are readily discernable by the fingers, and the same is true of fossils. Shells are ideally suited for a blind person like me.

In your research over the years, what are the main questions you have been trying to answer?
The questions have changed over the course of my career, but the overarching ones have been, What are the pathways of adaptation by which all the different lineages of organisms—not just molluscs, but all of life—have gotten here? How have the conditions to which organisms are exposed changed over time? How have organisms affected those conditions over time? I'm very interested in the history of life and how this history has been shaped.

What makes molluscs a good research focus for answering your questions?
Molluscs have several huge advantages. For me personally, of course, they are accessible. Most of them don't run away—squids and octopuses being exceptions. Their shells are extremely easy to observe with the hand, and importantly from a paleontologist's point of view, these hard mineralized objects have left a very good fossil record. That's a gigantic advantage. Not only can we trace molluscs all the way back through time, but because we know so much about how shells work, we can figure out how the extinct animals lived—even those that lived hundreds of millions of years ago.

What kinds of evolutionary insights can fossils provide that cannot be extracted from DNA evidence?
First of all, I should say that my collaborators and I do use DNA sequences ourselves to reconstruct the order of branching in evolutionary trees. But to estimate *when* these evolutionary lineages arose, we need to calibrate the tree with fossils of known age. Moreover, you can only get DNA from living things and a few rather recent fossils; so if you go back far enough, you find many lineages that no longer exist and for which, therefore, DNA evidence is simply unavailable. And yet these animals often have combinations of traits that we never see in living animals. Fossils give us a very good idea of what the ancestral organisms were like, which you couldn't get solely from DNA sequences of living organisms. So if you're trying to reconstruct early branches in the tree of life, fossils are very helpful.

How does your research relate to the mechanisms of evolution—to the principles as opposed to the pattern?
That's an important question. I do distinguish between describing what actually happened and the mechanisms that account for evolutionary events over time. A lot of our work is descriptive, figuring

out what happened and what extinct animals were like. But we also try to determine the mechanisms that account for the phenomena. And given that I work on adaptive characteristics and on the fit between animals and plants and their environments, I am particularly interested in the mechanisms by which organisms become adapted to their environments. That's not simply natural selection; it's also the modification of environments by the animals and plants that reside there.

Tell us how you go about your work.

I have done a lot of fieldwork all over the world. In the field I observe molluscs in nature and occasionally do some experiments with them. I want to understand how the molluscs relate to their environments, including their predators. I am interested in how they live—for example, how quickly they move—and how their performance levels compare with the performance of the agents that are out there making the world tough for them.

Recently I've spent more time in museum collections. I also maintain a very large research collection, most of which I've collected myself over the years. All of these collections are critical for learning what the shapes of organisms are in different evolutionary groups. I also visit and learn from other scientists. And I do an enormous amount of reading, because I like to synthesize information and ideas, to put things together. I read hundreds of papers a year about a very wide variety of subjects, everything from biology to geology to economics and history, so that I can place the particular work that I do into a larger context. As a scientist, you can never read enough.

When you do this kind of work, whether in collections of specimens or in the field or library, you always come across wonderful surprises—perhaps a shell with a feature you've never seen or even a book you didn't know about. Every single day for me is like that.

You have written about the "arms race" of evolution. What do you mean by that, and how has it played out in the creatures you've studied?

All living things are exposed to competition for resources and also to predation, where one animal eats another animal or part of another animal. The animals I am working on mostly don't move very fast, and one of the typical results of predation is that armor in the form of shells evolves in the prey; the mollusc shell probably first evolved as armor. But as predators become more powerful thanks to competition among themselves, the performance criteria for an effective shell also escalate. Nowadays, in order to survive in tropical shallow water environments where there are lots of predators, a mollusc needs a very well-armored shell—one that has thick walls, bumps all over the place, a narrow opening, and many other features. In fact, if you look at shell architecture over geological time, keeping habitat as constant as you can, you find that some of these protective features (the narrow opening, for example) are found only in the more recent evolutionary lineages and don't appear at all in the first couple of hundred million years of mollusc history. Meanwhile, all sorts of ways of overcoming mollusc defenses have evolved in predators. They have developed stronger, more powerful jaws or claws. They have "learned" how to drill a hole through the

> "When you do this kind of work . . . you always come across wonderful surprises. . . . Every single day for me is like that."

wall of a shell. They swallow or envelop larger prey. That tells us that there has been an arms race, an escalation of improvements in both shell architecture and methods of attack by predators.

In addition to arms races, what other kinds of ecological interactions have influenced evolutionary history?

Competition and predation are fundamental and inevitable, but the history of life from the very beginning is also a story of cooperation. The reason for that I think is simple: By cooperating, you can do things that neither party can do by itself. So, cooperation or some other kind of mutually beneficial relationship is a wonderful way to compete. Biology is absolutely filled with examples of social animals, mutually beneficial relationships between individuals of different species, and so forth. Cooperation is in some sense an emergent property of life as a whole. The interactions of organisms with one another give rise to properties that the individual components don't have. For example, a lichen, which is an alga and a fungus living together, has properties different from those of either participant.

How do the things you've been saying about the effects of ecological interactions on evolutionary history fit in with Darwin's main ideas?

Darwin was an incredibly smart guy. One of the many, many things that he got right was that natural selection is often brought about by the interactions of organisms with other organisms, as well as interactions of organisms with their physical environment. Natural selection isn't some nebulous agency out there that's choosing survivors over nonsurvivors.

Why is it important for people to understand evolution?

There are many reasons. An understanding of evolution is certainly of practical importance in medicine and agriculture. But an understanding of evolution also gives us a closer connection to the rest of life. Also, it's very important for people to understand that the theory of evolution, like all scientific theories, is a body of explanation and fact that explains natural phenomena and can predict them. A lot of the resistance to evolution comes down to the idea some people have that somehow evolution makes life meaningless or purposeless. To this I reply that meaning and purpose is an emergent property of evolution! It is our own responsibility to make life meaningful.

Geerat Vermeij (right) with Michael Cain (center) and Jane Reece

22

Descent with Modification: A Darwinian View of Life

▲ **Figure 22.1 How can this beetle survive in the desert, and what is it doing?**

OVERVIEW

Endless Forms Most Beautiful

In the coastal Namib desert of southwestern Africa, a land where fog is common but virtually no rain falls, lives the beetle *Onymacris unguicularis*. To obtain the water it needs to survive, this insect relies on a peculiar "headstanding" behavior

(Figure 22.1). Tilting head-downward, the beetle faces into the winds that blow fog across the dunes. Droplets of moisture from the fog collect on the beetle's body and run down into its mouth.

Interesting in its own right, this headstander beetle is also a member of an astonishingly diverse group: the more than 350,000 species of beetles. In fact, nearly one of every five known species is a beetle. These beetles all share similar features, such as six pairs of legs, a hard outer surface, and two pairs of wings. But they also differ from one another. How did there come to be so many beetles, and what causes their similarities and differences?

The headstander beetle and its many close relatives illustrate three key observations about life:

- the striking ways in which organisms are suited for life in their environments*
- the many shared characteristics (unity) of life
- the rich diversity of life

A century and a half ago, Charles Darwin was inspired to develop a scientific explanation for these three broad observations. When he published his hypothesis in *The Origin of Species*, Darwin ushered in a scientific revolution—the era of evolutionary biology.

For now, we will define **evolution** as *descent with modification*, a phrase Darwin used in proposing that Earth's many species are descendants of ancestral species that were different from the present-day species. Evolution can also be defined more narrowly as a change in the genetic composition of a population from generation to generation, as discussed further in Chapter 23.

Whether it is defined broadly or narrowly, we can view evolution in two related but different ways: as a pattern and as a process. The *pattern* of evolutionary change is revealed by data from a range of scientific disciplines, including biology, geology, physics, and chemistry. These data are facts—they are observations about the natural world. The *process* of evolution consists of the mechanisms that produce the observed pattern of change. These mechanisms represent natural causes of the natural phenomena we observe. Indeed, the power of evolution as a unifying theory is its ability to explain and connect a vast array of observations about the living world.

As with all general theories in science, we continue to test our understanding of evolution by examining whether it can account for new observations and experimental results. In this and the following chapters, we'll examine how ongoing discoveries shape what we know about the pattern and process of evolution. To set the stage, we'll first retrace Darwin's quest to explain the adaptations, unity, and diversity of what he called life's "endless forms most beautiful."

---

*Here and throughout this book, the term *environment* refers to other organisms as well as to the physical aspects of an organism's surroundings.

1795
Hutton proposes his principle of gradualism.

1798
Malthus publishes "Essay on the Principle of Population."

1809
Lamarck publishes his hypothesis of evolution.

1812
Cuvier publishes his extensive studies of vertebrate fossils.

1830
Lyell publishes *Principles of Geology*.

1858
While studying species in the Malay Archipelago, Wallace sends Darwin his hypothesis of natural selection.

1790

1809
Charles Darwin is born.

1831–36
Darwin travels around the world on HMS *Beagle*.

1844
Darwin writes his essay on descent with modification.

1859
On the Origin of Species is published.

1870

Marine iguana in the Galápagos Islands

▲ **Figure 22.2 The intellectual context of Darwin's ideas.**

CONCEPT ## 22.1

The Darwinian revolution challenged traditional views of a young Earth inhabited by unchanging species

What impelled Darwin to challenge the prevailing views about Earth and its life? Darwin's revolutionary proposal developed over time, influenced by the work of others and by his travels (**Figure 22.2**). As we'll see, his ideas had deep historical roots.

Scala Naturae and Classification of Species

Long before Darwin was born, several Greek philosophers suggested that life might have changed gradually over time. But one philosopher who greatly influenced early Western science, Aristotle (384–322 BCE), viewed species as fixed (un-

changing). Through his observations of nature, Aristotle recognized certain "affinities" among organisms. He concluded that life-forms could be arranged on a ladder, or scale, of increasing complexity, later called the *scala naturae* ("scale of nature"). Each form of life, perfect and permanent, had its allotted rung on this ladder.

These ideas were generally consistent with the Old Testament account of creation, which holds that species were individually designed by God and therefore perfect. In the 1700s, many scientists interpreted the often remarkable match of organisms to their environment as evidence that the Creator had designed each species for a particular purpose.

One such scientist was Carolus Linnaeus (1707–1778), a Swedish physician and botanist who sought to classify life's diversity, in his words, "for the greater glory of God." Linnaeus developed the two-part, or *binomial*, format for naming species (such as *Homo sapiens* for humans) that is still used today. In contrast to the linear hierarchy of the *scala naturae*, Linnaeus adopted a nested classification system, grouping similar species into increasingly general categories. For example, similar species are grouped in the same genus, similar genera (plural of genus) are grouped in the same family, and so on (see Figure 1.14).

Linnaeus did not ascribe the resemblances among species to evolutionary kinship, but rather to the pattern of their creation. A century later, however, Darwin argued that classification should be based on evolutionary relationships. He also noted that scientists using the Linnaean system often grouped organisms in ways that reflected those relationships.

Ideas About Change over Time

Darwin drew from the work of scientists studying **fossils**, the remains or traces of organisms from the past. Many fossils are found in sedimentary rocks formed from the sand and mud that settle to the bottom of seas, lakes, swamps, and other aquatic habitats (**Figure 22.3**). New layers of sediment cover older ones and compress them into superimposed layers of rock called **strata** (singular, *stratum*). The fossils in a particular stratum provide a glimpse of some of the organisms that populated Earth at the time that layer formed. Later, erosion may carve through upper (younger) strata, revealing deeper (older) strata that had been buried.

Paleontology, the study of fossils, was developed in large part by French scientist Georges Cuvier (1769–1832). In examining strata near Paris, Cuvier noted that the older the stratum, the more dissimilar its fossils were to current lifeforms. He also observed that from one layer to the next, some new species appeared while others disappeared. He inferred that extinctions must have been a common occurrence in the history of life. Yet Cuvier staunchly opposed the

idea of evolution. To explain his observations, he advocated **catastrophism**, the principle that events in the past occurred suddenly and were caused by mechanisms different from those operating in the present. Cuvier speculated that each boundary between strata represented a catastrophe, such as a flood, that had destroyed many of the species living at that time. He proposed that these periodic catastrophes were usually confined to local regions, which were later repopulated by different species immigrating from other areas.

In contrast, other scientists suggested that profound change could take place through the cumulative effect of slow but continuous processes. In 1795, Scottish geologist James Hutton (1726–1797) proposed that Earth's geologic features could be explained by gradual mechanisms still operating today. For example, he suggested that valleys were often formed by rivers wearing through rocks and that rocks containing marine fossils were formed when sediments that had eroded from the land were carried by rivers to the sea, where they buried dead marine organisms. The leading geologist of Darwin's time, Charles Lyell (1797–1875), incorporated Hutton's thinking into his principle of **uniformitarianism**, which stated that mechanisms of change are constant over time. Lyell proposed that the same geologic processes are operating today as in the past, and at the same rate.

Hutton and Lyell's ideas strongly influenced Darwin's thinking. Darwin agreed that if geologic change results from slow, continuous actions rather than from sudden events, then Earth must be much older than the widely accepted age of a few thousand years. It would, for example, take a very long time for a river to carve a canyon by erosion. He later reasoned that perhaps similarly slow and subtle processes could produce substantial biological change. Darwin was not the first to apply the idea of gradual change to biological evolution, however.

Lamarck's Hypothesis of Evolution

During the 18th century, several naturalists (including Darwin's grandfather, Erasmus Darwin) suggested that life evolves as environments change. But only one of Charles Darwin's predecessors proposed a mechanism for *how* life changes over time: French biologist Jean-Baptiste de Lamarck (1744–1829). Alas, Lamarck is primarily remembered today *not* for his visionary recognition that evolutionary change explains patterns in fossils and the match of organisms to their environments, but for the incorrect mechanism he proposed to explain how evolution occurs.

Lamarck published his hypothesis in 1809, the year Darwin was born. By comparing living species with fossil forms, Lamarck had found what appeared to be several lines of descent, each a chronological series of older to younger fossils leading to a living species. He explained his findings using two principles that were widely accepted at the time. The first was *use and disuse*, the idea that parts of the body that are used

① Rivers carry sediment into aquatic habitats such as seas and swamps. Over time, sedimentary rock layers (strata) form under water. Some strata contain fossils.

② As water levels change and the bottom surface is pushed upward, the strata and their fossils are exposed.

Younger stratum with more recent fossils

Older stratum with older fossils

▲ **Figure 22.3 Formation of sedimentary strata with fossils.**

▲ **Figure 22.4 Acquired traits cannot be inherited.** This bonsai tree was "trained" to grow as a dwarf by pruning and shaping. However, seeds from this tree would produce offspring of normal size.

extensively become larger and stronger, while those that are not used deteriorate. Among many examples, he cited a giraffe stretching its neck to reach leaves on high branches. The second principle, *inheritance of acquired characteristics*, stated that an organism could pass these modifications to its offspring. Lamarck reasoned that the long, muscular neck of the living giraffe had evolved over many generations as giraffes stretched their necks ever higher.

Lamarck also thought that evolution happens because organisms have an innate drive to become more complex. Darwin rejected this idea, but he, too, thought that variation was introduced into the evolutionary process in part through inheritance of acquired characteristics. Today, however, our understanding of genetics refutes this mechanism: Experiments show that traits acquired by use during an individual's life are not inherited in the way proposed by Lamarck **(Figure 22.4)**.

Lamarck was vilified in his own time, especially by Cuvier, who denied that species ever evolve. In retrospect, however, Lamarck did recognize that the match of organisms to their environments can be explained by gradual evolutionary change, and he did propose a testable explanation for how this change occurs.

CONCEPT CHECK 22.1

1. How did Hutton's and Lyell's ideas influence Darwin's thinking about evolution?
2. **MAKE CONNECTIONS** In Concept 1.3 (pp. 19–20), you read that scientific hypotheses must be testable and falsifiable. Applying these criteria, are Cuvier's explanation of the fossil record and Lamarck's hypothesis of evolution scientific? Explain your answer in each case.

For suggested answers, see Appendix A.

Descent with modification by natural selection explains the adaptations of organisms and the unity and diversity of life

As the 19th century dawned, it was generally thought that species had remained unchanged since their creation. A few clouds of doubt about the permanence of species were beginning to gather, but no one could have forecast the thundering storm just beyond the horizon. How did Charles Darwin become the lightning rod for a revolutionary view of life?

Darwin's Research

Charles Darwin (1809–1882) was born in Shrewsbury, in western England. Even as a boy, he had a consuming interest in nature. When he was not reading nature books, he was fishing, hunting, and collecting insects. Darwin's father, a physician, could see no future for his son as a naturalist and sent him to medical school in Edinburgh. But Charles found medicine boring and surgery before the days of anesthesia horrifying. He quit medical school and enrolled at Cambridge University, intending to become a clergyman. (At that time in England, many scholars of science belonged to the clergy.)

At Cambridge, Darwin became the protégé of the Reverend John Henslow, a botany professor. Soon after Darwin graduated, Henslow recommended him to Captain Robert FitzRoy, who was preparing the survey ship HMS *Beagle* for a long voyage around the world. Darwin would pay his own way and serve as a conversation partner to the young captain. FitzRoy, who was himself an accomplished scientist, accepted Darwin because he was a skilled naturalist and because they were of the same social class and close in age.

The Voyage of the Beagle

Darwin embarked from England on the *Beagle* in December 1831. The primary mission of the voyage was to chart poorly known stretches of the South American coastline. While the ship's crew surveyed the coast, Darwin spent most of his time on shore, observing and collecting thousands of South American plants and animals. He noted the characteristics of plants and animals that made them well suited to such diverse environments as the humid jungles of Brazil, the expansive grasslands of Argentina, and the towering peaks of the Andes.

Darwin observed that the plants and animals in temperate regions of South America more closely resembled species living in the South American tropics than species living in temperate regions of Europe. Furthermore, the fossils he found, though clearly different from living species, were distinctly South American in their resemblance to the living organisms of that continent.

▲ **Figure 22.5 The voyage of HMS *Beagle*.**

Darwin also spent much time thinking about geology. Despite bouts of seasickness, he read Lyell's *Principles of Geology* while aboard the *Beagle*. He experienced geologic change firsthand when a violent earthquake rocked the coast of Chile, and he observed afterward that rocks along the coast had been thrust upward by several feet. Finding fossils of ocean organisms high in the Andes, Darwin inferred that the rocks containing the fossils must have been raised there by many similar earthquakes. These observations reinforced what he had learned from Lyell: The physical evidence did not support the traditional view that Earth was only a few thousand years old.

Darwin's interest in the geographic distribution of species was further stimulated by the *Beagle*'s stop at the Galápagos, a group of volcanic islands located near the equator about 900 km west of South America **(Figure 22.5)**. Darwin was fascinated by the unusual organisms there. The birds he collected included the finches mentioned in Chapter 1 and several kinds of mockingbirds. These mockingbirds, though similar to each other, seemed to be different species. Some were unique to individual islands, while others lived on two or more adjacent islands. Furthermore, although the animals on the Galápagos resembled species living on the South American mainland, most of the Galápagos species were not known from anywhere else in the world. Darwin hypothesized that the Galápagos had been colonized by organisms that had strayed from South America and then diversified, giving rise to new species on the various islands.

Darwin's Focus on Adaptation

During the voyage of the *Beagle*, Darwin observed many examples of **adaptations**, inherited characteristics of organisms that enhance their survival and reproduction in specific environments. Later, as he reassessed his observations, he began to perceive adaptation to the environment and the origin of new species as closely related processes. Could a new species arise from an ancestral form by the gradual accumulation of adaptations to a different environment? From studies made years after Darwin's voyage, biologists have concluded that this is indeed what happened to the diverse group of Galápagos finches (see Figure 1.22). The finches' various beaks and behaviors are adapted to the specific foods available on their home islands **(Figure 22.6)**. Darwin realized that explaining such adaptations was essential to understanding evolution. As we'll explore further, his explanation of how adaptations arise centered on **natural selection**, a process in which individuals that have certain inherited traits tend to survive and reproduce at higher rates than other individuals *because of* those traits.

By the early 1840s, Darwin had worked out the major features of his hypothesis. He set these ideas on paper in 1844, when he wrote a long essay on descent with modification and its underlying mechanism, natural selection. Yet he was still reluctant to publish his ideas, apparently because he anticipated the uproar they would cause. During this time, Darwin continued to compile evidence in support of his hypothesis. By the mid-1850s, he had described his ideas to Lyell and a few others. Lyell, who was not yet convinced of evolution, nevertheless urged Darwin to publish on the subject before someone else came to the same conclusions and published first.

In June 1858, Lyell's prediction came true. Darwin received a manuscript from Alfred Russel Wallace (1823–1913), a British naturalist working in the South Pacific islands of the Malay Ar-

(a) Cactus-eater. The long, sharp beak of the cactus ground finch (*Geospiza scandens*) helps it tear and eat cactus flowers and pulp.

(b) Insect-eater. The green warbler finch (*Certhidea olivacea*) uses its narrow, pointed beak to grasp insects.

(c) Seed-eater. The large ground finch (*Geospiza magnirostris*) has a large beak adapted for cracking seeds that fall from plants to the ground.

▲ **Figure 22.6 Three examples of beak variation in Galápagos finches.** The Galápagos Islands are home to more than a dozen species of closely related finches, some found only on a single island. The most striking differences among them are their beaks, which are adapted for specific diets.

MAKE CONNECTIONS *Review Figure 1.22 (p. 17). To which of the other two species shown above is the cactus-eater more closely related (that is, with which does it share a more recent common ancestor)?*

chipelago (see Figure 22.2). Wallace had developed a hypothesis of natural selection nearly identical to Darwin's. He asked Darwin to evaluate his paper and forward it to Lyell if it merited publication. Darwin complied, writing to Lyell: "Your words have come true with a vengeance. . . . I never saw a more striking coincidence . . . so all my originality, whatever it may amount to, will be smashed." On July 1, 1858, Lyell and a colleague presented Wallace's paper, along with extracts from Darwin's unpublished 1844 essay, to the Linnean Society of London. Darwin quickly finished his book, titled *On the Origin of Species by Means of Natural Selection* (commonly referred to as *The Origin of Species*), and published it the next year. Although Wallace had submitted his ideas for publication first, he admired Darwin and thought that Darwin had developed the idea of natural selection so extensively that he should be known as its main architect.

Within a decade, Darwin's book and its proponents had convinced most scientists that life's diversity is the product of evolution. Darwin succeeded where previous evolutionists had failed, mainly by presenting a plausible scientific mechanism with immaculate logic and an avalanche of evidence.

The Origin of Species

In his book, Darwin amassed evidence that descent with modification by natural selection explains the three broad observations about nature listed in the Overview: the unity of life, the diversity of life, and the match between organisms and their environments.

Descent with Modification

In the first edition of *The Origin of Species*, Darwin never used the word *evolution* (although the final word of the book is

"evolved"). Rather, he discussed *descent with modification*, a phrase that summarized his view of life. Organisms share many characteristics, leading Darwin to perceive unity in life. He attributed the unity of life to the descent of all organisms from an ancestor that lived in the remote past. He also thought that as the descendants of that ancestral organism lived in various habitats over millions of years, they accumulated diverse modifications, or adaptations, that fit them to specific ways of life. Darwin reasoned that over long periods of time, descent with modification eventually led to the rich diversity of life we see today.

Darwin viewed the history of life as a tree, with multiple branchings from a common trunk out to the tips of the youngest twigs **(Figure 22.7)**. The tips of the twigs represent the diversity of organisms living in the present. Each fork of the tree represents the most recent common ancestor of all the lines of evolution that subsequently branch from that point. As an example, consider the three living species of elephants: the Asian elephant (*Elephas maximus*) and African elephants

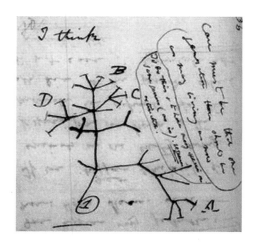

◀ **Figure 22.7 "I think. . ."** In this 1837 sketch, Darwin envisioned the branching pattern of evolution.

(*Loxodonta africana* and *L. cyclotis*). These closely related species are very similar because they shared the same line of descent until a relatively recent split from their common ancestor, as shown in the tree diagram in **Figure 22.8**. Note that seven lineages related to elephants have become extinct over the past 32 million years. As a result, there are no living species that fill the gap between the elephants and their nearest relatives today, the hyraxes and manatees. Such extinctions are not uncommon. In fact, many evolutionary branches, even some major ones, are dead ends: Scientists estimate that over 99% of all species that have ever lived are now extinct. As in Figure 22.8, fossils of extinct species can document the divergence of present-day groups by "filling in" gaps between them.

In his efforts at classification, Linnaeus had realized that some organisms resemble each other more closely than others, but he had not linked these resemblances to evolution. Nonetheless, because he had recognized that the great diversity of organisms could be organized into "groups subordinate to groups" (Darwin's phrase), Linnaeus's system meshed well with Darwin's hypothesis. To Darwin, the Linnaean hierarchy reflected the branching history of life, with organisms at the various levels related through descent from common ancestors.

Artificial Selection, Natural Selection, and Adaptation

Darwin proposed the mechanism of natural selection to explain the observable patterns of evolution. He crafted his argument carefully, to persuade even the most skeptical readers. First he discussed familiar examples of selective breeding of domesticated plants and animals. Humans have modified other species over many generations by selecting and breeding individuals that possess desired traits, a process called **artificial selection (Figure 22.9)**. As a result of artificial selection, crops, livestock animals, and pets often bear little resemblance to their wild ancestors.

Darwin then argued that a similar process occurs in nature. He based his argument on two observations, from which he drew two inferences:

Observation #1: Members of a population often vary in their inherited traits **(Figure 22.10)**.

Observation #2: All species can produce more offspring than their environment can support **(Figure 22.11)**, and many of these offspring fail to survive and reproduce.

Inference #1: Individuals whose inherited traits give them a higher probability of surviving and reproducing in a given environment tend to leave more offspring than other individuals.

Inference #2: This unequal ability of individuals to survive and reproduce will lead to the accumulation of favorable traits in the population over generations.

Darwin saw an important connection between natural selection and the

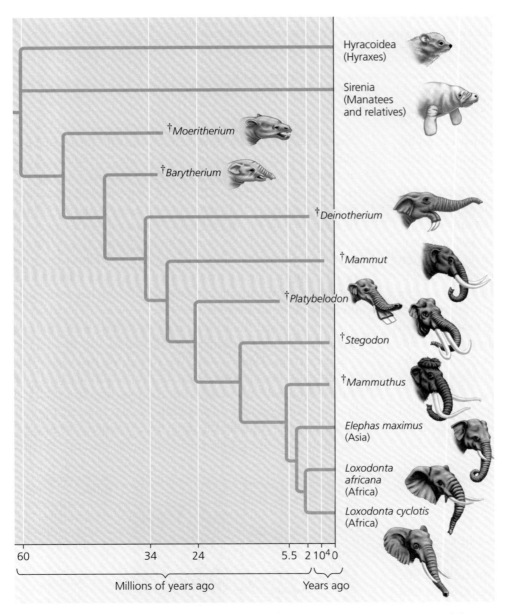

▲ **Figure 22.8 Descent with modification.** This evolutionary tree of elephants and their relatives is based mainly on fossils—their anatomy, order of appearance in strata, and geographic distribution. Note that most branches of descent ended in extinction (denoted by the dagger symbol †). (Time line not to scale.)

? *Based on the tree shown here, approximately when did the most recent ancestor shared by Mammuthus (woolly mammoths), Asian elephants, and African elephants live?*

► **Figure 22.9 Artificial selection.** These different vegetables have all been selected from one species of wild mustard. By selecting variations in different parts of the plant, breeders have obtained these divergent results.

Cabbage

Selection for apical (tip) bud

Brussels sprouts

Selection for axillary (side) buds

Broccoli

Selection for flowers and stems

Selection for stems

Selection for leaves

Kale

Wild mustard

Kohlrabi

▲ **Figure 22.10 Variation in a population.** Individuals in this population of Asian ladybird beetles vary in color and spot pattern. Natural selection may act on these variations only if (1) they are heritable and (2) they affect the beetles' ability to survive and reproduce.

► **Figure 22.11 Overproduction of offspring.** A single puffball fungus can produce billions of offspring. If all of these offspring and their descendants survived to maturity, they would carpet the surrounding land surface.

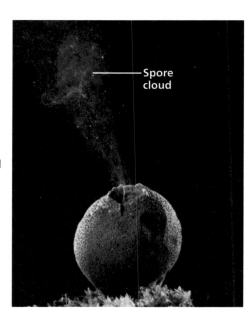

Spore cloud

capacity of organisms to "overreproduce." He began to make this connection after reading an essay by economist Thomas Malthus, who contended that much of human suffering—disease, famine, and war—was the inescapable consequence of the human population's potential to increase faster than food supplies and other resources. Darwin realized that the capacity to overreproduce was characteristic of all species. Of the many eggs laid, young born, and seeds spread, only a tiny fraction complete their development and leave offspring of their own. The rest are eaten, starved, diseased, unmated, or unable to tolerate physical conditions of the environment such as salinity or temperature.

An organism's heritable traits can influence not only its own performance, but also how well its offspring cope with environmental challenges. For example, an organism might have a trait that gives its offspring an advantage in escaping predators, obtaining food, or tolerating physical conditions. When such advantages increase the number of offspring that survive and reproduce, the traits that are favored will likely appear at a greater frequency in the next generation. Thus, over time, natural selection resulting from factors such as predators, lack of food, or adverse physical conditions can lead to an increase in the proportion of favorable traits in a population.

How rapidly do such changes occur? Darwin reasoned that if artificial selection can bring about dramatic change in a relatively short period of time, then natural selection should be capable of substantial modification of species over many hundreds of generations. Even if the advantages of some heritable traits over others are slight, the advantageous variations will gradually accumulate in the population, and less favorable variations will diminish. Over time, this process will increase the frequency of individuals with favorable adaptations and hence refine the match between organisms and their environment (see Figure 1.20).

Natural Selection: A Summary

Let's now recap the main ideas of natural selection:

- Natural selection is a process in which individuals that have certain heritable traits survive and reproduce at a higher rate than other individuals because of those traits.
- Over time, natural selection can increase the match between organisms and their environment **(Figure 22.12)**.
- If an environment changes, or if individuals move to a new environment, natural selection may result in adaptation to these new conditions, sometimes giving rise to new species.

One subtle but important point is that although natural selection occurs through interactions between individual organisms and their environment, *individuals do not evolve*. Rather, it is the population that evolves over time.

A second key point is that natural selection can amplify or diminish only those heritable traits that differ among the individuals in a population. Thus, even if a trait is heritable, if all the individuals in a population are genetically identical for that trait, evolution by natural selection cannot occur.

Third, remember that environmental factors vary from place to place and over time. A trait that is favorable in one place or time may be useless—or even detrimental—in other places or times. Natural selection is always operating, but which traits are favored depends on the context in which a species lives and mates.

Next, we'll survey the wide range of observations that support a Darwinian view of evolution by natural selection.

CONCEPT CHECK 22.2

1. How does the concept of descent with modification explain both the unity and diversity of life?
2. **WHAT IF?** If you discovered a fossil of an extinct mammal that lived high in the Andes, would you predict that it would more closely resemble present-day mammals from South American jungles or present-day mammals that live high in African mountains? Explain.
3. **MAKE CONNECTIONS** Review Figures 14.4 and 14.6 (pp. 265 and 267) on the relationship between genotype and phenotype. In a particular pea population, suppose that flowers with the white phenotype are favored by natural selection. Predict what would happen over time to the frequency of the p allele in the population, and explain your reasoning.

For suggested answers, see Appendix A.

CONCEPT 22.3

Evolution is supported by an overwhelming amount of scientific evidence

In *The Origin of Species*, Darwin marshaled a broad range of evidence to support the concept of descent with modification. Still—as he readily acknowledged—there were instances in which key evidence was lacking. For example, Darwin referred to the origin of flowering plants as an "abominable mystery," and he lamented the lack of fossils showing how earlier groups of organisms gave rise to new groups.

In the last 150 years, new discoveries have filled many of the gaps that Darwin identified. The origin of flowering plants, for example, is much better understood (see Chapter 30), and many fossils have been discovered that signify the origin of new groups of organisms (see Chapter 25). In this section, we'll consider four types of data that document the pattern of evolution and illuminate the processes by which it occurs: direct observations of evolution, homology, the fossil record, and biogeography.

Direct Observations of Evolutionary Change

Biologists have documented evolutionary change in thousands of scientific studies. We'll examine many such studies throughout this unit, but let's look at two examples here.

(a) A flower mantid in Malaysia

(b) A leaf mantid in Borneo

▲ **Figure 22.12 Camouflage as an example of evolutionary adaptation.** Related species of the insects called mantids have diverse shapes and colors that evolved in different environments.

? *Explain how these mantids demonstrate the three key observations about life introduced in this chapter's Overview: the match between organisms and their environments, unity, and diversity.*

Natural Selection in Response to Introduced Plant Species

Animals that eat plants, called herbivores, often have adaptations that help them feed efficiently on their primary food sources. What happens when herbivores begin to feed on a plant species with different characteristics than their usual food source?

An opportunity to study this question in nature is provided by soapberry bugs, which use their "beak," a hollow, needle-like mouthpart, to feed on seeds located within the fruits of various plants. In southern Florida, the soapberry bug *Jadera haematoloma* feeds on the seeds of a native plant, the balloon vine (*Cardiospermum corindum*). In central Florida, however, balloon vines have become rare. Instead, soapberry bugs in that region now feed on goldenrain tree (*Koelreuteria elegans*), a species recently introduced from Asia.

Soapberry bugs feed most effectively when their beak length closely matches the depth at which the seeds are found within the fruit. Goldenrain tree fruit consists of three flat lobes, and its seeds are much closer to the fruit surface than the seeds of the plump, round native balloon vine fruit. Researchers at the University of Utah predicted that in populations that feed on goldenrain tree, natural selection would result in beaks that are *shorter* than those in populations that feed on balloon vine (Figure 22.13). Indeed, beak lengths are shorter in the populations that feed on goldenrain tree.

Researchers have also studied beak length evolution in soapberry bug populations that feed on plants introduced to Louisiana, Oklahoma, and Australia. In each of these locations, the fruit of the introduced plants is larger than the fruit of the native plant. Thus, in populations feeding on introduced species in these regions, the researchers predicted that natural selection would result in the evolution of *longer* beak length. Again, data collected in field studies upheld this prediction.

The adaptation observed in these soapberry bug populations had important consequences: In Australia, for example, the increase in beak length nearly doubled the success with which soapberry bugs could eat the seeds of the introduced species. Furthermore, since historical data show that the goldenrain tree reached central Florida just 35 years before the scientific studies were initiated, the results demonstrate that natural selection can cause rapid evolution in a wild population.

The Evolution of Drug-Resistant Bacteria

An example of ongoing natural selection that dramatically affects humans is the evolution of drug-resistant pathogens (disease-causing organisms and viruses). This is a particular problem with bacteria and viruses because resistant strains of these pathogens can proliferate very quickly.

Consider the evolution of drug resistance in the bacterium *Staphylococcus aureus*. About one in three people harbor this species on their skin or in their nasal passages with no negative effects. However, certain genetic varieties (strains) of this species, known as methicillin-resistant *S. aureus* (MRSA), are

▼ **Figure 22.13**

INQUIRY

Can a change in a population's food source result in evolution by natural selection?

FIELD STUDY Soapberry bugs (*Jadera haematoloma*) feed most effectively when the length of their "beak" closely matches the depth within the fruits of the seeds they eat. Scott Carroll and his colleagues measured beak lengths in soapberry bug populations in southern Florida feeding on the native balloon vine. They also measured beak lengths in populations in central Florida feeding on the introduced goldenrain tree, which has a flatter fruit shape than the balloon vine. The researchers then compared the measurements to those of museum specimens collected in the two areas before the goldenrain tree was introduced.

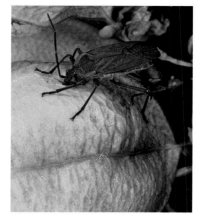

Soapberry bug with beak inserted in balloon vine fruit

RESULTS Beak lengths were shorter in populations feeding on the introduced species than in populations feeding on the native species, in which the seeds are buried more deeply. The average beak length in museum specimens from each population (indicated by red arrows) was similar to beak lengths in populations feeding on native species.

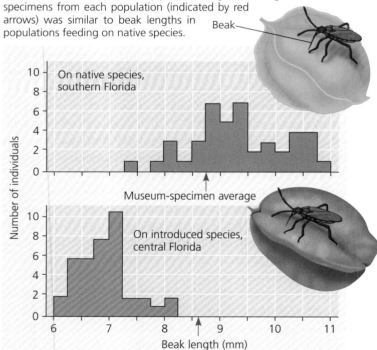

CONCLUSION Museum specimens and contemporary data suggest that a change in the size of the soapberry bug's food source can result in evolution by natural selection for matching beak size.

SOURCE S. P. Carroll and C. Boyd, Host race radiation in the soapberry bug: natural history with the history, *Evolution* 46: 1052–1069 (1992).

WHAT IF? When soapberry bug eggs from a population fed on balloon vine fruits were reared on goldenrain tree fruits (or vice versa), the beak lengths of the adult insects matched those in the population from which the eggs were obtained. Interpret these results.

formidable pathogens. The past decade has seen an alarming increase in virulent forms of MRSA such as clone USA300, a strain that can cause "flesh-eating disease" and potentially fatal infections (**Figure 22.14**). How did clone USA300 and other strains of MRSA become so dangerous?

The story begins in 1943, when penicillin became the first widely used antibiotic. Since then, penicillin and other antibiotics have saved millions of lives. However, by 1945, more than 20% of the *S. aureus* strains seen in hospitals were already resistant to penicillin. These bacteria had an enzyme, penicillinase, that could destroy penicillin. Researchers responded by developing antibiotics that were not destroyed by penicillinase, but some *S. aureus* populations developed resistance to each new drug within a few years.

In 1959, doctors began using the powerful antibiotic methicillin, but within two years, methicillin-resistant strains of *S. aureus* appeared. How did these resistant strains emerge? Methicillin works by deactivating a protein that bacteria use to synthesize their cell walls. However, *S. aureus* populations exhibited variations in how strongly their members were affected by the drug. In particular, some individuals were able to synthesize their cell walls using a different protein that was not affected by methicillin. These individuals survived the methicillin treatments and reproduced at higher rates than did other individuals. Over time, these resistant individuals became increasingly common, leading to the spread of MRSA.

Initially, MRSA could be controlled by antibiotics that worked differently from methicillin. But this has become increasingly difficult because some MRSA strains are resistant to multiple antibiotics—probably because bacteria can exchange genes with members of their own and other species (see Figure 27.13). Thus, the present-day multidrug-resistant strains may have emerged over time as MRSA strains that were resistant to different antibiotics exchanged genes.

The soapberry bug and *S. aureus* examples highlight two key points about natural selection. First, natural selection is a process of editing, not a creative mechanism. A drug does not *create* resistant pathogens; it *selects for* resistant individuals that are already present in the population. Second, natural selection depends on time and place. It favors those characteristics in a genetically variable population that provide advantage in the current, local environment. What is beneficial in one situation may be useless or even harmful in another. Beak lengths arise that match the size of the typical fruit eaten by a particular soapberry bug population. However, a beak length suitable for fruit of one size can be disadvantageous when the bug is feeding on fruit of another size.

Homology

A second type of evidence for evolution comes from analyzing similarities among different organisms. As we've discussed, evolution is a process of descent with modification: Characteristics present in an ancestral organism are altered (by natural

▼ **Figure 22.14**

IMPACT

The Rise of MRSA

Most methicillin-resistant *Staphylococcus aureus* (MRSA) infections are caused by recently appearing strains such as clone USA300. Resistant to multiple antibiotics and highly contagious, this strain and its close relatives can cause lethal infections of the skin, lungs, and blood. Researchers have identified key areas of the USA300 genome that code for its particularly virulent properties.

The circular chromosome of clone USA300 has been sequenced and contains 2,872,769 base pairs of DNA.

The highlighted regions contain genes that increase the strain's virulence (see the key).

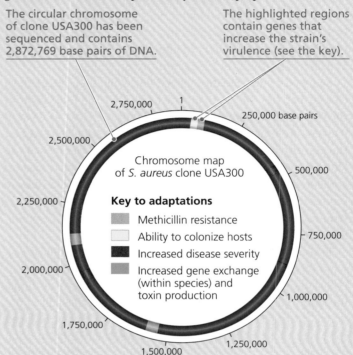

Chromosome map of *S. aureus* clone USA300

Key to adaptations

- Methicillin resistance
- Ability to colonize hosts
- Increased disease severity
- Increased gene exchange (within species) and toxin production

WHY IT MATTERS MRSA infections have proliferated dramatically in the past few decades, and the annual death toll in the United States is in the tens of thousands. There is grave concern about the continuing evolution of drug resistance and the resulting difficulty of treating MRSA infections. Ongoing studies of how MRSA strains colonize their hosts and cause disease may help scientists develop drugs to combat MRSA.

FURTHER READING General information about MRSA can be found on the Centers for Disease Control and Prevention (CDC) website (www.cdc.gov/mrsa) and in G. Taubes, The bacteria fight back, *Science* 321:356–361 (2008).

WHAT IF? Efforts are underway to develop drugs that target *S. aureus* specifically and to develop drugs that slow the growth of MRSA but do not kill it. Based on how natural selection works and on the fact that bacterial species can exchange genes, explain why each of these strategies might be effective.

selection) in its descendants over time as they face different environmental conditions. As a result, related species can have characteristics that have an underlying similarity yet function differently. Similarity resulting from common ancestry is known as **homology**. As this section will explain, an understanding of homology can be used to make testable predictions and explain observations that are otherwise puzzling.

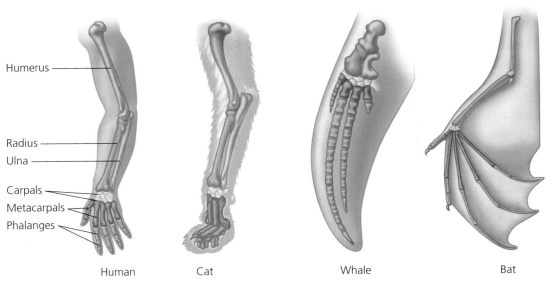

Humerus

Radius
Ulna

Carpals
Metacarpals
Phalanges

Human   Cat   Whale   Bat

◀ **Figure 22.15 Mammalian forelimbs: homologous structures.** Even though they have become adapted for different functions, the forelimbs of all mammals are constructed from the same basic skeletal elements: one large bone (purple), attached to two smaller bones (orange and tan), attached to several small bones (gold), attached to several metacarpals (green), attached to approximately five digits, or phalanges (blue).

Anatomical and Molecular Homologies

The view of evolution as a remodeling process leads to the prediction that closely related species should share similar features—and they do. Of course, closely related species share the features used to determine their relationship, but they also share many other features. Some of these shared features make little sense except in the context of evolution. For example, the forelimbs of all mammals, including humans, cats, whales, and bats, show the same arrangement of bones from the shoulder to the tips of the digits, even though these appendages have very different functions: lifting, walking, swimming, and flying **(Figure 22.15)**. Such striking anatomical resemblances would be highly unlikely if these structures had arisen anew in each species. Rather, the underlying skeletons of the arms, forelegs, flippers, and wings of different mammals are **homologous structures** that represent variations on a structural theme that was present in their common ancestor.

Comparing early stages of development in different animal species reveals additional anatomical homologies not visible in adult organisms. For example, at some point in their development, all vertebrate embryos have a tail located posterior to (behind) the anus, as well as structures called pharyngeal (throat) pouches **(Figure 22.16)**. These homologous throat pouches ultimately develop into structures with very different functions, such as gills in fishes and parts of the ears and throat in humans and other mammals.

Some of the most intriguing homologies concern "leftover" structures of marginal, if any, importance to the organism. These **vestigial structures** are remnants of features that served important functions in the organism's ancestors. For instance, the skeletons of some snakes retain vestiges of the pelvis and leg bones of walking ancestors. Another example is provided by eye remnants that are buried under scales in blind species of cave fishes. We would not expect to see these vestigial structures if snakes and blind cave fishes had origins separate from other vertebrate animals.

Biologists also observe similarities among organisms at the molecular level. All forms of life use the same genetic language of DNA and RNA, and the genetic code is essentially universal. Thus, it is likely that all species descended from common ancestors that used this code. But molecular homologies go beyond a shared code. For example, organisms as dissimilar as humans and bacteria share genes inherited from a very distant common ancestor. Some of these homologous genes have acquired new functions, while others, such as those coding for the ribosomal subunits used in protein synthesis (see Figure 17.17), have retained their original functions. It is also common for organisms to have genes that have lost their function, even though the homologous genes in related species may be fully functional. Like vestigial structures, it appears that such inactive "pseudogenes" may be present simply because a common ancestor had them.

Pharyngeal pouches

Post-anal tail

Chick embryo (LM)   Human embryo

▲ **Figure 22.16 Anatomical similarities in vertebrate embryos.** At some stage in their embryonic development, all vertebrates have a tail located posterior to the anus (referred to as a post-anal tail), as well as pharyngeal (throat) pouches. Descent from a common ancestor can explain such similarities.

Homologies and "Tree Thinking"

Some homologous characteristics, such as the genetic code, are shared by all species because they date to the deep ancestral past. In contrast, homologous characteristics that evolved more recently are shared only within smaller groups of organisms. Consider the *tetrapods* (from the Greek *tetra*, four, and *pod*, foot), the vertebrate group that consists of amphibians, mammals, and reptiles (including birds—see Figure 22.17). All tetrapods have limbs with digits (see Figure 22.15), whereas other vertebrates do not. Thus, homologous characteristics form a nested pattern: All life shares the deepest layer, and each successive smaller group adds its own homologies to those it shares with larger groups. This nested pattern is exactly what we would expect to result from descent with modification from a common ancestor.

Biologists often represent the pattern of descent from common ancestors and the resulting homologies with an **evolutionary tree**, a diagram that reflects evolutionary relationships among groups of organisms. We will explore in detail how evolutionary trees are constructed in Chapter 26, but for now, let's consider how we can interpret and use such trees.

Figure 22.17 is an evolutionary tree of tetrapods and their closest living relatives, the lungfishes. In this diagram, each branch point represents the common ancestor of all species that descended from it. For example, lungfishes and all tetrapods descended from ancestor ❶, whereas mammals, lizards and snakes, crocodiles, and birds all descended from ancestor ❸. As expected, the three homologies shown on the tree—limbs with digits, the amnion (a protective embryonic membrane), and feathers—form a nested pattern. Limbs with digits were present in common ancestor ❷ and hence are found in all of the descendants of that ancestor (the tetrapods). The amnion was present only in ancestor ❸ and hence is shared only by some tetrapods (mammals and reptiles). Feathers were present only in common ancestor ❻ and hence are found only in birds.

To explore "tree thinking" further, note that in Figure 22.17, mammals are positioned closer to amphibians than to birds. As a result, you might conclude that mammals are more closely related to amphibians than they are to birds. However, mammals are actually more closely related to birds than to amphibians because mammals and birds share a more recent common ancestor (ancestor ❸) than do mammals and amphibians (ancestor ❷). Ancestor ❷ is also the most recent common ancestor of birds and amphibians, making mammals and birds equally related to amphibians. Finally, note that the tree in Figure 22.17 shows the relative timing of evolutionary events but not their actual dates. Thus, we can conclude that ancestor ❷ lived before ancestor ❸, but we do not know when that was.

Evolutionary trees are hypotheses that summarize our current understanding of patterns of descent. Our confidence in these relationships, as with any hypothesis, depends on the strength of the supporting data. In the case of Figure 22.17, the tree is supported by a variety of independent data sets, including both anatomical and DNA sequence data. As a result, biologists feel confident that it accurately reflects evolutionary history. As you will read in Chapter 26, scientists can use such well-supported evolutionary trees to make specific and sometimes surprising predictions about organisms.

A Different Cause of Resemblance: Convergent Evolution

Although organisms that are closely related share characteristics because of common descent, distantly related organisms can resemble one another for a different reason: **convergent evolution**, the independent evolution of similar features in different lineages. Consider marsupial mammals, many of which live in Australia. Marsupials are distinct from another group of mammals—the eutherians—few of which live in Australia. (Eutherians complete their embryonic development in the uterus, whereas marsupials

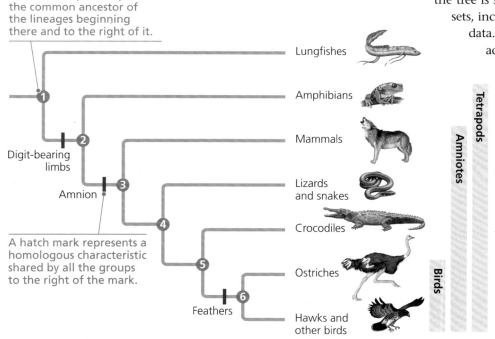

Each branch point represents the common ancestor of the lineages beginning there and to the right of it.

Digit-bearing limbs

Amnion

A hatch mark represents a homologous characteristic shared by all the groups to the right of the mark.

Feathers

Lungfishes
Amphibians
Mammals
Lizards and snakes
Crocodiles
Ostriches
Hawks and other birds

Tetrapods
Amniotes
Birds

▲ **Figure 22.17 Tree thinking: information provided in an evolutionary tree.** This evolutionary tree for tetrapods and their closest living relatives, the lungfishes, is based on anatomical and DNA sequence data. The purple bars indicate the origin of three important homologies, each of which evolved only once. Birds are nested within and evolved from reptiles; hence, the group of organisms called "reptiles" technically includes birds.

? *Are crocodiles more closely related to lizards or birds? Explain your answer.*

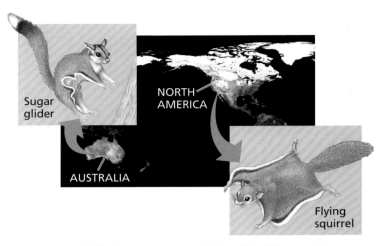

▲ **Figure 22.18 Convergent evolution.** The ability to glide through the air evolved independently in these two distantly related mammals.

are born as embryos and complete their development in an external pouch.) Some Australian marsupials have eutherian look-alikes with superficially similar adaptations. For instance, a forest-dwelling Australian marsupial called the sugar glider is superficially very similar to flying squirrels, gliding eutherians that live in North American forests (**Figure 22.18**). But the sugar glider has many other characteristics that make it a marsupial, much more closely related to kangaroos and other Australian marsupials than to flying squirrels or other eutherians. Once again, our understanding of evolution can explain these observations. Although they evolved independently from different ancestors, these two mammals have adapted to similar environments in similar ways. In such examples in which species share features because of convergent evolution, the resemblance is said to be **analogous**, not homologous. Analogous features share similar function, but not common ancestry, while homologous features share common ancestry, but not necessarily similar function.

The Fossil Record

A third type of evidence for evolution comes from fossils. As Chapter 25 discusses in more detail, the fossil record documents the pattern of evolution, showing that past organisms differed from present-day organisms and that many species have become extinct. Fossils also show the evolutionary changes that have occurred in various groups of organisms. To give one of hundreds of possible examples, researchers found that the pelvic bone in fossil stickleback fish became greatly reduced in size over time in a number of different lakes. The consistent nature of this change sug-

gests that the reduction in the size of the pelvic bone may have been driven by natural selection.

Fossils can also shed light on the origins of new groups of organisms. An example is the fossil record of cetaceans, the mammalian order that includes whales, dolphins, and porpoises. Some of these fossils provided an unexpected line of support for a hypothesis based on DNA data: that cetaceans are closely related to even-toed ungulates, a group that includes deer, pigs, camels, and cows (**Figure 22.19**). What else can fossils tell us about cetacean origins? The earliest cetaceans lived 50–60 million years ago. The fossil record indicates that prior to that time, most mammals were terrestrial. Although scientists had long realized that whales and other cetaceans originated from land mammals, few fossils had been found that revealed how cetacean limb structure had changed over time, leading eventually to the loss of hind limbs and the development of flippers and tail flukes. In the past few decades, however, a series of remarkable fossils have been discovered in Pakistan, Egypt, and North America. These fossils document steps in the transition from life on land to life in the sea, filling in some of the gaps between ancestral and living cetaceans (**Figure 22.20**, on the next page).

Collectively, the recent fossil discoveries document the formation of new species and the origin of a major new group of mammals, the cetaceans. These discoveries also show that cetaceans and their close living relatives (hippopotamuses, pigs, deer, and

▲ ***Diacodexis*, an early even-toed ungulate**

other even-toed ungulates) are much more different from each other than were *Pakicetus* and early even-toed ungulates, such as *Diacodexis*. Similar patterns are seen in fossils documenting the origins of other major new groups of organisms, including

▲ **Figure 22.19 Ankle bones: one piece of the puzzle.** Comparing fossils and present-day examples of the astragalus (a type of ankle bone) provides one line of evidence that cetaceans are closely related to even-toed ungulates. **(a)** In most mammals, the astragalus is shaped like that of a dog, with a double hump on one end (indicated by the red arrows) but not at the opposite end (blue arrow). **(b)** Fossils show that the early cetacean *Pakicetus* had an astragalus with double humps at both ends, a unique shape that is otherwise found only in even-toed ungulates, as shown here for **(c)** a pig and **(d)** a deer.

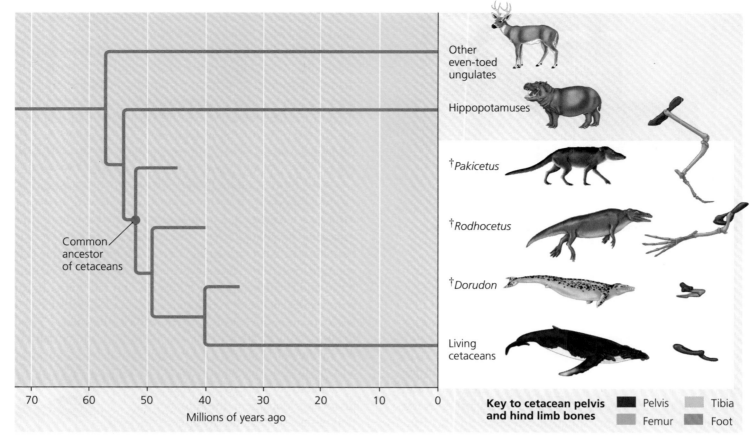

Key to cetacean pelvis and hind limb bones: Pelvis, Tibia, Femur, Foot

▲ **Figure 22.20 The transition to life in the sea.** Multiple lines of evidence support the hypothesis that cetaceans evolved from terrestrial mammals. Fossils document the reduction over time in the pelvis and hind limb bones of extinct cetacean ancestors, including *Pakicetus*, *Rodhocetus*, and *Dorudon*. DNA sequence data support the hypothesis that cetaceans are most closely related to hippopotamuses, even-toed ungulates.

? *Which happened first during the evolution of cetaceans: changes in hind limb structure or the origin of tail flukes?*

mammals (see Chapter 25), flowering plants (see Chapter 30), and tetrapods (see Chapter 34). In each of these cases, the fossil record shows that over time, descent with modification produced increasingly large differences among related groups of organisms, ultimately resulting in the diversity of life we see today.

Biogeography

A fourth type of evidence for evolution comes from **biogeography**, the geographic distribution of species. The geographic distribution of organisms is influenced by many factors, including *continental drift*, the slow movement of Earth's continents over time. About 250 million years ago, these movements united all of Earth's landmasses into a single large continent called **Pangaea** (see Figure 25.13). Roughly 200 million years ago, Pangaea began to break apart; by 20 million years ago, the continents we know today were within a few hundred kilometers of their present locations.

We can use our understanding of evolution and continental drift to predict where fossils of different groups of organisms might be found. For example, scientists have constructed evolutionary trees for horses based on anatomical data. These trees and the ages of fossils of horse ancestors suggest that present-day horse species originated 5 million years ago in North America. At that time, North and South America were close to their present locations, but they were not yet connected, making it difficult for horses to travel between them. Thus, we would predict that the oldest horse fossils should be found only on the continent on which horses originated—North America. This prediction and others like it for different groups of organisms have been upheld, providing more evidence for evolution.

We can also use our understanding of evolution to explain biogeographic data. For example, islands generally have many species of plants and animals that are **endemic**, which means they are found nowhere else in the world. Yet, as Darwin described in *The Origin of Species*, most island species are closely related to species from the nearest mainland or a neighboring island. He explained this observation by suggesting that islands are colonized by species from the nearest mainland. These colonists eventually give rise to new species as they adapt to their new environments. Such a process also explains why two islands with similar environments in distant parts of the world tend to be populated not by species that are closely related to each other, but rather by species related to those of the nearest mainland, where the environment is often quite different.

What Is Theoretical About Darwin's View of Life?

Some people dismiss Darwin's ideas as "just a theory." However, as we have seen, the *pattern* of evolution—the observation that life has evolved over time—has been documented directly and is supported by a great deal of evidence. In addition, Darwin's explanation of the *process* of evolution—that natural selection is the primary cause of the observed pattern of evolutionary change—makes sense of massive amounts of data. The effects of natural selection also can be observed and tested in nature.

What, then, is theoretical about evolution? Keep in mind that the scientific meaning of the term *theory* is very different from its meaning in everyday use. The colloquial use of the word *theory* comes close to what scientists mean by a hypothesis. In science, a theory is more comprehensive than a hypothesis. A theory, such as the theory of evolution by natural selection, accounts for many observations and explains and integrates a great variety of phenomena. Such a unifying theory does not become widely accepted unless its predictions stand up to thorough and continual testing by experiment and additional observation (see Chapter 1). As the next three chapters demonstrate, this has certainly been the case with the theory of evolution by natural selection.

The skepticism of scientists as they continue to test theories prevents these ideas from becoming dogma. For example, although Darwin thought that evolution was a very slow process, we now know that this isn't always true. New species can form in relatively short periods of time (a few thousand years or less; see Chapter 24). Furthermore, as we'll explore throughout this unit, evolutionary biologists now recognize that natural selection is not the only mechanism responsible for evolution. Indeed, the study of evolution today is livelier than ever as scientists find more ways to test predictions based on natural selection and other evolutionary mechanisms.

Although Darwin's theory attributes the diversity of life to natural processes, the diverse products of evolution nevertheless remain elegant and inspiring. As Darwin wrote in the final sentence of *The Origin of Species*, "There is grandeur in this view of life . . . [in which] endless forms most beautiful and most wonderful have been, and are being, evolved."

CONCEPT CHECK 22.3

1. Explain how the following statement is inaccurate: "Antibiotics have created drug resistance in MRSA."
2. How does evolution account for (a) the similar mammalian forelimbs with different functions shown in Figure 22.15 and (b) the similar lifestyle of the two distantly related mammals shown in Figure 22.18?
3. **WHAT IF?** The fossil record shows that dinosaurs originated 200–250 million years ago. Would you expect the geographic distribution of early dinosaur fossils to be broad (on many continents) or narrow (on one or a few continents only)? Explain.

For suggested answers, see Appendix A.

22 CHAPTER REVIEW

SUMMARY OF KEY CONCEPTS

CONCEPT 22.1

The Darwinian revolution challenged traditional views of a young Earth inhabited by unchanging species (pp. 453–455)

- Darwin proposed that life's diversity arose from ancestral species through natural selection, a departure from prevailing views.
- In contrast to **catastrophism** (the principle that events in the past occurred suddenly by mechanisms not operating today), Hutton and Lyell thought that geologic change results from mechanisms that operated in the past in the same manner as at the present time (**uniformitarianism**).
- Lamarck hypothesized that species evolve, but the underlying mechanisms he proposed are not supported by evidence.

? *Why was the age of Earth important for Darwin's ideas about evolution?*

CONCEPT 22.2

Descent with modification by natural selection explains the adaptations of organisms and the unity and diversity of life (pp. 455–460)

- Darwin's experiences during the voyage of the *Beagle* gave rise to his idea that new species originate from ancestral forms through the accumulation of **adaptations**. He refined his theory for many years and finally published it in 1859 after learning that Wallace had come to the same idea.
- In *The Origin of Species*, Darwin proposed that evolution occurs by **natural selection**.

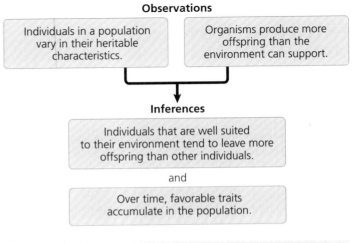

Observations

| Individuals in a population vary in their heritable characteristics. | Organisms produce more offspring than the environment can support. |

Inferences

Individuals that are well suited to their environment tend to leave more offspring than other individuals.

and

Over time, favorable traits accumulate in the population.

? *Describe how overreproduction and heritable variation relate to evolution by natural selection.*

Evolution is supported by an overwhelming amount of scientific evidence (pp. 460–467)

- Researchers have directly observed natural selection leading to adaptive evolution in many studies, including research on soapberry bug populations and on MRSA.
- Organisms share characteristics because of common descent (**homology**) or because natural selection affects independently evolving species in similar environments in similar ways (**convergent evolution**).
- Fossils show that past organisms differed from living organisms, that many species have become extinct, and that species have evolved over long periods of time; fossils also document the origin of major new groups of organisms.
- Evolutionary theory can explain biogeographic patterns.

? *Summarize the different lines of evidence supporting the hypothesis that cetaceans descended from land mammals and are closely related to even-toed ungulates.*

TEST YOUR UNDERSTANDING

Level 1: Knowledge/Comprehension

1. Which of the following is *not* an observation or inference on which natural selection is based?
   a. There is heritable variation among individuals.
   b. Poorly adapted individuals never produce offspring.
   c. Species produce more offspring than the environment can support.
   d. Individuals whose characteristics are best suited to the environment generally leave more offspring than those whose characteristics are less well suited.
   e. Only a fraction of an individual's offspring may survive.

2. Which of the following observations helped Darwin shape his concept of descent with modification?
   a. Species diversity declines farther from the equator.
   b. Fewer species live on islands than on the nearest continents.
   c. Birds can be found on islands located farther from the mainland than the birds' maximum nonstop flight distance.
   d. South American temperate plants are more similar to the tropical plants of South America than to the temperate plants of Europe.
   e. Earthquakes reshape life by causing mass extinctions.

Level 2: Application/Analysis

3. Within six months of effectively using methicillin to treat *S. aureus* infections in a community, all new infections were caused by MRSA. How can this result best be explained?
   a. *S. aureus* can resist vaccines.
   b. A patient must have become infected with MRSA from another community.
   c. In response to the drug, *S. aureus* began making drug-resistant versions of the protein targeted by the drug.
   d. Some drug-resistant bacteria were present at the start of treatment, and natural selection increased their frequency.
   e. The drug caused the *S. aureus* DNA to change.

4. The upper forelimbs of humans and bats have fairly similar skeletal structures, whereas the corresponding bones in whales have very different shapes and proportions. However, genetic data suggest that all three kinds of organisms diverged from a common ancestor at about the same time. Which of the following is the most likely explanation for these data?

   a. Humans and bats evolved by natural selection, and whales evolved by Lamarckian mechanisms.
   b. Forelimb evolution was adaptive in people and bats, but not in whales.
   c. Natural selection in an aquatic environment resulted in significant changes to whale forelimb anatomy.
   d. Genes mutate faster in whales than in humans or bats.
   e. Whales are not properly classified as mammals.

5. DNA sequences in many human genes are very similar to the sequences of corresponding genes in chimpanzees. The most likely explanation for this result is that
   a. humans and chimpanzees share a relatively recent common ancestor.
   b. humans evolved from chimpanzees.
   c. chimpanzees evolved from humans.
   d. convergent evolution led to the DNA similarities.
   e. humans and chimpanzees are not closely related.

Level 3: Synthesis/Evaluation

6. **EVOLUTION CONNECTION**
   Explain why anatomical and molecular features often fit a similar nested pattern. In addition, describe a process that can cause this not to be the case.

7. **SCIENTIFIC INQUIRY**
   DRAW IT Mosquitoes resistant to the pesticide DDT first appeared in India in 1959, but now are found throughout the world. (a) Graph the data in the table below. (b) Examining the graph, hypothesize why the percentage of mosquitoes resistant to DDT rose rapidly. (c) Suggest an explanation for the global spread of DDT resistance.

Month	0	8	12
Mosquitoes Resistant* to DDT	4%	45%	77%

   Source: C. F. Curtis et al., Selection for and against insecticide resistance and possible methods of inhibiting the evolution of resistance in mosquitoes, *Ecological Entomology* 3:273–287 (1978).
   *Mosquitoes were considered resistant if they were not killed within 1 hour of receiving a dose of 4% DDT.

8. **WRITE ABOUT A THEME**
   Environmental Interactions Write a short essay (about 100–150 words) evaluating whether changes to an organism's physical environment are likely to result in evolutionary change. Use an example to support your reasoning.

For selected answers, see Appendix A.

Mastering BIOLOGY www.masteringbiology.com

1. MasteringBiology® Assignments:

Tutorial Evidence for Evolution
Activities Artificial Selection • Darwin and the Galápagos Islands • The Voyage of the *Beagle*: Darwin's Trip Around the World • Discovery Channel Video: Charles Darwin • Natural Selection for Antibiotic Resistance • Reconstructing Forelimbs
Questions Student Misconceptions • Reading Quiz • Multiple Choice • End-of-Chapter

2. eText
Read your book online, search, take notes, highlight text, and more.

3. The Study Area
Practice Tests • Cumulative Test • *BioFlix* 3-D Animations • MP3 Tutor Sessions • Videos • Activities • Investigations • Lab Media • Audio Glossary • Word Study Tools • Art

23

The Evolution of Populations

▲ **Figure 23.1 Is this finch evolving?**

EVOLUTION

KEY CONCEPTS

23.1 Genetic variation makes evolution possible

23.2 The Hardy-Weinberg equation can be used to test whether a population is evolving

23.3 Natural selection, genetic drift, and gene flow can alter allele frequencies in a population

23.4 Natural selection is the only mechanism that consistently causes adaptive evolution

OVERVIEW

The Smallest Unit of Evolution

One common misconception about evolution is that individual organisms evolve. It is true that natural selection acts on individuals: Each organism's traits affect its survival and reproductive success compared with other individuals. But the evolutionary impact of natural selection is only apparent in the changes in a *population* of organisms over time.

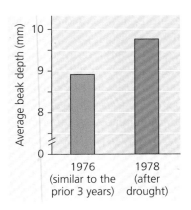

◀ **Figure 23.2 Evidence of selection by food source.** The data represent adult beak depth measurements of medium ground finches hatched in the generations before and after the 1977 drought. Beak sizes remained large until 1983, when changing conditions no longer favored large-beaked birds.

(MB) See the related Experimental Inquiry Tutorial in MasteringBiology.

Consider the medium ground finch (*Geospiza fortis*), a seed-eating bird that inhabits the Galápagos Islands (**Figure 23.1**). In 1977, the *G. fortis* population on the island of Daphne Major was decimated by a long period of drought: Of some 1,200 birds, only 180 survived. Researchers Peter and Rosemary Grant observed that during the drought, small, soft seeds were in short supply. The finches mostly fed on large, hard seeds that were more plentiful. Birds with larger, deeper beaks were better able to crack and eat these larger seeds, and they survived at a higher rate than finches with smaller beaks. Since beak depth is an inherited trait in these birds, the average beak depth in the next generation of *G. fortis* was greater than it had been in the pre-drought population (**Figure 23.2**). The finch population had evolved by natural selection. However, the *individual* finches did not evolve. Each bird had a beak of a particular size, which did not grow larger during the drought. Rather, the proportion of large beaks in the population increased from generation to generation: The population evolved, not its individual members.

Focusing on evolutionary change in populations, we can define evolution on its smallest scale, called **microevolution**, as change in allele frequencies in a population over generations. As we will see in this chapter, natural selection is not the only cause of microevolution. In fact, there are three main mechanisms that can cause allele frequency change: natural selection, genetic drift (chance events that alter allele frequencies), and gene flow (the transfer of alleles between populations). Each of these mechanisms has distinctive effects on the genetic composition of populations. However, only natural selection consistently improves the match between organisms and their environment (adaptation). Before we examine natural selection and adaptation more closely, let's revisit a prerequisite for these processes in a population: genetic variation.

CONCEPT 23.1

Genetic variation makes evolution possible

In *The Origin of Species*, Darwin provided abundant evidence that life on Earth has evolved over time, and he proposed natural selection as the primary mechanism for that change. He observed that individuals differed in their inherited traits and that selection acted on such differences, leading to evolutionary change. Thus, Darwin realized that variation in heritable traits was a prerequisite for evolution, but he did not know precisely how organisms pass heritable traits to their offspring.

Just a few years after Darwin published *The Origin of Species*, Gregor Mendel wrote a groundbreaking paper on inheritance in pea plants (see Chapter 14). In that paper, Mendel proposed a particulate model of inheritance in which organisms transmit discrete heritable units (now called genes) to their offspring. Although Darwin did not know about genes, Mendel's paper set the stage for understanding the genetic differences on which evolution is based. Here we'll examine such genetic differences and how they are produced.

Genetic Variation

You probably have no trouble recognizing your friends in a crowd. Each person is unique, exhibiting differences in their facial features, height, and voice. Indeed, individual variation occurs in all species. In addition to the differences that we can see or hear, individuals vary extensively at the molecular level. For example, you cannot identify a person's blood group (A, B, AB, or O) from his or her appearance, but this and many other molecular traits vary among individuals.

Individual variations often reflect **genetic variation**, differences among individuals in the composition of their genes or other DNA segments. As you read in earlier chapters, however, some phenotypic variation is not heritable (see **Figure 23.3** for a striking example in a caterpillar of the southwestern United States). Phenotype is the product of an inherited genotype and many environmental influences. In a human example, bodybuilders alter their phenotypes dramatically but do not pass their huge muscles on to the next generation. In general, only the genetically determined part of phenotypic variation can have evolutionary consequences. As

such, genetic variation provides the raw material for evolutionary change: Without genetic variation, evolution cannot occur.

Variation Within a Population

Characters that vary within a population may be discrete or quantitative. *Discrete characters*, such as the purple or white flower colors of Mendel's pea plants (see Figure 14.3), can be classified on an either-or basis (each plant has flowers that are either purple or white). Many discrete characters are determined by a single gene locus with different alleles that produce distinct phenotypes. However, most heritable variation involves *quantitative characters*, which vary along a continuum within a population. Heritable quantitative variation usually results from the influence of two or more genes on a single phenotypic character.

For both discrete and quantitative characters, biologists often need to describe how much genetic variation there is in a particular population. We can measure genetic variation at the whole-gene level (*gene variability*) and at the molecular level of DNA (*nucleotide variability*). Gene variability can be quantified as the **average heterozygosity**, the average percentage of loci that are heterozygous. (Recall that a heterozygous individual has two different alleles for a given locus, whereas a homozygous individual has two identical alleles for that locus.) As an example, on average the fruit fly *Drosophila melanogaster* is heterozygous for about 1,920 of its 13,700 loci (14%) and homozygous for all the rest. We can therefore say that a *D. melanogaster* population has an average heterozygosity of 14%. Analyses of this and many other species show that this level of genetic variation provides ample raw material for natural selection to operate, resulting in evolutionary change.

When determining gene variability, how do scientists identify heterozygous loci? One method is to survey the protein products of genes using gel electrophoresis (see Figure 20.9). However, this approach cannot detect silent mutations that

▲ **Figure 23.3 Nonheritable variation.** These caterpillars of the moth *Nemoria arizonaria* owe their different appearances to chemicals in their diets, not to differences in their genotypes. Caterpillars raised on a diet of oak flowers resembled the flowers **(a)**, whereas their siblings raised on oak leaves resembled oak twigs **(b)**.

alter the DNA sequence of a gene but not the amino acid sequence of the protein (see Figure 17.24). To include such silent mutations in their estimates of average heterozygosity, researchers must use other approaches, such as PCR-based methods and restriction fragment analyses (see Chapter 20).

To measure nucleotide variability, biologists compare the DNA sequences of two individuals in a population and then average the data from many such comparisons. The genome of *D. melanogaster* has about 180 million nucleotides, and the sequences of any two fruit flies differ on average by approximately 1.8 million (1%) of their nucleotides. Thus, the nucleotide variability of *D. melanogaster* populations is about 1%.

As in this example, gene variability tends to exceed nucleotide variability. Why is this true? Remember that a gene can consist of thousands of nucleotides. A difference at only one of these nucleotides can be sufficient to make two alleles of that gene different, increasing gene variability.

Variation Between Populations

In addition to variation observed within a population, species also exhibit **geographic variation**, differences in the genetic composition of separate populations. **Figure 23.4** illustrates geographic variation in populations of house mice (*Mus*

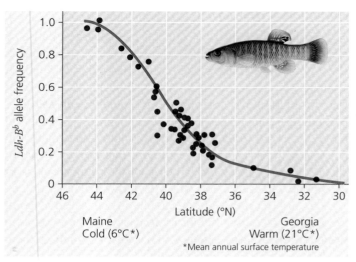

▲ **Figure 23.5 A cline determined by temperature.** In mummichog fish, the frequency of the *Ldh-B^b* allele for the enzyme lactate dehydrogenase-B (which functions in metabolism) decreases in fish sampled from Maine to Georgia. The *Ldh-B^b* allele codes for a form of the enzyme that is a better catalyst in cold water than are other versions of the enzyme. Individuals with the *Ldh-B^b* allele can swim faster in cold water than can individuals with other alleles.

musculus) separated by mountains on the Atlantic island of Madeira. Inadvertently introduced by Portuguese settlers in the 15th century, several populations of mice have evolved in isolation from one another. Researchers have observed differences in the karyotypes (chromosome sets) of these isolated populations. In certain populations, some of the chromosomes have become fused. However, the patterns of fused chromosomes differ from one population to another. Because these chromosome-level changes leave genes intact, their phenotypic effects on the mice seem to be neutral. Thus, the variation between these populations appears to have resulted from chance events (drift) rather than natural selection.

Other examples of geographic variation occur as a **cline**, a graded change in a character along a geographic axis. Some clines are produced by a gradation in an environmental variable, as illustrated by the impact of temperature on the frequency of a cold-adaptive allele in mummichog fish (*Fundulus heteroclitus*). Clines such as the one depicted in **Figure 23.5** probably result from natural selection—otherwise there would be no reason to expect a close association between the environmental variable and the frequency of the allele. But selection can only operate if multiple alleles exist for a given locus. Such variation in alleles can arise in several ways.

Sources of Genetic Variation

The genetic variation on which evolution depends originates when mutation, gene duplication, or other processes produce new alleles and new genes. Many new genetic variants can be produced in short periods of time in organisms that reproduce rapidly. Sexual reproduction can also result in genetic variation as existing genes are arranged in new ways.

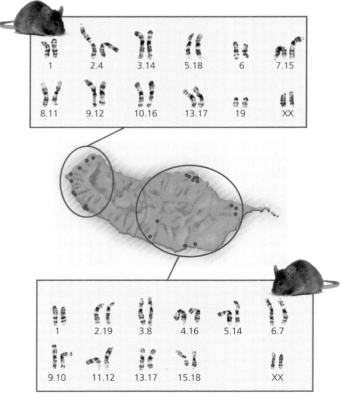

▲ **Figure 23.4 Geographic variation in isolated mouse populations on Madeira.** The number pairs represent fused chromosomes. For example, "2.4" indicates fusion of chromosome 2 and chromosome 4. Mice in the areas indicated by the blue dots have the set of fused chromosomes in the blue box; mice in the red-dot locales have the set of fused chromosomes in the red box.

Formation of New Alleles

As described in Chapters 17 and 21, new alleles can arise by *mutation*, a change in the nucleotide sequence of an organism's DNA. A mutation is like a shot in the dark—we cannot predict accurately which segments of DNA will be altered or in what way. In multicellular organisms, only mutations in cell lines that produce gametes can be passed to offspring. In plants and fungi, this is not as limiting as it may sound, since many different cell lines can produce gametes (see Figures 30.6 and 31.17). But in most animals, the majority of mutations occur in somatic cells and are lost when the individual dies.

A change of as little as one base in a gene, called a "point mutation," can have a significant impact on phenotype, as in sickle-cell disease (see Figure 17.23). Organisms reflect thousands of generations of past selection, and hence their phenotypes generally provide a close match to their environment. As a result, it's unlikely that a new mutation that alters a phenotype will improve it. In fact, most such mutations are at least slightly harmful. But much of the DNA in eukaryotic genomes does not code for protein products, and point mutations in these noncoding regions are often harmless. Also, because of the redundancy in the genetic code, even a point mutation in a gene that encodes a protein will have no effect on the protein's function if the amino acid composition is not changed. And even where there is a change in the amino acid, it may not affect the protein's shape and function. However, as will be discussed later in this chapter, a mutant allele may on rare occasions actually make its bearer better suited to the environment, enhancing reproductive success.

Altering Gene Number or Position

Chromosomal changes that delete, disrupt, or rearrange many loci at once are usually harmful. However, when such large-scale changes leave genes intact, their effects on organisms may be neutral (as in the case of the Madeira mice described in Figure 23.4). In rare cases, chromosomal rearrangements may even be beneficial. For example, the translocation of part of one chromosome to a different chromosome could link DNA segments in a way that results in a positive effect.

An important source of variation begins when genes are duplicated due to errors in meiosis (such as unequal crossing over), slippage during DNA replication, or the activities of transposable elements (see Chapters 15 and 21). Duplications of large chromosome segments, like other chromosomal aberrations, are often harmful, but the duplication of smaller pieces of DNA may not be. Gene duplications that do not have severe effects can persist over generations, allowing mutations to accumulate. The result is an expanded genome with new genes that may take on new functions.

Such beneficial increases in gene number appear to have played a major role in evolution. For example, the remote ancestors of mammals had a single gene for detecting odors that has since been duplicated many times. As a result, hu-mans today have about 1,000 olfactory receptor genes, and mice have 1,300. This dramatic proliferation of olfactory genes probably helped early mammals, enabling them to detect faint odors and to distinguish among many different smells. More recently, about 60% of human olfactory receptor genes have been inactivated by mutations, whereas mice have lost only 20% of theirs. Since mutation rates in humans and mice are similar, this difference is likely due to strong selection against mice with mutations that inactivate their olfactory genes. A versatile sense of smell appears to be much more important to mice than to humans!

Rapid Reproduction

Mutation rates tend to be low in plants and animals, averaging about one mutation in every 100,000 genes per generation, and they are often even lower in prokaryotes. But prokaryotes typically have short generation spans, so mutations can quickly generate genetic variation in populations of these organisms. The same is true of viruses. For instance, HIV has a generation span of about two days. It also has an RNA genome, which has a much higher mutation rate than a typical DNA genome because of the lack of RNA repair mechanisms in host cells (see Chapter 19). For this reason, it is unlikely that a single-drug treatment would ever be effective against HIV; mutant forms of the virus that are resistant to a particular drug would no doubt proliferate in relatively short order. The most effective AIDS treatments to date have been drug "cocktails" that combine several medications. It is less likely that multiple mutations conferring resistance to *all* the drugs will occur in a short time period.

Sexual Reproduction

In organisms that reproduce sexually, most of the genetic variation in a population results from the unique combination of alleles that each individual receives from its parents. Of course, at the nucleotide level, all the differences among these alleles have originated from past mutations and other processes that can produce new alleles. But it is the mechanism of sexual reproduction that shuffles existing alleles and deals them at random to produce individual genotypes.

As described in Chapter 13, three mechanisms contribute to this shuffling: crossing over, independent assortment of chromosomes, and fertilization. During meiosis, homologous chromosomes, one inherited from each parent, trade some of their alleles by crossing over. These homologous chromosomes and the alleles they carry are then distributed at random into gametes. Then, because myriad possible mating combinations exist in a population, fertilization brings together gametes that are likely to have different genetic backgrounds. The combined effects of these three mechanisms ensure that sexual reproduction rearranges existing alleles into fresh combinations each generation, providing much of the genetic variation that makes evolution possible.

UNIVERSITY OF ALBERTA FACULTY BIO

Stan Boutin BSc (University of Alberta); MSc and PhD (University of British Columbia)

Current Positions: Professor and NSERC Industrial Chair in Integrated Landscape Management, Department of Biological Sciences; Science Director, Alberta Biodiversity Monitoring Institute; Fellow of the Royal Society of Canada.

I completed my undergraduate degree at University of Alberta before going on to the University of British Columbia for my MSc and PhD where I studied the classic snowshoe hare-lynx population cycle. I teach Zoology 434 (Field Course in Animal Ecology), which is currently taught at the Kananaskis Field Station, and Biology 595 (Integrated Landscape Management).

The major focus of my research continues to be the population ecology of boreal mammals with an emphasis on the relationship between behavior and resources, parental investment and dispersal, and predator-prey relationships. My lab is involved with a long term study (1986) of the behaviour and population dynamics of red squirrels in the southwestern Yukon. My applied research is designed to allow stakeholders to make ecologically informed decisions regarding land-use.

My research group also studies causes behind the decline of woodland caribou in Alberta where caribou herds overlap with the highly valued oil sands. Woodland caribou live throughout much of Canada but their numbers have dwindled to the point that the subspecies is classified as "Threatened." Our work has uncovered a classic case of apparent competition. When moose and deer increase, caribou decline which looks like these species compete for food with caribou. However, the actual reason for the decline is increased mortality of caribou due to wolf predation. Wolves increase as their main prey (moose and deer) increase, but they also prey on caribou when they encounter them which results in the caribou decline.

1. (a) Explain why genetic variation within a population is a prerequisite for evolution. (b) What factors can produce genetic differences between populations?
2. Of all the mutations that occur in a population, why do only a small fraction become widespread?
3. **MAKE CONNECTIONS** If a population stopped reproducing sexually (but still reproduced asexually), how would its genetic variation be affected over time? Explain. (See Concept 13.4, pp. 257–259.)

For suggested answers, see Appendix A.

CONCEPT **23.2**

The Hardy-Weinberg equation can be used to test whether a population is evolving

Although the individuals in a population must differ genetically for evolution to occur, the presence of genetic variation does not guarantee that a population will evolve. For that to happen, one of the factors that cause evolution must be at work. In this section, we'll explore one way to test whether evolution is occurring in a population. The first step in this process is to clarify what we mean by a population.

Gene Pools and Allele Frequencies

A **population** is a group of individuals of the same species that live in the same area and interbreed, producing fertile offspring. Different populations of a single species may be isolated geographically from one another, thus exchanging genetic material only rarely. Such isolation is common for species that live on widely separated islands or in different lakes. But not all populations are isolated, nor must populations have sharp boundaries (**Figure 23.6**). Still, members of a population typically breed with one another and thus on average are more closely related to each other than to members of other populations.

We can characterize a population's genetic makeup by describing its **gene pool**, which consists of all copies of every type of allele at every locus in all members of the population. If only one allele exists for a particular locus in a population, that allele is said to be *fixed* in the gene pool, and all individuals are homozygous for that allele. But if there are two or more alleles for a particular locus in a population, individuals may be either homozygous or heterozygous.

Each allele has a frequency (proportion) in the population. For example, imagine a population of 500 wildflower plants with two alleles, C^R and C^W, for a locus that codes for flower pigment. These alleles show incomplete dominance (see Figure 14.10); thus, each genotype has a distinct phenotype.

▲ **Figure 23.6 One species, two populations.** These two caribou populations in the Yukon are not totally isolated; they sometimes share the same area. Still, members of either population are most likely to breed within their own population.

Plants homozygous for the C^R allele (C^RC^R) produce red pigment and have red flowers; plants homozygous for the C^W allele (C^WC^W) produce no red pigment and have white flowers; and heterozygotes (C^RC^W) produce some red pigment and have pink flowers.

In our population, suppose there are 320 plants with red flowers, 160 with pink flowers, and 20 with white flowers. Because these are diploid organisms, there are a total of 1,000 copies of the gene for flower color in the population of 500 individuals. The C^R allele accounts for 800 of these copies ($320 \times 2 = 640$ for C^RC^R plants, plus $160 \times 1 = 160$ for C^RC^W plants).

When studying a locus with two alleles, the convention is to use p to represent the frequency of one allele and q to represent the frequency of the other allele. Thus, p, the frequency of the C^R allele in the gene pool of this population, is $800/1,000 = 0.8 = 80\%$. And because there are only two alleles for this gene, the frequency of the C^W allele, represented by q, must be $200/1,000 = 0.2 = 20\%$. For loci that have more than two alleles, the sum of all allele frequencies must still equal 1 (100%).

Next we'll see how allele and genotype frequencies can be used to test whether evolution is occurring in a population.

The Hardy-Weinberg Principle

One way to assess whether natural selection or other factors are causing evolution at a particular locus is to determine what the genetic makeup of a population would be if it were *not* evolving at that locus. We can then compare that scenario with data from a real population. If there are no differences, we can conclude that the real population is not evolving. If there are differences, this suggests that the real population may be evolving—and then we can try to figure out why.

Hardy-Weinberg Equilibrium

The gene pool of a population that is not evolving can be described by the **Hardy-Weinberg principle**, named for the British mathematician and German physician, respectively, who independently derived it in 1908. This principle states that the frequencies of alleles and genotypes in a population will remain constant from generation to generation, provided that only Mendelian segregation and recombination of alleles are at work. Such a gene pool is in *Hardy-Weinberg equilibrium*.

To use the Hardy-Weinberg principle, it is helpful to think about genetic crosses in a new way. Previously, we used Punnett squares to determine the genotypes of offspring in a genetic cross (see Figure 14.5). Here, instead of considering the possible allele combinations from one cross, consider the combination of alleles in *all* of the crosses in a population.

Imagine that all the alleles for a given locus from all the individuals in a population were placed in a large bin (**Figure 23.7**).

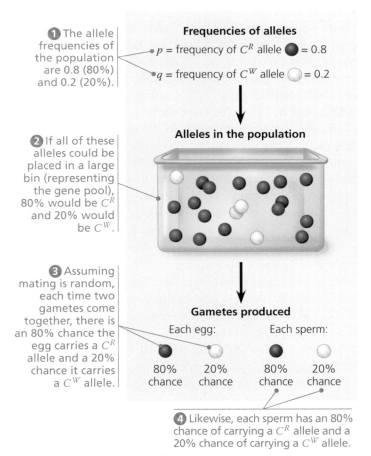

❶ The allele frequencies of the population are 0.8 (80%) and 0.2 (20%).

Frequencies of alleles

p = frequency of C^R allele ● = 0.8
q = frequency of C^W allele ○ = 0.2

❷ If all of these alleles could be placed in a large bin (representing the gene pool), 80% would be C^R and 20% would be C^W.

Alleles in the population

❸ Assuming mating is random, each time two gametes come together, there is an 80% chance the egg carries a C^R allele and a 20% chance it carries a C^W allele.

Gametes produced

Each egg:
80% chance   20% chance

Each sperm:
80% chance   20% chance

❹ Likewise, each sperm has an 80% chance of carrying a C^R allele and a 20% chance of carrying a C^W allele.

▲ **Figure 23.7 Selecting alleles at random from a gene pool.**

We can think of this bin as holding the population's gene pool for that locus. "Reproduction" occurs by selecting alleles at random from the bin; somewhat similar events occur in nature when fish release sperm and eggs into the water or when pollen (containing plant sperm) is blown about by the wind. By viewing reproduction as a process of randomly selecting and combining alleles from the bin (the gene pool), we are in effect assuming that mating occurs at random—that is, that all male-female matings are equally likely.

Let's apply the bin analogy to the hypothetical wildflower population discussed earlier. In that population of 500 flowers, the frequency of the allele for red flowers (C^R) is $p = 0.8$, and the frequency of the allele for white flowers (C^W) is $q = 0.2$. Thus, a bin holding all 1,000 copies of the flower-color gene in the population contains 800 C^R alleles and 200 C^W alleles. Assuming that gametes are formed by selecting alleles at random from the bin, the probability that an egg or sperm contains a C^R or C^W allele is equal to the frequency of these alleles in the bin. Thus, as shown in Figure 23.7, each egg has an 80% chance of containing a C^R allele and a 20% chance of containing a C^W allele; the same is true for each sperm.

Using the rule of multiplication (see Figure 14.9), we can now calculate the frequencies of the three possible genotypes, assuming random unions of sperm and eggs. The probability that two C^R alleles will come together is $p \times p = p^2 = 0.8 \times 0.8 = 0.64$. Thus, about 64% of the plants in the next generation will have the genotype $C^R C^R$. The frequency of $C^W C^W$ individuals is expected to be about $q \times q = q^2 = 0.2 \times 0.2 = 0.04$, or 4%. $C^R C^W$ heterozygotes can arise in two different ways. If the sperm provides the C^R allele and the egg provides the C^W allele, the resulting heterozygotes will be $p \times q = 0.8 \times 0.2 = 0.16$, or 16% of the total. If the sperm provides the C^W allele and the egg the C^R allele, the heterozygous offspring will make up $q \times p = 0.2 \times 0.8 = 0.16$, or 16%. The frequency of heterozygotes is thus the sum of these possibilities: $pq + qp = 2pq = 0.16 + 0.16 = 0.32$, or 32%.

As shown in **Figure 23.8** on the facing page, the genotype frequencies in the next generation must add up to 1 (100%). Thus, the equation for Hardy-Weinberg equilibrium states that at a locus with two alleles, the three genotypes will appear in the following proportions:

$$p^2 \quad + \quad 2pq \quad + \quad q^2 \quad = \quad 1$$

p^2	$2pq$	q^2
Expected frequency of genotype $C^R C^R$	Expected frequency of genotype $C^R C^W$	Expected frequency of genotype $C^W C^W$

Note that for a locus with two alleles, only three genotypes are possible (in this case, $C^R C^R$, $C^R C^W$, and $C^W C^W$). As a result, the sum of the frequencies of the three genotypes must equal 1 (100%) in *any* population—regardless of whether the population is in Hardy-Weinberg equilibrium. A population is in Hardy-Weinberg equilibrium only if the genotype frequencies are such that the actual frequency of

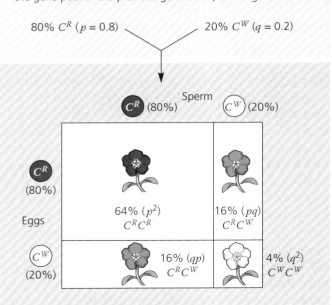

Gametes for each generation are drawn at random from the gene pool of the previous generation, as in Figure 23.7:

80% C^R (p = 0.8)   20% C^W (q = 0.2)

Sperm
C^R (80%) C^W (20%)

Eggs
C^R (80%)
C^W (20%)

64% (p^2)
$C^R C^R$

16% (pq)
$C^R C^W$

16% (qp)
$C^R C^W$

4% (q^2)
$C^W C^W$

If the gametes come together at random, the genotype frequencies of this generation are in Hardy-Weinberg equilibrium:

64% $C^R C^R$, 32% $C^R C^W$, and 4% $C^W C^W$

Gametes of this generation:

64% C^R
(from $C^R C^R$ plants) + 16% C^R
(from $C^R C^W$ plants) = 80% C^R = 0.8 = p

4% C^W
(from $C^W C^W$ plants) + 16% C^W
(from $C^R C^W$ plants) = 20% C^W = 0.2 = q

With random mating, these gametes will result in the same mix of genotypes in the next generation:

64% $C^R C^R$, 32% $C^R C^W$, and 4% $C^W C^W$ plants

▲ **Figure 23.8 The Hardy-Weinberg principle.** In our wildflower population, the gene pool remains constant from one generation to the next. Mendelian processes alone do not alter frequencies of alleles or genotypes.

? *If the frequency of the C^R allele is 60%, predict the frequencies of the $C^R C^R$, $C^R C^W$, and $C^W C^W$ genotypes.*

one homozygote is p^2, the actual frequency of the other homozygote is q^2, and the actual frequency of heterozygotes is $2pq$. Finally, as suggested by Figure 23.8, if a population such as our wildflowers is in Hardy-Weinberg equilibrium and its members continue to mate randomly generation after generation, allele and genotype frequencies will remain constant. The system operates somewhat like a deck of cards: No matter how many times the deck is reshuffled to deal out new hands, the deck itself remains the same. Aces do not grow more numerous than jacks. And the repeated shuffling of a

population's gene pool over the generations cannot, in itself, change the frequency of one allele relative to another.

Conditions for Hardy-Weinberg Equilibrium

The Hardy-Weinberg principle describes a hypothetical population that is not evolving. But in real populations, the allele and genotype frequencies often *do* change over time. Such changes can occur when at least one of the following five conditions of Hardy-Weinberg equilibrium is not met:

1. **No mutations.** The gene pool is modified if mutations alter alleles or if entire genes are deleted or duplicated.
2. **Random mating.** If individuals mate preferentially within a subset of the population, such as their close relatives (inbreeding), random mixing of gametes does not occur, and genotype frequencies change.
3. **No natural selection.** Differences in the survival and reproductive success of individuals carrying different genotypes can alter allele frequencies.
4. **Extremely large population size.** The smaller the population, the more likely it is that allele frequencies will fluctuate by chance from one generation to the next (a process called genetic drift).
5. **No gene flow.** By moving alleles into or out of populations, gene flow can alter allele frequencies.

Departure from these conditions usually results in evolutionary change, which, as we've already described, is common in natural populations. But it is also common for natural populations to be in Hardy-Weinberg equilibrium for specific genes. This apparent contradiction occurs because a population can be evolving at some loci, yet simultaneously be in Hardy-Weinberg equilibrium at other loci. In addition, some populations evolve so slowly that the changes in their allele and genotype frequencies are difficult to distinguish from those predicted for a nonevolving population.

Applying the Hardy-Weinberg Principle

The Hardy-Weinberg equation is often used as an initial test of whether evolution is occurring in a population (you'll encounter an example in Concept Check 23.2, question 3). The equation also has medical applications, such as estimating the percentage of a population carrying the allele for an inherited disease. For example, consider phenylketonuria (PKU), a metabolic disorder that results from homozygosity for a recessive allele and occurs in about one out of every 10,000 babies born in the United States. Left untreated, PKU results in mental disability and other problems. (Newborns are now tested for PKU, and symptoms can be largely avoided with a diet very low in phenylalanine. For this reason, products that contain phenylalanine, such as diet colas, carry warning labels.)

To apply the Hardy-Weinberg equation, we must assume that no new PKU mutations are being introduced into the population (condition 1), and that people neither choose their mates on the basis of whether or not they carry this gene nor generally mate with close relatives (condition 2). We must also ignore any effects of differential survival and reproductive success among PKU genotypes (condition 3) and assume that there are no effects of genetic drift (condition 4) or of gene flow from other populations into the United States (condition 5). These assumptions are reasonable: The mutation rate for the PKU gene is low, inbreeding is not common in the United States, selection occurs only against the rare homozygotes (and then only if dietary restrictions are not followed), the U.S. population is very large, and populations outside the country have PKU allele frequencies similar to those seen in the United States. If all these assumptions hold, then the frequency of individuals in the population born with PKU will correspond to q^2 in the Hardy-Weinberg equation (q^2 = frequency of homozygotes). Because the allele is recessive, we must estimate the number of heterozygotes rather than counting them directly as we did with the pink flowers. Since we know there is one PKU occurrence per 10,000 births (q^2 = 0.0001), the frequency of the recessive allele for PKU is

$$q = \sqrt{0.0001} = 0.01$$

and the frequency of the dominant allele is

$$p = 1 - q = 1 - 0.01 = 0.99$$

The frequency of carriers, heterozygous people who do not have PKU but may pass the PKU allele to offspring, is

$$2pq = 2 \times 0.99 \times 0.01 = 0.0198$$
(approximately 2% of the U.S. population)

Remember, the assumption of Hardy-Weinberg equilibrium yields an approximation; the real number of carriers may differ. Still, our calculations suggest that harmful recessive alleles at this and other loci can be concealed in a population because they are carried by healthy heterozygotes.

CONCEPT CHECK 23.2

1. Suppose a population of organisms with 20,000 gene loci is fixed at half of these loci and has two alleles at each of the other loci. How many different types of alleles are found in its entire gene pool? Explain.

2. If p is the frequency of allele A, use the Hardy-Weinberg equation to predict the frequency of individuals that have at least one A allele.

3. **WHAT IF?** A locus that affects susceptibility to a degenerative brain disease has two alleles, A and a. In a population, 16 people have genotype AA, 92 have genotype Aa, and 12 have genotype aa. Is this population evolving? Explain.

For suggested answers, see Appendix A.

CONCEPT 23.3

Natural selection, genetic drift, and gene flow can alter allele frequencies in a population

Note again the five conditions required for a population to be in Hardy-Weinberg equilibrium. A deviation from any of these conditions is a potential cause of evolution. New mutations (violation of condition 1) can alter allele frequencies, but because mutations are rare, the change from one generation to the next is likely to be very small. Nevertheless, as we'll see, mutation ultimately can have a large effect on allele frequencies when it produces new alleles that strongly influence fitness in a positive or negative way. Nonrandom mating (violation of condition 2) can affect the frequencies of homozygous and heterozygous genotypes but by itself usually has no effect on allele frequencies in the gene pool. The three mechanisms that alter allele frequencies directly and cause most evolutionary change are natural selection, genetic drift, and gene flow (violations of conditions 3–5).

Natural Selection

As you read in Chapter 22, Darwin's concept of natural selection is based on differential success in survival and reproduction: Individuals in a population exhibit variations in their heritable traits, and those with traits that are better suited to their environment tend to produce more offspring than those with traits that are not as well suited.

In genetic terms, we now know that selection results in alleles being passed to the next generation in proportions that differ from those in the present generation. For example, the fruit fly *D. melanogaster* has an allele that confers resistance to several insecticides, including DDT. This allele has a frequency of 0% in laboratory strains of *D. melanogaster* established from flies collected in the wild in the early 1930s, prior to DDT use. However, in strains established from flies collected after 1960 (following 20 or more years of DDT use), the allele frequency is 37%. We can infer that this allele either arose by mutation between 1930 and 1960 or that it was present in 1930, but very rare. In any case, the rise in frequency of this allele most likely occurred because DDT is a powerful poison that is a strong selective force in exposed fly populations.

As the *D. melanogaster* example shows, an allele that confers insecticide resistance will increase in frequency in a population exposed to that insecticide. Such changes are not coincidental. By consistently favoring some alleles over others, natural selection can cause *adaptive evolution* (evolution that results in a better match between organisms and their environment). We'll explore this process in more detail a little later in this chapter.

Genetic Drift

If you flip a coin 1,000 times, a result of 700 heads and 300 tails might make you suspicious about that coin. But if you flip a coin only 10 times, an outcome of 7 heads and 3 tails would not be surprising. The smaller the number of coin flips, the more likely it is that chance alone will cause a deviation from the predicted result. (In this case, the prediction is an equal number of heads and tails.) Chance events can also cause allele frequencies to fluctuate unpredictably from one generation to the next, especially in small populations—a process called **genetic drift**.

Figure 23.9 models how genetic drift might affect a small population of our wildflowers. In this example, an allele is lost from the gene pool, but it is a matter of chance that the C^W allele is lost and not the C^R allele. Such unpredictable changes in allele frequencies can be caused by chance events associated with survival and reproduction. Perhaps a large animal such as a moose stepped on the three $C^W C^W$ individuals in generation 2, killing them and increasing the chance that only the C^R allele would be passed to the next generation. Allele frequencies can also be affected by chance events that occur during fertilization. For example, suppose two individuals of genotype $C^R C^W$ had a small number of offspring. By chance alone, every egg and sperm pair that generated offspring could happen to have carried the C^R allele and not the C^W allele.

Certain circumstances can result in genetic drift having a significant impact on a population. Two examples are the founder effect and the bottleneck effect.

The Founder Effect

When a few individuals become isolated from a larger population, this smaller group may establish a new population whose gene pool differs from the source population; this is called the **founder effect**. The founder effect might occur, for example, when a few members of a population are blown by a storm to a new island. Genetic drift, in which chance events alter allele frequencies, will occur in such a case if the storm indiscriminately transports some individuals (and their alleles), but not others, from the source population.

The founder effect probably accounts for the relatively high frequency of certain inherited disorders among isolated human populations. For example, in 1814, 15 British colonists founded a settlement on Tristan da Cunha, a group of small islands in the Atlantic Ocean midway between Africa and South America. Apparently, one of the colonists carried a recessive allele for retinitis pigmentosa, a progressive form of blindness that afflicts homozygous individuals. Of the founding colonists' 240 descendants on the island in the late 1960s, 4 had retinitis pigmentosa. The frequency of the allele that causes this disease is ten times

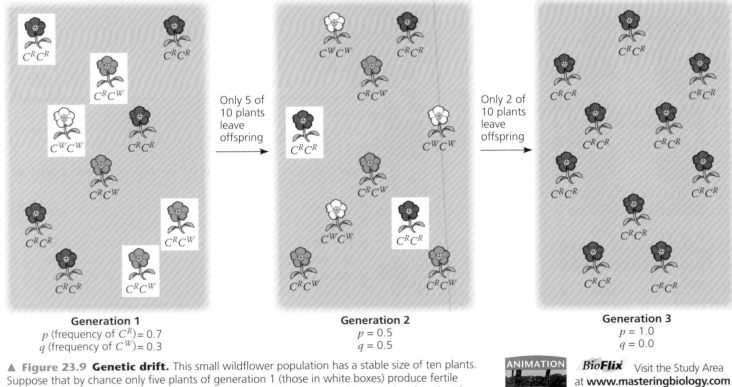

Generation 1
p (frequency of C^R) = 0.7
q (frequency of C^W) = 0.3

Generation 2
p = 0.5
q = 0.5

Generation 3
p = 1.0
q = 0.0

Only 5 of 10 plants leave offspring

Only 2 of 10 plants leave offspring

▲ **Figure 23.9 Genetic drift.** This small wildflower population has a stable size of ten plants. Suppose that by chance only five plants of generation 1 (those in white boxes) produce fertile offspring. (This could occur, for example, if only those plants happened to grow in a location that provided enough nutrients to support the production of offspring.) Again by chance, only two plants of generation 2 leave fertile offspring. As a result, by chance the frequency of the C^W allele first increases in generation 2, then falls to zero in generation 3.

ANIMATION **BioFlix** Visit the Study Area at **www.masteringbiology.com** for the BioFlix® 3-D Animation on Mechanisms of Evolution.

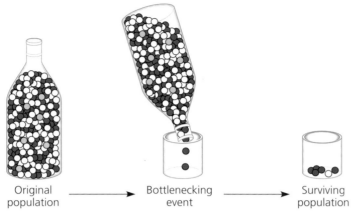

▲ **Figure 23.10 The bottleneck effect.** Shaking just a few marbles through the narrow neck of a bottle is analogous to a drastic reduction in the size of a population. By chance, blue marbles are overrepresented in the surviving population and gold marbles are absent.

higher on Tristan da Cunha than in the populations from which the founders came.

The Bottleneck Effect

A sudden change in the environment, such as a fire or flood, may drastically reduce the size of a population. A severe drop in population size can cause the **bottleneck effect**, so named because the population has passed through a "bottleneck" that reduces its size (**Figure 23.10**). By chance alone, certain alleles may be overrepresented among the survivors, others may be underrepresented, and some may be absent altogether. Ongoing genetic drift is likely to have substantial effects on the gene pool until the population becomes large enough that chance events have less impact. But even if a population that has passed through a bottleneck ultimately recovers in size, it may have low levels of genetic variation for a long period of time—a legacy of the genetic drift that occurred when the population was small.

One reason it is important to understand the bottleneck effect is that human actions sometimes create severe bottlenecks for other species, as the following example shows.

Case Study: *Impact of Genetic Drift on the Greater Prairie Chicken*

Millions of greater prairie chickens (*Tympanuchus cupido*) once lived on the prairies of Illinois. As these prairies were converted to farmland and other uses during the 19th and 20th centuries, the number of greater prairie chickens plummeted (**Figure 23.11a**). By 1993, only two Illinois populations remained, which together harbored fewer than 50 birds. The few surviving birds had low levels of genetic variation, and less than 50% of their eggs hatched, compared with much higher hatching rates of the larger populations in Kansas and Nebraska (**Figure 23.11b**).

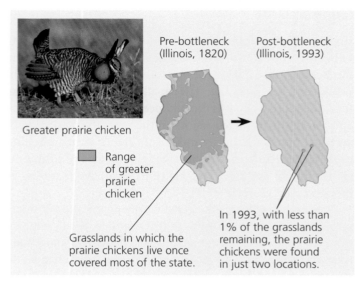

Greater prairie chicken

Range of greater prairie chicken

Pre-bottleneck (Illinois, 1820)   Post-bottleneck (Illinois, 1993)

Grasslands in which the prairie chickens live once covered most of the state.

In 1993, with less than 1% of the grasslands remaining, the prairie chickens were found in just two locations.

(a) The Illinois population of greater prairie chickens dropped from millions of birds in the 1800s to fewer than 50 birds in 1993.

Location	Population size	Number of alleles per locus	Percentage of eggs hatched
Illinois			
1930–1960s	1,000–25,000	5.2	93
1993	<50	3.7	<50
Kansas, 1998 (no bottleneck)	750,000	5.8	99
Nebraska, 1998 (no bottleneck)	75,000–200,000	5.8	96

(b) As a consequence of the drastic reduction in the size of the Illinois population, genetic drift resulted in a drop in the number of alleles per locus (averaged across six loci studied) and a decrease in the percentage of eggs that hatched.

▲ **Figure 23.11 Genetic drift and loss of genetic variation.**

These data suggest that genetic drift during the bottleneck may have led to a loss of genetic variation and an increase in the frequency of harmful alleles. To investigate this hypothesis, Juan Bouzat, of Bowling Green State University, Ohio, and his colleagues extracted DNA from 15 museum specimens of Illinois greater prairie chickens. Of the 15 birds, 10 had been collected in the 1930s, when there were 25,000 greater prairie chickens in Illinois, and 5 had been collected in the 1960s, when there were 1,000 greater prairie chickens in Illinois. By studying the DNA of these specimens, the researchers were able to obtain a minimum, baseline estimate of how much genetic variation was present in the Illinois population *before* the population shrank to extremely low numbers. This baseline estimate is a key piece of information that is not usually available in cases of population bottlenecks.

The researchers surveyed six loci and found that the 1993 Illinois greater prairie chicken population had lost nine alleles that were present in the museum specimens. The 1993 population also had fewer alleles per locus than the pre-bottleneck Illinois or the current Kansas and Nebraska populations (see Figure 23.11b). Thus, as predicted, drift had reduced the genetic variation of the small 1993 population. Drift may also have increased the frequency of harmful alleles, leading to the low egg-hatching rate. To counteract these negative effects, 271 birds from neighboring states were added to the Illinois population over four years. This strategy succeeded: New alleles entered the population, and the egg-hatching rate improved to over 90%. Overall, studies on the Illinois greater prairie chicken illustrate the powerful effects of genetic drift in small populations and provide hope that in at least some populations, these effects can be reversed.

Effects of Genetic Drift: A Summary

The examples we've described highlight four key points:

1. **Genetic drift is significant in small populations.** Chance events can cause an allele to be disproportionately over- or underrepresented in the next generation. Although chance events occur in populations of all sizes, they tend to alter allele frequencies substantially only in small populations.
2. **Genetic drift can cause allele frequencies to change at random.** Because of genetic drift, an allele may increase in frequency one year, then decrease the next; the change from year to year is not predictable. Thus, unlike natural selection, which in a given environment consistently favors some alleles over others, genetic drift causes allele frequencies to change at random over time.
3. **Genetic drift can lead to a loss of genetic variation within populations.** By causing allele frequencies to fluctuate randomly over time, genetic drift can eliminate alleles from a population. Because evolution depends on genetic variation, such losses can influence how effectively a population can adapt to a change in the environment.
4. **Genetic drift can cause harmful alleles to become fixed.** Alleles that are neither harmful nor beneficial can be lost or become fixed entirely by chance through genetic drift. In very small populations, genetic drift can also cause alleles that are slightly harmful to become fixed. When this occurs, the population's survival can be threatened (as for the greater prairie chicken).

Gene Flow

Natural selection and genetic drift are not the only phenomena affecting allele frequencies. Allele frequencies can also change by **gene flow**, the transfer of alleles into or out of a population due to the movement of fertile individuals or their gametes. For example, suppose that near our original hypothetical wildflower population there is another population

consisting primarily of white-flowered individuals ($C^W C^W$). Insects carrying pollen from these plants may fly to and pollinate plants in our original population. The introduced C^W alleles would modify our original population's allele frequencies in the next generation. Because alleles are exchanged between populations, gene flow tends to reduce the genetic differences between populations. In fact, if it is extensive enough, gene flow can result in two populations combining into a single population with a common gene pool.

Alleles transferred by gene flow can also affect how well populations are adapted to local environmental conditions. Researchers studying the songbird *Parus major* (great tit) on the small Dutch island of Vlieland noted survival differences between two populations on the island. Females born in the eastern population survive twice as well as females born in the central population, regardless of where the females eventually settle and raise offspring (Figure 23.12). This finding suggests that females born in the eastern population are better adapted to life on the island than females born in the

▲ **Figure 23.12 Gene flow and local adaptation.** In *Parus major* populations on Vlieland, the yearly survival rate of females born in the eastern population is higher than that of females born in the central population. Gene flow from the mainland to the central population is 3.3 times higher than it is to the eastern population, and birds from the mainland are selected against in both populations. These data suggest that gene flow from the mainland has prevented the central population from adapting fully to its local conditions.

central population. But extensive field studies also showed that the two populations are connected by high levels of gene flow (mating), which should reduce genetic differences between them. So how can the eastern population be better adapted to life on Vlieland than the central population? The answer lies in the unequal amounts of gene flow from the mainland. In any given year, 43% of the first-time breeders in the central population are immigrants from the mainland, compared with only 13% in the eastern population. Birds with mainland genotypes survive and reproduce poorly on Vlieland, and in the eastern population, selection reduces the frequency of these genotypes. In the central population, however, gene flow from the mainland is so high that it overwhelms the effects of selection. As a result, females born in the central population have many immigrant genes, reducing the degree to which members of that population are adapted to life on the island. Researchers are currently investigating why gene flow is so much higher in the central population and why birds with mainland genotypes have low fitness on Vlieland.

Gene flow can also transfer alleles that improve the ability of populations to adapt to local conditions. For example, gene flow has resulted in the worldwide spread of several insecticide-resistance alleles in the mosquito *Culex pipiens*, a vector of West Nile virus and other diseases. Each of these alleles has a unique genetic signature that allowed researchers to document that it arose by mutation in one or a few geographic locations. In their population of origin, these alleles increased because they provided insecticide resistance. These alleles were then transferred to new populations, where again, their frequencies increased as a result of natural selection.

Finally, gene flow has become an increasingly important agent of evolutionary change in human populations. Humans today move much more freely about the world than in the past. As a result, mating is more common between members of populations that previously had very little contact, leading to an exchange of alleles and fewer genetic differences between those populations.

CONCEPT CHECK 23.3

1. In what sense is natural selection more "predictable" than genetic drift?
2. Distinguish genetic drift from gene flow in terms of (a) how they occur and (b) their implications for future genetic variation in a population.
3. **WHAT IF?** Suppose two plant populations exchange pollen and seeds. In one population, individuals of genotype *AA* are most common (9,000 *AA*, 900 *Aa*, 100 *aa*), while the opposite is true in the other population (100 *AA*, 900 *Aa*, 9,000 *aa*). If neither allele has a selective advantage, what will happen over time to the allele and genotype frequencies of these populations?

For suggested answers, see Appendix A.

Natural selection is the only mechanism that consistently causes adaptive evolution

Evolution by natural selection is a blend of chance and "sorting": chance in the creation of new genetic variations (as in mutation) and sorting as natural selection favors some alleles over others. Because of this favoring process, the outcome of natural selection is *not* random. Instead, natural selection consistently increases the frequencies of alleles that provide reproductive advantage and thus leads to adaptive evolution.

A Closer Look at Natural Selection

In examining how natural selection brings about adaptive evolution, we'll begin with the concept of relative fitness and the different ways that an organism's phenotype is subject to natural selection.

Relative Fitness

The phrases "struggle for existence" and "survival of the fittest" are commonly used to describe natural selection, but these expressions are misleading if taken to mean direct competitive contests among individuals. There *are* animal species in which individuals, usually the males, lock horns or otherwise do combat to determine mating privilege. But reproductive success is generally more subtle and depends on many factors besides outright battle. For example, a barnacle that is more efficient at collecting food than its neighbors may have greater stores of energy and hence be able to produce a larger number of eggs. A moth may have more offspring than other moths in the same population because its body colors more effectively conceal it from predators, improving its chance of surviving long enough to produce more offspring. These examples illustrate how in a given environment, certain traits can lead to greater **relative fitness**: the contribution an individual makes to the gene pool of the next generation *relative to* the contributions of other individuals.

Although we often refer to the relative fitness of a genotype, remember that the entity that is subjected to natural selection is the whole organism, not the underlying genotype. Thus, selection acts more directly on the phenotype than on the genotype; it acts on the genotype indirectly, via how the genotype affects the phenotype.

Directional, Disruptive, and Stabilizing Selection

Natural selection can alter the frequency distribution of heritable traits in three ways, depending on which phenotypes in a population are favored. These three modes of selection are called directional selection, disruptive selection, and stabilizing selection.

Directional selection occurs when conditions favor individuals exhibiting one extreme of a phenotypic range, thereby shifting a population's frequency curve for the phenotypic character in one direction or the other **(Figure 23.13a)**. Directional selection is common when a population's environment changes or when members of a population migrate to a new (and different) habitat. For instance, an increase in the size of seeds available as food led to an increase in beak depth in a population of Galápagos finches (see Figure 23.1).

Disruptive selection (Figure 23.13b) occurs when conditions favor individuals at both extremes of a phenotypic range over individuals with intermediate phenotypes. One example is a population of black-bellied seedcracker finches in Cameroon whose members display two distinctly different beak sizes. Small-billed birds feed mainly on soft seeds, whereas large-billed birds specialize in cracking hard seeds. It appears that birds with intermediate-sized bills are relatively inefficient at cracking both types of seeds and thus have lower relative fitness.

Stabilizing selection (Figure 23.13c) acts against both extreme phenotypes and favors intermediate variants. This mode of selection reduces variation and tends to maintain the status quo for a particular phenotypic character. For example, the birth weights of most human babies lie in the range of 3–4 kg (6.6–8.8 pounds); babies who are either much smaller or much larger suffer higher rates of mortality.

Regardless of the mode of selection, however, the basic mechanism remains the same. Selection favors individuals whose heritable phenotypic traits provide higher reproductive success than do the traits of other individuals.

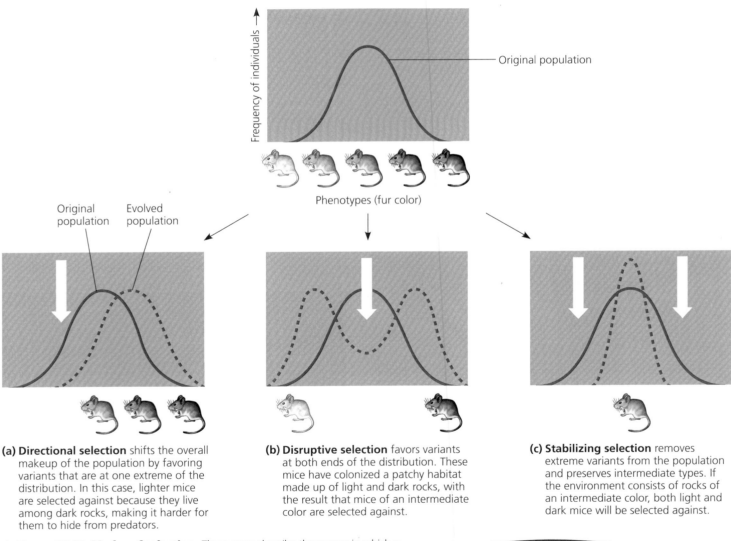

(a) Directional selection shifts the overall makeup of the population by favoring variants that are at one extreme of the distribution. In this case, lighter mice are selected against because they live among dark rocks, making it harder for them to hide from predators.

(b) Disruptive selection favors variants at both ends of the distribution. These mice have colonized a patchy habitat made up of light and dark rocks, with the result that mice of an intermediate color are selected against.

(c) Stabilizing selection removes extreme variants from the population and preserves intermediate types. If the environment consists of rocks of an intermediate color, both light and dark mice will be selected against.

▲ **Figure 23.13 Modes of selection.** These cases describe three ways in which a hypothetical deer mouse population with heritable variation in fur coloration from light to dark might evolve. The graphs show how the frequencies of individuals with different fur colors change over time. The large white arrows symbolize selective pressures against certain phenotypes.

MAKE CONNECTIONS *Review Figure 22.13 on p. 461. Which mode of selection has occurred in soapberry bug populations that feed on the introduced goldenrain tree? Explain.*

The Key Role of Natural Selection in Adaptive Evolution

The adaptations of organisms include many striking examples. Cuttlefish, for example, have the ability to change color rapidly, enabling them to blend into different backgrounds. Another example is the remarkable jaws of snakes **(Figure 23.14)**, which allow them to swallow prey much larger than their own head (a feat analogous to a person swallowing a whole watermelon). Other adaptations, such as a version of an enzyme that shows improved function in cold environments (see Figure 23.5), may be less visually dramatic but just as important for survival and reproduction.

Such adaptations can arise gradually over time as natural selection increases the frequencies of alleles that enhance survival and reproduction. As the proportion of individuals that have favorable traits increases, the match between a species and its environment improves; that is, adaptive evolution occurs. However, as we saw in Chapter 22, the physical and biological components of an organism's environment may change over time. As a result, what constitutes a "good match" between an organism and its environment can be a moving target, making adaptive evolution a continuous, dynamic process.

And what about the two other important mechanisms of evolutionary change in populations, genetic drift and gene flow? Both can, in fact, increase the frequencies of alleles that improve the match between organisms and their environ-ment, but neither does so consistently. Genetic drift can cause the frequency of a slightly beneficial allele to increase, but it also can cause the frequency of such an allele to decrease. Similarly, gene flow may introduce alleles that are advantageous or ones that are disadvantageous. Natural selection is the only evolutionary mechanism that consistently leads to adaptive evolution.

Sexual Selection

Charles Darwin was the first to explore the implications of **sexual selection**, a form of selection in which individuals with certain inherited characteristics are more likely than other individuals to obtain mates. Sexual selection can result in **sexual dimorphism**, a difference between the two sexes in secondary sexual characteristics **(Figure 23.15)**. These distinctions include differences in size, color, ornamentation, and behavior.

How does sexual selection operate? There are several ways. In **intrasexual selection**, meaning selection within the same sex, individuals of one sex compete directly for mates of the opposite sex. In many species, intrasexual selection occurs among males. For example, a single male may patrol a group of females and prevent other males from mating with them. The patrolling male may defend his status by defeating smaller, weaker, or less fierce males in combat. More often, this male is the psychological victor in ritualized displays that discourage would-be competitors but do not risk injury that would reduce his own fitness (see Figure 51.22). Intrasexual selection has also been observed among females in a variety of species, including ring-tailed lemurs and broad-nosed pipefish.

In **intersexual selection**, also called *mate choice*, individuals of one sex (usually the females) are choosy in selecting

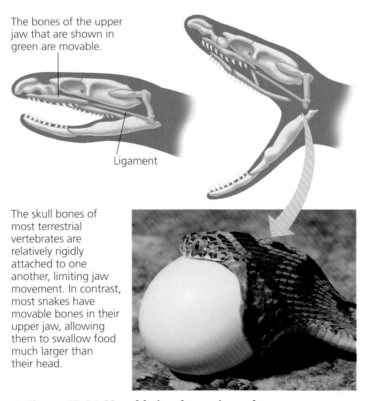

The bones of the upper jaw that are shown in green are movable.

Ligament

The skull bones of most terrestrial vertebrates are relatively rigidly attached to one another, limiting jaw movement. In contrast, most snakes have movable bones in their upper jaw, allowing them to swallow food much larger than their head.

▲ Figure 23.14 **Movable jaw bones in snakes.**

▲ Figure 23.15 **Sexual dimorphism and sexual selection.** Peacocks (above left) and peahens (above right) show extreme sexual dimorphism. There is intrasexual selection between competing males, followed by intersexual selection when the females choose among the showiest males.

their mates from the other sex. In many cases, the female's choice depends on the showiness of the male's appearance or behavior (see Figure 23.15). What intrigued Darwin about mate choice is that male showiness may not seem adaptive in any other way and may in fact pose some risk. For example, bright plumage may make male birds more visible to predators. But if such characteristics help a male gain a mate, and if this benefit outweighs the risk from predation, then both the bright plumage and the female preference for it will be reinforced because they enhance overall reproductive success.

How do female preferences for certain male characteristics evolve in the first place? One hypothesis is that females prefer male traits that are correlated with "good genes." If the trait preferred by females is indicative of a male's overall genetic quality, both the male trait and female preference for it should increase in frequency. **Figure 23.16** describes one experiment testing this hypothesis in gray tree frogs (*Hyla versicolor*).

Other researchers have shown that in several bird species, the traits preferred by females are related to overall male health. Here, too, female preference appears to be based on traits that reflect "good genes," in this case alleles indicative of a robust immune system.

The Preservation of Genetic Variation

Some of the genetic variation in populations represents **neutral variation**, differences in DNA sequence that do not confer a selective advantage or disadvantage. But variation is also found at loci affected by selection. What prevents natural selection from reducing genetic variation at those loci by culling all unfavorable alleles? The tendency for directional and stabilizing selection to reduce variation is countered by mechanisms that preserve or restore it.

Diploidy

In diploid eukaryotes, a considerable amount of genetic variation is hidden from selection in the form of recessive alleles. Recessive alleles that are less favorable than their dominant counterparts, or even harmful in the current environment, can persist by propagation in heterozygous individuals. This latent variation is exposed to natural selection only when both parents carry the same recessive allele and two copies end up in the same zygote. This happens only rarely if the frequency of the recessive allele is very low. Heterozygote protection maintains a huge pool of alleles that might not be favored under present conditions, but which could bring new benefits if the environment changes.

Balancing Selection

Selection itself may preserve variation at some loci. **Balancing selection** occurs when natural selection maintains two or

▼ **Figure 23.16** **INQUIRY**

Do females select mates based on traits indicative of "good genes"?

EXPERIMENT Female gray tree frogs (*Hyla versicolor*) prefer to mate with males that give long mating calls. Allison Welch and colleagues, at the University of Missouri, tested whether the genetic makeup of long-calling (LC) males is superior to that of short-calling (SC) males. The researchers fertilized half the eggs of each female with sperm from an LC male and fertilized the remaining eggs with sperm from an SC male. The resulting half-sibling offspring were raised in a common environment, and several measures of their "performance" were tracked for two years.

RESULTS

Offspring Performance	1995	1996
Larval survival	LC better	NSD
Larval growth	NSD	LC better
Time to metamorphosis	LC better (shorter)	LC better (shorter)

NSD = no significant difference; LC better = offspring of LC males superior to offspring of SC males.

CONCLUSION Because offspring fathered by an LC male outperformed their half-siblings fathered by an SC male, the team concluded that the duration of a male's mating call is indicative of the male's overall genetic quality. This result supports the hypothesis that female mate choice can be based on a trait that indicates whether the male has "good genes."

SOURCE A. M. Welch et al., Call duration as an indicator of genetic quality in male gray tree frogs, *Science* 280:1928–1930 (1998).

INQUIRY IN ACTION Read and analyze the original paper in *Inquiry in Action: Interpreting Scientific Papers.*

WHAT IF? Why did the researchers split each female frog's eggs into two batches for fertilization by different males? Why didn't they mate each female with a single male frog?

more forms in a population. This type of selection includes heterozygote advantage and frequency-dependent selection.

Heterozygote Advantage If individuals who are heterozygous at a particular locus have greater fitness than do both kinds of homozygotes, they exhibit **heterozygote advantage**. In such a case, natural selection tends to maintain two or more alleles at that locus. Note that heterozygote advantage is defined in terms of *genotype*, not phenotype. Thus, whether heterozygote advantage represents stabilizing or directional selection depends on the relationship between the genotype and the phenotype. For example, if the phenotype of a heterozygote is intermediate to the phenotypes of both homozygotes, heterozygote advantage is a form of stabilizing selection.

An example of heterozygote advantage occurs at the locus in humans that codes for the β polypeptide subunit of hemoglobin, the oxygen-carrying protein of red blood cells. In homozygous individuals, a certain recessive allele at that locus causes sickle-cell disease. The red blood cells of people with sickle-cell disease become distorted in shape, or *sickled*, under low-oxygen conditions (see Figure 5.21), as occurs in the capillaries. These sickled cells can clump together and block the flow of blood in the capillaries, resulting in serious damage to organs such as the kidney, heart, and brain. Although some red blood cells become sickled in heterozygotes, not enough become sickled to cause sickle-cell disease.

Heterozygotes for the sickle-cell allele are protected against the most severe effects of malaria, a disease caused by a parasite that infects red blood cells (see Figure 28.10). This partial protection occurs because the body destroys sickled red blood cells rapidly, killing the parasites they harbor (but not affecting parasites inside normal red blood cells). Protection against malaria is important in tropical regions where the disease is a major killer. In such regions, selection favors heterozygotes over homozygous dominant individuals, who are more vulnerable to the effects of malaria, and also over homozygous recessive individuals, who develop sickle-cell disease. The frequency of the sickle-cell allele in Africa is generally highest in areas where the malaria parasite is most common (**Figure 23.17**). In some populations, it accounts for 20% of the hemoglobin alleles in the gene pool, a very high frequency for such a harmful allele.

Frequency-Dependent Selection In **frequency-dependent selection**, the fitness of a phenotype depends on how common it is in the population. Consider the scale-eating fish (*Perissodus microlepis*) of Lake Tanganyika, in Africa. These fish attack other fish from behind, darting in to remove a few scales from the flank of their prey. Of interest here is a peculiar feature of the scale-eating fish: Some are "left-mouthed" and some are "right-mouthed." Simple Mendelian inheritance determines these phenotypes, with the right-mouthed allele being domi-

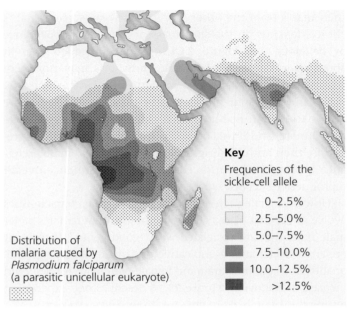

▲ **Figure 23.17 Mapping malaria and the sickle-cell allele.** The sickle-cell allele is most common in Africa, but it is not the only case of heterozygote advantage providing protection against malaria. Alleles at other loci (not shown on this map) are also favored by heterozygote advantage in populations near the Mediterranean Sea and in southeast Asia where malaria is widespread.

nant to the left-mouthed allele. Because their mouth twists to the left, left-mouthed fish always attack their prey's right flank (**Figure 23.18**). (To see why, twist your lower jaw and lips to the left and imagine trying to take a bite from the left side of a fish, approaching it from behind.) Similarly, right-mouthed fish always attack from the left. Prey species guard against attack from whatever phenotype of scale-eating fish is most common in the lake. Thus, from year to year, selection favors whichever mouth phenotype is least common. As a result, the frequency of left- and right-mouthed fish oscillates over time, and balancing selection (due to frequency dependence) keeps the frequency of each phenotype close to 50%.

Why Natural Selection Cannot Fashion Perfect Organisms

Though natural selection leads to adaptation, nature abounds with examples of organisms that are less than ideally "engineered" for their lifestyles. There are several reasons why.

1. **Selection can act only on existing variations.** Natural selection favors only the fittest phenotypes among those currently in the population, which may not be the ideal traits. New advantageous alleles do not arise on demand.

2. **Evolution is limited by historical constraints.** Each species has a legacy of descent with modification from ancestral forms. Evolution does not scrap the

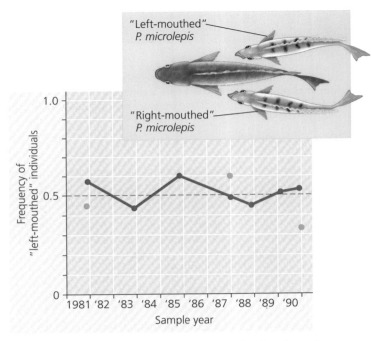

"Left-mouthed"
P. microlepis

"Right-mouthed"
P. microlepis

▲ **Figure 23.18 Frequency-dependent selection in scale-eating fish (*Perissodus microlepis*).** Michio Hori, of Kyoto University, Japan, noted that the frequency of left-mouthed individuals rises and falls in a regular manner. At each of three time periods when the phenotypes of breeding adults were assessed, adults that reproduced (represented by green dots) had the opposite phenotype of that which was most common in the population. Thus, it appeared that right-mouthed individuals were favored by selection when left-mouthed individuals were more common, and vice versa.

? *What did the researchers measure to determine which phenotype was favored by selection? Are any assumptions implied by this choice? Explain.*

ancestral anatomy and build each new complex structure from scratch; rather, evolution co-opts existing structures and adapts them to new situations. We could imagine that if a terrestrial animal were to adapt to an environment in which flight would be advantageous, it might be best just to grow an extra pair of limbs that would serve as wings. However, evolution does not work this way; instead, it operates on the traits an organism already has. Thus, in birds and bats, an existing pair of limbs took on new functions for flight as these organisms evolved from nonflying ancestors.

3. **Adaptations are often compromises.** Each organism must do many different things. A seal spends part of its time on rocks; it could probably walk better if it had legs instead of flippers, but then it would not swim nearly as well. We humans owe much of our versatility and athleticism to our prehensile hands and flexible limbs, but these also make us prone to sprains, torn ligaments, and dislocations: Structural reinforcement has been compromised for agility. **Figure 23.19** depicts another example of evolutionary compromise.

▲ **Figure 23.19 Evolutionary compromise.** The loud call that enables a Túngara frog to attract mates also attracts more dangerous characters in the neighborhood—in this case, a bat about to seize a meal.

4. **Chance, natural selection, and the environment interact.** Chance events can affect the subsequent evolutionary history of populations. For instance, when a storm blows insects or birds hundreds of kilometers over an ocean to an island, the wind does not necessarily transport those individuals that are best suited to the new environment. Thus, not all alleles present in the founding population's gene pool are better suited to the new environment than the alleles that are "left behind." In addition, the environment at a particular location may change unpredictably from year to year, again limiting the extent to which adaptive evolution results in a close match between the organism and current environmental conditions.

With these four constraints, evolution does not tend to craft perfect organisms. Natural selection operates on a "better than" basis. We can, in fact, see evidence for evolution in the many imperfections of the organisms it produces.

CONCEPT CHECK 23.4

1. What is the relative fitness of a sterile mule? Explain.
2. Explain why natural selection is the only evolutionary mechanism that consistently leads to adaptive evolution.
3. **WHAT IF?** Consider a population in which heterozygotes at a certain locus have an extreme phenotype (such as being larger than homozygotes) that confers a selective advantage. Does such a situation represent directional, disruptive, or stabilizing selection? Explain your answer.
4. **WHAT IF?** Would individuals who are heterozygous for the sickle-cell allele be selected for or against in a region free from malaria? Explain.

For suggested answers, see Appendix A.

SUMMARY OF KEY CONCEPTS

CONCEPT 23.1

Genetic variation makes evolution possible (pp. 469–473)

- **Genetic variation** refers to genetic differences among individuals within a population.
- The nucleotide differences that provide the basis of genetic variation arise by mutation and other processes that produce new alleles and new genes.
- New genetic variants are produced rapidly in organisms with short generation times. In sexually reproducing organisms, most of the genetic differences among individuals result from crossing over, the independent assortment of chromosomes, and fertilization.

? *Why do biologists estimate gene variability and nucleotide variability, and what do these estimates represent?*

CONCEPT 23.2

The Hardy-Weinberg equation can be used to test whether a population is evolving (pp. 473–476)

- A **population**, a localized group of organisms belonging to one species, is united by its **gene pool**, the aggregate of all the alleles in the population.
- The **Hardy-Weinberg principle** states that the allele and genotype frequencies of a population will remain constant if the population is large, mating is random, mutation is negligible, there is no gene flow, and there is no natural selection. For such a population, if p and q represent the frequencies of the only two possible alleles at a particular locus, then p^2 is the frequency of one kind of homozygote, q^2 is the frequency of the other kind of homozygote, and $2pq$ is the frequency of the heterozygous genotype.

? *Is it circular reasoning to calculate* p *and* q *from observed genotype frequencies and then use those values of* p *and* q *to test if the population is in Hardy-Weinberg equilibrium? Explain your answer. (Hint: Consider a specific case, such as a population with 195 individuals of genotype AA, 10 of genotype Aa, and 195 of genotype aa.)*

CONCEPT 23.3

Natural selection, genetic drift, and gene flow can alter allele frequencies in a population (pp. 476–480)

- In natural selection, individuals that have certain inherited traits tend to survive and reproduce at higher rates than other individuals *because of* those traits.
- In **genetic drift**, chance fluctuations in allele frequencies over generations tend to reduce genetic variation.
- **Gene flow**, the transfer of alleles between populations, tends to reduce genetic differences between populations over time.

? *Would two small, geographically isolated populations in very different environments be likely to evolve in similar ways? Explain.*

CONCEPT 23.4

Natural selection is the only mechanism that consistently causes adaptive evolution (pp. 480–485)

- One organism has greater **relative fitness** than a second organism if it leaves more fertile descendants than the second

organism. The modes of natural selection differ in how selection acts on phenotype (the white arrows in the summary diagram below represent selective pressure on a population).

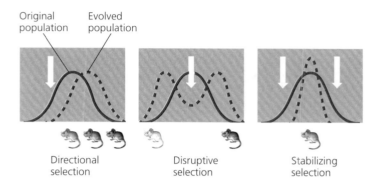

Original population   Evolved population

Directional selection   Disruptive selection   Stabilizing selection

- Unlike genetic drift and gene flow, natural selection consistently increases the frequencies of alleles that enhance survival and reproduction, thus improving the match between organisms and their environment.
- **Sexual selection** influences evolutionary change in secondary sex characteristics that can give individuals advantages in mating.
- Despite the winnowing effects of selection, populations have considerable genetic variation. Some of this variation represents **neutral variation**; additional variation can be maintained by diploidy and balancing selection.
- There are constraints to evolution: Natural selection can act only on available variation; structures result from modified ancestral anatomy; adaptations are often compromises; and chance, natural selection, and the environment interact.

? *How might secondary sex characteristics differ between males and females in a species in which females compete for mates?*

TEST YOUR UNDERSTANDING

LEVEL 1: KNOWLEDGE/COMPREHENSION

1. Natural selection changes allele frequencies because some _____ survive and reproduce more successfully than others.
   a. alleles
   b. loci
   c. gene pools
   d. species
   e. individuals

2. No two people are genetically identical, except for identical twins. The main source of genetic variation among human individuals is
   a. new mutations that occurred in the preceding generation.
   b. genetic drift due to the small size of the population.
   c. the reshuffling of alleles in sexual reproduction.
   d. geographic variation within the population.
   e. environmental effects.

3. Sparrows with average-sized wings survive severe storms better than those with longer or shorter wings, illustrating
   a. the bottleneck effect.
   b. disruptive selection.
   c. frequency-dependent selection.
   d. neutral variation.
   e. stabilizing selection.

LEVEL 2: APPLICATION/ANALYSIS

4. If the nucleotide variability of a locus equals 0%, what is the gene variability and number of alleles at that locus?
   a. gene variability = 0%; number of alleles = 0
   b. gene variability = 0%; number of alleles = 1
   c. gene variability = 0%; number of alleles = 2
   d. gene variability > 0%; number of alleles = 2
   e. Without more information, gene variability and number of alleles cannot be determined.

5. There are 40 individuals in population 1, all with genotype *A1A1*, and there are 25 individuals in population 2, all with genotype *A2A2*. Assume that these populations are located far from each other and that their environmental conditions are very similar. Based on the information given here, the observed genetic variation is most likely an example of
   a. genetic drift.   d. discrete variation.
   b. gene flow.   e. directional selection.
   c. disruptive selection.

6. A fruit fly population has a gene with two alleles, *A1* and *A2*. Tests show that 70% of the gametes produced in the population contain the *A1* allele. If the population is in Hardy-Weinberg equilibrium, what proportion of the flies carry both *A1* and *A2*?
   a. 0.7   b. 0.49   c. 0.21   d. 0.42   e. 0.09

LEVEL 3: SYNTHESIS/EVALUATION

7. EVOLUTION CONNECTION
How is the process of evolution revealed by the imperfections of living organisms?

8. SCIENTIFIC INQUIRY
DRAW IT Richard Koehn, of the State University of New York, Stony Brook, and Thomas Hilbish, of the University of South Carolina, studied genetic variation in the marine mussel *Mytilus edulis* around Long Island, New York. They measured the frequency of a particular allele (*lap*[94]) for an enzyme involved in regulating the mussel's internal saltwater balance. The researchers presented their data as a series of pie charts linked to sampling sites within Long Island Sound, where the salinity is highly variable, and along the coast of the open ocean, where salinity is constant:

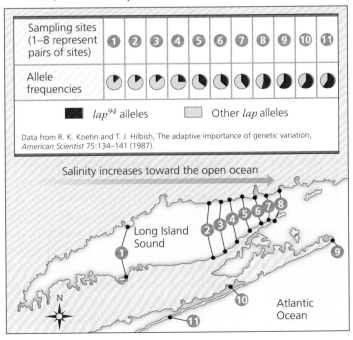

Data from R. K. Koehn and T. J. Hilbish, The adaptive importance of genetic variation, *American Scientist* 75:134–141 (1987).

(Question 8, continued)
Create a data table for the 11 sampling sites by estimating the frequency of *lap*[94] from the pie charts. (*Hint*: Think of each pie chart as a clock face to help you estimate the proportion of the shaded area.) Then graph the frequencies for sites 1–8 to show how the frequency of this allele changes with increasing salinity in Long Island Sound (from southwest to northeast). How do the data from sites 9–11 compare with the data from the sites within the Sound?

Construct a hypothesis that explains the patterns you observe in the data and that accounts for the following observations: (1) the *lap*[94] allele helps mussels maintain osmotic balance in water with a high salt concentration but is costly to use in less salty water; and (2) mussels produce larvae that can disperse long distances before they settle on rocks and grow into adults.

9. **WRITE ABOUT A THEME**
Emergent Properties Heterozygotes at the sickle-cell locus produce both normal and abnormal (sickle-cell) hemoglobin (see Concept 14.4). When hemoglobin molecules are packed into a heterozygote's red blood cells, some cells receive relatively large quantities of abnormal hemoglobin, making these cells prone to sickling. In a short essay (approximately 100–150 words), explain how these molecular and cellular events lead to emergent properties at the individual and population levels of biological organization.

For selected answers, see Appendix A.

Mastering BIOLOGY   www.masteringbiology.com

1. MasteringBiology® Assignments
Make Connections Tutorial Hardy-Weinberg Principle (Chapter 23) and Inheritance of Alleles (Chapter 14)
Experimental Inquiry Tutorial Did Natural Selection of Ground Finches Occur When the Environment Changed?
BioFlix Tutorial Mechanisms of Evolution
Tutorial Hardy-Weinberg Principle
Activities Genetic Variation from Sexual Recombination • The Hardy-Weinberg Principle • Causes of Evolutionary Change • Three Modes of Natural Selection
Questions Student Misconceptions • Reading Quiz • Multiple Choice • End-of-Chapter

2. eText
Read your book online, search, take notes, highlight text, and more.

3. The Study Area
Practice Tests • Cumulative Test • *BioFlix* 3-D Animations • MP3 Tutor Sessions • Videos • Activities • Investigations • Lab Media • Audio Glossary • Word Study Tools • Art

24

The Origin of Species

▲ **Figure 24.1 How did this flightless bird come to live on the isolated Galápagos Islands?**

OVERVIEW

That "Mystery of Mysteries"

Darwin came to the Galápagos Islands eager to explore landforms newly emerged from the sea. He noted that these volcanic islands, despite their geologic youth, were teeming with plants and animals found nowhere else in the world

(Figure 24.1). Later he realized that these species, like the islands, were relatively new. He wrote in his diary: "Both in space and time, we seem to be brought somewhat near to that great fact—that mystery of mysteries—the first appearance of new beings on this Earth."

The "mystery of mysteries" that captivated Darwin is **speciation**, the process by which one species splits into two or more species. Speciation fascinated Darwin (and many biologists since) because it is responsible for the tremendous diversity of life, repeatedly yielding new species that differ from existing ones. Speciation explains not only differences between species, but also similarities between them (the unity of life). When one species splits into two, the species that result share many characteristics because they are descended from this common ancestral species. For example, DNA similarities indicate that the flightless cormorant (*Phalacrocorax harrisi*) in Figure 24.1 is closely related to flying cormorants found in the Americas. This suggests that the flightless cormorant may have originated from an ancestral cormorant species that migrated from the mainland to the Galápagos.

Speciation also forms a conceptual bridge between **microevolution**, changes over time in allele frequencies in a population, and **macroevolution**, the broad pattern of evolution above the species level. An example of macroevolutionary change is the origin of new groups of organisms, such as mammals or flowering plants, through a series of speciation events. We examined microevolutionary mechanisms (mutation, natural selection, genetic drift, and gene flow) in Chapter 23, and we'll turn to macroevolution in Chapter 25. In this chapter, we will explore the "bridge"—the mechanisms by which new species originate from existing ones. First, however, we need to establish what we actually mean when we talk about "species."

CONCEPT **24.1**

The biological species concept emphasizes reproductive isolation

The word *species* is Latin for "kind" or "appearance." In daily life, we commonly distinguish between various "kinds" of organisms—dogs and cats, for instance—from differences in their appearance. But are organisms truly divided into the discrete units we call species, or is this classification an arbitrary attempt to impose order on the natural world? To answer this question, biologists compare not only the morphology (body form) of different groups of organisms but also less obvious differences in physiology, biochemistry, and DNA sequences. The results generally confirm that morphologically distinct species are indeed discrete groups, differing in many ways besides their body forms.

The Biological Species Concept

The primary definition of species used in this textbook is the **biological species concept**. According to this concept, a **species** is a group of populations whose members have the potential to interbreed in nature and produce viable, fertile offspring—but do not produce viable, fertile offspring with members of other such groups **(Figure 24.2)**. Thus, the members of a biological species are united by being repro-

(a) Similarity between different species. The eastern meadowlark (*Sturnella magna*, left) and the western meadowlark (*Sturnella neglecta*, right) have similar body shapes and colorations. Nevertheless, they are distinct biological species because their songs and other behaviors are different enough to prevent interbreeding should they meet in the wild.

(b) Diversity within a species. As diverse as we may be in appearance, all humans belong to a single biological species (*Homo sapiens*), defined by our capacity to interbreed successfully.

▲ **Figure 24.2 The biological species concept is based on the potential to interbreed rather than on physical similarity.**

ductively compatible, at least potentially. All human beings, for example, belong to the same species. A businesswoman in Manhattan may be unlikely to meet a dairy farmer in Mongolia, but if the two should happen to meet and mate, they could have viable babies that develop into fertile adults. In contrast, humans and chimpanzees remain distinct biological species even where they share territory, because many factors keep them from interbreeding and producing fertile offspring.

What holds the gene pool of a species together, causing its members to resemble each other more than they resemble other species? To answer this question, we need to return to the evolutionary mechanism called *gene flow*, the transfer of alleles between populations (see Chapter 23). Typically, gene flow occurs between the different populations of a species. This ongoing exchange of alleles tends to hold the populations together genetically. As we'll explore in the following sections, the absence of gene flow plays a key role in the formation of new species, as well as in keeping them apart once their potential to interbreed has been reduced.

Reproductive Isolation

Because biological species are defined in terms of reproductive compatibility, the formation of a new species hinges on **reproductive isolation**—the existence of biological factors (barriers) that impede members of two species from interbreeding and producing viable, fertile offspring. Such barriers block gene flow between the species and limit the formation of **hybrids**, offspring that result from an interspecific mating. Although a single barrier may not prevent all gene flow, a combination of several barriers can effectively isolate a species' gene pool.

Clearly, a fly cannot mate with a frog or a fern, but the reproductive barriers between more closely related species are not so obvious. These barriers can be classified according to whether they contribute to reproductive isolation before or after fertilization. **Prezygotic barriers** ("before the zygote") block fertilization from occurring. Such barriers typically act in one of three ways: by impeding members of different species from attempting to mate, by preventing an attempted mating from being completed successfully, or by hindering fertilization if mating is completed successfully. If a sperm cell from one species overcomes prezygotic barriers and fertilizes an ovum from another species, a variety of **postzygotic barriers** ("after the zygote") may contribute to reproductive isolation after the hybrid zygote is formed. For example, developmental errors may reduce survival among hybrid embryos. Or problems after birth may cause hybrids to be infertile or may decrease their chance of surviving long enough to reproduce. **Figure 24.3**, on the next two pages, describes prezygotic and postzygotic barriers in more detail.

Exploring Reproductive Barriers

Prezygotic barriers impede mating or hinder fertilization if mating does occur			
Habitat Isolation	**Temporal Isolation**	**Behavioral Isolation**	**Mechanical Isolation**

Individuals of different species → [MATING ATTEMPT]

Two species that occupy different habitats within the same area may encounter each other rarely, if at all, even though they are not isolated by obvious physical barriers, such as mountain ranges.

Species that breed during different times of the day, different seasons, or different years cannot mix their gametes.

Courtship rituals that attract mates and other behaviors unique to a species are effective reproductive barriers, even between closely related species. Such behavioral rituals enable *mate recognition*—a way to identify potential mates of the same species.

Mating is attempted, but morphological differences prevent its successful completion.

Example: Two species of garter snakes in the genus *Thamnophis* occur in the same geographic areas, but one lives mainly in water (a) while the other is primarily terrestrial (b).

Example: In North America, the geographic ranges of the eastern spotted skunk (*Spilogale putorius*) (c) and the western spotted skunk (*Spilogale gracilis*) (d) overlap, but *S. putorius* mates in late winter and *S. gracilis* mates in late summer.

Example: Blue-footed boobies, inhabitants of the Galápagos, mate only after a courtship display unique to their species. Part of the "script" calls for the male to high-step (e), a behavior that calls the female's attention to his bright blue feet.

Example: The shells of two species of snails in the genus *Bradybaena* spiral in different directions: Moving inward to the center, one spirals in a counterclockwise direction (f, left), the other in a clockwise direction (f, right). As a result, the snails' genital openings (indicated by arrows) are not aligned, and mating cannot be completed.

(a)

(c)

(e)

(f)

(b)

(d)

Gametic Isolation

Reduced Hybrid Viability

Reduced Hybrid Fertility

Hybrid Breakdown

FERTILIZATION

VIABLE, FERTILE OFFSPRING

Sperm of one species may not be able to fertilize the eggs of another species. For instance, sperm may not be able to survive in the reproductive tract of females of the other species, or biochemical mechanisms may prevent the sperm from penetrating the membrane surrounding the other species' eggs.

Example: Gametic isolation separates certain closely related species of aquatic animals, such as sea urchins (g). Sea urchins release their sperm and eggs into the surrounding water, where they fuse and form zygotes. It is difficult for gametes of different species, such as the red and purple urchins shown here, to fuse because proteins on the surfaces of the eggs and sperm bind very poorly to each other.

The genes of different parent species may interact in ways that impair the hybrid's development or survival in its environment.

Example: Some salamander subspecies of the genus *Ensatina* live in the same regions and habitats, where they may occasionally hybridize. But most of the hybrids do not complete development, and those that do are frail (h).

Even if hybrids are vigorous, they may be sterile. If the chromosomes of the two parent species differ in number or structure, meiosis in the hybrids may fail to produce normal gametes. Since the infertile hybrids cannot produce offspring when they mate with either parent species, genes cannot flow freely between the species.

Example: The hybrid offspring of a male donkey (i) and a female horse (j) is a mule (k), which is robust but sterile. A "hinny" (not shown), the offspring of a female donkey and a male horse, is also sterile.

Some first-generation hybrids are viable and fertile, but when they mate with one another or with either parent species, offspring of the next generation are feeble or sterile.

Example: Strains of cultivated rice have accumulated different mutant recessive alleles at two loci in the course of their divergence from a common ancestor. Hybrids between them are vigorous and fertile (l, left and right), but plants in the next generation that carry too many of these recessive alleles are small and sterile (l, center). Although these rice strains are not yet considered different species, they have begun to be separated by postzygotic barriers.

(i)

(g)

(h)

(j)

(k)

(l)

Limitations of the Biological Species Concept

One strength of the biological species concept is that it directs our attention to how speciation occurs: by the evolution of reproductive isolation. However, the number of species to which this concept can be usefully applied is limited. There is, for example, no way to evaluate the reproductive isolation of fossils. The biological species concept also does not apply to organisms that reproduce asexually all or most of the time, such as prokaryotes. (Many prokaryotes do transfer genes among themselves, as we will discuss in Chapter 27, but this is not part of their reproductive process.) Furthermore, in the biological species concept, species are designated by the *absence* of gene flow. But there are many pairs of species that are morphologically and ecologically distinct, and yet gene flow occurs between them. An example is the grizzly bear (*Ursus arctos*) and polar bear (*Ursus maritimus*), whose hybrid offspring have been dubbed "grolar bears" **(Figure 24.4)**. As we'll discuss, natural selection can cause such species to remain distinct even though some gene flow occurs between them. This observation has led some researchers to argue that the biological species concept overemphasizes gene flow and downplays the role of natural selection. Because of the limitations to the biological species concept, alternative species concepts are useful in certain situations.

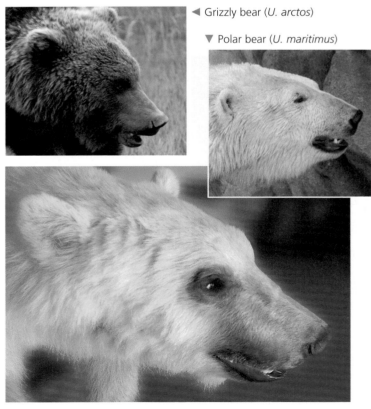

◀ Grizzly bear (*U. arctos*)

▼ Polar bear (*U. maritimus*)

▲ Hybrid "grolar bear"

▲ **Figure 24.4 Hybridization between two species of bears in the genus *Ursus*.**

Other Definitions of Species

While the biological species concept emphasizes the *separateness* of species from one another due to reproductive barriers, several other definitions emphasize the *unity within* a species. For example, the **morphological species concept** characterizes a species by body shape and other structural features. The morphological species concept can be applied to asexual and sexual organisms, and it can be useful even without information on the extent of gene flow. In practice, this is how scientists distinguish most species. One disadvantage, however, is that this definition relies on subjective criteria; researchers may disagree on which structural features distinguish a species.

The **ecological species concept** views a species in terms of its ecological niche, the sum of how members of the species interact with the nonliving and living parts of their environment. For example, two species of salamanders might be similar in appearance but differ in the foods they eat or in their ability to tolerate dry conditions. Unlike the biological species concept, the ecological species concept can accommodate asexual as well as sexual species. It also emphasizes the role of disruptive natural selection as organisms adapt to different environmental conditions.

The **phylogenetic species concept** defines a species as the smallest group of individuals that share a common ancestor, forming one branch on the tree of life. Biologists trace the phylogenetic history of a species by comparing its characteristics, such as morphology or molecular sequences, with those of other organisms. Such analyses can distinguish groups of individuals that are sufficiently different to be considered separate species. Of course, the difficulty with this species concept is determining the degree of difference required to indicate separate species.

In addition to those discussed here, more than 20 other species definitions have been proposed. The usefulness of each definition depends on the situation and the research questions being asked. For our purposes of studying how species originate, the biological species concept, with its focus on reproductive barriers, is particularly helpful.

CONCEPT CHECK 24.1

1. (a) Which species concept(s) could you apply to both asexual and sexual species? (b) Which would be most useful for identifying species in the field? Explain.
2. **WHAT IF?** Suppose you are studying two bird species that live in a forest and are not known to interbreed. One species feeds and mates in the treetops and the other on the ground. But in captivity, the birds can interbreed and produce viable, fertile offspring. What type of reproductive barrier most likely keeps these species separate in nature? Explain.

For suggested answers, see Appendix A.

CONCEPT 24.2

Speciation can take place with or without geographic separation

Now that we have a clearer sense of what constitutes a unique species, let's return to our discussion of the process by which such species arise from existing species. Speciation can occur in two main ways, depending on how gene flow is interrupted between populations of the existing species (**Figure 24.5**).

Allopatric ("Other Country") Speciation

In **allopatric speciation** (from the Greek *allos*, other, and *patra*, homeland), gene flow is interrupted when a population is divided into geographically isolated subpopulations. For example, the water level in a lake may subside, resulting in two or more smaller lakes that are now home to separated populations (see Figure 24.5a). Or a river may change course and divide a population of animals that cannot cross it. Allopatric speciation can also occur without geologic remodeling, such as when individuals colonize a remote area and their descendants become geographically isolated from the parent population. The flightless cormorant shown in Figure 24.1 most likely originated in this way from an ancestral flying species that reached the Galápagos Islands.

The Process of Allopatric Speciation

How formidable must a geographic barrier be to promote allopatric speciation? The answer depends on the ability of the organisms to move about. Birds, mountain lions, and coyotes can cross rivers and canyons—as can the windblown pollen of pine trees and the seeds of many flowering plants. In con-

▲ **Figure 24.6 Allopatric speciation of antelope squirrels on opposite rims of the Grand Canyon.** Harris's antelope squirrel (*Ammospermophilus harrisii*) inhabits the canyon's south rim (left). Just a few kilometers away on the north rim (right) lives the closely related white-tailed antelope squirrel (*Ammospermophilus leucurus*). Birds and other organisms that can disperse easily across the canyon have not diverged into different species on the two rims.

trast, small rodents may find a wide river or deep canyon a formidable barrier (**Figure 24.6**).

Once geographic separation has occurred, the separated gene pools may diverge. Different mutations arise, and natural selection and genetic drift may alter allele frequencies in different ways in the separated populations. Reproductive isolation may then arise as a by-product of selection or drift having caused the populations to diverge genetically. For example, on Andros Island, in the Bahamas, populations of the mosquitofish *Gambusia hubbsi* colonized a series of ponds that later became isolated from one another. Genetic analyses indicate that little or no gene flow currently occurs between the ponds. The environments of these ponds are very similar except that some contain many predatory fishes, while others do not. In the "high-predation" ponds, selection has favored the evolution of a mosquitofish body shape that enables rapid bursts of speed (**Figure 24.7**). In ponds lacking

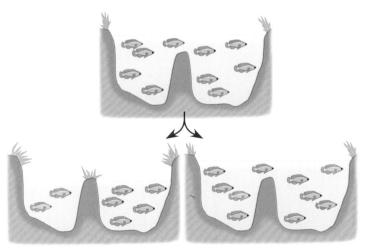

(a) Allopatric speciation. A population forms a new species while geographically isolated from its parent population.

(b) Sympatric speciation. A subset of a population forms a new species without geographic separation.

▲ **Figure 24.5 Two main modes of speciation.**

(a) Under high predation

(b) Under low predation

In ponds with predatory fishes, the head region of the mosquitofish is streamlined and the tail region is powerful, enabling rapid bursts of speed.

In ponds without predatory fishes, mosquitofish have a different body shape that favors long, steady swimming.

▲ **Figure 24.7 Reproductive isolation as a by-product of selection.** After bringing together mosquitofish from different ponds, researchers concluded that selection for traits that enable mosquitofish in high-predation ponds to avoid predators has isolated them reproductively from mosquitofish in low-predation ponds.

predatory fishes, selection has favored a different body shape, one that improves the ability to swim for long periods of time. How have these different selective pressures affected the evolution of reproductive barriers? Researchers answered this question by bringing together mosquitofish from the two types of ponds. They found that female mosquitofish prefer to mate with males whose body shape is similar to their own. This preference establishes a barrier to reproduction between mosquitofish from ponds with predators and those from ponds without predators. Thus, as a by-product of selection for avoiding predators, reproductive barriers have started to form in these allopatric populations.

Evidence of Allopatric Speciation

Many studies provide evidence that speciation can occur in allopatric populations. Consider the 30 species of snapping shrimp in the genus *Alpheus* that live off the Isthmus of Panama, the land bridge that connects South and North America (**Figure 24.8**). Fifteen of these species live on the Atlantic side of the isthmus, while the other 15 live on the Pacific side. Before the isthmus formed, gene flow could occur between the Atlantic and Pacific populations of snapping shrimp. Did the species on different sides of the isthmus orig-

inate by allopatric speciation? Morphological and genetic data group these shrimp into 15 pairs of *sibling species*, pairs whose member species are each other's closest relative. In each of these 15 pairs, one of the sibling species lives on the Atlantic side of the isthmus, while the other lives on the Pacific side, strongly suggesting that the two species arose as a consequence of geographic separation. Furthermore, genetic analyses indicate that the *Alpheus* species originated from 9 to 3 million years ago, with the sibling species that live in the deepest water diverging first. These divergence times are consistent with geologic evidence that the isthmus formed gradually, starting 10 million years ago, and closing completely about 3 million years ago.

The importance of allopatric speciation is also suggested by the fact that regions that are isolated or highly subdivided by barriers typically have more species than do otherwise similar regions that lack such features. For example, many unique plants and animals are found on the geographically isolated Hawaiian Islands (we'll return to the origin of Hawaiian species in Chapter 25). Similarly, unusually high numbers of butterfly species are found in South American regions that are subdivided by many rivers.

Laboratory and field tests also provide evidence that reproductive isolation between two populations generally increases as the distance between them increases. In a study of dusky salamanders (*Desmognathus ochrophaeus*), biologists brought individuals from different populations into the laboratory and tested their ability to produce viable, fertile offspring (**Figure 24.9**). The researchers observed little reproductive isolation in salamanders from neighboring populations. In contrast, salamanders from widely separated populations often failed to reproduce, a result consistent with allopatric speciation. In other studies, researchers have tested whether intrinsic reproductive barriers develop when populations are isolated

▼ **Figure 24.8 Allopatric speciation in snapping shrimp (*Alpheus*).** The shrimp pictured are just 2 of the 15 pairs of sibling species that arose as populations were divided by the formation of the Isthmus of Panama. The color-coded type indicates the sibling species.

▲ **Figure 24.9 Reproductive isolation increases with distance in populations of dusky salamanders.** The degree of reproductive isolation is represented here by an index ranging from 0 (no isolation) to 2 (complete isolation).

INQUIRY

Can divergence of allopatric populations lead to reproductive isolation?

EXPERIMENT Diane Dodd, then at Yale University, divided a laboratory population of the fruit fly *Drosophila pseudoobscura*, raising some flies on a starch medium and others on a maltose medium. After one year (about 40 generations), natural selection resulted in divergent evolution: Populations raised on starch digested starch more efficiently, while those raised on maltose digested maltose more efficiently. Dodd then put flies from the same or different populations in mating cages and measured mating frequencies. All flies used in the mating preference tests were reared for one generation on a standard cornmeal medium.

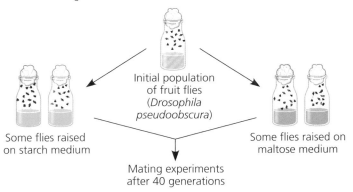

Initial population of fruit flies (*Drosophila pseudoobscura*)

Some flies raised on starch medium

Some flies raised on maltose medium

Mating experiments after 40 generations

RESULTS Mating patterns among populations of flies raised on different media are shown below. When flies from "starch populations" were mixed with flies from "maltose populations," the flies tended to mate with like partners. But in the control group (shown on the right), flies from different populations adapted to starch were about as likely to mate with each other as with flies from their own population; similar results were obtained for control groups adapted to maltose.

	Female	
Male	Starch	Maltose
Starch	22	9
Maltose	8	20

Number of matings in experimental group

	Female	
Male	Starch population 1	Starch population 2
Starch population 1	18	15
Starch population 2	12	15

Number of matings in control group

CONCLUSION In the experimental group, the strong preference of "starch flies" and "maltose flies" to mate with like-adapted flies indicates that a reproductive barrier was forming between these fly populations. Although this reproductive barrier was not absolute (some mating between starch flies and maltose flies did occur), after 40 generations it appeared to be under way. This barrier may have been caused by differences in courtship behavior that arose as an incidental by-product of differing selective pressures as these allopatric populations adapted to different sources of food.

SOURCE D. M. B. Dodd, Reproductive isolation as a consequence of adaptive divergence in *Drosophila pseudoobscura*, *Evolution* 43:1308–1311 (1989).

WHAT IF? Why were all flies used in the mating preference tests reared on a standard medium (rather than on a starch or maltose medium)?

experimentally and subjected to different environmental conditions. In such cases, too, the results provide strong support for allopatric speciation (**Figure 24.10**).

We need to emphasize here that although geographic isolation prevents interbreeding between allopatric populations, physical separation is not a biological barrier to reproduction. Biological reproductive barriers such as those described in Figure 24.3 are intrinsic to the organisms themselves. Hence, it is biological barriers that can prevent interbreeding when members of different populations come into contact with one another.

Sympatric ("Same Country") Speciation

In **sympatric speciation** (from the Greek *syn*, together), speciation occurs in populations that live in the same geographic area. How can reproductive barriers form between sympatric populations while their members remain in contact with each other? Although such contact (and the ongoing gene flow that results) makes sympatric speciation less common than allopatric speciation, sympatric speciation can occur if gene flow is reduced by such factors as polyploidy, habitat differentiation, and sexual selection. (Note that these factors can also promote allopatric speciation.)

Polyploidy

A species may originate from an accident during cell division that results in extra sets of chromosomes, a condition called **polyploidy**. Polyploid speciation occasionally occurs in animals; for example, the gray tree frog *Hyla versicolor* (see Figure 23.16) is thought to have originated in this way. However, polyploidy is far more common in plants. Botanists estimate that more than 80% of the plant species alive today are descended from ancestors that formed by polyploid speciation.

Two distinct forms of polyploidy have been observed in plant (and a few animal) populations. An **autopolyploid** (from the Greek *autos*, self) is an individual that has more than two chromosome sets that are all derived from a single species. In plants, for example, a failure of cell division could double a cell's chromosome number from the diploid number ($2n$) to a tetraploid number ($4n$).

$2n = 6$

Cell division error

Tetraploid cell $4n = 12$

A tetraploid can produce fertile tetraploid offspring by self-pollinating or by mating with other tetraploids. In addition, the tetraploids are reproductively isolated from diploid plants of the original population, because the

$2n$

$2n$

Gametes produced by tetraploids

New species ($4n$)

triploid (3*n*) offspring of such unions have reduced fertility. Thus, in just one generation, autopolyploidy can generate reproductive isolation without any geographic separation.

A second form of polyploidy can occur when two different species interbreed and produce hybrid offspring. Most such hybrids are sterile because the set of chromosomes from one species cannot pair during meiosis with the set of chromosomes from the other species. However, an infertile hybrid may be able to propagate itself asexually (as many plants can do). In subsequent generations, various mechanisms can change a sterile hybrid into a fertile polyploid called an **allopolyploid** (Figure 24.11). The allopolyploids are fertile when mating with each other but cannot interbreed with either parent species; thus, they represent a new biological species.

Although polyploid speciation is relatively rare, even in plants, scientists have documented that at least five new plant species have originated in this way since 1850. One of these examples involves the origin of a new species of goatsbeard plant (genus *Tragopogon*) in the Pacific Northwest. *Tragopogon* first arrived in the region when humans introduced three European species in the early 1900s. These three species are now common weeds in abandoned parking lots and other urban sites. In 1950, a new *Tragopogon* species was discovered near the Idaho-Washington border, a region where all three European species also were found. Genetic analyses revealed that this new species, *Tragopogon miscellus*, is a tetraploid hybrid of two of the European species. Although the *T. miscellus* population grows mainly by reproduction of its own members, additional episodes of hybridization between the parent species continue to add new members to the *T. miscellus* population—just one of many examples in which scientists have observed speciation in progress.

Many important agricultural crops—such as oats, cotton, potatoes, tobacco, and wheat—are polyploids. The wheat used for bread, *Triticum aestivum*, is an allohexaploid (six sets of chromosomes, two sets from each of three different species). The first of the polyploidy events that eventually led to modern wheat probably occurred about 8,000 years ago in the Middle East as a spontaneous hybrid of an early cultivated wheat species and a wild grass. Today, plant geneticists generate new polyploids in the laboratory by using chemicals that induce meiotic and mitotic errors. By harnessing the evolutionary process, researchers can produce new hybrid species with desired qualities, such as a hybrid that combines the high yield of wheat with the hardiness of rye.

Habitat Differentiation

Sympatric speciation can also occur when genetic factors enable a subpopulation to exploit a habitat or resource not used by the parent population. Such is the case with the North American apple maggot fly (*Rhagoletis pomonella*), a

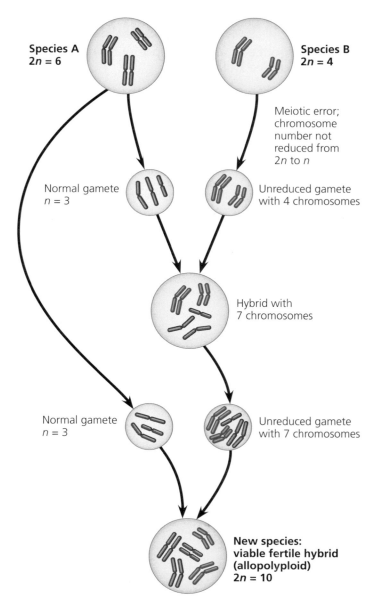

▲ Figure 24.11 **One mechanism for allopolyploid speciation in plants.** Most hybrids are sterile because their chromosomes are not homologous and cannot pair during meiosis. However, such a hybrid may be able to reproduce asexually. This diagram traces one mechanism that can produce fertile hybrids (allopolyploids) as new species. The new species has a diploid chromosome number equal to the sum of the diploid chromosome numbers of the two parent species.

pest of apples. The fly's original habitat was the native hawthorn tree, but about 200 years ago, some populations colonized apple trees that had been introduced by European settlers. As apples mature more quickly than hawthorn fruit, natural selection has favored apple-feeding flies with rapid development. These apple-feeding populations now show temporal isolation from the hawthorn-feeding *R. pomonella*, providing a prezygotic restriction to gene flow between the two populations. Researchers also have identified alleles that benefit the flies that use one host plant but harm the flies that use the other host plant. As a result, natural selection operating on these alleles provides a postzygotic barrier to reproduction, further limiting gene flow. Altogether, although the two populations are still classified as subspecies rather than separate species, sympatric speciation appears to be well under way.

Sexual Selection

There is evidence that sympatric speciation can also be driven by sexual selection. Clues to how this can occur have been found in cichlid fish from one of Earth's hot spots of animal speciation, East Africa's Lake Victoria. This lake was once home to as many as 600 species of cichlids. Genetic data indicate that these species originated within the last 100,000 years from a small number of colonizing species that arrived from rivers and lakes located elsewhere. How did so many species—more than double the number of freshwater fish species known in all of Europe—originate within a single lake?

One hypothesis is that subgroups of the original cichlid populations adapted to different food sources and that the resulting genetic divergence contributed to speciation in Lake Victoria. But sexual selection, in which (typically) females select males based on their appearance (see Chapter 23), may also have been a factor. Researchers have studied two closely related sympatric species of cichlids that differ mainly in the coloration of breeding males: Breeding *Pundamilia pundamilia* males have a blue-tinged back, whereas breeding *Pundamilia nyererei* males have a red-tinged back **(Figure 24.12)**. Their results suggest that mate choice based on male breeding coloration is the main reproductive barrier that normally keeps the gene pools of these two species separate.

Allopatric and Sympatric Speciation: A Review

Now let's recap the two main modes by which new species form. In allopatric speciation, a new species forms in geographic isolation from its parent population. Geographic isolation severely restricts gene flow. As a result, other reproductive barriers from the ancestral species may arise as a by-product of genetic changes that occur within the isolated population. Many different processes can produce such genetic changes, including natural selection under different environmental conditions, genetic drift, and sexual selection. Once formed, intrinsic reproductive barriers that arise in allopatric populations can prevent interbreeding with the parent population even if the populations come back into contact.

Sympatric speciation, in contrast, requires the emergence of a reproductive barrier that isolates a subset of a population

from the remainder of the population in the same area. Though rarer than allopatric speciation, sympatric speciation can occur when gene flow to and from the isolated subpopulation is blocked. This can occur as a result of polyploidy, a condition in which an organism has extra sets of chromosomes. Sympatric speciation also can occur when a subset of a population becomes reproductively isolated because of natural selection that results from a switch to a habitat or food source not used by the parent population. Finally, sympatric speciation can result from sexual selection.

Having reviewed the geographic context in which species originate, we'll next explore in more detail what can happen when new or partially formed species come into contact.

CONCEPT CHECK 24.2

1. Summarize key differences between allopatric and sympatric speciation. Which type of speciation is more common, and why?
2. Describe two mechanisms that can decrease gene flow in sympatric populations, thereby making sympatric speciation more likely to occur.
3. **WHAT IF?** Is allopatric speciation more likely to occur on an island close to a mainland or on a more isolated island of the same size? Explain your prediction.
4. **MAKE CONNECTIONS** After reviewing the process of meiosis in Figure 13.8 (p. 254), describe how an error during meiosis could lead to polyploidy.

For suggested answers, see Appendix A.

CONCEPT 24.3

Hybrid zones reveal factors that cause reproductive isolation

What happens if species with incomplete reproductive barriers come into contact with one another? One possible outcome is the formation of a **hybrid zone**, a region in which members of different species meet and mate, producing at least some offspring of mixed ancestry. In this section, we'll explore hybrid zones and what they reveal about factors that cause the evolution of reproductive isolation.

Patterns Within Hybrid Zones

Some hybrid zones form as narrow bands, such as the one depicted in **Figure 24.13** for two species of toads in the genus *Bombina*, the yellow-bellied toad (*B. variegata*) and the fire-bellied toad (*B. bombina*). This hybrid zone, represented by the red line on the map, extends for 4,000 km but is less than 10 km wide in most places. The hybrid zone occurs where the

Fire-bellied toad, *Bombina bombina*: lives at lower altitudes

Yellow-bellied toad, *Bombina variegata*: lives at higher altitudes

▲ **Figure 24.13 A narrow hybrid zone for *Bombina* toads in Europe.** The graph shows the pattern of species-specific allele frequencies across the width of the zone near Krakow, Poland. Individuals with frequencies close to 1.0 are yellow-bellied toads, individuals with frequencies close to 0.0 are fire-bellied toads, and individuals with intermediate frequencies are considered hybrids.

? *Does the graph indicate that gene flow is spreading fire-bellied toad alleles into the range of the yellow-bellied toad? Explain.*

higher-altitude habitat of the yellow-bellied toad meets the lowland habitat of the fire-bellied toad. Across a given "slice" of the zone, the frequency of alleles specific to yellow-bellied toads typically decreases from close to 100% at the edge where only yellow-bellied toads are found, to 50% in the central portion of the zone, to 0% at the edge where only fire-bellied toads are found.

What causes such a pattern of allele frequencies across a hybrid zone? We can infer that there is an obstacle to gene flow—otherwise, alleles from one parent species would also be common in the gene pool of the other parent species. Are geographic barriers reducing gene flow? Not in this case, since the toads can move throughout the hybrid zone. A more important factor is that hybrid toads have increased rates of embryonic mortality and a variety of morphological abnormalities, including ribs that are fused to the spine and malformed tadpole mouthparts. Because the hybrids have poor survival and reproduction, they produce few viable offspring with members of the parent species. As a result, hybrid individuals rarely serve as a stepping-stone from which alleles are passed from one species to the other. Outside the hybrid zone, additional obstacles to gene flow may be provided by natural selection in the different environments in which the parent species live.

Other hybrid zones have more complicated spatial patterns. For example, many plant species only occur in locations that have a very particular set of environmental conditions. Favorable "patches" that have such conditions are often scattered irregularly across the landscape and are isolated from one another. When two such plant species interbreed, the hybrid zone occurs in a group of disconnected patches, a more complex spatial pattern than the continuous band shown in Figure 24.13. But regardless of whether they have complex or simple spatial patterns, hybrid zones form when two species lacking complete barriers to reproduction come into contact. Once formed, how does a hybrid zone change over time?

Hybrid Zones over Time

Studying a hybrid zone is like observing a natural experiment on speciation. Will the hybrids become reproductively isolated from their parents and form a new species, as occurred by polyploidy in the goatsbeard plant of the Pacific Northwest? If not, there are three possible outcomes for the hybrid zone over time: reinforcement of barriers, fusion of species, or stability (Figure 24.14). Reproductive barriers between species may be reinforced over time (limiting the formation of hybrids) or weakened over time (causing the separating species to fuse into one species). Or hybrids may continue to be produced, creating a long-term and stable hybrid zone. Let's examine what studies in the field suggest about these three possibilities.

Reinforcement: Strengthening Reproductive Barriers

When hybrids are less fit than members of their parent species, as in the *Bombina* example, we might expect natural selection to strengthen prezygotic barriers to reproduction, thus reducing

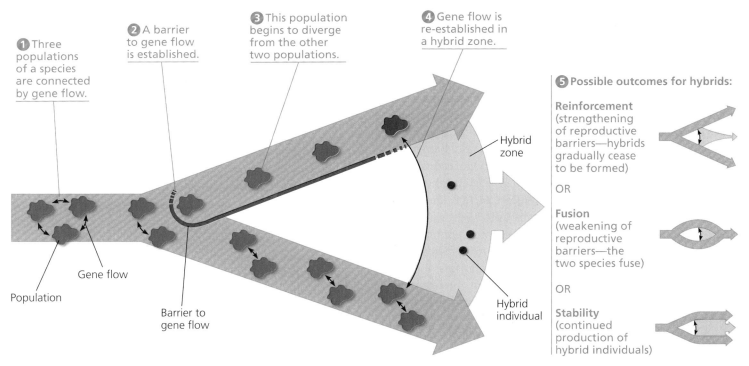

▲ **Figure 24.14 Formation of a hybrid zone and possible outcomes for hybrids over time.** The thick colored arrows represent the passage of time.

WHAT IF? *Predict what might happen if gene flow were re-established at step 3 in this process.*

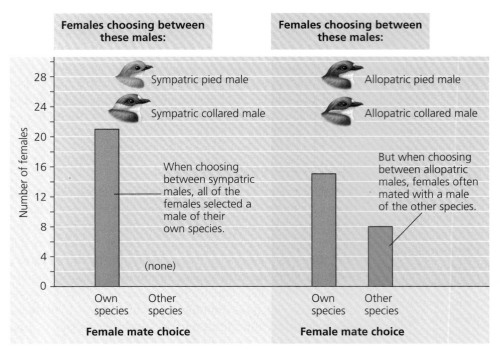

▲ **Figure 24.15 Reinforcement of barriers to reproduction in closely related species of European flycatchers.**

*Graph labels:*

Females choosing between these males:
- Sympatric pied male
- Sympatric collared male

When choosing between sympatric males, all of the females selected a male of their own species.

(none)

Number of females (y-axis: 0, 4, 8, 12, 16, 20, 24, 28)

Own species / Other species
Female mate choice

Females choosing between these males:
- Allopatric pied male
- Allopatric collared male

But when choosing between allopatric males, females often mated with a male of the other species.

Own species / Other species
Female mate choice

the formation of unfit hybrids. Because this process involves *reinforcing* reproductive barriers, it is called **reinforcement**. If reinforcement is occurring, a logical prediction is that barriers to reproduction between species should be stronger for sympatric populations than for allopatric populations.

As an example, let's consider the evidence for reinforcement in two closely related species of European flycatcher, the pied flycatcher and the collared flycatcher. In allopatric populations of these birds, males of the two species closely resemble one another. But in sympatric populations, the males of the two species look very different: Male pied flycatchers are a dull brown, whereas male collared flycatchers have enlarged patches of white. Female pied and collared flycatchers do not select males of the other species when given a choice between males from sympatric populations, but they frequently do make mistakes when selecting between males from allopatric populations **(Figure 24.15)**. Thus, barriers to reproduction appear to be stronger in birds from sympatric populations than in birds from allopatric populations, as you would predict if reinforcement is occurring. Similar results have been observed in a number of organisms, including fishes, insects, plants, and other birds. But interestingly, reinforcement does *not* appear to be at work in the case of the *Bombina* toads, as we'll discuss shortly.

Fusion: Weakening Reproductive Barriers

Next let's consider the case in which two species contact one another in a hybrid zone, but the barriers to reproduction are not strong. So much gene flow may occur that reproductive barriers weaken further and the gene pools of the two species become increasingly alike. In effect, the speciation process reverses, eventually causing the two hybridizing species to fuse into a single species.

Such a situation may be occurring among some of the Lake Victoria cichlids we discussed earlier. In the past 30 years, about 200 of the former 600 species of Lake Victoria cichlids have vanished. Some of these species were driven to extinction by an introduced predator, the Nile perch. But many species not eaten by Nile perch also have disappeared— perhaps in some cases by species fusion. Many pairs of ecologically similar cichlid species are reproductively isolated because the females of one species prefer to mate with males of one color, while females of the other species prefer to mate with males of a different color (see Figure 24.12). Researchers think that murky waters caused by pollution may have reduced the ability of females to use color to distinguish males of their own species from males of closely related species. If further evidence supports this hypothesis, it would seem that pollution in Lake Victoria has produced a cascade of related effects. First, by decreasing the ability of females to distinguish males of their own species, pollution has increased the frequency of mating between members of species that had been isolated reproductively from one another. Second, as a result of these matings, many hybrids have been produced, leading to fusion of the parent species' gene pools and a loss of species **(Figure 24.16)**.

Similar events may be affecting the polar bear (*Ursus maritimus*). Fossils and genetic analyses indicate that polar bears evolved from North American populations of grizzly bears (*U. arctos*) between 100,000 and 200,000 years ago. In recent decades, global warming has reduced the extent of the Arctic Ocean ice packs from which polar bears hunt for seals and other prey. As their ice-pack habitat disappears (placing them at risk of extinction), polar bears are more likely to be found on land, where they may encounter grizzly bears. Hybrid offspring of polar bears and grizzly bears in the wild have been documented (see Figure 24.4). As polar bear habitat continues to disappear, increasing numbers of such hybrids may cause the gene pools of these species to begin to fuse, thus contributing to the possible eventual extinction of the polar bear.

Pundamilia nyererei

Pundamilia pundamilia

Pundamilia "turbid water,"
hybrid offspring from a location
with turbid water

▲ **Figure 24.16 Fusion: The breakdown of reproductive barriers.** Increasingly cloudy water in Lake Victoria over the past 30 years may have weakened reproductive barriers between *P. nyererei* and *P. pundamilia*. In areas of cloudy water, the two species have hybridized extensively, causing their gene pools to fuse.

Stability: Continued Formation of Hybrid Individuals

Many hybrid zones are stable in the sense that hybrids continue to be produced. In some cases, this occurs because the hybrids survive or reproduce better than members of either parent species, at least in certain habitats or years. But stable hybrid zones have also been observed in cases where the hybrids are selected *against*—an unexpected result.

Recall that hybrids are at a strong disadvantage in the *Bombina* hybrid zone. As a result, the offspring of individuals that prefer to mate with members of their own species should survive or reproduce better than the unfit hybrid offspring of individuals that mate indiscriminately with members of the other species. This suggests that reinforcement should occur, strengthening reproductive barriers and thereby limiting the production of hybrid toads. But in more than 20 years of study, no evidence for reinforcement has been found, and hybrids continue to be produced.

What could explain this finding? One possibility relates to the narrowness of the *Bombina* hybrid zone (see Figure 24.13). Evidence suggests that members of both parent species migrate into the zone from the parent populations located outside the zone. Such movements lead to the continued production of hybrids, potentially overwhelming the selection for increased reproductive isolation inside the zone. If the hy-brid zone were wider, this would be less likely to occur, since the center of the zone would receive little gene flow from distant parent populations located outside the hybrid zone.

In short, sometimes the outcomes in hybrid zones match our predictions (European flycatchers and cichlid fishes), and sometimes they don't (*Bombina*). But whether our predictions are upheld or not, events in hybrid zones can shed light on how barriers to reproduction between closely related species change over time. In the next section, we'll examine how interactions between hybridizing species can also provide a glimpse into the speed and genetic control of speciation.

CONCEPT CHECK 24.3

1. What are hybrid zones, and why can they be viewed as "natural laboratories" in which to study speciation?
2. **WHAT IF?** Consider two species that diverged while geographically separated but resumed contact before reproductive isolation was complete. Predict what would happen over time if the two species mated indiscriminately and (a) hybrid offspring survived and reproduced more poorly than offspring from intraspecific matings or (b) hybrid offspring survived and reproduced as well as offspring from intraspecific matings.

For suggested answers, see Appendix A.

CONCEPT 24.4

Speciation can occur rapidly or slowly and can result from changes in few or many genes

Darwin faced many unanswered questions when he began to ponder that "mystery of mysteries"—speciation. As you read in Chapter 22, he found answers to some of those questions when he realized that evolution by natural selection helped explain both the diversity of life and the adaptations of organisms. But biologists since Darwin have continued to ask fundamental questions about speciation. For example, how long does it take for new species to form? And how many genes change when one species splits into two? Answers to these questions are also beginning to emerge.

The Time Course of Speciation

We can gather information about how long it takes new species to form from broad patterns in the fossil record and from studies that use morphological data (including fossils) or molecular data to assess the time interval between speciation events in particular groups of organisms.

(a) In a punctuated pattern, new species change most as they branch from a parent species and then change little for the rest of their existence.

Time ⟶

(b) Other species diverge from one another much more gradually over time.

▲ Figure 24.17 **Two models for the tempo of speciation.**

Patterns in the Fossil Record

The fossil record includes many episodes in which new species appear suddenly in a geologic stratum, persist essentially unchanged through several strata, and then disappear. For example, there are dozens of species of marine invertebrates that make their debut in the fossil record with novel morphologies, but then change little for millions of years before becoming extinct. Paleontologists Niles Eldredge, of the American Museum of Natural History, and Stephen Jay Gould, of Harvard University, coined the term **punctuated equilibria** to describe these periods of apparent stasis punctuated by sudden change **(Figure 24.17a)**. Other species do not show a punctuated pattern; instead, they change more gradually over long periods of time **(Figure 24.17b)**.

What do punctuated and gradual patterns tell us about how long it takes new species to form? Suppose that a species survived for 5 million years, but most of the morphological changes that caused it to be designated a new species occurred during the first 50,000 years of its existence—just 1% of its total lifetime. Time periods this short (in geologic terms) often cannot be distinguished in fossil strata, in part because the rate of sediment accumulation is too slow to separate layers this close in time. Thus, based on its fossils, the species would seem to have appeared suddenly and then lingered with little or no change before becoming extinct. Even though such a species may have originated more slowly than its fossils suggest (in this case taking 50,000 years), a punctuated pattern indicates that speciation occurred relatively rapidly. For species whose fossils changed much more gradually, we also cannot tell exactly when a new biological species formed, since information about reproductive isolation does not fossilize. However, it is likely that speciation in such groups occurred relatively slowly, perhaps taking millions of years.

Speciation Rates

The punctuated pattern suggests that once the process of speciation begins, it can be completed relatively rapidly—a suggestion supported by a growing number of studies.

For example, research conducted at Indiana University suggests that rapid speciation produced the wild sunflower *Helianthus anomalus*. Genetic evidence indicates that this species originated by the hybridization of two other sunflower species, *H. annuus* and *H. petiolaris*. The hybrid species *H. anomalus* is ecologically distinct and reproductively isolated from both parent species **(Figure 24.18)**. Unlike the outcome of allopolyploid speciation, in which there is a change in chromosome number after hybridization, in these sunflowers the two parent species and the hybrid all have the same number of chromosomes ($2n = 34$). How, then, did speciation occur? To answer this question, the researchers performed an

▲ Figure 24.18 **A hybrid sunflower species and its dry sand dune habitat.** The wild sunflower *Helianthus anomalus* originated via the hybridization of two other sunflowers, *H. annuus* and *H. petiolaris*, which live in nearby but moister environments.

INQUIRY

How does hybridization lead to speciation in sunflowers?

EXPERIMENT At Indiana University, Loren Rieseberg and his colleagues crossed the two parent sunflower species, *H. annuus* and *H. petiolaris*, to produce experimental hybrids in the laboratory (for each gamete, only two of the *n* = 17 chromosomes are shown).

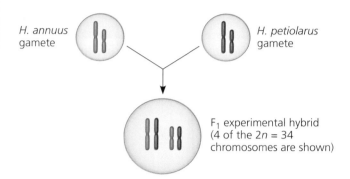

H. annuus gamete

H. petiolarus gamete

F_1 experimental hybrid (4 of the 2*n* = 34 chromosomes are shown)

Note that in the first (F_1) generation, each chromosome of the experimental hybrids consisted entirely of DNA from one or the other parent species. The researchers then tested whether the F_1 and subsequent generations of experimental hybrids were fertile. They also used species-specific genetic markers to compare the chromosomes in the experimental hybrids with the chromosomes in the naturally occurring hybrid *H. anomalus*.

RESULTS Although only 5% of the F_1 experimental hybrids were fertile, after just four more generations the hybrid fertility rose to more than 90%. The chromosomes of individuals from this fifth hybrid generation differed from those in the F_1 generation but were similar to those in *H. anomalus* individuals from natural populations:

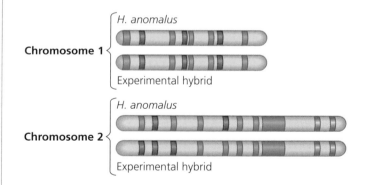

H. anomalus

Chromosome 1

Experimental hybrid

H. anomalus

Chromosome 2

Experimental hybrid

CONCLUSION Over time, the chromosomes in the population of experimental hybrids became similar to the chromosomes of *H. anomalus* individuals from natural populations. This suggests that the observed rise in the fertility of the experimental hybrids occurred as selection eliminated regions of DNA from the parent species that were not compatible with one another. Overall, it appeared that the initial steps of the speciation process occurred rapidly and could be mimicked in a laboratory experiment.

SOURCE L. H. Rieseberg et al., Role of gene interactions in hybrid speciation: evidence from ancient and experimental hybrids, *Science* 272:741–745 (1996).

WHAT IF? *The increased fertility of the experimental hybrids could have resulted from natural selection for thriving under laboratory conditions. Evaluate this alternative explanation for the results.*

experiment designed to mimic events in nature (**Figure 24.19**). Their results indicated that natural selection could produce extensive genetic changes in hybrid populations over short periods of time. These changes appear to have caused the hybrids to diverge reproductively from their parents and form a new species, *H. anomalus*.

The sunflower example, along with the apple maggot fly, Lake Victoria cichlid, and fruit fly examples discussed earlier, suggests that new species can arise rapidly *once divergence begins*. But what is the total length of time between speciation events? This interval consists of the time that elapses before populations of a newly formed species start to diverge from one another plus the time it takes for speciation to be complete once divergence begins. It turns out that the total time between speciation events varies considerably. For example, in a survey of data from 84 groups of plants and animals, the interval between speciation events ranged from 4,000 years (in cichlids of Lake Nabugabo, Uganda) to 40 million years (in some beetles). Overall, the time between speciation events averaged 6.5 million years and rarely took less than 500,000 years.

What can we learn from such data? First, the data suggest that on average, millions of years may pass before a newly formed species will itself give rise to another new species. As we'll see in Chapter 25, this result has implications for how long it takes life on Earth to recover from mass extinction events. Second, the extreme variability in the time it takes new species to form indicates that organisms do not have a "speciation clock" ticking inside them, causing them to produce new species at regular time intervals. Instead, speciation begins only after gene flow between populations is interrupted, perhaps by changing environmental conditions or by unpredictable events, such as a storm that transports a few individuals to an isolated area. Furthermore, once gene flow is interrupted, the populations must diverge genetically to such an extent that they become reproductively isolated— all before other events cause gene flow to resume, possibly reversing the speciation process (see Figure 24.16).

Studying the Genetics of Speciation

Studies of ongoing speciation (as in hybrid zones) can reveal traits that cause reproductive isolation. By identifying the genes that control those traits, scientists can explore a fundamental question of evolutionary biology: How many genes change when a new species forms?

In a few cases, the evolution of reproductive isolation is due to a change in a single gene. For example, in Japanese snails of the genus *Euhadra*, a change in a single gene can result in a mechanical barrier to reproduction. This gene controls the direction in which the shells spiral. When their shells spiral in different directions, the snails' genitalia are oriented in a manner that prevents mating (Figure 24.3f shows a similar example).

A major barrier to reproduction between two closely related species of monkey flower, *Mimulus cardinalis* and *M. lewisii*, also appears to be influenced by a relatively small number of genes. These two species are isolated by several prezygotic and postzygotic barriers. Of these, one prezygotic barrier, pollinator choice, accounts for most of the isolation: In a hybrid zone between *M. cardinalis* and *M. lewisii*, nearly 98% of pollinator visits were restricted to one species or the other.

The two monkey flower species are visited by different pollinators: Hummingbirds prefer the red-flowered *M. cardinalis*, and bumblebees prefer the pink-flowered *M. lewisii*. Douglas Schemske, of Michigan State University, and colleagues have shown that pollinator choice is affected by at least two loci in the monkey flowers, one of which, the "yellow upper," or *yup*, locus, influences flower color (**Figure 24.20**). By crossing the two parent species to produce F₁ hybrids and then performing repeated backcrosses of these F₁ hybrids to each parent species, Schemske and colleagues succeeded in transferring the *M. cardinalis* allele at this locus into *M. lewisii*, and vice versa. In a field experiment, *M. lewisii* plants with the *M. cardinalis yup* allele received 68-fold more visits from hummingbirds than did wild-type *M. lewisii*. Similarly, *M. cardinalis* plants with the *M. lewisii yup* allele received 74-fold more visits from bumblebees than did wild-type *M. cardinalis*. Thus, a mutation at a single locus can influence pollinator preference and hence contribute to reproductive isolation in monkey flowers.

In other organisms, the speciation process is influenced by larger numbers of genes and gene interactions. For example, hybrid sterility between two subspecies of the fruit fly *Drosophila pseudoobscura* results from gene interactions among at least four loci, and postzygotic isolation in the sunflower hybrid zone discussed earlier is influenced by at least 26 chromosome segments (and an unknown number of genes). Overall, studies suggest that few or many genes can influence the evolution of reproductive isolation and hence the emergence of a new species.

From Speciation to Macroevolution

As you've seen, speciation may begin with differences as seemingly small as the color on a cichlid's back. However, as speciation occurs again and again, such differences can accumulate and become more pronounced, eventually leading to the formation of new groups of organisms that differ greatly from their ancestors (as in the origin of whales from land-dwelling mammals; see Figure 22.20). Furthermore, as one group of organisms increases in size by producing many new species, another group of organisms may shrink, losing species to extinction. The cumulative effects of many such speciation and extinction events have helped shape the sweeping evolutionary changes that are documented in the fossil record. In the next chapter, we turn to such large-scale evolutionary changes as we begin our study of macroevolution.

(a) Typical *Mimulus lewisii*

(b) *M. lewisii* with an *M. cardinalis* flower-color allele

(c) Typical *Mimulus cardinalis*

(d) *M. cardinalis* with an *M. lewisii* flower-color allele

▲ **Figure 24.20 A locus that influences pollinator choice.** Pollinator preferences provide a strong barrier to reproduction between *Mimulus lewisii* and *M. cardinalis*. After transferring the *M. lewisii* allele for a flower-color locus into *M. cardinalis* and vice versa, researchers observed a shift in some pollinators' preferences.

WHAT IF? *If M. cardinalis individuals that had the M. lewisii yup allele were planted in an area that housed both monkey flower species, how might the production of hybrid offspring be affected?*

CONCEPT CHECK 24.4

1. Speciation can occur rapidly between diverging populations, yet the length of time between speciation events is often more than a million years. Explain this apparent contradiction.
2. Summarize evidence that the *yup* locus acts as a prezygotic barrier to reproduction in two species of monkey flowers. Do these results demonstrate that the *yup* locus alone controls barriers to reproduction between these species? Explain.
3. **MAKE CONNECTIONS** Compare Figure 13.11 (p. 259) with Figure 24.19 (p. 503). What cellular process could cause the hybrid chromosomes to contain DNA from both parent species? Explain.

For suggested answers, see Appendix A.

SUMMARY OF KEY CONCEPTS

CONCEPT 24.1

The biological species concept emphasizes reproductive isolation (pp. 488–492)

- A biological **species** is a group of populations whose individuals have the potential to interbreed and produce viable, fertile offspring with each other but not with members of other species. The **biological species concept** emphasizes reproductive isolation through prezygotic and postzygotic barriers that separate gene pools.
- Although helpful in thinking about how speciation occurs, the biological species concept has limitations. For instance, it cannot be applied to organisms known only as fossils or to organisms that reproduce only asexually. Thus, scientists use other species concepts, such as the **morphological species concept**, in certain circumstances.

? *Explain the importance of gene flow to the biological species concept.*

CONCEPT 24.2

Speciation can take place with or without geographic separation (pp. 493–498)

- In **allopatric speciation**, gene flow is reduced when two populations of one species become geographically separated from each other. One or both populations may undergo evolutionary change during the period of separation, resulting in the establishment of prezygotic or postzygotic barriers to reproduction.
- In **sympatric speciation**, a new species originates while remaining in the same geographic area as the parent species. Plant species (and, more rarely, animal species) have evolved sympatrically through polyploidy. Sympatric speciation can also result from habitat shifts and sexual selection.

Original population

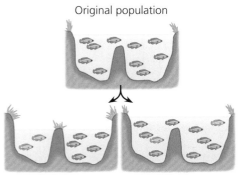
Allopatric speciation   Sympatric speciation

? *Can factors that cause sympatric speciation also cause allopatric speciation? Explain.*

CONCEPT 24.3

Hybrid zones reveal factors that cause reproductive isolation (pp. 498–501)

- Many groups of organisms form **hybrid zones** in which members of different species meet and mate, producing at least some offspring of mixed ancestry.

- Many hybrid zones are *stable* in that hybrid offspring continue to be produced over time. In others, **reinforcement** strengthens prezygotic barriers to reproduction, thus decreasing the formation of unfit hybrids. In still other hybrid zones, barriers to reproduction may weaken over time, resulting in the *fusion* of the species' gene pools (reversing the speciation process).

? *What factors can support the long-term stability of a hybrid zone if the parent species live in different environments?*

CONCEPT 24.4

Speciation can occur rapidly or slowly and can result from changes in few or many genes (pp. 501–504)

- New species can form rapidly once divergence begins—but it can take millions of years for that to happen. The time interval between speciation events varies considerably, from a few thousand years to tens of millions of years.
- New developments in genetics have enabled researchers to identify specific genes involved in some cases of speciation. Results show that speciation can be driven by few or many genes.

? *Is speciation something that happened only in the distant past, or are new species continuing to arise today? Explain.*

TEST YOUR UNDERSTANDING

LEVEL 1: KNOWLEDGE/COMPREHENSION

1. The *largest* unit within which gene flow can readily occur is a
   a. population.
   b. species.
   c. genus.
   d. hybrid.
   e. phylum.

2. Males of different species of the fruit fly *Drosophila* that live in the same parts of the Hawaiian Islands have different elaborate courtship rituals. These rituals involve fighting other males and making stylized movements that attract females. What type of reproductive isolation does this represent?
   a. habitat isolation
   b. temporal isolation
   c. behavioral isolation
   d. gametic isolation
   e. postzygotic barriers

3. According to the punctuated equilibria model,
   a. natural selection is unimportant as a mechanism of evolution.
   b. given enough time, most existing species will branch gradually into new species.
   c. most new species accumulate their unique features relatively rapidly as they come into existence, then change little for the rest of their duration as a species.
   d. most evolution occurs in sympatric populations.
   e. speciation is usually due to a single mutation.

LEVEL 2: APPLICATION/ANALYSIS

4. Bird guides once listed the myrtle warbler and Audubon's warbler as distinct species. Recently, these birds have been classified as eastern and western forms of a single species, the

yellow-rumped warbler. Which of the following pieces of evidence, if true, would be cause for this reclassification?
   a. The two forms interbreed often in nature, and their offspring have good survival and reproduction.
   b. The two forms live in similar habitats.
   c. The two forms have many genes in common.
   d. The two forms have similar food requirements.
   e. The two forms are very similar in coloration.

5. Which of the following factors would *not* contribute to allopatric speciation?
   a. A population becomes geographically isolated from the parent population.
   b. The separated population is small, and genetic drift occurs.
   c. The isolated population is exposed to different selection pressures than the ancestral population.
   d. Different mutations begin to distinguish the gene pools of the separated populations.
   e. Gene flow between the two populations is extensive.

6. Plant species A has a diploid number of 12. Plant species B has a diploid number of 16. A new species, C, arises as an allopolyploid from A and B. The diploid number for species C would probably be
   a. 12.   b. 14.   c. 16.   d. 28.   e. 56.

LEVEL 3: SYNTHESIS/EVALUATION

7. Suppose that a group of male pied flycatchers migrated from a region where there were no collared flycatchers to a region where both species were present (see Figure 24.15). Assuming events like this are very rare, which of the following scenarios is *least* likely?
   a. The frequency of hybrid offspring would increase.
   b. Migrant pied males would produce fewer offspring than would resident pied males.
   c. Pied females would rarely mate with collared males.
   d. Migrant males would mate with collared females more often than with pied females.
   e. The frequency of hybrid offspring would decrease.

8. **EVOLUTION CONNECTION**
   What is the biological basis for assigning all human populations to a single species? Can you think of a scenario by which a second human species could originate in the future?

9. **SCIENCE, TECHNOLOGY, AND SOCIETY**
   In the United States, the rare red wolf (*Canis lupus*) has been known to hybridize with coyotes (*Canis latrans*), which are much more numerous. Although red wolves and coyotes differ in terms of morphology, DNA, and behavior, genetic evidence suggests that living red wolf individuals are actually hybrids. Red wolves are designated as an endangered species and hence receive legal protection under the Endangered Species Act. Some people think that their endangered status should be withdrawn because the remaining red wolves are hybrids, not members of a "pure" species. Do you agree? Why or why not?

10. **SCIENTIFIC INQUIRY**
    DRAW IT   In this chapter, you read that bread wheat (*Triticum aestivum*) is an allohexaploid, containing two sets of chromosomes from each of three different parent species. Genetic analysis suggests that the three species pictured following this question each contributed chromosome sets to *T. aestivum*. (The capital letters here represent sets of chromosomes rather than individual genes.) Evidence also indicates that the first polyploidy event was a spontaneous hybridiza-

tion of the early cultivated wheat species *T. monococcum* and a wild *Triticum* grass species. Based on this information, draw a diagram of one possible chain of events that could have produced the allohexaploid *T. aestivum*.

Ancestral species:

AA

Triticum monococcum (2n = 14)

BB

Wild *Triticum* (2n = 14)

DD

Wild *T. tauschii* (2n = 14)

Product:

AA BB DD

T. aestivum (bread wheat) (2n = 42)

11. **WRITE ABOUT A THEME**
    The Genetic Basis of Life In sexually reproducing species, each individual begins life with DNA inherited from both parent organisms. In a short essay (100–150 words), apply this idea to what occurs when organisms of two species that have homologous chromosomes mate and produce (F_1) hybrid offspring. What percentage of the DNA in the F_1 hybrids' chromosomes comes from each parent species? As the hybrids mate and produce F_2 and later-generation hybrid offspring, describe how recombination and natural selection may affect whether the DNA in hybrid chromosomes is derived from one parent species or the other.

For selected answers, see Appendix A.

MasteringBIOLOGY®   www.masteringbiology.com

1. MasteringBiology® Assignments
Tutorial Defining Species
Activities Overview of Macroevolution • Allopatric Speciation • Speciation by Changes in Ploidy
Questions Student Misconceptions • Reading Quiz • Multiple Choice • End-of-Chapter

2. eText
Read your book online, search, take notes, highlight text, and more.

3. The Study Area
Practice Tests • Cumulative Test • *BioFlix* 3-D Animations • MP3 Tutor Sessions • Videos • Activities • Investigations • Lab Media • Audio Glossary • Word Study Tools • Art

UNIVERSITY OF ALBERTA FACULTY BIO

Philip J. Currie BSc Zoology (University of Toronto), MSc, PhD Paleontology (McGill University)

Current Positions: Professor and Canada Research Chair in Dinosaur Paleobiology, Department of Biological Sciences. Fellow of the Royal Society of Canada and member of Alberta Order of Excellence

I knew when I was 12 years old that I wanted to move to Alberta and study dinosaurs. As curator of Earth Sciences at the Provincial Museum of Alberta, I was part of a group that helped establish the Royal Tyrrell Museum of Paleontology. During my time as Curator of Dinosaurs, I became involved with the Canada-China Dinosaur Project, collaborating with Dale Russell of the Canadian Museum of Nature and Dong Zhiming of the Institute of Vertebrate Paleontology and Paleoanthropology in Beijing. This work in China set the foundation for our theory that birds are descended from dinosaurs.

I currently teach in Paleontology 400 (Paleontology Field School) and Paleontology 419 (Paleontology of the Higher Vertebrates). Not only have I published over 125 scientific papers, I am the author of 124 popular articles and 20 books.

My research focuses on the growth and variation of extinct reptiles, the anatomy and relationships of carnivorous dinosaurs, and the origin of birds. One current project in my lab concerns the armoured herbivorous dinosaurs known as ankylosaurs. I conduct field work in Alberta, British Columbia, the Canadian Arctic, Antarctica, Argentina, Mongolia, and China.

25

The History of Life on Earth

▲ **Figure 25.1 What does fossil evidence say about where these dinosaurs lived?**

Lost Worlds

Visitors to Antarctica today encounter one of Earth's harshest, most barren environments. In this land of extreme cold where there is almost no liquid water, life is sparse and small—the largest fully terrestrial animal is a fly that is 5 mm long. But even as early Antarctic explorers struggled to survive, some of them made an astonishing discovery:

▲ *Cryolophosaurus* **skull**

fossil evidence that life once thrived where it now barely exists. Fossils reveal that 500 million years ago, the ocean waters surrounding Antarctica were warm and teeming with tropical invertebrates. Later, the continent was covered in forests for hundreds of millions of years. At various times, a wide range of animals stalked through these forests, including 3-m-tall predatory "terror birds" and giant dinosaurs such as the voracious *Cryolophosaurus* **(Figure 25.1)**, a 7-m-long relative of *Tyrannosaurus rex*.

Fossils discovered in other parts of the world tell a similar, if not quite as surprising, story: Past organisms were very different from those presently living. The sweeping changes in life on Earth as revealed by fossils illustrate **macroevolution**, the broad pattern of evolution above the species level. Examples of macroevolutionary change include the emergence of terrestrial vertebrates through a series of speciation events, the impact of mass extinctions on the diversity of life, and the origin of key adaptations such as flight in birds.

Taken together, such changes provide a grand view of the evolutionary history of life on Earth. We'll examine that history in this chapter, beginning with hypotheses regarding the origin of life. The origin of life is the most speculative topic of the entire unit, for no fossil evidence of that seminal episode exists. We will then turn to evidence from the fossil record and what it tells us about major events in the history of life, paying particular attention to factors that have helped to shape the rise and fall of different groups of organisms over time.

CONCEPT **25.1**

Conditions on early Earth made the origin of life possible

Direct evidence of life on early Earth comes from fossils of microorganisms that are about 3.5 billion years old. But when and how did the first living cells appear? Observations and experiments in chemistry, geology, and physics have led scientists to propose one scenario that we'll examine here. They hypothesize that chemical and physical processes on early Earth, aided by the emerging force of natural selection, could have produced very simple cells through a sequence of four main stages:

1. The abiotic (nonliving) synthesis of small organic molecules, such as amino acids and nitrogenous bases
2. The joining of these small molecules into macromolecules, such as proteins and nucleic acids
3. The packaging of these molecules into **protocells**, droplets with membranes that maintained an internal chemistry different from that of their surroundings
4. The origin of self-replicating molecules that eventually made inheritance possible

Though speculative, this scenario leads to predictions that can be tested in the laboratory. In this section, we will examine some of the evidence for each stage.

Synthesis of Organic Compounds on Early Earth

There is scientific evidence that Earth and the other planets of the solar system formed about 4.6 billion years ago, condensing from a vast cloud of dust and rocks that surrounded the young sun. For the first few hundred million years, life probably could not have originated or survived on Earth because the planet was still being bombarded by huge chunks of rock and ice left over from the formation of the solar system. The collisions generated enough heat to vaporize the available water and prevent seas from forming. This early phase likely ended about 4.2–3.9 billion years ago.

As the bombardment of early Earth slowed, conditions on the planet were extremely different from those of today. The first atmosphere was probably thick with water vapor, along with various compounds released by volcanic eruptions, including nitrogen and its oxides, carbon dioxide, methane, ammonia, hydrogen, and hydrogen sulfide. As Earth cooled, the water vapor condensed into oceans, and much of the hydrogen escaped into space.

During the 1920s, Russian chemist A. I. Oparin and British scientist J. B. S. Haldane independently hypothesized that Earth's early atmosphere was a reducing (electron-adding) environment, in which organic compounds could have formed from simpler molecules. The energy for this organic synthesis could have come from lightning and intense UV radiation. Haldane suggested that the early oceans were a solution of organic molecules, a "primitive soup" from which life arose.

During 1953, Stanley Miller, working under the guidance of Harold Urey at the University of Chicago, tested the Oparin-Haldane hypothesis by creating laboratory conditions comparable to those that scientists at the time thought existed on early Earth (see Figure 4.2). His apparatus yielded a variety of amino acids found in organisms today, along with other organic compounds. Many laboratories have since repeated Miller's classic experiment using different recipes for the atmosphere, some of which also produced organic compounds.

However, it is unclear whether the atmosphere of early Earth contained enough methane and ammonia to be reducing. Some evidence suggests that the early atmosphere was made up primarily of nitrogen and carbon dioxide and was neither reducing nor oxidizing (electron-removing). Recent Miller-Urey-type experiments using such "neutral" atmospheres have also produced organic molecules. In addition, it is likely that small pockets of the early atmosphere—perhaps near the openings of volcanoes—were reducing. Perhaps the first organic compounds formed near volcanoes or deep-sea vents, where hot water and minerals gush into the ocean from Earth's interior. In a 2008 test of this volcanic-atmosphere hypothesis, researchers used modern equipment to reanalyze molecules that Miller had saved from one of his experiments. The study found that numerous amino acids had formed under conditions that simulated a volcanic eruption (**Figure 25.2**).

Miller-Urey-type experiments demonstrate that the abiotic synthesis of organic molecules is possible under various assumptions about the composition of the early atmosphere. A second source of organic molecules may have been meteorites. Among the meteorites that land on Earth are carbonaceous chondrites, rocks that are 1–2% carbon compounds by mass. Fragments of the Murchison meteorite, a 4.5-billion-year-old chondrite that fell to Australia in 1969, contain more than 80 amino acids, some in large amounts. These amino acids cannot be contaminants from Earth because they consist of an equal mix of D and L isomers (see Chapter 4). Organisms make and use only L isomers, with a few rare exceptions. Recent studies have shown that the Murchison meteorite also contained other key organic molecules, including lipids, simple sugars, and nitrogenous bases such as uracil.

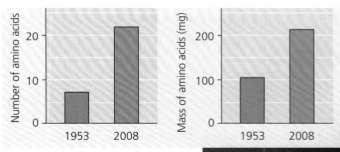

▲ **Figure 25.2 Amino acid synthesis in a simulated volcanic eruption.** In addition to his classic 1953 study, Miller also conducted an experiment simulating a volcanic eruption. In a 2008 reanalysis of those results, researchers found that far more amino acids were produced under simulated volcanic conditions than were produced in the conditions of the original 1953 experiment.

MAKE CONNECTIONS *After reviewing Concept 5.4 (pp. 78–80), explain how more than 20 amino acids could have been produced in the 2008 experiment.*

Abiotic Synthesis of Macromolecules

The presence of small organic molecules, such as amino acids and nitrogenous bases, is not sufficient for the emergence of life as we know it. Every cell has a vast assortment of macromolecules, including enzymes and other proteins and the nucleic acids that are essential for self-replication. Could such macromolecules have formed on early Earth? A 2009 study demonstrated that one key step, the abiotic synthesis of RNA monomers, can occur spontaneously from simple precursor molecules. In addition, by dripping solutions of amino acids or RNA nucleotides onto hot sand, clay, or rock, researchers have produced polymers of these molecules. The polymers formed spontaneously, without the help of enzymes or ribosomes. Unlike proteins, the amino acid polymers are a complex mix of linked and cross-linked amino acids. Nevertheless, it is possible that such polymers may have acted as weak catalysts for a variety of chemical reactions on early Earth.

Protocells

All organisms must be able to carry out reproduction and energy processing (metabolism). Life cannot persist without both of these functions. DNA molecules carry genetic information, including the instructions needed to replicate themselves accurately during reproduction. But the replication of DNA requires elaborate enzymatic machinery, along with a copious supply of nucleotide building blocks that are provided by the cell's metabolism (see Chapter 16). This suggests that self-replicating molecules and a metabolism-like source of the building blocks may have appeared together in early protocells. How did that happen?

The necessary conditions may have been met in *vesicles*, fluid-filled compartments bounded by a membrane-like structure. Recent experiments show that abiotically produced vesicles can exhibit certain properties of life, including simple reproduction and metabolism, as well as the maintenance of an internal chemical environment different from that of their surroundings.

For example, vesicles can form spontaneously when lipids or other organic molecules are added to water. When this occurs, the hydrophobic molecules in the mixture organize into a bilayer similar to the lipid bilayer of a plasma membrane. Adding substances such as *montmorillonite*, a soft mineral clay produced by the weathering of volcanic ash, greatly increases the rate of vesicle self-assembly **(Figure 25.3a)**. This clay, which is thought to have been common on early Earth, provides surfaces on which organic molecules become concentrated, increasing the likelihood that the molecules will react with each other and form vesicles. Abiotically produced vesicles can "reproduce" on their own **(Figure 25.3b)**, and they can increase in size ("grow") without dilution of their contents. Vesicles also can absorb montmorillonite particles, including those on which RNA and other organic molecules have become attached

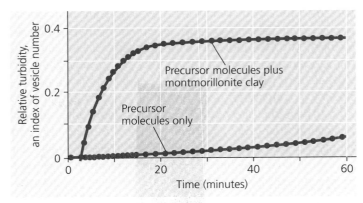

(a) Self-assembly. The presence of montmorillonite clay greatly increases the rate of vesicle self-assembly.

(b) Reproduction. Vesicles can divide on their own, as in this vesicle "giving birth" to smaller vesicles (LM).

(c) Absorption of RNA. This vesicle has incorporated montmorillonite clay particles coated with RNA (orange).

▲ **Figure 25.3 Features of abiotically produced vesicles.**

(Figure 25.3c). Finally, experiments have shown that some vesicles have a selectively permeable bilayer and can perform metabolic reactions using an external source of reagents—another important prerequisite for life.

Self-Replicating RNA and the Dawn of Natural Selection

The first genetic material was most likely RNA, not DNA. Thomas Cech, of the University of Colorado, and Sidney Altman, of Yale University, found that RNA, which plays a central role in protein synthesis, can also carry out a number of enzyme-like catalytic functions. Cech called these RNA catalysts **ribozymes**. Some ribozymes can make complementary copies of short pieces of RNA, provided that they are supplied with nucleotide building blocks.

Natural selection on the molecular level has produced ribozymes capable of self-replication in the laboratory. How does this occur? Unlike double-stranded DNA, which takes the form of a uniform helix, single-stranded RNA molecules assume a variety of specific three-dimensional shapes mandated by their nucleotide sequences. In a particular environment,

RNA molecules with certain base sequences are more stable and replicate faster and with fewer errors than other sequences. The RNA molecule whose sequence is best suited to the surrounding environment and has the greatest ability to replicate itself will leave the most descendant molecules. Occasionally, a copying error will result in a molecule that folds into a shape that is even more stable or more adept at self-replication than the ancestral sequence. Similar selection events may have occurred on early Earth. Thus, the molecular biology of today may have been preceded by an "RNA world," in which small RNA molecules that carried genetic information were able to replicate and to store information about the vesicles that carried them.

A vesicle with self-replicating, catalytic RNA would differ from its many neighbors that did not carry RNA or that carried RNA without such capabilities. If that vesicle could grow, split, and pass its RNA molecules to its daughters, the daughters would be protocells that had some of the properties of their parent. Although the first such protocells must have carried only limited amounts of genetic information, specifying only a few properties, their inherited characteristics could have been acted on by natural selection. The most successful of the early protocells would have increased in number because they could exploit their resources effectively and pass their abilities on to subsequent generations.

Once RNA sequences that carried genetic information appeared in protocells, many further changes would have been possible. For example, RNA could have provided the template on which DNA nucleotides were assembled. Double-stranded DNA is a more stable repository for genetic information than the more fragile single-stranded RNA. DNA also can be replicated more accurately. Accurate replication was advantageous as genomes grew larger through gene duplication and other processes and as more properties of the protocells became coded in genetic information. After DNA appeared, perhaps RNA molecules began to take on their present-day roles as regulators and intermediates in the translation of genes. The stage was now set for a blossoming of diverse life-forms—a change we see documented in the fossil record.

CONCEPT CHECK 25.1

1. What hypothesis did Miller test in his classic experiment?
2. How would the appearance of protocells have represented a key step in the origin of life?
3. **MAKE CONNECTIONS** In changing from an "RNA world" to today's "DNA world," genetic information must have flowed from RNA to DNA. After reviewing Figures 17.3 (p. 329) and 19.8 (p. 389), suggest how this could have occurred. Is such a flow a common occurrence today?

For suggested answers, see Appendix A.

CONCEPT 25.2

The fossil record documents the history of life

Starting with the earliest traces of life, the fossil record opens a window into the world of long ago and provides glimpses of the evolution of life over billions of years. In this section, we'll explore what the fossil record reveals about the major changes in the history of life—what those changes have been and how they may have occurred.

The Fossil Record

Recall from Chapter 22 that sedimentary rocks are the richest source of fossils. As a result, the fossil record is based primarily on the sequence in which fossils have accumulated in sedimentary rock layers, called *strata* (see Figure 22.3). Useful information is also provided by other types of fossils, such as insects preserved in amber (fossilized tree sap) and mammals frozen in ice.

The fossil record shows that there have been great changes in the kinds of organisms on Earth at different points in time **(Figure 25.4)**. Many past organisms were unlike today's organisms, and many organisms that once were common are now extinct. As we'll see later, fossils also document how new groups of organisms arose from previously existing ones.

As substantial and significant as the fossil record is, keep in mind that it is an incomplete chronicle of evolutionary change. Many of Earth's organisms did not die in the right place at the right time to be preserved as fossils. Of those fossils that were formed, many were destroyed by later geologic processes, and only a fraction of the others have been discovered. As a result, the known fossil record is biased in favor of species that existed for a long time, were abundant and widespread in certain kinds of environments, and had hard shells, skeletons, or other parts that facilitated their fossilization. Even with its limitations, however, the fossil record is a remarkably detailed account of biological change over the vast scale of geologic time. Furthermore, as shown by the recently unearthed fossils of whale ancestors with hind limbs (see Figures 22.19 and 22.20), gaps in the fossil record continue to be filled by new discoveries.

Although some of these new discoveries are fortuitous, others illustrate the predictive nature of paleontology. For instance, researchers seeking to discover a close ancestor of early terrestrial vertebrates predicted that such a fossil would most likely be located in a river bed (which would have sedimentary rocks) containing rocks that were 375 million years old (an age based on previously known fossils). After digging for several years in one of the few such places on Earth, their predictions bore fruit with the discovery of *Tiktaalik*, an aquatic organism closely related to the first vertebrates to walk on land (see Figures 25.4 and 34.20).

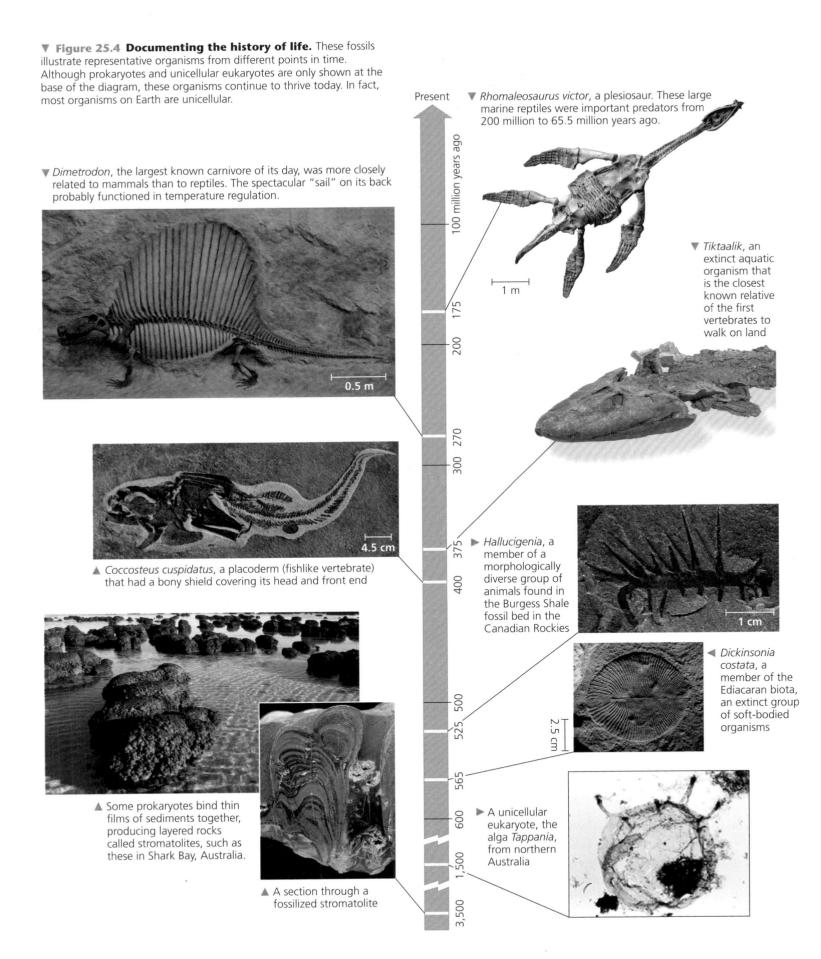

▼ **Figure 25.4 Documenting the history of life.** These fossils illustrate representative organisms from different points in time. Although prokaryotes and unicellular eukaryotes are only shown at the base of the diagram, these organisms continue to thrive today. In fact, most organisms on Earth are unicellular.

Present

100 million years ago

▼ *Rhomaleosaurus victor*, a plesiosaur. These large marine reptiles were important predators from 200 million to 65.5 million years ago.

1 m

▼ *Dimetrodon*, the largest known carnivore of its day, was more closely related to mammals than to reptiles. The spectacular "sail" on its back probably functioned in temperature regulation.

0.5 m

175

200

270

300

▼ *Tiktaalik*, an extinct aquatic organism that is the closest known relative of the first vertebrates to walk on land

▲ *Coccosteus cuspidatus*, a placoderm (fishlike vertebrate) that had a bony shield covering its head and front end

4.5 cm

375

400

► *Hallucigenia*, a member of a morphologically diverse group of animals found in the Burgess Shale fossil bed in the Canadian Rockies

1 cm

◄ *Dickinsonia costata*, a member of the Ediacaran biota, an extinct group of soft-bodied organisms

2.5 cm

▲ Some prokaryotes bind thin films of sediments together, producing layered rocks called stromatolites, such as these in Shark Bay, Australia.

500

525

565

600

► A unicellular eukaryote, the alga *Tappania*, from northern Australia

1,500

▲ A section through a fossilized stromatolite

3,500

How Rocks and Fossils Are Dated

Fossils are valuable data for reconstructing the history of life, but only if we can determine where they fit in that unfolding story. While the order of fossils in rock strata tells us the sequence in which the fossils were laid down—their relative ages—it does not tell us their actual (absolute) ages. Examining the relative positions of fossils in strata is like peeling off layers of wallpaper in an old house. You can determine the sequence in which the layers were applied, but not the year each layer was added.

How can we determine the absolute age of a fossil? (Note that "absolute" dating does not mean errorless dating, but only that an age is given in years rather than relative terms such as *before* and *after*.) One of the most common techniques is **radiometric dating**, which is based on the decay of radioactive isotopes (see Chapter 2). In this process, a radioactive "parent" isotope decays to a "daughter" isotope at a fixed rate. The rate of decay is expressed by the **half-life**, the time required for 50% of the parent isotope to decay **(Figure 25.5)**. Each type of radioactive isotope has a characteristic half-life, which is not affected by temperature, pressure, or other environmental variables. For example, carbon-14 decays relatively quickly; it has a half-life of 5,730 years. Uranium-238 decays slowly; its half-life is 4.5 billion years.

Fossils contain isotopes of elements that accumulated in the organisms when they were alive. For example, a living organism contains the most common carbon isotope, carbon-12, as well as a radioactive isotope, carbon-14. When the organism dies, it stops accumulating carbon, and the amount of carbon-12 in its tissues does not change over time. However, the carbon-14 that it contains at the time of death slowly decays into another element, nitrogen-14. Thus, by measuring the ratio of carbon-14 to carbon-12 in a fossil, we can determine the fossil's age. This method works for fossils up to about 75,000 years old; fossils older than that contain too little carbon-14 to be detected with current techniques. Radioactive isotopes with longer half-lives are used to date older fossils.

Determining the age of these older fossils in sedimentary rocks is challenging. Organisms do not use radioisotopes with long half-lives, such as uranium-238, to build their bones or shells. Moreover, the sedimentary rocks themselves tend to consist of sediments of differing ages. Though we usually cannot date these old fossils directly, an indirect method can be used to infer the age of fossils that are sandwiched between two layers of volcanic rocks. As lava cools into volcanic rock, radioisotopes from the surrounding environment become trapped in the newly formed rock. Some of the trapped radioisotopes have long half-lives, allowing geologists to estimate the ages of ancient volcanic rocks. If two volcanic layers surrounding fossils are determined to be 525 million and 535 million years old, for example, then the fossils are roughly 530 million years old.

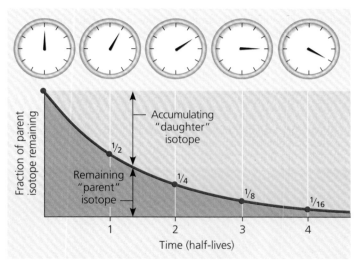

▲ **Figure 25.5 Radiometric dating.** In this diagram, each division of the clock face represents a half-life.

DRAW IT *Relabel the x-axis of this graph with time measurements in years to illustrate the radioactive decay of uranium-238 (half-life = 4.5 billion years).*

Now that we've seen how fossils can be dated, let's turn to an example of what we can learn from them.

The Origin of New Groups of Organisms

Some fossils provide a detailed look at the origin of new groups of organisms. Such fossils are central to our understanding of evolution; they illustrate how new features arise and how long it takes for such changes to occur. We'll examine one such case here: the origin of mammals.

Along with amphibians and reptiles, mammals belong to the group of animals called *tetrapods* (from the Greek *tetra*, four, and *pod*, foot), named for having four limbs. Mammals have a number of unique anatomical features that fossilize readily, allowing scientists to trace their origin. For example, the lower jaw is composed of one bone (the dentary) in mammals but several bones in other tetrapods. In addition, the lower and upper jaws hinge between a different set of bones in mammals than in other tetrapods. As we'll explore in Chapter 34, mammals also have a unique set of three bones that transmit sound in the middle ear (the hammer, anvil, and stirrup), whereas other tetrapods have only one such bone (the stirrup). Finally, the teeth of mammals are differentiated into incisors (for tearing), canines (for piercing), and the multi-pointed premolars and molars (for crushing and grinding). In contrast, the teeth of other tetrapods usually consist of a row of undifferentiated, single-pointed teeth.

As detailed in **Figure 25.6**, the fossil record shows that the unique features of mammalian jaws and teeth evolved gradually over time, in a series of steps. As you study Figure 25.6, bear in mind that it includes just a few examples of the fossil skulls that document the origin of mammals. If all the

Exploring The Origin of Mammals

Over the course of 120 million years, mammals originated gradually from a group of tetrapods called synapsids. Shown here are a few of the many fossil organisms whose morphological features represent intermediate steps between living mammals and their synapsid ancestors. The evolutionary context of the origin of mammals is shown in the tree diagram at right (the dagger symbol † indicates extinct lineages).

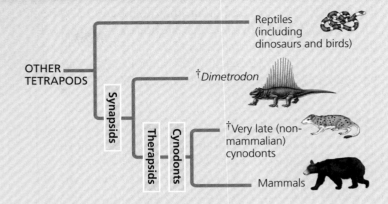

Key to skull bones

▨ Articular	▨ Dentary
▨ Quadrate	▧ Squamosal

Synapsid (300 mya)

Synapsids had multiple bones in the lower jaw and single-pointed teeth. The jaw hinge was formed by the articular and quadrate bones. Synapsids also had an opening called the *temporal fenestra* behind the eye socket. Powerful cheek muscles for closing the jaws probably passed through the temporal fenestra. Over time, this opening enlarged and moved in front of the hinge between the lower and upper jaws, thereby increasing the power and precision with which the jaws could be closed (much as moving a doorknob away from the hinge makes a door easier to close).

Therapsid (280 mya)

Later, a group of synapsids called therapsids appeared. Therapsids had large dentary bones, long faces, and the first examples of specialized teeth, large canines. These trends continued in a group of therapsids called cynodonts.

Early cynodont (260 mya)

In early cynodont therapsids, the dentary was the largest bone in the lower jaw, the temporal fenestra was large and positioned forward of the jaw hinge, and teeth with several cusps first appeared (not visible in the diagram). As in earlier synapsids, the jaw had an articular-quadrate hinge.

Later cynodont (220 mya)

Later cynodonts had teeth with complex cusp patterns and their lower and upper jaws hinged in two locations: They retained the original articular-quadrate hinge and formed a new, second hinge between the dentary and squamosal bones. (The temporal fenestra is not visible in this or the below cynodont skull at the angles shown.)

Very late cynodont (195 mya)

In some very late (non-mammalian) cynodonts and early mammals, the original articular-quadrate hinge was lost, leaving the dentary-squamosal hinge as the only hinge between the lower and upper jaws, as in living mammals. The articular and quadrate bones migrated into the ear region (not shown), where they functioned in transmitting sound. In the mammal lineage, these two bones later evolved into the familiar hammer (malleus) and anvil (incus) shown in Figure 34.31.

known fossils in the sequence were arranged by shape and placed side by side, their features would blend smoothly from one group to the next. Some of these fossils would reflect how the features of a group that dominates life today, the mammals, gradually arose in a previously existing group, the cynodonts. Others would reveal side branches on the tree of life—groups of organisms that thrived for millions of years but ultimately left no descendants that survive today.

CONCEPT CHECK 25.2

1. Your measurements indicate that a fossilized skull you unearthed has a carbon-14/carbon-12 ratio about ¹⁄₁₆ that of the skulls of present-day animals. What is the approximate age of the fossilized skull?
2. Describe an example from the fossil record that shows how life has changed over time.
3. **WHAT IF?** Suppose researchers discover a fossil of an organism that lived 300 million years ago but had mammalian teeth and a mammalian jaw hinge. What inferences might you draw from this fossil about the origin of mammals and the evolution of novel skeletal structures? Explain.

For suggested answers, see Appendix A.

CONCEPT 25.3

Key events in life's history include the origins of single-celled and multicelled organisms and the colonization of land

The study of fossils has helped geologists establish a **geologic record** of Earth's history, which is divided into three eons (**Table 25.1**, on the facing page). The first two eons—the Archaean and the Proterozoic—together lasted approximately 4 billion years. The Phanerozoic eon, roughly the last half billion years, encompasses most of the time that animals have existed on Earth. It is divided into three eras: the Paleozoic, Mesozoic, and Cenozoic. Each era represents a distinct age in the history of Earth and its life. For example, the Mesozoic era is sometimes called the "age of reptiles" because of its abundance of reptilian fossils, including those of dinosaurs. The boundaries between the eras correspond to major extinction events seen in the fossil record, when many forms of life disappeared and were replaced by forms that evolved from the survivors.

As we've seen, the fossil record provides a sweeping overview of the history of life over geologic time. Here we will focus on a few major events in that history, returning to study the details in Unit Five. **Figure 25.7** uses the analogy of a clock to place these events in the context of the geologic

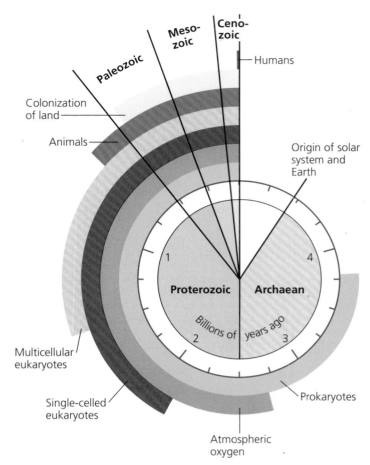

▲ **Figure 25.7 Clock analogy for some key events in Earth's history.** The clock ticks down from the origin of Earth 4.6 billion years ago to the present.

record. This clock will reappear at various points in this section as a quick visual reminder of when the events we are discussing took place.

The First Single-Celled Organisms

The earliest direct evidence of life, dating from 3.5 billion years ago, comes from fossilized stromatolites (see Figure 25.4). **Stromatolites** are layered rocks that form when certain prokaryotes bind thin films of sediment together. Present-day stromatolites are found in a few warm, shallow, salty bays. If microbial communities complex enough to form stromatolites existed 3.5 billion years ago, it is a reasonable hypothesis that single-celled organisms originated much earlier, perhaps as early as 3.9 billion years ago.

Early prokaryotes were Earth's sole inhabitants from at least 3.5 billion years ago to about 2.1 billion years ago. As we will see, these prokaryotes transformed life on our planet.

Table 25.1 The Geologic Record

Relative Duration of Eons	Era	Period	Epoch	Age (Millions of Years Ago)	Some Important Events in the History of Life
Phanerozoic	Cenozoic	Quaternary	Holocene		Historical time
				0.01	
			Pleistocene		Ice ages; origin of genus *Homo*
				2.6	
		Neogene	Pliocene		Appearance of bipedal human ancestors
				5.3	
			Miocene		Continued radiation of mammals and angiosperms; earliest direct human ancestors
				23	
		Paleogene	Oligocene		Origins of many primate groups
				33.9	
			Eocene		Angiosperm dominance increases; continued radiation of most present-day mammalian orders
				55.8	
			Paleocene		Major radiation of mammals, birds, and pollinating insects
				65.5	
	Mesozoic	Cretaceous			Flowering plants (angiosperms) appear and diversify; many groups of organisms, including most dinosaurs, become extinct at end of period
				145.5	
		Jurassic			Gymnosperms continue as dominant plants; dinosaurs abundant and diverse
				199.6	
		Triassic			Cone-bearing plants (gymnosperms) dominate landscape; dinosaurs evolve and radiate; origin of mammals
				251	
	Paleozoic	Permian			Radiation of reptiles; origin of most present-day groups of insects; extinction of many marine and terrestrial organisms at end of period
				299	
		Carboniferous			Extensive forests of vascular plants form; first seed plants appear; origin of reptiles; amphibians dominant
				359	
Proterozoic		Devonian			Diversification of bony fishes; first tetrapods and insects appear
				416	
		Silurian			Diversification of early vascular plants
				444	
		Ordovician			Marine algae abundant; colonization of land by diverse fungi, plants, and animals
				488	
		Cambrian			Sudden increase in diversity of many animal phyla (Cambrian explosion)
				542	
		Ediacaran			Diverse algae and soft-bodied invertebrate animals appear
				635	
				2,100	Oldest fossils of eukaryotic cells appear
				2,500	
Archaean				2,700	Concentration of atmospheric oxygen begins to increase
				3,500	Oldest fossils of cells (prokaryotes) appear
				3,800	Oldest known rocks on Earth's surface
				Approx. 4,600	Origin of Earth

Photosynthesis and the Oxygen Revolution

Atmospheric oxygen

Most atmospheric oxygen gas (O_2) is of biological origin, produced during the water-splitting step of photosynthesis. When oxygenic photosynthesis first evolved, the free O_2 it produced probably dissolved in the surrounding water until it reached a high enough concentration to react with dissolved iron. This would have caused the iron to precipitate as iron oxide, which accumulated as sediments. These sediments were compressed into banded iron formations, red layers of rock containing iron oxide that are a source of iron ore today. Once all of the dissolved iron had precipitated, additional O_2 dissolved in the water until the seas and lakes became saturated with O_2. After this occurred, the O_2 finally began to "gas out" of the water and enter the atmosphere. This change left its mark in the rusting of iron-rich terrestrial rocks, a process that began about 2.7 billion years ago. This chronology implies that bacteria similar to today's cyanobacteria (oxygen-releasing, photosynthetic bacteria) originated well before 2.7 billion years ago.

The amount of atmospheric O_2 increased gradually from about 2.7 to 2.3 billion years ago, but then shot up relatively rapidly to between 1% and 10% of its present level **(Figure 25.8)**. This "oxygen revolution" had an enormous impact on life. In certain of its chemical forms, oxygen attacks chemical bonds and can inhibit enzymes and damage cells. As a result, the rising concentration of atmospheric O_2 probably doomed many prokaryotic groups. Some species survived in habitats that remained anaerobic, where we find their descendants living today (see Chapter 27). Among other survivors, diverse adaptations to the changing atmosphere evolved, including cellular respiration, which uses O_2 in the process of harvesting the energy stored in organic molecules.

As mentioned previously, the early, gradual rise in atmospheric O_2 levels was probably brought about by ancient cyanobacteria. A few hundred million years later, the rise in O_2 accelerated. What caused this acceleration? One hypothesis is that this rise followed the evolution of eukaryotic cells containing chloroplasts, as we will discuss next.

The First Eukaryotes

Single-celled eukaryotes

The oldest widely accepted fossils of eukaryotic organisms are about 2.1 billion years old. Recall that eukaryotic cells have more complex organization than prokaryotic cells: Eukaryotic cells have a nuclear envelope, mitochondria, endoplasmic reticulum, and other internal structures that prokaryotes lack. Also, unlike prokaryotic cells, eukaryotic cells have a cytoskeleton, a feature that enables eukaryotic cells to change their shape and thereby surround and engulf other cells.

How did these eukaryotic features evolve from prokaryotic cells? A range of evidence supports the **endosymbiont theory**, which posits that mitochondria and plastids (a general term for chloroplasts and related organelles) were formerly small prokaryotes that began living within larger cells. The term *endosymbiont* refers to a cell that lives within another cell, called the *host cell*. The prokaryotic ancestors of mitochondria and plastids probably gained entry to the host cell as undigested prey or internal parasites. Though such a process may seem unlikely, scientists have directly observed cases in which endosymbionts that began as prey or parasites came to have a mutually beneficial relationship with the host in as little as five years.

By whatever means the relationships began, we can hypothesize how the symbiosis could have become mutually beneficial. A host that is a heterotroph (an organism that eats other organisms or substances derived from them) could use nutrients released from photosynthetic endosymbionts. And in a world that was becoming increasingly aerobic, a host that was itself an anaerobe would have benefited from endosymbionts that turned the oxygen to advantage. Over time, the host and endosymbionts would have become a single organism, its parts inseparable. Although all eukaryotes have mitochondria or remnants of these organelles, they do not all have plastids. Thus, the hypothesis of **serial endosymbiosis** supposes that mitochondria evolved before plastids through a sequence of endosymbiotic events **(Figure 25.9)**.

A great deal of evidence supports the endosymbiotic origin of mitochondria and plastids. The inner membranes of both organelles have enzymes and transport systems that are homologous to those found in the plasma membranes of

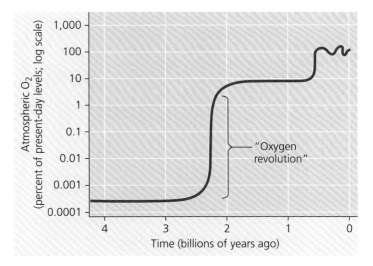

▲ **Figure 25.8 The rise of atmospheric oxygen.** Chemical analyses of ancient rocks have enabled this reconstruction of atmospheric oxygen levels during Earth's history.

Cytoplasm

DNA

Plasma
membrane

**Ancestral
prokaryote**

Infolding of
plasma membrane

Endoplasmic
reticulum

Nucleus

Nuclear envelope

Engulfing
of aerobic
heterotrophic
prokaryote

Cell with nucleus
and endomem-
brane system

Mitochondrion

Mitochondrion

Engulfing of
photosynthetic
prokaryote by
some cells

**Ancestral
heterotrophic
eukaryote**

Plastid

**Ancestral photosynthetic
eukaryote**

▲ **Figure 25.9 A hypothesis for the origin of eukaryotes
through serial endosymbiosis.** The proposed ancestors of
mitochondria were aerobic, heterotrophic prokaryotes (meaning they used
oxygen to metabolize organic molecules obtained from other organisms).
The proposed ancestors of plastids were photosynthetic prokaryotes. In
this figure, the arrows represent change over evolutionary time.

living prokaryotes. Mitochondria and plastids replicate by a splitting process that is similar to that of certain prokaryotes. In addition, each of these organelles contains a single, circular DNA molecule that, like the chromosomes of bacteria, is not associated with histones or large amounts of other proteins. As might be expected of organelles descended from free-living organisms, mitochondria and plastids also have the cellular machinery (including ribosomes) needed to transcribe and translate their DNA into proteins. Finally, in terms of size, RNA sequences, and sensitivity to certain antibiotics, the ribosomes of mitochondria and plastids are more similar to prokaryotic ribosomes than they are to the cytoplasmic ribosomes of eukaryotic cells.

The Origin of Multicellularity

An orchestra can play a greater variety of musical compositions than a violin soloist can; the increased complexity of the orchestra makes more variations possible. Likewise, the appearance of structurally complex eukaryotic cells sparked the evolution of greater morphological diversity than was possible for the simpler prokaryotic cells. After the first eukaryotes appeared, a great range of unicellular forms evolved, giving rise to the diversity of single-celled eukaryotes that continue to flourish today. Another wave of diversification also occurred: Some single-celled eukaryotes gave rise to multicellular forms, whose descendants include a variety of algae, plants, fungi, and animals.

The Earliest Multicellular Eukaryotes

Billions of years ago

Multicellular
eukaryotes

Based on comparisons of DNA sequences, researchers have suggested that the common ancestor of multicellular eukaryotes lived 1.5 billion years ago. This result is in rough agreement with the fossil record; the oldest known fossils of multicellular eukaryotes are of relatively small algae that lived about 1.2 billion years ago. Larger and more diverse multicellular eukaryotes do not appear in the fossil record until about 575 million years ago (see Figure 25.4). These fossils, referred to as the Ediacaran biota, were of soft-bodied organisms—some over 1 m long—that lived from 575 to 535 million years ago.

Why were multicellular eukaryotes limited in size and diversity until the late Proterozoic? One hypothesis stems from geologic evidence indicating that a series of severe ice ages occurred from 750 to 580 million years ago. At various times during this period, glaciers covered all of the planet's landmasses, and the seas were largely iced over. The "snowball Earth" hypothesis suggests that most life would have been confined to areas near deep-sea vents and hot springs or to equatorial regions of the ocean that lacked ice cover. The fossil record of the first major diversification of multicellular eukaryotes (beginning about 575 million years ago) corresponds roughly to the time when snowball Earth thawed. As that diversification came to a close about 40 million years later, the stage was set for another, even more spectacular burst of evolutionary change.

The Cambrian Explosion

Many present-day animal phyla appear suddenly in fossils formed early in the Cambrian period (535–525 million years ago), a phenomenon referred to as the **Cambrian explosion**. Fossils of several animal groups—sponges, cnidarians (sea anemones and their relatives), and molluscs—appear in even older rocks dating from the late Proterozoic **(Figure 25.10)**.

Prior to the Cambrian explosion, all large animals were soft-bodied. The fossils of large pre-Cambrian animals reveal little evidence of predation. Instead, these animals appear to have been grazers (feeding on algae), suspension feeders, or scavengers, not hunters. The Cambrian explosion changed

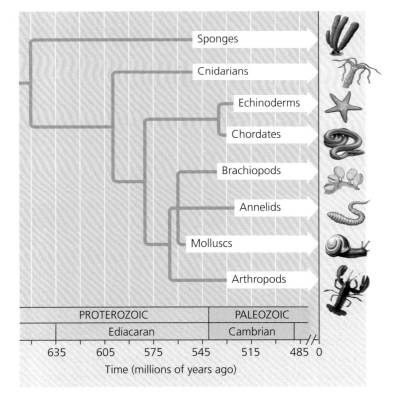

▲ **Figure 25.10 Appearance of selected animal groups.** The white bars indicate earliest appearances of these animal groups in the fossil record.

DRAW IT *Circle the branch point that represents the most recent common ancestor of chordates and annelids. What is a minimum estimate of that ancestor's age?*

(a) Two-cell stage 150 μm **(b) Later stage** 200 μm

▲ **Figure 25.11 Proterozoic fossils that may be animal embryos (SEM).**

all of that. In a relatively short period of time (10 million years), predators over 1 m in length emerged that had claws and other features for capturing prey; simultaneously, new defensive adaptations, such as sharp spines and heavy body armor, appeared in their prey (see Figure 25.4).

Although the Cambrian explosion had an enormous impact on life on Earth, it is possible that many animal phyla originated long before that time. Some DNA analyses suggest that most animal phyla originated and began to diverge from one another as early as 700 million to 1 billion years ago. Even if these estimates are not correct, recent fossil discoveries in China suggest that animals similar to members of living animal phyla were present tens of millions of years before the Cambrian explosion. The discoveries include 575-million-year-old fossils of beautifully preserved specimens interpreted by most scientists either as animal embryos or as members of extinct groups closely related to animals **(Figure 25.11)**. Overall, it appears that the Cambrian explosion had a "long fuse"—at least 40 million years long, based on the Chinese fossils. The fuse may have been hundreds of millions of years long if some animal phyla originated as far back as some DNA-based estimates suggest.

The Colonization of Land

The colonization of land was another milestone in the history of life. There is fossil evidence that cyanobacteria and other photosynthetic prokaryotes coated damp terrestrial surfaces well over a billion years ago. However, larger forms of life, such as fungi, plants, and animals, did not begin to colonize land until about 500 million years ago. This gradual evolutionary venture out of aquatic environments was associated with adaptations that made it possible to reproduce on land and that helped prevent dehydration. For example, many land plants today have a vascular system for transporting materials internally and a waterproof coating of wax on their leaves that slows the loss of water to the air. Early signs of these adaptations were present 420 million years ago, at which time small plants (about 10 cm high) existed that had a vascular system but lacked true roots or leaves. By about 50 million years later, plants had diversified greatly and included reeds and treelike plants with true roots and leaves.

Plants colonized land in the company of fungi. Even today, the roots of most plants are associated with fungi that aid in the absorption of water and minerals from the soil (see Chapter 31). These root fungi, in turn, obtain their organic nutrients from the plants. Such mutually beneficial associations of plants and fungi are evident in some of the oldest fossilized roots, dating this relationship back to the early spread of life onto land.

Although many animal groups are now represented in terrestrial environments, the most widespread and diverse land animals are arthropods (particularly insects and spiders) and tetrapods. Arthropods were the first animals to colonize land, roughly 420 million years ago. The earliest tetrapods found in the fossil record lived about 365 million years ago and appear to have evolved from a group of lobe-finned fishes (see Chapter 34). Tetrapods include humans, although we are late arrivals on the scene. The human lineage diverged from other primates around 6–7 million years ago, and our species originated only about 195,000 years ago. If the clock of Earth's history were rescaled to represent an hour, humans appeared less than 0.2 second ago.

CONCEPT CHECK 25.3

1. The first appearance of free oxygen in the atmosphere likely triggered a massive wave of extinctions among the prokaryotes of the time. Why?
2. What evidence supports the hypothesis that mitochondria preceded plastids in the evolution of eukaryotic cells?
3. **WHAT IF?** What would a fossil record of life today look like?

For suggested answers, see Appendix A.

CONCEPT 25.4

The rise and fall of groups of organisms reflect differences in speciation and extinction rates

From its beginnings, life on Earth has seen the rise and fall of groups of organisms. Anaerobic prokaryotes originated, flourished, and then declined as the oxygen content of the atmosphere rose. Billions of years later, the first tetrapods emerged from the sea, giving rise to several major new groups of organisms. One of these, the amphibians, went on to dominate life on land for 100 million years, until other tetrapods (including dinosaurs and, later, mammals) replaced them as the dominant terrestrial vertebrates.

The rise and fall of these and other major groups of organisms have shaped the history of life. Narrowing our focus, we can also see that the rise or fall of any particular group is related to the speciation and extinction rates of its member species. Just as a population increases in size when there are more births than deaths, the rise of a group of organisms occurs when it produces more new species than are lost to extinction. The reverse occurs when a group is in decline. As we'll see, such changes in the fates of groups of organisms have been influenced by large-scale processes such as plate tectonics, mass extinctions, and adaptive radiations.

Plate Tectonics

If photographs of Earth were taken from space every 10,000 years and spliced together to make a movie, it would show something many of us find hard to imagine: The seemingly "rock solid" continents we live on move over time. Since the origin of multicellular eukaryotes roughly 1.5 billion years ago, there have been three occasions (1.1 billion, 600 million, and 250 million years ago) when most of the landmasses of Earth came together to form a supercontinent, then later broke apart. Each time they yielded a different configuration of continents. Looking into the future, some geologists have estimated that the continents will come together again and form a new supercontinent roughly 250 million years from now.

According to the theory of **plate tectonics**, the continents are part of great plates of Earth's crust that essentially float on the hot, underlying portion of the mantle **(Figure 25.12)**. Movements in the mantle cause the plates to move over time in a process called *continental drift*. Geologists can measure the rate at which the plates are moving now, usually only a few centimeters per year. They can also infer the past locations of the continents using the magnetic signal recorded in rocks at the time of their formation. This method works because as a continent shifts its position over time, the direction of magnetic north recorded in its newly formed rocks also changes.

▶ **Figure 25.12 Cutaway view of Earth.** The thickness of the crust is exaggerated here.

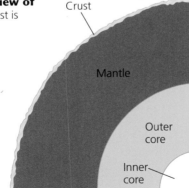

Crust

Mantle

Outer core

Inner core

Earth's major tectonic plates are shown in **Figure 25.13**. Many important geologic processes, including the formation of mountains and islands, occur at plate boundaries. In some cases, two plates are moving away from each other, as are the North American and Eurasian plates, which are currently drifting apart at a rate of about 2 cm per year. In other cases, two plates are sliding past each other, forming regions where earthquakes are common. California's infamous San Andreas Fault is part of a border where two plates slide past each other. In still other cases, two plates are colliding. Typically, oceanic plates (those found on the bottom of the ocean) are more dense than terrestrial plates. As a result, when an oceanic plate collides with a terrestrial plate, the oceanic plate usually sinks below the terrestrial plate. When two oceanic plates or two terrestrial plates collide with each other, violent upheavals occur and mountains form along the plate boundaries. One spectacular example of this occurred 45 million years ago, when the Indian plate crashed into the Eurasian plate, starting the formation of the Himalayan mountains.

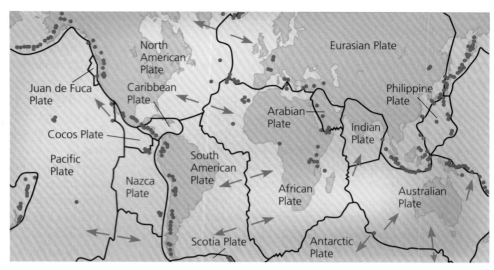

▲ **Figure 25.13 Earth's major tectonic plates.** The arrows indicate direction of movement. The reddish orange dots represent zones of violent tectonic activity.

Consequences of Continental Drift

Plate movements rearrange geography slowly, but their cumulative effects are dramatic. In addition to reshaping the physical features of our planet, continental drift also has a major impact on life on Earth.

One reason for its great impact on life is that continental drift alters the habitats in which organisms live. Consider the changes shown in **Figure 25.14**. About 250 million years ago, plate movements brought all the previously separated landmasses together into a supercontinent named **Pangaea**. Ocean basins became deeper, which lowered sea level and drained shallow coastal seas. At that time, as now, most marine species inhabited shallow waters, and the formation of Pangaea destroyed a considerable amount of that habitat. The interior of the vast continent was cold and dry, probably an even more severe environment than that of central Asia today. Overall, the formation of Pangaea had a tremendous impact on the physical environment and climate, which drove some species to extinction and provided new opportunities for groups of organisms that survived the crisis.

Another aspect of continental drift that affects organisms is the climate change that results when a continent shifts its location. The southern tip of Labrador, Canada, for example, once was located in the tropics but has moved 40° to the north over the last 200 million years. When faced with the changes in climate that such shifts in position entail, organisms adapt,

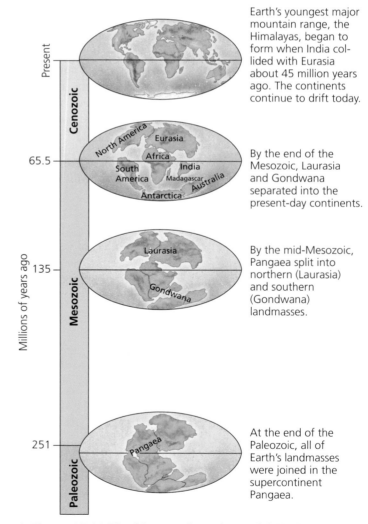

Earth's youngest major mountain range, the Himalayas, began to form when India collided with Eurasia about 45 million years ago. The continents continue to drift today.

By the end of the Mesozoic, Laurasia and Gondwana separated into the present-day continents.

By the mid-Mesozoic, Pangaea split into northern (Laurasia) and southern (Gondwana) landmasses.

At the end of the Paleozoic, all of Earth's landmasses were joined in the supercontinent Pangaea.

▲ **Figure 25.14 The history of continental drift during the Phanerozoic eon.**

move to a new location, or become extinct (this last outcome occurred for many organisms stranded on Antarctica).

Continental drift also promotes allopatric speciation on a grand scale. When supercontinents break apart, regions that once were connected become geographically isolated. As the continents drifted apart over the last 200 million years, each became a separate evolutionary arena, with lineages of plants and animals that diverged from those on other continents.

Finally, continental drift can help explain puzzles about the geographic distribution of extinct organisms, such as why fossils of the same species of Permian freshwater reptiles have been discovered in both Brazil and the West African nation of Ghana. These two parts of the world, now separated by 3,000 km of ocean, were joined together when these reptiles were living. Continental drift also explains much about the current distributions of organisms, such as why Australian fauna and flora contrast so sharply with those of the rest of the world. Marsupial mammals fill ecological roles in Australia analogous to those filled by eutherians (placental mammals) on other continents (see Figure 22.18). Fossil evidence suggests that marsupials originated in what is now Asia and reached Australia via South America and Antarctica while the continents were still joined. The subsequent breakup of the southern continents set Australia "afloat" like a giant raft of marsupials. In Australia, marsupials diversified, and the few eutherians that lived there became extinct; on other continents, most marsupials became extinct, and the eutherians diversified.

Mass Extinctions

The fossil record shows that the overwhelming majority of species that ever lived are now extinct. A species may become extinct for many reasons. Its habitat may have been destroyed, or its environment may have changed in a manner unfavorable to the species. For example, if ocean temperatures fall by even a few degrees, species that are otherwise well adapted may perish. Even if physical factors in the environment remain stable, biological factors may change—the origin of one species can spell doom for another.

Although extinction occurs on a regular basis, at certain times disruptive global environmental changes have caused the rate of extinction to increase dramatically. When this occurs, a **mass extinction** results, in which large numbers of species become extinct throughout Earth.

The "Big Five" Mass Extinction Events

Five mass extinctions are documented in the fossil record over the past 500 million years **(Figure 25.15)**. These events are particularly well documented for the decimation of hard-bodied animals that lived in shallow seas, the organisms for which the fossil record is most complete. In each mass extinction, 50% or more of Earth's marine species became extinct.

Two mass extinctions—the Permian and the Cretaceous—have received the most attention. The Permian mass extinction, which defines the boundary between the Paleozoic and Mesozoic eras (251 million years ago), claimed about 96% of marine animal species and drastically altered life in the ocean.

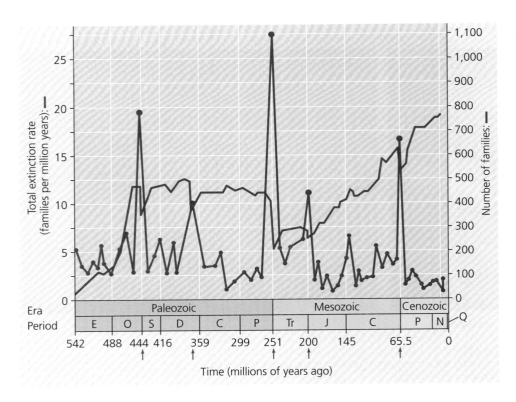

◀ **Figure 25.15 Mass extinction and the diversity of life.** The five generally recognized mass extinction events, indicated by red arrows, represent peaks in the extinction rate of marine animal families (red line and left vertical axis). These mass extinctions interrupted the overall increase in the number of marine animal families over time (blue line and right vertical axis).

? *96% of marine animal species became extinct in the Permian mass extinction. Explain why the blue curve shows only a 50% drop at that time.*

Terrestrial life was also affected. For example, 8 out of 27 known orders of insects were wiped out. This mass extinction occurred in less than 500,000 years, possibly in just a few thousand years—an instant in the context of geologic time.

The Permian mass extinction occurred at the time of enormous volcanic eruptions in what is now Siberia. This period was the most extreme episode of volcanism to have occurred during the past half billion years. Geologic data indicate that an area of 1.6 million km² (roughly half the size of western Europe) was covered with a layer of lava hundreds to thousands of meters thick. Besides spewing enormous amounts of lava and ash, the eruptions may have produced enough carbon dioxide to warm the global climate by an estimated 6°C. Reduced temperature differences between the equator and the poles would have slowed the mixing of ocean water, which in turn would have led to a widespread drop in oxygen concentrations. The resulting low-oxygen condition, called *ocean anoxia*, would have suffocated oxygen-breathers and promoted the growth of anaerobic bacteria that emit a poisonous metabolic by-product, hydrogen sulfide (H_2S) gas. As this gas bubbled into the atmosphere, it would have caused further extinctions by directly killing land plants and animals and by initiating chemical reactions that destroy the ozone layer, a "shield" that ordinarily protects organisms from life-threatening levels of UV radiation.

The Cretaceous mass extinction occurred about 65.5 million years ago and marks the boundary between the Mesozoic and Cenozoic eras. This event extinguished more than half of all marine species and eliminated many families of terrestrial plants and animals, including all dinosaurs (except birds,

which are members of the same group; see Chapter 34). One clue to a possible cause of the Cretaceous mass extinction is a thin layer of clay enriched in iridium that separates sediments from the Mesozoic and Cenozoic eras. Iridium is an element that is very rare on Earth but common in many of the meteorites and other extraterrestrial objects that occasionally fall to Earth. Walter Alvarez and the late Luis Alvarez, of the University of California, Berkeley, and their colleagues proposed that this clay is fallout from a huge cloud of debris that billowed into the atmosphere when an asteroid or large comet collided with Earth. This cloud would have blocked sunlight and severely disturbed the global climate for several months.

Is there evidence of such an asteroid or comet? Research has focused on the Chicxulub crater, a 65-million-year-old scar beneath sediments off the Yucatán coast of Mexico **(Figure 25.16)**. The crater is the right size to have been caused by an object with a diameter of 10 km. Critical evaluation of this and other hypotheses for mass extinctions continues.

Is a Sixth Mass Extinction Under Way?

As we will explore in Chapter 56, human actions, such as habitat destruction, are modifying the global environment to such an extent that many species are threatened with extinction. More than a thousand species have become extinct in the last 400 years. Scientists estimate that this rate is 100 to 1,000 times the typical background rate seen in the fossil record. Is a sixth mass extinction now in progress?

This question is difficult to answer, in part because it is hard to document the total number of extinctions occurring today. Tropical rain forests, for example, harbor many undiscovered

▲ **Figure 25.16 Trauma for Earth and its Cretaceous life.** Beneath the Caribbean Sea, the 65-million-year-old Chicxulub impact crater measures 180 km across. The horseshoe shape of the crater and the pattern of debris in sedimentary rocks indicate that an asteroid or comet struck at a low angle from the southeast. This artist's interpretation represents the impact and its immediate effect: a cloud of hot vapor and debris that could have killed many of the plants and animals in North America within hours.

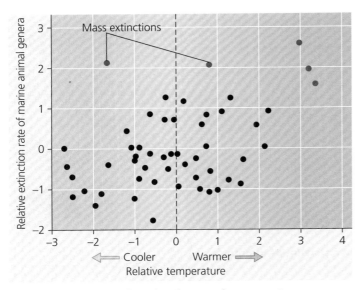

▲ **Figure 25.17 Fossil extinctions and temperature.**
Extinction rates increased when global temperatures were high. Temperatures were estimated using ratios of oxygen isotopes and converted to an index in which 0 is the overall average temperature.

species. As a result, destroying tropical forest may drive species to extinction before we even learn of their existence. Such uncertainties make it hard to assess the full extent of the current extinction crisis. Even so, it is clear that losses to date have not reached those of the "big five" mass extinctions, in which large percentages of Earth's species became extinct. This does not in any way discount the seriousness of today's situation. Monitoring programs show that many species are declining at an alarming rate, and studies on polar bears, pine trees, and other species suggest that climate change may hasten some of these declines. Indeed, the fossil record indicates that over the last 500 million years, extinction rates have tended to increase when global temperatures were high **(Figure 25.17)**. Overall, present-day and fossil evidence both suggest that unless dramatic actions are taken, a sixth, human-caused mass extinction is likely to occur within the next few centuries or millennia.

Consequences of Mass Extinctions

Mass extinctions have significant and long-term effects. By eliminating large numbers of species, a mass extinction can reduce a thriving and complex ecological community to a pale shadow of its former self. And once an evolutionary lineage disappears, it cannot reappear. The course of evolution is changed forever. Consider what would have happened if the early primates living 66 million years ago had died out in the Cretaceous mass extinction. Humans would not exist, and life on Earth would differ greatly from what it is today.

The fossil record shows that it typically takes 5–10 million years for the diversity of life to recover to previous levels after a mass extinction. In some cases, it has taken much longer than that: It took about 100 million years for the number of marine families to recover after the Permian mass extinction (see Figure 25.15). These data have sobering implications. If current trends continue and a sixth mass extinction occurs, it will take millions of years for life on Earth to recover.

Mass extinctions can also alter ecological communities by changing the types of organisms found in them. For example, after the Permian and Cretaceous mass extinctions, the percentage of marine organisms that were predators increased substantially **(Figure 25.18)**. A rise in the number of predator species can increase both the pressures faced by prey and the competition among predators for food. In addition, mass extinctions can curtail lineages with highly advantageous features. For example, in the late Triassic a group of gastropods (snails and their relatives) arose that could drill through the shells of bivalves (such as clams) and feed on the animals inside. Although shell drilling provided access to a new and abundant source of food, this newly formed group was wiped out during the mass extinction at the end of the Triassic (about 200 million years ago). Another 120 million years passed before another group of gastropods (the oyster drills) exhibited the ability to drill through shells. As their predecessors might have done if they had not originated at an unfortunate time, oyster

◀ **Figure 25.18 Mass extinctions and ecology.** The Permian and Cretaceous mass extinctions (indicated by red arrows) altered the ecology of the oceans by increasing the percentage of marine genera that were predators.

drills have since diversified into many new species. Finally, by eliminating so many species, mass extinctions can pave the way for adaptive radiations, in which new groups of organisms proliferate.

Adaptive Radiations

The fossil record indicates that the diversity of life has increased over the past 250 million years (see blue line in Figure 25.15). This increase has been fueled by **adaptive radiations**, periods of evolutionary change in which groups of organisms form many new species whose adaptations allow them to fill different ecological roles, or niches, in their communities. Large-scale adaptive radiations occurred after each of the big five mass extinctions, when survivors became adapted to the many vacant ecological niches. Adaptive radiations have also occurred in groups of organisms that possessed major evolutionary innovations, such as seeds or armored body coverings, or that colonized regions in which they faced little competition from other species.

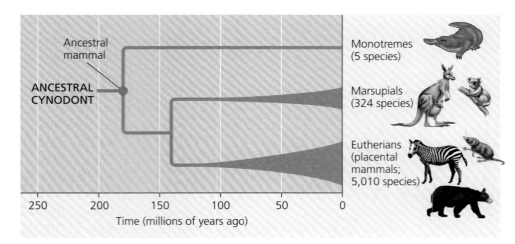

▲ **Figure 25.19 Adaptive radiation of mammals.**

Worldwide Adaptive Radiations

Fossil evidence indicates that mammals underwent a dramatic adaptive radiation after the extinction of terrestrial dinosaurs 65.5 million years ago (Figure 25.19). Although mammals originated about 180 million years ago, the mammal fossils older than 65.5 million years are mostly small and not morphologically diverse. Many species appear to have been nocturnal based on their large eye sockets, similar to those in living nocturnal mammals. A few early mammals were intermediate in size, such as *Repenomamus giganticus*, a 1-m-long predator that lived 130 million years ago—but none approached the size of many dinosaurs. Early mammals may have been restricted in size and diversity because they were eaten or outcompeted by the larger and more diverse dinosaurs. With the disappearance of the dinosaurs (except for birds), mammals expanded greatly in both diversity and size, filling the ecological roles once occupied by terrestrial dinosaurs.

The history of life has also been greatly altered by radiations in which groups of organisms increased in diversity as they came to play entirely new ecological roles in their communities. Examples include the rise of photosynthetic prokaryotes, the evolution of large predators in the Cambrian explosion, and the radiations following the colonization of land by plants, insects, and tetrapods. Each of these last three radiations was associated with major evolutionary innovations that facilitated life on land. The radiation of land plants, for example, was associated with key adaptations, such as stems that support plants against gravity and a waxy coat that protects leaves from water loss. Finally, organisms

that arise in an adaptive radiation can serve as a new source of food for still other organisms. In fact, the diversification of land plants stimulated a series of adaptive radiations in insects that ate or pollinated plants, one reason that insects are the most diverse group of animals on Earth today.

Regional Adaptive Radiations

Striking adaptive radiations have also occurred over more limited geographic areas. Such radiations can be initiated when a few organisms make their way to a new, often distant location in which they face relatively little competition from other organisms. The Hawaiian archipelago is one of the world's great showcases of this type of adaptive radiation (Figure 25.20). Located about 3,500 km from the nearest continent, the volcanic islands are progressively older as one follows the chain toward the northwest; the youngest island, Hawaii, is less than a million years old and still has active volcanoes. Each island was born "naked" and was gradually populated by stray organisms that rode the ocean currents and winds either from far-distant land areas or from older islands of the archipelago itself. The physical diversity of each island, including immense variation in elevation and rainfall, provides many opportunities for evolutionary divergence by natural selection. Multiple invasions followed by speciation events have ignited an explosion of adaptive radiation in Hawaii. Most of the thousands of species that inhabit the islands are found nowhere else on Earth.

CONCEPT CHECK 25.4

1. Explain the consequences of continental drift for life on Earth.
2. What factors promote adaptive radiations?
3. **WHAT IF?** If a mass extinction were caused by a sudden catastrophic event, would dates of the last observation in the fossil record of species lost in the extinction differ for rare versus common species? Explain.

For suggested answers, see Appendix A.

▲ **Figure 25.20 Adaptive radiation on the Hawaiian Islands.** Molecular analysis indicates that these remarkably varied Hawaiian plants, known collectively as the "silversword alliance," are all descended from an ancestral tarweed that arrived on the islands about 5 million years ago from North America. Members of the silversword alliance have since spread into different habitats and formed new species with strikingly different adaptations.

Close North American relative, the tarweed *Carlquistia muirii*

KAUAI 5.1 million years
OAHU 3.7 million years
MOLOKAI
LANAI
MAUI 1.3 million years
HAWAII 0.4 million years
N

Dubautia laxa

Dubautia waialealae

Dubautia scabra

Argyroxiphium sandwicense

Dubautia linearis

CONCEPT **25.5**

Major changes in body form can result from changes in the sequences and regulation of developmental genes

The fossil record tells us what the great changes in the history of life have been and when they occurred. Moreover, an understanding of plate tectonics, mass extinction, and adaptive radiation provides a picture of how those changes came about. But we can also seek to understand the intrinsic biological mechanisms that underlie changes seen in the fossil record. For this, we turn to genetic mechanisms of change, paying particular attention to genes that influence development.

Effects of Developmental Genes

As you read in Chapter 21, "evo-devo"—research at the interface between evolutionary biology and developmental biology—is illuminating how slight genetic divergences can produce major morphological differences between species. Genes that control development influence the rate, timing, and spatial pattern of change in an organism's form as it develops from a zygote into an adult.

Changes in Rate and Timing

Many striking evolutionary transformations are the result of **heterochrony** (from the Greek *hetero*, different, and *chronos*, time), an evolutionary change in the rate or timing of developmental events. For example, an organism's shape depends in part on the relative growth rates of different body parts

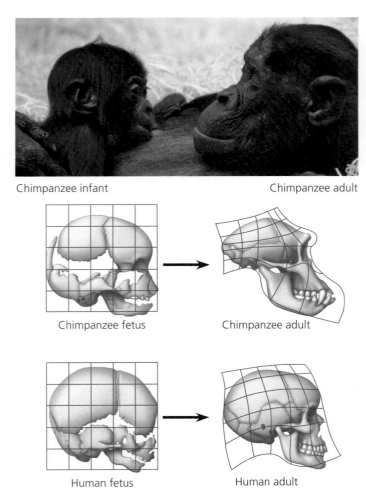

Chimpanzee infant

Chimpanzee adult

Chimpanzee fetus

Chimpanzee adult

Human fetus

Human adult

▲ **Figure 25.21 Relative skull growth rates.** In the human evolutionary lineage, mutations that slowed the growth of the jaw relative to other parts of the skull produced an adult whose head resembles that of a chimpanzee infant.

during development. Changes to these rates can alter the adult form substantially, as seen in the contrasting shapes of human and chimpanzee skulls **(Figure 25.21)**. Other examples of the dramatic evolutionary effects of heterochrony include how increased growth rates of finger bones yielded the skeletal structure of wings in bats (see Figure 22.15) and how slowed growth of leg and pelvic bones led to the reduction and eventual loss of hind limbs in whales (see Figure 22.20).

Heterochrony can also alter the timing of reproductive development relative to the development of nonreproductive organs. If reproductive organ development accelerates compared to other organs, the sexually mature stage of a species may retain body features that were juvenile structures in an ancestral species, a condition called **paedomorphosis** (from the Greek *paedos*, of a child, and *morphosis*, formation). For example, most salamander species have aquatic larvae that undergo metamorphosis in becoming adults. But some species grow to adult size and become sexually mature while retaining gills and other larval features **(Figure 25.22)**. Such an evolutionary alteration of developmental timing can produce animals that

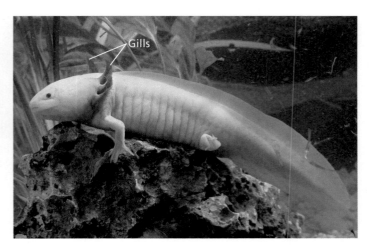

Gills

▲ **Figure 25.22 Paedomorphosis.** The adults of some species retain features that were juvenile in ancestors. This salamander is an axolotl, an aquatic species that grows to full size, becomes sexually mature, and reproduces while retaining certain larval (tadpole) characteristics, including gills.

appear very different from their ancestors, even though the overall genetic change may be small. Indeed, recent evidence indicates that a change at a single locus was probably sufficient to bring about paedomorphosis in the axolotl salamander, although other genes may have contributed as well.

Changes in Spatial Pattern

Substantial evolutionary changes can also result from alterations in genes that control the placement and spatial organization of body parts. For example, master regulatory genes called **homeotic genes** (described in Chapters 18 and 21) determine such basic features as where a pair of wings and a pair of legs will develop on a bird or how a plant's flower parts are arranged.

The products of one class of homeotic genes, the *Hox* genes, provide positional information in an animal embryo. This information prompts cells to develop into structures appropriate for a particular location. Changes in *Hox* genes or in how they are expressed can have a profound impact on morphology. For example, among crustaceans, a change in the location where two *Hox* genes (*Ubx* and *Scr*) are expressed correlates with the conversion of a swimming appendage to a feeding appendage. Large effects are also seen in snakes, where changes in how two *Hox* genes (*HoxC6* and *HoxC8*) are expressed suppresses limb formation **(Figure 25.23)**. Similarly, when comparing plant species, changes to the expression of homeotic genes known as *Mads-box* genes can produce flowers that differ dramatically in form (see Chapter 35).

The Evolution of Development

The 565-million-year-old fossils of Ediacaran animals in Figure 25.4 suggest that a set of genes sufficient to produce complex animals existed at least 30 million years *before* the Cambrian explosion. If such genes have existed for so long,

▲ **Figure 25.23** *Hox* **gene expression and limb development.** Regions of *HoxC6* gene expression (purple) correlate with limbless regions in the torsos of a snake embryo (left) and a chicken embryo (right).

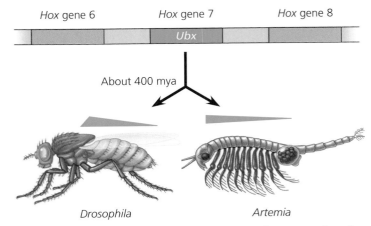

Hox gene 6   *Hox* gene 7   *Hox* gene 8

Ubx

About 400 mya

Drosophila   *Artemia*

▲ **Figure 25.24** **Origin of the insect body plan.** Expression of the *Hox* gene *Ubx* suppresses the formation of legs in fruit flies (*Drosophila*) but not in brine shrimp (*Artemia*), thus helping to build the insect body plan. Fruit fly and brine shrimp *Hox* genes have evolved independently for 400 million years. The green triangles indicate the relative amounts of *Ubx* expression in different body regions.

how can we explain the astonishing increases in diversity seen during and since the Cambrian explosion?

Adaptive evolution by natural selection provides one answer to this question. As we've seen throughout this unit, by sorting among differences in the sequences of protein-encoding genes, selection can improve adaptations rapidly. In addition, new genes (created by gene duplication events) can take on a wide range of new metabolic and structural functions. Thus, adaptive evolution of both new and existing genes may have played a key role in shaping the great diversity of life.

Examples in the previous section suggest that developmental genes may play a critical role. Next we'll examine how new morphological forms arise from changes in the nucleotide sequences or regulation of developmental genes.

Changes in Genes

New developmental genes arising after gene duplication events very likely facilitated the origin of novel morphological forms. But since other genetic changes also may have occurred at such times, it can be difficult to establish causal links between genetic and morphological changes that occurred in the past.

This difficulty was sidestepped in a recent study of developmental changes associated with the divergence of six-legged insects from crustacean-like ancestors that had more than six legs. In insects, such as *Drosophila*, the *Ubx* gene is expressed in the abdomen, while in crustaceans, such as *Artemia*, it is expressed in the main trunk of the body **(Figure 25.24)**. When expressed, the *Ubx* gene suppresses leg formation in insects but not in crustaceans. To examine the workings of this gene, researchers cloned the *Ubx* gene from *Drosophila* and *Artemia*. Next, they genetically engineered fruit fly embryos to express either the *Drosophila Ubx* gene or the *Artemia Ubx* gene throughout their bodies. The *Drosophila* gene suppressed 100% of the limbs in the embryos, as expected, whereas the *Artemia* gene suppressed only 15%.

The researchers then sought to uncover key steps involved in the evolutionary transition from a crustacean *Ubx* gene to an insect *Ubx* gene. Their approach was to identify mutations that would cause the *Artemia Ubx* gene to suppress leg formation, thus making the crustacean gene act more like an insect *Ubx* gene. To do this, they constructed a series of "hybrid" *Ubx* genes, each of which contained known segments of the *Drosophila Ubx* gene and known segments of the *Artemia Ubx* gene. By inserting these hybrid genes into fruit fly embryos (one hybrid gene per embryo) and observing their effects on leg development, the researchers were able to pinpoint the exact amino acid changes responsible for the suppression of additional limbs in insects. In so doing, this study provided evidence linking a particular change in the nucleotide sequence of a developmental gene to a major evolutionary change: the origin of the six-legged insect body plan.

Changes in Gene Regulation

Changes in the nucleotide sequence or regulation of developmental genes can result in morphological changes that harm the organism (see Chapter 18). Moreover, a change in the nucleotide sequence of a gene may affect its function wherever the gene is expressed. In contrast, changes in the regulation of gene expression can be limited to a single cell type (see Chapter 18). Thus, a change in the regulation of a developmental gene may have fewer harmful side effects than a change to the sequence of the gene. This line of reasoning has prompted researchers to suggest that changes in the form of organisms may often be caused by mutations that affect the regulation of developmental genes—not their sequences.

This idea is supported by studies in a variety of species, including threespine stickleback fish. These fish live in the open ocean and in shallow, coastal waters. In western Canada, they also live in lakes formed when the coastline receded during the past 12,000 years. Marine stickleback fish have a pair of spines on their ventral (lower) surface, which deter some predators. These spines are often reduced or absent in stickleback fish living in lakes that lack predatory fishes and that are also low in calcium. Spines may have been lost because they are not advantageous in the absence of predators, and the limited calcium is needed for purposes other than constructing spines.

At the genetic level, the developmental gene, *Pitx1*, was known to influence whether stickleback fish have ventral spines. Was the reduction of spines in some lake populations due to changes in the *Pitx1* gene or to changes in how the gene is expressed **(Figure 25.25)**? The researchers' results indicate that the regulation of gene expression has changed, not the DNA sequence of the gene. Furthermore, lake stickleback

▼ **Figure 25.25**

INQUIRY

What causes the loss of spines in lake stickleback fish?

EXPERIMENT Marine populations of the threespine stickleback fish (*Gasterosteus aculeatus*) have a set of protective spines on their lower (ventral) surface; however, these spines have been lost or reduced in some lake populations of this fish. Working at Stanford University, Michael Shapiro, David Kingsley, and colleagues performed genetic crosses and found that most of the reduction in spine size resulted from the effects of a single developmental gene, *Pitx1*. The researchers then tested two hypotheses about how *Pitx1* causes this morphological change.

Hypothesis A: A change in the DNA sequence of *Pitx1* had caused spine reduction in lake populations. To test this idea, the team used DNA sequencing to compare the coding sequence of the *Pitx1* gene between marine and lake stickleback populations.

Hypothesis B: A change in the regulation of the expression of *Pitx1* had caused spine reduction. To test this idea, the researchers monitored where in the developing embryo the *Pitx1* gene was expressed. They conducted whole-body *in situ* hybridization experiments (see Chapter 20) using *Pitx1* DNA as a probe to detect *Pitx1* mRNA in the fish.

Threespine stickleback
(*Gasterosteus aculeatus*)

RESULTS

Test of Hypothesis A: Are there differences in the coding sequence of the *Pitx1* gene in marine and lake stickleback fish? → **Result: No** → The 283 amino acids of the *Pitx1* protein are identical in marine and lake stickleback populations.

Test of Hypothesis B: Are there any differences in the regulation of expression of *Pitx1*? → **Result: Yes** → Red arrows ( ) indicate regions of *Pitx1* gene expression in the photographs below. *Pitx1* is expressed in the ventral spine and mouth regions of developing marine stickleback fish but only in the mouth region of developing lake stickleback fish.

Marine stickleback embryo

Close-up of mouth

Close-up of ventral surface

Lake stickleback embryo

CONCLUSION The loss or reduction of ventral spines in lake populations of threespine stickleback fish appears to have resulted primarily from a change in the regulation of *Pitx1* gene expression, not from a change in the gene's sequence.

SOURCE M. D. Shapiro et al., Genetic and developmental basis of evolutionary pelvic reduction in three-spine sticklebacks, *Nature* 428:717–723 (2004).

WHAT IF? Describe the set of results that would have led researchers to the conclusion that a change in the coding sequence of the *Pitx1* gene was more important than a change in regulation of gene expression.

fish do express the *Pitx1* gene in tissues not related to the production of spines (for example, the mouth), illustrating how morphological change can be caused by altering the expression of a developmental gene in some parts of the body but not others.

CONCEPT CHECK 25.5

1. How can heterochrony cause the evolution of different body forms?
2. Why is it likely that *Hox* genes have played a major role in the evolution of novel morphological forms?
3. **MAKE CONNECTIONS** Given that changes in morphology are often caused by changes in the regulation of gene expression, predict whether noncoding DNA is likely to be affected by natural selection. See Concept 18.3 (pp. 364–366) to review noncoding DNA and regulation of gene expression.

For suggested answers, see Appendix A.

CONCEPT 25.6
Evolution is not goal oriented

What does our study of macroevolution tell us about how evolution works? One lesson is that throughout the history of life, the origin of new species has been affected by both the bottom-up factors described in Chapter 24 (such as natural selection operating in populations) and the top-down factors described here (such as continental drift promoting bursts of speciation throughout the globe). Moreover, to paraphrase the Nobel Prize–winning geneticist François Jacob, evolution is like tinkering—a process in which new forms arise by the slight modification of existing forms. Even large changes, like the ones that produced the first mammals or the six-legged body plan of insects, can result from the modification of existing structures or existing developmental genes. Over time, such tinkering has led to three key features of the natural world described in Chapter 22: the striking ways in which organisms are suited for life in their environments; the many shared characteristics of life; and the rich diversity of life.

Evolutionary Novelties

François Jacob's view of evolution harkens back to Darwin's concept of descent with modification. As new species form, novel and complex structures can arise as gradual modifications of ancestral structures. In many cases, complex structures have evolved in increments from simpler versions that performed the same basic function. For example, consider the human eye, an intricate organ constructed from numerous parts that work together in forming an image and transmitting it to the brain. How could the human eye have evolved in gradual increments? Some argue that if the eye needs all of its components to function, a partial eye could not have been of use to our ancestors.

The flaw in this argument, as Darwin himself noted, lies in the assumption that only complicated eyes are useful. In fact, many animals depend on eyes that are far less complex than our own (Figure 25.26). The simplest eyes that we know of are patches of light-sensitive photoreceptor cells. These simple eyes appear to have had a single evolutionary origin and are now found in a variety of animals, including small molluscs called limpets. Such eyes have no equipment for focusing images, but they do enable the animal to distinguish light from dark. Limpets cling more tightly to their rock when a shadow falls on them, a behavioral adaptation that reduces the risk of being eaten. Because limpets have had a long evolutionary history, we can conclude that their "simple" eyes are quite adequate to support their survival and reproduction.

▼ **Figure 25.26 A range of eye complexity among molluscs.**

(a) Patch of pigmented cells

The limpet *Patella* has a simple patch of photoreceptors.

(b) Eyecup

The slit shell mollusc *Pleurotomaria* has an eyecup.

(c) Pinhole camera-type eye

The *Nautilus* eye functions like a pinhole camera (an early type of camera lacking a lens).

(d) Eye with primitive lens

The marine snail *Murex* has a primitive lens consisting of a mass of crystal-like cells. The cornea is a transparent region of tissue that protects the eye and helps focus light.

(e) Complex camera lens-type eye

The squid *Loligo* has a complex eye with features (cornea, lens, and retina) similar to those of vertebrate eyes. However, the squid eye evolved independently from vertebrate eyes.

In the animal kingdom, complex eyes have evolved independently from such basic structures many times. Some molluscs, such as squids and octopuses, have eyes as complex as those of humans and other vertebrates (see Figure 25.26). Although complex mollusc eyes evolved independently of vertebrate eyes, both evolved from a simple cluster of photoreceptor cells present in a common ancestor. In each case, the complex eye evolved through a series of incremental modifications that benefited the eyes' owners at every stage. Evidence of their independent evolution may also be found in their structure: Vertebrate eyes detect light at the back layer of the retina and conduct nerve impulses toward the front, while complex mollusc eyes do the reverse.

Throughout their evolutionary history, eyes retained their basic function of vision. But evolutionary novelties can also arise when structures that originally played one role gradually acquire a different one. For example, as cynodonts gave rise to early mammals, bones that formerly comprised the jaw hinge (the articular and quadrate; see Figure 25.6) were incorporated into the ear region of mammals, where they eventually took on a new function: the transmission of sound (see Chapter 34). Structures that evolve in one context but become co-opted for another function are sometimes called *exaptations* to distinguish them from the adaptive origin of the original structure. Note that the concept of exaptation does not imply that a structure somehow evolves in anticipation of future use. Natural selection cannot predict the future; it can only improve a structure in the context of its *current* utility. Novel features, such as the new jaw hinge and ear bones of early mammals, can arise gradually via a series of intermediate stages, each of which has some function in the organism's current context.

Evolutionary Trends

What else can we learn from patterns of macroevolution? Consider evolutionary "trends" observed in the fossil record. For instance, some evolutionary lineages exhibit a trend toward larger or smaller body size. An example is the evolution of the present-day horse (genus *Equus*), a descendant of the 55-million-year-old *Hyracotherium* (**Figure 25.27**). About the size of a large dog, *Hyracotherium* had four toes on its front feet, three toes on its hind feet, and teeth adapted for browsing on bushes and trees. In comparison, present-day horses are larger, have only one toe on each foot, and possess teeth modified for grazing on grasses.

Extracting a single evolutionary progression from the fossil record can be misleading, however; it is like describing a bush as growing toward a single point by tracing only the branches that lead to that twig. For example, by selecting certain species from the available fossils, it is possible to arrange a succession of animals intermediate between *Hyracotherium* and living horses that shows a trend toward large, single-toed

species (follow the yellow highlighting in Figure 25.27). However, if we consider *all* fossil horses known today, this apparent trend vanishes. The genus *Equus* did not evolve in a straight line; it is the only surviving twig of an evolutionary tree that is so branched that it is more like a bush. *Equus* actually descended through a series of speciation episodes that included several adaptive radiations, not all of which led to large, one-toed, grazing horses. In fact, phylogenetic analyses suggest that all lineages that include grazers are closely related to *Parahippus*; the many other horse lineages, all of which are now extinct, remained multi-toed browsers for 35 million years.

Branching evolution *can* result in a real evolutionary trend even if some species counter the trend. One model of long-term trends proposed by Steven Stanley, of Johns Hopkins University, views species as analogous to individuals: Speciation is their birth, extinction is their death, and new species that diverge from them are their offspring. In this model, Stanley suggests that just as populations of individual organisms undergo natural selection, species undergo *species selection*. The species that endure the longest and generate the most new offspring species determine the direction of major evolutionary trends. The species selection model suggests that "differential speciation success" plays a role in macroevolution similar to the role of differential reproductive success in microevolution. Evolutionary trends can also result directly from natural selection. For example, when horse ancestors invaded the grasslands that spread during the mid-Cenozoic, there was strong selection for grazers that could escape predators by running faster. This trend would not have occurred without open grasslands.

Whatever its cause, an evolutionary trend does not imply that there is some intrinsic drive toward a particular phenotype. Evolution is the result of the interactions between organisms and their current environments; if environmental conditions change, an evolutionary trend may cease or even reverse itself. The cumulative effect of these ongoing interactions between organisms and their environments is enormous: It is through them that the staggering diversity of life—Darwin's "endless forms most beautiful"—has arisen.

CONCEPT CHECK 25.6

1. How can the Darwinian concept of descent with modification explain the evolution of such complex structures as the vertebrate eye?
2. **WHAT IF?** The myxoma virus kills up to 99.8% of infected European rabbits in populations with no previous exposure to the virus. The virus is transmitted between living rabbits by mosquitoes. Describe an evolutionary trend (in either the rabbit or virus) that might occur after a rabbit population first encounters the virus.

For suggested answers, see Appendix A.

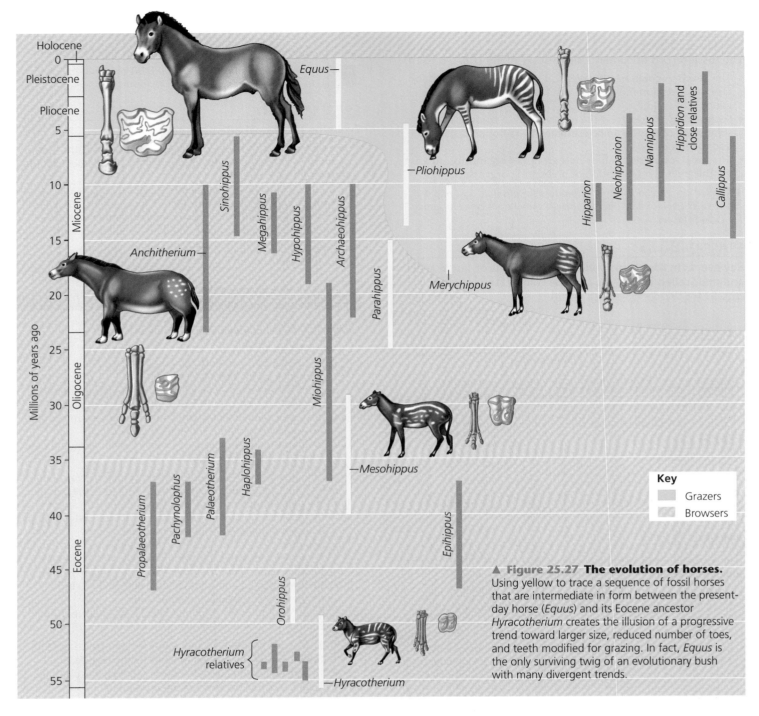

▲ **Figure 25.27 The evolution of horses.**
Using yellow to trace a sequence of fossil horses that are intermediate in form between the present-day horse (*Equus*) and its Eocene ancestor *Hyracotherium* creates the illusion of a progressive trend toward larger size, reduced number of toes, and teeth modified for grazing. In fact, *Equus* is the only surviving twig of an evolutionary bush with many divergent trends.

Key
Grazers
Browsers

25 CHAPTER REVIEW

SUMMARY OF KEY CONCEPTS

CONCEPT 25.1

Conditions on early Earth made the origin of life possible (pp. 507–510)

- Earth formed 4.6 billion years ago. Experiments simulating possible early atmospheres have produced organic molecules from inorganic precursors. Amino acids, lipids, sugars, and nitrogenous bases have also been found in meteorites.

- Amino acids and RNA nucleotides polymerize when dripped onto hot sand, clay, or rock. Organic compounds can spontaneously assemble into **protocells**, membrane-bounded droplets that have some properties of cells.

- The first genetic material may have been short pieces of RNA capable of guiding polypeptide synthesis and self-replication. Early protocells containing such RNA would have increased through natural selection.

❓ *Describe the roles that montmorillonite clay and vesicles may have played in the origin of life.*

CONCEPT 25.2

The fossil record documents the history of life (pp. 510–514)

- The **fossil record**, based largely on fossils found in sedimentary rocks, documents the rise and fall of different groups of organisms over time.
- Sedimentary strata reveal the relative ages of **fossils**. The absolute ages of fossils can be estimated by radiometric dating and other methods.
- The fossil record shows how new groups of organisms can arise via the gradual modification of preexisting organisms.

> ? *What are the challenges of estimating the absolute ages of old fossils? Explain how these challenges may be overcome in some circumstances.*

CONCEPT 25.3

Key events in life's history include the origins of single-celled and multicelled organisms and the colonization of land (pp. 514–519)

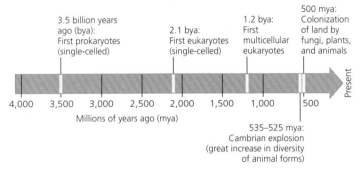

> ? *What is the "Cambrian explosion," and why is it significant?*

CONCEPT 25.4

The rise and fall of groups of organisms reflect differences in speciation and extinction rates (pp. 519–524)

- In **plate tectonics**, continental plates move gradually over time, altering the physical geography and climate of Earth. These changes lead to extinctions in some groups of organisms and bursts of speciation in others.
- Evolutionary history has been punctuated by five **mass extinctions** that radically altered the history of life. Some of these extinctions may have been caused by changes in continent positions, volcanic activity, or impacts from meteorites or comets.
- Large increases in the diversity of life have resulted from **adaptive radiations** that followed mass extinctions. Adaptive radiations have also occurred in groups of organisms that possessed major evolutionary innovations or that colonized new regions in which there was little competition from other organisms.

> ? *Explain how the broad evolutionary changes seen in the fossil record are the cumulative result of speciation and extinction events.*

CONCEPT 25.5

Major changes in body form can result from changes in the sequences and regulation of developmental genes (pp. 525–529)

- Developmental genes affect morphological differences between species by influencing the rate, timing, and spatial patterns of change in an organism's form as it develops into an adult.

- The evolution of new forms can be caused by changes in the nucleotide sequences or regulation of developmental genes.

> ? *How could changes in a single gene or DNA region ultimately lead to the origin of a new group of organisms?*

CONCEPT 25.6

Evolution is not goal oriented (pp. 529–531)

- Novel and complex biological structures can evolve through a series of incremental modifications, each of which benefits the organism that possesses it.
- Evolutionary trends can be caused by factors such as natural selection in a changing environment or species selection. Like all aspects of evolution, evolutionary trends result from interactions between organisms and their current environments.

> ? *Explain the reasoning behind the statement "Evolution is not goal oriented."*

TEST YOUR UNDERSTANDING

LEVEL 1: KNOWLEDGE/COMPREHENSION

1. Fossilized stromatolites
   a. all date from 2.7 billion years ago.
   b. formed around deep-sea vents.
   c. resemble structures formed by bacterial communities that are found today in some warm, shallow, salty bays.
   d. provide evidence that plants moved onto land in the company of fungi around 500 million years ago.
   e. contain the first undisputed fossils of eukaryotes and date from 2.1 billion years ago.

2. The oxygen revolution changed Earth's environment dramatically. Which of the following took advantage of the presence of free oxygen in the oceans and atmosphere?
   a. the evolution of cellular respiration, which used oxygen to help harvest energy from organic molecules
   b. the persistence of some animal groups in anaerobic habitats
   c. the evolution of photosynthetic pigments that protected early algae from the corrosive effects of oxygen
   d. the evolution of chloroplasts after early protists incorporated photosynthetic cyanobacteria
   e. the evolution of multicellular eukaryotic colonies from communities of prokaryotes

3. Which factor most likely caused animals and plants in India to differ greatly from species in nearby southeast Asia?
   a. The species became separated by convergent evolution.
   b. The climates of the two regions are similar.
   c. India is in the process of separating from the rest of Asia.
   d. Life in India was wiped out by ancient volcanic eruptions.
   e. India was a separate continent until 45 million years ago.

4. Adaptive radiations can be a direct consequence of four of the following five factors. Select the exception.
   a. vacant ecological niches
   b. genetic drift
   c. colonization of an isolated region that contains suitable habitat and few competitor species
   d. evolutionary innovation
   e. an adaptive radiation in a group of organisms (such as plants) that another group uses as food

5. Which of the following steps has *not* yet been accomplished by scientists studying the origin of life?
   a. synthesis of small RNA polymers by ribozymes
   b. abiotic synthesis of polypeptides

c. formation of molecular aggregates with selectively permeable membranes

d. formation of protocells that use DNA to direct the polymerization of amino acids

e. abiotic synthesis of organic molecules

6. **DRAW IT** Use the unlabeled clock diagram below to test your memory of the sequence of key events in the history of life described in this chapter by labeling the colored bars. As a visual aid to help you study, add labels that represent other significant events, including the Cambrian explosion, origin of mammals, and Permian and Cretaceous mass extinctions.

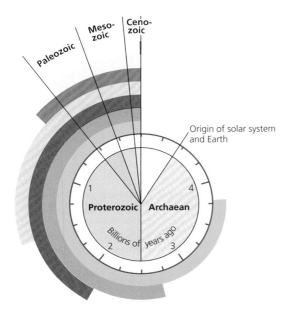

LEVEL 2: APPLICATION/ANALYSIS

7. A genetic change that caused a certain *Hox* gene to be expressed along the tip of a vertebrate limb bud instead of farther back helped make possible the evolution of the tetrapod limb. This type of change is illustrative of
   a. the influence of environment on development.
   b. paedomorphosis.
   c. a change in a developmental gene or in its regulation that altered the spatial organization of body parts.
   d. heterochrony.
   e. gene duplication.

8. A swim bladder is a gas-filled sac that helps fish maintain buoyancy. The evolution of the swim bladder from lungs of an ancestral fish is an example of
   a. an evolutionary trend.
   b. exaptation.
   c. changes in *Hox* gene expression.
   d. paedomorphosis.
   e. adaptive radiation.

LEVEL 3: SYNTHESIS/EVALUATION

9. **EVOLUTION CONNECTION**
   Describe how gene flow, genetic drift, and natural selection all can influence macroevolution.

10. **SCIENTIFIC INQUIRY**
    Herbivory (plant eating) has evolved repeatedly in insects, typically from meat-eating or detritus-feeding ancestors (detritus is dead organic matter). Moths and butterflies, for example, eat plants, whereas their "sister group" (the insect group

to which they are most closely related), the caddisflies, feed on animals, fungi, or detritus. As illustrated in the phylogenetic tree below, the combined moth/butterfly and caddisfly group shares a common ancestor with flies and fleas. Like caddisflies, flies and fleas are thought to have evolved from ancestors that did not eat plants.

There are 140,000 species of moths and butterflies and 7,000 species of caddisflies. State a hypothesis about the impact of herbivory on adaptive radiations in insects. How could this hypothesis be tested?

11. **SCIENCE, TECHNOLOGY, AND SOCIETY**
    Experts estimate that human activities cause the extinction of hundreds of species every year. In contrast, the natural rate of extinction is thought to average only a few species per year. If human actions continue to alter the global environment, especially by destroying tropical rain forests and changing Earth's climate, the likely result will be a wave of extinctions that could rival those at the end of the Cretaceous period. Considering that life has endured five mass extinctions, should we be concerned that we may cause a sixth mass extinction? How would such an extinction differ from previous extinctions? What might be some of the consequences?

12. **WRITE ABOUT A THEME**

    Structure and Function You have seen many examples of how form fits function at all levels of the biological hierarchy. However, we can imagine forms that would function better than some forms actually found in nature. For example, if the wings of a bird were not formed from its forelimbs, such a hypothetical bird could fly yet also hold objects with its forelimbs. In a short essay (100–150 words), use the concept of "evolution as tinkering" to explain why there are limits to the functionality of forms in nature.

For selected answers, see Appendix A.

1. MasteringBiology® Assignments
Tutorial Fossil Record
Activities Discovery Channel Video: Early Life • The History of Life • A Scrolling Geologic Record • Discovery Channel Video: Mass Extinctions • Adaptive Radiation • Allometric Growth
Questions Student Misconceptions • Reading Quiz • Multiple Choice • End-of-Chapter

2. eText
Read your book online, search, take notes, highlight text, and more.

3. The Study Area
Practice Tests • Cumulative Test • *BioFlix* 3-D Animations • MP3 Tutor Sessions • Videos • Activities • Investigations • Lab Media • Audio Glossary • Word Study Tools • Art

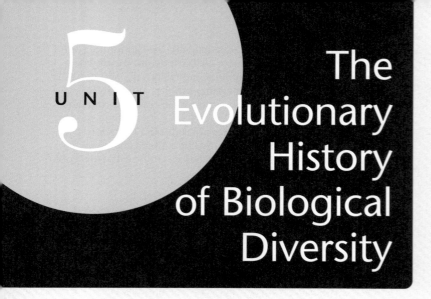

UNIT 5

The Evolutionary History of Biological Diversity

An Interview with

W. Ford Doolittle

Brimming with curiosity about nature, W. Ford Doolittle is a passionate advocate for both science and scientists. Dr. Doolittle holds degrees in molecular biology from Harvard and Stanford Universities. Since 1971 he has worked at Dalhousie University in Halifax, Canada, where he is now a Professor Emeritus. The author of more than 270 scientific articles, Dr. Doolittle is well known for his work on the molecular biology of cyanobacteria and archaea, early steps in the evolution of eukaryotes, and the importance of horizontal gene transfer in prokaryotes. He has also nurtured dozens of young scientists, making Dalhousie a world-renowned center for the study of evolution. The recipient of numerous awards and honorary degrees, Dr. Doolittle is an elected member of the Royal Society of Canada and the U.S. National Academy of Sciences. He is also an avid photographer, and in 2011 he will receive a B.F.A. in photography from the Nova Scotia College of Art and Design. Surrounded by stacks of journal articles, photography projects, and the bustle of a busy laboratory, Michael Cain and Jane Reece spoke with Dr. Doolittle in his office at Dalhousie.

How did you get started in science?
I hadn't planned on studying science until, as a high school student, I got a job washing glassware in Sol Spiegelman's lab at the University of Illinois. [Spiegelman was a molecular biologist whose work on RNA played a key role in developing understanding of biology's "central dogma" (see Chapter 17).] In college, I continued working in Sol's lab during the summer. It was a very exciting place to be, kind of like a hospital emergency ward where everything was important, everything was urgent. Some people worked all day, some people worked all night, some people worked all day and night! The lab was abuzz with simple and elegant experiments in molecular biology. I got the feeling that science was important, which I have never lost. And I got the feeling that science was important for its own sake, which I also have never lost. Doing science seems to fill our human need to know, to understand what the universe is like.

Did you become interested in evolution while working in Sol's lab?
Well, that came a little later. When I arrived at Dalhousie in 1971, I began studying blue-green algae (now called cyanobacteria) because they were a pretty color and few people were working on them. So the field was wide open. Lynn Margulis had just published her book *Origin of Eukaryotic Cells*, which put forward a startling idea—the endosymbiont hypothesis—positing that mitochondria and chloroplasts were formerly aerobic bacteria and cyanobacteria, respectively, that began living within larger cells, ultimately leading to the origin of eukaryotes. Then a fortuitous thing happened: I hired Linda Bonen, who brought a new technique to our lab, called RNA cataloging, from which you could get RNA sequence information. It's not a full sequence, but it was enough to start comparing ribosomal RNA molecules (rRNAs). I realized that we could use this technique to test the endosymbiont hypothesis for the origin of chloroplasts. We compared the sequences of rRNAs from chloroplasts with those from cyanobacteria and found they were similar, just as Margulis had predicted! From there, I became more and more interested in evolution, which continues to fascinate me today.

What are the main questions you are asking in your research?
I've had a long-standing interest in the evolution of genes and genomes. Most of my current work is on prokaryotes, but I've also been interested in questions about eukaryotes, such as, Where did introns come from? How did eukaryotic genomes originate? In recent years, my students and I have been occupied with two main research areas. One is *metagenomics*, where we collect environmental samples, such as mud from the bottom of harbors, and then sequence the prokaryotic DNA contained in the samples. We use these DNA sequences to shed light on how microbes interact with each other and their environment. The other main area of my current research is *horizontal gene transfer*, the transfer of genetic information—usually whole genes but not necessarily—from one species to another.

How can genes move from one prokaryotic species to another?
This can happen in a variety of ways, and such transfers turn out to be surprisingly common. Mechanisms have evolved in some bacteria enabling them to take up DNA molecules directly from the environment—and these DNA molecules may have come from individuals of other species that have died and broken apart. When this happens, sometimes the DNA is incorporated into the bacterial chromosomes and hence becomes part of their own genetic heritage. Many prokaryotes can also form temporary bridges that connect two or more individuals to one another, enabling genes to move from one species to another. And as we mentioned earlier, sometimes entire genomes are transferred in endosymbiosis. These and other processes that result in horizontal gene transfer have occurred throughout the nearly 4 billion years of life on Earth—and they continue to occur today.

What impact has horizontal gene transfer had on the evolutionary history of life?
Horizontal gene transfer, or HGT for short, has been a major force in the history of life. For instance, the endosymbiotic origins of mitochondria and chloroplasts were profoundly important events in the origin of eukaryotic cells. We humans wouldn't be here if it weren't for mitochondria, and of course without chloroplasts there wouldn't be any plants. Furthermore, HGT has been a dominant force in prokaryotic evolution—probably *the* dominant force. Genes that control key metabolic processes, such as photosynthesis and nitrogen fixation, can be transferred readily between species, and this has had an enormous impact on the ecological and evolutionary success of prokaryotes. And while one can construct evolutionary trees that identify major groups of prokaryotes, such trees can obscure the fact

that there has been a tremendous amount of HGT, affecting the majority of the genes.

Tell us more about evolutionary trees.

An evolutionary tree (or *phylogenetic tree*) is a branching diagram that represents the evolutionary history of a group of organisms. For example, we might use morphological and genetic data to figure out a phylogenetic tree of animals. Such a tree can provide a huge amount of information. For any particular group of animals, whether they be weevils, whales, or worms, our tree could identify the ancestors and closest relatives of the group. If we traced the history of animals all the way back, we could use the tree to help us answer questions such as, What did the earliest animals look like? What features did they pass on to all their descendants, including us? Phylogenetic trees also have great practical value. The same techniques we use to reconstruct evolutionary history have been used in forensics, where phylogenetic trees have helped solve criminal cases, and epidemiology, where trees have been used to estimate when and where diseases such as AIDS originated.

What have you learned during your career about the pattern and process of evolution?

We can document the *pattern* of evolution, the "what happened" part, with data from many scientific disciplines. For example, if we measure genetic change in a population, we are documenting an evolutionary pattern. The *process* of evolution is the "what caused it" part, which focuses on the mechanisms that produce the observed pattern. Sixty years ago, many scientists thought that natural selection was *the* mechanism that explained most evolutionary patterns. But we don't think that anymore; we now know that genetic drift and catastrophic events such as an asteroid striking Earth can explain many observed evolutionary patterns. I call this "process pluralism" to indicate that evolutionary patterns can result from many processes. Results from my research suggest that we should be considering "pattern pluralism" as well. Consider the tree of life, a phylogenetic tree that represents the history of all life as a series of branching events, in which a common ancestor gives rise to two descendant groups of organisms. This approach works well for organisms such as animals, but for prokaryotes the importance of HGT leads me to question whether the tree of life pattern is real. For prokaryotes, the pattern of evolution may be more like a tangled network of organisms exchanging DNA, not a simple branching tree.

Does this mean that Charles Darwin was wrong when he introduced the idea of a tree of life in *The Origin of Species*?

Darwin set out in his book to document the fact of evolution—the pattern of evolutionary change over time—and to show that natural selection could account for observed patterns of change. He did a great job on both accounts. We now recognize that well-understood genetic and ecological processes operating over nearly 4 billion years of evolution are adequate to explain diversity and adaptation in the living world. As for his ideas about the tree of life, Darwin was focused on plants and animals, two groups for which the tree of life idea works well. Remember, when Darwin formulated his ideas, many scientists still thought that bacteria formed spontaneously from

rotten meat. It wasn't even clear that bacteria were organisms. So I would say that Darwin's idea about the tree of life is still true, but that certain restrictions apply. It is similar to the situation in physics: Newton's laws work well under certain conditions, but not as well under other conditions. The tree of life still works well for plants and animals, but less well for prokaryotes due to HGT. And after all, most of life is prokaryotic.

Have recent discoveries altered our understanding of the evolutionary history of life?

Certainly. For one thing, our view of genomes and genome evolution has changed greatly in recent years. Who would have thought that we humans only have about the same number of genes as a 1-mm-long worm? It's astonishing. Not that long ago, little was known about endosymbiosis or HGT or the astoundingly rapid rates at which bacterial populations can evolve. Overall, the importance of prokaryotes and protists (single-celled eukaryotes) has really become clear. I mentioned metagenomics earlier, an approach that has already revealed previously unsuspected levels of microbial diversity. I think metagenomics will play an increasingly important role in future discoveries. It might even help us understand the consequences of increased atmospheric carbon dioxide (CO_2) and global warming, among the most important problems we face today. Microorganisms absorb vast amounts of CO_2 from the atmosphere. How will ongoing global warming affect microorganisms? Will they absorb even more CO_2, thus reducing effects of global warming? Or will the opposite occur? We don't know, but we can use metagenomics to figure out how climate change is currently affecting microbial communities. Once we understand what is going on, perhaps that can help us fix it.

You've devoted much time and effort to mentoring others. Can you comment on that?

Working in Sol Spiegelman's lab when I was young was a big turning point in my life. And as I gained experience, I tried to provide similar opportunities for others. One way I've done that is to establish programs that provide opportunities for young scientists to work together and to learn from each other and from more experienced scientists. I've always thought that it really helps to get experience early in your career, so I welcome people seeking such experience. One of the best ways to find what you really love doing is to try different things and see what most excites you. I did not plan to be a scientist, but I started doing science and I loved it. I'm a big believer in hands-on experience as a way of learning.

> "For prokaryotes, the pattern of evolution may be more like a tangled network of organisms exchanging DNA, not a simple branching tree."

W. Ford Doolittle (center) with Michael Cain (left) and Jane Reece

26

Phylogeny and the Tree of Life

▲ Figure 26.1 **What is this organism?**

OVERVIEW

Investigating the Tree of Life

Look closely at the organism in **Figure 26.1**. Although it resembles a snake, this animal is actually an Australian legless lizard known as the common scaly-foot (*Pygopus lepidopodus*). Why isn't the scaly-foot considered a snake? More generally, how do biologists distinguish and categorize the millions of species on Earth?

An understanding of evolutionary relationships suggests one way to address these questions: We can decide in which "container" to place a species by comparing its traits with those of potential close relatives. For example, the scaly-foot does not have a fused eyelid, a highly mobile jaw, or a short tail posterior to the anus, three traits shared by all snakes. These and other characteristics suggest that despite a superficial resemblance, the scaly-foot is not a snake. Furthermore, a survey of the lizards reveals that the scaly-foot is not alone; the legless condition has evolved independently in several different groups of lizards. Most legless lizards are burrowers or live in grasslands, and like snakes, these species lost their legs over generations as they adapted to their environments.

Snakes and lizards are part of the continuum of life extending from the earliest organisms to the great variety of species alive today. In this unit, we will survey this diversity and describe hypotheses regarding how it evolved. As we do so, our emphasis will shift from the *process* of evolution (the evolutionary mechanisms described in Unit Four) to its *pattern* (observations of evolution's products over time).

To set the stage for surveying life's diversity, in this chapter we consider how biologists trace **phylogeny**, the evolutionary history of a species or group of species. A phylogeny of lizards and snakes, for example, indicates that both the scaly-foot and snakes evolved from lizards with legs—but that they evolved from different lineages of legged lizards. Thus, it appears that their legless conditions evolved independently.

To construct phylogenies, biologists utilize **systematics**, a discipline focused on classifying organisms and determining their evolutionary relationships. Systematists use data ranging from fossils to molecules and genes to infer evolutionary relationships (**Figure 26.2**). This information is enabling biologists to construct a tree of all life, which will continue to be refined as additional data are collected.

▲ Figure 26.2 **An unexpected family tree.** What are the evolutionary relationships between a human, a mushroom, and a tulip? A phylogeny based on DNA data reveals that—despite appearances—animals (including humans) and fungi (including mushrooms) are more closely related to each other than either is to plants.

CONCEPT 26.1

Phylogenies show evolutionary relationships

As we discussed in Chapter 22, organisms share homologous characteristics because of common ancestry. As a result, we can learn a great deal about a species if we know its evolutionary history. For example, an organism is likely to share many of its genes, metabolic pathways, and structural proteins with its close relatives. We'll consider practical applications of such information at the close of this section, but first we'll examine how organisms are named and classified, the scientific discipline of **taxonomy**. We'll also look at how we can interpret and use diagrams that represent evolutionary history.

Binomial Nomenclature

Common names for organisms—such as monkey, finch, and lilac—convey meaning in casual usage, but they can also cause confusion. Each of these names, for example, refers to more than one species. Moreover, some common names do not accurately reflect the kind of organism they signify. Consider these three "fishes": jellyfish (a cnidarian), crayfish (a small lobsterlike crustacean), and silverfish (an insect). And of course, a given organism has different names in different languages.

To avoid ambiguity when communicating about their research, biologists refer to organisms by Latin scientific names. The two-part format of the scientific name, commonly called a **binomial**, was instituted in the 18th century by Carolus Linnaeus (see Chapter 22). The first part of a binomial is the name of the **genus** (plural, *genera*) to which the species belongs. The second part, called the specific epithet, is unique for each species within the genus. An example of a binomial is *Panthera pardus*, the scientific name for the large cat commonly called the leopard. Notice that the first letter of the genus is capitalized and the entire binomial is italicized. (Newly created scientific names are also "latinized": You can name an insect you discover after a friend, but you must add a Latin ending.) Many of the more than 11,000 binomials assigned by Linnaeus are still used today, including the optimistic name he gave our own species—*Homo sapiens*, meaning "wise man."

Hierarchical Classification

In addition to naming species, Linnaeus also grouped them into a hierarchy of increasingly inclusive categories. The first grouping is built into the binomial: Species that appear to be closely related are grouped into the same genus. For example, the leopard (*Panthera pardus*) belongs to a genus that also includes the African lion (*Panthera leo*), the tiger (*Panthera tigris*), and the jaguar (*Panthera onca*). Beyond genera, taxonomists employ progressively more comprehensive categories of classification. The taxonomic system named after Linnaeus, the

Linnaean system, places related genera in the same **family**, families into **orders**, orders into **classes**, classes into **phyla** (singular, *phylum*), phyla into **kingdoms**, and, more recently, kingdoms into **domains (Figure 26.3)**. The resulting biological classification of a particular organism is somewhat like a postal address identifying a person in a particular apartment, in a building with many apartments, on a street with many apartment buildings, in a city with many streets, and so on.

The named taxonomic unit at any level of the hierarchy is called a **taxon** (plural, *taxa*). In the leopard example, *Panthera* is a taxon at the genus level, and Mammalia is a taxon at the class level that includes all the many orders of mammals. Note that in the Linnaean system, taxa broader than the genus are not italicized, though they are capitalized.

Classifying species is a way to structure our human view of the world. We lump together various species of trees to which we give the common name of pines and distinguish them from other trees that we call firs. Taxonomists have decided

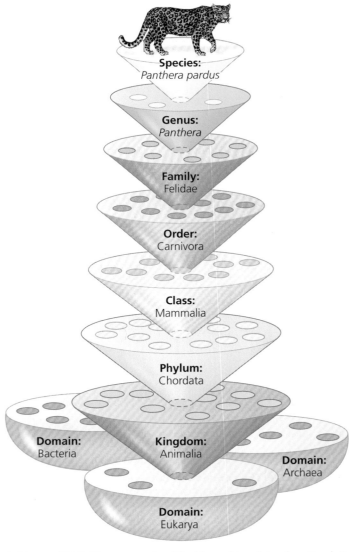

▲ **Figure 26.3 Linnaean classification.** At each level, or "rank," species are placed in groups within more inclusive groups.

that pines and firs are different enough to be placed in separate genera, yet similar enough to be grouped into the same family, Pinaceae. As with pines and firs, higher levels of classification are usually defined by particular characters chosen by taxonomists. However, characters that are useful for classifying one group of organisms may not be appropriate for other organisms. For this reason, the larger categories often are not comparable between lineages; that is, an order of snails does not exhibit the same degree of morphological or genetic diversity as an order of mammals. Furthermore, as we'll see, the placement of species into orders, classes, and so on, does not necessarily reflect evolutionary history.

Linking Classification and Phylogeny

The evolutionary history of a group of organisms can be represented in a branching diagram called a **phylogenetic tree**. As in **Figure 26.4**, the branching pattern often matches how taxonomists have classified groups of organisms nested within more inclusive groups. Sometimes, however, taxonomists have placed a species within a genus (or other group) to which it is *not* most closely related. One reason for misclassification might be that over the course of evolution, a species has lost a key feature shared by its close relatives. If DNA or other new evidence indicates that such a mistake has occurred, the organism may be reclassified to accurately reflect its evolutionary history. Another issue is that while the Linnaean system may distinguish groups, such as mammals, reptiles, birds, and other classes of vertebrates, it tells us nothing about these groups' evolutionary relationships to one another.

In fact, such difficulties in aligning Linnaean classification with phylogeny have led some systematists to propose that classification be based entirely on evolutionary relationships. A system called **PhyloCode**, for example, only names groups that include a common ancestor and all of its descendants. While PhyloCode would change the way taxa are defined and recognized, the taxonomic names of most species would remain the same. But groups would no longer have "ranks" attached to them, such as family or class. Also, some commonly recognized groups would become part of other groups previously of the same rank. For example, because birds evolved from a group of reptiles, Aves (the Linnaean class to which birds are assigned) would be considered a subgroup of Reptilia (also a class in the Linnaean system). Although PhyloCode is controversial, many systematists are adopting the phylogenetic approach on which it is based.

Whether groups are named according to PhyloCode or according to Linnaean classification, a phylogenetic tree represents a hypothesis about evolutionary relationships. These relationships often are depicted as a series of dichotomies, or two-way **branch points**. Each branch point represents the divergence of two evolutionary lineages from a common ancestor. In **Figure 26.5**, for example, branch point ❸ represents the common ancestor of taxa A, B, and C. The position of branch point ❹ to the right of ❸ indicates that taxa B and C diverged after their shared lineage split from that of taxon A. (Tree branches can be rotated around a branch point without changing their evolutionary relationships.)

In Figure 26.5, taxa B and C are **sister taxa**, groups of organisms that share an immediate common ancestor (branch

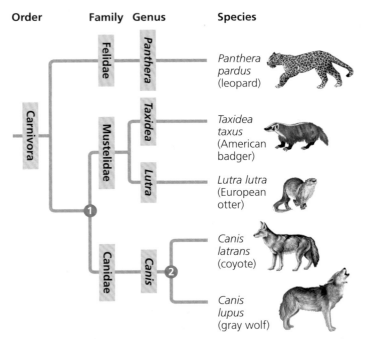

▲ **Figure 26.4 The connection between classification and phylogeny.** Hierarchical classification can reflect the branching patterns of phylogenetic trees. This tree traces possible evolutionary relationships between some of the taxa within order Carnivora, itself a branch of class Mammalia. The branch point ❶ represents the most recent common ancestor of all members of the weasel (Mustelidae) and dog (Canidae) families. The branch point ❷ represents the most recent common ancestor of coyotes and gray wolves.

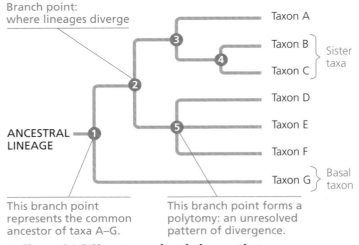

▲ **Figure 26.5 How to read a phylogenetic tree.**
DRAW IT *Redraw this tree, rotating the branches around branch points ❷ and ❹. Does your new version tell a different story about the evolutionary relationships between the taxa? Explain.*

point ④) and hence are each other's closest relatives. Note also that this tree, like most of the phylogenetic trees in this book, is **rooted**, which means that a branch point within the tree (often drawn farthest to the left) represents the most recent common ancestor of all taxa in the tree. The term **basal taxon** refers to a lineage that diverges early in the history of a group and hence, like taxon G in Figure 26.5, lies on a branch that originates near the common ancestor of the group. Finally, the lineage leading to taxa D–F includes a **polytomy**, a branch point from which more than two descendant groups emerge. A polytomy signifies that evolutionary relationships among the taxa are not yet clear.

What We Can and Cannot Learn from Phylogenetic Trees

Let's summarize three key points about phylogenetic trees. First, they are intended to show patterns of descent, not phenotypic similarity. Although closely related organisms often resemble one another due to their common ancestry, they may not if their lineages have evolved at different rates or faced very different environmental conditions. For example, even though crocodiles are more closely related to birds than to lizards (see Figure 22.17), they look more like lizards because morphology has changed dramatically in the bird lineage.

Second, the sequence of branching in a tree does not necessarily indicate the actual (absolute) ages of the particular species. For example, the tree in Figure 26.4 does not indicate that the wolf evolved more recently than the European otter; rather, the tree shows only that the most recent common ancestor of the wolf and otter (branch point ①) lived before the most recent common ancestor of the wolf and coyote (②). To indicate when wolves and otters evolved, the tree would need to include additional divergences in each evolutionary lineage, as well as the dates when those splits occurred. Generally, unless given specific information about what the branch lengths in a phylogenetic tree mean—for example, that they are proportional to time—we should interpret the diagram solely in terms of patterns of descent. No assumptions should be made about when particular species evolved or how much change occurred in each lineage.

Third, we should not assume that a taxon on a phylogenetic tree evolved from the taxon next to it. Figure 26.4 does not indicate that wolves evolved from coyotes or vice versa. We can infer only that the lineage leading to wolves and the lineage leading to coyotes both evolved from the common ancestor ②. That ancestor, which is now extinct, was neither a wolf nor a coyote. However, its descendants include the two *extant* (living) species shown here, wolves and coyotes.

Applying Phylogenies

Understanding phylogeny can have practical applications. Consider maize (corn), which originated in the Americas and is now an important food crop worldwide. From a phylogeny of maize based on DNA data, researchers have been able to identify two species of wild grasses that may be maize's closest living relatives. These two close relatives may be useful as "reservoirs" of beneficial alleles that can be transferred to cultivated maize by cross-breeding or genetic engineering (see Chapter 20).

A different use of phylogenetic trees is described in **Figure 26.6**: investigating whether whale meat samples had

▼ **Figure 26.6**

INQUIRY

What is the species identity of food being sold as whale meat?

EXPERIMENT C. S. Baker, then at the University of Auckland, New Zealand, and S. R. Palumbi, then at the University of Hawaii, purchased 13 samples of "whale meat" from Japanese fish markets. They sequenced a specific part of the mitochondrial DNA from each sample and compared their results with the comparable DNA sequence from known whale species. To infer the species identity of each sample, Baker and Palumbi constructed a *gene tree*, a phylogenetic tree that shows patterns of relatedness among DNA sequences rather than among taxa.

RESULTS The analysis yielded the following gene tree:

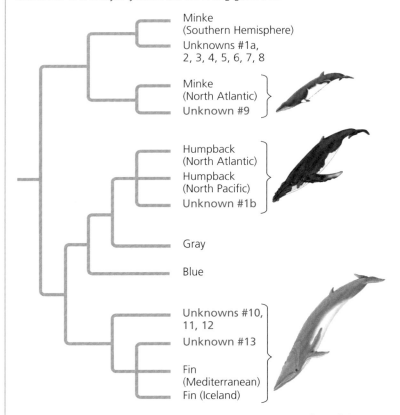

Minke (Southern Hemisphere)
Unknowns #1a, 2, 3, 4, 5, 6, 7, 8

Minke (North Atlantic)
Unknown #9

Humpback (North Atlantic)
Humpback (North Pacific)
Unknown #1b

Gray

Blue

Unknowns #10, 11, 12
Unknown #13

Fin (Mediterranean)
Fin (Iceland)

CONCLUSION This analysis indicated that DNA sequences of six of the unknown samples (in red) were most closely related to DNA sequences of whales that are not legal to harvest.

SOURCE C. S. Baker and S. R. Palumbi, Which whales are hunted? A molecular genetic approach to monitoring whaling, *Science* 265:1538–1539 (1994).

WHAT IF? What different results would have indicated that the whale meat had *not* been illegally harvested?

been illegally harvested from whale species protected under international law—rather than from species that can be harvested legally, such as Minke whales caught in the Southern Hemisphere. This phylogeny indicated that meat from humpback, fin, and Minke whales caught in the Northern Hemisphere was being sold illegally in some Japanese fish markets.

How do researchers construct trees like those we've considered here? In the next section, we'll begin to answer that question by examining the data used to determine phylogenies.

CONCEPT CHECK 26.1

1. Which levels of the classification in Figure 26.3 do humans share with leopards?
2. What does the phylogenetic tree in Figure 26.4 indicate about the evolutionary relationships of the leopard, badger, and wolf?
3. Which of the trees shown here depicts an evolutionary history different from the other two? Explain.

(a) (b) (c)

4. **WHAT IF?** Suppose new evidence indicates that taxon E in Figure 26.5 is the sister taxon of a group consisting of taxa D and F. Redraw the tree to accommodate this new finding.

For suggested answers, see Appendix A.

CONCEPT 26.2

Phylogenies are inferred from morphological and molecular data

To infer phylogeny, systematists must gather as much information as possible about the morphology, genes, and biochemistry of the relevant organisms. It is important to focus on features that result from common ancestry, because only such features reflect evolutionary relationships.

Morphological and Molecular Homologies

Recall that phenotypic and genetic similarities due to shared ancestry are called *homologies*. For example, the similarity in the number and arrangement of bones in the forelimbs of mammals is due to their descent from a common ancestor with the same bone structure; this is an example of a morphological homology (see Figure 22.15). In the same way, genes or other DNA sequences are homologous if they are descended from sequences carried by a common ancestor.

In general, organisms that share very similar morphologies or similar DNA sequences are likely to be more closely related than organisms with vastly different structures or sequences. In some cases, however, the morphological divergence between related species can be great and their genetic divergence small (or vice versa). Consider the Hawaiian silversword plants discussed in Chapter 25. These species vary dramatically in appearance throughout the islands. Some are tall, twiggy trees, and others are dense, ground-hugging shrubs (see Figure 25.20). But despite these striking phenotypic differences, the silverswords' genes are very similar. Based on these small molecular divergences, scientists estimate that the silversword group began to diverge 5 million years ago, which is also about the time when the oldest of the current islands formed. We'll discuss how scientists use molecular data to estimate such divergence times later in this chapter.

Sorting Homology from Analogy

A potential red herring in constructing a phylogeny is similarity due to convergent evolution—called **analogy**—rather than to shared ancestry (homology). As you read in Chapter 22, convergent evolution occurs when similar environmental pressures and natural selection produce similar (analogous) adaptations in organisms from different evolutionary lineages. For example, the two mole-like animals illustrated in **Figure 26.7** are very similar in their external appearance. However, their internal anatomy, physiology, and reproductive systems are very dissimilar. Australian "moles" are marsupials; their young complete their embryonic development in a pouch on the outside of the mother's body. North American moles, in contrast, are eutherians; their young complete

▲ **Figure 26.7 Convergent evolution of analogous burrowing characteristics.** An elongated body, enlarged front paws, small eyes, and a pad of thickened skin that protects a tapered nose all evolved independently in the marsupial Australian "mole" (top) and a eutherian North American mole (bottom).

their embryonic development in the uterus within the mother's body. Indeed, genetic comparisons and the fossil record provide evidence that the common ancestor of these moles lived 140 million years ago, about the time the marsupial and eutherian mammals diverged. This common ancestor and most of its descendants were not mole-like, but analogous characteristics evolved independently in these two mole lineages as they became adapted to similar lifestyles.

Distinguishing between homology and analogy is critical in reconstructing phylogenies. To see why, consider bats and birds, both of which have adaptations that enable flight. This superficial resemblance might imply that bats are more closely related to birds than they are to cats, which cannot fly. But a closer examination reveals that a bat's wing is far more similar to the forelimbs of cats and other mammals than to a bird's wing. Bats and birds descended from a common tetrapod ancestor that lived about 320 million years ago. This common ancestor could not fly. Thus, although the underlying skeletal systems of bats and birds are homologous, their *wings* are not. Flight is enabled in different ways—stretched membranes in the bat wing versus feathers in the bird wing. Fossil evidence also documents that bat wings and bird wings arose independently from the forelimbs of different tetrapod ancestors. Thus, with respect to flight, a bat's wing is *analogous*, not homologous, to a bird's wing. Analogous structures that arose independently are also called **homoplasies** (from the Greek, meaning "to mold in the same way").

Besides corroborative similarities and fossil evidence, another clue to distinguishing between homology and analogy is the complexity of the characters being compared. The more elements that are similar in two complex structures, the more likely it is that they evolved from a common ancestor. For instance, the skulls of an adult human and an adult chimpanzee both consist of many bones fused together. The compositions of the skulls match almost perfectly, bone for bone. It is highly improbable that such complex structures, matching in so many details, have separate origins. More likely, the genes involved in the development of both skulls were inherited from a common ancestor. The same argument applies to comparisons at the gene level. Genes are sequences of thousands of nucleotides, each of which represents an inherited character in the form of one of the four DNA bases: A (adenine), G (guanine), C (cytosine), or T (thymine). If genes in two organisms share many portions of their nucleotide sequences, it is likely that the genes are homologous.

Evaluating Molecular Homologies

Comparisons of DNA molecules often pose technical challenges for researchers. The first step after sequencing the molecules is to align comparable sequences from the species being studied. If the species are very closely related, the sequences probably differ at only one or a few sites. In contrast, comparable nucleic acid sequences in distantly related species usually have different bases at many sites and may have different lengths. This is because insertions and deletions accumulate over long periods of time.

Suppose, for example, that certain noncoding DNA sequences near a particular gene are very similar in two species, except that the first base of the sequence has been deleted in one of the species. The effect is that the remaining sequence shifts back one notch. A comparison of the two sequences that does not take this deletion into account would overlook what in fact is a very good match. To address such problems, researchers have developed computer programs that estimate the best way to align comparable DNA segments of differing lengths (**Figure 26.8**).

Such molecular comparisons reveal that many base substitutions and other differences have accumulated in the comparable genes of an Australian mole and a North American mole. The many differences indicate that their lineages have diverged greatly since their common ancestor; thus, we say that the living species are not closely related. In contrast, the high degree of gene sequence similarity among the silverswords indicates that they are all very closely related, in spite of their considerable morphological differences.

Just as with morphological characters, it is necessary to distinguish homology from analogy in evaluating molecular similarities for evolutionary studies. Two sequences that resemble each other at many points along their length most likely are

❶ These homologous DNA sequences are identical as species 1 and species 2 begin to diverge from their common ancestor.

1 C C A T C A G A G T C C
2 C C A T C A G A G T C C

❷ Deletion and insertion mutations shift what had been matching sequences in the two species.

Deletion

1 C C A T C A G A G T C C
2 C C A T C A G A G T C C

(G T A) Insertion

❸ Of the regions of the species 2 sequence that match the species 1 sequence, those shaded orange no longer align because of these mutations.

1 C C A T C A A G T C C
2 C C A T G T A C A G A G T C C

❹ The matching regions realign after a computer program adds gaps in sequence 1.

1 C C A T _ _ _ C A _ A G T C C
2 C C A T G T A C A G A G T C C

▲ **Figure 26.8 Aligning segments of DNA.** Systematists search for similar sequences along DNA segments from two species (only one DNA strand is shown for each species). In this example, 11 of the original 12 bases have not changed since the species diverged. Hence, those portions of the sequences still align once the length is adjusted.

ACGGATAGTCCACTAGGCACTA

TCACCGACAGGTCTTTGACTAG

▲ **Figure 26.9 A molecular homoplasy.** These two DNA sequences from organisms that are not closely related coincidentally share 25% of their bases. Statistical tools have been developed to determine whether DNA sequences that share more than 25% of their bases do so because they are homologous.

? *Why might you expect organisms that are not closely related to nevertheless share roughly 25% of their bases?*

homologous (see Figure 26.8). But in organisms that do not appear to be closely related, the bases that their otherwise very different sequences happen to share may simply be coincidental matches, called molecular homoplasies (**Figure 26.9**). Scientists have developed statistical tools that can help distinguish "distant" homologies from such coincidental matches in extremely divergent sequences.

To date, researchers have sequenced more than 110 billion bases of DNA from thousands of species. This enormous collection of data has fueled a boom in the study of phylogeny. The new data have supported earlier hypotheses regarding many evolutionary relationships, such as that between Australian and North American moles, and have clarified other relationships, such as those between the various silverswords. In the rest of this unit, you will see how our understanding of phylogeny has been transformed by **molecular systematics**, the discipline that uses data from DNA and other molecules to determine evolutionary relationships.

CONCEPT CHECK 26.2

1. Decide whether each of the following pairs of structures more likely represents analogy or homology, and explain your reasoning: (a) a porcupine's quills and a cactus's spines; (b) a cat's paw and a human's hand; (c) an owl's wing and a hornet's wing.
2. **WHAT IF?** Suppose that species 1 and species 2 have similar appearances but very divergent gene sequences and that species 2 and species 3 have very different appearances but similar gene sequences. Which pair of species is more likely to be closely related: 1 and 2, or 2 and 3? Explain.

For suggested answers, see Appendix A.

CONCEPT 26.3

Shared characters are used to construct phylogenetic trees

In reconstructing phylogenies, the first step is to distinguish homologous features from analogous ones (since only homology reflects evolutionary history). Next we must choose a method of inferring phylogeny from these homologous characters. A widely used set of methods is known as cladistics.

Cladistics

In the approach to systematics called **cladistics**, common ancestry is the primary criterion used to classify organisms. Using this methodology, biologists attempt to place species into groups called **clades**, each of which includes an ancestral species and all of its descendants (**Figure 26.10a**). Clades, like

▼ **Figure 26.10 Monophyletic, paraphyletic, and polyphyletic groups.**

(a) Monophyletic group (clade)

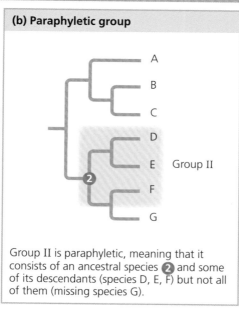

Group I, consisting of three species (A, B, C) and their common ancestor ❶, is a clade, also called a monophyletic group. A monophyletic group consists of an ancestral species and *all* of its descendants.

(b) Paraphyletic group

Group II is paraphyletic, meaning that it consists of an ancestral species ❷ and some of its descendants (species D, E, F) but not all of them (missing species G).

(c) Polyphyletic group

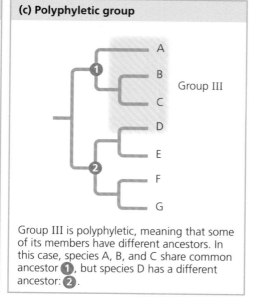

Group III is polyphyletic, meaning that some of its members have different ancestors. In this case, species A, B, and C share common ancestor ❶, but species D has a different ancestor: ❷.

taxonomic ranks, are nested within larger clades. In Figure 26.4, for example, the cat group (Felidae) represents a clade within a larger clade (Carnivora) that also includes the dog group (Canidae). However, a taxon is equivalent to a clade only if it is **monophyletic** (from the Greek, meaning "single tribe"), signifying that it consists of an ancestral species and all of its descendants (see Figure 26.10a). Contrast this with a **paraphyletic** ("beside the tribe") group, which consists of an ancestral species and some, but not all, of its descendants (Figure 26.10b), or a **polyphyletic** ("many tribes") group, which includes taxa with different ancestors (Figure 26.10c). Next we'll discuss how clades are identified using shared derived characters.

Shared Ancestral and Shared Derived Characters

As a result of descent with modification, organisms both share characteristics with their ancestors and differ from them. For example, all mammals have backbones, but a backbone does not distinguish mammals from other vertebrates because *all* vertebrates have backbones. The backbone predates the branching of mammals from other vertebrates. Thus for mammals, the backbone is a **shared ancestral character**, a character that originated in an ancestor of the taxon. In contrast, hair is a character shared by all mammals but *not* found in their ancestors. Thus, in mammals, hair is considered a **shared derived character**, an evolutionary novelty unique to a clade.

Note that it is a relative matter whether a particular character is considered ancestral or derived. A backbone can also qualify as a shared derived character, but only at a deeper branch point that distinguishes all vertebrates from other animals. Among mammals, a backbone is considered a shared ancestral character because it was present in the ancestor common to all mammals.

Inferring Phylogenies Using Derived Characters

Shared derived characters are unique to particular clades. Because all features of organisms arose at some point in the history of life, it should be possible to determine the clade in which each shared derived character first appeared and to use that information to infer evolutionary relationships.

To see how this analysis is done, consider the set of characters shown in **Figure 26.11a** for each of five vertebrates—a leopard, turtle, frog, bass, and lamprey (a jawless aquatic vertebrate). As a basis of comparison, we need to select an outgroup. An **outgroup** is a species or group of species from an evolutionary lineage that is known to have diverged before the lineage that includes the species we are studying (the **ingroup**). A suitable outgroup can be determined based on evidence from morphology, paleontology, embryonic development, and gene sequences. An appropriate outgroup for our example is the lancelet, a small animal that lives in mudflats and (like vertebrates) is a member of Chordata. Unlike the vertebrates, however, the lancelet does not have a backbone.

By comparing members of the ingroup with each other and with the outgroup, we can determine which characters were derived at the various branch points of vertebrate evolution. For example, *all* of the vertebrates in the ingroup have backbones: This character was present in the ancestral vertebrate, but not in the outgroup. Now note that hinged jaws are a character absent in lampreys but present in other members of the ingroup; this character helps us to identify an early branch point in the vertebrate clade. Proceeding in this way, we can translate the data in our table of characters into a phylogenetic tree that groups all the ingroup taxa into a hierarchy based on their shared derived characters (**Figure 26.11b**).

(a) **Character table.** A 0 indicates that a character is absent; a 1 indicates that a character is present.

(b) **Phylogenetic tree.** Analyzing the distribution of these derived characters can provide insight into vertebrate phylogeny.

▲ **Figure 26.11 Constructing a phylogenetic tree.** The characters used here include the amnion, a membrane that encloses the embryo inside a fluid-filled sac (see Figure 34.25).

DRAW IT *In (b), circle the most inclusive clade for which a hinged jaw is a shared ancestral character.*

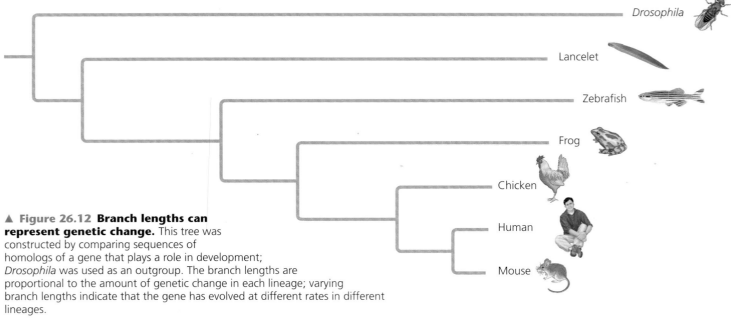

▲ **Figure 26.12 Branch lengths can represent genetic change.** This tree was constructed by comparing sequences of homologs of a gene that plays a role in development; *Drosophila* was used as an outgroup. The branch lengths are proportional to the amount of genetic change in each lineage; varying branch lengths indicate that the gene has evolved at different rates in different lineages.

? *In which vertebrate lineage has the studied gene evolved most rapidly? Explain.*

Phylogenetic Trees with Proportional Branch Lengths

In the phylogenetic trees we have presented so far, the lengths of the tree's branches do not indicate the degree of evolutionary change in each lineage. Furthermore, the chronology represented by the branching pattern of the tree is relative (earlier versus later) rather than absolute (how many millions of years ago). But in some tree diagrams, branch lengths are proportional to amount of evolutionary change or to the times at which particular events occurred.

In **Figure 26.12**, for example, the branch length of the phylogenetic tree reflects the number of changes that have taken place in a particular DNA sequence in that lineage. Note that the total length of the horizontal lines from the base of the tree to the mouse is less than that of the line leading to the outgroup species, the fruit fly *Drosophila*. This implies that in the time since the mouse and fly diverged from a common ancestor, more genetic changes have occurred in the *Drosophila* lineage than in the mouse lineage.

Even though the branches of a phylogenetic tree may have different lengths, among organisms alive today, all the different lineages that descend from a common ancestor have survived for the same number of years. To take an extreme example, humans and bacteria had a common ancestor that lived over 3 billion years ago. Fossils and genetic evidence indicate that this ancestor was a single-celled prokaryote. Even though bacteria have apparently changed little in their morphology since that common ancestor, there have nonetheless been 3 billion years of evolution in the bacterial lineage, just as there have been 3 billion years of evolution in the eukaryotic lineage that includes humans.

These equal spans of chronological time can be represented in a phylogenetic tree whose branch lengths are proportional to time **(Figure 26.13)**. Such a tree draws on fossil data to place branch points in the context of geologic time. Additionally, it is possible to combine these two types of trees by labeling branch points with information about rates of genetic change or dates of divergence.

Maximum Parsimony and Maximum Likelihood

As the growing database of DNA sequences enables us to study more species, the difficulty of building the phylogenetic tree that best describes their evolutionary history also grows. What if you are analyzing data for 50 species? There are 3×10^{76} different ways to arrange 50 species into a tree! And which tree in this huge forest reflects the true phylogeny? Systematists can never be sure of finding the most accurate tree in such a large data set, but they can narrow the possibilities by applying the principles of maximum parsimony and maximum likelihood.

According to the principle of **maximum parsimony**, we should first investigate the simplest explanation that is consistent with the facts. (The parsimony principle is also called "Occam's razor" after William of Occam, a 14th-century English philosopher who advocated this minimalist problem-solving approach of "shaving away" unnecessary complications.) In the case of trees based on morphology, the most parsimonious tree requires the fewest evolutionary events, as measured by the origin of shared derived morphological characters. For phylogenies based on DNA, the most parsimonious tree requires the fewest base changes.

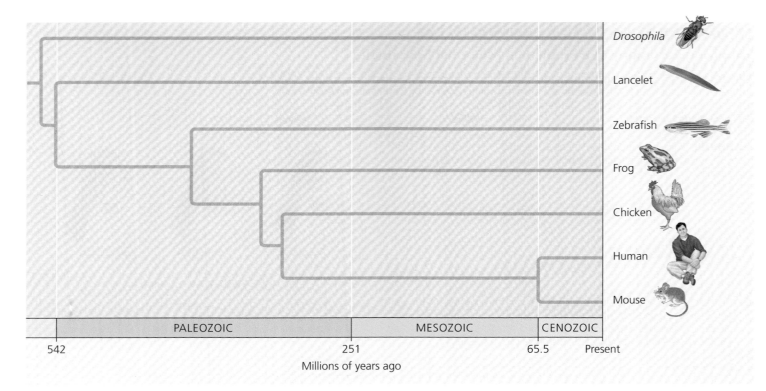

PALEOZOIC			MESOZOIC		CENOZOIC
542			251		65.5	Present

Millions of years ago

▲ **Figure 26.13 Branch lengths can indicate time.** This tree is based on the same molecular data as the tree in Figure 26.12, but here the branch points are mapped to dates based on fossil evidence. Thus, the branch lengths are proportional to time. Each lineage has the same total length from the base of the tree to the branch tip, indicating that all the lineages have diverged from the common ancestor for equal amounts of time.

The principle of **maximum likelihood** states that given certain probability rules about how DNA sequences change over time, a tree can be found that reflects the most likely sequence of evolutionary events. Maximum-likelihood methods are complex, but as a simple example, let us return to the phylogenetic relationships between a human, a mushroom, and a tulip. **Figure 26.14** shows two possible, equally parsimonious trees for this trio. Tree 1 is more likely if we assume that DNA changes have occurred at equal rates along all the branches of the tree from the common ancestor. Tree 2 requires assuming that the rate of evolution slowed greatly in the mushroom lineage and sped up greatly in the tulip lineage. Thus, assuming that equal rates are more common than unequal rates, tree 1 is more likely. We will soon see that many genes do evolve at approximately equal rates in different lineages. But note that if we find new evidence of unequal rates, tree 2 might be more likely! The likelihood of a tree depends on the assumptions on which it is based.

Scientists have developed many computer programs to search for trees that are parsimonious and likely. When a large amount of accurate data is available, the methods used in these programs usually yield similar trees. As an example of one

	Human	Mushroom	Tulip
Human	0	30%	40%
Mushroom		0	40%
Tulip			0

(a) Percentage differences between sequences

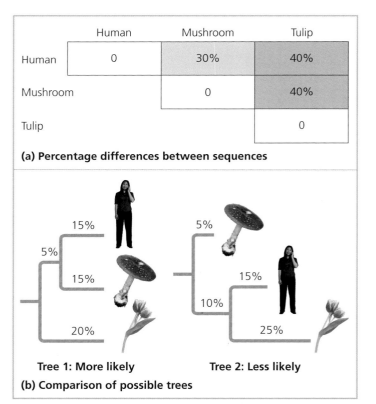

Tree 1: More likely   **Tree 2: Less likely**
(b) Comparison of possible trees

▲ **Figure 26.14 Trees with different likelihoods.** Based on percentage differences between genes in a human, a mushroom, and a tulip **(a)**, there are two phylogenetic trees with the same total branch length **(b)**. The sum of the percentages from a point of divergence in a tree equals the percentage differences in (a). For example, in tree 1, the human–tulip divergence is 15% + 5% + 20% = 40%. In tree 2, this divergence also equals 40% (15% + 25%). If the genes have evolved at the same rate in the different branches, tree 1 is more likely.

RESEARCH METHOD

Applying Parsimony to a Problem in Molecular Systematics

APPLICATION In considering possible phylogenies for a group of species, systematists compare molecular data for the species. An efficient way to begin is by identifying the most parsimonious hypothesis—the one that requires the fewest evolutionary events (molecular changes) to have occurred.

TECHNIQUE Follow the numbered steps as we apply the principle of parsimony to a hypothetical phylogenetic problem involving three closely related bird species.

Species I   Species II   Species III

① First, draw the three possible phylogenies for the species. (Although only 3 trees are possible when ordering 3 species, the number of possible trees increases rapidly with the number of species: There are 15 trees for 4 species and 34,459,425 trees for 10 species.)

Three phylogenetic hypotheses:

② Tabulate the molecular data for the species. In this simplified example, the data represent a DNA sequence consisting of just four nucleotide bases. Data from several outgroup species (not shown) were used to infer the ancestral DNA sequence.

	Site 1	Site 2	Site 3	Site 4
Species I	C	T	A	T
Species II	C	T	T	C
Species III	A	G	A	C
Ancestral sequence	A	G	T	T

③ Now focus on site 1 in the DNA sequence. In the tree on the left, a single base-change event, represented by the purple hatchmark on the branch leading to species I and II (and labeled 1/C, indicating a change at site 1 to nucleotide C), is sufficient to account for the site 1 data. In the other two trees, two base-change events are necessary.

④ Continuing the comparison of bases at sites 2, 3, and 4 reveals that each of the three trees requires a total of five additional base-change events (purple hatchmarks).

RESULTS To identify the most parsimonious tree, we total all of the base-change events noted in steps 3 and 4. We conclude that the first tree is the most parsimonious of the three possible phylogenies. (In a real example, many more sites would be analyzed. Hence, the trees would often differ by more than one base-change event.)

6 events   7 events   7 events

method, **Figure 26.15**, on the facing page, walks you through the process of identifying the most parsimonious molecular tree for a three-species problem. Computer programs use the principle of parsimony to estimate phylogenies in a similar way: They examine large numbers of possible trees and select the tree or trees that require fewest evolutionary changes.

Phylogenetic Trees as Hypotheses

This is a good place to reiterate that any phylogenetic tree represents a hypothesis about how the various organisms in the tree are related to one another. The best hypothesis is the one that best fits all the available data. A phylogenetic hypothesis may be modified when new evidence compels systematists to revise their trees. Indeed, while many older phylogenetic hypotheses have been supported by new morphological and molecular data, others have been changed or rejected.

Thinking of phylogenies as hypotheses also allows us to use them in a powerful way: We can make and test predictions based on the assumption that a phylogeny—our hypothesis—is correct. For example, in an approach known as *phylogenetic bracketing*, we can predict (by parsimony) that features shared by two groups of closely related organisms are present in their common ancestor and all of its descendants unless independent data indicate otherwise. (Note that "prediction" can refer to unknown past events as well as to evolutionary changes yet to occur.)

This approach has been used to make novel predictions about dinosaurs. For example, there is evidence that birds descended from the theropods, a group of bipedal saurischian dinosaurs. As seen in **Figure 26.16**, the closest living relatives of birds are crocodiles. Birds and crocodiles share numerous features: They have four-chambered hearts, they "sing" to defend territories and attract mates (although a crocodile's "song" is more like a bellow), and they build nests. Both birds and crocodiles also care for their eggs by *brooding*, a behavior in which a parent warms the eggs with its body. Birds brood by sitting on their eggs, whereas crocodiles cover their eggs with their neck. Reasoning that any feature shared by birds and crocodiles is likely to have been present in their common ancestor (denoted by the blue dot in Figure 26.16) and *all* of its descendants, biologists predicted that dinosaurs had four-chambered hearts, sang, built nests, and exhibited brooding.

Internal organs, such as the heart, rarely fossilize, and it is, of course, difficult to test whether dinosaurs sang to defend territories and attract mates. However, fossilized dinosaur eggs and nests have provided evidence supporting the prediction of brooding in dinosaurs. First, a fossil embryo of an *Oviraptor* dinosaur was found, still inside its egg. This egg was identical to those found in another fossil, one that showed an *Oviraptor* adult crouching over a group of eggs in a posture similar to that in brooding birds today **(Figure 26.17)**. Researchers suggested that the *Oviraptor* dinosaur preserved in this second fossil died while incubating or protecting its eggs. The broader conclusion that emerged from this work—that

(a) **Fossil remains of *Oviraptor* and eggs.** The orientation of the bones, which surround and cover the eggs, suggests that the dinosaur died while incubating or protecting its eggs.

(b) Artist's reconstruction of the dinosaur's posture based on the fossil findings.

▲ **Figure 26.17 Fossil support for a phylogenetic prediction: Dinosaurs built nests and brooded their eggs.**

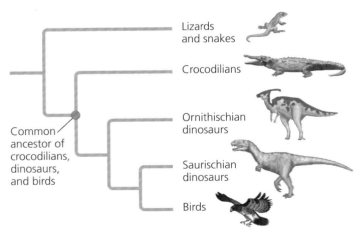

▲ **Figure 26.16 A phylogenetic tree of birds and their close relatives.**

? *What is the most basal taxon represented in this tree?*

dinosaurs built nests and exhibited brooding—has since been strengthened by additional fossil discoveries that show that other species of dinosaurs built nests and sat on their eggs. Finally, by supporting predictions based on the phylogenetic hypothesis shown in Figure 26.16, fossil discoveries of nests and brooding in dinosaurs provide independent data that suggest that the hypothesis is correct.

CONCEPT CHECK 26.3

1. To distinguish a particular clade of mammals within the larger clade that corresponds to class Mammalia, would hair be a useful character? Why or why not?

2. The most parsimonious tree of evolutionary relationships can be inaccurate. How can this occur?

3. **WHAT IF?** Draw a phylogenetic tree that includes the relationships from both Figure 25.6 and Figure 26.16. Traditionally, all the taxa shown besides birds and mammals were classified as reptiles. Would a cladistic approach support that classification? Explain.

For suggested answers, see Appendix A.

CONCEPT 26.4

An organism's evolutionary history is documented in its genome

As you have seen in this chapter, molecular systematics—using comparisons of nucleic acids or other molecules to deduce relatedness—is a valuable approach for tracing evolutionary history. The molecular approach helps us understand phylogenetic relationships that cannot be determined by nonmolecular methods such as comparative anatomy. For example, molecular systematics helps us uncover evolutionary relationships between groups that have little common ground for morphological comparison, such as animals and fungi. And molecular methods allow us to reconstruct phylogenies among groups of present-day organisms for which the fossil record is poor or lacking entirely. Overall, molecular biology has helped to extend systematics to evolutionary relationships far above and below the species level, ranging from the major branches of the tree of life to its finest twigs.

Different genes evolve at different rates, even in the same evolutionary lineage. As a result, molecular trees can represent short or long periods of time, depending on which genes are used. For example, the DNA that codes for ribosomal RNA (rRNA) changes relatively slowly. Therefore, comparisons of DNA sequences in these genes are useful for investigating relationships between taxa that diverged hundreds of millions of years ago. Studies of rRNA sequences indicate, for instance, that fungi are more closely related to animals than to green plants (see Figure 26.2). In contrast, mitochondrial DNA (mtDNA) evolves relatively rapidly and can be used to explore recent evolutionary events. One research team has traced the relationships among Native American groups through their mtDNA sequences. The molecular findings corroborate other evidence that the Pima of Arizona, the Maya of Mexico, and the Yanomami of Venezuela are closely related, probably descending from the first of three waves of immigrants that crossed the Bering land bridge from Asia to the Americas about 15,000 years ago.

Gene Duplications and Gene Families

What does molecular systematics reveal about the evolutionary history of genome change? Consider gene duplication, which plays a particularly important role in evolution because it increases the number of genes in the genome, providing more opportunities for further evolutionary changes. Molecular techniques now allow us to trace the phylogenies of gene duplications and the influence of these duplications on genome evolution. These molecular phylogenies must account for repeated duplications that have resulted in *gene families*, groups of related genes within an organism's genome (see Figure 21.11). Accounting for such duplications leads us to distinguish two types of homologous genes: orthologous genes and paralogous genes. **Orthologous genes** (from the Greek *orthos*, exact) are those found in different species, and their divergence traces back to the speciation events that produced the species (**Figure 26.18a**). The cytochrome *c* genes (which code for an electron transport chain protein) in humans and dogs are orthologous. In **paralogous genes** (from the Greek *para*, in parallel), the homology results from gene duplication; hence, multiple copies of these genes have diverged from one another within a species (**Figure 26.18b**). In Chapter 23, you encountered the example of olfactory receptor genes, which have undergone many gene duplications in vertebrates. Humans and mice both have huge families of more than 1,000 of these paralogous genes.

Note that orthologous genes can only diverge after speciation has taken place, that is, after the genes are found in separate gene pools. For example, although the cytochrome *c* genes in humans and dogs serve the same function, the gene's sequence in humans has diverged from that in dogs in the time since these species last shared a common ancestor. Paralogous genes, on the other hand, can diverge within a species because they are present in more than one copy in the genome. The paralogous genes that make up the olfactory receptor gene family in humans have diverged from each other during our long evolutionary history. They now specify proteins that confer sensitivity to a wide variety of molecules, ranging from food odors to sex pheromones.

Genome Evolution

Now that we can compare the entire genomes of different organisms, including our own, two patterns have emerged. First, lineages that diverged long ago can share orthologous genes. For

(a) Formation of orthologous genes: a product of speciation

Ancestral gene

Ancestral species

Speciation with divergence of gene

Orthologous genes

Species A   Species B

(b) Formation of paralogous genes: within a species

Ancestral gene

Species C

Gene duplication and divergence

Paralogous genes

Species C after many generations

example, though the human and mouse lineages diverged about 65 million years ago, 99% of the genes of humans and mice are orthologous. And 50% of human genes are orthologous with those of yeast, despite 1 billion years of divergent evolution. Such commonalities explain why disparate organisms nevertheless share many biochemical and developmental pathways.

Second, the number of genes a species has doesn't seem to increase through duplication at the same rate as perceived phenotypic complexity. Humans have only about four times as many genes as yeast, a single-celled eukaryote, even though—unlike yeast—we have a large, complex brain and a body with more than 200 different types of tissues. Evidence is emerging that many human genes are more versatile than those of yeast: A single human gene can encode multiple proteins that perform different tasks in various body tissues. Unraveling the mechanisms that cause this genomic versatility and phenotypic variation is an exciting challenge.

CONCEPT CHECK 26.4

1. Explain how comparing proteins of two species can yield data about the species' evolutionary relationship.
2. **WHAT IF?** Suppose gene A is orthologous in species 1 and species 2, and gene B is paralogous to gene A in species 1. Suggest a sequence of two evolutionary events that could result in the following: Gene A differs considerably between species, yet gene A and gene B show little divergence from each other.
3. **MAKE CONNECTIONS** Review Figure 18.13 (p. 363); then suggest how a particular gene could have different functions in different tissues within an organism.

For suggested answers, see Appendix A.

CONCEPT 26.5

Molecular clocks help track evolutionary time

One of the long-term goals of evolutionary biology is to understand the relationships among all organisms, including those for which there is no fossil record. When we extend molecular phylogenies beyond the fossil record, however, we must rely on an important assumption about how change occurs at the molecular level.

Molecular Clocks

We stated earlier that researchers have estimated that the common ancestor of Hawaiian silversword plants lived about 5 million years ago. How did they make this estimate? They relied on the concept of a **molecular clock**, a yardstick for measuring the absolute time of evolutionary change based on the observation that some genes and other regions of genomes appear to evolve at constant rates. The assumption underlying the molecular clock is that the number of nucleotide substitutions in orthologous genes is proportional to the time that has elapsed since the species branched from their common ancestor (divergence time). In the case of paralogous genes, the number of substitutions is proportional to the time since the ancestral gene was duplicated.

We can calibrate the molecular clock of a gene that has a reliable average rate of evolution by graphing the number of genetic differences—for example, nucleotide, codon, or amino acid differences—against the dates of evolutionary branch points that are known from the fossil record

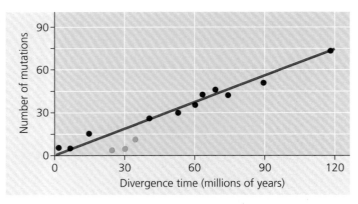

▲ **Figure 26.19 A molecular clock for mammals.** The number of accumulated mutations in seven proteins has increased over time in a consistent manner for most mammal species. The three green data points represent primate species, whose proteins appear to have evolved more slowly than those of other mammals. The divergence time for each data point was based on fossil evidence.

? *Use the graph to estimate the divergence time for a mammal with a total of 30 mutations in the seven proteins.*

(Figure 26.19). The average rates of genetic change inferred from such graphs can then be used to estimate the dates of events that cannot be discerned from the fossil record, such as the origin of the silverswords discussed earlier.

Of course, no gene marks time with complete precision. In fact, some portions of the genome appear to have evolved in irregular bursts that are not at all clocklike. And even those genes that seem to act as reliable molecular clocks are accurate only in the statistical sense of showing a fairly smooth *average* rate of change. Over time, there may still be deviations from that average rate. Furthermore, the same gene may evolve at different rates in different groups of organisms. And even among genes that are clocklike, the rate of the clock may vary greatly from one gene to another; some genes evolve a million times faster than others.

Neutral Theory

The observed regularity of change that enables us to use some genes as molecular clocks raises the possibility that many of the changes in these sequences result from mutations that have become fixed in a population by genetic drift (see Chapter 23) and that the changes are selectively neutral—neither beneficial nor detrimental. In the 1960s, Motoo Kimura, at the Japanese National Institute of Genetics, and Jack King and Thomas Jukes, at the University of California, Berkeley, independently published papers describing this **neutral theory**—that much evolutionary change in genes and proteins has no effect on fitness and therefore is not influenced by natural selection. Kimura pointed out that many new mutations are harmful and are removed quickly. But if most of the rest are neutral and have little or no effect on fitness, then the rate of molecular change should indeed be regular, like a clock. Differences in the clock rate for different genes are a function of how important a gene is. If the exact sequence of amino

acids that a gene specifies is essential to survival, most of the mutational changes will be harmful and only a few will be neutral. As a result, such genes change only slowly. But if the exact sequence of amino acids is less critical, fewer of the new mutations will be harmful and more will be neutral. Such genes change more quickly.

Problems with Molecular Clocks

In fact, molecular clocks do not run as smoothly as neutral theory predicts. Many irregularities are likely to be the result of natural selection in which certain DNA changes are favored over others. Consequently, some scientists question the utility of molecular clocks for timing evolution. Their skepticism is part of a broader debate about the extent to which neutral genetic variation can account for some kinds of DNA diversity. Indeed, evidence suggests that almost half the amino acid differences in proteins of two *Drosophila* species, *D. simulans* and *D. yakuba*, are not neutral but have resulted from directional natural selection. But because the direction of natural selection may change repeatedly over long periods of time (and hence may average out), some genes experiencing selection can nevertheless serve as approximate markers of elapsed time.

Another question arises when researchers attempt to extend molecular clocks beyond the time span documented by the fossil record. Although some fossils are more than 3 billion years old, these are very rare. An abundant fossil record extends back only about 550 million years, but molecular clocks have been used to date evolutionary divergences that occurred a billion or more years ago. These estimates assume that the clocks have been constant for all that time. Such estimates are highly uncertain.

In some cases, problems may be avoided by calibrating molecular clocks with many genes rather than just one or a few genes (as is often done). By using many genes, fluctuations in evolutionary rate due to natural selection or other factors that vary over time may average out. For example, one group of researchers constructed molecular clocks of vertebrate evolution from published sequence data for 658 nuclear genes. Despite the broad period of time covered (nearly 600 million years) and the fact that natural selection probably affected some of these genes, their estimates of divergence times agreed closely with fossil-based estimates.

Applying a Molecular Clock: The Origin of HIV

Researchers have used a molecular clock to date the origin of HIV infection in humans. Phylogenetic analysis shows that HIV, the virus that causes AIDS, is descended from viruses that infect chimpanzees and other primates. (Most of these viruses do not cause AIDS-like diseases in their native hosts.) When did HIV jump to humans? There is no simple answer, because the virus has spread to humans more than once. The multiple origins of HIV are reflected in the variety of strains

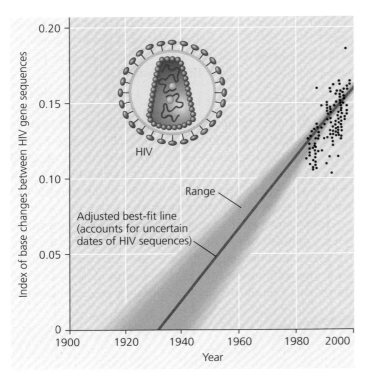

▲ **Figure 26.20 Dating the origin of HIV-1 M with a molecular clock.** The black data points are based on DNA sequences of an HIV gene in blood samples collected from patients. (The dates when these individual HIV gene sequences arose are not known with certainty because a person can harbor the virus for years before symptoms occur.) Projecting the gene's rate of change in the 1980s and 1990s backward in time suggests that the virus originated in the 1930s.

(genetic types) of the virus. HIV's genetic material is made of RNA, and like other RNA viruses, it evolves quickly.

The most widespread strain in humans is HIV-1 M. To pinpoint the earliest HIV-1 M infection, researchers compared samples of the virus from various times during the epidemic, including a sample from 1959. A comparison of gene sequences showed that the virus has evolved in a clocklike fashion (**Figure 26.20**). Extrapolating backward in time using the molecular clock indicates that the HIV-1 M strain first spread to humans during the 1930s.

CONCEPT CHECK 26.5

1. What is a molecular clock? What assumption underlies the use of a molecular clock?
2. **MAKE CONNECTIONS** Review Concept 17.5 (pp. 344–346). Then explain how numerous base changes could occur in an organism's DNA yet have no effect on its fitness.
3. **WHAT IF?** Suppose a molecular clock dates the divergence of two taxa at 80 million years ago, but new fossil evidence shows that the taxa diverged at least 120 million years ago. Explain how this could happen.

For suggested answers, see Appendix A.

New information continues to revise our understanding of the tree of life

The discovery that the scaly-foot in Figure 26.1 evolved from a different lineage of legless lizards than did snakes is one example of how systematics is used to reconstruct the evolutionary relationships of life's diverse forms. In recent decades, we have gained insight into even the very deepest branches of the tree of life through molecular systematics.

From Two Kingdoms to Three Domains

Early taxonomists classified all known species into two kingdoms: plants and animals. Even with the discovery of the diverse microbial world, the two-kingdom system persisted: Noting that bacteria had a rigid cell wall, taxonomists placed them in the plant kingdom. Eukaryotic unicellular organisms with chloroplasts were also considered plants. Fungi, too, were classified as plants, partly because most fungi, like most plants, are unable to move about (never mind the fact that fungi are not photosynthetic and have little in common structurally with plants!). In the two-kingdom system, unicellular eukaryotes that move and ingest food—protozoans—were classified as animals. Those such as *Euglena* that move and are photosynthetic were claimed by both botanists and zoologists and showed up in both kingdoms.

Taxonomic schemes with more than two kingdoms gained broad acceptance in the late 1960s, when many biologists recognized five kingdoms: Monera (prokaryotes), Protista (a diverse kingdom consisting mostly of unicellular organisms), Plantae, Fungi, and Animalia. This system highlighted the two fundamentally different types of cells, prokaryotic and eukaryotic, and set the prokaryotes apart from all eukaryotes by placing them in their own kingdom, Monera.

However, phylogenies based on genetic data soon began to reveal a problem with this system: Some prokaryotes differ as much from each other as they do from eukaryotes. Such difficulties have led biologists to adopt a three-domain system. The three domains—Bacteria, Archaea, and Eukarya—are a taxonomic level higher than the kingdom level. The validity of these domains is supported by many studies, including a recent study that analyzed nearly 100 completely sequenced genomes.

The domain Bacteria contains most of the currently known prokaryotes, including the bacteria closely related to chloroplasts and mitochondria. The second domain, Archaea, consists of a diverse group of prokaryotic organisms that inhabit a wide variety of environments. Some archaea can use hydrogen as an energy source, and others were the chief source of the natural gas deposits that are found throughout Earth's crust. As you will read in Chapter 27, bacteria differ from archaea in many structural, biochemical, and physiological characteristics. The third domain, Eukarya, consists of all the organisms that have cells containing true nuclei. This domain includes many groups of single-celled organisms (see Chapter 28) as well as multicellular plants (Chapters 29 and 30), fungi (Chapter 31), and animals (Chapters 32–34). **Figure 26.21** represents one possible phylogenetic tree for the three domains and the many lineages they encompass.

The three-domain system highlights the fact that much of the history of life has been about single-celled organisms. The two prokaryotic domains consist entirely of single-celled organisms, and even in Eukarya, only the branches shown in red (plants, fungi, and animals) are dominated by multicellular organisms. Of the five kingdoms previously recognized by taxonomists, most biologists continue to recognize Plantae, Fungi, and Animalia, but not Monera and Protista. The kingdom Monera is obsolete because it would have members in two different domains. As you'll read in Chapter 28, the kingdom Protista has also crumbled because it is polyphyletic—it includes members that are more closely related to plants, fungi, or animals than to other protists.

A Simple Tree of All Life

The evolutionary relationships shown in Figure 26.21 can be summarized in a simpler tree (see the figure legend question). In this tree, the first major split in the history of life occurred when bacteria diverged from other organisms. If this tree is correct, eukaryotes and archaea are more closely related to each other than either is to bacteria.

This reconstruction of the tree of life is based largely on sequence comparisons of rRNA genes, which code for the RNA components of ribosomes. Because ribosomes are fundamental to the workings of the cell, rRNA genes have evolved so slowly that homologies between distantly related organisms

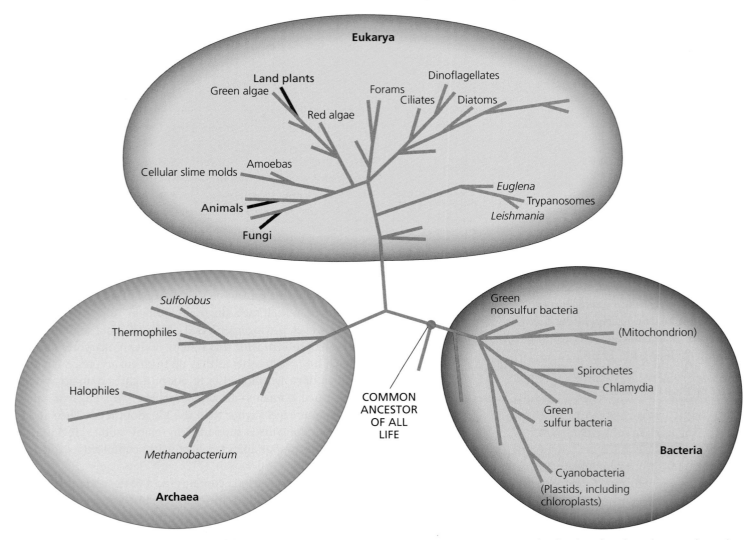

▲ **Figure 26.21 The three domains of life.** The phylogenetic tree shown here is based on rRNA gene sequences. Branch lengths are proportional to the amount of genetic change in each lineage. (To simplify the figure, only some branches are labeled.) In this diagram, the lineages within Eukarya that are dominated by multicellular organisms (plants, fungi, and animals) are shown in red. All other lineages consist solely or primarily of single-celled organisms.

DRAW IT Redraw this tree as a horizontal tree that has just three branches, one for each domain. Which domain was the first to diverge? Which is the sister domain to Eukarya?

can still be detected—making these genes very useful for determining evolutionary relationships between deep branches in the history of life. However, other genes reveal a different set of relationships. For example, researchers have found that many of the genes that influence metabolism in yeast (a unicellular eukaryote) are more similar to genes in the domain Bacteria than they are to genes in the domain Archaea—a finding that suggests that the eukaryotes may share a more recent common ancestor with bacteria than with archaea.

Comparisons of complete genomes from the three domains show that there have been substantial movements of genes between organisms in the different domains (Figure 26.22). These took place through **horizontal gene transfer**, a process in which genes are transferred from one genome to another through mechanisms such as exchange of transposable elements and plasmids, viral infection (see Chapter 19), and perhaps fusions of organisms. Recent research reinforces the view that horizontal gene transfer is important. For example, a 2008 analysis indicated that, on average, 80% of the genes in 181 prokaryotic genomes had moved between species at some point during the course of evolution. Because phylogenetic trees are based on the assumption that genes are passed vertically from one generation to the next, the occurrence of such horizontal transfer events helps to explain why trees built using different genes can give inconsistent results.

Is the Tree of Life Really a Ring?

Some biologists, including W. Ford Doolittle, interviewed on pages 534–535, have argued that horizontal gene transfer was

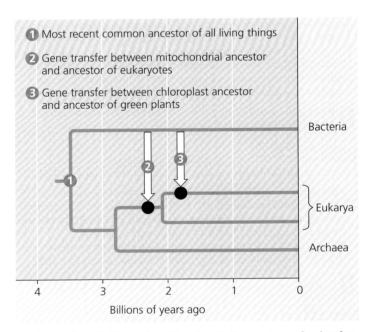

① Most recent common ancestor of all living things

② Gene transfer between mitochondrial ancestor and ancestor of eukaryotes

③ Gene transfer between chloroplast ancestor and ancestor of green plants

▲ **Figure 26.22 The role of horizontal gene transfer in the history of life.** This tree shows two major episodes of horizontal gene transfer, the dates of which are uncertain. It is known that many more such events occurred. (Because the tree is horizontal, the arrows representing "horizontal" transfer are vertical here.)

▲ **Figure 26.23 A ring of life.** In this hypothesis, the eukaryote lineage (orange) arose when an early archaean (teal) fused with an early bacterium (purple). Such an event is consistent with a "ring of life" but not with a tree of life. Three great domains (Archaea, Eukarya, and Bacteria) emerged from the ring and gave rise to the tremendous diversity of life we observe today.

so common that the early history of life should be represented as a tangled network of connected branches—not a simple, dichotomously branching tree like that in Figure 26.22. Others have suggested that relationships among early organisms are best represented by a ring, not a tree (Figure 26.23). In an analysis based on hundreds of genes, these researchers hypothesized that eukaryotes arose as a fusion between an early bacterium and an early archaean. If correct, eukaryotes are simultaneously most closely related to bacteria *and* archaea—an evolutionary relationship that cannot be depicted in a tree of life, but can be depicted in a *ring* of life.

Although scientists continue to debate whether early steps in the history of life are best represented as a tree, a ring, or a tangled web, in recent decades there have been many exciting discoveries about evolutionary events that occurred later in time. We'll explore such discoveries in the rest of this unit's chapters, beginning with Earth's earliest inhabitants, the prokaryotes.

CONCEPT CHECK 26.6

1. Why is the kingdom Monera no longer considered a valid taxon?
2. Explain why phylogenies based on different genes can yield different branching patterns for the tree of all life.
3. **WHAT IF?** Draw the three possible dichotomously branching trees showing evolutionary relationships for the domains Bacteria, Archaea, and Eukarya. Two of these trees have been supported by genetic data. Is it likely that the third tree might also receive such support? Explain your answer.

For suggested answers, see Appendix A.

26 CHAPTER REVIEW

SUMMARY OF KEY CONCEPTS

CONCEPT 26.1

Phylogenies show evolutionary relationships (pp. 537–540)

- Linnaeus's **binomial** classification system gives organisms two-part names: a **genus** plus a specific epithet.
- In the Linnaean system, species are grouped in increasingly broad taxa: Related genera are placed in the same family, families in orders, orders in classes, classes in phyla, phyla in kingdoms, and (more recently) kingdoms in domains.
- Systematists depict evolutionary relationships as branching **phylogenetic trees**. Many systematists propose that classification be based entirely on evolutionary relationships.

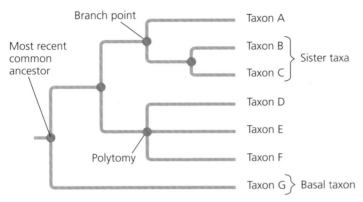

- Unless branch lengths are proportional to time or amount of genetic change, a phylogenetic tree indicates only patterns of descent.
- Much information can be learned about a species from its evolutionary history; hence, phylogenies are useful in a wide range of applications.

? *Humans and chimpanzees are sister species. Explain what that means.*

CONCEPT 26.2

Phylogenies are inferred from morphological and molecular data (pp. 540–542)

- Organisms with similar morphologies or DNA sequences are likely to be more closely related than organisms with very different structures and genetic sequences.
- To infer phylogeny, **homology** (similarity due to shared ancestry) must be distinguished from **analogy** (similarity due to convergent evolution).
- Computer programs are used to align comparable DNA sequences and to distinguish molecular homologies from coincidental matches between taxa that diverged long ago.

? *Why is it necessary to distinguish homology from analogy to infer phylogeny?*

CONCEPT 26.3

Shared characters are used to construct phylogenetic trees (pp. 542–548)

- A **clade** is a monophyletic grouping that includes an ancestral species and all of its descendants.

- Clades can be distinguished by their **shared derived characters**.

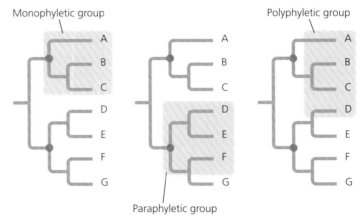

- Branch lengths can be drawn proportional to the amount of evolutionary change or time.
- Among phylogenies, the most parsimonious tree is the one that requires the fewest evolutionary changes. The most likely tree is the one based on the most likely pattern of changes.
- Well-supported phylogenetic hypotheses are consistent with a wide range of data.

? *Explain the logic of using shared derived characters to infer phylogeny.*

CONCEPT 26.4

An organism's evolutionary history is documented in its genome (pp. 548–549)

- **Orthologous genes** are homologous genes found in different species as a result of speciation. **Paralogous genes** are homologous genes within a species that result from gene duplication; such genes can diverge and potentially take on new functions.
- Distantly related species can have orthologous genes. The small variation in gene number in organisms of varying complexity suggests that genes are versatile and may have multiple functions.

? *When reconstructing phylogenies, is it better to compare orthologous or paralogous genes? Explain.*

CONCEPT 26.5

Molecular clocks help track evolutionary time (pp. 549–551)

- Some regions of DNA change at a rate consistent enough to serve as a **molecular clock**, in which the amount of genetic change is used to estimate the date of past evolutionary events. Other DNA regions change in a less predictable way.
- A molecular clock analysis suggests that the most common strain of HIV jumped from primates to humans in the 1930s.

? *Describe some assumptions and limitations of molecular clocks.*

CONCEPT 26.6

New information continues to revise our understanding of the tree of life (pp. 551–553)

- Past classification systems have given way to the current view of the tree of life, which consists of three great **domains**: Bacteria, Archaea, and Eukarya.

- Phylogenies based on rRNA genes suggest that eukaryotes are most closely related to archaea, while data from some other genes suggest a closer relationship to bacteria.
- Other genetic analyses suggest that eukaryotes arose as a fusion between a bacterium and an archaean, leading to a "ring of life" in which eukaryotes are equally closely related to bacteria and archaea.

? *Why was the five-kingdom system abandoned for a three-domain system?*

TESTING YOUR UNDERSTANDING

LEVEL 1: KNOWLEDGE/COMPREHENSION

1. In Figure 26.4, which similarly inclusive taxon descended from the same common ancestor as Canidae?
   a. Felidae
   b. Mustelidae
   c. Carnivora
   d. *Canis*
   e. *Lutra*

2. Three living species X, Y, and Z share a common ancestor T, as do extinct species U and V. A grouping that consists of species T, X, Y, and Z (but not U or V) makes up
   a. a valid taxon.
   b. a monophyletic clade.
   c. an ingroup, with species U as the outgroup.
   d. a paraphyletic group.
   e. a polyphyletic group.

3. In a comparison of birds and mammals, having four limbs is
   a. a shared ancestral character.
   b. a shared derived character.
   c. a character useful for distinguishing birds from mammals.
   d. an example of analogy rather than homology.
   e. a character useful for sorting bird species.

4. To apply parsimony to constructing a phylogenetic tree,
   a. choose the tree that assumes all evolutionary changes are equally probable.
   b. choose the tree in which the branch points are based on as many shared derived characters as possible.
   c. base phylogenetic trees only on the fossil record, as this provides the simplest explanation for evolution.
   d. choose the tree that represents the fewest evolutionary changes, in either DNA sequences or morphology.
   e. choose the tree with the fewest branch points.

LEVEL 2: APPLICATION/ANALYSIS

5. Based on this tree, which statement is *not* correct?

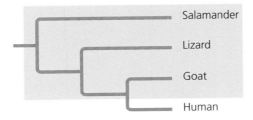

   a. The salamander lineage is a basal taxon.
   b. Salamanders are a sister group to the group containing lizards, goats, and humans.
   c. Salamanders are as closely related to goats as to humans.
   d. Lizards are more closely related to salamanders than to humans.
   e. The group highlighted by shading is paraphyletic.

6. If you were using cladistics to build a phylogenetic tree of cats, which of the following would be the best outgroup?
   a. lion   b. domestic cat   c. wolf   d. leopard   e. tiger

7. The relative lengths of the frog and mouse branches in the phylogeny in Figure 26.12 indicate that
   a. frogs evolved before mice.
   b. mice evolved before frogs.
   c. the genes of frogs and mice have only coincidental homoplasies.
   d. the homolog has evolved more slowly in mice.
   e. the homolog has evolved more rapidly in mice.

LEVEL 3: SYNTHESIS/EVALUATION

8. **EVOLUTION CONNECTION**
   Darwin suggested looking at a species' close relatives to learn what its ancestors may have been like. How does his suggestion anticipate recent methods, such as phylogenetic bracketing and the use of outgroups in cladistic analysis?

9. **SCIENTIFIC INQUIRY**
   DRAW IT (a) Draw a phylogenetic tree based on the first five characters in the table below. Place hatch marks on the tree to indicate the origin(s) of each of the six characters.
   (b) Assume that tuna and dolphins are sister species and redraw the phylogenetic tree accordingly. Place hatch marks on the tree to indicate the origin(s) of each of the six characters.
   (c) How many evolutionary changes are required in each tree? Which tree is most parsimonious?

Character	Lancelet (outgroup)	Lamprey	Tuna	Salamander	Turtle	Leopard	Dolphin
Backbone	0	1	1	1	1	1	1
Hinged jaw	0	0	1	1	1	1	1
Four limbs	0	0	0	1	1	1	1*
Amnion	0	0	0	0	1	1	1
Milk	0	0	0	0	0	1	1
Dorsal fin	0	0	1	0	0	0	1

*Although adult dolphins have only two obvious limbs (their flippers), as embryos they have two hind-limb buds, for a total of four limbs.

10. **WRITE ABOUT A THEME**
    The Cellular Basis of Life; The Genetic Basis of Life In a short essay (100–150 words), explain how these two themes—along with the process of descent with modification (see Chapter 22)—enable scientists to construct phylogenies that extend hundreds of millions of years back in time.

For selected answers, see Appendix A.

MasteringBIOLOGY® www.masteringbiology.com

1. MasteringBiology® Assignments
   Video Tutor Session Phylogenetic Trees
   Tutorial Constructing Phylogenetic Trees
   Activity Classification Schemes
   Questions Student Misconceptions • Reading Quiz • Multiple Choice • End-of-Chapter

2. eText
   Read your book online, search, take notes, highlight text, and more.

3. The Study Area
   Practice Tests • Cumulative Test • **BioFlix** 3-D Animations • MP3 Tutor Sessions • Videos • Activities • Investigations • Lab Media • Audio Glossary • Word Study Tools • Art

27

Bacteria and Archaea

▲ Figure 27.1 **Why is this lake's water pink?**

Masters of Adaptation

In the heat of summer, parts of Utah's Great Salt Lake turn pink **(Figure 27.1)**, a sign of waters so salty that they would dehydrate your skin if you took a dip. The salt concentration can reach 32%, nearly ten times that of seawater. Yet despite these harsh conditions, the dramatic color of these waters is caused not by minerals or other nonliving sources, but by living things. What organisms can live in such an inhospitable environment, and how do they do it?

The pink color in the Great Salt Lake comes from trillions of prokaryotes in the domains Archaea and Bacteria, including archaea in the genus *Halobacterium*. These archaea have red membrane pigments, some of which capture the light energy that drives ATP synthesis. *Halobacterium* species are among the most salt-tolerant organisms on Earth; they thrive in salinities that dehydrate and kill other cells. *Halobacterium* compensates for water lost through osmosis by pumping potassium ions (K^+) into the cell until the ionic concentration inside the cell matches the concentration outside.

Like *Halobacterium*, many other prokaryotes can tolerate extreme conditions. Examples include *Deinococcus radiodurans*, which can survive 3 million rads of radiation (3,000 times the dose fatal to humans), and *Picrophilus oshimae*, which can grow at a pH of 0.03 (acidic enough to dissolve metal). Other prokaryotes live in environments that are too cold or too hot for most other organisms, and some have even been found living in rocks 3.2 km (2 miles) below Earth's surface.

Prokaryotic species are also very well adapted to more "normal" habitats—the lands and waters in which most other species are found. Their ability to adapt to a broad range of habitats helps explain why prokaryotes are the most abundant organisms on Earth: The number of prokaryotes in a handful of fertile soil is greater than the number of people who have ever lived. In this chapter, we'll examine the adaptations, diversity, and enormous ecological impact of these tiny organisms.

CONCEPT **27.1**

Structural and functional adaptations contribute to prokaryotic success

As you read in Chapter 25, the first organisms to inhabit Earth were likely prokaryotes. Throughout their long evolutionary history, prokaryotic populations have been (and continue to be) subjected to natural selection in all kinds of environments, resulting in their enormous diversity today.

We'll begin by describing prokaryotes. Most prokaryotes are unicellular, although the cells of some species remain attached to each other after cell division. Prokaryotic cells typically have diameters of 0.5–5 μm, much smaller than the

10–100 μm diameter of many eukaryotic cells. (One notable exception, *Thiomargarita namibiensis*, can be 750 μm across—bigger than the dot on this i.) Prokaryotic cells have a variety of shapes **(Figure 27.2)**. Finally, although they are unicellular and small, prokaryotes are well organized, achieving all of an organism's life functions within a single cell.

(a) Spherical   **(b) Rod-shaped**   **(c) Spiral**

▲ **Figure 27.2 The most common shapes of prokaryotes.**
(a) Cocci (singular, *coccus*) are spherical prokaryotes. They occur singly, in pairs (diplococci), in chains of many cells (streptococci), and in clusters resembling bunches of grapes (staphylococci). **(b)** Bacilli (singular, *bacillus*) are rod-shaped prokaryotes. They are usually solitary, but in some forms the rods are arranged in chains (streptobacilli). **(c)** Spiral prokaryotes include spirilla, which range from comma-like shapes to loose coils, and spirochetes (shown here), which are corkscrew-shaped (colorized SEMs).

Cell-Surface Structures

A key feature of nearly all prokaryotic cells is the cell wall, which maintains cell shape, protects the cell, and prevents it from bursting in a hypotonic environment (see Chapter 7). In a hypertonic environment, most prokaryotes lose water and shrink away from their wall (plasmolyze), like other walled cells. Such water losses can inhibit cell reproduction. Thus, salt can be used to preserve foods because it causes prokaryotes to lose water, preventing them from rapidly multiplying.

The cell walls of prokaryotes differ in structure from those of eukaryotes. In eukaryotes that have cell walls, such as plants and fungi, the walls are usually made of cellulose or chitin (see Chapter 5). In contrast, most bacterial cell walls contain **peptidoglycan**, a polymer composed of modified sugars cross-linked by short polypeptides. This molecular fabric encloses the entire bacterium and anchors other molecules that extend from its surface. Archaeal cell walls contain a variety of polysaccharides and proteins but lack peptidoglycan.

Using a technique called the **Gram stain**, developed by the nineteenth-century Danish physician Hans Christian Gram, scientists can classify many bacterial species into two groups based on differences in cell wall composition. Samples are first stained with crystal violet dye and iodine, then rinsed in alcohol, and finally stained with a red dye such as safranin. The structure of a bacterium's cell wall determines the staining response **(Figure 27.3)**. **Gram-positive** bacteria have simpler walls with a relatively large amount of peptidoglycan. **Gram-negative** bacteria have less peptidoglycan and are structurally more complex, with an outer membrane that contains lipopolysaccharides (carbohydrates bonded to lipids).

▼ **Figure 27.3 Gram staining.**

(a) Gram-positive bacteria

Cell wall { Peptido-glycan layer

Plasma membrane

Gram-positive bacteria

Gram-positive bacteria have a thick cell wall made of peptidoglycan, which traps the crystal violet in the cytoplasm. The alcohol rinse does not remove the crystal violet, which masks the red safranin dye.

(b) Gram-negative bacteria

Gram-negative bacteria

Carbohydrate portion of lipopolysaccharide

Cell wall { Outer membrane / Peptido-glycan layer

Plasma membrane

Gram-negative bacteria have a thinner layer of peptidoglycan, and it is located in a layer between the plasma membrane and an outer membrane. The crystal violet is easily rinsed from the cytoplasm, and the cell appears pink or red from the dye.

10 μm

Bacterial cell wall

Bacterial capsule

Tonsil cell

200 nm

▲ **Figure 27.4 Capsule.** The polysaccharide capsule around this *Streptococcus* bacterium enables the prokaryote to attach to cells in the respiratory tract—in this colorized TEM, a tonsil cell.

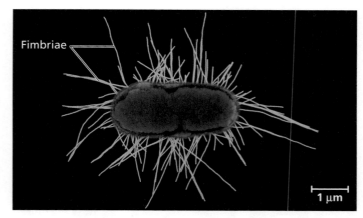

Fimbriae

1 μm

▲ **Figure 27.5 Fimbriae.** These numerous protein-containing appendages enable some prokaryotes to attach to surfaces or to other cells (colorized TEM).

Gram staining is a valuable tool in medicine for quickly determining if a patient's infection is due to gram-negative or to gram-positive bacteria. This information has treatment implications. The lipid portions of the lipopolysaccharides in the walls of many gram-negative bacteria are toxic, causing fever or shock. Furthermore, the outer membrane of a gram-negative bacterium helps protect it from the body's defenses. Gram-negative bacteria also tend to be more resistant than gram-positive species to antibiotics because the outer membrane impedes entry of the drugs. However, certain gram-positive species have virulent strains that are resistant to one or more antibiotics. (Figure 22.14 discusses one example: multidrug-resistant *Staphylococcus aureus*, which can cause lethal skin infections.)

The effectiveness of certain antibiotics, such as penicillin, derives from their inhibition of peptidoglycan cross-linking. The resulting cell wall may not be functional, particularly in gram-positive bacteria. Such drugs destroy many species of pathogenic bacteria without adversely affecting human cells, which do not have peptidoglycan.

The cell wall of many prokaryotes is surrounded by a sticky layer of polysaccharide or protein. This layer is called a **capsule** if it is dense and well-defined **(Figure 27.4)** or a *slime layer* if it is less well organized. Both kinds of sticky outer layers enable prokaryotes to adhere to their substrate or to other individuals in a colony. Some capsules and slime layers protect against dehydration, and some shield pathogenic prokaryotes from attacks by their host's immune system.

Some prokaryotes stick to their substrate or to one another by means of hairlike appendages called **fimbriae** (singular, *fimbria*) **(Figure 27.5)**. For example, the bacterium that causes gonorrhea, *Neisseria gonorrhoeae*, uses fimbriae to fasten itself to the mucous membranes of its host. Fimbriae are usually shorter and more numerous than **pili** (singular, *pilus*), appendages that pull two cells together prior to DNA transfer from one cell to the other (see Figure 27.12); pili are sometimes referred to as *sex pili*.

Motility

About half of all prokaryotes are capable of **taxis**, a directed movement toward or away from a stimulus (from the Greek *taxis*, to arrange). For example, prokaryotes that exhibit *chemotaxis* change their movement pattern in response to chemicals. They may move *toward* nutrients or oxygen (positive chemotaxis) or *away from* a toxic substance (negative chemotaxis). Some species can move at velocities exceeding 50 μm/sec—up to 50 times their body length per second. For perspective, consider that a person 1.7 m tall moving that fast would be running 306 km (190 miles) per hour!

Of the various structures that enable prokaryotes to move, the most common are flagella **(Figure 27.6)**. Flagella (singular, *flagellum*) may be scattered over the entire surface of the cell or concentrated at one or both ends. Prokaryotic flagella differ greatly from eukaryotic flagella: They are one-tenth the width and are not covered by an extension of the plasma membrane (see Figure 6.24). The flagella of prokaryotes are also very different in their molecular composition and their mechanism of propulsion. Among prokaryotes, bacterial and archaeal flagella are similar in size and rotation mechanism, but they are composed of different proteins. Overall, these structural and molecular comparisons suggest that the flagella of bacteria, archaea, and eukaryotes arose independently. Since the flagella of organisms in the three domains perform similar functions but probably are not related by common descent, it is likely that they are analogous, not homologous, structures.

Evolutionary Origins of Bacterial Flagella

The bacterial flagellum shown in Figure 27.6 has three main parts (the motor, hook, and filament) that are themselves composed of 42 different kinds of proteins. How could such a complex structure evolve? In fact, much evidence indicates that bacterial flagella originated as simpler structures that were modified in a stepwise fashion over time. As in the case of the

Flagellum

Filament

Hook

Motor

20 nm

Cell wall

Plasma membrane

Rod

Peptidoglycan layer

▲ **Figure 27.6 A prokaryotic flagellum.** The motor of a prokaryotic flagellum consists of a system of rings embedded in the cell wall and plasma membrane (TEM). ATP-driven pumps in the motor transport protons out of the cell. The diffusion of protons back into the cell provides the force that turns a curved hook and thereby causes the attached filament to rotate and propel the cell. (This diagram shows flagellar structures characteristic of gram-negative bacteria.)

human eye (see Concept 25.6), biologists asked whether a less complex version of the flagellum could still benefit its owner. Analyses of hundreds of bacterial genomes indicate that only half of the flagellum's protein components appear to be necessary for it to function; the others are inessential or not encoded in the genomes of some species. Of the 21 proteins required by all species studied to date, 19 are modified versions of proteins that perform other tasks in bacteria. For example, a set of 10 proteins in the motor are homologous to 10 similar proteins in a secretory system found in bacteria. (A secretory system is a protein complex that enables a cell to secrete certain macromolecules.)

Two other proteins in the motor are homologous to proteins that function in ion transport. The proteins that comprise the rod, hook, and filament are all related to each other and are descended from an ancestral protein that formed a pilus-like tube. These findings suggest that the bacterial flagellum evolved as other proteins were added to an ancestral secretory system. This is an example of *exaptation*, the process in which existing structures take on new functions through descent with modification.

Internal Organization and DNA

The cells of prokaryotes are simpler than those of eukaryotes in both their internal structure and the physical arrangement of their DNA (see Figure 6.5). Prokaryotic cells lack the complex compartmentalization found in eukaryotic cells. However, some prokaryotic cells do have specialized membranes that perform metabolic functions **(Figure 27.7)**. These membranes are usually infoldings of the plasma membrane.

The genome of a prokaryote is structurally different from a eukaryotic genome and in most cases has considerably less DNA. In the majority of prokaryotes, the genome consists of a circular chromosome with many fewer proteins than found in the linear chromosomes of eukaryotes **(Figure 27.8)**. Also

0.2 μm

Respiratory membrane

(a) Aerobic prokaryote

1 μm

Thylakoid membranes

(b) Photosynthetic prokaryote

▲ **Figure 27.7 Specialized membranes of prokaryotes.**
(a) Infoldings of the plasma membrane, reminiscent of the cristae of mitochondria, function in cellular respiration in some aerobic prokaryotes (TEM). **(b)** Photosynthetic prokaryotes called cyanobacteria have thylakoid membranes, much like those in chloroplasts (TEM).

Chromosome

Plasmids

1 μm

▲ **Figure 27.8 A prokaryotic chromosome and plasmids.** The thin, tangled loops surrounding this ruptured *E. coli* cell are parts of the cell's large, circular chromosome (colorized TEM). Three of the cell's plasmids, the much smaller rings of DNA, are also shown.

unlike eukaryotes, prokaryotes lack a membrane-bounded nucleus; their chromosome is located in the **nucleoid**, a region of cytoplasm that appears lighter than the surrounding cytoplasm in electron micrographs. In addition to its single chromosome, a typical prokaryotic cell may also have much smaller rings of independently replicating DNA molecules called **plasmids** (see Figure 27.8), most carrying only a few genes.

As explained in Chapters 16 and 17, DNA replication, transcription, and translation are fundamentally similar processes in prokaryotes and eukaryotes, although there are some differences. For example, prokaryotic ribosomes are slightly smaller than eukaryotic ribosomes and differ in their protein and RNA content. These differences allow certain antibiotics, such as erythromycin and tetracycline, to bind to ribosomes and block protein synthesis in prokaryotes but not in eukaryotes. As a result, people can use these antibiotics to kill or inhibit the growth of bacteria without harming themselves.

Reproduction and Adaptation

Prokaryotes are highly successful in part because of their potential to reproduce quickly in a favorable environment. By *binary fission* (see Figure 12.12), a single prokaryotic cell divides into 2 cells, which then divide into 4, 8, 16, and so on. Under optimal conditions, many prokaryotes can divide every 1–3 hours; some species can produce a new generation in only 20 minutes. If reproduction continued unchecked at this rate, a single prokaryotic cell could give rise to a colony outweighing Earth in only two days!

In reality, of course, prokaryotic reproduction is limited. The cells eventually exhaust their nutrient supply, poison themselves with metabolic wastes, face competition from other microorganisms, or are consumed by other organisms. For example, the well-studied bacterium *Escherichia coli* can divide every 20 minutes under ideal lab conditions, one reason it is used as a model organism in research. However, when growing in a human intestine, one of its natural environments, *E. coli* cells divide only once every 12–24 hours. But whether cell division occurs every 20 minutes or every few days, reproduction in prokaryotes draws attention to three key features of their biology: *They are small, they reproduce by binary fission, and they have short generation times.* As a result, prokaryotic populations can consist of many trillions of individuals—far more than populations of multicellular eukaryotes, such as plants and animals.

The ability of some prokaryotes to withstand harsh conditions also contributes to their success. Some, like *Halobacterium*, can survive in harsh environments because of particular biochemical adaptations; others, because of particular structural adaptations. Certain bacteria, for example, develop resistant cells called **endospores** when they lack an essential nutrient **(Figure 27.9)**. The original cell produces a copy of its chromosome and surrounds it with a tough multilayered structure,

▲ **Figure 27.9 An endospore.** *Bacillus anthracis*, the bacterium that causes the disease anthrax, produces endospores (TEM). An endospore's protective, multilayered coat helps it survive in the soil for years.

forming the endospore. Water is removed from the endospore, and its metabolism halts. The original cell then lyses, releasing the endospore. Most endospores are so durable that they can survive in boiling water; killing them requires heating lab equipment to 121°C under high pressure. In less hostile environments, endospores can remain dormant but viable for centuries, able to rehydrate and resume metabolism when their environment improves.

Finally, in part because of their short generation times, prokaryotic populations can evolve substantially in short periods of time. For example, in a remarkable study that spanned 20,000 generations (roughly eight years) of evolution, researchers at Michigan State University documented adaptive evolution in bacterial populations **(Figure 27.10)**. The ability of prokaryotes to adapt rapidly to new conditions highlights the point that although the structure of their cells is simpler than that of eukaryotic cells, prokaryotes are not "primitive" or "inferior" in an evolutionary sense. They are, in fact, highly evolved: For over 3.5 billion years, prokaryotic populations have responded successfully to many different types of environmental challenges. As we will see, one reason for this is that their populations harbor high levels of genetic diversity on which selection can act.

CONCEPT CHECK 27.1

1. Identify and explain at least two adaptations that enable prokaryotes to survive in environments too harsh for other organisms.
2. Contrast the cellular and DNA structures of prokaryotes and eukaryotes.
3. **MAKE CONNECTIONS** Suggest a hypothesis to explain why the thylakoid membranes of chloroplasts resemble those of cyanobacteria. Refer to Figure 6.18 (p. 111) and Figure 26.21 (p. 552).

For suggested answers, see Appendix A.

INQUIRY

Can prokaryotes evolve rapidly in response to environmental change?

EXPERIMENT Vaughn Cooper and Richard Lenski, of Michigan State University, tested the ability of *E. coli* populations to adapt to a new environment. They established 12 populations, each founded by a single cell from an *E. coli* strain, and followed these populations for 20,000 generations (3,000 days). To maintain a continual supply of resources, each day the researchers performed a *serial transfer*: They transferred 0.1 mL of each population to a new tube containing 9.9 mL of fresh growth medium. The growth medium used throughout the experiment provided a challenging environment that contained only low levels of glucose and other resources needed for growth.

Daily serial transfer

0.1 mL
(population sample)

Old tube
(discarded
after
transfer)

New tube
(9.9 mL
growth
medium)

Samples were periodically removed from the 12 populations and grown in competition with the common ancestral strain in the experimental (low-glucose) environment.

RESULTS The fitness of the experimental populations, as measured by the rate at which each population grew, increased rapidly for the first 5,000 generations (two years) and more slowly for the next 15,000 generations. The graph below shows the averages for the 12 populations.

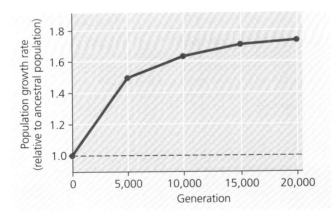

CONCLUSION Populations of *E. coli* continued to accumulate beneficial mutations for 20,000 generations, allowing rapid evolution of improved performance in their new environment.

SOURCE V. S. Cooper and R. E. Lenski, The population genetics of ecological specialization in evolving *Escherichia coli* populations, *Nature* 407:736–739 (2000).

WHAT IF? Suggest possible functions of the genes whose sequence or expression was altered as the experimental populations evolved in the low-glucose environment.

Rapid reproduction, mutation, and genetic recombination promote genetic diversity in prokaryotes

As we discussed in Unit Four, genetic variation is a prerequisite for natural selection to occur in a population. The diverse adaptations exhibited by prokaryotes suggest that their populations must have considerable genetic variation—and they do. For example, a ribosomal RNA gene can differ more between two strains of *E. coli* than it does between a human and a platypus. In this section, we'll examine three factors that give rise to high levels of genetic diversity in prokaryotes: rapid reproduction, mutation, and genetic recombination.

Rapid Reproduction and Mutation

In sexually reproducing species, the generation of a novel allele by a new mutation is rare for any particular gene. Instead, most of the genetic variation in sexual populations results from the way existing alleles are arranged in new combinations during meiosis and fertilization (see Chapter 13). Prokaryotes do not reproduce sexually, so at first glance their extensive genetic variation may seem puzzling. In fact, this variation can result from prokaryotes' rapid reproduction and mutation.

Consider a prokaryote reproducing by binary fission. After repeated rounds of division, most of the offspring cells are genetically identical to the original parent cell. However, if errors occur during DNA replication—such as insertions, deletions, or base-pair substitutions—some of the offspring cells may differ genetically. The probability of a spontaneous mutation occurring in a given *E. coli* gene averages only about one in 10 million (1×10^{-7}) per cell division. But among the 2×10^{10} new *E. coli* cells that arise each day in a person's intestine, there will be approximately $(2 \times 10^{10}) \times (1 \times 10^{-7}) = 2,000$ bacteria that have a mutation in that gene. The total number of mutations when all 4,300 *E. coli* genes are considered is about $4,300 \times 2,000 = 9$ million per day per human host.

The key point is that new mutations, though rare, can increase genetic diversity quickly in species with short generation times and large populations. This diversity, in turn, can lead to rapid evolution: Individuals that are genetically better equipped for their environment tend to survive and reproduce more prolifically than less fit individuals (see Figure 27.10).

Genetic Recombination

Although new mutations are a major source of variation in prokaryotic populations, additional diversity arises from *genetic recombination*, the combining of DNA from two sources. In eukaryotes, the sexual processes of meiosis and fertilization combine DNA from two individuals in a single zygote. But meiosis and fertilization do not occur in prokaryotes. Instead, three other mechanisms—transformation, transduction, and conjugation—can bring together prokaryotic DNA from different individuals (that is, cells). When the individuals are members of different species, this movement of genes from one organism to another is called *horizontal gene transfer*. Although scientists have found evidence that each of these mechanisms can transfer DNA within and between species in both domain Bacteria and domain Archaea, to date most of our knowledge comes from research on bacteria.

Transformation and Transduction

In **transformation**, the genotype and possibly phenotype of a prokaryotic cell are altered by the uptake of foreign DNA from its surroundings. For example, a harmless strain of *Streptococcus pneumoniae* can be transformed into pneumonia-causing cells if the cells are placed in a medium containing DNA from a pathogenic strain (see p. 306). This transformation occurs when a nonpathogenic cell takes up a piece of DNA carrying the allele for pathogenicity and replaces its own allele with the foreign allele, an exchange of homologous DNA segments. The cell is now a recombinant: Its chromosome contains DNA derived from two different cells.

For many years after transformation was discovered in laboratory cultures, most biologists thought the process to be too rare and haphazard to play an important role in natural bacterial populations. But researchers have since learned that many bacteria have cell-surface proteins that recognize DNA from closely related species and transport it into the cell. Once inside the cell, the foreign DNA can be incorporated into the genome by homologous DNA exchange.

In **transduction**, phages (from "bacteriophages," the viruses that infect bacteria) carry prokaryotic genes from one host cell to another. In most cases, transduction results from accidents that occur during the phage replicative cycle **(Figure 27.11)**. A virus that carries prokaryotic DNA may not be able to replicate because it lacks some or all of its own genetic material. However, the virus can attach to another prokaryotic cell (a recipient) and inject prokaryotic DNA acquired from the first cell (the donor). If some of this DNA is then incorporated into the recipient cell's chromosome by DNA recombination, a recombinant cell is formed.

Conjugation and Plasmids

In a process called **conjugation**, DNA is transferred between two prokaryotic cells (usually of the same species) that are temporarily joined. In bacteria, the DNA transfer is always one-way: One cell donates the DNA, and the other receives it. The best-understood mechanism is that used by *E. coli*, and we will focus on this organism for the rest of this section. In *E. coli*, a pilus of the donor cell attaches to the recipient **(Figure 27.12)**. The pilus then retracts, pulling the two cells together, much like a grappling hook. The next step is thought

1 A phage infects a bacterial cell that carries the A^+ and B^+ alleles on its chromosome (brown). This bacterium will be the "donor" cell.

Phage DNA

Donor cell

2 The phage DNA is replicated, and the cell makes many copies of the proteins encoded by its genes. Meanwhile, certain phage proteins halt the synthesis of proteins encoded by the host cell's DNA, and the host cell's DNA may be fragmented, as shown here.

3 As new phage particles assemble, a fragment of bacterial DNA carrying the A^+ allele happens to be packaged in a phage capsid.

A^+

Recombination

4 The phage carrying the A^+ allele from the donor cell infects a recipient cell with alleles A^- and B^-. Recombination between donor DNA (brown) and recipient DNA (green) occurs at two places (dotted lines).

Recipient cell

Recombinant cell

5 The genotype of the resulting recombinant cell (A^+B^-) differs from the genotypes of both the donor (A^+B^+) and the recipient (A^-B^-).

▲ **Figure 27.11 Transduction.** Phages may carry pieces of a bacterial chromosome from one cell (the donor) to another (the recipient). If recombination occurs after the transfer, genes from the donor may be incorporated into the recipient's genome.

? *Under what circumstances would transduction result in horizontal gene transfer?*

1 μm

Sex pilus

▲ **Figure 27.12 Bacterial conjugation.** The *E. coli* donor cell (left) extends a pilus that attaches to a recipient cell, a key first step in the transfer of DNA. The pilus is a flexible tube of protein subunits (TEM).

to be the formation of a temporary "mating bridge" between the two cells, through which the donor may transfer DNA to the recipient. This is an unsettled issue, however, and recent evidence indicates that DNA may pass directly through the pilus, which is hollow.

In either case, the ability to form pili and donate DNA during conjugation results from the presence of a particular piece of DNA called the **F factor** (F for *fertility*). The F factor of *E. coli* consists of about 25 genes, most required for the production of pili. The F factor can exist either as a plasmid or as a segment of DNA within the bacterial chromosome.

The F Factor as a Plasmid The F factor in its plasmid form is called the **F plasmid**. Cells containing the F plasmid, designated F$^+$ cells, function as DNA donors during conjugation. Cells lacking the F factor, designated F$^-$, function as DNA re-

cipients during conjugation. The F$^+$ condition is transferable in the sense that an F$^+$ cell converts an F$^-$ cell to F$^+$ if a copy of the entire F$^+$ plasmid is transferred **(Figure 27.13a)**.

The F Factor in the Chromosome Chromosomal genes can be transferred during conjugation when the donor cell's F factor is integrated into the chromosome. A cell with the F factor built into its chromosome is called an *Hfr cell* (for *h*igh *f*requency of *r*ecombination). Like an F$^+$ cell, an Hfr cell functions as a donor during conjugation with an F$^-$ cell **(Figure 27.13b)**. When chromosomal DNA from an Hfr cell enters an F$^-$ cell, homologous regions of the Hfr and F$^-$ chromosomes may align, allowing segments of their DNA to be exchanged. This results in the production of a recombinant bacterium that has genes derived from two different cells—a new genetic variant on which evolution can act.

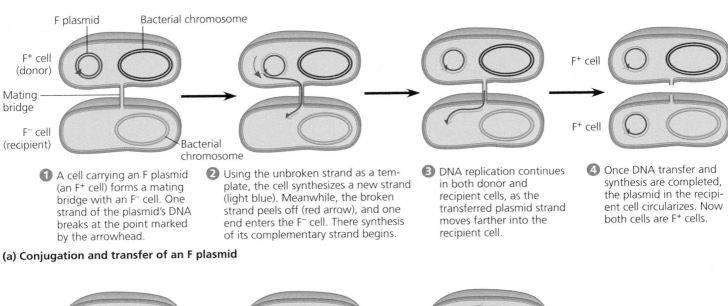

(a) Conjugation and transfer of an F plasmid

1. A cell carrying an F plasmid (an F$^+$ cell) forms a mating bridge with an F$^-$ cell. One strand of the plasmid's DNA breaks at the point marked by the arrowhead.

2. Using the unbroken strand as a template, the cell synthesizes a new strand (light blue). Meanwhile, the broken strand peels off (red arrow), and one end enters the F$^-$ cell. There synthesis of its complementary strand begins.

3. DNA replication continues in both donor and recipient cells, as the transferred plasmid strand moves farther into the recipient cell.

4. Once DNA transfer and synthesis are completed, the plasmid in the recipient cell circularizes. Now both cells are F$^+$ cells.

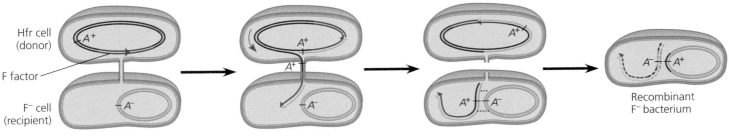

(b) Conjugation and transfer of part of an Hfr bacterial chromosome, resulting in recombination

1. In an Hfr cell, the F factor (dark blue) is integrated into the bacterial chromosome. Since an Hfr cell has all of the F-factor genes, it can form a mating bridge with an F$^-$ cell and transfer DNA.

2. A single strand of the F factor breaks and begins to move through the bridge. DNA replication occurs in both donor and recipient cells, resulting in double-stranded DNA (daughter strands shown in lighter color).

3. The mating bridge usually breaks before the entire chromosome is transferred. DNA recombination (indicated by dotted lines) can result in the exchange of homologous genes between the transferred DNA (brown) and the recipient's chromosome (green).

4. Cellular enzymes degrade any linear DNA not incorporated into the chromosome. The recipient cell, with a new combination of genes but no F factor, is now a recombinant F$^-$ cell.

▲ **Figure 27.13 Conjugation and recombination in *E. coli*.** The DNA replication that accompanies transfer of an F plasmid or part of an Hfr bacterial chromosome is called *rolling circle replication*. In effect, the intact circular parental DNA strand "rolls" as its other strand peels off and a new complementary strand is synthesized.

R Plasmids and Antibiotic Resistance During the 1950s in Japan, physicians started noticing that some hospital patients with bacterial dysentery, which produces severe diarrhea, did not respond to antibiotics that had generally been effective in the past. Apparently, resistance to these antibiotics had evolved in certain strains of *Shigella*, the bacterium that causes the disease.

Eventually, researchers began to identify the specific genes that confer antibiotic resistance in *Shigella* and other pathogenic bacteria. Sometimes, mutation in a chromosomal gene of the pathogen can confer resistance. For example, a mutation in one gene may make it less likely that the pathogen will transport a particular antibiotic into its cell. Mutation in a different gene may alter the intracellular target protein for an antibiotic molecule, reducing its inhibitory effect. In other cases, bacteria have "resistance genes," which code for enzymes that specifically destroy or otherwise hinder the effectiveness of certain antibiotics, such as tetracycline or ampicillin. Such resistance genes are carried by plasmids known as **R plasmids** (R for *resistance*).

Exposing a bacterial population to a specific antibiotic, whether in a laboratory culture or within a host organism, will kill antibiotic-sensitive bacteria but not those that happen to have R plasmids with genes that counter the antibiotic. Under these circumstances, we would predict that natural selection would cause the fraction of the bacterial population carrying genes for antibiotic resistance to increase, and that is exactly what happens. The medical consequences are also predictable: As you've read, resistant strains of pathogens are becoming more common, making the treatment of certain bacterial infections more difficult. The problem is compounded by the fact that many R plasmids, like F plasmids, have genes that encode pili and enable DNA transfer from one bacterial cell to another by conjugation. Making the problem still worse, some R plasmids carry as many as ten genes for resistance to that many antibiotics.

CONCEPT CHECK 27.2

1. What features of prokaryotes make it likely that considerable genetic variation will be added to their populations in each generation?
2. Distinguish between the three mechanisms of transferring DNA from one bacterial cell to another.
3. In a rapidly changing environment, which bacterial population would likely be more successful, one that includes individuals capable of conjugation or one that does not? Explain.
4. **WHAT IF?** If a nonpathogenic bacterium were to acquire resistance to antibiotics, could this strain pose a health risk to people? Explain. In general, how does DNA transfer among bacteria affect the spread of resistance genes?

For suggested answers, see Appendix A.

CONCEPT **27.3**

Diverse nutritional and metabolic adaptations have evolved in prokaryotes

The extensive genetic variation found in prokaryotic populations is reflected in the diverse nutritional adaptations of prokaryotes. Like all organisms, prokaryotes can be categorized by how they obtain energy and the carbon used in building the organic molecules that make up cells. Every type of nutrition observed in eukaryotes is represented among prokaryotes, along with some nutritional modes unique to prokaryotes. In fact, prokaryotes have an astounding range of metabolic adaptations, much broader than that found in eukaryotes.

Organisms that obtain energy from light are called *phototrophs*, and those that obtain energy from chemicals are called *chemotrophs*. Organisms that need only CO_2 in some form as a carbon source are called *autotrophs*. In contrast, *heterotrophs* require at least one organic nutrient, such as glucose, to make other organic compounds. Combining possible energy sources and carbon sources results in four major modes of nutrition, summarized in **Table 27.1**.

The Role of Oxygen in Metabolism

Prokaryotic metabolism also varies with respect to oxygen (O_2). **Obligate aerobes** must use O_2 for cellular respiration (see Chapter 9) and cannot grow without it. **Obligate anaerobes**, on the other hand, are poisoned by O_2. Some obligate anaerobes live exclusively by fermentation; others extract chemical energy by **anaerobic respiration**, in which substances other than O_2, such as nitrate ions (NO_3^-) or sulfate ions (SO_4^{2-}), accept electrons at the "downhill" end of electron transport chains. **Facultative anaerobes** use O_2 if it is present but can also carry out fermentation or anaerobic respiration in an anaerobic environment.

Nitrogen Metabolism

Nitrogen is essential for the production of amino acids and nucleic acids in all organisms. Whereas eukaryotes can obtain nitrogen from only a limited group of nitrogen compounds, prokaryotes can metabolize nitrogen in a wide variety of forms. For example, some cyanobacteria and some methanogens (a group of archaea) convert atmospheric nitrogen (N_2) to ammonia (NH_3), a process called **nitrogen fixation**. The cells can then incorporate this "fixed" nitrogen into amino acids and other organic molecules. In terms of their nutrition, nitrogen-fixing cyanobacteria are some of the most self-sufficient organisms, since they need only light, CO_2, N_2, water, and some minerals to grow.

Nitrogen fixation by prokaryotes has a large impact on other organisms. For example, nitrogen-fixing prokaryotes can increase the nitrogen available to plants, which cannot use

Table 27.1 Major Nutritional Modes			
Mode	Energy Source	Carbon Source	Types of Organisms
AUTOTROPH			
Photoautotroph	Light	CO_2, HCO_3^-, or related compound	Photosynthetic prokaryotes (for example, cyanobacteria); plants; certain protists (for example, algae)
Chemoautotroph	Inorganic chemicals (such as H_2S, NH_3, or Fe^{2+})	CO_2, HCO_3^-, or related compound	Unique to certain prokaryotes (for example, *Sulfolobus*)
HETEROTROPH			
Photoheterotroph	Light	Organic compounds	Unique to certain aquatic and salt-loving prokaryotes (for example, *Rhodobacter*, *Chloroflexus*)
Chemoheterotroph	Organic compounds	Organic compounds	Many prokaryotes (for example, *Clostridium*) and protists; fungi; animals; some plants

atmospheric nitrogen but can use the nitrogen compounds that the prokaryotes produce from ammonia.

Metabolic Cooperation

Cooperation between prokaryotic cells allows them to use environmental resources they could not use as individual cells. In some cases, this cooperation takes place between specialized cells of a filament. For instance, the cyanobacterium *Anabaena* has genes that encode proteins for photosynthesis and for nitrogen fixation, but a single cell cannot carry out both processes at the same time. The reason is that photosynthesis produces O_2, which inactivates the enzymes involved in nitrogen fixation. Instead of living as isolated cells, *Anabaena* forms filamentous chains **(Figure 27.14)**. Most cells in a filament carry out only photosynthesis, while a few specialized cells called **heterocysts** (sometimes called *heterocytes*) carry out only nitrogen fixation. Each heterocyst is surrounded by a thickened cell wall that restricts entry of O_2 produced by neighboring photosynthetic cells. Intercellular connections allow heterocysts to transport fixed nitrogen to neighboring cells and to receive carbohydrates.

Metabolic cooperation between different prokaryotic species often occurs in surface-coating colonies known as **biofilms**. Cells in a biofilm secrete signaling molecules that recruit nearby cells, causing the colonies to grow. The cells also produce polysaccharides and proteins that stick the cells to the substrate and to one another. Channels in the biofilm allow nutrients to reach cells in the interior and wastes to be expelled. Biofilms are common in nature, but they can cause problems by contaminating industrial products and medical equipment and contributing to tooth decay and more serious health problems. Altogether, damage caused by biofilms costs billions of dollars annually.

In another example of cooperation between prokaryotes, sulfate-consuming bacteria coexist with methane-consuming archaea in ball-shaped aggregates on the ocean floor. The bacteria appear to use the archaea's waste products, such as organic compounds and hydrogen. In turn, the bacteria produce sulfur compounds that the archaea use as oxidizing agents when they consume methane in the absence of oxygen. This partnership has global ramifications: Each year, these archaea consume an estimated 300 billion kilograms of methane, a major contributor to the greenhouse effect.

CONCEPT CHECK 27.3

1. Distinguish between the four major modes of nutrition, noting which are unique to prokaryotes.
2. A bacterium requires only the amino acid methionine as an organic nutrient and lives in lightless caves. What mode of nutrition does it employ? Explain.
3. **WHAT IF?** Describe what you might eat for a typical meal if humans, like cyanobacteria, could fix nitrogen.

For suggested answers, see Appendix A.

CONCEPT 27.4

Molecular systematics is illuminating prokaryotic phylogeny

Until the late 20th century, systematists based prokaryotic taxonomy on phenotypic criteria such as shape, motility, nutritional mode, and response to Gram staining. These criteria are still valuable in certain contexts, such as the rapid identification of pathogenic bacteria cultured from a patient's blood. But

▲ **Figure 27.14 Metabolic cooperation in a prokaryote.** In the filamentous cyanobacterium *Anabaena*, cells called heterocysts fix nitrogen, while the other cells carry out photosynthesis (LM). *Anabaena* is found in many freshwater lakes.

when it comes to prokaryotic phylogeny, comparing these characteristics does not reveal a clear evolutionary history. Applying molecular systematics to the investigation of prokaryotic phylogeny, however, has led to some dramatic conclusions.

Lessons from Molecular Systematics

As discussed in Chapter 26, microbiologists began comparing the sequences of prokaryotic genes in the 1970s. Using small-subunit ribosomal RNA as a marker for evolutionary relationships, Carl Woese and his colleagues concluded that many prokaryotes once classified as bacteria are actually more closely related to eukaryotes and belong in a domain of their own: Archaea. Microbiologists have since analyzed larger amounts of genetic data—including hundreds of entire genomes—and have concluded that a few traditional taxonomic groups, such as cyanobacteria, do appear to be monophyletic. However, other groups, such as gram-negative bacteria, are scattered throughout several lineages. **Figure 27.15** shows one phylogenetic hypothesis for some of the major taxa of prokaryotes based on molecular systematics.

One lesson from studying prokaryotic phylogeny is that the genetic diversity of prokaryotes is immense. When researchers began to sequence the genes of prokaryotes, they could investigate only the small fraction of species that could be cultured in the laboratory. In the 1980s, researchers began using the polymerase chain reaction (PCR; see Chapter 20) to analyze the genes of prokaryotes collected from the environment (such as from soil or water samples). Such "genetic prospecting" is now widely used; in fact, today entire prokaryotic genomes can be obtained from environmental samples using *metagenomics* (see Chapter 21). Each year these techniques add new branches to the tree of life. While only about 7,800 prokaryotic species have been assigned scientific names, a single handful of soil could contain 10,000 prokaryotic species by some estimates. Taking full stock of this diversity will require many years of research.

Another important lesson from molecular systematics is the apparent significance of horizontal gene transfer in the evolution of prokaryotes. Over hundreds of millions of years, prokaryotes have acquired genes from even distantly related species, and they continue to do so today. As a result, significant portions of the genomes of many prokaryotes are actually mosaics of genes imported from other species. As we saw in Chapter 26, such gene transfers can make it difficult to determine the root of the tree of life. Still, it is clear that for billions of years, the prokaryotes have evolved in two separate lineages, the archaea and the bacteria (see Figure 27.15).

Archaea

Archaea share certain traits with bacteria and other traits with eukaryotes **(Table 27.2)**. However, archaea also have many unique characteristics, as we would expect in a taxon that has followed a separate evolutionary path for so long.

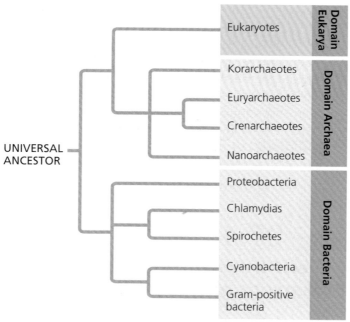

▲ **Figure 27.15 A simplified phylogeny of prokaryotes.** This phylogenetic tree based on molecular data shows one of several debated hypotheses of the relationships between the major prokaryotic groups discussed in this chapter. Within Archaea, the placement of the korarchaeotes and nanoarchaeotes remains unclear.

Table 27.2 A Comparison of the Three Domains of Life

CHARACTERISTIC	DOMAIN		
	Bacteria	**Archaea**	**Eukarya**
Nuclear envelope	Absent	Absent	Present
Membrane-enclosed organelles	Absent	Absent	Present
Peptidoglycan in cell wall	Present	Absent	Absent
Membrane lipids	Unbranched hydrocarbons	Some branched hydrocarbons	Unbranched hydrocarbons
RNA polymerase	One kind	Several kinds	Several kinds
Initiator amino acid for protein synthesis	Formyl-methionine	Methionine	Methionine
Introns in genes	Very rare	Present in some genes	Present in many genes
Response to the antibiotics streptomycin and chloramphenicol	Growth inhibited	Growth not inhibited	Growth not inhibited
Histones associated with DNA	Absent	Present in some species	Present
Circular chromosome	Present	Present	Absent
Growth at temperatures > 100°C	No	Some species	No

The first prokaryotes assigned to domain Archaea live in environments so extreme that few other organisms can survive there. Such organisms are called **extremophiles**, meaning "lovers" of extreme conditions (from the Greek *philos*, lover), and include extreme halophiles and extreme thermophiles.

Extreme halophiles (from the Greek *halo*, salt) live in highly saline environments, such as the Great Salt Lake and the Dead Sea (see Figure 27.1). Some species merely tolerate salinity, while others require an environment that is several times saltier than seawater (which has a salinity of 3.5%). For example, the proteins and cell wall of *Halobacterium* have unusual features that improve function in extremely salty environments but render these organisms incapable of survival if the salinity drops below 9%.

Extreme thermophiles (from the Greek *thermos*, hot) thrive in very hot environments **(Figure 27.16)**. For example, archaea in the genus *Sulfolobus* live in sulfur-rich volcanic springs as hot as 90°C. At temperatures this high, the cells of most organisms die because, for example, their DNA does not remain in a double helix and many of their proteins denature. *Sulfolobus* and other extreme thermophiles avoid this fate because their DNA and proteins have adaptations that make them stable at high temperatures. One extreme thermophile that lives near deep-sea hot springs called *hydrothermal vents* is informally known as "strain 121," since it can reproduce even at 121°C. Another extreme thermophile, *Pyrococcus furiosus*, is used in biotechnology as a source of DNA polymerase for the PCR technique (see Chapter 20).

Other archaea live in more moderate environments. Consider the **methanogens**, archaea that release methane as a byproduct of their unique ways of obtaining energy. Many methanogens use CO_2 to oxidize H_2, a process that produces both energy and methane waste. Among the strictest of anaerobes, methanogens are poisoned by O_2. Although some methanogens live in extreme environments, such as under kilometers of ice in Greenland, others live in swamps and marshes where other microorganisms have consumed all the O_2. The "marsh gas" found in such environments is the methane released by these archaea. Other species of methanogens inhabit the anaerobic environment within the guts of cattle, termites, and other herbivores, playing an essential role in the nutrition of these animals. Methanogens also have an important application as decomposers in sewage treatment facilities.

Many extreme halophiles and all known methanogens are archaea in the clade Euryarchaeota (from the Greek *eurys*, broad, a reference to the habitat range of these prokaryotes). The euryarchaeotes also include some extreme thermophiles, though most thermophilic species belong to a second clade, Crenarchaeota (*cren* means "spring," such as a hydrothermal spring). Recently, genetic prospecting has revealed many species of euryarchaeotes and crenarchaeotes that are not extremophiles. These archaea exist in habitats ranging from farm soils to lake sediments to the surface waters of the open ocean.

New findings continue to update the picture of archaeal phylogeny. In 1996, researchers sampling a hot spring in Yellowstone National Park discovered archaea that do not appear to belong to either Euryarchaeota or Crenarchaeota. They placed these archaea in a new clade, Korarchaeota (from the Greek *koron*, young man). In 2002, researchers exploring hydrothermal vents off the coast of Iceland discovered archaeal cells only 0.4 μm in diameter attached to a much larger crenarchaeote. The genome of the smaller archaean is one of the smallest known of any organism, containing only 500,000 base pairs. Genetic analysis indicates that this prokaryote belongs to a fourth archaeal clade, Nanoarchaeota (from the Greek *nanos*, dwarf). Within a year after this clade was named, three other DNA sequences from nanoarchaeote species were isolated: one from Yellowstone's hot springs, one from hot springs in Siberia, and one from a hydrothermal vent in the Pacific. As prospecting continues, it seems likely that the tree in Figure 27.15 will undergo further changes.

Bacteria

Bacteria include the vast majority of prokaryotic species of which most people are aware, from the pathogenic species that cause strep throat and tuberculosis to the beneficial species used to make Swiss cheese and yogurt. Every major mode of nutrition and metabolism is represented among bacteria, and even a small taxonomic group of bacteria may contain species exhibiting many different nutritional modes. As we'll see, the diverse nutritional and metabolic capabilities of bacteria—and archaea—are behind the great impact of these tiny organisms on Earth and its life. Examine **Figure 27.17**, on the following two pages, for a closer look at several major groups of bacteria.

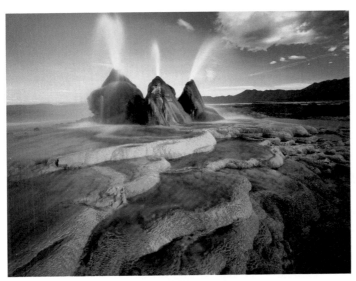

▲ **Figure 27.16 Extreme thermophiles.** Orange and yellow colonies of thermophilic prokaryotes grow in the hot water of a Nevada geyser.

MAKE CONNECTIONS *Review the discussion of enzymes in Concept 8.4 (pp. 155–156). How might the enzymes of thermophiles differ from those of other organisms?*

Exploring Major Groups of Bacteria

Proteobacteria

This large and diverse clade of gram-negative bacteria includes photo-autotrophs, chemoautotrophs, and heterotrophs. Some proteobacteria are anaerobic, while others are aerobic. Molecular systematists currently recognize five subgroups of proteobacteria; the phylogenetic tree at right shows their relationships based on molecular data.

Alpha
Beta
Gamma } Proteobacteria
Delta
Epsilon

Subgroup: Alpha Proteobacteria

Many of the species in this subgroup are closely associated with eukaryotic hosts. For example, *Rhizobium* species live in nodules within the roots of legumes (plants of the pea/bean family), where the bacteria convert atmospheric N_2 to compounds the host plant can use to make proteins. Species in the genus *Agrobacterium* produce tumors in plants; genetic engineers use these bacteria to carry foreign DNA into the genomes of crop plants (see Figure 20.26). As explained in Chapter 25, scientists hypothesize that mitochondria evolved from aerobic alpha proteobacteria through endosymbiosis.

Rhizobium (arrows) inside a root cell of a legume (TEM)

2.5 μm

Subgroup: Beta Proteobacteria

This nutritionally diverse subgroup includes *Nitrosomonas*, a genus of soil bacteria that play an important role in nitrogen recycling by oxidizing ammonium (NH_4^+), producing nitrite (NO_2^-) as a waste product.

Nitrosomonas (colorized TEM)

1 μm

Subgroup: Gamma Proteobacteria

This subgroup's autotrophic members include sulfur bacteria such as *Thiomargarita namibiensis* (see p. 557), which obtain energy by oxidizing H_2S, producing sulfur as a waste product (the small globules in the photograph at right). Some heterotrophic gamma proteobacteria are pathogens; for example, *Legionella* causes Legionnaires' disease, *Salmonella* is responsible for some cases of food poisoning, and *Vibrio cholerae* causes cholera. *Escherichia coli*, a common resident of the intestines of humans and other mammals, normally is not pathogenic.

Thiomargarita namibiensis containing sulfur wastes (LM)

200 μm

Subgroup: Delta Proteobacteria

This subgroup includes the slime-secreting myxobacteria. When the soil dries out or food is scarce, the cells congregate into a fruiting body that releases resistant "myxospores." These cells found new colonies in favorable environments. Another group of delta proteobacteria, the bdellovibrios, attack other bacteria, charging at up to 100 μm/sec (comparable to a human running 240 km/hr). The attack begins when a bdellovibrio attaches to specific molecules found on the outer covering of some bacterial species. The bdellovibrio then drills into its prey by using digestive enzymes and spinning at 100 revolutions per second.

Fruiting bodies of *Chondromyces crocatus*, a myxobacterium (SEM)

300 μm

Subgroup: Epsilon Proteobacteria

Most species in this subgroup are pathogenic to humans or other animals. Epsilon proteobacteria include *Campylobacter*, which causes blood poisoning and intestinal inflammation, and *Helicobacter pylori*, which causes stomach ulcers.

Helicobacter pylori (colorized TEM)

2 μm

Chlamydias

These parasites can survive only within animal cells, depending on their hosts for resources as basic as ATP. The gram-negative walls of chlamydias are unusual in that they lack peptidoglycan. One species, *Chlamydia trachomatis*, is the most common cause of blindness in the world and also causes nongonococcal urethritis, the most common sexually transmitted disease in the United States.

Chlamydia (arrows) inside an animal cell (colorized TEM)

2.5 μm

Spirochetes

These helical heterotrophs spiral through their environment by means of rotating, internal, flagellum-like filaments. Many spirochetes are free-living, but others are notorious pathogenic parasites: *Treponema pallidum* causes syphilis, and *Borrelia burgdorferi* causes Lyme disease (see Figure 27.20).

Leptospira, a spirochete (colorized TEM)

5 μm

Cyanobacteria

These photoautotrophs are the only prokaryotes with plantlike, oxygen-generating photosynthesis. (In fact, as we'll discuss in Chapter 28, chloroplasts likely evolved from an endosymbiotic cyanobacterium.) Both solitary and filamentous cyanobacteria are abundant components of freshwater and marine *phytoplankton*, the collection of photosynthetic organisms that drift near the water's surface. Some filaments have cells specialized for nitrogen fixation, the process that incorporates atmospheric N_2 into inorganic compounds that can be used in the synthesis of amino acids and other organic molecules (see Figure 27.14).

Oscillatoria, a filamentous cyanobacterium

40 μm

Gram-Positive Bacteria

Gram-positive bacteria rival the proteobacteria in diversity. Species in one subgroup, the actinomycetes (from the Greek *mykes*, fungus, for which these bacteria were once mistaken), form colonies containing branched chains of cells. Two species of actinomycetes cause tuberculosis and leprosy. However, most actinomycetes are free-living species that help decompose the organic matter in soil; their secretions are partly responsible for the "earthy" odor of rich soil. Soil-dwelling species in the genus *Streptomyces* (top) are cultured by pharmaceutical companies as a source of many antibiotics, including streptomycin.

Gram-positive bacteria include many solitary species, such as *Bacillus anthracis* (see Figure 27.9), which causes anthrax, and *Clostridium botulinum*, which causes botulism. The various species of *Staphylococcus* and *Streptococcus* are also gram-positive bacteria.

Mycoplasmas (bottom) are the only bacteria known to lack cell walls. They are also the tiniest known cells, with diameters as small as 0.1 μm, only about five times as large as a ribosome. Mycoplasmas have small genomes—*Mycoplasma genitalium* has only 517 genes, for example. Many mycoplasmas are free-living soil bacteria, but others are pathogens.

Streptomyces, the source of many antibiotics (SEM)

 5 μm

Hundreds of mycoplasmas covering a human fibroblast cell (colorized SEM)

2 μm

1. Explain how molecular systematics has contributed to our understanding of prokaryotic phylogeny.
2. How has genetic prospecting contributed to our understanding of prokaryotic diversity and phylogeny?
3. **WHAT IF?** What would the discovery of a bacterial species that is a methanogen imply about the evolution of the methane-producing pathway?

For suggested answers, see Appendix A.

CONCEPT 27.5

Prokaryotes play crucial roles in the biosphere

If humans were to disappear from the planet tomorrow, life on Earth would change for many species, but few would be driven to extinction. In contrast, prokaryotes are so important to the biosphere that if they were to disappear, the prospects of survival for many other species would be dim.

Chemical Recycling

The atoms that make up the organic molecules in all living things were at one time part of inorganic substances in the soil, air, and water. Sooner or later, those atoms will return there. Ecosystems depend on the continual recycling of chemical elements between the living and nonliving components of the environment, and prokaryotes play a major role in this process. For example, chemoheterotrophic prokaryotes function as **decomposers**, breaking down dead organisms as well as waste products and thereby unlocking supplies of carbon, nitrogen, and other elements. Without the actions of prokaryotes and other decomposers such as fungi, all life would cease. (See Chapter 55 for a detailed discussion of chemical cycles.)

Prokaryotes also convert some molecules to forms that can be taken up by other organisms. Cyanobacteria and other autotrophic prokaryotes use CO_2 to make organic compounds such as sugars, which are then passed up through food chains. Cyanobacteria also produce atmospheric O_2, and a variety of prokaryotes fix atmospheric nitrogen (N_2) into forms that other organisms can use to make the building blocks of proteins and nucleic acids. Under some conditions, prokaryotes can increase the availability of nutrients that plants require for growth, such as nitrogen, phosphorus, and potassium **(Figure 27.18)**. Prokaryotes can also *decrease* the availability of key plant nutrients; this occurs when prokaryotes "immobilize" nutrients by using them to synthesize molecules that remain within their cells. Thus, prokaryotes can have complex effects on soil nutrient concentrations. In marine environments, a 2005 study found that an archaean from the clade Crenarchaeota can perform nitrification, a key

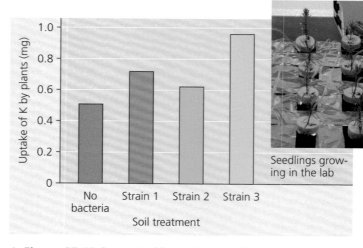

▲ **Figure 27.18 Impact of bacteria on soil nutrient availability.** Pine seedlings grown in sterile soils to which one of three strains of the bacterium *Burkholderia glathei* had been added absorbed more potassium (K) than did seedlings grown in soil without any bacteria. Other results (not shown) demonstrated that strain 3 increased the amount of K released from mineral crystals to the soil.

WHAT IF? *Estimate the average uptake of K for seedlings in soils with bacteria. What would you expect this average to be if bacteria had no effect on nutrient availability?*

step in the nitrogen cycle. Crenarchaeotes dominate the oceans by numbers, comprising an estimated 10^{28} cells. The sheer abundance of these organisms suggests that they may have a large impact on the global nitrogen cycle; scientists are investigating this possibility.

Ecological Interactions

Prokaryotes play a central role in many ecological interactions. Consider **symbiosis** (from a Greek word meaning "living together"), an ecological relationship in which two species live in close contact with each other. Prokaryotes often form symbiotic associations with much larger organisms. In general, the larger organism in a symbiotic relationship is known as the **host**, and the smaller is known as the **symbiont**. There are many cases in which a prokaryote and its host participate in **mutualism**, an ecological interaction between two species in which both benefit **(Figure 27.19)**. Other interactions take the form of **commensalism**, an ecological relationship in which one species benefits while the other is not harmed or helped in any significant way. For example, more than 150 bacterial species live on the surface of your body, covering portions of your skin with up to 10 million cells per square centimeter. Some of these species are commensalists: You provide them with food, such as the oils that exude from your pores, and a place to live, while they do not harm or benefit you. Finally, some prokaryotes engage in **parasitism**, an ecological relationship in which a **parasite** eats the cell contents, tissues, or body fluids of its host; as a group, parasites harm but usually do not kill their host, at least not immediately (unlike a predator). Parasites that cause disease are known as **pathogens**, many of which are prokaryotic.

UNIVERSITY OF ALBERTA FACULTY BIO

Julia Foght BSc and PhD Microbiology (University of Alberta)

Current Position: Professor, Department of Biological Sciences

I began undergraduate studies at the University of Alberta in Pharmacy but it just didn't suit me. In my second year I took the required full-year introductory microbiology course and fell in love with microbiology, particularly the labs. So I followed my passion, switched programs and graduated with a BSc, Specialization in Microbiology. I was a summer student in a research lab and after graduation worked as a research technologist on campus for 4 years. That is how I discovered that I wanted to direct my own research rather than conduct someone else's. I got a PhD from the University of Alberta, worked as a post-doctoral fellow (part-time for 5 years after my daughter was born) and a sessional instructor. I became an Assistant Professor in 1994.

My research initially focused on bioremediation of petroleum-contaminated environments but now my lab studies microbes in oil sands tailings ponds, as well as bacteria that thrive beneath glaciers. My job has taken me to every continent except Africa, including a sampling trip to Antarctica.

I love teaching, and helped design and teach the very first version of Biology 107 in 1995[R1]. Although I now teach upper-level courses, for many years I taught introductory microbiology (Microbiology 265), the course that catalyzed my scientific interests. Teaching that course always reminded me why I became a microbiologist. So, you do not have to know exactly what you want to be or do when you first enter the university. Follow your intellectual passion and, if you truly love it, your career will find you.

▲ **Figure 27.19 Mutualism: bacterial "headlights."** The glowing oval below the eye of the flashlight fish (*Photoblepharon palpebratus*) is an organ harboring bioluminescent bacteria. The fish uses the light to attract prey and to signal potential mates. The bacteria receive nutrients from the fish.

The very existence of an ecosystem can depend on prokaryotes. For example, consider the diverse ecological communities found at hydrothermal vents. These communities are densely populated by many different kinds of animals, including worms, clams, crabs, and fishes. But since sunlight does not penetrate to the deep ocean floor, the community does not include photosynthetic organisms. Instead, the energy that supports the community is derived from the metabolic activities of chemoautotrophic bacteria. These bacteria harvest chemical energy from compounds such as hydrogen sulfide (H_2S) that are released from the vent. An active hydrothermal vent may support hundreds of eukaryotic species, but when the vent stops releasing chemicals, the chemoautotrophic bacteria cannot survive. As a result, the entire vent community collapses.

CONCEPT CHECK 27.5

1. Explain how prokaryotes, though small, can be considered giants in their collective impact on Earth and its life.
2. **MAKE CONNECTIONS** After reviewing photosynthesis in Figure 10.6 (p. 188), summarize the main steps by which cyanobacteria produce O_2 and use CO_2 to make organic compounds.

For suggested answers, see Appendix A.

CONCEPT 27.6

Prokaryotes have both beneficial and harmful impacts on humans

Though the best-known prokaryotes tend to be the bacteria that cause illness in humans, these pathogens represent only a small fraction of prokaryotic species. Many other prokaryotes have positive interactions with humans, and some play essential roles in agriculture and industry.

Mutualistic Bacteria

As is true for many other eukaryotes, human well-being can depend on mutualistic prokaryotes. For example, our intestines are home to an estimated 500–1,000 species of bacteria; their cells outnumber all human cells in the body by a factor of ten. Different species live in different portions of the intestines, and they vary in their ability to process different foods. Many of these species are mutualists, digesting food that our own intestines cannot break down. In 2003, scientists published the first complete genome of one of these gut mutualists, *Bacteroides thetaiotaomicron*. The genome includes a large array of genes involved in synthesizing carbohydrates, vitamins, and other nutrients needed by humans. Signals from the bacterium activate human genes that build the network of intestinal blood vessels necessary to absorb nutrient molecules. Other signals induce human cells to produce antimicrobial compounds to which *B. thetaiotaomicron* is not susceptible. This action may reduce the population sizes of other, competing species, thus potentially benefiting both *B. thetaiotaomicron* and its human host.

Pathogenic Bacteria

All the pathogenic prokaryotes known to date are bacteria, and they deserve their negative reputation. Bacteria cause about half of all human diseases. Roughly 2 million people die each year of the lung disease tuberculosis, caused by *Mycobacterium tuberculosis*. And another 2 million people die each year from diarrheal diseases caused by various bacteria.

Some bacterial diseases are transmitted by other species, such as fleas or ticks. In the United States, the most widespread pest-carried disease is Lyme disease, which infects 15,000 to 20,000 people each year **(Figure 27.20)**. Caused by a bacterium carried by ticks that live on deer and field mice,

5 µm

▲ **Figure 27.20 Lyme disease.** Ticks in the genus *Ixodes* spread the disease by transmitting the spirochete *Borrelia burgdorferi* (colorized SEM). A rash may develop at the site of the tick's bite; the rash may be large and ring-shaped (as shown) or much less distinctive.

Lyme disease can result in debilitating arthritis, heart disease, nervous disorders, and death if untreated.

Pathogenic prokaryotes usually cause illness by producing poisons, which are classified as exotoxins or endotoxins. **Exotoxins** are proteins secreted by certain bacteria and other organisms. Cholera, a dangerous diarrheal disease, is caused by an exotoxin secreted by the proteobacterium *Vibrio cholerae*. The exotoxin stimulates intestinal cells to release chloride ions into the gut, and water follows by osmosis. In another example, the potentially fatal disease botulism is caused by botulinum toxin, an exotoxin secreted by the gram-positive bacterium *Clostridium botulinum* as it ferments various foods, including improperly canned meat, seafood, and vegetables. Like other exotoxins, the botulinum toxin can produce disease even if the bacteria that manufacture it are not present. In one such case, eight people contracted botulism after eating salted fish that did not contain any *C. botulinum* bacteria, but did contain the botulinum toxin. Even though the bacterium was no longer present, at some point in the fish preparation process, the bacterium had been able to grow and secrete the toxin.

Endotoxins are lipopolysaccharide components of the outer membrane of gram-negative bacteria. In contrast to exotoxins, endotoxins are released only when the bacteria die and their cell walls break down. Endotoxin-producing bacteria include species in the genus *Salmonella*, such as *Salmonella typhi*, which causes typhoid fever. You might have heard of food poisoning caused by other *Salmonella* species that are frequently found in poultry.

Since the 19th century, improved sanitation systems in the industrialized world have greatly reduced the threat of pathogenic bacteria. Antibiotics have saved a great many lives and reduced the incidence of disease. However, resistance to antibiotics is currently evolving in many bacterial strains. As you read earlier, the rapid reproduction of bacteria enables cells carrying resistance genes to quickly give rise to large populations as a result of natural selection, and these genes can also spread to other species by horizontal gene transfer.

Horizontal gene transfer can also spread genes associated with virulence, turning normally harmless bacteria into potent pathogens. *E. coli*, for instance, is ordinarily a harmless symbiont in the human intestines, but pathogenic strains that cause bloody diarrhea have emerged. One of the most dangerous strains, called O157:H7, is a global threat; in the United States alone, there are 75,000 cases of O157:H7 infection per year, often from contaminated beef or produce. In 2001, scientists sequenced the genome of O157:H7 and compared it with the genome of a harmless strain of *E. coli* called K-12. They discovered that 1,387 out of the 5,416 genes in O157:H7 have no counterpart in K-12. Many of these 1,387 genes are found in chromosomal regions that include phage DNA. This result suggests that at least some of the 1,387 genes were incorporated into the genome of O157:H7 through phage-mediated horizontal gene transfer (transduction). Some of the genes found only in O157:H7 are associated with virulence, including genes that code for adhesive fimbriae that enable O157:H7 to attach itself to the intestinal wall and extract nutrients.

Pathogenic bacteria also pose a potential threat as weapons of bioterrorism. For example, endospores of *Bacillus anthracis* sent through the mail in 2001 caused 18 people to develop inhalation anthrax, which was fatal in 5 of the cases. Such scenarios have stimulated more research on pathogenic prokaryotic species in the hope of developing new vaccines and antibiotics.

Prokaryotes in Research and Technology

On a positive note, we reap many benefits from the metabolic capabilities of both bacteria and archaea. For example, humans have long used bacteria to convert milk to cheese and yogurt. In recent years, our greater understanding of prokaryotes has led to an explosion of new applications in biotechnology; two examples are the use of *E. coli* in gene cloning and the use of *Agrobacterium tumefaciens* in producing transgenic plants such as Golden Rice (see Chapter 20).

Bacteria may soon figure prominently in a major industry: plastics. Globally, each year about 350 billion pounds of plastic are produced from petroleum and used to make toys, storage containers, soft drink bottles, and many other items. These products degrade slowly, creating environmental problems. Bacteria can now be used to make natural plastics **(Figure 27.21a)**. For example, some bacteria synthesize a type of polymer known as PHA (polyhydroxyalkanoate), which they use to store chemical energy. The PHA they produce can be extracted, formed into pellets, and used to make durable, biodegradable plastics.

▲ **Figure 27.21 Some applications of prokaryotes. (a)** These bacteria synthesize and store PHA, which can be extracted and used to make biodegradable plastic products. **(b)** Spraying fertilizers on an oil-soaked area stimulates growth of native bacteria that metabolize the oil, speeding the natural breakdown process up to fivefold. **(c)** Current research seeks to develop bacteria that produce ethanol (E-85) fuel efficiently from renewable plant products.

Another way to harness prokaryotes is in **bioremediation**, the use of organisms to remove pollutants from soil, air, or water. For example, anaerobic bacteria and archaea decompose the organic matter in sewage, converting it to material that can be used as landfill or fertilizer after chemical sterilization. Other bioremediation applications include cleaning up oil spills **(Figure 27.21b)** and precipitating radioactive material (such as uranium) out of groundwater.

Through genetic engineering, humans can now modify bacteria to produce vitamins, antibiotics, hormones, and other products (see Chapter 20). Researchers are seeking to reduce fossil fuel use by engineering bacteria that can produce ethanol from various forms of biomass, including agricultural waste, switchgrass, municipal waste (such as paper products that are not recycled), and corn **(Figure 27.21c)**.

The usefulness of prokaryotes largely derives from their diverse forms of nutrition and metabolism. All this metabolic versatility evolved prior to the appearance of the structural novelties that heralded the evolution of eukaryotic organisms, to which we devote the remainder of this unit.

CONCEPT CHECK 27.6

1. Identify at least two ways that prokaryotes have affected you positively today.
2. A pathogenic bacterium's toxin causes symptoms that increase the bacterium's chance of spreading from host to host. Does this information indicate whether the poison is an exotoxin or endotoxin? Explain.
3. **WHAT IF?** How might a sudden and dramatic change in your diet affect the diversity of prokaryotic species that live in your digestive tract?

For suggested answers, see Appendix A.

27 CHAPTER REVIEW

SUMMARY OF KEY CONCEPTS

CONCEPT 27.1

Structural and functional adaptations contribute to prokaryotic success (pp. 556–561)

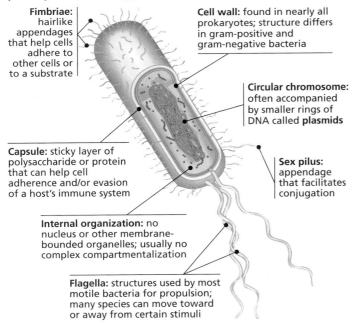

Fimbriae: hairlike appendages that help cells adhere to other cells or to a substrate

Cell wall: found in nearly all prokaryotes; structure differs in gram-positive and gram-negative bacteria

Circular chromosome: often accompanied by smaller rings of DNA called **plasmids**

Capsule: sticky layer of polysaccharide or protein that can help cell adherence and/or evasion of a host's immune system

Sex pilus: appendage that facilitates conjugation

Internal organization: no nucleus or other membrane-bounded organelles; usually no complex compartmentalization

Flagella: structures used by most motile bacteria for propulsion; many species can move toward or away from certain stimuli

- Prokaryotes can reproduce quickly by binary fission. Some form endospores, which can remain viable in harsh conditions for centuries. Prokaryotic populations can evolve in short periods of time in response to changing environmental conditions.

? *Describe features of prokaryotes that enable them to thrive in many different environments.*

CONCEPT 27.2

Rapid reproduction, mutation, and genetic recombination promote genetic diversity in prokaryotes (pp. 561–564)

- Because prokaryotes can often proliferate rapidly, mutations can quickly increase a population's genetic variation, making adaptive evolution possible.
- Genetic diversity in prokaryotes also can arise by recombination of the DNA from two different cells (via transformation, transduction, or conjugation). By transferring advantageous alleles, such as ones for antibiotic resistance, genetic recombination can promote adaptive evolution in prokaryotic populations.

? *Mutations are rare and prokaryotes reproduce asexually; yet their populations can have high genetic diversity. Explain how this can occur.*

CONCEPT 27.3

Diverse nutritional and metabolic adaptations have evolved in prokaryotes (pp. 564–565)

- Nutritional diversity is much greater in prokaryotes than in eukaryotes. As a group, prokaryotes perform all four modes of nutrition: **photoautotrophy**, **chemoautotrophy**, **photoheterotrophy**, and **chemoheterotrophy**.
- Among prokaryotes, **obligate aerobes** require O_2, **obligate anaerobes** are poisoned by O_2, and **facultative anaerobes** can survive with or without O_2.
- Unlike eukaryotes, prokaryotes can metabolize nitrogen in many different forms. Some can convert atmospheric nitrogen to ammonia, a process called **nitrogen fixation**.
- Prokaryotic cells and even species may cooperate metabolically. In *Anabaena*, photosynthetic cells and nitrogen-fixing cells exchange metabolic products. Metabolic cooperation also occurs in surface-coating **biofilms** that include different species.

? *Describe the range of prokaryotic metabolic adaptations.*

CONCEPT 27.4

Molecular systematics is illuminating prokaryotic phylogeny (pp. 565–570)

- Molecular systematics is leading to a phylogenetic classification of prokaryotes, allowing systematists to identify major new clades.
- Some archaea, such as extreme thermophiles and extreme halophiles, live in extreme environments. Other archaea live in moderate environments such as soils and lakes.
- Diverse nutritional types are scattered among the major groups of bacteria. The two largest groups are the proteobacteria and the gram-positive bacteria.

? *What impact have molecular data had on constructing prokaryotic phylogeny?*

CONCEPT 27.5

Prokaryotes play crucial roles in the biosphere (pp. 570–571)

- Decomposition by heterotrophic prokaryotes and the synthetic activities of autotrophic and nitrogen-fixing prokaryotes contribute to the recycling of elements in ecosystems.
- Many prokaryotes have a symbiotic relationship with a host; the relationships between prokaryotes and their hosts range from mutualism to commensalism to parasitism.

? *In what ways are prokaryotes key to the survival of many species?*

CONCEPT 27.6

Prokaryotes have both beneficial and harmful impacts on humans (pp. 571–573)

- Humans depend on mutualistic prokaryotes, including hundreds of species that live in our intestines and help digest food.
- Pathogenic bacteria typically cause disease by releasing **exotoxins** or **endotoxins** and are potential weapons of bioterrorism. Horizontal gene transfer can spread genes associated with virulence to harmless species or strains.
- Experiments with bacteria such as *E. coli* have led to important advances in DNA technology. Prokaryotes can be used in bioremediation, production of biodegradable plastics, and the synthesis of vitamins, antibiotics, and other products.

? *Describe beneficial and harmful impacts of prokaryotes on humans.*

TEST YOUR UNDERSTANDING

LEVEL 1: KNOWLEDGE/COMPREHENSION

1. Genetic variation in bacterial populations cannot result from
   a. transduction.
   b. transformation.
   c. conjugation.
   d. mutation.
   e. meiosis.

2. Photoautotrophs use
   a. light as an energy source and CO_2 as a carbon source.
   b. light as an energy source and methane as a carbon source.
   c. N_2 as an energy source and CO_2 as a carbon source.
   d. CO_2 as both an energy source and a carbon source.
   e. H_2S as an energy source and CO_2 as a carbon source.

3. Which of the following statements is *not* true?
   a. Archaea and bacteria have different membrane lipids.
   b. Both archaea and bacteria generally lack membrane-enclosed organelles.
   c. The cell walls of archaea lack peptidoglycan.
   d. Only bacteria have histones associated with DNA.
   e. Only some archaea use CO_2 to oxidize H_2, releasing methane.

4. Which of the following involves metabolic cooperation among prokaryotic cells?
   a. binary fission
   b. endospore formation
   c. endotoxin release
   d. biofilms
   e. photoautotrophy

5. Bacteria perform the following ecological roles. Which role typically does *not* involve symbiosis?
   a. skin commensalist
   b. decomposer
   c. aggregate with methane-consuming archaea
   d. gut mutualist
   e. pathogen

6. Plantlike photosynthesis that releases O_2 occurs in
   a. cyanobacteria.
   b. chlamydias.
   c. archaea.
   d. actinomycetes.
   e. chemoautotrophic bacteria.

LEVEL 2: APPLICATION/ANALYSIS

7. EVOLUTION CONNECTION

Health officials worldwide are concerned about antibiotic resistance in bacteria. In patients infected with nonresistant strains of the tuberculosis bacterium, antibiotics can relieve symptoms in a few weeks. However, it takes much longer to halt the infection, and patients may discontinue treatment while bacteria are still present. How might this result in the evolution of drug-resistant pathogens?

LEVEL 3: SYNTHESIS/EVALUATION

8. SCIENTIFIC INQUIRY

DRAW IT The nitrogen-fixing bacterium *Rhizobium* infects the roots of some plant species, forming a mutualism in which the bacterium provides nitrogen, and the plant provides carbohydrates. Scientists measured the 12-week growth of one such plant species (*Acacia irrorata*) when infected by six different *Rhizobium* strains. (a) Graph the data. (b) Interpret your graph.

Rhizobium strain	1	2	3	4	5	6
Plant mass (g)	0.91	0.06	1.56	1.72	0.14	1.03

Source: J. J. Burdon et al., Variation in the effectiveness of symbiotic associations between native rhizobia and temperate Australian *Acacia*: within species interactions, *Journal of Applied Ecology* 36:398–408 (1999).

Note: Without *Rhizobium*, after 12 weeks, *Acacia* plants have a mass of about 0.1 g.

9. **WRITE ABOUT A THEME**

Energy Transfer In a short essay (about 100–150 words), discuss how prokaryotes and other members of hydrothermal vent communities transfer and transform energy.

For selected answers, see Appendix A.

Mastering**BIOLOGY**   www.masteringbiology.com

1. MasteringBiology® Assignments
Tutorial Diversity in Bacteria
Activities Classification of Prokaryotes • The Tree of Life • Discovery Channel Videos: Bacteria; Antibiotics; Tasty Bacteria
Questions Student Misconceptions • Reading Quiz • Multiple Choice • End-of-Chapter

2. eText
Read your book online, search, take notes, highlight text, and more.

3. The Study Area
Practice Tests • Cumulative Test • *BioFlix* 3-D Animations • MP3 Tutor Sessions • Videos • Activities • Investigations • Lab Media • Audio Glossary • Word Study Tools • Art

28

Protists

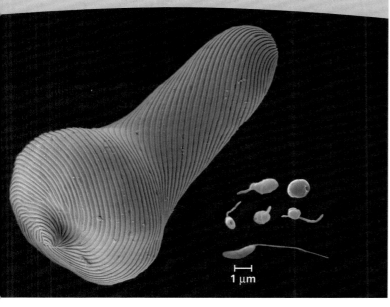

▲ **Figure 28.1 Which of these organisms are prokaryotes and which are eukaryotes?**

Living Small

Knowing that most prokaryotes are extremely small organisms, you might assume that **Figure 28.1** depicts six prokaryotes and one much larger eukaryote. But in fact, the only prokaryote is the organism immediately above the scale bar. The others are recently discovered members of diverse, mostly unicellular groups of eukaryotes informally known as **protists**. Very small eukaryotes have intrigued scientists for more than 300 years, ever since the Dutch microscopist Antoni van Leeuwenhoek first laid eyes on them. As he discovered, viewing a drop of pond water under a light microscope can reveal a fascinating world of unicellular protists and prokaryotes. Some protists propel themselves with whipping flagella, while others creep along by means of blob-like appendages. Some are shaped like tiny trumpets; others resemble miniature jewelry. Recalling his observations, van Leeuwenhoek wrote, "No more pleasant sight has met my eye than this, of so many thousands of living creatures in one small drop of water."

Until recently, biologists thought that 300 years of observation had uncovered a representative sample of living protist species. But in the last decade, genetic prospecting has turned up a treasure trove of previously unknown protists within the world of microscopic life. As shown in Figure 28.1, many of these newly discovered organisms are just 0.5–2 µm in diameter—as small as many prokaryotes.

The surprising discovery of many species of minuscule protists followed close on the heels of recent findings regarding protist phylogeny. All protists were once classified in a single kingdom, Protista, but advances in eukaryotic systematics have caused the kingdom to crumble. It has become clear that the kingdom Protista is in fact polyphyletic (see Figure 26.10): Some protists are more closely related to plants, fungi, or animals than they are to other protists. As a result, the kingdom Protista has been abandoned, and various lineages of protists are now recognized as kingdoms in their own right. Most biologists still use the term *protist*, but only as a convenient way to refer to eukaryotes that are not plants, animals, or fungi.

In this chapter, you will become acquainted with some of the most significant groups of protists. You will learn about their structural and biochemical adaptations as well as their enormous impact on ecosystems, agriculture, industry, and human health.

CONCEPT 28.1

Most eukaryotes are single-celled organisms

Protists, along with plants, animals, and fungi, are classified as eukaryotes; they are in domain Eukarya, one of the three domains of life. Unlike the cells of prokaryotes, eukaryotic cells have a nucleus and other membrane-bounded organelles, such as mitochondria and the Golgi apparatus. Such organelles provide specific locations in which particular cellular functions are accomplished, making the structure and organization of eukaryotic cells more complex than those of prokaryotic cells.

We'll survey the diversity of eukaryotes throughout the rest of this unit, beginning in this chapter with the protists. As you explore this material, bear in mind that

- the organisms in most eukaryotic lineages are protists, and
- most protists are unicellular.

Thus, life differs greatly from how most of us commonly think of it. The large, multicellular organisms that we know best (plants, animals, and fungi) are the tips of just a few branches on the great tree of life (see Figure 26.21).

Structural and Functional Diversity in Protists

Given the polyphyletic nature of the group once called Protista, it isn't surprising that few general characteristics of protists can be cited without exceptions. In fact, protists exhibit more structural and functional diversity than any other group of eukaryotes.

Most protists are unicellular, although there are some colonial and multicellular species. Single-celled protists are justifiably considered the simplest eukaryotes, but at the cellular level, many protists are very complex—the most elaborate of all cells. In multicellular organisms, essential biological functions are carried out by organs. Unicellular protists carry out the same essential functions, but they do so using subcellular organelles, not multicellular organs. The organelles that protists use are mostly those discussed in Chapter 6, including the nucleus, endoplasmic reticulum, Golgi apparatus, and lysosomes. Certain protists also rely on organelles not found in most other eukaryotic cells, such as contractile vacuoles that pump excess water from the protistan cell (see Figure 7.16).

Protists are more nutritionally diverse than other eukaryote groups. Some protists are photoautotrophs and contain chloroplasts. Some are heterotrophs, absorbing organic molecules or ingesting larger food particles. Still other protists, called **mixotrophs**, combine photosynthesis *and* heterotrophic nutrition. Photoautotrophy, heterotrophy, and mixotrophy have all arisen independently in many protist lineages.

Reproduction and life cycles also are highly varied among protists. Some protists are only known to reproduce asexually; others can also reproduce sexually or at least employ the sexual processes of meiosis and fertilization. All three basic types of sexual life cycles (see Figure 13.6) are represented among protists, along with some variations that do not quite fit any of these types. We will examine the life cycles of several protist groups later in this chapter.

Endosymbiosis in Eukaryotic Evolution

What gave rise to the enormous diversity of protists that exist today? There is abundant evidence that much of protist diversity has its origins in **endosymbiosis**, the process in which certain unicellular organisms engulf other cells, which become endosymbionts and ultimately organelles in the host cell. For example, as we discussed in Chapter 25, structural, biochemical, and DNA sequence data indicate that the first eukaryotes acquired mitochondria by engulfing an aerobic prokaryote (specifically, an alpha proteobacterium). The early origin of mitochondria is supported by the fact that all eukaryotes studied so far have either mitochondria or modified versions of them.

Much evidence also indicates that later in eukaryotic history, a lineage of heterotrophic eukaryotes acquired an additional endosymbiont—a photosynthetic cyanobacterium—that then evolved into plastids. As the hypothesis illustrated in **Figure 28.2** shows, this plastid-bearing lineage gave rise to two lineages of photosynthetic protists, or **algae:** red algae and green algae. This hypothesis is supported by the observation that the DNA of plastid genes in red algae and green algae closely resembles the DNA of cyanobacteria. In addition, plastids in red algae and green algae are surrounded by two membranes. Transport proteins in these membranes are homologous to proteins in the inner and outer membranes of cyanobacterial endosymbionts, providing further support for the hypothesis.

On several occasions during eukaryotic evolution, red algae and green algae underwent **secondary endosymbiosis**: They were ingested in the food vacuoles of heterotrophic eukaryotes and became endosymbionts themselves. For example, protists known as chlorarachniophytes likely evolved when a heterotrophic eukaryote engulfed a green alga. Evidence for this process can be found within the engulfed cell, which contains a tiny vestigial nucleus, called a *nucleomorph*. Genes from the nucleomorph are still transcribed, and their DNA sequences indicate the engulfed cell was a green alga. Also consistent with the hypothesis that chlorarachniophytes evolved from a eukaryote that engulfed another eukaryote, their plastids are surrounded by *four* membranes. The two inner membranes originated as the inner and outer membranes of the ancient cyanobacterium. The third membrane is derived from the engulfed alga's plasma membrane, and the outermost membrane is derived from the heterotrophic eukaryote's food vacuole. In some other protists, plastids acquired by secondary endosymbiosis are surrounded by three membranes, indicating that one of the original four membranes was lost during the course of evolution.

Five Supergroups of Eukaryotes

Our understanding of the evolutionary history of protists has been in a state of flux in recent years. Not only has kingdom Protista been abandoned, but a variety of other hypotheses have been discarded as well. For example, in the early 1990s,

▼ **Figure 28.2 Diversity of plastids produced by endosymbiosis.** Studies of plastid-bearing eukaryotes suggest that plastids evolved from a gram-negative cyanobacterium that was engulfed by an ancestral heterotrophic eukaryote (primary endosymbiosis). That ancestor then diversified into red algae and green algae, some of which were subsequently engulfed by other eukaryotes (secondary endosymbiosis).

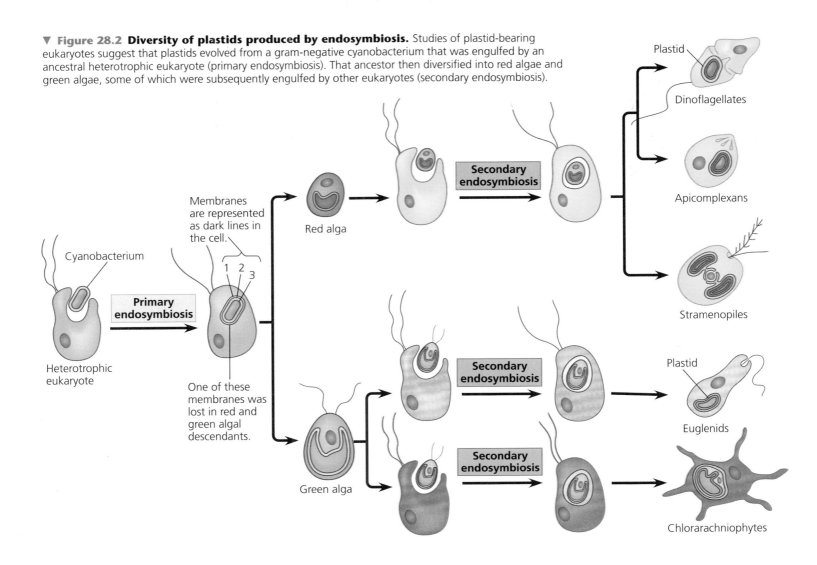

many biologists thought that the oldest lineage of living eukaryotes consisted of the *amitochondriate protists*, organisms without conventional mitochondria and with fewer membrane-bounded organelles than other protist groups. But recent structural and DNA data have undermined this hypothesis. Many of the so-called amitochondriate protists have been shown to have mitochondria—though reduced ones—and some of these organisms are now classified in entirely different groups. For example, microsporidians, once considered amitochondriate protists, are now classified as fungi.

The ongoing changes in our understanding of the phylogeny of protists pose challenges to students and instructors alike. Hypotheses about these relationships are a focus of scientific activity, changing rapidly as new data cause previous ideas to be modified or discarded. In this chapter, our discussion is organized around one current hypothesis: the five supergroups of eukaryotes shown in **Figure 28.3**, on the next two pages. Because the root of the eukaryotic tree is not known, all five supergroups are shown as diverging simultaneously from a common ancestor. We know that is not correct, but we do not know which organisms were the first to

diverge from the others. In addition, while some of the groups in Figure 28.3 are well supported by morphological and DNA data, others are more controversial. As you read this chapter, it may be helpful to focus less on the specific names of groups of organisms and more on why the organisms are important and how ongoing research is elucidating their evolutionary relationships.

CONCEPT CHECK 28.1

1. Cite at least four examples of structural and functional diversity among protists.
2. Summarize the role of endosymbiosis in eukaryotic evolution.
3. **WHAT IF?** After studying Figure 28.3, on the next two pages, draw a simplified version of the phylogenetic tree that shows only the five supergroups of eukaryotes. Now sketch how the tree would look if the unikonts were the first group of eukaryotes to diverge from other eukaryotes.

For suggested answers, see Appendix A.

Exploring Protistan Diversity

The tree below represents a phylogenetic hypothesis for the relationships among all the eukaryotes on Earth today. The eukaryotic groups at the branch tips are related in larger "supergroups," labeled vertically at the far right of the tree. The kingdoms Plantae (land plants), Fungi, and Animalia (animals) have survived from the five-kingdom system of classification. Groups that were formerly classified in the kingdom Protista are listed in beige boxes. Dotted lines indicate evolutionary relationships that are uncertain and proposed clades that are under active debate.

Diplomonads, Parabasalids, Euglenozoans — **Excavata**

Dinoflagellates, Apicomplexans, Ciliates — Alveolates
Diatoms, Golden algae, Brown algae, Oomycetes — Stramenopiles — **Chromalveolata**

Cercozoans, Forams, Radiolarians — **Rhizaria**

Red algae, Chlorophytes, Charophytes (Green algae), Land plants — **Archaeplastida**

Slime molds, Gymnamoebas, Entamoebas — Amoebozoans
Nucleariids, Fungi, Choanoflagellates, Animals — Opisthokonts — **Unikonta**

■ Excavata

Some members of this supergroup have an "excavated" groove on one side of the cell body. Two major clades (the parabasalids and diplomonads) have modified mitochondria; others (the euglenozoans) have flagella that differ in structure from those of other organisms. Excavates include parasites such as *Giardia*, as well as many predatory and photosynthetic species.

5 μm

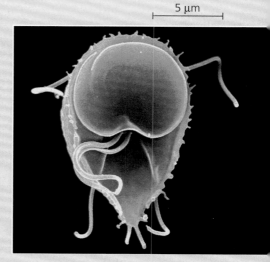

***Giardia intestinalis*, a diplomonad parasite.** This diplomonad (colorized SEM), which lacks the characteristic surface groove of the Excavata, can infect people when they drink water contaminated with feces containing *Giardia* cysts. Drinking such water—even from a seemingly pristine stream—can cause severe diarrhea. Boiling the water kills the parasite.

■ Chromalveolata

This group may have originated by an ancient secondary endosymbiosis event. Chromalveolates include some of the most important photosynthetic organisms on Earth, such as the diatoms shown here. The group also includes the brown algae that form underwater kelp "forests," as well as important pathogens, such as *Plasmodium*, which causes malaria, and *Phytophthora*, which caused the devastating potato famine in 19th-century Ireland.

50 μm

Diatom diversity. These beautiful single-celled protists are important photosynthetic organisms in aquatic communities (LM).

■ Rhizaria

This group contains many species of amoebas, most of which have pseudopodia that are threadlike in shape. Pseudopodia are extensions that can bulge from any portion of the cell; they are used in movement and in the capture of prey. Several recent molecular phylogenetic studies have suggested that Rhizaria should be nested within Chromalveolata; this hypothesis is currently being tested by other research groups.

100 μm

***Globigerina*, a foram in the supergroup Rhizaria.** Threadlike pseudopodia extend through pores in the shell, or *test* (LM). The inset SEM shows a foram test, which is hardened by calcium carbonate.

■ Archaeplastida

This group of eukaryotes includes red algae and green algae, along with land plants (kingdom Plantae, discussed in Chapters 29 and 30). Red algae and green algae include unicellular species, colonial species (such as the green alga *Volvox*), and multicellular species. Many of the large algae known informally as "seaweeds" are multicellular red or green algae. Protists in Archaeplastida include key photosynthetic species that form the base of the food web in some aquatic communities.

20 μm

50 μm

***Volvox*, a colonial freshwater green alga.** The colony is a hollow ball whose wall is composed of hundreds of biflagellated cells (see inset LM) embedded in a gelatinous matrix. The cells are usually connected by cytoplasmic strands; if isolated, these cells cannot reproduce. The large colonies seen here will eventually release the small "daughter" colonies within them (LM).

■ Unikonta

This group of eukaryotes includes amoebas that have lobe- or tube-shaped pseudopodia, as well as animals, fungi, and non-amoeba protists that are closely related to animals or fungi. According to one current hypothesis, the unikonts may have been the first group of eukaryotes to diverge from other eukaryotes (see Figure 28.23); however, this hypothesis has yet to be widely accepted.

100 μm

A unikont amoeba. This amoeba (*Amoeba proteus*) is using its pseudopodia to move.

CONCEPT 28.2

Excavates include protists with modified mitochondria and protists with unique flagella

Now that we have examined some of the broad patterns in eukaryotic evolution, we will look more closely at the five main groups of protists shown in Figure 28.3.

We begin this tour with **Excavata** (the excavates), a clade recently proposed based on morphological studies of the cytoskeleton. Some members of this diverse group also have an "excavated" feeding groove on one side of the cell body.

The excavates include the diplomonads, the parabasalids, and the euglenozoans. Molecular data indicate that each of these three groups is monophyletic, but the data have neither confirmed nor strongly refuted the monophyly of the excavate supergroup. Although many excavates share certain unique cytoskeletal features, we cannot yet tell whether that is because the excavates are monophyletic or because the common ancestor of eukaryotes had those features. Overall, support for the excavate clade is relatively weak, making it one of the more controversial of the five supergroups.

Diplomonads and Parabasalids

The protists in these two groups lack plastids and have modified mitochondria (until recently, they were thought to lack mitochondria altogether). Most diplomonads and parabasalids are found in anaerobic environments.

Diplomonads have modified mitochondria called *mitosomes*. These organelles lack functional electron transport chains and hence cannot use oxygen to help extract energy from carbohydrates and other organic molecules. Instead, diplomonads get the energy they need from anaerobic biochemical pathways.

Structurally, diplomonads have two equal-sized nuclei and multiple flagella. Recall that eukaryotic flagella are extensions of the cytoplasm, consisting of bundles of microtubules covered by the cell's plasma membrane (see Figure 6.24). They are quite different from prokaryotic flagella, which are filaments composed of the globular protein flagellin attached to the cell surface (see Figure 27.6).

Many diplomonads are parasites. An infamous example is *Giardia intestinalis* (also known as *Giardia lamblia*; see Figure 28.3), which inhabits the intestines of mammals.

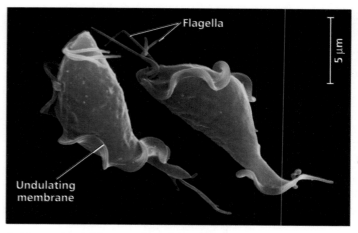

▲ **Figure 28.4 The parabasalid *Trichomonas vaginalis*** (colorized SEM).

Parabasalids also have reduced mitochondria; called *hydrogenosomes*, these organelles generate some energy anaerobically, releasing hydrogen gas as a by-product. The best-known parabasalid is *Trichomonas vaginalis*, a sexually transmitted parasite that infects some 5 million people each year. *T. vaginalis* travels along the mucus-coated lining of the human reproductive and urinary tracts by moving its flagella and by undulating part of its plasma membrane **(Figure 28.4)**. In females, if the vagina's normal acidity is disturbed, *T. vaginalis* can outcompete beneficial microorganisms there and infect the vagina. (*Trichomonas* infections also can occur in the urethra of males, though often without symptoms.) *T. vaginalis* has a gene that allows it to feed on the vaginal lining, promoting infection. Studies suggest that the protist acquired this gene by horizontal gene transfer from bacterial parasites in the vagina.

Euglenozoans

Protists called **euglenozoans** belong to a diverse clade that includes predatory heterotrophs, photosynthetic autotrophs, and parasites. The main morphological feature that distinguishes protists in this clade is the presence of a rod with either a spiral or a crystalline structure inside each of their flagella **(Figure 28.5)**. The two best-studied groups of euglenozoans are the kinetoplastids and the euglenids.

Kinetoplastids

Protists called **kinetoplastids** have a single, large mitochondrion that contains an organized mass of DNA called a *kinetoplast*. These protists include species that feed on prokaryotes in freshwater, marine, and moist terrestrial ecosystems, as well as species that parasitize animals, plants, and other protists. For example, kinetoplastids in the genus *Trypanosoma* infect humans and cause sleeping sickness, a neurological disease that is invariably fatal if not treated. The infection occurs via the bite of a vector (carrier) organism, the African tsetse fly **(Figure 28.6)**. Trypanosomes also cause Chagas' disease, which is

▲ Figure 28.5 Euglenozoan flagellum. Most euglenozoans have a crystalline rod inside one of their flagella (the TEM is a flagellum shown in cross section). The rod lies alongside the 9 + 2 ring of microtubules found in all eukaryotic flagella (compare with Figure 6.24).

Flagella

0.2 μm

8 μm

Crystalline rod (cross section)

Ring of microtubules (cross section)

9 μm

▲ Figure 28.6 *Trypanosoma*, the kinetoplastid that causes sleeping sickness. The purple, ribbon-shaped cells among these red blood cells are the trypanosomes (colorized SEM).

transmitted by bloodsucking insects and can lead to congestive heart failure.

Trypanosomes evade immune responses with an effective "bait-and-switch" defense. The surface of a trypanosome is coated with millions of copies of a single protein. However, before the host's immune system can recognize the protein and mount an attack, new generations of the parasite switch to another surface protein with a different molecular structure. Frequent changes in the surface protein prevent the host from developing immunity. About a third of *Trypanosoma*'s genome is dedicated to producing these surface proteins.

Euglenids

A **euglenid** has a pocket at one end of the cell from which one or two flagella emerge **(Figure 28.7)**. Many species of the euglenid *Euglena* are mixotrophs: In sunlight they are autotrophic, but when sunlight is unavailable, they can become heterotrophic, absorbing organic nutrients from their environment. Many other euglenids engulf prey by phagocytosis.

CONCEPT CHECK 28.2

1. Why do some biologists describe the mitochondria of diplomonads and parabasalids as "highly reduced"?
2. **WHAT IF?** DNA sequence data for a diplomonad, a euglenid, a plant, and an unidentified protist suggest that the unidentified species is most closely related to the diplomonad. Further studies reveal that the unknown species has fully functional mitochondria. Based on these data, at what point on the phylogenetic tree in Figure 28.3 did the mystery protist's lineage probably diverge from other eukaryote lineages? Explain.

For suggested answers, see Appendix A.

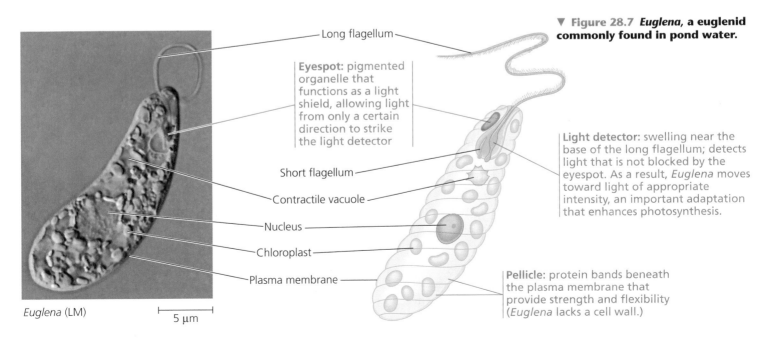

▼ Figure 28.7 *Euglena*, a euglenid commonly found in pond water.

Long flagellum

Eyespot: pigmented organelle that functions as a light shield, allowing light from only a certain direction to strike the light detector

Short flagellum

Contractile vacuole

Nucleus

Chloroplast

Plasma membrane

Light detector: swelling near the base of the long flagellum; detects light that is not blocked by the eyespot. As a result, *Euglena* moves toward light of appropriate intensity, an important adaptation that enhances photosynthesis.

Pellicle: protein bands beneath the plasma membrane that provide strength and flexibility (*Euglena* lacks a cell wall.)

Euglena (LM)

5 μm

CONCEPT 28.3

Chromalveolates may have originated by secondary endosymbiosis

The supergroup **Chromalveolata** (the chromalveolates), a large, extremely diverse clade of protists, has recently been proposed based on two lines of evidence. First, some (though not all) DNA sequence data suggest that the chromalveolates form a monophyletic group. Second, some data support the hypothesis that the chromalveolates originated more than a billion years ago, when a common ancestor of the group engulfed a single-celled, photosynthetic red alga. Because red algae are thought to have originated by primary endosymbiosis (see Figure 28.2), such an origin for the chromalveolates is referred to as secondary endosymbiosis.

How strong is the evidence that the chromalveolates originated by secondary endosymbiosis? Many species in the clade have plastids whose structure and DNA indicate that they are of red algal origin. Others have reduced plastids that seem to be derived from a red algal endosymbiont. Still other species lack plastids altogether, yet some of these species have plastid genes in their nuclear DNA. Such data have led researchers to suggest that the common ancestor of the chromalveolates had plastids of red algal origin, but that later, some evolutionary lineages within the group lost the plastids. Others question this idea, based on the absence of plastid genes in the genomes of several chromalveolates that lack plastids. Overall, the endosymbiotic origin of the chromalveolates is an interesting idea, but like any scientific hypothesis, new data may show it to be incorrect.

The chromalveolates are perhaps the most controversial of the five supergroups we describe in this chapter. Even so, for many scientists, this supergroup represents the best current hypothesis for the phylogeny of the two large protist clades to which we now turn: the alveolates and the stramenopiles.

Alveolates

The **alveolates** are a group of protists whose monophyly is well supported by molecular systematics. Structurally, species in this group have membrane-bounded sacs (alveoli) just under the plasma membrane **(Figure 28.8)**. The function of

the alveoli is unknown; researchers hypothesize that they may help stabilize the cell surface or regulate the cell's water and ion content.

The alveolates include three subgroups: a group of flagellates (the dinoflagellates), a group of parasites (the apicomplexans), and a group of protists that move using cilia (the ciliates).

Dinoflagellates

The **dinoflagellates** are characterized by cells that are reinforced by cellulose plates. Two flagella located in grooves in this "armor" make dinoflagellates (from the Greek *dinos*, whirling) spin as they move through the water **(Figure 28.9)**. Dinoflagellates are abundant components of both marine and freshwater plankton, communities of mostly microscopic organisms that drift in currents near the water's surface. These dinoflagellates include some of the most important species of *phytoplankton* (photosynthetic plankton, which include photosynthetic bacteria as well as algae). However, many photosynthetic dinoflagellates are mixotrophic, and roughly half of all dinoflagellates are purely heterotrophic.

▲ **Figure 28.8 Alveoli.** These sacs under the plasma membrane are a characteristic that distinguishes alveolates from other eukaryotes (TEM).

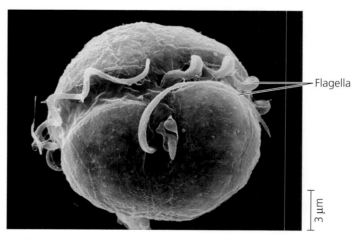

▲ **Figure 28.9 *Pfiesteria shumwayae*, a dinoflagellate.** Beating of the spiral flagellum, which lies in a groove that encircles the cell, makes this alveolate spin (colorized SEM).

Episodes of explosive population growth, or *blooms*, in dinoflagellates sometimes cause a phenomenon called "red tide." The blooms make coastal waters appear brownish red or pink because of the presence of carotenoids, the most common pigments in dinoflagellate plastids. Toxins produced by certain dinoflagellates (such as *Karenia brevis*, which inhabits the Gulf of Mexico) have caused massive kills of invertebrates and fishes. Humans who eat molluscs that have accumulated the toxins are affected as well, sometimes fatally.

Apicomplexans

Nearly all **apicomplexans** are parasites of animals, and some cause serious human diseases. The parasites spread through their host as tiny infectious cells called *sporozoites*. Apicomplexans are so named because one end (the *apex*) of

the sporozoite cell contains a *complex* of organelles specialized for penetrating host cells and tissues. Although apicomplex-

[handwritten note:]
- zygotic meiosis
- gametes are anisogamous
  - one large (female)
  - one small (male)
- massive mitotic divisions in RBC's cause fever in humans ③

▼ **Figure 28.10 The two-host life cycle of *Plasmodium*, the apicomplexan that causes malaria.**

? *Are morphological differences between sporozoites, merozoites, and gametocytes caused by different genomes or by differences in gene expression? Explain.*

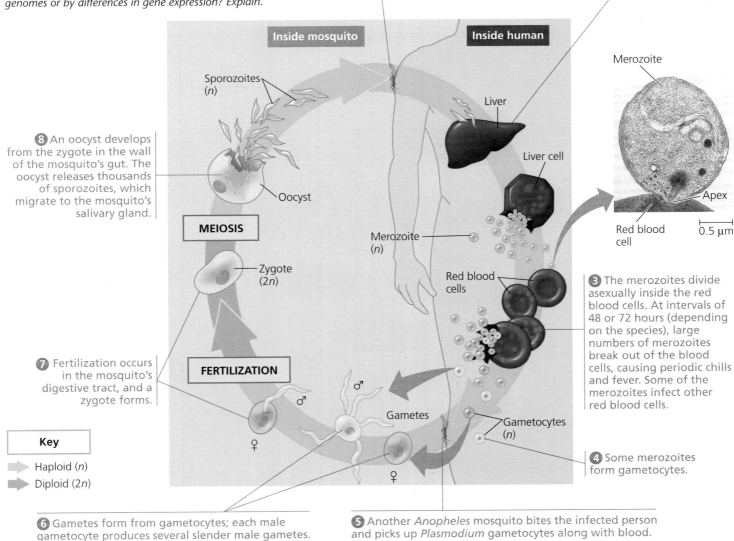

❶ An infected *Anopheles* mosquito bites a person, injecting *Plasmodium* sporozoites in its saliva.

❷ ... sporozoites undergo multiple divisions and become merozoites, which use their apical complex to penetrate red blood cells (see TEM below).

Inside mosquito

Inside human

Sporozoites (*n*)

Liver

Merozoite

❽ An oocyst develops from the zygote in the wall of the mosquito's gut. The oocyst releases thousands of sporozoites, which migrate to the mosquito's salivary gland.

Oocyst

Liver cell

MEIOSIS

Merozoite (*n*)

Apex

Red blood cell

0.5 μm

Zygote (2*n*)

Red blood cells

❸ The merozoites divide asexually inside the red blood cells. At intervals of 48 or 72 hours (depending on the species), large numbers of merozoites break out of the blood cells, causing periodic chills and fever. Some of the merozoites infect other red blood cells.

❼ Fertilization occurs in the mosquito's digestive tract, and a zygote forms.

FERTILIZATION

♂

♂

Gametes

Gametocytes (*n*)

Key

Haploid (*n*)

Diploid (2*n*)

♀

♀

❹ Some merozoites form gametocytes.

❻ Gametes form from gametocytes; each male gametocyte produces several slender male gametes.

❺ Another *Anopheles* mosquito bites the infected person and picks up *Plasmodium* gametocytes along with blood.

to a resurgence of malaria. About 250 million people in the tropics are currently infected, and 900,000 die each year.

The search for malarial vaccines has been hampered by the fact that *Plasmodium* lives mainly inside cells, hidden from the host's immune system. And, like trypanosomes, *Plasmodium* continually changes its surface proteins. The urgent need for treatments has inspired the sequencing of several *Plasmodium* genomes. Furthermore, researchers have now tracked the expression of most of the parasite's genes at numerous points

in its life cycle. This research could help identify vaccine targets. Drugs that target the apicoplast are also in development. This approach may be effective because the apicoplast, derived by secondary endosymbiosis from a prokaryote, has metabolic pathways different from those in humans.

Ciliates

Ciliates are a large, varied group of protists named for their use of cilia to move and feed **(Figure 28.11a)**. The cilia may

▼ **Figure 28.11 Structure and function in the ciliate *Paramecium caudatum*.**

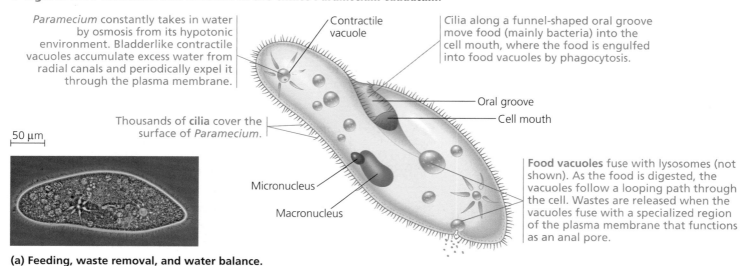

Paramecium constantly takes in water by osmosis from its hypotonic environment. Bladderlike contractile vacuoles accumulate excess water from radial canals and periodically expel it through the plasma membrane.

Thousands of **cilia** cover the surface of *Paramecium*.

50 µm

Contractile vacuole

Micronucleus

Macronucleus

Cilia along a funnel-shaped oral groove move food (mainly bacteria) into the cell mouth, where the food is engulfed into food vacuoles by phagocytosis.

Oral groove

Cell mouth

Food vacuoles fuse with lysosomes (not shown). As the food is digested, the vacuoles follow a looping path through the cell. Wastes are released when the vacuoles fuse with a specialized region of the plasma membrane that functions as an anal pore.

(a) Feeding, waste removal, and water balance.

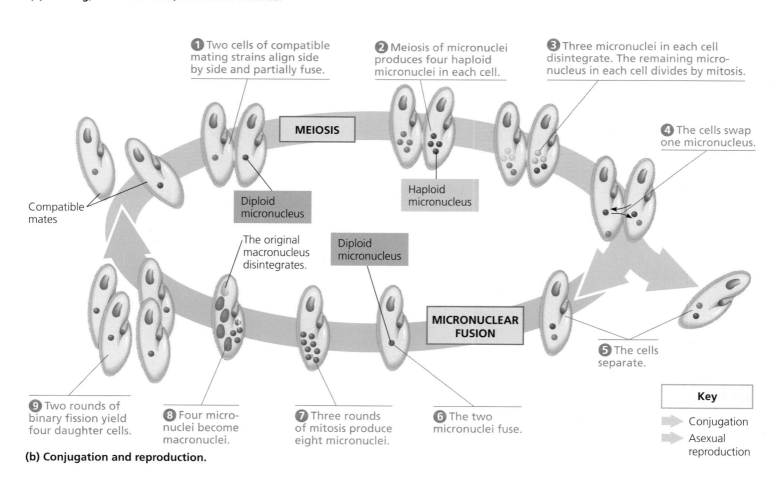

❶ Two cells of compatible mating strains align side by side and partially fuse.

❷ Meiosis of micronuclei produces four haploid micronuclei in each cell.

❸ Three micronuclei in each cell disintegrate. The remaining micronucleus in each cell divides by mitosis.

❹ The cells swap one micronucleus.

MEIOSIS

Haploid micronucleus

Diploid micronucleus

Compatible mates

The original macronucleus disintegrates.

Diploid micronucleus

MICRONUCLEAR FUSION

❺ The cells separate.

❾ Two rounds of binary fission yield four daughter cells.

❽ Four micronuclei become macronuclei.

❼ Three rounds of mitosis produce eight micronuclei.

❻ The two micronuclei fuse.

Key

➡ Conjugation
➡ Asexual reproduction

(b) Conjugation and reproduction.

completely cover the cell surface or may be clustered in a few rows or tufts. In certain species, rows of tightly packed cilia function collectively in locomotion. Other ciliates scurry about on leg-like structures constructed from many cilia bonded together.

A distinctive feature of ciliates is the presence of two types of nuclei: tiny micronuclei and large macronuclei. A cell has one or more nuclei of each type. Genetic variation results from **conjugation**, a sexual process in which two individuals exchange haploid micronuclei but do not reproduce **(Figure 28.11b)**. Ciliates generally reproduce asexually by binary fission, during which the existing macronucleus disintegrates and a new one is formed from the cell's micronuclei. Each macronucleus typically contains multiple copies of the ciliate's genome. Genes in the macronucleus control the everyday functions of the cell, such as feeding, waste removal, and maintaining water balance (see Figure 28.11a).

Stramenopiles

Another major subgroup of the chromalveolates is the **stramenopiles**, protists that include some of the most important photosynthetic organisms on the planet, as well as several clades of heterotrophs. Their name (from the Latin *stramen*, straw, and *pilos*, hair) refers to their characteristic flagellum, which has numerous fine, hairlike projections. In most stramenopiles, this "hairy" flagellum is paired with a shorter "smooth" (nonhairy) flagellum **(Figure 28.12)**. Here we'll focus on four groups of stramenopiles: diatoms, golden algae, brown algae, and oomycetes.

Diatoms

Diatoms are unicellular algae that have a unique glass-like wall made of hydrated silica (silicon dioxide) embedded in an organic matrix. The wall consists of two parts that overlap like a shoe box and its lid. These walls provide effective protection from the crushing jaws of predators: Live diatoms can withstand pressures as great as 1.4 million kg/m², equal to the pressure under each leg of a table supporting an elephant! Much of the diatoms' strength comes from the delicate lacework of holes and grooves in their walls **(Figure 28.13)**; if the walls were smooth, it would take 60% less force to crush them.

With an estimated 100,000 living species, diatoms are a highly diverse group of protists (see Figure 28.3). They are a major component of phytoplankton both in the ocean and in lakes: One bucket of water scooped from the surface of the sea may contain millions of these microscopic algae. The abundance of diatoms in the past is also evident in the fossil record, where massive accumulations of fossilized diatom walls are major constituents of sediments known as *diatomaceous earth*. These sediments are mined for their quality as a filtering medium and for many other uses.

▲ **Figure 28.12 Stramenopile flagella.** Most stramenopiles, such as *Synura petersenii*, have two flagella: one covered with fine, stiff hairs and a shorter one that is smooth.

5 µm

Hairy flagellum

Smooth flagellum

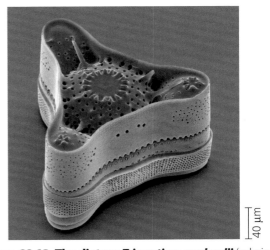

▲ **Figure 28.13 The diatom *Triceratium morlandii*** (colorized SEM).

40 µm

You might expect that since diatoms are so widespread and abundant, their photosynthetic activity would affect global carbon dioxide levels, and this is indeed the case. Diatoms have this effect in part because of the chain of events that follows their rapid population growth (a bloom) when ample nutrients are available. Typically, diatoms are eaten by a variety of protists and invertebrates, but during a bloom, many escape this fate. When these uneaten diatoms die, their bodies sink to the ocean floor. Diatoms that sink to the ocean floor are not very likely to be broken down by bacteria and other decomposers. Hence, the carbon in their bodies remains there, rather than being released as carbon dioxide as the decomposers respire. The overall effect of these events is that carbon dioxide absorbed by diatoms during photosynthesis is transported, or "pumped," to the ocean floor. With an eye toward reducing global warming by lowering atmospheric carbon dioxide levels, some scientists advocate promoting diatom blooms by fertilizing the ocean with essential nutrients such as iron. Other scientists question this strategy, noting that small-scale tests of this idea have yielded mixed results and that it is difficult to predict the effects of large-scale manipulations of ecological communities.

Flagellum
Outer container
Living cell

25 µm

▲ **Figure 28.14** *Dinobryon,* **a colonial golden alga found in fresh water** (LM).

Blade
Stipe
Holdfast

▲ **Figure 28.15** **Seaweeds: adapted to life at the ocean's margins.** The sea palm (*Postelsia*) lives on rocks along the coast of the northwestern United States and western Canada. The thallus of this brown alga is well adapted to maintaining a firm foothold despite the crashing surf.

Golden Algae

The characteristic color of **golden algae** results from their yellow and brown carotenoids. The cells of golden algae are typically biflagellated, with both flagella attached near one end of the cell.

Many golden algae are components of freshwater and marine plankton. While all golden algae are photosynthetic, some species are mixotrophic. These mixotrophs can absorb dissolved organic compounds or ingest food particles, including living cells, by phagocytosis. Most species are unicellular, but some, such as those in the freshwater genus *Dinobryon,* are colonial **(Figure 28.14)**. If environmental conditions deteriorate, many species form protective cysts that can survive for decades.

Brown Algae

The largest and most complex algae are **brown algae**. All are multicellular, and most are marine. Brown algae are especially common along temperate coasts, where the water is cool. They owe their characteristic brown or olive color to the carotenoids in their plastids.

Many of the species commonly called "seaweeds" are brown algae. (Some large, multicellular species of red and green algae are also referred to as seaweeds. We will examine them later in this chapter.) Brown algae include species that have the most complex multicellular anatomy of all algae; some even have specialized tissues and organs that resemble those in plants. But morphological and DNA evidence indicates that the similarities evolved independently in the algal and plant lineages and are thus analogous, not homologous.

The term **thallus** (plural, *thalli*; from the Greek *thallos,* sprout) refers to an algal body that is plantlike. Unlike the body of a plant, however, a thallus lacks true roots, stems, and leaves. A typical thallus consists of a rootlike **holdfast**, which anchors the alga, and a stemlike **stipe**, which supports leaflike **blades** **(Figure 28.15)**. The blades provide most of the alga's photosynthetic surface. Some brown algae are equipped with gas-filled, bubble-shaped floats, which help keep the blades up near the water surface. Beyond the intertidal zone in deeper waters live giant seaweeds known as kelps. The stipes of these brown algae may be as long as 60 m, more than half the length of a football field.

Brown algae that inhabit the intertidal zone must cope with water churned by waves and wind, along with low tides that expose the algae to the drying atmosphere and intense rays of the sun. Unique adaptations enable these seaweeds to survive. For example, their cell walls are composed of cellulose and gel-forming polysaccharides that help cushion the thalli from waves and reduce drying when the algae are exposed.

Brown algae are important commodities for humans. Some species are eaten, such as *Laminaria* (Japanese "kombu"), which is used in soups. In addition, the gel-forming substance in the cell walls of brown algae, called algin, is used to thicken many processed foods, including pudding and salad dressing.

Alternation of Generations

A variety of life cycles have evolved among the multicellular algae. The most complex life cycles include an **alternation of generations**, the alternation of multicellular haploid and diploid forms. Although haploid and diploid conditions [. . .] results [. . .] which matures and gives rise to a alternate in *all* sexual life cycles—human ga[. . .] ple, are haploid—the term *alternation of ge*[. . .] enerations are **heteromorphic**, only to life cycles in which both haploid an[. . .] tes and gametophytes are struc- are multicellular. As you will read in Chapter[. . .] life cycles have an alternation of generations also evolved in plants.

The complex life cycle of the brown alga *La*[. . .] each other, although they differ an example of alternation of generations (Figu[. . .] diploid individual is called the *sporophyte* becau[. . .] spores. The spores are haploid and move by me[. . .] *nd Their Relatives*) they are called zoospores. The zoospores develop[. . .] molds, the white rusts, and the multicellular male and female *gametophytes*, w[. . .] r morphology, these organisms gametes. The union of two gametes (fertilization[. . .] ungi (in fact, *oomycete* means

▲ **Figure 28.16 The life cycle of the brown alga *Laminaria*: an example of alternation of generations.**

? *Are the sperm shown in ⑤ genetically identical to one another? Are they genetically identical to the egg in ⑥? Explain.*

"egg fungus"). For example, many oomycetes have multinucleate filaments (hyphae) that resemble fungal hyphae **(Figure 28.17)**. However, there are key differences between oomycetes and fungi. Among the differences, oomycetes typically have cell walls made of cellulose, whereas the walls of fungi consist mainly of another polysaccharide, chitin. Data from molecular systematics have confirmed that oomycetes are not closely related to fungi. Their superficial similarity is a case of convergent evolution. In both oomycetes and fungi, the high surface-to-volume ratio of filamentous structures enhances the uptake of nutrients from the environment.

Although oomycetes descended from plastid-bearing ancestors, they no longer have plastids and do not perform photosynthesis. Instead, they typically acquire nutrients as decomposers or parasites. Most water molds are decomposers that grow as cottony masses on dead algae and animals, mainly in freshwater habitats (see Figure 28.17). White rusts and downy mildews generally live on land as plant parasites.

The ecological impact of oomycetes can be significant. For example, the oomycete *Phytophthora infestans* causes potato late blight, which turns the stalk and stem of potato plants to black slime. Late blight contributed to the devastating Irish famine of the 19th century, in which a million people died and at least that many were forced to leave Ireland. The disease remains a major problem today, causing crop losses of typically 15% in North America and as high as 70% in some parts of Russia where farmers cannot afford pesticides.

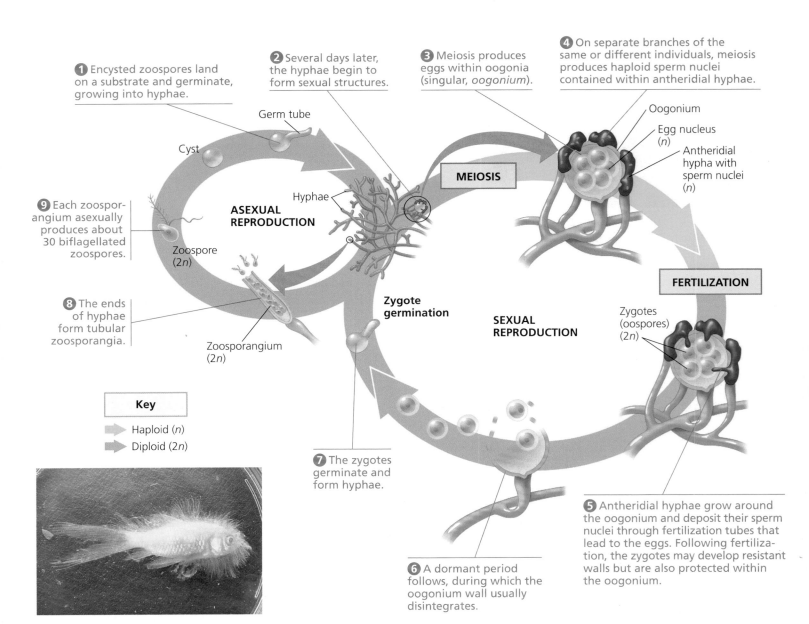

① Encysted zoospores land on a substrate and germinate, growing into hyphae.

② Several days later, the hyphae begin to form sexual structures.

③ Meiosis produces eggs within oogonia (singular, *oogonium*).

④ On separate branches of the same or different individuals, meiosis produces haploid sperm nuclei contained within antheridial hyphae.

⑨ Each zoosporangium asexually produces about 30 biflagellated zoospores.

⑧ The ends of hyphae form tubular zoosporangia.

⑦ The zygotes germinate and form hyphae.

⑥ A dormant period follows, during which the oogonium wall usually disintegrates.

⑤ Antheridial hyphae grow around the oogonium and deposit their sperm nuclei through fertilization tubes that lead to the eggs. Following fertilization, the zygotes may develop resistant walls but are also protected within the oogonium.

Germ tube

Cyst

Hyphae

ASEXUAL REPRODUCTION

Zoospore (2n)

Zoosporangium (2n)

Zygote germination

SEXUAL REPRODUCTION

MEIOSIS

Oogonium

Egg nucleus (n)

Antheridial hypha with sperm nuclei (n)

FERTILIZATION

Zygotes (oospores) (2n)

Key

Haploid (n)

Diploid (2n)

▲ **Figure 28.17 The life cycle of a water mold.** Water molds help decompose dead insects, fishes, and other animals in fresh water. (Note the hyphal mass growing on the goldfish in the photograph.)

To understand this pathogen better, molecular biologists have isolated DNA from a specimen of *P. infestans* preserved from the Irish potato blight of the 1840s. Genetic studies show that in recent decades, this oomycete has acquired genes that make it more aggressive and more resistant to pesticides. Scientists are looking within the genomes of both *Phytophthora* and potatoes to identify new weapons against the disease. Already, researchers have transferred genes from a blight-resistant strain of wild potato into domestic potatoes to produce a resistant crop strain.

CONCEPT CHECK 28.3

1. Summarize the evidence for and against the hypothesis that the species currently classified as chromalveolates are members of a single clade.
2. **WHAT IF?** Would you expect the plastid DNA of photosynthetic dinoflagellates, diatoms, and golden algae to be more similar to the nuclear DNA of plants (domain Eukarya) or to the chromosomal DNA of cyanobacteria (domain Bacteria)? Explain.
3. **MAKE CONNECTIONS** Which of the three life cycles in Figure 13.6 (p. 252) exhibits alternation of generations? How does it differ from the other two?

For suggested answers, see Appendix A.

CONCEPT 28.4

Rhizarians are a diverse group of protists defined by DNA similarities

The clade **Rhizaria** has recently been proposed based on results from molecular systematics. Although its members vary greatly in morphology, DNA evidence suggests that rhizarians are a monophyletic group. According to some recent phylogenetic studies, Rhizaria should be nested within Chromalveolata, as discussed in Figure 28.3.

Many species in Rhizaria are among the organisms referred to as amoebas. **Amoebas** were formerly defined as protists that move and feed by means of **pseudopodia**, extensions that may bulge from almost anywhere on the cell surface. An amoeba moves by extending a pseudopodium and anchoring the tip; more cytoplasm then streams into the pseudopodium. However, based on molecular systematics, it is now clear that amoebas do not constitute a monophyletic group but are dispersed across many distantly related eukaryotic

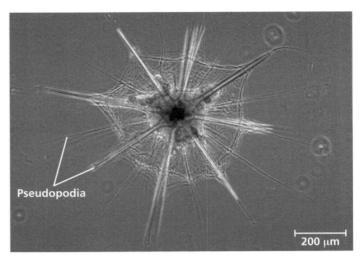

▲ **Figure 28.18 A radiolarian.** Numerous threadlike pseudopodia radiate from the central body of this radiolarian, which is found in the Red Sea (LM).

taxa. Most of those that belong to the clade Rhizaria are distinguished morphologically from other amoebas by having threadlike pseudopodia.

Rhizarians include three groups that we'll examine here: radiolarians, forams, and cercozoans.

Radiolarians

The protists called **radiolarians** have delicate, intricately symmetrical internal skeletons that are generally made of silica. The pseudopodia of these mostly marine protists radiate from the central body (**Figure 28.18**) and are reinforced by bundles of microtubules. The microtubules are covered by a thin layer of cytoplasm, which engulfs smaller microorganisms that become attached to the pseudopodia. Cytoplasmic streaming then carries the captured prey into the main part of the cell. After radiolarians die, their skeletons settle to the seafloor, where they have accumulated as an ooze that is hundreds of meters thick in some locations.

Forams

The protists called **foraminiferans** (from the Latin *foramen*, little hole, and *ferre*, to bear), or **forams**, are named for their porous shells, called **tests** (see Figure 28.3). Foram tests consist of a single piece of organic material hardened with calcium carbonate. The pseudopodia that extend through the pores function in swimming, test formation, and feeding. Many forams also derive nourishment from the photosynthesis of symbiotic algae that live within the tests.

Forams are found in both the ocean and fresh water. Most species live in sand or attach themselves to rocks or algae, but some are abundant in plankton. The largest forams, though single-celled, grow to a diameter of several centimeters.

Ninety percent of all identified species of forams are known from fossils. Along with the calcium-containing remains of other protists, the fossilized tests of forams are part of marine sediments, including sedimentary rocks that are now land formations. Foram fossils are excellent markers for correlating the ages of sedimentary rocks in different parts of the world.

Cercozoans

First identified in molecular phylogenies, the **cercozoans** form a large group that contains most of the amoeboid and flagellated protists that feed with threadlike pseudopodia. Cercozoan protists are common in marine, freshwater, and soil ecosystems.

Most cercozoans are heterotrophs. Many are parasites of plants, animals, or other protists; many others are predators. The predators include the most important consumers of bacteria in aquatic and soil ecosystems, along with species that eat other protists, fungi, and even small animals. One small group of cercozoans, the chlorarachniophytes (mentioned earlier in the discussion of secondary endosymbiosis), are mixotrophic: These organisms ingest smaller protists and bacteria as well as perform photosynthesis. At least one other cercozoan, *Paulinella chromatophora*, is an autotroph, deriving its energy from light and its carbon from carbon dioxide. This species has a distinctive sausage-shaped internal structure where photosynthesis is performed **(Figure 28.19)**. Genetic and morphological analyses indicate that these structures were derived from a cyanobacterium, although not the same cyanobacterium from which all other plastids were derived. As such, *Paulinella* appears to represent an intriguing additional evolutionary example of a eukaryotic lineage that obtained its photosynthetic apparatus directly from a cyanobacterium.

Chromatophore

5 µm

▲ **Figure 28.19 A second case of primary endosymbiosis?** The cercozoan *Paulinella* conducts photosynthesis in a unique structure called a chromatophore (LM). Chromatophores are surrounded by a membrane with a peptidoglycan layer, suggesting that they are derived from a bacterium. DNA evidence indicates that chromatophores are derived from a different cyanobacterium than that from which other plastids are derived.

CONCEPT CHECK 28.4

1. Explain why forams have such a well-preserved fossil record.
2. **WHAT IF?** Suppose DNA evidence suggests that a newly discovered amoeba is in the clade Rhizaria, yet its morphology is more similar to amoebas in other eukaryotic groups. Suggest an explanation that could account for these conflicting observations.
3. **MAKE CONNECTIONS** Review Figures 9.2 (p. 163) and 10.6 (p. 188), and then summarize how CO_2 and O_2 are both used and produced by chlorarachniophytes and other aerobic algae.

For suggested answers, see Appendix A.

CONCEPT 28.5

Red algae and green algae are the closest relatives of land plants

As we described in Chapter 25, molecular systematics and studies of cell structure support the following scenario: More than a billion years ago, a heterotrophic protist acquired a cyanobacterial endosymbiont, and the photosynthetic descendants of this ancient protist evolved into red algae and green algae. At least 475 million years ago, the lineage that produced green algae gave rise to land plants. Together, red algae, green algae, and land plants make up the fourth eukaryotic supergroup, which is called **Archaeplastida**. Archaeplastida is a monophyletic group that descended from the ancient protist that engulfed a cyanobacterium. We will examine land plants in Chapters 29 and 30; here we will look at the diversity of their closest algal relatives, red algae and green algae.

Red Algae

Many of the 6,000 known species of **red algae** (rhodophytes, from the Greek *rhodos*, red) are reddish, owing to a photosynthetic accessory pigment called phycoerythrin, which masks the green of chlorophyll **(Figure 28.20)**. However, species adapted to more shallow water have less phycoerythrin. As a result, red algal species may be greenish red in very shallow

▶ **Bonnemaisonia hamifera.** This red alga has a filamentous form.

20 cm

8 mm

◀ **Dulse (*Palmaria palmata*).** This edible species has a "leafy" form.

▼ **Nori.** The red alga *Porphyra* is the source of a traditional Japanese food.

The seaweed is grown on nets in shallow coastal waters.

The harvested seaweed is spread on bamboo screens to dry.

Paper-thin, glossy sheets of nori make a mineral-rich wrap for rice, seafood, and vegetables in sushi.

▲ **Figure 28.20 Red algae.**

water, bright red at moderate depths, and almost black in deep water. Some species lack pigmentation altogether and function heterotrophically as parasites on other red algae.

Red algae are the most abundant large algae in the warm coastal waters of tropical oceans. Their accessory pigments, including phycoerythrin, allow them to absorb blue and green light, which penetrate relatively far into the water. A

species of red alga has been discovered near the Bahamas at a depth of more than 260 m. There are also a small number of freshwater and terrestrial species.

Most red algae are multicellular. Although none are as big as the giant brown kelps, the largest multicellular red algae are included in the informal designation "seaweeds." You may have eaten one of these multicellular red algae, *Porphyra* (Japanese "nori"), as crispy sheets or as a wrap for sushi (see Figure 28.20). Red algae have especially diverse life cycles, and alternation of generations is common. But unlike other algae, they have no flagellated stages in their life cycle and depend on water currents to bring gametes together for fertilization.

Green Algae

The grass-green chloroplasts of **green algae** have a structure and pigment composition much like the chloroplasts of land plants. Molecular systematics and cellular morphology leave little doubt that green algae and land plants are closely related. In fact, some systematists now advocate including green algae in an expanded "plant" kingdom, Viridiplantae (from the Latin *viridis*, green). Phylogenetically, this change makes sense, since otherwise the green algae are a paraphyletic group.

Green algae are divided into two main groups, the charophytes and the chlorophytes. The charophytes are the algae most closely related to land plants, and so we will discuss them along with plants in Chapter 29.

The second group, the chlorophytes (from the Greek *chloros*, green), includes more than 7,000 species. Most live in fresh water, but there are also many marine and some terrestrial species. The simplest chlorophytes are unicellular organisms such as *Chlamydomonas*, which resemble gametes or zoospores of more complex chlorophytes. Various species of unicellular chlorophytes live in aquatic habitats as phytoplankton or inhabit damp soil. Some live symbiotically within other eukaryotes, contributing part of their photosynthetic output to the food supply of their hosts. Some chlorophytes have even adapted to one of the last habitats you might expect to find them: snow. These chlorophytes carry out photosynthesis despite subfreezing temperatures and intense visible and ultraviolet radiation. They are protected by the snow itself, which acts as a shield, and by radiation-blocking compounds in their cytoplasm. Other chlorophytes contain similar protective compounds in their cell wall or in a durable coat that surrounds the zygote.

Larger size and greater complexity evolved in chlorophytes by three different mechanisms:

1. The formation of colonies of individual cells, as seen in *Volvox* (see Figure 28.3) and in filamentous forms that contribute to the stringy masses known as pond scum

2. The formation of true multicellular bodies by cell division and differentiation, as in *Ulva* (**Figure 28.21a**)
3. The repeated division of nuclei with no cytoplasmic division, as in *Caulerpa* (**Figure 28.21b**)

Most chlorophytes have complex life cycles, with both sexual and asexual reproductive stages. Nearly all species of chlorophytes reproduce sexually by means of biflagellated gametes that have cup-shaped chloroplasts (**Figure 28.22**). Alternation of generations has evolved in some chlorophytes, including *Ulva*.

CONCEPT CHECK 28.5

1. Contrast red algae and brown algae.
2. Why is it accurate to say that *Ulva* is truly multicellular but *Caulerpa* is not?
3. **WHAT IF?** Suggest a possible reason why species in the green algal lineage may have been more likely to colonize land than species in the red algal lineage.

For suggested answers, see Appendix A.

(a) *Ulva*, or sea lettuce. This edible chlorophyte has a multicellular thallus differentiated into leaflike blades. Its rootlike holdfast anchors the alga.

(b) *Caulerpa*, an intertidal chlorophyte. The branched filaments lack cross-walls and thus are multinucleate. In effect, the thallus is one huge "supercell."

▲ **Figure 28.21 Multicellular chlorophytes.**

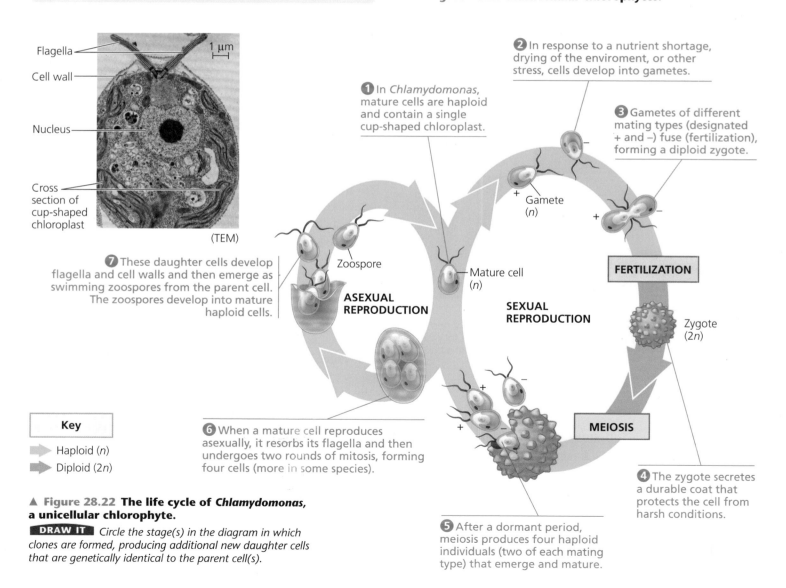

Flagella
Cell wall
Nucleus
Cross section of cup-shaped chloroplast
(TEM)
1 μm

1 In *Chlamydomonas*, mature cells are haploid and contain a single cup-shaped chloroplast.

2 In response to a nutrient shortage, drying of the enviroment, or other stress, cells develop into gametes.

3 Gametes of different mating types (designated + and −) fuse (fertilization), forming a diploid zygote.

Gamete (*n*)

Mature cell (*n*)

Zoospore

7 These daughter cells develop flagella and cell walls and then emerge as swimming zoospores from the parent cell. The zoospores develop into mature haploid cells.

ASEXUAL REPRODUCTION

SEXUAL REPRODUCTION

FERTILIZATION

Zygote (2*n*)

MEIOSIS

4 The zygote secretes a durable coat that protects the cell from harsh conditions.

5 After a dormant period, meiosis produces four haploid individuals (two of each mating type) that emerge and mature.

6 When a mature cell reproduces asexually, it resorbs its flagella and then undergoes two rounds of mitosis, forming four cells (more in some species).

Key

→ Haploid (*n*)
➔ Diploid (2*n*)

▲ **Figure 28.22 The life cycle of *Chlamydomonas*, a unicellular chlorophyte.**

DRAW IT *Circle the stage(s) in the diagram in which clones are formed, producing additional new daughter cells that are genetically identical to the parent cell(s).*

CONCEPT 28.6

Unikonts include protists that are closely related to fungi and animals

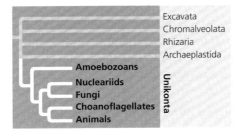

Unikonta is a recently proposed, extremely diverse supergroup of eukaryotes that includes animals, fungi, and some protists. There are two major clades of unikonts, the amoebozoans and the opisthokonts (animals, fungi, and closely related protist groups). Each of these two major clades is strongly supported by molecular systematics. The close relationship between amoebozoans and opisthokonts is more controversial. Support for this close relationship is provided by comparisons of myosin proteins and by several studies based on hundreds of genes, but not by other studies based on single genes.

Another controversy involving the unikonts concerns the root of the eukaryotic tree. Recall that the root of a phylogenetic tree anchors the tree in time: Branch points close to the root are the oldest. At present, the root of the eukaryotic tree is uncertain; thus, we do not know which group of eukaryotes was the first to diverge from other eukaryotes. Some hypotheses, such as the amitochondriate hypothesis described earlier, have been abandoned, but researchers have yet to agree on an alternative. If the root of the eukaryotic tree were known, scientists could infer characteristics of the common ancestor of all eukaryotes. Such information could help resolve some of the current debates about the five supergroups of eukaryotes.

In trying to determine the root of the eukaryotic tree, researchers have based their phylogenies on different sets of genes, producing conflicting results. Researchers at Oxford University have described a different approach, results from which support a radical new hypothesis about the root of the eukaryotic tree (**Figure 28.23**). According to their hypothesis, the unikonts were the first eukaryotes to diverge from other eukaryotes. This hypothesis proposes that animals and fungi belong to an early-diverging group of eukaryotes, while protists that lack typical mitochondria (such as the diplomonads and parabasalids) diverged much later in the history of life. This idea remains controversial and will require more supporting evidence to be widely accepted.

Amoebozoans

As already mentioned, **amoebozoans** form a clade that is well supported by molecular data. This clade includes many species

▼ Figure 28.23

INQUIRY

What is the root of the eukaryotic tree?

EXPERIMENT Responding to the difficulty in determining the root of the eukaryotic phylogenetic tree, Alexandra Stechmann and Thomas Cavalier-Smith, of Oxford University, proposed a new approach. They studied two genes, one for the enzyme dihydrofolate reductase (DHFR), the other for the enzyme thymidylate synthase (TS). Their approach took advantage of a rare evolutionary event: In some organisms, the DHFR and TS genes have fused, leading to the production of a single protein with both enzyme activities. Stechmann and Cavalier-Smith amplified (using PCR; see Figure 20.8) and sequenced DHFR and TS genes in nine species (one choanoflagellate; two amoebozoans; one euglenozoan; two chromalveolates; and three rhizarians). They combined their data with previously published data for species of bacteria, animals, plants, and fungi.

RESULTS The bacteria studied all have separate DHFR and TS genes, suggesting that this is the ancestral condition (red dot on the tree below). Other taxa with separate genes are denoted by red type. Fused genes are a derived character, found in certain members (blue type) of the supergroups Excavata, Chromalveolata, Rhizaria, and Archaeplastida:

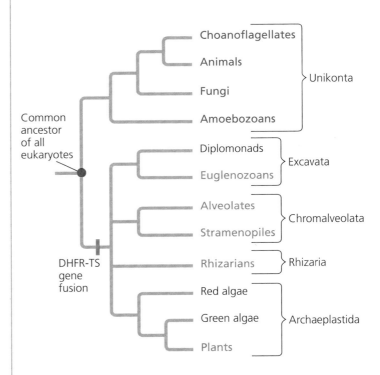

CONCLUSION These results support the hypothesis that the root of the tree is located between the unikonts and all other eukaryotes, suggesting that the unikonts were the first group of eukaryotes to diverge. Because support for this hypothesis is based on only one trait—the fusion of the DHFR and TS genes—more data are needed to evaluate its validity.

SOURCE A. Stechmann and T. Cavalier-Smith, Rooting the eukaryote tree by using a derived gene fusion, *Science* 297:89–91 (2002).

WHAT IF? Stechmann and Cavalier-Smith wrote that their conclusions are "valid only if the genes fused just once and were never secondarily split." Why is this assumption critical to their approach?

of amoebas that have lobe- or tube-shaped, rather than thread-like, pseudopodia. Amoebozoans include slime molds, gymnamoebas, and entamoebas.

Slime Molds

Slime molds, or mycetozoans (from the Latin, meaning "fungus animals"), were once thought to be fungi because, like fungi, they produce fruiting bodies that aid in spore dispersal. However, the resemblance between slime molds and fungi appears to be another example of evolutionary convergence. Molecular systematics places slime molds in Amoebozoa and suggests that they descended from unicellular ancestors. Slime molds have diverged into two main branches, plasmodial slime molds and cellular slime molds, distinguished in part by their unique life cycles.

Plasmodial Slime Molds Many **plasmodial slime molds** are brightly colored, often yellow or orange **(Figure 28.24)**. At one stage in their life cycle, they form a mass called a **plasmodium**, which may grow to a diameter of many centimeters. (Don't confuse a slime mold's plasmodium with the genus *Plasmodium*, which includes the parasitic apicomplexan that causes malaria.) Despite its size, the plasmodium is not multicellular; it is a single mass of cytoplasm that is undivided by plasma membranes and that contains many nuclei. This "supercell" is the product of mitotic nuclear divisions that are not followed by cytokinesis.

Within the plasmodium, cytoplasm streams first one way, then the other, in pulsing flows that are beautiful to watch through a microscope. This cytoplasmic streaming apparently helps distribute nutrients and oxygen. The plasmodium extends pseudopodia through moist soil, leaf mulch, or rotting

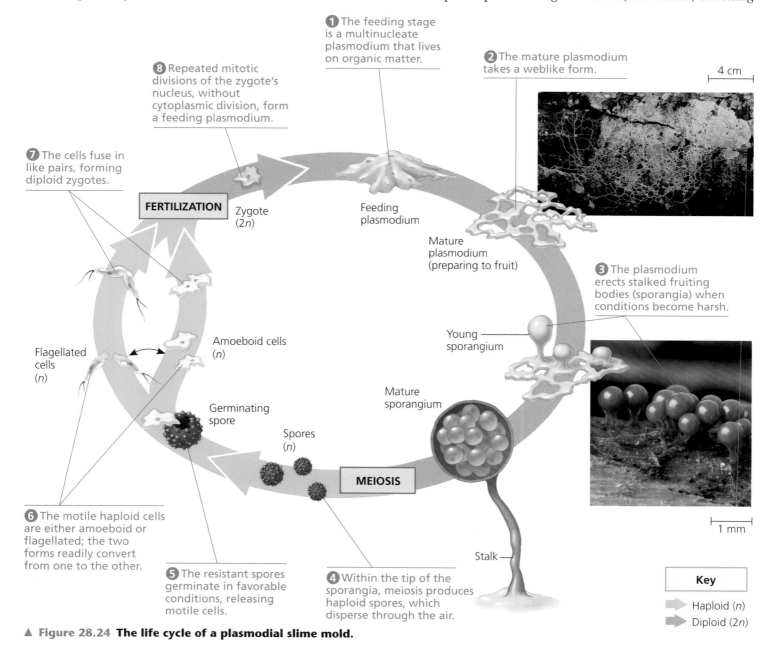

▲ **Figure 28.24 The life cycle of a plasmodial slime mold.**

logs, engulfing food particles by phagocytosis as it grows. If the habitat begins to dry up or there is no food left, the plasmodium stops growing and differentiates into fruiting bodies, which function in sexual reproduction.

Cellular Slime Molds The life cycle of the protists called **cellular slime molds** can prompt us to question what it means to be an individual organism. The feeding stage of these organisms consists of solitary cells that function individually, but when food is depleted, the cells form an aggregate that functions as a unit **(Figure 28.25)**. Although this mass of cells superficially resembles a plasmodial slime mold, the cells remain separated by their individual plasma membranes. Cellular slime molds also differ from plasmodial slime molds in

being haploid organisms (only the zygote is diploid) and in having fruiting bodies that function in asexual rather than sexual reproduction.

Dictyostelium discoideum, a cellular slime mold commonly found on forest floors, has become a model organism for studying the evolution of multicellularity. One line of research has focused on the slime mold's fruiting body stage. During this stage, the cells that form the stalk die as they dry out, while the spore cells at the top survive and have the potential to reproduce. Scientists have found that mutations in a single gene can turn individual *Dictyostelium* cells into "cheaters" that never become part of the stalk. Because these mutants gain a strong reproductive advantage over noncheaters, why don't all *Dictyostelium* cells cheat?

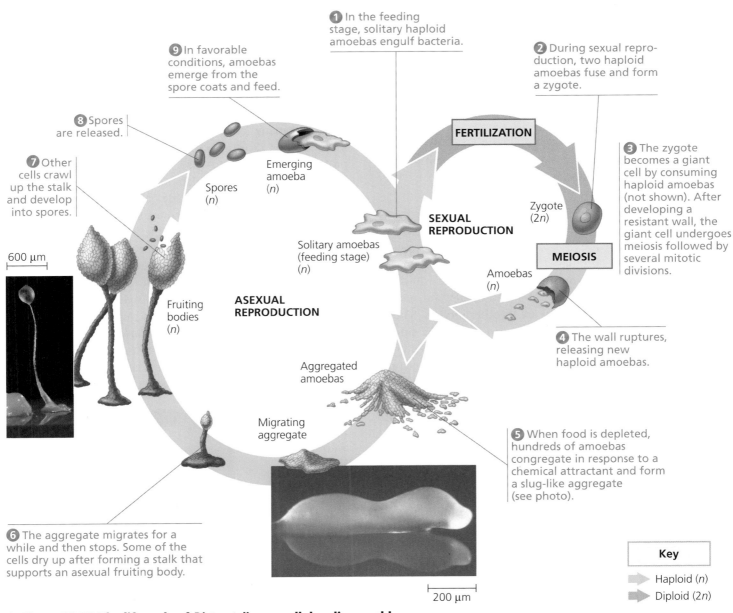

1 In the feeding stage, solitary haploid amoebas engulf bacteria.

9 In favorable conditions, amoebas emerge from the spore coats and feed.

2 During sexual reproduction, two haploid amoebas fuse and form a zygote.

8 Spores are released.

FERTILIZATION

7 Other cells crawl up the stalk and develop into spores.

Emerging amoeba (*n*)

Spores (*n*)

3 The zygote becomes a giant cell by consuming haploid amoebas (not shown). After developing a resistant wall, the giant cell undergoes meiosis followed by several mitotic divisions.

Zygote (2*n*)

SEXUAL REPRODUCTION

600 μm

Solitary amoebas (feeding stage) (*n*)

MEIOSIS

Fruiting bodies (*n*)

ASEXUAL REPRODUCTION

Amoebas (*n*)

4 The wall ruptures, releasing new haploid amoebas.

Aggregated amoebas

Migrating aggregate

5 When food is depleted, hundreds of amoebas congregate in response to a chemical attractant and form a slug-like aggregate (see photo).

6 The aggregate migrates for a while and then stops. Some of the cells dry up after forming a stalk that supports an asexual fruiting body.

200 μm

Key

Haploid (*n*)

Diploid (2*n*)

▲ **Figure 28.25 The life cycle of *Dictyostelium*, a cellular slime mold.**

Recent discoveries suggest an answer to this question. Cheating mutants lack a protein on their cell surface, and noncheating cells can recognize this difference. Noncheaters preferentially aggregate with other noncheaters, thus depriving cheaters of the opportunity to exploit them. Such a recognition system may have been important in the evolution of multicellular eukaryotes such as animals and plants.

Gymnamoebas

Gymnamoebas constitute a large and varied group of amoebozoans. These unicellular protists are ubiquitous in soil as well as freshwater and marine environments. Most are heterotrophs that actively seek and consume bacteria and other protists (see Figure 28.3). Some gymnamoebas also feed on detritus (nonliving organic matter).

Entamoebas

Whereas most amoebozoans are free-living, those that belong to the genus *Entamoeba* are parasites. They infect all classes of vertebrate animals as well as some invertebrates. Humans are host to at least six species of *Entamoeba*, but only one, *E. histolytica*, is known to be pathogenic. *E. histolytica* causes amebic dysentery and is spread via contaminated drinking water, food, or eating utensils. Responsible for up to 100,000 deaths worldwide every year, the disease is the third-leading cause of death due to eukaryotic parasites, after malaria (see Figure 28.10) and schistosomiasis (see Figure 33.11).

Opisthokonts

Opisthokonts are an extremely diverse group of eukaryotes that includes animals, fungi, and several groups of protists. We will discuss the evolutionary history of fungi and animals in Chapters 31–34. Of the opisthokont protists, we will discuss the nucleariids in Chapter 31 because they are more closely related to fungi than they are to other protists. Similarly, we will discuss choanoflagellates in Chapter 32, since they are more closely related to animals than they are to other protists. The nucleariids and choanoflagellates illustrate why scientists have abandoned the former kingdom Protista: A monophyletic group that included these single-celled eukaryotes would also have to include the multicellular animals and fungi that are closely related to them.

CONCEPT CHECK 28.6

1. Contrast the pseudopodia of amoebozoans and forams.
2. In what sense is "fungus animal" a fitting description of a slime mold? In what sense is it not fitting?
3. **WHAT IF?** If further evidence indicates that the root of the eukaryotic tree is as shown in Figure 28.23, would this evidence support, contradict, or have no bearing on the hypothesis that Excavata is monophyletic?

For suggested answers, see Appendix A.

CONCEPT 28.7

Protists play key roles in ecological communities

Most protists are aquatic, and they are found almost anywhere there is water, including moist terrestrial habitats such as damp soil and leaf litter. In oceans, ponds, and lakes, many protists are bottom-dwellers that attach to rocks and other substrates or creep through the sand and silt. Other protists are important constituents of plankton. We'll focus here on two key roles that protists play in the varied habitats in which they live: that of symbiont and that of producer.

Symbiotic Protists

Many protists form symbiotic associations with other species. For example, photosynthetic dinoflagellates are food-providing symbiotic partners of the coral polyps that build coral reefs. Coral reefs are highly diverse ecological communities. That diversity ultimately depends on corals—and on the mutualistic protist symbionts that nourish them. Corals support reef diversity by providing food to some species and habitat to many others.

Another example is the wood-digesting protists that inhabit the gut of many termite species **(Figure 28.26)**. Unaided, termites cannot digest wood, and they rely on protistan or prokaryotic symbionts to do so. Termites cause over $3.5 billion in damage annually to wooden homes in the United States.

Symbiotic protists also include parasites that have compromised the economies of entire countries. Consider the malaria-causing protist *Plasmodium*: Income levels in countries hard hit by malaria are 33% lower than in similar countries free of the disease. Protists can have devastating effects on other species too. Massive fish kills have been attributed to *Pfiesteria shumwayae* (see Figure 28.9), a dinoflagellate parasite that attaches to its victims and eats their skin. Among species that parasitize plants, the oomycete protist *Phytophthora ramorum* has emerged as a major new forest pathogen. This species causes sudden oak death (SOD), a disease that has killed millions of oaks and other trees in California and Oregon.

▶ **Figure 28.26 A symbiotic protist.** This organism is a hypermastigote, a member of a group of parabasalids that live in the gut of termites and certain cockroaches and enable the hosts to digest wood (SEM).

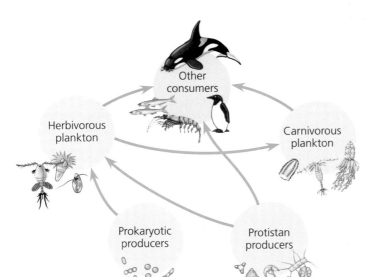

▲ **Figure 28.27 Protists: key producers in aquatic communities.** Arrows in this simplified food web lead from food sources to the organisms that eat them.

Photosynthetic Protists

Many protists are important **producers**, organisms that use energy from light (or inorganic chemicals) to convert carbon dioxide to organic compounds. Producers form the base of ecological food webs. In aquatic communities, the main producers are photosynthetic protists and prokaryotes. All other organisms in the community depend on them for food, either directly (by eating them) or indirectly (by eating an organism that ate a producer; **Figure 28.27**). Scientists estimate that roughly 30% of the world's photosynthesis is performed by diatoms, dinoflagellates, multicellular algae, and other aquatic protists. Photosynthetic prokaryotes contribute another 20%, and land plants are responsible for the remaining 50%.

Because producers form the foundation of food webs, factors that affect producers can dramatically affect their entire community. In aquatic environments, photosynthetic protists are often held in check by low concentrations of nitrogen, phosphorus, or iron. Various human actions can increase the concentrations of these elements in aquatic communities. For example, when fertilizer is applied to a field, some of the fertilizer may be washed by rainfall into a river that drains into a lake or ocean. When people add nutrients to aquatic communities in this or other ways, the abundance of photosynthetic protists can increase spectacularly. Such increases can alter the abundance of other species in the community.

A pressing question is how global warming will affect protists and other producers. Satellite data indicate that the growth and biomass of photosynthetic protists and prokaryotes have declined in many regions as sea surface temperatures have increased **(Figure 28.28)**. If sustained, these changes would likely have far-reaching effects on marine ecosystems, fishery yields, and the global carbon cycle. Global warming can also affect producers on land, but there the base of food webs is occupied not by protists but by land plants, which we will discuss in Chapters 29 and 30.

▼ **Figure 28.28**

IMPACT

Marine Protists in a Warmer World

Photosynthetic protists are important components of marine food webs, each day converting millions of tons of carbon in CO_2 to organic molecules on which other organisms depend. How has global warming affected these key marine producers? Satellite data indicate that the growth and biomass of marine producers are negatively correlated to sea surface temperature (SST). Their decline in tropical and midlatitude oceans (between the heavy black lines on the map below), where rising SSTs may have reduced the supply of nutrients available by forming a light, warm layer of water that acts as a barrier preventing the rise, or upwelling, of cold, nutrient-rich waters from below.

In regions between the black lines, a layer of warm water rests on top of colder waters.

In the yellow regions, high SSTs increase the temperature differences between warm and cold waters, which reduces upwelling. Marine producers rely on upwelled nutrients, so their growth decreases when upwelling decreases.

WHY IT MATTERS Major changes to marine ecosystems are expected if the growth and biomass of producers decrease as SSTs increase due to global warming. A decrease in diatom biomass, for example, would likely reduce both the amount of carbon pumped to the ocean floor and the catch of economically important fishes such as salmon and anchovies that feed on phytoplankton.

FURTHER READING M. J. Behrenfeld et al., Climate-driven trends in contemporary ocean productivity, *Nature* 444:752–755 (2006).

WHAT IF? If diatom populations continue to drop as the oceans warm, how might climate be affected in the future?

CONCEPT CHECK 28.7

1. Justify the claim that photosynthetic protists are among the biosphere's most important organisms.
2. Describe three symbioses that include protists.
3. **WHAT IF?** High water temperatures and pollution can cause corals to expel their dinoflagellate symbionts. Predict how such "coral bleaching" would affect corals and other species in the community.

For suggested answers, see Appendix A.

CONCEPT 28.1

Most eukaryotes are single-celled organisms (pp. 575–579)

- Protists are more diverse than all other eukaryotes and are no longer classified in a single kingdom. Most are unicellular. Protists include photoautotrophs, heterotrophs, and mixotrophs. Protists are characterized by a wide diversity of life cycles.
- Mitochondria and plastids are thought to be descendants of bacteria that were engulfed by other cells and became endosymbionts. The plastid-bearing lineage eventually evolved into red algae and green algae. Other protist groups evolved from secondary endosymbiosis events in which red algae or green algae were themselves engulfed.
- In one hypothesis, eukaryotes are grouped into five supergroups, each a monophyletic clade: Excavata, Chromalveolata, Rhizaria, Archaeplastida, and Unikonta.

? *Describe similarities and differences between protists and other eukaryotes.*

Key Concept/Eukaryote Supergroup	Major Groups	Key Morphological Characteristics	Specific Examples
CONCEPT 28.2 **Excavates include protists with modified mitochondria and protists with unique flagella (pp. 580–581)** **?** *What evidence indicates that the excavates form a clade?*	**Diplomonads and parabasalids**	Modified mitochondria	Giardia, Trichomonas
	Euglenozoans Kinetoplastids Euglenids	Spiral or crystalline rod inside flagella	Trypanosoma, Euglena
CONCEPT 28.3 **Chromalveolates may have originated by secondary endosymbiosis (pp. 582–589)** **?** *If Chromalveolata originated by secondary endosymbiosis, what can be inferred about the plastids of its members? Explain.*	**Alveolates** Dinoflagellates Apicomplexans Ciliates	Membrane-bounded sacs (alveoli) beneath plasma membrane	Pfiesteria, Plasmodium, Paramecium
	Stramenopiles Diatoms Golden algae Brown algae Oomycetes	Hairy and smooth flagella	Phytophthora, Laminaria
CONCEPT 28.4 **Rhizarians are a diverse group of protists defined by DNA similarities (pp. 589–590)** **?** *What are the main subgroups of rhizarians, and what unites these subgroups as a clade?*	**Radiolarians**	Amoebas with threadlike pseudopodia radiating from central body	Hexacontium
	Forams	Amoebas with threadlike pseudopodia and a porous shell	Globigerina
	Cercozoans	Amoebas and flagellated protists with threadlike pseudopodia	Paulinella
CONCEPT 28.5 **Red algae and green algae are the closest relatives of land plants (pp. 590–592) (Archaeplastida)** **?** *On what basis do some systematists place land plants in the same supergroup (Archaeplastida) as red and green algae?*	**Red algae**	Phycoerythrin (accessory pigment)	Porphyra
	Green algae	Plant-type chloroplasts	Chlamydomonas, Ulva
	Land plants	(See Chapters 29 and 30.)	Mosses, ferns, conifers, flowering plants
CONCEPT 28.6 **Unikonts include protists that are closely related to fungi and animals (pp. 593–596)** **?** *Describe a key feature for each of the main protist subgroups of Unikonta.*	**Amoebozoans** Slime molds Gymnamoebas Entamoebas	Amoebas with lobe-shaped pseudopodia	Amoeba, Entamoeba, Dictyostelium
	Opisthokonts	(Highly variable; see Chapters 31–34.)	Nucleariids, choanoflagellates, animals, fungi

Protists play key roles in ecological communities (pp. 596–597)

- Protists form a wide range of mutualistic and parasitic relationships that affect their symbiotic partners and many other members of the community.
- Photosynthetic protists are among the most important producers in aquatic communities. Because they are at the base of the food web, factors that affect photosynthetic protists affect many other species in the community.

 Describe several protists that are ecologically important.

TEST YOUR UNDERSTANDING

LEVEL 1: KNOWLEDGE/COMPREHENSION

1. Plastids that are surrounded by more than two membranes are evidence of
   a. evolution from mitochondria.
   b. fusion of plastids.
   c. origin of the plastids from archaea.
   d. secondary endosymbiosis.
   e. budding of the plastids from the nuclear envelope.

2. Biologists suspect that endosymbiosis gave rise to mitochondria before plastids partly because
   a. the products of photosynthesis could not be metabolized without mitochondrial enzymes.
   b. all eukaryotes have mitochondria (or their remnants), whereas many eukaryotes do not have plastids.
   c. mitochondrial DNA is less similar to prokaryotic DNA than is plastid DNA.
   d. without mitochondrial CO_2 production, photosynthesis could not occur.
   e. mitochondrial proteins are synthesized on cytosolic ribosomes, whereas plastids utilize their own ribosomes.

3. Which group is *incorrectly* paired with its description?
   a. rhizarians—morphologically diverse group defined by DNA similarities
   b. diatoms—important producers in aquatic communities
   c. red algae—acquired plastids by secondary endosymbiosis
   d. apicomplexans—parasites with intricate life cycles
   e. diplomonads—protists with modified mitochondria

4. Which protists are in the same eukaryotic supergroup as land plants?
   a. green algae
   b. dinoflagellates
   c. red algae
   d. brown algae
   e. both a and c

5. In life cycles with an alternation of generations, multicellular haploid forms alternate with
   a. unicellular haploid forms.
   b. unicellular diploid forms.
   c. multicellular haploid forms.
   d. multicellular diploid forms.
   e. multicellular polyploid forms.

LEVEL 2: APPLICATION/ANALYSIS

6. Based on the phylogenetic tree in Figure 28.3, which of the following statements is correct?
   a. The most recent common ancestor of Excavata is older than that of Chromalveolata.
   b. The most recent common ancestor of Chromalveolata is older than that of Rhizaria.
   c. The most recent common ancestor of red algae and land plants is older than that of nucleariids and fungi.
   d. The most basal (first to diverge) eukaryotic supergroup cannot be determined.
   e. Excavata is the most basal eukaryotic supergroup.

7. **EVOLUTION CONNECTION**
   DRAW IT Medical researchers seek to develop drugs that can kill or restrict the growth of human pathogens yet have few harmful effects on patients. These drugs often work by disrupting the metabolism of the pathogen or by targeting its structural features.

   Draw and label a phylogenetic tree that includes an ancestral prokaryote and the following groups of organisms: Excavata, Chromalveolata, Rhizaria, Archaeplastida, Unikonta, and, within Unikonta, amoebozoans, animals, choanoflagellates, fungi, and nucleariids. Based on this tree, hypothesize whether it would be most difficult to develop drugs to combat human pathogens that are prokaryotes, protists, animals, or fungi. (You do not need to consider the evolution of drug resistance by the pathogen.)

LEVEL 3: SYNTHESIS/EVALUATION

8. **SCIENTIFIC INQUIRY**
   Applying the "If . . . then" logic of science (see Chapter 1), what are a few of the predictions that arise from the hypothesis that plants evolved from green algae? Put another way, how could you test this hypothesis?

9. **WRITE ABOUT A THEME**
   Ecological Interactions Organisms interact with each other and the physical environment. In a short essay (100–150 words), explain how the response of diatom populations to a drop in nutrient availability can affect both other organisms and aspects of the physical environment (such as carbon dioxide concentrations).

For selected answers, see Appendix A.

 www.masteringbiology.com

1. MasteringBiology® Assignments
Tutorial Life Cycles of Protists
Activities Tentative Phylogeny of Eukaryotes • Alternation of Generations in a Protist • Life Cycle of a Malaria Parasite
Questions Student Misconceptions • Reading Quiz • Multiple Choice • End-of-Chapter

2. eText
Read your book online, search, take notes, highlight text, and more.

3. The Study Area
Practice Tests • Cumulative Test • *BioFlix* 3-D Animations • MP3 Tutor Sessions • Videos • Activities • Investigations • Lab Media • Audio Glossary • Word Study Tools • Art

Plant Diversity I: How Plants Colonized Land

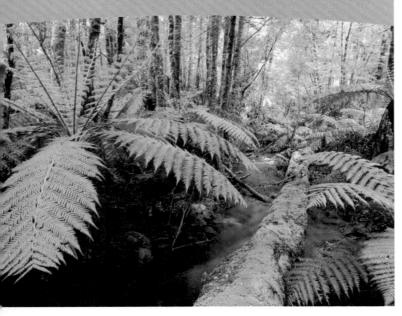

▲ **Figure 29.1 How did plants change the world?**

KEY CONCEPTS

29.1 Land plants evolved from green algae
29.2 Mosses and other nonvascular plants have life cycles dominated by gametophytes
29.3 Ferns and other seedless vascular plants were the first plants to grow tall

OVERVIEW

The Greening of Earth

Looking at a lush landscape, such as the forest scene in **Figure 29.1**, it is difficult to imagine the terrestrial environment without any plants or other organisms. Yet for more than 3 billion years of Earth's history, the land surface was largely lifeless. Geochemical evidence suggests that thin coatings of cyanobacteria existed on land about 1.2 billion years ago. But it was only within the last 500 million years that small plants as well as fungi and animals joined them

ashore. Finally, by about 385 million years ago, some plants appeared that could grow much taller, leading to the formation of the first forests (though with a very different set of species than those in Figure 29.1).

Since colonizing land, plants have diversified widely; today, there are more than 290,000 known plant species. Plants inhabit all but the harshest environments, such as some mountaintops, a few desert areas, and the polar regions. A few plant species, such as sea grasses, returned to aquatic habitats during their evolution, but most present-day plants live in terrestrial environments. In this chapter, we'll refer to all plants as *land* plants, even those that are now aquatic, to distinguish them from algae, which are photosynthetic protists.

The presence of land plants has enabled other life-forms—including animals—to survive on land. Plants supply oxygen and ultimately most of the food eaten by terrestrial animals. Also, plant roots create habitats for other organisms by stabilizing the soil in sand dunes and many other environments.

This chapter traces the first 100 million years of plant evolution, including the emergence of seedless plants such as mosses and ferns. Chapter 30 examines the later evolution of seed plants.

CONCEPT **29.1**

Land plants evolved from green algae

As you read in Chapter 28, researchers have identified green algae called charophytes as the closest relatives of land plants. What is the evidence for this relationship, and what does it suggest about the algal ancestors of land plants?

Morphological and Molecular Evidence

Many key traits of land plants also appear in some protists, primarily algae. For example, plants are multicellular, eukaryotic, photosynthetic autotrophs, as are brown, red, and certain green algae. Plants have cell walls made of cellulose, and so do green algae, dinoflagellates, and brown algae. And chloroplasts with chlorophylls *a* and *b* are present in green algae, euglenids, and a few dinoflagellates, as well as in plants.

However, the charophytes are the only algae that share the following four distinctive traits with land plants, strongly suggesting that they are the closest relatives of plants:

- **Rings of cellulose-synthesizing proteins.** The cells of both land plants and charophytes have distinctive circular rings of proteins in the plasma membrane (**Figure 29.2**). These protein rings synthesize the cellulose microfibrils of the cell wall. In contrast, noncharophyte algae have linear sets of proteins that synthesize cellulose.

- **Peroxisome enzymes.** The peroxisomes (see Figure 6.19) of both land plants and charophytes contain enzymes that help minimize the loss of organic products resulting from photorespiration (see Chapter 10).

▶ **Figure 29.2 Rings of cellulose-synthesizing proteins.** These circular sets of proteins embedded in the plasma membrane are found only in land plants and charophyte algae (SEM).

30 nm

- **Structure of flagellated sperm.** In species of land plants that have flagellated sperm, the structure of the sperm closely resembles that of charophyte sperm.
- **Formation of a phragmoplast.** Particular details of cell division occur only in land plants and certain charophytes, including the genera *Chara* and *Coleochaete*. For example, in land plants and certain charophytes, a group of microtubules known as the **phragmoplast** forms between the daughter nuclei of a dividing cell. A cell plate then develops in the middle of the phragmoplast, across the midline of the dividing cell (see Figure 12.10). The cell plate, in turn, gives rise to a new cross wall that separates the daughter cells.

Genetic evidence also supports the conclusion drawn from these four morphological and biochemical traits. Analyses of nuclear and chloroplast genes from a wide range of plants and algae indicate that charophytes—particularly *Chara* and *Coleochaete*—are the closest living relatives of land plants **(Figure 29.3)**. Note that this does not mean that plants are descended from these living algae; however, present-day charophytes may tell us something about what the algal ancestors of plants were like.

Adaptations Enabling the Move to Land

Many species of charophyte algae inhabit shallow waters around the edges of ponds and lakes, where they are subject to occasional drying. In such environments, natural selection favors individual algae that can survive periods when they are not submerged in water. In charophytes, a layer of a durable polymer called **sporopollenin** prevents exposed zygotes from drying out. A similar chemical adaptation is found in the tough sporopollenin walls that encase the spores of plants.

The accumulation of such traits by at least one population of charophyte ancestors probably enabled their descendants—the first land plants—to live permanently above the waterline. These evolutionary novelties opened a new frontier: a terrestrial habitat that offered enormous benefits. The bright sunlight was unfiltered by water and plankton; the atmosphere offered more plentiful carbon dioxide than did water; the soil by the water's edge was rich in some mineral nutrients; and initially there were relatively few herbivores and pathogens. But these benefits were accompanied by challenges: a relative scarcity of water and a lack of structural support against gravity. (To appreciate why such support is important, picture how the soft body of a jellyfish sags when taken out of water.) Land

5 mm

◀ *Chara* species, a pond organism

▼ *Coleochaete orbicularis*, a disk-shaped charophyte that also lives in ponds (LM)

40 µm

▲ **Figure 29.3 Examples of charophytes, the closest algal relatives of land plants.**

plants diversified as adaptations evolved that enabled plants to thrive despite these challenges.

Today, what adaptations are unique to plants? The answer to this question depends on where you draw the boundary dividing land plants from algae **(Figure 29.4)**. Many biologists equate the kingdom Plantae with embryophytes (plants with embryos). Others propose that the boundaries of the plant kingdom should be expanded to include some or all of the green algae (kingdoms Streptophyta and Viridiplantae). Since the debate is ongoing, this text retains the embryophyte definition of the plant kingdom and uses Plantae as the formal name for the taxon. In this context, let's now identify the derived traits that separate land plants from their closest algal relatives.

Derived Traits of Plants

Many of the adaptations that appear to have emerged after land plants diverged from their algal relatives facilitated survival and reproduction on dry land. **Figure 29.5**, on the next two pages, depicts four key traits that appear in land plants but not in the charophyte algae.

ANCESTRAL ALGA

Red algae

Chlorophytes

Charophytes

Embryophytes

Viridiplantae

Streptophyta

Plantae

▲ **Figure 29.4 Three possible "plant" kingdoms.**

▼ Figure 29.5

Exploring Derived Traits of Land Plants

Charophyte algae lack the four key traits of land plants described in this figure: alternation of generations (with an associated trait of multicellular, dependent embryos), walled spores produced in sporangia, multicellular gametangia, and apical meristems. This suggests that these four traits were absent in the ancestor common to land plants and charophytes but instead evolved as derived traits of land plants. Note that some of these traits are not unique to plants, having evolved independently in other lineages. And not every land plant exhibits all four of these traits; certain lineages of plants have lost some traits over time.

Alternation of Generations and Multicellular, Dependent Embryos

The life cycles of all land plants alternate between two generations of multicellular organisms: gametophytes and sporophytes. As shown in the diagram (using a fern as an example), each generation gives rise to the other, a process that is called **alternation of generations**. This type of reproductive cycle evolved in various groups of algae but does not occur in the charophytes, the algae most closely related to land plants.

Take care not to confuse the alternation of generations in plants with the haploid and diploid stages in the life cycles of other sexually reproducing organisms (see Figure 13.6). In humans, for example, meiosis produces haploid gametes that unite, forming diploid zygotes that divide and become multicellular. The haploid stage is represented only by single-celled gametes. In contrast, alternation of generations is distinguished by the fact that the life cycle includes both multicellular haploid organisms and multicellular diploid organisms. The multicellular haploid **gametophyte** ("gamete-producing plant") is named for its production by mitosis of haploid gametes—eggs and sperm—that fuse during fertilization, forming diploid zygotes. Mitotic division of the zygote produces a multicellular diploid **sporophyte** ("spore-producing plant"). Meiosis in a mature sporophyte produces haploid **spores**,

Alternation of generations: five generalized steps

1. The gametophyte produces haploid gametes by mitosis.

Gametophyte (n)

Mitosis

Gamete from another plant

Mitosis

2. Two gametes unite (fertilization) and form a diploid zygote.

Gamete

5. The spores develop into multicellular haploid gametophytes.

n

n — Spore

MEIOSIS

FERTILIZATION

4. The sporophyte produces haploid spores by meiosis.

2n — Zygote

3. The zygote develops into a multicellular diploid sporophyte.

Mitosis

Sporophyte (2n)

Key
Haploid (n)
Diploid (2n)

reproductive cells that can develop into a new haploid organism without fusing with another cell. Mitotic division of the spore cell produces a new multicellular gametophyte, and the cycle begins again. In many seedless plants, such as the fern in the diagram, the gametophyte and sporophyte look like different types of plants, even though they are forms of the same species. In seed plants, the gametophytes are microscopic; the familiar plants we see are the sporophytes.

As part of a life cycle with alternation of generations, multicellular plant embryos develop from zygotes that are retained within the tissues of the female parent (a gametophyte). The parental tissues provide the developing embryo with nutrients, such as sugars and amino acids. The embryo has specialized **placental transfer cells**, sometimes present in the adjacent maternal tissue as well, which enhance the transfer of nutrients from parent to embryo through elaborate ingrowths of the wall surface (plasma membrane and cell wall). This interface is analogous to the nutrient-transferring embryo-mother interface of eutherian (placental) mammals. The multicellular, dependent embryo of land plants is such a significant derived trait that land plants are also known as **embryophytes**.

Embryo (LM) and placental transfer cell (TEM) of *Marchantia* (a liverwort)

Embryo
Maternal tissue
2 μm
10 μm
Wall ingrowths
Placental transfer cell (outlined in blue)

MAKE CONNECTIONS *Review sexual life cycles in Figure 13.6 on p. 252. Identify which life cycle has alternation of generations, and summarize how it differs from other life cycles.*

Walled Spores Produced in Sporangia

Plant spores are haploid reproductive cells that can grow into multicellular haploid gametophytes by mitosis. The polymer sporopollenin makes the walls of plant spores tough and resistant to harsh environments. This chemical adaptation enables spores to be dispersed through dry air without harm.

The sporophyte has multicellular organs called **sporangia** (singular, *sporangium*) that produce the spores. Within a sporangium, diploid cells called **sporocytes**, or spore mother cells, undergo meiosis and generate the haploid spores. The outer tissues of the sporangium protect the developing spores until they are released into the air. Multicellular sporangia that produce spores with sporopollenin-enriched walls are key terrestrial adaptations of land plants. Although charophytes also produce spores, these algae lack multicellular sporangia, and their flagellated, water-dispersed spores lack sporopollenin.

Spores
Sporangium
Longitudinal section of *Sphagnum* sporangium (LM)
Sporophyte
Gametophyte

Sporophytes and sporangia of *Sphagnum* (a moss)

Multicellular Gametangia

Another feature distinguishing early land plants from their algal ancestors was the production of gametes within multicellular organs called **gametangia**. The female gametangia are called **archegonia** (singular, *archegonium*). Each archegonium is a pear-shaped organ that produces a single nonmotile egg retained within the bulbous part of the organ (the top for the species shown here). The male gametangia, called **antheridia** (singular, *antheridium*), produce sperm and release them into the environment. In many groups of present-day plants, the sperm have flagella and swim to the eggs through water droplets or a film of water. Each egg is fertilized within an archegonium, where the zygote develops into an embryo. As you will see in Chapter 30, the gametophytes of seed plants are so reduced in size that the archegonia and antheridia have been lost in many lineages.

Female gametophyte
Archegonia, each with an egg (yellow)
Antheridia (brown), containing sperm
Male gametophyte

Archegonia and antheridia of *Marchantia* (a liverwort)

Apical Meristems

In terrestrial habitats, a photosynthetic organism finds essential resources in two very different places. Light and CO_2 are mainly available above ground; water and mineral nutrients are found mainly in the soil. Though plants cannot move from place to place, their roots and shoots can elongate, increasing exposure to environmental resources. This growth in length is sustained throughout the plant's life by the activity of **apical meristems**, localized regions of cell division at the tips of roots and shoots. Cells produced by apical meristems differentiate into the outer epidermis, which protects the body, and various types of internal tissues. Shoot apical meristems also generate leaves in most plants. Thus, the complex bodies of plants have specialized below- and aboveground organs.

Apical meristems of plant roots and shoots. The LMs are longitudinal sections at the tips of a root and shoot.

Apical meristem of shoot
Developing leaves
Apical meristem of root
Root
100 μm
Shoot
100 μm

In addition to the four traits shown in Figure 29.5, other derived traits that relate to terrestrial life have evolved in many plant species. For example, the epidermis in many species has a covering, the **cuticle**, which consists of wax and other polymers. Permanently exposed to the air, land plants run a far greater risk of desiccation (drying out) than their algal ancestors. The cuticle acts as waterproofing, helping prevent excessive water loss from the aboveground plant organs, while also providing some protection from microbial attack.

Early land plants lacked true roots and leaves. Without roots, how did these plants absorb nutrients from the soil? Fossils dating from 420 million years ago reveal an adaptation that may have aided early plants in nutrient uptake: They formed symbiotic associations with fungi similar in structure to beneficial associations observed today between plants and fungi. We'll describe these associations, called *mycorrhizae*, and their benefits to both plants and fungi in more detail in Chapter 31. For now, the main point is that mycorrhizal fungi form extensive networks of filaments through the soil, enabling them to absorb nutrients more effectively than a plant can on its own. The fungi transfer nutrients to their symbiotic plant partner, a benefit that may have helped plants without roots to colonize land.

Finally, many land plants produce molecules called *secondary compounds*, so named because they are products of secondary metabolic pathways—side branches off the primary metabolic pathways that produce the lipids, carbohydrates, amino acids, and other compounds common to all organisms. Secondary compounds include compounds called alkaloids, terpenes, tannins, and flavonoids. Various alkaloids, terpenes, and tannins have a bitter taste, strong odor, or toxic effect that helps defend a plant against herbivores and parasites. Flavonoids absorb harmful UV radiation, and some related compounds deter attack by pathogens. Humans also benefit from secondary compounds in plants, many of which are used in spices, medicines, and other products.

The Origin and Diversification of Plants

Paleobotanists seeking the evolutionary origin of plants have long debated what constitutes the oldest fossil evidence of land plants. In the 1970s, researchers found fossil spores dating to the Ordovician period, up to 475 million years old. Although the fossil spores resemble those of living plants, they also have some striking differences. For example, spores of present-day plants are typically dispersed as single grains, but the fossil spores are fused together in groups of two or four. This difference raises the possibility that the fossil spores were not produced by plants, but by some extinct algal relative. Furthermore, the oldest known fragments of plant body tissues are 50 million years younger than the puzzling spores.

In 2003, scientists from Britain and the Middle Eastern country of Oman shed some light on this mystery when they extracted spores from 475-million-year-old rocks from Oman

(a) Fossilized spores. Unlike the spores of most living plants, which are single grains, these spores found in Oman are in groups of four (left; one hidden) and two (right).

(b) Fossilized sporophyte tissue. The spores were embedded in tissue that appears to be from plants.

▲ **Figure 29.6 Ancient plant spores and tissue** (colorized SEMs).

(Figure 29.6a). Unlike previously discovered spores of this age, these were embedded in plant cuticle material that is similar to spore-bearing tissue in living plants **(Figure 29.6b)**. After uncovering other small fragments of tissue that clearly belonged to plants, the scientists concluded that the spores from Oman represent fossil plants rather than algae.

Whatever the precise age of the first land plants, those ancestral species gave rise to the vast diversity of living plants. **Table 29.1** summarizes the ten extant phyla in the taxonomic scheme used in this text. (Extant lineages are those that have surviving members, not only extinct ones.) As you read the rest of this section, look at Table 29.1 together with **Figure 29.7**, which reflects a view of plant phylogeny based on plant morphology, biochemistry, and genetics.

One way to distinguish groups of plants is whether or not they have an extensive system of **vascular tissue**, cells joined into tubes that transport water and nutrients throughout the plant body. Most present-day plants have a complex vascular tissue system and are therefore called **vascular plants**. Plants that do not have an extensive transport system—liverworts, mosses, and hornworts—are described as "nonvascular" plants, even though some mosses do have simple vascular tissue. Nonvascular plants are often informally called **bryophytes** (from the Greek *bryon*, moss, and *phyton*, plant).

Although the term *bryophyte* is commonly used to refer to all nonvascular plants, molecular studies and morphological analyses of sperm structure have concluded that bryophytes do not form a monophyletic group (a clade). Debate continues, however, over the relationships of liverworts, mosses, and hornworts to each other and to vascular plants. Regardless of the outcome of this debate, bryophytes share some derived traits with vascular plants, such as multicellular

Table 29.1 Ten Phyla of Extant Plants		
	Common Name	Number of Known Species
Nonvascular Plants (Bryophytes)		
Phylum Hepatophyta	Liverworts	9,000
Phylum Bryophyta	Mosses	15,000
Phylum Anthocerophyta	Hornworts	100
Vascular Plants		
Seedless Vascular Plants		
Phylum Lycophyta	Lycophytes	1,200
Phylum Pterophyta	Pterophytes	12,000
Seed Plants		
Gymnosperms		
Phylum Ginkgophyta	Ginkgo	1
Phylum Cycadophyta	Cycads	130
Phylum Gnetophyta	Gnetophytes	75
Phylum Coniferophyta	Conifers	600
Angiosperms		
Phylum Anthophyta	Flowering plants	250,000

embryos and apical meristems, while lacking many innovations of vascular plants, such as roots and true leaves.

Vascular plants, which form a clade that comprises about 93% of all extant plant species, can be categorized further into smaller clades. Two of these clades are the **lycophytes** (club mosses and their relatives) and the **pterophytes** (ferns and their relatives). The plants in each of these clades lack seeds, which is why collectively the two clades are often informally called **seedless vascular plants**. However, notice in Figure 29.7 that seedless vascular plants are paraphyletic, not monophyletic. Groups such as the seedless vascular plants are sometimes referred to as a **grade**, a collection of organisms that share a key biological feature. Grades can be informative by grouping organisms according to features, such as lack of seeds. But members of a grade, unlike members of a clade, do not necessarily share the same ancestry. For example, even though pterophytes and lycophytes are all seedless plants, pterophytes share a more recent common ancestor with seed plants. As a result, we would expect pterophytes and seed plants to share key traits not found in lycophytes—and they do, as you'll read.

A third clade of vascular plants consists of seed plants, which represent the vast majority of living plant species. A **seed** is an embryo packaged with a supply of nutrients inside a protective coat. Seed plants can be divided into two groups, gymnosperms and angiosperms, based on the absence or

1 Origin of land plants (about 475 mya)
2 Origin of vascular plants (about 425 mya)
3 Origin of extant seed plants (about 305 mya)

▲ **Figure 29.7 Highlights of plant evolution.** The phylogeny shown here illustrates a leading hypothesis about the relationships between plant groups. The dotted lines indicate groups whose evolutionary relationships continue to be debated.

presence of enclosed chambers in which seeds mature. **Gymnosperms** (from the Greek *gymnos*, naked, and *sperm*, seed) are grouped together as "naked seed" plants because their seeds are not enclosed in chambers. Living gymnosperm species, the most familiar of which are the conifers, probably form a clade. **Angiosperms** (from the Greek *angion*, container) are a huge clade consisting of all flowering plants. Angiosperm seeds develop inside chambers called ovaries, which originate within flowers and mature into fruits. Nearly 90% of living plant species are angiosperms.

Note that the phylogeny depicted in Figure 29.7 focuses only on the relationships between extant plant lineages. Paleobotanists have also discovered fossils belonging to extinct plant lineages. As you'll read later in the chapter, many of these fossils reveal intermediate steps in the emergence of the distinctive plant groups found on Earth today.

CONCEPT CHECK 29.1

1. Why do researchers identify charophytes rather than another group as the closest relatives of land plants?
2. Identify three derived traits that distinguish plants from charophytes *and* facilitate life on land. Explain.
3. **WHAT IF?** What would the human life cycle be like if we had alternation of generations? Assume that the multicellular diploid stage is similar in form to an adult human.
4. **MAKE CONNECTIONS** Figure 29.7 identifies which lineages are land plants, nonvascular plants, vascular plants, seedless vascular plants, and seed plants. Which of these categories are monophyletic, and which are paraphyletic? Explain. See Figure 26.10 on p. 542.

For suggested answers, see Appendix A.

CONCEPT 29.2

Mosses and other nonvascular plants have life cycles dominated by gametophytes

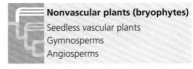

The nonvascular plants (bryophytes) are represented today by three phyla of small herbaceous (nonwoody) plants: **liverworts** (phylum Hepatophyta), **mosses** (phylum Bryophyta), and **hornworts** (phylum Anthocerophyta). Liverworts and hornworts are named for their shapes, plus the suffix *wort* (from the Anglo-Saxon for "herb"). Mosses are familiar to many people, although some plants commonly called "mosses" are not really mosses at all. These include Irish moss (a red seaweed), reindeer moss (a lichen), club mosses (seedless vascular plants), and Spanish mosses (lichens in some regions and flowering plants in others).

Note that the terms *Bryophyta* and *bryophyte* are not synonymous. Bryophyta is the formal taxonomic name for the phylum that consists solely of mosses. As mentioned earlier, the term *bryophyte* is used informally to refer to *all* nonvascular plants—liverworts, mosses, and hornworts.

Liverworts, mosses, and hornworts have acquired many unique adaptations over the long course of their evolution. Nevertheless, living bryophytes likely reflect some traits of the earliest plants. The oldest known fossils of plant fragments, for example, include tissues very similar to those inside liverworts. Researchers hope to discover more parts of these ancient plants to see if this resemblance is reflected more broadly.

Bryophyte Gametophytes

Unlike vascular plants, in all three bryophyte phyla the haploid gametophytes are the dominant stage of the life cycle: That is, they are usually larger and longer-living than the sporophytes, as shown in the moss life cycle in **Figure 29.8**. Sporophytes are typically present only part of the time.

When bryophyte spores are dispersed to a favorable habitat, such as moist soil or tree bark, they may germinate and grow into gametophytes. Germinating moss spores, for example, characteristically produce a mass of green, branched, one-cell-thick filaments known as a **protonema** (plural, *protonemata*; from the Greek *proto*, first, and *nema*, threads). A protonema has a large surface area that enhances absorption of water and minerals. In favorable conditions, a protonema produces one or more "buds." (Note that when referring to nonvascular plants, we typically use quotation marks for structures similar to the buds, stems, and leaves of vascular plants because the definitions of these terms are based on vascular plant organs.) Each of these bud-like growths has an apical meristem that generates a gamete-producing structure known as a **gametophore** ("gamete bearer"). Together, a protonema and one or more gametophores make up the body of a moss gametophyte.

Bryophyte gametophytes generally form ground-hugging carpets, partly because their body parts are too thin to support a tall plant. A second constraint on the height of many bryophytes is the absence of vascular tissue, which would enable long-distance transport of water and nutrients. (The thin structure of bryophyte organs makes it possible to distribute materials for short distances without specialized vascular tissue.) However, some mosses have conducting tissues in the center of their "stems." A few of these mosses can grow as tall as 2 m as a result. Phylogenetic analyses suggest that in these and some other bryophytes, conducting tissues similar to those of vascular plants arose independently by convergent evolution.

The gametophytes are anchored by delicate **rhizoids**, which are long, tubular single cells (in liverworts and hornworts) or filaments of cells (in mosses). Unlike roots, which are found in vascular plant sporophytes, rhizoids are not

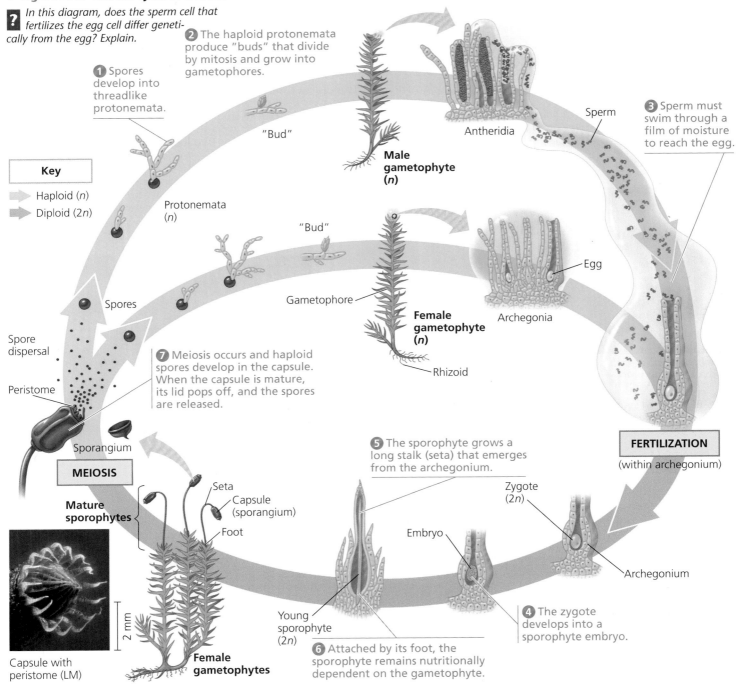

▼ **Figure 29.8 The life cycle of a moss.**

? *In this diagram, does the sperm cell that fertilizes the egg cell differ genetically from the egg? Explain.*

2 The haploid protonemata produce "buds" that divide by mitosis and grow into gametophores.

1 Spores develop into threadlike protonemata.

Key

→ Haploid (*n*)
→ Diploid (*2n*)

"Bud"

Antheridia

Sperm

Male gametophyte (*n*)

3 Sperm must swim through a film of moisture to reach the egg.

Protonemata (*n*)

Spores

Gametophore

"Bud"

Egg

Archegonia

Female gametophyte (*n*)

Spore dispersal

Rhizoid

Peristome

7 Meiosis occurs and haploid spores develop in the capsule. When the capsule is mature, its lid pops off, and the spores are released.

FERTILIZATION

(within archegonium)

5 The sporophyte grows a long stalk (seta) that emerges from the archegonium.

Sporangium

Zygote (*2n*)

MEIOSIS

Seta

Embryo

Mature sporophytes

Capsule (sporangium)

Foot

2 mm

Young sporophyte (*2n*)

Archegonium

4 The zygote develops into a sporophyte embryo.

Capsule with peristome (LM)

Female gametophytes

6 Attached by its foot, the sporophyte remains nutritionally dependent on the gametophyte.

composed of tissues. Bryophyte rhizoids also lack specialized conducting cells and do not play a primary role in water and mineral absorption.

Gametophytes can form multiple gametangia, each of which produces gametes and is covered by protective tissue. Each archegonium produces one egg, whereas each antheridium produces many sperm. Some bryophyte gametophytes are bisexual, but in mosses the archegonia and antheridia are typically carried on separate female and male gametophytes. Flagellated sperm swim through a film of water toward eggs, entering the archegonia in response to chemical attractants.

Eggs are not released but instead remain within the bases of archegonia. After fertilization, embryos are retained within the archegonia. Layers of placental transfer cells help transport nutrients to the embryos as they develop into sporophytes.

Bryophyte sperm typically require a film of water to reach the eggs. Given this requirement, it is not surprising that many bryophyte species are found in moist habitats. The fact that sperm swim through water to reach the egg also means that in species with separate male and female gametophytes (most mosses), sexual reproduction is likely to be more successful when individuals are located close to one another.

Exploring Bryophyte Diversity

Liverworts (Phylum Hepatophyta)

This phylum's common and scientific names (from the Latin *hepaticus*, liver) refer to the liver-shaped gametophytes of its members, such as *Marchantia*, shown below. In medieval times, their shape was thought to be a sign that the plants could help treat liver diseases. Some liverworts, including *Marchantia*, are described as "thalloid" because of the flattened shape of their gametophytes. (Recall from Chapter 28 that the body of a multicellular alga is called a thallus.) *Marchantia* gametangia are elevated on gametophores that look like miniature trees. You would need a magnifying glass to see the sporophytes, which have a short seta (stalk) with an oval or round capsule. Other liverworts, such as *Plagiochila*, below, are called "leafy" because their stemlike gametophytes have many leaflike appendages. There are many more species of leafy liverworts than thalloid liverworts.

Marchantia polymorpha,
a "thalloid" liverwort

Marchantia sporophyte (LM)

Thallus

Gametophore of female gametophyte

Sporophyte

Foot
Seta

Capsule (sporangium)

500 μm

***Plagiochila deltoidea,* a "leafy" liverwort**

Hornworts (Phylum Anthocerophyta)

This phylum's common and scientific names (from the Greek *keras*, horn) refer to the long, tapered shape of the sporophyte. A typical sporophyte can grow to about 5 cm high. Unlike a liverwort or moss sporophyte, a hornwort sporophyte lacks a seta and consists only of a sporangium. The sporangium releases mature spores by splitting open, starting at the tip of the horn. The gametophytes, which are usually 1–2 cm in diameter, grow mostly horizontally and often have multiple sporophytes attached. Hornworts are frequently among the first species to colonize open areas with moist soils; a symbiotic relationship with nitrogen-fixing cyanobacteria contributes to their ability to do this (nitrogen is often in short supply in such areas).

An *Anthoceros* hornwort species

Sporophyte

Gametophyte

Mosses (Phylum Bryophyta)

Moss gametophytes, which range in height from less than 1 mm to up to 2 m, are less than 15 cm tall in most species. The familiar carpet of moss you observe consists mainly of gametophytes. The blades of their "leaves" are usually only one cell thick, but more complex "leaves" that have ridges coated with cuticle can be found on the common hairy-cap moss (*Polytrichum*, below) and its close relatives. Moss sporophytes are typically elongated and visible to the naked eye, with heights ranging up to about 20 cm. Though green and photosynthetic when young, they turn tan or brownish red when ready to release spores.

***Polytrichum commune,* hairy-cap moss**

Capsule

Seta

Sporophyte (a sturdy plant that takes months to grow)

Gametophyte

Many bryophyte species can increase the number of individuals in a local area through various methods of asexual reproduction. For example, some mosses reproduce asexually by forming *brood bodies*, small plantlets (as shown at left) that detach from the parent plant and grow into new, genetically identical copies of their parent.

Bryophyte Sporophytes

Although bryophyte sporophytes are usually green and photosynthetic when young, they cannot live independently. They remain attached to their parental gametophytes, from which they absorb sugars, amino acids, minerals, and water.

Bryophytes have the smallest sporophytes of all extant plant groups, consistent with the hypothesis that larger sporophytes evolved only later, in the vascular plants. A typical bryophyte sporophyte consists of a foot, a seta, and a sporangium. Embedded in the archegonium, the **foot** absorbs nutrients from the gametophyte. The **seta** (plural, *setae*), or stalk, conducts these materials to the sporangium, also called a **capsule**, which uses them to produce spores by meiosis. One capsule can generate up to 50 million spores.

In most mosses, the seta becomes elongated, enhancing spore dispersal by elevating the capsule. Typically, the upper part of the capsule features a ring of interlocking, tooth-like structures known as the **peristome** (see Figure 29.8). These "teeth" open under dry conditions and close again when it is moist. This allows spores to be discharged gradually, via periodic gusts of wind that can carry them long distances.

Moss and hornwort sporophytes are often larger and more complex than those of liverworts. Both moss and hornwort sporophytes also have specialized pores called **stomata** (singular, *stoma*), which are also found in all vascular plants. These pores support photosynthesis by allowing the exchange of CO_2 and O_2 between the outside air and the sporophyte interior (see Figure 10.3). Stomata are also the main avenues by which water evaporates from the sporophyte. In hot, dry conditions, the stomata close, minimizing water loss.

The fact that stomata are present in mosses and hornworts but absent in liverworts suggests three possible hypotheses for their evolution. If liverworts are the deepest-branching lineage of land plants, as in Figure 29.7, then stomata may have evolved once in the ancestor of mosses, hornworts, and vascular plants. If hornworts are the deepest-branching lineage, stomata may have evolved once and then been lost in the liverwort lineage. Finally, if hornworts are the deepest-branching lineage and mosses are the closest relatives of vascular plants, it is also possible that hornworts acquired stomata independently of mosses and vascular plants. This question is important to understanding plant evolution because stomata play a crucial role in the success of vascular plants, as you will learn in Chapter 36.

Figure 29.9, on the facing page, shows some examples of gametophytes and sporophytes in the bryophyte phyla.

The Ecological and Economic Importance of Mosses

Wind dispersal of lightweight spores has distributed mosses throughout the world. These plants are particularly common and diverse in moist forests and wetlands. Some mosses colonize bare, sandy soil, where researchers have found they help retain nitrogen in the soil **(Figure 29.10)**. In northern coniferous forests, species such as the feather moss *Pleurozium* harbor nitrogen-fixing cyanobacteria that increase the availability of nitrogen in the ecosystem. Other mosses inhabit such extreme environments as mountaintops, tundra, and deserts. Many mosses are able to live in very cold or dry habitats because they can survive the loss of most of their body water, then rehydrate when moisture is available. Few vascular plants can survive the same degree of desiccation.

▼ **Figure 29.10**

INQUIRY

Can bryophytes reduce the rate at which key nutrients are lost from soils?

EXPERIMENT Soils in terrestrial ecosystems are often low in nitrogen, a nutrient required for normal plant growth. Richard Bowden, of Allegheny College, measured annual inputs (gains) and outputs (losses) of nitrogen in a sandy-soil ecosystem dominated by the moss *Polytrichum*. Nitrogen inputs were measured from rainfall (dissolved ions, such as nitrate, NO_3^-), biological N_2 fixation, and wind deposition. Nitrogen losses were measured in leached water (dissolved ions, such as NO_3^-) and gaseous emissions (such as NO_2 emitted by bacteria). Bowden measured losses for soils with *Polytrichum* and for soils where the moss was removed two months before the experiment began.

RESULTS A total of 10.5 kg of nitrogen per hectare (kg/ha) entered the ecosystem each year. Little nitrogen was lost by gaseous emissions (0.10 kg/ha·yr). The results of comparing nitrogen losses by leaching are shown below.

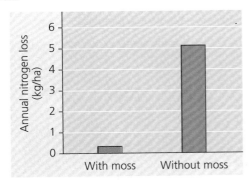

CONCLUSION The moss *Polytrichum* greatly reduced the loss of nitrogen by leaching in this ecosystem. Each year, the moss ecosystem retained over 95% of the 10.5 kg/ha of total nitrogen inputs (only 0.1 kg/ha and 0.3 kg/ha were lost to gaseous emissions and leaching, respectively).

SOURCE R. D. Bowden, Inputs, outputs, and accumulation of nitrogen in an early successional moss (*Polytrichum*) ecosystem, *Ecological Monographs* 61:207–223 (1991).

WHAT IF? How might the presence of *Polytrichum* affect plant species that typically colonize the sandy soils *after* the moss?

One wetland moss genus, *Sphagnum*, or "peat moss," is often a major component of deposits of partially decayed organic material known as **peat (Figure 29.11a)**. Boggy regions with thick layers of peat are called peatlands. *Sphagnum* does not decay readily, in part because of phenolic compounds embedded in its cell walls. The low temperature, pH, and oxygen level of peatlands also inhibit decay of moss and other organisms in these boggy wetlands. As a result, some peatlands have preserved corpses for thousands of years **(Figure 29.11b)**.

Peat has long been a fuel source in Europe and Asia, and it is still harvested for fuel today, notably in Ireland and Canada. Peat moss is also useful as a soil conditioner and for packing plant roots during shipment because it has large dead cells that can absorb roughly 20 times the moss's weight in water.

Peatlands cover 3% of Earth's land surface and contain roughly 30% of the world's soil carbon: Globally, an estimated 450 billion tons of organic carbon is stored as peat. These carbon reservoirs have helped to stabilize atmospheric CO_2

(a) Peat being harvested from a peatland

(b) "Tollund Man," a bog mummy dating from 405–100 B.C.E. The acidic, oxygen-poor conditions produced by *Sphagnum* can preserve human or other animal bodies for thousands of years.

▲ **Figure 29.11** *Sphagnum*, **or peat moss: a bryophyte with economic, ecological, and archaeological significance.**

concentrations. Current overharvesting of *Sphagnum* may reduce peat's beneficial ecological effects and contribute to global warming by releasing stored CO_2. In addition, if global temperatures continue to rise, the water levels of some peatlands are expected to drop. Such a change would expose peat to air and cause it to decompose, thereby releasing additional stored CO_2 and contributing further to global warming. The historical and expected future effects of *Sphagnum* on the global climate underscore the importance of preserving and managing peatlands.

CONCEPT CHECK 29.2

1. How do bryophytes differ from other plants?
2. Give three examples of how structure fits function in bryophytes.
3. **WHAT IF?** For each hypothesis of stomatal evolution, label each gain and loss of stomata on an appropriately modified version of the tree in Figure 29.7.

For suggested answers, see Appendix A.

CONCEPT 29.3

Ferns and other seedless vascular plants were the first plants to grow tall

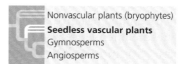

Nonvascular plants (bryophytes)
Seedless vascular plants
Gymnosperms
Angiosperms

During the first 100 million years of plant evolution, bryophytes or bryophyte-like plants were the prevalent vegetation. But it is vascular plants that dominate most landscapes today. Fossils and living seedless vascular plants can provide insights into plant evolution during the Devonian and Carboniferous periods, when vascular plants began to diversify but most groups of seed plants had not yet evolved. Fossils show that lycophytes, ferns, and other seedless vascular plants had well-developed vascular systems by the Devonian. As we'll see, this evolutionary innovation set the stage for vascular plants to grow taller than their bryophyte counterparts. As in nonvascular plants, however, the sperm of ferns and all other seedless vascular plants are flagellated and swim through a film of water to reach eggs. In part because of these swimming sperm, seedless vascular plants today are most common in damp environments.

Origins and Traits of Vascular Plants

Fossils of the forerunners of present-day vascular plants date back about 425 million years. Unlike the nonvascular plants, these species had branched sporophytes that were not dependent on gametophytes for nutrition **(Figure 29.12)**. Although these ancestors of vascular plants were only about

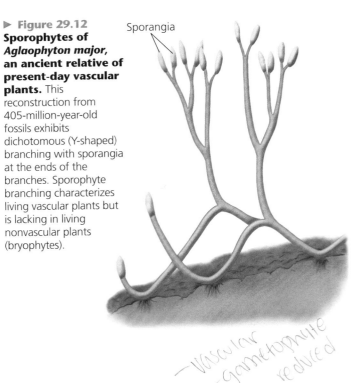

▶ **Figure 29.12 Sporophytes of *Aglaophyton major*, an ancient relative of present-day vascular plants.** This reconstruction from 405-million-year-old fossils exhibits dichotomous (Y-shaped) branching with sporangia at the ends of the branches. Sporophyte branching characterizes living vascular plants but is lacking in living nonvascular plants (bryophytes).

Sporangia

— vascular
— gametophyte
reduced

15 cm tall, their branching made possible more complex bodies with multiple sporangia. As plant bodies became increasingly complex, competition for space and sunlight probably increased. As we'll see, that competition may have stimulated still more evolution in vascular plants.

The ancestors of vascular plants already had some derived traits of today's vascular plants, but they lacked roots and some other adaptations that evolved later. This section describes the main traits that characterize living vascular plants: life cycles with dominant sporophytes, transport in vascular tissues called xylem and phloem, and well-developed roots and leaves, including spore-bearing leaves called sporophylls.

Life Cycles with Dominant Sporophytes

Fossils suggest that the ancestors of vascular plants had gametophytes and sporophytes that were about equal in size. Among living vascular plants, however, the sporophyte (diploid) generation is the larger and more complex plant in the alternation of generations (**Figure 29.13**). In ferns, for example, the familiar leafy plants are the sporophytes. You

▼ **Figure 29.13 The life cycle of a fern.**

WHAT IF? *If the ability to disperse sperm by wind evolved in a fern, how might its life cycle be affected?*

1 Sporangia release spores. Most fern species produce a single type of spore that develops into a bisexual photosynthetic gametophyte.

2 Each gametophyte develops sperm-producing organs called antheridia and egg-producing organs called archegonia. Although this simplified diagram shows a sperm fertilizing an egg from the same gametophyte, in most fern species a gametophyte produces sperm and eggs at different times. Therefore, typically an egg from one gametophyte is fertilized by a sperm from another gametophyte.

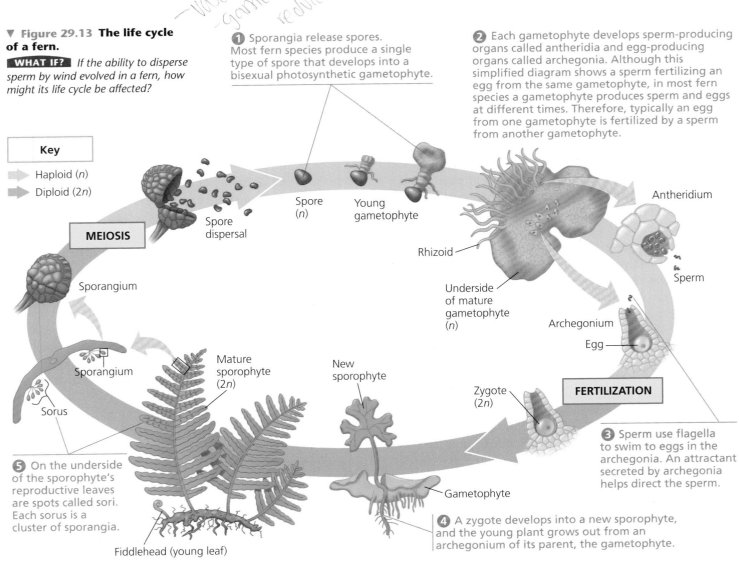

Key
Haploid (*n*)
Diploid (*2n*)

MEIOSIS

Spore dispersal

Sporangium

Sporangium

Sorus

5 On the underside of the sporophyte's reproductive leaves are spots called sori. Each sorus is a cluster of sporangia.

Mature sporophyte (*2n*)

Fiddlehead (young leaf)

Spore (*n*)

Young gametophyte

Rhizoid

Underside of mature gametophyte (*n*)

Antheridium

Sperm

Archegonium

Egg

New sporophyte

Zygote (*2n*)

FERTILIZATION

3 Sperm use flagella to swim to eggs in the archegonia. An attractant secreted by archegonia helps direct the sperm.

Gametophyte

4 A zygote develops into a new sporophyte, and the young plant grows out from an archegonium of its parent, the gametophyte.

would have to get down on your hands and knees and search the ground carefully to find fern gametophytes, which are tiny structures that often grow on or just below the soil surface. Until you have a chance to do that, you can study the sporophyte-dominant life cycle of seedless vascular plants in Figure 29.13, which uses a fern as an example. Then, for review, compare this life cycle with Figure 29.8, which represents a gametophyte-dominated life cycle typical of mosses and other nonvascular plants. In Chapter 30, you will see that gametophytes became even more reduced during the evolution of seed plants.

Transport in Xylem and Phloem

Vascular plants have two types of vascular tissue: xylem and phloem. **Xylem** conducts most of the water and minerals. The xylem of most vascular plants includes **tracheids**, tube-shaped cells that carry water and minerals up from roots (see Figure 35.10). (Tracheids have been lost in some highly specialized species, such as *Wolffia*, a tiny aquatic angiosperm.) Because nonvascular plants lack tracheids, vascular plants are sometimes referred to as tracheophytes. The water-conducting cells in vascular plants are *lignified*; that is, their cell walls are strengthened by the polymer **lignin**. The tissue called **phloem** has cells arranged into tubes that distribute sugars, amino acids, and other organic products (see Figure 35.10).

Lignified vascular tissue permitted vascular plants to grow tall. Their stems became strong enough to provide support against gravity, and they could transport water and mineral nutrients high above the ground. Tall plants could also out-compete short plants for access to the sunlight needed for photosynthesis. In addition, the spores of tall plants could disperse farther than those of short plants, enabling tall species to colonize new environments rapidly. Overall, the ability to grow tall was a major evolutionary innovation that gave vascular plants a competitive edge over nonvascular plants, which rarely grow above 20 cm in height. Competition among vascular plants also increased, and taller growth forms were favored by natural selection—such as the trees that formed the first forests about 385 million years ago.

Evolution of Roots

Lignified vascular tissue also provides benefits below ground. Instead of the rhizoids seen in bryophytes, roots evolved in the sporophytes of almost all vascular plants. **Roots** are organs that absorb water and nutrients from the soil. Roots also anchor vascular plants, hence allowing the shoot system to grow taller.

Root tissues of living plants closely resemble stem tissues of early vascular plants preserved in fossils. This suggests that roots may have evolved from the lowest belowground portions of stems in ancient vascular plants. It is unclear whether roots evolved only once in the common ancestor of all vascular plants or independently in different lineages.

Although the roots of living members of these lineages of vascular plants share many similarities, fossil evidence hints at convergent evolution. The oldest lycophyte fossils, for example, already displayed simple roots 400 million years ago, when the ancestors of ferns and seed plants still had none. Studying genes that control root development in different vascular plant species may help resolve this question.

Evolution of Leaves

Leaves increase the surface area of the plant body and serve as the primary photosynthetic organ of vascular plants. In terms of size and complexity, leaves can be classified as either microphylls or megaphylls. All of the lycophytes (the oldest lineage of present-day vascular plants)—and only the lycophytes—have **microphylls**, small, usually spine-shaped leaves supported by a single strand of vascular tissue. Almost all other vascular plants have **megaphylls**, leaves with a highly branched vascular system; a few species have reduced leaves that appear to have evolved from megaphylls. So named because they are typically larger than microphylls, megaphylls support greater photosynthetic productivity than microphylls as a result of the greater surface area served by their network of veins. Microphylls first appear in the fossil record 410 million years ago, but megaphylls do not emerge until about 370 million years ago, toward the end of the Devonian period.

According to one model of leaf evolution, microphylls originated from sporangia located on the side of the stem (Figure 29.14a). Megaphylls, by contrast, may have evolved from a series of branches lying close together on a stem. As one of these branches came to grow above, or *overtop*, the others, the lower branches became flattened and developed webbing that joined them to one another. These joined branches thus became a leaf attached to the branch that overtopped them (Figure 29.14b). To better understand the origin of leaves, scientists are exploring the genetic control of leaf development.

Sporophylls and Spore Variations

One milestone in the evolution of plants was the emergence of **sporophylls**, modified leaves that bear sporangia. Sporophylls vary greatly in structure. For example, fern sporophylls produce clusters of sporangia known as **sori** (singular, *sorus*), usually on the undersides of the sporophylls (see Figure 29.13). In many lycophytes and in most gymnosperms, groups of sporophylls form cone-like structures called **strobili** (singular, *strobilus*; from the Greek *strobilos*, cone). In Chapter 30, you will see how sporophylls form gymnosperm strobili and parts of angiosperm flowers.

Most seedless vascular plant species are **homosporous**: They have one type of sporangium that produces one type of spore, which typically develops into a bisexual gametophyte, as in most ferns. In contrast, a **heterosporous** species has

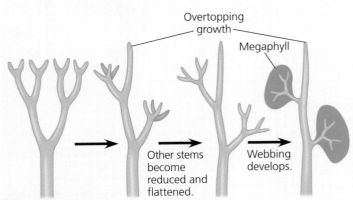

(a) **Microphylls**, such as those of lycophytes, may have originated from sporangia supported by single, unbranched strands of vascular tissue (shown in cross sections).

(b) **Megaphylls**, which have branched vascular systems, may have evolved by the fusion of branched stems.

▲ **Figure 29.14 Hypotheses for the evolution of leaves.**

two types of sporangia and produces two kinds of spores: Megasporangia on megasporophylls produce **megaspores**, which develop into female gametophytes; microsporangia on microsporophylls produce the comparatively smaller **microspores**, which develop into male gametophytes. All seed plants and a few seedless vascular plants are heterosporous. The following diagram compares the two conditions:

Classification of Seedless Vascular Plants

As we noted earlier, biologists recognize two clades of living seedless vascular plants: the lycophytes (phylum Lycophyta) and the pterophytes (phylum Pterophyta). The lycophytes include the club mosses, the spike mosses, and the quillworts. The pterophytes include the ferns, the horsetails, and the whisk ferns and their relatives. Because they differ greatly in appearance, the ferns, horsetails, and whisk ferns have long been considered separate phyla: phylum Pterophyta (ferns), phylum Sphenophyta (horsetails), and phylum Psilophyta (whisk ferns and a related genus). However, recent molecular comparisons provide convincing evidence that all three groups make up a clade. Accordingly, many systematists now classify them together as the phylum Pterophyta, as

we do in this chapter. Others refer to these groups as three separate phyla within a clade.

Figure 29.15, on the next page, describes the two main groups of seedless vascular plants.

Phylum Lycophyta: Club Mosses, Spike Mosses, and Quillworts

Present-day species of lycophytes, the most ancient group of vascular plants, are relics of a far more impressive past. By the Carboniferous period (359–299 million years ago), the lycophyte evolutionary lineage included small herbaceous plants and giant trees with diameters of more than 2 m and heights of more than 40 m. The giant lycophyte trees thrived for millions of years in moist swamps, but they became extinct when Earth's climate became drier at the end of the Carboniferous period. The small lycophytes survived, represented today by about 1,200 species. Though some are commonly called club mosses and spike mosses, they are not true mosses (which, as discussed earlier, are nonvascular plants).

Phylum Pterophyta: Ferns, Horsetails, and Whisk Ferns and Relatives

Ferns radiated extensively from their Devonian origins and grew alongside lycophyte trees and horsetails in the great Carboniferous swamp forests. Today, ferns are by far the most widespread seedless vascular plants, numbering more than 12,000 species. Though most diverse in the tropics, many ferns thrive in temperate forests, and some species are even adapted to arid habitats.

As mentioned earlier, ferns and other pterophytes are more closely related to seed plants than to lycophytes. As a result, pterophytes and seed plants share traits that are not found in lycophytes, including overtopping growth (see Figure 29.14b), megaphyll leaves, and roots that can branch at various points along the length of an existing root. In lycophytes,

Exploring Seedless Vascular Plant Diversity

Lycophytes (Phylum Lycophyta)

Many lycophytes grow on tropical trees as *epiphytes*, plants that use other plants as a substrate but are not parasites. Other species grow on temperate forest floors. In some species, the tiny gametophytes live above ground and are photosynthetic. Others live below ground, nurtured by symbiotic fungi.

Sporophytes have upright stems with many small leaves, as well as ground-hugging stems that produce dichotomously branching roots. Spike mosses are usually relatively small and often grow horizontally. In many club mosses and spike mosses, sporophylls are clustered into club-shaped cones (strobili). Quillworts, named for their leaf shape, form a single genus whose members live in marshy areas or as submerged aquatic plants. Club mosses are all homosporous, whereas spike mosses and quillworts are all heterosporous. The spores of club mosses are released in clouds and are so rich in oil that magicians and photographers once ignited them to create smoke or flashes of light.

2.5 cm

Selaginella moellendorffii, a spike moss

Isoetes gunnii, a quillwort

Strobili (clusters of sporophylls)

1 cm

Diphasiastrum tristachyum, a club moss

Pterophytes (Phylum Pterophyta)

Athyrium filix-femina, lady fern

25 cm

Equisetum arvense, field horsetail

Vegetative stem

Strobilus on fertile stem

1.5 cm

Psilotum nudum, a whisk fern

4 cm

Ferns

Unlike the lycophytes, ferns have megaphylls (see Figure 29.14b). The sporophytes typically have horizontal stems that give rise to large leaves called fronds, often divided into leaflets. A frond grows as its coiled tip, the fiddlehead, unfurls.

Almost all species are homosporous. The gametophyte in some species shrivels and dies after the young sporophyte detaches itself. In most species, sporophytes have stalked sporangia with springlike devices that catapult spores several meters. Airborne spores can be carried far from their origin. Some species produce more than a trillion spores in a plant's lifetime.

Horsetails

The group's name refers to the brushy appearance of the stems, which have a gritty texture that made them historically useful as "scouring rushes" for pots and pans. Some species have separate fertile (cone-bearing) and vegetative stems. Horsetails are homosporous, with cones releasing spores that typically give rise to bisexual gametophytes.

Horsetails are also called arthrophytes ("jointed plants") because their stems have joints. Rings of small leaves or branches emerge from each joint, but the stem is the main photosynthetic organ. Large air canals carry oxygen to the roots, which often grow in waterlogged soil.

Whisk Ferns and Relatives

Like primitive vascular plant fossils, the sporophytes of whisk ferns (genus *Psilotum*) have dichotomously branching stems but no roots. Stems have scalelike outgrowths that lack vascular tissue and may have resulted from the evolutionary reduction of leaves. Each yellow knob on a stem consists of three fused sporangia. Species of the genus *Tmesipteris*, closely related to whisk ferns and found only in the South Pacific, also lack roots but have small, leaflike outgrowths in their stems, giving them a vine-like appearance. Both genera are homosporous, with spores giving rise to bisexual gametophytes that grow underground and are only about a centimeter long.

by contrast, roots branch only at the growing tip of the root, forming a Y-shaped structure.

The pterophytes called horsetails were very diverse during the Carboniferous period, some growing as tall as 15 m. Today, only 15 species survive as a single, widely distributed genus, *Equisetum*, found in marshy places and along streams.

Psilotum (whisk ferns) and a closely related genus, *Tmesipteris*, form a clade consisting mainly of tropical epiphytes. Plants in these two genera, the only vascular plants lacking true roots, are called "living fossils" because of their resemblance to fossils of ancient relatives of living vascular plants (see Figures 29.12 and 29.15). However, much evidence, including analyses of DNA sequences and sperm structure, indicates that the genera *Psilotum* and *Tmesipteris* are closely related to ferns. This hypothesis suggests that their ancestor's true roots were lost during evolution. Today, plants in these two genera absorb water and nutrients through numerous absorptive rhizoids.

Fern   Lycophyte trees   Horsetail   Tree trunk covered with small leaves   Lycophyte tree reproductive structures

▲ **Figure 29.16 Artist's conception of a Carboniferous forest based on fossil evidence.** In addition to plants, animals, including giant dragonflies like the one in the foreground, also thrived in the "coal forests" of the Carboniferous.

WHAT IF? *What would this forest look like if few lycophyte trees were reproducing (as would often have been the case)?*

The Significance of Seedless Vascular Plants

The ancestors of living lycophytes, horsetails, and ferns, along with their extinct seedless vascular relatives, grew to great heights during the Devonian and early Carboniferous, forming the first forests (Figure 29.16). How did their dramatic growth affect Earth and its other life? With the evolution of vascular tissue, roots, and leaves, these plants accelerated their rate of photosynthesis, dramatically increasing the removal of CO_2 from the atmosphere. Scientists estimate that CO_2 levels dropped by as much as a factor of five during the Carboniferous, causing global cooling that resulted in widespread glacier formation. Ancient CO_2 levels can be estimated in several ways. These include counting the number of stomata in fossil leaves (data from living species show that this number increases as CO_2 levels drop) and measuring carbon isotope levels in fossils of plankton. Different methods yield similar results, suggesting that reconstructions of past climates are accurate.

The seedless vascular plants that formed the first forests eventually became coal. In the stagnant waters of Carboniferous swamps, dead plants did not completely decay. This organic material turned to thick layers of peat, later covered by the sea. Marine sediments piled on top, and over millions of years, heat and pressure converted the peat to coal. In fact, Carboniferous coal deposits are the most extensive ever formed. Coal was crucial to the Industrial Revolution, and people worldwide still burn 6 billion tons a year. It is ironic

that coal, formed from plants that contributed to a global cooling, now contributes to global warming by returning carbon to the atmosphere.

Growing along with the seedless plants in Carboniferous swamps were primitive seed plants. Though seed plants were not dominant at that time, they rose to prominence after the swamps began to dry up at the end of the Carboniferous period. The next chapter traces the origin and diversification of seed plants, continuing our story of adaptation to life on land.

CONCEPT CHECK 29.3

1. List the key derived traits found in pterophytes and seed plants, but not in lycophytes.
2. How do the main similarities and differences between seedless vascular plants and nonvascular plants influence function in these plants?
3. **WHAT IF?** If (contrary to the evidence) lycophytes and pterophytes formed a clade, what could you conclude about how members of this clade gained (or lost) traits shared by pterophytes and seed plants?
4. **MAKE CONNECTIONS** In Figure 29.13, if fertilization occurred between gametes from one gametophyte, how would this affect the production of genetic variation from sexual reproduction? See page 258 of Concept 13.4.

For suggested answers, see Appendix A.

SUMMARY OF KEY CONCEPTS

CONCEPT 29.1

Land plants evolved from green algae (pp. 600–606)

- Morphological and biochemical traits, as well as similarities in nuclear and chloroplast genes, suggest that charophytes are the closest living relatives of land plants.
- A protective layer of **sporopollenin** and other traits allow charophytes to tolerate occasional drying along the edges of ponds and lakes. Such traits may have enabled the algal ancestors of plants to survive in terrestrial conditions, opening the way to the colonization of dry land.
- Derived traits that distinguish the clade of land plants from charophytes, their closest algal relatives, include the four shown here:

❶ Alternation of generations

❷ Apical meristems

❸ Multicellular gametangia

❹ Walled spores in sporangia

- Fossil evidence indicates that plants were on land at least 475 million years ago. Subsequently, plants diverged into several major groups, including nonvascular plants (bryophytes); seedless vascular plants, such as lycophytes and ferns; and the two groups of seed plants: gymnosperms and angiosperms.

? *Draw a phylogenetic tree illustrating our current understanding of land plant phylogeny; label the common ancestor of land plants and the origins of multicellular gametangia, vascular tissue, and seeds.*

CONCEPT 29.2

Mosses and other nonvascular plants have life cycles dominated by gametophytes (pp. 606–610)

- Current evidence indicates that the three phyla of **bryophytes**—liverworts, mosses, and hornworts—do not form a clade.

- In bryophytes, the dominant and typically most visible generation consists of haploid **gametophytes**, such as those that make up a carpet of moss. **Rhizoids** anchor gametophytes to the substrate on which they grow. The flagellated sperm produced by **antheridia** require a film of water to travel to the eggs in the **archegonia**.
- The diploid stage of the bryophyte life cycle—the **sporophytes**—grow out of archegonia and are attached to the gametophytes and dependent on them for nourishment. Smaller and simpler than vascular plant sporophytes, they typically consist of a **foot**, **seta** (stalk), and **sporangium**.
- *Sphagnum*, or peat moss, is common in large regions known as peatlands and has many practical uses, including as a fuel.

? *Summarize the ecological importance of mosses.*

CONCEPT 29.3

Ferns and other seedless vascular plants were the first plants to grow tall (pp. 610–615)

- Fossils of the forerunners of today's vascular plants date back about 425 million years and show that these small plants had independent, branching sporophytes. However, these ancestral species lacked other derived traits of living vascular plants, such as a life cycle with dominant sporophytes; lignified vascular tissue; well-developed roots and leaves; and sporophylls.
- Seedless vascular plants include the **lycophytes** (phylum Lycophyta: club mosses, spike mosses, and quillworts) and the **pterophytes** (phylum Pterophyta: ferns, horsetails, and whisk ferns and relatives). Ancient lycophytes included both small herbaceous plants and large trees. Present-day lycophytes are small herbaceous plants.
- Seedless vascular plants dominated the earliest forests. Their growth may have helped produce the major global cooling that characterized the end of the Carboniferous period. The decaying remnants of the first forests eventually became coal.

? *What trait(s) allowed vascular plants to grow tall, and why might increased height have been advantageous?*

TEST YOUR UNDERSTANDING

LEVEL 1: KNOWLEDGE/COMPREHENSION

1. Which of the following is *not* evidence that charophytes are the closest algal relatives of plants?
   a. similar sperm structure
   b. the presence of chloroplasts
   c. similarities in cell wall formation during cell division
   d. genetic similarities in chloroplasts
   e. similarities in proteins that synthesize cellulose

2. Which of the following characteristics of plants is absent in their closest relatives, the charophyte algae?
   a. chlorophyll *b*
   b. cellulose in cell walls
   c. formation of a cell plate during cytokinesis
   d. sexual reproduction
   e. alternation of multicellular generations

3. In plants, which of the following are produced by meiosis?
   a. haploid sporophytes
   b. haploid gametes
   c. diploid gametes
   d. haploid spores
   e. diploid spores

4. Microphylls are found in which plant group?
   a. mosses
   b. liverworts
   c. lycophytes
   d. ferns
   e. hornworts

5. Which of the following is a land plant that has flagellated sperm and a sporophyte-dominated life cycle?
   a. fern
   b. moss
   c. liverwort
   d. charophyte
   e. hornwort

6. Identify each of the following structures as haploid or diploid.
   a. sporophyte
   b. spore
   c. gametophyte
   d. zygote
   e. sperm

LEVEL 2: APPLICATION/ANALYSIS

7. Suppose an efficient conducting system evolved in a moss that could transport water and other materials as high as a tall tree. Which of the following statements about "trees" of such a species would *not* be true?
   a. Fertilization would probably be more difficult.
   b. Spore dispersal distances would probably increase.
   c. Females could produce only one archegonium.
   d. Unless its body parts were strengthened, such a "tree" would probably flop over.
   e. Individuals would probably compete more effectively for access to light.

8. EVOLUTION CONNECTION

DRAW IT Draw a phylogenetic tree that represents our current understanding of evolutionary relationships between a moss, a gymnosperm, a lycophyte, and a fern. Use a charophyte alga as the outgroup. (See Chapter 26 to review phylogenetic trees.) Label each branch point of the phylogeny with at least one derived character unique to the clade descended from the common ancestor represented by the branch point.

LEVEL 3: SYNTHESIS/EVALUATION

9. SCIENTIFIC INQUIRY

DRAW IT The feather moss *Pleurozium schreberi* harbors species of symbiotic nitrogen-fixing bacteria. Scientists studying this moss in northern forests found that the percentage of the ground surface "covered" by the moss increased from about 5% in forests that had burned 35 to 41 years ago to about 70% in forests that had burned 170 or more years ago.

From mosses growing in these forests, they also obtained the following data on nitrogen fixation:

Age (years after fire)	N fixation rate (kg N per ha per yr)
35	0.001
41	0.005
78	0.08
101	0.3
124	0.9
170	2.0
220	1.3
244	2.1
270	1.6
300	3.0
355	2.3

Source: Data from O. Zackrisson et al., Nitrogen fixation increases with successional age in boreal forests, *Ecology* 85: 3327–3334 (2006).

a. Use the data to draw a line graph, with age on the *x*-axis and the nitrogen fixation rate on the *y*-axis.
b. Along with the nitrogen added by nitrogen fixation, about 1 kg of nitrogen per hectare per year is deposited into northern forests from the atmosphere as rain and small particles. Evaluate the extent to which *Pleurozium* affects nitrogen availability in northern forests of different ages.

10. **WRITE ABOUT A THEME**
   ENVIRONMENTAL INTERACTIONS Giant lycophyte trees had microphylls, whereas ferns and seed plants have megaphylls. Write a short essay (100–150 words) describing how a forest of lycophyte trees may have differed from a forest of large ferns or seed plants. In your answer, consider how the type of forest in which they grew may have affected interactions among small plants growing beneath the tall ones.

For selected answers, see Appendix A.

Mastering**BIOLOGY** www.masteringbiology.com

1. MasteringBiology® Assignments
Tutorial Nonvascular Plants
Activities Terrestrial Adaptations of Plants • Highlights of Plant Phylogeny • Moss Life Cycle • Fern Life Cycle
Questions Student Misconceptions • Reading Quiz • Multiple Choice • End-of-Chapter

2. eText
Read your book online, search, take notes, highlight text, and more.

3. The Study Area
Practice Tests • Cumulative Test • *BioFlix* 3-D Animations • MP3 Tutor Sessions • Videos • Activities • Investigations • Lab Media • Audio Glossary • Word Study Tools • Art

Plant Diversity II: The Evolution of Seed Plants

▲ **Figure 30.1 What human reproductive organ is functionally similar to this seed?**

EVOLUTION

KEY CONCEPTS

30.1 Seeds and pollen grains are key adaptations for life on land

30.2 Gymnosperms bear "naked" seeds, typically on cones

30.3 The reproductive adaptations of angiosperms include flowers and fruits

30.4 Human welfare depends greatly on seed plants

OVERVIEW

Transforming the World

Continuing the saga of how plants have transformed Earth, this chapter follows the emergence and diversification of seed plants. Fossils and comparative studies of living plants offer clues about the origin of seed plants some 360 million years ago. As this new group of plants became established, they dramatically altered the course of plant evolution. We'll begin our exploration of how this occurred by looking at the innovation for which seed plants are named: seeds **(Figure 30.1)**.

A **seed** consists of an embryo and its food supply, surrounded by a protective coat. When mature, seeds are dispersed from their parent by wind or other means. Because it nourishes and protects the embryo, yet can move away from the mother plant, a seed is analogous to a detachable and mobile version of a pregnant woman's uterus. As we'll see, seeds are a key adaptation that helped seed plants to become the dominant producers on land and to make up the vast majority of plant biodiversity today.

Seed plants have also had an enormous impact on human society. Starting about 12,000 years ago, humans began to cultivate wheat, figs, maize (commonly called corn in the United States), rice, and other wild seed plants. This practice emerged independently in various parts of the world, including the Near East, East Asia, Africa, and the Americas. One piece of evidence, the well-preserved squash seed in Figure 30.1, was found in a cave in Mexico and dates from between 8,000 and 10,000 years ago. This seed differs from wild squash seeds, suggesting that squash was being domesticated by that time. The domestication of seed plants, particularly angiosperms, produced the most important cultural change in human history, transforming most human societies from roving bands of hunter-gatherers to permanent settlements anchored by agriculture.

In this chapter, we will first examine the general characteristics of seed plants. Then we will look at the distinguishing features and evolution of gymnosperms and angiosperms.

CONCEPT 30.1

Seeds and pollen grains are key adaptations for life on land

We begin with an overview of terrestrial adaptations that seed plants added to those already present in nonvascular plants (bryophytes) and seedless vascular plants (see Chapter 29). In addition to seeds, the following are common to all seed plants: reduced gametophytes, heterospory, ovules, and pollen. As you'll read, these adaptations provided new ways for seed plants to cope with terrestrial conditions such as drought and exposure to the ultraviolet (UV) radiation in sunlight. Novel adaptations also freed seed plants from requiring water for fertilization, enabling reproduction to occur under a broader range of conditions than in seedless plants.

Advantages of Reduced Gametophytes

Mosses and other bryophytes have life cycles dominated by gametophytes, whereas ferns and other seedless vascular plants have sporophyte-dominated life cycles. The evolutionary trend of gametophyte reduction continued further in the vascular plant lineage that led to seed plants. While the gametophytes

PLANT GROUP		
Mosses and other nonvascular plants	**Ferns and other seedless vascular plants**	**Seed plants (gymnosperms and angiosperms)**
Gametophyte Dominant	Reduced, independent (photosynthetic and free-living)	Reduced (usually microscopic), dependent on surrounding sporophyte tissue for nutrition
Sporophyte Reduced, dependent on gametophyte for nutrition	Dominant	Dominant

Example

Sporophyte (2n)
Gametophyte (n)

Sporophyte (2n)
Gametophyte (n)

Gymnosperm
Microscopic female gametophytes (n) inside ovulate cone
Microscopic male gametophytes (n) inside pollen cone
Sporophyte (2n)

Angiosperm
Microscopic female gametophytes (n) inside these parts of flowers
Microscopic male gametophytes (n) inside these parts of flowers
Sporophyte (2n)

▲ **Figure 30.2 Gametophyte-sporophyte relationships in different plant groups.**
MAKE CONNECTIONS *In seed plants, how does retaining the gametophyte within the sporophyte likely affect embryo fitness? (See pp. 346, 472, and 480 in Chapters 17 and 23 to review mutagens, mutations, and fitness.)*

of seedless vascular plants are visible to the naked eye, the gametophytes of seed plants are mostly microscopic.

This miniaturization allowed for an important evolutionary innovation in seed plants: Their tiny gametophytes can develop from spores retained within the sporangia of the parental sporophyte. This arrangement protects the gametophytes from environmental stresses. The moist reproductive tissues of the sporophyte shield the gametophytes from UV radiation and protect them from drying out. This relationship also enables the dependent gametophytes to obtain nutrients from the sporophyte. In contrast, the free-living gametophytes of seedless plants must fend for themselves. **Figure 30.2** contrasts the gametophyte-sporophyte relationships in nonvascular plants, seedless vascular plants, and seed plants.

Heterospory: The Rule Among Seed Plants

You read in Chapter 29 that most seedless plants are *homosporous*—they produce one kind of spore, which usually gives rise to a bisexual gametophyte. Ferns and other close relatives

of seed plants are homosporous, suggesting that seed plants had homosporous ancestors. At some point, seed plants or their ancestors became *heterosporous*, producing two kinds of spores: Megasporangia produce *megaspores* that give rise to female gametophytes, and microsporangia produce *microspores* that give rise to male gametophytes. Each megasporangium has a single functional megaspore, whereas each microsporangium contains vast numbers of microspores.

As we noted previously, the miniaturization of seed plant gametophytes likely contributed to the great success of this clade. Next we will look at the development of the female gametophyte within an ovule and the development of the male gametophyte in a pollen grain. Then we will follow the transformation of a fertilized ovule into a seed.

Ovules and Production of Eggs

Although a few species of seedless plants are heterosporous, seed plants are unique in retaining the megasporangium within the parent sporophyte. A layer of sporophyte tissue

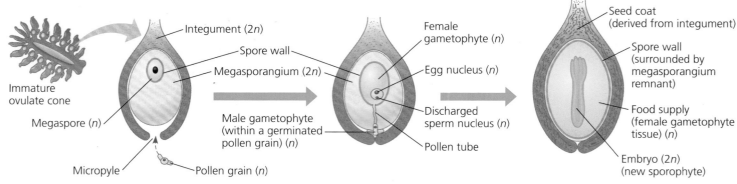

(a) Unfertilized ovule. In this longitudinal section through the ovule of a pine (a gymnosperm), a fleshy megasporangium is surrounded by a protective layer of tissue called an integument. The micropyle, the only opening through the integument, allows entry of a pollen grain.

(b) Fertilized ovule. A megaspore develops into a female gametophyte, which produces an egg. The pollen grain, which had entered through the micropyle, contains a male gametophyte. The male gametophyte develops a pollen tube that discharges sperm, thereby fertilizing the egg.

(c) Gymnosperm seed. Fertilization initiates the transformation of the ovule into a seed, which consists of a sporophyte embryo, a food supply, and a protective seed coat derived from the integument. The megasporangium dries out and collapses.

▲ **Figure 30.3 From ovule to seed in a gymnosperm.**

? *A gymnosperm seed contains cells from how many different plant generations? Identify the cells and whether each is haploid or diploid.*

called **integument** envelops and protects the megasporangium. Gymnosperm megasporangia are surrounded by one integument, whereas those in angiosperms usually have two integuments. The whole structure—megasporangium, megaspore, and their integument(s)—is called an **ovule** **(Figure 30.3a)**. Inside each ovule (from the Latin *ovulum*, little egg), a female gametophyte develops from a megaspore and produces one or more eggs.

Pollen and Production of Sperm

A microspore develops into a **pollen grain** that consists of a male gametophyte enclosed within the pollen wall. (The outer layer of the pollen wall is composed of molecules secreted by sporophyte cells; hence, we refer to the male gametophyte as being *in* the pollen grain, not *equivalent to* the pollen grain.) The tough pollen wall, which contains the polymer sporopollenin, protects a pollen grain as it is transported from the parent plant by wind, for example, or by hitchhiking on the body of an animal. The transfer of pollen to the part of a seed plant that contains the ovules is called **pollination**. If a pollen grain germinates (begins growing), it gives rise to a pollen tube that discharges sperm into the female gametophyte within the ovule, as shown in **Figure 30.3b**.

Recall that in nonvascular plants and seedless vascular plants such as ferns, free-living gametophytes release flagellated sperm that swim through a film of water to reach eggs. The distance for this sperm transport rarely exceeds a few centimeters. By contrast, in seed plants a sperm-producing male gametophyte inside a pollen grain can be carried long distances by wind or by animals, eliminating the dependence on water for sperm transport. The sperm of seed plants also do not require motility because sperm are carried directly to the eggs by pollen tubes. Living gymnosperms provide evidence of the evolutionary transition to nonmotile sperm. The sperm of some gymnosperm species (such as ginkgos and cycads, shown a little later in Figure 30.5) retain the ancient flagellated condition, but flagella have been lost in the sperm of most gymnosperms and all angiosperms.

The Evolutionary Advantage of Seeds

If a sperm fertilizes an egg of a seed plant, the zygote grows into a sporophyte embryo. As shown in **Figure 30.3c**, the whole ovule develops into a seed: the embryo, along with a food supply, packaged within a protective coat derived from the integument(s).

Until the advent of seeds, the spore was the only protective stage in any plant life cycle. Moss spores, for example, may survive even if the local environment becomes too cold, too hot, or too dry for the mosses themselves to live. Their tiny size enables the spores to be dispersed in a dormant state to a new area, where they can germinate and give rise to new moss gametophytes if and when conditions are favorable enough for them to break dormancy. Spores were the main way that mosses, ferns, and other seedless plants spread over Earth for the first 100 million years of plant life on land.

Although mosses and other seedless plants continue to be very successful today, seeds represent a major evolutionary innovation that contributed to the opening of new ways of life for seed plants. What advantages do seeds provide over spores? Spores are usually single-celled, whereas seeds are multicellular, consisting of an embryo protected by a layer of tissue, the seed coat. A seed can remain dormant for days, months, or even years after being released from the parent plant, whereas most spores have shorter lifetimes. Also, unlike spores, seeds have a supply of stored food. Under favorable conditions, the seed can emerge from dormancy and germinate, with its stored food providing critical support for growth as the sporophyte embryo emerges as a seedling. Most seeds land close to their parent sporophyte plant, but some are carried long distances (up to hundreds of kilometers) by wind or animals.

CONCEPT CHECK 30.1

1. Contrast sperm delivery in seedless plants with sperm delivery in seed plants.
2. What features not present in seedless plants have contributed to the enormous success of seed plants on land?
3. **WHAT IF?** If a seed could not enter dormancy, how might that affect the embryo's transport or survival?

For suggested answers, see Appendix A.

◀ **Figure 30.4 A progymnosperm.** *Archaeopteris,* which lived 380 million years ago, produced wood and was heterosporous, but it did not produce seeds. Growing up to 20 m tall, it had fernlike leaves.

CONCEPT 30.2

Gymnosperms bear "naked" seeds, typically on cones

Nonvascular plants (bryophytes)
Seedless vascular plants
Gymnosperms
Angiosperms

As shown in this phylogeny, extant seed plants form two sister clades: gymnosperms and angiosperms. Recall from Chapter 29 that gymnosperms have "naked" seeds that are not enclosed in ovaries. Their seeds are exposed on modified leaves (sporophylls) that usually form cones (strobili). (Angiosperm seeds are enclosed in fruits, which are mature ovaries.) We turn now to the origin of gymnosperms and other early seed plants.

Gymnosperm Evolution

Fossils reveal that by the late Devonian period (about 380 million years ago), some plants had acquired adaptations characteristic of seed plants. For example, *Archaeopteris* was a heterosporous tree with a woody stem (**Figure 30.4**). But it did not bear seeds. Such transitional species of seedless vascular plants are sometimes called **progymnosperms**.

The first seed plants to appear in the fossil record date from around 360 million years ago, 55 million years before the first gymnosperm fossils and more than 200 million years before the first angiosperm fossils. These early seed plants became extinct, as did several later lineages. It remains uncertain which of these extinct seed plant lineages ultimately gave rise to the gymnosperms.

The earliest fossils of gymnosperms are about 305 million years old. These early gymnosperms lived in Carboniferous ecosystems still dominated by lycophytes, horsetails, ferns, and other seedless vascular plants. As the Carboniferous period gave way to the Permian, markedly drier climatic conditions favored the spread of gymnosperms. The flora and fauna changed dramatically, as many groups of organisms disappeared and others became prominent (see Chapter 25). Though most pronounced in the seas, the changeover also affected terrestrial life. For example, in the animal kingdom, amphibians decreased in diversity and were replaced by reptiles, which were especially well adapted to the arid conditions. Similarly, the lycophytes, horsetails, and ferns that dominated the Carboniferous swamps were largely replaced by gymnosperms, which were more suited to the drier climate. Gymnosperms have the key terrestrial adaptations found in all seed plants, such as seeds and pollen. In addition, some gymnosperms were particularly well suited to arid conditions because of the thick cuticles and relatively small surface areas of their needle-shaped leaves.

Geologists consider the end of the Permian period, about 251 million years ago, to be the boundary between the Paleozoic ("old life") and Mesozoic ("middle life") eras. Life changed profoundly as gymnosperms dominated terrestrial ecosystems throughout much of the Mesozoic, serving as the food supply for giant herbivorous dinosaurs. Toward the end of the Mesozoic, angiosperms began to replace gymnosperms in some ecosystems. The Mesozoic era ended 65 million years ago with mass extinctions of dinosaurs and many other animal groups, and further increases in the biodiversity and importance of angiosperms. Although angiosperms now dominate most terrestrial ecosystems, many gymnosperms remain an important part of Earth's flora. For example, vast regions in northern latitudes are covered by forests of cone-bearing gymnosperms called **conifers**, which include spruce, pine, fir, and redwood (see Figure 52.12, p. 1155).

Of the ten plant phyla in the taxonomic scheme adopted by this textbook (see Table 29.1), four are gymnosperms: Cycadophyta, Ginkgophyta, Gnetophyta, and Coniferophyta. The relationships of these four phyla to each other are uncertain. **Figure 30.5**, on the next two pages, surveys the diversity of extant gymnosperms.

Exploring Gymnosperm Diversity

Phylum Cycadophyta

Cycads are the next largest group of gymnosperms after the conifers. They have large cones and palmlike leaves (true palm species are angiosperms). Only about 130 species survive today, but cycads thrived during the Mesozoic era, known as the age of cycads as well as the age of dinosaurs.

Cycas revoluta

Phylum Ginkgophyta

Ginkgo biloba is the only surviving species of this phylum. Also known as the maidenhair tree, it has deciduous fanlike leaves that turn gold in autumn. It is a popular ornamental tree in cities because it tolerates air pollution well. Landscapers often plant only pollen-producing trees because the fleshy seeds smell rancid as they decay.

Phylum Gnetophyta

Plants in the phylum Gnetophyta, called gnetophytes, consist of three genera: *Gnetum*, *Ephedra*, and *Welwitschia*. Some species are tropical, whereas others live in deserts. Although very different in appearance, the genera are grouped together based on molecular data.

▶ **Welwitschia.** This genus consists of one species, *Welwitschia mirabilis*, a plant that lives only in the deserts of southwestern Africa. Its straplike leaves are among the largest leaves known.

◀ **Gnetum.** This genus includes about 35 species of tropical trees, shrubs, and vines, mainly native to Africa and Asia. Their leaves look similar to those of flowering plants, and their seeds look somewhat like fruits.

Ovulate cones

▶ **Ephedra.** This genus includes about 40 species that inhabit arid regions worldwide. These desert shrubs, commonly called "Mormon tea," produce the compound ephedrine, which is used medicinally as a decongestant.

Phylum Coniferophyta

Phylum Coniferophyta is by far the largest of the gymnosperm phyla, consisting of about 600 species of conifers (from the Latin *conus*, cone, and *ferre*, to carry). Many are large trees, such as cypresses and redwoods. A few conifer species dominate vast forested regions of the Northern Hemisphere, where the growing season is relatively short because of latitude or altitude.

Most conifers are evergreens; they retain their leaves throughout the year. Even during winter, a limited amount of photosynthesis occurs on sunny days. When spring comes, conifers already have fully developed leaves that can take advantage of the sunnier, warmer days. Some conifers, such as the dawn redwood, tamarack, and larch, are deciduous trees that lose leaves each autumn.

▶ **Douglas fir.** This evergreen tree (*Pseudotsuga menziesii*) provides more timber than any other North American tree species. Some uses include house framing, plywood, pulpwood for paper, railroad ties, and boxes and crates.

▶ **Common juniper.** The "berries" of the common juniper (*Juniperus communis*) are actually ovule-producing cones consisting of fleshy sporophylls.

◀ **European larch.** The needle-like leaves of this deciduous conifer (*Larix decidua*) turn yellow before they are shed in autumn. Native to the mountains of central Europe, including Switzerland's Matterhorn, depicted here, this species is extremely cold-tolerant, able to survive winter temperatures that plunge to −50°C.

◀ **Wollemi pine.** Survivors of a conifer group once known only from fossils, living Wollemi pines (*Wollemia nobilis*) were discovered in 1994 in a national park only 150 km from Sydney, Australia. The species consists of just 40 known individuals in two small groves. The inset photo compares the leaves of this "living fossil" with actual fossils.

▶ **Sequoia.** This giant sequoia (*Sequoiadendron giganteum*) in California's Sequoia National Park weighs about 2,500 metric tons, equivalent to about 24 blue whales (the largest animals) or 40,000 people. The giant sequoia is one of the largest living organisms and also among the most ancient, with some individuals estimated to be between 1,800 and 2,700 years old. Their cousins, the coast redwoods (*Sequoia sempervirens*), grow to heights of more than 110 m (taller than the Statue of Liberty) and are found only in a narrow coastal strip of northern California and southern Oregon.

▶ **Bristlecone pine.** This species (*Pinus longaeva*), which is found in the White Mountains of California, includes some of the oldest living organisms, reaching ages of more than 4,600 years. One tree (not shown here) is called Methuselah because it may be the world's oldest living tree. To protect the tree, scientists keep its location a secret.

▼ **Figure 30.6 The life cycle of a pine.**

MAKE CONNECTIONS *What type of cell division occurs as a megaspore becomes a female gametophyte? (See Figure 13.9, p. 256.)*

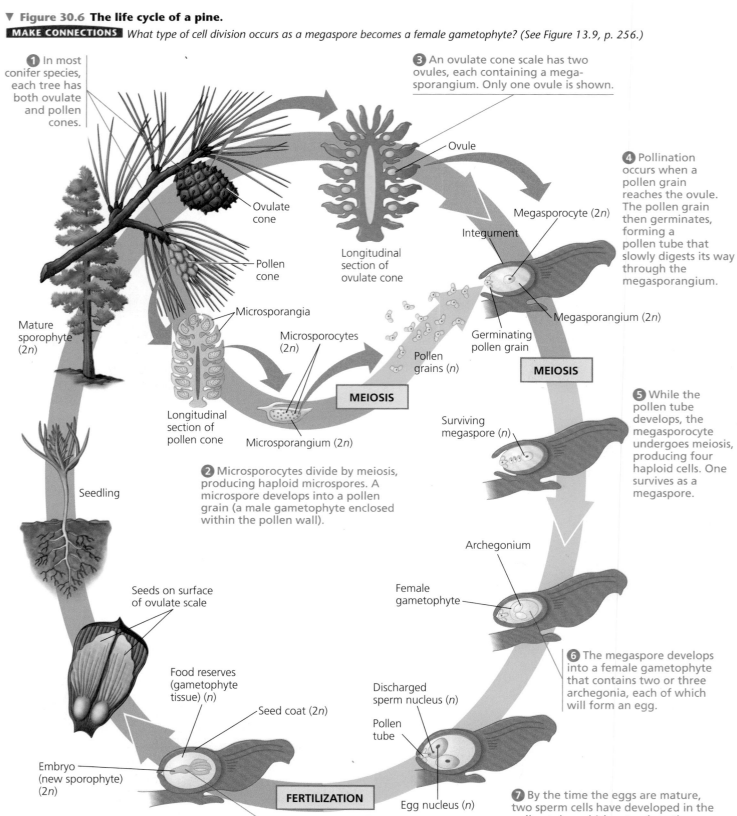

① In most conifer species, each tree has both ovulate and pollen cones.

③ An ovulate cone scale has two ovules, each containing a megasporangium. Only one ovule is shown.

Ovulate cone

Longitudinal section of ovulate cone

Ovule

④ Pollination occurs when a pollen grain reaches the ovule. The pollen grain then germinates, forming a pollen tube that slowly digests its way through the megasporangium.

Megasporocyte (2n)

Integument

Pollen cone

Microsporangia

Microsporocytes (2n)

Megasporangium (2n)

Germinating pollen grain

Pollen grains (n)

MEIOSIS

Mature sporophyte (2n)

MEIOSIS

Longitudinal section of pollen cone

Microsporangium (2n)

Surviving megaspore (n)

⑤ While the pollen tube develops, the megasporocyte undergoes meiosis, producing four haploid cells. One survives as a megaspore.

② Microsporocytes divide by meiosis, producing haploid microspores. A microspore develops into a pollen grain (a male gametophyte enclosed within the pollen wall).

Seedling

Archegonium

Female gametophyte

⑥ The megaspore develops into a female gametophyte that contains two or three archegonia, each of which will form an egg.

Seeds on surface of ovulate scale

Food reserves (gametophyte tissue) (n)

Discharged sperm nucleus (n)

Pollen tube

Seed coat (2n)

Embryo (new sporophyte) (2n)

FERTILIZATION

Egg nucleus (n)

⑦ By the time the eggs are mature, two sperm cells have developed in the pollen tube, which extends to the female gametophyte. Fertilization occurs when sperm and egg nuclei unite.

⑧ Fertilization usually occurs more than a year after pollination. All eggs may be fertilized, but usually only one zygote develops into an embryo. The ovule becomes a seed, consisting of an embryo, food supply, and seed coat.

Key

➤ Haploid (n)
➤ Diploid (2n)

The Life Cycle of a Pine: *A Closer Look*

As you read earlier, seed plant evolution has included three key reproductive adaptations: the increasing dominance of the sporophyte; the advent of the seed as a resistant, dispersible stage in the life cycle; and the appearance of pollen as an airborne agent that brings gametes together. **Figure 30.6**, on the facing page, shows how these adaptations come into play during the life cycle of a pine, a familiar conifer.

The pine tree is the sporophyte; its sporangia are located on scalelike structures packed densely in cones. Like all seed plants, conifers are heterosporous. In conifers, the two types of spores are produced by separate cones: small pollen cones and large ovulate cones. In most pine species, each tree has both types of cones. In pollen cones, microsporocytes (microspore mother cells) undergo meiosis, producing haploid microspores. Each microspore develops into a pollen grain containing a male gametophyte. In pines and other conifers, the yellow pollen is released in large amounts and carried by the wind, dusting everything in its path. Meanwhile, in ovulate cones, megasporocytes (megaspore mother cells) undergo meiosis and produce haploid megaspores inside the ovule. Surviving megaspores develop into multicellular female gametophytes, which are retained within the sporangia.

From the time young pollen and ovulate cones appear on the tree, it takes nearly three years for the male and female gametophytes to be produced and brought together and for mature seeds to form from the fertilized ovules. The scales of each ovulate cone then separate, and the seeds are dispersed by the wind. A seed that lands in a suitable environment then germinates, its embryo emerging as a pine seedling.

CONCEPT CHECK 30.2

1. Use examples from Figure 30.5 to describe how various gymnosperms are similar yet distinctive.
2. Explain how the pine life cycle in Figure 30.6 reflects the five adaptations common to all seed plants (see p. 618).
3. **MAKE CONNECTIONS** Does the hypothesis that gymnosperms and angiosperms are sister clades imply that they originated at the same time? (Review p. 538.)

For suggested answers, see Appendix A.

CONCEPT 30.3

The reproductive adaptations of angiosperms include flowers and fruits

Nonvascular plants (bryophytes)
Seedless vascular plants
Gymnosperms
Angiosperms

Commonly known as flowering plants, angiosperms are seed plants that produce the reproductive structures called flowers and fruits. The name *angiosperm* (from the Greek *angion*, container) refers to seeds contained in fruits, the mature ovaries. Today, angiosperms are the most diverse and widespread of all plants, with more than 250,000 species (about 90% of all plant species).

Characteristics of Angiosperms

All angiosperms are classified in a single phylum, Anthophyta (from the Greek *anthos*, flower). Before considering the evolution of angiosperms, we will examine their key adaptations—flowers and fruits—and the roles of these structures in the angiosperm life cycle.

Flowers

The **flower** is an angiosperm structure specialized for sexual reproduction. In many angiosperm species, insects or other animals transfer pollen from one flower to the sex organs on another flower, which makes pollination more directed than the wind-dependent pollination of most gymnosperms. However, some angiosperms *are* wind-pollinated, particularly those species that occur in dense populations, such as grasses and tree species in temperate forests.

A flower is a specialized shoot that can have up to four rings of modified leaves (sporophylls) called floral organs: sepals, petals, stamens, and carpels (**Figure 30.7**). Starting at the base of the flower are the **sepals**, which are usually green and enclose the flower before it opens (think of a rosebud). Interior to the sepals are the **petals**, which are brightly colored in most flowers and aid in attracting pollinators. Flowers that are wind-pollinated, however, generally lack brightly colored parts. In all angiosperms, the sepals and petals are sterile floral organs, meaning that they do not produce sperm or eggs. Within the petals are two whorls of fertile floral organs that produce spores,

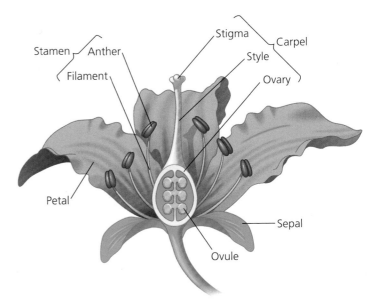

▲ Figure 30.7 **The structure of an idealized flower.**

the stamens and carpels. **Stamens** produce microspores that develop into pollen grains containing male gametophytes. A stamen consists of a stalk called the **filament** and a terminal sac, the **anther**, where pollen is produced. **Carpels** make megaspores and their products, female gametophytes. Some flowers have a single carpel, whereas others have multiple carpels, which are either separate or fused together. At the tip of the carpel is a sticky **stigma** that receives pollen. A **style** leads from the stigma to the **ovary** at the base of the carpel; the ovary contains one or more ovules. If fertilized, an ovule develops into a seed.

Fruits

A **fruit** typically consists of a mature ovary but can also include other flower parts. As seeds develop from ovules after fertilization, the ovary wall thickens. A pea pod is an example of a fruit, with seeds (mature ovules, the peas) encased in the ripened ovary (the pod). (We'll examine the developmental origin of fruits in Figure 38.10.)

Fruits protect dormant seeds and aid in their dispersal. Mature fruits can be either fleshy or dry **(Figure 30.8)**.

Tomatoes, plums, and grapes are examples of fleshy fruits, in which the wall (pericarp) of the ovary becomes soft during ripening. Dry fruits include beans, nuts, and grains. Some dry fruits split open at maturity to release seeds, whereas others remain closed. The dry, wind-dispersed fruits of grasses, harvested while on the plant, are major staple foods for humans. The cereal grains of maize, rice, wheat, and other grasses, though easily mistaken for seeds, are each actually a fruit with a dry outer covering (the former wall of the ovary) that adheres to the seed coat of the seed within.

As shown in **Figure 30.9**, various adaptations of fruits and seeds help to disperse seeds. The seeds of some flowering plants, such as dandelions and maples, are contained within fruits that function like parachutes or propellers, adaptations that enhance dispersal by wind. Some fruits, such as coconuts, are adapted to dispersal by water (see Figure 38.11). And many angiosperms rely on animals to carry seeds. Some of these plants have fruits modified as burrs that cling to animal fur (or the clothes of humans). Other angiosperms produce edible fruits, which are usually nutritious, sweet tasting, and vividly colored, advertising their ripeness. When an animal eats the fruit, it digests the fruit's fleshy part, but the tough seeds usually pass unharmed through the animal's digestive tract. Animals may deposit the seeds, along with a supply of natural fertilizer, many kilometers from where the fruit was eaten.

▼ Figure 30.8 **Some variations in fruit structure.**

▼ Tomato, a fleshy fruit with soft outer and inner layers of pericarp (fruit wall)

▼ Ruby grapefruit, a fleshy fruit with a firm outer layer and soft inner layer of pericarp

▶ Nectarine, a fleshy fruit with a soft outer layer and hard inner layer (pit) of pericarp

▼ Hazelnut, a dry fruit that remains closed at maturity

◀ Milkweed, a dry fruit that splits open at maturity

▼ Figure 30.9 **Fruit adaptations that enhance seed dispersal.**

▶ Wings enable maple fruits to be carried by the wind.

◀ Seeds within berries and other edible fruits are often dispersed in animal feces.

◀ The barbs of cockleburs facilitate seed dispersal by allowing the fruits to "hitchhike" on animals.

UNIVERSITY OF ALBERTA FACULTY BIO

Jocelyn Hall BSc University of Arizona; PhD University of Wisconsin-Madison

Current Positions: Assistant Professor, Department of Biological Sciences; Curator of the Vascular Plant Herbarium

I currently teach Biology 421/521 (Molecular Evolution and Systematics), Botany 205 (Fundamentals of Plant Biology) and Botany 321 (Flowering Plants).

The overarching research question in my lab is "how does morphological variation arise?" We employ a number of approaches to address this question: (1) using DNA variation to elucidate relationships among focal taxa, (2) conducting detailed comparative studies on a range of species to determine developmental patterns, (3) examining how differences in gene expression leads to morphological variation. We focus on understanding mechanisms underlying variation in two ecologically important plant traits: fruit structure and floral symmetry. For example, changes in flower symmetry affect plant-pollinator interactions and may promote speciation and diversification.

Cleomaceae, a plant family of about 180 species, is an ideal group to examine floral evolution. Members of this family have gorgeous flowers with four petals orientated upwards and the reproductive organs curved, resulting in bilaterally symmetrical flowers. Developmental studies of 11 species, published work that combined three undergraduate projects in my lab, led to the discovery that two distinct pathways in floral development produced seemingly similar morphologies. This research provided the framework for current projects in my lab that are investigating the genetic basis of bilaterally symmetrical flowers. The gene family *TCP* is responsible for this flower morphology across angiosperms and thus we are able to study the action of this gene in *Arabidopsis,* a widely used model organism for research on plant genetics which belongs to a plant family closely related to Cleomaceae.

The Angiosperm Life Cycle

You can follow a typical angiosperm life cycle in **Figure 30.10**. The flower of the sporophyte produces microspores that form male gametophytes and megaspores that form female gametophytes. The male gametophytes are in the pollen grains, which develop within microsporangia in the anthers. Each male gametophyte has two haploid cells: a *generative cell* that divides, forming two sperm, and a *tube cell* that produces a pollen tube. Each ovule, which develops in the ovary, con-

tains a female gametophyte, also known as an **embryo sac**. The embryo sac consists of only a few cells, one of which is the egg. (We will discuss gametophyte development in more detail in Chapter 38.)

After its release from the anther, the pollen is carried to the sticky stigma at the tip of a carpel. Although some flowers self-pollinate, most have mechanisms that ensure **cross-pollination**, which in angiosperms is the transfer of pollen from an anther of a flower on one plant to the stigma of a flower on another plant of the same species. Cross-pollination enhances genetic

▼ **Figure 30.10 The life cycle of an angiosperm.**

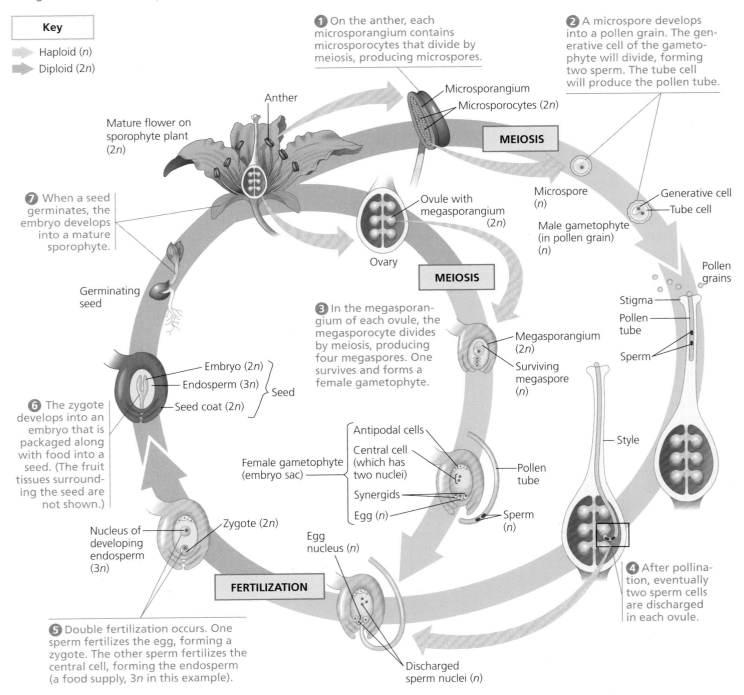

Key

Haploid (*n*)

Diploid (*2n*)

1 On the anther, each microsporangium contains microsporocytes that divide by meiosis, producing microspores.

2 A microspore develops into a pollen grain. The generative cell of the gametophyte will divide, forming two sperm. The tube cell will produce the pollen tube.

Anther

Microsporangium

Microsporocytes (*2n*)

Mature flower on sporophyte plant (*2n*)

MEIOSIS

Microspore (*n*)

Generative cell

Tube cell

Male gametophyte (in pollen grain) (*n*)

Ovule with megasporangium (*2n*)

Ovary

7 When a seed germinates, the embryo develops into a mature sporophyte.

MEIOSIS

Pollen grains

Stigma

Pollen tube

Sperm

Germinating seed

3 In the megasporangium of each ovule, the megasporocyte divides by meiosis, producing four megaspores. One survives and forms a female gametophyte.

Megasporangium (*2n*)

Surviving megaspore (*n*)

Embryo (*2n*)

Endosperm (*3n*) } Seed

Seed coat (*2n*)

6 The zygote develops into an embryo that is packaged along with food into a seed. (The fruit tissues surrounding the seed are not shown.)

Antipodal cells

Central cell (which has two nuclei)

Style

Female gametophyte (embryo sac)

Pollen tube

Synergids

Egg (*n*)

Sperm (*n*)

Nucleus of developing endosperm (*3n*)

Zygote (*2n*)

Egg nucleus (*n*)

FERTILIZATION

4 After pollination, eventually two sperm cells are discharged in each ovule.

5 Double fertilization occurs. One sperm fertilizes the egg, forming a zygote. The other sperm fertilizes the central cell, forming the endosperm (a food supply, *3n* in this example).

Discharged sperm nuclei (*n*)

variability. In some species, stamens and carpels of a single flower may mature at different times, or they may be so arranged that self-pollination is unlikely.

The pollen grain absorbs water and germinates after it adheres to the stigma of a carpel. The tube cell produces a pollen tube that grows down within the style of the carpel. After reaching the ovary, the pollen tube penetrates through the **micropyle**, a pore in the integuments of the ovule, and discharges two sperm cells into the female gametophyte (embryo sac). One sperm fertilizes the egg, forming a diploid zygote. The other sperm fuses with the two nuclei in the large central cell of the female gametophyte, producing a triploid cell. This type of **double fertilization**, in which one fertilization event produces a zygote and the other produces a triploid cell, is unique to angiosperms.

After double fertilization, the ovule matures into a seed. The zygote develops into a sporophyte embryo with a rudimentary root and one or two seed leaves called **cotyledons**. The triploid central cell of the female gametophyte develops into **endosperm**, tissue rich in starch and other food reserves that nourish the developing embryo.

What is the function of double fertilization in angiosperms? One hypothesis is that double fertilization synchronizes the development of food storage in the seed with the development of the embryo. If a particular flower is not pollinated or sperm cells are not discharged into the embryo sac, fertilization does not occur, and neither endosperm nor embryo forms. So perhaps double fertilization is an adaptation that prevents flowering plants from squandering nutrients on infertile ovules.

Another type of double fertilization occurs in some gymnosperm species belonging to the phylum Gnetophyta. However, double fertilization in these species gives rise to two embryos rather than to an embryo and endosperm.

As you read earlier, the seed consists of the embryo, the endosperm, and a seed coat derived from the integuments. An ovary develops into a fruit as its ovules become seeds. After being dispersed, a seed may germinate if environmental conditions are favorable. The coat ruptures and the embryo emerges as a seedling, using food stored in the endosperm and cotyledons until it can produce its own food by photosynthesis.

Angiosperm Evolution

Clarifying the origin of angiosperms—what Charles Darwin once called an "abominable mystery"—poses fascinating challenges to evolutionary biologists.

Angiosperms originated at least 140 million years ago, and during the late Mesozoic, the major branches of the clade diverged from their common ancestor. By the mid-Cretaceous period (100 million years ago), angiosperms began to dominate many terrestrial ecosystems. Landscapes changed dramatically as conifers, cycads, and other gymnosperms gave way to flowering plants in many parts of the world.

The flowers and fruits of angiosperms distinguish them markedly from living gymnosperms, which makes the origins of angiosperms puzzling. To understand how the angiosperm body plan emerged, scientists are studying fossils, refining angiosperm phylogeny, and elucidating developmental patterns that underlie flowers and other angiosperm innovations. As we'll see, much progress has been made toward solving Darwin's mystery—but we still do not fully understand how angiosperms originated from earlier seed plants.

Fossil Angiosperms

In the late 1990s, scientists in China discovered several intriguing fossils of 125-million-year-old angiosperms. These fossils, now named *Archaefructus liaoningensis* and *Archaefructus sinensis* (**Figure 30.11**), share some traits with living angiosperms but lack others. *Archaefructus sinensis*, for example, has anthers and also has seeds inside closed carpels but lacks petals and sepals. In 2002, scientists completed a phylogenetic comparison of *Archaefructus* with 173 living plant species. The researchers concluded that *Archaefructus* may belong to the earliest-diverging group of angiosperms known.

(a) *Archaefructus sinensis*, **a 125-million-year-old fossil.** This species may represent the sister group to all other angiosperms, or it may belong to the water lily group (see Figure 30.12). Researchers are testing these two hypotheses with phylogenetic analyses.

(b) Artist's reconstruction of *Archaefructus sinensis*

▲ **Figure 30.11** **An early flowering plant.**

Based on *Archaefructus* fossils, can we infer traits of the common ancestor of *Archaefructus* and living angiosperms? The fossils indicate that *Archaefructus* had simple flowers and was herbaceous with bulbous structures that may have served as floats, suggesting it was aquatic. But investigating whether the angiosperm common ancestor had simple flowers and was herbaceous and aquatic also requires examining fossils of other seed plants thought to have been closely related to angiosperms. All of those plants were woody, indicating that the common ancestor was probably woody. Furthermore, paleobotanists have found angiosperm fossils from later-diverging lineages that became aquatic and have flowers resembling those of *Archaefructus*. This suggests that simple flowers and an aquatic growth form may have been derived traits of *Archaefructus* rather than traits of the common ancestor. Overall, while most researchers agree that the angiosperm common ancestor was woody, debate continues about many of its other features.

Angiosperm Phylogeny

To shed light on the body plan of early angiosperms, scientists have long sought to identify which seed plants, including fossil species, are most closely related to angiosperms. Molecular and morphological evidence suggests that living gymnosperms are a monophyletic group whose earliest lineages diverged from the ancestors of angiosperms about 305 million years ago. Note that this does not necessarily imply that angiosperms originated 305 million years ago, but that the most recent common ancestor of gymnosperms and angiosperms lived at that time. Angiosperms may in fact be most closely related to extinct seed plants such as the Bennettitales, a group with flowerlike structures that may have been pollinated by insects **(Figure 30.12a)**. Systematists hope to resolve this issue through phylogenetic studies that combine data from fossil and living species of a wide range of seed plants.

Making sense of the origin of angiosperms also depends on working out the order in which angiosperm clades diverged from one another. Here, dramatic progress has been made in recent years. Molecular and morphological evidence suggests that a small South Pacific shrub called *Amborella trichopoda* and water lilies are living representatives of two of the most ancient angiosperm lineages **(Figure 30.12b)**.

Developmental Patterns in Angiosperms

Additional clues about the origin of flowering plants are emerging from studies of plant development. For example, a 2006 study demonstrated that in *Amborella*, eggs form from precursor cells that differ from the egg precursor cells of most other living angiosperms. Intriguingly, the way in which eggs form in *Amborella* has similarities to how eggs

(a) A possible ancestor of the angiosperms?
This reconstruction shows a cross section through the flowerlike structures found in the Bennettitales, an extinct group of seed plants hypothesized to be more closely related to angiosperms than to gymnosperms.

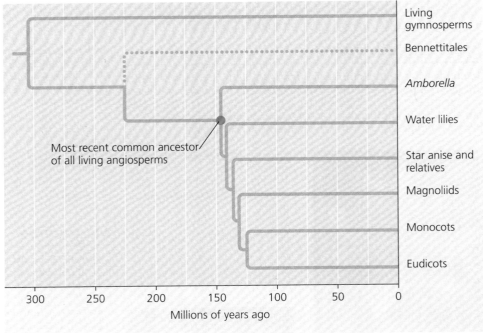

(b) Angiosperm phylogeny. This tree represents one current hypothesis of angiosperm evolutionary relationships, based on morphological and molecular evidence. Angiosperms originated at least 140 million years ago. The dotted line indicates the uncertain position of the Bennettitales, a possible sister group to the angiosperms.

▲ **Figure 30.12 Angiosperm evolutionary history.**

? *Would the branching order of the phylogeny in (b) necessarily have to be redrawn if a 150-million-year-old fossil monocot were discovered? Explain.*

form in gymnosperms—a possible link to the ancient common ancestor of gymnosperms and angiosperms. Other studies suggest that in a variety of early angiosperms (as well as in *Amborella*), the outer of the two protective integuments appears to be a modified leaf that originates separately from the inner integument. Because gymnosperms have only one integument, scientists are curious about exactly how the second integument originated in angiosperms. Researchers are also studying key developmental genes in gymnosperms and angiosperms, including genes that control flower development in angiosperms. Early results have uncovered developmental pathways shared by gymnosperms and angiosperms. These shared pathways may reveal clues about steps leading to the origin of flowering plants.

Angiosperm Diversity

From their humble beginnings in the Mesozoic, angiosperms have diversified into more than 250,000 living species. Until the late 1990s, most systematists divided flowering plants into two groups, based partly on the number of cotyledons, or seed leaves, in the embryo. Species with one cotyledon were called **monocots**, and those with two were called **dicots**. Other features, such as flower and leaf structure, were also used to define the two groups. For example, monocots typically have parallel leaf veins (think of a grass blade), whereas the veins of most dicots have a netlike pattern (think of an oak leaf). Some examples of monocots are orchids, palms, and grain crops such as maize, wheat, and rice. Some examples of dicots are roses, peas, sunflowers, and maples.

Recent DNA studies, however, indicate that the monocot-dicot distinction does not completely reflect evolutionary relationships. Current research supports the hypothesis that monocots form a clade but reveals that the species traditionally called dicots are polyphyletic. The vast majority of species once categorized as dicots form a large clade, now known as **eudicots** ("true" dicots). The rest of the former dicots are now grouped into several small lineages. Three of these lineages are informally called **basal angiosperms** because they appear to include the flowering plants belonging to the oldest lineages. A fourth lineage, called the **magnoliids**, evolved later. **Figure 30.13** provides an overview of angiosperm diversity.

▼ Figure 30.13

Exploring Angiosperm Diversity

Basal Angiosperms

Surviving basal angiosperms are currently thought to consist of three lineages comprising only about 100 species. The oldest lineage seems to be represented by a single species, *Amborella trichopoda* (right). The other surviving lineages diverged later: a clade that includes water lilies and a clade consisting of the star anise and its relatives.

Water lily (*Nymphaea "Rene Gerard"*). Water lilies are living members of a clade that may be predated only by the *Amborella* lineage.

Star anise (*Illicium floridanum*). This species represents a third surviving lineage of basal angiosperms.

Amborella trichopoda. This small shrub, found only on the South Pacific island of New Caledonia, may be the sole survivor of a branch at the base of the angiosperm tree. *Amborella* lacks vessels, which are present in angiosperms in later-developing lineages. Consisting of xylem cells arranged in continuous tubes, vessels transport water more efficiently than tracheids. Their absence in *Amborella* indicates they may have evolved after the lineage that gave rise to *Amborella* diverged.

Magnoliids

Magnoliids consist of about 8,000 species, most notably magnolias, laurels, and black pepper plants. They include both woody and herbaceous species. Although they share some traits with basal angiosperms, such as a typically spiral rather than whorled arrangement of floral organs, magnoliids are more closely related to eudicots and monocots.

Southern magnolia (*Magnolia grandiflora*). This member of the magnolia family is a woody magnoliid. The variety of southern magnolia shown here, called "Goliath," has flowers that measure up to about a foot across.

Monocots

About one-quarter of angiosperm species are monocots—about 70,000 species. These examples represent some of the largest families.

Eudicots

More than two-thirds of angiosperm species are eudicots—roughly 170,000 species. Below is a sampling of eudicot floral diversity.

Orchid (*Lemboglossum rossii*)

California poppy (*Eschscholzia californica*)

Monocot Characteristics		Eudicot Characteristics
	Embryos	
One cotyledon		Two cotyledons
	Leaf venation	
Veins usually parallel		Veins usually netlike
	Stems	
Vascular tissue scattered		Vascular tissue usually arranged in ring
	Roots	
Root system usually fibrous (no main root)		Taproot (main root) usually present
	Pollen	
Pollen grain with one opening		Pollen grain with three openings
	Flowers	
Floral organs usually in multiples of three		Floral organs usually in multiples of four or five

Pygmy date palm (*Phoenix roebelenii*)

Lily (*Lilium "Enchantment"*)

Dog rose (*Rosa canina*), a wild rose

Pyrenean oak (*Quercus pyrenaica*)

Snow pea (*Pisum sativum*), a legume

Anther

Stigma

Filament

Ovary

Barley (*Hordeum vulgare*), a grass

Zucchini (*Cucurbita pepo*) flowers

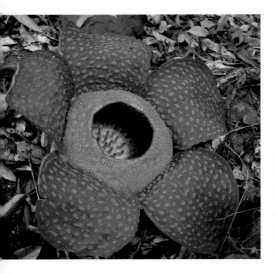

◀ **Figure 30.14 A plant pollinated by flies.** *Rafflesia arnoldii,* the "monster flower" of Indonesia, is the size of an automobile tire. It attracts fly pollinators with an odor like that of a decaying corpse.

Evolutionary Links Between Angiosperms and Animals

Ever since they colonized land, animals have influenced the evolution of terrestrial plants, and vice versa. For example, herbivores can reduce a plant's reproductive success by eating its roots, leaves, or seeds. As a result, if a novel and effective defense against herbivores originates in a group of plants, those plants may be favored by natural selection—as will any herbivores that can overcome this new defense. Plant-pollinator and other mutually beneficial interactions can have similar evolutionary effects, as seen in **Figure 30.14**.

In the examples we just discussed, interactions between plants and animals led to reciprocal evolution in the particular pairs of species involved. However, interactions between plants and animals also may have affected broader patterns in the history of life, such as rates at which new species form. Consider the evolutionary impact of how flower petals are arranged. Flower petals can be symmetrical in one direction only (*bilateral symmetry,* as in the pea blossom in Figure 30.13), or they can be symmetrical in all directions (*radial symmetry,* as in the dog rose in Figure 30.13). On a flower with bilateral symmetry, an insect pollinator may be able to obtain nectar only when it approaches the flower from a certain direction **(Figure 30.15)**. This constraint can make it more likely that

◀ **Figure 30.15 Pollinating a bilaterally symmetrical flower.** To harvest nectar (a sugary solution secreted by flower glands) from this bilaterally symmetrical Scottish broom flower, a honeybee must land as shown. This releases a tripping mechanism that arches the flower's stamens over the bee and dusts it with pollen. Later, some of this pollen will rub off onto the stigma of the next flower of this species that the bee visits.

as an insect moves from flower to flower, pollen is placed on a part of the insect's body that will come into contact with the stigma of a flower of the same species. Such specificity of pollen transfer tends to reduce gene flow between diverging populations and hence could lead to increased rates of plant speciation.

How can this hypothesis be tested? One approach is illustrated in this diagram:

A key step is to identify cases in which a clade with bilaterally symmetrical flowers shares an immediate common ancestor with a clade whose members have radially symmetrical flowers. One recent study identified 19 such pairs of closely related "bilateral" and "radial" clades. On average, the clade with bilaterally symmetrical flowers had nearly 2,400 more species than did its closely related clade with radially symmetrical flowers. This result suggests that flower shape can affect the rate at which new species form, with speciation occurring more rapidly in clades with bilateral symmetry. Overall, the effects of plant-pollinator interactions are thought to have contributed to the increasing dominance of flowering plants in the Cretaceous period, helping to make angiosperms of central importance in ecological communites.

CONCEPT CHECK 30.3

1. It has been said that an oak is an acorn's way of making more acorns. Write an explanation that includes these terms: sporophyte, gametophyte, ovule, seed, ovary, and fruit.
2. Compare and contrast a pine cone and a flower in terms of structure and function.
3. **WHAT IF?** Do speciation rates in closely related clades of flowering plants show that flower shape is *correlated with* the rate at which new species form, or that flower shape is *responsible for* this rate? Explain.

For suggested answers, see Appendix A.

CONCEPT 30.4

Human welfare depends greatly on seed plants

Throughout Unit Five, we are highlighting the ways in which humans depend on various organisms. In forests and on farms, seed plants are key sources of food, fuel, wood products, and medicine. Our reliance on them makes the preservation of plant diversity critical.

Products from Seed Plants

Most of our food comes from angiosperms. Just six crops—maize, rice, wheat, potatoes, cassava, and sweet potatoes—yield 80% of all the calories consumed by humans. We also depend on angiosperms to feed livestock: It takes 5–7 kg of grain to produce 1 kg of grain-fed beef.

Today's crops are the products of artificial selection—the result of plant domestication that began about 12,000 years ago. To appreciate the scale of this transformation, note how the number and size of seeds in domesticated plants are greater than those of their wild relatives, as in the case of maize and the grass teosinte (see Figure 38.16). Scientists can glean information about domestication by comparing the genes of crops with those of wild relatives. With maize, dramatic changes such as increased cob size and loss of the hard coating around teosinte kernels may have been initiated by as few as five mutations.

Flowering plants also provide other edible products. Two popular beverages come from tea leaves and coffee beans, and you can thank the tropical cacao tree for cocoa and chocolate. Spices are derived from various plant parts, such as flowers (cloves, saffron), fruits and seeds (vanilla, black pepper, mustard), leaves (basil, mint, sage), and even bark (cinnamon).

Many seed plants are sources of wood, which is absent in all living seedless plants. Wood consists of tough-walled xylem cells (see Figure 35.22). It is the primary source of fuel for much of the world, and wood pulp, typically derived from conifers such as fir and pine, is used to make paper. Wood also remains the most widely used construction material.

For centuries, humans have also depended on seed plants for medicines. Many cultures use herbal remedies, and scientists have extracted and identified the relevant secondary compounds (see p. 604) from many of these plants, and later synthesized them. Willow leaves and bark, for instance, have long been used in pain-relieving remedies, including prescriptions by the Greek physician Hippocrates. In the 1800s, scientists traced the willow's medicinal property to the chemical salicin. A synthesized derivative, acetylsalicylic acid, is what we call aspirin. Plants also remain a direct source of medicinal compounds. In the United States, about 25% of prescription drugs contain an active ingredient from plants, typically seed plants. Other ingredients were discovered in seed plants and then synthesized artificially. **Table 30.1** lists some medicinal uses of secondary compounds found in seed plants.

Table 30.1 Examples of Plant-Derived Medicines

Compound	Source	Use
Atropine	Belladonna plant	Eye pupil dilator
Digitalin	Foxglove	Heart medication
Menthol	Eucalyptus tree	Throat soother
Quinine	Cinchona tree	Malaria preventive
Taxol	Pacific yew	Ovarian cancer drug
Tubocurarine	Curare tree	Muscle relaxant
Vinblastine	Periwinkle	Leukemia drug

Threats to Plant Diversity

Although plants may be a renewable resource, plant diversity is not. The exploding human population and its demand for space and resources are extinguishing plant species at a high rate. The problem is especially severe in the tropics, where more than two-thirds of the human population live and where population growth is fastest. About 55,000 km² (14 million acres) of tropical rain forest are cleared each year **(Figure 30.16)**, a rate that would completely eliminate the remaining 11 million km²

▼ **Figure 30.16**

IMPACT

Clear-Cutting of Tropical Forests

Over the past several hundred years, nearly half of Earth's tropical forests have been cut down and converted to farmland and other uses. Satellite images, such as those below, show that together these regions cover an area roughly the size of Canada. Living trees release large quantities of water to the atmosphere, cooling the local environment (much as evaporation of sweat cools your body) and putting moisture into the air that is recycled as rain. When trees are cut down, less moisture is released to the atmosphere, causing increased temperatures and decreased rainfall. Tree removal also reduces the absorption of atmospheric carbon dioxide (CO_2) that occurs during photosynthesis.

A satellite image from 2000 shows clear-cut areas in Brazil surrounded by dense tropical forest.

By 2009, much more of this same tropical forest had been cut down.

WHY IT MATTERS Higher temperatures and increased atmospheric CO_2 resulting from destruction of tropical forests contribute to global warming, making preservation of these forests a high priority. Moreover, changes in rainfall patterns are expected to reduce agricultural production in some of the poorest countries. Finally, tropical forests harbor 50% or more of all species on Earth. Hence, higher temperatures, reduced rainfall, and habitat loss caused by clear-cutting tropical forests may lead to extinction of many species.

FURTHER READING G. P. Asner, T. K. Rudel, T. M. Aide, R. Defries, and R. Emerson, A contemporary assessment of change in humid tropical forests, *Conservation Biology* 23:1386–1395 (2009).

WHAT IF? How would clear-cutting affect the temperature and moisture along the edges of a remaining forest fragment?

of tropical forests in 200 years. The most common cause of this destruction is slash-and-burn clearing of forests for agricultural use. As forests disappear, so do large numbers of plant species. Of course, once a species becomes extinct, it can never return.

The loss of plant species is often accompanied by the loss of insects and other rain forest animals. Researchers estimate that habitat destruction in rain forests and other ecosystems is pushing hundreds of species toward extinction each year. If current rates of loss in the tropics and elsewhere continue, scientists estimate that within the next few centuries, 50% or more of Earth's species will become extinct. Such losses would constitute a global mass extinction, rivaling the Permian and Cretaceous mass extinctions and forever changing the evolutionary history of land plants (and many other organisms).

Many people have ethical concerns about contributing to the extinction of living forms. In addition, there are practical reasons to be concerned about the loss of plant diversity. So far, we have explored the potential uses of only a tiny fraction of the more than 290,000 known plant species. For example, almost all our food is based on the cultivation of only about two dozen species of seed plants. And fewer than 5,000 plant species have been studied as potential sources of medicines. The tropical rain forest may be a medicine chest of healing plants that could be extinct before we even know they exist. If we begin to view rain forests and other ecosystems as living treasures that can regenerate only slowly, we may learn to harvest their products at sustainable rates. What else can we do to preserve plant diversity? Few questions are as important, as we'll explore more fully in Unit Eight (Ecology).

CONCEPT CHECK 30.4

1. Explain why plant diversity can be considered a non-renewable resource.
2. **WHAT IF?** How could phylogenies be used to help researchers search more efficiently for novel medicines derived from seed plants?

For suggested answers, see Appendix A.

30 CHAPTER REVIEW

SUMMARY OF KEY CONCEPTS

CONCEPT 30.1

Seeds and pollen grains are key adaptations for life on land (pp. 618–621)

Five Derived Traits of Seed Plants		
Reduced gametophytes	Microscopic male and female gametophytes (n) are nourished and protected by the sporophyte (2n)	Male gametophyte / Female gametophyte
Heterospory	Microspore (gives rise to a male gametophyte) / Megaspore (gives rise to a female gametophyte)	
Ovules	Ovule (gymnosperm) { Integument (2n) / Megaspore (n) / Megasporangium (2n) }	
Pollen	Pollen grains make water unnecessary for fertilization	
Seeds	Seeds: survive better than unprotected spores, can be transported long distances { Seed coat / Food supply / Embryo }	

? *Describe how the parts of an ovule (integument, megaspore, megasporangium) correspond to the parts of a seed.*

CONCEPT 30.2

Gymnosperms bear "naked" seeds, typically on cones (pp. 621–625)

- Gymnosperms appear early in the plant fossil record and dominated many Mesozoic terrestrial ecosystems. Living seed plants can be divided into two monophyletic groups: gymnosperms and angiosperms. Extant gymnosperms include cycads, *Ginkgo biloba*, gnetophytes, and conifers.
- Dominance of the sporophyte generation, the development of seeds from fertilized ovules, and the role of pollen in transferring sperm to ovules are key features of a typical gymnosperm life cycle.

? *Although there are fewer than 1,000 species of gymnosperms, the group is still very successful in terms of its evolutionary longevity, adaptations, and geographic distribution. Explain.*

CONCEPT 30.3

The reproductive adaptations of angiosperms include flowers and fruits (pp. 625–632)

- Flowers generally consist of four whorls of modified leaves: sepals, petals, stamens (which produce pollen), and carpels (which produce ovules). Ovaries ripen into fruits, which often carry seeds by wind, water, or animals to new locations.
- An adaptive radiation of angiosperms occurred during the Cretaceous period. Fossils, phylogenetic analyses, and developmental studies offer insights into the origin of flowers.
- Several groups of basal angiosperms have been identified. Other major clades of angiosperms include magnoliids, monocots, and eudicots.

- Pollination and other interactions between angiosperms and animals may have contributed to the success of flowering plants during the last 100 million years.

? *What makes the origin of angiosperms puzzling? Has Darwin's "abominable mystery" been solved? Explain.*

CONCEPT 30.4

Human welfare depends greatly on seed plants (pp. 632–634)

- Humans depend on seed plants for products such as food, wood, and many medicines.
- Destruction of habitat threatens the extinction of many plant species and the animal species they support.

? *Explain why destroying the remaining tropical forests might harm humans and lead to a mass extinction.*

TEST YOUR UNDERSTANDING

LEVEL 1: KNOWLEDGE/COMPREHENSION

1. Where in an angiosperm would you find a megasporangium?
   a. in the style of a flower
   b. inside the tip of a pollen tube
   c. enclosed in the stigma of a flower
   d. within an ovule contained within an ovary of a flower
   e. packed into pollen sacs within the anthers found on a stamen

2. A fruit is most commonly
   a. a mature ovary.   d. a modified root.
   b. a thickened style.   e. a mature female gametophyte.
   c. an enlarged ovule.

3. With respect to angiosperms, which of the following is *incorrectly* paired with its chromosome count?
   a. egg—n d. zygote—$2n$
   b. megaspore—$2n$ e. sperm—n
   c. microspore—n

4. Which of the following is *not* a characteristic that distinguishes gymnosperms and angiosperms from other plants?
   a. alternation of generations   d. pollen
   b. ovules   e. dependent gametophytes
   c. integuments

5. Gymnosperms and angiosperms have the following in common *except*
   a. seeds.   d. ovaries.
   b. pollen.   e. ovules.
   c. vascular tissue.

LEVEL 2: APPLICATION/ANALYSIS

6. **DRAW IT** Use the letters a–d to label where on the phylogenetic tree each of the following derived characters appear.
   a. flowers   c. seeds
   b. embryos   d. vascular tissue

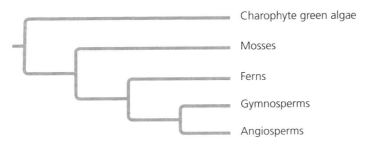

Charophyte green algae

Mosses

Ferns

Gymnosperms

Angiosperms

7. EVOLUTION CONNECTION
The history of life has been punctuated by several mass extinctions. For example, the impact of a meteorite may have wiped out most of the dinosaurs and many forms of marine life at the end of the Cretaceous period (see Chapter 25). Fossils indicate that plants were less severely affected by this and other mass extinctions. What adaptations may have enabled plants to withstand these disasters better than animals?

LEVEL 3: SYNTHESIS/EVALUATION

8. **SCIENTIFIC INQUIRY**
   DRAW IT As will be described in detail in Chapter 38, the female gametophyte of angiosperms typically has seven cells, one of which, the central cell, contains two haploid nuclei. After double fertilization, the central cell develops into endosperm, which is triploid. Because magnoliids, monocots, and eudicots typically have female gametophytes with seven cells and triploid endosperm, scientists assumed that this was the ancestral state for angiosperms. Consider, however, the following recent discoveries:
   - Our understanding of angiosperm phylogeny has changed to that shown in Figure 30.12b.
   - *Amborella trichopoda* has eight-celled female gametophytes and triploid endosperm.
   - Water lilies and star anise have four-celled female gametophytes and diploid endosperm.
     a. Draw a phylogeny of the angiosperms (see Figure 30.12b), incorporating the data given above about the number of cells in female gametophytes and the ploidy of the endosperm. Assume that all of the star anise relatives have four-celled female gametophytes and diploid endosperm.
     b. What does your labeled phylogeny suggest about the evolution of the female gametophyte and endosperm in angiosperms?

9. **WRITE ABOUT A THEME**
   The Cellular Basis of Life Cells are the basic units of structure and function in all organisms. A key feature in the life cycle of plants is the alternation of multicellular haploid and diploid generations. Imagine a lineage of flowering plants in which mitotic cell division did not occur between the events of meiosis and fertilization (see Figure 30.10). In a short essay (100–150 words), describe how this change in the timing of cell division would affect the structure and life cycle of plants in this lineage.

For selected answers, see Appendix A.

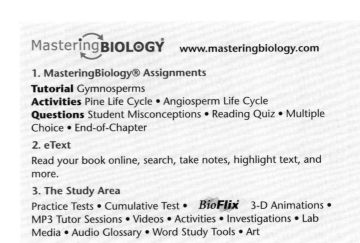

Mastering**BIOLOGY**   www.masteringbiology.com

1. MasteringBiology® Assignments
Tutorial Gymnosperms
Activities Pine Life Cycle • Angiosperm Life Cycle
Questions Student Misconceptions • Reading Quiz • Multiple Choice • End-of-Chapter

2. eText
Read your book online, search, take notes, highlight text, and more.

3. The Study Area
Practice Tests • Cumulative Test • *BioFlix* 3-D Animations • MP3 Tutor Sessions • Videos • Activities • Investigations • Lab Media • Audio Glossary • Word Study Tools • Art

31

Fungi

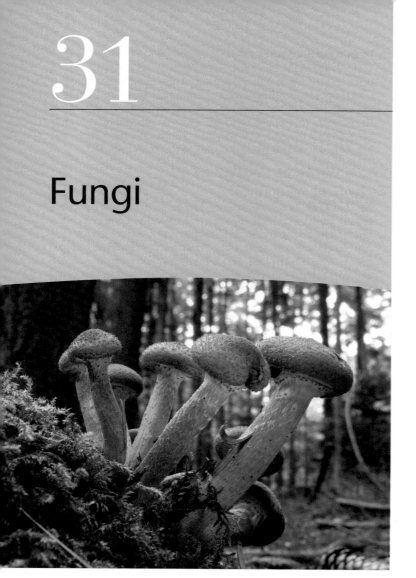

▲ **Figure 31.1 Can you spot the largest organism in this forest?**

KEY CONCEPTS

31.1 Fungi are heterotrophs that feed by absorption
31.2 Fungi produce spores through sexual or asexual life cycles
31.3 The ancestor of fungi was an aquatic, single-celled, flagellated protist
31.4 Fungi have radiated into a diverse set of lineages
31.5 Fungi play key roles in nutrient cycling, ecological interactions, and human welfare

OVERVIEW

Mighty Mushrooms

Hiking through the Malheur National Forest in eastern Oregon, you might notice a few clusters of honey mushrooms (*Armillaria ostoyae*) scattered here and there beneath the towering trees **(Figure 31.1)**. The trees appear to dwarf the mushrooms, but as strange as it sounds, the reverse is actually true.

All these mushrooms are just the aboveground portion of a single enormous fungus. Its subterranean network of filaments spreads through 965 hectares of the forest—more than the area of 1,800 football fields. Based on its current growth rate, scientists estimate that this fungus, which weighs hundreds of tons, has been growing for more than 1,900 years.

The inconspicuous honey mushrooms on the forest floor are a fitting symbol of the neglected grandeur of the kingdom Fungi. Most of us are barely aware of these eukaryotes beyond the mushrooms we eat or the occasional brush with athlete's foot. Yet fungi are a huge and important component of the biosphere. While about 100,000 species have been described, it is estimated that there are actually as many as 1.5 million species of fungi. Some fungi are exclusively single-celled, though most have complex multicellular bodies, which in many cases include the structures we know as mushrooms. These diverse organisms are found in just about every imaginable terrestrial and aquatic habitat; airborne spores have even been found 160 km above ground.

Fungi are not only diverse and widespread; they are also essential for the well-being of most ecosystems. They break down organic material and recycle nutrients, allowing other organisms to assimilate essential chemical elements. Humans make use of fungi as a food source, for applications in agriculture and forestry, and in manufacturing products ranging from bread to antibiotics. But it is also true that some fungi cause disease in plants and animals.

In this chapter, we will investigate the structure and evolutionary history of fungi, survey the major groups of fungi, and discuss their ecological and commercial significance.

CONCEPT **31.1**

Fungi are heterotrophs that feed by absorption

Despite their vast diversity, all fungi share some key traits, most importantly the way they derive nutrition. In addition, many fungi grow by forming multicellular filaments, a body structure that plays an important role in how they obtain food.

Nutrition and Ecology

Like animals, fungi are heterotrophs: They cannot make their own food as plants and algae can. But unlike animals, fungi do not ingest (eat) their food. Instead, a fungus absorbs nutrients from the environment outside of its body. Many fungi accomplish this task by secreting powerful hydrolytic enzymes into their surroundings. These enzymes break down complex molecules to smaller organic compounds that the fungi can absorb into their bodies and use. Other fungi use enzymes to penetrate the walls of cells, enabling the fungi to absorb nutrients from the cells. Collectively, the different enzymes found in various fungal species can digest compounds from a wide range of sources, living or dead.

This diversity of food sources corresponds to the varied roles of fungi in ecological communities, with different species living as decomposers, parasites, or mutualists. Decomposer fungi break down and absorb nutrients from non-living organic material, such as fallen logs, animal corpses, and the wastes of living organisms. Parasitic fungi absorb nutrients from the cells of living hosts. Some parasitic fungi are pathogenic, including many species that cause diseases in plants. Mutualistic fungi also absorb nutrients from a host organism, but they reciprocate with actions that benefit the host. For example, mutualistic fungi that live inside certain termite species use their enzymes to break down wood, as do mutualistic protists in other termite species (see Figure 28.26).

The versatile enzymes that enable fungi to digest a wide range of food sources are not the only reason for their ecological success. Another important factor is how their body structure increases the efficiency of nutrient absorption.

Body Structure

The most common fungal body structures are multicellular filaments and single cells (**yeasts**). Many species can grow as both filaments and yeasts, but even more grow only as filaments; relatively few species grow only as yeasts. Yeasts often inhabit moist environments, including plant sap and animal tissues, where there is a ready supply of soluble nutrients, such as sugars and amino acids. We'll discuss yeasts again later in the chapter.

The morphology of multicellular fungi enhances their ability to grow into and absorb nutrients from their surroundings (**Figure 31.2**). The bodies of these fungi typically form a network of tiny filaments called **hyphae** (singular, *hypha*). Hyphae consist of tubular cell walls surrounding the plasma membrane and cytoplasm of the cells. Unlike plant cell walls, which contain cellulose, fungal cell walls are strengthened by **chitin**. This strong but flexible nitrogen-containing polysaccharide is also found in the external skeletons of insects and other arthropods.

Fungal hyphae form an interwoven mass called a **mycelium** (plural, *mycelia*) that infiltrates the material on which the fungus feeds. A mycelium's structure maximizes its surface-to-volume ratio, making feeding very efficient. Just 1 cm³ of rich soil may contain as much as 1 km of hyphae with a total surface area of 300 cm² in contact with the soil. A fungal mycelium grows rapidly, as proteins and other materials synthesized by the fungus are channeled through cytoplasmic streaming to the tips of the extending hyphae. The fungus concentrates its energy and resources on adding hyphal length and thus overall absorptive surface area, rather than on increasing hyphal girth. Fungi are not motile in the typical sense—they cannot run, swim, or fly in search of food or mates. However, as they grow, fungi can move into new territory, swiftly extending the tips of their hyphae.

In most fungi, the hyphae are divided into cells by cross-walls, or **septa** (singular, *septum*) (**Figure 31.3a**). Septa generally have pores large enough to allow ribosomes, mitochondria, and even nuclei to flow from cell to cell. Some fungi lack septa (**Figure 31.3b**). Known as **coenocytic fungi**, these organisms consist of a continuous cytoplasmic mass having hundreds or thousands of nuclei. The coenocytic condition results from the repeated division of nuclei without cytokinesis. This description

▲ **Figure 31.3 Two forms of hyphae.**

▲ **Figure 31.2 Structure of a multicellular fungus.** The top photograph shows the sexual structures, in this case called mushrooms, of the penny bun fungus (*Boletus edulis*). The bottom photograph shows a mycelium growing on fallen conifer needles. The inset SEM shows hyphae.

? *Although the mushrooms in the top photograph appear to be different individuals, could their DNA be identical? Explain.*

may remind you of the plasmodial slime molds you read about in Chapter 28, which also consist of cytoplasmic masses containing many nuclei. This similarity is one reason that slime molds were once classified as fungi; molecular data have since shown that slime molds and fungi belong to distinct clades.

Specialized Hyphae in Mycorrhizal Fungi

Some fungi have specialized hyphae that allow them to feed on living animals (**Figure 31.4a**). Other fungal species have specialized hyphae called **haustoria**, which the fungi use to extract nutrients from, or exchange nutrients with, their plant hosts (**Figure 31.4b**). Mutually beneficial relationships between such fungi and plant roots are called **mycorrhizae** (the term means "fungus roots").

Mycorrhizal fungi (fungi that form mycorrhizae) can improve delivery of phosphate ions and other minerals to plants because the vast mycelial networks of the fungi are more efficient than the plants' roots at acquiring these minerals from the soil. In exchange, the plants supply the fungi with organic nutrients such as carbohydrates. There are two main types of mycorrhizal fungi. **Ectomycorrhizal fungi** (from the Greek *ektos*, out) form sheaths of hyphae over the surface of a root and typically grow into the extracellular spaces of the root cortex. **Arbuscular mycorrhizal fungi** (from the Latin *arbor*, tree) extend branching hyphae through the root cell wall and into tubes formed by invagination (pushing inward) of the root cell plasma membrane.

Mycorrhizae are enormously important in natural ecosystems and agriculture. Almost all vascular plants have mycorrhizae and rely on their fungal partners for essential nutrients. Many studies have demonstrated the significance of mycorrhizae by comparing the growth of plants with and without them. Foresters commonly inoculate pine seedlings with mycorrhizal fungi to promote growth. In the absence of human intervention, mycorrhizal fungi colonize soils by dispersing haploid cells called **spores** that form new mycelia after germinating. Spore dispersal is a key component of how fungi reproduce and spread to new areas, as we discuss next.

(a) Hyphae adapted for trapping and killing prey. In *Arthrobotrys*, a soil fungus, portions of the hyphae are modified as hoops that can constrict around a nematode (roundworm) in less than a second. The fungus then penetrates its prey with hyphae and digests the prey's inner tissues (SEM).

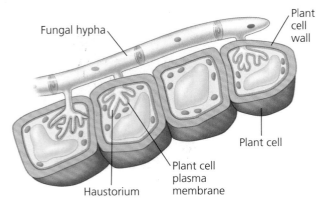

(b) Haustoria. Some mutualistic and parasitic fungi grow specialized hyphae called haustoria that can extract nutrients from living plant cells. Haustoria remain separated from a plant cell's cytoplasm by the plasma membrane of the plant cell (orange).

▲ **Figure 31.4 Specialized hyphae.**

CONCEPT CHECK 31.1

1. Compare and contrast the nutritional mode of a fungus with your own nutritional mode.
2. **WHAT IF?** Suppose a certain fungus is a mutualist that lives within an insect host, yet its ancestors were parasites that grew in and on the insect's body. What derived traits might you find in this mutualistic fungus?
3. **MAKE CONNECTIONS** Review Figure 10.4 (p. 186) and Figure 10.6 (p. 188). If a plant has mycorrhizae, where might carbon that enters the plant's stomata as CO_2 eventually be deposited: in the plant, in the mycorrhizal fungus, or in both? Explain.

For suggested answers, see Appendix A.

CONCEPT 31.2

Fungi produce spores through sexual or asexual life cycles

Most fungi propagate themselves by producing vast numbers of spores, either sexually or asexually. For example, puffballs, the reproductive structures of certain fungal species, may release trillions of spores in cloud-like bursts (see Figure 31.18). Spores can be carried long distances by wind or water. If they land in a moist place where there is food, they germinate, producing new mycelia. To appreciate how effective spores are at dispersing, leave a slice of melon exposed to the air. Even without a visible source of spores nearby, within a week or so, you will likely observe fuzzy mycelia growing from the microscopic spores that have fallen onto the melon.

▲ Figure 31.5 Generalized life cycle of fungi. Many—but not all—fungi reproduce both sexually and asexually. Some reproduce only sexually, others only asexually.

Figure 31.5 generalizes the many different life cycles that can produce fungal spores. In this section, we will survey general aspects of the sexual and asexual life cycles of fungi. Later, we'll examine more closely the life cycles of specific fungi.

Sexual Reproduction

The nuclei of fungal hyphae and the spores of most fungal species are haploid, although many fungi have transient diploid stages that form during sexual life cycles. In fungi, sexual reproduction often begins when hyphae from two mycelia release sexual signaling molecules called **pheromones**. If the mycelia are of different mating types, the pheromones from each partner bind to receptors on the other, and the hyphae extend toward the source of the pheromones. When the hyphae meet, they fuse. In species with such a "compatibility test," this process contributes to genetic variation by preventing hyphae from fusing with other hyphae from the same mycelium or another genetically identical mycelium.

The union of the cytoplasms of two parent mycelia is known as **plasmogamy**. In most fungi, the haploid nuclei contributed by each parent do not fuse right away. Instead, parts of the fused mycelium contain coexisting, genetically different nuclei. Such a mycelium is said to be a **heterokaryon** (meaning "different nuclei"). In some species, the different nuclei may even exchange chromosomes and genes in a process similar to crossing over (see Chapter 13). In other species, the haploid nuclei pair off two to a cell, one from each parent. Such a mycelium is **dikaryotic** (meaning "two nuclei"). As a dikaryotic mycelium grows, the two nuclei in each cell divide in tandem without fusing. Because these cells retain two separate haploid nuclei, they differ from diploid cells, which have pairs of homologous chromosomes within a single nucleus.

Hours, days, or (in some fungi) even centuries may pass between plasmogamy and the next stage in the sexual cycle, **karyogamy**. During karyogamy, the haploid nuclei contributed by the two parents fuse, producing diploid cells. Zygotes and other transient structures form during karyogamy, the only diploid stage in most fungi. Meiosis then restores the haploid condition, leading to the formation of spores that enable the fungus to disperse.

The sexual processes of karyogamy and meiosis generate extensive genetic variation, a prerequisite for natural selection. (See Chapters 13 and 23 to review how sex can increase genetic diversity in a population.) The heterokaryotic condition also offers some of the advantages of diploidy in that one haploid genome may compensate for harmful mutations in the other.

Asexual Reproduction

Many fungi can reproduce both sexually and asexually. Some 20,000 fungal species are only known to reproduce asexually. As with sexual reproduction, the processes of asexual reproduction vary widely among fungi.

Many fungi reproduce asexually by growing as filamentous fungi that produce (haploid) spores by mitosis; such species are known informally as **molds** if they form visible mycelia. Depending on your housekeeping habits, you may have observed molds in your kitchen, forming furry carpets on fruit, bread, and other foods **(Figure 31.6)**. Molds typically grow rapidly and produce many spores asexually, enabling the fungi to colonize new sources of food. Many species that produce such spores can also reproduce sexually if they happen to contact a member of their species of a different mating type.

1.5 μm

▲ Figure 31.6 *Penicillium*, a mold commonly encountered as a decomposer of food. The bead-like clusters in the colorized SEM are conidia, structures involved in asexual reproduction.

Other fungi reproduce asexually by growing as single-celled yeasts. Instead of producing spores, asexual reproduction in yeasts occurs by ordinary cell division or by the pinching of small "bud cells" off a parent cell (Figure 31.7). As already mentioned, some fungi that grow as yeasts can also grow as filamentous mycelia, depending on the availability of nutrients.

▲ Figure 31.7 The yeast *Saccharomyces cerevisiae* in several stages of budding (SEM).

Many yeasts and filamentous fungi have no known sexual stage in their life cycle. Since early mycologists (biologists who study fungi) classified fungi based mainly on their type of sexual structure, this posed a problem. Mycologists have traditionally lumped all fungi lacking sexual reproduction into a group called **deuteromycetes** (from the Greek *deutero*, second, and *mycete*, fungus). Whenever a sexual stage is discovered for a so-called deuteromycete, the species is reclassified in a particular phylum, depending on the type of sexual structures it forms. In addition to searching for sexual stages of such unassigned fungi, mycologists can now use genetic techniques to classify them.

CONCEPT CHECK 31.2

1. **MAKE CONNECTIONS** Compare Figure 31.5 with Figure 13.6 (p. 252). In terms of haploidy versus diploidy, how do the life cycles of fungi and humans differ?

2. **WHAT IF?** Suppose that you sample the DNA of two mushrooms on opposite sides of your yard and find that they are identical. Propose two hypotheses that could reasonably account for this result.

For suggested answers, see Appendix A.

CONCEPT 31.3

The ancestor of fungi was an aquatic, single-celled, flagellated protist

Data from both paleontology and molecular systematics offer insights into the early evolution of fungi. As a result, systematists now recognize that fungi and animals are more closely related to each other than either group is to plants or most other eukaryotes.

The Origin of Fungi

Phylogenetic systematics suggests that fungi evolved from a flagellated ancestor. While the majority of fungi lack flagella, some of the earliest-diverging lineages of fungi (the chytrids, discussed later in this chapter) do have flagella. Moreover, most of the protists that share a close common ancestor with animals and fungi also have flagella. DNA sequence data indicate that these three groups of eukaryotes—the fungi, the animals, and their protistan relatives—form a clade (Figure 31.8). As discussed in Chapter 28, members of this clade are called **opisthokonts**, a name that refers to the posterior (*opistho-*) location of the flagellum in these organisms.

DNA sequence data also indicate that fungi are more closely related to several groups of single-celled protists than they are to animals, suggesting that the ancestor of fungi was unicellular. One such group of unicellular protists, the **nucleariids**, consists of amoebas that feed on algae and bacteria. DNA evidence further indicates that animals are more closely related to a *different* group of protists (the choanoflagellates) than they are to either fungi or nucleariids. Together, these results suggest that multicellularity must have evolved in animals and fungi independently, from different single-celled ancestors.

Based on molecular clock analysis (see Chapter 26), scientists have estimated that the ancestors of animals and fungi diverged into separate lineages about 1 billion years ago. However, the oldest undisputed fossils of fungi are only about 460 million years old (Figure 31.9). One possible explanation for this discrepancy is that the microscopic ancestors of today's terrestrial fungi fossilized poorly.

▲ Figure 31.8 Fungi and their close relatives. Molecular evidence indicates that the nucleariids, a group of single-celled protists, are the closest living relatives of fungi. The three parallel lines leading to the chytrids indicate that this group may be paraphyletic.

▶ Figure 31.9 Fossil fungal hyphae and spores from the Ordovician period (about 460 million years ago) (LM).

50 μm

▲ **Figure 31.10 A eukaryotic cell infected by microsporidia.**
A large vacuole inside this host eukaryotic cell contains spores and
developing forms of the parasite *Encephalitozoon intestinalis* (TEM).

Are Microsporidia Fungi?

In addition to animals and protists such as the nucleariids, another group of organisms, the microsporidia, are closely related to fungi—and may in fact be fungi. Microsporidia are unicellular parasites of animals and protists (Figure 31.10). They are often used to control insect pests. While microsporidia do not normally cause illness in humans, they do pose a risk to people with AIDS and other immune-compromised conditions.

In many ways, microsporidia are unlike most other eukaryotes. They do not have conventional mitochondria, for example. As a result, microsporidia have been something of a taxonomic mystery, thought by some researchers to be a basal lineage of eukaryotes. In recent years, however, researchers have discovered that microsporidia actually have tiny organelles derived from mitochondria. In addition, most molecular comparisons indicate that microsporidia are fungi, suggesting that they are highly derived parasites. One such study, a 2006 analysis of DNA sequence data from six genes in nearly 200 fungal species, concluded that microsporidia are members of an early-diverging lineage of fungi. Additional genetic data from species belonging to early-diverging lineages of fungi are needed to fully resolve whether microsporidia are fungi or are a closely related but distinct group of organisms.

The Move to Land

Much of the fungal diversity we observe today may have originated during an adaptive radiation that began when multicellular plants and animals colonized land. For example, fossils of the earliest known vascular plants from the late Silurian period (420 million years ago) contain evidence of mycorrhizal relationships between plants and fungi. This evidence includes fossils of hyphae that have penetrated within plant cells and formed structures that closely resemble the haustoria of arbuscular mycorrhizae. Indeed, plants probably

existed in beneficial relationships with fungi from the earliest periods of colonization of land.

CONCEPT 31.4

Fungi have radiated into a diverse set of lineages

The phylogeny of fungi is currently the subject of much research. In the past decade, molecular analyses have helped clarify the evolutionary relationships between fungal groups, although there are still areas of uncertainty. Figure 31.11, on the next page, presents a simplified version of one current hypothesis. In this section, we will survey each of the major fungal groups identified in this phylogenetic tree.

Chytrids

Chytrids
Zygomycetes
Glomeromycetes
Ascomycetes
Basidiomycetes

The fungi classified in the phylum Chytridiomycota, called **chytrids**, are ubiquitous in lakes and soil. Some of the approximately 1,000 chytrid species are decomposers, while others are parasites of protists, other fungi, plants, or animals; as we'll see later in the chapter, one such chytrid parasite has likely contributed to the global decline of amphibian populations. Still other chytrids are important mutualists. For example, anaerobic chytrids that live in the digestive tracts of sheep and cattle help to break down plant matter, thereby contributing significantly to the animal's growth.

Molecular evidence supports the hypothesis that chytrids diverged early in fungal evolution. Like other fungi, chytrids have cell walls made of chitin, and they also share certain key enzymes and metabolic pathways with other fungal groups. Some chytrids form colonies with hyphae, while others exist as single spherical cells. But chytrids are unique among fungi in having flagellated spores, called **zoospores (Figure 31.12)**.

Flagellum

4 µm

▲ **Figure 31.12 Flagellated chytrid zoospore** (TEM).

Exploring Fungal Diversity

Most mycologists currently recognize five major groups of fungi, although the chytrids and zygomycetes are probably paraphyletic (as indicated by the parallel lines).

Chytrids (1,000 species)

In chytrids such as *Chytridium*, the globular fruiting body forms multicellular, branched hyphae (LM); other species are single-celled. Chytrids have flagellated spores and are thought to include some of the earliest fungal groups to diverge from other fungi.

Zygomycetes (1,000 species)

The hyphae of some zygomycetes, including this mold in the genus *Mucor* (LM), grow rapidly into foods such as fruits and bread. As such, the fungi may act as decomposers (if the food is not alive) or parasites; other species live as neutral (commensal) symbionts. According to some recent analyses, the zygomycetes include the enigmatic group known as microsporidia; other studies have classified microsporidia as chytrids.

Glomeromycetes (160 species)

The glomeromycetes (arbuscular mycorrhizal fungi) are of great ecological importance. Many plants form mycorrhizal associations with these fungi. This LM shows glomeromycete hyphae (stained dark blue) within a plant root.

Ascomycetes (65,000 species)

Also called sac fungi, members of this diverse group are common to many marine, freshwater, and terrestrial habitats. The cup-shaped ascocarp (fruiting body) of the ascomycete shown here (*Aleuria aurantia*) gives this species its common name: orange peel fungus.

Basidiomycetes (30,000 species)

Often important as decomposers and ectomycorrhizal fungi, basidiomycetes, or club fungi, are unusual in having a long-lived, dikaryotic mycelium. The fruiting bodies—commonly called mushrooms—of this fly agaric (*Amanita muscaria*) are a familiar sight in coniferous forests of the Northern Hemisphere.

Zygomycetes

Chytrids
Zygomycetes
Glomeromycetes
Ascomycetes
Basidiomycetes

There are approximately 1,000 known species of **zygomycetes**, fungi in the phylum Zygomycota. This diverse phylum includes species of fast-growing molds responsible for causing foods such as bread, peaches, strawberries, and sweet potatoes to rot during storage. Other zygomycetes live as parasites or as commensal (neutral) symbionts of animals.

The life cycle of *Rhizopus stolonifer* (black bread mold) is fairly typical of zygomycete species **(Figure 31.13)**. Its hyphae

spread out over the food surface, penetrate it, and absorb nutrients. The hyphae are coenocytic, with septa found only where reproductive cells are formed. In the asexual phase, bulbous black sporangia develop at the tips of upright hyphae. Within each sporangium, hundreds of haploid spores develop and are dispersed through the air. Spores that happen to land on moist food germinate, growing into new mycelia.

If environmental conditions deteriorate—for instance, if the mold consumes all its food—*Rhizopus* may reproduce sexually. The parents in a sexual union are mycelia of different mating types, which possess different chemical markers but may appear identical. Plasmogamy produces a sturdy

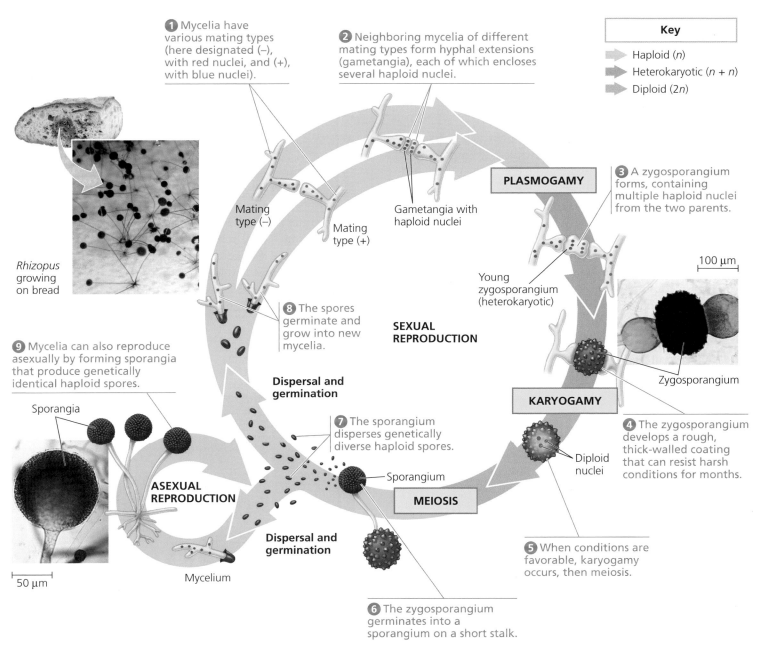

▲ Figure 31.13 **The life cycle of the zygomycete *Rhizopus stolonifer* (black bread mold).**

▲ **Figure 31.14** *Pilobolus* **aiming its sporangia.** This zygomycete decomposes animal dung. Its spore-bearing hyphae bend toward light, where there are likely to be openings in the vegetation through which spores may reach fresh grass. The fungus then launches its sporangia in a jet of water that can travel up to 2.5 m. Grazing animals ingest the fungi with the grass and then scatter the spores in feces, thereby enabling the next generation of fungi to grow.

▲ **Figure 31.15** **Arbuscular mycorrhizae.** Most glomeromycetes form arbuscular mycorrhizae with plant roots, supplying minerals and other nutrients to the roots. This SEM depicts the branched hyphae— an arbuscule—of *Glomus mosseae* bulging into a root cell by pushing in the membrane (the root has been treated to remove the cytoplasm).

structure called a **zygosporangium**, in which karyogamy and then meiosis occur. Note that while a zygosporangium represents the zygote (2*n*) stage in the life cycle, it is not a zygote in the usual sense (that is, a cell with one diploid nucleus). Rather, a zygosporangium is a multinucleate structure, first heterokaryotic with many haploid nuclei from the two parents, then with many diploid nuclei after karyogamy.

Zygosporangia are resistant to freezing and drying and are metabolically inactive. When conditions improve, the nuclei of the zygosporangium undergo meiosis, the zygosporangium germinates into a sporangium, and the sporangium releases genetically diverse haploid spores that may colonize a new substrate. Some zygomycetes, such as *Pilobolus*, can actually "aim" and then shoot their sporangia toward bright light **(Figure 31.14)**.

Glomeromycetes

Chytrids
Zygomycetes
Glomeromycetes
Ascomycetes
Basidiomycetes

The **glomeromycetes**, fungi assigned to the phylum Glomeromycota, were formerly thought to be zygomycetes. But recent molecular studies, including a phylogenetic analysis of DNA sequence data from hundreds of fungal species, indicate that glomeromycetes form a separate clade (monophyletic group). Although only 160 species have been identified to date, the glomeromycetes are an ecologically significant group in that nearly all of them form arbuscular mycorrhizae **(Figure 31.15)**. The tips of the hyphae that push into plant root cells branch into tiny treelike arbuscules. About 90% of all plant species have such mutualistic partnerships with glomeromycetes.

Ascomycetes

Chytrids
Zygomycetes
Glomeromycetes
Ascomycetes
Basidiomycetes

Mycologists have described 65,000 species of **ascomycetes**, fungi in the phylum Ascomycota, from a wide variety of marine, freshwater, and terrestrial habitats. The defining feature of ascomycetes is the production of spores in saclike **asci** (singular, *ascus*) during sexual reproduction; thus, they are commonly called *sac fungi*. Unlike zygomycetes, during their sexual stage most ascomycetes develop fruiting bodies, called **ascocarps**, which range in size from microscopic to macroscopic **(Figure 31.16)**. The ascocarps contain the spore-forming asci.

▼ The edible ascocarp of *Morchella esculenta*, the tasty morel, is often found under trees in orchards.

▼ *Tuber melanosporum* is a truffle species that forms ectomycorrhizae with trees. The ascocarp grows underground and emits a strong odor. These ascocarps have been dug up and the middle one sliced open.

▲ **Figure 31.16** **Ascomycetes (sac fungi).**

? *Ascomycetes vary greatly in morphology (see also Figure 31.11). How could you confirm that a fungus is an ascomycete?*

Ascomycetes vary in size and complexity from unicellular yeasts to elaborate cup fungi and morels (see Figure 31.16). They include some of the most devastating plant pathogens, which we will discuss later. However, many ascomycetes are important decomposers, particularly of plant material. More than 25% of all ascomycete species live with green algae or cyanobacteria in beneficial symbiotic associations called lichens. Some ascomycetes form mycorrhizae with plants. Many others live between mesophyll cells in leaves; some of these species release toxic compounds that help protect the plant from insects.

Although the life cycles of various ascomycete groups differ in the details of their reproductive structures and processes,

we'll illustrate some common elements using the bread mold *Neurospora crassa* (**Figure 31.17**). Ascomycetes reproduce asexually by producing enormous numbers of asexual spores called **conidia** (singular, *conidium*). Conidia are not formed inside sporangia, as are the asexual spores of most zygomycetes. Rather, they are produced externally at the tips of specialized hyphae called conidiophores, often in clusters or long chains, from which they may be dispersed by the wind.

Conidia may also be involved in sexual reproduction, fusing with hyphae from a mycelium of a different mating type, as occurs in *Neurospora*. Fusion of two different mating types is followed by plasmogamy, resulting in the formation of dikaryotic cells, each with two haploid nuclei representing

1 Ascomycete mycelia can reproduce asexually by producing pigmented haploid spores (conidia).

Conidia; mating type (–)

Dispersal

Germination

ASEXUAL REPRODUCTION

Hypha

Conidiophore

Mycelia

Mycelium

Germination

Dispersal

Ascocarp

Asci

Eight ascospores

Four haploid nuclei

7 The ascospores are discharged forcibly from the asci through an opening in the ascocarp. Germinating ascospores give rise to new mycelia.

6 Each haploid nucleus divides once by mitosis, yielding eight nuclei. Cell walls and plasma membranes develop around the nuclei, forming ascospores (LM).

2 *Neurospora* can also reproduce sexually by producing specialized hyphae. Conidia of the opposite mating type fuse to these hyphae.

Key

Haploid (*n*)
Dikaryotic (*n* + *n*)
Diploid (2*n*)

Mating type (+)

PLASMOGAMY

3 The dikaryotic hyphae that result from plasmogamy produce many dikaryotic asci, two of which are shown here.

Ascus (dikaryotic)

Dikaryotic hyphae

SEXUAL REPRODUCTION

KARYOGAMY

Diploid nucleus (zygote)

4 Karyogamy occurs within each ascus, producing a diploid nucleus.

MEIOSIS

5 Each diploid nucleus divides by meiosis, yielding four haploid nuclei.

▲ **Figure 31.17 The life cycle of *Neurospora crassa*, an ascomycete.** *Neurospora* is a bread mold and research organism that also grows in the wild on burned vegetation.

the two parents. The cells at the tips of these dikaryotic hyphae develop into many asci. Within each ascus, karyogamy combines the two parental genomes, and then meiosis forms four genetically different nuclei. This is usually followed by a mitotic division, forming eight ascospores. The ascospores develop in and are eventually discharged from the ascocarp.

In contrast to the life cycle of zygomycetes, the extended dikaryotic stage of ascomycetes (and also basidiomycetes) provides increased opportunity for genetic recombination. In *Neurospora*, for example, many dikaryotic cells can develop into asci, recombining genomes during meiosis and resulting in a multitude of genetically different offspring from one mating event (see steps 2 and 3 in Figure 31.17).

Neurospora has a significant history in biological research. As we discussed in Chapter 17, biologists in the 1930s used *Neurospora* in research that led to the one gene–one enzyme hypothesis. Today, this ascomycete continues to serve as a model research organism. In 2003, its entire genome was published. With 10,000 genes, this tiny fungus has about three-fourths as many genes as the fruit fly *Drosophila* and about half as many as a human. The *Neurospora* genome is relatively compact, having few of the stretches of noncoding DNA that occupy so much space in the genomes of humans and many other eukaryotes. In fact, there is evidence that *Neurospora* has a genomic defense system that prevents noncoding DNA such as transposons from accumulating.

Basidiomycetes

Chytrids
Zygomycetes
Glomeromycetes
Ascomycetes
Basidiomycetes

Approximately 30,000 species, including mushrooms, puffballs, and shelf fungi, are called **basidiomycetes** and are classified in the phylum Basidiomycota **(Figure 31.18)**. This phylum also includes mutualists that form mycorrhizae and two groups of destructive plant parasites: rusts and smuts. The name of the phylum derives from the **basidium** (Latin for "little pedestal"), a cell in which karyogamy occurs, followed immediately by meiosis. The club-like shape of the basidium also gives rise to the common name *club fungus*.

Basidiomycetes are important decomposers of wood and other plant material. Of all the fungi, certain basidiomycetes are the best at decomposing the complex polymer lignin, an abundant component of wood. Many shelf fungi break down the wood of weak or damaged trees and continue to decompose the wood after the tree dies.

The life cycle of a basidiomycete usually includes a long-lived dikaryotic mycelium **(Figure 31.19)**. As in ascomycetes, this extended dikaryotic stage provides opportunities for many genetic recombination events, in effect multiplying the result of a single mating. Periodically, in response to environmental stimuli, the mycelium reproduces sexually by producing elaborate fruiting bodies called **basidiocarps**. The

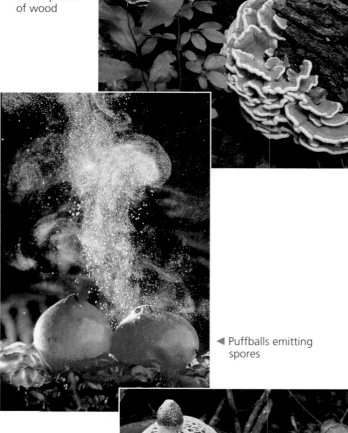

▶ Shelf fungi, important decomposers of wood

◀ Puffballs emitting spores

▶ Maiden veil fungus (*Dictyphora*), a fungus with an odor like rotting meat

▲ **Figure 31.18 Basidiomycetes (club fungi).**

common white mushrooms in the supermarket are familiar examples of a basidiocarp.

By concentrating growth in the hyphae of mushrooms, a basidiomycete mycelium can erect its fruiting structures in just a few hours; a mushroom pops up as it absorbs water and as cytoplasm streams in from the dikaryotic mycelium. By this process, a ring of mushrooms, popularly called a "fairy ring," may appear literally overnight **(Figure 31.20)**. The mycelium below the fairy ring expands outward at a rate of about 30 cm per year, decomposing organic matter in the soil as it grows. Some giant fairy rings are produced by mycelia that are centuries old.

The numerous basidia in a basidiocarp are the sources of sexual spores called basidiospores. After a mushroom forms,

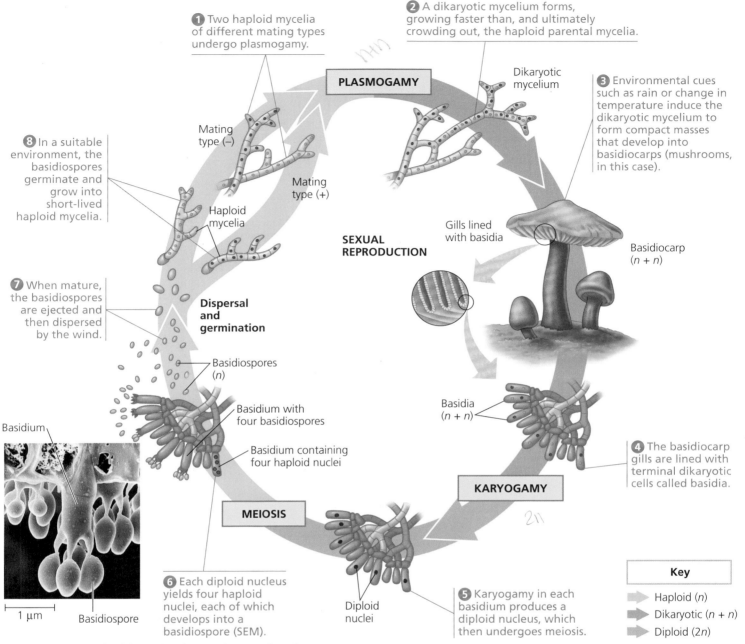

① Two haploid mycelia of different mating types undergo plasmogamy.

PLASMOGAMY

② A dikaryotic mycelium forms, growing faster than, and ultimately crowding out, the haploid parental mycelia.

Dikaryotic mycelium

③ Environmental cues such as rain or change in temperature induce the dikaryotic mycelium to form compact masses that develop into basidiocarps (mushrooms, in this case).

Mating type (–)

Mating type (+)

⑧ In a suitable environment, the basidiospores germinate and grow into short-lived haploid mycelia.

Haploid mycelia

SEXUAL REPRODUCTION

Gills lined with basidia

Basidiocarp (n + n)

⑦ When mature, the basidiospores are ejected and then dispersed by the wind.

Dispersal and germination

Basidiospores (n)

Basidia (n + n)

Basidium with four basidiospores

Basidium containing four haploid nuclei

④ The basidiocarp gills are lined with terminal dikaryotic cells called basidia.

Basidium

MEIOSIS

KARYOGAMY

Key

⑥ Each diploid nucleus yields four haploid nuclei, each of which develops into a basidiospore (SEM).

Diploid nuclei

⑤ Karyogamy in each basidium produces a diploid nucleus, which then undergoes meiosis.

Haploid (n)

Dikaryotic (n + n)

Diploid (2n)

1 µm

Basidiospore

▲ **Figure 31.19 The life cycle of a mushroom-forming basidiomycete.**

its cap supports and protects a large surface area of dikaryotic basidia on gills. During karyogamy, the two nuclei in each basidium fuse, producing a diploid nucleus (see Figure 31.19). This nucleus then undergoes meiosis, yielding four haploid nuclei. The basidium then grows four appendages, and one haploid nucleus enters each appendage and develops into a basidiospore. Large numbers of basidiospores are produced: The gills of a common white mushroom have a surface area of about 200 cm² and may release a billion basidiospores, which drop from the bottom of the cap and are blown away.

▲ **Figure 31.20 A fairy ring.** According to legend, these mushrooms spring up where fairies have danced in a ring on a moonlit night. (The text provides a biological explanation of how fairy rings form.)

1. What feature of chytrids supports the hypothesis that they represent an early-diverging fungal lineage?
2. Give examples of how form fits function in zygomycetes, glomeromycetes, ascomycetes, and basidiomycetes.
3. **WHAT IF?** Suppose that the mutation of an ascomycete changed its life cycle so that plasmogamy, karyogamy, and meiosis occurred in quick succession. How might this affect the ascospores and ascocarp?

For suggested answers, see Appendix A.

CONCEPT 31.5

Fungi play key roles in nutrient cycling, ecological interactions, and human welfare

In our survey of fungal classification, we've touched on some of the ways fungi influence other organisms. We will now look more closely at these impacts, focusing on how fungi act as decomposers, mutualists, and pathogens.

Fungi as Decomposers

Fungi are well adapted as decomposers of organic material, including the cellulose and lignin of plant cell walls. In fact, almost any carbon-containing substrate—even jet fuel and house paint—can be consumed by at least some fungi. As you might expect, researchers are developing ways to use a variety of fungal species in bioremediation projects. In addition, fungi and bacteria are primarily responsible for keeping ecosystems stocked with the inorganic nutrients essential for plant growth. Without these decomposers, carbon, nitrogen, and other elements would remain tied up in organic matter. Plants and the animals that eat them could not exist because elements taken from the soil would not be returned. Without decomposers, life as we know it would cease.

Fungi as Mutualists

Fungi may form mutualistic relationships with plants, algae, cyanobacteria, and animals. All of these relationships have profound ecological effects, often affecting the growth, survival, or reproduction of many species in a community.

Fungus-Plant Mutualisms

We've already considered the enormous importance of the mutualistic associations that most vascular plants form with mycorrhizal fungi. In addition, all plant species studied to date appear to harbor symbiotic **endophytes**, fungi that live inside leaves or other plant parts without causing harm. Most

▼ Figure 31.21

INQUIRY

Do endophytes benefit a woody plant?

EXPERIMENT Endophytes are symbiotic fungi found within the bodies of all plants examined to date. A. Elizabeth Arnold, at the University of Arizona, Tucson, and colleagues tested whether endophytes benefit the cacao tree (*Theobroma cacao*). This tree, whose name means "food of the gods" in Greek, is the source of the beans used to make chocolate, and it is cultivated throughout the tropics. Endophytes were added to the leaves of some cacao seedlings, but not others. (In cacao, endophytes colonize leaves after the seedling germinates.) The seedlings were then inoculated with a virulent pathogen, the protist *Phytophthora* (see Chapter 28).

RESULTS Fewer leaves were killed by the pathogen in seedlings with endophytes than in seedlings without endophytes. Among leaves that survived, pathogens damaged less of the leaf surface area in seedlings with endophytes than in seedlings without endophytes.

Endophyte not present; pathogen present (E–P+)
Both endophyte and pathogen present (E+P+)

CONCLUSION The presence of endophytes appears to benefit cacao trees by reducing the leaf mortality and damage caused by *Phytophthora*.

SOURCE A. E. Arnold et al., Fungal endophytes limit pathogen damage in a tropical tree, *Proceedings of the National Academy of Sciences* 100:15649–15654 (2003).

WHAT IF? Arnold and colleagues also performed control treatments. Suggest two controls they might have used, and explain how each would be helpful in interpreting the results described here.

endophytes identified to date are ascomycetes. Endophytes have been shown to benefit certain grasses and other nonwoody plants by making toxins that deter herbivores or by increasing host plant tolerance of heat, drought, or heavy metals. Seeking to discover how endophytes affect a woody plant, researchers tested whether leaf endophytes benefit seedlings of the cacao tree, *Theobroma cacao* (**Figure 31.21**). Their findings show that the endophytes of woody flowering plants can play an important role in defending against pathogens.

Fungus-Animal Symbioses

As mentioned earlier, some fungi share their digestive services with animals, helping break down plant material in the guts of cattle and other grazing mammals. Many species of ants take advantage of the digestive power of fungi by raising them in "farms." Leaf-cutter ants, for example, scour tropical forests in search of leaves, which they cannot digest on their own but

▲ **Figure 31.22 Fungus-gardening insects.** These leaf-cutting ants depend on fungi to convert plant material to a form the insects can digest. The fungi, in turn, depend on the nutrients from the leaves the ants feed them.

carry back to their nests and feed to the fungi (**Figure 31.22**). As the fungi grow, their hyphae develop specialized swollen tips that are rich in proteins and carbohydrates. The ants feed primarily on these nutrient-rich tips. The fungi break down plant leaves into substances the insects can digest, and they also detoxify plant defensive compounds that would otherwise kill or harm the ants. In some tropical forests, the fungi have helped these insects become the major consumers of leaves.

The evolution of such farmer ants and that of their fungal "crops" have been tightly linked for over 50 million years. The fungi have become so dependent on their caretakers that in many cases they can no longer survive without the ants, and vice versa.

Lichens

A **lichen** is a symbiotic association between a photosynthetic microorganism and a fungus in which millions of photosynthetic cells are held in a mass of fungal hyphae. Lichens grow on the surfaces of rocks, rotting logs, trees, and roofs in various forms (**Figure 31.23**). The photosynthetic partners are unicellular or filamentous green algae or cyanobacteria. The fungal component is most often an ascomycete, but one glomeromycete and 75 basidiomycete lichens are known. The fungus usually gives a lichen its overall shape

and structure, and tissues formed by hyphae account for most of the lichen's mass. The algae or cyanobacteria generally occupy an inner layer below the lichen surface (**Figure 31.24**).

The merger of fungus and alga or cyanobacterium is so complete that lichens are given scientific names as though they were single organisms; to date, 17,000 lichen species have been described. As might be expected of such "dual organisms," asexual reproduction as a symbiotic unit is common. This can occur either by fragmentation of the parental lichen or by the formation of **soredia**, small clusters of hyphae with embedded algae (see Figure 31.24). The fungi of many lichens also reproduce sexually, and lichen algae can reproduce independently of the fungus by asexual cell division.

In most lichens, each partner provides something the other could not obtain on its own. The algae provide carbon compounds; the cyanobacteria also fix nitrogen (see Chapter 27) and provide organic nitrogen compounds. The fungi provide their photosynthetic partners with a suitable environment for growth. The physical arrangement of hyphae allows for gas

▼ **Figure 31.23 Variation in lichen growth forms.**

▼ A foliose (leaflike) lichen

▼ Crustose (encrusting) lichens

▶ A fruticose (shrublike) lichen

▼ **Figure 31.24 Anatomy of an ascomycete lichen** (colorized SEM).

Ascocarp of fungus

Fungal hyphae

Algal layer

Soredia

50 μm

Fungal hyphae

Algal cell

exchange, protects the photosynthetic partner, and retains water and minerals, most of which are absorbed either from airborne dust or from rain. The fungi also secrete acids, which aid in the uptake of minerals.

Lichens are important pioneers on cleared rock and soil surfaces, such as volcanic flows and burned forests. They break down the surface by physically penetrating and chemically attacking it, and they trap windblown soil. Nitrogen-fixing lichens also add organic nitrogen to some ecosystems. These processes make it possible for a succession of plants to grow. Lichens may also have aided the colonization of land by plants. Fossils of lichens or lichen-like organisms date to 550–600 million years ago, long before plants grew on land. Early lichens may have modified rocks and soil much as they do today, helping pave the way for plants.

As tough as lichens are, however, many do not stand up well to air pollution. Their passive mode of mineral uptake from rain and moist air makes them particularly sensitive to sulfur dioxide and other airborne poisons.

Fungi as Pathogens

About 30% of the 100,000 known species of fungi make a living as parasites or pathogens, mostly of plants **(Figure 31.25)**. For example, *Cryphonectria parasitica*, the ascomycete fungus that causes chestnut blight, dramatically changed the landscape of the northeastern United States. Accidentally introduced on trees imported from Asia in the early 1900s, spores of the fungus enter cracks in the bark of American chestnut trees and produce hyphae, killing the tree. The once-common chestnuts now survive mainly as sprouts from the stumps of former trees. Another ascomycete, *Fusarium circinatum*, causes pine pitch canker, a disease that threatens pines throughout the world. Between 10% and 50% of the world's fruit harvest is lost annually due to fungi, and grain crops also suffer major losses each year.

Some fungi that attack food crops produce compounds that are toxic to humans. Certain species of the ascomycete *Aspergillus* contaminate grain and peanuts by secreting compounds called aflatoxins. Another example is the ascomycete *Claviceps purpurea*, which grows on rye plants, forming purple structures called ergots. If infected rye is milled into flour, toxins from the ergots can cause ergotism, characterized by gangrene, nervous spasms, burning sensations, hallucinations, and temporary insanity. An epidemic of ergotism around 944 CE killed more than 40,000 people in France. One compound that has been isolated from ergots is lysergic acid, the raw material from which the hallucinogen LSD is made.

Although animals are less susceptible to parasitic fungi than are plants, about 500 fungi are known to parasitize animals. One such parasite, the chytrid *Batrachochytrium dendrobatidis*, has been implicated in the recent decline or extinction of about 200 species of frogs and other amphibians **(Figure 31.26)**. This chytrid can cause severe skin infections, leading to massive

(a) Corn smut on corn

(b) Tar spot fungus on maple leaves

(c) Ergots on rye

▲ Figure 31.25 **Examples of fungal diseases of plants.**

die-offs. Field observations and studies of museum specimens indicate that *B. dendrobatidis* first appeared in frog populations shortly before their declines in Australia, Costa Rica, the United States, and other countries. In addition, in regions where it infects frogs, this chytrid has very low levels of genetic diversity. These findings are consistent with the hypothesis that *B. dendrobatidis* has emerged recently and spread rapidly across the globe, decimating many amphibian populations.

The general term for an infection caused by a fungal parasite is **mycosis**. In humans, skin mycoses include the disease ringworm, so named because it appears as circular red areas on the skin. The ascomycetes that cause ringworm can infect almost any skin surface. Most commonly, they grow on the feet, causing the intense itching and blisters known as athlete's foot. Though highly contagious, athlete's foot and other ringworm infections can be treated with fungicidal lotions and powders.

Systemic mycoses, by contrast, spread through the body and usually cause very serious illnesses. They are typically caused by inhaled spores. For example, coccidioidomycosis is a systemic mycosis that produces tuberculosis-like symptoms in the lungs. Each year, hundreds of cases in North America require treatment with antifungal drugs, without which the disease would be fatal.

Some mycoses are opportunistic, occurring only when a change in the body's microorganisms, chemical environment, or immune system allows fungi to grow unchecked. *Candida albicans*, for example, is one of the normal inhabitants of moist epithelia, such as the vaginal lining. Under certain circumstances, *Candida* can grow too rapidly and become pathogenic, leading to so-called "yeast infections." Many other opportunistic mycoses in humans have become more common in recent decades, due in part to AIDS, which compromises the immune system.

IMPACT

Amphibians Under Attack

Could a fungal parasite have caused the hundreds of amphibian population declines and extinctions during the last three decades? While habitat losses resulting from human activities have often been the culprit, the underlying causes have been unknown for nearly half the declining species. However, recent studies have implicated the global spread of a parasitic fungus, the chytrid *Batrachochytrium dendrobatidis*. For example, Vance Vredenburg, at San Francisco State University, and colleagues showed that the number of yellow-legged frogs (*Rana muscosa*) plummeted after the chytrid reached the Sixty Lake Basin area of California. Prior to the chytrid's 2004 arrival, on average there were 2,325 frogs in these lakes. By 2009, only 38 frogs remained. All the surviving frogs were in two lakes (yellow) where researchers had applied a fungicide to reduce the chytrid's impact.

▲ Yellow-legged frogs killed by *B. dendrobatidis* infection

Key

--- Boundary of chytrid spread

Lake status in 2009:

■ Frog population extinct

□ Treatment lake: frogs treated with fungicides and released

WHY IT MATTERS Worldwide, over one-third of amphibian species are suffering serious population declines. Information about the causes of these declines is essential if we are to protect these animals from extinction. Furthermore, because about 60% of human diseases originate from diseases in other animals, it is in our best interest to understand emerging diseases in amphibians.

FURTHER READING V. T. Vredenburg, et al., Large-scale amphibian die-offs driven by the dynamics of an emerging infectious disease, *Proceedings of the National Academy of Sciences* 107:9689-9694 (2010).

WHAT IF? Do the data depicted indicate that the chytrid *caused* or *is correlated to* the drop in frog numbers? Explain.

Practical Uses of Fungi

The dangers posed by fungi should not overshadow their immense benefits. We depend on their ecological services as decomposers and recyclers of organic matter. And without mycorrhizae, farming would be far less productive.

Mushrooms are not the only fungi of interest for human consumption. Fungi are used to ripen Roquefort and other blue cheeses. A species of *Aspergillus* produces citric acid used in colas. Morels and truffles, the edible fruiting bodies of various ascomycetes, are highly prized for their complex flavors (see Figure 31.16). These fungi can sell for hundreds to thousands of dollars a pound. Truffles release strong odors that attract mammals and insects, which in nature feed on them and disperse their spores. In some cases, the odors mimic the pheromones (sex attractants) of certain mammals. For example, the odors of several European truffles mimic the pheromones released by male pigs, which explains why *female* pigs are used to help find these delicacies.

Humans have used yeasts to produce alcoholic beverages and bread for thousands of years. Under anaerobic conditions, yeasts ferment sugars to alcohol and CO_2, which causes dough to rise. Only relatively recently have the yeasts involved been separated into pure cultures for more controlled use. The yeast *Saccharomyces cerevisiae* is the most important of all cultured fungi (see Figure 31.7). It is available as many strains of baker's yeast and brewer's yeast.

Many fungi have great medical value as well. For example, a compound extracted from ergots is used to reduce high blood pressure and to stop maternal bleeding after childbirth. Some fungi produce antibiotics that are effective in treating bacterial infections. In fact, the first antibiotic discovered was penicillin, made by the ascomycete mold *Penicillium* (**Figure 31.27**). Other examples of pharmaceuticals derived from fungi include cholesterol-lowering drugs and cyclosporine, a drug used to suppress the immune system after organ transplants.

Fungi also figure prominently in research. For example, the yeast *Saccharomyces cerevisiae* is used to study the molecular genetics of eukaryotes because its cells are easy to culture and manipulate. Scientists are gaining insight into the genes involved in Parkinson's disease and other human diseases by examining the functions of homologous genes in *S. cerevisiae*.

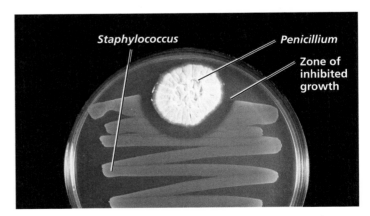

▲ **Figure 31.27 Fungal production of an antibiotic.** The mold *Penicillium* produces an antibiotic (penicillin) that inhibits the growth of *Staphylococcus* bacteria, resulting in the clear area between the mold and the bacteria.

Genetically modified fungi hold much promise. Although bacteria such as *Escherichia coli* can produce some useful proteins, they cannot synthesize glycoproteins because they lack enzymes that can attach carbohydrates to proteins. Fungi, on the other hand, do produce such enzymes. In 2003, scientists succeeded in engineering a strain of *S. cerevisiae* that produces human glycoproteins, including insulin-like growth factor. Such fungus-produced glycoproteins have the potential to treat people with medical conditions that prevent them from producing these compounds. Meanwhile, other researchers are sequencing the genome of the wood-digesting basidiomycete *Phanerochaete chrysosporium*, one of many "white rot" fungi. They hope to decipher the metabolic pathways by which white rot breaks down wood, with the goal of harnessing these pathways to produce paper pulp.

Having now completed our survey of the kingdom Fungi, we will turn in the remaining chapters of this unit to the closely related kingdom Animalia, to which we humans belong.

CONCEPT CHECK 31.5

1. What are some of the benefits that lichen algae can derive from their relationship with fungi?
2. What characteristics of pathogenic fungi result in their being efficiently transmitted?
3. **WHAT IF?** How might life on Earth differ from what we know today if no mutualistic relationships between fungi and other organisms had ever evolved?

For suggested answers, see Appendix A.

31 CHAPTER REVIEW

SUMMARY OF KEY CONCEPTS

CONCEPT 31.1

Fungi are heterotrophs that feed by absorption (pp. 636–638)

- All **fungi** (including decomposers and symbionts) are heterotrophs that acquire nutrients by absorption. Many fungi secrete enzymes that break down complex molecules to smaller molecules that can be absorbed.
- Most fungi grow as thin, multicellular filaments called **hyphae**; relatively few species grow only as single-celled **yeasts**. In their multicellular form, fungi consist of **mycelia**, networks of branched hyphae adapted for absorption. Mycorrhizal fungi have specialized hyphae that enable them to form a mutually beneficial relationship with plants.

? *How does the morphology of multicellular fungi affect the efficiency of nutrient absorption?*

CONCEPT 31.2

Fungi produce spores through sexual or asexual life cycles (pp. 638–640)

- The sexual cycle involves cytoplasmic fusion (**plasmogamy**) and nuclear fusion (**karyogamy**), with an intervening heterokaryotic stage in which cells have haploid nuclei from two parents. The diploid cells resulting from karyogamy are short-lived and undergo meiosis, producing haploid **spores**.
- Many fungi can reproduce asexually as filamentous fungi or yeasts. DNA sequence data now allow mycologists to classify all fungi, even those lacking a known sexual cycle.

DRAW IT *Draw a fungal life cycle, labeling asexual and sexual reproduction, meiosis, plasmogamy, karyogamy, and the points in the cycle when spores and the zygote are produced.*

CONCEPT 31.3

The ancestor of fungi was an aquatic, single-celled, flagellated protist (pp. 640–641)

- Molecular evidence supports the hypothesis that fungi and animals diverged from a common ancestor that was unicellular and had a flagellum.

- Unicellular parasites called microsporidia appear to be an early-diverging fungal lineage.
- Fungi were among the earliest colonizers of land, including species that were symbionts with early land plants.

? *Did multicellularity originate independently in fungi and animals? Explain.*

CONCEPT 31.4

Fungi have radiated into a diverse set of lineages (pp. 641–648)

Fungal Phylum	Distinguishing Features of Morphology and Life Cycles	
Chytridiomycota (**chytrids**)	Flagellated spores	
Zygomycota (**zygote fungi**)	Resistant zygosporangium as sexual stage	
Glomeromycota (**arbuscular mycorrhizal fungi**)	Arbuscular mycorrhizae formed with plants	
Ascomycota (**ascomycetes**, or **sac fungi**)	Sexual spores (ascospores) borne internally in sacs called asci; vast numbers of asexual spores (conidia) produced	
Basidiomycota (**basidiomycetes**, or **club fungi**)	Elaborate fruiting body (basidiocarp) containing many basidia that produce sexual spores (basidiospores)	

DRAW IT *Draw a phylogenetic tree showing relationships among the five major groups of fungi.*

Fungi play key roles in nutrient cycling, ecological interactions, and human welfare (pp. 648–652)

- Fungi perform essential recycling of chemical elements between the living and nonliving world.
- Some **endophytes** help protect plants from herbivores and pathogens, while other fungi help certain animals digest plant tissue. **Lichens** are highly integrated symbiotic associations of fungi and algae or cyanobacteria.
- About 30% of all known fungal species are parasites, mostly of plants. Some fungi also cause disease in animals.
- Humans eat many fungi and use others to make cheeses, alcoholic beverages, and bread. Antibiotics produced by fungi treat bacterial infections. Genetic research on fungi is leading to applications in biotechnology.

? *Summarize how fungi are important as decomposers, mutualists, and pathogens.*

TEST YOUR UNDERSTANDING

LEVEL 1: KNOWLEDGE/COMPREHENSION

1. *All* fungi share which of the following characteristics?
   a. symbiotic
   b. heterotrophic
   c. flagellated
   d. pathogenic
   e. act as decomposers

2. Which feature seen in chytrids supports the hypothesis that they diverged earliest in fungal evolution?
   a. the absence of chitin within the cell wall
   b. coenocytic hyphae
   c. flagellated spores
   d. formation of resistant zygosporangia
   e. parasitic lifestyle

3. Which of the following cells or structures are associated with *asexual* reproduction in fungi?
   a. ascospores
   b. basidiospores
   c. zygosporangia
   d. conidiophores
   e. ascocarps

4. The photosynthetic symbiont of a lichen is often
   a. a moss.
   b. a green alga.
   c. a brown alga.
   d. an ascomycete.
   e. a small vascular plant.

5. Among the organisms listed here, which are thought to be the closest relatives of fungi?
   a. animals
   b. vascular plants
   c. mosses
   d. brown algae
   e. slime molds

LEVEL 2: APPLICATION/ANALYSIS

6. The adaptive advantage associated with the filamentous nature of fungal mycelia is primarily related to
   a. the ability to form haustoria and parasitize other organisms.
   b. avoiding sexual reproduction until the environment changes.
   c. the potential to inhabit almost all terrestrial habitats.
   d. the increased probability of contact between different mating types.
   e. an extensive surface area well suited for invasive growth and absorptive nutrition.

7. **SCIENTIFIC INQUIRY**
   DRAW IT The grass *Dichanthelium languinosum* lives in hot soils and houses fungi of the genus *Curvularia* as endophytes. Regina Redman, of Montana State University, and colleagues performed field experiments to test the impact of *Curvularia* on the heat tolerance of this grass. They grew plants without (E−) and with (E+) *Curvularia* endophytes in soils of different temperatures and measured plant mass and the number of new shoots the plants produced. Draw a bar graph of the results for plant mass versus temperature and interpret it.

Soil Temp.	*Curvularia* Presence	Plant Mass (g)	Number of New Shoots
30°C	E−	16.2	32
	E+	22.8	60
35°C	E−	21.7	43
	E+	28.4	60
40°C	E−	8.8	10
	E+	22.2	37
45°C	E−	0	0
	E+	15.1	24

Source: R. S. Redman et al., Thermotolerance generated by plant/fungal symbiosis, *Science* 298:1581 (2002).

LEVEL 3: SYNTHESIS/EVALUATION

8. **EVOLUTION CONNECTION**
   The fungus-alga symbiosis that makes up a lichen is thought to have evolved multiple times independently in different fungal groups. However, lichens fall into three well-defined growth forms (see Figure 31.23). What research could you perform to test the following hypotheses?

   Hypothesis 1: Crustose, foliose, and fruticose lichens each represent a monophyletic group.

   Hypothesis 2: Each lichen growth form represents convergent evolution by taxonomically diverse fungi.

9. **WRITE ABOUT A THEME**
   Emergent Properties As you read in this chapter, fungi have long formed symbiotic associations with plants and with algae. In a short essay (100–150 words), describe how these two types of associations may lead to emergent properties in biological communities.

For selected answers, see Appendix A.

Mastering**BIOLOGY**®   www.masteringbiology.com

1. MasteringBiology® Assignments
Tutorial Fungal Morphology and Nutrition
Activities Fungal Reproduction and Nutrition • Fungal Life Cycles • Life Cycle of a Mushroom • Discovery Channel Videos: Fungi; Leafcutter Ants
Questions Student Misconceptions • Reading Quiz • Multiple Choice • End-of-Chapter

2. eText
Read your book online, search, take notes, highlight text, and more.

3. The Study Area
Practice Tests • Cumulative Test • *BioFlix* 3-D Animations • MP3 Tutor Sessions • Videos • Activities • Investigations • Lab Media • Audio Glossary • Word Study Tools • Art

An Overview of Animal Diversity

▲ **Figure 32.1 Which of these organisms are animals?**

KEY CONCEPTS

32.1 Animals are multicellular, heterotrophic eukaryotes with tissues that develop from embryonic layers

32.2 The history of animals spans more than half a billion years

32.3 Animals can be characterized by "body plans"

32.4 New views of animal phylogeny are emerging from molecular data

OVERVIEW

Welcome to Your Kingdom

Reading the last few chapters, you may have felt like a tourist among some unfamiliar organisms, such as slime molds, whisk ferns, and sac fungi. You probably are more at home with the topic introduced in this chapter—the animal

kingdom, which of course includes yourself. But animal diversity extends far beyond humans and the dogs, cats, birds, and other animals we humans regularly encounter. For example, the diverse organisms in **Figure 32.1** are all animals, including those that appear to resemble lacy branches, thick stems, and curly leaves. To date, biologists have identified 1.3 million extant (living) species of animals. Estimates of the actual number of animal species run far higher. This vast diversity encompasses a spectacular range of morphological variation, from corals to cockroaches to crocodiles.

In this chapter, we embark on a tour of the animal kingdom that will continue in the next two chapters. We will consider the characteristics that all animals share, as well as those that distinguish various taxonomic groups. This information is central to understanding animal phylogeny, a topic that is a lively arena of biological research and debate, as you will read.

CONCEPT 32.1

Animals are multicellular, heterotrophic eukaryotes with tissues that develop from embryonic layers

Listing features shared by all animals is challenging, as there are exceptions to nearly every criterion for distinguishing animals from other life-forms. When taken together, however, several characteristics of animals sufficiently describe the group for our discussion.

Nutritional Mode

Animals differ from both plants and fungi in their mode of nutrition. Plants are autotrophic eukaryotes capable of generating organic molecules through photosynthesis. Fungi are heterotrophs that grow on or near their food and that feed by absorption (often after they have released enzymes that digest the food outside their bodies). Unlike plants, animals cannot construct all of their own organic molecules and so, in most cases, they ingest them—either by eating other living organisms or by eating nonliving organic material. But unlike fungi, most animals do not feed by absorption; instead, animals ingest their food and then use enzymes to digest it within their bodies.

Cell Structure and Specialization

Animals are eukaryotes, and like plants and most fungi, animals are multicellular. In contrast to plants and fungi, however, animals lack the structural support of cell walls. Instead, a variety of proteins external to the cell membrane provide structural support to animal cells and connect them to one another (see Figure 6.30). The most abundant of these proteins is collagen, which is found only in animals.

Many animals have two types of specialized cells not found in other multicellular organisms: muscle cells and nerve cells. In most animals, these cells are organized into **tissues**, groups of cells that have a common structure, function, or both. Muscle tissue and nervous tissue are responsible for moving the body and conducting nerve impulses, respectively. The ability to move and conduct nerve impulses underlies many of the adaptations that differentiate animals from plants and fungi. For this reason, muscle and nerve cells are central to the animal lifestyle.

Reproduction and Development

Most animals reproduce sexually, and the diploid stage usually dominates the life cycle. In the haploid stage, sperm and egg cells are produced directly by meiotic division, unlike what occurs in plants and fungi (see Figure 13.6). In most animal species, a small, flagellated sperm fertilizes a larger, nonmotile egg, forming a diploid zygote. The zygote then undergoes **cleavage**, a succession of mitotic cell divisions without cell growth between the divisions. During the development of most animals, cleavage leads to the formation of a multicellular stage called a **blastula**, which in many animals takes the form of a hollow ball **(Figure 32.2)**. Following the blastula stage is the process of **gastrulation**, during which the layers of embryonic tissues that will develop into adult body parts are produced. The resulting developmental stage is called a **gastrula**.

Although some animals, including humans, develop directly into adults, the life cycles of most animals include at least one larval stage. A **larva** is a sexually immature form of an animal that is morphologically distinct from the adult, usually eats different food, and may even have a different habitat than the adult, as in the case of the aquatic larva of a mosquito or dragonfly. Animal larvae eventually undergo **metamorphosis**, a developmental transformation that turns the animal into a juvenile that resembles an adult but is not yet sexually mature.

Although adult animals vary widely in morphology, the genes that control animal development are similar across a broad range of taxa. All animals have developmental genes that regulate the expression of other genes, and many of these regulatory genes contain sets of DNA sequences called *homeoboxes* (see Chapter 21). Most animals share a unique homeobox-containing family of genes, known as *Hox* genes. *Hox* genes play important roles in the development of animal embryos, controlling the expression of dozens or even hundreds of other genes that influence animal morphology (see Chapter 25).

Sponges, which are among the simplest extant animals, lack *Hox* genes. However, they have other homeobox genes that influence their shape, such as those that regulate the formation of water channels in the body wall, a key feature of sponge morphology (see Figure 33.4). In the ancestors of more complex animals, the *Hox* gene family arose via the duplication of

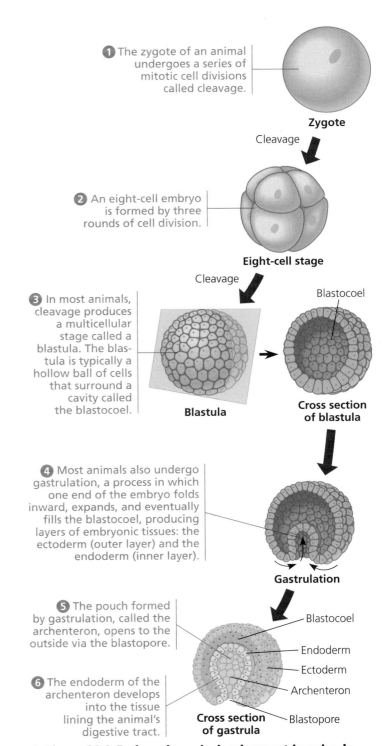

① The zygote of an animal undergoes a series of mitotic cell divisions called cleavage.

Zygote

Cleavage

② An eight-cell embryo is formed by three rounds of cell division.

Eight-cell stage

Cleavage

③ In most animals, cleavage produces a multicellular stage called a blastula. The blastula is typically a hollow ball of cells that surround a cavity called the blastocoel.

Blastocoel

Blastula

Cross section of blastula

④ Most animals also undergo gastrulation, a process in which one end of the embryo folds inward, expands, and eventually fills the blastocoel, producing layers of embryonic tissues: the ectoderm (outer layer) and the endoderm (inner layer).

Gastrulation

⑤ The pouch formed by gastrulation, called the archenteron, opens to the outside via the blastopore.

⑥ The endoderm of the archenteron develops into the tissue lining the animal's digestive tract.

Blastocoel

Endoderm

Ectoderm

Archenteron

Blastopore

Cross section of gastrula

▲ **Figure 32.2 Early embryonic development in animals.**

earlier homeobox genes. Over time, the *Hox* gene family underwent a series of duplications, yielding a versatile "toolkit" for regulating development. In vertebrates, insects, and most other animals, *Hox* genes regulate the formation of the anterior-posterior (front-to-back) axis, as well as other aspects of development. Similar sets of conserved genes govern the development of both flies and humans, despite their obvious differences and hundreds of millions of years of divergent evolution.

CONCEPT **32.2**

The history of animals spans more than half a billion years

The animal kingdom includes not only a great diversity of living species, but an even greater diversity of extinct ones. (Some paleontologists have estimated that over 99% of all animal species are extinct.) Various studies suggest that this great diversity originated during the last billion years. For example, some estimates based on molecular clocks suggest that the ancestors of animals diverged from the ancestors of fungi about a billion years ago. Other such studies have estimated that the common ancestor of living animals lived sometime between 800 and 675 million years ago.

To learn what this common ancestor may have been like, scientists have sought to identify protist groups that are closely related to animals. As shown in **Figure 32.3**, a combination of morphological and molecular evidence indicates that choanoflagellates are among the closest living relatives of animals. Based on such evidence, researchers hypothesize that the common ancestor of living animals may have been a suspension feeder similar to present-day choanoflagellates. We will next survey the fossil evidence for how animals evolved from their distant common ancestor over four geologic eras (see Table 25.1 to review the geologic time scale).

Neoproterozoic Era (1 Billion–542 Million Years Ago)

Despite the molecular data indicating an earlier origin of animals, the first generally accepted macroscopic fossils of animals date from 565 to 550 million years ago. These fossils are members of an early group of soft-bodied multicellular eukaryotes, known collectively as the **Ediacaran biota**. The name comes from the Ediacara Hills of Australia, where these animals were first discovered **(Figure 32.4)**. Similar fossils have since been found on other continents.

▼ **Figure 32.3** **Three lines of evidence that choanoflagellates are closely related to animals.**

? *Are the data described in consistent with predictions that could be made from the evidence in and ? Explain.*

Choanoflagellates

OTHER EUKARYOTES

Sponges

Animals

Other animals

Individual choanoflagellate

1 Morphologically, choanoflagellate cells and the collar cells (or *choanocytes*) of sponges are almost indistinguishable.

Collar cell (choanocyte)

3 DNA sequence data indicate that choanoflagellates and animals are sister groups. In addition, genes for signaling and adhesion proteins previously known only from animals have been discovered in choanoflagellates.

2 Similar collar cells have been identified in other animals, including cnidarians, flatworms, and echinoderms—but they have never been observed in non-choanoflagellate protists or in plants or fungi.

1.5 cm

0.4 cm

(a) *Mawsonites spriggi*   **(b)** *Spriggina floundersi*

▲ **Figure 32.4 Ediacaran fossils.** Fossils dating to 565–550 million years ago include animals **(a)** with simple, radial forms and **(b)** with many body segments.

▲ **Figure 32.5 A Cambrian seascape.** This artist's reconstruction depicts a diverse array of organisms found in fossils from the Burgess Shale site in British Columbia, Canada. The animals include *Pikaia* (eel-like chordate at top left), *Marella* (arthropod swimming at left), *Anomalocaris* (large animal with anterior grasping limbs and a circular mouth), and *Hallucigenia* (animals with toothpick-like spikes on the seafloor).

Some are sponges, while others may be related to living cnidarians. Still others of these fossil organisms have proved difficult to classify, as they do not seem to be closely related to any living animal or algal groups.

In addition to these macroscopic fossils, Neoproterozoic rocks have also yielded what may be microscopic signs of early animals. As you read in Chapter 25, 575-million-year-old microfossils discovered in China appear to exhibit the basic structural organization of present-day animal embryos. However, debate continues about whether the fossil embryos are animals or are members of extinct groups that are closely related to animals (but are not actually animals). Though older fossils of animals may be discovered in the future, the fossil record as it is known today shows that the late Neoproterozoic era was a time of increasing animal diversity.

Paleozoic Era (542–251 Million Years Ago)

Another wave of animal diversification occurred 535–525 million years ago, during the Cambrian period of the Paleozoic era—a phenomenon referred to as the **Cambrian explosion** (see Chapter 25). In strata formed before the Cambrian explosion, only a few animal phyla have been observed. But in strata that are 535–525 million years old, paleontologists have found the oldest fossils of about half of all extant animal phyla, including the first arthropods, chordates, and echinoderms. Many of these distinctive fossils, which include the first animals with hard, mineralized skeletons, look very different from most living animals **(Figure 32.5)**. But for the most part, paleontologists have established that these Cambrian fossils are members of extant animal phyla, or at least are close relatives.

The increase in the diversity of animal phyla during the Cambrian was accompanied by a decline in the diversity of Ediacaran life-forms. What caused these trends? There are several current hypotheses. Some evidence suggests that during the Cambrian period, predators acquired novel adaptations,

such as forms of locomotion that helped them catch prey, while prey species acquired new defenses, such as protective shells. As new predator-prey relationships emerged, natural selection may have led to the decline of some groups and the rise of others. Another hypothesis focuses on an increase in atmospheric oxygen that preceded the Cambrian explosion. More plentiful oxygen would have enabled animals with higher metabolic rates and larger body sizes to thrive, while potentially harming other species. A third hypothesis proposes that the origin of *Hox* genes and other genetic changes affecting the regulation of developmental genes facilitated the evolution of new body forms. These hypotheses are not mutually exclusive, however; predator-prey relationships, atmospheric changes, and changes in the regulation of development may each have played a role.

The Cambrian period was followed by the Ordovician, Silurian, and Devonian periods, when animal diversity continued to increase, although punctuated by episodes of mass extinction (see Figure 25.15). Vertebrates (fishes) emerged as the top predators of the marine food web. By 460 million years ago, groups that diversified during the Cambrian period were making an impact on land. Arthropods began to adapt to terrestrial habitats, as indicated by the appearance of millipedes and centipedes. Another clue is seen in fossilized fern galls—enlarged cavities that fern plants form in response to stimulation by resident insects, which then use the galls for protection. Fossils indicate that fern galls date back at least

302 million years, suggesting that insects and plants were influencing each other's evolution by that time.

Vertebrates made the transition to land around 365 million years ago and diversified into numerous terrestrial groups. Two of these survive today: the amphibians (such as frogs and salamanders) and the amniotes (reptiles, including birds, and mammals). We will explore these groups, known collectively as the tetrapods, in more detail in Chapter 34.

Mesozoic Era (251–65.5 Million Years Ago)

The animal phyla that had evolved during the Paleozoic now began to spread into new habitats. In the oceans, the first coral reefs formed, providing other marine animals with new habitats. Some reptiles returned to the water, leaving plesiosaurs (see Figure 25.4) and other large aquatic predators as their descendants. On land, descent with modification in some tetrapods led to the origin of wings and other flight equipment in pterosaurs and birds. Large and small dinosaurs emerged, both as predators and herbivores. At the same time, the first mammals—tiny nocturnal insect-eaters—appeared on the scene. In addition, as you read in Chapter 30, flowering plants (angiosperms) and insects both underwent dramatic diversifications during the late Mesozoic.

Cenozoic Era (65.5 Million Years Ago to the Present)

Mass extinctions of both terrestrial and marine animals ushered in a new era, the Cenozoic. Among the groups of species that disappeared were the large, nonflying dinosaurs and the marine reptiles. The fossil record of the early Cenozoic documents the rise of large mammalian herbivores and predators as mammals began to exploit the vacated ecological niches. The global climate gradually cooled throughout the Cenozoic, triggering significant shifts in many animal lineages. Among primates, for example, some species in Africa adapted to the open woodlands and savannas that replaced many of the former dense forests. The ancestors of our own species were among those grassland apes.

CONCEPT CHECK 32.2

1. Put the following milestones in animal evolution in chronological order from oldest to most recent: (a) origin of mammals, (b) earliest evidence of terrestrial arthropods, (c) Ediacaran fauna, (d) extinction of large, nonflying dinosaurs.
2. **WHAT IF?** Suppose the most recent common ancestor of fungi and animals lived 1 billion years ago. If the first fungi lived 990 million years ago, would animals also have been alive at that time? Explain.

For suggested answers, see Appendix A.

CONCEPT 32.3

Animals can be characterized by "body plans"

Animal species vary tremendously in morphology, but their great diversity in form can be described by a relatively small number of major "body plans." A **body plan** is a particular set of morphological and developmental traits, integrated into a functional whole—the living animal. The term *plan* here does not imply that animal forms are the result of conscious planning or invention. But body plans do provide a succinct way to compare and contrast key animal features. They also are of interest in the study of *evo-devo*, the interface between evolution and development (see Chapters 21 and 25).

Like all features of organisms, animal body plans have evolved over time. Some of the evolutionary changes appear to have occurred early in the history of animal life. For example, recent research suggests that a key step in the molecular control of gastrulation has remained unchanged for more than 500 million years (**Figure 32.6**). This early evolutionary innovation was of fundamental importance: Gastrulation helps to explain why most animals are not a hollow ball of cells. As we'll discuss, however, other aspects of animal body plans have changed multiple times over the course of evolution. Thus, as we explore the major features of animal body plans, bear in mind that similar body forms may have evolved independently in different lineages. In addition, body features can be lost over the course of evolution, causing some closely related species to look very different from one another.

Symmetry

A basic feature of animal bodies is their type of symmetry—or absence of symmetry. (Many sponges, for example, lack symmetry altogether.) Some animals exhibit **radial symmetry**, the type of symmetry found in a flowerpot (**Figure 32.7a**). Sea anemones, for example, have a top side (where the mouth is located) and a bottom side. But they have no front and back ends and no left and right sides.

The two-sided symmetry seen in a shovel is an example of **bilateral symmetry** (**Figure 32.7b**). A bilateral animal has two axes of orientation: front to back and top to bottom. Such animals have a **dorsal** (top) side and a **ventral** (bottom) side, a left side and a right side, and an **anterior** (front) end and a **posterior** (back) end. Many animals with a bilaterally symmetrical body plan (such as arthropods and mammals) have sensory equipment concentrated at their anterior end, including a central nervous system ("brain") in the head—an evolutionary trend called **cephalization** (from the Greek *kephale*, head).

The symmetry of an animal generally fits its lifestyle. Many radial animals are sessile (living attached to a substrate) or planktonic (drifting or weakly swimming, such as jellies,

▼ Figure 32.6

INQUIRY

Did β-catenin play an ancient role in the molecular control of gastrulation?

EXPERIMENT In most animals, gastrulation leads to the formation of three layers of embryonic cells. In some of these species, such as worms, sea urchins, and vertebrates, the protein β-catenin marks the site of gastrulation and activates the transcription of genes necessary for the process. Athula Wikramanayake and Mark Martindale, of the University of Hawaii, and colleagues tested whether β-catenin also helps to control gastrulation in the sea anemone *Nematostella vectensis*. This species is a member of the phylum Cnidaria, a group that predates the origin of animals whose embryos form three layers of cells.

RESULTS

1 In early stages of development, β-catenin (here labeled with green fluorescent protein) is found throughout the *N. vectensis* embryo.

100 μm

2 By the 32-cell stage, β-catenin is concentrated on the side of the embryo where gastrulation will occur.

Site of gastrulation

3 In the early gastrula stage, β-catenin activity (here stained a darker red) occurs in the inner layer of cells.

Site of gastrulation

4 In embryos in which β-catenin activity is blocked (by a protein that binds to β-catenin), gastrulation does not occur.

CONCLUSION In *N. vectensis*, β-catenin is required for gastrulation to occur and may help to determine the site of gastrulation. Since the fossil record indicates that cnidarians diverged more than 500 million years ago from species in which β-catenin is known to influence gastrulation, it seems likely that β-catenin played an ancient role in the molecular control of gastrulation.

SOURCE A. H. Wikramanayake et al., An ancient role for nuclear β-catenin in the evolution of axial polarity and germ layer segregation, *Nature* 426:446–450 (2003).

WHAT IF? β-catenin binds to DNA, thereby stimulating the transcription of genes necessary for gastrulation. Based on this information, suggest a different experiment that could be used to confirm the results in step 4. What would be the purpose of performing such an experiment?

(a) Radial symmetry. A radial animal, such as a sea anemone (phylum Cnidaria), does not have a left side and a right side. Any imaginary slice through the central axis divides the animal into mirror images.

(b) Bilateral symmetry. A bilateral animal, such as a lobster (phylum Arthropoda), has a left side and a right side. Only one imaginary cut divides the animal into mirror-image halves.

▲ **Figure 32.7 Body symmetry.** The flowerpot and shovel are included to help you remember the radial-bilateral distinction.

commonly called jellyfishes). Their symmetry equips them to meet the environment equally well from all sides. In contrast, bilateral animals typically move actively from place to place. Most bilateral animals have a central nervous system that enables them to coordinate the complex movements involved in crawling, burrowing, flying, or swimming. Fossil evidence indicates that these two fundamentally different kinds of symmetry have been present for at least 550 million years.

Tissues

Animal body plans also vary with regard to tissue organization. In animals, true tissues are collections of specialized cells isolated from other tissues by membranous layers. While sponges and a few other groups lack true tissues, in all other animals, the embryo becomes layered through the process of gastrulation (see Figure 32.2). As development progresses, these concentric layers, called *germ layers*, form the various tissues and organs of the body. **Ectoderm**, the germ layer covering the surface of the embryo, gives rise to the outer covering of the animal and, in some phyla, to the central nervous system. **Endoderm**, the innermost germ layer, lines the pouch that forms during gastrulation (the archenteron) and gives rise to the lining of the digestive tract (or cavity) and organs such as the liver and lungs of vertebrates.

Animals that have only these two germ layers are said to be **diploblastic**. Diploblasts include the animals called cnidarians (jellies and corals, for example) as well as the comb jellies (see Chapter 33). All bilaterally symmetrical animals have a third germ layer, called the **mesoderm**, which fills much of the space between the ectoderm and endoderm. Thus, animals with bilateral symmetry are also said to be **triploblastic** (having three germ layers). In triploblasts, the mesoderm forms the muscles and most other organs between the digestive tract and the outer covering of the animal. Triploblasts include a broad range of animals, from flatworms to arthropods to vertebrates. (Although some diploblasts actually do have a third germ layer, it is not nearly as well developed as the mesoderm of animals considered to be triploblastic.)

Body Cavities

Most triploblastic animals have a **body cavity**, a fluid- or air-filled space located between the digestive tract and the outer body wall. This body cavity is also called a **coelom** (from the Greek *koilos*, hollow). A so-called "true" coelom forms from tissue derived from mesoderm. The inner and outer layers of tissue that surround the cavity connect and form structures that suspend the internal organs. Animals with a true coelom are known as **coelomates** (Figure 32.8a).

Some triploblastic animals have a body cavity that is formed from mesoderm and endoderm (Figure 32.8b). Such a cavity is called a "pseudocoelom" (from the Greek *pseudo*, false), and the animals that have one are called **pseudocoelomates**. Despite its name, however, a pseudocoelom is not false; it is a fully functional body cavity. Finally, some triploblastic animals lack a body cavity altogether (Figure 32.8c). They are known collectively as **acoelomates** (from the Greek *a-*, without).

A body cavity has many functions. Its fluid cushions the suspended organs, helping to prevent internal injury. In soft-bodied coelomates, such as earthworms, the coelom contains noncompressible fluid that acts like a skeleton against which muscles can work. The cavity also enables the internal organs to grow and move independently of the outer body wall. If it were not for your coelom, for example, every beat of your heart or ripple of your intestine would warp your body's surface.

Terms such as *coelomates* and *pseudocoelomates* refer to organisms that have a similar body plan and hence belong to the same *grade* (a group whose members share key biological features). However, phylogenetic studies show that true coeloms and pseudocoeloms have been independently gained or lost multiple times in the course of animal evolution. As illustrated by this example, a grade is not necessarily equivalent to a *clade* (a group that includes an ancestral species and all of its descendants). Thus, while describing an organism as a coelomate or pseudocoelomate can be helpful in describing certain of its features, these terms must be interpreted with caution when seeking to understand evolutionary history.

Protostome and Deuterostome Development

Based on certain aspects of early development, many animals can be described as having one of two developmental modes: **protostome development** or **deuterostome**

▼ **Figure 32.8 Body cavities of triploblastic animals.** The various organ systems of a triploblastic animal develop from the three germ layers that form in the embryo. Blue represents tissue derived from ectoderm, red from mesoderm, and yellow from endoderm.

(a) Coelomate

Coelomate, such as earthworms, have a true coelom, a body cavity completely lined by tissue derived from mesoderm.

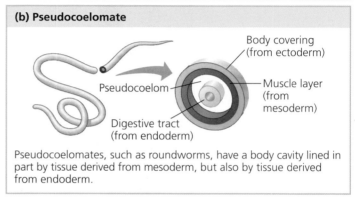

(b) Pseudocoelomate

Pseudocoelomates, such as roundworms, have a body cavity lined in part by tissue derived from mesoderm, but also by tissue derived from endoderm.

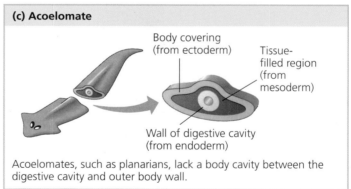

(c) Acoelomate

Acoelomates, such as planarians, lack a body cavity between the digestive cavity and outer body wall.

development. These modes can generally be distinguished by differences in cleavage, coelom formation, and fate of the blastopore.

Cleavage

Many animals with protostome development undergo **spiral cleavage**, in which the planes of cell division are diagonal to the vertical axis of the embryo; as seen in the eight-cell stage of the embryo, smaller cells are centered over the grooves between larger, underlying cells (Figure 32.9a, left). Furthermore, the so-called **determinate cleavage** of some animals with protostome development rigidly casts ("determines") the developmental fate of each embryonic cell very early. A cell

► **Figure 32.9** **A comparison of protostome and deuterostome development.** These are useful general distinctions, though there are many variations and exceptions to these patterns.

MAKE CONNECTIONS *Review Figure 20.21 (p. 415). As an early embryo, which would more likely have stem cells capable of giving rise to cells of any type: an animal with protostome development or with deuterostome development? Explain.*

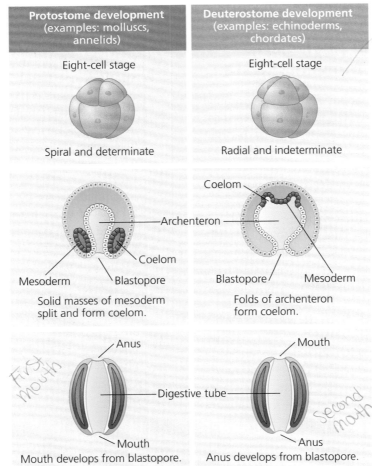

Protostome development (examples: molluscs, annelids)

Deuterostome development (examples: echinoderms, chordates)

Eight-cell stage

Eight-cell stage

Spiral and determinate

Radial and indeterminate

indeterminate results in embryonic stem cells

Coelom

Archenteron

Mesoderm   Blastopore   Coelom

Blastopore   Mesoderm

Solid masses of mesoderm split and form coelom.

Folds of archenteron form coelom.

Anus

Mouth

First mouth

Digestive tube

Second mouth

Mouth

Anus

Mouth develops from blastopore.

Anus develops from blastopore.

Key
- ▨ Ectoderm
- ▨ Mesoderm
- ▨ Endoderm

(a) Cleavage. In general, protostome development begins with spiral, determinate cleavage. Deuterostome development is characterized by radial, indeterminate cleavage.

(b) Coelom formation. Coelom formation begins in the gastrula stage. In protostome development, the coelom forms from splits in the mesoderm. In deuterostome development, the coelom forms from mesodermal outpocketings of the archenteron.

(c) Fate of the blastopore. In protostome development, the mouth forms from the blastopore. In deuterostome development, the mouth forms from a secondary opening.

isolated from a snail at the four-cell stage, for example, cannot develop into a whole animal. Instead, after repeated divisions, such a cell will form an inviable embryo that lacks many parts.

In contrast to the spiral cleavage pattern, deuterostome development is predominantly characterized by **radial cleavage**. The cleavage planes are either parallel or perpendicular to the vertical axis of the embryo; as seen at the eight-cell stage, the tiers of cells are aligned, one directly above the other (see Figure 32.9a, right). Most animals with deuterostome development also have **indeterminate cleavage**, meaning that each cell produced by early cleavage divisions retains the capacity to develop into a complete embryo. For example, if the cells of a sea urchin embryo are separated at the four-cell stage, each can form a complete larva. Similarly, it is the indeterminate cleavage of the human zygote that makes identical twins possible.

Coelom Formation

During gastrulation, an embryo's developing digestive tube initially forms as a blind pouch, the **archenteron**, which becomes the gut **(Figure 32.9b)**. As the archenteron forms in protostome development, initially solid masses of mesoderm split and form the coelom. In contrast, in deuterostome development, the mesoderm buds from the wall of the archenteron, and its cavity becomes the coelom.

Fate of the Blastopore

Protostome and deuterostome development often differ in the fate of the **blastopore**, the indentation that during gastrulation leads to the formation of the archenteron **(Figure 32.9c)**. After the archenteron develops, in most animals a second opening forms at the opposite end of the gastrula. In many species, the blastopore and this second opening become the two openings of the digestive tube: the mouth and the anus. In protostome development, the mouth generally develops from the first opening, the blastopore, and it is for this characteristic that the term *protostome* derives (from the Greek *protos*, first, and *stoma*, mouth). In deuterostome development (from the Greek *deuteros*, second), the mouth is derived from the secondary opening, and the blastopore usually forms the anus.

CONCEPT CHECK 32.3

1. Distinguish the terms *grade* and *clade*.
2. Compare three aspects of the early development of a snail (a mollusc) and a human (a chordate).
3. **WHAT IF?** Evaluate this claim: Ignoring the details of their specific anatomy, worms, humans, and most other triploblasts have a shape analogous to that of a doughnut.

For suggested answers, see Appendix A.

New views of animal phylogeny are emerging from molecular data

Zoologists currently recognize about three dozen animal phyla. But the boundaries of and relationships between these phyla continue to be debated. Although it might be frustrating that the phylogenies in textbooks cannot be memorized as set-in-stone truths, the uncertainty inherent in these diagrams is a healthy reminder that science is an ongoing, dynamic process of inquiry.

Researchers have long based their hypotheses about animal phylogeny on morphological data. Now biologists also reconstruct phylogenies using molecular data. Additional clues have come from studies of lesser-known animal phyla, along with fossil data that help clarify when key morphological traits arose in various groups.

Another important change has been the use of cladistics (see Chapter 26). Phylogenetic systematists seek to place organisms into clades, each of which includes an ancestral species and all of its descendants. Based on cladistic methods, a phylogenetic tree takes shape as a hierarchy of clades nested within larger clades—the finer and thicker branches of the tree, respectively. Clades are inferred from shared derived characters that are unique to members of the clade. For example, a clade might be inferred from key anatomical and embryological similarities that researchers conclude are homologous. Molecular data such as DNA sequences are another source of information for inferring common ancestry. But whether the data used are "traditional" morphological characters or "new" molecular sequences or a combination, the goal is the same: to reconstruct evolutionary history.

To get a sense of the debates in animal systematics, we'll compare a traditional view of animal phylogeny, based primarily on morphological data (**Figure 32.10**), with a more current view, based mainly on molecular data (**Figure 32.11**).

Points of Agreement

These two views agree on several significant aspects of animal phylogeny. Notice how the following points are reflected in Figures 32.10 and 32.11.

1. **All animals share a common ancestor.** Both trees indicate that animals are monophyletic, forming a clade called Metazoa. All extant and extinct animal lineages have descended from a common ancestor.
2. **Sponges are basal animals.** Among the extant taxa, sponges (phylum Porifera) branch from the base of both animal trees. Morphological and molecular analyses published in 2009 indicate that sponges are monophyletic, as shown here; some earlier studies had suggested that sponges are paraphyletic.
3. **Eumetazoa is a clade of animals with true tissues.** All animals except for sponges and a few others belong to a clade of **eumetazoans** ("true animals"). True tissues evolved in the common ancestor of living eumetazoans. Basal eumetazoans, which include the phyla Ctenophora (comb jellies) and Cnidaria, are diploblastic and generally have radial symmetry.
4. **Most animal phyla belong to the clade Bilateria.** Bilateral symmetry and the presence of three germ layers are shared derived characters that help define the clade Bilateria. This clade contains the majority of animal phyla, and its members are known as **bilaterians**. The Cambrian explosion was primarily a rapid diversification of bilaterians.

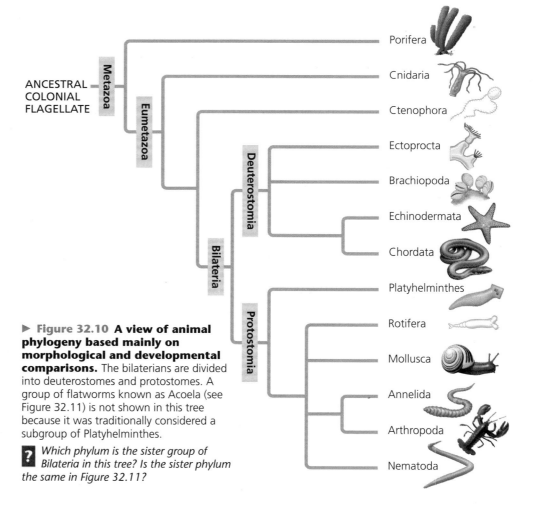

▶ **Figure 32.10 A view of animal phylogeny based mainly on morphological and developmental comparisons.** The bilaterians are divided into deuterostomes and protostomes. A group of flatworms known as Acoela (see Figure 32.11) is not shown in this tree because it was traditionally considered a subgroup of Platyhelminthes.

❓ *Which phylum is the sister group of Bilateria in this tree? Is the sister phylum the same in Figure 32.11?*

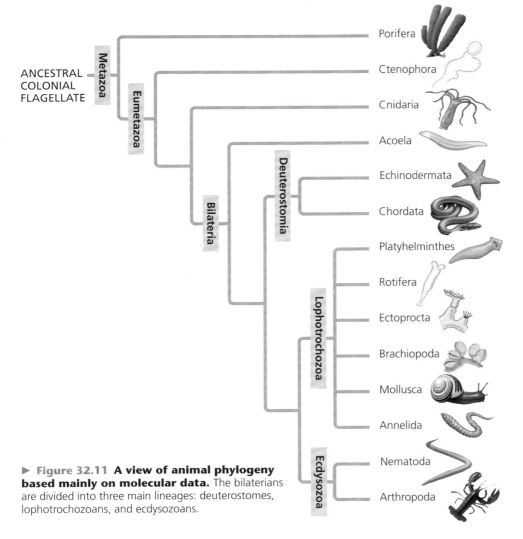

Porifera

Ctenophora

Cnidaria

Acoela

Echinodermata

Chordata

Platyhelminthes

Rotifera

Ectoprocta

Brachiopoda

Mollusca

Annelida

Nematoda

Arthropoda

ANCESTRAL COLONIAL FLAGELLATE

Metazoa

Eumetazoa

Bilateria

Deuterostomia

Lophotrochozoa

Ecdysozoa

▶ **Figure 32.11 A view of animal phylogeny based mainly on molecular data.** The bilaterians are divided into three main lineages: deuterostomes, lophotrochozoans, and ecdysozoans.

5. **Chordates and some other phyla belong to the clade Deuterostomia.** The term *deuterostome* refers not only to a mode of animal development, but also to the members of a clade that includes vertebrates and other chordates. (Note, however, that the traditional and molecular views of animal phylogeny disagree as to which other phyla are also deuterostomes.)

Progress in Resolving Bilaterian Relationships

While evolutionary relationships inferred from morphological data and molecular data are similar in many respects, there are some differences. For example, the morphology-based tree in Figure 32.10 divides the bilaterians into deuterostomes and protostomes. This view assumes that these two modes of development reflect a phylogenetic pattern. Within the protostomes, arthropods (such as insects and crustaceans) are grouped with annelids. Both groups have segmented bodies (think of the tail of a lobster, which is an arthropod, and an earthworm, which is an annelid).

A different view has emerged from molecular phylogenies based on ribosomal genes, *Hox* genes, and dozens of other protein-coding nuclear genes, as well as mitochondrial genes. Collectively, these studies indicate that there are three major clades of bilaterally symmetrical animals: the Deuterostomia, Lophotrochozoa, and Ecdysozoa (see Figure 32.11). In contrast to the traditional morphological view, the molecular phylogeny holds that the arthropods and annelids are not closely related to one another. Note also that Figure 32.11 includes a group of acoelomate flatworms (Acoela) not shown in Figure 32.10. Traditionally, acoelomate flatworms were classified with other flatworms in the phylum Platyhelminthes. However, recent research indicates that acoelomate flatworms are basal bilaterians, and not members of the phylum Platyhelminthes. Acoela's basal position suggests that the bilaterians may have descended from a common ancestor that resembled living acoelomate flatworms—that is, from an ancestor that had a simple nervous system, a saclike gut with a single opening (the "mouth"), and no excretory system.

As seen in Figure 32.11, the molecular phylogeny assigns the animal phyla that are not in Deuterostomia to two taxa rather than one: the **ecdysozoans** and the **lophotrochozoans**. The clade name Ecdysozoa refers to a characteristic shared by nematodes, arthropods, and some of the other ecdysozoan phyla that are not included in our survey. These animals secrete external skeletons (exoskeletons); the stiff covering of a cicada or cricket is an example. As the animal grows, it molts, squirming out of its old exoskeleton and secreting a larger one. The process of shedding the old exoskeleton is called *ecdysis* **(Figure 32.12).** Though named for this characteristic, the

◀ **Figure 32.12 Ecdysis.** This molting cicada is in the process of emerging from its old exoskeleton. The animal will now secrete a new, larger exoskeleton.

clade was proposed mainly on the basis of molecular data that support the common ancestry of its members. Furthermore, some taxa excluded from this clade by their molecular data, such as certain species of leeches, do in fact molt.

The name Lophotrochozoa refers to two different features observed in some animals belonging to this clade. Some lophotrochozoans, such as ectoprocts, develop a structure called a **lophophore** (from the Greek *lophos*, crest, and *pherein*, to carry), a crown of ciliated tentacles that function in feeding (**Figure 32.13a**). Individuals in other phyla, including molluscs and annelids, go through a distinctive developmental stage called the **trochophore larva** (**Figure 32.13b**)—hence the name lophotrochozoan.

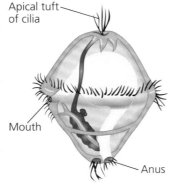

(a) Lophophore feeding structures of an ectoproct

(b) Structure of a trochophore larva

▲ **Figure 32.13 Morphological characteristics of lophotrochozoans.**

Future Directions in Animal Systematics

Like any area of scientific inquiry, animal systematics is a work in progress. At present, most systematists think that the tree shown in Figure 32.11 is more strongly supported than is the tree shown in Figure 32.10. Of course, as new information emerges, our understanding of the evolutionary relationships shown in these trees may change. Researchers continue to conduct large-scale analyses of multiple genes and morphological traits across a wide sample of animal phyla. A better understanding of the relationships between these phyla will give scientists a clearer picture of how the diversity of animal body plans arose. In Chapters 33 and 34, we will take a closer look at the diverse phyla of extant animals and their evolutionary history.

CONCEPT CHECK 32.4

1. Describe the evidence that cnidarians share a more recent common ancestor with other animals than with sponges.
2. How do the phylogenetic hypotheses presented in Figures 32.10 and 32.11 differ in structuring the major branches within the clade Bilateria?
3. **MAKE CONNECTIONS** Based on the phylogeny in Figure 32.11 and the information in Figure 25.10 (p. 518), evaluate this statement: "The Cambrian explosion actually consists of three explosions, not one."

For suggested answers, see Appendix A.

32 CHAPTER REVIEW

SUMMARY OF KEY CONCEPTS

CONCEPT 32.1

Animals are multicellular, heterotrophic eukaryotes with tissues that develop from embryonic layers (pp. 654–656)

- Animals are heterotrophs that ingest their food.
- Animals are multicellular eukaryotes. Their cells are supported and connected to one another by collagen and other structural proteins located outside the cell membrane. Nervous tissue and muscle tissue are key animal features.
- In most animals, **gastrulation** follows the formation of the **blastula** and leads to the formation of embryonic tissue layers. All animals have *Hox* genes that regulate the development of body form. Although *Hox* genes have been highly conserved over the course of evolution, they can produce a wide diversity of animal morphology.

❓ *Describe key ways that animals differ from plants and fungi.*

CONCEPT 32.2

The history of animals spans more than half a billion years (pp. 656–658)

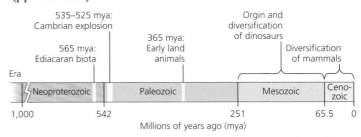

❓ *What caused the Cambrian explosion? Describe current hypotheses.*

CONCEPT 32.3

Animals can be characterized by "body plans" (pp. 658–661)

- Animals may lack symmetry or may have radial or bilateral symmetry. Bilaterally symmetrical animals have dorsal and ventral sides, as well as anterior and posterior ends.

- Among eumetazoans (animals with true tissues), embryos may be **diploblastic** (having two germ layers) or **triploblastic** (having three germ layers).
- In triploblastic animals, a body cavity may be present or absent. A body cavity can be a **pseudocoelom** (derived from both mesoderm and endoderm) or a true **coelom** (derived only from mesoderm).
- **Protostome** and **deuterostome** development often differ in patterns of cleavage, coelom formation, and blastopore fate.

? *Describe how body plans provide useful information yet should be interpreted cautiously when scientists are trying to understand evolutionary relationships.*

CONCEPT 32.4

New views of animal phylogeny are emerging from molecular data (pp. 662–664)

This phylogenetic tree shows key steps in animal evolution:

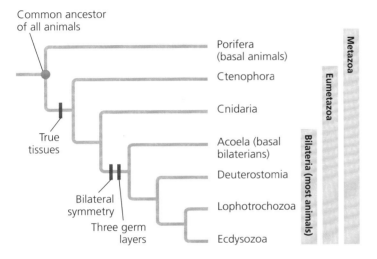

? *Describe the data and methods used today to reconstruct animal phylogeny.*

TEST YOUR UNDERSTANDING

LEVEL 1: KNOWLEDGE/COMPREHENSION

1. Among the characteristics unique to animals is
   - a. gastrulation.
   - b. multicellularity.
   - c. sexual reproduction.
   - d. flagellated sperm.
   - e. heterotrophic nutrition.

2. The distinction between sponges and other animal phyla is based mainly on the absence versus the presence of
   - a. a body cavity.
   - b. a complete digestive tract.
   - c. a circulatory system.
   - d. true tissues.
   - e. mesoderm.

3. Acoelomates are characterized by
   - a. the absence of a brain.
   - b. the absence of mesoderm.
   - c. deuterostome development.
   - d. a coelom that is not completely lined with mesoderm.
   - e. a solid body without a cavity surrounding internal organs.

4. Which of the following was probably the *least* important factor in bringing about the Cambrian explosion?
   - a. the emergence of predator-prey relationships among animals
   - b. the accumulation of diverse adaptations, such as shells and different modes of locomotion
   - c. the movement of animals onto land
   - d. the origin of *Hox* genes and other genetic changes affecting the regulation of developmental genes
   - e. the accumulation of sufficient atmospheric oxygen to support the more active metabolism of mobile animals

LEVEL 2: APPLICATION/ANALYSIS

5. Which of these is a point of conflict between the phylogenetic analyses presented in Figures 32.10 and 32.11?
   - a. the monophyly of the animal kingdom
   - b. the relationship of taxa of segmented animals to taxa of nonsegmented animals
   - c. that sponges are basal animals
   - d. that chordates are deuterostomes
   - e. the monophyly of the bilaterians

LEVEL 3: SYNTHESIS/EVALUATION

6. **EVOLUTION CONNECTION**
   A professor begins a lecture on animal phylogeny by saying, "We are all worms." In this context, what did she mean?

7. **SCIENTIFIC INQUIRY**
   DRAW IT Redraw the bilaterian portion of Figure 32.11 for the nine phyla in the table below. Consider these blastopore fates: protostomy (mouth develops from the blastopore), deuterostomy (anus develops from the blastopore), or neither (the blastopore closes and the mouth develops elsewhere). Depending on the blastopore fate of its members, label each branch that leads to a phylum with P, D, N, or a combination of these letters. What is the ancestral blastopore fate? How many times has blastopore fate changed over the course of evolution? Explain.

Blastopore Fate	Phyla
Protostomy (P)	Platyhelminthes, Rotifera, Nematoda; most Mollusca, most Annelida; few Arthropoda
Deuterostomy (D)	Echinodermata, Chordata; most Arthropoda; few Mollusca, few Annelida
Neither (N)	Acoela

Source: A. Hejnol and M. Martindale, The mouth, the anus, and the blastopore—open questions about questionable openings. In *Animal Evolution: Genomes, Fossils and Trees,* eds. D. T. J. Littlewood and M. J. Telford, Oxford University Press, pp. 33–40 (2009).

8. **WRITE ABOUT A THEME**
   Feedback Regulation Animal life changed greatly during the Cambrian explosion, with some groups expanding in diversity and others declining. Write a short essay (100–150 words) interpreting these events as feedback regulation at the level of the biological community.

For selected answers, see Appendix A.

 www.masteringbiology.com

1. MasteringBiology® Assignments
Tutorial Animal Body Plans
Activities Protostome Diversity • Animal Phylogenetic Tree
Questions Student Misconceptions • Reading Quiz • Multiple Choice • End-of-Chapter

2. eText
Read your book online, search, take notes, highlight text, and more.

3. The Study Area
Practice Tests • Cumulative Test • *BioFlix* 3-D Animations • MP3 Tutor Sessions • Videos • Activities • Investigations • Lab Media • Audio Glossary • Word Study Tools • Art

33

An Introduction to Invertebrates

▲ Figure 33.1 **What function do the red whorls of this organism have?**

Life Without a Backbone

At first glance, you might mistake the organism shown in **Figure 33.1** for a type of seaweed. But this colorful inhabitant of coral reefs is actually an animal, not an alga. Specifically, it is a species of segmented worm known as a Christmas tree worm (*Spirobranchus giganteus*). The two tree-shaped whorls are tentacles, which the worm uses for gas exchange and for removing small food particles from the surrounding water. The tentacles emerge from a tube of calcium carbonate secreted by the worm that protects and supports its soft body. Light-sensitive structures on the tentacles can detect the shadow cast by a predator, triggering the worm to contract muscles that rapidly withdraw the tentacles into the tube.

Christmas tree worms are **invertebrates**—animals that lack a backbone. Invertebrates account for 95% of known animal species. They occupy almost every habitat on Earth, from the scalding water released by deep-sea hydrothermal vents to the rocky, frozen ground of Antarctica. Adaptation to these varied environments has produced an immense diversity of forms, ranging from a species consisting of a flat bilayer of cells to other species with features such as silk-spinning glands, pivoting spines, and tentacles covered with suction cups. Invertebrate species also show enormous variation in size, from microscopic organisms to organisms that can grow to 18 m long (1.5 times the length of a school bus).

In this chapter, we'll take a tour of the invertebrate world, using the phylogenetic tree in **Figure 33.2** as a guide. **Figure 33.3**, on the next three pages, surveys 23 invertebrate phyla. Serving as representatives of invertebrate diversity, many of those phyla are explored in more detail in the rest of this chapter.

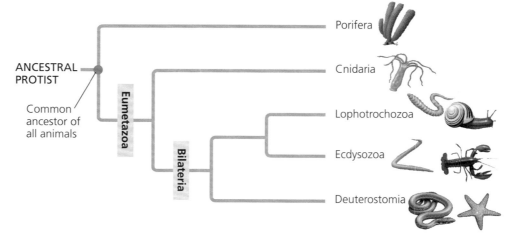

▲ Figure 33.2 **Review of animal phylogeny.** Except for sponges (basal animals in phylum Porifera) and a few other groups, all animals have tissues and are in the clade Eumetazoa. Most animals are in the diverse clade Bilateria. The evolutionary tree shown here provides an overview of material covered in Chapter 32 but omits many groups; for a more complete view of animal relationships, see Figure 32.11.

▼ Figure 33.3

Exploring Invertebrate Diversity

Kingdom Animalia encompasses 1.3 million known species, and estimates of total species range as high as 10–20 million species. Of the 23 phyla surveyed here, 12 are discussed more fully in this chapter, Chapter 32, or Chapter 34; cross-references are given at the end of their descriptions.

Porifera (5,500 species)

Animals in this phylum are informally called sponges. Sponges are sessile animals that lack true tissues. They live as suspension feeders, trapping particles that pass through the internal channels of their body (see Concept 33.1).

A sponge

Cnidaria (10,000 species)

Cnidarians include corals, jellies, and hydras. These animals have a diploblastic, radially symmetrical body plan that includes a gastrovascular cavity with a single opening that serves as both mouth and anus (see Concept 33.2).

A jelly

Acoela (400 species)

Acoel flatworms have a simple nervous system and a saclike gut, and thus were once placed in phylum Platyhelminthes. Molecular analyses, however, indicate that Acoela is a separate lineage that diverged before the three main bilaterian clades (see Concept 32.4).

Acoel flatworms (LM)

Placozoa (1 species)

The single known species in this phylum, *Trichoplax adhaerens*, doesn't even look like an animal. It consists of a simple bilayer of a few thousand cells. Placozoans are thought to be basal animals, but it is not yet known how they are related to other early-diverging animal groups such as Porifera and Cnidaria. *Trichoplax* can reproduce by dividing into two individuals or by budding off many multicellular individuals.

A placozoan (LM)

Ctenophora (100 species)

Ctenophores (comb jellies) are diploblastic and radially symmetrical like cnidarians, suggesting that both phyla diverged from other animals very early (see Figure 32.11). Comb jellies make up much of the ocean's plankton. They have many distinctive traits, including eight "combs" of cilia that propel the animals through the water. When a small animal contacts the tentacles of some comb jellies, specialized cells burst open, covering the prey with sticky threads.

A ctenophore, or comb jelly

Lophotrochozoans

Platyhelminthes (20,000 species)

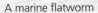

Flatworms (including tapeworms, planarians, and flukes) have bilateral symmetry and a central nervous system that processes information from sensory structures. They have no body cavity or organs for circulation (see Concept 33.3).

A marine flatworm

Ectoprocta (4,500 species)

Ectoprocts (also known as bryozoans) live as sessile colonies and are covered by a tough exoskeleton (see Concept 33.3).

Ectoprocts

Rotifera (1,800 species)

Despite their microscopic size, rotifers have specialized organ systems, including an *alimentary canal* (a digestive tract with both a mouth and an anus). They feed on microorganisms suspended in water (see Concept 33.3).

A rotifer (LM)

Brachiopoda (335 species)

Brachiopods, or lamp shells, may be easily mistaken for clams or other molluscs. However, most brachiopods have a unique stalk that anchors them to their substrate, as well as a crown of cilia called a lophophore (see Concept 33.3).

A brachiopod

Continued on next page

Exploring Invertebrate Diversity

Lophotrochozoa (continued)

Acanthocephala (1,100 species)

Acanthocephalans are called spiny-headed worms because of the curved hooks on the proboscis at the anterior end of their body. All species are parasites. Some acanthocephalans manipulate the behavior of their intermediate hosts (generally arthropods) in ways that increase their chances of reaching their final hosts (generally vertebrates). For example, acanthocephalans that infect New Zealand mud crabs force their hosts to move to more visible areas on the beach, where the crabs are more likely to be eaten by birds, the worms' final hosts. Some phylogenetic analyses place the acanthocephalans within Rotifera.

Curved hooks

An acanthocephalan (LM)

Nemertea (900 species)

Also called proboscis worms or ribbon worms, nemerteans swim through water or burrow in sand, extending a unique proboscis to capture prey. Like flatworms, they lack a true coelom. However, unlike flatworms, nemerteans have an alimentary canal and a closed circulatory system in which the blood is contained in vessels and hence is distinct from fluid in the body cavity.

A ribbon worm

Cycliophora (1 species)

100 μm

A cycliophoran (colorized SEM)

The only known cycliophoran species, *Symbion pandora*, was discovered in 1995 on the mouthparts of a lobster. This tiny, vase-shaped creature has a unique body plan and a particularly bizarre life cycle. Males impregnate females that are still developing in their mothers' bodies. The fertilized females then escape, settle elsewhere on the lobster, and release their offspring. The offspring apparently leave that lobster and search for another one to which they attach.

Annelida (16,500 species)

Annelids, or segmented worms, are distinguished from other worms by their body segmentation. Earthworms are the most familiar annelids, but the phylum consists primarily of marine and freshwater species (see Concept 33.3).

A marine annelid

Mollusca (93,000 species)

Molluscs (including snails, clams, squids, and octopuses) have a soft body that in many species is protected by a hard shell (see Concept 33.3).

An octopus

Ecdysozoa

Loricifera (10 species)

Loriciferans (from the Latin *lorica*, corset, and *ferre*, to bear) are tiny animals that inhabit the deep-sea bottom. A loriciferan can telescope its head, neck, and thorax in and out of the lorica, a pocket formed by six plates surrounding the abdomen. Though the natural history of loriciferans is mostly a mystery, at least some species likely eat bacteria.

50 μm

A loriciferan (LM)

Priapula (16 species)

A priapulan

Priapulans are worms with a large, rounded proboscis at the anterior end. (They are named after Priapos, the Greek god of fertility, who was symbolized by a giant penis.) Ranging from 0.5 mm to 20 cm in length, most species burrow through seafloor sediments. Fossil evidence suggests that priapulans were among the major predators during the Cambrian period.

Ecdysozoa (continued)

Onychophora (110 species)

An onychophoran

Onychophorans, also called velvet worms, originated during the Cambrian explosion (see Chapter 32). Originally, they thrived in the ocean, but at some point they succeeded in colonizing land. Today they live only in humid forests. Onychophorans have fleshy antennae and several dozen pairs of saclike legs.

Tardigrada (800 species)

Tardigrades (from the Latin *tardus*, slow, and *gradus*, step) are sometimes called water bears for their rounded shape, stubby appendages, and lumbering, bearlike gait. Most tardigrades are less than 0.5 mm in length. Some live in oceans or fresh water, while others live on plants or animals. As many as 2 million tardigrades can be found on a square meter of moss. Harsh conditions may cause tardigrades to enter a state of dormancy; while dormant, they can survive temperatures as low as −272°C, close to absolute zero!

100 μm

Tardigrades (colorized SEM)

Nematoda (25,000 species)

A roundworm (colored SEM)

Also called roundworms, nematodes are enormously abundant and diverse in the soil and in aquatic habitats; many species parasitize plants and animals. Their most distinctive feature is a tough cuticle that coats the body (see Concept 33.4).

Arthropoda (1,000,000 species)

The vast majority of known animal species, including insects, crustaceans, and arachnids, are arthropods. All arthropods have a segmented exoskeleton and jointed appendages (see Concept 33.4).

A scorpion (an arachnid)

Deuterostomia

Hemichordata (85 species)

An acorn worm

Like echinoderms and chordates, hemichordates are members of the deuterostome clade (see Chapter 32). Hemichordates share some traits with chordates, such as gill slits and a dorsal nerve cord. The largest group of hemichordates is the enteropneusts, or acorn worms. Acorn worms are marine and generally live buried in mud or under rocks; they may grow to more than 2 m in length.

Chordata (52,000 species)

More than 90% of all known chordate species have backbones (and thus are vertebrates). However, the phylum Chordata also includes three groups of invertebrates: lancelets, tunicates, and hagfishes. See Chapter 34 for a full discussion of this phylum.

A tunicate

Echinodermata (7,000 species)

Echinoderms, such as sand dollars, sea stars, and sea urchins, are marine animals in the deuterostome clade that are bilaterally symmetrical as larvae but not as adults. They move and feed by using a network of internal canals to pump water to different parts of their body (see Concept 33.5).

A sea urchin

CONCEPT 33.1

Sponges are basal animals that lack true tissues

Porifera
Cnidaria
Lophotrochozoa
Ecdysozoa
Deuterostomia

Animals in the phylum Porifera are known informally as sponges. (Recent molecular studies indicate that sponges are monophyletic, and that is the phylogeny we follow here; this remains under debate, however, as some studies suggest that sponges are paraphyletic.) Among the simplest of animals, sponges are sedentary and were mistaken for plants by the ancient Greeks. They range in size from a few millimeters to a few meters, and most species are marine, though a few live in fresh water. Sponges are **suspension feeders**: They capture food particles suspended in the water that passes through their body, which in some species resembles a sac perforated with pores. Water is drawn through the pores into a central cavity, the **spongocoel**, and then flows out of the sponge through a larger opening called the **osculum** **(Figure 33.4)**. More complex sponges have folded body walls, and many contain branched water canals and several oscula.

Sponges are basal animals; that is, they represent a lineage that originates near the root of the phylogenetic tree of animals. Unlike nearly all other animals, sponges lack true tissues, groups of similar cells that act as a functional unit and are isolated from other tissues by membranous layers. However, the sponge body does contain several different cell types. For example, lining the interior of the spongocoel are flagellated **choanocytes**, or collar cells (named for the finger-like projections that form a "collar" around the flagellum). These cells engulf bacteria and other food particles by phagocytosis. The similarity between choanocytes and the cells of choanoflagellates supports molecular evidence suggesting that animals evolved from a choanoflagellate-like ancestor (see Figure 32.3).

The body of a sponge consists of two layers of cells separated by a gelatinous region called the **mesohyl**. Because both cell layers are in contact with water, processes such as gas exchange and waste removal can occur by diffusion across the membranes of these cells. Other tasks are performed by cells called **amoebocytes**, named for their use of pseudopodia. These cells move through the mesohyl and have many functions. For example, they take up food from the surrounding water and from choanocytes, digest it, and carry nutrients to other cells. Amoebocytes also manufacture tough skeletal fibers within the mesohyl. In some sponges, these fibers are sharp spicules made from calcium carbonate or silica. Other sponges produce more flexible fibers composed of a protein called spongin; you may have seen these pliant skeletons

▼ **Figure 33.4 Anatomy of a sponge.**

Azure vase sponge (*Callyspongia plicifera*)

❺ Choanocytes. The spongocoel is lined with flagellated cells called choanocytes. By beating flagella, the choanocytes create a current that draws water in through the pores and out through the osculum.

Osculum

❹ Spongocoel. Water passing through pores enters a cavity called the spongocoel.

❸ Pores. Water enters the sponge through pores formed by doughnut-shaped cells that span the body wall.

❷ Epidermis. The outer layer consists of tightly packed epidermal cells.

Water flow

❶ Mesohyl. The wall of this sponge consists of two layers of cells separated by a gelatinous matrix, the mesohyl ("middle matter").

Spicules

Flagellum   Food particles in mucus   Choanocyte
Collar
Phagocytosis of food particles
Amoebocyte

❻ The movement of a choanocyte's flagellum also draws water through its collar of finger-like projections. Food particles are trapped in the mucus that coats the projections, engulfed by phagocytosis, and either digested or transferred to amoebocytes.

❼ Amoebocytes. These cells can transport nutrients to other cells of the sponge body, produce materials for skeletal fibers (spicules), or become any type of sponge cell as needed.

being sold as brown bath sponges. Finally, and perhaps most importantly, amoebocytes are capable of becoming other types of sponge cells. This gives the sponge body remarkable flexibility, enabling it to adjust its shape in response to changes in its physical environment (such as the direction of water currents).

Most sponges are **hermaphrodites**, meaning that each individual functions as both male and female in sexual reproduction by producing sperm *and* eggs. Almost all sponges exhibit sequential hermaphroditism: They function first as one sex and then as the other.

Sponge gametes arise from choanocytes or amoebocytes. Eggs reside in the mesohyl, but sperm are carried out of the sponge by the water current. Cross-fertilization results from some of the sperm being drawn into neighboring individuals. Fertilization occurs in the mesohyl, where the zygotes develop into flagellated, swimming larvae that disperse from the parent sponge. After settling on a suitable substrate, a larva develops into a sessile adult.

Sponges produce a variety of antibiotics and other defensive compounds. Researchers are now isolating these compounds, which hold promise for fighting human diseases. For example, a compound called cribrostatin isolated from marine sponges can kill penicillin-resistant strains of the bacterium *Streptococcus*. Other sponge-derived compounds are being tested as possible anticancer agents.

CONCEPT CHECK 33.1

1. Describe how sponges feed.
2. **WHAT IF?** Some molecular evidence suggests that the sister group of animals is not the choanoflagellates, but rather a group of parasitic protists, Mesomycetozoa. Given that these parasites lack collar cells, can this hypothesis be correct? Explain.

For suggested answers, see Appendix A.

CONCEPT 33.2

Cnidarians are an ancient phylum of eumetazoans

All animals except sponges and a few other groups belong to the clade Eumetazoa, animals with true tissues (see Chapter 32). One of the oldest lineages in this clade is the phylum Cnidaria. Cnidarians have diversified into a wide range of sessile and motile forms, including hydras, corals, and jellies (commonly called "jellyfish"). Yet most cnidarians still exhibit the relatively simple, diploblastic, radial body plan that existed in early members of the group some 560 million years ago.

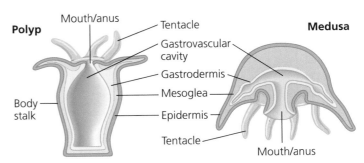

▲ **Figure 33.5 Polyp and medusa forms of cnidarians.** The body wall of a cnidarian has two layers of cells: an outer layer of epidermis (darker blue; derived from ectoderm) and an inner layer of gastrodermis (yellow; derived from endoderm). Digestion begins in the gastrovascular cavity and is completed inside food vacuoles in the gastrodermal cells. Flagella on the gastrodermal cells keep the contents of the gastrovascular cavity agitated and help distribute nutrients. Sandwiched between the epidermis and gastrodermis is a gelatinous layer, the mesoglea.

The basic body plan of a cnidarian is a sac with a central digestive compartment, the **gastrovascular cavity**. A single opening to this cavity functions as both mouth and anus. There are two variations on this body plan: the sessile polyp and the motile medusa **(Figure 33.5)**. **Polyps** are cylindrical forms that adhere to the substrate by the aboral end of their body (the end opposite the mouth) and extend their tentacles, waiting for prey. Examples of the polyp form include hydras and sea anemones. A **medusa** (plural, *medusae*) resembles a flattened, mouth-down version of the polyp. It moves freely in the water by a combination of passive drifting and contractions of its bell-shaped body. Medusae include free-swimming jellies. The tentacles of a jelly dangle from the oral surface, which points downward. Some cnidarians exist only as polyps or only as medusae; others have both a polyp stage and a medusa stage in their life cycle.

Cnidarians are carnivores that often use tentacles arranged in a ring around their mouth to capture prey and push the food into their gastrovascular cavity, where digestion begins. Enzymes are secreted into the cavity, thus breaking down the prey into a nutrient-rich broth. Cells lining the cavity then absorb these nutrients and complete the digestive process; any undigested remains are expelled through the mouth/anus. The tentacles are armed with batteries of **cnidocytes**, cells unique to cnidarians that function in defense and prey capture **(Figure 33.6)**. Cnidocytes contain *cnidae* (from the Greek *cnide*, nettle), capsule-like organelles that are capable of exploding outward and that give phylum Cnidaria its name. Specialized cnidae called **nematocysts** contain a stinging thread that can penetrate the body wall of the cnidarian's prey. Other kinds of cnidae have long threads that stick to or entangle small prey that bump into the cnidarian's tentacles.

Contractile tissues and nerves occur in their simplest forms in cnidarians. Cells of the epidermis (outer layer) and gastrodermis (inner layer) have bundles of microfilaments arranged into contractile fibers (see Chapter 6). The gastrovascular

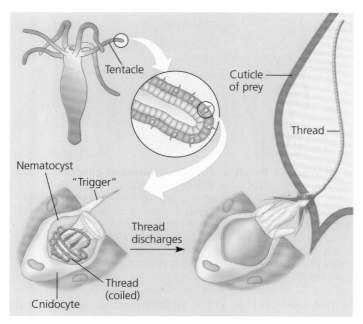

▲ **Figure 33.6 A cnidocyte of a hydra.** This type of cnidocyte contains a stinging capsule, the nematocyst, which contains a coiled thread. When a "trigger" is stimulated by touch or by certain chemicals, the thread shoots out, puncturing and injecting poison into prey.

cavity acts as a hydrostatic skeleton against which the contractile cells can work. When a cnidarian closes its mouth, the volume of the cavity is fixed, and contraction of selected cells causes the animal to change shape. Movements are coordinated by a nerve net. Cnidarians have no brain, and the noncentralized nerve net is associated with sensory structures that are distributed around the body. Thus, the animal can detect and respond to stimuli from all directions.

The phylum Cnidaria is divided into four major clades: Hydrozoa, Scyphozoa, Cubozoa, and Anthozoa **(Figure 33.7)**.

Hydrozoans

Most hydrozoans alternate between the polyp and medusa forms, as seen in the life cycle of *Obelia* **(Figure 33.8)**. The polyp stage, a colony of interconnected polyps in the case of *Obelia*, is more conspicuous than the medusa. Hydras, among the few cnidarians found in fresh water, are unusual hydrozoans in that they exist only in polyp form. When environmental conditions are favorable, a hydra reproduces asexually by budding, forming outgrowths that pinch off from the parent and live independently (see Figure 13.2). When conditions deteriorate, hydras can reproduce sexually, forming resistant zygotes that remain dormant until conditions improve.

Scyphozoans

The medusa is the predominant stage in the life cycle of most scyphozoans. The medusae of most species live among the plankton as jellies. Most coastal scyphozoans go through a stage as small polyps during their life cycle, whereas those that live in the open ocean generally lack the polyp stage altogether.

Cubozoans

As their name (which means "cube animals") suggests, cubozoans have a box-shaped medusa stage. Cubozoans can be distinguished from scyphozoans in other ways, such as having complex eyes embedded in the fringe of their medusae. They also are comparatively strong swimmers and as a result are less likely to be stranded on shore. Most cubozoans live in tropical oceans and are equipped with highly toxic cnidocytes. The sea wasp (*Chironex fleckeri*), a cubozoan that lives off the coast of northern Australia, is one of the deadliest organisms known: Its sting causes intense pain and can lead to respiratory failure, cardiac arrest, and death within minutes. The poison of sea wasps isn't universally fatal, however; sea turtles have defenses against it, allowing them to eat the cubozoan in great quantities.

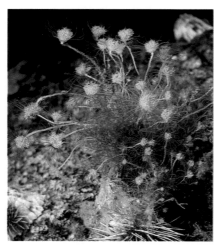

(a) Hydrozoa. Some species, such as this one, live as colonial polyps.

(b) Scyphozoa. Many jellies are bioluminescent. Food captured by nematocyst-bearing tentacles is transferred to specialized oral arms (that lack nematocysts) for transport to the mouth.

(c) Cubozoa. A notorious example is the sea wasp (*Chironex fleckeri*). Its poison, which can subdue fish and other large prey, is more potent than cobra venom.

(d) Anthozoa. Sea anemones and other anthozoans exist only as polyps. Many anthozoans form symbiotic relationships with photosynthetic algae.

▲ **Figure 33.7 Cnidarians.**

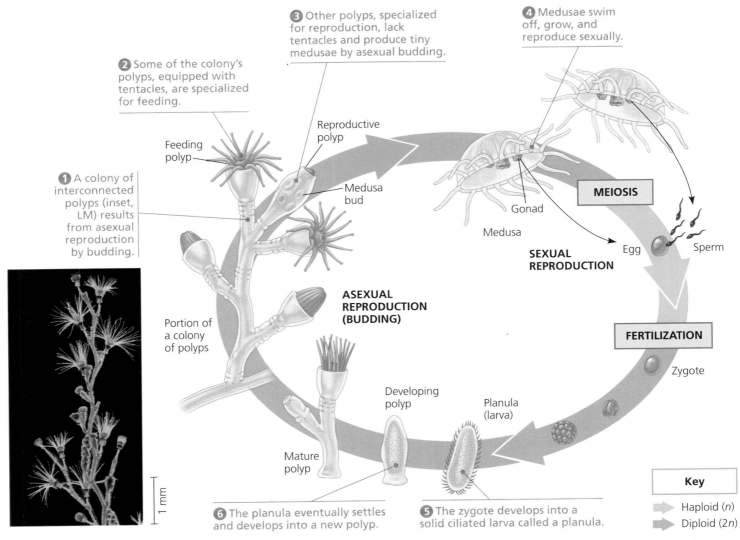

① A colony of interconnected polyps (inset, LM) results from asexual reproduction by budding.

② Some of the colony's polyps, equipped with tentacles, are specialized for feeding.

③ Other polyps, specialized for reproduction, lack tentacles and produce tiny medusae by asexual budding.

④ Medusae swim off, grow, and reproduce sexually.

Feeding polyp

Reproductive polyp

Medusa bud

MEIOSIS

Gonad

Medusa

SEXUAL REPRODUCTION

Egg

Sperm

ASEXUAL REPRODUCTION (BUDDING)

Portion of a colony of polyps

FERTILIZATION

Zygote

Developing polyp

Planula (larva)

Mature polyp

1 mm

⑥ The planula eventually settles and develops into a new polyp.

⑤ The zygote develops into a solid ciliated larva called a planula.

Key

Haploid (*n*)

Diploid (2*n*)

▲ **Figure 33.8 The life cycle of the hydrozoan *Obelia*.** The polyp is asexual, and the medusa is sexual, releasing eggs and sperm. These two stages alternate, one producing the other. Do not confuse this with the alternation of generations that occurs in plants and some algae: In *Obelia*, both the polyp and the medusa are diploid organisms. Typical of animals, only the single-celled gametes are haploid. By contrast, plants have a multicellular haploid generation and a multicellular diploid generation.

WHAT IF? *Suppose that* Obelia *medusae and gametes were haploid, but all other stages were diploid. What aspects of its actual life cycle would have to change for this to occur?*

Anthozoans

Sea anemones (see Figure 33.7d) and corals belong to the clade Anthozoa (meaning "flower animals"). These cnidarians occur only as polyps. Corals live as solitary or colonial forms, often forming symbioses with algae (see Chapter 28). Many species secrete a hard external skeleton of calcium carbonate. Each polyp generation builds on the skeletal remains of earlier generations, constructing "rocks" with shapes characteristic of their species. These skeletons are what we usually think of as coral.

Coral reefs are to tropical seas what rain forests are to tropical land areas: They provide habitat for many other species. Unfortunately, these reefs are being destroyed at an alarming rate. Pollution and overfishing are major threats, and global warming may also be contributing to their demise by raising seawater temperatures above the narrow range in which corals thrive.

CONCEPT CHECK 33.2

1. Compare and contrast the polyp and medusa forms of cnidarians.
2. Describe the structure and function of the stinging cells for which cnidarians are named.
3. **MAKE CONNECTIONS** As you read in Concept 25.3 (pp. 518–519), many new animal body plans emerged during and after the Cambrian explosion. In contrast, cnidarians today retain the same diploblastic, radial body plan found in cnidarians 560 million years ago. Are cnidarians therefore less successful or less "highly evolved" than other animal groups? Explain. (See also Concept 25.6, pp. 529–530.)

For suggested answers, see Appendix A.

CONCEPT 33.3

Lophotrochozoans, a clade identified by molecular data, have the widest range of animal body forms

Porifera
Cnidaria
Lophotrochozoa
Ecdysozoa
Deuterostomia

The vast majority of animal species belong to the clade Bilateria, whose members exhibit bilateral symmetry and triploblastic development (see Chapter 32). Most bilaterians also have a digestive tract with two openings (a mouth and an anus) and a coelom. While the sequence of bilaterian evolution is a subject of active investigation, the most recent common ancestor of living bilaterians probably existed in the late Proterozoic eon (about 575 million years ago). Many of the major groups of bilaterians first appeared in the fossil record during the Cambrian explosion.

As you read in Chapter 32, molecular evidence suggests that there are three major clades of bilaterally symmetrical animals: Lophotrochozoa, Ecdysozoa, and Deuterostomia. This section will focus on the first of these clades, the lophotrochozoans. Concepts 33.4 and 33.5 will explore the other two clades.

Although the clade Lophotrochozoa was identified by molecular data, its name comes from features found in some of its members. Some lophotrochozoans develop a structure called a *lophophore*, a crown of ciliated tentacles that functions in feeding, while others go through a distinctive stage called the *trochophore larva* (see Figure 32.13). Other members of the group have neither of these features. Few other unique morphological features are widely shared within the group—in fact, the lophotrochozoans are the most diverse bilaterian clade in terms of body plan. This diversity in form is reflected in the number of phyla classified in the group: Lophotrochozoa includes about 18 phyla, more than twice the number in any other clade of bilaterians.

We'll now introduce six diverse lophotrochozoan phyla: the flatworms, rotifers, ectoprocts, brachiopods, molluscs, and annelids.

Flatworms

Flatworms (phylum Platyhelminthes) live in marine, freshwater, and damp terrestrial habitats. In addition to free-living species, flatworms include many parasitic species, such as flukes and tapeworms. Flatworms are so named because they have thin bodies that are flattened dorsoventrally (between the dorsal and ventral surfaces); the word *platyhelminth* means "flat worm." (Note that *worm* is not a formal taxonomic name but rather refers to a grade of animals with long, thin bodies.) The smallest flatworms are nearly microscopic free-living species, while some tapeworms are more than 20 m long.

Although flatworms undergo triploblastic development, they are acoelomates (animals that lack a body cavity). Their flat shape places all their cells close to water in the surrounding environment or in their gut. Because of this proximity to water, gas exchange and the elimination of nitrogenous waste (ammonia) can occur by diffusion across the body surface. Flatworms have no organs specialized for gas exchange, and their relatively simple excretory apparatus functions mainly to maintain osmotic balance with their surroundings. This apparatus consists of **protonephridia**, networks of tubules with ciliated structures called *flame bulbs* that pull fluid through branched ducts opening to the outside (see Figure 44.11). Most flatworms have a gastrovascular cavity with only one opening. Though flatworms lack a circulatory system, the fine branches of the gastrovascular cavity distribute food directly to the animal's cells.

Early in their evolutionary history, flatworms separated into two lineages, Catenulida and Rhabditophora. Catenulida is a small clade of about 100 flatworm species, most of which live in freshwater habitats. Catenulids typically reproduce asexually by budding at their posterior end. The offspring often produce their own buds before detaching from the parent, thereby forming a chain of two to four genetically identical individuals—hence their informal name, "chain worms."

The other ancient flatworm lineage, Rhabditophora, is a diverse clade of about 20,000 freshwater and marine species, one example of which is shown in **Figure 33.9**. We'll explore this group in more detail, focusing on free-living and parasitic members of this clade.

Free-Living Species

Free-living rhabditophorans are important as predators and scavengers in a wide range of freshwater and marine habitats. The best-known members of this group are freshwater species in the genus *Dugesia*, commonly called **planarians**. Abundant in unpolluted ponds and streams, planarians prey on

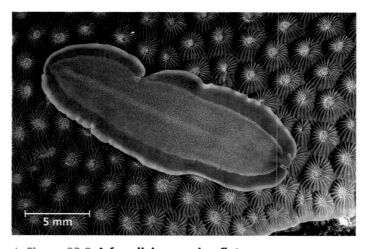

5 mm

▲ Figure 33.9 **A free-living marine flatworm.**

674 UNIT FIVE The Evolutionary History of Biological Diversity

smaller animals or feed on dead animals. They move by using cilia on their ventral surface, gliding along a film of mucus they secrete. Some other rhabditophorans also use their muscles to swim through water with an undulating motion.

A planarian's head is equipped with a pair of light-sensitive eyespots and lateral flaps that function mainly to detect specific chemicals. The planarian nervous system is more complex and centralized than the nerve nets of cnidarians (Figure 33.10). Experiments have shown that planarians can learn to modify their responses to stimuli.

Some planarians can reproduce asexually through fission. The parent constricts roughly in the middle of its body, separating into a head end and a tail end; each end then regenerates the missing parts. Sexual reproduction also occurs. Planarians are hermaphrodites, and copulating mates typically cross-fertilize each other.

Parasitic Species

More than half of the known species of rhabditophorans live as parasites in or on other animals. Many have suckers that attach to the internal organs or outer surfaces of the host animal. In most species, a tough covering helps protect the parasites within their hosts. Reproductive organs occupy nearly the entire interior of these worms. We'll discuss two ecologically and economically important subgroups of parasitic rhabditophorans, the trematodes and the tapeworms.

Trematodes As a group, trematodes parasitize a wide range of hosts, and most species have complex life cycles with alternating sexual and asexual stages. Many trematodes require an intermediate host in which larvae develop before infecting the final host (usually a vertebrate), where the adult worms live. For example, trematodes that parasitize humans spend part of their lives in snail hosts (Figure 33.11). Around the world, some 200 million people are infected with trematodes called blood flukes (*Schistosoma*) and suffer from schistosomiasis, a disease whose symptoms include pain, anemia, and diarrhea.

Living within different hosts puts demands on trematodes that free-living animals don't face. A blood fluke, for instance, must evade the immune systems of both snails and humans. By mimicking the surface proteins of its hosts, the blood fluke creates a partial immunological camouflage for itself. It

▼ **Figure 33.10** **Anatomy of a planarian.**

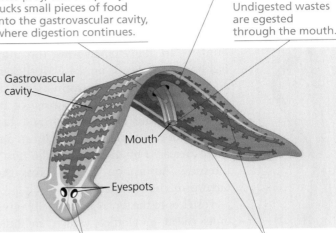

Pharynx. The mouth is at the tip of a muscular pharynx. Digestive juices are spilled onto prey, and the pharynx sucks small pieces of food into the gastrovascular cavity, where digestion continues.

Digestion is completed within the cells lining the gastrovascular cavity, which has many fine subbranches that provide an extensive surface area.

Undigested wastes are egested through the mouth.

Gastrovascular cavity

Mouth

Eyespots

Ganglia. At the anterior end of the worm, near the main sources of sensory input, is a pair of ganglia, dense clusters of nerve cells.

Ventral nerve cords. From the ganglia, a pair of ventral nerve cords runs the length of the body.

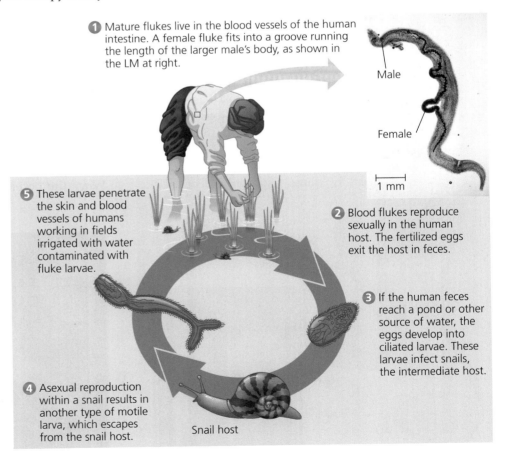

① Mature flukes live in the blood vessels of the human intestine. A female fluke fits into a groove running the length of the larger male's body, as shown in the LM at right.

Male

Female

1 mm

⑤ These larvae penetrate the skin and blood vessels of humans working in fields irrigated with water contaminated with fluke larvae.

② Blood flukes reproduce sexually in the human host. The fertilized eggs exit the host in feces.

③ If the human feces reach a pond or other source of water, the eggs develop into ciliated larvae. These larvae infect snails, the intermediate host.

④ Asexual reproduction within a snail results in another type of motile larva, which escapes from the snail host.

Snail host

▲ **Figure 33.11** **The life cycle of a blood fluke (*Schistosoma mansoni*), a trematode.**

WHAT IF? *Snails eat algae, whose growth is stimulated by nutrients found in fertilizer. How would the contamination of irrigation water with fertilizer likely affect the occurrence of schistosomiasis? Explain.*

also releases molecules that manipulate the hosts' immune systems into tolerating the parasite's existence. These defenses are so effective that individual blood flukes can survive in humans for more than 40 years.

Tapeworms The tapeworms are a second large and diverse group of parasitic rhabditophorans **(Figure 33.12)**. The adults live mostly inside vertebrates, including humans. In many tapeworms, the anterior end, or scolex, is armed with suckers and often hooks that the worm uses to attach itself to the intestinal lining of its host. Tapeworms lack a mouth and gastrovascular cavity; they simply absorb nutrients released by digestion in the host's intestine. Absorption occurs across the tapeworm's body surface.

Posterior to the scolex is a long ribbon of units called proglottids, which are little more than sacs of sex organs. After sexual reproduction, proglottids loaded with thousands of fertilized eggs are released from the posterior end of a tapeworm and leave the host's body in feces. In one type of life cycle, feces carrying the eggs contaminate the food or water of intermediate hosts, such as pigs or cattle, and the tapeworm eggs develop into larvae that encyst in muscles of these animals. A human acquires the larvae by eating undercooked meat containing the cysts, and the worms develop into mature adults within the human. Large tapeworms can block the intestines and rob enough nutrients from the human host to cause nutritional deficiencies.

Doctors have patients take the drug niclosamide by mouth to kill the adult worms.

Rotifers

Rotifers (phylum Rotifera) are tiny animals that inhabit freshwater, marine, and damp soil habitats. Ranging in size from about 50 μm to 2 mm, rotifers are smaller than many protists but nevertheless are multicellular and have specialized organ systems **(Figure 33.13)**. In contrast to cnidarians and flatworms, which have a gastrovascular cavity, rotifers have an **alimentary canal**, a digestive tube with two openings, a mouth and an anus. Internal organs lie within the pseudocoelom, a body cavity that is not completely lined by mesoderm (see Figure 32.8b). Fluid in the pseudocoelom serves as a hydrostatic skeleton. Movement of a rotifer's body distributes the fluid throughout the body, circulating nutrients.

The word *rotifer* is derived from the Latin meaning "wheelbearer," a reference to the crown of cilia that draws a vortex of water into the mouth. Posterior to the mouth, a region of the digestive tract called the pharynx bears jaws called trophi that grind up food, mostly microorganisms suspended in the water. Digestion is then completed farther along the alimentary canal. Most other bilaterians also have an alimentary canal, which enables the stepwise digestion of a wide range of food particles.

Rotifers exhibit some unusual forms of reproduction. Some species consist only of females that produce more females from unfertilized eggs, a type of asexual reproduction called **parthenogenesis**. Some other invertebrates (for example, aphids and some bees) and even some vertebrates (for example, some lizards and some fishes) can also reproduce in this way. In addition to being able to produce females by parthenogeneis, some rotifers can also reproduce sexually under certain conditions, such as high levels of crowding. When this occurs, a female produces two types of eggs. Eggs

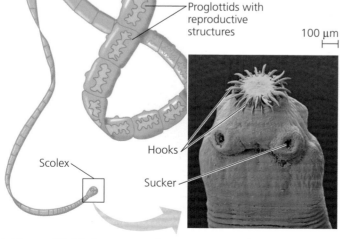

100 μm

Proglottids with reproductive structures

Scolex

Hooks

Sucker

▲ **Figure 33.12 Anatomy of a tapeworm.** The inset shows a close-up of the scolex (colorized SEM).

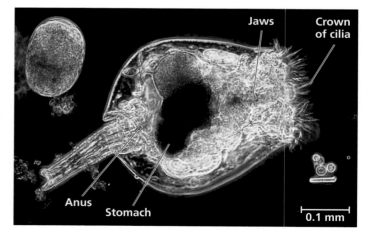

Jaws

Crown of cilia

Anus

Stomach

0.1 mm

▲ **Figure 33.13 A rotifer.** These pseudocoelomates, smaller than many protists, are generally more anatomically complex than flatworms (LM).

of one type develop into females, and eggs of the other type develop into males. In some cases, the males do not feed and survive only long enough to fertilize eggs. The fertilized eggs develop into resistant embryos capable of remaining dormant for years. Once the embryos break dormancy, they develop into a new female generation that reproduces by parthenogenesis until conditions once again favor sexual reproduction.

It is puzzling that many rotifer species survive without males. The vast majority of animals and plants reproduce sexually at least some of the time, and sexual reproduction has certain advantages over asexual reproduction (see Concept 46.1). For example, species that reproduce asexually tend to accumulate harmful mutations in their genomes faster than sexually reproducing species. As a result, asexual species should experience higher rates of extinction and lower rates of speciation.

Seeking to understand this unusual group, researchers have been studying a clade of asexual rotifers named Bdelloidea. Some 360 species of bdelloid rotifers are known, and all of them reproduce by parthenogenesis without any males. Paleontologists have discovered bdelloid rotifers preserved in 35-million-year-old amber, and the morphology of these fossils resembles only the female form, with no evidence of males. By comparing the DNA of bdelloids with that of their closest sexually reproducing rotifer relatives, scientists have concluded that bdelloids have likely been asexual for 100 million years. How these animals manage to flout the general rule against long-lasting asexuality remains a puzzle.

Lophophorates: Ectoprocts and Brachiopods

Bilaterians in the phyla Ectoprocta and Brachiopoda are among those known as lophophorates. These animals have a *lophophore*, a crown of ciliated tentacles around their mouth (see Figure 32.13a). As the cilia draw water toward the mouth, the tentacles trap suspended food particles. Other similarities, such as a U-shaped alimentary canal and the absence of a distinct head, reflect these organisms' sessile existence. In contrast to flatworms, which lack a body cavity, and rotifers, which have a pseudocoelom, lophophorates have a true coelom that is completely lined by mesoderm (see Figure 32.8a).

Ectoprocts (from the Greek *ecto*, outside, and *procta*, anus) are colonial animals that superficially resemble clumps of moss. (In fact, their common name, bryozoans, means "moss animals.") In most species, the colony is encased in a hard **exoskeleton** (external skeleton) studded with pores through which the lophophores extend **(Figure 33.14a)**. Most ectoproct species live in the sea, where they are among the most widespread and numerous sessile animals. Several species are important reef builders. Ectoprocts also live in lakes and rivers. Colonies of the freshwater ectoproct *Pectinatella magnifica* grow on submerged sticks or rocks and can grow into a gelatinous, ball-shaped mass more than 10 cm across.

(a) Ectoprocts, such as this creeping bryozoan (*Plumatella repens*), are colonial lophophorates.

(b) Brachiopods, such as this lampshell (*Terebratulina retusa*), have a hinged shell. The two parts of the shell are dorsal and ventral.

▲ **Figure 33.14 Lophophorates.**

Brachiopods, or lamp shells, superficially resemble clams and other hinge-shelled molluscs, but the two halves of the brachiopod shell are dorsal and ventral rather than lateral, as in clams **(Figure 33.14b)**. All brachiopods are marine. Most live attached to the seafloor by a stalk, opening their shell slightly to allow water to flow through the lophophore. The living brachiopods are remnants of a much richer past that included 30,000 species in the Paleozoic and Mesozoic eras. Some living brachiopods, such as those in the genus *Lingula*, appear nearly identical to fossils of species that lived 400 million years ago.

Molluscs

Snails and slugs, oysters and clams, and octopuses and squids are all molluscs (phylum Mollusca). There are 93,000 known species, making them the second most diverse phylum of animals (after the arthropods, discussed later). Although the majority of molluscs are marine, roughly 8,000 species inhabit fresh water, and 28,000 species of snails and slugs live on land. All molluscs are soft-bodied (from the Latin *molluscus*, soft), and most secrete a hard protective shell made of calcium carbonate. Slugs, squids, and octopuses have a reduced internal shell or have lost their shell completely during their evolution.

Despite their apparent differences, all molluscs have a similar body plan **(Figure 33.15**, on the next page). Molluscs are coelomates, and their bodies have three main parts: a muscular **foot**, usually used for movement; a **visceral mass** containing most of the internal organs; and a **mantle**, a fold of tissue that drapes over the visceral mass and secretes a shell (if one is present). In many molluscs, the mantle extends beyond the visceral mass, producing a water-filled chamber, the **mantle cavity**, which houses the gills, anus, and excretory pores. Many molluscs feed by using a straplike organ called a **radula** to scrape up food.

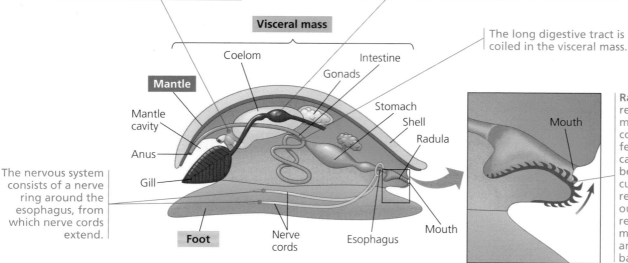

Nephridium. Excretory organs called nephridia remove metabolic wastes from the hemolymph.

Heart. Most molluscs have an open circulatory system. The dorsally located heart pumps circulatory fluid called hemolymph through arteries into sinuses (body spaces). The organs of the mollusc are thus continually bathed in hemolymph.

The long digestive tract is coiled in the visceral mass.

Visceral mass

Coelom

Mantle

Intestine

Gonads

Mantle cavity

Stomach

Shell

Radula

Anus

The nervous system consists of a nerve ring around the esophagus, from which nerve cords extend.

Gill

Foot

Nerve cords

Esophagus

Mouth

Mouth

Radula. The mouth region in many mollusc species contains a rasp-like feeding organ called a radula. This belt of backward-curved teeth repeatedly thrusts outward and then retracts into the mouth, scraping and scooping like a backhoe.

▲ **Figure 33.15 The basic body plan of a mollusc.**

Most molluscs have separate sexes, and their gonads (ovaries or testes) are located in the visceral mass. Many snails, however, are hermaphrodites. The life cycle of many marine molluscs includes a ciliated larval stage, the trochophore (see Figure 32.13b), which is also characteristic of marine annelids (segmented worms) and some other lophotrochozoans.

The basic body plan of molluscs has evolved in various ways in the phylum's seven or eight clades (experts disagree on the number). We'll examine four of those clades here: Polyplacophora (chitons), Gastropoda (snails and slugs), Bivalvia (clams, oysters, and other bivalves), and Cephalopoda (squids, octopuses, cuttlefishes, and chambered nautiluses). We will then focus on threats facing some groups of molluscs.

Chitons

Chitons have an oval-shaped body and a shell composed of eight dorsal plates **(Figure 33.16)**. The chiton's body itself, however, is unsegmented. You can find these marine animals clinging to rocks along the shore during low tide. If you try to dislodge a chiton by hand, you will be surprised at how well its foot, acting as a suction cup, grips the rock. A chiton can also use its foot to creep slowly over the rock surface. Chitons use their radula to scrape algae off the rock surface.

Gastropods

About three-quarters of all living species of molluscs are gastropods **(Figure 33.17)**. Most gastropods are marine, but there are also freshwater species. Still other gastropods have adapted to life on land, where snails and slugs thrive in habitats ranging from deserts to rain forests.

▲ **Figure 33.16 A chiton.** Note the eight-plate shell characteristic of molluscs in the clade Polyplacophora.

(a) A land snail

(b) A sea slug. Nudibranchs, or sea slugs, lost their shell during their evolution.

▲ **Figure 33.17 Gastropods.**

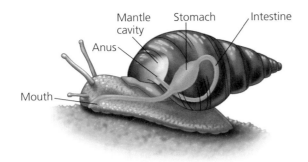

▲ **Figure 33.18 The results of torsion in a gastropod.**
Because of torsion (twisting of the visceral mass) during embryonic development, the digestive tract is coiled and the anus is near the anterior end of the animal.

Gastropods undergo a distinctive developmental process known as **torsion**. As a gastropod embryo develops, its visceral mass rotates up to 180°, causing the animal's anus and mantle cavity to wind up above its head **(Figure 33.18)**. After torsion, some organs that were bilateral may be reduced in size, while others may be lost on one side of the body. Torsion should not be confused with the formation of a coiled shell, which is a separate developmental process.

Most gastropods have a single, spiraled shell into which the animal can retreat when threatened. The shell is often conical but is somewhat flattened in abalones and limpets. Many gastropods have a distinct head with eyes at the tips of tentacles. Gastropods move literally at a snail's pace by a rippling motion of their foot or by means of cilia, often leaving a trail of slime in their wake. Most gastropods use their radula to graze on algae or plants. Several groups, however, are predators, and their radula has become modified for boring holes in the shells of other molluscs or for tearing apart prey. In the cone snails, the teeth of the radula act as poison darts that are used to subdue prey (see the Unit 7 interview with Baldomero Olivera on pp. 850–851 to learn more about cone snails and their venom).

Terrestrial snails lack the gills typical of most aquatic gastropods. Instead, the lining of their mantle cavity functions as a lung, exchanging respiratory gases with the air.

Bivalves

The molluscs of the clade Bivalvia are all aquatic and include many species of clams, oysters, mussels, and scallops. Bivalves have a shell divided into two halves **(Figure 33.19)**. The halves are hinged, and powerful adductor muscles draw them tightly together to protect the animal's soft body. Bivalves have no distinct head, and the radula has been lost. Some bivalves have eyes and sensory tentacles along the outer edge of their mantle.

The mantle cavity of a bivalve contains gills that are used for gas exchange as well as feeding in most species **(Figure 33.20)**. Most bivalves are suspension feeders. They trap small food

▲ **Figure 33.19 A bivalve.** This scallop has many eyes (dark blue spots) lining each half of its hinged shell.

particles in mucus that coats their gills, and cilia then convey those particles to the mouth. Water enters the mantle cavity through an incurrent siphon, passes over the gills, and then exits the mantle cavity through an excurrent siphon.

Most bivalves lead sedentary lives, a characteristic suited to suspension feeding. Mussels secrete strong threads that tether them to rocks, docks, boats, and the shells of other animals. However, clams can pull themselves into the sand or mud, using their muscular foot for an anchor, and scallops can skitter along the seafloor by flapping their shells, rather like the mechanical false teeth sold in novelty shops.

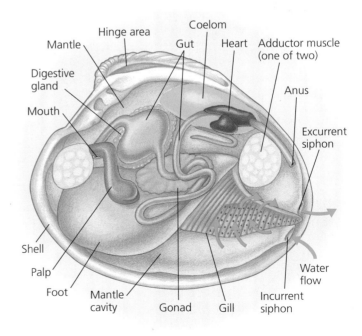

▲ **Figure 33.20 Anatomy of a clam.** Food particles suspended in water that enters through the incurrent siphon are collected by the gills and passed via cilia and the palps to the mouth.

Cephalopods

Cephalopods are active marine predators (Figure 33.21). They use their tentacles to grasp prey, which they then bite with beak-like jaws and immobilize with a poison present in their saliva. The foot of a cephalopod has become modified into a muscular excurrent siphon and part of the tentacles. Squids dart about by drawing water into their mantle cavity and then firing a jet of water through the excurrent siphon; they steer by pointing the siphon in different directions. Octopuses use a similar mechanism to escape predators.

The mantle covers the visceral mass of cephalopods, but the shell is generally reduced and internal (in most species) or missing altogether (in some cuttlefishes and some octopuses). One small group of cephalopods with external shells, the chambered nautiluses, survives today.

Cephalopods are the only molluscs with a *closed circulatory system*, in which the blood remains separate from fluid in the body cavity. They also have well-developed sense organs and a complex brain. The ability to learn and behave in a complex manner is probably more critical to fast-moving predators than to sedentary animals such as clams.

The ancestors of octopuses and squids were probably shelled molluscs that took up a predatory lifestyle; the shell was lost in later evolution. Shelled cephalopods called **ammonites**, some of them as large as truck tires, were the dominant invertebrate predators of the seas for hundreds of millions of years until their disappearance during the mass extinction at the end of the Cretaceous period, 65.5 million years ago (see Table 25.1).

Most species of squid are less than 75 cm long, but some are considerably larger. The giant squid *Architeuthis dux* was for a long time the largest squid known, with a mantle up to 2.25 m long and a total length of 18 m. In 2003, however, a specimen of the rare species *Mesonychoteuthis hamiltoni* was caught near Antarctica; its mantle was 2.5 m long. Some biologists think that this specimen was a juvenile and estimate that adults of its species could be twice as large! Unlike *A. dux*, which has large suckers and small teeth on its tentacles, *M. hamiltoni* has two rows of sharp hooks at the ends of its tentacles that can inflict deadly lacerations.

It is likely that *A. dux* and *M. hamiltoni* spend most of their time in the deep ocean, where they may feed on large fishes. Remains of both giant squid species have been found in the stomachs of sperm whales, which are probably their only natural predator. In 2005, scientists reported the first observations of *A. dux* in the wild, photographed while attacking baited hooks at a depth of 900 m. *M. hamiltoni* has yet to be observed in nature. Overall, these marine giants remain among the great mysteries of invertebrate life.

Protecting Freshwater and Terrestrial Molluscs

Species extinction rates have increased dramatically in the last 400 years, raising concern that a sixth, human-caused mass extinction may be under way (see Chapter 25). Among the many taxa under threat, molluscs have the dubious distinction of being the animal group with the largest number of documented extinctions (Figure 33.22).

Threats to molluscs are especially severe in two groups, freshwater bivalves and terrestrial gastropods. The pearl mussels, a group of freshwater bivalves that can make natural pearls (gems that form when a mussel or oyster secretes layers of a lustrous coating around a grain of sand or other small irritant), are among the world's most endangered animals. Roughly 10% of the 300 pearl mussel species that once lived in North America have become extinct in the last 100 years, and over two-thirds of those that remain are threatened by extinction. Terrestrial gastropods, such as the snail in Figure 33.22, fare no better. Hundreds of Pacific island land snails have disappeared since 1800. Overall, more than 50% of the Pacific island land snails are extinct or under imminent threat of extinction.

Threats faced by freshwater and terrestrial molluscs include habitat loss, pollution, and competition or predation by non-native species introduced by people. Is it too late to protect these molluscs? In some locations, reducing water pollution and changing how water is released from dams have led to dramatic rebounds in pearl mussel populations. Such results provide hope that with corrective measures, other endangered mollusc species can be revived.

◄ Squids are speedy carnivores with beak-like jaws and well-developed eyes.

► Octopuses are considered among the most intelligent invertebrates.

◄ Chambered nautiluses are the only living cephalopods with an external shell.

▲ **Figure 33.21 Cephalopods.**

Figure 33.22

IMPACT

Molluscs: The Silent Extinction

Molluscs account for a largely unheralded but sobering 40% of all documented extinctions of animal species. These extinctions have resulted from habitat loss, pollution, introduced species, overharvesting, and other human actions. Many pearl mussel populations, for example, were driven to extinction by overharvesting for their shells, which were used to make buttons and other goods. Today, remaining populations of these and other freshwater bivalves face threats from pollution and introduced species. Terrestrial gastropods such as the species pictured above are highly vulnerable to the same threats and are among the world's most imperiled animal groups.

▲ An endangered Pacific island land snail, *Partula suturalis*

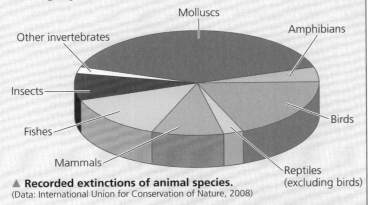

▲ **Recorded extinctions of animal species.**
(Data: International Union for Conservation of Nature, 2008)

▲ Workers on a mound of pearl mussels killed to make buttons (ca. 1919)

WHY IT MATTERS The extinctions of molluscs represent an irreversible loss of biological diversity and greatly threaten other organisms, too. Land snails, for example, play a key role in nutrient cycling, while the filtering activities of freshwater bivalves purify the waters of streams, rivers, and lakes.

FURTHER READING C. Lydeard et al., The global decline of nonmarine mollusks, *BioScience* 54:321–330 (2004).

MAKE CONNECTIONS Freshwater bivalves feed on and can reduce the abundance of photosynthetic protists and bacteria. As such, would the extinction of freshwater bivalves likely have weak or strong effects on aquatic communities (see Concept 28.7, p. 597)? Explain.

◀ **Figure 33.23 A polychaete.** *Hesiolyra bergi* lives on the seafloor around deep-sea hydrothermal vents.

Annelids

Annelida means "little rings," referring to the annelid body's resemblance to a series of fused rings. Annelids are segmented worms that live in the sea, in most freshwater habitats, and in damp soil. Annelids are coelomates, and they range in length from less than 1 mm to more than 3 m, the length of a giant Australian earthworm.

The phylum Annelida can be divided into two main groups: Polychaeta (the polychaetes) and Oligochaeta (the earthworms and their relatives, and the leeches). Some recent phylogenetic analyses have suggested that the oligochaetes are actually a subgroup of the polychaetes. However, since this idea continues to be debated, we discuss polychaetes and oligochaetes separately.

Polychaetes

Each segment of a polychaete (from the Greek *poly*, many, and *chaitē*, long hair) has a pair of paddle-like or ridge-like structures called parapodia ("beside feet") that function in locomotion **(Figure 33.23)**. Each parapodium has numerous chaetae, bristles made of chitin. In many polychaetes, the parapodia are richly supplied with blood vessels and also function as gills.

Polychaetes make up a large and diverse group, most of whose members are marine. A few species drift and swim among the plankton, many crawl on or burrow in the seafloor, and many others live in tubes. Some tube-dwellers, such as the fan worms, build their tubes by mixing mucus with bits of sand and broken shells. Others, such as Christmas tree worms (see Figure 33.1), construct tubes using only their own secretions.

Oligochaetes

Oligochaetes (*oligos*, few, and *chaitē*, long hair) are named for their relatively sparse chaetae (far fewer per segment than in polychaetes). Molecular data indicate that these segmented worms form a diverse clade that includes the earthworms and their aquatic relatives, along with the leeches.

Earthworms Earthworms eat their way through the soil, extracting nutrients as the soil passes through the alimentary canal.

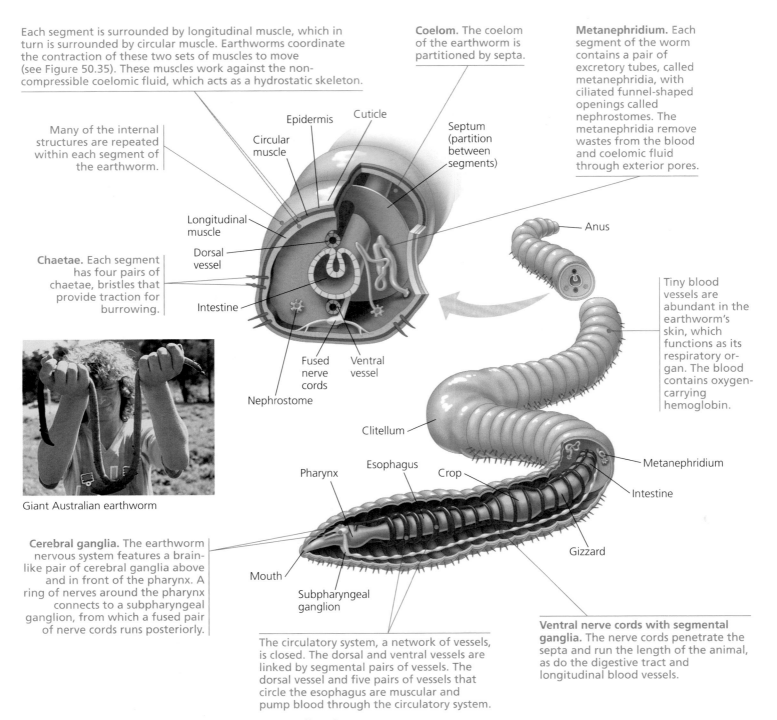

Each segment is surrounded by longitudinal muscle, which in turn is surrounded by circular muscle. Earthworms coordinate the contraction of these two sets of muscles to move (see Figure 50.35). These muscles work against the non-compressible coelomic fluid, which acts as a hydrostatic skeleton.

Many of the internal structures are repeated within each segment of the earthworm.

Chaetae. Each segment has four pairs of chaetae, bristles that provide traction for burrowing.

Giant Australian earthworm

Cerebral ganglia. The earthworm nervous system features a brain-like pair of cerebral ganglia above and in front of the pharynx. A ring of nerves around the pharynx connects to a subpharyngeal ganglion, from which a fused pair of nerve cords runs posteriorly.

Coelom. The coelom of the earthworm is partitioned by septa.

Metanephridium. Each segment of the worm contains a pair of excretory tubes, called metanephridia, with ciliated funnel-shaped openings called nephrostomes. The metanephridia remove wastes from the blood and coelomic fluid through exterior pores.

Epidermis
Cuticle
Circular muscle
Septum (partition between segments)
Longitudinal muscle
Dorsal vessel
Intestine
Fused nerve cords
Ventral vessel
Nephrostome

Anus

Tiny blood vessels are abundant in the earthworm's skin, which functions as its respiratory organ. The blood contains oxygen-carrying hemoglobin.

Clitellum
Pharynx
Esophagus
Crop
Metanephridium
Mouth
Subpharyngeal ganglion
Intestine
Gizzard

The circulatory system, a network of vessels, is closed. The dorsal and ventral vessels are linked by segmental pairs of vessels. The dorsal vessel and five pairs of vessels that circle the esophagus are muscular and pump blood through the circulatory system.

Ventral nerve cords with segmental ganglia. The nerve cords penetrate the septa and run the length of the animal, as do the digestive tract and longitudinal blood vessels.

▲ **Figure 33.24 Anatomy of an earthworm, an oligochaete.**

Undigested material, mixed with mucus secreted into the canal, is eliminated as fecal castings through the anus. Farmers value earthworms because the animals till and aerate the earth, and their castings improve the texture of the soil. (Charles Darwin estimated that a single acre of British farmland contains about 50,000 earthworms, producing 18 tons of castings per year.)

A guided tour of the anatomy of an earthworm, which is representative of annelids, is shown in **Figure 33.24**. Earthworms are hermaphrodites, but they do cross-fertilize. Two earthworms mate by aligning themselves in opposite directions in such a way that they exchange sperm, and then they separate. The received sperm are stored temporarily while an organ called the clitellum secretes a cocoon of mucus. The cocoon slides along the worm, picking up the eggs and then the stored sperm. The cocoon then slips off the worm's head and remains in the soil while the embryos develop. Some earthworms can also reproduce asexually by fragmentation followed by regeneration.

▶ **Figure 33.25 A leech.** A nurse applied this medicinal leech (*Hirudo medicinalis*) to a patient's sore thumb to drain blood from a hematoma (an abnormal accumulation of blood around an internal injury).

Leeches Most leeches inhabit fresh water, but there are also marine species and terrestrial leeches, which live in moist vegetation. Leeches range in length from 1 to 30 cm. Many are predators that feed on other invertebrates, but some are parasites that suck blood by attaching temporarily to other animals, including humans **(Figure 33.25)**. Some parasitic species use bladelike jaws to slit the skin of their host, whereas others secrete enzymes that digest a hole through the skin. The host is usually oblivious to this attack because the leech secretes an anesthetic. After making the incision, the leech secretes another chemical, hirudin, which keeps the blood of the host from coagulating near the incision. The parasite then sucks as much blood as it can hold, often more than ten times its own weight. After this gorging, a leech can last for months without another meal.

Until the 20th century, leeches were frequently used for bloodletting. Today they are used to drain blood that accumulates in tissues following certain injuries or surgeries. Researchers have also investigated the potential use of purified hirudin to dissolve unwanted blood clots that form during surgery or as a result of heart disease. Several forms of hirudin have been developed using recombinant DNA techniques; two of these were recently approved for clinical use.

As a group, Lophotrochozoa encompasses a remarkable range of body plans, as illustrated by members of such phyla as Rotifera, Ectoprocta, Mollusca, and Annelida. Next we'll explore the diversity of Ecdysozoa, a dominant presence on Earth in terms of sheer number of species.

CONCEPT CHECK 33.3

1. Explain how tapeworms can survive without a coelom, a mouth, a digestive system, or an excretory system.
2. Annelid anatomy can be described as "a tube within a tube." Explain.
3. **MAKE CONNECTIONS** Explain how the molluscan foot in gastropods and the excurrent siphon in cephalopods represent an example of descent with modification (see Concept 22.2, pp. 457–460).

For suggested answers, see Appendix A.

CONCEPT 33.4

Ecdysozoans are the most species-rich animal group

Porifera
Cnidaria
Lophotrochozoa
Ecdysozoa
Deuterostomia

Although defined primarily by molecular evidence, the clade Ecdysozoa includes animals that shed a tough external coat (**cuticle**) as they grow; in fact, the group derives its name from this process, which is called *ecdysis*, or **molting**. Ecdysozoa consists of about eight animal phyla and contains more known species than all other animal, protist, fungus, and plant groups combined. Here we'll focus on the two largest ecdysozoan phyla, the nematodes and arthropods, which are among the most successful and abundant of all animal groups.

Nematodes

Among the most ubiquitous of animals, nematodes (phylum Nematoda), or roundworms, are found in most aquatic habitats, in the soil, in the moist tissues of plants, and in the body fluids and tissues of animals. In contrast to annelids, nematodes do not have segmented bodies. The cylindrical bodies of nematodes range from less than 1 mm to more than 1 m long, often tapering to a fine tip at the posterior end and to a blunter tip at the anterior end **(Figure 33.26)**. A nematode's body is covered by a tough cuticle (a type of exoskeleton); as the worm grows, it periodically sheds its old cuticle and secretes a new, larger one. Nematodes have an alimentary canal, though they lack a circulatory system. Nutrients are transported throughout the body via fluid in the pseudocoelom. The body wall muscles are all longitudinal, and their contraction produces a thrashing motion.

Nematodes usually reproduce sexually, by internal fertilization. In most species, the sexes are separate and females are larger than males. A female may deposit 100,000 or more fertilized eggs (zygotes) per day. The zygotes of most species are resistant cells that can survive harsh conditions.

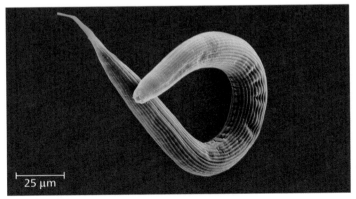

25 μm

▲ **Figure 33.26 A free-living nematode** (colorized SEM).

Multitudes of nematodes live in moist soil and in decomposing organic matter on the bottoms of lakes and oceans. While 25,000 species are known, perhaps 20 times that number actually exist. It has been said that if nothing of Earth or its organisms remained but nematodes, they would still preserve the outline of the planet and many of its features. These free-living worms play an important role in decomposition and nutrient cycling, but little is known about most species. One species of soil nematode, *Caenorhabditis elegans*, however, is very well studied and has become a model research organism in biology (see Chapter 47). Ongoing studies of *C. elegans* are revealing some of the mechanisms involved in aging in humans, among other findings.

Phylum Nematoda includes many species that parasitize plants, and some are major agricultural pests that attack the roots of crops. Other nematodes parasitize animals. Some of these species benefit humans by attacking insects such as cutworms that feed on the roots of crop plants. On the other hand, humans are hosts to at least 50 nematode species, including various pinworms and hookworms. One notorious nematode is *Trichinella spiralis*, the worm that causes trichinosis **(Figure 33.27)**. Humans acquire this nematode by eating raw or undercooked pork or other meat (including wild game such as bear or walrus) that has juvenile worms encysted in the muscle tissue. Within the human intestines, the juveniles develop into sexually mature adults. Females burrow into the intestinal muscles and produce more juveniles, which bore through the body or travel in lymphatic vessels to other organs, including skeletal muscles, where they encyst.

Parasitic nematodes have an extraordinary molecular toolkit that enables them to redirect some of the cellular functions of their hosts and thus evade their immune systems. Some species inject their plant hosts with molecules that induce the development of root cells, which then supply nutrients to the parasites. *Trichinella*, which parasitizes animals, controls the expression of specific muscle cell genes that code for proteins that make the cell elastic enough to house the nematode. Additionally, the infected muscle cell releases signals that promote the growth of new blood vessels, which then supply the nematode with nutrients.

Arthropods

Zoologists estimate that there are about a billion billion (10^{18}) arthropods living on Earth. More than 1 million arthropod species have been described, most of which are insects. In fact, two out of every three known species are arthropods, and members of the phylum Arthropoda can be found in nearly all habitats of the biosphere. By the criteria of species diversity, distribution, and sheer numbers, arthropods must be regarded as the most successful of all animal phyla.

Arthropod Origins

Biologists hypothesize that the diversity and success of **arthropods** are related to their body plan—their segmented body, hard exoskeleton, and jointed appendages (*arthropod* means "jointed feet"). The earliest fossils with this body plan are from the Cambrian explosion (535–525 million years ago), indicating that the arthropods are at least that old.

Along with arthropods, the fossil record of the Cambrian explosion contains many species of *lobopods*, an extinct group from which arthropods may have evolved. Lobopods such as *Hallucigenia* (see Figure 25.4) had segmented bodies, but most of their body segments were identical to one another. Early arthropods, such as the trilobites, also showed little variation from segment to segment **(Figure 33.28)**. As arthropods continued to evolve, the segments tended to fuse and become fewer, and the appendages became specialized for a variety of functions. These evolutionary changes resulted not only in great diversification but also in an efficient body plan that permits the division of labor among different body regions.

Encysted juveniles   Muscle tissue   50 μm

▲ **Figure 33.27 Juveniles of the parasitic nematode *Trichinella spiralis* encysted in human muscle tissue** (LM).

▶ **Figure 33.28 A trilobite fossil.** Trilobites were common denizens of the shallow seas throughout the Paleozoic era but disappeared with the great Permian extinctions about 250 million years ago. Paleontologists have described about 4,000 trilobite species.

UNIVERSITY OF ALBERTA FACULTY BIO

Heather C. Proctor BSc Zoology (University of Alberta) MSc Biological Science (University of Calgary) PhD Zoology (University of Toronto)

Current Position: Professor, Department of Biological Sciences

I've taught a wide range of courses in the Department of Biological Sciences since arriving here in 2002, but my mainstays are Biology 108 (Introduction to Biological Diversity), Biology 321 (Mechanisms of Evolution) and Zoology 351 (Freshwater Invertebrate Diversity). This array of courses reflects my own research orientation. My interests are in the origin and maintenance of organismal diversity, from morphological, behavioural, phylogenetic, and ecological standpoints. Questions I have worked on include: What determines size of pollen packets across different species of orchids? Why is courtship behaviour simple in some species and very complex in others? Why do some animals host very few species of symbiotic arthropods and others a large number? How might climate change affect diversity and body size of soil invertebrates?

One of my most productive areas of research focuses on mites (Arachnida: Acari) associated with birds. I began this line of investigation during my 5 years as a lecturer in Australia, where the avian diversity is astounding. There, with the aid of colleagues from Queensland, Tasmania, Poland and Russia, I was able to study bird families that have been rarely explored for feather mites, including megapodes, parrots, cassowaries, and even penguins. Unsurprisingly, I discovered many new species of mite, and even new genera, that live on these birds. Since returning to Canada, I have continued working with bird mites with my graduate students. Although finding a new species of mite on a Canadian bird species might seem unlikely, my student Wayne Knee discovered and described 6 new species—all found during his 2 year MSc project! There is so much unknown about the biology of mites and other invertebrates that you are almost guaranteed to discover new things, even in your own backyard.

INQUIRY

Did the arthropod body plan result from new Hox genes?

EXPERIMENT How did the highly successful arthropod body plan arise? One hypothesis suggests that it resulted from the origin (by a gene duplication event) of two unusual *Hox* genes found in arthropods: *Ultrabithorax* (*Ubx*) and *abdominal-A* (*abd-A*). To test this hypothesis, Sean Carroll, of the University of Wisconsin, Madison, and colleagues turned to the onychophorans, a group of invertebrates closely related to arthropods. Unlike many living arthropods, onychophorans have a body plan in which most body segments are identical to one another. Thus, Carroll and colleagues reasoned that if the origin of the *Ubx* and *abd-A Hox* genes drove the evolution of body segment diversity in arthropods, these genes probably arose on the arthropod branch of the evolutionary tree:

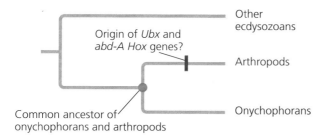

According to this hypothesis, *Ubx* and *abd-A* would not have been present in the common ancestor of arthropods and onychophorans; hence, onychophorans should not have these genes. To find out whether this was the case, Carroll and colleagues examined the *Hox* genes of the onychophoran *Acanthokara kaputensis*.

RESULTS The onychophoran *A. kaputensis* has all arthropod *Hox* genes, including *Ubx* and *abd-A*.

Red indicates the body regions of this onychophoran embryo in which *Ubx* or *abd-A* genes were expressed. (The inset shows this area enlarged.)

Ant = antenna
J = jaws
L1–L15 = body segments

CONCLUSION Since *A. kaputensis*, an onychophoran, has the arthropod *Hox* genes, the evolution of increased body segment diversity in arthropods must not have been related to the origin of new *Hox* genes.

SOURCE J. K. Grenier, S. Carroll, et al., Evolution of the entire arthropod *Hox* gene set predated the origin and radiation of the onychophoran/arthropod clade, *Current Biology* 7:547–553 (1997).

WHAT IF? If Carroll and colleagues had found that *A. kaputensis* did *not* have the *Ubx* and *abd-A Hox* genes, how would their conclusion have been affected? Explain.

What genetic changes led to the increasing complexity of the arthropod body plan? Arthropods today have two unusual *Hox* genes, both of which influence segmentation. To test whether these genes could have driven the evolution of increased body segment diversity in arthropods, researchers studied *Hox* genes in onychophorans (see Figure 33.3), close relatives of arthropods **(Figure 33.29)**. Their results indicate that arthropod body plan diversity did *not* arise from the acquisition of new *Hox* genes. Instead, the evolution of body segment diversity in arthropods may have been driven by changes in the sequence or regulation of existing *Hox* genes. (See Chapter 25 for a discussion of how changes in form can result from changes in the sequence or regulation of developmental genes such as *Hox* genes.)

General Characteristics of Arthropods

Over the course of evolution, the appendages of some arthropods have become modified, specializing in functions such as walking, feeding, sensory reception, reproduction, and defense. Like the appendages from which they were derived, these modified structures are jointed and come in pairs. **Figure 33.30** illustrates the diverse appendages and other arthropod characteristics of a lobster.

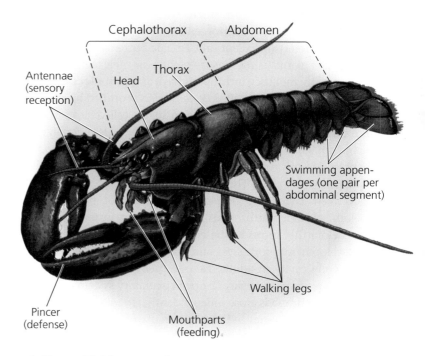

▲ **Figure 33.30 External anatomy of an arthropod.** Many of the distinctive features of arthropods are apparent in this dorsal view of a lobster, along with some uniquely crustacean characteristics. The body is segmented, but this characteristic is obvious only in the abdomen. The appendages (including antennae, pincers, mouthparts, walking legs, and swimming appendages) are jointed. The head bears a pair of compound (multilens) eyes, each situated on a movable stalk. The whole body, including appendages, is covered by an exoskeleton.

The body of an arthropod is completely covered by the cuticle, an exoskeleton constructed from layers of protein and the polysaccharide chitin. The cuticle can be thick and hard over some parts of the body and paper-thin and flexible over others, such as the joints. The rigid exoskeleton protects the animal and provides points of attachment for the muscles that move the appendages. But it also means that an arthropod cannot grow without occasionally shedding its exoskeleton and producing a larger one. This molting process is energetically expensive. A molting or recently molted arthropod is also vulnerable to predation and other dangers until its new, soft exoskeleton hardens.

When the arthropod exoskeleton first evolved in the sea, its main functions were probably protection and anchorage for muscles, but it later enabled certain arthropods to live on land. The exoskeleton's relative impermeability to water helped prevent desiccation, and its strength solved the problem of support when arthropods left the buoyancy of water. Arthropods began to diversify on land following the colonization of land by plants in the early Paleozoic. Evidence includes a 428-million-year-old fossil of a millipede found in 2004 by an amateur fossil hunter in Scotland. Fossilized tracks of other terrestrial arthropods date from about 450 million years ago.

Arthropods have well-developed sensory organs, including eyes, olfactory (smell) receptors, and antennae that function in both touch and smell. Most sensory organs are concentrated at the anterior end of the animal, although there are interesting exceptions. Female butterflies, for example, "taste" plants using sensory organs on their feet.

Like many molluscs, arthropods have an **open circulatory system**, in which fluid called *hemolymph* is propelled by a heart through short arteries and then into spaces called sinuses surrounding the tissues and organs. (The term *blood* is generally reserved for fluid in a closed circulatory system.) Hemolymph reenters the arthropod heart through pores that are usually equipped with valves. The hemolymph-filled body sinuses are collectively called the *hemocoel*, which is not part of the coelom. Although arthropods are coelomates, in most species the coelom that forms in the embryo becomes much reduced as development progresses, and the hemocoel becomes the main body cavity in adults. Despite their similarity, phylogenetic analyses suggest that the open circulatory systems of molluscs and arthropods arose independently.

A variety of specialized gas exchange organs have evolved in arthropods. These organs allow the diffusion of respiratory gases in spite of the exoskeleton. Most aquatic species have gills with thin, feathery extensions that place an extensive surface area in contact with the surrounding water. Terrestrial arthropods generally have internal surfaces specialized for gas exchange. Most insects, for instance, have tracheal systems, branched air ducts leading into the interior from pores in the cuticle.

▲ **Figure 33.31 Horseshoe crabs (*Limulus polyphemus*).** Common on the Atlantic and Gulf coasts of the United States, these "living fossils" have changed little in hundreds of millions of years. They are surviving members of a rich diversity of chelicerates that once filled the seas.

Morphological and molecular evidence suggests that living arthropods consist of four major lineages that diverged early in the evolution of the phylum: **chelicerates** (sea spiders, horseshoe crabs, scorpions, ticks, mites, and spiders); **myriapods** (centipedes and millipedes); **hexapods** (insects and their wingless, six-legged relatives); and **crustaceans** (crabs, lobsters, shrimps, barnacles, and many others).

Chelicerates

Chelicerates (subphylum Chelicerata; from the Greek *cheilos*, lips, and *cheir*, arm) are named for clawlike feeding appendages called **chelicerae**, which serve as pincers or fangs. Chelicerates have an anterior cephalothorax and a posterior abdomen. They lack antennae, and most have simple eyes (eyes with a single lens).

The earliest chelicerates were **eurypterids**, or water scorpions. These marine and freshwater predators grew up to 3 m long; it is thought that some species could have walked on land, much as land crabs do today. Most of the marine chelicerates, including all of the eurypterids, are extinct. Among the marine chelicerates that survive today are the sea spiders (pycnogonids) and horseshoe crabs **(Figure 33.31)**.

The bulk of modern chelicerates are **arachnids**, a group that includes scorpions, spiders, ticks, and mites **(Figure 33.32)**. Ticks and many mites are among a large group of parasitic arthropods. Nearly all ticks are bloodsucking parasites that live on the body surfaces of reptiles or mammals. Parasitic mites live on or in a wide variety of vertebrates, invertebrates, and plants.

Arachnids have a cephalothorax that has six pairs of appendages: the chelicerae; a pair of appendages called *pedipalps* that function in sensing, feeding, or reproduction; and four pairs of walking legs **(Figure 33.33)**. Spiders use their fang-like chelicerae, which are equipped with poison glands, to attack

▲ Scorpions have pedipalps that are pincers specialized for defense and the capture of food. The tip of the tail bears a poisonous stinger.

50 µm

▲ Dust mites are ubiquitous scavengers in human dwellings but are harmless except to those people who are allergic to them (colorized SEM).

◄ Web-building spiders are generally most active during the daytime.

▲ **Figure 33.32 Arachnids.**

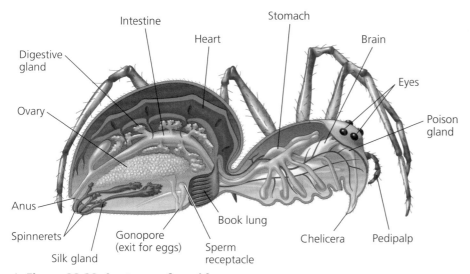

Digestive gland

Intestine

Heart

Stomach

Brain

Eyes

Ovary

Poison gland

Anus

Spinnerets

Book lung

Silk gland

Gonopore (exit for eggs)

Sperm receptacle

Chelicera

Pedipalp

▲ **Figure 33.33 Anatomy of a spider.**

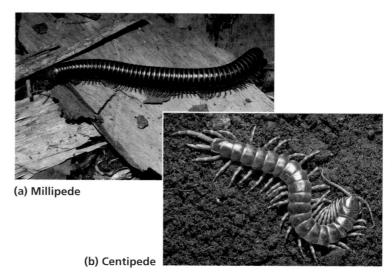

(a) Millipede

(b) Centipede

▲ **Figure 33.34 Myriapods.**

prey. As the chelicerae pierce the prey, the spider secretes digestive juices onto the prey's torn tissues. The food softens, and the spider sucks up the liquid meal.

In most spiders, gas exchange is carried out by **book lungs**, stacked platelike structures contained in an internal chamber (see Figure 33.33). The extensive surface area of these respiratory organs is a structural adaptation that enhances the exchange of O_2 and CO_2 between the hemolymph and air.

A unique adaptation of many spiders is the ability to catch insects by constructing webs of silk, a liquid protein produced by specialized abdominal glands. The silk is spun by organs called spinnerets into fibers that then solidify. Each spider engineers a web characteristic of its species and builds it perfectly on the first try, indicating that this complex behavior is inherited. Various spiders also use silk in other ways: as droplines for rapid escape, as a cover for eggs, and even as "gift wrap" for food that males offer females during courtship. Many small spiders also extrude silk into the air and let themselves be transported by wind, a behavior known as "ballooning."

Myriapods

Millipedes and centipedes belong to the subphylum Myriapoda **(Figure 33.34)**. All living myriapods are terrestrial. The myriapod head has a pair of antennae and three pairs of appendages modified as mouthparts, including the jaw-like **mandibles**.

Millipedes have a large number of legs, though fewer than the thousand their name implies. Each trunk segment is formed from two fused segments and bears two pairs of legs (see Figure 33.34a). Millipedes eat decaying leaves and other plant matter. They may have been among the earliest animals on land, living on mosses and primitive vascular plants.

Unlike millipedes, centipedes are carnivores. Each segment of a centipede's trunk region has one pair of legs (see Figure 33.34b). Centipedes have poison claws on their foremost trunk segment that paralyze prey and aid in defense.

Insects

Insects and their relatives (subphylum Hexapoda) are more species-rich than all other forms of life combined. They live in almost every terrestrial habitat and in fresh water, and flying insects fill the air. Insects are rare, though not absent, in marine habitats, where crustaceans are the dominant arthropods. The internal anatomy of an insect includes several complex organ systems, which are highlighted in **Figure 33.35**.

The oldest insect fossils date from the Devonian period, which began about 416 million years ago. However, when insect flight evolved during the Carboniferous and Permian periods, it spurred an explosion in insect diversity. A fossil record of diverse insect mouthparts indicates that specialized feeding on gymnosperms and other Carboniferous plants also contributed to early adaptive radiations of insects. Later, a major increase in insect diversity appears to have been stimulated by the evolutionary expansion of flowering plants during the mid-Cretaceous period (about 90 million years ago). Although insect and plant diversity decreased during the Cretaceous mass extinction, both groups rebounded over the next 65 million years. Studies indicate that increases in the diversity of particular insect groups often were associated with radiations of the flowering plants on which they fed.

Flight is obviously one key to the great success of insects. An animal that can fly can escape many predators, find food and mates, and disperse to new habitats much faster than an animal that must crawl about on the ground. Many insects have one or two pairs of wings that emerge from the dorsal side of the thorax **(Figure 33.36)**. Because the wings are extensions of the cuticle and not true appendages, insects can fly without sacrificing any walking legs. By contrast, the flying vertebrates—birds and bats—have one of their two pairs of walking legs modified into wings, making some of these species clumsy on the ground.

Insect wings may have first evolved as extensions of the cuticle that helped the insect body absorb heat, only later becoming organs for flight. Other hypotheses suggest that wings allowed terrestrial insects to glide from vegetation to the ground or that they served as gills in aquatic insects. Still another hypothesis is that insect wings functioned for swimming before they functioned for flight.

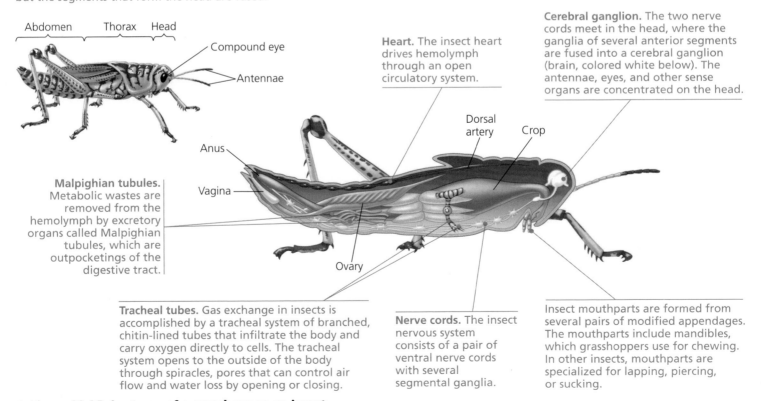

The insect body has three regions: head, thorax, and abdomen. The segmentation of the thorax and abdomen is obvious, but the segments that form the head are fused.

Abdomen   Thorax   Head

Compound eye

Antennae

Heart. The insect heart drives hemolymph through an open circulatory system.

Cerebral ganglion. The two nerve cords meet in the head, where the ganglia of several anterior segments are fused into a cerebral ganglion (brain, colored white below). The antennae, eyes, and other sense organs are concentrated on the head.

Dorsal artery   Crop

Anus

Malpighian tubules. Metabolic wastes are removed from the hemolymph by excretory organs called Malpighian tubules, which are outpocketings of the digestive tract.

Vagina

Ovary

Tracheal tubes. Gas exchange in insects is accomplished by a tracheal system of branched, chitin-lined tubes that infiltrate the body and carry oxygen directly to cells. The tracheal system opens to the outside of the body through spiracles, pores that can control air flow and water loss by opening or closing.

Nerve cords. The insect nervous system consists of a pair of ventral nerve cords with several segmental ganglia.

Insect mouthparts are formed from several pairs of modified appendages. The mouthparts include mandibles, which grasshoppers use for chewing. In other insects, mouthparts are specialized for lapping, piercing, or sucking.

▲ **Figure 33.35 Anatomy of a grasshopper, an insect.**

UNIVERSITY OF ALBERTA FACULTY BIO

 Maya Evenden BSc Biology (University of Victoria); MPM (Master of Pest Management, Simon Fraser University); PhD Biological Sciences (Simon Fraser University)

Current Position: Associate Professor, Department of Biological Sciences

My teaching includes Entomology 220 (Insect Biology), Entomology 207 (Agricultural Entomology), Entomology 401/501 (Current Topics in Arthropod Biology), and Biology 434/534 (Chemical Ecology).

I am broadly interested in the chemical ecology of insects and how message-bearing chemicals (semiochemicals) can be exploited for pest management. I approach this research from behavioural, physiological, ecological and evolutionary perspectives. Although this research is applicable to a wide range of organisms, for my study systems I target moth species (Lepidoptera) considered to be pests in a variety of managed ecosystems.

A recent research focus in my lab has been the study of plasticity in chemical communication in long-lived moths. In collaboration with PhD students Joelle Lemmen and Tyler Wist, we study the effect of physiological state on response to sex pheromone and volatile plant host cues. We have shown that both threshold and breadth of pheromone response are plastic and depend on a moth's physiological state. Pheromone response is regulated in part by juvenile hormone that acts at the level of the peripheral nervous system. This research is the first evidence that antennal response to pheromone can be plastic in Lepidoptera.

► Figure 33.36
**Ladybird beetle
in flight.**

Morphological and molecular data indicate that wings evolved only once in insects. Dragonflies, which have two similar pairs of wings, were among the first insects to fly. Several insect orders that evolved later than dragonflies have modified flight equipment. The wings of bees and wasps, for instance, are hooked together and move as a single pair. Butterfly wings operate in a similar fashion because the anterior pair overlaps the posterior wings. In beetles, the posterior wings function in flight, while the anterior ones are modified as covers that protect the flight wings when the beetle is walking on the ground or burrowing.

Many insects undergo metamorphosis during their development. In the **incomplete metamorphosis** of grasshoppers and some other insect groups, the young (called nymphs) resemble adults but are smaller, have different body proportions, and lack wings. The nymph undergoes a series of molts, each time looking more like an adult. With the final molt, the insect reaches full size, acquires wings, and becomes sexually mature. Insects with **complete metamorphosis** have larval stages specialized for eating and growing that are known by such names as caterpillar, maggot, or grub. The larval stage looks entirely different from the adult stage, which is specialized for dispersal and reproduction. Metamorphosis from the larval stage to the adult occurs during a pupal stage **(Figure 33.37)**.

Reproduction in insects is usually sexual, with separate male and female individuals. Adults come together and recognize each other as members of the same species by advertising with bright colors (as in butterflies), sounds (as in crickets), or odors (as in moths). Fertilization is generally internal. In most species, sperm are deposited directly into the female's vagina at the time of copulation, though in some species the male deposits a sperm packet outside the female, and the female picks it up. An internal structure in the female called the spermatheca stores the sperm, usually enough to fertilize more than one batch of eggs. Many insects mate only once in a lifetime. After mating, a female often lays her eggs on an appropriate food source where the next generation can begin eating as soon as it hatches.

Insects are classified in more than 30 orders, 8 of which are introduced in **Figure 33.38**.

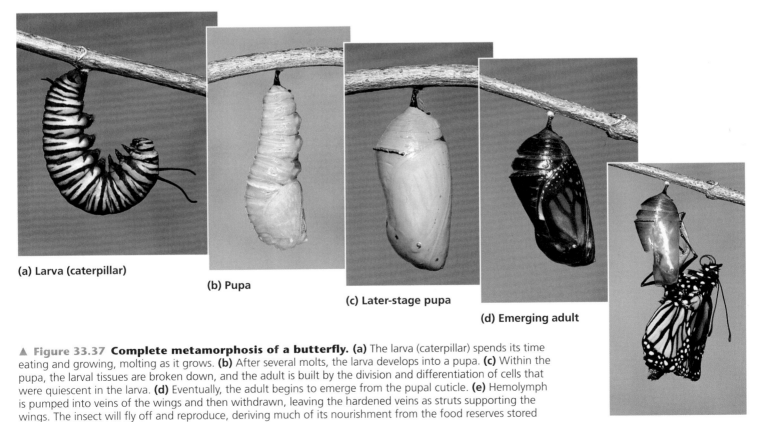

(a) Larva (caterpillar)

(b) Pupa

(c) Later-stage pupa

(d) Emerging adult

(e) Adult

▲ **Figure 33.37 Complete metamorphosis of a butterfly. (a)** The larva (caterpillar) spends its time eating and growing, molting as it grows. **(b)** After several molts, the larva develops into a pupa. **(c)** Within the pupa, the larval tissues are broken down, and the adult is built by the division and differentiation of cells that were quiescent in the larva. **(d)** Eventually, the adult begins to emerge from the pupal cuticle. **(e)** Hemolymph is pumped into veins of the wings and then withdrawn, leaving the hardened veins as struts supporting the wings. The insect will fly off and reproduce, deriving much of its nourishment from the food reserves stored by the feeding larva.

Exploring Insect Diversity

Although there are more than 30 orders of insects, we'll focus on just 8 here. Two early-diverging groups of wingless insects are the bristletails (Archaeognatha) and silverfish (Thysanura). Evolutionary relationships among the other groups discussed here are under debate and so are not depicted on the tree.

Archaeognatha (bristletails; 350 species)

These wingless insects are found under bark and in other moist, dark habitats such as leaf litter, compost piles, and rock crevices. They feed on algae, plant debris, and lichens.

Thysanura (silverfish; 450 species)

These small, wingless insects have a flattened body and reduced eyes. They live in leaf litter or under bark. They can also infest buildings, where they can become pests.

Winged insects (many orders)

Complete metamorphosis

Coleoptera (beetles; 350,000 species)

Beetles, such as this male snout weevil (*Rhiastus lasternus*), constitute the most species-rich order of insects. They have two pairs of wings, one of which is thick and stiff, the other membranous. They have an armored exoskeleton and mouthparts adapted for biting and chewing.

Diptera (151,000 species)

Dipterans have one pair of wings; the second pair has become modified into balancing organs called halteres. Their mouthparts are adapted for sucking, piercing, or lapping. Flies and mosquitoes are among the best-known dipterans, which live as scavengers, predators, and parasites. Like many other insects, flies such as this red tachinid (*Adejeania vexatrix*) have well-developed compound eyes that provide a wide-angle view and excel at detecting fast movements.

Hymenoptera (125,000 species)

Most hymenopterans, which include ants, bees, and wasps, are highly social insects. They have two pairs of membranous wings, a mobile head, and chewing or sucking mouthparts. The females of many species have a posterior stinging organ. Many species, such as this European paper wasp (*Polistes dominulus*), build elaborate nests.

Lepidoptera (120,000 species)

Proboscis

Butterflies and moths have two pairs of wings covered with tiny scales. To feed, they uncoil a long proboscis, visible in this photograph of a hummingbird hawkmoth (*Macroglossum stellatarum*). This moth's name refers to its ability to hover in the air while feeding from a flower. Most lepidopterans feed on nectar, but some species feed on other substances, including animal blood or tears.

Incomplete metamorphosis

Hemiptera (85,000 species)

Hemipterans include so-called "true bugs," such as stink bugs, bed bugs, and assassin bugs. (Insects in other orders are sometimes erroneously called bugs.) Hemipterans have two pairs of wings, one pair partly leathery, the other pair membranous. They have piercing or sucking mouthparts and undergo incomplete metamorphosis, as shown in this image of an adult stink bug guarding its offspring (nymphs).

Orthoptera (13,000 species)

Grasshoppers, crickets, and their relatives are mostly herbivorous. They have large hind legs adapted for jumping, two pairs of wings (one leathery, one membranous), and biting or chewing mouthparts. This aptly named spear-bearer katydid (*Cophiphora* sp.) has a face and legs well adapted to making a threatening display. Male orthopterans commonly make courtship sounds by rubbing together body parts, such as ridges on their hind legs.

Animals as numerous, diverse, and widespread as insects are bound to affect the lives of most other terrestrial organisms, including humans. Insects consume enormous quantities of plant matter; play key roles as predators, parasites, and decomposers; and are an essential source of food for larger animals such as lizards, rodents, and birds. Humans depend on bees, flies, and many other insects to pollinate crops and orchards. In addition, people in many parts of the world eat insects as an important source of protein. On the other hand, insects are carriers for many diseases, including African sleeping sickness (spread by tsetse flies that carry the protist *Trypanosoma*; see Figure 28.6) and malaria (spread by mosquitoes that carry the protist *Plasmodium*; see Figure 28.10).

Insects also compete with humans for food. In parts of Africa, for instance, insects claim about 75% of the crops. In the United States, billions of dollars are spent each year on pesticides, spraying crops with massive doses of some of the deadliest poisons ever invented. Try as they may, not even humans have challenged the preeminence of insects and their arthropod kin. As Cornell University entomologist Thomas Eisner puts it: "Bugs are not going to inherit the Earth. They own it now. So we might as well make peace with the landlord."

Crustaceans

While arachnids and insects thrive on land, crustaceans, for the most part, have remained in marine and freshwater environments. Crustaceans (subphylum Crustacea) typically have highly specialized appendages. Lobsters and crayfishes, for instance, have a toolkit of 19 pairs of appendages (see Figure 33.30). The anterior-most appendages are antennae; crustaceans are the only arthropods with two pairs. Three or more pairs of appendages are modified as mouthparts, including the hard mandibles. Walking legs are present on the thorax, and, unlike insects, crustaceans also have appendages on their abdomen. A lost appendage can be regenerated at the next molt.

Small crustaceans exchange gases across thin areas of the cuticle; larger species have gills. Nitrogenous wastes also diffuse through thin areas of the cuticle, but a pair of glands regulates the salt balance of the hemolymph.

Sexes are separate in most crustaceans. In the case of lobsters and crayfishes, the male uses a specialized pair of abdominal appendages to transfer sperm to the reproductive pore of the female during copulation. Most aquatic crustaceans go through one or more swimming larval stages.

One of the largest groups of crustaceans (numbering over 11,000 species) is the **isopods**, which include terrestrial, freshwater, and marine species. Some isopod species are abundant in habitats at the bottom of the deep ocean. Among the terrestrial isopods are the pill bugs, or wood lice, common on the undersides of moist logs and leaves.

Lobsters, crayfishes, crabs, and shrimps are all relatively large crustaceans called **decapods** (Figure 33.39a). The cuticle of

(a) Ghost crabs live on sandy ocean beaches worldwide. Primarily nocturnal, they take shelter in burrows during the day.

(b) Planktonic crustaceans known as krill are consumed in vast quantities by some whales.

(c) The jointed appendages projecting from the shells of these barnacles capture organisms and organic particles suspended in the water.

▲ **Figure 33.39 Crustaceans.**

decapods is hardened by calcium carbonate; the portion that covers the dorsal side of the cephalothorax forms a shield called the carapace. Most decapod species are marine. Crayfishes, however, live in fresh water, and some tropical crabs live on land.

Many small crustaceans are important members of marine and freshwater plankton communities. Planktonic crustaceans include many species of **copepods**, which are among the most numerous of all animals. Some copepods are grazers that feed upon algae, while others are predators that eat small animals (including smaller copepods!). Copepods are rivaled in abundance by the shrimplike krill, which grow to about 5 cm long (Figure 33.39b). A major food source for baleen whales (including blue whales, humpbacks, and right whales), krill are now being harvested in great numbers by humans for food and agricultural fertilizer. The larvae of many larger-bodied crustaceans are also planktonic.

With the exception of a few parasitic species, barnacles are a group of sessile crustaceans whose cuticle is hardened into a shell containing calcium carbonate (Figure 33.39c). Most barnacles anchor themselves to rocks, boat hulls, pilings, and other submerged surfaces. Their natural adhesive is as strong as synthetic glues. These barnacles feed by extending appendages from their shell to strain food from the water. Barnacles were not recognized as crustaceans until the 1800s, when naturalists discovered that barnacle larvae resemble the larvae of other crustaceans. The remarkable mix of unique traits and crustacean homologies found in barnacles was a major inspiration to Charles Darwin as he developed his theory of evolution.

CONCEPT CHECK 33.4

1. How do nematode and annelid body plans differ?
2. Describe two adaptations that have enabled insects to thrive on land.
3. In contrast to mammalian jaws, which move up and down, the mouthparts of arthropods move side to side. Explain this feature of arthropods in terms of the origin of their mouthparts.
4. **MAKE CONNECTIONS** Traditionally, annelids and arthropods were viewed as closely related because both have body segmentation. Yet DNA sequence data indicate that annelids belong to one clade (Lophotrochozoa) and arthropods to another (Ecdysozoa). Could traditional and molecular hypotheses be tested by studying the expression of *Hox* genes that control body segmentation (see Concept 21.6, pp. 442–447)? Explain.

For suggested answers, see Appendix A.

CONCEPT 33.5

Echinoderms and chordates are deuterostomes

Porifera
Cnidaria
Lophotrochozoa
Ecdysozoa
Deuterostomia

Sea stars, sea urchins, and other echinoderms (phylum Echinodermata) may seem to have little in common with vertebrates (animals that have a backbone) and other members of phylum Chordata. Nevertheless, DNA evidence indicates that echinoderms and chordates are closely related, with both phyla belonging to the Deuterostomia clade of bilaterian animals. Echinoderms and chordates also share features characteristic of a deuterostome mode of development, such as radial cleavage and formation of the anus from the blastopore (see Figure 32.9). As discussed in Chapter 32, however, some animal phyla with members that have deuterostome developmental features, including ectoprocts and brachiopods, are not in the deuterostome clade. Hence, despite its name, the clade Deuterostomia is defined primarily by DNA similarities—not developmental similarities.

Echinoderms

Sea stars (commonly called starfish) and most other **echinoderms** (from the Greek *echin*, spiny, and *derma*, skin) are slow-moving or sessile marine animals. A thin epidermis covers an endoskeleton of hard calcareous plates. Most echinoderms are prickly from skeletal bumps and spines. Unique to echinoderms is the **water vascular system**, a network of hydraulic canals branching into extensions called **tube feet** that function in locomotion and feeding (Figure 33.40). Sexual reproduction of echinoderms usually involves separate male and female individuals that release their gametes into the water.

The internal and external parts of most adult echinoderms radiate from the center, often as five spokes. However, echinoderm larvae have bilateral symmetry. Furthermore, the symmetry of adult echinoderms is not truly radial. For example, the opening (madreporite) of a sea star's water vascular system is not central but shifted to one side.

Living echinoderms are divided into five clades.

Asteroidea: Sea Stars and Sea Daisies

Sea stars have arms radiating from a central disk; the undersurfaces of the arms bear tube feet. By a combination of muscular and chemical actions, the tube feet can attach to or detach from a substrate. The sea star adheres firmly to rocks or creeps along slowly as its tube feet extend, grip, release, extend, and grip again. Although the base of the tube foot has a flattened disk that resembles a suction cup, the gripping action results from adhesive chemicals, not suction (see Figure 33.40).

Sea stars also use their tube feet to grasp prey, such as clams and oysters. The arms of the sea star embrace the closed bivalve, clinging tightly with their tube feet. The sea star then turns part of its stomach inside out, everting it through its mouth and into the narrow opening between the halves of the bivalve's shell. Next, the digestive system of the sea star secretes juices that begin digesting the mollusc within its own shell. The stomach is then brought back inside the seastar's body, where digestion of the mollusc's (now liquefied) body is completed. The ability to begin the digestive process outside of its body allows a sea star to consume bivalves and other prey species that are much larger than its mouth.

Sea stars and some other echinoderms have considerable powers of regeneration. Sea stars can regrow lost arms, and members of one genus can even regrow an entire body from a single arm if part of the central disk remains attached.

The clade Asteroidea, to which sea stars belong, also includes a small group of armless species, the *sea daisies*. Discovered in 1986, only three species of sea daisies are known, all of which live on submerged wood. A sea daisy's body is typically disk-shaped; it has a five-sided organization and measures less than a centimeter in diameter (Figure 33.41). The edge of the body is ringed with small spines. Sea daisies absorb nutrients through a membrane that surrounds their body.

A short digestive tract runs from the mouth on the bottom of the central disk to the anus on top of the disk.

The surface of a sea star is covered by spines that help defend against predators, as well as by small gills that provide gas exchange.

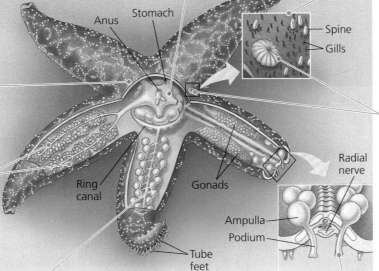

Central disk. The central disk has a nerve ring and nerve cords radiating from the ring into the arms.

Digestive glands secrete digestive juices and aid in the absorption and storage of nutrients.

Anus

Stomach

Spine

Gills

Madreporite. Water can flow in or out of the water vascular system into the surrounding water through the madreporite.

Radial nerve

Gonads

Ring canal

Ampulla

Podium

Tube feet

Radial canal. The water vascular system consists of a ring canal in the central disk and five radial canals, each running in a groove down the entire length of an arm. Branching from each radial canal are hundreds of hollow, muscular tube feet filled with fluid.

Each tube foot consists of a bulb-like ampulla and a podium (foot portion). When the ampulla squeezes, water is forced into the podium, which expands and contacts the substrate. Adhesive chemicals are then secreted from the base of the podium, attaching it to the substrate. To detach the tube foot, de-adhesive chemicals are secreted and muscles in the podium contract, forcing water back into the ampulla and shortening the podium. As it moves, a sea star leaves an observable "footprint" of adhesive material on the substrate.

▲ **Figure 33.40 Anatomy of a sea star, an echinoderm.**

▶ **Figure 33.41 A sea daisy (clade Asteroidea).**

Ophiuroidea: Brittle Stars

Brittle stars have a distinct central disk and long, flexible arms **(Figure 33.42)**. They move primarily by lashing their arms in serpentine movements. The base of a brittle star tube foot lacks the flattened disk found in sea stars but does secrete adhesive

▲ **Figure 33.42 A brittle star (clade Ophiuroidea).**

chemicals. Hence, like sea stars and other echinoderms, brittle stars can use their tube feet to grip substrates. Some species are suspension feeders; others are predators or scavengers.

▲ **Figure 33.43 A sea urchin (clade Echinoidea).**

▲ **Figure 33.45 A sea cucumber (clade Holothuroidea).**

Echinoidea: Sea Urchins and Sand Dollars

Sea urchins and sand dollars have no arms, but they do have five rows of tube feet that function in slow movement. Sea urchins also have muscles that pivot their long spines, which aid in locomotion as well as protection **(Figure 33.43)**. The mouth of a sea urchin is ringed by highly complex, jaw-like structures that are well adapted to eating seaweed. Sea urchins are roughly spherical, whereas sand dollars are flat disks.

Crinoidea: Sea Lilies and Feather Stars

Sea lilies live attached to the substrate by a stalk; feather stars crawl about by using their long, flexible arms. Both use their arms in suspension feeding. The arms encircle the mouth, which is directed upward, away from the substrate **(Figure 33.44)**. Crinoidea is an ancient group whose morphology has changed little over the course of evolution; fossilized sea lilies some 500 million years old are extremely similar to present-day members of the clade.

▲ **Figure 33.44 A feather star (clade Crinoidea).**

Holothuroidea: Sea Cucumbers

On casual inspection, sea cucumbers do not look much like other echinoderms. They lack spines, and their endoskeleton is much reduced. They are also elongated in their oral-aboral axis, giving them the shape for which they are named and further disguising their relationship to sea stars and sea urchins **(Figure 33.45)**. Closer examination, however, reveals that sea cucumbers have five rows of tube feet. Some of the tube feet around the mouth are developed as feeding tentacles.

Chordates

Phylum Chordata consists of two subphyla of invertebrates, as well as the hagfishes and the vertebrates. Chordates are bilaterally symmetrical coelomates with segmented bodies. The close relationship between echinoderms and chordates does not mean that one phylum evolved from the other. In fact, echinoderms and chordates have evolved independently of one another for over 500 million years. We will trace the phylogeny of chordates in Chapter 34, focusing on the history of vertebrates.

CONCEPT CHECK 33.5

1. How do sea star tube feet attach to substrates?
2. **WHAT IF?** The insect *Drosophila melanogaster* and the nematode *Caenorhabditis elegans* are prominent model organisms. Are these species the most appropriate invertebrates for making inferences about humans and other vertebrates? Explain.
3. **MAKE CONNECTIONS** Describe how the features and diversity of echinoderms illustrate the unity of life, the diversity of life, and the match between organisms and their environments (see Concept 22.2, pp. 455–460).

For suggested answers, see Appendix A.

SUMMARY OF KEY CONCEPTS

The table below summarizes the groups of animals surveyed in this chapter.

Selected Animal Phyla

Key Concept					Phylum	Description
Concept 33.1 Sponges are basal animals that lack true tissues (pp. 670–671) **?** *Lacking tissues and organs, how do sponges accomplish tasks such as gas exchange, nutrient transport, and waste removal?*	Metazoa				Porifera (sponges)	Lack true tissues; have choanocytes (collar cells—flagellated cells that ingest bacteria and tiny food particles)
Concept 33.2 Cnidarians are an ancient phylum of eumetazoans (pp. 671–673) **?** *Describe the cnidarian body plan and its two major variations.*		Eumetazoa			Cnidaria (hydras, jellies, sea anemones, corals)	Unique stinging structures (nematocysts) housed in specialized cells (cnidocytes); diploblastic; radially symmetrical; gastrovascular cavity (digestive compartment with a single opening)
Concept 33.3 Lophotrochozoans, a clade identified by molecular data, have the widest range of animal body forms (pp. 674–683) **?** *Is the lophotrochozoan clade united by unique morphological features shared by all of its members? Explain.*			Bilateria	Lophotrochozoa	Platyhelminthes (flatworms)	Dorsoventrally flattened, unsegmented acoelomates; gastrovascular cavity or no digestive tract
					Rotifera (rotifers)	Pseudocoelomates with alimentary canal (digestive tube with mouth and anus); jaws (trophi) in pharynx; head with ciliated crown
					Lophophorates: Ectoprocta, Brachiopoda	Coelomates with lophophores (feeding structures bearing ciliated tentacles)
					Mollusca (clams, snails, squids)	Coelomates with three main body parts (muscular foot, visceral mass, mantle); coelom reduced; most have hard shell made of calcium carbonate
					Annelida (segmented worms)	Coelomates with segmented body wall and internal organs (except digestive tract, which is unsegmented)
Concept 33.4 Ecdysozoans are the most species-rich animal group (pp. 683–692) **?** *Describe ecological roles of nematodes and arthropods.*				Ecdysozoa	Nematoda (roundworms)	Cylindrical, unsegmented pseudocoelomates with tapered ends; no circulatory system; undergo ecdysis
					Arthropoda (crustaceans, insects, spiders)	Coelomates with segmented body, jointed appendages, and exoskeleton made of protein and chitin
Concept 33.5 Echinoderms and chordates are deuterostomes (pp. 692–694) **?** *You've read that echinoderms and chordates are closely related and have evolved independently for over 500 million years. Explain how both of these statements can be correct.*				Deuterostomia	Echinodermata (sea stars, sea urchins)	Coelomates with bilaterally symmetrical larvae and five-part body organization as adults; unique water vascular system; endoskeleton
					Chordata (lancelets, tunicates, vertebrates)	Coelomates with notochord; dorsal, hollow nerve cord; pharyngeal slits; post-anal tail (see Chapter 34)

LEVEL 1: KNOWLEDGE/COMPREHENSION

1. A land snail, a clam, and an octopus all share
   a. a mantle.
   b. a radula.
   c. gills.
   d. embryonic torsion.
   e. distinct cephalization.

2. Which phylum is characterized by animals that have a segmented body?
   a. Cnidaria
   b. Platyhelminthes
   c. Porifera
   d. Arthropoda
   e. Mollusca

3. The water vascular system of echinoderms
   a. functions as a circulatory system that distributes nutrients to body cells.
   b. functions in locomotion and feeding.
   c. is bilateral in organization, even though the adult animal is not bilaterally symmetrical.
   d. moves water through the animal's body during suspension feeding.
   e. is analogous to the gastrovascular cavity of flatworms.

4. Which of the following combinations of phylum and description is *incorrect?*
   a. Echinodermata—bilateral symmetry as a larva, coelom present
   b. Nematoda—roundworms, pseudocoelomate
   c. Cnidaria—radial symmetry, polyp and medusa body forms
   d. Platyhelminthes—flatworms, gastrovascular cavity, acoelomate
   e. Porifera—gastrovascular cavity, coelom present

LEVEL 2: APPLICATION/ANALYSIS

5. In Figure 33.2, which two main clades branch from the most recent common ancestor of the eumetazoans?
   a. Porifera and Cnidaria
   b. Lophotrochozoa and Ecdysozoa
   c. Cnidaria and Bilateria
   d. Rotifera and Deuterostomia
   e. Deuterostomia and Bilateria

6. **MAKE CONNECTIONS** In Figure 33.8, assume that the two medusae shown at step 4 were produced by one polyp colony. Review Concept 12.1 (pp. 229–230) and Concept 13.4 (pp. 257–260), and then use your understanding of mitosis and meiosis to evaluate whether the following sentence is true or false. If false, select the answer that provides the correct reason.

   Although the two medusae are genetically identical, a sperm produced by one will differ genetically from an egg produced by the other.

   a. F (the medusae are genetically identical, but so are the gametes)
   b. F (neither the medusae or the gametes are genetically identical)
   c. F (the medusae are not identical but the gametes are)
   d. T

LEVEL 3: SYNTHESIS/EVALUATION

7. **EVOLUTION CONNECTION**
   DRAW IT Draw a phylogenetic tree of Bilateria that includes the ten phyla of bilaterians discussed in detail in this chapter. Label each branch that leads to a phylum with a C, P, or A, depending on whether members of the phylum are coelomates (C), pseudocoelomates (P), or acoelomates (A). Use your labeled tree to answer the following questions:
   a. For each of the three major clades of bilaterians, what (if anything) can be inferred about whether the common ancestor of the clade had a true coelom?
   b. To what extent has the presence of a true coelom in animals changed over the course of evolution?

8. **SCIENTIFIC INQUIRY**
   Bats emit ultrasonic sounds and then use the returning echoes of those sounds to locate and capture flying insects, such as moths, in the dark. In response to bat attacks, some tiger moths make ultrasonic clicks of their own. Researchers hypothesize that tiger moth clicks likely either (1) jam the bat's sonar or (2) warn the bat about the moth's toxic chemical defenses. The graph below shows two patterns observed in studies of moth capture rates over time.

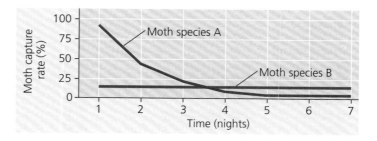

   Bats in these experiments were "naive," meaning that prior to the study the bats had not previously hunted tiger moths. Do the results support hypothesis (1), hypothesis (2), or both? Why did the researchers use naive bats? Explain.

9. **WRITE ABOUT A THEME**
   Structure and Function Write a short essay (100–150 words) that explains how the structure of the digestive tract in different invertebrate groups affects the size of the organisms that they can eat.

For selected answers, see Appendix A.

MasteringBIOLOGY® www.masteringbiology.com

1. MasteringBiology® Assignments
Tutorial Ecdysozoans
Activities Characteristics of Invertebrates • Discovery Channel Video: Invertebrates
Questions Student Misconceptions • Multiple Choice • Reading Quiz • End-of-Chapter

2. eText
Read your book online, search, take notes, highlight text, and more.

3. The Study Area
Practice Tests • Cumulative Test • **BioFlix®** 3-D Animations • MP3 Tutor Sessions • Videos • Activities • Investigations • Lab Media • Audio Glossary • Word Study Tools • Art

34

The Origin and Evolution of Vertebrates

▲ **Figure 34.1 What is the relationship of this ancient organism to humans?**

KEY CONCEPTS

34.1 Chordates have a notochord and a dorsal, hollow nerve cord

34.2 Craniates are chordates that have a head

34.3 Vertebrates are craniates that have a backbone

34.4 Gnathostomes are vertebrates that have jaws

34.5 Tetrapods are gnathostomes that have limbs

34.6 Amniotes are tetrapods that have a terrestrially adapted egg

34.7 Mammals are amniotes that have hair and produce milk

34.8 Humans are mammals that have a large brain and bipedal locomotion

Half a Billion Years of Backbones

Early in the Cambrian period, some 530 million years ago, an immense variety of invertebrate animals inhabited Earth's oceans. Predators used sharp claws and mandibles to skewer their prey. Many animals had protective spikes or armor as well as modified mouthparts that enabled their bearers to filter food from the water. Worms slithered in the bottom muck, feeding on organic matter. Amidst this bustle, it would have been easy to overlook certain slender, 3-cm-long creatures gliding through the water: *Myllokunmingia fengjiaoa* **(Figure 34.1)**. Although lacking armor and appendages, this ancient species was closely related to one of the most successful groups of animals ever to swim, walk, slither, or fly: the **vertebrates**, which derive their name from vertebrae, the series of bones that make up the vertebral column, or backbone.

For more than 150 million years, vertebrates were restricted to the oceans, but about 365 million years ago, the evolution of limbs in one lineage of vertebrates set the stage for these vertebrates to colonize land. There they diversified into amphibians, reptiles (including birds), and mammals.

There are approximately 52,000 species of vertebrates, a relatively small number compared to, say, the 1 million insect species on Earth. But what vertebrates lack in species diversity they make up for in *disparity*, varying enormously in characteristics such as body mass. Vertebrates include the heaviest animals ever to walk on land, plant-eating dinosaurs as massive as 40,000 kg (more than 13 pickup trucks). They also include the biggest animal ever to exist on Earth, the blue whale, which can exceed a mass of 100,000 kg. On the other end of the spectrum, a fish discovered in 2004 is just 8.4 mm long and has a mass roughly 100 billion times smaller than that of a blue whale.

In this chapter, you will learn about current hypotheses regarding the origins of vertebrates from invertebrate ancestors. We will track the evolution of the vertebrate body plan, from a notochord to a head to a mineralized skeleton. We'll also explore the major groups of vertebrates (both living and extinct), as well as the evolutionary history of our own species.

CONCEPT **34.1**

Chordates have a notochord and a dorsal, hollow nerve cord

Vertebrates are members of the phylum Chordata, the chordates. **Chordates** are bilaterian (bilaterally symmetrical) animals, and within Bilateria, they belong to the clade of animals known as Deuterostomia (see Chapter 32). The best-known deuterostomes, aside from vertebrates, are the echinoderms, the group that includes sea stars and sea urchins.

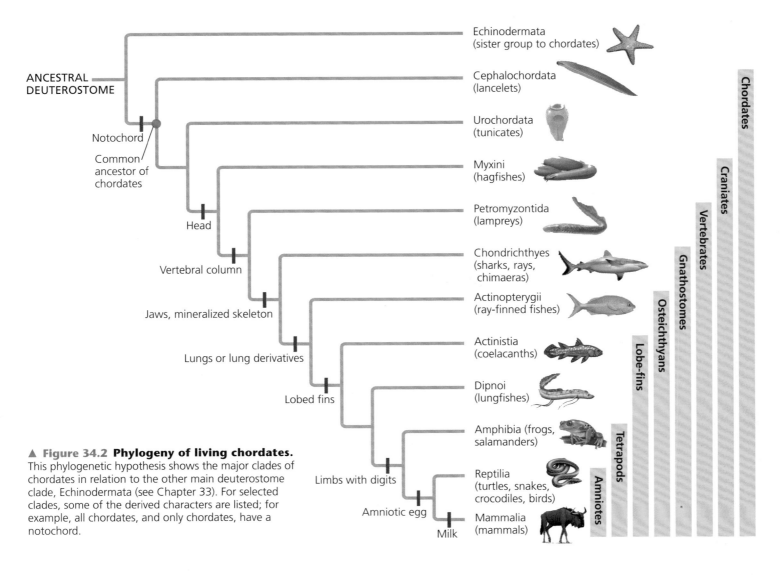

▲ **Figure 34.2 Phylogeny of living chordates.**
This phylogenetic hypothesis shows the major clades of
chordates in relation to the other main deuterostome
clade, Echinodermata (see Chapter 33). For selected
clades, some of the derived characters are listed; for
example, all chordates, and only chordates, have a
notochord.

However, as shown in **Figure 34.2**, the cephalochordates and
the urochordates are two groups of invertebrate deuterostomes that are more closely related to vertebrates than to
other invertebrates. Along with the hagfishes and the vertebrates, they make up the chordates.

Derived Characters of Chordates

All chordates share a set of derived characters, though many
species possess some of these traits only during embryonic
development. **Figure 34.3** illustrates four key characters of
chordates: a notochord; a dorsal, hollow nerve cord; pharyngeal slits or clefts; and a muscular, post-anal tail.

Notochord

Chordates are named for a skeletal structure, the notochord,
present in all chordate embryos as well as in some adult chordates. The **notochord** is a longitudinal, flexible rod located
between the digestive tube and the nerve cord. It is composed
of large, fluid-filled cells encased in fairly stiff, fibrous tissue.
The notochord provides skeletal support throughout most of

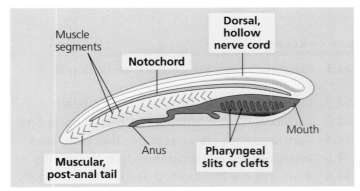

▲ **Figure 34.3 Chordate characteristics.** All chordates possess
the four highlighted structural trademarks at some point during their
development.

the length of a chordate, and in larvae or adults that retain it, it
also provides a firm but flexible structure against which muscles can work during swimming. In most vertebrates, a more
complex, jointed skeleton develops around the ancestral notochord, and the adult retains only remnants of the embryonic

notochord. In humans, the notochord is reduced and forms part of the gelatinous disks sandwiched between the vertebrae.

Dorsal, Hollow Nerve Cord

The nerve cord of a chordate embryo develops from a plate of ectoderm that rolls into a tube located dorsal to the notochord. The resulting dorsal, hollow nerve cord is unique to chordates. Other animal phyla have solid nerve cords, and in most cases they are ventrally located. The nerve cord of a chordate embryo develops into the central nervous system: the brain and spinal cord.

Pharyngeal Slits or Clefts

The digestive tube of chordates extends from the mouth to the anus. The region just posterior to the mouth is the pharynx. In all chordate embryos, a series of pouches separated by grooves forms along the sides of the pharynx. In most chordates, these grooves (known as **pharyngeal clefts**) develop into slits that open to the outside of the body. These **pharyngeal slits** allow water entering the mouth to exit the body without passing through the entire digestive tract. Pharyngeal slits function as suspension-feeding devices in many invertebrate chordates. In vertebrates (with the exception of vertebrates with limbs, the tetrapods), these slits and the structures that support them have been modified for gas exchange and are known as gill slits. In tetrapods, the pharyngeal clefts do not develop into slits. Instead, they play an important role in the development of parts of the ear and other structures in the head and neck.

Muscular, Post-Anal Tail

Chordates have a tail that extends posterior to the anus, although in many species it is greatly reduced during embryonic development. In contrast, most nonchordates have a digestive tract that extends nearly the whole length of the body. The chordate tail contains skeletal elements and muscles, and it helps propel many aquatic species in the water.

Lancelets

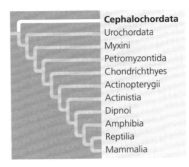

The most basal (earliest-diverging) group of living chordates are animals called **lancelets** (Cephalochordata), which get their name from their bladelike shape **(Figure 34.4)**. As larvae, lancelets develop a notochord, a dorsal, hollow nerve cord, numerous pharyngeal slits, and a post-anal tail. The larvae feed on plankton in the water column, alternating between upward swimming and passive sinking. As the larvae sink, they trap plankton and other suspended particles in their pharynx.

Adult lancelets can reach 6 cm in length. They retain key chordate traits, closely resembling the idealized chordate shown in Figure 34.3. Following metamorphosis, an adult lancelet swims down to the seafloor and wriggles backward into the sand, leaving only its anterior end exposed. Cilia draw seawater into the lancelet's mouth. A net of mucus secreted across the pharyngeal slits removes tiny food particles as the water passes through the slits, and the trapped food enters the intestine. The pharynx and pharyngeal slits play a minor role in gas exchange, which occurs mainly across the external body surface.

A lancelet frequently leaves its burrow to swim to a new location. Though feeble swimmers, these invertebrate chordates display, in a simple form, the swimming mechanism of fishes.

◀ **Figure 34.4 The lancelet _Branchiostoma_, a cephalochordate.** This small invertebrate displays all four main chordate characters. Water enters the mouth and passes through the pharyngeal slits into the atrium, a chamber that vents to the outside via the atriopore; large particles are blocked from entering the mouth by tentacle-like cirri. The serially arranged segmental muscles produce the lancelet's wavelike swimming movements.

Coordinated contraction of muscles arranged like rows of chevrons (<<<<) along the sides of the notochord flexes the notochord, producing side-to-side undulations that thrust the body forward. This serial arrangement of muscles is evidence of the lancelet's segmentation. The muscle segments develop from blocks of mesoderm called *somites*, which are found along each side of the notochord in all chordate embryos.

Globally, lancelets are rare, but in a few regions (including Tampa Bay, along the Florida coast), they occasionally reach densities in excess of 5,000 individuals per square meter.

Tunicates

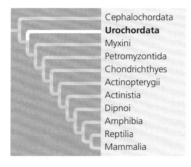

Cephalochordata
Urochordata
Myxini
Petromyzontida
Chondrichthyes
Actinopterygii
Actinistia
Dipnoi
Amphibia
Reptilia
Mammalia

Contrary to what was formerly thought, recent molecular studies suggest that the **tunicates** (Urochordata) are more closely related to other chordates than are lancelets. The chordate characters of tunicates are most apparent during their larval stage, which may be as brief as a few minutes (**Figure 34.5a**). In many species, the larva uses its tail muscles and notochord to swim through water in search of a suitable substrate on which it can settle, guided by cues it receives from light- and gravity-sensitive cells.

Once a tunicate has settled on a substrate, it undergoes a radical metamorphosis in which many of its chordate characters disappear. Its tail and notochord are resorbed; its nervous system degenerates; and its remaining organs rotate 90°. As an adult, a tunicate draws in water through an incurrent siphon;

the water then passes through the pharyngeal slits into a chamber called the atrium and exits through an excurrent siphon (**Figure 34.5b** and **c**). Food particles are filtered from the water by a mucous net and transported by cilia to the esophagus. The anus empties into the excurrent siphon. Some tunicate species shoot a jet of water through their excurrent siphon when attacked, earning them the informal name of "sea squirts."

The loss of chordate characters in the adult stage of tunicates appears to have occurred after the tunicate lineage branched off from other chordates. Even the tunicate larva appears to be highly derived. For example, tunicates have 9 *Hox* genes, whereas all other chordates studied to date—including the early-diverging lancelets—share a set of 13 *Hox* genes. The apparent loss of 4 *Hox* genes indicates that the chordate body plan of a tunicate larva is built using a different set of genetic controls than other chordates.

Early Chordate Evolution

Although lancelets and tunicates are relatively obscure animals, they occupy key positions in the history of life and can provide clues about the evolutionary origin of vertebrates. As you have read, for example, lancelets display key chordate characters as adults, and their lineage branches from the base of the chordate phylogenetic tree. These findings suggest that the ancestral chordate may have looked something like a lancelet—that is, it had an anterior end with a mouth; a notochord; a dorsal, hollow nerved cord; pharyngeal slits; and a post-anal tail.

Research on lancelets has also revealed important clues about the evolution of the chordate brain. Rather than a full-fledged brain, lancelets have only a slightly swollen tip on the anterior end of their dorsal nerve cord. But the same *Hox* genes that organize major regions of the forebrain, midbrain,

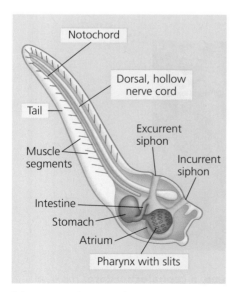

(a) A tunicate larva is a free-swimming but nonfeeding "tadpole" in which all four main characters of chordates are evident.

(b) In the adult, prominent pharyngeal slits function in suspension feeding, but other chordate characters are not obvious.

(c) An adult tunicate, or sea squirt, is a sessile animal (photo is approximately life-sized).

▲ **Figure 34.5 A tunicate, a urochordate.**

▲ **Figure 34.6 Expression of developmental genes in lancelets and vertebrates.** *Hox* genes (including *BF1*, *Otx*, and *Hox3*) control the development of major regions of the vertebrate brain. These genes are expressed in the same anterior-to-posterior order in lancelets and vertebrates. Each colored bar is positioned above the portion of the brain whose development that gene controls.

MAKE CONNECTIONS *What do these results and those in Figure 21.18 indicate about* Hox *genes and their evolution?*

and hindbrain of vertebrates express themselves in a corresponding pattern in this small cluster of cells in the lancelet's nerve cord **(Figure 34.6)**. This suggests that the vertebrate brain is an elaboration of an ancestral structure similar to the lancelet's simple nerve cord tip.

As for tunicates, their genome has been completely sequenced and can be used to identify genes likely to have been present in early chordates. Researchers taking this approach have suggested that ancestral chordates had genes associated with vertebrate organs such as the heart and thyroid gland. These genes are found in tunicates and vertebrates but are absent from nonchordate invertebrates. In contrast, tunicates lack many genes that in vertebrates are associated with the long-range transmission of nerve impulses. This result suggests that such genes arose in an early vertebrate and are unique to the vertebrate evolutionary lineage.

CONCEPT CHECK 34.1

1. Identify four derived characters that all chordates have at some point during their life.
2. You are a chordate, yet you lack most of the main derived characters of chordates. Explain.
3. **WHAT IF?** Suppose lancelets lacked a gene found in tunicates and vertebrates. Would this imply that the chordates' most recent common ancestor also lacked this gene? Explain.

For suggested answers, see Appendix A.

CONCEPT 34.2

Craniates are chordates that have a head

After the evolution of the basic chordate body plan, that seen in lancelets and tunicate larvae, the next major transition in chordate evolution was the appearance of a head. Chordates with a head are known as **craniates** (from the word *cranium*, skull). The origin of a head—consisting of a brain at the anterior end of the dorsal nerve cord, eyes and other sensory organs, and a skull—enabled chordates to coordinate more complex movement and feeding behaviors. (Note that heads evolved independently in other animal lineages as well; see Chapter 33.)

Derived Characters of Craniates

Living craniates share a set of derived characters that distinguish them from other chordates. As a result of gene duplication, craniates possess two or more sets of *Hox* genes (lancelets and tunicates have only one). Other important families of genes that produce signaling molecules and transcription factors are also duplicated in craniates. Divergence of sequences in the duplicate genes led to additional genetic complexity. This may have made it possible for craniates to develop more complex morphologies than those of lancelets and tunicates.

One feature unique to craniates is the **neural crest**, a collection of cells that appears near the dorsal margins of the closing neural tube in an embryo **(Figure 34.7)**. Neural crest cells disperse throughout the body, where they give rise to a variety of structures, including teeth, some of the bones and cartilage of the skull, the inner layer of skin (dermis) of the facial region, several types of neurons, and the sensory capsules in which eyes and other sense organs develop.

In aquatic craniates, the pharyngeal clefts evolved into gill slits. Unlike the pharyngeal slits of lancelets, which are used primarily for suspension feeding, gill slits are associated with muscles and nerves that allow water to be pumped through

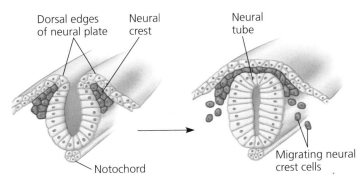

(a) The neural crest consists of bilateral bands of cells near the margins of the embryonic folds that form the neural tube.

(b) Neural crest cells migrate to distant sites in the embryo.

(c) The migrating neural crest cells give rise to some of the anatomical structures unique to vertebrates, including some of the bones and cartilage of the skull. (A fetal human skull is depicted here.)

▲ **Figure 34.7 The neural crest, embryonic source of many unique craniate characters.**

the slits. This pumping can assist in sucking in food, and it facilitates gas exchange. (In terrestrial craniates, the pharyngeal clefts develop into other structures, as we'll explain later.)

Craniates, which are more active than lancelets and tunicates, also have a higher metabolic rate and a much more extensive muscular system. Muscles lining their digestive tract aid digestion by moving food through the tract. Craniates also have a heart with at least two chambers, red blood cells with hemoglobin, and kidneys that remove waste products from the blood.

The Origin of Craniates

In the late 1990s, paleontologists working in China discovered a vast supply of fossils of early chordates that appear to straddle the transition to craniates. The fossils were formed during the Cambrian explosion 530 million years ago, when many groups of animals were diversifying (see Chapter 32).

The most primitive of the fossils are the 3-cm-long *Haikouella* (**Figure 34.8**). In many ways, *Haikouella* resembled a lancelet. Its mouth structure indicates that, like lancelets, it probably was a suspension feeder. However, *Haikouella* also had some of the characters of craniates. For example, it had a well-formed brain, small eyes, and muscle segments along the body, as do the vertebrate fishes. It also had respiratory gills in its pharynx, which all the more basal chordates lack. However, *Haikouella* did not have a skull or ear organs, suggesting that these characters emerged with further innovations to the

chordate nervous system. (The earliest "ears" were organs for maintaining balance, a function still performed by the ears of humans and other living vertebrates.)

In other Cambrian rocks, paleontologists have found fossils of more advanced chordates, such as *Myllokunmingia* (see Figure 34.1). About the same size as *Haikouella*, *Myllokunmingia* had ear capsules and eye capsules, parts of the skull that surround these organs. Based on these and other characters, paleontologists have identified *Myllokunmingia* as a true craniate.

Hagfishes

The most basal group of craniates is Myxini, the hagfishes (**Figure 34.9**). Hagfishes have a skull made of cartilage, but they lack jaws and vertebrae. They swim in a snakelike fashion by using their segmental muscles to exert force against their notochord, which they retain in adulthood as a strong, flexible rod of cartilage. Hagfishes have a small brain, eyes, ears, and a nasal opening that connects with the pharynx. Their mouths contain toothlike formations made of the protein keratin.

All of the 30 living species of hagfishes are marine. Measuring up to 60 cm in length, most are bottom-dwelling scavengers that feed on worms and sick or dead fish. Rows of slime glands on a hagfish's flanks secrete a substance that absorbs water, forming a slime that may repulse other scavengers when a hagfish is feeding (see Figure 34.9). When attacked by a predator, a hagfish can produce several liters of slime in less than a minute. The slime coats the gills of the attacking fish, sending it into retreat or even suffocating it. Several teams of biologists and engineers are investigating the properties of hagfish slime in hopes of producing an artificial slime that could act as a space-filling gel. Such a gel might be used, for instance, to curtail bleeding during surgery.

▲ **Figure 34.8 Fossil of an early chordate.** Discovered in 1999 in southern China, *Haikouella* had eyes and a brain but lacked a skull, a derived trait of craniates. The colors in the illustration are fanciful.

▲ **Figure 34.9 A hagfish.**

CONCEPT **34.3**

Vertebrates are craniates that have a backbone

During the Cambrian period, a lineage of craniates gave rise to vertebrates. With a more complex nervous system and a more elaborate skeleton than those of their ancestors, vertebrates became more efficient at two essential tasks: capturing food and avoiding being eaten.

Derived Characters of Vertebrates

After vertebrates branched off from other craniates, they underwent another gene duplication, this one involving a group of transcription factor genes called the *Dlx* family. The resulting additional genetic complexity may be associated with innovations in the vertebrate nervous system and skeleton, including a more extensive skull and a backbone composed of vertebrae. In some vertebrates, the vertebrae are little more than small prongs of cartilage arrayed dorsally along the notochord. In the majority of vertebrates, however, the vertebrae enclose the spinal cord and have taken over the mechanical roles of the notochord. Aquatic vertebrates also acquired dorsal, ventral, and anal fins stiffened by bony structures called fin rays, which provide thrust and steering control when swimming after prey or away from predators. Faster swimming was supported by other adaptations, including a more efficient gas exchange system in the gills.

Lampreys

Lampreys (Petromyzontida) are the most basal lineage of living vertebrates. Like hagfishes, lampreys may offer clues to early chordate evolution, but they have also acquired unique characters.

There are about 35 species of lampreys inhabiting

▲ **Figure 34.10 A sea lamprey.** Most lampreys use their mouth (inset) and tongue to bore a hole in the side of a fish. The lamprey then ingests the blood and other tissues of its host.

various marine and freshwater environments (**Figure 34.10**). Most are parasites that feed by clamping their round, jawless mouth onto the flank of a live fish. They then use their rasping tongue to penetrate the skin of the fish and ingest the fish's blood.

As larvae, lampreys live in freshwater streams. The larva is a suspension feeder that resembles a lancelet and spends much of its time partially buried in sediment. Some species of lampreys feed only as larvae; following several years in streams, they mature sexually, reproduce, and die within a few days. Most lampreys, however, migrate to the sea or lakes as they mature into adults. Sea lampreys (*Petromyzon marinus*) have invaded the Great Lakes over the past 170 years and have devastated a number of fisheries there.

The skeleton of lampreys is made of cartilage. Unlike the cartilage found in most vertebrates, lamprey cartilage contains no collagen. Instead, it is a stiff matrix of other proteins. The notochord of lampreys persists as the main axial skeleton in the adult, as it does in hagfishes. However, lampreys also have a flexible sheath around their rodlike notochord. Along the length of this sheath, pairs of cartilaginous projections related to vertebrae extend dorsally, partially enclosing the nerve cord.

Fossils of Early Vertebrates

After the ancestors of lampreys branched off from other vertebrates during the Cambrian period, many other lineages of vertebrates emerged. Like lampreys, the early members of these lineages lacked jaws, but the resemblance stopped there.

Conodonts were slender, soft-bodied vertebrates with prominent eyes controlled by numerous muscles. Most conodonts were 3–10 cm in length, although some may have been as long as 30 cm. They probably hunted with the help of their large eyes, impaling prey on a set of barbed hooks at the anterior end of their mouth. These hooks were made of dental tissues that were *mineralized*—composed of minerals such as calcium that provide rigidity (**Figure 34.11**). The food was then passed back to the pharynx, where a different set of dental elements sliced and crushed the food.

▲ **Figure 34.11** **A conodont.** Conodonts were early vertebrates that lived from the late Cambrian until the late Triassic. Unlike lampreys, conodonts had mineralized mouthparts, which they used for either predation or scavenging.

Dental elements (within head)

Conodonts were extremely abundant for over 300 million years. Their fossilized dental elements are so plentiful that they have been used for decades by petroleum geologists as guides to the age of rock layers in which they search for oil. (These elements also gave conodonts their name, which means "cone teeth.")

Vertebrates with additional innovations emerged during the Ordovician, Silurian, and Devonian periods. These vertebrates had paired fins and, as in lampreys, an inner ear with two semi-circular canals that provided a sense of balance. Although they, too, lacked jaws, they had a muscular pharynx, which they may have used to suck in bottom-dwelling organisms or detritus. They were also armored with mineralized bone, which covered varying amounts of their body **(Figure 34.12)**. The armor, which in some species included spines, may have offered protection from predators. There were many species of these

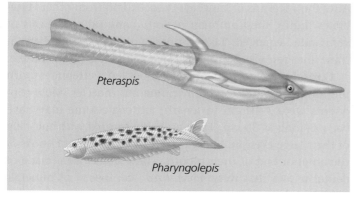

▲ **Figure 34.12** **Jawless armored vertebrates.** *Pteraspis* and *Pharyngolepis* were two of many genera of jawless vertebrates that emerged during the Ordovician, Silurian, and Devonian periods.

Pteraspis

Pharyngolepis

jawless, armored swimming vertebrates, but they all became extinct by the end of the Devonian period.

Origins of Bone and Teeth

The human skeleton is heavily mineralized bone, whereas cartilage plays a fairly minor role. But a bony skeleton was a relatively late development in the history of vertebrates. As we've seen, the vertebrate skeleton evolved initially as a structure made of unmineralized cartilage.

What initiated the process of mineralization in vertebrates? One hypothesis is that mineralization was associated with a transition in feeding mechanisms. Early chordates probably were suspension feeders, like lancelets, but over time they became larger and were able to ingest larger particles, including some small animals. The earliest known mineralized structures in vertebrates—conodont dental elements—were an adaptation that may have allowed these animals to become scavengers and predators. In addition, when the bony armor of later jawless vertebrates was examined under the microscope, scientists found that it was composed of small tooth-like structures. These findings suggest that mineralization of the vertebrate body may have begun in the mouth and later was incorporated into protective armor. Only in more derived vertebrates did the endoskeleton begin to mineralize, starting with the skull. As you'll read in the next section, more recent lineages of vertebrates underwent even further mineralization.

CONCEPT CHECK 34.3

1. How are differences in the anatomy of lampreys and conodonts reflected in each animal's feeding method?
2. **WHAT IF?** Suggest key roles that mineralized bone might have played in early vertebrates.

For suggested answers, see Appendix A.

CONCEPT **34.4**

Gnathostomes are vertebrates that have jaws

Hagfishes and lampreys are survivors from the early Paleozoic era, when jawless craniates were common. Since then, jawless vertebrates have been far outnumbered by jawed vertebrates, known as **gnathostomes**. Living gnathostomes are a diverse group that includes sharks and their relatives, ray-finned fishes, lobe-finned fishes, amphibians, reptiles (including birds), and mammals.

Derived Characters of Gnathostomes

Gnathostomes ("jaw mouth") are named for their jaws, hinged structures that, especially with the help of teeth, enable gnathostomes to grip food items firmly and slice them.

► **Figure 34.13 Hypothesis for the evolution of vertebrate jaws.** The skeleton of the jaws and their supports may have evolved from two pairs of skeletal rods (red and green) located between gill slits near the mouth. According to this hypothesis, pairs of rods anterior to those that formed the jaws were either lost or incorporated into the cranium or jaws.

0.5 m

▲ **Figure 34.14 Fossil of an early gnathostome.** The placoderm *Dunkleosteus* grew up to 10 m in length. A 2006 analysis of its jaw structure concluded that *Dunkleosteus* could exert a force of 560 kg/cm² (8,000 pounds per square inch) at the tip of its jaws.

According to one hypothesis, gnathostome jaws evolved by modification of the skeletal rods that had previously supported the anterior pharyngeal (gill) slits **(Figure 34.13)**. The remaining gill slits, no longer required for suspension feeding, remained as the major sites of respiratory gas exchange with the external environment.

Gnathostomes share other derived characters besides jaws. The common ancestors of all gnathostomes underwent an additional duplication of *Hox* genes, such that the single set present in early chordates became four. In fact, the entire genome appears to have duplicated, and together these genetic changes likely enabled the origin of jaws and other novel features in gnathostomes. The gnathostome forebrain is enlarged compared to that of other craniates, mainly in association with enhanced senses of smell and vision. Another characteristic of aquatic gnathostomes is the **lateral line system**, organs that form a row along each side of the body and are sensitive to vibrations in the surrounding water. Precursors of these organs were present in the head shields of some jawless vertebrates.

Fossil Gnathostomes

Gnathostomes appeared in the fossil record in the late Ordovician period, about 450 million years ago, and steadily became more diverse. Their success probably resulted from a combination of anatomical features: Their paired fins and tail (which were also found in jawless vertebrates) allowed them to swim efficiently after prey, and their jaws enabled them to grab prey or simply bite off chunks of flesh.

The earliest gnathostomes in the fossil record include extinct lineages of armored vertebrates known as **placoderms**,

which means "plate-skinned." Most placoderms were less than a meter long, though some giants measured more than 10 m **(Figure 34.14)**. Other groups of jawed vertebrates, collectively called **acanthodians**, emerged at roughly the same time and radiated during the Silurian and Devonian periods (444–359 million years ago). Placoderms had disappeared by 359 million years ago, and acanthodians became extinct about 70 million years later.

In the past several years, new fossil discoveries have revealed that 450–420 million years ago was a period of tumultuous evolutionary change. Gnathostomes that lived during this period had highly variable forms, and by 420 million years ago, they had diverged into the three lineages of jawed vertebrates that survive today: chondrichthyans, ray-finned fishes, and lobe-fins.

Chondrichthyans (Sharks, Rays, and Their Relatives)

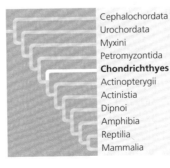

Cephalochordata
Urochordata
Myxini
Petromyzontida
Chondrichthyes
Actinopterygii
Actinistia
Dipnoi
Amphibia
Reptilia
Mammalia

Sharks, rays, and their relatives include some of the biggest and most successful vertebrate predators in the oceans. They belong to the clade Chondrichthyes, which means "cartilage fish." As their name indicates, the **chondrichthyans** have a skeleton composed predominantly of cartilage, though often impregnated with calcium.

When the name Chondrichthyes was first coined in the 1800s, scientists thought that chondrichthyans represented an early stage in the evolution of the vertebrate skeleton and that mineralization had evolved only in more derived lineages (such as "bony fishes"). However, as conodonts and armored jawless vertebrates demonstrate, the mineralization of the vertebrate skeleton had already begun before the chondrichthyan lineage branched off from other vertebrates. Moreover, bone-like tissues have been found in early chondrichthyans, such as the fin skeleton of a shark that lived in the Carboniferous period. Traces of bone can also be found in living chondrichthyans—in their scales, at the base of their teeth, and, in some sharks, in a thin layer on the surface of their vertebrae. Such findings strongly suggest that the restricted distribution of bone in the chondrichthyan body is a derived condition, emerging after chondrichthyans diverged from other gnathostomes.

There are about 1,000 species of living chondrichthyans. The largest and most diverse group consists of the sharks, rays, and skates (**Figure 34.15a** and **b**). A second group is composed of a few dozen species of ratfishes, or chimaeras (**Figure 34.15c**).

Most sharks have a streamlined body and are swift swimmers, but they do not maneuver very well. Powerful movements of the trunk and the tail fin propel them forward. The dorsal fins function mainly as stabilizers, and the paired pectoral (fore) and pelvic (hind) fins are important for maneuvering. Although a shark gains buoyancy by storing a large amount of oil in its huge liver, the animal is still more dense than water, and if it stops swimming it sinks. Continual swimming also ensures that water flows into the shark's mouth and out through the gills, where gas exchange occurs. However, some sharks and many skates and rays spend a good deal of time resting on the seafloor. When resting, they use muscles of their jaws and pharynx to pump water over the gills.

The largest sharks and rays are suspension feeders that consume plankton. Most sharks, however, are carnivores that swallow their prey whole or use their powerful jaws and sharp teeth to tear flesh from animals too large to swallow in one piece. Sharks have several rows of teeth that gradually move to the front of the mouth as old teeth are lost. The digestive tract of many sharks is proportionately shorter than that of many other vertebrates. Within the shark intestine is a *spiral valve*, a corkscrew-shaped ridge that increases surface area and prolongs the passage of food through the digestive tract.

Acute senses are adaptations that go along with the active, carnivorous lifestyle of sharks. Sharks have sharp vision but cannot distinguish colors. The nostrils of sharks, like those of most aquatic vertebrates, open into dead-end cups. They function only for olfaction (smelling), not for breathing. Like some other vertebrates, sharks have a pair of regions in the skin of their head that can detect electric fields generated by the muscle contractions of nearby animals. Like all (non-mammalian) aquatic vertebrates, sharks have no eardrums, structures that terrestrial vertebrates use to transmit sound waves in air to the auditory organs. Sound reaches a shark through water, and the animal's entire body transmits the sound to the hearing organs of the inner ear.

(a) Blacktip reef shark (*Carcharhinus melanopterus*). Sharks are fast swimmers with acute senses. Like all gnathosomes, they have paired pectoral and pelvic fins.

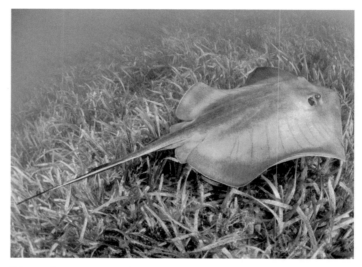

(b) Southern stingray (*Dasyatis americana*). Most rays are bottom-dwellers that feed on molluscs and crustaceans. Some rays cruise in open water and scoop food into their gaping mouth.

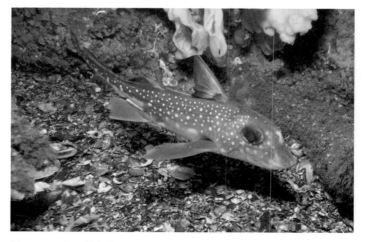

(c) Spotted ratfish (*Hydrolagus colliei*). Ratfishes, or chimaeras, typically live at depths greater than 80 m and feed on shrimp, molluscs, and sea urchins. Some species have a venomous spine at the front of their first dorsal fin.

▲ **Figure 34.15 Chondrichthyans.**

Shark eggs are fertilized internally. The male has a pair of claspers on its pelvic fins that transfer sperm into the reproductive tract of the female. Some species of sharks are **oviparous**; they lay eggs that hatch outside the mother's body. These sharks release their eggs after encasing them in protective coats. Other species are **ovoviviparous**; they retain the fertilized eggs in the oviduct. Nourished by the egg yolk, the embryos develop into young that are born after hatching within the uterus. A few species are **viviparous**; the young develop within the uterus and obtain nourishment prior to birth by receiving nutrients from the mother's blood through a yolk sac placenta, by absorbing a nutritious fluid produced by the uterus, or by eating other eggs. The reproductive tract of the shark empties along with the excretory system and digestive tract into the **cloaca**, a common chamber that has a single opening to the outside.

Although rays are closely related to sharks, they have adopted a very different lifestyle. Most rays are bottom-dwellers that feed by using their jaws to crush molluscs and crustaceans. They have a flattened shape and use their greatly enlarged pectoral fins like water wings to propel themselves through the water. The tail of many rays is whiplike and, in some species, bears venomous barbs that function in defense.

Chondrichthyans have thrived for over 400 million years. Today, however, they are severely threatened with overfishing. A recent report indicated that shark stocks in the northwest Atlantic had declined 75% over a 15-year period.

Ray-Finned Fishes and Lobe-Fins

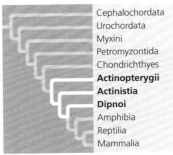

Cephalochordata
Urochordata
Myxini
Petromyzontida
Chondrichthyes
Actinopterygii
Actinistia
Dipnoi
Amphibia
Reptilia
Mammalia

The vast majority of vertebrates belong to the clade of gnathostomes called Osteichthyes. Unlike chondrichthyans, nearly all living **osteichthyans** have an ossified (bony) endoskeleton with a hard matrix of calcium phosphate. Like many other taxonomic names, the name Osteichthyes ("bony fish") was coined long before the advent of phylogenetic systematics. When it was originally defined, the group excluded tetrapods, but we now know that such a taxon would be paraphyletic (see Figure 34.2). Therefore, systematists today include tetrapods along with bony fishes in the clade Osteichthyes. Clearly, the name of the group does not accurately describe all of its members.

In this section, we'll discuss the aquatic osteichthyans known informally as fishes. Most fishes breathe by drawing water over four or five pairs of gills located in chambers covered by a protective bony flap called the **operculum** (Figure 34.16). Water is drawn into the mouth, through the pharynx, and out between the gills by movement of the operculum and contraction of muscles surrounding the gill chambers.

Most fishes can control their buoyancy with an air sac known as a **swim bladder**. Movement of gases from the blood to the swim bladder increases buoyancy, making the animal rise; transfer of gas back to the blood causes the animal to sink. Charles Darwin proposed that the lungs of tetrapods evolved from swim bladders, but strange as it may sound, the opposite seems to be true. Osteichthyans in many early-branching lineages have lungs, which they use to breathe air as a supplement to gas exchange in their gills. The weight of evidence indicates that lungs arose in early osteichthyans; later, swim bladders evolved from lungs in some lineages.

In nearly all fishes, the skin is covered by flattened, bony scales that differ in structure from the tooth-like scales of sharks. Glands in the skin secrete a slimy mucus over the skin, an adaptation that reduces drag during swimming. Like the ancient aquatic gnathostomes mentioned earlier, fishes have a lateral line system, which is evident as a row of tiny pits in the skin on either side of the body.

The details of fish reproduction vary extensively. Most species are oviparous, reproducing by external fertilization after the female sheds large numbers of small eggs. However, internal fertilization and birthing characterize other species.

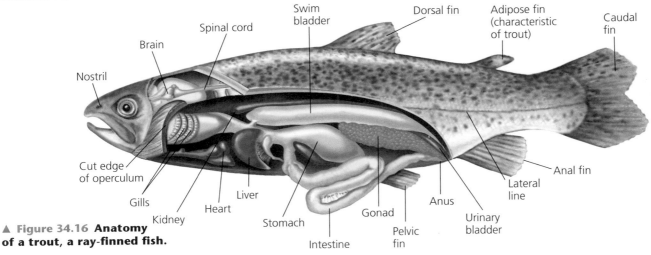

▲ **Figure 34.16 Anatomy of a trout, a ray-finned fish.**

Brain · Spinal cord · Swim bladder · Dorsal fin · Adipose fin (characteristic of trout) · Caudal fin · Nostril · Cut edge of operculum · Gills · Kidney · Heart · Liver · Stomach · Intestine · Gonad · Pelvic fin · Anus · Urinary bladder · Lateral line · Anal fin

Ray-Finned Fishes

Nearly all the aquatic osteichthyans familiar to us are among the over 27,000 species of **ray-finned fishes** (Actinopterygii) **(Figure 34.17)**. Named for the bony rays that support their fins, the ray-finned fishes originated during the Silurian period (444–416 million years ago). The group has diversified greatly since that time, as suggested by modifications in body form and fin structure that affect maneuvering, defense, and other functions (see Figure 34.17).

▲ Yellowfin tuna (*Thunnus albacares*) is a fast-swimming, schooling fish that is commercially important worldwide.

▶ Native to coral reefs of the Pacific Ocean, the brightly colored red lionfish (*Pterois volitans*) can inject venom through its spines, causing a severe and painful reaction in humans.

▲ The sea horse has a highly modified body form, as exemplified by *Hippocampus ramulosus,* shown above. Sea horses are unusual among animals in that the male carries the young during their embryonic development.

▲ The fine-spotted moray eel (*Gymnothorax dovii*) is a predator that ambushes prey from crevices in its coral reef habitat.

▲ **Figure 34.17 Ray-finned fishes (Actinopterygii).**

Ray-finned fishes serve as a major source of protein for humans, who have harvested them for thousands of years. However, industrial-scale fishing operations appear to have driven some of the world's biggest fisheries to collapse. For example, after decades of abundant harvests, in the 1990s the catch of cod (*Gadus morhua*) in the northwest Atlantic plummeted to just 5% of its historic maximum, bringing codfishing there to a near halt. Despite ongoing restrictions on the fishery, cod populations have yet to recover to sustainable levels. Ray-finned fishes also face other pressures from humans, such as the diversion of rivers by dams. Changing water flow patterns can hamper the fishes' ability to obtain food and interferes with migratory pathways and spawning grounds.

Lobe-Fins

Like the ray-finned fishes, the other major lineage of osteichthyans, the **lobe-fins** (Sarcopterygii), also originated during the Silurian period **(Figure 34.18)**. The key derived character of lobe-fins is the presence of rod-shaped bones surrounded by a thick layer of muscle in their pectoral and pelvic fins. During the Devonian (416–359 million years ago), many lobe-fins lived in brackish waters, such as in coastal wetlands. There they may have used their lobed fins to swim and "walk" underwater across the substrate (as do some living lobe-fins). Some Devonian lobe-fins were gigantic predators. It is not uncommon to find spike-shaped fossils of Devonian lobe-fin teeth as big as your thumb.

By the end of the Devonian period, lobe-fin diversity was dwindling, and today only three lineages survive. One lineage,

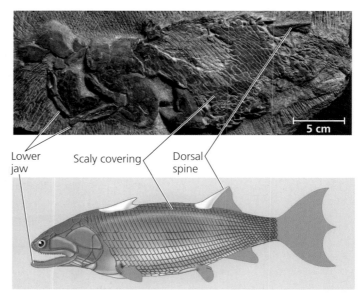

▲ **Figure 34.18 A reconstruction of an ancient lobe-fin.** Discovered in 2009, *Guiyu oneiros* is the earliest known lobe-fin, dating to 420 million years ago. The fossil of this species was nearly complete, allowing for an accurate reconstruction.

▲ **Figure 34.19 A coelacanth (*Latimeria*).** These lobe-fins were found living off the coasts of southern Africa and Indonesia.

the coelacanths (Actinistia), was thought to have become extinct 75 million years ago. However, in 1938, fishermen caught a living coelacanth off the east coast of South Africa (Figure 34.19). Until the 1990s, all subsequent discoveries were near the Comoros Islands in the western Indian Ocean. Since 1999, coelacanths have also been found at various places along the eastern coast of Africa and in the eastern Indian Ocean, near Indonesia. The Indonesian population may represent a second species.

The second lineage of living lobe-fins, the lungfishes (Dipnoi), is represented today by six species in three genera, all of which are found in the Southern Hemisphere. Lungfishes arose in the ocean but today are found only in fresh water, generally in stagnant ponds and swamps. They surface to gulp air into lungs connected to their pharynx. Lungfishes also have gills, which are the main organs for gas exchange in Australian lungfishes. When ponds shrink during the dry season, some lungfishes can burrow into the mud and estivate (wait in a state of torpor; see Chapter 40).

The third lineage of lobe-fins that survives today is far more diverse than the coelacanths or the lungfishes. During the mid-Devonian, these organisms adapted to life on land and gave rise to vertebrates with limbs and feet, called tetrapods—a lineage that includes humans. The tetrapod clade is the topic of the next section.

CONCEPT CHECK 34.4

1. What derived characters do sharks and tuna share? What are some characteristics that distinguish tuna from sharks?
2. Describe key adaptations of aquatic gnathostomes.
3. **WHAT IF?** Imagine that we could replay the history of life. Is it possible that a group of vertebrates that colonized land could have arisen from aquatic gnathostomes other than the lobe-fins? Explain.

For suggested answers, see Appendix A.

Tetrapods are gnathostomes that have limbs

One of the most significant events in vertebrate history took place about 365 million years ago, when the fins of some lobe-fins evolved into the limbs and feet of tetrapods. Until then, all vertebrates had shared the same basic fishlike anatomy. After tetrapods moved onto land, they took on many new forms, from leaping frogs to flying eagles to bipedal humans.

Derived Characters of Tetrapods

The most significant character of **tetrapods** gives the group its name, which means "four feet" in Greek. In place of pectoral and pelvic fins, tetrapods have limbs with digits. Limbs support a tetrapod's weight on land, while feet with digits efficiently transmit muscle-generated forces to the ground when it walks.

Life on land brought numerous other changes to the tetrapod body plan. In tetrapods, the head is separated from the body by a neck that originally had one vertebra on which the skull could move up and down. Later, with the origin of a second vertebra in the neck, the head could also swing from side to side. The bones of the pelvic girdle, to which the hind legs are attached, are fused to the backbone, permitting forces generated by the hind legs against the ground to be transferred to the rest of the body. Except for some fully aquatic species (such as the axolotl discussed below), the adults of living tetrapods do not have gills; during embryonic development, the pharyngeal clefts instead give rise to parts of the ears, certain glands, and other structures.

As you will see, some of these characters were dramatically altered or lost in various lineages of tetrapods. In birds, for example, the pectoral limbs became wings, and in whales, the entire body converged toward a fishlike shape.

The Origin of Tetrapods

As you have read, the Devonian coastal wetlands were home to a wide range of lobe-fins. Those that entered particularly shallow, oxygen-poor water could use their lungs to breathe air. Some species probably used their stout fins to help them move across logs or the muddy bottom. Thus, the tetrapod body plan did not evolve "out of nowhere" but was simply a modification of a preexisting body plan.

The recent discovery of a fossil called *Tiktaalik* has provided new details on how this process occurred. Like a fish, this species had fins, gills, and lungs, and its body was covered in scales. But unlike a fish, *Tiktaalik* had a full set of ribs

IMPACT

Discovery of a "Fishapod": *Tiktaalik*

Paleontologists were on the hunt for fossils that could shed light on the evolutionary origin of tetrapods. Based on the ages of previously discovered fossils, researchers were looking for a dig site with rocks about 365–385 million years old. Ellesmere Island, in the Canadian Arctic, was one of the few such sites likely to contain fossils, because it was once a river. The search at this site was rewarded by the discovery of fossils of a 375-million-year-old lobe-fin, named *Tiktaalik*. As shown in the chart and photographs below, *Tiktaalik* exhibits both fish and tetrapod characters. (Figure 34.21, on the facing page, includes an artist's conception of what *Tiktaalik* might have looked like.)

WHY IT MATTERS As the most tetrapod-like fish known, *Tiktaalik* documents key steps in the vertebrate transition from water to land. Since *Tiktaalik* predates the oldest known tetrapod by 10 million years, its features suggest that key "tetrapod" traits, such as a wrist, ribs, and a neck, were in fact ancestral to the tetrapod lineage. The discovery also shows the predictive capacity of paleontology in identifying likely locations of fossils of interest.

FURTHER READING E. B. Daeschler, N. H. Shubin, and F. A. Jenkins, A Devonian tetrapod-like fish and the evolution of the tetrapod body plan, *Nature* 440:757–763 (2006).

MAKE CONNECTIONS Describe how *Tiktaalik*'s features illustrate Darwin's concept of descent with modification (see Concept 22.2, pp. 457–460).

Fish Characters	Tetrapod Characters
Scales	Neck
Fins	Ribs
Gills and lungs	Fin skeleton
	Flat skull
	Eyes on top of skull

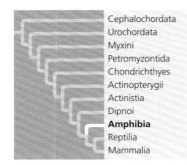

Shoulder bones

Neck

Head

Eyes on top of skull

Flat skull

Ribs

Scales

Humerus

Ulna

"Wrist"

Elbow

Radius

Fin

Fin skeleton

that would have helped it breathe air and support its body (**Figure 34.20**). Also unlike a fish, *Tiktaalik* had a neck and shoulders, allowing it to move its head about. Finally, the bones of *Tiktaalik*'s front fin have the same basic pattern found in all limbed animals: one bone (the humerus), followed by two bones (the radius and ulna), followed by a group of small bones that comprise the wrist. Although it is unlikely that *Tiktaalik* could walk on land, its front fin skeleton suggests that it could prop itself up in water on its fins.

Tiktaalik and other extraordinary fossil discoveries have allowed paleontologists to reconstruct how fins became progressively more limb-like over time, culminating in the appearance of the first tetrapods 365 million years ago (**Figure 34.21**). Over the next 60 million years, a great diversity of tetrapods arose. Judging from the morphology and locations of their fossils, most of these early tetrapods probably remained tied to water, a characteristic they share with some members of a group of living tetrapods called amphibians.

Amphibians

Cephalochordata
Urochordata
Myxini
Petromyzontida
Chondrichthyes
Actinopterygii
Actinistia
Dipnoi
Amphibia
Reptilia
Mammalia

The **amphibians** (class Amphibia) are represented today by about 6,150 species of salamanders (order Urodela, "tailed ones"), frogs (order Anura, "tail-less ones"), and caecilians (order Apoda, "legless ones").

About 550 species of urodeles are known. Some are entirely aquatic, but others live on land as adults or

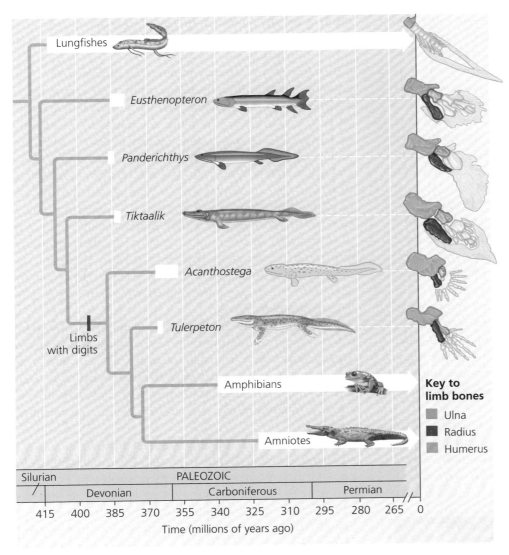

Lungfishes

Eusthenopteron

Panderichthys

Tiktaalik

Acanthostega

Tulerpeton

Limbs
with digits

Amphibians

Amniotes

Key to
limb bones
■ Ulna
■ Radius
■ Humerus

Silurian	PALEOZOIC		
	Devonian	Carboniferous	Permian

415 400 385 370 355 340 325 310 295 280 265 0

Time (millions of years ago)

◀ **Figure 34.21 Steps in the origin of limbs with digits.** The white bars on the branches of this diagram place known fossils in time; arrowheads indicate lineages that extend to today. The drawings of extinct organisms are based on fossilized skeletons, but the colors are fanciful.

WHAT IF? *If the most recent common ancestor of* Tulerpeton *and living tetrapods originated 380 million years ago, what range of dates would include the origin of amphibians?*

throughout life. Most salamanders that live on land walk with a side-to-side bending of the body, a trait also found in early terrestrial tetrapods **(Figure 34.22a)**. Paedomorphosis is common among aquatic salamanders; the axolotl, for instance, retains larval features even when it is sexually mature (see Figure 25.22).

Anurans, numbering about 5,420 species, are more specialized than urodeles for moving on land **(Figure 34.22b)**. Adult frogs use their powerful hind legs to hop along the terrain. Although often distinctive in appearance, the animals known as "toads" are simply frogs that have leathery skin or other adaptations for life on land. A frog nabs insects and other prey by flicking out its long, sticky tongue, which is attached to the front of the mouth. Frogs display a great variety of adaptations that help them avoid being eaten by larger predators. Their skin glands secrete distasteful or even poisonous mucus. Many poisonous species have bright coloration, which predators apparently associate with danger. Other frogs have color patterns that camouflage them.

(a) Order Urodela. Urodeles (salamanders) retain their tail as adults.

(b) Order Anura. Anurans, such as this poison dart frog, lack a tail as adults.

▶ **Figure 34.22 Amphibians.**

(c) Order Apoda. Apodans, or caecilians, are legless, mainly burrowing amphibians.

Apodans, the caecilians (about 170 species), are legless and nearly blind, and superficially they resemble earthworms **(Figure 34.22c)**. Their absence of legs is a secondary adaptation, as they evolved from a legged ancestor. Caecilians inhabit tropical areas, where most species burrow in moist forest soil. A few South American species live in freshwater ponds and streams.

Amphibian (derived from *amphibious*, meaning "both ways of life") refers to the life stages of many frog species that live first in water and then on land **(Figure 34.23)**. The larval stage of a frog, called a tadpole, is usually an aquatic herbivore with gills, a lateral line system resembling that of aquatic vertebrates, and a long, finned tail. The tadpole initially lacks legs; it swims by undulating its tail. During the metamorphosis that leads to the "second life," the tadpole develops legs, lungs, a pair of external eardrums, and a digestive system adapted to a carnivorous diet. At the same time, the gills disappear; the lateral line system also disappears in most species. The young frog crawls onto shore and becomes a terrestrial hunter. In spite of their name, however, many amphibians do not live a dual—aquatic and terrestrial—life. There are some strictly aquatic or strictly terrestrial frogs, salamanders, and caecilians. Moreover, salamander and caecilian larvae look much like the adults, and typically both the larvae and the adults are carnivorous.

Most amphibians are found in damp habitats such as swamps and rain forests. Even those adapted to drier habitats spend much of their time in burrows or under moist leaves, where humidity is high. Amphibians generally rely heavily on their moist skin for gas exchange with the environment. Some terrestrial species lack lungs and breathe exclusively through their skin and oral cavity.

Fertilization is external in most amphibians; the male grasps the female and spills his sperm over the eggs as the female sheds them (see Figure 34.23c). Amphibians typically lay their eggs in water or in moist environments on land; the eggs lack a shell and dehydrate quickly in dry air. Some amphibian species lay vast numbers of eggs in temporary pools, and egg mortality is high. In contrast, other species lay relatively few eggs and display various types of parental care. Depending on the species, either males or females may house eggs on their back **(Figure 34.24)**, in their mouth, or even in their stomach. Certain tropical tree frogs stir their egg masses into moist, foamy nests that resist drying. There are also some ovoviviparous and viviparous species that retain the eggs in the female reproductive tract, where embryos can develop without drying out.

Many amphibians exhibit complex and diverse social behaviors, especially during their breeding seasons. Frogs are usually quiet, but the males of many species vocalize to defend their breeding territory or to attract females. In some species, migrations to specific breeding sites may involve vocal communication, celestial navigation, or chemical signaling.

Over the past 30 years, zoologists have documented a rapid and alarming decline in amphibian populations in locations throughout the world. There appear to be several causes, including the spread of a disease-causing chytrid fungus (see Figure 31.26), habitat loss, climate change, and pollution. These and other factors have not only reduced populations, but led to extinctions. A recent study indicates that at least 9 amphibian species have become extinct since 1980; more than 100 other species have not been seen since that time and are considered possibly extinct.

(a) The tadpole is an aquatic herbivore with a fishlike tail and internal gills.

(b) During metamorphosis, the gills and tail are resorbed, and walking legs develop. The adult frog will live on land.

(c) The adults return to water to mate. The male grasps the female, stimulating her to release eggs. The eggs are laid and fertilized in water. They have a jelly coat but lack a shell and would desiccate in air.

▲ **Figure 34.23 The "dual life" of a frog (*Rana temporaria*).**

▲ **Figure 34.24 A mobile nursery.** A female pygmy marsupial frog, *Flectonotus pygmaeus,* incubates her eggs in a pouch of skin on her back, helping to protect the eggs from predators. When the eggs hatch, the female deposits the tadpoles in water where they begin life on their own.

1. Describe the origin of tetrapods and identify some of their key derived traits.
2. Some amphibians never leave the water, whereas others can survive in relatively dry terrestrial environments. Contrast the adaptations that facilitate these two lifestyles.
3. **WHAT IF?** Scientists think that amphibian populations may provide an early warning system of environmental problems. What features of amphibians might make them particularly sensitive to environmental problems?

For suggested answers, see Appendix A.

Amniotes are tetrapods that have a terrestrially adapted egg

The **amniotes** are a group of tetrapods whose extant members are the reptiles (including birds) and mammals (**Figure 34.25**). During their evolution, amniotes acquired a number of new adaptations to life on land.

Derived Characters of Amniotes

Amniotes are named for the major derived character of the clade, the **amniotic egg**, which contains four specialized membranes: the amnion, the chorion, the yolk sac, and the

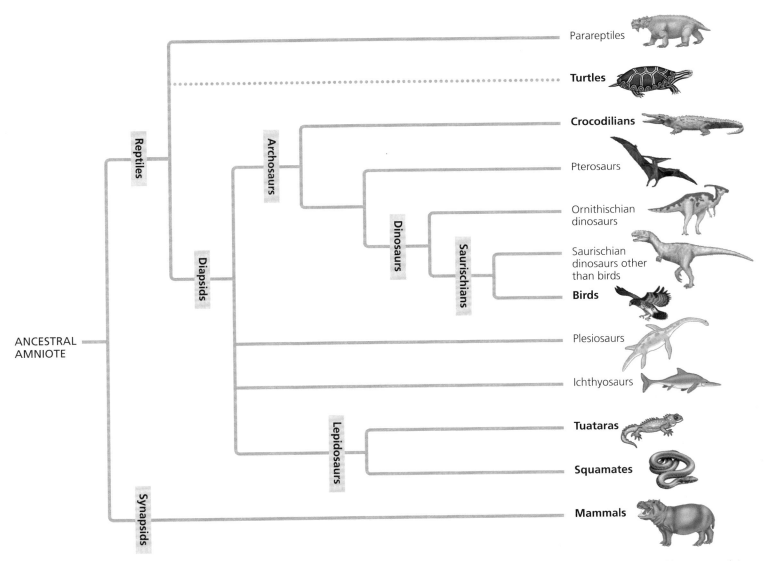

▲ **Figure 34.25 A phylogeny of amniotes.** Extant groups are named at the tips of the branches in boldface type. The dotted line of the turtle branch indicates the uncertain relationship of turtles to other reptiles. Turtles may be a sister group to parareptiles (as indicated by some morphological data), or they may be diapsids more closely related to lepidosaurs (as indicated by other morphological analyses) or to archosaurs (as indicated by many molecular studies).

? *Based on this phylogeny, DNA sequences in birds are likely most similar to DNA sequences in which other extant group of amniotes? Explain.*

▶ **Figure 34.26 The amniotic egg.**
The embryos of reptiles and mammals form four extraembryonic membranes: the amnion, chorion, yolk sac, and allantois. This diagram shows these membranes in the shelled egg of a reptile.

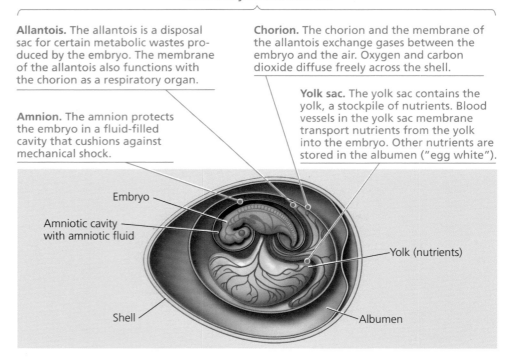

Extraembryonic membranes

Allantois. The allantois is a disposal sac for certain metabolic wastes produced by the embryo. The membrane of the allantois also functions with the chorion as a respiratory organ.

Chorion. The chorion and the membrane of the allantois exchange gases between the embryo and the air. Oxygen and carbon dioxide diffuse freely across the shell.

Amnion. The amnion protects the embryo in a fluid-filled cavity that cushions against mechanical shock.

Yolk sac. The yolk sac contains the yolk, a stockpile of nutrients. Blood vessels in the yolk sac membrane transport nutrients from the yolk into the embryo. Other nutrients are stored in the albumen ("egg white").

Embryo

Amniotic cavity with amniotic fluid

Yolk (nutrients)

Shell

Albumen

allantois (**Figure 34.26**). Called *extraembryonic membranes* because they are not part of the body of the embryo itself, these membranes develop from tissue layers that grow out from the embryo. The amniotic egg is named for the amnion, which encloses a compartment of fluid that bathes the embryo and acts as a hydraulic shock absorber. The other membranes in the egg function in gas exchange, the transfer of stored nutrients to the embryo, and waste storage. The amniotic egg was a key evolutionary innovation for terrestrial life: It allowed the embryo to develop on land in its own private "pond," hence reducing the dependence of tetrapods on an aqueous environment for reproduction.

In contrast to the shell-less eggs of amphibians, the amniotic eggs of most reptiles and some mammals have a shell. The shells of bird eggs are calcareous (made of calcium carbonate) and inflexible, while the eggshells of many other reptiles are leathery and flexible. Either kind of shell significantly slows dehydration of the egg in air, an adaptation that helped amniotes to occupy a wider range of terrestrial habitats than amphibians, their closest living relatives. (Seeds played a similar role in the evolution of land plants, as we discussed in Chapter 30.) Most mammals have dispensed with the eggshell over the course of their evolution, and the embryo avoids desiccation by developing within the amnion inside the mother's body.

Amniotes have acquired other key adaptations to life on land. For example, amniotes use their rib cage to ventilate their lungs. This method is more efficient than throat-based ventilation, which amphibians use as a supplement to breathing through their skin. The increased efficiency of rib cage ventilation may

have allowed amniotes to abandon breathing through their skin and develop less permeable skin, thereby conserving water.

Early Amniotes

The most recent common ancestor of living amphibians and amniotes likely lived about 350 million years ago. No fossils of amniotic eggs have been found from that time, which is not surprising given how delicate they are. Thus, it is not yet possible to say when the amniotic egg evolved, although it must have existed in the last common ancestor of living amniotes, which all have amniotic eggs.

Based on where their fossils have been found, the earliest amniotes lived in warm, moist environments, as did the first tetrapods. Over time, however, early amniotes expanded into a wide range of new environments, including dry and high-latitude regions. The earliest amniotes were small and had sharp teeth, a sign that they were predators (**Figure 34.27**). Later groups also included herbivores, as evidenced by their grinding teeth and other features.

▲ **Figure 34.27 Artist's reconstruction of *Hylonomus*, an early amniote.** About 25 cm long, this species lived 310 million years ago and probably ate insects and other small invertebrates.

UNIVERSITY OF ALBERTA FACULTY BIO

 Michael Caldwell BPEd Exercise Physiology; BSc Paleontology (University of Alberta); PhD (McGill University)

Current Position: Professor Vertebrate Paleontology and Chair, Department of Biological Sciences

My most recent teaching has been in Paleontology 418 (Paleobiology of Lower Vertebrates) and Paleontology 419 (Paleobiology of Higher Vertebrates). I have also contributed teaching in two graduate courses, Paleontology 512 (Problems in Paleontology) and Paleontology 520 (Problems in Vertebrate Paleontology).

My research is focused on the paleontology and evolution of squamate reptiles (snakes and lizards), and in particular on mosasaurs (gigantic extinct marine lizards) and fossil snakes. In 1997 my colleague, Michael S.Y. Lee and I described the first known fossil snake with legs found in 95 million year old rocks near Jerusalem. Since then, I have authored more than 80 research papers examining the evolution and origins of snakes, mosasaurs and other lizards. My work, along with that of my graduate students, has taken me around the world digging fossils and studying specimens in museums in Argentina, Japan, Israel, Egypt, Morocco, all of Europe, Australia and New Zealand, the Canadian Arctic and throughout North America.

Reptiles

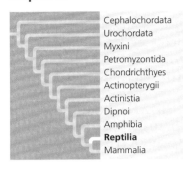

Cephalochordata
Urochordata
Myxini
Petromyzontida
Chondrichthyes
Actinopterygii
Actinistia
Dipnoi
Amphibia
Reptilia
Mammalia

The **reptile** clade includes tuataras, lizards, snakes, turtles, crocodilians, and birds, along with a number of extinct groups, such as plesiosaurs and ichthyosaurs (see Figure 34.25).

Fossil evidence indicates that the earliest reptiles lived about 310 million years ago and resembled lizards. Reptiles have diverged greatly since that time, but as a group they share several derived characters that distinguish them from other tetrapods. For example, unlike amphibians, reptiles have scales that contain the protein keratin (as does a human nail). Scales help protect the animal's skin from desiccation and abrasion. In addition, most reptiles lay their shelled eggs on land **(Figure 34.28)**. Fertilization must occur internally, before the eggshell is secreted. Many species of snakes and lizards are viviparous; in such species, the extraembryonic membranes form a kind of placenta that enables the embryo to obtain nutrients from its mother.

Reptiles such as lizards and snakes are sometimes described as "cold-blooded" because they do not use their metabolism extensively to control their body temperature. However, they do regulate their body temperature by using behavioral adaptations. For example, many lizards bask in the sun when the air is cool and seek shade when the air is too warm. A more accurate description of these reptiles is to say that they are **ectothermic**, which means that they absorb external heat as their main source of body heat. (This topic is discussed in more detail in Chapter 40.) By warming themselves directly with solar energy rather than through the metabolic breakdown of food, an ectothermic reptile can survive on less than 10% of the food energy required by a mammal of the same size. But the reptile clade is not entirely ectothermic; birds are **endothermic**, capable of maintaining body temperature through metabolic activity.

The Origin and Evolutionary Radiation of Reptiles

The oldest reptilian fossils, found in rocks from Nova Scotia, date from the late Carboniferous period. As reptiles diverged from their lizard-like ancestors, one of the first major groups to emerge were the **parareptiles**, which were mostly large, stocky, quadrupedal herbivores. Some parareptiles had plates on their skin that may have provided them with defense against predators. Parareptiles died out by about 200 million years ago, at the end of the Triassic period.

As parareptiles were dwindling, another ancient clade of reptiles, the **diapsids**, was diversifying. One of the most obvious derived characters of diapsids is a pair of holes on each side of the skull, behind the eye socket; muscles pass through these holes and attach to the jaw, controlling jaw movement. The diapsids are composed of two main lineages. One lineage gave rise to the **lepidosaurs**, which include tuataras, lizards, and snakes. This lineage also produced a number of marine reptiles, including the giant mososaurs. Some of these marine species rivaled today's whales in length; all of them are extinct. (We'll say more about living lepidosaurs shortly.)

The other diapsid lineage, the **archosaurs**, produced the crocodilians (which we'll discuss later), pterosaurs, and dinosaurs. **Pterosaurs**, which originated in the late Triassic, were the first tetrapods to exhibit flapping flight. The pterosaur wing was completely different from the wings of birds and bats. It consisted of a collagen-strengthened membrane that stretched between the trunk or hind leg and a very long digit on the foreleg. Well-preserved fossils show evidence of muscles, blood vessels, and nerves in the wing membranes, suggesting that pterosaurs could dynamically adjust their membranes to assist their flight.

The smallest pterosaurs were no bigger than a sparrow, and the largest had a wingspan of nearly 11 m. They appear to have converged on many of the ecological roles later played by birds; some were insect-eaters, others grabbed fish out of the ocean, and still others filtered small animals through thousands of fine needlelike teeth. But by the end of the Cretaceous period 65 million years ago, pterosaurs had become extinct.

On land, the **dinosaurs** diversified into a vast range of shapes and sizes, from bipeds the size of a pigeon to 45-m-long quadrupeds with necks long enough to let them browse the tops of trees. One lineage of dinosaurs, the ornithischians, were herbivores; they included many species with elaborate defenses against predators, such as tail clubs and horned crests. The other main lineage of dinosaurs, the saurischians, included the

▲ **Figure 34.28 Hatching reptiles.** These bushmaster snakes (*Lachesis muta*) are breaking out of their parchment-like shells, a common type of shell among living reptiles other than birds.

long-necked giants and a group called the **theropods**, which were bipedal carnivores. Theropods included the famous *Tyrannosaurus rex* as well as the ancestors of birds.

There is continuing debate about the metabolism of dinosaurs. Some researchers have pointed out that the Mesozoic climate over much of the dinosaurs' range was relatively warm and unvarying, and they have suggested that the low surface-to-volume ratios of large dinosaurs combined with behavioral adaptations such as basking may have been sufficient for an ectotherm to maintain a suitable body temperature. However, some anatomical evidence supports the hypothesis that at least some dinosaurs were endotherms. Furthermore, paleontologists have found fossils of dinosaurs in both Antarctica and the Arctic; although the climate in these areas was milder when dinosaurs existed than it is today, it was cool enough that small dinosaurs may have had difficulty maintaining a high body temperature through ectothermy. The dinosaur that gave rise to birds was *certainly* endothermic, as are all birds.

Traditionally, dinosaurs were considered slow, sluggish creatures. Since the early 1970s, however, fossil discoveries and research have led to the conclusion that many dinosaurs were agile and fast moving. Dinosaurs had a limb structure that enabled them to walk and run more efficiently than could earlier tetrapods, which had a sprawling gait. Fossilized footprints and other evidence suggest that some species were social—they lived and traveled in groups, much as many mammals do today. Paleontologists have also discovered evidence that some dinosaurs built nests and brooded their eggs, as birds do today (see Figure 26.17).

All dinosaurs except birds became extinct by the end of the Cretaceous period. Their extinction may have been caused at least in part by the asteroid or comet impact you read about in Chapter 25. Some analyses of the fossil record are consistent with this idea in that they show a sudden decline in dinosaur diversity at the end of the Cretaceous. However, other analyses indicate that the number of dinosaur species had begun to decline several million years before the Cretaceous ended. Further fossil discoveries and new analyses will be needed to resolve this debate.

Lepidosaurs

One surviving lineage of lepidosaurs is represented by two species of lizard-like reptiles called tuataras (**Figure 34.29a**). Fossil evidence indicates that tuatara ancestors lived at least 220 million years ago. These organisms thrived on many

▼ **Figure 34.29 Extant reptiles (other than birds).**

(a) Tuatara (*Sphenodon punctatus*)

(b) Australian thorny devil lizard (*Moloch horridus*)

(c) Wagler's pit viper (*Tropidolaemus wagleri*)

(d) Eastern box turtle (*Terrapene carolina carolina*)

(e) American alligator (*Alligator mississippiensis*)

continents well into the Cretaceous period, reaching up to a meter in length. Today, however, tuataras are found only on 30 islands off the coast of New Zealand. When humans arrived in New Zealand 750 years ago, the rats that accompanied them devoured tuatara eggs, eventually eliminating the reptiles on the main islands. The tuataras that remain on the outlying islands are about 50 cm long and feed on insects, small lizards, and bird eggs and chicks. They can live to be over 100 years old. Their future survival depends on whether their remaining habitats are kept rat-free.

The other major living lineage of lepidosaurs consists of the lizards and snakes, or squamates, which number about 7,900 species. Lizards are the most numerous and diverse reptiles (apart from birds) alive today **(Figure 34.29b)**. Many lizards are small; the Jaragua lizard, discovered in the Dominican Republic in 2001, is only 16 mm long—small enough to fit comfortably on a dime. In contrast, the Komodo dragon of Indonesia is a lizard that can reach a length of 3 m. It hunts deer and other large prey, delivering venom with its bite.

Snakes are legless lepidosaurs **(Figure 34.29c)**. As described in Chapter 26, snakes descended from lizards with legs. Today, some species of snakes retain vestigial pelvic and limb bones, providing evidence of their ancestry. Despite their lack of legs, snakes are quite proficient at moving on land, most often by producing waves of lateral bending that pass from head to tail. Force exerted by the bends against solid objects pushes the snake forward. Snakes can also move by gripping the ground with their belly scales at several points along the body while the scales at intervening points are lifted slightly off the ground and pulled forward.

Snakes are carnivorous, and a number of adaptations aid them in hunting and eating prey. They have acute chemical sensors, and though they lack eardrums, they are sensitive to ground vibrations, which helps them detect the movements of prey. Heat-detecting organs between the eyes and nostrils of pit vipers, including rattlesnakes, are sensitive to minute temperature changes, enabling these night hunters to locate warm animals. Venomous snakes inject their toxin through a pair of sharp teeth that may be hollow or grooved. The flicking tongue is not venomous but helps fan odors toward olfactory (smell) organs on the roof of the mouth. Loosely articulated jawbones and elastic skin enable most snakes to swallow prey larger than the diameter of the snake's head (see Figure 23.14).

Turtles

Turtles are one of the most distinctive group of reptiles alive today. All turtles have a boxlike shell made of upper and lower shields that are fused to the vertebrae, clavicles (collarbones), and ribs **(Figure 34.29d)**. Most of the 307 known species of turtles have a hard shell, providing excellent defense against predators. A 2008 study reported the discovery of the oldest known fossil of the turtle lineage, dating to 220 million years ago. This fossil has a complete lower shell but an incomplete upper shell, suggesting that turtles may have acquired full shells in stages. The marine sediments in which this fossil was found also suggest that turtles may have originated in shallow coastal waters. However, as other scientists have argued, it is also possible that turtles originated on land and that the incomplete upper shell of this fossil may have been a specialized adaptation for an aquatic lifestyle. Scientists continue to hunt for fossils that could shed light on the origin of the turtle shell.

The earliest turtles could not retract their head into their shell, but mechanisms for doing so evolved independently in two separate branches of turtles. The side-necked turtles fold their neck horizontally, while the vertical-necked turtles fold their neck vertically.

Some turtles have adapted to deserts, and others live almost entirely in ponds and rivers. Still others have returned to the sea. Sea turtles have a reduced shell and enlarged forelimbs that function as flippers. They include the largest living turtles, the deep-diving leatherbacks, which can exceed a mass of 1,500 kg and feed on jellies. Leatherbacks and other sea turtles are endangered by being caught in fishing nets, as well as by development of the beaches where the turtles lay their eggs.

Alligators and Crocodiles

Alligators and crocodiles (collectively called crocodilians) belong to a lineage that reaches back to the late Triassic **(Figure 34.29e)**. The earliest members of this lineage were small terrestrial quadrupeds with long, slender legs. Later species became larger and adapted to aquatic habitats, breathing air through their upturned nostrils. Some Mesozoic crocodilians grew as long as 12 m and may have attacked dinosaurs and other prey at the water's edge.

The 23 known species of living crocodilians are confined to warm regions of the globe. Alligators in the southeastern United States have made a comeback after spending years on the endangered species list.

Birds

There are about 10,000 species of birds in the world. Like crocodilians, birds are archosaurs, but almost every feature of their anatomy has been modified in their adaptation to flight.

Derived Characters of Birds Many of the characters of birds are adaptations that facilitate flight, including weight-saving modifications that make flying more efficient. For example, birds lack a urinary bladder, and the females of most species have only one ovary. The gonads of both females and males are usually small, except during the breeding season, when they increase in size. Living birds are also toothless, an adaptation that trims the weight of the head.

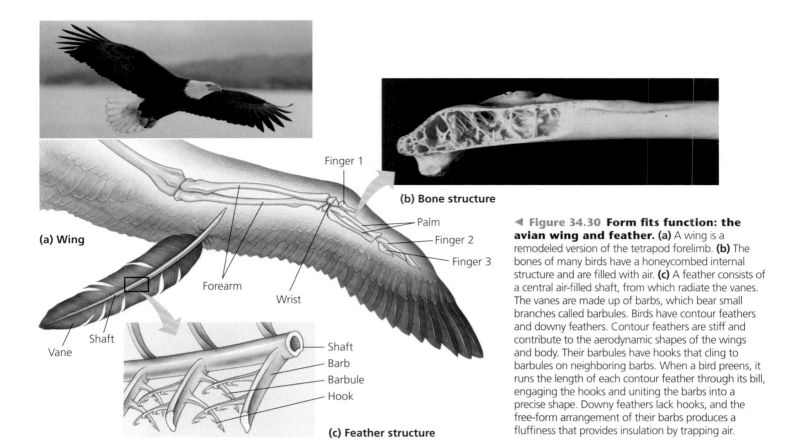

(a) Wing

Finger 1

Palm

Finger 2

Finger 3

Forearm

Wrist

(b) Bone structure

Shaft

Vane

Shaft
Barb
Barbule
Hook

(c) Feather structure

◀ **Figure 34.30 Form fits function: the avian wing and feather. (a)** A wing is a remodeled version of the tetrapod forelimb. **(b)** The bones of many birds have a honeycombed internal structure and are filled with air. **(c)** A feather consists of a central air-filled shaft, from which radiate the vanes. The vanes are made up of barbs, which bear small branches called barbules. Birds have contour feathers and downy feathers. Contour feathers are stiff and contribute to the aerodynamic shapes of the wings and body. Their barbules have hooks that cling to barbules on neighboring barbs. When a bird preens, it runs the length of each contour feather through its bill, engaging the hooks and uniting the barbs into a precise shape. Downy feathers lack hooks, and the free-form arrangement of their barbs produces a fluffiness that provides insulation by trapping air.

A bird's most obvious adaptations for flight are its wings and feathers **(Figure 34.30)**. Feathers are made of the protein β-keratin, which is also found in the scales of other reptiles. The shape and arrangement of the feathers form the wings into airfoils, and they illustrate some of the same principles of aerodynamics as the wings of an airplane. Power for flapping the wings comes from contractions of large pectoral (breast) muscles anchored to a keel on the sternum (breastbone). Some birds, such as eagles and hawks, have wings adapted for soaring on air currents and flap their wings only occasionally; other birds, including hummingbirds, must flap continuously to stay aloft (see Figure 34.34). Among the fastest birds are the appropriately named swifts, which can fly up to 170 km/hr.

Flight provides numerous benefits. It enhances hunting and scavenging; many birds consume flying insects, an abundant, highly nutritious food resource. Flight also provides ready escape from earthbound predators and enables some birds to migrate great distances to exploit different food resources and seasonal breeding areas.

Flying requires a great expenditure of energy from an active metabolism. Birds are endothermic; they use their own metabolic heat to maintain a high, constant body temperature. Feathers and in some species a layer of fat provide insulation that enables birds to retain body heat. The lungs have

tiny tubes leading to and from elastic air sacs that improve airflow and oxygen uptake. This efficient respiratory system and a circulatory system with a four-chambered heart keep tissues well supplied with oxygen and nutrients, supporting a high rate of metabolism.

Flight also requires both acute vision and fine muscle control. Birds have color vision and excellent eyesight. The visual and motor areas of the brain are well developed, and the brain is proportionately larger than those of amphibians and nonbird reptiles.

Birds generally display very complex behaviors, particularly during breeding season, when they engage in elaborate courtship rituals. Because eggs have shells by the time they are laid, fertilization must be internal. Copulation usually involves contact between the mates' vents, the openings to their cloacas. After eggs are laid, the avian embryo must be kept warm through brooding by the mother, the father, or both, depending on the species.

The Origin of Birds Cladistic analyses of birds and reptilian fossils indicate that birds belong to the group of bipedal saurischian dinosaurs called theropods. Since the late 1990s, Chinese paleontologists have unearthed a spectacular trove of feathered theropod fossils that are shedding light on the origin of birds. Several species of dinosaurs closely related to birds had feathers with vanes, and a wider range of species had filamentous feathers. Such findings imply that feathers evolved long before powered flight. Among the possible functions of these early feathers were insulation, camouflage, and courtship display.

How did flight evolve in the theropods? In one scenario, feathers may have enabled small, running dinosaurs chasing prey or escaping predators to gain extra lift as they jumped into the air. Or small dinosaurs could have gained traction as they ran up hills by flapping their feathered forelimbs—a behavior seen in some birds today. In a third scenario, some dinosaurs could have climbed trees and glided, aided by feathers. Whether birds took to the air from the ground up or the trees down, an essential question being studied by scientists ranging from paleontologists to engineers is how their efficient flight stroke evolved.

By 150 million years ago, feathered theropods had evolved into birds. *Archaeopteryx*, which was discovered in a German limestone quarry in 1861, remains the earliest known bird **(Figure 34.31)**. It had feathered wings but retained ancestral characters such as teeth, clawed digits in its wings, and a long tail. *Archaeopteryx* flew well at high speeds, but unlike a present-day bird, it could not take off from a standing position. Fossils of later birds from the Cretaceous show a gradual loss of certain ancestral dinosaur features, such as teeth and clawed forelimbs, as well as the acquisition of innovations found in extant birds, including a short tail covered by a fan of feathers.

▲ **Figure 34.32 An emu (*Dromaius novaehollandiae*), a flightless bird native to Australia.**

Living Birds Clear evidence of Neornithes, the clade that includes the 28 orders of living birds, can be found before the Cretaceous-Paleogene boundary 65.5 million years ago. Several groups of living and extinct birds include one or more flightless species. The **ratites** (order Struthioniformes), which consist of the ostrich, rhea, kiwi, cassowary, and emu, are all flightless **(Figure 34.32)**. In ratites, the sternal keel is absent, and the pectoral muscles are small relative to those of birds that can fly.

Penguins make up the flightless order Sphenisciformes, but, like flying birds, they have powerful pectoral muscles. They use these muscles to "fly" in the water: As they swim, they flap their flipper-like wings in a manner that resembles the flight stroke of a more typical bird **(Figure 34.33)**. Certain species of rails, ducks, and pigeons are also flightless.

Although the demands of flight have rendered the general body forms of many flying birds similar to one another, experienced bird-watchers can distinguish species by their profile, colors, flying style, behavior, and beak shape. The skeleton of a hummingbird wing is unique, making them the only birds

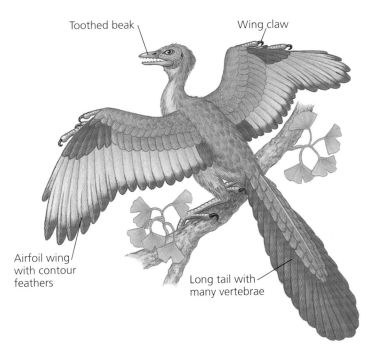

Toothed beak

Wing claw

Airfoil wing with contour feathers

Long tail with many vertebrae

▲ **Figure 34.31 Artist's reconstruction of *Archaeopteryx*, the earliest known bird.** Fossil evidence indicates that *Archaeopteryx* was capable of powered flight but retained many characters of nonbird dinosaurs.

▲ **Figure 34.33 A king penguin (*Aptenodytes patagonicus*) "flying" underwater.** With their streamlined shape and powerful pectoral muscles, penguins are fast and agile swimmers.

◀ **Figure 34.34 Hummingbird feeding while hovering.** A hummingbird can rotate its wings in all directions, enabling it to hover and fly backwards.

that can hover and fly backwards (**Figure 34.34**). Adult birds lack teeth, but during the course of avian evolution their beaks have taken on a variety of shapes suited to different diets. Some birds, such as parrots, have crushing beaks with which they can crack open hard nuts and seeds. Other birds, such as flamingoes, are filter feeders. Their beaks have remarkable 'strainers' that enable them to capture food particles from the water (**Figure 34.35**). Foot structure, too, shows considerable variation. Various birds use their feet for perching on branches (**Figure 34.36**), grasping food, defense, swimming or walking, and even courtship (see Figure 24.3e).

◀ **Figure 34.35 Specialized beaks.** This greater flamingo (*Phoenicopterus ruber*) dips its beak into the water and strains out the food.

▲ **Figure 34.36 Feet adapted to perching.** This great tit (*Parus major*) is a member of the Passeriformes, the perching birds. The toes of these birds can lock around a branch or wire, enabling the bird to rest for long periods.

CONCEPT CHECK 34.6

1. Describe three key amniote adaptations for life on land.
2. Are snakes tetrapods? Explain.
3. Identify four avian adaptations for flight.
4. **WHAT IF?** Suppose turtles are more closely related to lepidosaurs than to other reptiles. Redraw Figure 34.25 to show this relationship, and mark the node that represents the most recent common ancestor shared by all living reptiles. Defining the reptile clade as consisting of all descendants of that ancestor, list the reptiles.

For suggested answers, see Appendix A.

CONCEPT **34.7**

Mammals are amniotes that have hair and produce milk

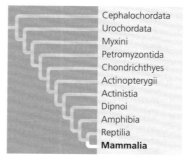

Cephalochordata
Urochordata
Myxini
Petromyzontida
Chondrichthyes
Actinopterygii
Actinistia
Dipnoi
Amphibia
Reptilia
Mammalia

The reptiles we have been discussing represent one of the two living lineages of amniotes. The other amniote lineage is our own, the **mammals** (class Mammalia). Today, there are more than 5,300 known species of mammals on Earth.

Derived Characters of Mammals

The distinctive character from which mammals derive their name is their mammary glands, which produce milk for offspring. All mammalian mothers nourish their young with milk, a balanced diet rich in fats, sugars, proteins, minerals, and vitamins. Hair, another mammalian characteristic, and a fat layer under the skin help the body retain heat. Like birds, mammals are endothermic, and most have a high metabolic rate. Efficient respiratory and circulatory systems (including a four-chambered heart) support a mammal's metabolism. A sheet of muscle called the diaphragm helps ventilate the lungs.

Like birds, mammals generally have a larger brain than other vertebrates of equivalent size, and many species are capable learners. And as in birds, the relatively long duration of parental care extends the time for offspring to learn important survival skills by observing their parents.

Differentiated teeth are another important mammalian trait. Whereas the teeth of reptiles are generally uniform in size and shape, the jaws of mammals bear a variety of teeth with sizes and shapes adapted for chewing many kinds of foods. Humans, like most mammals, have teeth modified for shearing (incisors and canine teeth) and for crushing and grinding (premolars and molars; see Figure 41.16).

Early Evolution of Mammals

Mammals belong to a group of amniotes known as **synapsids**. Early nonmammalian synapsids lacked hair, had a sprawling gait, and laid eggs. A distinctive characteristic of synapsids is the single temporal fenestra, a hole behind the eye socket on each side of the skull. Humans retain this feature; your jaw muscles pass through the temporal fenestra and anchor on your temple. Fossil evidence shows that the jaw was remodeled as mammalian features arose gradually in successive lineages of earlier synapsids (see Figure 25.6); in all, these changes took more than 100 million years. In addition, two of the bones that formerly made up the jaw joint were incorporated into the mammalian middle ear **(Figure 34.37)**. This evolutionary change is reflected in changes that occur during development. For example, as a mammalian embryo grows, the posterior region of its jaw—which in a reptile forms the articular bone—can be observed to detach from the jaw and migrate to the ear, where it forms the malleus.

Synapsids evolved into large herbivores and carnivores during the Permian period, and for a time they were the dominant tetrapods. However, the Permian-Triassic extinctions took a heavy toll on them, and their diversity fell during the Triassic (251–200 million years ago). Increasingly mammal-like synapsids emerged by the end of the Triassic. While not true mammals, these synapsids had acquired a number of the derived characters that distinguish mammals

from other amniotes. They were small and probably hairy, and they likely fed on insects at night. Their bones show that they grew faster than other synapsids, suggesting that they probably had a relatively high metabolic rate; however, they still laid eggs.

During the Jurassic (200–145 million years ago), the first true mammals arose and diversified into many short-lived lineages. A diverse set of mammal species coexisted with dinosaurs in Jurassic and Cretaceous periods, but these species were not abundant or dominant members of their community, and most measured less than 1 m. One possible explanation for their small size is that dinosaurs already occupied ecological niches of large-bodied animals.

By the early Cretaceous, the three major lineages of mammals had emerged: those leading to monotremes (egg-laying mammals), marsupials (mammals with a pouch), and eutherians (placental mammals). After the extinction of large dinosaurs, pterosaurs, and marine reptiles during the late Cretaceous period, mammals underwent an adaptive radiation, giving rise to large predators and herbivores as well as flying and aquatic species.

Monotremes

Monotremes are found only in Australia and New Guinea and are represented by one species of platypus and four species of echidnas (spiny anteaters). Monotremes lay eggs, a character that is ancestral for amniotes and retained in most

(a) In *Biarmosuchus*, the articular and quadrate bones formed the jaw joint.

Key

- Articular
- Quadrate
- Dentary
- Squamosal

◀ **Figure 34.37 The evolution of the mammalian ear bones.** *Biarmosuchus* was a synapsid, a lineage that eventually gave rise to the mammals. Bones that transmit sound in the ear of mammals arose from the modification of bones in the jaw of nonmammalian synapsids.

MAKE CONNECTIONS *Review the definition of* exaptation *in Concept 25.6 (p. 530). Summarize the process by which exaptation occurs and explain how the incorporation of the articular and quadrate bones into the mammalian inner ear is an example.*

Present-day reptile

Present-day mammal

(b) During the evolutionary remodeling of the mammalian skull, a new jaw joint formed between the dentary and squamosal bones (see Figure 25.6). No longer used in the jaw, the quadrate and articular bones became incorporated into the middle ear as two of the three bones that transmit sound from the eardrum to the inner ear.

▲ **Figure 34.38 Short-beaked echidna (*Tachyglossus aculeatus*), an Australian monotreme.** Monotremes have hair and produce milk, but they lack nipples. Monotremes are the only mammals that lay eggs (inset).

(a) A young brushtail possum. The offspring of marsupials are born very early in their development. They finish their growth while nursing from a nipple (in their mother's pouch in most species).

(b) Long-nosed bandicoot. Most bandicoots are diggers and burrowers that eat mainly insects but also some small vertebrates and plant material. Their rear-opening pouch helps protect the young from dirt as the mother digs. Other marsupials, such as kangaroos, have a pouch that opens to the front.

▲ **Figure 34.39 Australian marsupials.**

reptiles **(Figure 34.38)**. Like all mammals, monotremes have hair and produce milk, but they lack nipples. Milk is secreted by glands on the belly of the mother. After hatching, the baby sucks the milk from the mother's fur.

Marsupials

Opossums, kangaroos, and koalas are examples of **marsupials**. Both marsupials and eutherians share derived characters not found among monotremes. They have higher metabolic rates and nipples that provide milk, and they give birth to live young. The embryo develops inside the uterus of the female's reproductive tract. The lining of the uterus and the extraembryonic membranes that arise from the embryo form a **placenta**, a structure in which nutrients diffuse into the embryo from the mother's blood.

A marsupial is born very early in its development and completes its embryonic development while nursing. In most species, the nursing young are held within a maternal pouch called a *marsupium* **(Figure 34.39a)**. A red kangaroo, for instance, is about the size of a honeybee at its birth, just 33 days after fertilization. Its back legs are merely buds, but its front legs are strong enough for it to crawl from the exit of its mother's reproductive tract to a pouch that opens to the front of her body, a journey that lasts a few minutes. In other species, the marsupium opens to the rear of the mother's body; in bandicoots, this protects the young as their mother burrows in the dirt **(Figure 34.39b)**.

Marsupials existed worldwide during the Mesozoic era, but today they are found only in the Australian region and in North and South America. The biogeography of marsupials is an example of the interplay between biological and geologic evolution (see Concept 25.4). After the breakup of the supercontinent Pangaea, South America and Australia became island continents, and their marsupials diversified in isolation from the eutherians that began an adaptive radiation on the northern continents. Australia has not been in contact with another continent since early in the Cenozoic era, about 65 million years ago. In Australia, convergent evolution has resulted in a diversity of marsupials that resemble eutherians in similar ecological roles in other parts of the world **(Figure 34.40)**. In contrast, although South America had a diverse marsupial fauna throughout the Paleogene, it has experienced several migrations of eutherians. One of the most important migrations occurred about 3 million years ago, when North and South America joined at the Panamanian isthmus and extensive two-way traffic of animals took place over the land bridge. Today, only three families of marsupials live outside the Australian region, and the only marsupials found in the wild in North America are a few species of opossum.

UNIVERSITY OF ALBERTA FACULTY BIO

Andrew E. Derocher BSc Forest Biology (University of British Columbia) MSc and PhD Zoology (University of Alberta)

Current Position: Professor, Department of Biological Sciences

I started my undergraduate program in zoology at the University of British Columbia but I finished in Forest Biology (Honours) because most wildlife in B.C. lives in forest habitats. After a stint studying grizzly bears, I was presented with an opportunity, more by chance than design, to study polar bears at the University of Alberta for my Masters degree. The Arctic drew me in and I stayed for my PhD, still studying polar bears. After holding various positions, including 7 years working for the Norwegian Polar Institute as a polar bear research scientist, I returned to University of Alberta as a professor of Biological Sciences. I now teach Northern Ecology (Biology 366) and Biology of Mammals (Zoology 408).

My research still focuses on the ecology and conservation of polar bears. As an Arctic nation, Canada's north offers amazing opportunities for research. My group also studies grizzly bears, caribou, peregrine falcons, Dall sheep, and wolves. Topics range from studies of habitat selection, behaviour, predator-prey relationships, movement ecology, population structure, ecotoxicology, as well as anthropogenic and climate change effects on wildlife. Many of these studies have a conservation or management focus, but others are curiosity driven.

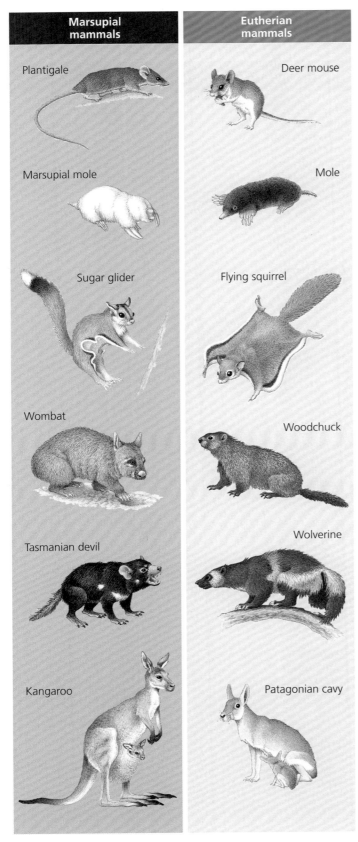

Marsupial mammals	Eutherian mammals
Plantigale	Deer mouse
Marsupial mole	Mole
Sugar glider	Flying squirrel
Wombat	Woodchuck
Tasmanian devil	Wolverine
Kangaroo	Patagonian cavy

▲ **Figure 34.40 Convergent evolution of marsupials and eutherians (placental mammals).** (Drawings are not to scale.)

Eutherians (Placental Mammals)

Eutherians are commonly called placental mammals because their placentas are more complex than those of marsupials. Eutherians have a longer pregnancy than marsupials. Young eutherians complete their embryonic development within the uterus, joined to their mother by the placenta. The eutherian placenta provides an intimate and long-lasting association between the mother and her developing young.

The major groups of living eutherians are thought to have diverged from one another in a burst of evolutionary change. The timing of this burst is uncertain: It is dated to 100 million years ago by molecular data and 60 million years ago by morphological data. **Figure 34.41**, on the next two pages, explores the major eutherian orders and their possible phylogenetic relationships with each other as well as with the monotremes and marsupials.

Primates

The mammalian order Primates includes the lemurs, tarsiers, monkeys, and apes. Humans are members of the ape group.

Derived Characters of Primates Most primates have hands and feet adapted for grasping, and their digits have flat nails instead of the narrow claws of other mammals. There are other characteristic features of the hands and feet, too, such as skin ridges on the fingers (which account for human fingerprints). Relative to other mammals, primates have a large brain and short jaws, giving them a flat face. Their forward-looking eyes are close together on the front of the face. Primates also exhibit relatively well-developed parental care and complex social behavior.

The earliest known primates were tree-dwellers, and many of the characteristics of primates are adaptations to the demands of living in the trees. Grasping hands and feet allow primates to hang onto tree branches. All living primates, except humans, have a big toe that is widely separated from the other toes, enabling them to grasp branches with their feet. All primates also have a thumb that is relatively movable and separate from the fingers, but monkeys and apes have a fully **opposable thumb**; that is, they can touch the ventral surface (fingerprint side) of the tip of all four fingers with the ventral surface of the thumb of the same hand. In monkeys and apes other than humans, the opposable thumb functions in a grasping "power grip." In humans, a distinctive bone structure at the base of the thumb allows it to be used for more precise manipulation. The unique dexterity of humans represents descent with modification from our tree-dwelling ancestors. Arboreal maneuvering also requires excellent eye-hand coordination. The overlapping visual fields of the two forward-facing eyes enhance depth perception, an obvious advantage when brachiating (traveling by swinging from branch to branch in trees).

Exploring Mammalian Diversity

Phylogenetic Relationships of Mammals

Evidence from numerous fossils and molecular analyses indicates that monotremes diverged from other mammals about 180 million years ago and that marsupials diverged from eutherians (placental mammals) about 140 million years ago. Molecular systematics has helped to clarify the evolutionary relationships between the eutherian orders, though there is still no broad consensus on a phylogenetic tree. One current hypothesis, represented by the tree shown below, clusters the eutherian orders into four main clades.

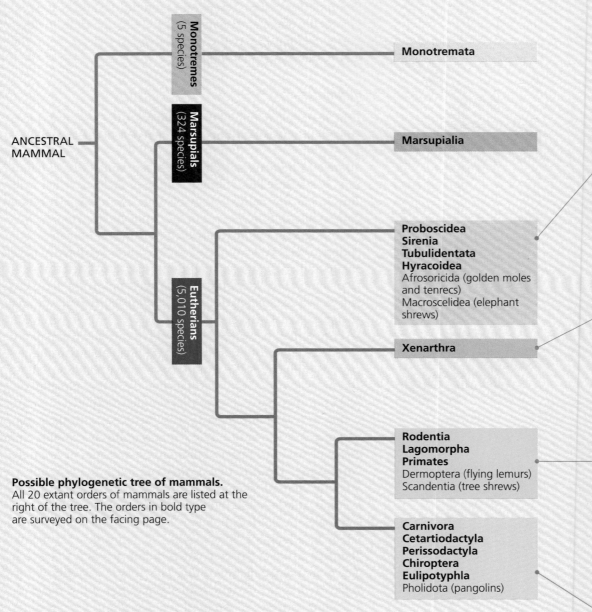

Possible phylogenetic tree of mammals.
All 20 extant orders of mammals are listed at the right of the tree. The orders in bold type are surveyed on the facing page.

This clade of eutherians evolved in Africa when the continent was isolated from other landmasses. It includes Earth's largest living land animal (the African elephant), as well as species that weigh less than 10 g.

All members of this clade, which underwent an adaptive radiation in South America, belong to the order Xenarthra. One species, the nine-banded armadillo, is found in the southern United States.

This is the largest eutherian clade. It includes the rodents, which make up the largest mammalian order by far, with about 1,770 species. Humans belong to the order Primates.

This diverse clade includes terrestrial and marine mammals as well as bats, the only flying mammals. A growing body of evidence, including Eocene fossils of whales with feet, supports putting whales in the same order (Cetartiodactyla) as pigs, cows, and hippos (see Figures 22.19 and 22.20).

Orders and Examples	Main Characteristics	Orders and Examples	Main Characteristics
Monotremata Platypuses, echidnas Echidna	Lay eggs; no nipples; young suck milk from fur of mother	**Marsupialia** Kangaroos, opossums, koalas Koala	Completes embryonic development in pouch on mother's body
Proboscidea Elephants African elephant	Long, muscular trunk; thick, loose skin; upper incisors elongated as tusks	**Tubulidentata** Aardvarks Aardvark	Teeth consisting of many thin tubes cemented together; eats ants and termites
Sirenia Manatees, dugongs Manatee	Aquatic; finlike fore-limbs and no hind limbs; herbivorous	**Hyracoidea** Hyraxes Rock hyrax	Short legs; stumpy tail; herbivorous; complex, multi-chambered stomach
Xenarthra Sloths, anteaters, armadillos Tamandua	Reduced teeth or no teeth; herbivorous (sloths) or carnivorous (anteaters, armadillos)	**Rodentia** Squirrels, beavers, rats, porcupines, mice Red squirrel	Chisel-like, continuously growing incisors worn down by gnawing; herbivorous
Lagomorpha Rabbits, hares, picas Jackrabbit	Chisel-like incisors; hind legs longer than forelegs and adapted for running and jumping; herbivorous	**Primates** Lemurs, monkeys, chimpanzees, gorillas, humans Golden lion tamarin	Opposable thumbs; forward-facing eyes; well-developed cerebral cortex; omnivorous
Carnivora Dogs, wolves, bears, cats, weasels, otters, seals, walruses Coyote	Sharp, pointed canine teeth and molars for shearing; carnivorous	**Perissodactyla** Horses, zebras, tapirs, rhinoceroses Indian rhinoceros	Hooves with an odd number of toes on each foot; herbivorous
Cetartiodactyla Artiodactyls Sheep, pigs, cattle, deer, giraffes Bighorn sheep	Hooves with an even number of toes on each foot; herbivorous	**Chiroptera** Bats Frog-eating bat	Adapted for flight; broad skinfold that extends from elongated fingers to body and legs; carnivorous or herbivorous
Cetaceans Whales, dolphins, porpoises Pacific white-sided porpoise	Aquatic; streamlined body; paddle-like fore-limbs and no hind limbs; thick layer of insulating blubber; carnivorous	**Eulipotyphla** "Core insectivores": some moles, some shrews Star-nosed mole	Eat mainly insects and other small invertebrates

Living Primates There are three main groups of living primates: (1) the lemurs of Madagascar **(Figure 34.42)** and the lorises and bush babies of tropical Africa and southern Asia; (2) the tarsiers, which live in Southeast Asia; and (3) the **anthropoids**, which include monkeys and apes and are found worldwide. The first group—lemurs, lorises, and bush babies—probably resemble early arboreal primates. The oldest known anthropoid fossils, discovered in China in mid-Eocene strata dating to 45 million years ago, indicate that tarsiers are more closely related to anthropoids than to the lemur group **(Figure 34.43)**.

You can see in Figure 34.38 that monkeys do not form a clade but rather consist of two groups, the New and Old World monkeys. Both of these groups are thought to have originated in Africa or Asia. The fossil record indicates that New World monkeys first colonized South America roughly 25 million years ago. By that time, South America and Africa had drifted apart, and monkeys may have reached South America from Africa by rafting on logs or other debris. What is certain is that New World monkeys and Old World monkeys underwent separate adaptive radiations during their many millions of years of separation **(Figure 34.44)**. All species of New World monkeys are arboreal, whereas Old World monkeys include ground-dwelling as well as arboreal species. Most monkeys in both groups are diurnal (active during the day) and usually live in bands held together by social behavior.

The other group of anthropoids consists of primates informally called apes **(Figure 34.45)**. The ape group includes the genera *Hylobates* (gibbons), *Pongo* (orangutans), *Gorilla* (gorillas), *Pan* (chimpanzees and bonobos), and *Homo* (humans).

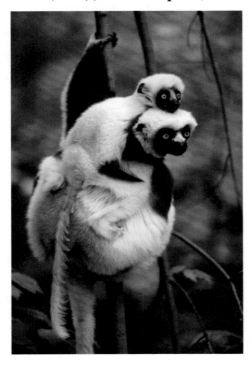

▶ **Figure 34.42 Coquerel's sifakas (*Propithecus verreauxi coquereli*), a type of lemur.**

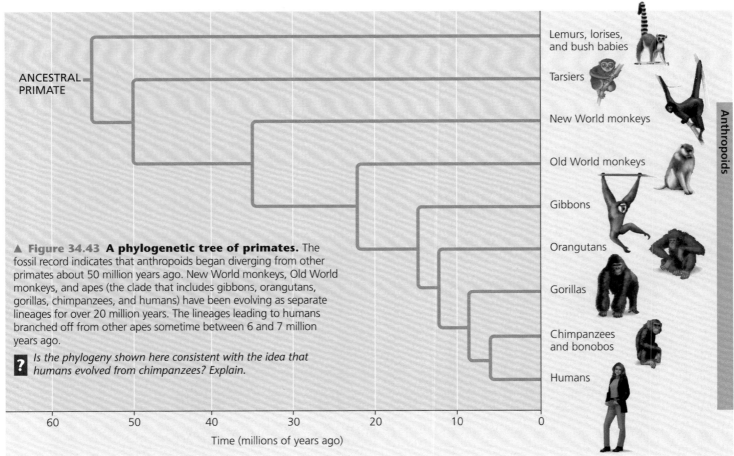

▲ **Figure 34.43 A phylogenetic tree of primates.** The fossil record indicates that anthropoids began diverging from other primates about 50 million years ago. New World monkeys, Old World monkeys, and apes (the clade that includes gibbons, orangutans, gorillas, chimpanzees, and humans) have been evolving as separate lineages for over 20 million years. The lineages leading to humans branched off from other apes sometime between 6 and 7 million years ago.

? *Is the phylogeny shown here consistent with the idea that humans evolved from chimpanzees? Explain.*

ANCESTRAL PRIMATE

Lemurs, lorises, and bush babies
Tarsiers
New World monkeys
Old World monkeys
Gibbons
Orangutans
Gorillas
Chimpanzees and bonobos
Humans

Anthropoids

Time (millions of years ago)
60   50   40   30   20   10   0

▼ **Figure 34.44 New World monkeys and Old World monkeys.**

(a) New World monkeys, such as spider monkeys (shown here), squirrel monkeys, and capuchins, have a prehensile tail and nostrils that open to the sides.

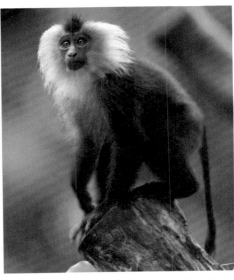

(b) Old World monkeys lack a prehensile tail, and their nostrils open downward. This group includes macaques (shown here), mandrils, baboons, and rhesus monkeys.

The apes diverged from Old World monkeys about 20–25 million years ago. Today, nonhuman apes are found exclusively in tropical regions of the Old World. With the exception of gibbons, living apes are larger than either New or Old World monkeys. All living apes have relatively long arms, short legs, and no tail. Although all nonhuman apes spend time in trees, only gibbons and orangutans are primarily arboreal. Social organization varies among the apes; gorillas and chimpanzees are highly social. Finally, compared to other primates, apes have a larger brain in proportion to their body size, and their behavior is more flexible. These two characteristics are especially prominent in the next group we'll consider, the hominins.

(a) Gibbons, such as this Muller's gibbon, are found only in southeastern Asia. Their very long arms and fingers are adaptations for brachiating (swinging by the arms from branch to branch).

(b) Orangutans are shy apes that live in the rain forests of Sumatra and Borneo. They spend most of their time in trees; note the foot adapted for grasping and the opposable thumb.

(c) Gorillas are the largest apes; some males are almost 2 m tall and weigh about 200 kg. Found only in Africa, these herbivores usually live in groups of up to about 20 individuals.

(d) Chimpanzees live in tropical Africa. They feed and sleep in trees but also spend a great deal of time on the ground. Chimpanzees are intelligent, communicative, and social.

(e) Bonobos are in the same genus (*Pan*) as chimpanzees but are smaller. They survive today only in the African nation of Congo.

▲ **Figure 34.45 Nonhuman apes.**

CONCEPT 34.8

Humans are mammals that have a large brain and bipedal locomotion

In our tour of Earth's biodiversity, we come at last to our own species, *Homo sapiens*, which is about 200,000 years old. When you consider that life has existed on Earth for at least 3.5 billion years, we are clearly evolutionary newcomers.

Derived Characters of Humans

Many characters distinguish humans from other apes. Most obviously, humans stand upright and are bipedal (walk on two legs). Humans have a much larger brain and are capable of language, symbolic thought, artistic expression, and the manufacture and use of complex tools. Humans also have reduced jawbones and jaw muscles, along with a shorter digestive tract.

At the molecular level, the list of derived characters of humans is growing as scientists compare the genomes of humans and chimpanzees. Although the two genomes are 99% identical, a difference of 1% can translate into a large number of changes in a genome that contains 3 billion base pairs. Furthermore, changes in a small number of genes can have large effects. This point was highlighted by recent results showing that humans and chimpanzees differ in the expression of 19 regulatory genes. These genes turn other genes on and off and hence may account for many differences between humans and chimpanzees.

Bear in mind that such genomic differences—and whatever derived phenotypic traits they code for—separate humans from other *living* apes. But many of these new characters first emerged in our ancestors, long before our own species appeared. We will consider some of these ancestors to see how these characters originated.

The Earliest Hominins

The study of human origins is known as **paleoanthropology**. Paleoanthropologists have unearthed fossils of approximately 20 extinct species that are more closely related to humans than to chimpanzees. These species are known as **hominins** (**Figure 34.46**, on the facing page). (Although a majority of anthropologists now use the term *hominin*, its older synonym, *hominid*, continues to be used by some). Since 1994, fossils of four hominin species dating to more than 4 million years ago have been discovered. The oldest of these hominins, *Sahelanthropus tchadensis*, lived about 6.5 million years ago.

Sahelanthropus and other early hominins shared some of the derived characters of humans. For example, they had reduced canine teeth, and some fossils suggest that they had relatively flat faces. They also show signs of having been more upright and bipedal than other apes. One clue to their upright stance can be found in the foramen magnum, the hole at the base of the skull through which the spinal cord exits. In chimpanzees, the foramen magnum is relatively far back on the skull, while in early hominins (and in humans), it is located underneath the skull. This position allows us to hold our head directly over our body, as apparently early hominins did as well. The pelvis, leg bones, and feet of the 4.4-million-year-old *Ardipithecus ramidus* also suggest that early hominins were increasingly bipedal (**Figure 34.47**). (We will return to the subject of bipedalism later.)

Note that the characters that distinguish humans from other living apes did not all evolve in tight unison. While early hominins were showing signs of bipedalism, their brains remained small—about 300–450 cm^3 in volume, compared with an average of 1,300 cm^3 for *Homo sapiens*. The earliest hominins were also small overall. *A. ramidus*, for example, is

◀ **Figure 34.47** The skeleton of "Ardi," a 4.4-million-year-old hominin, *Ardipithecus ramidus*.

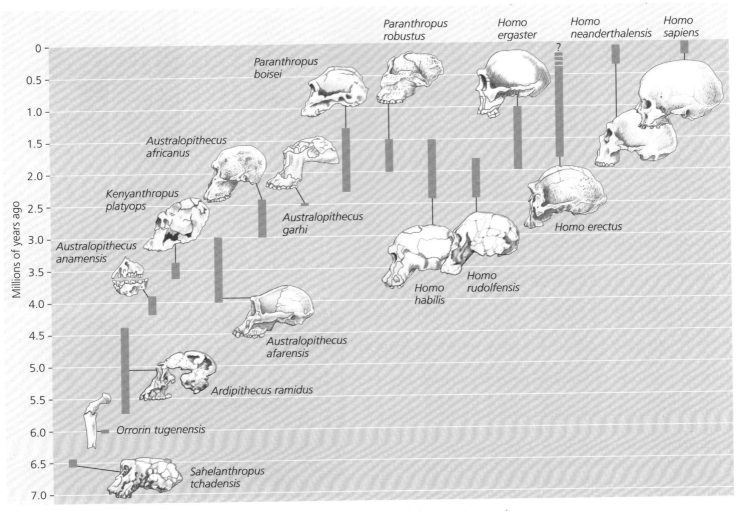

▲ **Figure 34.46 A timeline for some selected hominin species.** Most of these fossils come from sites in eastern and southern Africa. Note that at most times in hominin history, two or more hominin species were contemporaries. Some of the species are controversial, reflecting phylogenetic debates about the interpretation of skeletal details and biogeography.

estimated to have weighed only 50 kg, with relatively large teeth and a jaw that projected beyond the upper part of the face. Humans, in contrast, have a relatively flat face; compare your own face with that of the chimpanzees in Figure 34.45d.

It's important to avoid two common misconceptions when considering early hominins. One is to think of them either as chimpanzees or as having evolved from chimpanzees. Chimpanzees represent the tip of a separate branch of evolution, and they acquired derived characters of their own after they diverged from their common ancestor with humans.

Another misconception is to think of human evolution as a ladder leading directly from an ancestral ape to *Homo sapiens*. This error is often illustrated as a parade of fossil species that become progressively more like ourselves as they march across the page. If human evolution is a parade, it is a very disorderly one, with many groups breaking away to wander other evolutionary paths. At times, several hominin species coexisted. These species often differed in skull shape, body size, and diet

(as inferred from their teeth). Ultimately, all but one lineage— the one that gave rise to *Homo sapiens*—ended in extinction. But when the characteristics of all hominins that lived over the past 6 million years are considered, *H. sapiens* appears not as the end result of a straight evolutionary path, but rather as the only surviving member of a highly branched evolutionary tree.

Australopiths

The fossil record indicates that hominin diversity increased dramatically between 4 and 2 million years ago. Many of the hominins from this period are collectively called australopiths. Their phylogeny remains unresolved on many points, but as a group, they are almost certainly paraphyletic. The earliest member of the group, *Australopithecus anamensis*, lived 4.2–3.9 million years ago, close in time to older hominins such as *Ardipithecus ramidus*.

Australopiths got their name from the 1924 discovery in South Africa of *Australopithecus africanus* ("southern ape of

Africa"), which lived between 3 and 2.4 million years ago. With the discovery of more fossils, it became clear that *A. africanus* walked fully erect (was bipedal) and had human-like hands and teeth. However, its brain was only about one-third the size of the brain of a present-day human.

In 1974, in the Afar region of Ethiopia, paleoanthropologists discovered a 3.2-million-year-old *Australopithecus* skeleton that was 40% complete. "Lucy," as the fossil was named, was short—only about 1 m tall. Lucy and similar fossils have been given the species name *Australopithecus afarensis* (for the Afar region). Fossils discovered in the early 1990s show that *A. afarensis* existed as a species for at least 1 million years.

At the risk of oversimplifying, we could say that *A. afarensis* had fewer of the derived characters of humans above the neck than below. Lucy's brain was the size of a softball, a size similar to that expected for a chimpanzee of Lucy's body size. *A. afarensis* skulls also have a long lower jaw. Skeletons of *A. afarensis* suggest that these hominins were capable of arboreal locomotion, with arms that were relatively long in proportion to body size (compared to the proportions in humans). However, fragments of pelvic and skull bones indicate that *A. afarensis* walked on two legs. Fossilized footprints in Laetoli, Tanzania, corroborate the skeletal evidence that hominins living at the time of *A. afarensis* were bipedal **(Figure 34.48)**.

Another lineage of australopiths consisted of the "robust" australopiths. These hominins, which included species such as *Paranthropus boisei*, had sturdy skulls with powerful jaws and large teeth, adapted for grinding and chewing hard, tough foods. They contrast with the "gracile" (slender) australopiths, including *A. afarensis* and *A. africanus*, which had lighter feeding equipment adapted for softer foods.

Combining evidence from the earliest hominins with the much richer fossil record of later australopiths makes it possible to formulate hypotheses about significant trends in hominin evolution. Let's consider two of these trends: the emergence of bipedalism and tool use.

Bipedalism

Our anthropoid ancestors of 35–30 million years ago were still tree-dwellers. But by about 10 million years ago, the Himalayan mountain range had formed, thrust up in the aftermath of the Indian plate's collision with the Eurasian plate (see Figure 25.13). The climate became drier, and the forests of what are now Africa and Asia contracted. The result was an increased area of savanna (grassland) habitat, with fewer trees. For decades, paleoanthropologists have seen a strong connection between the rise of savannas and the rise of bipedal hominins. According to one hypothesis, tree-dwelling hominins could no longer move through the canopy, so natural selection favored adaptations that made moving over open ground more efficient. Underlying this idea is the fact that while nonhuman apes are superbly adapted for climbing trees, they are less well suited for

▶ **Figure 34.48**
Evidence that hominins walked upright 3.5 million years ago.

(a) The Laetoli footprints, more than 3.5 million years old, confirm that upright posture evolved quite early in hominin history.

(b) An artist's reconstruction of *A. afarensis*, a hominin alive at the time of the Laetoli footprints.

ground travel. For example, as a chimpanzee walks, it uses four times the amount of energy used by a human.

Although elements of this hypothesis survive, the picture now appears somewhat more complex. Although all recently discovered fossils of early hominins show indications of bipedalism, none of these hominins lived in savannas. Instead, they lived in mixed habitats ranging from forests to open woodlands. Furthermore, whatever the selective pressure that led to bipedalism, hominins did not become more bipedal in a simple, linear fashion. *Ardipithecus* had skeletal elements indicating that it could switch to upright walking but also was well suited for climbing trees. Australopiths seem to have had various locomotor styles, and some species spent more time on the ground than others. Only about 1.9 million years ago did hominins begin to walk long distances on two legs. These hominins lived in more arid environments, where bipedal walking requires less energy than walking on all fours.

Tool Use

As you read earlier, the manufacture and use of complex tools is a derived behavioral character of humans. Determining the origin of tool use in hominin evolution is one of paleoanthropolgy's great challenges. Other apes are capable of surprisingly sophisticated tool use. Orangutans, for example, can fashion sticks into probes for retrieving insects from their nests. Chimpanzees are even more adept, using rocks to smash open food and putting leaves on their feet to walk over thorns. It's likely that early hominins were capable of this sort of simple tool use, but finding fossils of modified sticks or leaves that were used as shoes is practically impossible.

The oldest generally accepted evidence of tool use by hominins is 2.5-million-year-old cut marks on animal bones found in Ethiopia. These marks suggest that hominins cut flesh from the bones of animals using stone tools. Interestingly, the hominins whose fossils were found near the site where the bones were discovered had a relatively small brain. If these hominins, which have been named *Australopithecus garhi*, were in fact the creators of the stone tools used on the bones, that would suggest that stone tool use originated before the evolution of large brains in hominins.

Early *Homo*

The earliest fossils that paleoanthropologists place in our genus, *Homo*, include those of the species *Homo habilis*. These fossils, ranging in age from about 2.4 to 1.6 million years, show clear signs of certain derived hominin characters above the neck. Compared to the australopiths, *H. habilis* had a shorter jaw and a larger brain volume, about 600–750 cm^3. Sharp stone tools have also been found with some fossils of *H. habilis* (the name means "handy man").

Fossils from 1.9 to 1.5 million years ago mark a new stage in hominin evolution. A number of paleoanthropologists recognize these fossils as those of a distinct species, *Homo ergaster*. *Homo ergaster* had a substantially larger brain than *H. habilis* (over 900 cm^3), as well as long, slender legs with hip joints well adapted for long-distance walking (Figure 34.49). The fingers were relatively short and straight, suggesting that *H. ergaster* did not climb trees like earlier hominins. *Homo ergaster* fossils have been discovered in far more arid environments than earlier hominins and have been associated with more sophisticated stone tools. Its smaller teeth also suggest that *H. ergaster* either ate different foods than australopiths (more meat and less plant material) or prepared some of its food before chewing, perhaps by cooking or mashing the food.

Homo ergaster marks an important shift in the relative sizes of the sexes. In primates, a size difference between males and females is a major component of sexual dimorphism (see Chapter 23). On average, male gorillas and orangutans weigh about twice as much as females of their species. In chimpanzees and bonobos, males are only about 1.35 times as heavy as females, on average. In *Australopithecus afarensis*, males were 1.5 times as heavy as females. But in early *Homo*, sexual dimorphism was significantly reduced, and this trend continues through our own species: Human males average about 1.2 times the weight of females.

► **Figure 34.49 Fossil of *Homo ergaster*.** This 1.7-million-year-old fossil from Kenya belongs to a young *Homo ergaster* male. This individual was tall, slender, and fully bipedal, and he had a relatively large brain.

The reduced sexual dimorphism may offer some clues to the social systems of extinct hominins. In extant primates, extreme sexual dimorphism is associated with intense male-male competition for multiple females. In species that undergo more pair-bonding (including our own), sexual dimorphism is less dramatic. In *H. ergaster*, therefore, males and females may have engaged in more pair-bonding than earlier hominins did. This shift may have been associated with long-term care of the young by both parents. Human babies depend on their parents for food and protection much longer than do the young of other apes.

Fossils now generally recognized as *H. ergaster* were originally considered early members of another species, *Homo erectus*, and some paleoanthropologists still hold this position. *Homo erectus* originated in Africa and was the first hominin to migrate out of Africa. The oldest fossils of hominins outside Africa, dating back 1.8 million years, were discovered in 2000 in the former Soviet Republic of Georgia. *Homo erectus* eventually migrated as far as the Indonesian archipelago. Fossil evidence indicates that *H. erectus* became extinct sometime after 200,000 years ago; one group may have persisted on Java until roughly 50,000 years ago.

Neanderthals

In 1856, miners discovered some mysterious human fossils in a cave in the Neander Valley in Germany. The 40,000-year-old fossils belonged to a thick-boned hominin with a prominent brow. The hominin was named *Homo neanderthalensis* and is commonly called a Neanderthal. Neanderthals were living in Europe by 350,000 years ago and later spread to the Near East, central Asia, and southern Siberia. They had a brain as large as that of present-day humans, buried their dead, and made hunting tools from stone and wood. But despite their adaptations and culture, Neanderthals apparently became extinct about 28,000 years ago.

At one time, many paleoanthropologists considered Neanderthals to be a stage in the evolution of *Homo erectus* into *Homo sapiens*. Now most have abandoned this view, partly due to the analysis of mitochondrial DNA **(Figure 34.50)**. These and other genetic results suggest that Neanderthals may have contributed little to the gene pool of *H. sapiens*. However, a 2010 analysis of the DNA sequence of the Neanderthal genome appears to be consistent with limited gene flow between the two species. In addition, some researchers have argued that evidence of gene flow can be found in fossils that show a mixture of *H. sapiens* and Neanderthal characteristics. Further genetic analyses and fossil discoveries will be needed to resolve the ongoing debate over the extent of genetic exchange between the two species.

Homo sapiens

Evidence from fossils, archaeology, and DNA studies has led to a compelling hypothesis about how our own species, *Homo sapiens*, emerged and spread around the world.

Fossil evidence indicates that the ancestors of humans originated in Africa. Older species (perhaps *H. ergaster* or *H. erectus*) gave rise to later species, ultimately including *H. sapiens*. Furthermore, the oldest known fossils of our own species have been found at two different sites in Ethiopia and include specimens that are 195,000 and 160,000 years old **(Figure 34.51)**. These early humans had less pronounced browridges than found in *H. erectus* and Neanderthals, and they were more slender than other recent hominins.

The Ethiopian fossils support inferences about the origin of humans from molecular evidence. As shown in Figure 34.50, DNA analyses indicate that all living humans are more closely related to one another than to Neanderthals. Other studies on human DNA show that Europeans and Asians share a relatively recent common ancestor and that many African lineages branched off more basal positions on the human family tree. These findings strongly suggest that all living humans have ancestors that originated as *H. sapiens* in Africa, which is further supported by analysis of mitochondrial DNA and Y chromosomes from members of various human populations.

The oldest fossils of *H. sapiens* outside Africa are from the Middle East and date back about 115,000 years.

▲ **Figure 34.51 A 160,000-year-old fossil of *Homo sapiens*.** This skull, discovered in Ethiopia in 2003, differs little from the skulls of living humans.

▼ **Figure 34.50**

INQUIRY

Did Neanderthals give rise to European humans?

EXPERIMENT People have long been fascinated by Neanderthals and their relationship to *Homo sapiens*. Several fossils discovered in Europe have been interpreted by some researchers as showing a mixture of Neanderthal and human features, leading to the suggestion that European humans bred extensively with or descended from Neanderthals. Igor Ovchinnikov and William Goodwin, then at the University of Glasgow, and their team used genetic methods to assess the relationship between Neanderthals and *H. sapiens*. The team extracted mitochondrial DNA (mtDNA) from a Neanderthal fossil (Neanderthal 1) and compared its sequence to an mtDNA sequence that other researchers had obtained three years earlier from a different Neanderthal fossil (Neanderthal 2). Mitochondrial DNA sequences were also obtained for a number of living humans from Europe, Africa, and Asia. The researchers then used Neanderthal and *H. sapiens* mtDNA sequences to construct a phylogenetic tree for Neanderthals and humans; data from chimpanzees were used to root the tree. This approach permitted the researchers to test the following hypothesis:

Hypothesis: Neanderthals gave rise to European humans.

Expected phylogeny:

- Chimpanzees
- Neanderthals
- Living Europeans
- Other living humans

RESULTS The two Neanderthal mtDNA sequences differed at 3.5% of the bases, whereas on average, the Neanderthal and *H. sapiens* mtDNA differed at 24% of the bases. The phylogenetic analysis yielded the following tree:

- Chimpanzees
- Neanderthal 1
- Neanderthal 2
- European and other living humans

CONCLUSION The Neanderthals form one clade, and living humans form another, separate clade. Thus, it is not likely that Neanderthals gave rise to European humans.

SOURCE I. V. Ovchinnikov et al., Molecular analysis of Neanderthal DNA from the northern Caucasus, *Nature* 404:490–493 (2000).

WHAT IF? The human and chimpanzee lineages diverged about 6 million years ago. Can the phylogeny shown in RESULTS be used to infer when Neanderthal and human lineages diverged? Explain.

Studies of the human Y chromosome suggest that humans spread beyond Africa in one or more waves, first into Asia and then to Europe and Australia. The date of the first arrival of humans in the New World is uncertain, although the oldest generally accepted evidence puts that date at about 15,000 years ago.

New findings continually update our understanding of the evolution of *H. sapiens*. For example, in 2004, researchers reported an astonishing find: skeletal remains of adult hominins dating from just 18,000 years ago and representing a previously unknown species, which they named *Homo floresiensis*. Discovered in a limestone cave on the Indonesian island of Flores, the individuals were much shorter and had a much smaller brain volume than *H. sapiens*—more similar, in fact, to an australopith. The researchers who discovered these fossils argue that the skeletons also display many derived traits, including skull thickness and proportions and teeth shape, suggesting that the species is descended from the larger *H. erectus*. Not convinced, some researchers have argued that the fossils represent small *H. sapiens* individuals with deformed, miniature brains, a condition called microcephaly.

However, a 2007 study found that the wrist bones of the Flores fossils are similar in shape to those of nonhuman apes and early hominins, but different from those of Neanderthals and *H. sapiens*. These researchers concluded that the Flores fossils represent a species whose lineage branched off before the origin of the clade that includes Neanderthals and humans. A later study comparing the foot bones of the Flores fossils with those of other hominins also indicated that *H. floresiensis* arose before *H. sapiens*; in fact, these researchers suggested that *H. floresiensis* may have descended from an as-yet-unidentified hominin that lived even earlier than *H. erectus*.

If further evidence continues to support the designation of *H. floresiensis* as a new hominin, one intriguing explanation for this species' apparent "shrinkage" is that isolation on the island may have resulted in selection for greatly reduced size. Such dramatic size reduction is well studied in other dwarf mammalian species that are endemic to islands, including primitive pygmy elephants found near the Flores fossils. One such study found that on islands, the brains of dwarf fossil hippos were proportionally even smaller than their bodies. One possible explanation for this finding is that smaller brains resulted from selection for reduced energy consumption (the mammalian brain uses large amounts of energy). Applying their results to the Flores fossils, the researchers concluded that the brain size of *H. floresiensis* closely matches that predicted for a dwarf hominin of its body size. Compelling questions that may yet be answered from the cache of anthropological and archaeological finds on Flores include how *H. floresiensis* originated and whether it encountered *H. sapiens*, which also was living in Indonesia 18,000 years ago.

The rapid expansion of our species may have been spurred by changes in human cognition as *H. sapiens* evolved in Africa. Evidence of sophisticated thought in *H. sapiens* includes a 2002 discovery in South Africa of 77,000-year-old art—geometric markings made on pieces of ochre (**Figure 34.52**). And in 2004, archaeologists working in southern and eastern Africa found 75,000-year-old ostrich eggs and snail shells with holes neatly drilled through them. By 36,000 years ago, humans were producing spectacular cave paintings. While these developments can help us understand the spread of *H. sapiens*, it is not clear whether they played a role in the extinction of other hominins. Neanderthals, for example, also made complex

▲ **Figure 34.52 Art, a human hallmark.** The engravings on this 77,000-year-old piece of ochre, discovered in South Africa's Blombos Cave, are among the earliest signs of symbolic thought in humans.

tools and showed a capacity for symbolic thought. As a result, the earlier suggestion that Neanderthals were driven to extinction by competition with *H. sapiens* is now being questioned by some scientists.

Our discussion of humans brings this unit on biological diversity to an end. But this organization isn't meant to imply that life consists of a ladder leading from lowly microorganisms to lofty humanity. Biological diversity is the product of branching phylogeny, not ladderlike "progress," however we choose to measure it. The fact that there are more species of ray-finned fishes alive today than all other vertebrates combined is a clear indication that our finned relatives are not outmoded underachievers that failed to leave the water. The tetrapods—amphibians, reptiles, and mammals—are derived from one lineage of lobe-finned vertebrates. As tetrapods diversified on land, fishes continued their branching evolution in the greatest portion of the biosphere's volume. Similarly, the ubiquity of diverse prokaryotes throughout the biosphere today is a reminder of the enduring ability of these relatively simple organisms to keep up with the times through adaptive evolution. Biology exalts life's diversity, past and present.

CONCEPT CHECK 34.8

1. Identify some characters that distinguish hominins from other apes.
2. Provide an example in which different features of organisms in the hominin evolutionary lineage evolved at different rates.
3. **WHAT IF?** Some genetic studies suggest that the most recent common ancestor of *Homo sapiens* that lived outside of Africa spread from Africa about 50,000 years ago. Compare this date with the dates of fossils given in the text. Can both the genetic results and the dates ascribed to the fossils be correct? Explain.

For suggested answers, see Appendix A.

34 CHAPTER REVIEW

SUMMARY OF KEY CONCEPTS

Nested clade labels (brackets spanning the table):
- **Chordates:** notochord; dorsal, hollow nerve cord; pharyngeal slits; post-anal tail
- **Craniates:** two sets of *Hox* genes, neural crest
- **Vertebrates:** *Dlx* genes duplication, backbone of vertebrae
- **Gnathostomes:** hinged jaws, four sets of *Hox* genes
- **Osteichthyans:** bony skeleton
- **Lobe-fins:** muscular fins or limbs
- **Tetrapods:** four limbs, neck, fused pelvic girdle
- **Amniotes:** amniotic egg, rib cage ventilation

Key Concept	Clade	Description
Concept 34.1 Chordates have a notochord and a dorsal, hollow nerve cord (pp. 697–701) ▶ *Describe likely features of the chordate common ancestor and explain your reasoning.*	Cephalochordata (lancelets)	Basal chordates; marine suspension feeders that exhibit four key derived characters of chordates
	Urochordata (tunicates)	Marine suspension feeders; larvae display the derived traits of chordates
Concept 34.2 Craniates are chordates that have a head (pp. 701–703) ▶ *Compare the typical lifestyle of craniates with that of lancelets and tunicates.*	Myxini (hagfishes and relatives)	Jawless marine organisms; have head that includes a skull and brain, eyes, and other sensory organs
Concept 34.3 Vertebrates are craniates that have a backbone (pp. 703–704) ▶ *Identify the shared features of early fossil vertebrates.*	Petromyzontida (lampreys)	Jawless vertebrates; typically feed by attaching to a live fish and ingesting its blood
Concept 34.4 Gnathostomes are vertebrates that have jaws (pp. 704–709) ▶ *How would the appearance of organisms with jaws have altered ecological interactions? Provide supporting evidence.*	Chondrichthyes (sharks, rays, skates, ratfishes)	Aquatic gnathostomes; have cartilaginous skeleton, a derived trait formed by the reduction of an ancestral mineralized skeleton
	Actinopterygii (ray-finned fishes)	Aquatic gnathostomes; have bony skeleton and maneuverable fins supported by rays
	Actinistia (coelacanths)	Ancient lineage of aquatic lobe-fins still surviving in Indian Ocean
	Dipnoi (lungfishes)	Freshwater lobe-fins with both lungs and gills; sister group of tetrapods
Concept 34.5 Tetrapods are gnathostomes that have limbs (pp. 709–713) ▶ *Which features of amphibians restrict most species to living in aquatic or moist terrestrial habitats?*	Amphibia (salamanders, frogs, caecilians)	Have four limbs descended from modified fins; most have moist skin that functions in gas exchange; many live both in water (as larvae) and on land (as adults)
Concept 34.6 Amniotes are tetrapods that have a terrestrially adapted egg (pp. 713–720) ▶ *Explain why birds are considered reptiles.*	Reptilia (tuataras, lizards and snakes, turtles, crocodilians, birds)	One of two groups of living amniotes; have amniotic eggs and rib cage ventilation, key adaptations for life on land
Concept 34.7 Mammals are amniotes that have hair and produce milk (pp. 720–728) ▶ *Describe the origin and early evolution of mammals.*	Mammalia (monotremes, marsupials, eutherians)	Evolved from synapsid ancestors; include egg-laying monotremes (echidnas, platypus); pouched marsupials (such as kangaroos, opossums); and eutherians (placental mammals, such as rodents, primates)

734 UNIT FIVE The Evolutionary History of Biological Diversity

Humans are mammals that have a large brain and bipedal locomotion (pp. 728–733)

- Derived characters of humans include that we are bipedal and have a larger brain and reduced jaw compared with other apes.
- Hominins—humans and species that are more closely related to humans than to chimpanzees—originated in Africa at least 6 million years ago. Early hominins had a small brain but probably walked upright.
- The oldest evidence of tool use is 2.5 million years old.
- *Homo ergaster* was the first fully bipedal, large-brained hominin. *Homo erectus* was the first hominin to leave Africa.
- Neanderthals lived in Europe and the Near East from about 350,000 to 28,000 years ago.
- *Homo sapiens* originated in Africa about 195,000 years ago and began to spread to other continents about 115,000 years ago.

? *Explain why it is misleading to portray human evolution as a "ladder" leading to* Homo sapiens.

TEST YOUR UNDERSTANDING

LEVEL 1: KNOWLEDGE/COMPREHENSION

1. Vertebrates and tunicates share
   a. jaws adapted for feeding.
   b. a high degree of cephalization.
   c. the formation of structures from the neural crest.
   d. an endoskeleton that includes a skull.
   e. a notochord and a dorsal, hollow nerve cord.

2. Some animals that lived 530 million years ago resembled lancelets but had a brain and a skull. These animals may represent
   a. the first chordates.
   b. a "missing link" between urochordates and cephalochordates.
   c. early craniates.
   d. marsupials.
   e. nontetrapod gnathostomes.

3. Which of the following could be considered the most recent common ancestor of living tetrapods?
   a. a sturdy-finned, shallow-water lobe-fin whose appendages had skeletal supports similar to those of terrestrial vertebrates
   b. an armored, jawed placoderm with two pairs of appendages
   c. an early ray-finned fish that developed bony skeletal supports in its paired fins
   d. a salamander that had legs supported by a bony skeleton but moved with the side-to-side bending typical of fishes
   e. an early terrestrial caecilian whose legless condition had evolved secondarily

4. Unlike eutherians, *both* monotremes and marsupials
   a. lack nipples.
   b. have some embryonic development outside the uterus.
   c. lay eggs.
   d. are found in Australia and Africa.
   e. include only insectivores and herbivores.

5. Which clade does *not* include humans?
   a. synapsids
   b. lobe-fins
   c. diapsids
   d. craniates
   e. osteichthyans

6. As hominins diverged from other primates, which of the following appeared first?
   a. reduced jawbones
   b. language
   c. bipedal locomotion
   d. the making of stone tools
   e. an enlarged brain

LEVEL 2: APPLICATION/ANALYSIS

7. **EVOLUTION CONNECTION**
   A scientist comments that living members of a vertebrate lineage can be very different from early members of the lineage and that evolutionary reversals (character losses) are common. Give specific examples that illustrate these observations, and explain the evolutionary mechanism(s) that cause them.

LEVEL 3: SYNTHESIS/EVALUATION

8. **SCIENTIFIC INQUIRY**
   DRAW IT As a consequence of size alone, organisms that are large tend to have larger brains than organisms that are small. However, some organisms have brains that are considerably larger than expected for an animal of their size. There are high energetic costs associated with the development and maintenance of brains that are large relative to body size.
   a. The fossil record documents trends in which brains that are large relative to body size evolved in certain lineages, including hominins. In such lineages, what can you infer about the relative magnitude of the costs and benefits of large brains?
   b. Hypothesize how natural selection might favor the evolution of large brains despite their high maintenance costs.
   c. Data for 14 bird species are listed below. Graph the data, placing deviation from expected brain size on the *x*-axis and mortality rate on the *y*-axis. What can you conclude about the relationship between brain size and mortality?

Deviation from Expected Brain Size*	-2.4	-2.1	2.0	-1.8	-1.0	0.0	0.3	0.7	1.2	1.3	2.0	2.3	3.0	3.2
Mortality Rate	0.9	0.7	0.5	0.9	0.4	0.7	0.8	0.4	0.8	0.3	0.6	0.6	0.3	0.6

D. Sol et al., Big-brained birds survive better in nature, *Proceedings of the Royal Society B* 274:763–769 (2007).

*Values <0 indicate brain sizes smaller than expected; values >0 indicate sizes larger than expected.

9. **WRITE ABOUT A THEME**
   Emergent Properties Early tetrapods had a sprawling gait (like that of a lizard): As the right front foot moved forward, the body twisted to the left and the left rib cage and lung were compressed; the reverse occurred with the next step. Normal breathing, in which both lungs expand equally with each breath, was hindered during walking and prevented during running. In a short essay (100–150 words), explain how the origin of organisms such as dinosaurs, whose gait allowed them to move without compressing their lungs, could have led to emergent properties in biological communities.

For selected answers, see Appendix A.

MasteringBIOLOGY www.masteringbiology.com

1. MasteringBiology® Assignments
Activities Characteristics of Chordates • Primate Diversity • Human Evolution
Questions Student Misconceptions • Reading Quiz • Multiple Choice • End-of-Chapter

2. eText
Read your book online, search, take notes, highlight text, and more.

3. The Study Area
Practice Tests • Cumulative Test • *BioFlix* 3-D Animations • MP3 Tutor Sessions • Videos • Activities • Investigations • Lab Media • Audio Glossary • Word Study Tools • Art

Plant Form and Function

An Interview with
Luis Herrera-Estrella

Luis Herrera-Estrella is a leading advocate for the use of genetic engineering to improve the lives of poor farmers in Mexico and other developing countries. He graduated with a B.Sc. in Biochemical Engineering from the National Polytechnic Institute (NPI) in Mexico City in 1978. In 1980 he received his M.Sc. from the Center for Research and Advanced Studies at NPI (where he heads a laboratory today) and in 1984 his Ph.D. from Ghent University, in Belgium. While still a graduate student, he published the first report of the successful transfer and expression of a bacterial gene in plant cells. He also pioneered the development of selectable markers and the use of reporter genes for plant systems, which have since become two of the most important tools in developing gene transfer systems for crops. More recently, his work has focused on improving plant tolerance to acidic and phosphate-deficient soils. Among other honors, Dr. Herrera is a Scholar of the Howard Hughes Biomedical Institute, a member of the Mexican Academy of Sciences, a foreign associate member of the U.S. National Academy of Sciences, and a past president of the International Society for Plant Molecular Biology.

What sparked your interest in science?

My childhood interest in science came from reading books and watching TV programs about science and technology. As a child, I wanted to be an inventor. However, because I came from a lower middle-class family in Mexico and had no contact with scientists or academics, I didn't really know what science or research was. When I finished high school, I wanted to become a nuclear physicist, but I was told that nuclear physics didn't have a future in Mexico. So I studied biochemical engineering. I had an inspirational teacher, a microbiologist who taught me about molecular biology. I was fascinated and decided to pursue a Ph.D.

How did you become interested in plant molecular biology?

I thought about how I could use molecular biology. Agriculture is important in Mexico, so I decided to study plant molecular biology even though I had absolutely no background in plant biology! When I reached this decision, Francisco Bolivar, one of the scientists who had developed a type of plasmid widely used in genetic engineering, had just returned to Mexico. So I asked him if I could work with him before entering a Ph.D. program. Very kindly, he accepted me. When I was in his lab, a visiting scientist from Belgium, Marc van Montagu, gave a seminar about *Agrobacterium* and the potential use of this bacterium for genetically modifying plants. I immediately thought, "That's my future!"

Agrobacterium tumefaciens is a bacterial pathogen that causes crown gall disease. How does one make the creative leap to change a disease into a useful tool?

Agrobacterium causes disease by transferring genes into the host plant's chromosomes and modifying the cell's metabolism for its own benefit. When I went to Belgium, the plant molecular biologist Patricia Zambryski was already studying the mechanism by which tumor-inducing (Ti) plasmids of *Agrobacterium* integrate into plant chromosomes. She had been able to produce "disarmed Ti plasmids"—modified plasmids that failed to produce tumors or alter the host's metabolism but were still effective in DNA transfer. But we didn't have a way to quickly identify which cells were modified because the transformed cells had no selective advantage. I started working on a way to get plant cells to express foreign genes. Scientists had just identified the sequences of two genes in the DNA transferred by *Agrobacterium* to its host. So I figured that the promoter sequence and terminator sequences of these genes could be used to express any gene we chose. We took a gene that confers resistance to the protein synthesis inhibitor kanamycin (because we could select for that gene) and integrated it into a disarmed Ti plasmid. We then transformed plant cells with these plasmids and obtained transgenic plant cells that were resistant to kanamycin! The next question was whether genetic transformation had affected the ability of the cells to regenerate from tiny clumps of cells into whole plants. It was exciting to see that when we put these cells in tissue culture medium, little plants emerged, and they were still kanamycin resistant. Finally, we determined that the transgenes were passed on according to Mendel's laws, just like any other gene!

How is your more recent research contributing to agriculture?

One of the major problems faced by farmers in the tropics is acidic soil. The problem stems from the fact that aluminum, which is high in tropical soils, becomes soluble under acidic conditions, and the ions are quite toxic to plants. We have been able to genetically alter plants to secrete more organic acids from their roots. The organic anions bind the aluminum cations and eliminate the toxicity.

We are also interested in how plants alter their architecture in response to deficiencies in phosphorus, an essential plant nutrient. Phosphorus availability is one of the most limiting factors for plant productivity in many natural and agricultural ecosystems. We have found that in low-phosphorus conditions, root systems become more branched, and root hairs become denser and longer. What controls these changes? You don't see this in animals. We don't develop extra arms or extra legs in response to environmental changes.

What are the steps for transferring the results of basic research to products in the field, and why do some people oppose genetically engineered crops?

To go from a discovery in the lab to the commercial release of a transgenic plant is a long process that requires extensive testing in the lab, in the greenhouse, and eventually in the field. You have to demonstrate that the transgenic crop performs consistently under different environments and that it has no negative effects on yield or quality. And then you have to go through the process of approval for human consumption and show that the protein that you introduce is not toxic or allergenic. Unfortunately, it can cost $10–50 million to go through this regulatory process. Nowadays, the only organizations that can afford to commercialize transgenic plants are large, multinational companies.

Because multinational companies have monopolized the commercialization of transgenic plants, there has been a strong reaction from people who oppose the control of food production by such companies. Other issues are raised—for example, that GMOs (genetically modified organisms) could harm the environment or human health. But in fact most of the products commercially released to date have been shown to be totally innocuous for human and animal health and have no different impact on the environment than traditional crops. The opposition to GMOs initially started in Europe, where most people have enough money to buy food and don't need transgenic crops. It's not the same case in other countries where any technology that helps to produce more and better food is strongly needed. I do not think that recombinant technology is a miracle that is going to solve the problem of hunger in the world, but it's going to be a very important tool for making agriculture more productive.

Tell us about the debate surrounding GMOs in Mexico.
When I returned to Mexico in 1986, some field trials of transgenic plants were under way. There wasn't much controversy because few people knew what a transgenic plant was. Government officials had heard about the potential applications of genetic engineering, and they were happy that Mexico was involved in this new technology. But then people who oppose multinational companies and some ecologists started to protest, and the government officials became concerned. The government decided that if the scientists couldn't agree, then it would be better to err on the side of caution, and an official moratorium was imposed against planting transgenic crops in Mexico. The farmers, however, wanted the technology, and they began smuggling the seeds of genetically modified plants, especially maize, into Mexico and planting them illegally. This is a bad situation because you don't know what, where, or how much they are planting. We argued that the only way of assessing whether GMOs are actually going to have a negative effect on the environment and alter the genomes of indigenous varieties of maize is to do small, controlled experiments employing every conceivable biological safety measure. Eventually, the government agreed and lifted the moratorium.

Maize cross-fertilizes very easily and over long distances, so it's impossible to avoid the transfer of genes from transgenic maize into Mexico's indigenous varieties of maize. Is this a problem? Personally, I don't think so. Plants, particularly maize, are full of transposable elements that jump from one place in the genome to another. So, the maize genome is already a "mess." Introducing one more gene is not going to be any different from a transposon moving an enhancer or a complete gene from one place in the genome to another. Of course we have to analyze each transgenic line to make sure that the gene is not going to cause any problem for the environment or for the health of humans or other animals.

How can genetic engineering improve the welfare of poor farmers in developing countries?
Those who would benefit the most from genetic engineering are the poorest farmers. For example, the average production of maize in Mexico is about 2.5 tons per acre. But in central Mexico, where I live, the production of maize is around 8–10 tons per acre. That means that in many places, people are producing only 1 ton per acre. If, by using recombinant DNA technology, we can increase the yields of these poor farmers to 3 tons per acre, these people will triple their incomes. Of course, the big seed companies tailor their products for large farms, but they are willing to donate their expertise toward programs aimed at developing the types of crop varieties needed by subsistence farmers. People who oppose the use of the transgenic crops simply because they are controlled by large companies are making it more difficult for scientists in the developing world to create the varieties that are needed by the poor farmers in their countries.

By altering plants you are continuing a great and ancient Mexican tradition: plant domestication. How did farmers create maize over 10,000 years ago?
Well, first I must say that our attempts to modify maize are quite modest compared with what the ancient Native American farmers accomplished. Maize is derived from a wild grass called teosinte. The two plants look fairly similar. It's very hard, for example, to distinguish between the leaves of teosinte and maize. The really fantastic difference is in the reproductive organs. When a teosinte seed matures, it goes "pop!" and lands on the ground. Picking up these small seeds is laborious, so the ancient farmers selected plants that had cobs that held onto their seeds. Also, because teosinte seeds have a very hard coat, making them difficult to cook, the farmers selected for a thinner seed coat. And teosinte has only a single row of seeds, so these early farmers selected for two rows of seeds, and then four and eight, and so on. What we are doing now with genetic engineering is absolutely nothing compared with the domestication of maize.

You have published research on plants, fungi, and bacteria. What has led you to cast such a wide intellectual net?
Curiosity about life and nature and the world around me. I don't share the ambition of people who embrace a single question, topic, or model system at the beginning of their career and then die studying the same thing. I'm always eager to explore new processes and new phenomena, even if I have to switch to a completely different field. Currently, I'm sequencing the genome of plant species native to Mexico—but truthfully, I don't know what I'm going to be doing in four years.

"... our attempts to modify maize are quite modest compared with what the ancient Native American farmers accomplished."

Luis Herrera-Estrella (right) with Peter Minorsky (left) and Jane Reece

35

Plant Structure, Growth, and Development

▲ Figure 35.1 **Computer art?**

OVERVIEW

Are Plants Computers?

The object in **Figure 35.1** is not the creation of a computer genius with a flair for the artistic. It is a head of romanesco, an edible relative of broccoli. Romanesco's mesmerizing beauty is attributable to the fact that each of its smaller buds resembles in miniature the entire vegetable. (Mathematicians refer to such repetitive patterns as *fractals*.) Romanesco looks as if it were generated by a computer because its growth pattern follows a repetitive sequence of instructions. As in most plants, the growing shoot tips lay down a pattern of leaf . . . bud . . . stem, over and over again. These repetitive developmental patterns are genetically determined and subject to natural selection. For example, a mutation that shortens the stem segments between leaves will generate a bushier plant. If this altered architecture enhances the plant's ability to access resources such as light and, by doing so, to leave more offspring, then this trait will occur more frequently in later generations—evolution will have occurred.

Romanesco is unusual in adhering so rigidly to its basic body organization. Most plants show much greater diversity in their individual forms because the growth of most plants, much more than in animals, is affected by local environmental conditions. All lions, for example, have four legs and are of roughly the same size, but oak trees vary in the number and arrangement of their branches. This is because lions and other animals respond to challenges and opportunities in their local environment by movement, whereas plants respond by altering their growth. Illumination of a plant from the side, for example, creates asymmetries in its basic body plan. Branches grow more quickly from the illuminated side of a shoot than from the shaded side, an architectural change of obvious benefit for photosynthesis. Recognizing the highly adaptive development of plants is critical for understanding how plants interact with their environment.

Chapters 29 and 30 described the evolution of plants from green algae to angiosperms (flowering plants). In Unit Six, we focus primarily on angiosperms because they serve as the primary producers in many ecosystems and are of great agricultural importance. We begin by discussing the structure of flowering plants and how these plants develop.

CONCEPT **35.1**

Plants have a hierarchical organization consisting of organs, tissues, and cells

Plants, like most animals, have organs composed of different tissues, which in turn are composed of different cell types. A **tissue** is a group of cells, consisting of one or more cell types, that together perform a specialized function. An **organ** consists of several types of tissues that together carry out particular functions. In looking at the hierarchy of plant organs, tissues, and cells, we begin with organs because they are the most familiar and easily observed plant structures. As you learn about the hierarchy of plant structure, keep in mind how natural selection has produced plant forms that fit plant function at all levels of organization.

UNIVERSITY OF ALBERTA FACULTY BIO

Janice Cooke BSc Biology (University of Victoria): PhD Biological Sciences (University of Alberta)

Current Position: Assistant Professor Plant Biology, Department of Biological Sciences.

I knew from an early age that I wanted to be a biologist. I actually began my scientific career in animal biochemistry, but after a job in which I had to take samples from lab rats, I decided that animal research was not for me. I've been involved in forest tree research ever since.

I currently teach Botany 205 (Fundamentals of Plant Biology), Botany 340 (Plant Physiology), Botany 445/545 (Molecular Plant Physiology), and Botany 464/564 (Plant Functional Genomics).

My lab is investigating many aspects of forest tree biology. Forest trees are cool because they are long-lived plants that in many cases are keystone species in ecosystems. Imagine a world without forest trees! Our main interest is to understand how tree growth is affected by the environment. Trees are constantly faced with stresses like nutrient limitation, harsh winter conditions, and attack by pests and pathogens. Trees can not run away from these stresses, so how do they respond? What genes control these responses? How do these responses impact trees' growth, development and ability to thrive in their environment? Our experiments take place in both the lab and the field, where we use a lot of different tools to investigate these questions, such as genomics, molecular biology, microscopy, physiology, biochemistry, and genetics.

The Three Basic Plant Organs: Roots, Stems, and Leaves

The basic morphology of vascular plants reflects their evolutionary history as terrestrial organisms that inhabit and draw resources from two very different environments—below the ground and above the ground. They must absorb water and minerals from below the ground surface and CO_2 and light from above the ground surface. The ability to acquire these resources efficiently is traceable to the evolution of three basic organs—roots, stems, and leaves. These organs form a **root system** and a **shoot system**, the latter consisting of stems and leaves **(Figure 35.2)**. With few exceptions, vascular plants rely completely on both systems for survival. Roots typically are not photosynthetic; they starve unless *photosynthates*, the sugars and other carbohydrates produced during photosynthesis, are imported from the shoot system. Conversely, the shoot system depends on the water and minerals that roots absorb from the soil.

Vegetative growth—production of nonreproductive leaves, stems, and roots—is only one stage in a plant's life. Most plants also undergo growth relating to sexual reproduction. In angiosperms, reproductive shoots bear flowers, which consist of leaves that are highly modified for sexual reproduction.

Later in this chapter, we'll discuss the transition from vegetative shoot formation to reproductive shoot formation.

In describing plant organs, we'll draw examples mainly from the two major groups of angiosperms: monocots and eudicots (see Figure 30.13).

Roots

A **root** is an organ that anchors a vascular plant in the soil, absorbs minerals and water, and often stores carbohydrates. Most eudicots and gymnosperms have a *taproot system*, consisting of one main vertical root, the **taproot**, which develops from an embryonic root. The taproot gives rise to **lateral roots**, also called branch roots (see Figure 35.2). Taproot systems generally penetrate deeply and are therefore well adapted to deep soils, where the groundwater is not close to the surface.

In most monocots, such as grasses, the embryonic root dies early on and does not form a taproot. Instead, many small roots emerge from the stem. Such roots are said to be *adventitious* (from the Latin *adventicus*, extraneous), a term describing a plant organ that grows in an unusual location, such as roots arising from stems or leaves. Each small root forms its own lateral roots. The result is a *fibrous root system*—a mat of generally thin roots spreading out below the soil surface (see Figure 30.13). Fibrous root systems usually do not penetrate deeply and are therefore best adapted to shallow soils or regions where rainfall is light and does not moisten the soil much below the surface layer. Most grasses have shallow roots, concentrated in the upper few centimeters of the soil. Because these shallow roots hold the topsoil in place, grass makes excellent ground cover for preventing erosion.

Although the entire root system helps anchor a plant, in most plants the absorption of water and minerals occurs primarily near the tips of roots, where vast numbers of **root hairs** emerge and increase the surface area of the root enormously **(Figure 35.3)**. A root hair is a thin, tubular extension of a root epidermal cell. It should not be confused with a lateral root, which is an organ. Despite their great surface

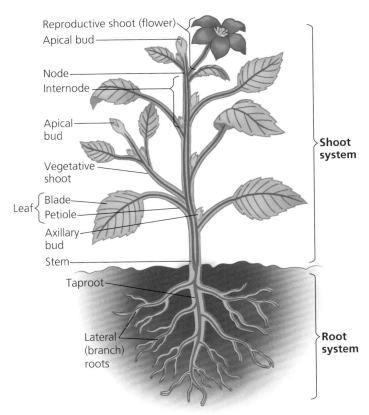

▲ Figure 35.2 An overview of a flowering plant. The plant body is divided into a root system and a shoot system, connected by vascular tissue (purple strands in this diagram) that is continuous throughout the plant. The plant shown is an idealized eudicot.

◄ Figure 35.3 Root hairs of a radish seedling. Root hairs grow by the thousands just behind the tip of each root. By increasing the root's surface area, they greatly enhance the absorption of water and minerals from the soil.

area, root hairs, unlike lateral roots, contribute little to plant anchorage. Their main function is absorption.

Many plants have root adaptations with specialized functions (**Figure 35.4**). Some of these arise from the roots, and others are adventitious, developing from stems or, in rare cases, leaves. Some modified roots add support and anchorage. Others store water and nutrients or absorb oxygen from the air.

Stems

A **stem** is an organ that raises or separates leaves, exposing them to sunlight. Stems also raise reproductive structures, facilitating dispersal of pollen and fruit. Each stem consists of an alternating system of **nodes**, the points at which leaves are attached, and **internodes**, the stem segments between nodes (see Figure 35.2). In the upper angle (axil) formed by each leaf and the stem is an **axillary bud**, a structure that can form a lateral shoot, commonly called a branch. Young axillary buds typically grow very slowly: Most of the growth of a young shoot is concentrated near the shoot tip, which consists of an **apical bud**, or terminal bud, that is composed of developing leaves and a compact series of nodes and internodes.

The proximity of the axillary buds to the apical bud is partly responsible for their dormancy. The inhibition of axillary buds by an apical bud is called **apical dominance**. If an animal eats the end of the shoot or if shading results in

▼ Figure 35.4 **Evolutionary adaptations of roots.**

▲ **Prop roots.** The aerial roots of hala trees are examples of prop roots, so named because they support the tall, top-heavy trees. Hala trees grow along coastal areas in the South Pacific where the sandy soils are shallow and unstable.

◀ **Storage roots.** Many plants, such as the common beet, store food and water in their roots.

◀ **"Strangling" aerial roots.** The seeds of this strangler fig germinate in the branches of tall trees of other species and send numerous aerial roots to the ground. These snakelike roots gradually wrap around the host tree and objects such as this Cambodian temple ruin. Eventually, the host tree dies of shading by the fig leaves.

▼ **Buttress roots.** Because of moist conditions in the tropics, root systems of many of the tallest trees are surprisingly shallow. Aerial roots that look like buttresses, such as seen in this ceiba tree in Central America, give architectural support to the trunks of such trees.

▲ **Pneumatophores.** Also known as air roots, pneumatophores are produced by trees such as mangroves that inhabit tidal swamps. By projecting above the water's surface, they enable the root system to obtain oxygen, which is lacking in the thick, waterlogged mud.

the light being more intense to the side of the shoot, axillary buds break dormancy; that is, they start growing. A growing axillary bud gives rise to a lateral shoot, complete with its own apical bud, leaves, and axillary buds. Removing the apical bud stimulates the growth of axillary buds, resulting in more lateral shoots. That is why pruning trees and shrubs and pinching back houseplants will make them bushier.

Some plants have stems with additional functions, such as food storage and asexual reproduction. These modified stems, which include rhizomes, bulbs, stolons, and tubers, are often mistaken for roots (**Figure 35.5**).

▼ **Figure 35.5 Evolutionary adaptations of stems.**

◀ **Rhizomes.** The base of this iris plant is an example of a rhizome, a horizontal shoot that grows just below the surface. Vertical shoots emerge from axillary buds on the rhizome.

▶ **Bulbs.** Bulbs are vertical underground shoots consisting mostly of the enlarged bases of leaves that store food. You can see the many layers of modified leaves attached to the short stem by slicing an onion bulb lengthwise.

▶ **Stolons.** Shown here on a strawberry plant, stolons are horizontal shoots that grow along the surface. These "runners" enable a plant to reproduce asexually, as plantlets form at nodes along each runner.

◀ **Tubers.** Tubers, such as these potatoes, are enlarged ends of rhizomes or stolons specialized for storing food. The "eyes" of a potato are clusters of axillary buds that mark the nodes.

Leaves

In most vascular plants, the **leaf** is the main photosynthetic organ, although green stems also perform photosynthesis. Leaves vary extensively in form but generally consist of a flattened **blade** and a stalk, the **petiole**, which joins the leaf to the stem at a node (see Figure 35.2). Grasses and many other monocots lack petioles; instead, the base of the leaf forms a sheath that envelops the stem.

Monocots and eudicots differ in the arrangement of **veins**, the vascular tissue of leaves. Most monocots have parallel major veins that run the length of the blade. Eudicots generally have a branched network of major veins (see Figure 30.13).

In identifying angiosperms according to structure, taxonomists rely mainly on floral morphology, but they also use variations in leaf morphology, such as leaf shape, the branching pattern of veins, and the spatial arrangement of leaves. **Figure 35.6** illustrates a difference in leaf shape: simple versus compound. Many leaves, such as those of poison ivy, are

▼ **Figure 35.6 Simple versus compound leaves.**

Simple leaf

A simple leaf has a single, undivided blade. Some simple leaves are deeply lobed, as shown here.

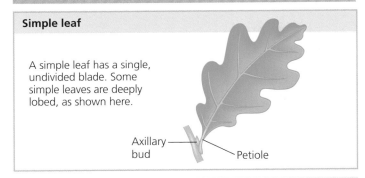

Axillary bud — Petiole

Compound leaf

In a compound leaf, the blade consists of multiple leaflets. A leaflet has no axillary bud at its base.

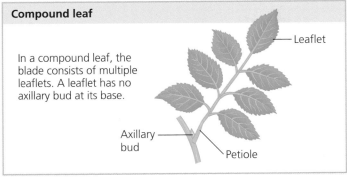

Leaflet

Axillary bud — Petiole

Doubly compound leaf

In a doubly compound leaf, each leaflet is divided into smaller leaflets.

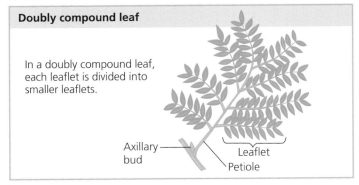

Axillary bud — Leaflet — Petiole

compound or doubly compound. This structural adaptation may enable leaves to withstand strong wind with less tearing. It may also confine some pathogens (disease-causing organisms and viruses) that invade the leaf to a single leaflet, rather than allowing them to spread to the entire leaf.

Almost all leaves are specialized for photosynthesis. However, some species have leaves with adaptations that enable them to perform additional functions, such as support, protection, storage, or reproduction (**Figure 35.7**).

▼ **Figure 35.7** **Evolutionary adaptations of leaves.**

▶ **Tendrils.** The tendrils by which this pea plant clings to a support are modified leaves. After it has "lassoed" a support, a tendril forms a coil that brings the plant closer to the support. Tendrils are typically modified leaves, but some tendrils are modified stems, as in grapevines.

◀ **Spines.** The spines of cacti, such as this prickly pear, are actually leaves; photosynthesis is carried out by the fleshy green stems.

◀ **Storage leaves.** Most succulents, such as this ice plant, have leaves adapted for storing water.

◀ **Reproductive leaves.** The leaves of some succulents, such as *Kalanchoë daigremontiana*, produce adventitious plantlets, which fall off the leaf and take root in the soil.

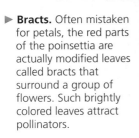

▶ **Bracts.** Often mistaken for petals, the red parts of the poinsettia are actually modified leaves called bracts that surround a group of flowers. Such brightly colored leaves attract pollinators.

Dermal, Vascular, and Ground Tissues

Each plant organ—root, stem, or leaf—has dermal, vascular, and ground tissues. Each of these three categories forms a **tissue system**, a functional unit connecting all of the plant's organs. Although each tissue system is continuous throughout the plant, specific characteristics of the tissues and their spatial relationships to one another vary in different organs (**Figure 35.8**).

The **dermal tissue system** is the plant's outer protective covering. Like our skin, it forms the first line of defense against physical damage and pathogens. In nonwoody plants, it is usually a single tissue called the **epidermis**, a layer of tightly packed cells. In leaves and most stems, the **cuticle**, a waxy coating on the epidermal surface, helps prevent water loss. In woody plants, protective tissues called **periderm** replace the epidermis in older regions of stems and roots. In addition to protecting the plant from water loss and disease, the epidermis has specialized characteristics in each organ. For example, a root hair is an extension of an epidermal cell near the tip of a root. *Trichomes* are hairlike outgrowths of the shoot epidermis. In some desert species, they reduce water loss and reflect excess light, but their most common function

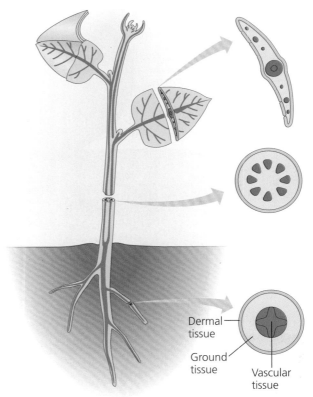

Dermal tissue

Ground tissue

Vascular tissue

▲ **Figure 35.8** **The three tissue systems.** The dermal tissue system (blue) provides a protective cover for the entire body of a plant. The vascular tissue system (purple), which transports materials between the root and shoot systems, is also continuous throughout the plant, but is arranged differently in each organ. The ground tissue system (yellow), which is responsible for most of the plant's metabolic functions, is located between the dermal tissue and the vascular tissue in each organ.

is to provide defense against insects by forming a barrier or by secreting sticky fluids or toxic compounds. For instance, the trichomes on aromatic leaves such as mint secrete oils that protect the plants from herbivores and disease. **Figure 35.9** describes an investigation of the relationship between trichome density on soybean pods and damage by beetles.

▼ Figure 35.9

INQUIRY

Do soybean pod trichomes deter herbivores?

EXPERIMENT Bean leaf beetles (*Cerotoma trifurcata*) feed on developing legume pods, causing pod scarring and decreased seed quality. W. F. Lam and L. P. Pedigo, of Purdue University, investigated whether the stiff trichomes on soybean pods (*Glycine max*) physically deter these beetles. The researchers placed hungry beetles in muslin bags and sealed the bags around the pods of adjacent plants expressing different pod hairiness. The amount of damage to the pods was assessed after 24 hours.

Very hairy pod (10 trichomes/mm²)   Slightly hairy pod (2 trichomes/mm²)   Bald pod (no trichomes)

RESULTS Beetle damage to very hairy soybean pods was much lower than damage to the other pod types.

Very hairy pod: 10% damage   Slightly hairy pod: 25% damage   Bald pod: 40% damage

CONCLUSION Soybean pod trichomes protect against beetle damage.

SOURCE W. F. Lam and L. P. Pedigo, Effect of trichome density on soybean pod feeding by adult bean leaf beetles (Coleoptera: Chrysomelidae), *Journal of Economic Entomology* 94:1459–1463 (2001).

WHAT IF? The pod trichomes of most soybean varieties are white, but some varieties have tan-colored trichomes. Suppose that the effects of trichome density on beetle feeding were observed only in tan-haired varieties. What might this finding suggest about how these trichomes deter beetles?

The **vascular tissue system** carries out long-distance transport of materials between the root and shoot systems. The two types of vascular tissues are xylem and phloem. **Xylem** conducts water and dissolved minerals upward from roots into the shoots. **Phloem** transports sugars, the products of photosynthesis, from where they are made (usually the leaves) to where they are needed—usually roots and sites of growth, such as developing leaves and fruits. The vascular tissue of a root or stem is collectively called the **stele** (the Greek word for "pillar"). The arrangement of the stele varies, depending on the species and organ. In angiosperms, for example, the root stele is a solid central *vascular cylinder* of xylem and phloem, whereas the stele of stems and leaves consists of *vascular bundles*, separate strands containing xylem and phloem (see Figure 35.8). Both xylem and phloem are composed of a variety of cell types, including cells that are highly specialized for transport or support.

Tissues that are neither dermal nor vascular are part of the **ground tissue system**. Ground tissue that is internal to the vascular tissue is known as **pith**, and ground tissue that is external to the vascular tissue is called **cortex**. The ground tissue system is not just filler. It includes various cells specialized for functions such as storage, photosynthesis, and support.

Common Types of Plant Cells

Like any multicellular organism, a plant is characterized by cell differentiation, the specialization of cells in structure and function. Cell differentiation may involve changes both in the cytoplasm and its organelles and in the cell wall. **Figure 35.10**, on the next two pages, focuses on the major types of plant cells: parenchyma cells, collenchyma cells, sclerenchyma cells, the water-conducting cells of the xylem, and the sugar-conducting cells of the phloem. Notice the structural adaptations in the different cells that make their specific functions possible. You may also wish to review Figures 6.9 and 6.28, which show basic plant cell structure.

CONCEPT CHECK 35.1

1. How does the vascular tissue system enable leaves and roots to function together in supporting growth and development of the whole plant?
2. What plant structure is each of the following? (a) brussels sprouts; (b) celery; (c) onions; (d) carrots
3. **WHAT IF?** If humans were photoautotrophs, making food by capturing light energy for photosynthesis, how might our anatomy be different?
4. **MAKE CONNECTIONS** Explain how central vacuoles and cellulose cell walls contribute to plant growth (see Chapter 6, pp. 108 and 118–119).

For suggested answers, see Appendix A.

Exploring Examples of Differentiated Plant Cells

Parenchyma Cells

Mature **parenchyma cells** have primary walls that are relatively thin and flexible, and most lack secondary walls. (See Figure 6.28 to review primary and secondary cell walls.) When mature, parenchyma cells generally have a large central vacuole. Parenchyma cells perform most of the metabolic functions of the plant, synthesizing and storing various organic products. For example, photosynthesis occurs within the chloroplasts of parenchyma cells in the leaf. Some parenchyma cells in stems and roots have colorless plastids that store starch. The fleshy tissue of many fruits is composed mainly of parenchyma cells. Most parenchyma cells retain the ability to divide and differentiate into other types of plant cells under particular conditions—during wound repair, for example. It is even possible to grow an entire plant from a single parenchyma cell.

Parenchyma cells in *Elodea* leaf, with chloroplasts (LM)   60 µm

Collenchyma Cells

Grouped in strands, **collenchyma cells** (seen here in cross section) help support young parts of the plant shoot. Collenchyma cells are generally elongated cells that have thicker primary walls than parenchyma cells, though the walls are unevenly thickened. Young stems and petioles often have strands of collenchyma cells just below their epidermis (for example, the "strings" of a celery stalk, which is a petiole). Collenchyma cells provide flexible support without restraining growth. At maturity, these cells are living and flexible, elongating with the stems and leaves they support—unlike sclerenchyma cells, which we discuss next.

Collenchyma cells (in *Helianthus* stem) (LM)   5 µm

Sclerenchyma Cells

5 µm

Sclereid cells in pear (LM)

25 µm

Cell wall

Fiber cells (cross section from ash tree) (LM)

Sclerenchyma cells also function as supporting elements in the plant, but are much more rigid than collenchyma cells. The secondary walls of sclerenchyma cells are thick and contain large amounts of lignin. This relatively indigestible strengthening polymer accounts for more than a quarter of the dry mass of wood. Lignin is present in all vascular plants, but not in bryophytes. Mature sclerenchyma cells cannot elongate, and they occur in regions of the plant that have stopped growing in length. Sclerenchyma cells are so specialized for support that many are dead at functional maturity, but they produce secondary walls before the protoplast (the living part of the cell) dies. The rigid walls remain as a "skeleton" that supports the plant, in some cases for hundreds of years.

Two types of sclerenchyma cells, known as **sclereids** and **fibers**, are specialized entirely for support and strengthening. Sclereids, which are boxier than fibers and irregular in shape, have very thick, lignified secondary walls. Sclereids impart the hardness to nutshells and seed coats and the gritty texture to pear fruits. Fibers, which are usually grouped in strands, are long, slender, and tapered. Some are used commercially, such as hemp fibers for making rope and flax fibers for weaving into linen.

Water-Conducting Cells of the Xylem

The two types of water-conducting cells, **tracheids** and **vessel elements**, are tubular, elongated cells that are dead at functional maturity. Tracheids are in the xylem of nearly all vascular plants. In addition to tracheids, most angiosperms, as well as a few gymnosperms and a few seedless vascular plants, have vessel elements. When the living cellular contents of a tracheid or vessel element disintegrate, the cell's thickened walls remain behind, forming a nonliving conduit through which water can flow. The secondary walls of tracheids and vessel elements are often interrupted by pits, thinner regions where only primary walls are present (see Figure 6.28 to review primary and secondary walls). Water can migrate laterally between neighboring cells through pits.

Tracheids are long, thin cells with tapered ends. Water moves from cell to cell mainly through the pits, where it does not have to cross thick secondary walls.

Vessel elements are generally wider, shorter, thinner walled, and less tapered than the tracheids. They are aligned end to end, forming long micropipes known as **vessels**. The end walls of vessel elements have perforation plates that enable water to flow freely through the vessels.

The secondary walls of tracheids and vessel elements are hardened with lignin. This hardening prevents collapse under the tensions of water transport and also provides support.

Tracheids and vessels
(colorized SEM)

Vessel   Tracheids   100 µm

Perforation plate

Pits

Vessel element

Vessel elements, with perforated end walls

Tracheids

Sugar-Conducting Cells of the Phloem

Unlike the water-conducting cells of the xylem, the sugar-conducting cells of the phloem are alive at functional maturity. In seedless vascular plants and gymnosperms, sugars and other organic nutrients are transported through long, narrow cells called sieve cells. In the phloem of angiosperms, these nutrients are transported through sieve tubes, which consist of chains of cells called **sieve-tube elements**, or sieve-tube members.

Though alive, sieve-tube elements lack a nucleus, ribosomes, a distinct vacuole, and cytoskeletal elements. This reduction in cell contents enables nutrients to pass more easily through the cell. The end walls between sieve-tube elements, called **sieve plates**, have pores that facilitate the flow of fluid from cell to cell along the sieve tube. Alongside each sieve-tube element is a nonconducting cell called a **companion cell**, which is connected to the sieve-tube element by numerous channels called plasmodesmata (see Figure 6.28). The nucleus and ribosomes of the companion cell serve not only that cell itself but also the adjacent sieve-tube element. In some plants, the companion cells in leaves also help load sugars into the sieve-tube elements, which then transport the sugars to other parts of the plant.

3 µm

Sieve-tube element (left) and companion cell: cross section (TEM)

Sieve-tube elements: longitudinal view

Sieve-tube elements: longitudinal view (LM)

Sieve plate

Companion cells

Sieve-tube elements

Plasmodesma

Sieve plate

Nucleus of companion cell

30 µm

15 µm

Sieve plate with pores (LM)

CONCEPT 35.2

Meristems generate cells for primary and secondary growth

How do plant cells and tissues develop into mature organs? A major difference between plants and most animals is that plant growth is not limited to an embryonic or juvenile period. Instead, growth occurs throughout the plant's life, a process known as **indeterminate growth**. At any given time, a typical plant has embryonic, developing, and mature organs. Except for dormant periods, most plants grow continuously. In contrast, most animals and some plant organs—such as leaves, thorns, and flowers—undergo **determinate growth**; that is, they stop growing after reaching a certain size.

Plants are capable of indeterminate growth because they have perpetually undifferentiated tissues called **meristems** that divide when conditions permit, leading to new cells that can elongate. There are two main types of meristems: apical meristems and lateral meristems (**Figure 35.11**). **Apical meristems**, located at the tips of roots and shoots and in axillary buds of shoots, provide additional cells that enable growth in length, a process known as **primary growth**. Primary growth allows roots to extend throughout the soil and shoots to increase their exposure to light. In herbaceous (nonwoody) plants, primary growth produces all, or almost all, of the plant body. Woody plants, however, also grow in circumference in the parts of stems and roots that no longer grow in length. This growth in thickness, known as **secondary growth**, is caused by **lateral meristems** called the vascular

cambium and cork cambium. These cylinders of dividing cells extend along the length of roots and stems. The **vascular cambium** adds layers of vascular tissue called secondary xylem (wood) and secondary phloem. The **cork cambium** replaces the epidermis with the thicker, tougher periderm.

The cells within meristems divide relatively frequently, generating additional cells. Some new cells remain in the meristem and produce more cells, while others differentiate and are incorporated into tissues and organs of the growing plant. Cells that remain as sources of new cells have traditionally been called *initials* but are increasingly being called *stem cells* to correspond to animal stem cells that also perpetually divide and remain undifferentiated. The new cells displaced from the meristem, called *derivatives*, divide until the cells they produce become specialized in mature tissues.

The relationship between primary and secondary growth is clearly seen in the winter twig of a deciduous tree. At the shoot tip is the dormant apical bud, enclosed by scales that protect its apical meristem (**Figure 35.12**). In spring, the bud sheds its scales and begins a new spurt of primary growth, producing a series of nodes and internodes. Along each growth segment, nodes are marked by scars that were left when leaves fell. Above each leaf scar is an axillary bud or a branch formed by an axillary bud. Farther down the twig are bud scars from the whorls of scales that enclosed the apical bud during the previous winter. During each growing season, primary growth extends the shoots, and secondary growth thickens the parts that formed in previous years.

Although plants grow throughout their lives, they do die, of course. Based on the length of their life cycle, flowering

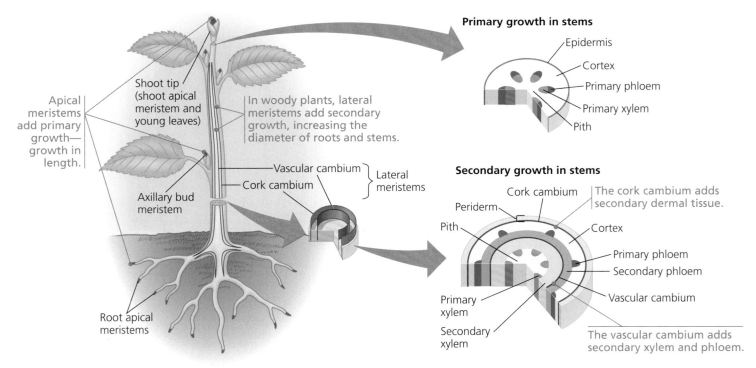

▲ Figure 35.11 **An overview of primary and secondary growth.**

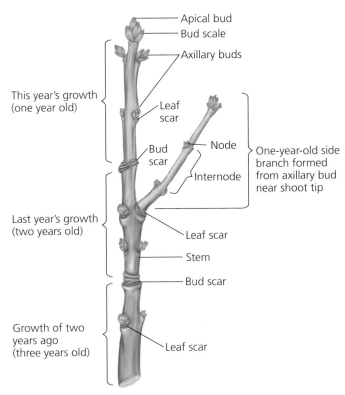

Apical bud
Bud scale
Axillary buds

This year's growth (one year old)

Leaf scar

Bud scar
Node
One-year-old side branch formed from axillary bud near shoot tip
Internode

Last year's growth (two years old)

Leaf scar

Stem

Bud scar

Growth of two years ago (three years old)

Leaf scar

▲ Figure 35.12 **Three years' growth in a winter twig.**

plants can be categorized as annuals, biennials, or perennials. *Annuals* complete their life cycle—from germination to flowering to seed production to death—in a single year or less. Many wildflowers are annuals, as are most staple food crops, including legumes and cereal grains such as wheat and rice. *Biennials*, such as turnips, generally require two growing seasons to complete their life cycle, flowering and fruiting only in their second year. *Perennials* live many years and include trees, shrubs, and some grasses. Some buffalo grass of the North American plains is thought to have been growing for 10,000 years from seeds that sprouted at the close of the last ice age.

CONCEPT CHECK 35.2

1. Distinguish between primary and secondary growth.
2. Cells in lower layers of your skin divide and replace dead cells sloughed from the surface. Are such regions of cell division comparable to a plant meristem? Explain your answer.
3. Roots and stems grow indeterminately, but leaves do not. How might this benefit the plant?
4. **WHAT IF?** Suppose a gardener uproots some carrots after one season and sees they are too small. Carrots are biennials, and so the gardener leaves the remaining plants in the ground, thinking their roots will grow larger during their second year. Is this a good idea? Explain.

For suggested answers, see Appendix A.

SUMMARY OF KEY CONCEPTS

CONCEPT 35.1

Plants have a hierarchical organization consisting of organs, tissues, and cells (pp. 738–745)

- Vascular plants have shoots consisting of **stems**, **leaves**, and, in angiosperms, flowers. **Roots** anchor the plant, absorb and conduct water and minerals, and store food. Leaves are attached to stem **nodes** and are the main **organs** of photosynthesis. **Axillary buds**, in axils of leaves and stems, give rise to branches. Plant organs may be adapted for specialized functions.

- Vascular plants have three **tissue systems**—dermal, vascular, and ground—which are continuous throughout the plant. **Dermal tissue** protects against pathogens, herbivores, and drought and aids in the absorption of water, minerals, and carbon dioxide. **Vascular tissues** (**xylem** and **phloem**) facilitate the long-distance transport of substances. **Ground tissues** function in storage, metabolism, and regeneration.

- **Parenchyma cells** are relatively unspecialized and thin-walled cells that retain the ability to divide; they perform most of the plant's metabolic functions of synthesis and storage. **Collenchyma cells** have unevenly thickened walls; they support young, growing parts of the plant. **Sclerenchyma cells**—fibers and sclereids—have thick, lignified walls that help support mature, nongrowing parts of the plant. **Tracheids** and **vessel elements**, the water-conducting cells of xylem, have thick walls and are dead at functional maturity. **Sieve-tube elements** are living but highly modified cells that are largely devoid of internal organelles; they function in the transport of sugars through the phloem of angiosperms.

> **?** *Describe at least three specializations in plant organs and plant cells that are adaptations to life on land.*

CONCEPT 35.2

Meristems generate cells for primary and secondary growth (pp. 746–747)

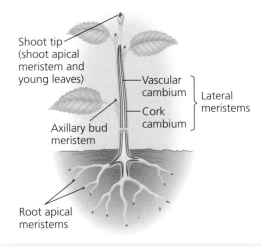

> **?** *Which plant organs originate from the activity of meristems?*

LEVEL 1: KNOWLEDGE/COMPREHENSION

1. Most of the growth of a plant body is the result of
   a. cell differentiation.
   b. morphogenesis.
   c. cell division.
   d. cell elongation.
   e. reproduction.

2. The innermost layer of the root cortex is the
   a. core.
   b. pericycle.
   c. endodermis.
   d. pith.
   e. vascular cambium.

3. Heartwood and sapwood consist of
   a. bark.
   b. periderm.
   c. secondary xylem.
   d. secondary phloem.
   e. cork.

4. The phase change of an apical meristem from the juvenile to the mature vegetative phase is often revealed by
   a. a change in the morphology of the leaves produced.
   b. the initiation of secondary growth.
   c. the formation of lateral roots.
   d. a change in the orientation of preprophase bands and cytoplasmic microtubules in lateral meristems.
   e. the activation of floral meristem identity genes.

LEVEL 2: APPLICATION/ANALYSIS

5. Based on the ABC hypothesis, what would be the structure of a flower from the outermost whorl that had normal expression of genes *A* and *C* and expression of gene *B* in all four whorls?
   a. carpel-petal-petal-carpel
   b. petal-petal-stamen-stamen
   c. sepal-carpel-carpel-sepal
   d. sepal-sepal-carpel-carpel
   e. carpel-carpel-carpel-carpel

6. Which of the following arise, directly or indirectly, from meristematic activity?
   a. secondary xylem
   b. leaves
   c. dermal tissue
   d. tubers
   e. all of the above

7. Which of the following would not be seen in a cross-section through the woody part of a root?
   a. sclerenchyma cells
   b. parenchyma cells
   c. sieve-tube elements
   d. root hairs
   e. vessel elements

8. **DRAW IT** On this cross section from a woody eudicot, label a growth ring, late wood, early wood, and a vessel element. Then draw an arrow in the pith-to-cork direction.

LEVEL 3: SYNTHESIS/EVALUATION

9. **EVOLUTION CONNECTION**
   Evolutionary biologists have coined the term *exaptation* to describe a common occurrence in the evolution of life: A limb or organ evolves in a particular context but over time takes on a new function (see Chapter 25). What are some examples of exaptations in plant organs?

10. **SCIENTIFIC INQUIRY**
    Grasslands typically do not flourish when large herbivores are removed. In fact, they are soon replaced by broad-leaved herbaceous eudicots, shrubs, and trees. Based on your knowledge of the structure and growth habits of monocots versus eudicots, suggest a reason why.

11. **SCIENCE, TECHNOLOGY, AND SOCIETY**
    Hunger and malnutrition are urgent problems for many poor countries, and yet plant biologists in wealthy nations have focused most of their research efforts on *Arabidopsis thaliana*. Some people have argued that if plant biologists are truly concerned about fighting world hunger, they should focus their studies on crops such as cassava and plantain because they are staples for many of the world's poor. If you were an *Arabidopsis* researcher, how might you respond to these arguments?

12. **WRITE ABOUT A THEME**
    Structure and Function In a short essay (100–150 words), explain how the evolution of lignin affected vascular plant structure and function.

For selected answers, see Appendix A.

MasteringBIOLOGY®   www.masteringbiology.com

1. MasteringBiology® Assignments:
   BioFlix Tutorial Tour of a Plant Cell
   Tutorials Primary and Secondary Growth in Plants • Developmental Biology of Plants
   Activities Root, Stem, and Leaf Sections • Plant Growth • Primary and Secondary Growth
   Questions Student Misconceptions • Reading Quiz • Multiple Choice • End-of-Chapter

2. eText
   Read your book online, search, take notes, highlight text, and more.

3. The Study Area
   Practice Tests • Cumulative Test • **BioFlix** 3-D Animations • MP3 Tutor Sessions • Videos • Activities • Investigations • Lab Media • Audio Glossary • Word Study Tools • Art

36

Resource Acquisition and Transport in Vascular Plants

▲ Figure 36.1 **Plants or pebbles?**

KEY CONCEPTS

36.1 Adaptations for acquiring resources were key steps in the evolution of vascular plants
36.2 Different mechanisms transport substances over short or long distances
36.3 Transpiration drives the transport of water and minerals from roots to shoots via the xylem
36.4 The rate of transpiration is regulated by stomata

OVERVIEW

Underground Plants

The Kalahari Desert of southern Africa receives only about 20 cm of precipitation a year, almost entirely during the summer, when daytime temperatures reach a scorching 35–45°C (95–113°F). Many animals escape the desert heat by seeking shelter underground. A peculiar genus of peren-

nial plants called stone plants (*Lithops*) has a similar, mostly subterranean lifestyle (**Figure 36.1**). Except for the tips of two succulent leaves that are exposed to the surface, a stone plant lives entirely below ground. Each leaf tip has a region of clear, lens-like cells that allow light to penetrate to the photosynthetic tissues underground. These adaptations enable stone plants to conserve moisture, hide from grazing tortoises, and avoid the potentially harmful temperatures and high light intensities of the desert.

The remarkable growth habit of *Lithops* reminds us that the success of plants depends largely on their ability to gather and conserve resources from their environment. Through natural selection, many plant species have become highly proficient in acquiring or conserving resources that are especially limited in their environment, but there are often trade-offs in such specializations. For example, the mostly subterranean lifestyle of stone plants reduces water loss from evaporation but inhibits photosynthesis. As a result, stone plants grow very slowly.

The first concept in this chapter examines structural features of shoot and root systems that increase their efficiency in acquiring resources. Resource acquisition, however, is not the end of the story but the beginning. Resources must be transported within the plant to where they are needed. Therefore, the rest of the chapter focuses on how water, minerals, and the products of photosynthesis (sugars) are transported in vascular plants.

CONCEPT 36.1

Adaptations for acquiring resources were key steps in the evolution of vascular plants

EVOLUTION Land plants typically inhabit two worlds—above ground, where their shoot systems acquire sunlight and CO_2, and below ground, where their root systems acquire water and minerals. Without adaptations that allow acquisition of these resources, plants could not have colonized land.

The algal ancestors of land plants absorbed water, minerals, and CO_2 directly from the water in which they lived. Transport in these algae was relatively simple because every cell was close to the source of these substances. The earliest land plants were nonvascular plants that grew photosynthetic shoots above the shallow fresh water in which they lived. These leafless shoots typically had waxy cuticles and few stomata, which allowed them to avoid excessive water loss while still permitting some exchange of CO_2 and O_2 for photosynthesis. The anchoring and absorbing functions of early land plants were assumed by the base of the stem or by threadlike rhizoids (see Figure 29.8).

As land plants evolved and increased in number, competition for light, water, and nutrients intensified. Taller plants with broad, flat appendages had an advantage in absorbing light. This increase in surface area, however, resulted in more evaporation and therefore a greater need for water. Larger shoots also required more anchorage. These needs favored the production of multicellular, branching roots. Meanwhile, as greater shoot heights further separated the top of the photosynthetic shoot from the nonphotosynthetic parts below ground, natural selection favored plants capable of efficient long-distance transport of water, minerals, and products of photosynthesis.

The evolution of vascular tissue consisting of xylem and phloem made possible the development of extensive root and shoot systems that carry out long-distance transport (see Figure 35.10). The xylem transports water and minerals from roots to shoots. The phloem transports products of photosynthesis from where they are made or stored to where they are needed. **Figure 36.2** provides an overview of resource acquisition and transport in a vascular plant.

Because plant success depends on photosynthesis, evolution has resulted in many structural adaptations for efficiently acquiring light from the sun, CO_2 from the air, and water from the ground. Perhaps just as importantly, land plants must minimize the evaporative loss of water, particularly in environments where water is scarce. The adaptations

of each species represent compromises between enhancing photosynthesis and minimizing water loss in the species' particular habitat. Later in the chapter, we discuss how plants enhance CO_2 uptake and minimize water loss by regulating stomatal pores. Here, we examine how the basic architecture of shoots and roots helps plants acquire resources.

Shoot Architecture and Light Capture

In shoot systems, stems serve as supporting structures for leaves and as conduits for the transport of water and nutrients. Variations in shoot systems arise largely from the form and arrangement of leaves, the outgrowth of axillary buds, and the relative growth in stem length and thickness.

Leaf size and structure account for much of the outward diversity in plant form. Leaves range in length from the minuscule 1.3-mm leaves of the pygmy weed (*Crassula erecta*), a native of dry, sandy regions in the western United States, to the 20-m leaves of the palm *Raphia regalis*, a native of African rain forests. These species represent extreme examples of a general correlation observed between water availability and leaf size. The largest leaves are typically found in species from tropical rain forests, whereas the smallest are usually found in species from dry or very cold environments, where liquid water is scarce and evaporative loss from leaves is potentially more problematic.

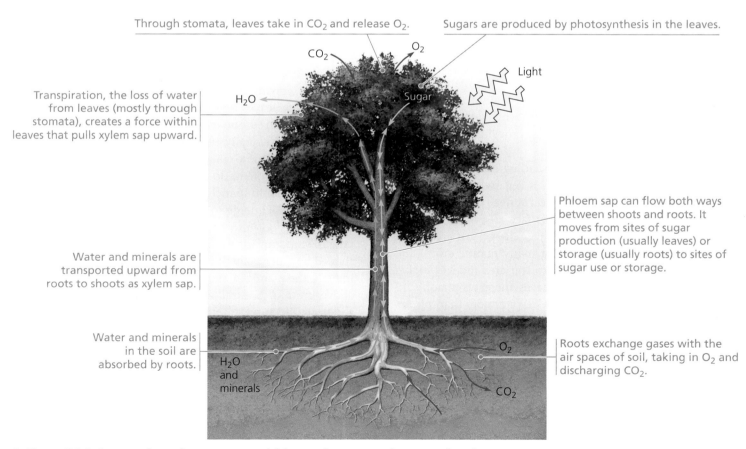

Through stomata, leaves take in CO_2 and release O_2.

Sugars are produced by photosynthesis in the leaves.

CO_2 O_2 Light

Transpiration, the loss of water from leaves (mostly through stomata), creates a force within leaves that pulls xylem sap upward.

H_2O Sugar

Phloem sap can flow both ways between shoots and roots. It moves from sites of sugar production (usually leaves) or storage (usually roots) to sites of sugar use or storage.

Water and minerals are transported upward from roots to shoots as xylem sap.

Water and minerals in the soil are absorbed by roots.

H_2O and minerals O_2

Roots exchange gases with the air spaces of soil, taking in O_2 and discharging CO_2.

CO_2

▲ **Figure 36.2 An overview of resource acquisition and transport in a vascular plant.**

▲ **Figure 36.3 Emerging phyllotaxy of Norway spruce.** This SEM, taken from above a shoot tip, shows the pattern of emergence of leaves. The leaves are numbered, with 1 being the youngest. (Some numbered leaves are not visible in the close-up.)

? *With your finger, trace the progression of leaf emergence, starting with leaf number 29. What is the pattern?*

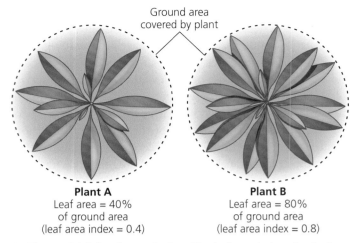

▲ **Figure 36.4 Leaf area index.** The leaf area index of a single plant is the ratio of the total area of the top surfaces of the leaves to the area of ground covered by the plant, as shown in this illustration of two plants viewed from the top. With many layers of leaves, a leaf area index value can easily exceed 1.

? *Would a higher leaf area index always increase the amount of photosynthesis? Explain.*

The arrangement of leaves on a stem, known as **phyllotaxy**, is an architectural feature of immense importance in light capture. Phyllotaxy is determined by the shoot apical meristem (see Figure 35.16) and is specific to each species **(Figure 36.3)**. A species may have one leaf per node (alternate, or spiral, phyllotaxy), two leaves per node (opposite phyllotaxy), or more (whorled phyllotaxy). Most angiosperms have alternate phyllotaxy, with leaves arranged in an ascending spiral around the stem, each successive leaf emerging 137.5° from the site of the previous one. Why 137.5°? Mathematical analyses suggest that this angle minimizes shading of the lower leaves by those above. In environments where intense sunlight can harm leaves, the greater shading provided by oppositely arranged leaves may be advantageous.

Plant features that reduce self-shading increase light capture. A useful measurement in this regard is the *leaf area index*, the ratio of the total upper leaf surface of a single plant or an entire crop divided by the surface area of the land on which the plant or crop grows **(Figure 36.4)**. Leaf area index values of up to 7 are common for many mature crops, and there is little agricultural benefit to leaf area indexes higher than this value. Adding more leaves increases shading of lower leaves to the point that they respire more than photosynthesize. When this happens, the nonproductive leaves or branches undergo programmed cell death and are eventually shed, a process called *self-pruning*.

Another factor affecting light capture is leaf orientation. Some plants have horizontally oriented leaves; others, such as grasses, have leaves that are vertically oriented. In low-light conditions, horizontal leaves capture sunlight much more effectively than vertical leaves. In grasslands or other sunny regions, however, horizontal orientation may expose upper leaves

to overly intense light, injuring leaves and reducing photosynthesis. But if a plant's leaves are nearly vertical, light rays are essentially parallel to the leaf surfaces, so no leaf receives too much light, and light penetrates more deeply to the lower leaves.

The height of shoots and their branching patterns are two other architectural features affecting light capture. Plants that grow tall avoid shading from neighboring plants. Most tall plants require thick stems, which enable greater vascular flow to the leaves and mechanical support for them. Vines are an exception, relying on other structures (usually other plants) to raise their leaves higher. In woody plants, stems become thicker through secondary growth (see Figure 35.11).

Branching generally enables plants to harvest sunlight for photosynthesis more effectively. However, some species, such as the coconut palm, do not branch at all. Why is there so much variation in branching patterns? Plants have only a finite amount of energy to devote to shoot growth. If most of that energy goes into branching, there is less energy to devote toward growing tall, and there is increased risk of being shaded by taller plants. If most of the energy goes into growing tall, the plants are not optimally exploiting the resources above ground. Natural selection has produced varieties of shoot architectures among species, optimizing light absorption in the ecological niche each species occupies.

Root Architecture and Acquisition of Water and Minerals

Just as carbon dioxide and sunlight are resources exploited by the shoot system, soil contains resources mined by the root system. The evolution of root branching enabled land plants to more effectively acquire water and nutrients from the soil while also providing strong anchorage. The tallest plant species, including gymnosperms and eudicots, are typically anchored by strong taproot systems with numerous branches (see Figure 35.2). Although there are exceptions, such as palms, most monocots do not reach treelike heights because their fibrous root systems do not anchor a tall plant as strongly as a taproot system (see Figure 30.13).

Plants can rapidly adjust the architecture and physiology of their roots to exploit patches of available nutrients in the soil. The roots of many plants, for example, respond to pockets of low nitrate availability in soils by extending straight through the pockets instead of branching within them. Conversely, when encountering a pocket rich in nitrate, a root will often branch extensively there. Root cells also respond to high soil nitrate levels by synthesizing more proteins involved in nitrate transport and assimilation. Thus, not only does the plant devote more of its mass to exploiting a nitrate-rich patch; the cells also absorb nitrate more efficiently.

Researchers have uncovered a fascinating physiological mechanism that reduces competition within the root system of a plant. Cuttings from the stolons of buffalo grass (*Buchloe dactyloides*) develop fewer and shorter roots in the presence of cuttings from the same plant than they do in the presence of cuttings from another buffalo grass plant. Although the mechanism underlying this ability to distinguish self from nonself is unknown, avoiding competition between roots of the same plant for the same limited pool of resources certainly seems beneficial.

The evolution of mutualistic associations between roots and fungi called **mycorrhizae (Figure 36.5)** was a critical step in the successful colonization of land by vascular plants, especially given the poorly developed soils available at that time. About 80% of extant land plant species form mycorrhizal associations. Mycorrhizal hyphae endow the fungus and plant roots with an enormous surface area for absorbing water and minerals, particularly phosphate.

Once acquired, resources must be transported to other parts of the plant that need them. In the next section, we examine the processes and pathways that enable resources such as water, minerals, and sugars to be transported throughout the plant.

CONCEPT CHECK 36.1

1. Why is long-distance transport important for vascular plants?
2. What architectural features influence self-shading?
3. Some plants can detect increased levels of light reflected from leaves of encroaching neighbors. This detection elicits stem elongation, production of erect leaves, and reduced lateral branching. How do these responses help the plant compete?
4. **WHAT IF?** If you prune a plant's shoot tips, what will be the short-term effect on the plant's branching and leaf area index?
5. **MAKE CONNECTIONS** Explain how fungal hyphae provide more surface area for nutrient absorption. See pp. 637–638 of Concept 31.1.

For suggested answers, see Appendix A.

CONCEPT 36.2
Different mechanisms transport substances over short or long distances

Given the diversity of substances that move through plants and the great range of distances and barriers over which such substances must be transported, it is not surprising that plants employ a variety of transport processes. Before examining these processes, however, we will look at the two major pathways of transport: the apoplast and the symplast.

The Apoplast and Symplast: Transport Continuums

Plant tissues may be viewed as having two major compartments—the apoplast and the symplast. The **apoplast** consists of everything external to the plasma membranes of living cells and includes cell walls, extracellular spaces, and the interior of dead cells such as vessel elements and tracheids (see Figure 35.10). The **symplast** consists of the entire mass of cytosol of all the living cells in a plant, as well as the plasmodesmata, the cytoplasmic channels that interconnect them.

Roots

Fungus

▲ **Figure 36.5 A mycorrhiza, a mutualistic association of fungus and roots.** The fine fungal hyphae provide an extensive surface area for the absorption of water and minerals.

▶ **Figure 36.6 Cell compartments and routes for short-distance transport.** Some substances may use more than one transport route.

The compartmental structure of plants provides three routes for transport within a plant tissue or organ: the apoplastic, symplastic, and transmembrane routes **(Figure 36.6)**. In the *apoplastic route*, water and solutes (dissolved chemicals) move along the continuum of cell walls and extracellular spaces. In the *symplastic route*, water and solutes move along the continuum of cytosol. This route requires substances to cross a plasma membrane once, when they first enter the plant. After entering one cell, substances can move from cell to cell via plasmodesmata. In the *transmembrane route*, water and solutes move out of one cell, across the cell wall, and into the neighboring cell, which may pass them to the next cell in the same way. The transmembrane route requires repeated crossings of plasma membranes as substances exit one cell and enter the next. These three routes are not mutually exclusive, and some substances may use more than one route to varying degrees.

Short-Distance Transport of Solutes Across Plasma Membranes

In plants, as in any organism, the selective permeability of the plasma membrane controls the short-distance movement of substances into and out of cells (see Chapter 7). Both active and passive transport mechanisms occur in plants, and plant cell membranes are equipped with the same general types of pumps and transport proteins (channel proteins, carrier proteins, and cotransporters) that function in other cells. In this section, we focus on some ways that plants differ from animals in solute transport across plasma membranes.

Hydrogen ions (H^+), rather than sodium ions (Na^+), play the primary role in basic transport processes in plant cells. For example, in plant cells the membrane potential (the voltage across the membrane) is established mainly through the pumping of H^+ by proton pumps **(Figure 36.7a)**, rather than the pumping of Na^+ by sodium-potassium pumps. Also, H^+ is most often cotransported in plants, whereas Na^+ is typically cotransported in animals. During cotransport,

plant cells use the energy in the H^+ gradient and membrane potential to drive the active transport of many different solutes. For instance, cotransport with H^+ is responsible for absorption of neutral solutes, such as the sugar sucrose, by phloem cells and other plant cells. An H^+/sucrose cotransporter couples movement of sucrose against its concentration gradient with movement of H^+ down its electrochemical gradient **(Figure 36.7b)**. Cotransport with H^+ also facilitates movement of ions, as in the uptake of nitrate (NO_3^-) by root cells **(Figure 36.7c)**.

The membranes of plant cells also have ion channels that allow only certain ions to pass **(Figure 36.7d)**. As in animal cells, most channels are gated, opening or closing in response to stimuli such as chemicals, pressure, or voltage. Later in this chapter, we discuss how K^+ ion channels in guard cells function in opening and closing stomata. Ion channels are also involved in producing electrical signals analogous to the action potentials of animals. However, these signals are 1,000 times slower and employ Ca^{2+}-activated anion channels rather than the Na^+ ion channels used by animal cells.

Short-Distance Transport of Water Across Plasma Membranes

The absorption or loss of water by a cell occurs by **osmosis**, the diffusion of free water—water that is not bound to solutes or surfaces—across a membrane (see Figure 7.14). The physical property that predicts the direction in which water will flow is called **water potential**, a quantity that includes the effects of solute concentration and physical pressure. Free water moves from regions of higher water potential to regions of lower water potential if there is no barrier to its flow. For example, if a plant cell is immersed in a solution that has a higher water potential than the cell, water will move into the cell. As it moves, water can perform work, such as cell expansion. The word *potential* in the term *water potential* refers to water's potential energy—

(a) H⁺ and membrane potential. The plasma membranes of plant cells use ATP-dependent proton pumps to pump H⁺ out of the cell. These pumps contribute to the membrane potential and the establishment of a pH gradient across the membrane. These two forms of potential energy can drive the transport of solutes.

(b) H⁺ and cotransport of neutral solutes. Neutral solutes such as sugars can be loaded into plant cells by cotransport with H⁺ ions. H⁺/sucrose cotransporters, for example, play a key role in loading sugar into the phloem prior to its transport throughout the plant.

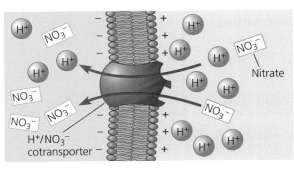

(c) H⁺ and cotransport of ions. Cotransport mechanisms involving H⁺ also participate in regulating ion fluxes into and out of cells. For example, H⁺/NO₃⁻ cotransporters in the plasma membranes of root cells are important for the uptake of NO₃⁻ by plant roots.

(d) Ion channels. Plant ion channels open and close in response to voltage, stretching of the membrane, and chemical factors. When open, ion channels allow specific ions to diffuse across membranes. For example, a K⁺ ion channel is involved in the release of K⁺ from guard cells when stomata close.

▲ **Figure 36.7 Solute transport across plant cell plasma membranes.**

? *Assume that a plant cell has all four of the plasma membrane transport proteins shown above. Assume also that you have specific inhibitors for each of the four transport proteins. Then predict what effect the individual application of each inhibitor would have on the cell's membrane potential.*

living plant cell due to the osmotic uptake of water is approximately 0.5 MPa, about twice the air pressure inside an inflated car tire.

How Solutes and Pressure Affect Water Potential

Both solute concentration and physical pressure can affect water potential, as expressed in the *water potential equation*:

$$\psi = \psi_S + \psi_P$$

where ψ is the water potential, ψ_S is the solute potential (osmotic potential), and ψ_P is the pressure potential. The **solute potential** (ψ_S) of a solution is directly proportional to its molarity. Solute potential is also called *osmotic potential* because solutes affect the direction of osmosis. The solutes in plants are typically mineral ions and sugars. By definition, the ψ_S of pure water is 0. When solutes are added, they bind water molecules. As a result, there are fewer free water molecules, reducing the capacity of the water to move and do work. In this way, an increase in solutes has a negative effect on water potential, which is why the ψ_S of a solution is always expressed as a negative number. For example, a 0.1 *M* solution of a sugar has a ψ_S of -0.23 MPa. As the solute concentration increases, ψ_S becomes more negative.

Pressure potential (ψ_P) is the physical pressure on a solution. Unlike ψ_S, ψ_P can be positive or negative relative to atmospheric pressure. For example, the water in the hollow nonliving xylem cells (tracheids and vessel elements) of a plant is often under a negative pressure potential (tension) of less than -2 MPa. Conversely, much like the air in a tire's inner tube, the water in living cells is usually under positive pressure due to the osmotic uptake of water. Specifically, the cell contents press the plasma membrane against the cell wall, and the cell wall then presses against the **protoplast** (the living part of the cell, which also includes the plasma membrane), producing what is called **turgor pressure**. This internal pressure is critical for plant function because it helps maintain the stiffness of plant tissues and also serves as the driving force for cell elongation.

water's capacity to perform work when it moves from a region of higher water potential to a region of lower water potential.

Water potential is abbreviated by the Greek letter ψ (psi, pronounced "sigh"). Plant biologists measure ψ in a unit of pressure called a **megapascal** (abbreviated MPa). By definition, the ψ of pure water in a container open to the atmosphere under standard conditions (at sea level and at room temperature) is 0 MPa. One MPa is equal to about 10 times atmospheric pressure at sea level. The internal pressure of a

A U-shaped tube can be used to demonstrate the effects of solutes and pressure on water movement across a selectively permeable membrane (**Figure 36.8**). As you consider this model, keep in mind the key point: *Water moves from regions of higher water potential to regions of lower water potential.*

Water Movement Across Plant Cell Membranes

Now let's consider how water potential affects absorption and loss of water by a living plant cell. First, imagine a cell that is **flaccid** (limp) as a result of losing water. The cell has a ψ_P of 0 MPa. Suppose this flaccid cell is bathed in a solution of higher solute concentration (more negative solute potential) than the cell itself (**Figure 36.9a**). Since the external solution has the lower (more negative) water potential, water diffuses out of the cell. The cell's protoplast undergoes **plasmolysis**—that is, it shrinks and pulls away from the cell wall. If we place the same flaccid cell in pure water ($\psi = 0$ MPa) (**Figure 36.9b**), the cell, because it contains solutes, has a lower water potential than the water, and water enters the cell by osmosis. The contents of the cell begin to swell and press the plasma membrane against the cell wall. The partially elastic wall, exerting turgor pressure, confines the pressurized protoplast. When this pressure is enough to offset the tendency for water to enter because of the solutes in the cell, then ψ_P and ψ_S are equal, and $\psi = 0$. This matches the water potential of the extracellular environment—in this example, 0 MPa. A dynamic equilibrium has been reached, and there is no further net movement of water.

In contrast to a flaccid cell, a walled cell with a greater solute concentration than its surroundings is **turgid**, or very firm. When turgid cells in a nonwoody tissue push against each other, the tissue is stiffened. The effects of turgor loss are seen during **wilting**, when leaves and stems droop as a result of cells losing water.

Turgid

Wilted

▼ Figure 36.8 **Effects of solutes and pressure on water potential (ψ) and water movement.**

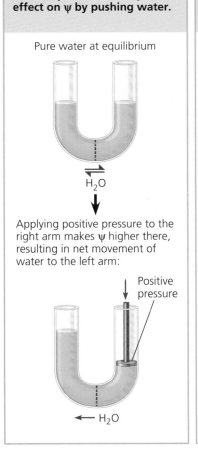

Solutes have a negative effect on ψ by binding water molecules.

Pure water at equilibrium

H_2O

Adding solutes to the right arm makes ψ lower there, resulting in net movement of water to the right arm:

Pure water

Membrane
$H_2O \rightarrow$
Solutes

Positive pressure has a positive effect on ψ by pushing water.

Pure water at equilibrium

H_2O

Applying positive pressure to the right arm makes ψ higher there, resulting in net movement of water to the left arm:

Positive pressure

$\leftarrow H_2O$

Solutes and positive pressure have opposing effects on water movement.

Pure water at equilibrium

H_2O

In this example, the effect of adding solutes is offset by positive pressure, resulting in no net movement of water:

Positive pressure

Solutes

H_2O

Negative pressure (tension) has a negative effect on ψ by pulling water.

Pure water at equilibrium

H_2O

Applying negative pressure to the right arm makes ψ lower there, resulting in net movement of water to the right arm:

Negative pressure

$H_2O \rightarrow$

Initial flaccid cell:
$\psi_P = 0$
$\psi_S = -0.7$
$\overline{\psi \ = -0.7 \text{ MPa}}$

0.4 *M* sucrose solution:
$\psi_P = 0$
$\psi_S = -0.9$
$\overline{\psi \ = -0.9 \text{ MPa}}$

Pure water:
$\psi_P = 0$
$\psi_S = 0$
$\overline{\psi \ = 0 \text{ MPa}}$

Plasmolyzed cell
at osmotic equilibrium
with its surroundings
$\psi_P = 0$
$\psi_S = -0.9$
$\overline{\psi \ = -0.9 \text{ MPa}}$

Turgid cell
at osmotic equilibrium
with its surroundings
$\psi_P = 0.7$
$\psi_S = -0.7$
$\overline{\psi \ = 0 \text{ MPa}}$

(a) Initial conditions: cellular ψ > environmental ψ. The cell loses water and plasmolyzes. After plasmolysis is complete, the water potentials of the cell and its surroundings are the same.

(b) Initial conditions: cellular ψ < environmental ψ. There is a net uptake of water by osmosis, causing the cell to become turgid. When this tendency for water to enter is offset by the back pressure of the elastic wall, water potentials are equal for the cell and its surroundings. (The volume change of the cell is exaggerated in this diagram.)

▲ **Figure 36.9 Water relations in plant cells.** In these experiments, flaccid cells (cells in which the protoplast contacts the cell wall but lacks turgor pressure) are placed in two environments. Blue arrows indicate initial net water movement.

Aquaporins: Facilitating Diffusion of Water

A difference in water potential determines the *direction* of water movement across membranes, but how do water molecules actually cross the membranes? Water molecules are small enough to diffuse across the phospholipid bilayer, even though the bilayer's interior is hydrophobic. However, their movement across biological membranes is too rapid to be explained by unaided diffusion. The transport of water molecules across membranes is facilitated by transport proteins called **aquaporins** (see Chapter 7). These selective channels affect the *rate* at which water moves osmotically across the membrane. Aquaporin channel proteins are highly dynamic: Their permeability is decreased by increases in cytosolic Ca^{2+} or decreases in cytosolic pH.

Long-Distance Transport: The Role of Bulk Flow

Diffusion is an effective transport mechanism over the spatial scales typically found at the cellular level. However, diffusion is much too slow to function in long-distance transport within a plant. Although diffusion from one end of a cell to the other takes just seconds, diffusion from the roots to the top of a giant redwood would take several centuries. Instead, long-distance transport occurs through **bulk flow**, the movement of liquid in response to a pressure gradient. The bulk flow of material always occurs from higher to lower pressure. Unlike osmosis, bulk flow is independent of solute concentration.

Long-distance bulk flow occurs within the tracheids and vessel elements of the xylem and within the sieve-tube elements of the phloem. The structures of these conducting cells facilitate bulk flow. As you saw in Figure 35.10, mature tracheids and vessel elements are dead cells and therefore have no cytoplasm, and the cytoplasm of sieve-tube elements is almost devoid of internal organelles. If you have ever dealt with a partially clogged drain, you know that the volume of flow depends on the pipe's diameter. Clogs reduce the effective diameter of the drainpipe. Such experiences help us understand how the structures of plant cells specialized for bulk flow fit their function. Like the unplugging of a kitchen drain, the absence or reduction of cytoplasm in a plant's "plumbing" allows for efficient bulk flow through the xylem and phloem. Bulk flow is also enhanced by the perforation plates at the ends of vessel elements and the porous sieve plates connecting sieve-tube elements.

Diffusion, active transport, and bulk flow act in concert to transport resources throughout the whole plant. For example, bulk flow due to a pressure difference is the mechanism of long-distance transport of sugars in the phloem, but active transport of sugar at the cellular level maintains this pressure difference. In the next three sections, we examine in more detail the transport of water and minerals from roots to shoots, the control of evaporation, and the transport of sugars.

CONCEPT CHECK 36.2

1. If a plant cell immersed in distilled water has a ψ_S of −0.7 MPa and a ψ of 0 MPa, what is the cell's ψ_P? If you put it in an open beaker of solution that has a ψ of −0.4 MPa, what would be its ψ_P at equilibrium?
2. How would a reduction in the number of aquaporin channels affect a plant cell's ability to adjust to new osmotic conditions?
3. How would the long-distance transport of water be affected if tracheids and vessel elements were alive at maturity? Explain.
4. **WHAT IF?** What would happen if you put plant protoplasts in pure water? Explain.

For suggested answers, see Appendix A.

CONCEPT 36.3

Transpiration drives the transport of water and minerals from roots to shoots via the xylem

Picture yourself struggling to carry a 19-L (5-gallon) container of water weighing 19 kg (42 pounds) up several flights of stairs. Imagine doing this 40 times a day. Then consider the fact that an averaged-sized tree, despite having neither heart nor muscle, transports a similar volume of water effortlessly on a daily basis. How do trees accomplish this feat? To answer this question, we'll follow each step in the journey of water and minerals from the tips of roots to leaves.

Absorption of Water and Minerals by Root Cells

Although all living plant cells absorb nutrients across their plasma membranes, the cells near the tips of roots are particularly important because most of the absorption of water and minerals occurs there. In this region, the epidermal cells are permeable to water, and many are differentiated into root hairs, modified cells that account for much of the absorption of water by roots (see Figure 35.3). The root hairs absorb the soil solution, which consists of water molecules and dissolved mineral ions that are not bound tightly to soil particles. The soil solution is drawn into the hydrophilic walls of epidermal cells and passes freely along the cell walls and the extracellular spaces into the root cortex. This flow enhances the exposure of the cells of the cortex to the soil solution, providing a much greater membrane surface area for absorption than the surface area of the epidermis alone. Although the soil solution usually has a low mineral concentration, active transport enables roots to accumulate essential minerals, such as K^+, to concentrations hundreds of times greater than in the soil.

Transport of Water and Minerals into the Xylem

Water and minerals that pass from the soil into the root cortex cannot be transported to the rest of the plant until they enter the xylem of the vascular cylinder, or stele. The **endodermis**, the innermost layer of cells in the root cortex, functions as a last checkpoint for the selective passage of minerals from the cortex into the vascular cylinder (**Figure 36.10**). Minerals already in the symplast when they reach the endodermis continue through the plasmodesmata of endodermal cells and pass into the vascular cylinder. These minerals were already screened by the plasma membrane they had to cross to enter the symplast in the epidermis or cortex. Those minerals that reach the endodermis via the apoplast encounter a dead end that blocks their passage into the vascular cylinder. This barrier, located in the transverse and radial walls of each endodermal cell, is the **Casparian strip**, a belt made of suberin, a

waxy material impervious to water and dissolved minerals (see Figure 36.10). Thus, water and minerals cannot cross the endodermis and enter the vascular cylinder via the apoplast. The Casparian strip forces water and minerals that are passively moving through the apoplast to cross the plasma membrane of an endodermal cell before they can enter the vascular cylinder.

The endodermis, with its Casparian strip, ensures that no minerals can reach the vascular tissue of the root without crossing a selectively permeable plasma membrane. The endodermis also prevents solutes that have accumulated in the xylem from leaking back into the soil solution. The structure of the endodermis and its strategic location fit its function as an apoplastic barrier between the cortex and the vascular cylinder. The endodermis transports needed minerals from the soil into the xylem and keeps many unneeded or toxic substances out.

The last segment in the soil-to-xylem pathway is the passage of water and minerals into the tracheids and vessel elements of the xylem. These water-conducting cells lack protoplasts when mature and are therefore parts of the apoplast. Endodermal cells, as well as living cells within the vascular cylinder, discharge minerals from their protoplasts into their own cell walls. Both diffusion and active transport are involved in this transfer of solutes from symplast to apoplast, and the water and minerals are now free to enter the tracheids and vessel elements, where they are transported to the shoot system by bulk flow.

Bulk Flow Transport via the Xylem

Water and minerals from the soil enter the plant through the epidermis of roots, cross the root cortex, and pass into the vascular cylinder. From there the **xylem sap**, the water and dissolved minerals in the xylem, gets transported long distances by bulk flow to the veins that branch throughout each leaf. As noted earlier, bulk flow is much faster than diffusion or active transport. Peak velocities in the transport of xylem sap can range from 15 to 45 m/hr for trees with wide vessel elements. Stems and leaves depend on this efficient delivery system for their supply of water and minerals.

The process of transporting xylem sap involves the loss of an astonishing amount of water by **transpiration**, the loss of water vapor from leaves and other aerial parts of the plant. A single maize plant, for example, transpires 60 L of water (the equivalent of 170 12-ounce bottles) during a growing season. A maize crop growing at a typical density of 60,000 plants per hectare transpires almost 4 million L of water per hectare every growing season (about 400,000 gallons of water per acre per growing season). Unless the transpired water is replaced by water transported up from the roots, the leaves will wilt, and the plants will eventually die.

Xylem sap rises to heights of more than 120 m in the tallest trees. Is the sap mainly *pushed* upward from the roots, or is it mainly *pulled* upward? Let's evaluate the relative contributions of these two mechanisms.

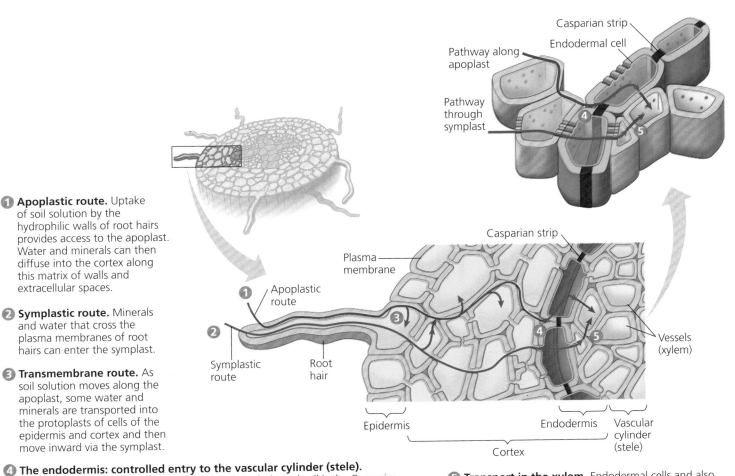

1 Apoplastic route. Uptake of soil solution by the hydrophilic walls of root hairs provides access to the apoplast. Water and minerals can then diffuse into the cortex along this matrix of walls and extracellular spaces.

2 Symplastic route. Minerals and water that cross the plasma membranes of root hairs can enter the symplast.

3 Transmembrane route. As soil solution moves along the apoplast, some water and minerals are transported into the protoplasts of cells of the epidermis and cortex and then move inward via the symplast.

4 The endodermis: controlled entry to the vascular cylinder (stele).
Within the transverse and radial walls of each endodermal cell is the Casparian strip, a belt of waxy material (purple band) that blocks the passage of water and dissolved minerals. Only minerals already in the symplast or entering that pathway by crossing the plasma membrane of an endodermal cell can detour around the Casparian strip and pass into the vascular cylinder (stele).

5 Transport in the xylem. Endodermal cells and also living cells within the vascular cylinder discharge water and minerals into their walls (apoplast). The xylem vessels then transport the water and minerals by bulk flow upward into the shoot system.

▲ **Figure 36.10** **Transport of water and minerals from root hairs to the xylem.**

? *How does the Casparian strip force water and minerals to pass through the plasma membranes of endodermal cells?*

Pushing Xylem Sap: Root Pressure

At night, when there is almost no transpiration, root cells continue actively pumping mineral ions into the xylem of the vascular cylinder. Meanwhile, the Casparian strip of the endodermis prevents the ions from leaking back out into the cortex and soil. The resulting accumulation of minerals lowers the water potential within the vascular cylinder. Water flows in from the root cortex, generating **root pressure**, a push of xylem sap. The root pressure sometimes causes more water to enter the leaves than is transpired, resulting in **guttation**, the exudation of water droplets that can be seen in the morning on the tips or edges of some plant leaves **(Figure 36.11)**. Guttation fluid should not be confused with dew, which is condensed atmospheric moisture.

In most plants, root pressure is a minor mechanism driving the ascent of xylem sap, at most pushing water only a few

▲ **Figure 36.11** **Guttation.** Root pressure is forcing excess water from this strawberry leaf.

meters. The positive pressures produced are simply too weak to overcome the gravitational force of the water column in the xylem, particularly in tall plants. Many plants do not generate any root pressure or do so only during part of the growing season. Even in plants that display guttation, root pressure cannot keep pace with transpiration after sunrise. For the most part, xylem sap is not pushed from below by root pressure but is pulled up.

Pulling Xylem Sap: The Cohesion-Tension Hypothesis

As we have seen, root pressure, which depends on the active transport of solutes by plants, is only a minor force in the ascent of xylem sap. Far from depending on the metabolic activity of cells, most of the xylem sap that rises through a tree does not even require living cells to do so. As demonstrated by Eduard Strasburger in 1891, leafy stems with their lower end immersed in toxic solutions of copper sulfate or acid will readily draw these poisons up if the stem is cut below the surface of the liquid. As the toxic solutions ascend, they kill all living cells in their path, eventually arriving in the transpiring leaves and killing the leaf cells as well. Nevertheless, as Strasburger noted, the uptake of the toxic solutions and the loss of water from the dead leaves can continue for weeks.

In 1894, a few years after Strasburger's findings, two Irish scientists, John Joly and Henry Dixon, put forward a hypothesis that remains the leading explanation of the ascent of xylem sap. According to their **cohesion-tension hypothesis**, transpiration provides the pull for the ascent of xylem sap, and

the cohesion of water molecules transmits this pull along the entire length of the xylem from shoots to roots. Hence, xylem sap is normally under negative pressure, or tension. Since transpiration is a "pulling" process, our exploration of the rise of xylem sap by the cohesion-tension mechanism begins not with the roots but with the leaves, where the driving force for transpirational pull begins.

Transpirational Pull Stomata on a leaf's surface lead to a maze of internal air spaces that expose the mesophyll cells to the CO_2 they need for photosynthesis. The air in these spaces is saturated with water vapor because it is in contact with the moist walls of the cells. On most days, the air outside the leaf is drier; that is, it has lower water potential than the air inside the leaf. Therefore, water vapor in the air spaces of a leaf diffuses down its water potential gradient and exits the leaf via the stomata. It is this loss of water vapor by diffusion and evaporation that we call transpiration.

But how does loss of water vapor from the leaf translate into a pulling force for upward movement of water through a plant? The negative pressure potential that causes water to move up through the xylem develops at the surface of mesophyll cell walls in the leaf (**Figure 36.12**). The cell wall acts like a very thin capillary network. Water adheres to the cellulose microfibrils and other hydrophilic components of the cell wall. As water evaporates from the water film that covers the cell walls of mesophyll cells, the air-water interface retreats farther into the cell wall. Because of the high surface tension of water, the curvature of the interface induces a tension, or negative pressure potential, in the water. As more

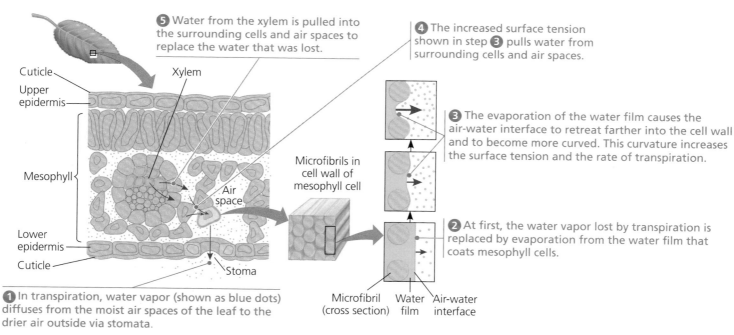

5 Water from the xylem is pulled into the surrounding cells and air spaces to replace the water that was lost.

4 The increased surface tension shown in step **3** pulls water from surrounding cells and air spaces.

3 The evaporation of the water film causes the air-water interface to retreat farther into the cell wall and to become more curved. This curvature increases the surface tension and the rate of transpiration.

Microfibrils in cell wall of mesophyll cell

Cuticle
Upper epidermis
Xylem
Mesophyll
Air space
Lower epidermis
Cuticle
Stoma

2 At first, the water vapor lost by transpiration is replaced by evaporation from the water film that coats mesophyll cells.

1 In transpiration, water vapor (shown as blue dots) diffuses from the moist air spaces of the leaf to the drier air outside via stomata.

Microfibril (cross section)   Water film   Air-water interface

▲ **Figure 36.12 Generation of transpirational pull.** Negative pressure (tension) at the air-water interface in the leaf is the basis of transpirational pull, which draws water out of the xylem.

water evaporates from the cell wall, the curvature of the air-water interface increases and the pressure of the water becomes more negative. Water molecules from the more hydrated parts of the leaf are then pulled toward this area, reducing the tension. These pulling forces are transferred to the xylem because each water molecule is cohesively bound to the next by hydrogen bonds. Thus, transpirational pull depends on several of the properties of water discussed in Chapter 3: adhesion, cohesion, and surface tension.

The role of negative pressure potential in transpiration is consistent with the water potential equation because negative pressure potential (tension) *lowers* water potential (see Figure 36.8). Because water moves from areas of higher water potential to areas of lower water potential, the more negative pressure potential at the air-water interface causes water in xylem cells to be "pulled" into mesophyll cells, which lose water to the air spaces, the water diffusing out through stomata. In this way, the negative water potential of leaves provides the "pull" in transpirational pull. The transpirational pull on xylem sap is transmitted all the way from the leaves to the root tips and even into the soil solution (**Figure 36.13**).

Adhesion and Cohesion in the Ascent of Xylem Sap Adhesion and cohesion facilitate the transport of water by bulk flow. Adhesion is the attractive force between water molecules and other polar substances. Because both water and cellulose are polar molecules, there is a strong attraction between water molecules and the cellulose molecules in the xylem cell walls. Cohesion is the attractive force between molecules of the same substance. Water has an unusually high cohesive force due to the hydrogen bonds each water molecule can potentially make with other water molecules. It is estimated that water's cohesive force within the xylem gives it a tensile strength equivalent to that of a steel wire of similar diameter. The cohesion of water makes it possible to pull a column of xylem sap from above without the water molecules separating. Water molecules exiting the xylem in the leaf tug on adjacent water molecules, and this pull is relayed, molecule by molecule, down the entire column of water

in the xylem. Meanwhile, the strong adhesion of water molecules (again by hydrogen bonds) to the hydrophilic walls of xylem cells helps offset the downward force of gravity.

The upward pull on the sap creates tension within the vessel elements and tracheids, which are like elastic pipes. Positive pressure causes an elastic pipe to swell, whereas tension pulls the walls of the pipe inward. On a warm day, a decrease in the diameter of a tree trunk can even be measured. As transpirational pull puts the vessel elements and tracheids under tension, their thick secondary walls prevent them from collapsing, much as wire rings maintain the shape of a vacuum-cleaner hose. The tension produced by transpirational pull

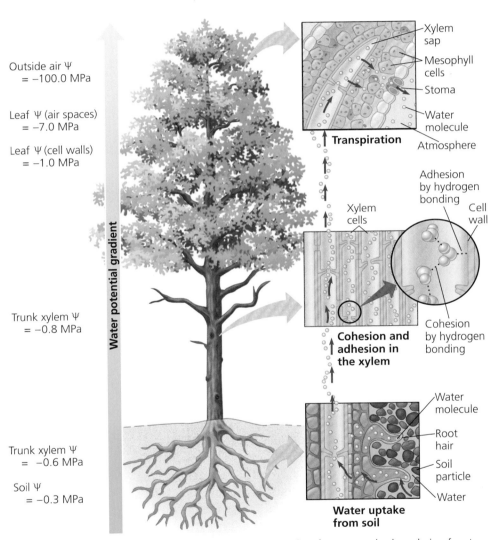

Outside air Ψ = −100.0 MPa

Leaf Ψ (air spaces) = −7.0 MPa

Leaf Ψ (cell walls) = −1.0 MPa

Trunk xylem Ψ = −0.8 MPa

Trunk xylem Ψ = −0.6 MPa

Soil Ψ = −0.3 MPa

Water potential gradient

Xylem sap
Mesophyll cells
Stoma
Water molecule
Transpiration
Atmosphere

Adhesion by hydrogen bonding
Cell wall
Xylem cells
Cohesion by hydrogen bonding
Cohesion and adhesion in the xylem

Water molecule
Root hair
Soil particle
Water
Water uptake from soil

▲ **Figure 36.13 Ascent of xylem sap.** Hydrogen bonding forms an unbroken chain of water molecules extending from leaves to the soil. The force driving the ascent of xylem sap is a gradient of water potential (ψ). For bulk flow over long distance, the ψ gradient is due mainly to a gradient of the pressure potential (ψ_P). Transpiration results in the ψ_P at the leaf end of the xylem being lower than the ψ_P at the root end. The ψ values shown at the left are a "snapshot." They may vary during daylight, but the direction of the ψ gradient remains the same.

ANIMATION   **BioFlix**   Visit the Study Area at **www.masteringbiology.com** for the BioFlix® 3-D Animation on Water Transport in Plants.

lowers water potential in the root xylem to such an extent that water flows passively from the soil, across the root cortex, and into the vascular cylinder.

Transpirational pull can extend down to the roots only through an unbroken chain of water molecules. Cavitation, the formation of a water vapor pocket, breaks the chain. It is more common in wide vessel elements than in tracheids and can occur during drought stress or when xylem sap freezes in winter. The air bubbles resulting from cavitation expand and block water channels of the xylem. The rapid expansion of air bubbles produces clicking noises that can be heard by placing sensitive microphones at the surface of the stem.

The interruption of xylem sap transport by cavitation is not always permanent. The chain of water molecules can detour around the air bubbles through pits between adjacent tracheids or vessel elements (see Figure 35.10). Moreover, root pressure enables small plants to refill blocked vessel elements. Recent evidence suggests that cavitation may even be repaired when the xylem sap is under negative pressure, although the mechanism by which this occurs is uncertain. In addition, secondary growth adds a layer of new xylem each year. Only the youngest, outermost secondary xylem layers transport water. Although the older secondary xylem no longer transports water, it does provide support for the tree.

Xylem Sap Ascent by Bulk Flow: *A Review*

The cohesion-tension mechanism that transports xylem sap against gravity is an excellent example of how physical principles apply to biological processes. In the long-distance transport of water from roots to leaves by bulk flow, the movement of fluid is driven by a water potential difference at opposite ends of xylem tissue. The water potential difference is created at the leaf end of the xylem by the evaporation of water from leaf cells. Evaporation lowers the water potential at the air-water interface, thereby generating the negative pressure (tension) that pulls water through the xylem.

Bulk flow in the xylem differs from diffusion in some key ways. First, it is driven by differences in pressure potential (ψ_P); solute potential (ψ_S) is not a factor. Therefore, the water potential gradient within the xylem is essentially a pressure gradient. Also, the flow does not occur across plasma membranes of living cells, but instead within hollow, dead cells. Furthermore, it moves the entire solution together—not just water or solutes—and at much greater speed than diffusion.

The plant expends no energy to lift xylem sap by bulk flow. Instead, the absorption of sunlight drives most of transpiration by causing water to evaporate from the moist walls of mesophyll cells and by lowering the water potential in the air spaces within a leaf. Thus, the ascent of xylem sap, like the process of photosynthesis, is ultimately solar powered.

CONCEPT CHECK 36.3

1. How do xylem cells facilitate long-distance transport?
2. A horticulturalist notices that when *Zinnia* flowers are cut at dawn, a small drop of water collects at the surface of the stump. However, when the flowers are cut at noon, no drop is observed. Suggest an explanation.
3. A scientist adds a water-soluble inhibitor of photosynthesis to roots of a transpiring plant, but photosynthesis is not reduced. Why?
4. **WHAT IF?** Suppose an *Arabidopsis* mutant lacking functional aquaporin proteins has a root mass three times greater than that of wild-type plants. Suggest an explanation.
5. **MAKE CONNECTIONS** How are the Casparian strip and tight junctions similar? See Figure 6.32 on p. 121.

For suggested answers, see Appendix A.

CONCEPT 36.4

The rate of transpiration is regulated by stomata

Leaves generally have large surface areas and high surface-to-volume ratios. The large surface area enhances light absorption for photosynthesis. The high surface-to-volume ratio aids in CO_2 absorption during photosynthesis as well as in the release of O_2, a by-product of photosynthesis. Upon diffusing through the stomata, CO_2 enters a honeycomb of air spaces formed by the spongy mesophyll cells (see Figure 35.18). Because of the irregular shapes of these cells, the leaf's internal surface area may be 10 to 30 times greater than the external surface area.

Although large surface areas and high surface-to-volume ratios increase the rate of photosynthesis, they also increase water loss by way of the stomata. Thus, a plant's tremendous requirement for water is largely a consequence of the shoot system's need for ample exchange of CO_2 and O_2 for photosynthesis. By opening and closing the stomata, guard cells help balance the plant's requirement to conserve water with its requirement for photosynthesis (Figure 36.14).

Stomata: Major Pathways for Water Loss

About 95% of the water a plant loses escapes through stomata, although these pores account for only 1–2% of the external leaf surface. The waxy cuticle limits water loss through the remaining surface of the leaf. Each stoma is flanked by a pair of guard cells. Guard cells control the diameter of the stoma by changing shape, thereby widening or narrowing the gap between the guard cell pair. Under the same environmental conditions, the amount of water lost by a leaf

▲ **Figure 36.14 An open stoma (left) and closed stoma** (LMs).

depends largely on the number of stomata and the average size of their pores.

The stomatal density of a leaf, which may be as high as 20,000 per square centimeter, is under both genetic and environmental control. For example, as a result of evolution by natural selection, desert plants are genetically programmed to have lower stomatal densities than do marsh plants. Stomatal density, however, is a developmentally plastic feature of many plants. High light exposures and low CO_2 levels during leaf development lead to increased density in many species. By measuring the stomatal density of leaf fossils, scientists have gained insight into the levels of atmospheric CO_2 in past climates. A recent British survey found that stomatal density of many woodland species has decreased since 1927, when a similar survey was made. This observation is consistent with other findings that atmospheric CO_2 levels increased dramatically during the late 20th century.

Mechanisms of Stomatal Opening and Closing

When guard cells take in water from neighboring cells by osmosis, they become more turgid. In most angiosperm species, the cell walls of guard cells are uneven in thickness, and the cellulose microfibrils are oriented in a direction that causes the guard cells to bow outward when turgid **(Figure 36.15a)**. This bowing outward increases the size of the pore between the guard cells. When the cells lose water and become flaccid, they become less bowed, and the pore closes.

The changes in turgor pressure in guard cells result primarily from the reversible absorption and loss of K^+. Stomata open when guard cells actively accumulate K^+ from neighboring epidermal cells **(Figure 36.15b)**. The flow of K^+ across the plasma membrane of the guard cell is coupled to the generation of a membrane potential by proton pumps (see Figure 36.7a). Stomatal opening correlates with active transport of H^+ out of the guard cell. The resulting voltage (membrane potential) drives K^+ into the cell through specific membrane channels.

Guard cells turgid/Stoma open   Guard cells flaccid/Stoma closed

(a) Changes in guard cell shape and stomatal opening and closing (surface view). Guard cells of a typical angiosperm are illustrated in their turgid (stoma open) and flaccid (stoma closed) states. The radial orientation of cellulose microfibrils in the cell walls causes the guard cells to increase more in length than width when turgor increases. Since the two guard cells are tightly joined at their tips, they bow outward when turgid, causing the stomatal pore to open.

(b) Role of potassium in stomatal opening and closing. The transport of K^+ (potassium ions, symbolized here as red dots) across the plasma membrane and vacuolar membrane causes the turgor changes of guard cells. The uptake of anions, such as malate and chloride ions (not shown), also contributes to guard cell swelling.

▲ **Figure 36.15 Mechanisms of stomatal opening and closing.**

The absorption of K^+ causes the water potential to become more negative within the guard cells, and the cells become more turgid as water enters by osmosis. Because most of the K^+ and water are stored in the vacuole, the vacuolar membrane also plays a role in regulating guard cell dynamics. Stomatal closing results from a loss of K^+ from guard cells to neighboring cells, which leads to an osmotic loss of water. Aquaporins also help regulate the osmotic swelling and shrinking of guard cells.

Stimuli for Stomatal Opening and Closing

In general, stomata are open during the day and mostly closed at night, preventing the plant from losing water under conditions when photosynthesis cannot occur. At least three cues contribute to stomatal opening at dawn: light, CO_2 depletion, and an internal "clock" in guard cells.

The light stimulates guard cells to accumulate K^+ and become turgid. This response is triggered by illumination of blue-light receptors in the plasma membrane of guard cells. Activation of these receptors stimulates the activity of proton pumps in the plasma membrane of the guard cells, in turn promoting absorption of K^+.

The stomata also open in response to depletion of CO_2 within the leaf's air spaces as a result of photosynthesis. As CO_2 concentrations decrease during the day, the stomata progressively open if sufficient water is supplied to the leaf.

A third cue, the internal "clock" in the guard cells, ensures that stomata continue their daily rhythm of opening and closing. This rhythm occurs even if a plant is kept in a dark location. All eukaryotic organisms have internal clocks that regulate cyclic processes. Cycles with intervals of approximately 24 hours are called **circadian rhythms**.

Environmental stresses, such as drought, high temperature, and wind, can cause stomata to close during the daytime. When the plant has a water deficiency, guard cells may lose turgor and close stomata. In addition, a hormone called **abscisic acid (ABA)**, produced in roots and leaves in response to water deficiency, signals guard cells to close stomata. This response reduces wilting but also restricts CO_2 absorption, thereby slowing photosynthesis. Since turgor is necessary for cell elongation, growth ceases throughout the plant. These are some reasons why droughts reduce crop yields.

Guard cells control the photosynthesis-transpiration compromise on a moment-to-moment basis by integrating a variety of internal and external stimuli. Even the passage of a cloud or a transient shaft of sunlight through a forest can affect the rate of transpiration.

Effects of Transpiration on Wilting and Leaf Temperature

As long as most stomata remain open, transpiration is greatest on a day that is sunny, warm, dry, and windy because these environmental factors increase evaporation. If transpiration cannot pull sufficient water to the leaves, the shoot becomes slightly wilted as cells lose turgor pressure. Although plants respond to such mild drought stress by rapidly closing stomata, some evaporative water loss still occurs through the cuticle. Under prolonged drought conditions, leaves can become severely wilted and irreversibly injured.

Transpiration also results in evaporative cooling, which can lower a leaf's temperature by as much as 10°C compared with the surrounding air. This cooling prevents the leaf from reaching temperatures that could denature enzymes involved in photosynthesis and other metabolic processes.

Adaptations That Reduce Evaporative Water Loss

Plants adapted to arid environments, such as the stone plants of the Kalahari Desert (see Figure 36.1), are called **xerophytes** (from the Greek *xero*, dry). **Figure 36.16** shows other examples. Dry soils are relatively unproductive because plants need a sufficient quantity of liquid water to carry out photosynthesis. However, the reason why water availability is so tied to plant productivity is not related to photosynthesis's direct need for water as a substrate but rather because freely available water allows plants to keep stomata open and take up more CO_2.

Many species of desert plants avoid drying out by completing their short life cycles during the brief rainy seasons. Rain comes infrequently in deserts, but when it arrives, the vegetation is transformed as dormant seeds of annual species quickly germinate and bloom, completing their life cycle before dry conditions return. Longer-lived species have unusual physiological or morphological adaptations that enable them to withstand the harsh desert conditions. Many xerophytes, such as cacti, have highly reduced leaves that resist excessive water loss; they carry out photosynthesis mainly in their stems. The stems of many xerophytes are fleshy because they store water for use during long dry periods. Some desert plants, such as mesquite, have roots more than 20 m long, allowing them to acquire moisture at or near the water table.

Another adaptation to arid habitats is crassulacean acid metabolism (CAM), a specialized form of photosynthesis found in succulents of the family Crassulaceae and several other families (see Figure 10.21). Because the leaves of CAM plants take in CO_2 at night, the stomata can remain closed during the day, when evaporative stresses are greater. Stomata are the most important mediators of the conflicting demands of CO_2 acquisition and water retention.

CONCEPT CHECK 36.4

1. What are the stimuli that control the opening and closing of stomata?
2. The pathogenic fungus *Fusicoccum amygdali* secretes a toxin called fusicoccin that activates the plasma membrane proton pumps of plant cells and leads to uncontrolled water loss. Suggest a mechanism by which the activation of proton pumps could lead to severe wilting.
3. **WHAT IF?** If you buy cut flowers, why might the florist recommend cutting the stems underwater and then transferring the flowers to a vase while the cut ends are still wet?
4. **MAKE CONNECTIONS** Explain why the evaporation of water from leaves lowers their temperature. See p. 49 of Concept 3.2.

For suggested answers, see Appendix A.

▼ **Figure 36.16 Some xerophytic adaptations.**

▶ Ocotillo (*Fouquieria splendens*) is common in the southwestern region of the United States and northern Mexico. It is leafless during most of the year, thereby avoiding excessive water loss (right). Immediately after a heavy rainfall, it produces small leaves (below and inset). As the soil dries, the leaves quickly shrivel and die.

▼ Oleander (*Nerium oleander*), shown in the inset, is commonly found in arid climates. Its leaves have a thick cuticle and multiple-layered epidermal tissue that reduce water loss. Stomata are recessed in cavities called "crypts," an adaptation that reduces the rate of transpiration by protecting the stomata from hot, dry wind. Trichomes help minimize transpiration by breaking up the flow of air, allowing the chamber of the crypt to have a higher humidity than the surrounding atmosphere (LM).

Cuticle Upper epidermal tissue

100 μm

Trichomes ("hairs") Crypt Stoma Lower epidermal tissue

▶ This is a close-up view of stems of old man cactus (*Cephalocereus senilis*), a Mexican desert plant. The long, white, hairlike bristles help reflect the sun.

SUMMARY OF KEY CONCEPTS

CONCEPT 36.1

Adaptations for acquiring resources were key steps in the evolution of vascular plants (pp. 764–767)

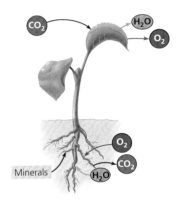

- Leaves typically function in gathering sunlight and CO_2. Stems serve as supporting structures for leaves and as conduits for the long-distance transport of water and nutrients. Roots mine the soil for water and minerals and anchor the whole plant. **Mycorrhizae** are mutualistic associations formed between roots and certain soil fungi that aid in the absorption of minerals and water.
- Natural selection has produced plant architectures that optimize resource acquisition in the ecological niche in which the plant species naturally exists.

? *How did the evolution of xylem and phloem contribute to the successful colonization of land by vascular plants?*

CONCEPT 36.2

Different mechanisms transport substances over short or long distances (pp. 767–771)

- The selective permeability of the plasma membrane controls the movement of substances into and out of cells. Both active and passive transport mechanisms occur in plants.
- Plant tissues have two major compartments: the **apoplast** (everything outside the cells' plasma membranes) and the **symplast** (the cytosol and connecting plasmodesmata).
- The direction of water movement depends on the **water potential**, a quantity incorporating solute concentration and phys-

ical pressure. The osmotic uptake of water by plant cells and the resulting internal pressure that builds up make plant cells **turgid**.
- Long-distance transport occurs through **bulk flow**, the movement of liquid in response to a pressure gradient. Bulk flow occurs within the tracheids and vessel elements of the xylem and within the sieve-tube elements of the phloem.

? *Is xylem sap usually pulled or pushed up the plant?*

CONCEPT 36.3

Transpiration drives the transport of water and minerals from roots to shoots via the xylem (pp. 772–776)

- Water and minerals from the soil enter the plant through the epidermis of roots, cross the root cortex, and then pass into the vascular cylinder by way of the selectively permeable cells of the **endodermis**. From the vascular cylinder, the **xylem sap** is transported long distances by bulk flow to the veins that branch throughout each leaf.
- The **cohesion-tension hypothesis** proposes that the movement of xylem sap is driven by a water potential difference created at the leaf end of the xylem by the evaporation of water from leaf cells. Evaporation lowers the water potential at the air-water interface, thereby generating the negative pressure that pulls water through the xylem.

? *Why is the ability of water molecules to form hydrogen bonds important for the movement of xylem sap?*

CONCEPT 36.4

The rate of transpiration is regulated by stomata (pp. 776–778)

- **Transpiration** is the loss of water vapor from plants. **Wilting** occurs when the water lost by transpiration is not replaced by absorption from roots.
- Stomata are the major pathway for water loss from plants. Guard cells widen or narrow the stomatal pores. When guard cells take up K^+, the pore widens. The opening and closing of stomata is controlled by light, CO_2, the drought hormone **abscisic acid**, and a **circadian rhythm**.
- Reduced leaves and CAM photosynthesis are examples of adaptations to arid environments.

? *Why are stomata necessary?*

LEVEL 1: KNOWLEDGE/COMPREHENSION

1. The symplast transports all of the following *except*
   a. sugars.   d. proteins.
   b. mRNA.   e. viruses.
   c. DNA.

2. Which of the following is an adaptation that enhances the uptake of water and minerals by roots?
   a. mycorrhizae
   b. cavitation
   c. active uptake by vessel elements
   d. rhythmic contractions by cortical cells
   e. pumping through plasmodesmata

3. Which structure or compartment is part of the symplast?
   a. the interior of a vessel element
   b. the interior of a sieve tube
   c. the cell wall of a mesophyll cell
   d. an extracellular air space
   e. the cell wall of a root hair

4. Movement of phloem sap from a source to a sink
   a. occurs through the apoplast of sieve-tube elements.
   b. depends ultimately on the activity of proton pumps.
   c. depends on tension, or negative pressure potential.
   d. depends on pumping water into sieve tubes at the source.
   e. results mainly from diffusion.

LEVEL 2: APPLICATION/ANALYSIS

5. Photosynthesis ceases when leaves wilt, mainly because
   a. the chlorophyll in wilting leaves is degraded.
   b. flaccid mesophyll cells are incapable of photosynthesis.
   c. stomata close, preventing CO_2 from entering the leaf.
   d. photolysis, the water-splitting step of photosynthesis, cannot occur when there is a water deficiency.
   e. accumulation of CO_2 in the leaf inhibits enzymes.

6. What would enhance water uptake by a plant cell?
   a. decreasing the ψ of the surrounding solution
   b. increasing the pressure exerted by the cell wall
   c. the loss of solutes from the cell
   d. increasing the ψ of the cytoplasm
   e. positive pressure on the surrounding solution

7. A plant cell with a ψ_S of –0.65 MPa maintains a constant volume when bathed in a solution that has a ψ_S of –0.30 MPa and is in an open container. The cell has a
   a. ψ_P of +0.65 MPa.   d. ψ_P of +0.30 MPa.
   b. ψ of –0.65 MPa.   e. ψ of 0 MPa.
   c. ψ_P of +0.35 MPa.

8. Compared with a cell with few aquaporin proteins in its membrane, a cell containing many aquaporin proteins will
   a. have a faster rate of osmosis.
   b. have a lower water potential.
   c. have a higher water potential.
   d. have a faster rate of active transport.
   e. accumulate water by active transport.

9. Which of the following would tend to increase transpiration?
   a. a rainstorm   d. higher stomatal density
   b. sunken stomata   e. spiny leaves
   c. a thicker cuticle

10. **DRAW IT** Trace the uptake of water and minerals from root hairs to the endodermis in a root, following a symplastic route and an apoplastic route. Label the routes on the diagram below.

LEVEL 3: SYNTHESIS/EVALUATION

11. **EVOLUTION CONNECTION**
    Large brown algae called kelps can grow as tall as 25 m. Kelps consist of a holdfast anchored to the ocean floor, blades that float at the surface and collect light, and a long stalk connecting the blades to the holdfast (see Figure 28.15). Specialized cells in the stalk, although nonvascular, can transport sugar. Suggest a reason why these structures analogous to sieve-tube elements might have evolved in kelps.

12. **SCIENTIFIC INQUIRY**
    Cotton plants wilt within a few hours of flooding their roots. The flooding leads to low-oxygen conditions, increases in cytosolic Ca^{2+}, and decreases in cytosolic pH. Suggest a hypothesis to explain how flooding leads to wilting.

13. **WRITE ABOUT A THEME**
    Structure and Function Natural selection has led to changes in the architecture of plants that enable them to photosynthesize more efficiently in the ecological niches they occupy. In a short essay (100–150 words), explain how shoot architecture enhances photosynthesis.

For selected answers, see Appendix A.

Mastering BIOLOGY®   www.masteringbiology.com

1. MasteringBiology® Assignments:
Make Connections Tutorial Ascent of Xylem Sap (Chapter 36) and Hydrogen Bonding (Chapter 3)
BioFlix Tutorials Water Transport in Plants: The Transpiration-Cohesion-Tension Mechanism • Water Transport in Plants: Transpiration
Activities Transport of Xylem Sap • Translocation of Phloem Sap • Solute Transport in Plants
Questions Student Misconceptions • Reading Quiz • Multiple Choice • End-of-Chapter

2. eText
Read your book online, search, take notes, highlight text, and more.

3. The Study Area
Practice Tests • Cumulative Test • **BioFlix** 3-D Animations • MP3 Tutor Sessions • Videos • Activities • Investigations • Lab Media • Audio Glossary • Word Study Tools • Art

38

Angiosperm Reproduction and Biotechnology

▲ **Figure 38.1 Why is this wasp trying to mate with this flower?**

KEY CONCEPTS

38.1 Flowers, double fertilization, and fruits are unique features of the angiosperm life cycle

38.2 Flowering plants reproduce sexually, asexually, or both

38.3 Humans modify crops by breeding and genetic engineering

Flowers of Deceit

Male wasps of the species *Campsoscolia ciliata* often attempt to copulate with the flowers of the Mediterranean orchid *Ophrys speculum* (**Figure 38.1**). During this encounter, a sac of pollen becomes glued to the insect's body. Eventually frustrated, the wasp flies off and deposits the pollen onto another *Ophrys* flower that has become the object of his misplaced ardor. *Ophrys* flowers offer no reward such as nectar to the male wasps, only sexual frustration. So what makes the male wasps so enamored of this orchid? The traditional answer has been that the shape of the orchid's largest petal and the frill of orange bristles around it vaguely resemble the female wasp. These visual cues, however, are only part of the deception: *Ophrys* orchids also emit chemicals with a scent similar to that produced by sexually receptive female wasps.

This orchid and its wasp pollinators are one example of the amazing ways in which angiosperms (flowering plants) reproduce sexually with spatially distant members of their own species. Sex, however, is not their only means of reproduction. Many species also reproduce asexually, creating offspring that are genetically identical to the parent.

An unusual aspect of the orchid and wasp example is that the insect does not profit from interacting with the flower. In fact, by wasting time and energy, the wasp is probably rendered less fit. More typically, a plant lures an animal pollinator to its flowers not with offers of sex but with rewards of energy-rich nectar or pollen. Thus, both plant and pollinator benefit; that is, the symbiotic relationship is mutualistic. Participating in mutualistic relationships with other organisms is very common in the plant kingdom. In fact, in recent evolutionary times, some flowering plants have formed mutualistic relationships with an animal that not only disperses their seeds but also provides the plants with water and mineral nutrients and vigorously protects them from encroaching competitors, pathogens, and predators. In return for these favors, the animal typically gets to eat a fraction of the plants' seeds and fruits. The plant symbionts involved in these remarkable mutualistic interactions are called crops; the animal symbionts are called humans.

Since the origins of crop domestication over 10,000 years ago, plant breeders have genetically manipulated the traits of a few hundred wild angiosperm species by artificial selection, transforming them into the crops we grow today. Genetic engineering has dramatically increased the variety of ways and the speed with which we can now modify plants.

In Chapters 29 and 30, we approached plant reproduction from an evolutionary perspective, tracing the descent of land plants from algal ancestors. Here, we'll explore the reproductive biology of flowering plants in greater detail because they are the most important group of plants in most terrestrial ecosystems and in agriculture. After discussing the sexual and asexual reproduction of angiosperms, we'll examine the role of humans in genetically altering crop species, as well as the controversies surrounding modern plant biotechnology.

CONCEPT 38.1

Flowers, double fertilization, and fruits are unique features of the angiosperm life cycle

The life cycles of plants are characterized by an alternation of generations, in which multicellular haploid (n) and diploid ($2n$)

generations take turns producing each other (see Figures 29.5 and 30.10). The diploid plant, the sporophyte, produces haploid spores by meiosis. These spores divide by mitosis, giving rise to the multicellular gametophytes, the male and female haploid plants that produce gametes (sperm and eggs). **Fertilization**, the fusion of gametes, results in diploid zygotes, which divide by mitosis and form new sporophytes. In angiosperms, the sporophyte is the dominant generation: It is larger, more conspicuous, and longer-lived than the gametophyte. Over the course of seed plant evolution, gametophytes became reduced in size and wholly dependent on the sporophyte for nutrients. Angiosperm gametophytes are the most reduced of all plants, consisting of only a few cells. **Figure 38.2** reviews the angiosperm life cycle, which is shown in more detail in Figure 30.10. The key derived traits of the angiosperm life cycle can be remembered as the "three Fs"—*f*lowers, double *f*ertilization, and *f*ruits. Since angiosperms, along with gymnosperms, are seed plants, a knowledge of seed structure and function is also critical to understanding the angiosperm life cycle.

Flower Structure and Function

Flowers, the reproductive shoots of angiosperm sporophytes, are typically composed of four whorls of modified leaves called floral organs. Unlike vegetative shoots, flowers are determinate shoots; they cease growing after the flower and fruit are formed.

Floral organs—**sepals**, **petals**, **stamens**, and **carpels**—are attached to a part of the stem called the **receptacle**. Stamens and carpels are reproductive organs, whereas sepals and petals are sterile. Sepals, which enclose and protect unopened floral buds, are usually more leafy in appearance than the other floral organs. Petals are typically more brightly colored than sepals and advertise the flower to insects and other pollinators.

A stamen consists of a stalk called the *filament* and a terminal structure called the **anther**; within the anther are chambers called microsporangia (pollen sacs) that produce pollen. A carpel has an **ovary** at its base and a long, slender neck called the **style**. At the top of the style is a generally sticky structure called the **stigma** that captures pollen. Within the ovary are one or more **ovules**; the number of ovules depends on the species. The flower shown in Figure 38.2 has a single carpel, but many species have multiple carpels. In most species, two or more carpels are fused into a single structure; the result is an ovary with two or more chambers, each containing one or more ovules. The term **pistil** is sometimes used to refer to a single carpel or two or more fused carpels.

Complete flowers have all four basic floral organs (see Figure 38.2a). Some species have **incomplete flowers**, lacking sepals, petals, stamens, or carpels. For example, most grass flowers lack petals. Some incomplete flowers are sterile, lacking functional stamens and carpels; others are *unisexual*, lacking either stamens or carpels. Flowers also vary in size, shape, color, odor, organ arrangement, and time of opening. Some are borne singly, while others are arranged in showy clusters called **inflorescences**. For example, a sunflower's central disk consists of hundreds of tiny incomplete flowers, and what look like petals are actually sterile flowers (see Figure 1.3). Much of floral diversity represents adaptation to specific pollinators.

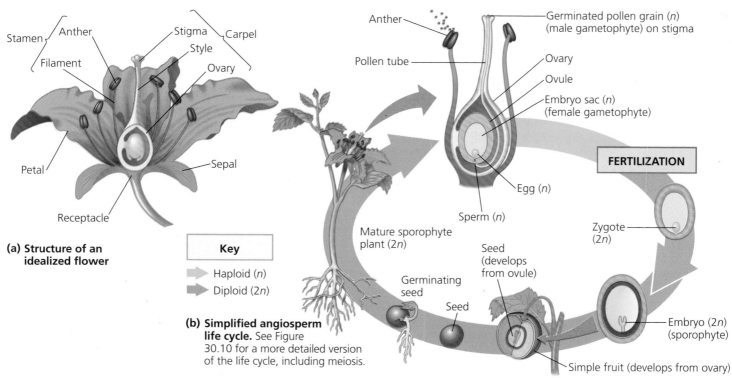

(a) Structure of an idealized flower

Key
Haploid (*n*)
Diploid (*2n*)

(b) Simplified angiosperm life cycle. See Figure 30.10 for a more detailed version of the life cycle, including meiosis.

▲ **Figure 38.2 An overview of angiosperm reproduction.**

Development of Male Gametophytes in Pollen Grains

Each anther contains four microsporangia, also known as pollen sacs. Within the microsporangia are many diploid cells called *microsporocytes,* or microspore mother cells **(Figure 38.3a)**. Each microsporocyte undergoes meiosis, forming four haploid **microspores**, each of which eventually gives rise to a haploid male gametophyte. Each microspore then undergoes mitosis, producing a male gametophyte consisting of only two cells: the *generative cell* and the *tube cell*. Together, these two cells and the spore wall constitute a **pollen grain**. The spore wall, which consists of material produced by both the microspore and the anther, usually exhibits an elaborate pattern unique to the species. During maturation of the male gametophyte, the generative cell passes into the tube cell, and the spore wall is completed. The tube cell now has a completely free-standing cell inside it. After the microsporangium breaks open and releases the pollen, a pollen grain may be transferred to a receptive surface of a stigma. There, the tube cell produces the **pollen tube**, a long cellular protuberance that delivers sperm to the female gametophyte. Pollen tubes can grow very quickly, at rates of 1 cm/hr or more. As a pollen tube elongates through the style, the generative cell usually divides and produces two sperm cells, which remain inside the tube cell (see Figure 30.10). The pollen tube grows through the style and into the ovary, where it releases the sperm cells in the vicinity of the female gametophyte.

Development of Female Gametophytes (Embryo Sacs)

Among angiosperm species, there are over 15 variations in the development of the female gametophyte, also known as an **embryo sac**. We'll focus on just one common variation. The entire process occurs in a tissue within each ovule called the megasporangium. Two *integuments* (layers of protective sporophytic tissue that will develop into the seed coat) surround each megasporangium except at a gap called the *micropyle*. Female gametophyte development begins when one cell in the megasporangium of each ovule, the *megasporocyte* (or megaspore mother cell), enlarges and undergoes meiosis, producing four haploid **megaspores** **(Figure 38.3b)**. Only one megaspore survives; the others degenerate.

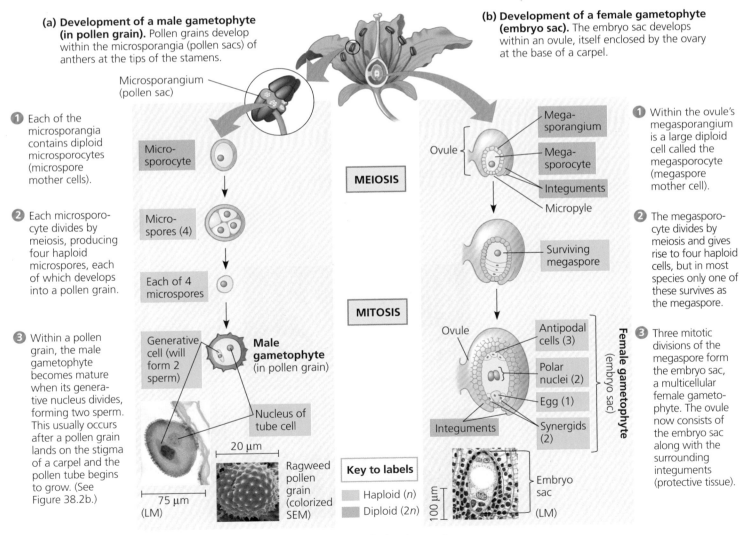

(a) **Development of a male gametophyte (in pollen grain).** Pollen grains develop within the microsporangia (pollen sacs) of anthers at the tips of the stamens.

(b) **Development of a female gametophyte (embryo sac).** The embryo sac develops within an ovule, itself enclosed by the ovary at the base of a carpel.

Microsporangium (pollen sac)

❶ Each of the microsporangia contains diploid microsporocytes (microspore mother cells).

❷ Each microsporocyte divides by meiosis, producing four haploid microspores, each of which develops into a pollen grain.

❸ Within a pollen grain, the male gametophyte becomes mature when its generative nucleus divides, forming two sperm. This usually occurs after a pollen grain lands on the stigma of a carpel and the pollen tube begins to grow. (See Figure 38.2b.)

Micro-sporocyte

Micro-spores (4)

Each of 4 microspores

MEIOSIS

MITOSIS

Generative cell (will form 2 sperm)

Male gametophyte (in pollen grain)

Nucleus of tube cell

20 μm

75 μm (LM)

Ragweed pollen grain (colorized SEM)

Key to labels

Haploid (*n*)
Diploid (*2n*)

Ovule

Mega-sporangium
Mega-sporocyte
Integuments
Micropyle

Surviving megaspore

Ovule

Antipodal cells (3)
Polar nuclei (2)
Egg (1)
Synergids (2)

Integuments

Female gametophyte (embryo sac)

Embryo sac

100 μm

(LM)

❶ Within the ovule's megasporangium is a large diploid cell called the megasporocyte (megaspore mother cell).

❷ The megasporocyte divides by meiosis and gives rise to four haploid cells, but in most species only one of these survives as the megaspore.

❸ Three mitotic divisions of the megaspore form the embryo sac, a multicellular female gametophyte. The ovule now consists of the embryo sac along with the surrounding integuments (protective tissue).

▲ **Figure 38.3 The development of male and female gametophytes in angiosperms.**

The nucleus of the surviving megaspore divides by mitosis three times without cytokinesis, resulting in one large cell with eight haploid nuclei. The multinucleate mass is partitioned by membranes into a multicellular female gametophyte—the embryo sac. The cell fates of the nuclei are determined by a gradient of the hormone auxin originating near the micropyle. At the micropylar end, two cells called synergids flank the egg and help attract and guide the pollen tube to the embryo sac. At the opposite end of the embryo sac are three antipodal cells of unknown function. The other two nuclei, called polar nuclei, are not partitioned into separate cells but share the cytoplasm of the large central cell of the embryo sac. The ovule, which will become a seed, now consists of the embryo sac and two surrounding integuments.

▼ Figure 38.4

Exploring Flower Pollination

Most angiosperm species rely on a living (biotic) or nonliving (abiotic) pollinating agent that can move pollen from the anther of a flower on one plant to the stigma of a flower on another plant. Approximately 80% of all angiosperm pollination is biotic, employing animal go-betweens. Among abiotically pollinated species, 98% rely on wind and 2% on water. (Some angiosperm species can self-pollinate, but such species are limited to inbreeding in nature.)

Abiotic Pollination by Wind

About 20% of all angiosperm species are wind-pollinated. Since their reproductive success does not depend on attracting pollinators, there has been no selective pressure favoring colorful or scented flowers. Accordingly, the flowers of wind-pollinated species are often small, green, and inconspicuous, and they produce neither nectar nor scent. Most temperate trees and grasses are wind-pollinated. The flowers of hazel (*Corylus avellana*, shown here) and many other temperate, wind-pollinated trees appear in the early spring, when leaves are not present to interfere with pollen movement. The relative inefficiency of wind pollination is compensated for by production of copious amounts of pollen grains. Wind tunnel studies reveal that wind pollination is often more efficient than it appears because floral structures can create eddy currents that aid in pollen capture.

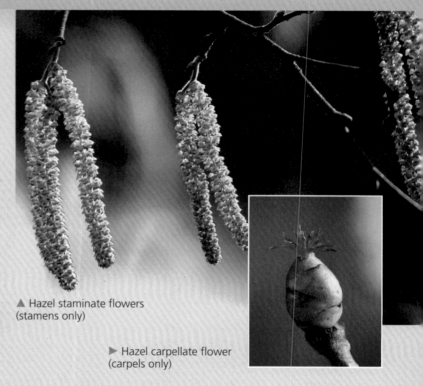

▲ Hazel staminate flowers (stamens only)

▶ Hazel carpellate flower (carpels only)

Pollination by Bees

About 65% of all flowering plants require insects for pollination; the percentage is even greater for major crops. Bees are the most important insect pollinators, and there is great concern in Europe and North America that honeybee populations have shrunk. Pollinating bees depend on nectar and pollen for food. Typically, bee-pollinated flowers have a delicate, sweet fragrance. Bees are attracted to bright colors, primarily yellow and blue. Red appears dull to them, but they can see ultraviolet radiation. Many bee-pollinated flowers, such as the common dandelion (*Taraxacum vulgare*), have ultraviolet markings called "nectar guides" that help insects locate the nectaries (nectar-producing glands) but are only visible to human eyes under ultraviolet light.

▲ Common dandelion under normal light

▲ Common dandelion under ultraviolet light

Pollination

In angiosperms, **pollination** is the transfer of pollen from an anther to a stigma. It is accomplished by wind, water, or animals (**Figure 38.4**). In wind-pollinated species, including grasses and many trees, the release of enormous quantities of smaller-sized pollen compensates for the randomness of dispersal by the wind. At certain times of the year, the air is loaded with pollen grains, as anyone who is plagued with pollen allergies can attest. Some species of aquatic plants rely on water to disperse pollen. Most angiosperm species, however, depend on insects, birds, or other animal pollinators to transfer pollen directly from one flower to another. If pollination is successful, a pollen grain produces a pollen tube, which then grows down into the ovary via the style.

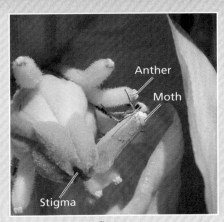

▲ Moth on yucca flower

▲ Blowfly on carrion flower

▲ Long-nosed bat feeding on cactus flower at night

Pollination by Moths and Butterflies

Moths and butterflies detect odors, and the flowers they pollinate are often sweetly fragrant. Butterflies perceive many bright colors, but moth-pollinated flowers are usually white or yellow, which stand out at night when moths are active. A yucca plant (shown here) is typically pollinated by a single species of moth with appendages that pack pollen onto the stigma. The moth then deposits eggs directly into the ovary. The larvae eat some developing seeds, but this cost is outweighed by the benefit of an efficient and reliable pollinator. If a moth deposits too many eggs, the flower aborts and drops off, selecting against individuals that overexploit the plant.

? *What are the benefits and dangers to a plant of having a highly specific animal pollinator?*

Pollination by Flies

Many fly-pollinated flowers are reddish and fleshy, with an odor like rotten meat. Blowflies visiting carrion flowers (*Stapelia* species) mistake the flower for a rotting corpse and lay their eggs on it. In the process, the blowflies become dusted with pollen that they carry to other flowers. When the eggs hatch, the larvae find no carrion to eat and therefore die.

Pollination by Birds

Bird-pollinated flowers, such as columbine flowers, are usually large and bright red or yellow, but they have little odor. Since birds often do not have a well-developed sense of smell, there has been no selective pressure favoring scent production. However, the flowers produce the sugary solution called nectar that helps meet the high energy demands of the pollinating birds. The primary function of nectar, which is produced by nectaries at the base of many flowers, is to "reward" the pollinator. The petals of such flowers are often fused, forming a bent floral tube that fits the curved beak of the bird.

Pollination by Bats

Bat-pollinated flowers, like moth-pollinated flowers, are light-colored and aromatic, attracting their nocturnal pollinators. The lesser long-nosed bat (*Leptonycteris curasoae yerbabuenae*) feeds on the nectar and pollen of agave and cactus flowers in the southwestern United States and Mexico. In feeding, the bats transfer pollen from plant to plant. Long-nosed bats are an endangered species.

▶ Hummingbird drinking nectar of columbine flower

Coevolution of Flower and Pollinator

EVOLUTION The joint evolution of two interacting species, each in response to selection imposed by the other, is called **coevolution**. Many species of flowering plants have co-evolved with specific pollinators. Natural selection favors individual plants or insects having slight deviations of structure that enhance the flower-pollinator mutualism. For example, some species have flower petals fused together, forming long, tube-like structures bearing nectaries tucked deep inside. Charles Darwin suggested that a race between flower and insect might lead to correspondences between the length of a floral tube and the length of an insect's proboscis, a straw-like mouthpart. Imagine an insect with a tongue long enough to drink the nectar of flowers without picking up pollen on its body. The resulting failure of these plants to fertilize others would render them less evolutionarily fit. Natural selection would then favor flowers with longer tubes. At the same time, an insect with a tongue that was too short for the tube wouldn't be able to use the nectar as a food source and therefore would be at a selective disadvantage compared with long-tongued rivals. As a result, the shapes and sizes of flowers often show a close correspondence to the pollen-adhering parts of their animal pollinators. In fact, based on the length of a long, tubular flower that grows in Madagascar, Darwin predicted the existence of a pollinating moth with a 28-cm-long proboscis. Such a moth was discovered two decades after Darwin's death **(Figure 38.5)**.

▲ **Figure 38.5 Coevolution of a flower and an insect pollinator.** The long floral tube of the Madagascar orchid *Angraecum sesquipedale* has coevolved with the 28-cm-long proboscis of its pollinator, the hawkmoth *Xanthopan morganii praedicta*. The moth is named in honor of Darwin's prediction of its existence.

Double Fertilization

At the time of pollination, the pollen grain typically consists of only the tube cell and the generative cell. After a pollen grain lands on a suitable stigma, it absorbs water and germinates by producing a pollen tube, which grows between the cells of the style toward the ovary **(Figure 38.6)**. The nucleus of the generative cell divides by mitosis and forms two sperm. In response to chemical attractants produced by the synergids, the tip of the pollen tube grows toward the micropyle. Its arrival initiates the death of one of the two synergids, thereby providing a passageway into the embryo sac for the two sperm that are discharged from the pollen tube.

Upon reaching the female gametophyte, one sperm fertilizes the egg, forming the zygote. The other sperm combines with the two polar nuclei, forming a triploid (3n) nucleus in the

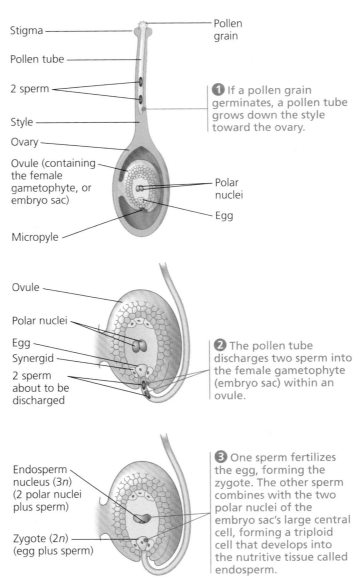

❶ If a pollen grain germinates, a pollen tube grows down the style toward the ovary.

Stigma
Pollen tube
2 sperm
Style
Ovary
Ovule (containing the female gametophyte, or embryo sac)
Micropyle
Pollen grain
Polar nuclei
Egg

❷ The pollen tube discharges two sperm into the female gametophyte (embryo sac) within an ovule.

Ovule
Polar nuclei
Egg
Synergid
2 sperm about to be discharged

❸ One sperm fertilizes the egg, forming the zygote. The other sperm combines with the two polar nuclei of the embryo sac's large central cell, forming a triploid cell that develops into the nutritive tissue called endosperm.

Endosperm nucleus (3n) (2 polar nuclei plus sperm)
Zygote (2n) (egg plus sperm)

▲ **Figure 38.6 Growth of the pollen tube and double fertilization.**

center of the large central cell of the female gametophyte. This large cell will give rise to the **endosperm**, a food-storing tissue of the seed. The union of two sperm cells with different nuclei of the female gametophyte is called **double fertilization**. Double fertilization ensures that endosperm develops only in ovules where the egg has been fertilized, thereby preventing angiosperms from squandering nutrients on infertile ovules.

The tissues surrounding the female gametophyte have prevented researchers from directly observing fertilization in plants grown under normal conditions. Scientists have, however, isolated sperm from germinated pollen grains and eggs from female gametophytes and observed the merging of plant gametes *in vitro* (in an artificial environment). The first cellular event that takes place after gamete fusion is an increase in the levels of cytoplasmic calcium ions (Ca^{2+}) in the egg, as also occurs during animal gamete fusion (see Chapter 47). Another similarity to animals is the establishment of a block to *polyspermy*, the fertilization of an egg by multiple sperm. Thus, sperm cannot fuse with zygotes even *in vitro*. In maize (*Zea mays*), for example, this barrier to polyspermy is established as early as 45 seconds after the initial fusion of sperm with egg.

Seed Development, Form, and Function

After double fertilization, each ovule develops into a seed, and the ovary develops into a fruit enclosing the seed(s). As the embryo develops from the zygote, the seed stockpiles proteins, oils, and starch to varying degrees, depending on the species. This is why seeds are such a major nutrient drain. Initially, carbohydrates and other nutrients are stored in the seed's endosperm, but later, depending on the species, the swelling cotyledons (seed leaves) of the embryo may take over this function.

Endosperm Development

Endosperm usually develops before the embryo does. After double fertilization, the triploid nucleus of the ovule's central cell divides, forming a multinucleate "supercell" that has a milky consistency. This liquid mass, the endosperm, becomes multicellular when cytokinesis partitions the cytoplasm by forming membranes between the nuclei. Eventually, these "naked" cells produce cell walls, and the endosperm becomes solid. Coconut "milk" and "meat" are examples of liquid and solid endosperm, respectively. The white fluffy part of popcorn is also endosperm.

In grains and most other species of monocots, as well as many eudicots, the endosperm stores nutrients that can be used by the seedling after germination. In other eudicot seeds, the food reserves of the endosperm are completely exported to the cotyledons before the seed completes its development; consequently, the mature seed lacks endosperm.

Embryo Development

The first mitotic division of the zygote splits the fertilized egg into a basal cell and a terminal cell **(Figure 38.7)**. The

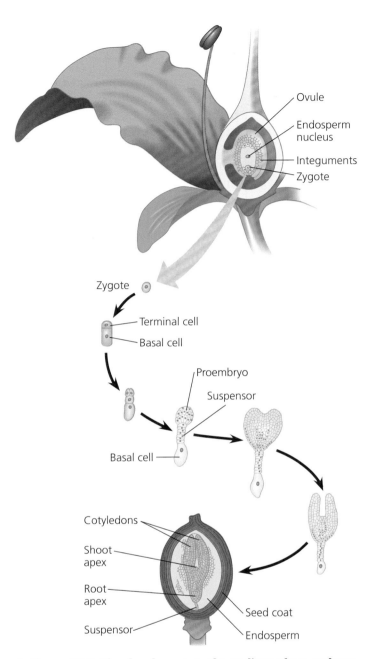

▲ **Figure 38.7 The development of a eudicot plant embryo.** By the time the ovule becomes a mature seed and the integuments harden and thicken into the seed coat, the zygote has given rise to an embryonic plant with rudimentary organs.

terminal cell eventually gives rise to most of the embryo. The basal cell continues to divide, producing a thread of cells called the *suspensor*, which anchors the embryo to the parent plant. The suspensor helps in transferring nutrients to the embryo from the parent plant and, in some species of plants, from the endosperm. As the suspensor elongates, it pushes the embryo deeper into the nutritive and protective tissues. Meanwhile, the terminal cell divides several times and forms a spherical proembryo (early embryo) attached to the suspensor. The cotyledons begin to form as bumps on the proembryo. A eudicot, with its two cotyledons, is heart-shaped at this stage. Only one cotyledon develops in monocots.

Soon after the rudimentary cotyledons appear, the embryo elongates. Cradled between the two cotyledons is the embryonic shoot apex. At the opposite end of the embryo's axis, where the suspensor attaches, an embryonic root apex forms. After the seed germinates—indeed, for the rest of the plant's life—the apical meristems at the apices of shoots and roots sustain primary growth (see Figure 35.11).

Structure of the Mature Seed

During the last stages of its maturation, the seed dehydrates until its water content is only about 5–15% of its weight. The embryo, which is surrounded by a food supply (cotyledons, endosperm, or both), enters **dormancy**; that is, it stops growing and its metabolism nearly ceases. The embryo and its food supply are enclosed by a hard, protective **seed coat** formed from the integuments of the ovule. In some species, dormancy is imposed by the presence of an intact seed coat rather than by the embryo itself.

You can take a closer look at one type of eudicot seed by splitting open the seed of a common garden bean. The embryo consists of an elongate structure, the embryonic axis, attached to fleshy cotyledons (**Figure 38.8a**). Below where the cotyledons are attached, the embryonic axis is called the **hypocotyl** (from the Greek *hypo*, under). The hypocotyl terminates in the **radicle**, or embryonic root. The portion of the embryonic axis above where the cotyledons are attached and below the first pair of miniature leaves is the **epicotyl** (from the Greek *epi*, on, over). The epicotyl, young leaves, and shoot apical meristem are collectively called the *plumule*.

The cotyledons of the common garden bean are packed with starch before the seed germinates because they absorbed carbohydrates from the endosperm when the seed was developing. However, the seeds of some eudicot species, such as castor beans (*Ricinus communis*), retain their food supply in the endosperm and have very thin cotyledons (**Figure 38.8b**). The cotyledons absorb nutrients from the endosperm and transfer them to the rest of the embryo when the seed germinates.

The embryos of monocots possess only a single cotyledon (**Figure 38.8c**). Grasses, including maize and wheat, have a specialized cotyledon called a *scutellum* (from the Latin *scutella*, small shield, a reference to its shape). The scutellum, which has a large surface area, is pressed against the endosperm, from which it absorbs nutrients during germination. The embryo of a grass seed is enclosed within two protective sheaths: a **coleoptile**, which covers the young shoot, and a **coleorhiza**, which covers the young root. Both structures aid in soil penetration after germination.

Seed weights range from less than 1 µg for some orchids to 20 kg for coco-de-mer palms. Orchid seeds have almost no

(a) Common garden bean, a eudicot with thick cotyledons. The fleshy cotyledons store food absorbed from the endosperm before the seed germinates.

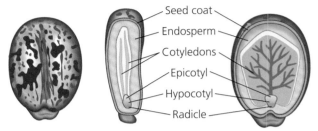

(b) Castor bean, a eudicot with thin cotyledons. The narrow, membranous cotyledons (shown in edge and flat views) absorb food from the endosperm when the seed germinates.

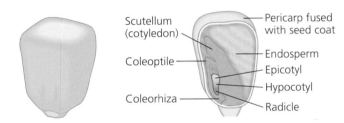

(c) Maize, a monocot. Like all monocots, maize has only one cotyledon. Maize and other grasses have a large cotyledon called a scutellum. The rudimentary shoot is sheathed in a structure called the coleoptile, and the coleorhiza covers the young root.

▲ **Figure 38.8 Seed structure.**
MAKE CONNECTIONS *In addition to cotyledon number, what are some others ways that the structures of monocots and eudicots differ? (See Figure 30.13 on p. 631.)*

food reserves and must bond symbiotically with mycorrhizae prior to germination. Large, endosperm-rich palm seeds are an adaptation for seedling establishment on nutrient-poor beaches.

Seed Dormancy: An Adaptation for Tough Times

Environmental conditions required to break seed dormancy vary among species. Seeds of some species germinate as soon as they are in a suitable environment. Others remain dormant, even if sown in a favorable place, until a specific environmental cue causes them to break dormancy.

The requirement for specific cues to break seed dormancy increases the chances that germination will occur at a time and place most advantageous to the seedling. Seeds of many desert plants, for instance, germinate only after a substantial rainfall. If they were to germinate after a mild drizzle, the soil might soon become too dry to support the seedlings. Where natural fires are common, many seeds require intense heat or smoke to break dormancy; seedlings are therefore most abundant after fire has cleared away competing vegetation. Where winters are harsh, seeds may require extended exposure to cold. Seeds sown during summer or fall will then not germinate until the following spring, ensuring a long growth season before the next winter. Certain small seeds, such as those of some lettuce varieties, require light for germination and will break dormancy only if buried shallow enough for the seedlings to poke through the soil surface. Some seeds have coats that must be weakened by chemical attack as they pass through an animal's digestive tract and thus are usually carried a considerable distance before germinating from dropped feces.

The length of time a dormant seed remains viable and capable of germinating varies from a few days to decades or even longer, depending on the plant species and environmental conditions. The oldest carbon-14–dated seed that has grown into a viable plant was a 2,000-year-old date palm seed recovered from excavations of Herod's palace in Israel. Most seeds are durable enough to last a year or two until conditions are favorable for germinating. Thus, the soil has a bank of ungerminated seeds that may have accumulated for several years. This is one reason vegetation reappears so rapidly after an environmental disruption such as fire.

Seed Germination and Seedling Development

Germination depends on **imbibition**, the uptake of water due to the low water potential of the dry seed. Imbibing water causes the seed to expand and rupture its coat and also triggers metabolic changes in the embryo that enable it to resume growth. Following hydration, enzymes begin digesting the storage materials of the endosperm or cotyledons, and the nutrients are transferred to the growing regions of the embryo.

The first organ to emerge from the germinating seed is the radicle, the embryonic root. Next, the shoot tip must break through the soil surface. In garden beans and many other eudicots, a hook forms in the hypocotyl, and growth pushes the hook above ground **(Figure 38.9a)**. In response to light, the hypocotyl straightens, the cotyledons separate, and the delicate epicotyl, now exposed, spreads its first true leaves (as distinct from the cotyledons, or seed leaves). These leaves expand, become green, and begin making food by photosynthesis. The cotyledons shrivel and fall away from the seedling, their food reserves having been exhausted by the germinating embryo.

Some monocots, such as maize and other grasses, use a different method for breaking ground when they germinate **(Figure 38.9b)**. The coleoptile, the sheath enclosing and protecting the embryonic shoot, pushes upward through the soil and into the air. The shoot tip then grows straight up through the tunnel provided by the tubular coleoptile and eventually breaks out through the coleoptile's tip.

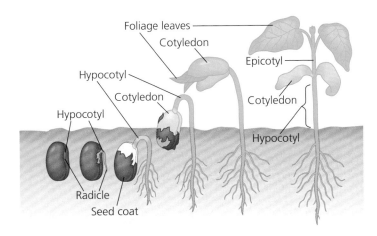

(a) **Common garden bean.** In common garden beans, straightening of a hook in the hypocotyl pulls the cotyledons from the soil.

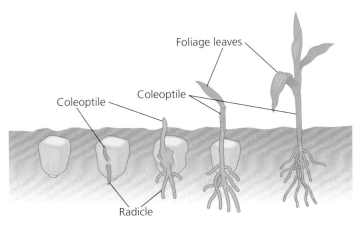

(b) **Maize.** In maize and other grasses, the shoot grows straight up through the tube of the coleoptile.

▲ **Figure 38.9 Two common types of seed germination.**

? *How do bean and maize seedlings protect their shoot systems as they push through the soil?*

Fruit Form and Function

While the seeds are developing from ovules, the ovary of the flower is developing into a **fruit**, which protects the enclosed seeds and, when mature, aids in their dispersal by wind or animals. Fertilization triggers hormonal changes that cause the ovary to begin its transformation into a fruit. If a flower has not been pollinated, fruit typically does not develop, and the entire flower usually withers and falls away.

During fruit development, the ovary wall becomes the pericarp, the thickened wall of the fruit. As the ovary grows, the other parts of the flower usually wither and are shed. For example, the pointed tip of a pea pod is the withered remains of the pea flower's stigma.

Fruits are classified into several types, depending on their developmental origin. Most fruits are derived from a single

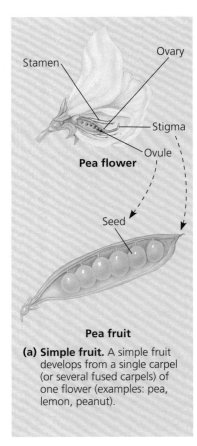

Pea flower

Stamen
Ovary
Stigma
Ovule
Seed

Pea fruit

(a) Simple fruit. A simple fruit develops from a single carpel (or several fused carpels) of one flower (examples: pea, lemon, peanut).

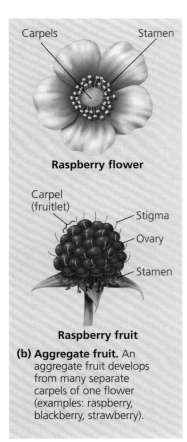

Raspberry flower

Carpels
Stamen

Carpel (fruitlet)
Stigma
Ovary
Stamen

Raspberry fruit

(b) Aggregate fruit. An aggregate fruit develops from many separate carpels of one flower (examples: raspberry, blackberry, strawberry).

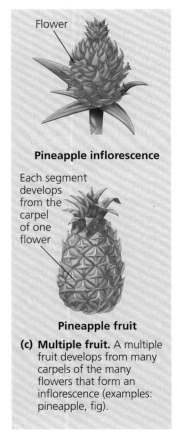

Pineapple inflorescence

Flower

Each segment develops from the carpel of one flower

Pineapple fruit

(c) Multiple fruit. A multiple fruit develops from many carpels of the many flowers that form an inflorescence (examples: pineapple, fig).

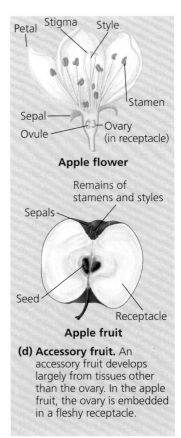

Apple flower

Petal
Stigma
Style
Stamen
Sepal
Ovule
Ovary (in receptacle)

Remains of stamens and styles
Sepals
Seed
Receptacle

Apple fruit

(d) Accessory fruit. An accessory fruit develops largely from tissues other than the ovary. In the apple fruit, the ovary is embedded in a fleshy receptacle.

▲ **Figure 38.10 Developmental origin of fruits.**

carpel or several fused carpels and are called **simple fruits** (**Figure 38.10a**). Some simple fruits are dry, such as a pea pod or a nut, whereas others are fleshy, such as a nectarine (see Figure 30.8). An **aggregate fruit** results from a single flower that has more than one separate carpel, each forming a small fruit (**Figure 38.10b**). These "fruitlets" are clustered together on a single receptacle, as in a raspberry. A **multiple fruit** develops from an inflorescence, a group of flowers tightly clustered together. When the walls of the many ovaries start to thicken, they fuse together and become incorporated into one fruit, as in a pineapple (**Figure 38.10c**).

In some angiosperms, other floral parts contribute to what we commonly call the fruit. Such fruits are called **accessory fruits**. In apple flowers, the ovary is embedded in the receptacle, and the fleshy part of this simple fruit is derived mainly from the enlarged receptacle; only the apple core develops from the ovary (**Figure 38.10d**). Another example is the strawberry, an aggregate fruit consisting of an enlarged receptacle studded with tiny, partially embedded fruits, each bearing a single seed.

A fruit usually ripens about the same time that its seeds complete their development. Whereas the ripening of a dry fruit, such as a soybean pod, involves the aging and drying out of fruit tissues, the process in a fleshy fruit is more elaborate. Complex interactions of hormones result in an edible fruit that entices animals that help disperse the seeds. The fruit's "pulp" becomes softer as a result of enzymes digesting components of the cell walls. The color usually changes from green to another color, such as red, orange, or yellow. The fruit becomes sweeter as organic acids or starch molecules are converted to sugar, which may reach a concentration of as much as 20% in a ripe fruit. **Figure 38.11** examines some mechanisms of fruit dispersal in more detail.

In this section, you have learned about the unique features of sexual reproduction in angiosperms—flowers, fruits, and double fertilization. Next, we'll examine asexual reproduction.

CONCEPT CHECK 38.1

1. Distinguish between pollination and fertilization.
2. What is the benefit of seed dormancy?
3. **WHAT IF?** If flowers had shorter styles, pollen tubes would more easily reach the embryo sac. Suggest an explanation for why very long styles have evolved in most flowering plants.
4. **MAKE CONNECTIONS** Does the life cycle of animals have any structures analogous to plant gametophytes? Explain your answer. (See Figure 13.6 on p. 252.)

For suggested answers, see Appendix A.

Exploring Fruit and Seed Dispersal

A plant's life depends on finding fertile ground. But a seed that falls and sprouts beneath the parent plant will stand little chance of competing successfully for nutrients. To prosper, seeds must be widely dispersed. Plants use biotic dispersal agents as well as abiotic agents such as water and wind.

Dispersal by Water

▶ Some buoyant seeds and fruits can survive months or years at sea. In coconut, the seed embryo and fleshy white "meat" (endosperm) are within a hard layer (endocarp) surrounded by a thick and buoyant fibrous husk.

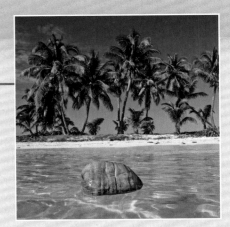

Dispersal by Wind

▶ The winged seed of the tropical Asian climbing gourd *Alsomitra macrocarpa* glides through the air of the rain forest in wide circles when released.

▼ The winged fruit of a maple spins like a helicopter blade, slowing descent and increasing the chance of being carried farther by horizontal winds.

Dandelion fruit

▶ Tumbleweeds break off at the ground and tumble across the terrain, scattering their seeds.

▲ Some seeds and fruits are attached to umbrella-like "parachutes" that are made of intricately branched hairs and often produced in puffy clusters. These dandelion "seeds" (actually one-seeded fruits) are carried aloft by the slightest gust of wind.

Dispersal by Animals

◀ The sharp, tack-like spines on the fruits of puncture vine (*Tribulus terrestris*) can pierce bicycle tires and injure animals, including humans. When these painful "tacks" are removed and discarded, the seeds are dispersed.

◀ Some animals, such as squirrels, hoard seeds or fruits in underground caches. If the animal dies or forgets the cache's location, the buried seeds are well positioned to germinate.

▶ Seeds in edible fruits are often dispersed in feces, such as the black bear feces shown here. Such dispersal may carry seeds far from the parent plant.

▶ Ants are chemically attracted to seeds with "food bodies" rich in fatty acids, amino acids, and sugars. The ants carry the seed to their underground nest, where the food body (the lighter-colored portion shown here) is removed and fed to larvae. Due to the seed's size, unwieldy shape, or hard coating, the remainder is usually left intact in the nest, where it germinates.

Flowering plants reproduce sexually, asexually, or both

Imagine chopping off your finger and watching it develop into an exact copy of you. If this could actually occur, it would be an example of **asexual reproduction**, in which offspring are derived from a single parent without fusion of egg and sperm. The result would be a clone, an asexually produced, genetically identical organism. Asexual reproduction is common in angiosperms, as well as in other plants, and for some plant species it is the predominant mode of reproduction.

Mechanisms of Asexual Reproduction

Asexual reproduction in plants is typically an extension of the capacity for indeterminate growth. As described in Concept 35.2, plant growth can be sustained or renewed indefinitely by meristems, regions of undifferentiated, dividing cells. In addition, parenchyma cells throughout the plant can divide and differentiate into more specialized types of cells, enabling plants to regenerate lost parts. Detached vegetative fragments of some plants can develop into whole offspring; for example, pieces of a potato with an "eye" (vegetative bud) can each regenerate a whole plant. Such **fragmentation**, the separation of a parent plant into parts that develop into whole plants, is one of the most common modes of asexual reproduction. The adventitious plantlets on *Kalanchoë* leaves exemplify an unusual type of fragmentation (see Figure 35.7). In other cases, the root system of a single parent, such as an aspen tree, can give rise to many adventitious shoots that become separate shoot systems **(Figure 38.12)**. One aspen clone in Utah has been estimated to be composed of 47,000 stems of genetically

identical trees. Although it is likely that some of the root system connections have been severed, making some of the trees isolated from the rest of the clone, each tree still shares a common genome.

An entirely different mechanism of asexual reproduction has evolved in dandelions and some other plants. These plants can sometimes produce seeds without pollination or fertilization. This asexual production of seeds is called **apomixis** (from the Greek words meaning "away from the act of mixing") because there is no joining or, indeed, production of sperm and egg. Instead, a diploid cell in the ovule gives rise to the embryo, and the ovules mature into seeds, which in the dandelion are dispersed by windblown fruits. Thus, these plants clone themselves by an asexual process but have the advantage of seed dispersal, usually associated with sexual reproduction. Introducing apomixis into hybrid crops is of great interest to plant breeders because apomixis would allow hybrid plants to pass on their desirable genomes intact to their offspring.

Advantages and Disadvantages of Asexual Versus Sexual Reproduction

An advantage of asexual reproduction is that there is no need for a pollinator. This may be beneficial in situations where plants of the same species are sparsely distributed and unlikely to be visited by the same pollinator. Asexual reproduction also allows the plant to pass on all of its genetic legacy intact to its progeny. In contrast, when reproducing sexually, a plant passes on only half of its alleles. If a plant is superbly suited to its environment, asexual reproduction can be advantageous. A vigorous plant can potentially clone many copies of itself, and if the environmental circumstances remain stable, these offspring will also be genetically well adapted to the same environmental conditions under which the parent flourished.

Generally, the progeny produced by asexual reproduction are stronger than seedlings produced by sexual reproduction. The offspring usually arise from mature vegetative fragments from the parent plant, which is why asexual reproduction in plants is also known as **vegetative reproduction**. In contrast, seed germination is a precarious stage in a plant's life. The tough seed gives rise to a fragile seedling that may face exposure to predators, parasites, wind, and other hazards. In the wild, only a small fraction of seedlings survive to become parents themselves. Production of enormous numbers of seeds compensates for the odds against individual survival and gives natural selection ample genetic variations to screen. However, this is an expensive means of reproduction in terms of the resources consumed in flowering and fruiting.

Because sexual reproduction generates variation in offspring and populations, it can be advantageous in unstable environments where evolving pathogens and other fluctuating conditions affect survival and reproductive success. In contrast, the genotypic uniformity of asexually produced plants puts them at great risk of local extinction if there is a

▲ **Figure 38.12 Asexual reproduction in aspen trees.** Some aspen groves, such as those shown here, consist of thousands of trees descended by asexual reproduction. Each grove of trees derives from the root system of one parent. Thus, the grove is a clone. Notice that genetic differences between groves descended from different parents result in different timing for the development of fall color.

catastrophic environmental change, such as a new strain of disease. Moreover, seeds (which are almost always produced sexually) facilitate the dispersal of offspring to more distant locations. Finally, seed dormancy allows growth to be suspended until environmental conditions become more favorable.

Although sexual reproduction involving two genetically different plants has the benefit of producing the most genetically diverse offspring, some plants, such as garden peas, usually self-fertilize. This process, called "selfing," can be a desirable attribute in some crop plants because it ensures that every ovule will develop into a seed. In many angiosperm species, however, mechanisms have evolved that make it difficult or impossible for a flower to fertilize itself, as we'll discuss next.

Mechanisms That Prevent Self-Fertilization

The various mechanisms that prevent self-fertilization contribute to genetic variety by ensuring that the sperm and egg come from different parents. In the case of **dioecious** species, plants cannot self-fertilize because different individuals have either staminate flowers (lacking carpels) or carpellate flowers (lacking stamens) **(Figure 38.13a)**. Other plants have flowers with functional stamens and carpels that mature at different times or are structurally arranged in such a way that it is unlikely that an animal pollinator could transfer pollen from an

(a) Some species, such as *Sagittaria latifolia* (common arrowhead), are dioecious, having plants that produce only staminate flowers (left) or carpellate flowers (right).

Thrum flower   Pin flower

(b) Some species, such as *Oxalis alpina* (alpine woodsorrel), produce two types of flowers on different individuals: "thrums," which have short styles and long stamens, and "pins," which have long styles and short stamens. An insect foraging for nectar would collect pollen on different parts of its body; thrum pollen would be deposited on pin stigmas, and vice versa.

▲ **Figure 38.13 Some floral adaptations that prevent self-fertilization.**

anther to a stigma of the same flower **(Figure 38.13b)**. However, the most common anti-selfing mechanism in flowering plants is **self-incompatibility**, the ability of a plant to reject its own pollen and sometimes the pollen of closely related individuals. If a pollen grain lands on a stigma of a flower on the same plant, a biochemical block prevents the pollen from completing its development and fertilizing an egg.

Researchers are unraveling the molecular mechanisms involved in self-incompatibility. This plant response is analogous to the immune response of animals in that both are based on the ability to distinguish the cells of "self" from those of "nonself." The key difference is that the animal immune system rejects nonself, as when the system mounts a defense against a pathogen or rejects a transplanted organ. Self-incompatibility in plants, in contrast, is a rejection of self.

Recognition of "self" pollen is based on genes for self-incompatibility, called *S*-genes. In the gene pool of a plant population, there can be dozens of alleles of an *S*-gene. If a pollen grain has an allele that matches an allele of the stigma on which it lands, the pollen tube fails to grow. Depending on the species, self-recognition blocks pollen tube growth by one of two molecular mechanisms: gametophytic self-incompatibility or sporophytic self-incompatibility.

In gametophytic self-incompatibility, the *S*-allele in the pollen genome governs the blocking of fertilization. For example, an S_1 pollen grain from an S_1S_2 parental sporophyte cannot fertilize eggs of an S_1S_2 flower but can fertilize an S_2S_3 flower. An S_2 pollen grain cannot fertilize either flower. Self-recognition of this kind involves the enzymatic destruction of RNA within a pollen tube. RNA-hydrolyzing enzymes are produced by the style and enter the pollen tube. If the pollen tube is a "self" type, these enzymes destroy its RNA.

In sporophytic self-incompatibility, fertilization is blocked by *S*-allele gene products in tissues of the parental sporophyte that adhere to the pollen grain wall. For example, neither an S_1 nor S_2 pollen grain from an S_1S_2 parental sporophyte can fertilize eggs of an S_1S_2 flower or S_2S_3 flower, due to the S_1S_2 parental tissue attached to the pollen wall. Sporophytic incompatibility involves a signal transduction pathway in epidermal cells of the stigma that prevents germination of the pollen grain.

Some crops, such as peas, maize, and tomatoes, routinely self-fertilize with satisfactory results. However, plant breeders frequently hybridize different varieties of a crop plant to combine the best traits of the varieties and counter the loss of vigor that can often result from excessive inbreeding. To obtain hybrid seeds, plant breeders today must prevent self-fertilization either by laboriously removing the anthers from the parent plants that provide the seeds (as Mendel did) or by developing male-sterile plants. The latter option is increasingly common. Eventually, it may also be possible to impose self-incompatibility genetically on crop species that are normally self-compatible. Basic research on mechanisms of self-incompatibility may thus have agricultural applications.

Vegetative Propagation and Agriculture

With the objective of improving crops and ornamental plants, humans have devised various methods for asexual propagation of angiosperms. Most of these methods are based on the ability of plants to form adventitious roots or shoots.

Clones from Cuttings

Most houseplants, woody ornamentals, and orchard trees are asexually reproduced from plant fragments called cuttings. In some cases, shoot cuttings are used. At the cut end of the shoot, a mass of dividing, undifferentiated cells called a **callus** forms, and adventitious roots then develop from the callus. If the shoot fragment includes a node, then adventitious roots form without a callus stage. Some plants, including African violets, can be propagated from single leaves rather than stems. For other plants, cuttings are taken from specialized storage stems, such as potato tubers. The Bartlett pear and the Red Delicious apple are examples of varieties that have been propagated asexually for over 150 years.

Grafting

In a modification of vegetative reproduction from cuttings, a twig or bud from one plant can be grafted onto a plant of a closely related species or a different variety of the same species. Grafting makes it possible to combine the best qualities of different species or varieties into a single plant. The plant that provides the root system is called the **stock**; the twig grafted onto the stock is referred to as the **scion**. For example, scions from French varieties of vines that produce superior wine grapes are grafted onto rootstocks of American varieties that produce inferior grapes but are more resistant to certain soil pathogens. The genes of the scion determine the quality of the fruit.

Test-Tube Cloning and Related Techniques

Plant biologists have adopted *in vitro* methods to clone novel plant varieties. They can grow whole plants by culturing small pieces of tissue from the parent plant on an artificial medium containing nutrients and hormones. The cells or tissues can come from any part of a plant, but growth may vary depending on the plant part, species, and artificial medium. In some media, the cultured cells divide and form a callus of undifferentiated cells **(Figure 38.14a)**. When the concentrations of hormones and nutrients are manipulated appropriately, a callus can sprout shoots and roots with fully differentiated cells **(Figure 38.14b,c)**. The plantlets can then be transferred to soil, where they continue their growth. A single plant can be cloned into thousands of copies by dividing calluses as they grow. This method is now used for propagating orchids as well as a wide variety of trees and shrubs.

▲ **Figure 38.14 Cloning a garlic plant. (a)** A root from a garlic clove gave rise to this callus culture, a mass of undifferentiated cells. **(b and c)** The differentiation of a callus into a plantlet depends on the nutrient levels and hormone concentrations in the artificial medium, as can be seen in these cultures grown for different lengths of time.

Plant tissue culture also facilitates genetic engineering. Most techniques for the introduction of foreign genes into plants require small pieces of plant tissue or single plant cells as the starting material. The term **transgenic** is used to describe genetically modified (GM) organisms that have been engineered to express a gene from another species. Test-tube culture makes it possible to regenerate GM plants from a single plant cell into which the foreign DNA has been incorporated. The techniques of genetic engineering are discussed in more detail in Chapter 20.

Some researchers couple a technique known as **protoplast fusion** with tissue culture methods to invent new plant varieties that can be cloned. Protoplasts are plant cells with their cell walls removed by treatment with enzymes (cellulases and pectinases) isolated from fungi **(Figure 38.15)**. In some cases, it is possible to fuse two protoplasts from different plant species that would otherwise be reproductively incompatible and then culture the hybrid protoplasts. Each protoplast can regenerate a wall and eventually form a hybrid plantlet. The hybrid produced by the protoplast fusion

◄ **Figure 38.15 Protoplasts.** These plant cells without walls are prepared by treating cells or tissues with wall-degrading enzymes isolated from certain fungi. Researchers can fuse protoplasts from different species to make hybrid cells and can then culture the cells to produce a new plant (LM).

50 μm

of two *Datura species*, for example, produces fertile seeds and is considered a new species. This hybrid can grow larger than the two parent species and is about 25% richer in medicinal alkaloids.

The *in vitro* culturing of plant cells and tissues is fundamental to most types of plant biotechnology. The other basic process is the production of transgenic plants through various methods of genetic engineering. In the next section, we take a closer look at plant biotechnology.

CONCEPT CHECK 38.2

1. The seedless banana, the world's most popular fruit, is losing the battle against two fungal epidemics. Why do such epidemics generally pose a greater risk to asexually propagated crops?
2. Self-fertilization, or selfing, seems to have obvious disadvantages as a reproductive "strategy" in nature, and it has even been called an "evolutionary dead end." So it is surprising that about 20% of angiosperm species primarily rely on selfing. Suggest a reason why selfing might be advantageous and yet still be an evolutionary dead end.
3. **WHAT IF?** Potatoes (*Solanum tuberosum*) and tomatoes (*Solanum lycopersicum*) are fairly closely related species. If you managed to cross the two, would it be possible to have a hybrid that makes potato-like tubers and tomato-like fruits on the same plant?

For suggested answers, see Appendix A.

CONCEPT 38.3

Humans modify crops by breeding and genetic engineering

Humans have intervened in the reproduction and genetic makeup of plants since the dawn of agriculture. As explained by Luis Herrera-Estrella in the Unit Six interview (see pp. 736–737), maize owes its existence to humans. Left on its own in nature, maize would soon become extinct for the simple reason that it cannot spread its seeds. Maize kernels are not only permanently attached to the central axis (the "cob") but also permanently protected by tough, overlapping leaf sheaths (the "husk") **(Figure 38.16)**. These attributes arose by artificial selection by humans. (See Chapter 22 to review the basic concept of artificial selection.) Despite having no understanding of the scientific principles underlying plant breeding, Neolithic (late Stone Age) humans domesticated most of our crop species over a relatively short period about 10,000 years ago. But genetic modification began long before humans started altering crops by artificial selection. For example,

▲ **Figure 38.16 Maize: a product of artificial selection.** Modern maize (bottom) was derived from teosinte (top). Teosinte kernels are tiny, and each row has a husk that must be removed to get at the kernel. The seeds are loose at maturity, allowing dispersal, which probably made harvesting difficult for early farmers. Neolithic farmers selected seeds from plants with larger cob and kernel size as well as the permanent attachment of seeds to the cob and the encasing of the entire cob by a tough husk.

the wheat species we rely on for much of our food evolved by the natural hybridization between different species of grasses. Such hybridization is common in plants and has long been exploited by breeders to introduce genetic variation for artificial selection and crop improvement.

Plant Breeding

The art of recognizing valuable traits is important in plant breeding. Breeders scrutinize their fields carefully and travel to other countries searching for domesticated varieties or wild relatives with desirable traits. Such traits occasionally arise spontaneously through mutation, but the natural rate of mutation is too slow and unreliable to produce all the mutations that breeders would like to study. Breeders sometimes hasten mutations by treating large batches of seeds or seedlings with radiation or chemicals.

When a desirable trait is identified in a wild species, the wild species is crossed with a domesticated variety. Generally, those progeny that have inherited the desirable trait from the wild parent have also inherited many traits that are not desirable for agriculture, such as small fruits or low yields. The progeny that express the desired trait are again crossed with members of the domesticated species and their progeny examined for the desired trait. This process is continued until the progeny with the desired wild trait resemble the original domesticated parent in their other agricultural attributes.

While most breeders cross-pollinate plants of a single species, some breeding methods rely on hybridization between two distant species of the same genus. Such crosses often result in the abortion of the hybrid seed during development. Very often the embryo begins to develop, but the endosperm does not. Hybrid embryos are sometimes rescued by surgically removing them from the ovule and culturing them *in vitro*.

Less commonly, hybridization is carried out on members of two different genera. A cross between wheat (*Triticum aestivum*) and rye (*Secale cereale*), for example, produced a novel grain called triticale, which contains a copy of all the chromosomes from both species. When triticale was first produced in the 1870s, it was considered little more than a botanical oddity. In the mid-1900s, however, plant breeders realized that triticale could potentially be developed into a crop with the yield and quality of bread wheat and with rye's tolerance of cold stress, moisture stress, and acidic soils. The early triticales were plagued with problems. These tall, late-maturing plants tended to fall over, were partially sterile, and were low yielding. They typically produced shriveled seeds that germinated poorly and were of poor quality for milling and baking. But through continued artificial selection, these problems were overcome, and triticale is now grown worldwide on more than 1 million hectares of marginal (poor-quality) farmland (1 ha = 2.47 acres). If we are to feed the rapidly growing world population in the 21st century, such marginal lands will have to become increasingly productive.

Plant Biotechnology and Genetic Engineering

Plant biotechnology has two meanings. In the general sense, it refers to innovations in the use of plants (or substances obtained from plants) to make products of use to humans—an endeavor that began in prehistory. In a more specific sense, biotechnology refers to the use of GM organisms in agriculture and industry. Indeed, in the last two decades, genetic engineering has become such a powerful force that the terms *genetic engineering* and *biotechnology* have become synonymous in the media.

Unlike traditional plant breeders, modern plant biotechnologists, using techniques of genetic engineering, are not limited to the transfer of genes between closely related species or genera. For example, traditional breeding techniques could not be used to insert a desired gene from daffodil into rice because the many intermediate species between rice and daffodil and their common ancestor are extinct. In theory, if breeders had the intermediate species, over the course of several centuries they could probably introduce a daffodil gene into rice by traditional hybridization and breeding methods. With genetic engineering, however, such gene transfers can be done more quickly, more specifically, and without the need for intermediate species.

In the remainder of this chapter, we expand on discussions in Chapter 20 by examining the prospects and controversies surrounding the use of GM crops. The advocates of plant biotechnology believe that the genetic engineering of crop plants is the key to overcoming some of the most pressing problems of the 21st century, including world hunger and fossil fuel dependency.

Reducing World Hunger and Malnutrition

Currently, 800 million people suffer from nutritional deficiencies, with 40,000 dying each day of malnutrition, half of them children. There is much disagreement about the causes of such hunger. Some argue that food shortages arise from inequities in distribution and that the dire poor simply cannot afford food. Others regard food shortages as evidence that the world is overpopulated—that the human species has exceeded the carrying capacity of the planet. Whatever the social and demographic causes of malnutrition, increasing food production is a humane objective. Because land and water are the most limiting resources, the best option is to increase yields on already existing farmland. Indeed, there is very little "extra" land that can be farmed, especially if the few remaining pockets of wilderness are to be preserved. Based on conservative estimates of population growth, farmers will have to produce 40% more grain per hectare to feed the human population in 2030. Plant biotechnology can help make these crop yields possible.

The commercial use of transgenic crops has been one of the most dramatic examples of rapid technology adoption in the history of agriculture. These crops include varieties and hybrids of cotton, maize, and potatoes that contain genes from the bacterium *Bacillus thuringiensis*. These "transgenes" encode a protein (*Bt* toxin) that is toxic to insect pests. The use of such plant varieties greatly reduces the need for chemical insecticides. The *Bt* toxin used in crops is produced in the plant as a harmless protoxin that only becomes toxic if activated by alkaline conditions, such as occur in the guts of insects. Because vertebrates have highly acidic stomachs, protoxin consumed by humans or farm animals is destroyed without becoming active.

Considerable progress has also been made in developing transgenic crops that tolerate certain herbicides. The cultivation of these plants may reduce production costs by enabling farmers to "weed" crops with herbicides that do not damage the transgenic crop plants, instead of using heavy tillage, which can cause soil erosion. Researchers are also engineering plants with enhanced resistance to disease. In one case, a transgenic papaya resistant to a ring spot virus was introduced into Hawaii, thereby saving its papaya industry.

The nutritional quality of plants is also being improved. For example, some 250,000 to 500,000 children go blind each year because of vitamin A deficiencies. More than half of these children die within a year of becoming blind. In response to this crisis, genetic engineers have created "Golden Rice," a transgenic variety supplemented with two daffodil genes that enable it to produce grain containing beta-carotene, a precursor of vitamin A. Another target for improvement by genetic

IMPACT

Fighting World Hunger with Transgenic Cassava

Plant biologists are racing to mold cassava (*Manihot esculenta*) into the perfect food. This starchy root crop is plentiful and easy to grow and is the primary food for 800 million of the world's poor. But it has several drawbacks. Composed almost entirely of carbohydrates, it provides plenty of calories but not a complete and balanced diet. Moreover, it must be processed to remove chemicals that release cyanide, and workers can be sickened by chronic exposure to this toxin. However, transgenic cassava plants have been developed with greatly enriched levels of protein, iron, and beta-carotene (a vitamin A precursor), and cyanide-producing chemicals have been almost eliminated from the roots. Researchers have also created cassava plants with root masses twice the normal size.

Cassava roots harvested in Thailand

WHY IT MATTERS Feeding the world's hungry will continue to be a daunting challenge in the 21st century because their population continues to climb. Untold human misery can be avoided if plant biologists can produce a cassava variety so nutritious that a 500-gram serving a day will provide a full and healthy diet.

FURTHER READING N. Nassar and R. Ortiz, Breeding cassava to feed the poor, *Scientific American* 302:78–84 (2010).

MAKE CONNECTIONS Genetic transformation using *Agrobacterium tumefaciens*, which causes crown gall disease, is the preferred method for transporting new genes into cassava cells. Review Concept 20.4, page 421, and explain why the use of this pathogen in genetic engineering does not produce crown gall disease in transgenic plants.

engineering is cassava, a staple for 800 million of the poorest people on our planet **(Figure 38.17)**.

Reducing Fossil Fuel Dependency

Global sources of inexpensive fossil fuels, particularly oil, are rapidly being depleted. Moreover, most climatologists attribute global warming mainly to the rampant burning of fossil fuels, such as coal and oil, and the resulting release of the greenhouse gas CO_2. How can the world meet its energy demands in the 21st century in an economical and nonpolluting way? In certain localities, wind or solar power may become economically viable, but such alternative energy sources are unlikely to fill the global energy demands completely. Many scientists predict that biomass from extremely fast-growing plants, such as switchgrass (*Panicum virgatum*) and poplar (*Populus trichocarpa*), could produce a sizable fraction of the world's energy needs in the not-too-distant future.

Under optimal conditions, poplars can grow 3–4 m each year, and switchgrass grows well under a wide variety of conditions found in regions where most types of agriculture are not economically viable. Scientists do not envisage the plant biomass being burned directly. Instead, the polymers in cell walls, such as cellulose and hemicellulose, which constitute the most abundant organic compounds on Earth, would be broken down into sugars by enzymatic reactions. These sugars, in turn, would be fermented into alcohol and distilled to yield **biofuels**.

The use of biofuels from plant biomass would reduce the net emission of CO_2. Whereas burning fossil fuels increases atmospheric CO_2 concentrations, biofuel crops reabsorb by photosynthesis the CO_2 emitted when biofuels are burned, creating a cycle that is carbon neutral. Plant breeders are trying to genetically engineer faster-growing poplar trees that produce more readily convertible biomass.

Biofuel technology does have its critics. For example, ecologist David Pimentel, of Cornell University, and geoengineer Tad Patzek, of the University of California, Berkeley, have estimated that more energy may be required to produce biofuels than would be produced from combustion of these products. Biofuel advocates, in turn, have questioned the accuracy of the data underlying these estimates.

The Debate over Plant Biotechnology

Much of the debate about GM organisms (GMOs) in agriculture is political, social, economic, or ethical and therefore outside the scope of this book. But we *should* consider the biological concerns about GM crops. Some biologists, particularly ecologists, are concerned about the unknown risks associated with the release of GMOs into the environment. The debate centers on the extent to which GMOs could harm the environment or human health. Those who want to proceed more slowly with agricultural biotechnology (or end it) are concerned about the unstoppable nature of the "experiment." If a drug trial produces unanticipated harmful results, the trial is stopped. But we may not be able to stop the "trial" of introducing novel organisms into the biosphere.

Chapter 20 introduced the key concerns regarding biotechnology in general. Here we take a closer look at some issues as they relate to plant biotechnology. Laboratory and field studies continue to examine the possible consequences of using GM crops, including the effects on human health and non-target organisms and the potential for transgene escape.

Issues of Human Health

Many GMO opponents worry that genetic engineering may inadvertently transfer allergens, molecules to which some people are allergic, from a species that produces an allergen to a plant used for food. However, biotechnologists are already engaged in removing genes that encode allergenic proteins from soybeans and other crops. So far, there is no credible evidence that GM plants specifically designed for human consumption have adverse effects on human health. In fact, some GM foods are potentially healthier than non-GM foods. For example, *Bt* maize (the transgenic variety with the *Bt* toxin) contains 90% less of a cancer-causing and birth defect–causing fungal toxin than non-*Bt* maize. Called fumonisin, this toxin is highly resistant to degradation and has been found in alarmingly high concentrations in some batches of processed maize products, ranging from cornflakes to beer. Fumonisin is produced by a fungus (*Fusarium*) that infects insect-damaged maize. Because *Bt* maize generally suffers less insect damage than non-GM maize, it contains much less fumonisin.

Nevertheless, because of health concerns, GMO opponents lobby for the clear labeling of all foods containing products of GMOs. Some also argue for strict regulations against the mixing of GM foods with non-GM foods during food transport, storage, and processing. Biotechnology advocates, however, note that similar demands were not made when "transgenic" crops produced by traditional plant-breeding techniques were put on the market. There are, for example, some commercially grown varieties of wheat derived by traditional plant-breeding techniques that contain entire chromosomes (and thousands of genes) from rye.

Possible Effects on Nontarget Organisms

Many ecologists are concerned that the growing of GM crops might have unforeseen effects on nontarget organisms. One laboratory study indicated that the larvae (caterpillars) of monarch butterflies responded adversely and even died after eating milkweed leaves (their preferred food) heavily dusted with pollen from transgenic *Bt* maize. This study has since been discredited, affording a good example of the self-correcting nature of science. As it turns out, when the original researchers shook the male maize inflorescences onto the milkweed leaves in the laboratory, the filaments of stamens, opened microsporangia, and other floral parts also rained onto the leaves. Subsequent research found that it was these other floral parts, *not* the pollen, that contained *Bt* toxin in high concentrations. Unlike pollen, these floral parts would not be carried by the wind to neighboring milkweed plants when shed under natural field conditions. Only one *Bt* maize line, accounting for less than 2% of commercial *Bt* maize production (and now discontinued), produced pollen with high *Bt* toxin concentrations.

In considering the negative effects of *Bt* pollen on monarch butterflies, one must also weigh the effects of an alternative to the cultivation of *Bt* maize—the spraying of non-*Bt* maize with chemical pesticides. Recent studies have shown that such spraying is much more harmful to nearby monarch populations than is *Bt* maize production. Although the effects of *Bt* maize pollen on monarch butterfly larvae appear to be minor, the controversy has emphasized the need for accurate field testing of all GM crops and the importance of targeting gene expression to specific tissues to improve safety.

Addressing the Problem of Transgene Escape

Perhaps the most serious concern raised about GM crops is the possibility of the introduced genes escaping from a transgenic crop into related weeds through crop-to-weed hybridization. The fear is that the spontaneous hybridization between a crop engineered for herbicide resistance and a wild relative might give rise to a "superweed" that would have a selective advantage over other weeds in the wild and would be much more difficult to control in the field. Some crops *do* hybridize with weedy relatives, and crop-to-weed transgene escape is a possibility. Its likelihood depends on the ability of the crop and weed to hybridize and on how the transgenes affect the overall fitness of the hybrids. A desirable crop trait—a dwarf phenotype, for example—might be disadvantageous to a weed growing in the wild. In other instances, there are no weedy relatives nearby with which to hybridize; soybean, for example, has no wild relatives in the United States. However, canola, sorghum, and many other crops do hybridize readily with weeds.

Many different strategies are being pursued with the goal of preventing transgene escape. For example, if male sterility could be engineered into plants, these plants would still produce seeds and fruit if pollinated by nearby nontransgenic plants, but they would produce no viable pollen. A second approach involves genetically engineering apomixis into transgenic crops. When a seed is produced by apomixis, the embryo and endosperm develop without fertilization. The transfer of this trait to transgenic crops would therefore minimize the possibility of transgene escape via pollen because plants could be male-sterile without compromising seed or fruit production. A third approach is to engineer the transgene into the chloroplast DNA of the crop. Chloroplast DNA in many plant species is inherited strictly from the egg, so transgenes in the chloroplast cannot be transferred by pollen (see Chapter 15 to review maternal inheritance). A fourth approach for preventing transgene escape is to genetically engineer flowers that develop normally but fail to open. Consequently, self-pollination would occur, but pollen would be unlikely to escape from the flower. This solution would require modifications to flower design. Several floral genes have been identified that could be manipulated to this end.

The continuing debate about GMOs in agriculture exemplifies one of this textbook's recurring ideas: the relationship of science and technology to society. Technological advances almost always involve some risk of unintended outcomes. In plant biotechnology, zero risk is probably unattainable. Therefore, scientists and the public must assess on a case-by-case basis the possible benefits of transgenic products versus the risks that society is willing to take. The best scenario is for these discussions and decisions to be based on sound scientific information and rigorous testing rather than on reflexive fear or blind optimism.

CONCEPT CHECK **38.3**

1. Compare traditional plant-breeding methods with genetic engineering.
2. Explain some benefits and risks of GM crops.
3. Why does *Bt* maize have less fumonisin than non-GM maize?
4. **WHAT IF?** In a few species, chloroplast genes are inherited only from sperm. How might this influence efforts to prevent transgene escape?

For suggested answers, see Appendix A.

38 CHAPTER REVIEW

SUMMARY OF KEY CONCEPTS

CONCEPT **38.1**

Flowers, double fertilization, and fruits are unique features of the angiosperm life cycle (pp. 801–811)

- Angiosperm reproduction involves an alternation of generations between a multicellular diploid sporophyte generation and a multicellular haploid gametophyte generation. Flowers, produced by the sporophyte, function in sexual reproduction.
- The four floral organs are sepals, petals, stamens, and carpels. **Sepals** protect the floral bud. **Petals** help attract pollinators. **Stamens** bear anthers in which haploid **microspores** develop into **pollen grains** containing a male gametophyte. **Carpels** contain ovules (immature seeds) in their swollen bases. Within the ovules, **embryos sacs** (female gametophytes) develop from megaspores.
- **Pollination**, which precedes fertilization, is the placing of pollen on the stigma of a carpel. After pollination, the pollen tube discharges two sperm into the female gametophyte. Two sperm are needed for **double fertilization**, a process in which one sperm fertilizes the egg, forming a zygote and eventually an embryo, while the other sperm combines with the polar nuclei, giving rise to food-storing endosperm.

Endosperm nucleus (3*n*) (2 polar nuclei plus sperm)

Zygote (2*n*) (egg plus sperm)

- The **seed coat** encloses the embryo along with a food supply stocked in either the **endosperm** or the **cotyledons**. Seed **dormancy** ensures that seeds germinate only when conditions for seedling survival are optimal. The breaking of dormancy often requires environmental cues, such as temperature or lighting changes.
- The **fruit** protects the enclosed seeds and aids in wind dispersal or in the attraction of seed-dispersing animals.

> **?** *What changes occur to the four types of floral parts as a flower changes into a fruit?*

CONCEPT **38.2**

Flowering plants reproduce sexually, asexually, or both (pp. 812–815)

- **Asexual reproduction** enables successful plants to proliferate quickly. Sexual reproduction generates most of the genetic variation that makes evolutionary adaptation possible.
- Plants have evolved many mechanisms to avoid self-fertilization, including dioecy (male and female flowers on different individuals), nonsynchronous production of male and female parts within a single flower, and **self-incompatibility** reactions in which pollen grains that bear an allele identical to one in the female are rejected.
- Plants can be cloned from single cells, which can be genetically manipulated before being allowed to develop into a plant.

> **?** *What are the advantages and disadvantages of asexual reproduction?*

CONCEPT **38.3**

Humans modify crops by breeding and genetic engineering (pp. 815–819)

- Hybridization of different varieties and even species of plants is common in nature and has been used by breeders, ancient and modern, to introduce new genes into crops. After two plants are successfully hybridized, plant breeders select those progeny that have the desired traits.
- In genetic engineering, genes from unrelated organisms are incorporated into plants. Genetically modified (GM) plants have the potential of increasing the quality and quantity of food worldwide and may also become increasingly important as biofuels.
- Two important GM crops are Golden Rice, which provides more vitamin A, and *Bt* maize, which is insect resistant.
- There are concerns about the unknown risks of releasing GM organisms into the environment, but the potential benefits of transgenic crops need to be considered.

> **?** *Give three examples of how genetic engineering has improved food quality or agricultual productivity.*

TEST YOUR UNDERSTANDING

LEVEL 1: KNOWLEDGE/COMPREHENSION

1. A seed develops from
   a. an ovum.
   b. a pollen grain.
   c. an ovule.
   d. an ovary.
   e. an embryo.

2. A fruit is
   a. a mature ovary.
   b. a mature ovule.
   c. a seed plus its integuments.
   d. a fused carpel.
   e. an enlarged embryo sac.

3. Double fertilization means that
   a. flowers must be pollinated twice to yield fruits and seeds.
   b. every egg must receive two sperm to produce an embryo.
   c. one sperm is needed to fertilize the egg, and a second sperm is needed to fertilize the polar nuclei.
   d. the egg of the embryo sac is diploid.
   e. every sperm has two nuclei.

4. "Golden Rice"
   a. is resistant to various herbicides, making it practical to weed rice fields with those herbicides.
   b. is resistant to a virus that commonly attacks rice fields.
   c. includes bacterial genes that produce a toxin that reduces damage from insect pests.
   d. produces larger, golden grains that increase crop yields.
   e. contains daffodil genes that increase vitamin A content.

5. Which statement concerning grafting is correct?
   a. Stocks and scions refer to twigs of different species.
   b. Stocks come from vines, but scions come from trees.
   c. Stocks provide root systems for grafting.
   d. Grafting creates new species.
   e. Stocks and scions must come from unrelated species.

LEVEL 2: APPLICATION/ANALYSIS

6. Some dioecious species have the XY genotype for male and XX for female. After double fertilization, what would be the genotypes of the embryos and endosperm nuclei?
   a. embryo X/endosperm XX or embryo Y/endosperm XY
   b. embryo XX/endosperm XX or embryo XY/endosperm XY
   c. embryo XX/endosperm XXX or embryo XY/endosperm XYY
   d. embryo XX/endosperm XXX or embryo XY/endosperm XXY
   e. embryo XY/endosperm XXX or embryo XX/endosperm XXY

7. A small flower with green petals is most likely
   a. bee-pollinated.
   b. bird-pollinated.
   c. bat-pollinated.
   d. wind-pollinated.
   e. moth-pollinated.

8. The pollen produced by wind-pollinated plants is often smaller than the pollen produced by animal-pollinated plants. A reason for this might be that
   a. wind-pollinated plants, in general, are smaller than animal pollinated plants.
   b. wind-pollinated plants release pollen in the spring, before the plant has stored enough energy to make large pollen grains.
   c. small pollen grains can be carried farther by the wind.
   d. animal pollinators are more facile at picking up large pollen grains.
   e. wind-pollinated flowers don't need large pollen grains because they don't have to attract animal pollinators.

9. The black dots that cover strawberries are actually individual fruits. The fleshy and tasty portion of a strawberry derives from the receptacle of a flower with many separate carpels. Therefore, a strawberry is
   a. both a multiple fruit and an aggregate fruit.
   b. both a multiple fruit and an accessory fruit.
   c. both a simple fruit and an aggregate fruit.
   d. both an aggregate fruit and an accessory fruit.
   e. a simple fruit with many seeds.

10. **DRAW IT** Draw and label the parts of a flower.

LEVEL 3: SYNTHESIS/EVALUATION

11. **EVOLUTION CONNECTION**
    With respect to sexual reproduction, some plant species are fully self-fertile, others are fully self-incompatible, and some exhibit a "mixed strategy" with partial self-incompatibility. These reproductive strategies differ in their implications for evolutionary potential. How, for example, might a self-incompatible species fare as a small founder population or remnant population in a severe population bottleneck (see Chapter 23), as compared with a self-fertile species?

12. **SCIENTIFIC INQUIRY**
    Critics of GM foods have argued that foreign genes may disturb normal cellular functioning, causing unexpected and potentially harmful substances to appear inside cells. Toxic intermediary substances that normally occur in very small amounts may arise in larger amounts, or new substances may appear. The disruption may also lead to loss of substances that help maintain normal metabolism. If you were your nation's chief scientific advisor, how would you respond to these criticisms?

13. **SCIENCE, TECHNOLOGY, AND SOCIETY**
    Humans have engaged in genetic manipulation for millennia, producing plant and animal varieties through selective breeding and hybridization processes that significantly modify the genomes of organisms. Why do you think modern genetic engineering, which often entails introducing or modifying only one or a few genes, has met with so much public opposition? Should some forms of genetic engineering be of greater concern than others? Explain.

14. **WRITE ABOUT A THEME**
    Emergent Properties In a short essay (100–150 words), discuss how the ability of a flower to reproduce with other flowers of the same species is an emergent property that arises from its floral parts and their organization.

For selected answers, see Appendix A.

MasteringBIOLOGY®   www.masteringbiology.com

1. MasteringBiology® Assignments
Tutorial Angiosperm Life Cycle
Activities Discovery Channel Video: Plant Pollination • Reproduction in Flowering Plants • Fruit Structure and Development • Discovery Channel Video: Colored Cotton
Questions Student Misconceptions • Reading Quiz • Multiple Choice • End-of-Chapter

2. eText
Read your book online, search, take notes, highlight text, and more.

3. The Study Area
Practice Tests • Cumulative Test • *BioFlix* 3-D Animations • MP3 Tutor Sessions • Videos • Activities • Investigations • Lab Media • Audio Glossary • Word Study Tools • Art

Animal Form and Function

An Interview with

Baldomero M. Olivera

Growing up in the Philippines, Baldomero (Toto) Olivera collected the shells of venomous cone snails as a hobby. Today, he is a leading expert on the use of cone snail toxins for exploring and modifying the activity of the mammalian nervous system. After graduating summa cum laude from the University of the Philippines, he earned a Ph.D. in Chemistry from the California Institute of Technology (Caltech). In 1970, Dr. Olivera joined the faculty at the University of Utah, where he is now a Distinguished Professor of Biology. In 2009, he became the first Filipino to be elected to the U.S. National Academy of Sciences.

How did you get started in science?

In high school I had a great teacher in both biology and chemistry. After I finished college, she encouraged me to go on to graduate school. She put an article in front of me about Caltech and told me to apply there. Fortunately, they accepted me.

When I got to Caltech, I assumed that since I'd taken five courses at a time as an undergraduate, I'd be expected to take even more in graduate school, so in my first semester I was taking seven courses. One was the only statistical mechanics course at Caltech, so not only chemists like me, but also physicists took it. The first day, the professor, Norman Davidson, reviewed all of classical mechanics, which I had never had. The second day he reviewed all of quantum mechanics. After the fourth lecture I went to him and said, "You know, Professor, I haven't understood a word you've said." He said, "Don't worry about it. Just hang in there." I did, and I ended up doing my Ph.D. research in his lab, studying DNA.

After graduate school I went to Stanford and continued to work on DNA as a postdoctoral fellow. I then took a faculty job in the Philippines, but soon found out that I probably would have no large lab equipment for at least a year. I decided to look for a project that we could start immediately with no equipment and, if at all possible, that would have some local advantages. Since I'd collected shells as a hobby, I knew that some of the local snails, called cone snails, had a venomous sting that could kill people. So we set out to purify the substances in the venom that were lethal to mammals.

Why do cone snails produce venom?

Not much was known about this until 1956, when a Yale graduate student, Alan Kohn, discovered that a cone snail he had in an aquarium hunted fish. (Kohn went on to become a leading expert on the ecology and taxonomy of cone snails.) We now know that about 100 of the 500–700 species of cone snails hunt fish. A similar number hunt other molluscs, and the rest hunt marine worms.

When a cone snail hunts, it first sniffs the fish by means of chemoreceptors, specialized cells that function in sensing smell or taste. Chemoreception by a cone snail in the marine environment is amazing. For example, fish-hunting cone snails in a large aquarium react the moment you drop in a fish. They move their siphon, which is sensory, back and forth so they can locate the fish. When the siphon touches fish skin, a disposable, harpoon-like tooth shoots out of the snail's proboscis and pierces the scales of the fish. The venom flows through the tooth into the fish. So the tooth, which is barbed, is both a harpoon and a hypodermic needle. The venom very rapidly immobilizes the harpooned fish, which the cone snail can then consume.

Some other animals hunt cone snails, which explains their cone-like shape. Among the major predators are crabs. If you're a crab, you grab the snail's shell and try to break it. But if the snail is cone-shaped, the crab claw slips, making it hard to break the shell. So the cone shape is a defensive adaptation. However, a cone-shaped snail shell that narrows to a point has an opening too small to allow a large prey animal to be pulled into the shell. So fish-hunting cone snails tend to be more cylindrical.

What did you hope to learn by studying cone snail venom?

We knew that venoms could be useful because the toxins of the pufferfish—*fugu* in Japanese—and the krait, a cobra-like snake, had been used to study ion channels in the nervous system. Ion channels are found on the surface of neurons, and they let ions in and out of the cell. This movement of ions mediates the electrical signaling within neurons and controls the transfer of a signal from one neuron to another. Venoms that interfere with that ion movement wipe out the prey animal's nervous system—that's why they're deadly.

The toxins in venoms are quite specific. The toxin of the pufferfish targets a sodium ion channel. The toxin of the krait targets a different type of ion channel, called a nicotinic receptor. By using these toxins in the lab to interfere with the function of particular kinds of ion channels, you can learn a great deal about how the nervous system normally functions.

How did you study the cone snail toxins?

In the Philippines, people eat marine snails, and the shells are by-products. Since I'd collected shells, I knew the people who sold them commercially and asked them to get me some live snails.

When you work with cone snails, you of course don't want to be stung. We put the snails on ice and they became very lethargic. We then dissected out the venom duct and pressed out the venom. The next step was to measure the activity of the venom. The medical literature said people stung by cone snails died because their diaphragms became paralyzed. So we assayed (tested) for paralysis. We would inject mice with various fractions of the venom and then immediately put them on a wire screen, upside down. Mice can actually stay attached this way indefinitely, but when paralysis sets in, they fall off. All we did was measure the time until they fell. It turns out that the falling time changes with the amount of toxin in a very reproducible way.

Using this falling-time assay, we purified an active peptide from two different fractions of the venom of the species *Conus geographus*. One of these peptides has only 13 amino acids; the other has 22. We found out that the peptide with 13 amino acids bound to exactly the same site on an ion channel as the krait toxin, which has about 80 amino acids. It was remarkable that a toxin had evolved in snails that was so much smaller but had the same activity.

How did the big breakthrough in your cone snail studies come about?

When I started as a full-time faculty member here at Utah, all our funding was still for experiments with DNA, and my graduate students all studied DNA. So we started recruiting undergraduates to work on the cone snail project—and that led to a very lucky break. One of the undergraduates, Craig Clark, said, "You guys are injecting into the body cavity of the mice. I think we should inject directly into the central nervous system." That was purely his idea. I thought it would probably just kill the mice.

At the time, we were beginning to use new techniques to separate the venom into many fractions, each containing different peptides. Using our falling-time assay, most fractions were inactive. But when Craig started injecting fractions into the central nervous system, the results were truly astonishing. Almost every fraction changed the mice's behavior in some way, and many of the effects were really bizarre. Some fractions made mice run around in circles. Others made mice scratch themselves. Still others made mice get up on their hind legs and move their front legs as if they were boxing. There was even a fraction that put juvenile, but not adult, mice into a sleeplike state. Craig purified the peptide with that activity, which he called the "sleeper peptide." I think the reason why university research is typically the most creative is that students sometimes do what they want, not what their professors tell them to do!

From then on, we let undergraduates pick which active fraction they wanted to study. Their job was to purify the peptide, which we would then synthesize and work on further.

Why and how did so much toxin diversity evolve in cone snails?

My suspicion is that if your survival depends on influencing the behavior of another animal and your strategy is purely chemical, it takes a very complex strategy for that to be successful in evolution. The adaptations that evolved in cone snails are in essence what we're just discovering in modern medical practice. To treat cancer or AIDS effectively, you can't use just one chemical; you use combination drug therapy. I think the evolution of venoms in cone snails followed the same principle.

For the cone snail toxins there are a few gene superfamilies, and they are subject to very accelerated evolution. There are parallels to the vertebrate adaptive immune system in that there are conserved and highly variable regions in the genes. The conserved regions are mostly all cut out. So, if you like, a cone snail peptide is equivalent to the highly variable part that makes an antibody very specific.

How did your studies with snails lead to a discovery that was medically important?

After Craig discovered that you could study the effects of toxins by injecting them into the central nervous system of mice, he recruited a high school student, Michael McIntosh, to the lab. Mike decided to work with a different snail, called *Conus magus*, or the magician's cone. One of the most striking discoveries he made was a peptide that gave mice a characteristic tremor, or shake.

When Mike purified the "shaker peptide," we learned that it blocks a certain type of calcium channel. In fish these calcium channels control the release of the neurotransmitter that carries signals from nerve to muscle. When shaker peptide blocks these channels, the neurotransmitter is not released, and the fish becomes paralyzed. In mammals, this type of calcium channel is found only in the pain circuitry. When you experience severe pain, pain fibers send signals to a nerve cell in your spinal cord that takes the pain signal up to your brain. The pain fibers in mammals release signals to the nerves using the same type of calcium channel that in fish carries signals to muscles to direct movement. This difference in receptor location and function is why the shaker peptide paralyzes and kills fish, but not mammals.

The shaker peptide is now an approved drug. If a patient has very severe pain and the shaker peptide is injected where the pain fiber connects to the nerve, the perception of pain stops because the pain fiber no longer releases the chemical signal to the nerve. Doctors are using the shaker peptide in this way for people who are suffering from severe pain and no longer get pain relief from morphine due to tolerance built up over time. A surgically implanted pump introduces the shaker peptide to the spinal cord at the site where the pain fiber makes its connection.

What other discoveries do you hope to see come out of studying cone snails?

There are 500–700 species of cone snails, but the total biodiversity of molluscs with venom is probably 12,000 species. The biggest group is the turrids. You don't find many of them in shallow water, but at 400 meters, where there are no cone snails, you find hundreds of species of turrids. Many of them are just a few millimeters in length, and nobody knows anything about their biology. Fortunately, hobbyists are extremely interested in their tiny shells, so fishermen in the Philippines gather them. They tie all their broken fine-mesh fishing nets into bundles, which they sink in water for 3 to 6 months. When they lift these bundles, each will contain several thousand marine animals, almost all of them alive. For gastropods alone, a net will hold something like 250 different species, of which 40 are venomous. Each venom has 200 compounds. So this is a vast new world.

What advice would you give students interested in biology or medicine?

One piece of advice is to get as good a basic science background as you possibly can. I started out with very basic chemistry and very basic biology, and then of course the science grew as my research career grew. Having strong basic science training allows you to feel confident that even if you don't understand a problem at first (like quantum mechanics), you can still tackle it. A second thing is that you ought to know what it is in science that really turns you on. Third, keep in mind that it is always fun to learn something new.

> "The adaptations that evolved in cone snails are in essence what we're just discovering in modern medical practice."

Baldomero Olivera (center) with Jane Reece and Steve Wasserman (right)

Basic Principles of Animal Form and Function

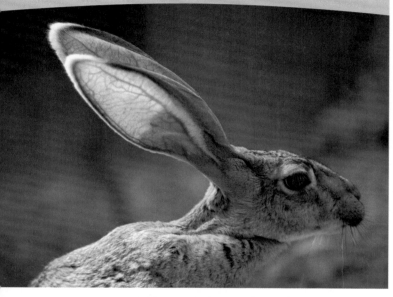

▲ **Figure 40.1 How does a jackrabbit keep from overheating?**

KEY CONCEPTS

40.1 Animal form and function are correlated at all levels of organization

40.2 Feedback control maintains the internal environment in many animals

40.3 Homeostatic processes for thermoregulation involve form, function, and behavior

40.4 Energy requirements are related to animal size, activity, and environment

OVERVIEW

Diverse Forms, Common Challenges

The ears of the jackrabbit (*Lepus alleni*) in **Figure 40.1** are thin and remarkably large. They provide this hare with an acute sense of hearing, a primary defense against predators. The ears also help the jackrabbit shed excess heat. Blood flowing through each ear's network of vessels transfers heat to the surrounding air. However, when the air is warmer than the jackrabbit, blood passing through the ears could absorb heat, raising body temperature to a dangerous level. How, then, does a big-eared jackrabbit survive in the midday desert heat? To answer this question, we need to look more closely at the biological form, or **anatomy**, of the animal.

Over the course of its life, a jackrabbit faces the same fundamental challenges as any other animal, whether hydra, hawk, or human. All animals must obtain oxygen and nutrients, fight off infection, and produce offspring. Given that they share these and other basic requirements, why do species vary so enormously in makeup, complexity, organization, and appearance? The answer is adaptation: Natural selection favors those variations in a population that increase relative fitness (see Chapter 23). The solutions to the challenges of survival vary among environments and species, but they frequently result in a close match of form to function.

Because form and function are correlated, examining anatomy often provides clues to **physiology**—biological function. In the case of the jackrabbit, researchers noted that its large, pink-tinged ears turn pale when the air temperature exceeds 40°C (104°F), the normal temperature of the jackrabbit's body. The color change reflects a temporary narrowing of blood vessels in response to a hot environment. With their blood supply reduced, the ears can absorb heat without overheating the rest of the body. When the air cools, blood flow increases, and the large ears again help release excess heat.

In this chapter, we will begin our study of animal form and function by examining the levels of organization in the animal body and the systems for coordinating the activities of distinct body parts. Next, we will use the example of body temperature regulation to illustrate how animals control their internal environment. Finally, we will explore how anatomy and physiology relate to an animal's interactions with the environment and its management of energy use.

CONCEPT 40.1

Animal form and function are correlated at all levels of organization

An animal's size and shape are fundamental aspects of form that significantly affect the way the animal interacts with its environment. Although we may refer to size and shape as elements of a "body plan" or "design," this does not imply a process of conscious invention. The body plan of an animal is the result of a pattern of development programmed by the genome, itself the product of millions of years of evolution.

Evolution of Animal Size and Shape

EVOLUTION Many different body plans have arisen during the course of evolution, but these variations fall within certain bounds. Physical laws that govern strength, diffusion, movement, and heat exchange limit the range of animal forms.

As an example of how physical laws constrain evolution, let's consider how some properties of water limit the possible shapes for animals that are fast swimmers. Water is about a thousand times denser than air and also far more viscous. Therefore, any bump on an animal's body surface that causes drag impedes a swimmer more than it would a runner or flyer. Tuna and other fast ray-finned fishes can swim at speeds up to 80 km/hr (50 miles/hour). Sharks, penguins, dolphins, and seals are also fast swimmers. As is apparent in the examples in **Figure 40.2**, such animals share a streamlined body contour: a shape that is fusiform, meaning tapered on both ends. The similar shape found in these speedy vertebrates is an example of convergent evolution (see Chapter 22). Natural selection often results in similar adaptations when diverse organisms face the same environmental challenge, such as overcoming drag during swimming.

Physical laws also influence animal body plans with regard to maximum size. As body dimensions increase, thicker skeletons are required to maintain adequate support. This limitation affects internal skeletons, such as those of vertebrates, as well as external skeletons, such as those of insects and other arthropods. In addition, as bodies increase in size, the muscles required for locomotion must represent an ever-larger fraction of the total body mass. At some point, mobility becomes limited. By considering the fraction of

▲ **Seal**

▲ **Penguin**

▲ **Tuna**

▲ **Figure 40.2 Convergent evolution in fast swimmers.**

body mass in leg muscles and the effective force such muscles generate, scientists can estimate maximum running speed for a wide range of body plans. Such calculations indicate that the dinosaur *Tyrannosaurus rex*, which stood more than 6 m tall, probably could reach speeds of 30 km/hr (19 miles/hour), about as fast as the fastest humans can run.

Exchange with the Environment

Animals must exchange materials with their environment, and this requirement imposes limitations on their body plans (as it does for all multicellular organisms). Exchange occurs as substances dissolved in an aqueous solution move across the plasma membrane of each cell. The rates of exchange for nutrients, waste products, and gases are proportional to membrane surface area, whereas the amount of material that must be exchanged to sustain life is proportional to cell volume.

The opportunity for exchange depends on the number of cells in an organism's body. A single-celled organism, such as the amoeba in **Figure 40.3a**, has a sufficient membrane surface area in contact with its environment to carry out all necessary exchange. In contrast, an animal is composed of many cells, each with its own plasma membrane across which exchange must occur. A multicellular organization therefore works only if every cell has access to a suitable aqueous environment, either inside or outside the animal's body.

Many animals with a simple internal organization have body plans that enable direct exchange between almost all their cells and the external environment. For example, a pond-dwelling hydra, which has a saclike body plan, has a body wall only two cell layers thick (**Figure 40.3b**). Because its

(a) Single cell   **(b) Two layers of cells**

Mouth

Gastrovascular cavity

Exchange

Exchange

Exchange

0.1 mm

1 mm

▲ **Figure 40.3 Contact with the environment. (a)** In a single-celled organism, such as an amoeba, the entire surface area contacts the environment. **(b)** Although all animals are multicellular, some have a simple organization in which all or nearly all cells contact the environment. For example, a hydra's body consists of two layers of cells. As fluid moves in and out of the hydra's mouth, every body cell can exchange material directly with the aqueous environment.

gastrovascular cavity opens to the external environment, both the outer and inner layers of cells are constantly bathed by pond water. Another common body plan that maximizes exposure to the surrounding medium is a flat shape. Consider, for instance, a parasitic tapeworm, which can reach several meters in length (see Figure 33.12). A thin, flat shape places most cells of the worm in direct contact with its particular environment—the nutrient-rich intestinal fluid of a vertebrate host.

The bodies of most animals are composed of compact masses of cells, with an internal organization much more complex than that of a hydra or a tapeworm. For such a body plan, increasing the number of cells decreases the ratio of outer surface area to total volume. As an extreme comparison, the ratio of outer surface to volume for a whale is hundreds of thousands of times smaller than that for a water flea (*Daphnia*). Nevertheless, every cell in the whale must be bathed in fluid and have access to oxygen, nutrients, and other resources. How is this accomplished?

In whales and most other animals, the evolutionary adaptations that enable sufficient exchange with the environment are specialized surfaces that are extensively branched or folded **(Figure 40.4)**. In almost all cases, these exchange surfaces lie within the body, an arrangement that protects their delicate tissues from abrasion or dehydration and allows for streamlined body contours. In humans, the internal exchange surfaces of the digestive, respiratory, and circulatory systems each have an area more than 25 times that of the skin.

Internal body fluids link exchange surfaces to body cells. The spaces between cells are filled with fluid, in many animals called **interstitial fluid** (from the Latin for "stand between"). Complex body plans also include a circulatory fluid, such as blood. Exchange between the interstitial fluid and the circulatory fluid enables cells throughout the body to obtain nutrients and get rid of wastes (see Figure 40.4).

Despite the greater challenges of exchange with the environment, complex body plans have distinct benefits over simple

A microscopic view of the lung reveals that it is much more sponge-like than balloon-like. This construction provides an expansive wet surface for gas exchange with the environment (SEM).

The lining of the small intestine has finger-like projections that expand the surface area for nutrient absorption (SEM).

Within the kidney, blood is filtered across the surface of long, narrow blood vessels packed into ball-shaped structures (SEM).

▲ **Figure 40.4 Internal exchange surfaces of complex animals.** This diagram provides an overview of chemical exchange between an animal body and the environment. Most animals have surfaces that are specialized for exchanging chemicals with the surroundings. These exchange surfaces are usually internal but are connected to the environment via openings on the body surface (the mouth, for example). The exchange surfaces are finely branched or folded, giving them a very large area. The digestive, respiratory, and excretory systems all have such exchange surfaces. The circulatory system carries chemicals transported across these surfaces throughout the body.

? *In what sense are exchange surfaces such as the lining of the digestive system both internal and external?*

ones. For example, an external skeleton can protect against predators, and sensory organs can provide detailed information on the animal's surroundings. Internal digestive organs can break down food gradually, controlling the release of stored energy. In addition, specialized filtration systems can adjust the composition of the internal fluid that bathes the animal's body cells. In this way, an animal can maintain a relatively stable internal environment while living in a changeable external environment. A complex body plan is especially advantageous for animals living on land, where the external environment may be highly variable.

Hierarchical Organization of Body Plans

Cells form a functional animal body through their emergent properties. Recall from Chapter 1 that emergent properties arise by way of successive levels of structural and functional organization. Cells are organized into **tissues**, groups of cells with a similar appearance and a common function. Different types of tissues are further organized into functional units called **organs**. (The simplest animals, such as sponges, lack organs or even true tissues.) Groups of organs that work together provide an additional level of organization and coordination and make up an **organ system** (Table 40.1). Thus, for example, the skin is an organ of the integumentary system, which protects against infection and helps regulate body temperature.

Many organs contain tissues with distinct physiological roles. In some cases, the roles are different enough that we consider the organ to belong to more than one organ sys-

tem. The pancreas, for instance, produces enzymes critical to the function of the digestive system and also regulates the level of sugar in the blood as a vital part of the endocrine system.

Just as viewing the body's organization from the "bottom up" (from cells to organ systems) reveals emergent properties, a "top-down" view of the hierarchy reveals the multilayered basis of specialization. Consider the human digestive system: the mouth, pharynx, esophagus, stomach, small and large intestines, accessory organs, and anus. Each organ has specific roles in digestion. One function of the stomach, for example, is to initiate the breakdown of proteins. This process requires a churning motion powered by stomach muscles, as well as digestive juices secreted by the stomach lining. Producing digestive juices, in turn, requires highly specialized cell types: One cell type secretes a protein-digesting enzyme, a second generates concentrated hydrochloric acid, and a third produces mucus, which protects the stomach lining.

The specialized and complex organ systems of animals are built from a limited set of cell and tissue types. For example, lungs and blood vessels have distinct functions but are lined by tissues that are of the same basic type and that therefore share many properties.

There are four main types of animal tissues: epithelial, connective, muscle, and nervous. **Figure 40.5**, on the next three pages, explores the structure and function of each type. In later chapters, we'll discuss how the tissues described here contribute to the functions of each organ system.

Table 40.1 Organ Systems in Mammals

Organ System	Main Components	Main Functions
Digestive	Mouth, pharynx, esophagus, stomach, intestines, liver, pancreas, anus	Food processing (ingestion, digestion, absorption, elimination)
Circulatory	Heart, blood vessels, blood	Internal distribution of materials
Respiratory	Lungs, trachea, other breathing tubes	Gas exchange (uptake of oxygen; disposal of carbon dioxide)
Immune and lymphatic	Bone marrow, lymph nodes, thymus, spleen, lymph vessels, white blood cells	Body defense (fighting infections and cancer)
Excretory	Kidneys, ureters, urinary bladder, urethra	Disposal of metabolic wastes; regulation of osmotic balance of blood
Endocrine	Pituitary, thyroid, pancreas, adrenal, and other hormone-secreting glands	Coordination of body activities (such as digestion and metabolism)
Reproductive	Ovaries or testes and associated organs	Reproduction
Nervous	Brain, spinal cord, nerves, sensory organs	Coordination of body activities; detection of stimuli and formulation of responses to them
Integumentary	Skin and its derivatives (such as hair, claws, skin glands)	Protection against mechanical injury, infection, dehydration; thermoregulation
Skeletal	Skeleton (bones, tendons, ligaments, cartilage)	Body support, protection of internal organs, movement
Muscular	Skeletal muscles	Locomotion and other movement

Exploring Structure and Function in Animal Tissues

Epithelial Tissue

Occurring as sheets of cells, **epithelial tissues**, or **epithelia** (singular, *epithelium*), cover the outside of the body and line organs and cavities within the body. Because epithelial cells are closely packed, often with tight junctions (see Figure 6.32), they function as a barrier against mechanical injury, pathogens, and fluid loss. Epithelia also form active interfaces with the environment. For example, the epithelium that lines the nasal passages is crucial for olfaction, the sense of smell. Note how different cell shapes and arrangements correlate with distinct functions.

Stratified squamous epithelium

A stratified squamous epithelium is multilayered and regenerates rapidly. New cells formed by division near the basal lamina (see micrograph below) push outward, replacing cells that are sloughed off. This epithelium is commonly found on surfaces subject to abrasion, such as the outer skin and the linings of the mouth, anus, and vagina.

Cuboidal epithelium

Cuboidal epithelium, with dice-shaped cells specialized for secretion, makes up the epithelium of kidney tubules and many glands, including the thyroid gland and salivary glands.

Simple columnar epithelium

The large, brick-shaped cells of simple columnar epithelia are often found where secretion or active absorption is important. For example, a simple columnar epithelium lines the intestines, secreting digestive juices and absorbing nutrients.

Simple squamous epithelium

The single layer of platelike cells that form a simple squamous epithelium functions in the exchange of material by diffusion. This type of epithelium, which is thin and leaky, lines blood vessels and the air sacs of the lungs, where diffusion of nutrients and gases is critical.

Pseudostratified columnar epithelium

A pseudostratified epithelium consists of a single layer of cells varying in height. In many vertebrates, a pseudostratified epithelium of ciliated cells forms a mucous membrane that lines portions of the respiratory tract. The beating cilia sweep the film of mucus along the surface.

Apical surface

Basal surface

Basal lamina

40 μm

Polarity of epithelia

All epithelia are polarized, meaning that they have two different sides. The *apical* surface faces the lumen (cavity) or outside of the organ and is therefore exposed to fluid or air. Specialized projections often cover this surface. For example, the apical surface of the epithelium lining the small intestine is covered with microvilli, projections that increase the surface area available for absorbing nutrients. The opposite side of each epithelium is the *basal* surface. The basal surface is attached to a *basal lamina*, a dense mat of extracellular matrix that separates the epithelium from the underlying tissue.

(All photos in figure are LMs.)

Connective Tissue

Connective tissue, consisting of a sparse population of cells scattered through an extracellular matrix, holds many tissues and organs together and in place. The matrix generally consists of a web of fibers embedded in a liquid, jellylike, or solid foundation. Within the matrix are numerous cells called **fibroblasts**, which secrete fiber proteins, and **macrophages**, which engulf foreign particles and any cell debris by phagocytosis (see Chapter 6).

Connective tissue fibers are of three kinds: *Collagenous fibers* provide strength and flexibility, *reticular fibers* join connective tissue to adjacent tissues, and *elastic fibers* make tissues elastic. If you pinch a fold of tissue on the back of your hand, the collagenous and reticular fibers prevent the skin from being pulled far from the bone, whereas the elastic fibers restore the skin to its original shape when you release your grip. Different mixtures of fibers and foundation form the major types of connective tissue shown below.

Loose connective tissue

The most widespread connective tissue in the vertebrate body is *loose connective tissue,* which binds epithelia to underlying tissues and holds organs in place. Loose connective tissue gets its name from the loose weave of its fibers, which include all three types. It is found in the skin and throughout the body.

120 µm

Collagenous fiber

Elastic fiber

Fibrous connective tissue

Fibrous connective tissue is dense with collagenous fibers. It is found in **tendons**, which attach muscles to bones, and in **ligaments**, which connect bones at joints.

30 µm

Nuclei

Bone

The skeleton of most vertebrates is made of **bone**, a mineralized connective tissue. Bone-forming cells called *osteoblasts* deposit a matrix of collagen. Calcium, magnesium, and phosphate ions combine into a hard mineral within the matrix. The microscopic structure of hard mammalian bone consists of repeating units called *osteons*. Each osteon has concentric layers of the mineralized matrix, which are deposited around a central canal containing blood vessels and nerves.

Central canal

700 µm

Osteon

Adipose tissue

Adipose tissue is a specialized loose connective tissue that stores fat in adipose cells distributed throughout its matrix. Adipose tissue pads and insulates the body and stores fuel as fat molecules (see Figure 4.6). Each adipose cell contains a large fat droplet that swells when fat is stored and shrinks when the body uses that fat as fuel.

Fat droplets

150 µm

Blood

Blood has a liquid extracellular matrix called plasma, which consists of water, salts, and dissolved proteins. Suspended in plasma are erythrocytes (red blood cells), leukocytes (white blood cells), and cell fragments called platelets. Red cells carry oxygen, white cells function in defense, and platelets aid in blood clotting.

Plasma

White blood cells

55 µm

Red blood cells

Cartilage

Cartilage contains collagenous fibers embedded in a rubbery protein-carbohydrate complex called chondroitin sulfate. Cells called *chondrocytes* secrete the collagen and chondroitin sulfate, which together make cartilage a strong yet flexible support material. The skeletons of many vertebrate embryos contain cartilage that is replaced by bone as the embryo matures. Cartilage remains in some locations, such as the disks that act as cushions between vertebrae.

Chondrocytes

100 µm

Chondroitin sulfate

Exploring Structure and Function in Animal Tissues

Muscle Tissue

The tissue responsible for nearly all types of body movement is **muscle tissue**. All muscle cells consist of filaments containing the proteins actin and myosin, which together enable muscles to contract. There are three types of muscle tissue in the vertebrate body: skeletal, smooth, and cardiac.

Skeletal muscle

Attached to bones by tendons, **skeletal muscle**, or *striated muscle,* is responsible for voluntary movements. Skeletal muscle consists of bundles of long cells called muscle fibers. During development, skeletal muscle fibers form by the fusion of many cells, resulting in multiple nuclei in each muscle cell or fiber. The arrangement of contractile units, or sarcomeres, along the fibers gives the cells a striped (striated) appearance. In adult mammals, building muscle increases the size but not the number of muscle fibers.

Smooth muscle

Smooth muscle, which lacks striations, is found in the walls of the digestive tract, urinary bladder, arteries, and other internal organs. The cells are spindle-shaped. Smooth muscles are responsible for involuntary body activities, such as churning of the stomach and constriction of arteries.

Cardiac muscle

Cardiac muscle forms the contractile wall of the heart. It is striated like skeletal muscle and has similar contractile properties. Unlike skeletal muscle, however, cardiac muscle has fibers that interconnect via intercalated disks, which relay signals from cell to cell and help synchronize heart contraction.

Nuclei

Muscle fiber

Sarcomere

100 μm

Nucleus   Muscle fibers   25 μm

Nucleus   Intercalated disk   50 μm

Nervous Tissue

Nervous tissue functions in the receipt, processing, and transmission of information. Nervous tissue contains **neurons**, or nerve cells, which transmit nerve impulses, as well as support cells called **glial cells**, or simply **glia.** In many animals, a concentration of nervous tissue forms a brain, an information-processing center.

Neurons

Neurons are the basic units of the nervous system. A neuron receives nerve impulses from other neurons via its cell body and multiple extensions called dendrites. Neurons transmit impulses to neurons, muscles, or other cells via extensions called axons, which are often bundled together into nerves.

Neuron:

Dendrites

Cell body

Axon

40 μm

(Fluorescent LM)

Glia

The various types of glia help nourish, insulate, and replenish neurons, and in some cases, modulate neuron function.

Glia

15 μm

Axons of neurons

Blood vessel

(Confocal LM)

UNIVERSITY OF ALBERTA FACULTY BIO

Declan Ali BSc Biology and Physics (University of Toronto); PhD Neuroscience (University of Toronto)

Current Position: Professor, Department of Biological Sciences

After completing my PhD at the University of Toronto, I did Post-Doctoral research at McGill University and the Hospital for Sick Children in Toronto. I had the opportunity to teach at the Woods Hole Oceanographic Institute. Currently, I teach a third year neurobiology class (Zoology 342). I also participate in second-year cell biology and physiology classes. I contribute guest lectures at the fourth year and graduate levels.

My research has contributed towards an understanding of synaptic development in the central nervous system and at the neuromuscular junction. More specifically, my lab is investigating the cellular signals that underlie postsynaptic maturation at excitatory synapses. These intricate developmental processes have puzzled biologists for decades, and are currently the focus of great attention. To do this research, graduate students in my lab use electrophysiological tools to record currents and voltages from embryonic neurons in zebrafish. The ultimate goal is to determine what drives synaptic development so that we may have a better understanding of the cellular processes that underly nervous system development and regeneration following injury and neurotrauma.

Coordination and Control

An animal's tissues, organs, and organ systems must act in concert with one another. For example, during long dives, the harbor seal in Figure 40.2 slows its heart rate, collapses its lungs, and lowers its body temperature while propelling itself forward with its hind flippers. Coordinating activity across an animal's body in this way requires communication between different locations in the body. What signals are used? How do the signals move within the body? There are two sets of answers to these questions, reflecting the two major systems for controlling and coordinating responses to stimuli (Figure 40.6).

In the endocrine system, signaling molecules released into the bloodstream by endocrine cells reach all locations in the body. In the nervous system, neurons transmit signals, called nerve impulses, between specific locations in the body. In each system, the type of pathway used is the same regardless of whether the signal reaches across the length of the body or ends up just a few cell diameters away.

The signaling molecules broadcast throughout the body by the endocrine system are called **hormones**. Different hormones cause distinct effects, and only cells that have receptors for a particular hormone respond (Figure 40.6a). Depending on which cells have receptors for that hormone, the hormone may have an effect in just a single location or in sites throughout the body. For example, only cells of the thyroid gland have the receptor for thyroid-stimulating hormone (TSH). Upon binding TSH, thyroid cells release thyroid hormone, which acts directly on cells in nearly every tissue to increase oxygen consumption and heat production.

Hormones are relatively slow acting. It takes many seconds for TSH and other hormones to be released into the bloodstream and carried throughout the body. The effects of hormones are often long-lasting, however, because hormones remain in the bloodstream for seconds, minutes, or even hours.

In the nervous system, signals are not broadcast throughout the entire body. Instead, each nerve impulse travels to specific target cells along dedicated communication lines consisting mainly of axons (Figure 40.6b). Four types of cells can receive nerve impulses: other neurons, muscle cells, endocrine cells, and exocrine cells. Unlike the endocrine system, the nervous system conveys information by the *pathway* the signal takes. For example, a person can distinguish different musical notes because each note's frequency activates different neurons connecting the ear to the brain.

Communication in the nervous system usually involves more than one type of signal. Nerve impulses travel along axons, sometimes over long distances, as changes in voltage. But in many cases, passing information from one neuron to another involves very short-range chemical signals. Overall, transmission is extremely fast; nerve impulses take only a fraction of a second to reach the target and last only a fraction of a second.

Because the two major communication systems of the body differ in signal type, transmission, speed, and duration, they are adapted to different functions. The endocrine system is well suited for coordinating gradual changes that affect the entire body, such as growth and development, reproduction, metabolic processes, and digestion. The nervous system is well suited for directing immediate and rapid responses to the environment, especially in controlling fast locomotion and behavior.

Although the functions of the endocrine and nervous systems are distinct, the two systems often work in close coordination. Both contribute to maintaining a stable internal environment, our next topic of discussion.

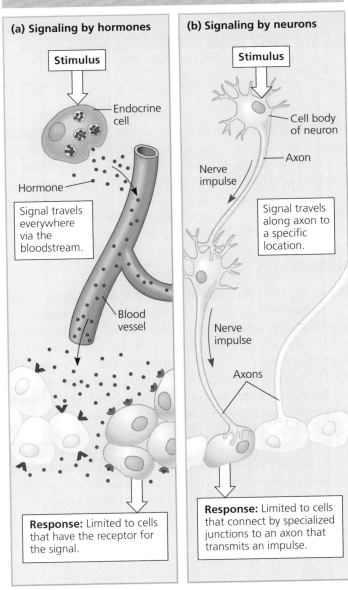

▼ **Figure 40.6 Signaling in the endocrine and nervous systems**

(a) Signaling by hormones

Stimulus

Endocrine cell

Hormone

Signal travels everywhere via the bloodstream.

Blood vessel

Response: Limited to cells that have the receptor for the signal.

(b) Signaling by neurons

Stimulus

Cell body of neuron

Axon

Nerve impulse

Signal travels along axon to a specific location.

Nerve impulse

Axons

Response: Limited to cells that connect by specialized junctions to an axon that transmits an impulse.

CONCEPT CHECK 40.1

1. What properties are shared by all types of epithelia?
2. In cool weather, jackrabbits sometimes flatten their ears against their body. What advantage and disadvantage do you think this body posture offers for survival?
3. **WHAT IF?** Suppose you are standing at the edge of a cliff and suddenly slip—you barely manage to keep your balance and avoid falling. As your heart races, you feel a burst of energy, due in part to a surge of blood into dilated (widened) vessels in your muscles and an upward spike in the level of glucose in your blood. Why might you expect that this "fight-or-flight" response requires both the nervous and endocrine systems?

For suggested answers, see Appendix A.

CONCEPT 40.2

Feedback control maintains the internal environment in many animals

Imagine that your body temperature soared every time you took a hot shower or drank a freshly brewed cup of coffee. Managing the state of the internal environment is a major challenge for the animal body. Faced with environmental fluctuations, animals manage their internal environment by either regulating or conforming.

Regulating and Conforming

An animal is said to be a **regulator** for a particular environmental variable if it uses internal mechanisms to control internal change in the face of external fluctuation. The river otter in **Figure 40.7** is a regulator for temperature, keeping its body at a temperature that is largely independent of that of the water in which it swims.

An animal is said to be a **conformer** for a particular environmental variable if it allows its internal condition to change in accordance with external changes in the variable. The largemouth bass in Figure 40.7 conforms to the temperature of the lake it inhabits. As the water warms or cools, so does the body of the bass. Some animals conform to more constant environments. For example, many marine invertebrates, such as spider crabs of the genus *Libinia*, let their internal solute concentration conform to the relatively stable solute concentration (salinity) of their ocean environment.

Regulating and conforming represent extremes on a continuum. An animal may regulate some internal conditions while allowing others to conform to the environment. For ex-

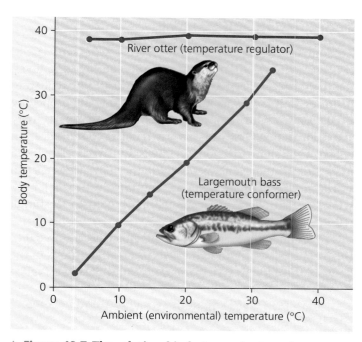

▲ Figure 40.7 **The relationship between body and environmental temperatures in an aquatic temperature regulator and an aquatic temperature conformer.** The river otter regulates its body temperature, keeping it stable across a wide range of environmental temperatures. The largemouth bass, meanwhile, allows its internal environment to conform to the water temperature.

ample, even though the bass conforms to the temperature of the surrounding water, the solute concentration in its blood and interstitial fluid differs from the solute concentration of the fresh water in which it lives. This difference occurs because the fish's anatomy and physiology enable it to regulate internal changes in solute concentration. (You will learn more about the mechanisms of this regulation in Chapter 44.)

Homeostasis

The steady body temperature of a river otter and the stable concentration of solutes in a freshwater bass are examples of **homeostasis**, which means "steady state," referring to the maintenance of internal balance. In achieving homeostasis, animals maintain a relatively constant internal environment even when the external environment changes significantly.

Like many animals, humans exhibit homeostasis for a range of physical and chemical properties. For example, the human body maintains a fairly constant temperature of about 37°C (98.6°F) and a pH of the blood and interstitial fluid within 0.1 pH unit of 7.4. The body also regulates the concentration of glucose in the bloodstream so that it remains predominantly in the range of 70–110 mg of glucose per 100 mL of blood.

Mechanisms of Homeostasis

Before exploring homeostasis in animals, let's first consider a nonliving example: the regulation of room temperature

Response:
Heating stops.

Sensor/control center:
Thermostat turns heater off.

Room temperature decreases.

Stimulus:
Room temperature increases.

Set point:
Room temperature at 20°C

Room temperature increases.

Stimulus:
Room temperature decreases.

Response:
Heating starts.

Sensor/control center:
Thermostat turns heater on.

▲ **Figure 40.8 A nonliving example of temperature regulation: control of room temperature.** Regulating room temperature depends on a control center (a thermostat) that detects temperature change and activates mechanisms that reverse that change. **WHAT IF?** *How would adding an air conditioner to the system contribute to homeostasis?*

(Figure 40.8). Let's assume you want to keep a room at 20°C (68°F), a comfortable temperature for normal activity. You adjust a control device—the thermostat—to 20°C and allow a thermometer in the thermostat to monitor temperature. If the room temperature falls below 20°C, the thermostat responds by turning on a radiator, furnace, or other heater. Heat is produced until the room reaches 20°C, at which point the thermostat switches off the heater. Whenever the temperature in the room again drifts below 20°C, the thermostat activates another heating cycle.

Like a home heating system, an animal achieves homeostasis by maintaining a variable, such as body temperature or solute concentration, at or near a particular value, or **set point**. Fluctuations in the variable above or below the set point serve as the **stimulus** detected by a receptor, or **sensor**. Upon receiving a signal from the sensor, a *control center* generates output that triggers a **response**, a physiological activity that helps return the variable to the set point. In the home heating example, a drop in temperature

below the set point acts as a stimulus, the thermostat serves as the sensor and control center, and the heater produces the response.

Feedback Control in Homeostasis

Like the regulatory circuit shown in Figure 40.8, homeostasis in animals relies largely on **negative feedback**, a control mechanism that reduces, or "damps," the stimulus. For example, when you exercise vigorously, you produce heat, which increases body temperature. Your nervous system detects this increase and triggers sweating. As you sweat, the evaporation of moisture from your skin cools your body, helping return your body temperature to its set point.

Homeostasis is a dynamic equilibrium, the interplay between external factors that tend to change the internal environment and internal control mechanisms that oppose such changes. Note that physiological responses to stimuli are not instantaneous, just as switching on a furnace does not immediately warm a room. As a result, homeostasis moderates but doesn't eliminate changes in the internal environment. Additional fluctuation occurs if a variable has a *normal range*—an upper and lower limit—rather than a single set point. This is equivalent to a heating system that begins producing heat when the room temperature drops to 19°C (66°F) and stops heating when the temperature reaches 21°C (70°F). Regardless of whether there is a set point or a normal range, homeostasis is enhanced by adaptations that reduce fluctuations, such as insulation in the case of temperature and physiological buffers in the case of pH.

Unlike negative feedback, **positive feedback** is a control mechanism that amplifies rather than reduces the stimulus (see Figure 1.13). Positive-feedback loops in animals do not play a major role in homeostasis, but instead help drive processes to completion. During childbirth, for instance, the pressure of the baby's head against receptors near the opening of the mother's uterus stimulates the uterus to contract. These contractions result in greater pressure against the opening of the uterus, heightening the contractions and thereby causing even greater pressure, until the baby is born.

Alterations in Homeostasis

The set points and normal ranges for homeostasis can change under various circumstances. In fact, *regulated changes* in the internal environment are essential to normal body functions. Some regulated changes are associated with a particular stage in life, such as the radical shift in hormone balance that occurs during puberty. Other regulated changes are cyclic, such as the variation in hormone levels responsible for a woman's menstrual cycle (see Figure 46.14).

In all animals (and plants, too), certain cyclic alterations in metabolism reflect a **circadian rhythm**, a set of physiological changes that occur roughly every 24 hours. For example, your body temperature typically undergoes a cyclic rise and fall of more than 0.6°C (1°F) in every 24-hour period. Remarkably, a biological clock maintains this rhythm even when variations in human activity, room temperature, and light levels are minimized (Figure 40.9a). A circadian rhythm is thus intrinsic to the body, although the biological clock is normally coordinated with the cycle of light and darkness in the environment (Figure 40.9b). For example, the hormone melatonin is secreted at night, and more is released during the longer nights of winter. External stimuli can reset the biological clock, but the effect is not immediate. That is why flying across several time zones results in jet lag, a mismatch between

the circadian rhythm and local environment that persists until the clock fully resets.

One way in which the normal range of homeostasis may change is through **acclimatization**, the gradual process by which an animal adjusts to changes in its external environment. For example, when an elk or other mammal moves up into the mountains from sea level, physiological changes that occur over several days facilitate activity at the higher elevations. The lower oxygen concentration in the air stimulates the animal to breathe more rapidly and deeply. It therefore loses more CO_2 through exhalation, raising blood pH above its set point. As the animal acclimatizes, changes in kidney function result in excretion of more alkaline urine, returning blood pH to its normal range. Other changes during acclimatization to a higher altitude include increased production of red blood cells, which carry oxygen. Note that acclimatization, a temporary change during an animal's lifetime, should not be confused with adaptation, a process of change in a population brought about by natural selection acting over many generations.

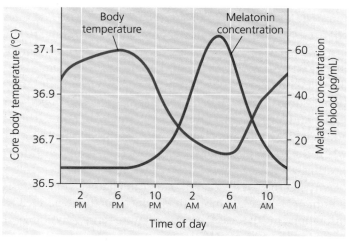

(a) **Variation in core body temperature and melatonin concentration in blood.** Researchers measured these two variables in resting but awake volunteers in an isolation chamber with constant temperature and low light. (Melatonin is a hormone that appears to be involved in sleep/wake cycles.)

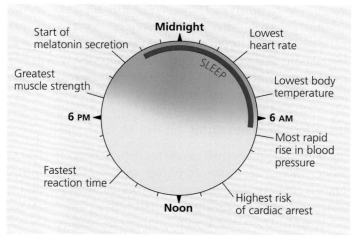

(b) **The human circadian clock.** Metabolic activities undergo daily cycles in response to the circadian clock. As illustrated for a typical individual who rises early in the morning, eats lunch around noon, and sleeps at night, this variation in metabolism is apparent both day and night.

▲ **Figure 40.9 Human circadian rhythm.**

CONCEPT CHECK 40.2

1. **MAKE CONNECTIONS** Figure 8.21 (p. 160) illustrates feedback inhibition in an enzyme-catalyzed biosynthetic process. How does this type of negative feedback differ from that in thermoregulation?
2. If you were deciding where to put the thermostat in a house, what factors would govern your decision? How do these factors relate to the fact that many homeostatic control sensors in humans are located in the brain?
3. **MAKE CONNECTIONS** Like animals, cyanobacteria have a circadian rhythm. By analyzing the genes that maintain biological clocks, scientists were able to conclude that the 24-hour rhythms of humans and cyanobacteria reflect convergent evolution (see Concept 26.2, pp. 540–541). What evidence would have supported this conclusion? Explain.

For suggested answers, see Appendix A.

CONCEPT 40.3

Homeostatic processes for thermoregulation involve form, function, and behavior

In this section, we will examine the regulation of body temperature as an example of how form and function work together in regulating an animal's internal environment. Later chapters in this unit will discuss other physiological systems involved in maintaining homeostasis.

Thermoregulation is the process by which animals maintain an internal temperature within a tolerable range. Thermoregulation is critical to survival because most biochemical and physiological processes are very sensitive to changes in body temperature. For every 10°C (18°F) decrease in temperature, the rates of most enzyme-mediated reactions decrease two- to threefold. Increases in temperature speed up reactions but cause some proteins to become less active. For instance, the oxygen carrier molecule hemoglobin becomes less effective at binding oxygen as temperature increases. Membranes can also change fluidity, becoming increasingly fluid or rigid as temperatures rise or fall, respectively.

Each animal species has an optimal temperature range. Thermoregulation helps maintain body temperature within that optimal range, enabling cells to function effectively even as the external temperature fluctuates.

Endothermy and Ectothermy

Internal metabolism and the external environment are the sources of heat for thermoregulation. Birds and mammals are mainly **endothermic**, meaning that they are warmed mostly by heat generated by metabolism. A few nonavian reptiles, some fishes, and many insect species are also mainly endothermic. In contrast, amphibians, lizards, snakes, turtles, many fishes, and most invertebrates are mainly **ectothermic**, meaning that they gain most of their heat from external sources.

Animals that are mainly endothermic are referred to as endotherms; those that are mainly ectothermic are known as ectotherms. Keep in mind, though, that endothermy and ectothermy are not mutually exclusive modes of thermoregulation. For example, a bird is mainly endothermic, but it may warm itself in the sun on a cold morning, much as an ectothermic lizard does.

Endotherms can maintain a stable body temperature even in the face of large fluctuations in the environmental temperature. For example, few ectotherms are active in the below-freezing weather that prevails during winter over much of Earth's surface, but many endotherms function very well in these conditions **(Figure 40.10a)**. In a cold environment, an endotherm generates enough heat to keep its body substantially warmer than its surroundings. In a hot environment, endothermic vertebrates have mechanisms for cooling their bodies, enabling them to withstand heat loads that are intolerable for most ectotherms.

Because their heat source is largely environmental, ectotherms generally need to consume much less food than endotherms of equivalent size—an advantage if food supplies are limited. Ectotherms also usually tolerate larger fluctuations in their internal temperature. Although ectotherms do not generate enough heat for thermoregulation, many adjust body temperature by behavioral means, such as seeking out shade

(a) A walrus, an endotherm

(b) A lizard, an ectotherm

▲ Figure 40.10 **Endothermy and ectothermy.**

or basking in the sun **(Figure 40.10b)**. Overall, ectothermy is an effective and successful strategy in most environments, as shown by the abundance and diversity of ectothermic animals.

Variation in Body Temperature

Animals can have either a variable or a constant body temperature. An animal whose body temperature varies with its environment is called a *poikilotherm* (from the Greek *poikilos*, varied). In contrast, a *homeotherm* has a relatively constant body temperature. For example, the largemouth bass is a poikilotherm, and the river otter is a homeotherm (see Figure 40.7).

From the descriptions of ectotherms and endotherms, it might seem that all ectotherms are poikilothermic and all endotherms are homeothermic. In fact, there is no fixed relationship between the source of heat and the stability of body temperature. For example, many ectothermic marine fishes and invertebrates inhabit waters with such stable temperatures that their body temperature varies less than that of endotherms such as humans and other mammals. Conversely, the body temperature of a few endotherms varies considerably. For example, bats and hummingbirds may periodically enter an inactive state in which they maintain a lower body temperature.

It is a common misconception that ectotherms are "cold-blooded" and endotherms are "warm-blooded." Ectotherms do not necessarily have low body temperatures. In fact, when sitting in the sun, many ectothermic lizards have higher body temperatures than mammals. Thus, the terms *cold-blooded* and *warm-blooded* are misleading and are avoided in scientific communication.

Balancing Heat Loss and Gain

Thermoregulation depends on an animal's ability to control the exchange of heat with its environment. Any organism, like any object, exchanges heat by four physical processes: radiation, evaporation, convection, and conduction. **Figure 40.11** distinguishes these processes, which account for the flow of heat both within an organism and between an organism and its external environment. Note that heat is always transferred from an object of higher temperature to one of lower temperature.

The essence of thermoregulation is maintaining rates of heat gain that equal rates of heat loss. Animals do this through mechanisms that either reduce heat exchange overall or favor heat exchange in a particular direction. In mammals, several of these mechanisms involve the **integumentary system**,

the outer covering of the body, consisting of the skin, hair, and nails (claws or hooves in some species).

Insulation

A major thermoregulatory adaptation in mammals and birds is insulation, which reduces the flow of heat between an animal and its environment. Sources of insulation include hair, feathers, and layers of fat formed by adipose tissue.

Many animals that rely on insulation to reduce overall heat exchange also adjust their insulating layers to help thermoregulate. Most land mammals and birds, for example, react to cold by raising their fur or feathers. This action traps a thicker layer of air, thereby increasing the insulating power of the fur or feather layer. To repel water that would reduce the insulating capacity of feathers or fur, some animals secrete oily substances, such as the oils that birds apply to their feathers during preening. Lacking feathers or fur, humans must rely primarily on fat for insulation. "Goose bumps" are a vestige of hair raising inherited from our furry ancestors.

Insulation is particularly important for marine mammals, such as whales and walruses. These animals swim in water colder than their body core, and many species spend at least part of the year in nearly freezing polar seas. The problem of thermoregulation is made worse by the fact that the transfer of heat to water occurs 50 to 100 times more rapidly than heat transfer to air. Just under their skin, marine mammals have a very thick layer of insulating fat called blubber. The insulation that blubber provides is so effective that marine mammals can maintain body core temperatures of about 36–38°C (97–100°F) without requiring much more energy from food than land mammals of similar size.

Circulatory Adaptations

Circulatory systems provide a major route for heat flow between the interior and exterior of the body. Adaptations that regulate the extent of blood flow near the body surface or that trap heat within the body core play a significant role in thermoregulation.

In response to changes in the temperature of their surroundings, many animals alter the amount of blood (and hence heat) flowing between their body core and their skin. Nerve signals that relax the muscles of the vessel walls result in *vasodilation*, a widening of superficial blood vessels (those near the body surface). As a consequence of the increase in vessel diameter, blood flow in the skin increases. In endotherms, vasodilation usually warms the skin and increases the transfer of body heat to the environment by radiation, conduction, and convection (see Figure 40.11). The reverse process, *vasoconstriction*, reduces blood flow and heat transfer by decreasing the diameter of superficial vessels. It is vasoconstriction in blood vessels of the ear that allows the jackrabbit shown in Figure 40.1 to avoid overheating on hot desert days.

Radiation is the emission of electromagnetic waves by all objects warmer than absolute zero. Here, a lizard absorbs heat radiating from the distant sun and radiates a smaller amount of energy to the surrounding air.

Evaporation is the removal of heat from the surface of a liquid that is losing some of its molecules as gas. Evaporation of water from a lizard's moist surfaces that are exposed to the environment has a strong cooling effect.

Convection is the transfer of heat by the movement of air or liquid past a surface, as when a breeze contributes to heat loss from a lizard's dry skin or when blood moves heat from the body core to the extremities.

Conduction is the direct transfer of thermal motion (heat) between molecules of objects in contact with each other, as when a lizard sits on a hot rock.

▲ **Figure 40.11 Heat exchange between an organism and its environment.**

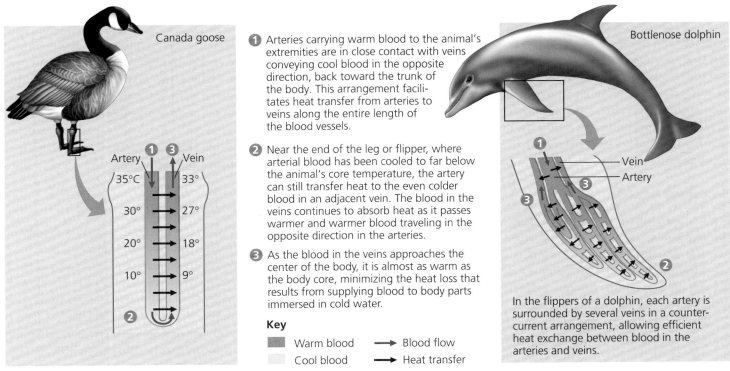

1 Arteries carrying warm blood to the animal's extremities are in close contact with veins conveying cool blood in the opposite direction, back toward the trunk of the body. This arrangement facilitates heat transfer from arteries to veins along the entire length of the blood vessels.

2 Near the end of the leg or flipper, where arterial blood has been cooled to far below the animal's core temperature, the artery can still transfer heat to the even colder blood in an adjacent vein. The blood in the veins continues to absorb heat as it passes warmer and warmer blood traveling in the opposite direction in the arteries.

3 As the blood in the veins approaches the center of the body, it is almost as warm as the body core, minimizing the heat loss that results from supplying blood to body parts immersed in cold water.

Key

| | Warm blood | → Blood flow |
| | Cool blood | → Heat transfer |

In the flippers of a dolphin, each artery is surrounded by several veins in a countercurrent arrangement, allowing efficient heat exchange between blood in the arteries and veins.

▲ **Figure 40.12 Countercurrent heat exchangers.** A countercurrent exchange system traps heat in the body core, thus reducing heat loss from the extremities, particularly when they are immersed in cold water or in contact with ice or snow. In essence, heat in the arterial blood emerging from the body core is transferred directly to the returning venous blood instead of being lost to the environment.

Like endotherms, some ectotherms control heat exchange by regulating blood flow. For example, when the marine iguana of the Galápagos Islands swims in the cold ocean, its superficial blood vessels undergo vasoconstriction. This process routes more blood to the central core of the iguana's body, conserving body heat.

In many birds and mammals, reducing heat loss from the body relies on **countercurrent exchange**, the transfer of heat (or solutes) between fluids that are flowing in opposite directions. In a countercurrent heat exchanger, arteries and veins are located adjacent to each other **(Figure 40.12)**. As warm blood moves from the body core in the arteries, it transfers heat to the colder blood returning from the extremities in the veins. Because blood flows through the arteries and veins in opposite directions, heat is transferred along the entire length of the exchanger, maximizing the rate of heat exchange.

Certain sharks, fishes, and insects also use countercurrent heat exchange. Although most sharks and fishes are temperature conformers, countercurrent heat exchangers are found in some large, powerful swimmers, including great white sharks, bluefin tuna, and swordfish. By keeping the main swimming muscles several degrees warmer than tissues near the animal's surface, this adaptation enables the vigorous, sustained activity that is characteristic of these animals. Similarly, many endothermic insects (bumblebees, honeybees, and some moths) have a countercurrent exchanger that helps maintain a high temperature in their thorax, where flight muscles are located.

In controlling heat gain and loss, some species regulate the extent of blood flow to the countercurrent exchanger. By allowing blood to pass through the heat exchanger or diverting it to other blood vessels, these animals alter the rate of heat loss as their physiological state or environment changes. For example, insects flying in hot weather run the risk of overheating because of the large amount of heat produced by working flight muscles. In some species, the countercurrent mechanism can be "shut down," allowing muscle-produced heat to be lost from the thorax to the abdomen and then to the environment.

Cooling by Evaporative Heat Loss

Many mammals and birds live in places where thermoregulation requires cooling as well as warming. If the environmental temperature is above their body temperature, animals gain heat from the environment as well as from metabolism, and evaporation is the only way to keep body temperature from rising. Terrestrial animals lose water by evaporation from their skin and respiratory surfaces. Water absorbs considerable heat when it evaporates (see Chapter 3); this heat is carried away from the body surface with the water vapor.

Some animals have adaptations that can greatly augment the cooling effect of evaporation. Panting is important in birds and many mammals. Some birds have a pouch richly supplied with blood vessels in the floor of the mouth; fluttering the pouch increases evaporation. Pigeons, for example, can use this adaptation to keep their body temperature close to 40°C (104°F) in air temperatures as high as 60°C (140°F), as long as they have sufficient water. Sweating or bathing moistens the skin and enhances evaporative cooling. Many terrestrial mammals have sweat glands that are controlled by the nervous system.

Behavioral Responses

Both endotherms and ectotherms control body temperature through behavioral responses to changes in the environment. Many ectotherms maintain a nearly constant body temperature by engaging in relatively simple behaviors. More extreme behavioral adaptations in some animals include hibernation or migration to a more suitable climate.

All amphibians and most reptiles other than birds are ectothermic. Therefore, these organisms control body temperature mainly by behavior. When cold, they seek warm places, orienting themselves toward heat sources and expanding the portion of their body surface exposed to the heat source (see Figure 40.10b). When hot, they move to cool areas or turn in another direction.

Many terrestrial invertebrates can adjust internal temperature by the same behavioral mechanisms used by vertebrate ectotherms. The desert locust (*Schistocerca gregaria*), for example, must reach a certain temperature to become active, and on cold days it orients itself in a direction that maximizes the absorption of sunlight. Other terrestrial invertebrates have certain postures that enable them to maximize or minimize their absorption of heat from the sun **(Figure 40.13)**.

Honeybees use a thermoregulatory mechanism that depends on social behavior. In cold weather, they increase heat production and huddle together, thereby retaining heat. Individuals move between the cooler outer edges of

▶ **Figure 40.13**
Thermoregulatory behavior in a dragonfly. This dragonfly's "obelisk" posture is an adaptation that minimizes the amount of body surface exposed to the sun. This posture helps reduce heat gain by radiation.

the cluster and the warmer center, thus circulating and distributing the heat. Even when huddling, honeybees must expend considerable energy to keep warm during long periods of cold weather. (This is the main function of storing large quantities of fuel in the hive in the form of honey.) In hot weather, honeybees cool the hive by transporting water to the hive and fanning with their wings, promoting evaporation and convection. Thus, a colony of honeybees uses many of the mechanisms of thermoregulation seen in individual organisms.

Adjusting Metabolic Heat Production

Because endotherms generally maintain a body temperature considerably higher than that of the environment, they must counteract continual heat loss. Endotherms can vary heat production—*thermogenesis*—to match changing rates of heat loss. Thermogenesis is increased by such muscle activity as moving or shivering. For example, shivering helps chickadees (genus *Poecile*), birds with a body mass of only 20 g, remain active and hold their body temperature nearly constant at 40°C (104°F) in environmental temperatures as low as −40°C (−40°F), as long as they have adequate food.

In some mammals, certain hormones can cause mitochondria to increase their metabolic activity and produce heat instead of ATP. This process, called *nonshivering thermogenesis,* takes place throughout the body; some mammals also have a tissue called *brown fat* in their neck and between their shoulders that is specialized for rapid heat production. (In human infants, brown fat represents about 5% of total body weight. In 2009, brown fat was found for the first time in human adults, with greater amounts being detected when outdoor temperatures were lower.) Through shivering and nonshivering thermogenesis, mammals and birds in cold environments can increase their metabolic heat production by as much as five to ten times the levels that occur in warm conditions.

A few large reptiles become endothermic in particular circumstances. In the early 1960s, Herndon Dowling documented this phenomenon for a female Burmese python (*Python molurus bivittatus*). Placing temperature-recording devices along the snake's coils, Dowling found that the snake maintained a body temperature roughly 6°C (11°F) above that of the surrounding air during the month when she was incubating eggs. Where did the heat come from? Further studies by Dowling and colleagues showed that pythons, like mammals and birds, can raise their body temperature through shivering **(Figure 40.14)**. These and other findings have led to new insights into thermoregulation in reptiles and have contributed to the idea, still under debate, that certain groups of Mesozoic dinosaurs were endothermic (see Chapter 34).

As mentioned earlier, many species of flying insects, such as bees and moths, are endothermic—the smallest of all endotherms. The capacity of such endothermic insects to elevate

▼ Figure 40.14
INQUIRY

How does a Burmese python generate heat while incubating eggs?

EXPERIMENT Herndon Dowling, graduate student Allen Vinegar, and the student's research supervisor, Victor Hutchison, at the Bronx Zoo in New York, observed that when a female Burmese python incubated eggs by wrapping her body around them, she raised her body temperature and frequently contracted the muscles in her coils. To learn if the contractions were elevating her body temperature, they placed the python and her eggs in a chamber. As they varied the chamber's temperature, they monitored the python's muscle contractions as well as her oxygen uptake, a measure of her rate of cellular respiration.

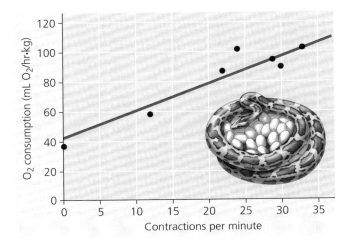

RESULTS The python's oxygen consumption increased when the temperature in the chamber decreased. Her oxygen consumption also increased with the rate of muscle contraction.

CONCLUSION Because oxygen consumption generates heat through cellular respiration and increases linearly with the rate of muscle contraction, the researchers concluded that the muscle contractions, a form of shivering, were the source of the Burmese python's elevated body temperature.

SOURCE V. H. Hutchison, H. G. Dowling, and A. Vinegar, Thermoregulation in a brooding female Indian python, *Python molurus bivittatus*, *Science* 151:694–696 (1966).

WHAT IF? Suppose you varied air temperature and measured oxygen consumption for a female Burmese python without a clutch of eggs. Since she would not show shivering behavior, how would you expect the snake's oxygen consumption to vary with environmental temperature?

body temperature depends on powerful flight muscles, which generate large amounts of heat when contracting. Many endothermic insects warm up by shivering before taking off. As they contract their flight muscles in synchrony, only slight wing movements occur, but considerable heat is produced. Chemical reactions, and hence cellular respiration, speed up in the warmed-up flight "motors," enabling these insects to fly even when the air is cold (**Figure 40.15**).

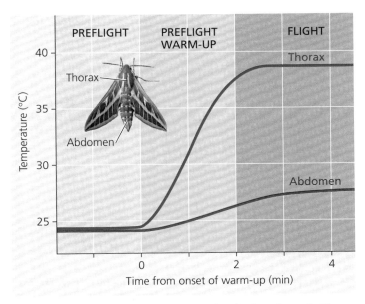

▲ **Figure 40.15 Preflight warm-up in the hawkmoth.** The hawkmoth (*Manduca sexta*) is one of many insect species that use a shivering-like mechanism for preflight warm-up of thoracic flight muscles. Warming up helps these muscles produce enough power to let the animal take off. Once the moth is airborne, flight muscle activity maintains a high thoracic temperature.

Acclimatization in Thermoregulation

Acclimatization contributes to thermoregulation in many animal species. In birds and mammals, acclimatization to seasonal temperature changes often includes adjusting insulation—growing a thicker coat of fur in the winter and shedding it in the summer, for example. These changes help endotherms keep a constant body temperature year-round.

Acclimatization in ectotherms often includes adjustments at the cellular level. Cells may produce variants of enzymes that have the same function but different optimal temperatures. Also, the proportions of saturated and unsaturated lipids in membranes may change; unsaturated lipids help keep membranes fluid at lower temperatures (see Figure 7.5). Some ectotherms that experience subzero body temperatures protect themselves by producing "antifreeze" compounds that prevent ice formation in their cells. In the Arctic Ocean and Southern (Antarctic) Ocean, these compounds enable certain fishes to survive in water as cold as −2°C (28°F), below the freezing point of unprotected body fluids (about −1°C, or 30°F).

Physiological Thermostats and Fever

The regulation of body temperature in humans and other mammals is brought about by a complex system based on feedback mechanisms. The sensors for thermoregulation are concentrated in a brain region called the **hypothalamus**. A group of nerve cells in the hypothalamus functions as a thermostat, responding to body temperatures outside a normal range by activating mechanisms that promote heat loss

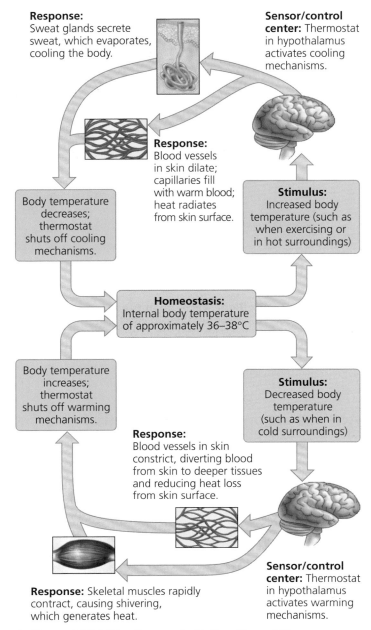

Response:
Sweat glands secrete sweat, which evaporates, cooling the body.

Sensor/control center: Thermostat in hypothalamus activates cooling mechanisms.

Response:
Blood vessels in skin dilate; capillaries fill with warm blood; heat radiates from skin surface.

Body temperature decreases; thermostat shuts off cooling mechanisms.

Stimulus: Increased body temperature (such as when exercising or in hot surroundings)

Homeostasis: Internal body temperature of approximately 36–38°C

Body temperature increases; thermostat shuts off warming mechanisms.

Stimulus: Decreased body temperature (such as when in cold surroundings)

Response:
Blood vessels in skin constrict, diverting blood from skin to deeper tissues and reducing heat loss from skin surface.

Sensor/control center: Thermostat in hypothalamus activates warming mechanisms.

Response: Skeletal muscles rapidly contract, causing shivering, which generates heat.

▲ **Figure 40.16 The thermostatic function of the hypothalamus in human thermoregulation.**

or gain **(Figure 40.16)**. Warm receptors signal the hypothalamic thermostat when temperatures increase; cold receptors signal when temperatures decrease. (Because the same blood vessel supplies the hypothalamus and ears, an ear thermometer records the temperature detected by the hypothalamic thermostat.) At body temperatures below the normal range, the thermostat inhibits heat loss mechanisms and activates heat-saving ones, such as vasoconstriction and the raising of fur, while stimulating heat-generating mechanisms (shivering and nonshivering thermogenesis). In response to elevated body temperature, the thermostat shuts down heat retention mechanisms and promotes cooling the body by vasodilation, sweating, or panting.

In the course of certain bacterial and viral infections, mammals and birds develop fever, an elevated body temperature. A variety of experiments have shown that fever reflects an increase in the set point for the biological thermostat. For example, artificially raising the temperature of the hypothalamus in an infected animal reduces fever in the rest of the body!

Although only endotherms develop fever, lizards exhibit a related response. When infected with certain bacteria, the desert iguana (*Dipsosaurus dorsalis*) seeks a warmer environment and then maintains a body temperature that is elevated by 2–4°C (4–7°F). Similar observations in fishes, amphibians, and even cockroaches indicate that this response to certain infections is a common feature of many animal species.

Having explored thermoregulation in depth, we'll now consider some other energy-consuming processes and the different ways that animals allocate, use, and conserve energy.

CONCEPT CHECK 40.3

1. What mode of heat exchange is involved in "wind chill," when moving air feels colder than still air at the same temperature? Explain.
2. Flowers differ in how much sunlight they absorb. Why might this matter to a hummingbird seeking nectar on a cool morning?
3. **WHAT IF?** Suppose at the end of a hard run on a hot day you find that there are no drinks left in the cooler. If, out of desperation, you dunk your head into the cooler, how might the ice-cold water affect the rate at which your body temperature returns to normal?

For suggested answers, see Appendix A.

CONCEPT 40.4

Energy requirements are related to animal size, activity, and environment

One of the unifying themes of biology introduced in Chapter 1 is that life requires energy transfer and transformation. Like other organisms, animals use chemical energy for growth, repair, activity, and reproduction. The overall flow and transformation of energy in an animal—its **bioenergetics**—determines nutritional needs and is related to the animal's size, activity, and environment.

Energy Allocation and Use

As we have discussed in other chapters, organisms can be classified by how they obtain chemical energy. Most autotrophs, such as plants, use light energy to build energy-rich organic molecules and then use those organic molecules for fuel. Most heterotrophs, such as animals, must obtain their chemical

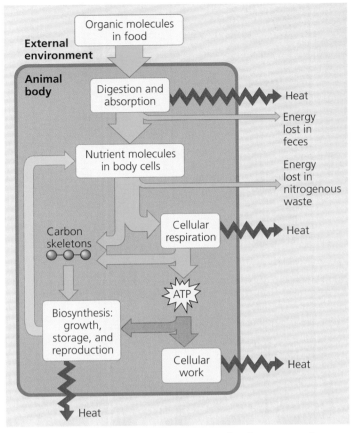

▲ Figure 40.17 Bioenergetics of an animal: an overview.

MAKE CONNECTIONS *Review the idea of energy coupling in Concept 8.3 (pp. 149–151). Then use that idea to explain why heat is produced in the absorption of nutrients, in cellular respiration, and in the synthesis of biopolymers.*

energy from food, which contains organic molecules synthesized by other organisms.

Animals use chemical energy harvested from the food they eat to fuel metabolism and activity **(Figure 40.17)**. Food is digested by enzymatic hydrolysis (see Figure 5.2b), and nutrients are absorbed by body cells. Most nutrient molecules are used to generate ATP. ATP produced by cellular respiration and fermentation powers cellular work, enabling cells, organs, and organ systems to perform the functions that keep an animal alive. Energy in the form of ATP is also used in biosynthesis, which is needed for body growth and repair, synthesis of storage material such as fat, and production of gametes. The production and use of ATP generates heat, which the animal eventually gives off to its surroundings.

Quantifying Energy Use

How much of the total energy an animal obtains from food does it need just to stay alive? How much energy must be expended to walk, run, swim, or fly from one place to another? What fraction of the energy intake is used for reproduction? Physiologists answer such questions by measuring the rate at

▲ Figure 40.18 Measuring the rate of oxygen consumption by a swimming shark. A researcher monitors the drop in oxygen level in the recirculating water of a juvenile hammerhead's tank.

which an animal uses chemical energy and how this rate changes in different circumstances.

The amount of energy an animal uses in a unit of time is called its **metabolic rate**—the sum of all the energy used in biochemical reactions over a given time interval. Energy is measured in joules (J) or in calories (cal) and kilocalories (kcal). (A kilocalorie equals 1,000 calories, or 4,184 joules. The unit Calorie, with a capital C, as used by many nutritionists, is actually a kilocalorie.)

Metabolic rate can be determined in several ways. Because nearly all of the chemical energy used in cellular respiration eventually appears as heat, metabolic rate can be measured by monitoring an animal's rate of heat loss. For this approach, researchers use a calorimeter, which is a closed, insulated chamber equipped with a device that records an animal's heat loss. Metabolic rate can also be determined from the amount of oxygen consumed or carbon dioxide produced by an animal's cellular respiration **(Figure 40.18)**. To calculate metabolic rate over longer periods, researchers record the rate of food consumption, the energy content of the food (about 4.5–5 kcal per gram of protein or carbohydrate and about 9 kcal per gram of fat), and the chemical energy lost in waste products (feces and nitrogenous waste).

Minimum Metabolic Rate and Thermoregulation

Animals must maintain a minimum metabolic rate for basic functions such as cell maintenance, breathing, and heartbeat. Researchers measure this minimum metabolic rate differently for endotherms and ectotherms. The minimum metabolic rate of a nongrowing endotherm that is at rest, has an empty stomach, and is not experiencing stress is called the **basal metabolic rate (BMR)**. BMR is measured under a "comfortable" temperature range—a range that requires no generation or shedding of heat above the minimum. The minimum metabolic rate of ectotherms is determined at a specific temperature because changes in the environmental temperature alter body temperature and therefore metabolic rate. The metabolic rate of a fasting, nonstressed ectotherm at rest at a particular temperature is called its **standard metabolic rate (SMR)**.

Comparisons of minimum metabolic rates reveal that endothermy and ectothermy have different energy costs. The BMR for humans averages 1,600–1,800 kcal per day for adult males and 1,300–1,500 kcal per day for adult females. These BMRs are about equivalent to the rate of energy use by a 75-watt light bulb. In contrast, the SMR of an American alligator is only about 60 kcal per day at 20°C (68°F). Since this represents less than $\frac{1}{20}$ the energy used by a comparably sized adult human, the lower energetic requirement of ectothermy is readily apparent.

Influences on Metabolic Rate

Metabolic rate is affected by many factors besides whether the animal is an endotherm or an ectotherm. Some key factors are age, sex, size, activity, temperature, and nutrition. Here we'll examine the effects of size and activity.

Size and Metabolic Rate

Larger animals have more body mass and therefore require more chemical energy. Remarkably, the relationship between overall metabolic rate and body mass is constant across a wide range of sizes and forms, as illustrated for various mammals in **Figure 40.19a**. In fact, for even more varied organisms ranging in size from bacteria to blue whales, metabolic rate remains roughly proportional to body mass to the three-quarter power ($m^{3/4}$). Scientists are still researching the basis of this relationship, which applies to ectotherms as well as endotherms.

The relationship of metabolic rate to size profoundly affects energy consumption by body cells and tissues. As shown in **Figure 40.19b**, the energy it takes to maintain each gram of body mass is inversely related to body size. Each gram of a mouse, for instance, requires about 20 times as many calories as a gram of an elephant, even though the whole elephant uses far more calories than the whole mouse. The smaller animal's higher metabolic rate per gram demands a higher rate of oxygen delivery. Correlated with its higher metabolic rate per gram, the smaller animal has a higher breathing rate, blood volume (relative to its size), and heart rate. Also, it must eat much more food per unit of body mass.

Bioenergetic considerations associated with body size provide a clear example of how trade-offs shape the evolution of body plans. As body size becomes smaller, each gram of tissue increases in energy cost. As body size increases, energy costs per gram of tissue decrease, but an ever-larger fraction of body tissue is required for exchange, support, and locomotion.

Activity and Metabolic Rate

For both ectotherms and endotherms, activity greatly affects metabolic rate. Even a person reading quietly at a desk or an

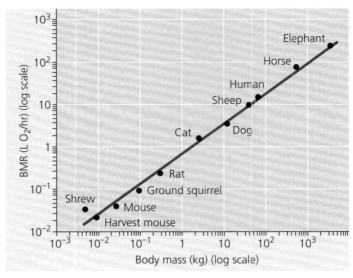

(a) Relationship of basal metabolic rate (BMR) to body size for various mammals. From shrew to elephant, size increases 1 millionfold.

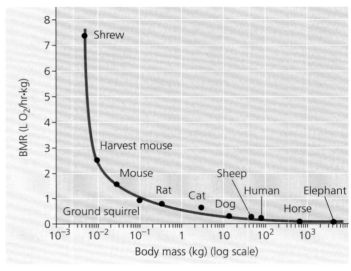

(b) Relationship of BMR per kilogram of body mass to body size for the same mammals as in (a).

▲ **Figure 40.19 The relationship of metabolic rate to body size.**

insect twitching its wings consumes energy beyond the BMR or SMR. Maximum metabolic rates (the highest rates of ATP use) occur during peak activity, such as lifting heavy weights, sprinting, or high-speed swimming. In general, the maximum metabolic rate an animal can sustain is inversely related to the duration of activity.

For most terrestrial animals, the average daily rate of energy consumption is 2 to 4 times BMR (for endotherms) or SMR (for ectotherms). Humans in most developed countries have an unusually low average daily metabolic rate of about 1.5 times BMR—an indication of their relatively sedentary lifestyles.

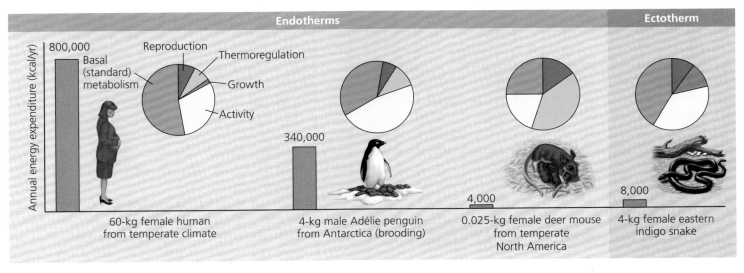

▲ **Figure 40.20 Energy budgets for four animals.** The slices of the pie charts indicate annual energy expenditures for various functions.

Energy Budgets

As we have seen, the ways in which animals use the chemical energy of food depend on environment, behavior, size, and thermoregulation. To understand how these influences affect bioenergetics in animal bodies, let's consider typical annual energy "budgets" of four terrestrial vertebrates varying in size and thermoregulatory strategy: a 60-kg female human, a 4-kg male Adélie penguin, a 25-g (0.025-kg) female deer mouse, and a 4-kg female eastern indigo snake (**Figure 40.20**). Reproduction is included in these energy budgets because it can greatly influence energy allocation and is critical to species survival.

The female human, an endothermic mammal, spends the largest fraction of her annual energy budget for BMR and comparatively less for activity and thermoregulation. The small amount of growth, about 1%, is equivalent to adding about 1 kg of body fat or 5–6 kg of other tissues. (Growth is not shown in the budgets for the penguin and deer mouse because these animals don't typically gain weight year to year after they are adults.) The cost of nine months of pregnancy and several months of breast-feeding is only 5–8% of the mother's energy requirements for a year.

A male penguin spends the largest fraction of his energy for activity because he must swim to catch food. Being well insulated and fairly large, he has relatively low costs of thermoregulation in spite of living in the cold Antarctic. His reproductive costs, about 6% of annual energy expenditures, come mainly from incubating eggs (brooding) and bringing food to his chicks.

Despite living in a temperate climate, the female deer mouse spends a large fraction of her energy budget for temperature regulation. Because of the high surface-to-volume ratio that goes with small size, deer mice lose body heat rapidly and must constantly generate metabolic heat to maintain body temperature.

In contrast with these endothermic animals, the ectothermic snake has no thermoregulation costs. Like most snakes, she grows continuously throughout her life. In the example in Figure 40.20, the snake adds about 750 g of new body tissue in a year. She also produces about 650 g of eggs. The snake's economical ectothermic strategy is revealed by her very low energy expenditure, only $\frac{1}{40}$ the energy expended by the similarly sized endothermic penguin.

For all the animals in Figure 40.20, locomotion and other activities are a major part of the energy budget. Some animals can conserve energy by temporarily decreasing their activity to a very low level, a process we will consider next.

Torpor and Energy Conservation

Despite their many adaptations for homeostasis, animals may encounter conditions that severely challenge their abilities to balance their heat, energy, and materials budgets. For example, at certain times of the day or year, their surroundings may be extremely hot or cold, or food may be unavailable. **Torpor**, a physiological state of decreased activity and metabolism, is an adaptation that enables animals to save energy while avoiding difficult and dangerous conditions.

Many small mammals and birds exhibit a daily torpor that seems to be adapted to feeding patterns. For instance, some bats feed at night and go into torpor in daylight. Chickadees and hummingbirds feed during the day and often go into torpor on cold nights; the body temperature of chickadees drops as much as 10°C (18°F) at night, and the temperature of hummingbirds can fall 25°C (45°F) or more. All endotherms that exhibit daily torpor are relatively small; when active, they have high metabolic rates and thus very high rates of energy consumption.

Hibernation is long-term torpor that is an adaptation to winter cold and food scarcity. When a mammal enters hibernation, its body temperature declines as its body's thermostat is turned down. The temperature reduction may be dramatic: Some hibernating mammals cool to as low as 1–2°C (34–36°F), and at least one, the Arctic ground squirrel (*Spermophilus parryii*), can enter a supercooled (unfrozen) state in which its body temperature dips below 0°C (32°F). Periodically, perhaps every two weeks or so, hibernating animals undergo arousal,

raising their body temperature and becoming active briefly before resuming hibernation. Nevertheless, the energy savings from hibernation are huge: Metabolic rates during hibernation can be 20 times lower than if the animal attempted to maintain normal body temperatures of 36–38°C (97–100°F). As a result, hibernators such as the ground squirrel can survive through the winter on limited supplies of energy stored in the body tissues or as food cached in a burrow. Similarly, the slow metabolism and inactivity of *estivation*, or summer torpor, enables animals to survive long periods of high temperatures and scarce water supplies.

What happens to the circadian rhythm in hibernating animals? In the past, some researchers have reported detecting daily biological rhythms in hibernating animals. However, in some cases the animals were probably in a state of torpor, from which they could readily arouse, rather than "deep" hibernation. Recently, a group of researchers in France addressed this question in a different way, examining the machinery of the biological clock rather than the rhythms it controls **(Figure 40.21)**. Working with the European hamster, they found that molecular components of the clock stopped oscillating during hibernation. These findings support the hypothesis that the circadian clock ceases operation during hibernation, at least in this species.

From discussing body shape to considering energy conservation, this chapter has focused on the whole animal. We surveyed common tissue types that make up organs and organ systems. We also investigated how body plans provide for exchange of materials with the environment, how some animals maintain a constant internal environment, and how size and activity affect metabolic rate. For much of the rest of this unit, we'll explore how specialized organs and organ systems enable animals to meet the basic challenges of life.

▼ **Figure 40.21**

INQUIRY

What happens to the circadian clock during hibernation?

EXPERIMENT To determine whether the 24-hour biological clock continues to run during hibernation, Paul Pévet and colleagues at the University of Louis Pasteur in Strasbourg, France, studied molecular components of the circadian clock in the European hamster (*Cricetus cricetus*). The researchers measured RNA levels for two clock genes—*Per2* and *Bmal1*—during normal activity (euthermia) and during hibernation in constant darkness. The RNA samples were obtained from the suprachiasmatic nuclei (SCN), a pair of structures in the mammalian brain that control circadian rhythms.

RESULTS

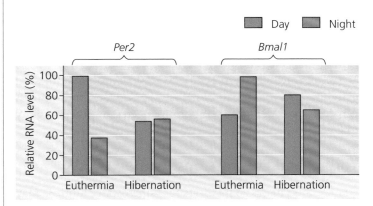

CONCLUSION Hibernation disrupted circadian variation in the hamster's clock gene RNA levels. Further experiments demonstrated that this disruption was not simply due to the dark environment during hibernation, since for nonhibernating animals RNA levels during a darkened daytime were the same as in daylight. The researchers concluded that the biological clock stops running in hibernating European hamsters and, perhaps, in other hibernators as well.

SOURCE F. G. Revel et al., The circadian clock stops ticking during deep hibernation in the European hamster, *Proceedings of the National Academy of Sciences USA* 104:13816–13820 (2007).

WHAT IF? Suppose you discovered a new hamster gene and found that the levels of RNA for this gene were constant during hibernation. What could you conclude about the day and night RNA levels for this gene during euthermia?

CONCEPT CHECK 40.4

1. If a mouse and a small lizard of the same mass (both at rest) were placed in experimental chambers under identical environmental conditions, which animal would consume oxygen at a higher rate? Explain.
2. Which animal must eat a larger proportion of its weight in food each day: a house cat or an African lion caged in a zoo? Explain.
3. **WHAT IF?** If you monitored energy allocation in the penguin in Figure 40.20 for just a few months instead of an entire year, you might find the "growth" category to be a significant part of the pie chart. Given that adult penguins don't grow from year to year, how would you explain this finding?

For suggested answers, see Appendix A.

40 CHAPTER REVIEW

SUMMARY OF KEY CONCEPTS

CONCEPT 40.1

Animal form and function are correlated at all levels of organization (pp. 852–860)

- Physical laws constrain the evolution of an animal's size and shape. These constraints contribute to convergent evolution, the similar but independent adaptations of different species to a common environmental challenge.
- Each animal cell must have access to an aqueous environment. Simple two-layered sacs and flat shapes maximize exposure to the surrounding medium. More complex body plans have highly folded internal surfaces specialized for exchanging materials.
- In the hierarchical organization of animal bodies, groups of cells with a common structure and function make up **tissues**. Different tissues make up **organs**, which together make up **organ systems**. Animal tissues fall into four main groups, each with distinct functions. **Epithelial tissue** forms active interfaces with the environment on external and internal surfaces of the body. **Connective tissue** binds and supports other tissues. **Muscle tissue** contracts, moving the parts of the body. **Nervous tissue** transmits nerve impulses throughout the body.
- The endocrine and nervous systems are the two means of communication between different locations in the body. The endocrine system broadcasts signaling molecules called **hormones** everywhere via the bloodstream, but only certain cells are responsive to each hormone. The nervous system uses dedicated cellular circuits involving electrical and chemical signals to send information to specific locations.

? For a large animal, what challenges would a spherical shape pose for carrying out exchange with the environment?

CONCEPT 40.2

Feedback control maintains the internal environment in many animals (pp. 860–862)

- Faced with environmental fluctuations, animals *regulate* (control) certain internal variables while allowing other internal variables to *conform* to (correspond to) external changes. **Homeostasis** is the maintenance of a steady state despite internal and external changes.
- Homeostatic mechanisms are usually based on **negative feedback**, in which the **response** reduces the **stimulus**.

In contrast, **positive feedback** involves amplification of a stimulus by the response and often brings about a change in state, such as the transition from pregnancy to childbirth.

- Regulated change in the internal environment is essential to normal function. **Circadian rhythms** are daily fluctuations in metabolism and behavior tuned to the cycles of light and dark in the environment. Other environmental changes may trigger **acclimatization**, a temporary shift in the steady state.

? Is it accurate to define homeostasis as a constant internal environment? Explain.

CONCEPT 40.3

Homeostatic processes for thermoregulation involve form, function, and behavior (pp. 862–868)

- An animal maintains its internal temperature within a tolerable range by **thermoregulation**. **Endotherms** are warmed mostly by heat generated by metabolism. **Ectotherms** get most of their heat from external sources. Endothermy requires a greater expenditure of energy. Body temperature may vary with environmental temperature, as in *poikilotherms*, or be relatively constant, as in *homeotherms*.
- In thermoregulation, physiological and behavioral adjustments balance heat gain and loss, which occur through **radiation**, **evaporation**, **convection**, and **conduction**. Insulation and **countercurrent exchange** reduce heat loss, whereas panting, sweating, and bathing increase evaporation, cooling the body. Both ectotherms and endotherms adjust their rate of heat exchange with their surroundings by vasodilation or vasoconstriction and by behavioral responses.
- Many mammals and birds adjust their amount of body insulation in response to changes in environmental temperature. Ectotherms undergo a variety of changes at the cellular level to acclimatize to shifts in temperature.
- The **hypothalamus** acts as the thermostat in mammalian regulation of body temperature. Fever reflects a resetting of this thermostat to a higher set point in response to infection.

? Given that humans thermoregulate, explain why your skin is cooler than your body core.

CONCEPT 40.4

Energy requirements are related to animal size, activity, and environment (pp. 868–872)

- Animals obtain chemical energy from food, storing it for short-term use in ATP. The total amount of energy used in a unit of time defines an animal's **metabolic rate**. Metabolic rates are generally higher for endotherms than for ectotherms.
- Under similar conditions and for animals of the same size, the **basal metabolic rate** of endotherms is substantially higher than the **standard metabolic rate** of ectotherms. Minimum metabolic rate per gram is inversely related to body size among similar animals. Animals allocate energy for basal (or standard) metabolism, activity, homeostasis, growth, and reproduction.
- **Torpor**, a state of decreased activity and metabolism, conserves energy during environmental extremes. Animals may enter torpor during sleep periods (daily torpor), in winter (**hibernation**), or in summer (estivation).

? Most hibernators are small. After reviewing Figure 40.19, suggest an explanation for this observation.

LEVEL 1: KNOWLEDGE/COMPREHENSION

1. The body tissue that consists largely of material located out-side of cells is
   a. epithelial tissue.
   b. connective tissue.
   c. skeletal muscle.
   d. smooth muscle.
   e. nervous tissue.

2. Which of the following would increase the rate of heat ex-change between an animal and its environment?
   a. feathers or fur
   b. vasoconstriction
   c. wind blowing across the body surface
   d. countercurrent heat exchanger
   e. blubber or fat layer

3. Consider the energy budgets for a human, an elephant, a pen-guin, a mouse, and a snake. The _____ would have the highest total annual energy expenditure, and the _____ would have the highest energy expenditure per unit mass.
   a. elephant; mouse
   b. elephant; human
   c. human; penguin
   d. mouse; snake
   e. penguin; mouse

LEVEL 2: APPLICATION/ANALYSIS

4. Compared with a smaller cell, a larger cell of the same shape has
   a. less surface area.
   b. less surface area per unit of volume.
   c. the same surface-to-volume ratio.
   d. a smaller average distance between its mitochondria and the external source of oxygen.
   e. a smaller cytoplasm-to-nucleus ratio.

5. An animal's inputs of energy and materials would exceed its outputs
   a. if the animal is an endotherm, which must always take in more energy because of its high metabolic rate.
   b. if it is actively foraging for food.
   c. if it is hibernating.
   d. if it is growing and increasing its mass.
   e. never; homeostasis makes these energy and material budgets always balance.

6. You are studying a large tropical reptile that has a high and relatively stable body temperature. How would you determine whether this animal is an endotherm or an ectotherm?
   a. You know from its high and stable body temperature that it must be an endotherm.
   b. You know that it is an ectotherm because it is not a bird or mammal.
   c. You subject this reptile to various temperatures in the lab and find that its body temperature and metabolic rate change with the ambient temperature. You conclude that it is an ectotherm.
   d. You note that its environment has a high and stable temper-ature. Because its body temperature matches the environ-mental temperature, you conclude that it is an ectotherm.
   e. You measure the metabolic rate of the reptile, and because it is higher than that of a related species that lives in temperate forests, you conclude that this reptile is an endotherm and its relative is an ectotherm.

7. Which of the following animals uses the largest percentage of its energy budget for homeostatic regulation?
   a. a hydra
   b. a marine jelly (an invertebrate)
   c. a snake in a temperate forest
   d. a desert insect
   e. a desert bird

8. **DRAW IT** Draw a model of the control circuit(s) required for driving an automobile at a fairly constant speed over a hilly road. Indicate each feature that represents a sensor, stim-ulus, or response.

LEVEL 3: SYNTHESIS/EVALUATION

9. **EVOLUTION CONNECTION**
   In 1847, the German biologist Christian Bergmann noted that mammals and birds living at higher latitudes (farther from the equator) are on average larger and bulkier than related species found at lower latitudes. Suggest an evolutionary hypothesis to explain this observation.

10. **SCIENTIFIC INQUIRY**
    Eastern tent caterpillars (*Malacosoma americanum*) live in large groups in silk nests, or tents, which they build in trees. They are among the first insects to be active in early spring, when daily temperature fluctuates from freezing to very hot. Over the course of a day, they display striking differences in behavior: Early in the morning, they rest in a tightly packed group on the tent's east-facing surface. In midafternoon, they are on its un-dersurface, each caterpillar hanging by a few of its legs. Propose a hypothesis to explain this behavior. How could you test it?

11. **SCIENCE, TECHNOLOGY, AND SOCIETY**
    Medical researchers are investigating artificial substitutes for various human tissues. Why might artificial blood or skin be useful? What characteristics would these substitutes need in order to function well in the body? Why do real tissues work better? Why not use the real tissues if they work better? What other artificial tissues might be useful? What problems do you anticipate in developing and applying them?

12. **WRITE ABOUT A THEME**
    Feedback Regulation In a short essay (about 100–150 words) focusing on feedback control in thermoregulation, explain why shivering is likely during the onset of a fever.

For selected answers, see Appendix A.

MasteringBIOLOGY   www.masteringbiology.com

1. MasteringBiology® Assignments
Tutorial Thermoregulation
Activities Overview of Animal Tissues • Epithelial Tissue • Connective Tissue • Muscle Tissue • Nervous Tissue • Homeostasis • Regulation: Negative and Positive Feedback • Discovery Channel Video: An Introduction to the Human Body
Questions Student Misconceptions • Reading Quiz • Multiple Choice • End-of-Chapter

2. eText
Read your book online, search, take notes, highlight text, and more.

3. The Study Area
Practice Tests • Cumulative Test • *BioFlix* 3-D Animations • MP3 Tutor Sessions • Videos • Activities • Investigations • Lab Media • Audio Glossary • Word Study Tools • Art

41

Animal Nutrition

▲ **Figure 41.1 How does a lean fish help a bear make fat?**

KEY CONCEPTS

41.1 An animal's diet must supply chemical energy, organic molecules, and essential nutrients

41.2 The main stages of food processing are ingestion, digestion, absorption, and elimination

The Need to Feed

Dinnertime has arrived for the Kodiak bear in **Figure 41.1** (and for the salmon, though in quite a different sense). The skin, muscles, and other parts of the fish will be chewed into pieces, broken down by acid and enzymes in the bear's digestive system, and finally absorbed as small molecules into the body of the bear. Such a process is what is meant by animal **nutrition**: food being taken in, taken apart, and taken up.

Although a diet of fish plucked from a waterfall is not common, all animals eat other organisms—dead or alive, piecemeal or whole. Unlike plants, animals must consume food for both energy and the organic molecules used to assemble new molecules, cells, and tissues. Despite this shared need, animals have diverse diets. **Herbivores**, such as cattle, sea slugs, and termites, dine mainly on plants or algae. **Carnivores**, such as sharks, hawks, and spiders, mostly eat other animals. Bears and other **omnivores** (from the Latin *omni*, all) don't in fact eat everything, but they do regularly consume animals as well as plants or algae. We humans are typically omnivores, as are cockroaches and crows.

The terms *herbivore*, *carnivore*, and *omnivore* represent the kinds of food an animal usually eats. Keep in mind, however, that most animals are opportunistic feeders, eating foods outside their standard diet when their usual foods aren't available. For example, deer are herbivores, but in addition to feeding on grass and other plants, they occasionally eat insects, worms, or bird eggs. Note as well that microorganisms are an unavoidable "supplement" in every animal's diet.

Animals must eat. But to survive and reproduce, they must also balance their consumption, storage, and use of food. Bears, for example, store energy, largely in the form of body fat, in preparation for winter sleep. Eating too little food, too much food, or the wrong mixture of foods can endanger an animal's health. In this chapter, we will survey the nutritional requirements of animals, explore some of the diverse evolutionary adaptations for obtaining and processing food, and investigate the regulation of energy intake and expenditure.

CONCEPT 41.1

An animal's diet must supply chemical energy, organic molecules, and essential nutrients

Overall, an adequate diet must satisfy three nutritional needs: chemical energy for cellular processes, organic building blocks for macromolecules, and essential nutrients.

The activities of cells, tissues, organs, and whole animals depend on sources of chemical energy in the diet. This energy is used to produce ATP, which powers processes ranging from DNA replication and cell division to vision and flight. To meet the continuous requirement for ATP, animals ingest and digest nutrients, including carbohydrates, proteins, and lipids, for use in cellular respiration and energy storage.

In addition to providing fuel for ATP production, an animal's diet must supply the raw materials needed for biosynthesis. To build the complex molecules it needs to grow, maintain itself, and reproduce, an animal must obtain two types of organic precursors from its food. Animals need a source of organic carbon (such as sugar) and a source of organic nitrogen (such as protein). Starting with these materials, animals can construct a great variety of organic molecules.

The materials that an animal's cells require but cannot synthesize are called **essential nutrients**. Obtained from dietary sources, these nutrients include certain minerals and preassembled organic molecules. Some nutrients are essential for all animals, whereas others are needed only by certain species. For instance, ascorbic acid (vitamin C) is an essential nutrient for humans and other primates, guinea pigs, and some birds and snakes, but not for most other animals.

Essential Nutrients

There are four classes of essential nutrients: essential amino acids, essential fatty acids, vitamins, and minerals.

Essential Amino Acids

Animals require 20 amino acids to make proteins (see Figure 5.16). The majority of animal species have the enzymes to synthesize about half of these amino acids, as long as their diet includes sulfur and organic nitrogen. The remaining amino acids must be obtained from food in prefabricated form and are therefore called **essential amino acids**. Most animals, including adult humans, require eight amino acids in their diet (infants also need a ninth, histidine).

The proteins in animal products such as meat, eggs, and cheese are "complete," which means that they provide all the essential amino acids in their proper proportions. In contrast, most plant proteins are "incomplete," being deficient in one or more essential amino acids. Corn (maize), for example, is deficient in tryptophan and lysine, whereas beans are lacking in methionine. However, vegetarians can easily obtain all of the essential amino acids by eating a varied diet of plant proteins.

Some animals have adaptations that help them through periods when their bodies demand extraordinary amounts of protein. In penguins, for example, muscle protein provides a source of amino acids for making new proteins when feathers are replaced after molting **(Figure 41.2)**.

Essential Fatty Acids

Animals produce the enzymes to synthesize most, but not all, of the fatty acids they need. The **essential fatty acids**, the ones they cannot make, are certain fatty acids that contain

▲ **Figure 41.2 Storing protein for growth.** Penguins, such as this Adélie from Antarctica, must make an abundance of new proteins when they molt and grow new feathers. Because of the temporary loss of their insulating coat of feathers, penguins cannot swim—or feed—when molting. How, then, do they obtain amino acids for production of feather protein? Before molting, a penguin greatly increases its muscle mass. The penguin then breaks down the extra muscle protein, which supplies the amino acids for growing new feathers.

MAKE CONNECTIONS *Taking into account the examples in Figure 5.15, what generalization can you make about the circumstances under which animals commonly use proteins for amino acid storage?*

one or more double bonds and are thus unsaturated (see Figure 5.11). For example, humans require linoleic acid to make some membrane phospholipids. Because seeds, grains, and vegetables in the diets of humans and other animals generally furnish ample quantities of essential fatty acids, deficiencies in this class of nutrients are rare.

Vitamins

As Nobel Prize winner Albert Szent-Gyorgyi pointed out, "A vitamin is a substance that makes you ill if you *don't* eat it." **Vitamins** are organic molecules that have diverse functions and are required in the diet in very small amounts. Vitamin B_2, for example, is converted in the body to FAD, a coenzyme used in many metabolic processes, including cellular respiration (see Figure 9.12). For humans, 13 vitamins have been identified. Depending on the vitamin, the required amount ranges from about 0.01 to 100 mg per day.

Vitamins are classified as water-soluble or fat-soluble **(Table 41.1)**. The water-soluble vitamins include the B vitamins, which are compounds that generally function as coenzymes, and vitamin C, which is required for the production of connective tissue. Among the fat-soluble vitamins are vitamin A, which is incorporated into visual pigments of the eye, and vitamin K, which functions in blood clotting. Another is vitamin D, which aids in calcium absorption and bone formation.

Table 41.1 Vitamin Requirements of Humans

Vitamin	Major Dietary Sources	Major Functions in the Body	Symptoms of Deficiency
Water-Soluble Vitamins			
B_1 (thiamine)	Pork, legumes, peanuts, whole grains	Coenzyme used in removing CO_2 from organic compounds	Beriberi (tingling, poor coordination, reduced heart function)
B_2 (riboflavin)	Dairy products, meats, enriched grains, vegetables	Component of coenzymes FAD and FMN	Skin lesions, such as cracks at corners of mouth
B_3 (niacin)	Nuts, meats, grains	Component of coenzymes NAD^+ and $NADP^+$	Skin and gastrointestinal lesions, delusions, confusion
B_5 (pantothenic acid)	Meats, dairy products, whole grains, fruits, vegetables	Component of coenzyme A	Fatigue, numbness, tingling of hands and feet
B_6 (pyridoxine)	Meats, vegetables, whole grains	Coenzyme used in amino acid metabolism	Irritability, convulsions, muscular twitching, anemia
B_7 (biotin)	Legumes, other vegetables, meats	Coenzyme in synthesis of fat, glycogen, and amino acids	Scaly skin inflammation, neuromuscular disorders
B_9 (folic acid)	Green vegetables, oranges, nuts, legumes, whole grains	Coenzyme in nucleic acid and amino acid metabolism	Anemia, birth defects
B_{12} (cobalamin)	Meats, eggs, dairy products	Production of nucleic acids and red blood cells	Anemia, numbness, loss of balance
C (ascorbic acid)	Citrus fruits, broccoli, tomatoes	Used in collagen synthesis; antioxidant	Scurvy (degeneration of skin and teeth), delayed wound healing
Fat-Soluble Vitamins			
A (retinol)	Dark green and orange vegetables and fruits, dairy products	Component of visual pigments; maintenance of epithelial tissues	Blindness, skin disorders, impaired immunity
D	Dairy products, egg yolk	Aids in absorption and use of calcium and phosphorus	Rickets (bone deformities) in children, bone softening in adults
E (tocopherol)	Vegetable oils, nuts, seeds	Antioxidant; helps prevent damage to cell membranes	Nervous system degeneration
K (phylloquinone)	Green vegetables, tea; also made by colon bacteria	Important in blood clotting	Defective blood clotting

Our dietary requirement for vitamin D is variable because we synthesize this vitamin from other molecules when the skin is exposed to sunlight.

For people with poorly balanced diets, taking vitamin supplements that provide recommended daily levels is certainly reasonable. It is much less clear whether massive doses of vitamins confer any health benefits or are, in fact, safe. Moderate overdoses of water-soluble vitamins are probably harmless because excesses of these vitamins are excreted in urine. However, excesses of fat-soluble vitamins are deposited in body fat, so overconsumption may result in accumulating toxic levels of these compounds.

Minerals

Dietary **minerals** are inorganic nutrients, such as iron and sulfur, that are usually required in small amounts—from less than 1 mg to about 2,500 mg per day. As shown in **Table 41.2** on the next page, minerals have diverse functions in animal physiology. Some are cofactors built into the structure of enzymes; magnesium, for example, is present in enzymes that split ATP. In contrast, sodium, potassium, and chloride are important in the functioning of nerves and in maintaining osmotic balance between cells and the surrounding body fluid. Vertebrates use one mineral—iodine—specifically to make thyroid hormones, which regulate metabolic rate. Vertebrates also require relatively large quantities of calcium and phosphorus for building and maintaining bone.

Ingesting large amounts of some minerals can upset homeostatic balance and impair health. For example, excess salt (sodium chloride) intake can contribute to high blood pressure. This is a particular problem in the United States, where the typical person consumes enough salt to provide about 20 times the required amount of sodium. Packaged (prepared) foods often contain large amounts of sodium chloride, even if they do not taste very salty. Excessive consumption of iron can also endanger health: Liver damage due to iron overload affects as much as 10% of the human population in some regions of Africa where the water supply is especially iron-rich.

Table 41.2 Mineral Requirements of Humans*			
Mineral	**Major Dietary Sources**	**Major Functions in the Body**	**Symptoms of Deficiency**
Calcium (Ca)	Dairy products, dark green vegetables, legumes	Bone and tooth formation, blood clotting, nerve and muscle function	Impaired growth, loss of bone mass
Phosphorus (P)	Dairy products, meats, grains	Bone and tooth formation, acid-base balance, nucleotide synthesis	Weakness, loss of minerals from bone, calcium loss
Sulfur (S)	Proteins from many sources	Component of certain amino acids	Impaired growth, fatigue, swelling
Potassium (K)	Meats, dairy products, many fruits and vegetables, grains	Acid-base balance, water balance, nerve function	Muscular weakness, paralysis, nausea, heart failure
Chlorine (Cl)	Table salt	Acid-base balance, formation of gastric juice, nerve function, osmotic balance	Muscle cramps, reduced appetite
Sodium (Na)	Table salt	Acid-base balance, water balance, nerve function	Muscle cramps, reduced appetite
Magnesium (Mg)	Whole grains, green leafy vegetables	Enzyme cofactor; ATP bioenergetics	Nervous system disturbances
Iron (Fe)	Meats, eggs, legumes, whole grains, green leafy vegetables	Component of hemoglobin and of electron carriers; enzyme cofactor	Iron-deficiency anemia, weakness, impaired immunity
Fluorine (F)	Drinking water, tea, seafood	Maintenance of tooth structure	Higher frequency of tooth decay
Iodine (I)	Seafood, iodized salt	Component of thyroid hormones	Goiter (enlarged thyroid gland)

The first seven minerals (Calcium through Magnesium) are grouped under the bracket labeled "Greater than 200 mg per day required."

*Additional minerals required in trace amounts are chromium (Cr), cobalt (Co), copper (Cu), manganese (Mn), molybdenum (Mo), selenium (Se), and zinc (Zn). All of these minerals, as well as those in the table, are harmful when consumed in excess.

Dietary Deficiencies

A diet that lacks one or more essential nutrients or consistently supplies less chemical energy than the body requires results in *malnutrition*, a failure to obtain adequate nutrition. Malnutrition resulting from either type of dietary deficiency can have negative impacts on health and survival.

Deficiencies in Essential Nutrients

Insufficient intake of essential nutrients can cause deformities, disease, and even death. For example, cattle, deer, and other herbivores may develop dangerously fragile bones if they graze on plants growing in soil that lacks phosphorus. Some grazing animals obtain otherwise missing nutrients by consuming concentrated sources of salt or other minerals **(Figure 41.3)**. Among carnivores, spiders have been found to adjust for dietary deficiencies by switching to prey that restores nutritional balance.

Like other animals, humans sometimes suffer from diets lacking in essential nutrients. A diet that provides insufficient amounts of one or more essential amino acids causes protein deficiency, the most common type of malnutrition among humans. For example, protein deficiency may arise if a child's diet shifts from consisting of breast milk to consisting solely of foods that provide almost all of their calories in the form of starch and other carbohydrates. Such children, if they survive infancy, often have impaired physical and mental development.

▲ **Figure 41.3 Obtaining essential nutrients.** A juvenile chamois (*Rupicapra rupicapra*), an herbivore, licks exposed salts and minerals in its rocky alpine habitat. This behavior is common among herbivores living where soils and plants provide insufficient amounts of essential nutrients, such as sodium, calcium, phosphorus, and iron.

Among populations subsisting on simple rice diets, individuals are often afflicted with vitamin A deficiency, which can cause blindness or death. To overcome this problem, scientists have engineered a strain of rice to synthesize beta-carotene, the orange-colored pigment that is abundant in carrots. Once absorbed into the body, beta-carotene is converted to vitamin A.

The potential benefit of this "Golden Rice" (see Chapter 38) is enormous because 1–2 million young children worldwide die every year from vitamin A deficiency.

Undernutrition

A diet that fails to provide adequate sources of chemical energy results in *undernutrition*. When an animal is undernourished, a series of events unfold: The body uses up stored carbohydrates and fat and then begins breaking down its own proteins for fuel; muscles begin to decrease in size; and the brain may become protein-deficient. If energy intake remains less than energy expenditures, the animal will eventually die. Even if a seriously undernourished animal survives, some of the damage may be irreversible.

Human undernutrition is most common when drought, war, or another crisis severely disrupts the food supply. In sub-Saharan Africa, where the AIDS epidemic has crippled both rural and urban communities, approximately 200 million children and adults cannot obtain enough food.

Sometimes undernutrition occurs within well-fed human populations as a result of eating disorders. For example, anorexia nervosa leads individuals, usually female, to starve themselves compulsively.

Assessing Nutritional Needs

Determining the ideal diet for the human population is an important but difficult problem for scientists. As objects of study, people present many challenges. Unlike laboratory animals, humans are genetically diverse. They also live in settings far more varied than the stable and uniform environment that scientists use to facilitate comparisons in laboratory experiments. Ethical concerns present an additional barrier. For example, it is not acceptable to investigate the nutritional needs of children in a way that might harm a child's growth or development.

The methods used to study human nutrition have changed dramatically over time. To avoid harming others, several of the researchers who discovered vitamins a century ago used themselves as subject animals. Today, researchers typically rely on the study of genetic defects that disrupt food uptake, storage, or use. For example, a genetic disorder called hemochromatosis causes iron buildup in the absence of any abnormal iron consumption or exposure. Fortunately, this common disorder is remarkably easy to treat: Drawing blood regularly removes enough iron from the body to restore homeostasis. By studying the defective genes that can cause the disease, scientists have learned a great deal about the regulation of iron absorption.

Many insights into human nutrition have come from *epidemiology*, the study of human health and disease at the population level. In the 1970s, for instance, researchers

▼ **Figure 41.4**

INQUIRY

Can diet influence the frequency of birth defects?

EXPERIMENT Richard Smithells, of the University of Leeds, in England, examined the effect of vitamin supplementation on the risk of neural tube defects. Women who had had one or more babies with such a defect were put into two study groups. The experimental group consisted of those who were planning a pregnancy and began taking a multivitamin at least four weeks before attempting conception. The control group, who were not given vitamins, included women who declined them and women who were already pregnant. The numbers of neural tube defects resulting from the pregnancies were recorded for each group.

RESULTS

Group	Number of infants/fetuses studied	Infants/fetuses with a neural tube defect
Vitamin supplements (experimental group)	141	1 (0.7%)
No vitamin supplements (control group)	204	12 (5.9%)

CONCLUSION This study provided evidence that vitamin supplementation protects against neural tube defects, at least after the first pregnancy. Follow-up trials demonstrated that folic acid alone provided an equivalent protective effect.

SOURCE R. W. Smithells et al., Possible prevention of neural-tube defects by periconceptional vitamin supplementation, *Lancet* 315: 339–340 (1980).

INQUIRY IN ACTION Read and analyze the original paper in *Inquiry in Action: Interpreting Scientific Papers.*

WHAT IF? Subsequent studies were designed to learn if folic acid supplements prevent neural tube defects during first-time pregnancies. To determine the required number of subjects, what type of additional information did the researchers need?

discovered that children born to women of low socioeconomic status were more likely to have neural tube defects, which occur when tissue fails to enclose the developing brain and spinal cord (see Chapter 47). The English scientist Richard Smithells thought that malnutrition among these women might be responsible. As described in **Figure 41.4**, he found that vitamin supplementation greatly reduced the risk of neural tube defects. In other studies, he obtained evidence that folic acid (vitamin B_9) was the specific vitamin responsible, a finding confirmed by other researchers. Based on this evidence, the United States in 1998 began to require that folic acid be added to enriched grain products used to make bread, cereals, and other foods. Follow-up studies have documented the effectiveness of this program in reducing the frequency of neural tube defects. Thus, at a time when microsurgery and sophisticated diagnostic imaging dominate the headlines, a simple dietary change such as folic acid supplementation or consumption of Golden Rice may be among the greatest contributors to human health.

CONCEPT **41.2**

The main stages of food processing are ingestion, digestion, absorption, and elimination

In this section, we turn from nutritional requirements to the mechanisms by which animals process food. Food processing can be divided into four distinct stages: ingestion, digestion, absorption, and elimination (**Figure 41.5**). The first stage, **ingestion**, is the act of eating or feeding. **Figure 41.6** surveys and classifies the principal feeding mechanisms that have evolved in animals. Given the variation in food sources among animal species, it is not surprising that strategies for extracting resources from food also differ widely. We will focus, however, on the shared processes, pausing periodically to consider some adaptations to particular diets or environments.

In **digestion**, the second stage of food processing, food is broken down into molecules small enough for the body to absorb. Mechanical digestion, such as chewing, typically precedes chemical digestion. Mechanical digestion breaks food into smaller pieces, increasing the surface area available for

① Ingestion ② Digestion ③ Absorption ④ Elimination

▲ **Figure 41.5 The four stages of food processing.**

chemical processes. Chemical digestion is necessary because animals cannot directly use the proteins, carbohydrates, nucleic acids, fats, and phospholipids in food. One problem is that these molecules are too large to pass through membranes and enter the cells of the animal. In addition, the large molecules in food are not all identical to those the animal needs for its particular tissues and functions. When large molecules in food are broken down into their components, however, the animal can use these smaller molecules to assemble the large molecules it needs. For example, although fruit flies and humans have very different diets, both convert proteins in their food to the same 20 amino acids from which they assemble all of the proteins specific for their species.

Recall from Chapter 5 that a cell makes a macromolecule or fat by linking together smaller components; it does so by removing a molecule of water for each new covalent bond formed. Chemical digestion by enzymes reverses this process by breaking bonds with the addition of water (see Figure 5.2). This splitting process is called *enzymatic hydrolysis*. A variety of enzymes catalyze the digestion of large molecules in food. Polysaccharides and disaccharides are split into simple sugars; proteins are broken down into amino acids; and nucleic acids are cleaved into nucleotides and their components. Enzymatic hydrolysis also releases fatty acids and other components from fats and phospholipids.

The last two stages of food processing occur after the food is digested. In the third stage, **absorption**, the animal's cells take up (absorb) small molecules such as amino acids and simple sugars. **Elimination** completes the process as undigested material passes out of the digestive system.

Digestive Compartments

In our overview of food processing, we have seen that digestive enzymes hydrolyze the same biological materials (such as proteins, fats, and carbohydrates) that make up the bodies of the animals themselves. How, then, are animals able to digest food without digesting their own cells and tissues? The evolutionary adaptation found across a wide range of animal species is the processing of food within specialized compartments. Such compartments can be intracellular, in the form of food vacuoles, or extracellular, as in digestive organs and systems.

Intracellular Digestion

Food vacuoles—cellular organelles in which hydrolytic enzymes break down food—are the simplest digestive compartments. The hydrolysis of food inside vacuoles, called *intracellular digestion*, begins after a cell engulfs solid food by phagocytosis or liquid food by pinocytosis (see Figure 7.22). Newly formed food vacuoles fuse with lysosomes, organelles containing hydrolytic enzymes. This fusion of organelles brings food in contact with the enzymes, allowing digestion to occur safely within a compartment

▼ Figure 41.6

Exploring Four Main Feeding Mechanisms of Animals

Suspension Feeders and Filter Feeders

Baleen

Many aquatic animals are **suspension feeders**, which eat small organisms or food particles suspended in the water. For example, clams and oysters feed on tiny morsels of food in the water that passes over their gills; cilia sweep the food particles to the animal's mouth in a film of mucus. **Filter feeders** such as the humpback whale shown above move water through a filtering structure to obtain food. Attached to the whale's upper jaw are comblike plates called baleen, which strain small invertebrates and fish from enormous volumes of water.

Substrate Feeders

Substrate feeders are animals that live in or on their food source. This leaf miner caterpillar, the larva of a moth, is eating through the soft tissue of an oak leaf, leaving a dark trail of feces in its wake. Some other substrate feeders include maggots (fly larvae), which burrow into animal carcasses.

Caterpillar   Feces

Fluid Feeders

Fluid feeders suck nutrient-rich fluid from a living host. This mosquito has pierced the skin of its human host with hollow, needlelike mouthparts and is consuming a blood meal (colorized SEM). Similarly, aphids are fluid feeders that tap the phloem sap of plants. In contrast to such parasites, some fluid feeders actually benefit their hosts. For example, hummingbirds and bees move pollen between flowers as they fluid-feed on nectar.

Bulk Feeders

Most animals, including humans, are **bulk feeders**, which eat relatively large pieces of food. Their adaptations include tentacles, pincers, claws, poisonous fangs, jaws, and teeth that kill their prey or tear off pieces of meat or vegetation. In this amazing scene, a rock python is beginning to ingest a gazelle it has captured and killed. Snakes cannot chew their food into pieces and must swallow it whole—even if the prey is much bigger than the diameter of the snake. They can do so because the lower jaw is loosely hinged to the skull by an elastic ligament that permits the mouth and throat to open very wide. After swallowing its prey, which may take more than an hour, the python will spend two weeks or more digesting its meal.

enclosed by a protective membrane. A few animals, such as sponges, digest their food entirely by this intracellular mechanism (see Figure 33.4).

Extracellular Digestion

In most animal species, at least some hydrolysis occurs by *extracellular digestion*, the breakdown of food in compartments that are continuous with the outside of the animal's body. Having one or more extracellular compartments for digestion enables an animal to devour much larger pieces of food than can be ingested by phagocytosis.

Many animals with relatively simple body plans have a digestive compartment with a single opening **(Figure 41.7)**. This pouch, called a **gastrovascular cavity**, functions in digestion as well as in the distribution of nutrients throughout the body (hence the *vascular* part of the term). The carnivorous cnidarians called hydras provide a good example of how a gastrovascular cavity works. A hydra uses its tentacles to stuff captured prey through its mouth into its gastrovascular cavity. Specialized gland cells of the hydra's gastrodermis, the tissue layer that lines the cavity, then secrete digestive enzymes that break the soft tissues of the prey into tiny pieces. Other cells of the gastrodermis engulf these food particles, and most of the hydrolysis of macromolecules occurs intracellularly, as in sponges. After a hydra has digested its meal, undigested materials that remain in the gastrovascular cavity, such as exoskeletons of small crustaceans, are eliminated through the same opening by which food entered. Many flatworms also have a gastrovascular cavity with a single opening (see Figure 33.10).

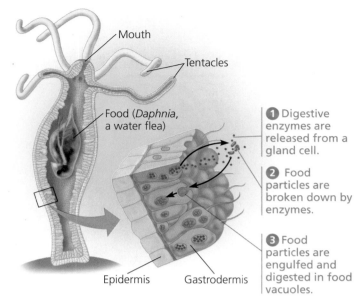

① Digestive enzymes are released from a gland cell.

② Food particles are broken down by enzymes.

③ Food particles are engulfed and digested in food vacuoles.

▲ **Figure 41.7 Digestion in a hydra.** Digestion begins in the gastrovascular cavity and is completed intracellularly after small food particles are engulfed by specialized cells of the gastrodermis.

In contrast with cnidarians and flatworms, most animals have a digestive tube extending between two openings, a mouth and an anus **(Figure 41.8)**. Such a tube is called a *complete digestive tract* or, more commonly, an **alimentary canal**. Because food moves along the alimentary canal in a single direction, the tube can be organized into specialized compartments that carry out digestion and nutrient absorption in a stepwise fashion. An animal with an alimentary canal can ingest food while earlier meals are still being digested, a feat that

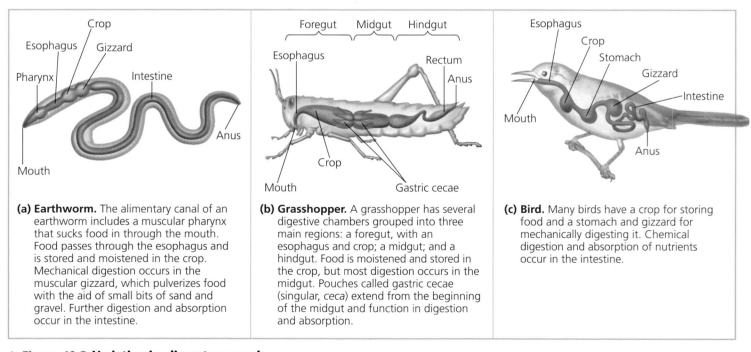

(a) Earthworm. The alimentary canal of an earthworm includes a muscular pharynx that sucks food in through the mouth. Food passes through the esophagus and is stored and moistened in the crop. Mechanical digestion occurs in the muscular gizzard, which pulverizes food with the aid of small bits of sand and gravel. Further digestion and absorption occur in the intestine.

(b) Grasshopper. A grasshopper has several digestive chambers grouped into three main regions: a foregut, with an esophagus and crop; a midgut; and a hindgut. Food is moistened and stored in the crop, but most digestion occurs in the midgut. Pouches called gastric cecae (singular, *ceca*) extend from the beginning of the midgut and function in digestion and absorption.

(c) Bird. Many birds have a crop for storing food and a stomach and gizzard for mechanically digesting it. Chemical digestion and absorption of nutrients occur in the intestine.

▲ **Figure 41.8 Variation in alimentary canals.**

is likely to be difficult or inefficient for animals with gastrovascular cavities. In the next section, we'll explore the spatial and functional organization of an alimentary canal.

CONCEPT CHECK 41.2

1. Distinguish the overall structure of a gastrovascular cavity from that of an alimentary canal.
2. In what sense are nutrients from a recently ingested meal not really "inside" your body prior to the absorption stage of food processing?
3. **WHAT IF?** Thinking in broad terms, what similarities can you identify between digestion in an animal body and the breakdown of gasoline in an automobile? (You don't have to know about auto mechanics.)

For suggested answers, see Appendix A.

SUMMARY OF KEY CONCEPTS

- Animals have diverse diets. **Herbivores** mainly eat plants; **carnivores** mainly eat other animals; and **omnivores** eat both. Animals must balance consumption, storage, and use of food.

CONCEPT 41.1

An animal's diet must supply chemical energy, organic molecules, and essential nutrients (pp. 875–880)

- Food provides animals with energy for ATP production, carbon skeletons for biosynthesis, and **essential nutrients**—nutrients that must be supplied in preassembled form. Essential nutrients include certain amino acids and fatty acids that animals cannot synthesize; **vitamins**, which are organic molecules; and **minerals**, which are inorganic substances.
- Animals can suffer from two types of malnutrition: an inadequate intake of essential nutrients and a deficiency in sources of chemical energy. Studies of genetic defects and of disease at the population level help researchers determine human dietary requirements.

> **?** *Propose a reason why the diet of many mammals doesn't need to include vitamin C, a substance that is important for collagen synthesis.*

CONCEPT 41.2

The main stages of food processing are ingestion, digestion, absorption, and elimination (pp. 880–883)

- Food processing in animals involves **ingestion** (eating), **digestion** (enzymatic breakdown of large molecules), **absorption** (uptake of nutrients by cells), and **elimination** (passage of undigested materials out of the body in feces).
- Animals differ in the ways they obtain and ingest food. Most animals are **bulk feeders**, eating large pieces of food.
- Compartmentalization is necessary to avoid self-digestion. In intracellular digestion, food particles are engulfed by endocytosis and digested within food vacuoles that have fused with lysosomes. In extracellular digestion, which is used by most animals, enzymatic hydrolysis occurs outside cells in a **gastrovascular cavity** or **alimentary canal**.

> **?** *Propose an artificial diet that would eliminate the need for one of the first three steps in food processing.*

LEVEL 1: KNOWLEDGE/COMPREHENSION

1. Which of the following animals is *incorrectly* paired with its feeding mechanism?
   a. lion—substrate feeder
   b. baleen whale—suspension feeder
   c. aphid—fluid feeder
   d. clam—suspension feeder
   e. snake—bulk feeder

2. The mammalian trachea and esophagus both connect to the
   a. large intestine.
   b. stomach.
   c. pharynx.
   d. rectum.
   e. epiglottis.

3. Which of the following organs is *incorrectly* paired with its function?
   a. stomach—protein digestion
   b. oral cavity—starch digestion
   c. large intestine—bile production
   d. small intestine—nutrient absorption
   e. pancreas—enzyme production

4. Which of the following is *not* a major activity of the stomach?
   a. mechanical digestion
   b. HCl secretion
   c. mucus secretion
   d. nutrient absorption
   e. enzyme secretion

LEVEL 2: APPLICATION/ANALYSIS

5. After surgical removal of an infected gallbladder, a person must be especially careful to restrict dietary intake of
   a. starch.   b. protein.   c. sugar.   d. fat.   e. water.

6. If you were to jog 1 km a few hours after lunch, which stored fuel would you probably tap?
   a. muscle proteins
   b. muscle and liver glycogen
   c. fat stored in the liver
   d. fat stored in adipose tissue
   e. blood proteins

LEVEL 3: SYNTHESIS/EVALUATION

7. **DRAW IT** Make a flowchart of the events that occur after partially digested food leaves the stomach. Use the following terms: bicarbonate secretion, circulation, decrease in acidity, secretin secretion, increase in acidity, signal detection. Next to each term, indicate the compartment(s) involved. You may use a term more than once.

8. **EVOLUTION CONNECTION**
   The human esophagus and trachea share a passage leading from the mouth and nasal passages, which can cause problems. After reviewing vertebrate evolution in Chapter 34, explain the evolutionary basis for this "imperfect" anatomy.

9. **SCIENTIFIC INQUIRY**
   In human populations of northern European origin, the disorder called hemochromatosis causes excess iron uptake from food and affects one in 200 adults. Men are ten times as likely as women to suffer from iron overload. Devise a hypothesis for the difference in the disease between the two sexes.

10. **WRITE ABOUT A THEME**
   Emergent Properties Hair is largely made up of the protein keratin. In a short essay (100–150 words), explain why a shampoo containing protein is not effective in replacing the protein in damaged hair.

For selected answers, see Appendix A.

MasteringBIOLOGY®   www.masteringbiology.com

1. MasteringBiology® Assignments
Make Connections Tutorial Fat Absorption (Chapter 41) and Fat Structure (Chapter 5).
Experimental Inquiry Tutorial What Role Do Genes Play in Appetite Regulation?
BioFlix Tutorials Membrane Transport • Homeostasis: Regulating Blood Sugar
Tutorial Vitamins
Activities Digestive System Function • Hormonal Control of Digestion • The Digestion and Absorption of Food • Discovery Channel Video: Nutrition
Questions Student Misconceptions • Reading Quiz • Multiple Choice • End-of-Chapter

2. eText
Read your book online, search, take notes, highlight text, and more.

3. The Study Area
Practice Tests • Cumulative Test • *BioFlix* 3-D Animations • MP3 Tutor Sessions • Videos • Activities • Investigations • Lab Media • Audio Glossary • Word Study Tools • Art

42

Circulation and Gas Exchange

▲ **Figure 42.1 How does a feathery fringe help this animal survive?**

KEY CONCEPTS

42.1 Circulatory systems link exchange surfaces with cells throughout the body

42.5 Gas exchange occurs across specialized respiratory surfaces

Trading Places

The animal in **Figure 42.1** may look like a creature from a science fiction film, but it's actually an axolotl, a salamander native to shallow ponds in central Mexico. The feathery red appendages jutting out from the head of this albino adult are gills. Although external gills are uncommon in adult animals, they help satisfy the need shared by all animals to exchange substances with their environment.

Exchange between an axolotl or any other animal and its surroundings ultimately occurs at the cellular level. The resources that animal cells require, such as nutrients and oxygen (O_2), enter the cytoplasm by crossing the plasma membrane. Metabolic by-products, such as carbon dioxide (CO_2), exit the cell by crossing the same membrane. In unicellular organisms, exchange occurs directly with the external environment. For most multicellular organisms, however, direct transfer of materials between every cell and the environment is not possible. Instead, these organisms rely on specialized systems that carry out exchange with the environment and that transport materials between sites of exchange and the rest of the body.

The reddish color and branching structure of the axolotl's gills reflect the intimate association between exchange and transport. Tiny blood vessels lie close to the surface of each filament in the gills. Across this surface, there is a net diffusion of O_2 from the surrounding water into the blood and of CO_2 from the blood into the water. The short distances involved allow diffusion to be rapid. Pumping of the axolotl's heart propels the oxygen-rich blood from the gill filaments to all other tissues of the body. There, more short-range exchange occurs, involving nutrients and O_2 as well as CO_2 and other wastes.

Because internal transport and gas exchange are functionally related in most animals, not just axolotls, we will examine both circulatory and respiratory systems in this chapter. We will explore the remarkable variation in form and organization of these systems by considering examples from a number of species. We will also highlight the roles of circulatory and respiratory systems in maintaining homeostasis under a range of physiological and environmental conditions.

CONCEPT 42.1

Circulatory systems link exchange surfaces with cells throughout the body

The molecular trade that an animal carries out with its environment—gaining O_2 and nutrients while shedding CO_2 and other waste products—must ultimately involve every cell in the body. As you learned in Chapter 7, small, nonpolar molecules such as O_2 and CO_2 can move between cells and their immediate surroundings by diffusion. But diffusion is very slow for distances of more than a few millimeters. That's because the time it takes for a substance to diffuse from one place to another is proportional to the *square* of the distance. For example, if it takes 1 second for a given quantity of glucose to diffuse 100 μm, it will take 100 seconds for the same quantity to diffuse 1 mm and almost 3 hours to diffuse 1 cm! This relationship between diffusion time and distance places a substantial constraint on the body plan of any animal.

Given that diffusion is rapid only over very small distances, how does each cell of an animal participate in exchange? Natural selection has resulted in two general solutions to this problem. The first solution is a body size and shape that keep many or all cells in direct contact with the environment. Each cell can thus exchange materials directly with the surrounding medium. This type of body plan is found only in certain invertebrates, including cnidarians and flatworms. The second solution, found in all other animals, is a circulatory system that moves fluid between each cell's immediate surroundings and the tissues where exchange with the environment occurs.

Gastrovascular Cavities

Let's begin by looking at animals that lack a distinct circulatory system. In hydras, jellies, and other cnidarians, a central gastrovascular cavity functions in the distribution of substances throughout the body and in digestion (see Figure 41.7). An opening at one end connects the cavity to the surrounding water. In a hydra, thin branches of the gastrovascular cavity extend into the animal's tentacles. In jellies and some other cnidarians, the gastrovascular cavity has a much more elaborate branching pattern (**Figure 42.2a**).

In animals with a gastrovascular cavity, fluid bathes both the inner and outer tissue layers, facilitating exchange of gases and cellular waste. Only the cells lining the cavity have direct access to nutrients released by digestion. However, because the body wall is a mere two cells thick, nutrients need diffuse only a short distance to reach the cells of the outer tissue layer.

Planarians and most other flatworms also survive without a circulatory system. Their combination of a gastrovascular cavity and a flat body is well suited for exchange with the environment (**Figure 42.2b**). A flat body

▶ **Figure 42.2 Internal transport in gastrovascular cavities.**

WHAT IF? *Suppose a gastrovascular cavity were open at two ends, with fluid entering one end and leaving the other. How would this affect the gastrovascular cavity's functions in gas exchange and digestion?*

optimizes diffusional exchange by increasing surface area and minimizing diffusion distances.

Evolutionary Variation in Circulatory Systems

EVOLUTION For animals with many cell layers, diffusion distances are too great for adequate exchange of nutrients and wastes by a gastrovascular cavity. In these organisms, a circulatory system minimizes the distances that substances must diffuse to enter or leave a cell.

General Properties of Circulatory Systems

A circulatory system has three basic components: a circulatory fluid, a set of interconnecting vessels, and a muscular pump, the **heart**. The heart powers circulation by using metabolic energy to elevate the hydrostatic pressure of the circulatory fluid, which then flows through the vessels and back to the heart.

By transporting fluid throughout the body, the circulatory system functionally connects the aqueous environment of the body cells to the organs that exchange gases, absorb nutrients, and dispose of wastes. In mammals, for example, O_2 from inhaled air diffuses across only two layers of cells in the lungs before reaching the blood. The circulatory system, powered by the heart, then carries the oxygen-rich blood to all parts of the body. As the blood streams throughout the body tissues in tiny blood vessels, O_2 in the blood diffuses only a short distance before entering the fluid that directly bathes the cells.

Several basic types of circulatory systems have arisen during evolution, each representing adaptations to constraints imposed by anatomy and environment. Circulatory systems are either open or closed, vary with regard to the number of circuits in the body, and rely on pumps that differ in structure and organization. We'll examine each of these variations and their physiological consequences in turn.

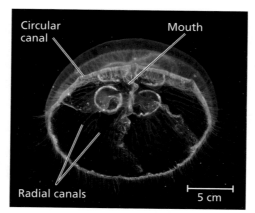

(a) The moon jelly *Aurelia*, a cnidarian. The jelly is viewed here from its underside (oral surface). The mouth leads to an elaborate gastrovascular cavity that consists of radial canals leading to and from a circular canal. Ciliated cells lining the canals circulate fluid within the cavity.

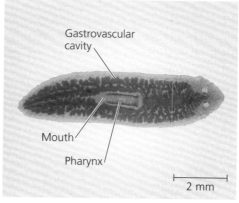

(b) The planarian *Dugesia*, a flatworm. The mouth and pharynx on the ventral side lead to the highly branched gastrovascular cavity, stained dark red in this specimen (LM).

Open and Closed Circulatory Systems

Arthropods and most molluscs have an **open circulatory system**, in which the circulatory fluid bathes the organs directly **(Figure 42.3a)**. In these animals, the circulatory fluid, called **hemolymph**, is also the *interstitial fluid* that bathes body cells. Contraction of one or more hearts pumps the hemolymph through the circulatory vessels into interconnected sinuses, spaces surrounding the organs. Within the sinuses, chemical exchange occurs between the hemolymph and body cells. Relaxation of the heart draws hemolymph

▼ **Figure 42.3 Open and closed circulatory systems.**

(a) An open circulatory system

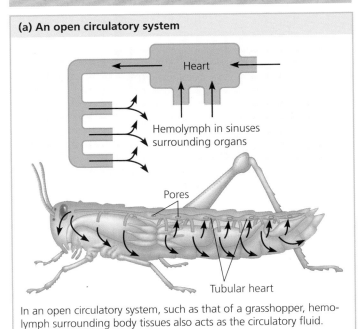

In an open circulatory system, such as that of a grasshopper, hemolymph surrounding body tissues also acts as the circulatory fluid.

(b) A closed circulatory system

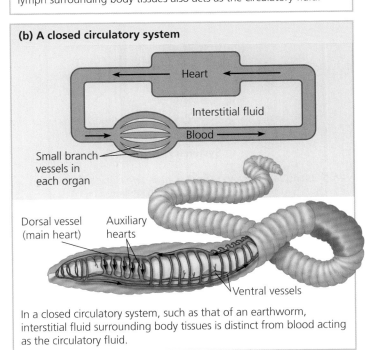

In a closed circulatory system, such as that of an earthworm, interstitial fluid surrounding body tissues is distinct from blood acting as the circulatory fluid.

back in through pores, which are equipped with valves that close when the heart contracts. Body movements help circulate the hemolymph by periodically squeezing the sinuses. The open circulatory system of larger crustaceans, such as lobsters and crabs, includes a more extensive system of vessels as well as an accessory pump.

In a **closed circulatory system**, a circulatory fluid called **blood** is confined to vessels and is distinct from the interstitial fluid **(Figure 42.3b)**. One or more hearts pump blood into large vessels that branch into smaller ones that infiltrate the organs. Chemical exchange occurs between the blood and the interstitial fluid, as well as between the interstitial fluid and body cells. Annelids (including earthworms), cephalopods (including squids and octopuses), and all vertebrates have closed circulatory systems.

The fact that both open and closed circulatory systems are widespread among animals suggests that there are advantages to each system. The lower hydrostatic pressures associated with open circulatory systems make them less costly than closed systems in terms of energy expenditure. In some invertebrates, open circulatory systems serve additional functions. For example, spiders use the hydrostatic pressure generated by their open circulatory system to extend their legs.

The benefits of closed circulatory systems include relatively high blood pressures, which enable the effective delivery of O_2 and nutrients to the cells of larger and more active animals. Among the molluscs, for instance, closed circulatory systems are found in the largest and most active species, the squids and octopuses. Closed systems are also particularly well suited to regulating the distribution of blood to different organs, as you'll learn later in this chapter. In examining closed circulatory systems in more detail, we will focus on the vertebrates.

Organization of Vertebrate Circulatory Systems

The closed circulatory system of humans and other vertebrates is often called the **cardiovascular system**. Blood circulates to and from the heart through an amazingly extensive network of vessels: The total length of blood vessels in an average human adult is twice Earth's circumference at the equator!

Arteries, veins, and capillaries are the three main types of blood vessels. Within each type, blood flows in only one direction. **Arteries** carry blood away from the heart to organs throughout the body. Within organs, arteries branch into **arterioles**, small vessels that convey blood to the capillaries. **Capillaries** are microscopic vessels with very thin, porous walls. Networks of these vessels, called **capillary beds**, infiltrate every tissue, passing within a few cell diameters of every cell in the body. Across the thin walls of capillaries, chemicals, including dissolved gases, are exchanged by diffusion between the blood and the interstitial fluid around the tissue cells. At their "downstream" end, capillaries converge into **venules**, and venules converge into **veins**, the vessels that carry blood back to the heart.

Arteries and veins are distinguished by the *direction* in which they carry blood, not by the O_2 content or other characteristics of the blood they contain. Arteries carry blood from the heart *toward* capillaries, and veins return blood to the heart *from* capillaries. The only exceptions are the portal veins, which carry blood between pairs of capillary beds. The hepatic portal vein, for example, carries blood from capillary beds in the digestive system to capillary beds in the liver (see Chapter 41). From the liver, blood passes into the hepatic veins, which conduct blood toward the heart.

The hearts of all vertebrates contain two or more muscular chambers. The chambers that receive blood entering the heart are called **atria** (singular, *atrium*). The chambers responsible for pumping blood out of the heart are called **ventricles**. The number of chambers and the extent to which they are separated from one another differ substantially among groups of vertebrates, as we will discuss next. These important differences reflect the close fit of form to function that arises from natural selection.

Single Circulation

In bony fishes, rays, and sharks, the heart consists of two chambers: an atrium and a ventricle. The blood passes through the heart once in each complete circuit, an arrangement called **single circulation** (Figure 42.4a). Blood entering the heart collects in the atrium before transfer to the ventricle. Contraction of the ventricle pumps blood to the gills, where there is a net diffusion of O_2 into the blood and of CO_2 out of the blood. As blood leaves the gills, the capillaries converge into a vessel that carries oxygen-rich blood to capillary beds throughout the body. Blood then returns to the heart.

In single circulation, blood that leaves the heart passes through two capillary beds before returning to the heart. When blood flows through a capillary bed, blood pressure drops substantially, for reasons we will explain shortly. The drop in blood pressure in the gills limits the rate of blood flow in the rest of the animal's body. As the animal swims, however, the contraction and relaxation of its muscles help accelerate the relatively sluggish pace of circulation.

Double Circulation

The circulatory systems of amphibians, reptiles, and mammals have two circuits, an arrangement called **double circulation** (Figure 42.4b). The pumps for the two circuits are combined into a single organ, the heart. Having both pumps within a single heart simplifies coordination of the pumping cycles.

One pump, the right side of the heart, delivers oxygen-poor blood to the capillary beds of the gas exchange tissues, where there is a net movement of O_2 into the blood and of CO_2 out of the blood. This part of the circulation is called a **pulmonary circuit** if the capillary beds involved are all in the lungs, as in reptiles and mammals. It is called a **pulmocutaneous circuit** if it includes capillaries in both the lungs and the skin, as in many amphibians.

▼ **Figure 42.4 Single and double circulation in vertebrates.**

(a) Single circulation

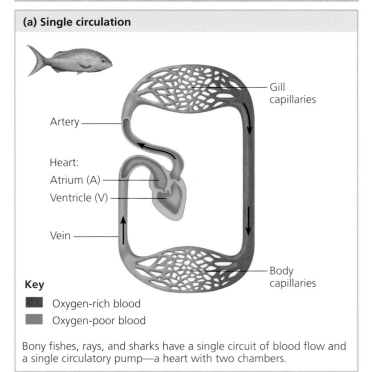

Key

■ Oxygen-rich blood

■ Oxygen-poor blood

Bony fishes, rays, and sharks have a single circuit of blood flow and a single circulatory pump—a heart with two chambers.

(b) Double circulation

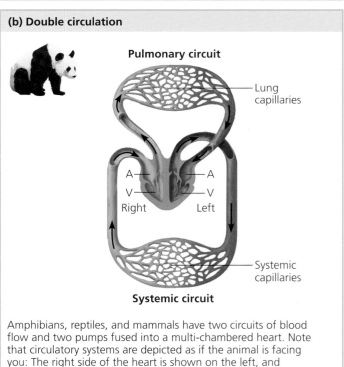

Amphibians, reptiles, and mammals have two circuits of blood flow and two pumps fused into a multi-chambered heart. Note that circulatory systems are depicted as if the animal is facing you: The right side of the heart is shown on the left, and vice versa.

After the oxygen-enriched blood leaves the gas exchange tissues, it enters the other pump, the left side of the heart. Contraction of the heart propels this blood to capillary beds in organs and tissues throughout the body. Following the exchange of O_2 and CO_2, as well as nutrients and waste products, the now oxygen-poor blood returns to the heart, completing the **systemic circuit**.

Double circulation provides a vigorous flow of blood to the brain, muscles, and other organs because the heart repressurizes the blood destined for these tissues after it passes through the capillary beds of the lungs or skin. Indeed, blood pressure is often much higher in the systemic circuit than in the gas exchange circuit. This contrasts sharply with single circulation, in which blood flows under reduced pressure directly from the gas exchange organs to other organs.

To explore the adaptations of double circulation that meet the particular needs of different vertebrates, we conclude our overview of circulatory systems with **Figure 42.5**. In the next section, we will restrict our focus to circulation in mammals and to the anatomy and physiology of the key circulatory organ—the heart.

▼ Figure 42.5

Exploring Double Circulation in Vertebrates

Amphibians

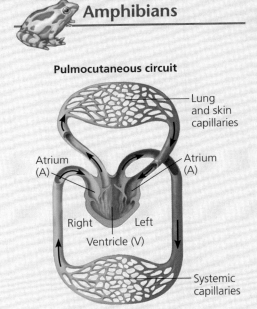

Pulmocutaneous circuit

Lung and skin capillaries

Atrium (A)

Atrium (A)

Right   Left

Ventricle (V)

Systemic capillaries

Systemic circuit

Reptiles (Except Birds)

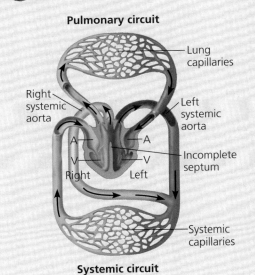

Pulmonary circuit

Lung capillaries

Right systemic aorta

Left systemic aorta

A — A
V — V
Right   Left

Incomplete septum

Systemic capillaries

Systemic circuit

Mammals and Birds

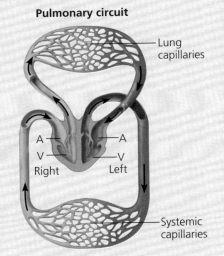

Pulmonary circuit

Lung capillaries

A — A
V — V
Right   Left

Systemic capillaries

Systemic circuit

Key
■ Oxygen-rich blood
■ Oxygen-poor blood

Frogs and other amphibians have a heart with three chambers: two atria and one ventricle. A ridge within the ventricle diverts most (about 90%) of the oxygen-poor blood from the right atrium into the pulmocutaneous circuit and most of the oxygen-rich blood from the left atrium into the systemic circuit. When underwater, a frog adjusts its circulation, for the most part shutting off blood flow to its temporarily ineffective lungs. Blood flow continues to the skin, which acts as the sole site of gas exchange while the frog is submerged.

In the three-chambered heart of turtles, snakes, and lizards, an incomplete septum partially divides the single ventricle into separate right and left chambers. Two major arteries, called aortas, lead to the systemic circulation. The detailed anatomy of the heart varies among these three groups of reptiles, with some adaptations allowing control of the relative amount of blood flowing to the lungs and the body.

In alligators, caimans, and other crocodilians, the ventricles are divided by a complete septum (not shown), but the pulmonary and systemic circuits connect where the arteries exit the heart. This connection enables arterial valves to shunt blood flow away from the lungs temporarily, such as when the animal is underwater.

In mammals and birds, there are two atria and two completely divided ventricles. The left side of the heart receives and pumps only oxygen-rich blood, while the right side receives and pumps only oxygen-poor blood. (In birds, the major vessels near the heart are slightly different than shown.) As endotherms, mammals and birds use about ten times as much energy as equal-sized ectotherms. Their circulatory systems therefore need to deliver about ten times as much fuel and O_2 to their tissues (and remove ten times as much CO_2 and other wastes). This large traffic of substances is made possible by separate and independently powered systemic and pulmonary circuits and by large hearts that pump the necessary volume of blood. A powerful four-chambered heart arose independently in the distinct ancestors of mammals and birds and thus reflects convergent evolution (see Chapter 34).

1. How is the flow of hemolymph through an open circulatory system similar to the flow of water through an outdoor fountain?

2. Three-chambered hearts with incomplete septa were once viewed as being less adapted to circulatory function than mammalian hearts. What advantage of such hearts did this viewpoint overlook?

3. **WHAT IF?** The heart of a normally developing human fetus has a hole between the left and right atria. In some cases, this hole does not close completely before birth. If the hole weren't surgically corrected, how would it affect the O_2 content of the blood entering the systemic circuit?

For suggested answers, see Appendix A.

CONCEPT 42.5

Gas exchange occurs across specialized respiratory surfaces

In the remainder of this chapter, we will focus on the process of **gas exchange**. Although this process is often called respiratory exchange or respiration, it should not be confused with the energy transformations of cellular respiration. Gas exchange is the uptake of molecular O_2 from the environment and the discharge of CO_2 to the environment.

Partial Pressure Gradients in Gas Exchange

To understand the driving forces for gas exchange, we must calculate **partial pressure**, which is simply the pressure exerted by a particular gas in a mixture of gases. To do so, we need to know the pressure that the mixture exerts and the fraction of the mixture represented by a particular gas. Let's consider O_2 as an example. At sea level, the atmosphere exerts a downward force equal to that of a column of mercury (Hg) 760 mm high. Therefore, atmospheric pressure at sea level is 760 mm Hg. Since the atmosphere is 21% O_2 by volume, the partial pressure of O_2 is 0.21×760, or about 160 mm Hg. This value is called the *partial pressure* of O_2 (abbreviated P_{O_2}) because it is the part of atmospheric pressure contributed by O_2. The partial pressure of CO_2 (abbreviated P_{CO_2}) is much less, only 0.29 mm Hg at sea level.

Partial pressures also apply to gases dissolved in a liquid, such as water. When water is exposed to air, an equilibrium is reached in which the partial pressure of each gas in the water equals the partial pressure of that gas in the air. Thus, water exposed to air at sea level has a P_{O_2} of 160 mm Hg, the same as in the atmosphere. However, the *concentrations* of O_2 in the air and water differ substantially because O_2 is much less soluble in water than in air.

Once we have calculated partial pressures, we can readily predict the net result of diffusion at gas exchange surfaces: A gas always diffuses from a region of higher partial pressure to a region of lower partial pressure.

Respiratory Media

The conditions for gas exchange vary considerably, depending on whether the respiratory medium—the source of O_2—is air or water. As already noted, O_2 is plentiful in air, making up about 21% of Earth's atmosphere by volume. Compared to water, air is much less dense and less viscous, so it is easier to move and to force through small passageways. As a result, breathing air is relatively easy and need not be particularly efficient. Humans, for example, extract only about 25% of the O_2 in inhaled air.

Gas exchange with water as the respiratory medium is much more demanding. The amount of O_2 dissolved in a given volume of water varies but is always less than in an equivalent volume of air: Water in many marine and freshwater habitats contains only 4–8 mL of dissolved O_2 per liter, a concentration roughly 40 times less than in air. The warmer and saltier the water is, the less dissolved O_2 it can hold. Water's lower O_2 content, greater density, and greater viscosity mean that aquatic animals such as fishes and lobsters must expend considerable energy to carry out gas exchange. In the context of these challenges, adaptations have evolved that enable most aquatic animals to be very efficient in gas exchange. Many of these adaptations involve the organization of the surfaces dedicated to exchange.

Respiratory Surfaces

Specialization for gas exchange is apparent in the structure of the respiratory surface, the part of an animal's body where gas exchange occurs. Like all living cells, the cells that carry out gas exchange have a plasma membrane that must be in contact with an aqueous solution. Respiratory surfaces are therefore always moist.

The movement of O_2 and CO_2 across moist respiratory surfaces takes place entirely by diffusion. The rate of diffusion is proportional to the surface area across which it occurs and inversely proportional to the square of the distance through which molecules must move. In other words, gas exchange is fast when the area for diffusion is large and the path for diffusion is short. As a result, respiratory surfaces tend to be large and thin.

In some relatively simple animals, such as sponges, cnidarians, and flatworms, every cell in the body is close enough to the external environment that gases can diffuse quickly between all cells and the environment. In many animals, however, the bulk of the body's cells lack immediate access to the environment. The respiratory surface in these animals is a thin, moist epithelium that constitutes a respiratory organ.

The skin serves as a respiratory organ in some animals, including earthworms and some amphibians. Just below the skin, a dense network of capillaries facilitates the exchange of gases between the circulatory system and the environment. Because the respiratory surface must remain moist, earthworms and many other skin-breathers can survive for extended periods only in damp places.

The general body surface of most animals lacks sufficient area to exchange gases for the whole organism. The evolutionary solution to this limitation is a respiratory organ that is extensively folded or branched, thereby enlarging the available surface area for gas exchange. Gills, tracheae, and lungs are three such organs.

Gills in Aquatic Animals

Gills are outfoldings of the body surface that are suspended in the water. As illustrated in **Figure 42.22**, the distribution of gills over the body can vary considerably. Regardless of their distribution, gills often have a total surface area much greater than that of the rest of the body's exterior.

Movement of the respiratory medium over the respiratory surface, a process called **ventilation**, maintains the partial pressure gradients of O_2 and CO_2 across the gill that

Parapodium (functions as gill)

(a) Marine worm. Many polychaetes (marine worms of the phylum Annelida) have a pair of flattened appendages called parapodia on each body segment. The parapodia serve as gills and also function in crawling and swimming.

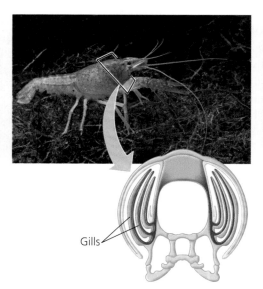

Gills

(b) Crayfish. Crayfish and other crustaceans have long, feathery gills covered by the exoskeleton. Specialized body appendages drive water over the gill surfaces.

Coelom

Gills

Tube foot

(c) Sea star. The gills of a sea star are simple tubular projections of the skin. The hollow core of each gill is an extension of the coelom (body cavity). Gas exchange occurs by diffusion across the gill surfaces, and fluid in the coelom circulates in and out of the gills, aiding gas transport. The surfaces of a sea star's tube feet also function in gas exchange.

▲ **Figure 42.22 Diversity in the structure of gills, external body surfaces that function in gas exchange.**

MAKE CONNECTIONS *As shown in Figure 32.11, animals with bilateral symmetry are divided into three main lineages. What are those lineages? How many are represented by the gilled animals shown above?*

are necessary for gas exchange. To promote ventilation, most gill-bearing animals either move their gills through the water or move water over their gills. For example, crayfish and lobsters have paddle-like appendages that drive a current of water over the gills, whereas mussels and clams move water with cilia. Octopuses and squids ventilate their gills by taking in and ejecting water, with the side benefit of locomotion by jet propulsion. Fishes use the motion of swimming or coordinated movements of the mouth and gill covers to ventilate their gills. In both cases, a current of water enters the mouth, passes through slits in the pharynx, flows over the gills, and then exits the body (Figure 42.23).

The arrangement of capillaries in a fish gill allows for **countercurrent exchange**, the exchange of a substance or heat between two fluids flowing in opposite directions. In a fish gill, this process maximizes gas exchange efficiency. Because blood flows in the direction opposite to that of water passing over the gills, at each point in its travel blood is less saturated with O_2 than the water it meets (see Figure 42.23). As blood enters a gill capillary, it encounters water that is completing its passage through the gill. Depleted of much of its dissolved O_2, this water nevertheless has a higher P_{O_2} than the incoming blood, and O_2 transfer takes place. As the blood continues its passage, its P_{O_2} steadily increases, but so does that of the water it encounters, since each successive position

in the blood's travel corresponds to an earlier position in the water's passage over the gills. Thus, a partial pressure gradient favoring the diffusion of O_2 from water to blood exists along the entire length of the capillary.

Countercurrent exchange mechanisms are remarkably efficient. In the fish gill, more than 80% of the O_2 dissolved in the water is removed as it passes over the respiratory surface. In other settings, countercurrent exchange contributes to temperature regulation (see Chapter 40) and to the functioning of the mammalian kidney, as we will see in Chapter 44.

Gills are generally unsuitable for an animal living on land. An expansive surface of wet membrane exposed directly to air currents in the environment would lose too much water by evaporation. Furthermore, the gills would collapse as their fine filaments, no longer supported by water, stuck together. In most terrestrial animals, respiratory surfaces are enclosed within the body, exposed to the atmosphere only through narrow tubes.

Tracheal Systems in Insects

Although the most familiar respiratory structure among terrestrial animals is the lung, the most common is actually the **tracheal system** of insects. Made up of air tubes that branch throughout the body, this system is one variation on the theme of an internal respiratory surface. The largest

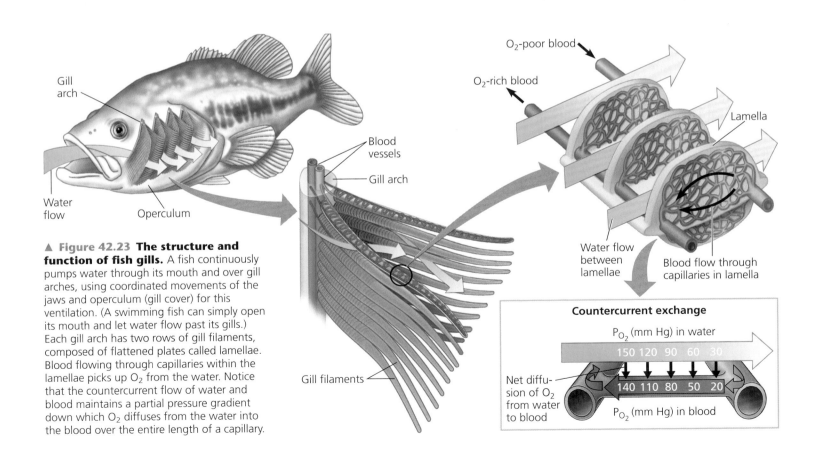

▲ **Figure 42.23 The structure and function of fish gills.** A fish continuously pumps water through its mouth and over gill arches, using coordinated movements of the jaws and operculum (gill cover) for this ventilation. (A swimming fish can simply open its mouth and let water flow past its gills.) Each gill arch has two rows of gill filaments, composed of flattened plates called lamellae. Blood flowing through capillaries within the lamellae picks up O_2 from the water. Notice that the countercurrent flow of water and blood maintains a partial pressure gradient down which O_2 diffuses from the water into the blood over the entire length of a capillary.

Gill arch

Water flow

Operculum

Blood vessels

Gill arch

Gill filaments

O_2-poor blood

O_2-rich blood

Lamella

Water flow between lamellae

Blood flow through capillaries in lamella

Countercurrent exchange

P_{O_2} (mm Hg) in water

150   120   90   60   30

Net diffusion of O_2 from water to blood

140   110   80   50   20

P_{O_2} (mm Hg) in blood

Tracheoles   Mitochondria   Muscle fiber

2.5 μm

(a) The respiratory system of an insect consists of branched internal tubes. The largest tubes, called tracheae, connect to external openings spaced along the insect's body surface. Air sacs formed from enlarged portions of the tracheae are found near organs that require a large supply of oxygen.

(b) Rings of chitin keep the tracheae open, allowing air to enter and pass into smaller tubes called tracheoles. The branched tracheoles deliver air directly to cells throughout the body. Tracheoles have closed ends filled with fluid (blue-gray). When the animal is active and using more O_2, most of the fluid is withdrawn into the body. This increases the surface area of air-filled tracheoles in contact with cells.

(c) The TEM above shows cross sections of tracheoles in a tiny piece of insect flight muscle. Each of the numerous mitochondria in the muscle cells lies within about 5 μm of a tracheole.

▲ **Figure 42.24 Tracheal systems.**

tubes, called tracheae, open to the outside **(Figure 42.24a)**. The finest branches extend close to the surface of nearly every cell, where gas is exchanged by diffusion across the moist epithelium that lines the tips of the tracheal branches **(Figure 42.24b)**. Because the tracheal system brings air within a very short distance of virtually every body cell in an insect, it can transport O_2 and CO_2 without the participation of the animal's open circulatory system.

For small insects, diffusion through the tracheae brings in enough O_2 and removes enough CO_2 to support cellular respiration. Larger insects meet their higher energy demands by ventilating their tracheal systems with rhythmic body movements that compress and expand the air tubes like bellows. For example, consider an insect in flight, which has a very high metabolic rate, consuming 10 to 200 times more O_2 than it does at rest. In many flying insects, alternating contraction and relaxation of the flight muscles pumps air rapidly through the tracheal system. The flight muscle cells are packed with mitochondria that support the high metabolic rate, and the tracheal tubes supply these ATP-generating organelles with ample O_2 **(Figure 42.24c)**. Thus, adaptations of tracheal systems are directly related to bioenergetics.

Lungs

Unlike tracheal systems, which branch throughout the insect body, **lungs** are localized respiratory organs. Representing an infolding of the body surface, they are typically subdivided into numerous pockets. Because the respiratory surface of a lung is not in direct contact with all other parts of the body, the gap must be bridged by the circulatory system, which transports gases between the lungs and the rest of the body. Lungs have evolved in organisms with open

circulatory systems, such as spiders and land snails, as well as in vertebrates.

Among vertebrates that lack gills, the use of lungs for gas exchange varies. Amphibian lungs, when present, are relatively small and lack an extensive surface for exchange. Amphibians instead rely heavily on diffusion across other body surfaces, such as the skin, to carry out gas exchange. In contrast, most reptiles (including all birds) and all mammals depend entirely on lungs for gas exchange. Turtles are an exception; they supplement lung breathing with gas exchange across moist epithelial surfaces continuous with their mouth or anus. Lungs and air breathing have evolved in a few aquatic vertebrates (including lungfishes) as adaptations to living in oxygen-poor water or to spending part of their time exposed to air (for instance, when the water level of a pond recedes).

Mammalian Respiratory Systems: A Closer Look

In mammals, a system of branching ducts conveys air to the lungs, which are located in the thoracic cavity **(Figure 42.25)**. Air enters through the nostrils and is then filtered by hairs, warmed, humidified, and sampled for odors as it flows through a maze of spaces in the nasal cavity. The nasal cavity leads to the pharynx, an intersection where the paths for air and food cross. When food is swallowed, the **larynx** (the upper part of the respiratory tract) moves upward and tips the epiglottis over the glottis (the opening of the **trachea**, or windpipe). This allows food to go down the esophagus to the stomach (see Figure 41.11). The rest of the time, the glottis is open, enabling breathing.

From the larynx, air passes into the trachea. Cartilage reinforcing the walls of both the larynx and the trachea keeps this part of the airway open. Within the larynx of most mammals,

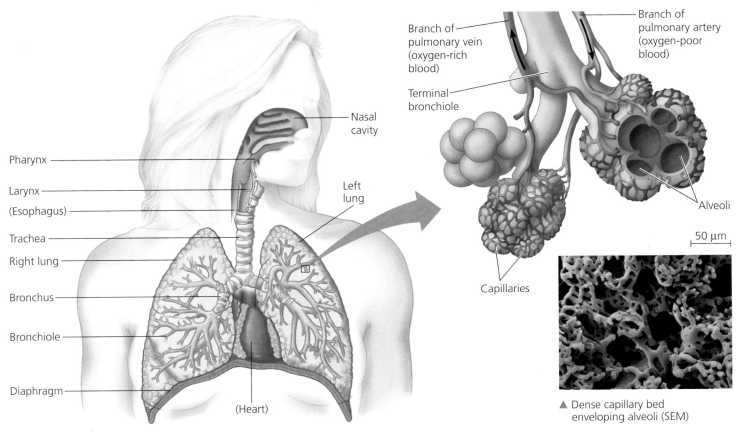

Pharynx

Larynx

(Esophagus)

Trachea

Right lung

Bronchus

Bronchiole

Diaphragm

(Heart)

Nasal cavity

Left lung

Branch of pulmonary vein (oxygen-rich blood)

Terminal bronchiole

Branch of pulmonary artery (oxygen-poor blood)

Alveoli

Capillaries

50 μm

▲ Dense capillary bed enveloping alveoli (SEM)

▲ **Figure 42.25 The mammalian respiratory system.** From the nasal cavity and pharynx, inhaled air passes through the larynx, trachea, and bronchi to the bronchioles, which end in microscopic alveoli lined by a thin, moist epithelium. Branches of the pulmonary arteries convey oxygen-poor blood to the alveoli; branches of the pulmonary veins transport oxygen-rich blood from the alveoli back to the heart.

exhaled air rushes by a pair of elastic bands of muscle called *vocal folds*, or, in humans, *vocal cords*. Sounds are produced when muscles in the larynx are tensed, stretching the cords so they vibrate. High-pitched sounds result from tightly stretched cords vibrating rapidly; low-pitched sounds come from less tense cords vibrating slowly.

The trachea branches into two **bronchi** (singular, *bronchus*), one leading to each lung. Within the lung, the bronchi branch repeatedly into finer and finer tubes called **bronchioles**. The entire system of air ducts has the appearance of an inverted tree, the trunk being the trachea. The epithelium lining the major branches of this respiratory tree is covered by cilia and a thin film of mucus. The mucus traps dust, pollen, and other particulate contaminants, and the beating cilia move the mucus upward to the pharynx, where it can be swallowed into the esophagus. This process, sometimes referred to as the "mucus escalator," plays a crucial role in cleansing the respiratory system.

Gas exchange in mammals occurs in **alveoli** (singular, *alveolus*; see Figure 42.25), air sacs clustered at the tips of the tiniest bronchioles. Human lungs contain millions of alveoli, which together have a surface area of about 100 m², 50 times

that of the skin. Oxygen in the air entering the alveoli dissolves in the moist film lining their inner surfaces and rapidly diffuses across the epithelium into a web of capillaries that surrounds each alveolus. Net diffusion of carbon dioxide occurs in the opposite direction, from the capillaries across the epithelium of the alveolus and into the air space.

Lacking cilia or significant air currents to remove particles from their surface, alveoli are highly susceptible to contamination. White blood cells patrol alveoli, engulfing foreign particles. However, if too much particulate matter reaches the alveoli, the defenses can be overwhelmed, leading to inflammation and irreversible damage. For example, particulates from cigarette smoke that enter alveoli can cause a permanent reduction in lung capacity. For coal miners, inhalation of large amounts of coal dust can lead to silicosis, a disabling, irreversible, and sometimes fatal lung disease.

The film of liquid that lines alveoli is subject to surface tension, an attractive force that acts to minimize the surface area of a liquid (see Chapter 3). Given their tiny diameter (about 0.25 mm), why don't alveoli collapse under high surface tension? Researchers reasoned that alveoli must be coated with a material that reduces surface tension. In 1955, English biophysicist Richard Pattle obtained experimental evidence for such a material, now called a **surfactant**, for *surf*ace-*active* agent. In addition, he proposed that the absence of surfactant might cause *respiratory distress syndrome (RDS)*, a disease common among preterm infants born 6 weeks or more before their due dates. In the 1950s, RDS killed 10,000 infants annually in the United States alone.

In the late 1950s, Mary Ellen Avery carried out the first experiment linking RDS to a surfactant deficiency **(Figure 42.26)**. Subsequent studies revealed that surfactant contains a mixture of phospholipids and proteins and typically appears in the lungs after 33 weeks of development. (The average full-term pregnancy lasts 38 weeks in humans.) Artificial surfactants are now used routinely to treat early preterm infants. Treated babies with a body mass over 900 g (2 pounds) at birth usually survive without long-term health problems. For her contributions, Avery received the National Medal of Science in 1991.

Having surveyed the route that air follows when we breathe, we will turn next to the process of breathing itself.

▼ **Figure 42.26**

INQUIRY

What causes respiratory distress syndrome?

EXPERIMENT Mary Ellen Avery, a research fellow working with Jere Mead at Harvard University Medical School, wondered whether a lack of surfactant caused respiratory distress syndrome (RDS) in preterm infants. She obtained autopsy samples of lungs from infants that had died of RDS and from infants that had died of other causes. She extracted material from the samples and allowed it to form a film on a water surface. Then Dr. Avery measured the tension (in dynes per centimeter) across the surface of the water and recorded the lowest surface tension observed for each sample.

RESULTS

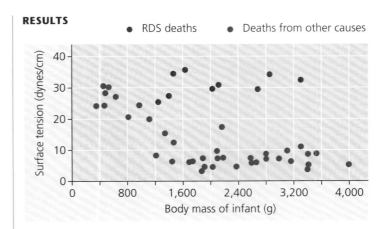

CONCLUSION The lungs of infants with a body mass over 1,200 g (2.7 pounds) contain a substance that reduces surface tension. That substance is absent in the lungs of infants with RDS.

SOURCE M. E. Avery and J. Mead, Surface properties in relation to atelectasis and hyaline membrane disease, *American Journal of Diseases of Children* 97:517–523 (1959).

WHAT IF? Suppose you repeated this experiment but instead measured the amount of surfactant in lung samples. Describe the graph you would expect if you plotted the amount of surfactant versus infant weight.

CONCEPT CHECK 42.5

1. Why is the position of lung tissues *within* the body an advantage for terrestrial animals?
2. After a heavy rain, earthworms come to the surface. How would you explain this behavior in terms of an earthworm's requirements for gas exchange?
3. **MAKE CONNECTIONS** Describe how countercurrent exchange can facilitate both thermoregulation (see Concept 40.3, p. 865) and respiration.

For suggested answers, see Appendix A.

SUMMARY OF KEY CONCEPTS

CONCEPT 42.1

Circulatory systems link exchange surfaces with cells throughout the body (pp. 897–902)

- In animals with simple body plans, gastrovascular cavities mediate exchange between the environment and cells that can be reached by diffusion. Because diffusion is slow over long distances, most complex animals have a circulatory system that moves fluid between cells and the organs that carry out exchange with the environment. Arthropods and most molluscs have an **open circulatory system**, in which **hemolymph** bathes organs directly. Vertebrates have a **closed circulatory system**, in which **blood** circulates in a closed network of pumps and vessels.

- The closed circulatory system of vertebrates consists of blood, **blood vessels**, and a two- to four-chambered **heart**. Blood pumped by a heart **ventricle** passes to **arteries** and then to **capillaries**, the sites of chemical exchange between blood and interstitial fluid. **Veins** return blood from capillaries to an **atrium**, which passes blood to a ventricle. Fishes, rays, and sharks have a single pump in their circulation. Air-breathing vertebrates have two pumps combined in a single heart. Variations in ventricle number and separation reflect adaptations to different environments and metabolic needs.

> **?** *How does the flow of a fluid in a closed circulatory system differ from the movement of molecules between cells and their environment with regard to distance traveled, direction traveled, and driving force?*

Gas exchange occurs across specialized respiratory surfaces (pp. 915–920)

- At all sites of **gas exchange**, a gas diffuses from where its **partial pressure** is higher to where it is lower. Air is more conducive to gas exchange than water because air has a higher O_2 content, lower density, and lower viscosity. Regardless of whether the respiratory medium is air or water, adequate diffusion of O_2 and CO_2 between the medium and an animal's cells requires large, moist respiratory surfaces.
- The structure and organization of respiratory surfaces differ among animal species. Gills are outfoldings of the body surface specialized for gas exchange in water. The effectiveness of gas exchange in some gills, including those of fishes, is increased by **ventilation** and **countercurrent exchange** between blood and water. Gas exchange in insects relies on a **tracheal system** consisting of tiny, branching tubes that penetrate the body, bringing O_2 directly to cells. Spiders, land snails, and most terrestrial vertebrates have internal **lungs**. In mammals, air inhaled through the nostrils passes through the pharynx into the **trachea, bronchi, bronchioles**, and dead-end **alveoli**, where gas exchange occurs.

? *Why does altitude have almost no effect on an animal's ability to rid itself of CO_2 through gas exchange?*

LEVEL 1: KNOWLEDGE/COMPREHENSION

1. Which of the following respiratory systems is not closely associated with a blood supply?
   a. the lungs of a vertebrate
   b. the gills of a fish
   c. the tracheal system of an insect
   d. the skin of an earthworm
   e. the parapodia of a polychaete worm

2. Blood returning to the mammalian heart in a pulmonary vein drains first into the
   a. vena cava.
   b. left atrium.
   c. right atrium.
   d. left ventricle.
   e. right ventricle.

3. Pulse is a direct measure of
   a. blood pressure.
   b. stroke volume.
   c. cardiac output.
   d. heart rate.
   e. breathing rate.

4. When you hold your breath, which of the following blood gas changes first leads to the urge to breathe?
   a. rising O_2
   b. falling O_2
   c. rising CO_2
   d. falling CO_2
   e. rising CO_2 and falling O_2

5. One feature that amphibians and humans have in common is
   a. the number of heart chambers.
   b. the type of gas exchange tissues.
   c. a complete separation of circuits for circulation.
   d. the number of circuits for circulation.
   e. a low blood pressure in the systemic circuit.

LEVEL 2: APPLICATION/ANALYSIS

6. If a molecule of CO_2 released into the blood in your left toe is exhaled from your nose, it must pass through all of the following except
   a. the pulmonary vein.
   b. an alveolus.
   c. the trachea.
   d. the right atrium.
   e. the right ventricle.

7. Compared with the interstitial fluid that bathes active muscle cells, blood reaching these cells in arteries has a
   a. higher P_{O_2}.
   b. higher P_{CO_2}.
   c. greater bicarbonate concentration.
   d. lower pH.
   e. lower osmotic pressure.

8. Which of the following reactions prevails in red blood cells traveling through alveolar capillaries? (Hb = hemoglobin)
   a. $Hb + 4 O_2 \rightarrow Hb(O_2)_4$
   b. $Hb(O_2)_4 \rightarrow Hb + 4 O_2$
   c. $CO_2 + H_2O \rightarrow H_2CO_3$
   d. $H_2CO_3 \rightarrow H^+ + HCO_3^-$
   e. $Hb + 4 CO_2 \rightarrow Hb(CO_2)_4$

LEVEL 3: SYNTHESIS/EVALUATION

9. **DRAW IT** Plot blood pressure against time for one cardiac cycle in humans, drawing separate lines for the pressure in the aorta, the left ventricle, and the right ventricle. Below the time axis, add a vertical arrow pointing to the time when you expect a peak in atrial blood pressure.

10. **EVOLUTION CONNECTION**
    One of the many mutant opponents that the movie monster Godzilla contends with is Mothra, a giant mothlike creature with a wingspan of several dozen meters. Science fiction creatures like these can be critiqued on the grounds of biomechanical and physiological principles. What problems of respiration and gas exchange would Mothra face? The largest insects that have ever lived are Paleozoic dragonflies with half-meter wingspans. Why do you think truly giant insects are improbable?

11. **SCIENTIFIC INQUIRY**
    The hemoglobin of a human fetus differs from adult hemoglobin. Compare the dissociation curves of the two hemoglobins in the graph at right. Propose a hypothesis to explain the benefit of this difference between these two hemoglobins.

12. **SCIENCE, TECHNOLOGY, AND SOCIETY**
    Hundreds of studies have linked smoking with cardiovascular and lung disease. According to most health authorities, smoking is the leading cause of preventable, premature death in the United States. Antismoking groups have proposed that cigarette advertising in all media be banned entirely. What are some arguments in favor of a total ban on cigarette advertising? What are arguments in opposition? Do you favor or oppose such a ban? Defend your position.

13. **WRITE ABOUT A THEME**
    Environmental Interactions Some athletes prepare for competition at sea level by sleeping in a tent in which P_{O_2} is kept artificially low. When climbing very high peaks, some mountaineers breathe from bottles of pure O_2. In a short essay (100–150 words), relate these behaviors to the mechanism of O_2 transport in the human body and to our physiological interactions with our gaseous environment.

For selected answers, see Appendix A.

 www.masteringbiology.com

1. MasteringBiology® Assignments
  BioFlix **Tutorial** Gas Exchange
  Tutorial Gas Transport in Blood
  Activities Mammalian Cardiovascular System Structure • The Human Heart • Path of Blood Flow in Mammals • Mammalian Cardiovascular System Function • Discovery Channel Video: Blood • The Human Respiratory System • Gas Exchange in the Lungs and Tissues • Transport of Respiratory Gases
  Questions Student Misconceptions • Reading Quiz • Multiple Choice • End-of-Chapter

2. eText
Read your book online, search, take notes, highlight text, and more.

3. The Study Area
Practice Tests • Cumulative Test • *BioFlix* 3-D Animations • MP3 Tutor Sessions • Videos • Activities • Investigations • Lab Media • Audio Glossary • Word Study Tools • Art

UNIVERSITY OF ALBERTA FACULTY BIO

Greg Goss BSc Biology (McMaster University); PhD. Biology (University of Ottawa)

Current Position: Professor, Department of Biological Sciences

My teaching includes Zoology 344 (Laboratory Exercises in Animal Physiology), Zoology 340 (Environmental Physiology), Biology 445/545 (Seminars in Cell Physiology) and Zoology 441/541 (Homeostasis).

My research group interests are in the twin areas of molecular animal physiology and toxicology. In the area of animal physiology, I investigate the mechanisms of ion and acid base regulation in fishes and other animals including mosquitoes and crustaceans. Currently I have students and a post-doctoral researcher working in this area on a number of projects. A significant part of this research in comparative physiology takes place at Bamfield Marine Sciences Centre.

In the area of toxicology, I have a very large research program investigating the impact of a variety of toxicants on fishes. My research program in this area focuses on the effects of municipal wastewater on fish, oil-sands affected water and even the potential impacts of new nanomaterials and other microcontaminants. We use a variety of tests such as molecular and biochemical biomarker analysis, proteomic analysis, or whole animals studies to inform the public, government regulators and industry about these environmental risks.

44

Osmoregulation and Excretion

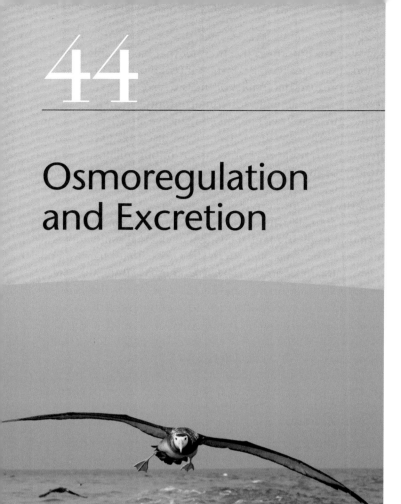

▲ **Figure 44.1 How does an albatross drink salt water without ill effect?**

OVERVIEW

A Balancing Act

With a wingspan that can reach 3.5 m, the largest of any living bird, a wandering albatross (*Diomedea exulans*) soaring over the ocean is hard to miss (Figure 44.1). Yet the albatross commands attention for more than just its size. This massive bird remains at sea day and night throughout the year, returning to land only to reproduce. A human with only seawater to drink would die of dehydration, but faced with the same conditions, the albatross thrives.

For both albatross and human, maintaining the fluid environment of their cells, tissues, and organs requires keeping relative concentrations of water and solutes within fairly narrow limits. In addition, ions such as sodium and calcium must be maintained at concentrations that permit normal activity of muscles, neurons, and other body cells. Homeostasis thus requires **osmoregulation**, the general term for the processes by which animals control solute concentrations and balance water gain and loss.

A number of strategies for water and solute control have arisen during evolution, reflecting the varied and often severe osmoregulatory challenges presented by an animal's surroundings. The arid environment of a desert, for instance, can quickly deplete an animal of body water. Despite a quite different environment, albatrosses and other marine animals also face potential dehydration. The success of animals in an ocean environment depends critically on conserving water and, for marine birds and fishes, eliminating excess salts. In contrast, freshwater animals live in an environment that threatens to flood and dilute their body fluids. These organisms survive by conserving solutes and absorbing salts from their surroundings.

In safeguarding their internal fluid environment, animals must also deal with a hazardous metabolite produced by the dismantling of proteins and nucleic acids. Breakdown of *nitrogenous* (nitrogen-containing) molecules releases ammonia, a very toxic compound. Several different mechanisms have evolved for **excretion**, the process that rids the body of nitrogenous metabolites and other metabolic waste products. Because systems for excretion and osmoregulation are structurally and functionally linked in many animals, we will consider both of these processes in this chapter.

CONCEPT 44.1

Osmoregulation balances the uptake and loss of water and solutes

Just as thermoregulation depends on balancing heat loss and gain (see Chapter 40), regulating the chemical composition of body fluids depends on balancing the uptake and loss of water and solutes. This process of osmoregulation is based largely on the controlled movement of solutes between internal fluids and the external environment. Because solute movement results in the movement of water by osmosis, the net effect is to regulate both solutes and water.

Osmosis and Osmolarity

All animals—regardless of habitat or type of waste produced—face the same need to balance water uptake and loss. If water

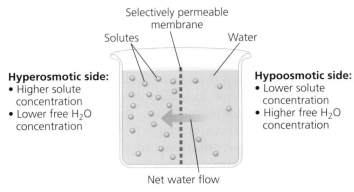

Selectively permeable
membrane
Solutes   Water

Hyperosmotic side:
• Higher solute
  concentration
• Lower free H$_2$O
  concentration

Hypoosmotic side:
• Lower solute
  concentration
• Higher free H$_2$O
  concentration

Net water flow

▲ **Figure 44.2 Solute concentration and osmosis.**

MAKE CONNECTIONS *Review types of membrane proteins and their functions in Concepts 7.1 and 7.2 (pp. 129–132). Which membrane proteins allow water, but not solutes, to diffuse across a lipid bilayer?*

uptake is excessive, animal cells swell and burst; if water loss is substantial, they shrivel and die (see Figure 7.15).

Water enters and leaves cells by osmosis. Recall from Chapter 7 that osmosis, a special case of diffusion, is the movement of water across a selectively permeable membrane. It occurs whenever two solutions separated by the membrane differ in osmotic pressure, or **osmolarity** (total solute concentration expressed as molarity, that is, moles of solute per liter of solution). The unit of measurement for osmolarity used in this chapter is milliOsmoles per liter (mOsm/L). Seawater has an osmolarity of about 1,000 mOsm/L (equivalent to a total solute concentration of 1 *M*), while the osmolarity of human blood is about 300 mOsm/L.

If two solutions separated by a selectively permeable membrane have the same osmolarity, they are said to be *isoosmotic*. Water molecules continually cross the membrane, but under these conditions they do so at equal rates in both directions. Thus, there is no *net* movement of water by osmosis between isoosmotic solutions. When two solutions differ in osmolarity, the one with the greater concentration of solutes is said to be *hyperosmotic*, and the more dilute solution is said to be *hypoosmotic* (**Figure 44.2**). Water flows by osmosis from a hypoosmotic solution to a hyperosmotic one.*

Osmotic Challenges

Given the chemical principles that govern osmotic flow, an animal can maintain water balance in two ways. One is to be an **osmoconformer**: to be isoosmotic with its surroundings. The second is to be an **osmoregulator**: to control internal osmolarity independent of that of its environment.

All osmoconformers are marine animals. Because an osmoconformer's internal osmolarity is the same as that of its environment, there is no tendency to gain or lose water.

---

*In this chapter, we use the terms *isoosmotic*, *hypoosmotic*, and *hyperosmotic*, which refer specifically to osmolarity, instead of *isotonic*, *hypotonic*, and *hypertonic*. The latter set of terms applies to the response of animal cells—whether they swell or shrink—in solutions of known solute concentrations.

Many osmoconformers live in water that has a stable composition and hence have a constant internal osmolarity.

Osmoregulation enables animals to live in environments that are uninhabitable for osmoconformers, such as freshwater and terrestrial habitats. To survive in a hypoosmotic environment, an osmoregulator must discharge excess water. In a hyperosmotic environment, an osmoregulator must instead take in water to offset osmotic loss. Osmoregulation also allows many marine animals to maintain an internal osmolarity different from that of seawater.

Most animals, whether osmoconformers or osmoregulators, cannot tolerate substantial changes in external osmolarity and are said to be *stenohaline* (from the Greek *stenos*, narrow, and *halos*, salt). In contrast, *euryhaline* animals (from the Greek *eurys*, broad) can survive large fluctuations in external osmolarity. Euryhaline osmoconformers include many barnacles and mussels, which are continually covered and uncovered by ocean tides; examples of euryhaline osmoregulators are the striped bass and the various species of salmon.

Next we'll examine some adaptations for osmoregulation that have evolved in marine, freshwater, and terrestrial animals.

Marine Animals

Most marine invertebrates are osmoconformers. Their osmolarity is the same as that of seawater. They therefore face no substantial challenges in water balance. However, because these animals differ considerably from seawater in the concentrations of *specific* solutes, they must actively transport these solutes to maintain homeostasis. For example, although the concentration of magnesium ions (Mg^{2+}) in seawater is 50 m*M* (millimolar, or 10^{-3} mol/L), homeostatic mechanisms in the Atlantic lobster (*Homarus americanus*) result in a Mg^{2+} concentration of less than 9 m*M* in this animal's hemolymph (circulatory fluid).

Many marine vertebrates and some marine invertebrates are osmoregulators. For most of these animals, the ocean is a strongly dehydrating environment. For example, marine fishes, such as the cod in **Figure 44.3a**, constantly lose water by osmosis. Such fishes balance the water loss by drinking large amounts of seawater. In ridding themselves of salts, they make use of both their gills and kidneys. In the gills, specialized *chloride cells* actively transport chloride ions (Cl$^-$) out and allow sodium ions (Na$^+$) to follow passively. In the kidneys, excess calcium, magnesium, and sulfate ions are excreted with the loss of only small amounts of water.

A distinct osmoregulatory strategy evolved in marine sharks and most other chondrichthyans (cartilaginous animals; see Chapter 34). Like "bony fishes" (as we'll refer collectively to ray-finned and lobe-finned fishes in this chapter), sharks have an internal salt concentration much lower than that of seawater. Thus, salt tends to diffuse into their bodies from the water, especially across their gills. Unlike bony fishes, however, marine sharks are not hypoosmotic to seawater. The explanation

(a) Osmoregulation in a marine fish

Gain of water and salt ions from food

Excretion of salt ions from gills

Osmotic water **loss** through gills and other parts of body surface

Gain of water and salt ions from drinking seawater

Excretion of salt ions and small amounts of water in scanty urine from kidneys

SALT WATER

(b) Osmoregulation in a freshwater fish

Gain of water and some ions in food

Uptake of salt ions by gills

Osmotic water **gain** through gills and other parts of body surface

FRESH WATER

Excretion of salt ions and large amounts of water in dilute urine from kidneys

Key

⇨ Water
➡ Salt

▲ **Figure 44.3 Osmoregulation in marine and freshwater bony fishes: a comparison.**

is that shark tissue contains high concentrations of urea, a nitrogenous waste product of protein and nucleic acid metabolism (see Figure 44.8). A shark's body fluids also contain trimethylamine oxide (TMAO), an organic molecule that protects proteins from damage by urea. Together, the salts, urea, TMAO, and other compounds maintained in the body fluids of sharks result in an osmolarity very close to that of seawater. For this reason, sharks are often considered osmoconformers. However, because the solute concentration in their body fluids is actually somewhat higher than 1,000 mOsm/L, water slowly *enters* the shark's body by osmosis and in food (sharks do not drink). This small influx of water is disposed of in urine produced by the shark's kidneys. The urine also removes some of the salt that diffuses into the shark's body; the rest is lost in feces or is secreted from a specialized gland.

Freshwater Animals

The osmoregulatory problems of freshwater animals are the opposite of those of marine animals. The body fluids of freshwater animals must be hyperosmotic because animal cells cannot tolerate salt concentrations as low as that of lake or river water. Having internal fluids with an osmolarity higher than that of their surroundings, freshwater animals face the problem of gaining water by osmosis and losing salts by diffusion. Many freshwater animals, including bony fishes, solve the problem of water balance by drinking almost no water and excreting large amounts of very dilute urine. At the same time, salts lost by diffusion and in the urine are replenished by eating. Freshwater fishes, such as the perch in **Figure 44.3b**, also replenish salts by uptake across the gills. Chloride cells in the gills of the fish actively transport Cl^- into the body, and Na^+ follows.

Salmon and other euryhaline fishes that migrate between fresh water and seawater undergo dramatic changes in osmoregulatory status **(Figure 44.4)**. When living in rivers and streams, salmon osmoregulate like other freshwater fishes,

▲ **Figure 44.4 Sockeye salmon (*Oncorhynchus nerka*), euryhaline osmoregulators.**

producing large amounts of dilute urine and taking up salt from the dilute environment through their gills. When they migrate to the ocean, salmon acclimatize. They produce more of the steroid hormone cortisol, which increases the number and size of salt-secreting chloride cells. As a result of these and other physiological changes, salmon in salt water excrete excess salt from their gills and produce only small amounts of urine—just like bony fishes that spend their entire lives in salt water.

Animals That Live in Temporary Waters

Extreme dehydration, or *desiccation*, is fatal for most animals. However, a few aquatic invertebrates that live in temporary ponds and in films of water around soil particles can lose almost all their body water and survive. These animals enter a dormant state when their habitats dry up, an adaptation called **anhydrobiosis** ("life without water"). Among the

50 μm

(a) Hydrated tardigrade

50 μm

(b) Dehydrated tardigrade

▲ **Figure 44.5 Anhydrobiosis.** SEM images of tardigrades (water bears), which inhabit temporary ponds as well as droplets of water in soil and on moist plants.

most striking examples are the tardigrades, or water bears **(Figure 44.5).** Less than 1 mm long, these tiny invertebrates are found in marine, freshwater, and moist terrestrial environments. In their active, hydrated state, they contain about 85% water by weight, but they can dehydrate to less than 2% water and survive in an inactive state, dry as dust, for a decade or more. Just add water, and within hours the rehydrated tardigrades are moving about and feeding.

Anhydrobiosis requires adaptations that keep cell membranes intact. Researchers are just beginning to learn how tardigrades survive drying out, but studies of anhydrobiotic roundworms (phylum Nematoda; see Chapter 33) show that desiccated individuals contain large amounts of sugars. In particular, a disaccharide called trehalose seems to protect the cells by replacing the water that is normally associated with proteins and membrane lipids. Many insects that survive freezing in the winter also use trehalose as a membrane protectant, as do some plants resistant to desiccation.

Land Animals

The threat of dehydration is a major regulatory problem for terrestrial plants and animals. Humans, for example, die if they lose as little as 12% of their body water (desert camels can withstand approximately twice that level of dehydration). Adaptations that reduce water loss are key to survival on land. Much as a waxy cuticle contributes to the success of land plants, the body coverings of most terrestrial animals help prevent dehydration. Examples are the waxy layers of insect exoskeletons, the shells of land snails, and the layers of dead, keratinized skin cells covering most terrestrial vertebrates, including humans. Many terrestrial animals, especially desert-dwellers, are nocturnal, which reduces evaporative water loss because of the lower temperature and higher humidity of night air.

Despite these and other adaptations, most terrestrial animals lose water through many routes: in urine and feces, across their skin, and from the surfaces of gas exchange organs. Land animals maintain water balance by drinking and

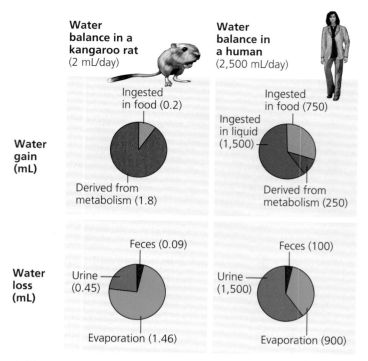

▲ **Figure 44.6 Water balance in two terrestrial mammals.** Kangaroo rats, which live in the American Southwest, eat mostly dry seeds and do not drink water. A kangaroo rat gains water mainly from cellular metabolism and loses water mainly by evaporation during gas exchange. In contrast, a human gains water in food and drink and loses the largest fraction of it in urine.

eating moist foods and by producing water metabolically through cellular respiration. A number of desert animals, including many insect-eating birds and other reptiles, are well enough adapted for minimizing water loss that they can survive for long periods of time without drinking. A noteworthy example is the kangaroo rat: It typically loses so little water that 90% is replaced by water it generates metabolically **(Figure 44.6);** the remaining 10% comes from the small amount of water in its diet of seeds. During particularly hot periods, kangaroo rats supplement their diet with juicy insects, thereby maintaining their water balance.

Energetics of Osmoregulation

Maintaining an osmolarity difference between an animal's body and its external environment carries an energy cost. Because diffusion tends to equalize concentrations in a system, osmoregulators must expend energy to maintain the osmotic gradients that cause water to move in or out. They do so by using active transport to manipulate solute concentrations in their body fluids.

The energy cost of osmoregulation depends on how different an animal's osmolarity is from its surroundings, how easily water and solutes can move across the animal's surface, and how much work is required to pump solutes across the membrane. Osmoregulation accounts for 5% or more of the resting metabolic rate of many freshwater and marine bony fishes. For brine shrimp, small crustaceans that live in extremely salty lakes, the gradient between internal and external osmolarity is very large, and the cost of osmoregulation is correspondingly high—as much as 30% of the resting metabolic rate.

The energy cost to an animal of maintaining water and salt balance is minimized by having body fluids that are adapted to the salinity of the animal's habitat. Thus, the body fluids of most animals that live in fresh water (which has an osmolarity of 0.5–15 mOsm/L) have lower solute concentrations than the body fluids of their closest relatives that live in seawater (1,000 mOsm/L). For instance, whereas marine molluscs have body fluids with solute concentrations of approximately 1,000 mOsm/L, some freshwater molluscs maintain the osmolarity of their body fluids at just 40 mOsm/L. In each case, minimizing the osmotic difference between body fluids and the surrounding environment decreases the energy the animal expends for osmoregulation.

Transport Epithelia in Osmoregulation

The ultimate function of osmoregulation is to control solute concentrations in cells, but most animals do this indirectly by managing the solute content of an internal body fluid that bathes the cells. In insects and other animals with an open circulatory system, the fluid surrounding cells is hemolymph. In vertebrates and other animals with a closed circulatory system, the cells are bathed in an interstitial fluid that contains a mixture of solutes controlled indirectly by the blood. Maintaining the composition of such fluids depends on structures ranging from individual cells that regulate solute movement to complex organs such as the vertebrate kidney.

In most animals, osmoregulation and metabolic waste disposal rely on **transport epithelia**—one or more layers of epithelial cells specialized for moving particular solutes in controlled amounts in specific directions. Transport epithelia are typically arranged into complex tubular networks with extensive surface areas. Some transport epithelia face the outside environment directly, while others line channels connected to the outside by an opening on the body surface.

The transport epithelium that enables the albatross to survive on seawater remained undiscovered for many years. Some scientists suggested that marine birds do not actually drink water, asserting that although the birds take water into their mouths, they do not swallow. Questioning this idea, Knut Schmidt-Nielsen and colleagues at the Mount Desert Island Laboratory, in Maine, gave captive marine birds only seawater to drink. The researchers found that while very little salt appeared in the birds' urine, fluid dripping from the tip of their beaks was a concentrated solution of salt (NaCl). Where did this fluid come from? As Schmidt-Nielsen demonstrated, the salt solution was produced by a pair of structures called the nasal glands. Similar structures, called salt glands, eliminate excess salt from the bodies of sea turtles and marine iguanas.

As shown in **Figure 44.7**, the nasal gland removes excess NaCl (in the form of Na^+ and Cl^-) from the blood

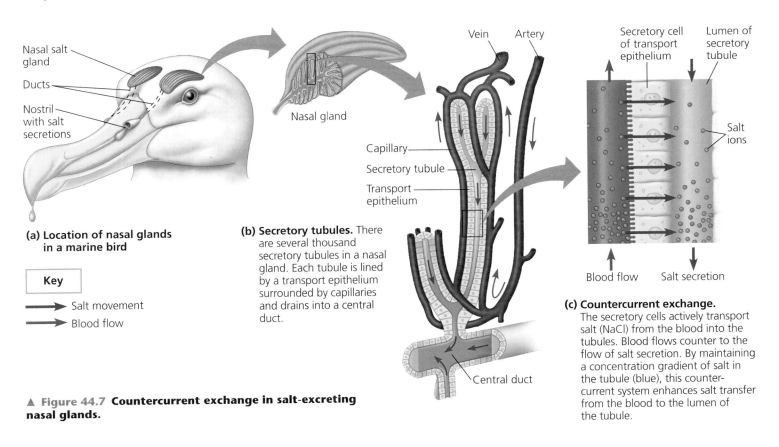

(a) **Location of nasal glands in a marine bird**

Key

→ Salt movement
→ Blood flow

(b) **Secretory tubules.** There are several thousand secretory tubules in a nasal gland. Each tubule is lined by a transport epithelium surrounded by capillaries and drains into a central duct.

(c) **Countercurrent exchange.** The secretory cells actively transport salt (NaCl) from the blood into the tubules. Blood flows counter to the flow of salt secretion. By maintaining a concentration gradient of salt in the tubule (blue), this countercurrent system enhances salt transfer from the blood to the lumen of the tubule.

▲ **Figure 44.7 Countercurrent exchange in salt-excreting nasal glands.**

by countercurrent exchange. Recall from Chapter 40 that countercurrent exchange occurs between two fluids separated by one or more membranes and flowing in opposite directions. In the albatross's nasal gland, the net result is the secretion of fluid much saltier than the ocean. Thus, even though drinking seawater brings in a lot of salt, the bird achieves a net gain of water. By contrast, humans who drink a given volume of seawater must use a *greater* volume of water to excrete the salt load, with the result that they become dehydrated.

Transport epithelia that function in maintaining water balance also often function in disposal of metabolic wastes. We will see examples of this coordinated function in our upcoming consideration of earthworm and insect excretory systems as well as the vertebrate kidney.

CONCEPT CHECK 44.1

1. The movement of salt from the surrounding water to the blood of a freshwater fish requires the expenditure of energy in the form of ATP. Why?
2. Why aren't any freshwater animals osmoconformers?
3. **WHAT IF?** Researchers found that a camel standing in the sun required much more water when its fur was shaved off, although its body temperature remained the same. What can you conclude about the relationship between osmoregulation and the insulation provided by fur?

For suggested answers, see Appendix A.

CONCEPT 44.2

An animal's nitrogenous wastes reflect its phylogeny and habitat

Because most metabolic wastes must be dissolved in water to be excreted from the body, the type and quantity of an animal's waste products may have a large impact on its water balance. In this regard, some of the most significant waste products are the nitrogenous breakdown products of proteins and nucleic acids **(Figure 44.8)**. When proteins and nucleic acids are broken apart for energy or converted to carbohydrates or fats, enzymes remove nitrogen in the form of **ammonia** (NH_3). Ammonia is very toxic, in part because its ion, ammonium (NH_4^+), interferes with oxidative phosphorylation. Although some animals excrete ammonia directly, many species expend energy to convert it to less toxic compounds prior to excretion.

Forms of Nitrogenous Waste

Animals excrete nitrogenous wastes as ammonia, urea, or uric acid. These different forms vary significantly in their toxicity and the energy costs of producing them.

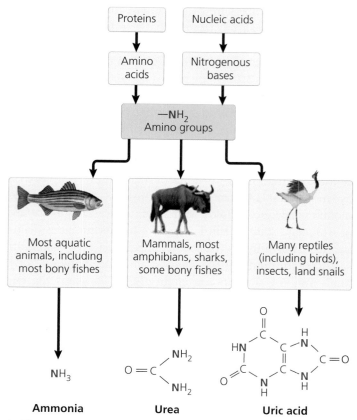

▲ Figure 44.8 **Forms of nitrogenous waste.**

Ammonia

Because ammonia can be tolerated only at very low concentrations, animals that excrete nitrogenous wastes as ammonia need access to lots of water. Therefore, ammonia excretion is most common in aquatic species. Being highly soluble, ammonia molecules easily pass through membranes and are readily lost by diffusion to the surrounding water. In many invertebrates, ammonia release occurs across the whole body surface. In fishes, most of the ammonia is lost as NH_4^+ across the epithelium of the gills; the kidneys excrete only minor amounts of nitrogenous waste.

Urea

Although ammonia excretion works well in many aquatic species, it is much less suitable for land animals. Ammonia is so toxic that it can be transported and excreted only in large volumes of very dilute solutions. As a result, most terrestrial animals and many marine species (principally those that tend to lose water to their environment by osmosis) simply do not have access to sufficient water to routinely excrete ammonia. Instead, mammals, most adult amphibians, sharks, and some marine bony fishes and turtles mainly excrete a different nitrogenous waste, **urea**. Produced in the vertebrate liver, urea is the product of a metabolic cycle that combines ammonia with carbon dioxide.

The main advantage of urea is its very low toxicity. Animals can transport urea in the circulatory system and store it safely at high concentrations. Furthermore, much less water is lost when a given quantity of nitrogen is excreted in a concentrated solution of urea rather than a dilute solution of ammonia.

The main disadvantage of urea is its energy cost: Animals must expend energy to produce urea from ammonia. From a bioenergetic standpoint, we would predict that animals that spend part of their lives in water and part on land would switch between excreting ammonia (thereby saving energy) and excreting urea (reducing excretory water loss). Indeed, many amphibians excrete mainly ammonia when they are aquatic tadpoles and switch largely to urea excretion when they become land-dwelling adults.

Uric Acid

Insects, land snails, and many reptiles, including birds, excrete **uric acid** as their primary nitrogenous waste. (Bird droppings, or *guano*, are a mixture of white uric acid and brown feces.) Uric acid is relatively nontoxic and does not readily dissolve in water. It therefore can be excreted as a semisolid paste with very little water loss. This is a great advantage for animals with little access to water, but there is a cost: Uric acid is even more energetically expensive to produce than urea, requiring considerable ATP for synthesis from ammonia.

Because uric acid releases nitrates to soil, bird guano can be used as fertilizer in agriculture. Before synthetic fertilizers were developed, this "waste" was so valued that nations fought wars over South American islands covered with piles of seabird guano as tall as 12-story buildings! Recently, interest in organic fertilizers has revived the commercial trade in guano (**Figure 44.9**).

While not primarily uric acid producers, humans and some other animals generate a small amount of uric acid as a product of purine breakdown. Diseases that alter this process reflect the problems that can arise when a metabolic product is

insoluble. For example, a genetic defect in purine metabolism predisposes Dalmatian dogs to form uric acid stones in their bladder. In humans, adult males are particularly susceptible to *gout*, a painful joint inflammation caused by deposits of uric acid crystals. Meals containing purine-rich animal tissues can increase the inflammation. Some dinosaurs appear to have been similarly affected: Fossilized bones of *Tyrannosaurus rex* exhibit joint damage characteristic of gout.

The Influence of Evolution and Environment on Nitrogenous Wastes

EVOLUTION In general, the kind of nitrogenous wastes an animal excretes depends on both the species' evolutionary history (phylogeny) and its habitat, especially the availability of water. For example, terrestrial turtles (which often live in dry areas) excrete mainly uric acid, whereas aquatic turtles excrete both urea and ammonia. Another factor affecting the primary type of nitrogenous waste produced by a particular group of animals is the immediate environment of the animal egg. For example, soluble wastes can diffuse out of a shell-less amphibian egg or be carried away from a mammalian embryo by the mother's blood. However, the shelled eggs produced by birds and other reptiles (see Figure 34.25) are permeable to gases but not to liquids, which means that soluble nitrogenous wastes released by an embryo would be trapped within the egg and could accumulate to dangerous levels. (Although urea is much less harmful than ammonia, it is toxic at very high concentrations.) Using uric acid as a waste product conveys a selective advantage because it precipitates out of solution and can be stored within the egg as a harmless solid left behind when the animal hatches.

Regardless of the type of nitrogenous waste, the amount produced is coupled to the animal's energy budget. Endotherms, which use energy at high rates, eat more food and produce more nitrogenous waste than ectotherms. The amount of nitrogenous waste is also linked to diet. Predators, which derive much of their energy from protein, excrete more nitrogen than animals that rely mainly on lipids or carbohydrates as energy sources.

Having surveyed the forms of nitrogenous waste and their interrelationship with evolutionary lineage, habitat, and energy consumption, we will turn next to the processes and systems animals use to excrete these and other wastes.

▼ **Figure 44.9 Recycling nitrogenous waste.** Seabirds nesting on islands off Peru annually produce 12,000 tons of guano, which workers collect for sale as organic fertilizer.

CONCEPT CHECK 44.2

1. What advantage does uric acid offer as a nitrogenous waste in arid environments?
2. **WHAT IF?** Suppose a bird and a human both have gout. Why might reducing purine in their diets help the human much more than the bird?

For suggested answers, see Appendix A.

CONCEPT 44.3

Diverse excretory systems are variations on a tubular theme

Whether an animal lives on land, in salt water, or in fresh water, water balance depends on the regulation of solute movement between internal fluids and the external environment. Much of this movement is handled by excretory systems. These systems are central to homeostasis because they dispose of metabolic wastes and control body fluid composition. Before we describe particular excretory systems, let's consider a generalized version of the process of excretion.

Excretory Processes

Animals across a wide range of species produce a fluid waste called urine through the basic steps shown in **Figure 44.10**. In the first step, body fluid (blood, coelomic fluid, or hemolymph) is brought in contact with the selectively permeable membrane of a transport epithelium. In most cases, hydrostatic pressure (blood pressure in many animals) drives a process of **filtration**. Cells, as well as proteins and other large molecules, cannot cross the epithelial membrane and remain in the body fluid. In contrast, water and small solutes, such as salts, sugars, amino acids, and nitrogenous wastes, cross the membrane, forming a solution called the **filtrate**.

The filtrate is converted to a waste fluid by the specific transport of materials into or out of the filtrate. The process of selective **reabsorption** recovers useful molecules and water from the filtrate and returns them to the body fluids. Valuable solutes—including glucose, certain salts, vitamins, hormones, and amino acids—are reabsorbed by active transport. Nonessential solutes and wastes are left in the filtrate or are added to it by selective **secretion**, which also occurs by active transport. The pumping of various solutes adjusts the osmotic movement of water into or out of the filtrate. In the last step—excretion—the processed filtrate containing nitrogenous wastes is released from the body as urine.

Survey of Excretory Systems

The systems that perform the basic excretory functions vary widely among animal groups. However, they are generally built on a complex network of tubules that provide a large surface area for the exchange of water and solutes, including nitrogenous wastes. We'll examine the excretory systems of flatworms, earthworms, insects, and vertebrates as examples of evolutionary variations on tubule networks.

Protonephridia

Flatworms (phylum Platyhelminthes) have excretory systems called **protonephridia** (singular, *protonephridium*), which form a network of dead-end tubules (**Figure 44.11**). The

① Filtration. The excretory tubule collects a filtrate from the blood. Water and solutes are forced by blood pressure across the selectively permeable membranes of a cluster of capillaries and into the excretory tubule.

Capillary

Filtrate

Excretory tubule

② Reabsorption. The transport epithelium reclaims valuable substances from the filtrate and returns them to the body fluids.

③ Secretion. Other substances, such as toxins and excess ions, are extracted from body fluids and added to the contents of the excretory tubule.

Urine

④ Excretion. The altered filtrate (urine) leaves the system and the body.

▲ **Figure 44.10 Key steps of excretory system function: an overview.** Most excretory systems produce a filtrate by pressure-filtering body fluids and then modify the filtrate's contents. This diagram is modeled after the vertebrate excretory system.

▶ **Figure 44.11 Protonephridia: the flame bulb system of a planarian.** Protonephridia are branching internal tubules that function mainly in osmoregulation.

Nucleus of cap cell

Cilia

Interstitial fluid filters through membrane where cap cell and tubule cell interlock.

Tubule cell

Flame bulb

Tubule

Tubules of protonephridia

Opening in body wall

tubules, which are connected to external openings, branch throughout the flatworm body, which lacks a coelom or body cavity. Cellular units called flame bulbs cap the branches of each protonephridium. Consisting of a tubule cell and a cap cell, each flame bulb has a tuft of cilia projecting into the tubule. During filtration, the beating of the cilia draws water and solutes from the interstitial fluid through the flame bulb, releasing filtrate into the tubule network. (The moving cilia resemble a flickering flame, hence the name *flame bulb*.) The processed filtrate then moves outward through the tubules and empties as urine into the external environment. The urine excreted by freshwater flatworms has a low solute concentration, helping to balance the osmotic uptake of water from the environment.

Protonephridia are also found in rotifers, some annelids, mollusc larvae, and lancelets (see Figure 34.4). Among these animals, the function of the protonephridia varies. In the freshwater flatworms, protonephridia serve chiefly in osmoregulation. Most metabolic wastes diffuse out of the animal across the body surface or are excreted into the gastrovascular cavity and eliminated through the mouth (see Figure 33.10). However, in some parasitic flatworms, which are isoosmotic to the surrounding fluids of their host organisms, the main function of protonephridia is the disposal of nitrogenous wastes. Natural selection has thus adapted protonephridia to different tasks in different environments.

Metanephridia

Most annelids, such as earthworms, have **metanephridia** (singular, *metanephridium*), excretory organs that collect fluid directly from the coelom **(Figure 44.12)**. Each segment of a worm has a pair of metanephridia, which are immersed in coelomic fluid and enveloped by a capillary network. A ciliated funnel surrounds the internal opening. As the cilia beat, fluid is drawn into a collecting tubule, which includes a storage bladder that opens to the outside.

The metanephridia of an earthworm have both excretory and osmoregulatory functions. As urine moves along the tubule, the transport epithelium bordering the lumen reabsorbs most solutes and returns them to the blood in the capillaries. Nitrogenous wastes remain in the tubule and are excreted to the outside. Earthworms inhabit damp soil and usually experience a net uptake of water by osmosis through their skin. Their metanephridia balance the water influx by producing urine that is dilute (hypoosmotic to body fluids).

Malpighian Tubules

Insects and other terrestrial arthropods have organs called **Malpighian tubules** that remove nitrogenous wastes and that also function in osmoregulation **(Figure 44.13)**. The Malpighian tubules extend from dead-end tips immersed in hemolymph (circulatory fluid) to openings into the digestive tract. The filtration step common to other excretory systems is absent. Instead, the transport epithelium that lines the tubules secretes certain solutes, including nitrogenous wastes, from the hemolymph into the lumen of the tubule. Water follows the solutes into the tubule by osmosis, and the fluid then passes into the rectum. There, most solutes are pumped back into the hemolymph, and water reabsorption by osmosis follows. The nitrogenous wastes—mainly insoluble

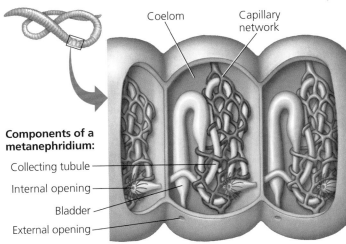

▲ **Figure 44.12 Metanephridia of an earthworm.** Each segment of the worm contains a pair of metanephridia, which collect coelomic fluid from the adjacent anterior segment. The region highlighted in yellow illustrates the organization of one metanephridium of a pair; the other would be behind it.

Coelom

Capillary network

Components of a metanephridium:

Collecting tubule

Internal opening

Bladder

External opening

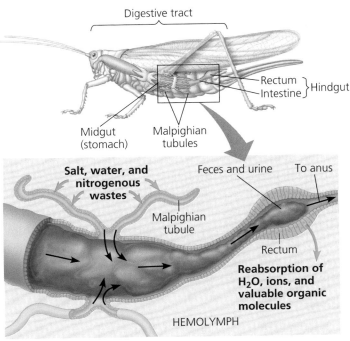

Digestive tract

Rectum
Intestine } Hindgut

Midgut (stomach)

Malpighian tubules

Salt, water, and nitrogenous wastes

Feces and urine

To anus

Malpighian tubule

Rectum

Reabsorption of H₂O, ions, and valuable organic molecules

HEMOLYMPH

▲ **Figure 44.13 Malpighian tubules of insects.** Malpighian tubules are outpocketings of the digestive tract that remove nitrogenous wastes and function in osmoregulation.

Exploring the Mammalian Excretory System

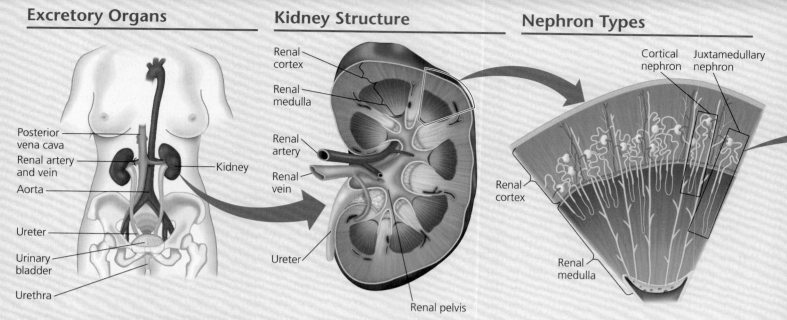

Excretory Organs

In humans, the excretory system consists of a pair of **kidneys**, bean-shaped organs about 10 cm in length, as well as organs for transporting and storing urine. Urine produced by each kidney exits through a duct called the **ureter**; the two ureters drain into a common sac called the **urinary bladder**. During urination, urine is expelled from the bladder through a tube called the **urethra**, which empties to the outside near the vagina in females and through the penis in males. Sphincter muscles near the junction of the urethra and bladder regulate urination.

Kidney Structure

Each kidney has an outer **renal cortex** and an inner **renal medulla**. Both regions are supplied with blood by a renal artery and drained by a renal vein. Within the cortex and medulla lie tightly packed excretory tubules and associated blood vessels. The inner **renal pelvis** collects urine from the excretory tubules and passes it to the urinary bladder.

Nephron Types

Weaving back and forth across the renal cortex and medulla are the **nephrons**, the functional units of the vertebrate kidney. Of the roughly 1 million nephrons in a human kidney, 85% are **cortical nephrons**, which reach only a short distance into the medulla. The remainder, the **juxtamedullary nephrons**, extend deep into the medulla. Juxtamedullary nephrons are essential for production of urine that is hyperosmotic to body fluids, a key adaptation for water conservation in mammals.

---

uric acid—are eliminated as nearly dry matter along with the feces. Capable of conserving water very effectively, the insect excretory system is a key adaptation contributing to these animals' tremendous success on land.

Some terrestrial insects have an additional adaptation for water balance: The rectal end of their gut enables water uptake from the air. Although some species absorb water from air only when it is very humid, others, such as fleas (genus *Xenopsylla*), can capture water from the atmosphere when relative humidity is as low as 50%.

Kidneys

In vertebrates and some other chordates, a specialized organ called the kidney functions in both osmoregulation and excretion. Like the excretory organs of most animal phyla, kidneys consist of tubules. The numerous tubules of these compact organs are arranged in a highly organized manner and are closely associated with a network of capillaries. The vertebrate excretory system also includes ducts and other structures that carry urine from the tubules out of the kidney and, eventually, the body.

Vertebrate kidneys are typically nonsegmented. However, hagfishes, which are invertebrate chordates, have kidneys with segmentally arranged excretory tubules. This suggests that the excretory structures of vertebrate ancestors also may have been segmented.

Because kidney organization is integral to kidney function, we begin with **Figure 44.14**, an exploration of the anatomy of the mammalian kidney and associated structures. Familiarizing yourself with the terms and diagrams in this figure will provide you with a solid foundation for learning about filtrate processing in the kidney, our focus in the next concept.

Nephron Organization

Afferent arteriole from renal artery
Glomerulus
Bowman's capsule
Proximal tubule
Peritubular capillaries
Distal tubule
Efferent arteriole from glomerulus
Branch of renal vein
Descending limb
Vasa recta
Loop of Henle
Collecting duct
Ascending limb

Each nephron consists of a single long tubule as well as a ball of capillaries called the **glomerulus**. The blind end of the tubule forms a cup-shaped swelling, called **Bowman's capsule**, which surrounds the glomerulus. Filtrate is formed when blood pressure forces fluid from the blood in the glomerulus into the lumen of Bowman's capsule. Processing occurs as the filtrate passes through three major regions of the nephron: the **proximal tubule**, the **loop of Henle** (a hairpin turn with a descending limb and an ascending limb), and the **distal tubule**. A **collecting duct** receives processed filtrate from many nephrons and transports it to the renal pelvis.

Each nephron is supplied with blood by an *afferent arteriole*, an offshoot of the renal artery that branches and forms the capillaries of the glomerulus. The capillaries converge as they leave the glomerulus, forming an *efferent arteriole*. Branches of this vessel form the **peritubular capillaries**, which surround the proximal and distal tubules. Other branches extend downward and form the **vasa recta**, hairpin-shaped capillaries that serve the renal medulla, including the long loop of Henle of juxtamedullary nephrons.

▶ In this SEM of densely packed blood vessels from a human kidney, arterioles and peritubular capillaries appear pink; the glomeruli appear yellow.

200 μm

CONCEPT CHECK **44.3**

1. Compare and contrast the different ways that metabolic waste products enter the excretory systems of flatworms, earthworms, and insects.

2. What is the function of the filtration step in excretory systems?

3. **WHAT IF?** Kidney failure is often treated by hemodialysis, in which blood diverted out of the body is filtered and then allowed to flow on one side of a semipermeable membrane. Fluid called dialysate flows in the opposite direction on the other side of the membrane. In replacing the reabsorption and secretion of solutes in a functional kidney, the makeup of the starting dialysate is critical. What initial solute composition would work well?

For suggested answers, see Appendix A.

CONCEPT 44.1

Osmoregulation balances the uptake and loss of water and solutes (pp. 953–958)

- Cells balance water gain and loss through **osmoregulation**, a process based on the controlled movement of solutes between internal fluids and the external environment and on the movement of water, which follows by osmosis. **Osmoconformers** are isoosmotic with their marine environment and do not regulate their **osmolarity**. In contrast, **osmoregulators** control water uptake and loss in a hypoosmotic or hyperosmotic environment, respectively. Water-conserving excretory organs help terrestrial animals to avoid desiccation. Animals that live in temporary waters may be **anhydrobiotic** for one stage of life.

Animal	Inflow/Outflow	Urine
Freshwater fish. Lives in water less concentrated than body fluids; fish tends to gain water, lose salt	Does not drink water Salt in H₂O in (active transport by gills) Salt out	▶ Large volume of urine ▶ Urine is less concentrated than body fluids
Marine bony fish. Lives in water more concentrated than body fluids; fish tends to lose water, gain salt	Drinks water Salt in H₂O out Salt out (active transport by gills)	▶ Small volume of urine ▶ Urine is slightly less concentrated than body fluids
Terrestrial vertebrate. Terrestrial environment; tends to lose body water to air	Drinks water Salt in (by mouth) H₂O and salt out	▶ Moderate volume of urine ▶ Urine is more concentrated than body fluids

- **Transport epithelia** contain specialized epithelial cells that regulate the solute movements required for waste disposal and for tempering changes in body fluids.

? *Under what environmental conditions does water move into a cell by osmosis?*

CONCEPT 44.2

An animal's nitrogenous wastes reflect its phylogeny and habitat (pp. 958–959)

- Protein and nucleic acid metabolism generates **ammonia**. Most aquatic animals excrete ammonia. Mammals and most adult amphibians convert ammonia to the less toxic **urea**, which is excreted with a minimal loss of water. Insects and many reptiles, including birds, convert ammonia to **uric acid**, a mostly insoluble waste excreted in a paste-like urine.
- The kind of nitrogenous waste excreted depends on an animal's evolutionary history and habitat. The amount of nitrogenous waste produced is coupled to the animal's energy budget and amount of dietary protein.

DRAW IT *Construct a table summarizing the three major types of nitrogenous wastes and their relative toxicity, energy content, and associated water loss during excretion.*

CONCEPT 44.3

Diverse excretory systems are variations on a tubular theme (pp. 960–963)

- Most excretory systems carry out **filtration**, **reabsorption**, **secretion**, and **excretion**. The **protonephridia** of the flatworm flame bulb excrete a dilute **filtrate**. An earthworm has pairs of open-ended **metanephridia** in each segment that produce urine. In insects, **Malpighian tubules** function in osmoregulation and removal of nitrogenous wastes. **Kidneys** function in both excretion and osmoregulation in vertebrates.
- Excretory tubules (consisting of **nephrons** and **collecting ducts**) and blood vessels pack the mammalian kidney. Blood pressure forces fluid from blood in the **glomerulus** into the lumen of **Bowman's capsule**. Following reabsorption and secretion, filtrate flows into a collecting duct. The **ureter** conveys urine from the **renal pelvis** to the **urinary bladder**.

? *Given that a typical excretory system selectively absorbs and secretes materials, what function does filtration serve?*

LEVEL 1: KNOWLEDGE/COMPREHENSION

1. *Unlike* an earthworm's metanephridia, a mammalian nephron
   a. is intimately associated with a capillary network.
   b. forms urine by changing fluid composition inside a tubule.
   c. functions in both osmoregulation and excretion.
   d. receives filtrate from blood instead of coelomic fluid.
   e. has a transport epithelium.

2. Which process in the nephron is *least* selective?
   a. filtration
   b. reabsorption
   c. active transport
   d. secretion
   e. salt pumping by the loop of Henle

3. Which of the following animals generally has the lowest volume of urine production?
   a. a vampire bat
   b. a salmon in fresh water
   c. a marine bony fish
   d. a freshwater bony fish
   e. a shark inhabiting freshwater Lake Nicaragua

LEVEL 2: APPLICATION/ANALYSIS

4. The high osmolarity of the renal medulla is maintained by all of the following *except*
   a. diffusion of salt from the thin segment of the ascending limb of the loop of Henle.
   b. active transport of salt from the upper region of the ascending limb.
   c. the spatial arrangement of juxtamedullary nephrons.
   d. diffusion of urea from the collecting duct.
   e. diffusion of salt from the descending limb of the loop of Henle.

5. Natural selection should favor the highest proportion of juxtamedullary nephrons in which of the following species?
   a. a river otter
   b. a mouse species living in a tropical rain forest
   c. a mouse species living in a temperate broadleaf forest
   d. a mouse species living in a desert
   e. a beaver

6. African lungfish, which are often found in small stagnant pools of fresh water, produce urea as a nitrogenous waste. What is the advantage of this adaptation?
   a. Urea takes less energy to synthesize than ammonia.
   b. Small stagnant pools do not provide enough water to dilute the toxic ammonia.
   c. The highly toxic urea makes the pool uninhabitable to potential competitors.
   d. Urea forms an insoluble precipitate.
   e. Urea makes lungfish tissue hypoosmotic to the pool.

LEVEL 3: SYNTHESIS/EVALUATION

7. **DRAW IT** Using Figure 44.3 as an example, sketch the exchange of salt (NaCl) and water between a shark and its marine environment.

8. **EVOLUTION CONNECTION**
   Merriam's kangaroo rats (*Dipodomys merriami*) live in North American habitats ranging from moist, cool woodlands to hot deserts. Assuming that natural selection has resulted in differences in water conservation between *D. merriami* populations, propose a hypothesis concerning the relative rates of evaporative water loss by populations that live in moist versus dry environments. Using a humidity sensor to detect evaporative water loss by kangaroo rats, how could you test your hypothesis?

9. **SCIENTIFIC INQUIRY**
   You are exploring kidney function in kangaroo rats. You measure urine volume and osmolarity, as well as the amount of chloride (Cl^-) and urea in the urine. If the water source provided to the animals were switched from tap water to a 2% NaCl solution, what change in urine osmolarity would you expect? How would you determine if this change was more likely due to a change in the excretion of Cl^- or urea?

10. **WRITE ABOUT A THEME**
    Structure and Function In a short essay (100–150 words), compare how membrane structures in the loop of Henle and collecting duct of the mammalian kidney enable water to be recovered from filtrate in the process of osmoregulation.

For selected answers, see Appendix A.

MasteringBIOLOGY® www.masteringbiology.com

1. **MasteringBiology® Assignments**
   Make Connections Tutorial Kidney Function (Chapter 44) and Passive and Active Transport (Chapter 7)
   Tutorial Kidney Structure and Function
   Activities Structure of the Human Excretory System • The Mammalian Kidney • Nephron Function • Control of Water Reabsorption
   Questions Student Misconceptions • Reading Quiz • Multiple Choice • End-of-Chapter

2. **eText**
   Read your book online, search, take notes, highlight text, and more.

3. **The Study Area**
   Practice Tests • Cumulative Test • *BioFlix* 3-D Animations • MP3 Tutor Sessions • Videos • Activities • Investigations • Lab Media • Audio Glossary • Word Study Tools • Art

46

Animal Reproduction

▲ **Figure 46.1 How can each of these sea slugs be both male and female?**

KEY CONCEPTS

46.1 Both asexual and sexual reproduction occur in the animal kingdom

46.2 Fertilization depends on mechanisms that bring together sperm and eggs of the same species

OVERVIEW

Pairing Up for Sexual Reproduction

The sea slugs, or nudibranchs (*Nembrotha rutilans*), in **Figure 46.1** are mating. If not disturbed, these marine molluscs may remain joined for hours. Sperm will be transferred and will fertilize eggs. A few weeks later, sexual reproduction will be complete. New individuals will hatch, but which parent is the mother? The answer is simple yet probably unexpected: both. In fact, each sea slug produces eggs *and* sperm.

As humans, we tend to think of reproduction in terms of the mating of males and females and the fusion of sperm and eggs. Animal reproduction, however, takes many forms. In some species, individuals change their sex during their lifetime; in other species, such as sea slugs, an individual is both male and female. There are animals that can fertilize their own eggs, as well as others that can reproduce without any form of sex. For certain species, such as honeybees, only a few individuals within a large population reproduce.

A population outlives its members only by reproduction, the generation of new individuals from existing ones. In this chapter, we will compare the diverse reproductive mechanisms that have evolved in the animal kingdom. We will then examine details of mammalian reproduction, particularly that of humans. We will focus on the physiology of reproduction mostly from the parents' perspective, deferring the details of embryonic development until the next chapter.

CONCEPT ## 46.1

Both asexual and sexual reproduction occur in the animal kingdom

There are two modes of animal reproduction—sexual and asexual. In **sexual reproduction**, the fusion of haploid gametes forms a diploid cell, the **zygote**. The animal that develops from a zygote can in turn give rise to gametes by meiosis (see Figure 13.8). The female gamete, the **egg**, is a large, nonmotile cell. The male gamete, the **sperm**, is generally a much smaller, motile cell. **Asexual reproduction** is the generation of new individuals without the fusion of egg and sperm. In most asexual animals, reproduction relies entirely on mitotic cell division.

For the vast majority of animals, reproduction is primarily or exclusively sexual. However, there are species that have a primarily asexual mode of reproduction, including a few all-female species for which reproduction is exclusively asexual. These include the microscopic bdelloid rotifer (see p. 677), as well as certain species of whiptail lizard (*Aspidoscelis*), which we will discuss shortly.

Mechanisms of Asexual Reproduction

Several forms of asexual reproduction are found only among invertebrates. One of these is **fission**, the separation of a parent organism into two individuals of approximately equal size **(Figure 46.2)**. Also common among invertebrates is **budding**, in which new individuals arise from outgrowths of existing ones (see Figure 13.2). In stony corals, for example, buds form and remain attached to the parent. The eventual result is a

▲ **Figure 46.2 Asexual reproduction of a sea anemone (*Anthopleura elegantissima*).** The large individual in the center of this photograph is undergoing fission, a type of asexual reproduction. Two smaller individuals will form as the parent divides approximately in half. Each offspring will be a genetic copy of the parent.

colony more than 1 m across, consisting of thousands of connected individuals. In another form of asexual reproduction, some invertebrates, including certain sponges, release specialized groups of cells that can grow into new individuals.

Another process of asexual reproduction involves two steps: *fragmentation*, the breaking of the body into several pieces, followed by *regeneration*, the regrowth of lost body parts. If more than one piece grows and develops into a complete animal, the net effect is reproduction. For example, certain annelid worms can split their body into several fragments, each regenerating a complete worm in less than a week. Numerous sponges, cnidarians, bristle worms, and sea squirts also reproduce by fragmentation and regeneration.

Parthenogenesis is asexual reproduction in which an egg develops without being fertilized. Among invertebrates, parthenogenesis occurs in certain species of bees, wasps, and ants. The progeny can be either haploid or diploid. If haploid, the offspring develop into adults that produce eggs or sperm without meiosis. In the case of honeybees, males (drones) are fertile haploid adults that arise by parthenogenesis. (In contrast, female honeybees, including both the sterile workers and the fertile queens, are diploid adults that develop from fertilized eggs.) Among vertebrates, parthenogenesis has been observed in about one in every thousand species. Recently, zookeepers discovered parthenogenesis in the Komodo dragon and in a species of hammerhead shark. In both cases, females had been kept completely isolated from males of their species but nevertheless produced offspring.

Sexual Reproduction: An Evolutionary Enigma

EVOLUTION Sex must enhance reproductive success or survival because it would otherwise rapidly disappear. To see why, consider an animal population in which half the females reproduce sexually and half reproduce asexually **(Figure 46.3)**. We'll assume that the number of offspring per female is a constant, two in this case. The two offspring of an asexual female will both be daughters that will each give birth to two more reproductive daughters. In contrast, half of a sexual female's offspring will be male. The number of sexual offspring will remain the same at each generation, because both a male and a female are required to reproduce. Thus, the asexual condition will increase in frequency at each generation. Yet despite this "twofold cost," sex is maintained even in animal species that can also reproduce asexually.

What advantage does sex provide? The answer remains elusive. Most hypotheses focus on the unique combinations of parental genes formed during meiotic recombination and fertilization. By producing offspring of varied genotypes, sexual reproduction may enhance the reproductive success of parents when environmental factors, such as pathogens, change relatively rapidly. In contrast, asexual reproduction is expected to be most advantageous in stable, favorable environments because it perpetuates successful genotypes faithfully and precisely.

There are a number of reasons why the unique gene combinations formed during sexual reproduction might be advantageous. One is that beneficial gene combinations arising through recombination might speed up adaptation. Although this idea appears straightforward, the theoretical advantage is significant only when the rate of beneficial mutations is high and population size is small. Another idea is that the shuffling of genes during sexual reproduction might allow a population to rid itself of sets of harmful genes

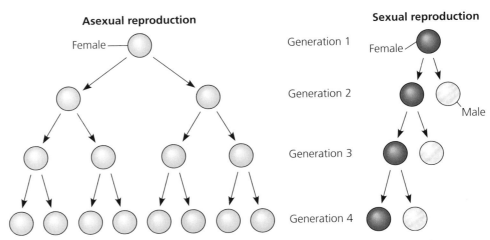

▲ **Figure 46.3 The "reproductive handicap" of sex.** These diagrams contrast the reproductive output of females (blue spheres) over four generations for asexual versus sexual reproduction, assuming two surviving offspring per female. The asexual population rapidly outgrows the sexual one.

more readily. Experiments to test these and other hypotheses are ongoing in many laboratories.

Reproductive Cycles

Most animals exhibit cycles in reproductive activity, often related to changing seasons. In this way, animals conserve resources, reproducing only when sufficient energy sources or stores are available and when environmental conditions favor the survival of offspring. For example, ewes (female sheep) have a reproductive cycle lasting 15–17 days. **Ovulation**, the release of mature eggs, occurs at the midpoint of each cycle. A ewe's cycle generally occurs only during fall and early winter, and the length of any resulting pregnancy is 5 months. Thus, most lambs are born in the early spring, when their chances of survival are optimal. Reproductive cycles are controlled by hormones, which in turn are regulated by environmental cues. Common environmental cues are changes in day length, seasonal temperature, rainfall, and lunar cycles.

Because seasonal temperature is often an important cue for reproduction, climate change can decrease reproductive success. Researchers in Denmark have demonstrated just such an effect on caribou (wild reindeer). In spring, caribou migrate to calving grounds to eat sprouting green plants, give birth, and care for their new calves **(Figure 46.4)**. Changes in the length of daylight trigger the migration, while the seasonal rise in temperature that thaws the tundra causes plants to sprout. Prior to 1993, the arrival of the caribou at the calving grounds coincided with the brief period during which the plants were nutritious and digestible. Between 1993 and 2006, average spring temperatures in the calving grounds increased by more than 4°C, and the plants now sprout two weeks earlier. Since the length of daylight is unaffected by climate change, the timing

of the caribou migration has not changed. The result is a timing mismatch between new plant growth and caribou birthing. Without adequate nutrition for the nursing females, production of caribou offspring has declined by 75%.

Reproductive cycles are also found among animals that can reproduce both sexually and asexually. Consider, for instance, the water flea (genus *Daphnia*). A *Daphnia* female can produce eggs of two types. One type of egg requires fertilization to develop, but the other type does not and develops instead by parthenogenesis. Asexual reproduction occurs when environmental conditions are favorable, whereas sexual reproduction occurs during times of environmental stress. As a result, the switch between sexual and asexual reproduction is roughly linked to season.

A very different type of reproductive cycle is found among animals that only reproduce asexually. Several genera of fishes, amphibians, and reptiles engage in a complex form of parthenogenesis that involves the doubling of chromosomes after meiosis, producing diploid offspring. Among these are about 15 species of whiptail lizards in the genus *Aspidoscelis*. There are no males, but courtship and mating behaviors are typical of sexual species of the same genus. During the breeding season, one female of each mating pair mimics a male **(Figure 46.5a)**. Each member of the pair alternates roles two or three times during the season. An individual adopts female behavior prior to ovulation, when the level of the female sex hormone estradiol is high, then switches to male-like behavior after ovulation, when the level of progesterone is highest **(Figure 46.5b)**. Ovulation is more likely to occur if the individual is mounted during the critical time of the hormone cycle; isolated lizards lay fewer eggs than those that go through the motions of sex. These observations support the hypothesis that these parthenogenetic lizards evolved from species having two sexes and still require certain sexual stimuli for maximum reproductive success.

Variation in Patterns of Sexual Reproduction

For many animals, finding a partner for sexual reproduction can be challenging. Adaptations that arose during the evolution of some species meet this challenge in a novel way—by blurring the strict distinction between male and female. One such adaptation arose among sessile (stationary) animals, such as barnacles; burrowing animals, such as clams; and some parasites, including tapeworms. Lacking locomotion, these animals have a very limited opportunity to find a mate. An evolutionary solution to this problem is **hermaphroditism**, in which each individual has both male and female reproductive systems (the term *hermaphrodite* merges the names Hermes and Aphrodite, a Greek god and goddess). Because each hermaphrodite reproduces as both a male and a female, *any* two individuals can mate. Each animal donates and receives sperm during mating, as the sea slugs in Figure 46.1 are doing. In some species, hermaphrodites are

▲ **Figure 46.4 Caribou (*Rangifer tarandus*) mother and calf.** As a result of warming due to global climate change, the number of caribou offspring in a West Greenland study site has fallen fourfold.

(a) Both lizards in this photograph are *A. uniparens* females. The one on top is playing the role of a male. Every two or three weeks during the breeding season, individuals switch sex roles.

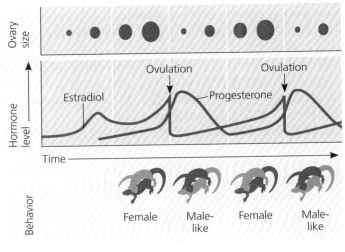

(b) The sexual behavior of *A. uniparens* is correlated with the cycle of ovulation mediated by sex hormones. As the blood level of estradiol rises, the ovaries grow, and the lizard behaves as a female. After ovulation, the estradiol level drops abruptly, and the progesterone level rises; these hormone levels correlate with male-like behavior.

▲ **Figure 46.5 Sexual behavior in parthenogenetic lizards.** The desert-grassland whiptail lizard (*Aspidoscelis uniparens*) is an all-female species. These reptiles reproduce by parthenogenesis, the development of an unfertilized egg. Nevertheless, ovulation is stimulated by mating behavior.

also capable of self-fertilization, allowing a form of sexual reproduction that doesn't require any partner.

The bluehead wrasse (*Thalassoma bifasciatum*), a coral reef fish, provides a well-studied example of a quite different variation in sexual reproduction. These wrasses live in harems, each consisting of a single male and several females. When the lone male dies, the opportunity for sexual reproduction would appear lost. Instead, a female wrasse undergoes sex reversal, a change in sex. Within a week, the transformed individual is producing sperm instead of eggs. Scientists have observed that it is the largest (and usually oldest) female in the harem that undergoes sex reversal. What advantage did this offer in the evolution of this wrasse? Because it is the male that defends a harem against intruders, a larger size may be more important for males than females in ensuring successful reproduction.

Certain oyster species also undergo sex reversal. In this case, individuals reproduce as males and then later as females, when their size is greatest. Since the number of gametes produced generally increases with size much more for females than for males, sex reversal in this direction maximizes gamete production. The result is enhanced reproductive success: Because oysters are sedentary animals and release their gametes into the surrounding water rather than mating directly, releasing more gametes tends to result in more offspring.

CONCEPT CHECK 46.1

1. Compare and contrast the outcomes of asexual and sexual reproduction.
2. Parthenogenesis is the most common form of asexual reproduction in animals that at other times reproduce sexually. What characteristic of parthenogenesis might explain this observation?
3. **WHAT IF?** If a hermaphrodite self-fertilizes, will the offspring be identical to the parent? Explain.
4. **MAKE CONNECTIONS** What examples of plant reproduction are most similar to asexual reproduction in animals? (See Concept 38.2, p. 812.)

For suggested answers, see Appendix A.

CONCEPT 46.2

Fertilization depends on mechanisms that bring together sperm and eggs of the same species

The union of sperm and egg—**fertilization**—can be either external or internal. In species with **external fertilization**, the female releases eggs into the environment, where the male then fertilizes them. Other species have **internal fertilization**: Sperm are deposited in or near the female reproductive tract, and fertilization occurs within the tract. (We'll discuss the cellular and molecular details of fertilization in Chapter 47.)

A moist habitat is almost always required for external fertilization, both to prevent the gametes from drying out and to allow the sperm to swim to the eggs. Many aquatic invertebrates simply shed their eggs and sperm into the surroundings, and fertilization occurs without the parents making physical contact. However, timing is crucial to ensure that mature sperm and eggs encounter one another.

Among some species with external fertilization, individuals clustered in the same area release their gametes into the water at the same time, a process known as *spawning*. In some cases, chemical signals that one individual generates in releasing gametes trigger others to release gametes. In other cases, environmental cues, such as temperature or day length, cause a whole population to release gametes at one time. For example, the palolo worm, native to coral reefs of the South Pacific, times its spawning to both the season and the lunar cycle. In spring, when the moon is in its last quarter, palolo worms break in half, releasing tail segments engorged with sperm or eggs. These packets rise to the ocean surface and burst in such vast numbers that the sea appears milky with gametes. The sperm quickly fertilize the floating eggs, and within hours, the palolo's once-a-year reproductive frenzy is complete.

When external fertilization is not synchronous across a population, individuals may exhibit specific mating behaviors leading to the fertilization of the eggs of one female by one male (**Figure 46.6**). Such "courtship" behavior has two important benefits: It allows mate choice (see Chapter 23) and, by triggering the release of both sperm and eggs, increases the probability of successful fertilization.

Internal fertilization is an adaptation that enables sperm to reach an egg efficiently, even when the environment is dry. It typically requires cooperative behavior that leads to copulation, as well as sophisticated and compatible reproductive systems. The male copulatory organ delivers sperm, and the female reproductive tract often has receptacles for storage and delivery of sperm to mature eggs.

No matter how fertilization occurs, the mating animals may make use of *pheromones*, chemicals released by one organism that can influence the physiology and behavior of other individuals of the same species. Pheromones are small, volatile or water-soluble molecules that disperse into the environment and, like hormones, are active in tiny amounts. Many pheromones function as mate attractants, enabling

▲ **Figure 46.6 External fertilization.** Many species of amphibians reproduce by external fertilization. In most of these species, behavioral adaptations ensure that a male is present when the female releases eggs. Here, a female frog (on bottom) has released a mass of eggs in response to being clasped by a male. The male released sperm (not visible) at the same time, and external fertilization has already occurred in the water.

some female insects to be detected by males from as far away as a mile. (We will discuss mating behavior and pheromones further in Chapter 51.)

Ensuring the Survival of Offspring

Comparing internal and external fertilization across many species reveals that internal fertilization is typically associated with the production of fewer gametes but the survival of a higher fraction of zygotes. Better zygote survival is due in part to the fact that eggs fertilized internally are sheltered from potential predators. However, internal fertilization is also more often associated with mechanisms that provide greater protection of the embryos and parental care of the young. For example, the internally fertilized eggs of many species of terrestrial animals exhibit adaptations that protect against water loss and physical damage during their external development. In the case of birds and other reptiles, as well as monotremes (egg-laying mammals), the zygotes consist of eggs with calcium- and protein-containing shells and several internal membranes (see Figure 34.25). In contrast, the fertilized eggs of fishes and amphibians have only a gelatinous coat and lack internal membranes.

Rather than secreting a protective eggshell, some animals retain the embryo for a portion of its development within the female's reproductive tract. Embryos of marsupial mammals, such as kangaroos and opossums, spend only a short period in the uterus; the embryos then crawl out and complete fetal development attached to a mammary gland in the mother's pouch. However, embryos of eutherian (placental) mammals, such as humans, remain in the uterus throughout fetal development. There they are nourished by the mother's blood supply through a temporary organ, the placenta. The embryos of some fishes and sharks also complete development internally, although typically the embryo and mother in such species lack a connection dedicated to nutrient exchange.

When a baby eagle hatches out of an egg or when a human is born, the newborn is not yet capable of independent existence. Instead, adult birds feed their young and mammals nurse their offspring. Parental care is in fact much more widespread than you might suspect. For example, there are many invertebrates that provide parental care (**Figure 46.7**). Among vertebrates, the gastric brooding frogs (genus *Rheobatrachus*) of Australia provided a particularly unusual example prior to their extinction in the 1980s. During reproduction, the female frog would carry the tadpoles in her stomach until they underwent metamorphosis and hopped out of her mouth as young frogs.

Gamete Production and Delivery

Sexual reproduction in animals relies on sets of cells that are precursors for eggs and sperm. A group of cells dedicated to this purpose is often established very early in the formation of the embryo and remains in an inactive state while the body plan

▲ **Figure 46.7 Parental care in an invertebrate.** Compared with many other insects, giant water bugs of the genus *Belostoma* produce relatively few offspring, but offer much greater parental protection. Following internal fertilization, the female glues her fertilized eggs to the back of the male (shown here). The male carries them for days, frequently fanning water over them to keep the eggs moist, aerated, and free of parasites.

develops. Cycles of growth and mitosis then increase, or *amplify*, the number of cells available for making eggs or sperm.

In producing gametes from the amplified precursor cells and making them available for fertilization, animals employ a variety of reproductive systems. The simplest systems do not even include discrete **gonads**, the organs that produce gametes in most animals. The palolo and most other polychaete worms (phylum Annelida) have separate sexes but do not have distinct gonads; rather, the eggs and sperm develop from undifferentiated cells lining the coelom (body cavity). As the gametes mature, they are released from the body wall and fill the coelom. Depending on the species, mature gametes may be shed through the excretory opening, or the swelling mass of eggs may split a portion of the body open, spilling the eggs into the environment.

More elaborate reproductive systems include sets of accessory tubes and glands that carry, nourish, and protect the gametes and sometimes the developing embryos. Most insect species, for example, have separate sexes with complex reproductive systems **(Figure 46.8)**. In the males, sperm develop in a pair of testes and are passed along a coiled duct to two seminal vesicles for storage. During mating, sperm are ejaculated into the female reproductive system. There, eggs develop in a pair of ovaries and are conveyed through ducts to the uterus. Eggs are fertilized in the uterus and then expelled for development outside the body. In many insect species, the female reproductive system includes one or more **spermathecae** (singular, spermatheca), sacs in which sperm may be stored for extended periods, a year or more in some species. Because the female releases male gametes from the spermatheca only in response to the appropriate stimuli, fertilization occurs

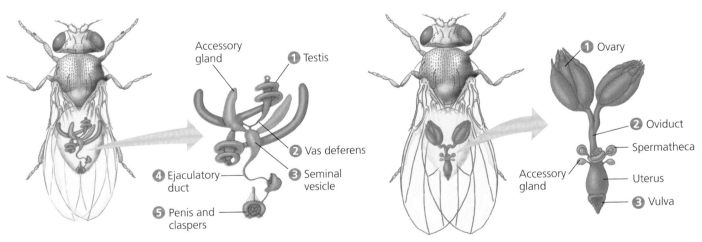

(a) Male fruit fly. Sperm form in the testes, pass through the sperm ducts (vas deferens), and are stored in the seminal vesicles. The male ejaculates sperm along with fluid from the accessory glands. (Males of some species of insects and other arthropods have appendages called claspers that grasp the female during copulation.)

(b) Female fruit fly. Eggs develop in the ovaries and then travel through the oviducts to the uterus. After mating, sperm are stored in the spermathecae, which are connected to the uterus by short ducts. The female uses a stored sperm to fertilize each egg as it enters the uterus before she passes the egg out through the vulva.

▲ **Figure 46.8 Insect reproductive anatomy.** Circled numbers indicate sequences of sperm and egg movement.

under conditions likely to be well suited to embryonic development. Even more complex reproductive systems can be found in some animals whose body plans are otherwise fairly simple, such as parasitic flatworms.

The basic plans of all vertebrate reproductive systems are quite similar, but there are some important variations. In many nonmammalian vertebrates, the digestive, excretory, and reproductive systems have a common opening to the outside, the **cloaca**, a structure that was probably also present in the ancestors of all vertebrates. In contrast, mammals generally lack a cloaca and have a separate opening for the digestive tract. In addition, most female mammals have separate openings for the excretory and reproductive systems. Among most vertebrates, the uterus is partly or completely divided into two chambers. However, in humans and other mammals that produce only one or a few young at a time, as well as in birds and many snakes, the uterus is a single structure. Male reproductive systems differ mainly in the copulatory organs. Many nonmammalian vertebrates, including all reptiles and amphibians, lack a well-developed penis and instead ejaculate sperm by turning the cloaca inside out.

Although fertilization involves the union of a single egg and sperm, animals often mate with more than one member of the other sex. Indeed, monogamy, the sustained sexual partnership of two individuals, is relatively rare among animals, including most mammals. Mechanisms have evolved, however, that enhance the reproductive success of a male with a particular female and diminish the chance of that female mating successfully with another partner. For example, some male insects transfer secretions that make a female less receptive to courtship, thereby reducing the likelihood of her mating again.

Can females also influence the relative reproductive success of their mates? This question intrigued two scientific collaborators working in Europe. Studying female fruit flies that copulated with one male and then another, the researchers traced the fate of sperm transferred in the first mating. As shown in **Figure 46.9**, they found that female fruit flies play a major role in determining the reproductive outcome of multiple matings. Nevertheless, the processes by which gametes and individuals compete during reproduction are only partly understood and remain a vibrant research area.

CONCEPT CHECK 46.2

1. How does internal fertilization facilitate life on land?
2. What mechanisms have evolved in animals with (a) external fertilization and (b) internal fertilization that help ensure that offspring survive to adulthood?
3. **MAKE CONNECTIONS** What are the shared and distinct functions of the uterus of an insect and the ovary of a flowering plant? (See Figure 38.6, p. 806.)

For suggested answers, see Appendix A.

▼ **Figure 46.9** **INQUIRY**

Why is sperm usage biased when female fruit flies mate twice?

EXPERIMENT When a female fruit fly mates twice, 80% of the offspring result from the second mating. Scientists had postulated that ejaculate from the second mating displaces stored sperm. To test this hypothesis, Rhonda Snook, at the University of Sheffield, and David Hosken, at the University of Zurich, used mutant males with altered reproductive systems. "No-ejaculate" males mate, but do not transfer sperm or fluid to females. "No-sperm" males mate and ejaculate, but make no sperm. The researchers allowed females to mate with wild-type males and then mate with wild-type males, no-sperm males, or no-ejaculate males. As a control, some females were mated only once. The scientists then dissected each female under a microscope and recorded whether sperm were absent from the spermatheca, the major sperm storage organ.

RESULTS

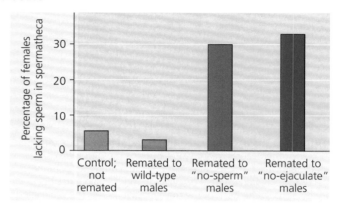

CONCLUSION Because remating reduces sperm storage when no sperm or fluids are transferred, the hypothesis that ejaculate from a second mating displaces stored sperm is incorrect. Instead, it appears that females sometimes get rid of stored sperm in response to remating. This might represent a way for females to replace stored sperm, possibly of diminished fitness, with fresh sperm.

SOURCE R. R. Snook and D. J. Hosken, Sperm death and dumping in *Drosophila*, *Nature* 428:939–941 (2004).

WHAT IF? Suppose males in the first mating had a mutant allele for the dominant trait of smaller eyes. What fraction of the females would produce some offspring with smaller eyes?

46 CHAPTER REVIEW

SUMMARY OF KEY CONCEPTS

CONCEPT 46.1

Both asexual and sexual reproduction occur in the animal kingdom (pp. 996–999)

- Animals reproduce either asexually or sexually. **Sexual reproduction** requires the fusion of male and female gametes, forming a diploid **zygote**. **Asexual reproduction** is the production of offspring without gamete fusion. Fission, budding, fragmentation with regeneration, and **parthenogenesis** are mechanisms of asexual reproduction in various invertebrates. Facilitating selection for or against sets of genes may explain why sexual reproduction is widespread among animal species.

- Although most animals reproduce exclusively sexually or asexually, some alternate between the two. Variations on these two modes are made possible through parthenogenesis, **hermaphroditism**, and sex reversal. Hormones and environmental cues control reproductive cycles.

? *Would a pair of haploid offspring produced by parthenogenesis be genetically identical?*

CONCEPT 46.2

Fertilization depends on mechanisms that bring together sperm and eggs of the same species (pp. 999–1002)

- Fertilization can occur externally or internally with regard to the mother's body. In either case, fertilization requires coordinated timing, which may be mediated by environmental cues, pheromones, or courtship behavior. Internal fertilization is typically often associated both with relatively fewer offspring and with greater protection of offspring by the parents. Systems for gamete production and delivery range from undifferentiated cells in the body cavity to complex **gonads** with accessory tubes and glands that carry and protect gametes and embryos. Although sexual reproduction involves a partnership, it also provides an opportunity for competition between individuals and between gametes.

? *Identify which of the following are unique to mammals: a female uterus and a male vas deferens, extended internal development, parental care of newborns.*

LEVEL 1: KNOWLEDGE/COMPREHENSION

1. Which of the following characterizes parthenogenesis?
   a. An individual may change its sex during its lifetime.
   b. Specialized groups of cells grow into new individuals.
   c. An organism is first a male and then a female.
   d. An egg develops without being fertilized.
   e. Both mates have male and female reproductive organs.

2. In male mammals, excretory and reproductive systems share
   a. the testes.
   b. the urethra.
   c. the seminal vesicle.
   d. the vas deferens.
   e. the prostate.

3. Which of the following is *not* properly paired?
   a. seminiferous tubule—cervix
   b. Sertoli cells—follicle cells
   c. testosterone—estradiol
   d. scrotum—labia majora
   e. vas deferens—oviduct

4. Peaks of LH and FSH production occur during
   a. the menstrual flow phase of the uterine cycle.
   b. the beginning of the follicular phase of the ovarian cycle.
   c. the period just before ovulation.
   d. the end of the luteal phase of the ovarian cycle.
   e. the secretory phase of the menstrual cycle.

5. During human gestation, rudiments of all organs develop
   a. in the first trimester.
   b. in the second trimester.
   c. in the third trimester.
   d. while the embryo is in the oviduct.
   e. during the blastocyst stage.

LEVEL 2: APPLICATION/ANALYSIS

6. Which of the following is a true statement?
   a. All mammals have menstrual cycles.
   b. The endometrial lining is shed in menstrual cycles but reabsorbed in estrous cycles.
   c. Estrous cycles are more frequent than menstrual cycles.
   d. Estrous cycles are not controlled by hormones.
   e. Ovulation occurs before the endometrium thickens in estrous cycles.

7. For which of the following is the number the same in spermatogenesis and oogenesis?
   a. interruptions in meiotic divisions
   b. functional gametes produced by meiosis
   c. meiotic divisions required to produce each gamete
   d. gametes produced in a given time period
   e. different cell types produced by meiosis

8. Which statement about human reproduction is false?
   a. Fertilization occurs in the oviduct.
   b. Effective hormonal contraceptives are currently available only for females.
   c. An oocyte completes meiosis after a sperm penetrates it.
   d. The earliest stages of spermatogenesis occur closest to the lumen of the seminiferous tubules.
   e. Spermatogenesis and oogenesis require different temperatures.

LEVEL 3: SYNTHESIS/EVALUATION

9. **DRAW IT** In human spermatogenesis, mitosis of a stem cell gives rise to one cell that remains a stem cell and one cell that becomes a spermatogonium. (a) Draw four rounds of mitosis for a stem cell, and label the daughter cells. (b) For one spermatogonium, draw the cells it would produce from one round of mitosis followed by meiosis. Label the cells, and label mitosis and meiosis. (c) What would happen if stem cells divided like spermatogonia?

10. **EVOLUTION CONNECTION**
Hermaphroditism is often found in animals that are fixed to a surface. Motile species are less often hermaphroditic. Why?

11. **SCIENTIFIC INQUIRY**
You discover a new egg-laying worm species. You dissect four adults and find both oocytes and sperm in each. Cells outside the gonad contain five chromosome pairs. Lacking genetic variants, how would you determine whether the worms can self-fertilize?

12. **WRITE ABOUT A THEME**
Energy Transfer In reproducing, animals transfer energy to their offspring. In a short essay (100–150 words), discuss how distinct investments of energy by females contribute to the reproductive success of a frog, a chicken, and a human.

For selected answers, see Appendix A.

1. MasteringBiology® Assignments
Tutorial Sex Hormones and Mammalian Reproduction
Activities Reproductive System of the Human Female • Reproductive System of the Human Male • Human Gametogenesis • Human Reproduction
Questions Student Misconceptions • Reading Quiz • Multiple Choice • End-of-Chapter

2. eText
Read your book online, search, take notes, highlight text, and more.

3. The Study Area
Practice Tests • Cumulative Test • *BioFlix* 3-D Animations • MP3 Tutor Sessions • Videos • Activities • Investigations • Lab Media • Audio Glossary • Word Study Tools • Art

UNIVERSITY OF ALBERTA FACULTY BIO

Sally Leys BSc Zoology, (University of British Columbia); PhD Biology (University of Victoria)

Current Position: Professor and Canada Research Chair in Evolutionary and Developmental Biology, Department of Biological Sciences

I currently teach Zoology 250 (Survey of Invertebrates) and Zoology 450/550 (Development and Evolution of Form). In past years I have taught Biology 361 (Marine Science), Zoology 303 (Animal Development), and Zoology 402 (Topics in Developmental Biology).

I am interested in how basic features of the animal body plan such as the body axis, tissue layers, nerves and muscle came about during evolution. Sponges (Phylum Porifera) are currently understood to be the first multicellular animals to have arisen from a unicellular (or colonial) flagellate. They also are the only animal group that lacks nerves and muscle, and therefore are good models for studying what systems early animals possessed prior to the advent of complex tissues and neurosensory coordination systems.

Sponges are sessile, aquatic animals that filter vast amounts of water daily for feeding and respiration. Because of their unusual lifestyle and body plans, my students and I use a variety of approaches including physiology, molecular biology, and even ecology to understand how the sponge body plan is adapted to its environment today, and how it may have changed over time. Our discoveries are exciting. Recently for example, we cultured sponge tissues on minute filters in the lab and showed that sponges have sealed epithelia that generate a transepithelial potential like other animal epithelia. Using tiny freshwater sponges we collect by snorkeling in lakes, we have shown that sponges can be made to 'sneeze' by exposure to sediment or vigorous shaking. Intriguingly the sneeze contractions are also triggered by glutamate and inhibited by GABA (gamma-Aminobutyric acid) so sponges, like other animals, have glutaminergic signaling. My students have cleverly developed tools to manipulate sponge morphology and are the first lab ever to generate artificial sponges with many oscula (excurrent vents). We are now looking at the molecular signals that generate normal and abnormal patterns during sponge development.

47

Animal Development

1 mm

▲ Figure 47.1 **How did a single cell develop into this intricately detailed embryo?**

KEY CONCEPTS

47.1 Fertilization and cleavage initiate embryonic development

47.2 Morphogenesis in animals involves specific changes in cell shape, position, and survival

47.3 Cytoplasmic determinants and inductive signals contribute to cell fate specification

OVERVIEW

A Body-Building Plan

The 7-week-old human embryo in **Figure 47.1** has already achieved a remarkable number of milestones in its development. Its heart—the red spot in the center—is beating, and a digestive tract traverses the length of its body. Its

brain is forming (at the upper left in the photo), while the blocks of tissue that will give rise to the vertebrae are lined up along its back.

Development occurs at many points in the life cycle of an animal **(Figure 47.2)**. In a frog, for example, a major developmental period is metamorphosis, when the larva (tadpole) is transformed into an adult. Other developmental events in the adult gonads produce sperm and eggs (gametes). In this chapter, our focus is on embryonic development.

Across a range of animal species, embryonic development involves common stages that occur in a set order. As shown in Figure 47.2, the first is fertilization, the fusion of sperm and egg, which forms a zygote. Development proceeds with the cleavage stage, during which a series of cell divisions divide, or cleave, the zygote into a many-celled embryo. These cleavage divisions, which typically are rapid and lack accompanying cell growth, convert the embryo to a hollow ball of cells called a blastula. Next, the blastula folds in on itself, rearranging into a three-layered embryo, the gastrula, in a process called gastrulation. During organogenesis, the last major stage of embryonic development, local changes in cell shape and large-scale changes in cell location generate the rudimentary organs from which adult structures grow.

By combining molecular genetics with classical embryology, developmental biologists have learned a great deal about the transformation of a fertilized egg into an adult. As an embryo develops, specific patterns of gene expression direct cells to adopt distinct fates. Although animals display

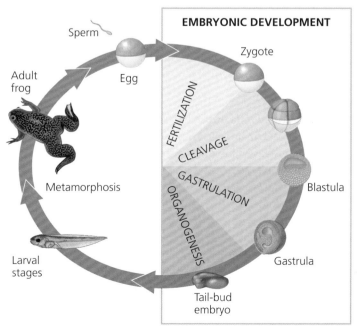

▲ Figure 47.2 **Developmental events in the life cycle of a frog.**

widely differing body plans, they share many basic mechanisms of development and use a common set of regulatory genes. For example, the gene that specifies heart location in a human embryo (such as the one in Figure 47.1) has a close counterpart with a nearly identical function in the fruit fly, *Drosophila*. (Noting that the fly heart fails to develop when this gene is defective, researchers named the *Drosophila* gene *tinman*, after the similarly affected character from *The Wizard of Oz*.)

In studying development, biologists frequently make use of **model organisms**, species chosen for the ease with which they can be studied in the laboratory. *Drosophila* is a useful model organism: Its life cycle is short, and mutants can be readily identified and studied (see Chapters 15 and 18). In this chapter, we will concentrate on four other model organisms: the sea urchin, the frog, the chick, and the nematode (roundworm). We will also explore some aspects of human embryonic development. Even though humans are not model organisms, we are, of course, intensely interested in our own species.

Our exploration of embryonic development will begin with a description of the basic stages common to most animals. We will then look at some of the cellular mechanisms that generate body form. Finally, we will consider how a cell becomes committed to a particular specialized role.

CONCEPT 47.1

Fertilization and cleavage initiate embryonic development

With the preceding overview of embryonic development in mind, let's take a closer look at the events surrounding **fertilization**, the formation of a diploid zygote from a haploid egg and sperm.

Fertilization

Molecules and events at the egg surface play a crucial role in each step of fertilization. First, sperm dissolve or penetrate any protective layer surrounding the egg to reach the plasma membrane. Next, molecules on the sperm surface bind to receptors on the egg surface, helping ensure that a sperm of the same species fertilizes the egg. Finally, changes at the surface of the egg prevent *polyspermy*, the entry of multiple sperm nuclei into the egg. If polyspermy were to occur, the resulting abnormal number of chromosomes in the embryo would be lethal.

The cell surface events that take place during fertilization have been studied most extensively in sea urchins (members of the phylum Echinodermata; see Figure 33.43). Sea urchin gametes are easy to collect, and fertilization is external.

As a result, researchers can observe fertilization and subsequent events simply by combining eggs and sperm in seawater in the laboratory. Furthermore, fertilization in sea urchins provides a good general model for the same process in vertebrates.

The Acrosomal Reaction

When sea urchins release their gametes into the water, the jelly coat that surrounds the egg exudes soluble molecules that attract the sperm, which swim toward the egg. As soon as the head of a sea urchin sperm contacts the jelly coat of a sea urchin egg, molecules in the jelly coat trigger the **acrosomal reaction** in the sperm (**Figure 47.3**). This reaction begins with the discharge of hydrolytic enzymes from the **acrosome**, a specialized vesicle at the tip of the sperm. These enzymes partially digest the jelly coat, enabling a sperm structure called the *acrosomal process* to elongate and penetrate the coat. Protein molecules on the tip of the extended acrosomal process bind to specific receptor proteins that jut out from the egg plasma membrane. This "lock-and-key" recognition is especially important for sea urchins and other species with external fertilization because the surrounding water may contain gametes of other species.

Contact between the tip of the acrosomal process and the receptors on the egg leads to the fusion of the sperm and egg plasma membranes. The sperm nucleus then enters the egg cytoplasm as ion channels open in the egg's plasma membrane. Sodium ions diffuse into the egg and cause *depolarization*, a decrease in the membrane potential (see Chapter 7). The depolarization occurs within about 1–3 seconds after a sperm binds to an egg. By preventing additional sperm from fusing with the egg's plasma membrane, this depolarization acts as a **fast block to polyspermy**.

The Cortical Reaction

Membrane depolarization lasts for only a minute or so. A longer-lasting block to polyspermy is established by vesicles that lie just beneath the egg plasma membrane, in the rim of cytoplasm known as the *cortex*. Within seconds after a sperm binds to the egg, these vesicles, called cortical granules, fuse with the egg plasma membrane (see Figure 47.3, ❹). The contents of the cortical granules are released into the space between the plasma membrane and the surrounding *vitelline layer*, a structure formed by the extracellular matrix of the egg. Enzymes and other macromolecules from the granules trigger a cortical reaction, which lifts the vitelline layer away from the egg and hardens the layer into a protective fertilization envelope. Additional enzymes clip off and release the external portions of the remaining receptor proteins, along with any attached sperm. Together, the fertilization envelope

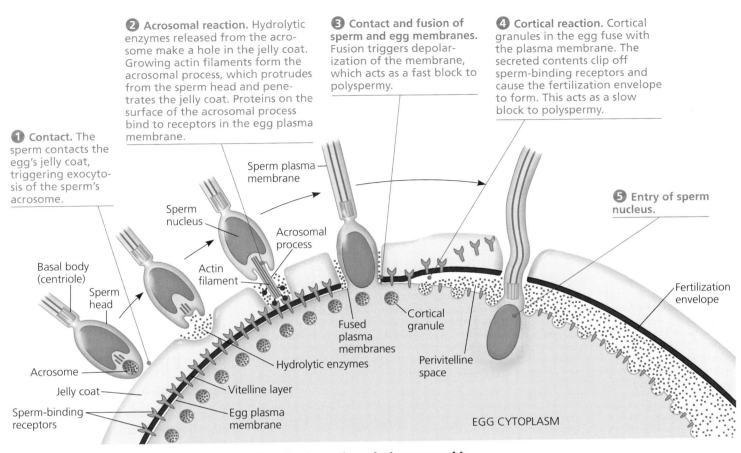

2 Acrosomal reaction. Hydrolytic enzymes released from the acrosome make a hole in the jelly coat. Growing actin filaments form the acrosomal process, which protrudes from the sperm head and penetrates the jelly coat. Proteins on the surface of the acrosomal process bind to receptors in the egg plasma membrane.

1 Contact. The sperm contacts the egg's jelly coat, triggering exocytosis of the sperm's acrosome.

3 Contact and fusion of sperm and egg membranes. Fusion triggers depolarization of the membrane, which acts as a fast block to polyspermy.

4 Cortical reaction. Cortical granules in the egg fuse with the plasma membrane. The secreted contents clip off sperm-binding receptors and cause the fertilization envelope to form. This acts as a slow block to polyspermy.

5 Entry of sperm nucleus.

Sperm plasma membrane

Sperm nucleus

Acrosomal process

Basal body (centriole)

Sperm head

Actin filament

Acrosome

Jelly coat

Sperm-binding receptors

Hydrolytic enzymes

Vitelline layer

Egg plasma membrane

Fused plasma membranes

Cortical granule

Perivitelline space

Fertilization envelope

EGG CYTOPLASM

▲ **Figure 47.3 The acrosomal and cortical reactions during sea urchin fertilization.** The events following contact of a single sperm and egg ensure that the nucleus of only one sperm enters the egg cytoplasm.

The icon above is a simplified drawing of an adult sea urchin. Throughout the chapter, this and other icons of an adult frog, chicken, nematode, and human indicate the animals whose embryos are featured in certain figures.

and other changes in the egg's surface impede the entry of additional sperm nuclei and thus act as a longer-term **slow block to polyspermy**.

Formation of the fertilization envelope requires a high concentration of calcium ions (Ca^{2+}) in the egg. Does a change in the Ca^{2+} concentration trigger the cortical reaction? To answer this question, researchers at the University of California, Berkeley, used a calcium-sensitive dye to assess the amount and distribution of Ca^{2+} in the egg during fertilization. As described in **Figure 47.4**, on the next page, they found that Ca^{2+} spread across the egg in a wave that correlated with the appearance of the fertilization envelope. Further studies demonstrated that release of Ca^{2+} into the cytosol from the endoplasmic reticulum is controlled by a signal transduction pathway activated by sperm binding. The resulting increase in Ca^{2+} levels causes cortical granules to fuse with the plasma membrane. Although understood in greatest detail in sea urchins, the cortical reaction triggered by Ca^{2+} also occurs in vertebrates such as fishes and mammals.

Egg Activation

A major function of fertilization is the combining of haploid sets of chromosomes from two individuals into a single diploid cell, the zygote. However, the events of fertilization also initiate metabolic reactions that trigger the onset of embryonic development, thus "activating" the egg. There is, for example, a marked increase in the rates of cellular respiration and protein synthesis in the egg following fertilization.

What triggers egg activation? Studies show that injecting Ca^{2+} into an unfertilized egg activates egg metabolism in many species, despite the absence of sperm. Researchers therefore conclude that the rise in Ca^{2+} concentration that causes the cortical reaction also causes egg activation. Further experiments have revealed that artificial activation is possible even if the nucleus has been removed from the egg. This finding indicates that egg activation requires only the proteins and mRNAs already present in the egg cytoplasm.

▼ Figure 47.4

INQUIRY

Does the distribution of Ca²⁺ in an egg correlate with formation of the fertilization envelope?

EXPERIMENT During fertilization, fusion of cortical granules with the egg plasma membrane causes the fertilization envelope to rise and spread around the egg from the point of sperm binding.

10 sec after fertilization   25 sec   35 sec   1 min   ⊢━━━━⊣ 500 μm

Calcium ion (Ca^{2+}) signaling is involved in fusion of vesicles with the plasma membrane during neurotransmitter release, insulin secretion, and plant pollen tube formation. Rick Steinhardt, Gerald Schatten, and colleagues, then at the University of California at Berkeley, hypothesized that an increase in Ca^{2+} levels similarly triggers cortical granule fusion. To test this hypothesis, they tracked the release of free Ca^{2+} in sea urchin eggs after sperm binding to see if it correlated with formation of the fertilization envelope. A fluorescent dye that glows when it binds free Ca^{2+} was injected into unfertilized eggs. The researchers then added sea urchin sperm and observed the eggs with a fluorescence microscope. Schatten and colleagues later repeated the experiment using a more sensitive dye, producing the results shown here.

RESULTS A rise in cytosolic Ca^{2+} concentration began at the point of sperm entry and spread in a wave to the other side of the egg. Soon after the wave passed, the fertilization envelope rose.

1 sec before fertilization   10 sec after fertilization   20 sec   30 sec   ⊢━━━━⊣ 500 μm

CONCLUSION The researchers concluded that Ca^{2+} release is correlated with the cortical reaction and formation of the fertilization envelope, supporting their hypothesis that an increase in Ca^{2+} levels triggers cortical granule fusion.

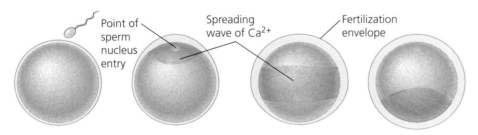

Point of sperm nucleus entry — Spreading wave of Ca^{2+} — Fertilization envelope

SOURCE R. Steinhardt et al., Intracellular calcium release at fertilization in the sea urchin egg, *Developmental Biology* 58:185–197 (1977). M. Hafner et al., Wave of free calcium at fertilization in the sea urchin egg visualized with Fura-2, *Cell Motility and the Cytoskeleton* 9:271–277 (1988).

(MB) See the related Experimental Inquiry Tutorial in MasteringBiology.

WHAT IF? Suppose you were given a chemical compound that could enter the egg and bind to Ca^{2+}, blocking its function. How would you use this compound to further test the hypothesis that a rise in Ca^{2+} levels triggers cortical granule fusion?

About 20 minutes after the sperm nucleus enters the sea urchin egg, the sperm and egg nuclei fuse. DNA synthesis begins, and the first cell division occurs after about 90 minutes, marking the end of the fertilization stage.

Fertilization in other species shares many features with the process in sea urchins. However, the timing of events differs, as does the stage of meiosis the egg has reached by the time it is fertilized. Sea urchin eggs have already completed meiosis when they are released from the female. In other species, eggs are arrested at a specific stage of meiosis and do not complete the meiotic divisions until fertilization occurs. Human eggs, for example, are arrested at metaphase of meiosis II prior to fertilization.

Fertilization in Mammals

Unlike sea urchins and most other marine invertebrates, terrestrial animals, including mammals, fertilize eggs internally. Secretions in the mammalian female reproductive tract not only provide a moist environment for the sperm, but also bring about changes in sperm motility and structure. Only after these changes occur do sperm have the capacity to fertilize an egg. In humans, this process of *capacitation* occurs during the first 6 hours after the sperm enter the female reproductive tract.

Support cells of the developing follicle surround the mammalian egg and remain with it during and after ovulation. A sperm must travel through this layer of follicle cells before it reaches the **zona pellucida**, the extracellular matrix of the egg. Within the zona pellucida is a component that functions as a receptor for sperm. Binding of a sperm to this receptor induces an acrosomal reaction, facilitating sperm passage through the zona pellucida to the egg. This binding also exposes a protein on the sperm that binds with the egg plasma membrane. At this point, the two cells fuse **(Figure 47.5)**.

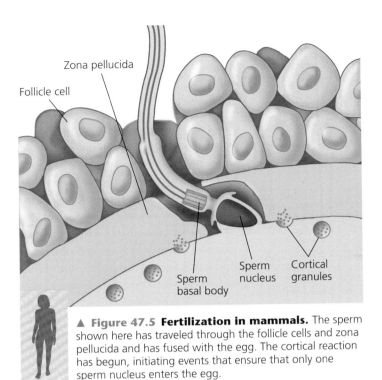

Zona pellucida

Follicle cell

Sperm basal body

Sperm nucleus

Cortical granules

▲ **Figure 47.5 Fertilization in mammals.** The sperm shown here has traveled through the follicle cells and zona pellucida and has fused with the egg. The cortical reaction has begun, initiating events that ensure that only one sperm nucleus enters the egg.

As in sea urchin fertilization, sperm binding triggers changes within the mammalian egg that lead to a cortical reaction, the release of enzymes from cortical granules to the outside of the cell. These enzymes catalyze changes in the zona pellucida, which then functions as the slow block to polyspermy. (No fast block to polyspermy has been identified in mammals.)

After the egg and sperm membranes fuse, the whole sperm is taken into the egg. Once the envelopes of both haploid nuclei have dispersed, the sperm and egg chromosomes are organized onto a single mitotic spindle. Only after the first division is there a true diploid nucleus with a nuclear membrane.

Overall, fertilization is much slower in mammals than in sea urchins: The first cell division occurs 12–36 hours after sperm binding in mammals, compared with about 90 minutes in sea urchins. This cell division marks the end of fertilization and the beginning of the next stage, cleavage.

Cleavage

Once fertilization is complete, many animal species undergo a succession of rapid cell divisions that characterize the **cleavage** stage of early development. During cleavage, the cell cycle consists primarily of the S (DNA synthesis) and M (mitosis) phases. Cells essentially skip the G_1 and G_2 (gap) phases, and little or no protein synthesis occurs (see Figure 12.6 for a review of the cell cycle). As a result, cleavage partitions the cytoplasm of the large fertilized egg into many smaller cells called **blastomeres**, as shown in **Figure 47.6**.

The first five to seven cleavage divisions produce a hollow ball of cells, the **blastula**, surrounding a fluid-filled cavity called the **blastocoel** (see Figure 47.6).

Cleavage Patterns

In frogs and many other animals, the distribution of **yolk** (stored nutrients) is a key factor influencing the pattern of cleavage. Yolk is often concentrated toward one pole of the egg, called the **vegetal pole**. The yolk concentration decreases significantly toward the opposite pole, the **animal pole**. This difference in yolk distribution results

50 μm

(a) Fertilized egg. Shown here is the zygote shortly before the first cleavage division, surrounded by the fertilization envelope.

(b) Four-cell stage. Remnants of the mitotic spindle can be seen between the two pairs of cells that have just completed the second cleavage division.

(c) Early blastula. After further cleavage divisions, the embryo is a multicellular ball that is still surrounded by the fertilization envelope. The blastocoel has begun to form in the center.

(d) Later blastula. A single layer of cells surrounds a large blastocoel. Although not visible here, the fertilization envelope is still present; the embryo will soon hatch from it and begin swimming.

▲ **Figure 47.6 Cleavage in an echinoderm embryo.** Cleavage is a series of mitotic cell divisions that transform the fertilized egg into a blastula, a hollow ball composed of cells called blastomeres. These light micrographs show the cleavage stages of a sand dollar embryo, which are virtually identical to those of a sea urchin.

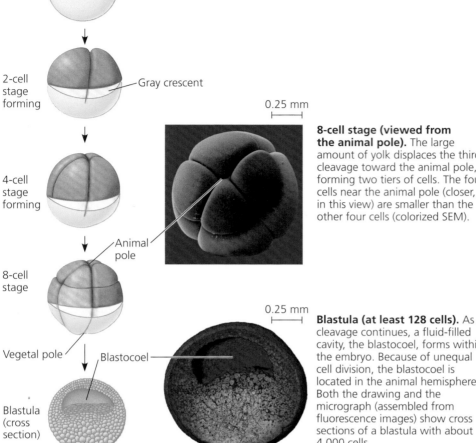

Zygote

2-cell stage forming — Gray crescent

4-cell stage forming

Animal pole

8-cell stage

0.25 mm

8-cell stage (viewed from the animal pole). The large amount of yolk displaces the third cleavage toward the animal pole, forming two tiers of cells. The four cells near the animal pole (closer, in this view) are smaller than the other four cells (colorized SEM).

Vegetal pole — Blastocoel

0.25 mm

Blastula (at least 128 cells). As cleavage continues, a fluid-filled cavity, the blastocoel, forms within the embryo. Because of unequal cell division, the blastocoel is located in the animal hemisphere. Both the drawing and the micrograph (assembled from fluorescence images) show cross sections of a blastula with about 4,000 cells.

Blastula (cross section)

▲ **Figure 47.7 Cleavage in a frog embryo.** The cleavage planes in the first and second divisions extend from the animal pole to the vegetal pole, but the third cleavage is perpendicular to the polar axis. In some species, the first division bisects the gray crescent, a lighter-colored region that appears opposite the site of sperm entry.

in animal and vegetal hemispheres that differ in appearance **(Figure 47.7)**.

During cell division, an indentation called a *cleavage furrow* forms in the cell surface as cytokinesis divides the cell in half. As shown in Figure 47.7, the first two cleavage furrows in the frog lie parallel to the line (or meridian) connecting the two poles. The second cell division begins before the first is complete, so the second cleavage furrow further divides the animal hemisphere while the first furrow is dividing the yolky cytoplasm of the vegetal hemisphere. Nevertheless, the first two divisions eventually produce four blastomeres of equal size, each extending from the animal pole to the vegetal pole.

During the third division of the frog egg, the asymmetric distribution of yolk in the embryo affects the relative size of cells produced in the two hemispheres. This division is equatorial (perpendicular to the line connecting the poles) and produces an eight-celled embryo. However, as each of the four blastomeres begins this division, the high concentration of yolk around the

vegetal pole displaces the mitotic apparatus toward the animal pole. Consequently, the cleavage furrow is also displaced from the egg equator toward the animal pole, yielding smaller blastomeres in the animal hemisphere than in the vegetal hemisphere. The displacing effect of the yolk persists in the subsequent divisions that produce a blastula. In frogs, these unequal cell divisions cause the blastocoel to form entirely in the animal hemisphere (see Figure 47.7).

Although yolk affects where division occurs in the eggs of frogs and other amphibians, the cleavage furrow still passes entirely through the egg. Cleavage in amphibian development is thus said to be **holoblastic** (from the Greek *holos*, complete). Holoblastic cleavage is also seen in many other groups of animals, including echinoderms, mammals, and annelids. The orientation of the cleavage furrows varies within these groups, resulting in blastulas that vary considerably in appearance. In those animals whose eggs contain relatively little yolk, the blastocoel forms centrally and the blastomeres are often of similar size, particularly during the first few divisions (see Figure 47.6). This is the case for humans, whose embryos complete three divisions in the first 3 days after fertilization.

Yolk is most plentiful and has its most pronounced effect on cleavage in the eggs of birds, other reptiles, many fishes, and insects. In these animals, the volume of yolk is so great that cleavage furrows cannot pass through it, and only the region of the egg lacking yolk undergoes cleavage. This incomplete cleavage of a yolk-rich egg is said to be **meroblastic** (from the Greek *meros*, partial).

In birds, the part of the egg commonly called the yolk is actually the entire egg cell, swollen with yolk nutrients. Cell divisions are limited to a small whitish area at the animal pole. These divisions produce a cap of cells that sort into upper and lower layers. The cavity between these two layers is the avian version of the blastocoel.

In the eggs of *Drosophila* and most other insects, the sperm and egg nuclei fuse *within* a mass of yolk. Multiple rounds of mitosis occur without cytokinesis. In other words, no cell membranes form around the early nuclei. The first several hundred nuclei spread throughout the yolk and later migrate to the outer edge of the embryo. After several more rounds of mitosis, a plasma membrane forms around each nucleus, and the embryo, now the equivalent of a blastula, consists of a single layer of about 6,000 cells surrounding a mass of yolk (see Figure 18.22).

Regulation of Cleavage

The number of cleavage divisions varies among animals but appears to be controlled by a shared mechanism. Experimental results support the hypothesis that an animal embryo finishes the cleavage stage when the ratio of material in each nucleus to that in the cytoplasm is sufficiently large. One line of evidence comes from experiments in which researchers changed the starting amount of cytoplasm and then counted the cleavage divisions that occurred. For example, when half the normal amount of cytoplasm surrounds the newly formed zygotic nucleus, one fewer cleavage division occurs, consistent with the nuclear-cytoplasmic ratio reaching the threshold after one fewer cell cycle.

What is the adaptive advantage of linking the duration of the cleavage stage to the ratio of material in the nucleus and cytoplasm? The single nucleus in a newly fertilized egg has too little DNA to produce the amount of messenger RNA required to meet the cell's need for new proteins. Instead, the initial stages of development are carried out by RNA and proteins deposited in the egg during oogenesis. After cleavage, the egg cytoplasm has been divided among the many blastomeres, each with its own nucleus. Because each blastomere is much smaller than the entire egg or embryo, its nucleus can make enough RNA to program the cell's metabolism and its further development. The increase in the number of cells also sets the stage for morphogenesis, the transformation of embryo organization and shape.

CONCEPT CHECK 47.1

1. How does the fertilization envelope form in sea urchins? What is its function?
2. **WHAT IF?** Predict what would happen if you injected Ca^{2+} into an unfertilized sea urchin egg.
3. **MAKE CONNECTIONS** Review Figure 12.17 on page 240. Would you expect MPF activity to fluctuate or remain steady during cleavage? Explain your logic.

For suggested answers, see Appendix A.

CONCEPT 47.2

Morphogenesis in animals involves specific changes in cell shape, position, and survival

After cleavage, the rate of cell division slows considerably as the normal cell cycle is restored. The last two stages of embryonic development are responsible for **morphogenesis**, the cellular and tissue-based processes by which the animal body takes shape. During **gastrulation**, a set of cells at or near the surface of the blastula moves to an interior location, cell layers are established, and a primitive digestive tube is formed. Further transformation occurs during **organogenesis**, the formation of organs. We will discuss these two stages in turn, focusing in each case on the development of a few model organisms.

Gastrulation

Gastrulation is a dramatic reorganization of the hollow blastula into a two-layered or three-layered embryo called a **gastrula**. The cell layers produced by gastrulation are collectively called the embryonic **germ layers** (from the Latin *germen*, to sprout or germinate). In the late gastrula, **ectoderm** forms the outer layer and **endoderm** lines the embryonic digestive compartment or tract. In cnidarians and a few other radially symmetrical animals, only these two germ layers form during gastrulation. Such animals are called diploblasts (see Chapter 32). In contrast, animals with bilateral symmetry are triploblasts, having a third germ layer, the **mesoderm,** between the ectoderm and the endoderm.

Each germ layer contributes to a distinct set of structures in the adult animal **(Figure 47.8)**. Note that some organs and many organ systems of the adult derive from more than one germ layer. For example, the adrenal gland has both ectodermal and mesoderm tissue, and many other endocrine glands contain endodermal tissue.

ECTODERM (outer layer of embryo)

- Epidermis of skin and its derivatives (including sweat glands, hair follicles)
- Nervous and sensory systems
- Pituitary gland, adrenal medulla
- Jaws and teeth
- Germ cells

MESODERM (middle layer of embryo)

- Skeletal and muscular systems
- Circulatory and lymphatic systems
- Excretory and reproductive systems (except germ cells)
- Dermis of skin
- Adrenal cortex

ENDODERM (inner layer of embryo)

- Epithelial lining of digestive tract and associated organs (liver, pancreas)
- Epithelial lining of respiratory, excretory, and reproductive tracts and ducts
- Thymus, thyroid, and parathyroid glands

▲ **Figure 47.8 Major derivatives of the three embryonic germ layers in vertebrates.**

▶ **Figure 47.9 Gastrulation in a sea urchin embryo.** The movement of cells during gastrulation forms an embryo with a primitive digestive tube and three germ layers. Some of the mesodermal mesenchyme cells that migrate inward (step ❶) will eventually secrete calcium carbonate and form a simple internal skeleton. Embryos in steps ❶–❸ are viewed from the front, those in ❹ and ❺ from the side.

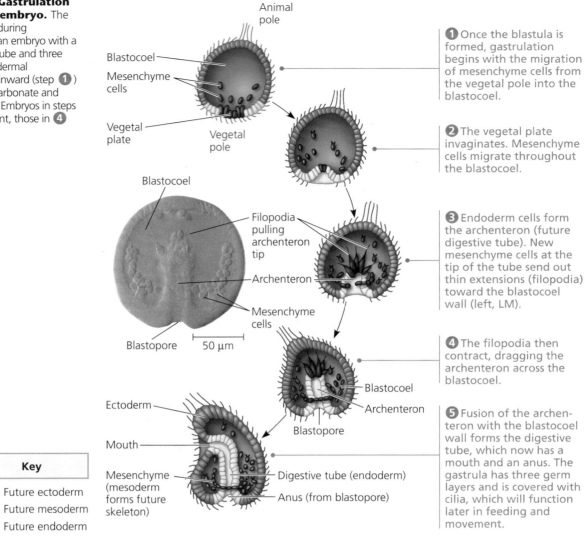

❶ Once the blastula is formed, gastrulation begins with the migration of mesenchyme cells from the vegetal pole into the blastocoel.

❷ The vegetal plate invaginates. Mesenchyme cells migrate throughout the blastocoel.

❸ Endoderm cells form the archenteron (future digestive tube). New mesenchyme cells at the tip of the tube send out thin extensions (filopodia) toward the blastocoel wall (left, LM).

❹ The filopodia then contract, dragging the archenteron across the blastocoel.

❺ Fusion of the archenteron with the blastocoel wall forms the digestive tube, which now has a mouth and an anus. The gastrula has three germ layers and is covered with cilia, which will function later in feeding and movement.

Key
- ▉ Future ectoderm
- ▉ Future mesoderm
- ▉ Future endoderm

Gastrulation in Sea Urchins

Gastrulation in the sea urchin begins at the vegetal pole of the blastula **(Figure 47.9)**. There, cells called *mesenchyme cells* individually detach from the blastocoel wall and enter the blastocoel. The remaining cells near the vegetal pole flatten slightly and cause that end of the embryo to buckle inward as a result of cell shape changes we will discuss later. This process—the infolding of a sheet of cells into the embryo—is called *invagination*. Extensive rearrangement of cells transforms the shallow depression into a deeper, narrower, blind-ended tube called the **archenteron**. The open end of the archenteron, which will become the anus, is called the **blastopore**. A second opening, which will become the mouth, forms when the opposite end of the archenteron touches the inside of the ectoderm and the two layers fuse, producing a rudimentary digestive tube.

As you learned in Chapter 32, animals can be categorized by whether the mouth develops from the first opening that forms in the embryo (protostomes) or the second (deuterostomes).

Sea urchins and other echinoderms are deuterostomes, as are chordates like ourselves and other vertebrates.

Upon completing gastrulation, sea urchin embryos develop into ciliated larvae that drift in ocean surface waters as zooplankton, feeding on bacteria and unicellular algae. Eventually, each larva metamorphoses into the adult form of the sea urchin, which takes up residence on the ocean floor.

Gastrulation in Frogs

The frog blastula contains large, yolk-laden cells in the vegetal hemisphere and a blastocoel wall that in most species is more than one cell thick. Recall from Chapter 32 that frogs and other bilaterally symmetrical animals have a dorsal (top) side and a ventral (bottom) side, a left side and a right side, and an anterior (front) end and a posterior (back) end. As shown in **Figure 47.10**, frog gastrulation begins when a group of cells on the dorsal side of the blastula begins to invaginate. This process forms a crease along the region where the gray crescent formed (see Figure 47.7). It may help to

① Gastrulation begins when a small indented crease, the blastopore, appears on the dorsal side of the late blastula. The crease is formed by cells changing shape and invaginating. Sheets of outer cells then roll inward over the dorsal lip (involution) and move into the interior (shown by the dashed arrow), where they will form endoderm and mesoderm. Meanwhile, cells at the animal pole change shape and begin spreading over the outer surface.

SURFACE VIEW · CROSS SECTION

Animal pole

Blastocoel

Dorsal lip of blasto-pore

Dorsal lip of blastopore

Blastopore

Early gastrula

Vegetal pole

② The blastopore extends around both sides of the embryo (red arrows) as more cells invaginate. When the ends meet, the blastopore forms a circle that becomes smaller as ectoderm spreads downward over the surface. Internally, continued involution expands the endoderm and mesoderm, and the archenteron begins to form; as a result, the blastocoel becomes smaller.

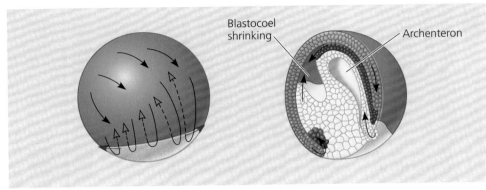

Blastocoel shrinking

Archenteron

③ Late in gastrulation, the endoderm-lined archenteron has completely replaced the blastocoel and the three germ layers are in place. The circular blastopore surrounds a plug of yolk-filled cells.

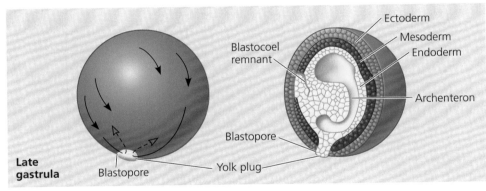

Ectoderm

Mesoderm

Endoderm

Blastocoel remnant

Archenteron

Blastopore

Yolk plug

Key	

▬ Future ectoderm
▬ Future mesoderm
▢ Future endoderm

Late gastrula

Blastopore

▲ **Figure 47.10 Gastrulation in a frog embryo.** In the frog blastula, the blastocoel is displaced toward the animal pole and is surrounded by a wall several cells thick. The cell movements that begin gastrulation occur on the dorsal side of the blastula, opposite where the sperm entered the egg.

think of this crease as the site where two thin lips are pressed together. The part above the crease becomes the dorsal side of the blastopore, called the **dorsal lip**.

As the blastopore is forming, a sheet of cells begins to spread out of the animal hemisphere. Some of these cells roll over the edge of the lip into the interior of the embryo, a process called *involution*. Once inside the embryo, these cells move away from the blastopore toward the animal pole and become organized into layers of endoderm and mesoderm, with the endoderm on the inside. Cells continue to spread over the gastrula surface, shifting and shrinking the blastopore. In the interior of the embryo, an archenteron forms and grows as the blastocoel shrinks and eventually disappears.

At the end of gastrulation, the cells remaining on the surface make up the ectoderm, the tube of endoderm is the innermost layer, and the mesoderm lies between them. As in the sea urchin, the frog's anus develops from the blastopore, and the mouth eventually breaks through at the opposite end of the archenteron.

Gastrulation in Chicks

The starting point for gastrulation in chicks is an embryo consisting of upper and lower layers—the *epiblast* and *hypoblast*—lying atop a yolk mass. All the cells that will form the embryo come from the epiblast. During gastrulation, some epiblast cells move toward the midline of the blastoderm, detach, and

▲ **Figure 47.11 Gastrulation in a chick embryo.**
The chick blastula consists of an upper layer of cells, the epiblast, and a lower layer, the hypoblast, with a space (the blastocoel) between them. This is a cross section at a right angle to the primitive streak, looking toward the anterior end of a gastrulating embryo. During gastrulation, some cells of the epiblast migrate (arrows) into the interior of the embryo through the primitive streak. Some of these cells move downward and form endoderm, pushing aside the hypoblast cells, while others migrate laterally and form mesoderm. The cells left behind on the surface of the embryo at the end of gastrulation will become ectoderm.

move inward toward the yolk **(Figure 47.11)**. The pileup of cells moving inward at the blastoderm's midline produces a thickening called the **primitive streak**. Although the hypoblast contributes no cells to the embryo, it is required for normal development and seems to help direct the formation of the primitive streak before the onset of gastrulation. The hypoblast cells later segregate from the endoderm and eventually form part of the sac that surrounds the yolk and also part of the stalk that connects the yolk mass to the embryo.

Gastrulation in Humans

Unlike the large, yolky eggs of many vertebrates, human eggs are quite small, storing little in the way of food reserves. Fertilization takes place in the oviduct, and the earliest stages of development occur while the embryo completes its journey down the oviduct to the uterus (see Figure 46.15). Knowledge about gastrulation in humans is therefore largely based on what we can extrapolate from other mammals, such as the mouse, and on observation of very early human development following *in vitro* fertilization.

Figure 47.12 depicts development of the human embryo starting about 6 days after fertilization. The description on page 1031 follows the numbered stages in the figure.

① Blastocyst reaches uterus.

② Blastocyst implants (7 days after fertilization).

③ Extraembryonic membranes start to form (10–11 days), and gastrulation begins (13 days).

④ Gastrulation has produced a three-layered embryo with four extraembryonic membranes.

▲ **Figure 47.12 Four stages in the early embryonic development of a human.**

❶ At the end of cleavage, the embryo has more than 100 cells arranged around a central cavity and has traveled down the oviduct to the uterus. At this stage of development, the embryo is called a **blastocyst**, the mammalian version of a blastula. Clustered at one end of the blastocyst cavity is a group of cells called the **inner cell mass**, which will develop into the embryo proper. It is the cells of the very early blastocyst stage that are the source of embryonic stem cell lines.

❷ The **trophoblast**, the outer epithelium of the blastocyst, does not contribute to the embryo itself but instead supports embryo growth in a number of ways. It initiates implantation by secreting enzymes that break down molecules of the endometrium, the lining of the uterus. This allows the blastocyst to invade the endometrium. As the trophoblast thickens through cell division, it extends finger-like projections into the surrounding maternal tissue. Invasion by the trophoblast leads to erosion of capillaries in the endometrium, causing blood to spill out and bathe trophoblast tissues. Around the time of implantation, the inner cell mass of the blastocyst forms a flat disk with an upper layer of cells, the *epiblast*, and a lower layer, the *hypoblast*. As in birds, the human embryo develops almost entirely from epiblast cells.

❸ Following implantation, the trophoblast continues to expand into the endometrium, and four new membranes appear. Although these **extraembryonic membranes** are formed by the embryo, they enclose specialized structures located outside the embryo. As implantation is completed, gastrulation begins. Cells move inward from the epiblast through a primitive streak and form mesoderm and endoderm, just as in the chick (see Figure 47.11).

❹ By the end of gastrulation, the embryonic germ layers have formed. Extraembryonic mesoderm and the four extraembryonic membranes now surround the embryo. As development proceeds, the invading trophoblast, cells from the epiblast, and adjacent endometrial tissue will all contribute to formation of the placenta. This vital organ mediates exchange of nutrients, gases, and nitrogenous wastes between the embryo and the mother.

Developmental Adaptations of Amniotes

EVOLUTION As you read in Chapter 34, birds and other reptiles, like mammals, form four extraembryonic membranes. In all these groups, such membranes provide a "life-support system" for further embryonic development. Why, then, did this adaptation appear in the evolutionary history of reptiles and mammals but not other vertebrates, such as fishes and amphibians? We can formulate a reasonable hypothesis by considering a few basic facts about embryonic development. All vertebrate embryos require an aqueous environment for their development. The embryos of fishes and amphibians usually develop in the surrounding sea or pond and need no specialized water-filled enclosure. However, the extensive colonization of land by vertebrates was possible only after the evolution of structures that would allow reproduction in dry environments. Two such structures exist today: (1) the shelled egg of birds and other reptiles as well as a few mammals (the monotremes) and (2) the uterus of marsupial and eutherian mammals. Inside the shell or uterus, the embryos of these animals are surrounded by fluid within a sac formed by one of the extraembryonic membranes, the amnion. Mammals and reptiles, including birds, are therefore called **amniotes** (see Chapter 34).

We can explore the evolution of extraembryonic membranes by comparing their functions in different groups of amniotes. For the purposes of this discussion, you may find it useful to refer to Figure 34.26, which describes the functions of the extraembryonic membranes in the egg of a reptile.

For the most part, the extraembryonic membranes have similar functions in mammals and reptiles, consistent with a common evolutionary origin. The chorion is the site of gas exchange, and the fluid within the amnion physically protects the developing embryo. (This amniotic fluid is released from the vagina when a pregnant woman's "water breaks" just before childbirth.) The allantois, which disposes of wastes in the reptilian egg, is incorporated into the umbilical cord in mammals. There it forms blood vessels that transport oxygen and nutrients from the placenta to the embryo and rid the embryo of carbon dioxide and nitrogenous wastes. The fourth extraembryonic membrane, the yolk sac, encloses yolk in the eggs of reptiles. In mammals it is a site of early formation of blood cells, which later migrate into the embryo proper. Thus, although the extraembryonic membranes of reptiles were conserved in mammals in the course of evolution, modifications appeared that were adapted to development within the uterus of the mother.

After gastrulation is complete and any extraembryonic membranes are formed, the next stage of embryonic development begins: organ formation.

Organogenesis

During organogenesis, regions of the three embryonic germ layers develop into the rudiments of organs. Whereas gastrulation involves mass movements of cells, organogenesis involves

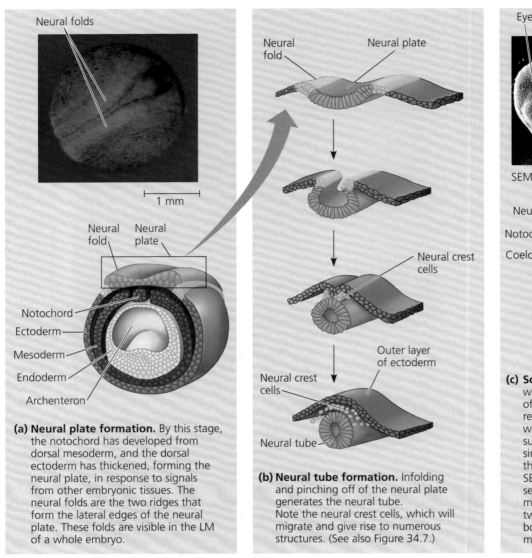

Neural folds

1 mm

Neural fold | Neural plate

Notochord
Ectoderm
Mesoderm
Endoderm
Archenteron

(a) Neural plate formation. By this stage, the notochord has developed from dorsal mesoderm, and the dorsal ectoderm has thickened, forming the neural plate, in response to signals from other embryonic tissues. The neural folds are the two ridges that form the lateral edges of the neural plate. These folds are visible in the LM of a whole embryo.

Neural fold | Neural plate

Neural crest cells

Outer layer of ectoderm

Neural crest cells

Neural tube

(b) Neural tube formation. Infolding and pinching off of the neural plate generates the neural tube. Note the neural crest cells, which will migrate and give rise to numerous structures. (See also Figure 34.7.)

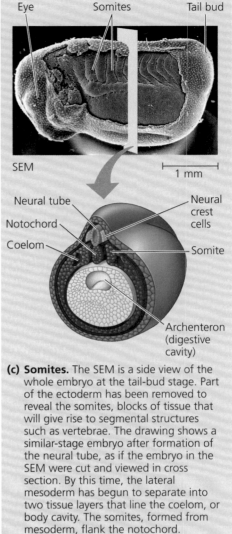

Eye   Somites   Tail bud

SEM   1 mm

Neural tube
Notochord
Coelom

Neural crest cells
Somite

Archenteron (digestive cavity)

(c) Somites. The SEM is a side view of the whole embryo at the tail-bud stage. Part of the ectoderm has been removed to reveal the somites, blocks of tissue that will give rise to segmental structures such as vertebrae. The drawing shows a similar-stage embryo after formation of the neural tube, as if the embryo in the SEM were cut and viewed in cross section. By this time, the lateral mesoderm has begun to separate into two tissue layers that line the coelom, or body cavity. The somites, formed from mesoderm, flank the notochord.

▲ **Figure 47.13 Neurulation in a frog embryo.**

more localized changes. To illustrate the basic principles of this process, we'll focus on *neurulation*, the first steps in the formation of the brain and spinal cord in vertebrates.

Neurulation begins as cells from the dorsal mesoderm come together to form the **notochord**, the rod that extends along the dorsal side of the chordate embryo, seen in **Figure 47.13a** for the frog. Signaling molecules secreted by these mesodermal cells and other tissues induce the ectoderm above the notochord to become the *neural plate*. Next, the cells of the neural plate change shape, curving the neural plate inward. In this way, the neural plate rolls itself into the **neural tube**, which runs along the anterior-posterior axis of the embryo **(Figure 47.13b)**. The neural tube will become the brain in the head and the spinal cord along the rest of the body.

In vertebrate embryos, two sets of cells develop near the neural tube and then migrate elsewhere in the body. The first set is a band of cells called the **neural crest**, which develops along the borders where the neural tube pinches off from the ectoderm. Neural crest cells subsequently migrate to many parts of the embryo, forming a variety of tissues that include peripheral nerves as well as parts of the teeth and skull bones. The second set of migratory cells is formed when groups of cells located in strips of mesoderm lateral to the notochord separate into blocks called **somites (Figure 47.13c)**. The somites are arranged serially on both sides along the length of the notochord. Parts of the somites dissociate into mesenchyme cells, which migrate individually to new locations.

Somites play a major role in organizing the segmented structure of the vertebrate body. One of the major functions of the mesenchyme cells that leave the somites is formation of the vertebrae. Although the notochord disappears before birth, parts of the notochord persist as the inner portions of

► **Figure 47.14**
Organogenesis in a chick embryo.

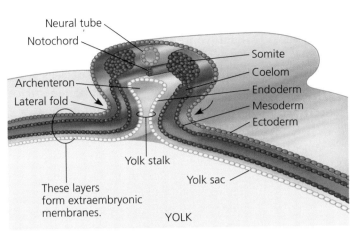

Labels in diagram (a): Neural tube, Notochord, Somite, Coelom, Archenteron, Endoderm, Lateral fold, Mesoderm, Ectoderm, Yolk stalk, These layers form extraembryonic membranes., Yolk sac, YOLK

(a) Early organogenesis. The archenteron forms when lateral folds pinch the embryo away from the yolk. The embryo remains open to the yolk, attached by the yolk stalk, about midway along its length, as shown in this cross section. The notochord, neural tube, and somites subsequently develop much as they do in the frog. The germ layers lateral to the embryo itself form extraembryonic membranes.

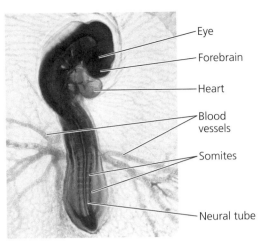

Labels in photo (b): Eye, Forebrain, Heart, Blood vessels, Somites, Neural tube

(b) Late organogenesis. Rudiments of most major organs have already formed in this chick embryo, which is 3 days old and about 2–3 mm long. The extraembryonic membranes eventually are supplied by blood vessels extending from the embryo; several major blood vessels are seen here (LM).

the vertebral disks in adults. (These are the disks that can herniate or rupture, causing back pain.) Somite cells that become mesenchymal later form the muscles associated with the vertebral column and the ribs. Through these processes, serially repeating structures of the embryo (somites) form repeated structures in the adult. Chordates can thus be described as segmented animals, although the segmentation becomes less obvious later in development. Lateral to the somites, the mesoderm splits into two layers that form the lining of the body cavity, or coelom (see Figure 32.8).

Early organogenesis in other vertebrates is quite similar to that in the frog. In the chick, for example, the borders of the blastoderm fold downward and come together, pinching the embryo into a three-layered tube joined under the middle of the body to the yolk **(Figure 47.14a)**. By the time the chick embryo is 3 days old, rudiments of the major organs, including the brain, eyes, and heart, are readily apparent **(Figure 47.14b)**.

In humans, an error in neural tube formation results in *spina bifida*, the most common disabling birth defect in the United States. In spina bifida, a portion of the neural tube fails to develop or close properly, leaving an opening in the spinal column and causing nerve damage. Although the opening can be surgically repaired shortly after birth, the nerve damage is permanent, resulting in varying degrees of leg paralysis.

Organogenesis is somewhat different in invertebrates, which is not surprising, given that their body plans diverge significantly from those of vertebrates. The underlying mechanisms, however, involve many of the same cellular activities: cell migration, cell signaling between different tissues, and cell shape changes generating new organs. In insects, for example, tissues of the nervous system form when ectoderm

along the anterior-posterior axis rolls into a tube inside the embryo, similar to the vertebrate neural tube. Interestingly, the tube is on the ventral side of the insect embryo rather than the dorsal side, where it is in vertebrates. In spite of the different locations, the molecular signaling pathways that bring about the events in the two groups are very similar, underscoring their ancient shared evolutionary history.

As we have seen in our consideration of gastrulation and organogenesis, changes in cell shape and location are essential to early development. We will turn now to an exploration of how these changes take place.

Mechanisms of Morphogenesis

Morphogenesis is a major stage of development in both animals and plants, but only in animals does it involve the *movement* of cells. The rigid cell wall that surrounds plant cells prevents complex movements like those that occur during gastrulation and organogenesis. In animals, movement of parts of a cell can bring about changes in cell shape or enable a cell to migrate from one place to another within the embryo. Here we will consider some of the cellular components that contribute to these events. We'll begin with the roles of the microtubules and microfilaments that make up the cytoskeleton (see Table 6.1).

The Cytoskeleton in Morphogenesis

Reorganization of the cytoskeleton is a major force in changing cell shape during development. As an example, let's return to the topic of neurulation. At the onset of neural tube formation, microtubules oriented from dorsal to ventral in a sheet of ectodermal cells help lengthen the cells along that

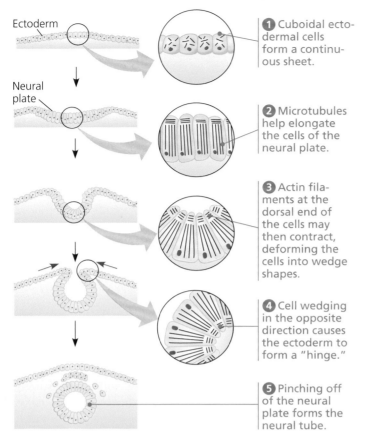

Ectoderm

❶ Cuboidal ecto-dermal cells form a continu-ous sheet.

Neural plate

❷ Microtubules help elongate the cells of the neural plate.

❸ Actin fila-ments at the dorsal end of the cells may then contract, deforming the cells into wedge shapes.

❹ Cell wedging in the opposite direction causes the ectoderm to form a "hinge."

❺ Pinching off of the neural plate forms the neural tube.

▲ **Figure 47.15 Change in cell shape during morphogenesis.** Reorganization of the cytoskeleton is associated with morphogenetic changes in embryonic tissues, as shown here for the formation of the neural tube in vertebrates.

axis **(Figure 47.15)**. At the dorsal end of each cell is a bundle of actin filaments (microfilaments) oriented crosswise. These actin filaments contract, giving the cells a wedge shape that bends the ectoderm layer inward. Similar changes in cell shape occur at the hinge regions where the neural tube is pinching off from the ectoderm. However, the generation of wedge-shaped cells is not limited to neurulation or even to vertebrates. In *Drosophila* gastrulation, for instance, the for-mation of wedge-shaped cells along the ventral surface is re-sponsible for invagination of a tube of cells that form the mesoderm.

The cytoskeleton directs a different type of morpho-genetic movement in promoting elongation of the archen-teron in the sea urchin embryo (see Figure 47.9). In this case, cytoskeletal changes direct **convergent extension**, a rearrangement of the cells of a tissue layer that causes the sheet to become narrower (converge) while it becomes longer (extends). It's as if a crowd of people waiting to

enter a theater for a concert began to form a single-file line; the line would become much longer as it narrowed. In the embryo, the cells elongate, with their ends pointing in the direction they will move, and they wedge between each other into fewer columns of cells **(Figure 47.16)**. Conver-gent extension is also important in other developmental settings, such as involution in the frog gastrula. There, con-vergent extension changes the gastrulating embryo from a spherical shape to the rounded rectangular shape seen in Figure 47.13c.

The cytoskeleton is responsible not only for cell shape changes but also for cell migration. During organogenesis in vertebrates, cells from the neural crest and from somites mi-grate to locations throughout the embryo. Cells "crawl" within the embryo by using cytoskeletal fibers to extend and retract cellular protrusions. This type of motility is akin to the amoeboid movement described in Figure 6.27b. Trans-membrane glycoproteins called *cell adhesion molecules* play a key role in cell migration by promoting interaction between pairs of cells. Cell migration also involves the *extracellular ma-trix* (*ECM*), the meshwork of secreted glycoproteins and other macromolecules lying outside the plasma membranes of cells (see Figure 6.30). The ECM helps to guide cells in many types of movements, such as migration of individual cells and shape changes of cell sheets. Cells that line migration path-ways regulate movement of migrating cells by secreting spe-cific molecules into the ECM.

Programmed Cell Death

Just as certain cells of the embryo are programmed to change shape or location, others are programmed to die. A type of *programmed cell death* called **apoptosis** is in fact a common feature of animal development. At various times in develop-ment, individual cells, sets of cells, or whole tissues cease to develop and are engulfed by neighboring cells. In some cases, a structure functions in a larval or other immature form of the organism and then is eliminated during later develop-ment. One familiar example is provided by the cells in the tail of a tadpole, which undergo apoptosis during frog meta-morphosis. Apoptosis can also occur when cells compete with one another for survival. For instance, many more neu-rons are produced during development of the vertebrate nervous system than exist in the adult. In general, neurons survive if they make functional connections with other neu-rons and die if they do not.

Some cells that undergo apoptosis don't seem to have any function in the developing embryo. Why do such cells form? The answer can be found by considering the evolution of

▶ **Figure 47.16 Convergent extension of a sheet of cells.** In this simplified diagram, the cells elongate in a particular direction and crawl between each other (convergence) as the sheet becomes longer and narrower (extension).

Convergence

Extension

amphibians, birds, and mammals. When these groups began to diverge during evolution, the developmental program for making a vertebrate body was already in place. The differences in present-day body forms arose through modification of that common developmental program (which is why the early embryos of all vertebrates look so similar). As these groups evolved, many structures produced by the ancestral program that no longer offered a selective advantage were targeted for cell death. For example, the shared developmental program generates webbing between the embryonic digits, but in many birds and mammals the webbing is eliminated by apoptosis.

As you have seen, cell behavior and the molecular mechanisms underlying it are crucial to the morphogenesis of the embryo. In the next section, you'll learn that a shared set of cellular and genetic processes ensure that the various types of cells end up in the right places in each embryo.

CONCEPT CHECK 47.2

1. In the frog embryo, convergent extension elongates the notochord. Explain how the words *convergent* and *extension* apply to this process.
2. **WHAT IF?** Predict what would happen if, just before neural tube formation, you treated embryos with a drug that blocks the function of microfilaments.
3. **MAKE CONNECTIONS** Unlike some other types of birth defects, neural tube defects are largely preventable. Explain (see Figure 41.4, p. 879).

For suggested answers, see Appendix A.

CONCEPT 47.3

Cytoplasmic determinants and inductive signals contribute to cell fate specification

During embryonic development, cells arise by division, take up particular locations in the body, and become specialized in structure and function. Where a cell resides, how it appears, and what it does define its development fate. Developmental biologists use the terms **determination** to refer to the process by which a cell or group of cells becomes committed to a particular fate and **differentiation** to refer to the resulting specialization in structure and function.

Every diploid cell formed during an animal's development has the same genome. With the exception of certain mature immune cells, the collection of genes present is the same throughout the cell's life. How, then, do cells acquire different fates? As discussed in Concept 18.4, particular tissues, and often cells within a tissue, differ from one another by expressing distinct sets of genes from their shared genome.

A major focus of developmental biology is to uncover the mechanisms that direct the differences in gene expression underlying developmental fates. As one step toward this goal, scientists often seek to trace tissues and cell types back to their origins in the early embryo.

Fate Mapping

One way to trace the ancestry of embryonic cells is direct observation through the microscope. Such studies produced the first **fate maps**, diagrams showing the structures arising from each region of an embryo. In the 1920s, German embryologist Walther Vogt used this approach to determine where groups of cells from the blastula end up in the gastrula (**Figure 47.17a**). Later researchers developed techniques that allowed them to mark an individual blastomere during cleavage and then follow the marker as it was distributed to all the mitotic descendants of that cell (**Figure 47.17b**).

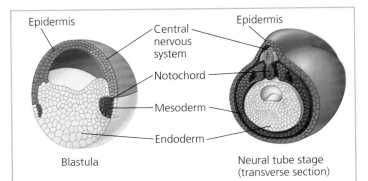

Epidermis / Central nervous system / Epidermis / Notochord / Mesoderm / Endoderm

Blastula / Neural tube stage (transverse section)

(a) Fate map of a frog embryo. The fates of groups of cells in a frog blastula (left) were determined in part by marking different regions of the blastula surface with nontoxic dyes of various colors. The embryos were sectioned at later stages of development, such as the neural tube stage shown on the right, and the locations of the dyed cells determined. The two embryonic stages shown here represent the result of numerous such experiments.

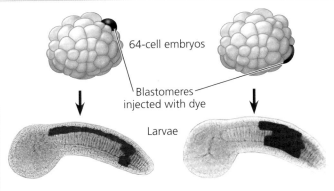

64-cell embryos

Blastomeres injected with dye

Larvae

(b) Cell lineage analysis in a tunicate. In lineage analysis, an individual blastomere is injected with a dye during cleavage, as indicated in the drawings of 64-cell embryos of a tunicate, an invertebrate chordate (top). The dark regions in the light micrographs of larvae (bottom) correspond to the cells that developed from the two different blastomeres indicated in the drawings.

▲ **Figure 47.17 Fate mapping for two chordates.**

A much more comprehensive approach to fate mapping has been carried out on the soil-dwelling nematode *Caenorhabditis elegans*. This roundworm is about 1 mm long, has a simple, transparent body with only a few types of cells, and develops into a mature adult hermaphrodite in only 3½ days in the laboratory. These attributes allowed Sydney Brenner, Robert Horvitz, and John Sulston to determine the complete cell lineage of *C. elegans*. They found that every adult hermaphrodite has exactly 959 somatic cells, which arise from the fertilized egg in virtually the same way for every individual. Careful microscopic observations of worms at all stages of development, coupled with experiments in which particular cells or groups of cells were destroyed by a laser beam or through mutations, resulted in the cell lineage diagram shown in **Figure 47.18**.

As an example of a particular cell fate, we'll consider *germ cells*, the specialized cells that give rise to eggs or sperm. In all animals studied, complexes of RNA and protein are involved in the specification of germ cell fate. In *C. elegans*, such complexes, called *P granules*, persist throughout development and can be detected in the germ cells of the adult gonad **(Figure 47.19)**.

▲ **Figure 47.19 Determination of germ cell fate in *C. elegans*.** Labeling with an antibody specific for a *C. elegans* P granule protein (green) reveals the specific incorporation of P granules into the cells of the adult worm that will produce sperm or eggs.

Tracing the position of the P granules provides a dramatic illustration of cell fate specification during development. The P granules are distributed throughout the newly fertilized egg but move to the posterior end of the zygote before the first cleavage division **(Figure 47.20 ❶ and ❷)**. As a result, only the posterior of the two cells formed by the first division contains P granules **(Figure 47.20 ❸)**. The P granules continue to be asymmetrically partitioned during subsequent divisions **(Figure 47.20 ❹)**. Thus, the P granules act as cytoplasmic determinants (see Concept 18.4), fixing germ cell fate at the earliest stage of *C. elegans* development.

Fate mapping in *C. elegans* paved the way for major discoveries about programmed cell death. Lineage analysis demonstrated that exactly 131 cells die during normal *C. elegans* development. In the 1980s, researchers found that a mutation inactivating a single gene allows all 131 cells to live. Further research revealed that this gene is part of a pathway that controls and carries out apoptosis in a wide range of animals, including humans. In 2002, Brenner, Horvitz, and Sulston shared a Nobel Prize for their use of the *C. elegans* fate map in studies of programmed cell death and organogenesis.

Having established fate maps for early development, scientists were positioned to answer questions about underlying mechanisms, such as how the basic axes of the embryo are established, a process known as axis formation.

Axis Formation

A body plan with bilateral symmetry is found across a range of animals, including nematodes, echinoderms, and vertebrates (see Chapter 32). As shown for a frog tadpole in **Figure 47.21a**, this body plan exhibits asymmetry along the dorsal-ventral and anterior-posterior axes. The right-left axis is largely symmetrical, as

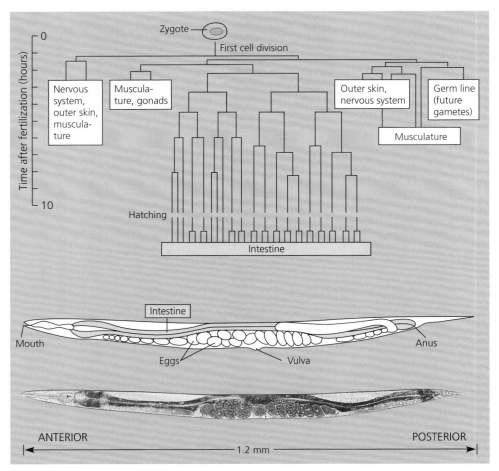

▲ **Figure 47.18 Cell lineage in *Caenorhabditis elegans*.** The *C. elegans* embryo is transparent, making it possible for researchers to trace the lineage of every cell, from the zygote to the adult worm (LM). The diagram shows a detailed lineage only for the intestine, which is derived exclusively from one of the first four cells formed from the zygote. The eggs will be fertilized internally and released through the vulva.

1 Newly fertilized egg

2 Zygote prior to first division

3 Two-cell embryo

4 Four-cell embryo

▲ **Figure 47.20 Partitioning of P granules during C. elegans development.** The differential interference contrast micrographs (left) highlight the boundaries of nuclei and cells through the first two cell divisions. The immunofluorescence micrographs (right) show identically staged embryos stained with a labeled antibody specific for a P granule protein.

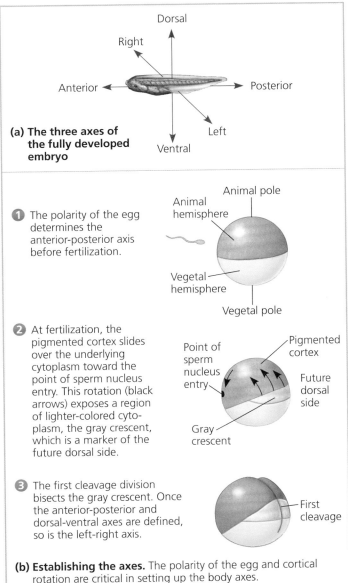

(a) The three axes of the fully developed embryo

Dorsal, Right, Anterior, Posterior, Left, Ventral

1 The polarity of the egg determines the anterior-posterior axis before fertilization.

Animal pole, Animal hemisphere, Vegetal hemisphere, Vegetal pole

2 At fertilization, the pigmented cortex slides over the underlying cytoplasm toward the point of sperm nucleus entry. This rotation (black arrows) exposes a region of lighter-colored cytoplasm, the gray crescent, which is a marker of the future dorsal side.

Point of sperm nucleus entry, Pigmented cortex, Future dorsal side, Gray crescent

3 The first cleavage division bisects the gray crescent. Once the anterior-posterior and dorsal-ventral axes are defined, so is the left-right axis.

First cleavage

(b) Establishing the axes. The polarity of the egg and cortical rotation are critical in setting up the body axes.

▲ **Figure 47.21 The body axes and their establishment in an amphibian.** All three axes are established before the zygote begins to undergo cleavage.

WHAT IF? *To study axis establishment, researchers can block cortical rotation or force it to occur in a specific direction. One such study resulted in a two-headed embryo because the "back" developed on both sides. What do you think the researchers did to obtain such an embryo?*

the two sides are roughly mirror images of each other. These three body axes are established early in development.

The anterior-posterior axis of the frog embryo is determined during oogenesis. Asymmetry is apparent in the formation of two distinct hemispheres: Dark melanin granules are embedded in the cortex of the animal hemisphere, whereas a yellow yolk fills the vegetal hemisphere. This animal-vegetal asymmetry dictates where the anterior-posterior axis forms in the embryo. Note, however, that the anterior-posterior and

animal-vegetal axes are not the same; that is, the head of the embryo does not form at the animal pole.

The dorsal-ventral axis of the frog embryo is not determined until fertilization. Upon fusion of the egg and the sperm, the egg surface—the plasma membrane and associated cortex—rotates with respect to the inner cytoplasm, a movement called *cortical rotation*. From the perspective of the animal pole, this rotation is always toward the point of sperm entry **(Figure 47.21b)**.

How does cortical rotation establish the dorsal-ventral axis? Cortical rotation allows molecules in one portion of the vegetal cortex to interact with molecules in the inner cytoplasm of the animal hemisphere. These inductive interactions activate regulatory factors in specific portions of the vegetal cortex, leading to expression of different sets of genes in dorsal and ventral regions of the embryo.

In chicks, gravity is apparently involved in establishing the anterior-posterior axis as the egg travels down the hen's oviduct before being laid. Later, pH differences between the two sides of the blastoderm cells establish the dorsal-ventral axis. If the pH is artificially reversed above and below the blastoderm, the cells' fates will be reversed: The side facing the egg white will become the ventral part of the embryo, whereas the side facing the yolk will become the dorsal part.

In mammals, no polarity is obvious until after cleavage. However, the results of recent experiments suggest that the orientation of the egg and sperm nuclei before they fuse influences the location of the first cleavage plane and thus may play a role in establishing the embryonic axes. In insects, morphogen gradients establish both the anterior-posterior and dorsal-ventral axes (see Chapter 18).

Once the anterior-posterior and dorsal-ventral axes are established, the position of the left-right axis is fixed. Nevertheless, specific molecular mechanisms must establish which side is left and which is right. In vertebrates, there are marked left-right differences in the location of internal organs as well as in the organization and structure of the heart and brain. Recent research has revealed that cilia are involved in setting up this left-right asymmetry. We will discuss this and other developmental roles of cilia at the end of this chapter.

Restricting Developmental Potential

Earlier we described determination in terms of commitment to a particular cell fate. Is cell fate commitment immediately irreversible, or is there a period of time during which cell fate can be modified? The German zoologist Hans Spemann addressed this question in 1938. By manipulating embryos to perturb normal development and then examining cell fate after the manipulation, he was able to assay a

cell's *developmental potential*, the range of structures to which it can give rise **(Figure 47.22)**. Spemann found that the fates of embryonic cells are affected by both the distribution of determinants and the pattern of cleavage relative to this distribution. Furthermore, the work of Spemann and others demonstrated that the first two blastomeres of the frog embryo are **totipotent**, meaning that they can each develop into all the different cell types of that species.

In mammals, embryonic cells remain totipotent through the eight-cell stage, much longer than in many other animals. Recent work, however, indicates that the very early cells (even the first two) are not actually equivalent in a normal embryo. Rather, their totipotency when isolated likely

▼ **Figure 47.22**

INQUIRY

How does distribution of the gray crescent affect the developmental potential of the first two daughter cells?

EXPERIMENT Hans Spemann, at the University of Freiburg-im-Breisgau, in Germany, carried out the following experiment in 1938 to test whether substances were located asymmetrically in the gray crescent.

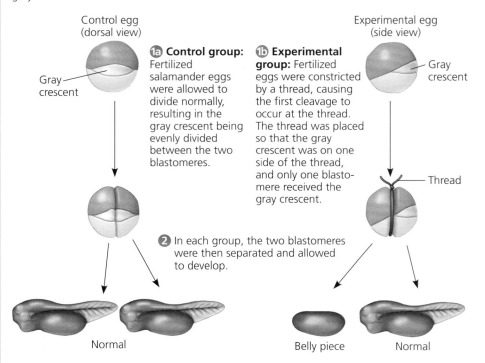

1a Control group: Fertilized salamander eggs were allowed to divide normally, resulting in the gray crescent being evenly divided between the two blastomeres.

1b Experimental group: Fertilized eggs were constricted by a thread, causing the first cleavage to occur at the thread. The thread was placed so that the gray crescent was on one side of the thread, and only one blastomere received the gray crescent.

2 In each group, the two blastomeres were then separated and allowed to develop.

RESULTS Blastomeres that received half or all of the material in the gray crescent developed into normal embryos, but a blastomere that received none of the gray crescent gave rise to an abnormal embryo without dorsal structures. Spemann called it a "belly piece."

CONCLUSION The developmental potential of the two blastomeres normally formed during the first cleavage division depends on their acquisition of cytoplasmic determinants localized in the gray crescent.

SOURCE H. Spemann, *Embryonic Development and Induction*, Yale University Press, New Haven, CT (1938).

WHAT IF? In a similar experiment 40 years earlier, embryologist Hans Roux allowed the first cleavage to occur and then used a needle to kill just one blastomere. The embryo that developed from the remaining blastomere (plus remnants of the dead cell) was abnormal, resembling a half-embryo. Propose a hypothesis to explain why Roux's result differed from the control result in Spemann's experiment.

means that the cells can regulate their fate in response to their embryonic environment. Once the 16-cell stage is reached, mammalian cells are determined to form the trophoblast or the inner cell mass. Although the cells have a limited developmental potential from this point onward, their nuclei remain totipotent, as demonstrated in cloning experiments like that described in Figure 20.19.

As you learned in Chapter 46, identical (monozygotic) twins can develop when embryonic cells become separated. If the separation occurs before the trophoblast and inner cell mass become differentiated, two embryos grow, each with its own chorion and amnion. This is the case for about a third of identical twins. For the rest, the two embryos that develop share a chorion and, in very rare cases where separation is particularly late, an amnion as well.

Regardless of how uniform or varied early embryonic cells are in a particular species, the progressive restriction of developmental potential is a general feature of development in all animals. In general, the tissue-specific fates of cells are fixed in a late gastrula, but not always so in an early gastrula. For example, if the dorsal ectoderm of an early amphibian gastrula is experimentally replaced with ectoderm from some other location in the same gastrula, the transplanted tissue forms a neural plate. But if the same experiment is performed on a late-stage gastrula, the transplanted ectoderm does not respond to its new environment and does not form a neural plate.

Cell Fate Determination and Pattern Formation by Inductive Signals

As embryonic cells acquire distinct fates, the cells begin to influence each other's fates by induction. At the molecular level, the response to an inductive signal is usually to switch on a set of genes that make the receiving cells differentiate into a specific tissue. Here we will examine two examples of induction, an essential process in the development of many tissues in most animals.

The "Organizer" of Spemann and Mangold

Before his studies of totipotency in the fertilized frog egg, Spemann had investigated cell fate determination during gastrulation. In these experiments, he and his student Hilde Mangold transplanted tissues between early gastrulas. In their most famous such experiment, summarized in **Figure 47.23**, they made a remarkable discovery. Not only did a transplanted dorsal lip of the blastopore continue to be a blastopore lip, but it also triggered gastrulation of the surrounding tissue. They concluded that the dorsal lip of the blastopore in the early gastrula functions as an "organizer" of the embryo's body plan, inducing changes in surrounding tissue that direct formation of the notochord, the neural tube, and other organs.

Nearly a century later, developmental biologists are still actively studying the basis of induction by *Spemann's organizer*. An important clue has come from studies of a growth factor called

▼ Figure 47.23

Can the dorsal lip of the blastopore induce cells in another part of the amphibian embryo to change their developmental fate?

EXPERIMENT In 1924, Hans Spemann and Hilde Mangold, at the University of Freiburg-im-Breisgau, in Germany, transplanted a piece of the dorsal lip from a pigmented newt gastrula to the ventral side of a nonpigmented newt gastrula to investigate the inductive ability of the dorsal lip. Cross sections of the gastrulas are shown here.

Dorsal lip of blastopore

Pigmented gastrula (donor embryo)

Nonpigmented gastrula (recipient embryo)

RESULTS The recipient embryo formed a second notochord and neural tube in the region of the transplant, and eventually most of a second embryo developed. Examination of the interior of the double embryo revealed that the secondary structures were formed partly, but not wholly, from recipient tissue.

Primary embryo

Secondary (induced) embryo

Primary structures:
Neural tube
Notochord

Secondary structures:
Notochord (pigmented cells)
Neural tube (mostly nonpigmented cells)

CONCLUSION The transplanted dorsal lip was able to induce cells in a different region of the recipient to form structures different from their normal fate. In effect, the transplanted dorsal lip "organized" the later development of an entire extra embryo.

SOURCE H. Spemann and H. Mangold, Induction of embryonic primordia by implantation of organizers from a different species, Trans. V. Hamburger (1924). Reprinted in *International Journal of Developmental Biology* 45:13–38 (2001).

WHAT IF? Because the transplanted dorsal lip caused the recipient tissue to become something it would not otherwise have become, a signal of some sort must have passed from the dorsal lip. If you identified a protein candidate for the signaling molecule, how could you test whether it actually functions in signaling?

bone morphogenetic protein 4 (BMP-4). (Bone morphogenetic proteins, a family of related proteins with a variety of developmental roles, derive their name from members of the family that are important in bone formation.) One major function of the cells of the organizer seems to be to *inactivate* BMP-4 on the dorsal side of the embryo. Inactivation of BMP-4 allows cells on the dorsal side to make dorsal structures, such as the notochord and neural tube. Proteins related to BMP-4 and its inhibitors are also found in other animals, including invertebrates such as the fruit fly, where they also regulate the dorsal-ventral axis.

Formation of the Vertebrate Limb

Inductive signals play a major role in **pattern formation**, the development of an animal's spatial organization, the arrangement of organs and tissues in their characteristic places in three-dimensional space. The molecular cues that control pattern formation, called **positional information**, tell a cell where it is with respect to the animal's body axes and help to determine how the cell and its descendants will respond to molecular signaling.

In Chapter 18, we discussed pattern formation in the development of *Drosophila*. For the study of pattern formation in vertebrates, a classic model system has been limb development in the chick. The wings and legs of chicks, like all vertebrate limbs, begin as limb buds, bumps of mesodermal tissue covered by a layer of ectoderm **(Figure 47.24a)**. Each component of a chick limb, such as a specific bone or muscle, develops with a precise location and orientation relative to three axes: the proximal-distal axis (the "shoulder-to-fingertip" axis), the anterior-posterior axis (the "thumb-to-little finger" axis), and the dorsal-ventral axis (the "knuckle-to-palm" axis). The embryonic cells within a limb bud respond to positional information indicating location along these three axes **(Figure 47.24b)**.

Two regions in a limb bud have profound effects on the limb's development. These regions are present in all vertebrate limb buds, including those that will develop into forelimbs (such as wings or arms) and those destined to become hind limbs. The cells of these regions secrete proteins that provide key positional information to the other cells of the bud.

One region regulating limb-bud development is the **apical ectodermal ridge (AER)**, a thickened area of ectoderm at the tip of the bud (see Figure 47.24a). Removing the AER blocks outgrowth of the limb along the proximal-distal axis. The cells of the AER secrete several protein signals in the fibroblast growth factor (FGF) family that promote limb-bud outgrowth. If the AER is surgically removed and beads soaked with FGF are put in its place, a nearly normal limb will develop. In 2006, researchers identified an FGF-secreting AER that appears to be responsible for building a shark's unpaired (median) fins. This finding suggests that the specific function of the AER predated the appearance of paired limbs in the vertebrate lineage.

The second major limb-bud regulatory region is the **zone of polarizing activity (ZPA)**, a block of mesodermal tissue located underneath the ectoderm where the posterior side of the bud is attached to the body (see Figure 47.24a). The ZPA is necessary for proper pattern formation along the anterior-posterior axis of the limb. Cells nearest the ZPA give rise to the posterior structures, such as the most posterior of the chick's three digits (positioned like our little finger); cells

(a) Organizer regions. Vertebrate limbs develop from protrusions called limb buds, each consisting of mesoderm cells covered by a layer of ectoderm. Two regions in each limb bud, the apical ectodermal ridge (AER, shown in this SEM) and the zone of polarizing activity (ZPA), play key roles as organizers in limb pattern formation.

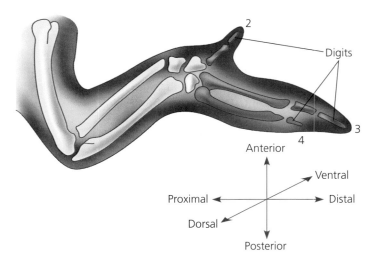

(b) Wing of chick embryo. As the bud develops into a limb, a specific pattern of tissues emerges. In the chick wing, for example, the digits are always present in the arrangement shown here. Pattern formation requires each embryonic cell to receive some kind of positional information indicating location along the three axes of the limb. The AER and ZPA secrete molecules that help provide this information. (Numbers are assigned to the digits based on a convention established for vertebrate limbs. The chicken wing has only four digits; the first digit points backward and is not shown in the diagram.)

▲ **Figure 47.24 Vertebrate limb development.**

farthest from the ZPA form anterior structures, including the most anterior digit (like our thumb).

The tissue transplantation experiment outlined in **Figure 47.25** supports the hypothesis that the inductive signal produced by the ZPA conveys positional information indicating "posterior." Indeed, researchers have discovered that the cells of the ZPA secrete a growth factor called Sonic hedgehog. (Sonic hedgehog gets its name from two sources: its similarity to a *Drosophila* protein called Hedgehog, which is involved in segmentation of the fly embryo, and a video game character.) If cells genetically engineered to produce large amounts of Sonic hedgehog are implanted in the anterior region of a normal limb bud, a mirror-image limb results—just as if a ZPA had been grafted there. Studies of the mouse version of Sonic hedgehog suggest that extra toes in mice—and perhaps also in humans—can result when this protein is produced in part of the limb bud where it is normally absent. Sonic hedgehog and other similar Hedgehog proteins function in many developmental settings and organisms, including pattern formation in *Drosophila* and regulation of cell fate and number in the vertebrate nervous system.

Signaling by Sonic hedgehog plays a vital role in limb-bud development, but what determines whether a limb bud develops into a forelimb or a hind limb? It turns out that the cells receiving the Hedgehog signals from the AER and ZPA respond according to their developmental histories. Before the AER or ZPA issues its signals, earlier developmental signaling sets up specific spatial patterns of *Hox* gene expression (see Figure 21.18). Differences in *Hox* gene expression cause cells of the forelimb and hind limb buds—and cells in different parts of each limb bud—to react differently to the same positional cues.

Hedgehog, FGF, and BMP-4 are examples of a much larger set of signaling molecules that govern cell fates in animals. Having mapped out many of the basic functions of these molecules in embryonic development, researchers are now addressing their role in organogenesis, focusing in particular on the development of the brain.

Cilia and Cell Fate

For many years, developmental biologists largely ignored the cellular organelles known as cilia. That is no longer the case. There is now good experimental evidence that ciliary function is essential for proper specification of cell fate in the human embryo.

Like other mammals, humans have stationary and motile cilia (see Figure 6.24). Stationary primary cilia, or *monocilia*, exist as a single projection on the surface of nearly all cells. Motile cilia are found on cells that propel fluid over their surface, such as the epithelial cells of airways, and on sperm (in the form of flagella that propel sperm movement). Both stationary and motile cilia play vital roles in development.

In 2003, geneticists discovered that certain mutations disrupting development of the mouse nervous system affect

---

---

genes that function in the assembly of monocilia. Other researchers found that mutations responsible for a severe kidney disease in mice alter a gene important for the transport of materials up and down monocilia. Mutations that block the function of monocilia have also been linked to cystic kidney disease in humans.

Given that monocilia are stationary, how do they function in development? The answer is that each acts as an antenna on the cell surface, receiving signals from multiple signaling

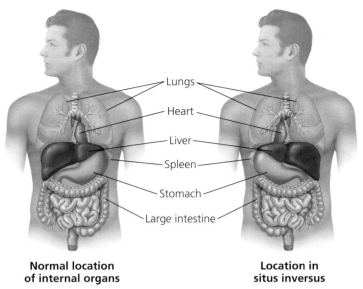

Lungs
Heart
Liver
Spleen
Stomach
Large intestine

Normal location
of internal organs

Location in
situs inversus

▲ Figure 47.26 **Situs inversus, a reversal of normal left-right asymmetry in the chest and abdomen.**

proteins, including Sonic hedgehog. When the monocilia are defective, signaling is disrupted.

Research on the role of motile cilia in development grew from the observation that certain individuals share a particular set of medical conditions, later named Kartagener's syndrome. Such individuals are prone to infections of the nasal sinuses and bronchi. Males with Kartagener's syndrome also produce immotile sperm. But the most intriguing feature of this syndrome is *situs inversus*, a reversal of the normal left-right asymmetry of the organs in the chest and abdomen (**Figure 47.26**). For example, in situs inversus, the heart is on the right side rather than the left. (About one in 10,000 individuals have situs inversus, which causes no significant medical problems by itself.)

The conditions associated with Kartagener's syndrome all result from a defect that makes cilia immotile. Without motility, sperm tails cannot beat and airway cells cannot sweep

mucus and microbes out of the airway. But what causes situs inversus in these individuals? The current model proposes that ciliary motion in a particular part of the embryo is essential for normal development. Evidence indicates that movement of the cilia generates a leftward fluid flow, breaking the symmetry between left and right sides. Without that flow, asymmetry along the left-right axis arises randomly, and half of the affected embryos develop situs inversus.

If we step back from the specification of particular cell fates to consider development as a whole, we see a sequence of events marked by cycles of signaling and differentiation. Initial cell asymmetries allow different types of cells to influence each other, resulting in the expression of specific sets of genes. The products of these genes then direct cells to differentiate into specific types. Through pattern formation and morphogenesis, differentiated cells ultimately produce a complex arrangement of tissues and organs, each functioning in its appropriate location and in coordination with other cells, tissues, and organs throughout the organism.

CONCEPT CHECK 47.3

1. How do axis formation and pattern formation differ?
2. **MAKE CONNECTIONS** How does a morphogen gradient differ from cytoplasmic determinants and inductive interactions with regard to the set of cells it affects (see Concept 18.4, p. 367)?
3. **WHAT IF?** If the ventral cells of an early frog gastrula are experimentally induced to express large amounts of a protein that inhibits BMP-4, could a second embryo develop? Explain.
4. **WHAT IF?** If you removed the ZPA from a limb bud and then placed a bead soaked in Sonic hedgehog in the middle of the limb bud, what would be the most likely result?

For suggested answers, see Appendix A.

47 CHAPTER REVIEW

SUMMARY OF KEY CONCEPTS

CONCEPT 47.1

Fertilization and cleavage initiate embryonic development (pp. 1022–1027)

- **Fertilization** brings together the nuclei of sperm and egg, forming a diploid zygote, and activates the egg, initiating embryonic development. The **acrosomal reaction**, which is triggered when the sperm meets the egg, releases hydrolytic enzymes that digest material surrounding the egg. Gamete contact and/or fusion depolarizes the egg cell membrane and sets up a **fast block to polysperm** in many animals. Sperm-egg fusion also initiates the cortical reaction.

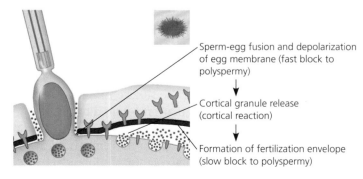

Sperm-egg fusion and depolarization of egg membrane (fast block to polyspermy)

↓

Cortical granule release (cortical reaction)

↓

Formation of fertilization envelope (slow block to polyspermy)

In mammalian fertilization, the cortical reaction modifies the zona pellucida as a **slow block to polyspermy**.

- Fertilization is followed by **cleavage**, a period of rapid cell division without growth, which results in the production of a large number of cells called **blastomeres**. In many species, cleavage creates a multicellular ball called the **blastula**, which contains a fluid-filled cavity, the **blastocoel**. **Holoblastic** cleavage (division of the entire egg) occurs in species whose eggs have little or moderate amounts of **yolk** (as in sea urchins, frogs, and mammals). **Meroblastic** cleavage (incomplete division of the egg) occurs in species with yolk-rich eggs (as in birds and other reptiles).

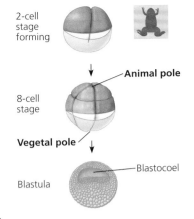

2-cell stage forming

8-cell stage — Animal pole

Vegetal pole

Blastula — Blastocoel

? What cell-surface barrier prevents fertilization of an egg by a sperm of a different species?

CONCEPT 47.2

Morphogenesis in animals involves specific changes in cell shape, position, and survival (pp. 1027–1035)

- **Gastrulation** converts the blastula to a **gastrula**, which has a primitive digestive cavity and three **germ layers**: ectoderm (blue), **mesoderm** (red), and **endoderm** (yellow).

- Mammalian eggs are small, store few nutrients, exhibit holoblastic cleavage, and show no obvious polarity. However, gastrulation and organogenesis in mammals resemble the processes in birds and other reptiles. After fertilization and early cleavage in the oviduct, the **blastocyst** implants in the uterus. The **trophoblast** initiates formation of the fetal portion of the placenta, and the embryo proper develops from a single layer of cells, the epiblast, within the blastocyst.
- The embryos of birds, other reptiles, and mammals develop within a fluid-filled sac that is contained within a shell or the uterus. In these organisms, the three germ layers give rise not only to embryonic tissue but also to the four **extraembryonic membranes**: the amnion, chorion, yolk sac, and allantois.
- The organs of the animal body develop from specific portions of the three embryonic germ layers. Early events in **organogenesis** in vertebrates include neurulation: formation of the **notochord** by cells of the dorsal mesoderm and development of the **neural tube** from infolding of the ectodermal neural plate.

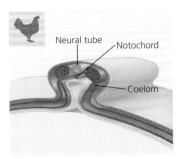

Neural tube — Notochord — Coelom

Neural tube — Notochord — Coelom

- Cytoskeletal rearrangements are responsible for changes in the shape of cells that underlie cell movements in gastrulation and organogenesis, including invaginations and **convergent extension**. The cytoskeleton is also involved in cell migration, which relies on cell adhesion molecules and the extracellular matrix to help cells reach specific destinations.

? How does the neural tube form? How do neural crest cells arise?

CONCEPT 47.3

Cytoplasmic determinants and inductive signals contribute to cell fate specification (pp. 1035–1042)

- Experimentally derived **fate maps** of embryos show that specific regions of the zygote or blastula develop into specific parts of older embryos. The complete cell lineage has been worked out for *C. elegans*. Mechanisms for establishing cellular asymmetries include morphogen gradients, localized determinants, and inductive interactions. As embryonic development proceeds, the developmental potential of cells becomes progressively more limited in all species.
- Cells in a developing embryo receive and respond to **positional information** that varies with location. This information is often in the form of signaling molecules secreted by cells in specific regions of the embryo, such as the dorsal lip of the blastopore in the amphibian gastrula and the **apical ectodermal ridge** and **zone of polarizing activity** of the vertebrate limb bud. The signaling molecules influence gene expression in the cells that receive them, leading to **differentiation** and the development of particular structures.

? Suppose you found two classes of mouse mutations, one that affected limb development only and one that affected both limb and kidney development. Which class would be more likely to alter the function of monocilia? Explain.

TEST YOUR UNDERSTANDING

LEVEL 1: KNOWLEDGE/COMPREHENSION

1. The cortical reaction of sea urchin eggs functions directly in
   a. the formation of a fertilization envelope.
   b. the production of a fast block to polyspermy.
   c. the release of hydrolytic enzymes from the sperm.
   d. the generation of an electrical impulse by the egg.
   e. the fusion of egg and sperm nuclei.

2. Which of the following is common to the development of both birds and mammals?
   a. holoblastic cleavage
   b. epiblast and hypoblast
   c. trophoblast
   d. yolk plug
   e. gray crescent

3. The archenteron develops into
   a. the mesoderm.
   b. the blastocoel.
   c. the endoderm.
   d. the placenta.
   e. the lumen of the digestive tract.

4. What structural adaptation in chickens allows them to lay their eggs in arid environments rather than in water?
   a. extraembryonic membranes
   b. yolk
   c. cleavage
   d. gastrulation
   e. development of the brain from ectoderm

LEVEL 2: APPLICATION/ANALYSIS

5. In an egg cell treated with EDTA, a chemical that binds calcium and magnesium ions,
   a. the acrosomal reaction would be blocked.
   b. the fusion of sperm and egg nuclei would be blocked.
   c. the fast block to polyspermy would not occur.
   d. the fertilization envelope would not form.
   e. the zygote would not contain maternal and paternal chromosomes.

6. In humans, identical twins are possible because
   a. cytoplasmic determinants are distributed unevenly in unfertilized eggs.
   b. extraembryonic cells interact with the zygote nucleus.
   c. convergent extension occurs.
   d. early blastomeres can form a complete embryo if isolated.
   e. the gray crescent divides the dorsal-ventral axis into new cells.

7. Cells transplanted from the neural tube of a frog embryo to the ventral part of another embryo develop into nervous system tissues. This result indicates that the transplanted cells were
   a. totipotent.
   b. determined.
   c. differentiated.
   d. mesenchymal.
   e. apoptotic.

8. **DRAW IT** Fill in the blanks in the figure below, and draw arrows showing the movement of ectoderm, mesoderm, and endoderm.

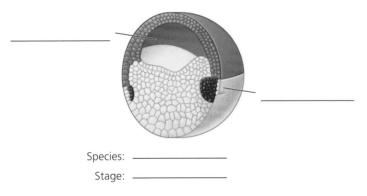

Species: _____

Stage: _____

LEVEL 3: SYNTHESIS/EVALUATION

9. **EVOLUTION CONNECTION**
   Evolution in insects and vertebrates has involved the repeated duplication of body segments, followed by fusion of some segments and specialization of their structure and function. What parts of vertebrate anatomy reflect the vertebrate segmentation pattern?

10. **SCIENTIFIC INQUIRY**
    The "snout" of a frog tadpole bears a sucker. A salamander tadpole has a mustache-shaped structure called a balancer in the same area. Suppose that you perform an experiment in which you transplant ectoderm from the side of a young salamander embryo to the snout of a frog embryo. The tadpole that develops has a balancer. When you transplant ectoderm from the side of a slightly older salamander embryo to the snout of a frog embryo, the frog tadpole ends up with a patch of salamander skin on its snout. Suggest a hypothesis to explain these results in terms of developmental mechanisms. How might you test your hypothesis?

11. **SCIENCE, TECHNOLOGY, AND SOCIETY**
    Many scientists think that fetal tissue transplants offer great potential for treating Parkinson's disease, epilepsy, diabetes, Alzheimer's disease, and spinal cord injuries. Why might tissues from a fetus be particularly useful for replacing diseased or damaged cells in patients with such conditions? Some people would allow only tissues from miscarriages to be used in fetal transplant research. However, most researchers prefer to use tissues from surgically aborted fetuses. Why? Explain your position on this controversial issue.

12. **WRITE ABOUT A THEME**
    Emergent Properties In a short essay (100–150 words), describe how the emergent properties of the cells of the gastrula direct embryonic development.

For selected answers, see Appendix A.

MasteringBIOLOGY®   www.masteringbiology.com

1. MasteringBiology® Assignments
Experimental Inquiry Tutorial How Do Calcium Ions Help to Prevent Polyspermy During Egg Fertilization?
Tutorial Embryonic Development
Activities Early Stages of Animal Development • Sea Urchin Development • Frog Development
Questions Student Misconceptions • Reading Quiz • Multiple Choice • End-of-Chapter

2. eText
Read your book online, search, take notes, highlight text, and more.

3. The Study Area
Practice Tests • Cumulative Test • *BioFlix* 3-D Animations • MP3 Tutor Sessions • Videos • Activities • Investigations • Lab Media • Audio Glossary • Word Study Tools • Art

49

Nervous Systems

▲ **Figure 49.1 How do scientists identify individual neurons in the brain?**

KEY CONCEPTS

49.1 Nervous systems consist of circuits of neurons and supporting cells

49.2 The vertebrate brain is regionally specialized

OVERVIEW

Command and Control Center

What happens in your brain when you solve a math problem or listen to music? Until quite recently, scientists had little hope of answering that question. The human brain contains an estimated 10^{11} (100 billion) neurons. Interconnecting these brain cells are circuits more complex than those of even the most powerful supercomputers. Yet the circuitry of the brain has been largely hidden from view. That's no

longer the case, thanks in part to several exciting new technologies.

One recent advance in exploring the brain relies on a method for expressing random combinations of colored proteins in brain cells—such that each cell shows up in a different color. The result is a "brainbow" like the one in **Figure 49.1**, which highlights neurons in the brain of a mouse. In this image, each neuron expresses one of more than 90 different color combinations of four fluorescent proteins. Using the brainbow technology, neuroscientists hope to develop detailed maps of the connections that transfer information between particular regions of the brain.

Another breakthrough came with the development of powerful imaging techniques that reveal activity in the working brain. Researchers can monitor multiple areas of the human brain while a subject is performing various tasks, such as speaking, looking at pictures, or forming a mental image of a person's face. They can use these techniques to look for a correlation between a particular task and activity in specific brain areas.

In this chapter, we will discuss the organization and evolution of animal nervous systems, exploring how groups of neurons function in specialized circuits dedicated to specific tasks. First we'll focus on specialization in regions of the vertebrate brain. We will then turn to the ways in which brain activity makes information storage and organization possible. Finally, we'll consider several disorders of the nervous system that are the subject of intense research today.

CONCEPT 49.1

Nervous systems consist of circuits of neurons and supporting cells

The ability to sense and react originated billions of years ago with prokaryotes that could detect changes in their environment and respond in ways that enhanced their survival and reproductive success. For example, bacteria keep moving in a particular direction as long as they encounter increasing concentrations of a food source. Later in evolution, modification of simple recognition and response processes provided multicellular organisms with a mechanism for communication between cells of the body. By the time of the Cambrian explosion more than 500 million years ago (see Chapter 32), systems of neurons allowing animals to sense and move rapidly were present in essentially their current forms.

Hydras, jellies, and other cnidarians are the simplest animals with nervous systems. As you read in Chapters 33 and 41, these animals have radially symmetrical bodies organized around a central digestive compartment, the gastrovascular cavity. In most cnidarians, interconnected nerve cells form a diffuse **nerve net** (**Figure 49.2a**), which controls the contraction and expansion of the gastrovascular cavity. Unlike the nervous systems of other animals, the nerve net of cnidarians lacks clusters of neurons that perform specialized functions.

In more complex animals, the axons of multiple nerve cells are often bundled together, forming **nerves**. These fibrous structures channel and organize information flow along specific routes through the nervous system. For example, sea stars have a set of radial nerves connecting to a central nerve ring (**Figure 49.2b**). Within each arm of a sea star, the radial nerve is linked to a nerve net from which it receives input and to which it sends signals controlling muscle contraction.

Animals that have elongated, bilaterally symmetrical bodies have even more specialized nervous systems. Such animals exhibit cephalization, an evolutionary trend toward a clustering of sensory neurons and interneurons at the anterior (front) end of the body. These anterior neurons communicate with cells elsewhere in the body, including neurons located in one or more nerve cords extending toward the posterior (rear) end. In nonsegmented worms, such as the planarian shown in **Figure 49.2c**, a small brain and longitudinal nerve cords constitute the simplest clearly defined *central nervous system* (*CNS*). In some such animals, the entire nervous system is constructed from only a small number of cells, as shown by studies of another nonsegmented worm, the nematode *Caenorhabditis elegans*. In this species, an adult worm (hermaphrodite) has exactly 302 neurons, no more and no fewer. More complex invertebrates, such as segmented worms

(annelids; **Figure 49.2d**) and arthropods (**Figure 49.2e**), have many more neurons. The behavior of such invertebrates is regulated by more complicated brains and by ventral nerve cords containing ganglia, segmentally arranged clusters of neurons.

Within an animal group, nervous system organization often correlates with lifestyle. Among the molluscs, for example, sessile and slow-moving species, such as clams and chitons, have relatively simple sense organs and little or no cephalization (**Figure 49.2f**). In contrast, active predatory molluscs, such as octopuses and squids (**Figure 49.2g**), have the most sophisticated nervous systems of any invertebrates, rivaling those of some vertebrates. With their large, image-forming eyes and a brain containing millions of neurons, octopuses can learn to discriminate between visual patterns and to perform complex tasks.

In vertebrates (**Figure 49.2h**), the brain and the spinal cord form the CNS; nerves and ganglia form the *peripheral nervous system* (*PNS*). Regional specialization is a hallmark of both systems, as we will see throughout the remainder of this chapter.

Organization of the Vertebrate Nervous System

In the vertebrate CNS, the functions of the brain and spinal cord are tightly coordinated. The brain provides the integrative power that underlies the complex behavior of vertebrates. The spinal cord, which runs lengthwise inside the vertebral column (spine), conveys information to and from the brain

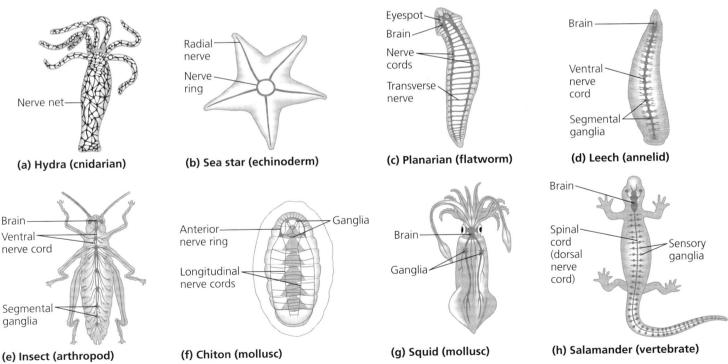

(a) Hydra (cnidarian) — Nerve net

(b) Sea star (echinoderm) — Radial nerve, Nerve ring

(c) Planarian (flatworm) — Eyespot, Brain, Nerve cords, Transverse nerve

(d) Leech (annelid) — Brain, Ventral nerve cord, Segmental ganglia

(e) Insect (arthropod) — Brain, Ventral nerve cord, Segmental ganglia

(f) Chiton (mollusc) — Anterior nerve ring, Longitudinal nerve cords, Ganglia

(g) Squid (mollusc) — Brain, Ganglia

(h) Salamander (vertebrate) — Brain, Spinal cord (dorsal nerve cord), Sensory ganglia

▲ **Figure 49.2 Nervous system organization. (a)** A hydra contains individual neurons (purple) organized in a diffuse nerve net. **(b–h)** Animals with more sophisticated nervous systems contain groups of neurons (blue) organized into nerves and often ganglia and a brain.

② Sensors detect a sudden stretch in the quadriceps.

③ **Sensory neurons** convey the information to the spinal cord.

④ In response to signals from the sensory neurons, **motor neurons** convey signals to the quadriceps, causing it to contract and jerking the lower leg forward.

Cell body of sensory neuron in dorsal root ganglion

Gray matter

Quadriceps muscle

① The reflex is initiated artificially by tapping the tendon connected to the quadriceps muscle.

White matter

⑤ Sensory neurons also communicate with **interneurons** in the spinal cord.

⑥ The interneurons inhibit motor neurons that lead to the hamstring muscle. This inhibition prevents contraction of the hamstring, which would resist the action of the quadriceps.

Hamstring muscle

Spinal cord (cross section)

- Sensory neuron
- Motor neuron
- Interneuron

▲ **Figure 49.3 The knee-jerk reflex.** Many neurons are involved in the reflex, but for simplicity, only a few neurons are shown.

MAKE CONNECTIONS *Using the nerve signals to the hamstring and quadriceps in this reflex as an example, propose a model for regulation of smooth muscle activity in the esophagus during the swallowing reflex (see Figure 41.10, p. 884).*

and generates basic patterns of locomotion. The spinal cord also acts independently of the brain as part of the simple nerve circuits that produce **reflexes**, the body's automatic responses to certain stimuli.

A reflex protects the body by triggering a rapid, involuntary response to a particular stimulus. If you put your hand on a hot burner, a reflex begins to pull your hand back well before the sensation of pain has been processed in your brain. Similarly, if your knees buckle when you pick up a heavy object, the tension across your knees triggers a reflex that contracts the thigh muscles, helping you stay upright and support the load. During a physical exam, your doctor may trigger this knee-jerk reflex with a mallet to help assess nervous system function **(Figure 49.3)**.

Whereas the nerve cord of many invertebrates is located ventrally, the spinal cord of vertebrates runs along the dorsal side of the body **(Figure 49.4)**. An underlying segmental organization is apparent in the arrangement of neurons within the spinal cord and in the distribution of spinal nerves and ganglia just outside the spinal cord.

During embryonic development in vertebrates, the central nervous system develops from the hollow dorsal nerve cord—a hallmark of chordates (see Chapter 34). The cavity

Central nervous system (CNS)

Peripheral nervous system (PNS)

Brain

Cranial nerves

Spinal cord

Ganglia outside CNS

Spinal nerves

▲ **Figure 49.4 The vertebrate nervous system.** The central nervous system consists of the brain and spinal cord (yellow). Left-right pairs of cranial nerves, spinal nerves, and ganglia make up most of the peripheral nervous system (dark gold).

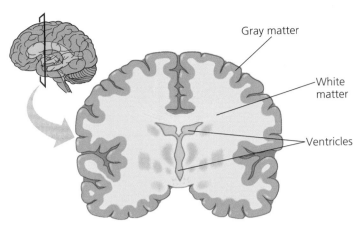

▲ Figure 49.5 Ventricles, gray matter, and white matter. Ventricles deep in the brain's interior contain cerebrospinal fluid. Most of the gray matter is on the surface of the brain, surrounding the white matter.

of the nerve cord gives rise to the narrow **central canal** of the spinal cord as well as the **ventricles** of the brain **(Figure 49.5)**. Both the canal and ventricles fill with **cerebrospinal fluid**, which is formed in the brain by filtration of arterial blood. The cerebrospinal fluid circulates slowly through the central canal and ventricles and then drains into the veins. This circulation supplies the brain

with nutrients and hormones and carries away wastes. In mammals, the cerebrospinal fluid also cushions the brain and spinal cord by circulating between layers of connective tissue that surround the CNS.

In addition to these fluid-filled spaces, the brain and spinal cord contain gray matter and white matter (see Figure 49.5). **Gray matter** consists mainly of neuron cell bodies, dendrites, and unmyelinated axons. In contrast, **white matter** consists of bundled axons that have myelin sheaths, which give the axons a whitish appearance. White matter in the spinal cord lies on the outside, consistent with its function in linking the CNS to sensory and motor neurons of the PNS. White matter in the brain is predominantly on the inside, reflecting the role of signaling between neurons of the brain in learning, feeling emotions, processing sensory information, and generating commands.

Glia

The glia present throughout the vertebrate brain and spinal cord carry out functions crucial for the activity of the nervous system. **Figure 49.6** illustrates the major types of glia in the adult nervous system and provides an overview of the ways in which they nourish, support, and regulate the functioning of neurons.

Ependymal cells line the ventricles and have cilia that promote circulation of the cerebrospinal fluid.

Oligodendrocytes myelinate axons in the CNS. Myelination greatly increases the conduction speed of action potentials.

Schwann cells myelinate axons in the PNS.

Microglia are immune cells that protect against pathogens.

Astrocytes (from the Greek *astron*, star) facilitate information transfer at synapses and in some instances release neurotransmitters. Astrocytes next to active neurons cause nearby blood vessels to dilate, increasing blood flow and enabling the neurons to obtain oxygen and glucose more quickly. Astrocytes also regulate extracellular concentrations of ions and neurotransmitters.

The green cells in this mammalian brain tissue are astrocytes labeled with a fluorescent antibody.

A blue dye that binds DNA in the nuclei of all cells reveals the intermingling of astrocytes with other cells, predominantly neurons.

▲ Figure 49.6 Glia in the vertebrate nervous system.

Glia also have an essential role in development of the nervous system. In embryos, cells called *radial glia* form tracks along which newly formed neurons migrate from the neural tube, the structure that gives rise to the CNS (see Figure 47.13). Later, astrocytes induce cells that line the capillaries in the CNS to form tight junctions (see Figure 6.32). The result is the *blood-brain barrier*, which controls the extracellular environment of the CNS by restricting the entry of most substances from the blood.

Both radial glia and astrocytes can also act as stem cells, generating new neurons and glia. Researchers view these multipotent precursors as a potential means for replacing neurons and glia that are lost to injury or disease, a topic we'll explore further in Concept 49.4.

The Peripheral Nervous System

The PNS transmits information to and from the CNS and plays a large role in regulating an animal's movement and internal environment **(Figure 49.7)**. Sensory information reaches the CNS along PNS neurons designated as *afferent* (from the Latin, meaning "to carry toward"). Following information processing within the CNS, instructions then travel to muscles, glands, and endocrine cells along PNS neurons designated as *efferent* (from the Latin, meaning "to carry away"). Most nerves contain both afferent and efferent neurons. One exception is the olfactory nerve, which conveys only sensory information from the nose to the brain.

The PNS has two efferent components: the motor system and the autonomic nervous system (see Figure 49.7). The **motor system** consists of neurons that carry signals to skeletal muscles. This control of skeletal muscles can be voluntary, as when you raise your hand to ask a question, or involuntary, as in the knee-jerk reflex controlled by the spinal cord. In contrast, regulation of smooth and cardiac muscles by the **autonomic nervous system** is generally involuntary. The three divisions of the autonomic nervous system—sympathetic, parasympathetic, and enteric—together control the organs of the digestive, cardiovascular, excretory, and endocrine systems.

The sympathetic and parasympathetic divisions of the autonomic nervous system have largely antagonistic (opposite) functions in regulating organ function **(Figure 49.8)**. Activation of

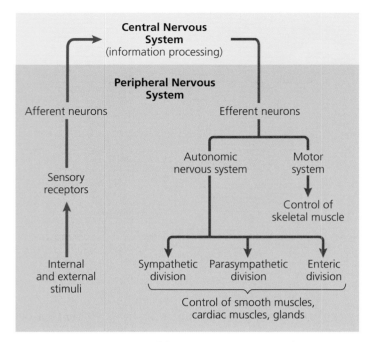

▲ **Figure 49.7 Functional hierarchy of the vertebrate peripheral nervous system.**

▲ **Figure 49.8 The parasympathetic and sympathetic divisions of the autonomic nervous system.** Most pathways in each division consist of preganglionic neurons (having cell bodies in the CNS) and postganglionic neurons (having cell bodies in ganglia in the PNS).

the **sympathetic division** corresponds to arousal and energy generation (the "fight-or-flight" response). For example, the heart beats faster, digestion is inhibited, the liver converts glycogen to glucose, and the adrenal medulla increases secretion of epinephrine (adrenaline) and norepinephrine. Activation of the **parasympathetic division** generally causes opposite responses that promote calming and a return to self-maintenance functions ("rest and digest"). Thus, heart rate decreases, digestion is enhanced, and glycogen production increases. In regulating reproductive activity, however, the parasympathetic division complements rather than antagonizes the sympathetic division (see Figure 49.8).

Networks of neurons that form the **enteric division** of the PNS are active in the digestive tract, pancreas, and gallbladder. Within these organs, the enteric division regulates secretion and peristalsis (see Chapter 41). The sympathetic and parasympathetic divisions normally regulate the enteric division, although it is capable of independent activity.

Homeostasis often relies on cooperation between the motor and autonomic nervous systems. In response to a drop in body temperature, for example, the hypothalamus signals the motor system to cause shivering, which increases heat production. At the same time, the hypothalamus signals the autonomic nervous system to constrict surface blood vessels, reducing heat loss.

CONCEPT CHECK 49.1

1. Which division of the autonomic nervous system would likely be activated if a student learned that an exam she had forgotten about would start in 5 minutes? Explain your answer.

2. The parasympathetic and sympathetic divisions of the PNS (see Figure 49.8) use the same neurotransmitters at the axon terminals of preganglionic neurons, but different neurotransmitters at the axon terminals of postganglionic neurons. How does this difference correlate with the function of the axons bringing signals into and out of the ganglia in the two divisions?

3. **WHAT IF?** Suppose a person had an accident that severed a small nerve required to move some of the fingers of the right hand. Would you also expect an effect on sensation from those fingers?

4. **MAKE CONNECTIONS** Most tissues regulated by the autonomic nervous system receive both sympathetic and parasympathetic input from postganglionic neurons. Responses are typically local. In contrast, the adrenal medulla receives input only from the sympathetic division and only from preganglionic neurons, yet responses are observed throughout the body. Explain why.

For suggested answers, see Appendix A.

CONCEPT 49.2

The vertebrate brain is regionally specialized

Having considered some of the basic functions of the PNS, we turn now to the brain. Images of the human brain in popular culture almost always focus on the cerebrum, the part of the brain whose surface lies just beneath the skull. The cerebrum is responsible for many activities we commonly associate with the brain, such as calculation, contemplation, and memory. Underneath the cerebrum, however, are additional brain structures with important and diverse activities, including homeostasis, coordination, and information transfer.

Figure 49.9, on pages 1068–1069, explores the origin, form, and function of major regions of the human brain. It outlines how brain structures arise during embryonic development, illustrates their size, shape, and location in the adult, and summarizes their best-understood functions. Figure 49.9 will serve as an introduction to the regional specialization in the brain and provide a useful point of reference for later discussions of specific brain functions.

To learn more about how brain organization relates to brain function, we'll first consider activity cycles of the brain and the physiological basis of emotion. Then, in Concept 49.3, we'll shift our attention to regional specialization within the cerebrum.

Arousal and Sleep

If you've ever drifted off to sleep while listening to a lecture (or reading a book), you know that your attentiveness and mental alertness can change rapidly. Such transitions are regulated by the brainstem and cerebrum, which control arousal and sleep. Arousal is a state of awareness of the external world. Sleep is a state in which external stimuli are received but not consciously perceived.

Contrary to appearances, sleep is an active state, at least for the brain. By placing electrodes at multiple sites on the scalp, we can record patterns of electrical activity called brain waves in an electroencephalogram (EEG). These recordings reveal that brain wave frequencies change as the brain progresses through distinct stages of sleep.

Although sleep is essential for survival, we still know very little about its function. One hypothesis is that sleep and dreams are involved in consolidating learning and memory. This hypothesis is supported by the finding that test subjects who are kept awake for 36 hours have a reduced ability to remember when particular events occurred, even if they first "perk up" with caffeine. Other experiments show that regions of the brain that are activated during a learning task can become active again during sleep.

Exploring The Organization of the Human Brain

The brain is the most complex organ in the human body. Surrounded by the thick bones of the skull, the brain is divided into a set of distinctive structures, some of which are visible in the magnetic resonance image (MRI) of an adult's head shown at right. The diagram below traces the development of these structures in the embryo. Their major functions are explained on the facing page.

Human Brain Development

As a human embryo develops, the neural tube forms three anterior bulges—the **forebrain**, **midbrain**, and **hindbrain**—that together produce the adult brain. The midbrain and a part of the hindbrain give rise to the **brainstem**, a stalk that joins with the spinal cord at the base of the brain. The rest of the hindbrain gives rise to the **cerebellum**, which lies behind the brainstem. The third anterior bulge, the forebrain, develops into the diencephalon, including the neuroendocrine tissues of the brain, and the telencephalon, which becomes the **cerebrum**. Rapid, expansive growth of the telencephalon during the second and third months causes the outer portion, or cortex, of the cerebrum to extend over and around much of the rest of the brain.

The Cerebrum

The cerebrum controls skeletal muscle contraction and is the center for learning, emotion, memory, and perception. It is divided into right and left **cerebral hemispheres**. The **cerebral cortex** is vital for perception, voluntary movement, and learning. Like the rest of the cerebrum, the cerebral cortex is divided into right and left sides. The left side receives information from, and controls the movement of, the right side of the body, and vice versa. A thick band of axons known as the **corpus callosum** enables the right and left cerebral cortices to communicate. Deep within the white matter, clusters of neurons called *basal nuclei* serve as centers for planning and learning movement sequences. Damage to these sites during fetal development can result in cerebral palsy, a disorder resulting from a disruption in the transmission of motor commands to the muscles.

The Cerebellum

The cerebellum coordinates movement and balance and helps in learning and remembering motor skills. The cerebellum receives sensory information about the positions of the joints and the lengths of the muscles, as well as input from the auditory (hearing) and visual systems. It also monitors motor commands issued by the cerebrum. The cerebellum integrates this information as it carries out coordination and error checking during motor and perceptual functions. Hand-eye coordination is an example of cerebellar control; if the cerebellum is damaged, the eyes can follow a moving object, but they will not stop at the same place as the object. Hand movement toward the object will also be erratic.

Adult brain viewed from the rear

Labels: Left cerebral hemisphere; Right cerebral hemisphere; Cerebral cortex; Corpus callosum; Basal nuclei; Cerebrum; Cerebellum

The Diencephalon

The diencephalon gives rise to the thalamus, hypothalamus, and epithalamus. The **thalamus** is the main input center for sensory information going to the cerebrum. Incoming information from all the senses is sorted in the thalamus and sent to the appropriate cerebral centers for further processing. The thalamus is formed by two masses, each roughly the size and shape of a walnut. A much smaller structure, the **hypothalamus**, contains the body's thermostat as well as the central biological clock. Through its control of the pituitary gland, the hypothalamus regulates hunger and thirst, plays a role in sexual and mating behaviors, and controls the fight-or-flight response. The hypothalamus is also the source of posterior pituitary hormones and of releasing hormones that act on the anterior pituitary. The *epithalamus* includes the pineal gland, the source of melatonin. It also contains one of several clusters of capillaries that generate cerebrospinal fluid from blood.

Labels: Diencephalon; Thalamus; Pineal gland; Hypothalamus; Pituitary gland; Spinal cord

The Brainstem

The brainstem consists of the midbrain, the **pons**, and the **medulla oblongata** (commonly called the *medulla*). The midbrain receives and integrates several types of sensory information and sends it to specific regions of the forebrain. All sensory axons involved in hearing either terminate in the midbrain or pass through it on their way to the cerebrum. In addition, the midbrain coordinates visual reflexes, such as the peripheral vision reflex: The head turns toward an object approaching from the side without the brain having formed an image of the object.

A major function of the pons and medulla is to transfer information between the PNS and the midbrain and forebrain. The pons and medulla also help coordinate large-scale body movements, such as running and climbing. Most axons that carry instructions about these movements cross from one side of the CNS to the other in the medulla. As a result, the right side of the brain controls much of the movement of the left side of the body, and vice versa. An additional function of the medulla is the control of several automatic, homeostatic functions, including breathing, heart and blood vessel activity, swallowing, vomiting, and digestion. The pons also participates in some of these activities; for example, it regulates the breathing centers in the medulla.

Labels: Brainstem; Midbrain; Pons; Medulla oblongata

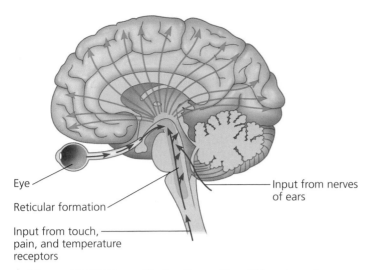

Eye

Reticular formation

Input from touch, pain, and temperature receptors

Input from nerves of ears

▲ **Figure 49.10 The reticular formation.** This system of neurons distributed throughout the core of the brainstem filters sensory input (blue arrows), blocking familiar and repetitive information that constantly enters the nervous system. It sends the filtered input to the cerebral cortex (green arrows).

Location	Time: 0 hours	Time: 1 hour
Left hemisphere	∿∿∿	∿∿∿
Right hemisphere	∿∿∿	∿∿∿

▲ **Figure 49.11 Dolphins can be asleep and awake at the same time.** EEG recordings were made separately for the two sides of a dolphin's brain. Low-frequency activity was recorded in one hemisphere while higher-frequency activity typical of being awake was recorded in the other hemisphere.

Arousal and sleep are controlled in part by the **reticular formation**, a diffuse network of neurons in the core of the brainstem **(Figure 49.10)**. Acting as a sensory filter, the reticular formation determines which incoming information reaches the cerebrum. The more information the cerebrum receives, the more alert and aware a person is, although the brain often ignores certain stimuli while actively processing other inputs. Besides the diffuse reticular formation, there are also specific parts of the brainstem that regulate sleep and wakefulness: The pons and medulla contain centers that cause sleep when stimulated, and the midbrain has a center that causes arousal.

All birds and mammals show characteristic sleep/wake cycles. Melatonin, a hormone produced by the pineal gland, appears to play an important role in these cycles. Peak melatonin secretion occurs at night.

Some animals display evolutionary adaptations that allow for substantial activity during sleep. Bottlenose dolphins, for example, swim while sleeping, rising to the surface to breathe air on a regular basis. How do they manage this feat? A critical clue came from American physiologist John Lilly, who in 1964 observed that dolphins sleep with one eye open and one closed. As in humans and other mammals, the forebrain of dolphins is physically and functionally divided into two halves, the right and left hemispheres. Lilly suggested that a dolphin sleeping with one eye closed could mean that just one side of the brain was asleep. In 1977, Russian scientist Lev Mukhametov set out to test Lilly's hypothesis by collecting EEG recordings from each hemisphere of sleeping dolphins **(Figure 49.11)**. Mukhametov's findings demonstrate that dolphins do in fact sleep with one brain hemisphere at a time.

Biological Clock Regulation

Cycles of sleep and wakefulness are just one example of a circadian rhythm, a daily cycle of biological activity. Such cycles occur in organisms ranging from bacteria to fungi, plants, insects, birds, and humans. As in other organisms, circadian rhythms in mammals rely on a **biological clock**, a molecular mechanism that directs periodic gene expression and cellular activity. Although biological clocks are typically synchronized to the cycles of light and dark in the environment, they can maintain a roughly 24-hour cycle even in the absence of environmental cues (see Figure 40.9). For example, humans kept in a constant environment exhibit a cycle length of 24.2 hours, with very little variation among individuals.

What normally links an animal's biological clock to environmental cycles of light and dark? In mammals, circadian rhythms are coordinated by a group of neurons in the hypothalamus called the **suprachiasmatic nucleus**, or **SCN**. (Certain clusters of neurons in the CNS are referred to as "nuclei.") In response to transmission of sensory information by the eyes, the SCN acts as a pacemaker, synchronizing the biological clock in cells throughout the body to the natural cycles of day length. By surgically removing the SCN from laboratory animals and then observing their behavior, scientists demonstrated that the SCN is required for circadian rhythms: Animals without an SCN lack rhythmicity in behaviors and in electrical activity of the brain. These experiments did not, however, reveal whether rhythms originate in the SCN or elsewhere. In 1990, researchers answered this question with the aid of a mutation that changes the circadian rhythm of hamsters **(Figure 49.12)**. By transplanting brain tissue between normal and mutant hamsters, these scientists demonstrated that the SCN determines the circadian rhythm of the whole animal.

▼ **Figure 49.12**

INQUIRY

Which cells control the circadian rhythm in mammals?

EXPERIMENT The τ (tau) mutation alters the period of the circadian rhythm in Syrian (golden) hamsters (*Mesocricetus auratus*). Whereas wild-type hamsters have a circadian cycle lasting 24 hours in the absence of external cues, hamsters homozygous for the τ mutation have a cycle lasting only about 20 hours. To determine if the SCN controls the circadian rhythm, Michael Menaker and colleagues at the University of Virginia surgically removed the SCN from wild-type and τ hamsters. Several weeks later, each of these hamsters received a transplant of an SCN from a hamster of the opposite genotype. The researchers then measured the circadian cycle period of the transplant recipients.

RESULTS In 80% of the hamsters in which the SCN had been removed, transplanting an SCN from another hamster restored rhythmic activity. For hamsters in which an SCN transplant restored a circadian rhythm, the net effect of the two procedures (SCN destruction and replacement) on circadian rhythm is graphed below. Each of the eight lines represents the change in the observed circadian cycle period for an individual hamster.

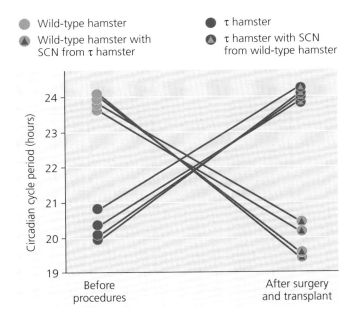

- Wild-type hamster
- Wild-type hamster with SCN from τ hamster
- τ hamster
- τ hamster with SCN from wild-type hamster

CONCLUSION Because the circadian rhythm of the animal that received the transplant was that of the donor animal, regardless of whether the recipient was wild-type or τ mutant, cells associated with the suprachiasmatic nucleus must determine the period of the circadian rhythm.

SOURCE M. R. Ralph, R. G. Foster, F. C. Davis, and M. Menaker, Transplanted suprachiasmatic nucleus determines circadian period, *Science* 247:975–978 (1990).

WHAT IF? Suppose in the course of your research you identified a hamster mutant that lacked rhythmic activity. How might you use this mutant in transplant experiments with wild-type or τ mutant hamsters to demonstrate that the mutation affected the pacemaker function of the SCN?

Emotions

Whereas a single structure in the brain controls the biological clock, the generation and experience of emotions depend on many brain structures, including the amygdala, hippocampus, and parts of the thalamus **(Figure 49.13)**. These structures border the brainstem in mammals and are therefore grouped as the *limbic system* (from the Latin *limbus*, border). The limbic system, however, is not dedicated solely to emotion. It also functions in motivation, olfaction (the sense of smell), behavior, and memory.

Generating emotion and experiencing emotion require parts of the brain in addition to the limbic system. For example, emotions that manifest themselves in behaviors such as laughing and crying involve an interaction of parts of the limbic system with sensory areas of the cerebrum. Structures in the forebrain also attach emotional "feelings" to basic, survival-related functions controlled by the brainstem, including aggression, feeding, and sexuality.

Emotional experiences are often stored as memories that can be recalled by similar circumstances. In the case of fear, emotional memory is stored separately from the memory system that supports explicit recall of events. The brain structure with the most important role in storage of emotional memory is the **amygdala**, an almond-shaped mass of nuclei (clusters of neurons) located near the base of the cerebrum.

To study the function of the human amygdala, researchers sometimes present adult subjects with an image followed by an unpleasant experience, such as a mild electrical shock. After several trials, study participants experience *autonomic arousal*—as measured by increased heart rate or sweating—if they see the image again. Subjects with brain damage confined to the amygdala can recall the image because their explicit memory is intact. However, they do not exhibit autonomic arousal, indicating that damage to the amygdala has resulted in a reduced capacity for emotional memory.

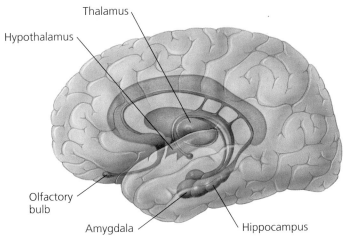

▲ **Figure 49.13 The limbic system.**

Today, the amygdala and other brain structures are being studied with functional imaging methods that are transforming our understanding of the normal and diseased brain (Figure 49.14)

▼ Figure 49.14

IMPACT

Using Functional Brain Imaging to Map Activity in the Working Brain

Techniques for mapping brain activity have transformed the study of human brain function. The first widely used technique was positron-emission tomography (PET; see Figure 2.7). After injecting radioactive glucose into the blood of a subject, researchers can use PET scans to monitor metabolic activity across the brain. Further progress has come with functional magnetic resonance imaging (fMRI). In fMRI, the subject lies with his or her head in the center of a large, doughnut-shaped magnet. When the brain is scanned with electromagnetic waves, changes in blood oxygen concentration in active parts of the brain generate a signal that can be recorded.

Functional brain imaging has been applied to the study of human cognition, consciousness, and emotion. For example, functional imaging suggests that consciousness may be an emergent property of the brain based on activity in many areas of the cortex. In the experiment shown here, researchers explored differences in brain activity associated with music that listeners described as happy or sad. Listening to happy music activated the *nucleus accumbens*, a brain structure important for the perception of pleasure. In contrast, subjects who heard sad music had increased activity in the amygdala, a brain structure that serves as a center for emotional memory.

Nucleus accumbens | Amygdala

Happy music | Sad music

WHY IT MATTERS Functional brain imaging is aiding the investigation of recovery from stroke and other brain traumas, as well as helping map abnormalities in migraine headaches, dyslexia, and many psychiatric disorders. Functional imaging is also having a major impact on brain surgery. For example, for patients with epilepsy that is not responsive to drug therapy, functional imaging can pinpoint the region of abnormal function, increasing the effectiveness of surgery and enhancing recovery. Finally, functional imaging has been used to explore sex-based differences in the CNS, demonstrating, for instance, that cerebral blood flow is higher on average in women than in men.

FURTHER READING R. C. deCharms, Applications of real-time fMRI, *Nature Reviews Neuroscience* 9:720–729 (2008).

WHAT IF? In the experiment illustrated above, some regions of the brain showed activity under all conditions. What function might such regions carry out?

CONCEPT CHECK 49.2

1. When you wave your right hand, what part of your brain initiates the action?
2. When a police officer stops a driver for driving erratically and suspects that the person is intoxicated, the officer may ask the driver to close his or her eyes and touch his or her nose. What can you deduce from this test about one of the brain regions affected by alcohol?
3. **WHAT IF?** Suppose you examine individuals with damage to the CNS that has resulted in either coma (a prolonged state of unconsciousness) or general paralysis (a loss of skeletal muscle function throughout the body). Relative to the position of the reticular formation, where would you predict the site of injury to lie in each group of patients? Explain.

For suggested answers, see Appendix A.

SUMMARY OF KEY CONCEPTS

CONCEPT 49.1

Nervous systems consist of circuits of neurons and supporting cells (pp. 1062–1067)

- Invertebrate nervous systems range in complexity from simple **nerve nets** to highly centralized nervous systems having complicated brains and ventral nerve cords.

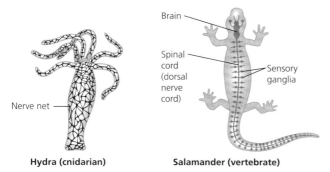

Hydra (cnidarian)   **Salamander (vertebrate)**

In vertebrates, the central nervous system (CNS), consisting of the brain and the spinal cord, integrates information, while the **nerves** of the peripheral nervous system (PNS) transmit sensory and motor signals between the CNS and the rest of the body. The simplest circuits in the vertebrate nervous system control **reflex** responses, in which sensory input is linked to motor output without involvement of the brain. Vertebrate neurons are supported by several types of glia, including **astrocytes**, oligodendrocytes, Schwann cells, and ependymal cells.

- Afferent neurons carry sensory signals to the CNS. Efferent neurons function in either the **motor system**, which carries signals to skeletal muscles, or the **autonomic nervous system**, which regulates smooth and cardiac muscles. The **sympathetic** and **parasympathetic divisions** of the autonomic nervous system have antagonistic effects on a diverse set of target organs, while the **enteric division** controls the activity of many digestive organs.

? *How does the circuitry of a reflex facilitate a rapid response?*

CONCEPT 49.2

The vertebrate brain is regionally specialized (pp. 1067–1072)

- The cerebrum has two hemispheres, each of which consists of cortical **gray matter** overlying **white matter** and basal nuclei, which are important in planning and learning movements. A thick band of axons, the **corpus callosum**, provides communication between the right and left cerebral cortices.
- Within each region of the brain, particular structures have specialized functions. The **pons** and **medulla oblongata** are relay stations for information traveling between the PNS and the cerebrum. The **reticular formation**, a network of neurons within the **brainstem**, regulates sleep and arousal. The **cerebellum** helps coordinate motor, perceptual, and cognitive functions. It is also involved in learning and remembering

motor skills. The **thalamus** is the main center through which sensory and motor information passes to the **cerebrum**. The **hypothalamus** regulates homeostasis and basic survival behaviors. Within the hypothalamus, the **suprachiasmatic nucleus (SCN)** acts as the pacemaker for circadian rhythms.

- The generation and experience of emotions involve many regions of the brain. However, the **amygdala** plays a key role in recognizing and recalling a number of emotions.

? *What role do particular regions of the brain play in vision and responses to visual input?*

LEVEL 1: KNOWLEDGE/COMPREHENSION

1. Wakefulness is regulated by the reticular formation, which is present in the
   a. basal nuclei.
   b. cerebral cortex.
   c. brainstem.
   d. limbic system.
   e. spinal cord.

2. Which of the following structures or regions is *incorrectly* paired with its function?
   a. limbic system—motor control of speech
   b. medulla oblongata—homeostatic control
   c. cerebellum—coordination of movement and balance
   d. corpus callosum—communication between the left and right cerebral cortices
   e. amygdala—emotional memory

3. Patients with damage to Wernicke's area have difficulty
   a. coordinating limb movement.
   b. generating speech.
   c. recognizing faces.
   d. understanding language.
   e. experiencing emotion.

4. The cerebral cortex plays a major role in all of the following *except*
   a. short-term memory.
   b. long-term memory.
   c. circadian rhythm.
   d. foot-tapping rhythm.
   e. breath holding.

LEVEL 2: APPLICATION/ANALYSIS

5. After suffering a stroke, a patient can see objects anywhere in front of him but pays attention only to objects in his right field of vision. When asked to describe these objects, he has difficulty judging their size and distance. What part of the brain was likely damaged by the stroke?
   a. the left frontal lobe
   b. the right frontal lobe
   c. the left parietal lobe
   d. the right parietal lobe
   e. the corpus callosum

6. Injury localized to the hypothalamus would most likely disrupt
   a. short-term memory.
   b. coordination during locomotion.
   c. executive functions, such as decision making.
   d. sorting of sensory information.
   e. regulation of body temperature.

7. **DRAW IT** The reflex that pulls your hand away when you prick your finger on a sharp object relies on a simple neuronal circuit with two synapses in the spinal cord. (a) Using a circle to represent a cross section of the spinal cord, draw the circuit, labeling the types of neurons, the direction of information flow in each, and the locations of synapses. (b) Draw a simple diagram of the brain indicating where pain would eventually be perceived.

LEVEL 3: SYNTHESIS/EVALUATION

8. **EVOLUTION CONNECTION**
   Scientists often use measures of "higher-order thinking" to assess intelligence in other animals. For example, birds are judged to have sophisticated thought processes because they can use tools and make use of abstract concepts. What problems do you see in defining intelligence in these ways?

9. **SCIENTIFIC INQUIRY**
   Consider an individual who had been fluent in American Sign Language before suffering damage to the left cerebral hemisphere. After the injury, this person could still understand signs, but could not readily generate signs that represented his thoughts. What two hypotheses could explain this finding, and how might you distinguish between them?

10. **SCIENCE, TECHNOLOGY, AND SOCIETY**
    With increasingly sophisticated methods for scanning brain activity, scientists are rapidly developing the ability to detect an individual's particular emotions and thought processes from outside the body. What benefits and problems do you envision when such technology becomes readily available?

11. **WRITE ABOUT A THEME**
    The Genetic Basis of Life In a short essay (100–150 words), explain how specification of the adult nervous system by the genome is incomplete.

For selected answers, see Appendix A.

MasteringBIOLOGY® www.masteringbiology.com

1. MasteringBiology® Assignments
Tutorial The Vertebrate Nervous System
Activities Discovery Channel Video: Teen Brains • Signal Transmission at a Chemical Synapse
Questions Student Misconceptions • Reading Quiz • Multiple Choice • End-of-Chapter

2. eText
Read your book online, search, take notes, highlight text, and more.

3. The Study Area
Practice Tests • Cumulative Test • *BioFlix* 3-D Animations • MP3 Tutor Sessions • Videos • Activities • Investigations • Lab Media • Audio Glossary • Word Study Tools • Art

51

Animal Behavior

▲ **Figure 51.1 What prompts a fiddler crab to wave its giant claw?**

KEY CONCEPTS

51.1 Discrete sensory inputs can stimulate both simple and complex behaviors

51.2 Learning establishes specific links between experience and behavior

51.3 Selection for individual survival and reproductive success can explain most behaviors

51.4 Inclusive fitness can account for the evolution of behavior, including altruism

OVERVIEW

The How and Why of Animal Activity

Unlike most animals, male fiddler crabs (genus *Uca*) are highly asymmetrical: One claw grows to giant proportions, half the mass of the entire body **(Figure 51.1)**. The name *fiddler* comes from the crab's appearance as it feeds on algae from the mudflats where it lives: The smaller front claw moves to and from the mouth in front of the enlarged claw.

Sometimes, however, the male waves his large claw in the air. What triggers this behavior? What purpose does it serve?

Claw waving by a male fiddler crab has two functions. Waving the claw, which can be used as a weapon, helps the crab *repel* other males wandering too close to his burrow. Vigorous claw waving also helps him *attract* females, who wander through the crab colony in search of a mate. After the male fiddler crab lures a female to his burrow, he seals her in with mud or sand in preparation for mating.

Animal behavior, be it solitary or social, fixed or variable, is based on physiological systems and processes. An individual **behavior** is an action carried out by muscles under control of the nervous system in response to a stimulus. Examples include an animal using its chest and throat muscles to produce a song, releasing a scent to mark its territory, or simply waving a claw. Behavior is an essential part of acquiring nutrients for digestion and finding a partner for sexual reproduction. Behavior also contributes to homeostasis, as in honeybees huddling to conserve heat (see Chapter 40). In short, all of animal physiology contributes to behavior, and animal behavior influences all of physiology.

Being essential for survival and reproduction, behavior is subject to substantial natural selection over time. This evolutionary process of selection also affects anatomy because the recognition and communication that underlie many behaviors depend on body form and appearance. Thus, the enlarged claw of the male fiddler crab is an adaptation that enables the display essential for recognition by other members of the species. Similarly, the positioning of the eyes on stalks held well above the crab's head enables him to see intruders from far off.

In this chapter, we'll examine how behavior is controlled, how it develops during an animal's life, and how it is influenced by genes and the environment. We'll also explore the ways in which behavior evolves over many generations. In moving from our study of an animal's inner workings to its interactions with the outside world, we will also provide a transition to ecology, the focus of Unit Eight.

CONCEPT 51.1

Discrete sensory inputs can stimulate both simple and complex behaviors

What approach do biologists use to determine how behaviors arise and what functions they serve? The Dutch scientist Niko Tinbergen, a pioneer in the study of animal behavior, suggested that understanding any behavior requires answering four questions, which can be summarized as follows:

1. What stimulus elicits the behavior, and what physiological mechanisms mediate the response?
2. How does the animal's experience during growth and development influence the response?

3. How does the behavior aid survival and reproduction?

4. What is the behavior's evolutionary history?

Tinbergen's first two questions ask about *proximate causation*: "how" a behavior occurs or is modified. The last two questions ask about *ultimate causation*: "why" a behavior occurs in the context of natural selection.

Today, Tinbergen's questions and the associated ideas of causation underlie **behavioral ecology**, the study of the ecological and evolutionary basis for animal behavior. As we explore this vibrant area of modern biological research, we will also review studies by Tinbergen and two other early researchers—Karl von Frisch and Konrad Lorenz—that earned the three scientists a Nobel Prize in 1973.

In addressing Tinbergen's first question, the nature of the stimuli that trigger behavior, we'll begin with behavioral responses to well-defined stimuli, starting with an example from Tinbergen's own experiments.

Fixed Action Patterns

As part of his research, Tinbergen kept fish tanks containing three-spined sticklebacks (*Gasterosteus aculeatus*). Male sticklebacks, which have red bellies, attack other males that invade their nesting territories. Tinbergen noticed that his male sticklebacks also behaved aggressively when a red truck passed in front of their tank. Inspired by this chance observation, he carried out experiments showing that the red color of an intruder's underside is what provokes the attack behavior. A male stickleback will not attack a fish lacking red coloration (note that female sticklebacks never have red bellies), but will attack even unrealistic models if they contain areas of red color **(Figure 51.2)**.

The territorial response of male sticklebacks is an example of a **fixed action pattern**, a sequence of unlearned acts directly linked to a simple stimulus. Fixed action patterns are essentially unchangeable and, once initiated, usually carried to completion. The trigger for the behavior is an external cue called a **sign stimulus**, such as a red object prompting the male stickleback's aggressive behavior.

Migration

Environmental stimuli not only trigger behaviors but also provide cues that animals use to carry out those behaviors. For example, a wide variety of birds, fishes, and other animals use environmental cues to guide **migration**—a regular, long-distance change in location **(Figure 51.3)**.

Many migrating animals pass through environments they have not previously encountered. How, then, do they find their way in these foreign settings?

Some migrating animals track their position relative to the sun, even though the sun's position relative to Earth changes throughout the day. Animals can adjust for these changes by means of a *circadian clock*, an internal mechanism that maintains a 24-hour activity rhythm or cycle (see Chapter 49). For

(a) A male stickleback fish attacks other male sticklebacks that invade its nesting territory. The red belly of the intruding male (left) acts as the sign stimulus that releases the aggressive behavior.

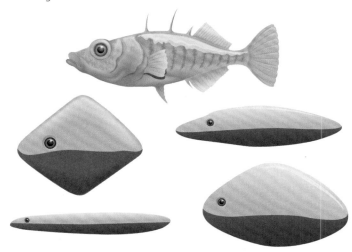

(b) The realistic model at the top, without a red underside, produces no aggressive response in a male three-spined stickleback. The other models, with red undersides, produce strong responses.

▲ **Figure 51.2 Sign stimuli in a classic fixed action pattern.**

❓ *Suggest an explanation for why this behavior evolved (its ultimate causation).*

▲ **Figure 51.3 Migration.** Each spring, snow geese (*Chen caerulescens*) migrate from their wintering grounds, which may be as far south as Mexico, to their breeding grounds in Greenland, Canada, and Alaska. In the autumn, they return to their wintering grounds.

example, experiments have shown that migrating birds orient differently relative to the sun at distinct times of the day. Nocturnal animals can instead use the North Star, which has a constant position in the night sky.

Although the sun and stars can provide useful clues for navigation, these landmarks can be obscured by clouds. How do migrating animals overcome this problem? A simple experiment with homing pigeons provides one answer. On an overcast day, placing a small magnet on the head of a homing pigeon prevents it from returning efficiently to its roost. Researchers concluded that pigeons can sense their position relative to Earth's magnetic field and thereby navigate without solar or celestial cues.

The way in which animals detect Earth's magnetic field remains a matter of debate. It is known that the heads of migrating fishes and birds contain bits of magnetite, a magnetic iron mineral. This fact leads some scientists to hypothesize that Earth's pull on magnetite-containing structures triggers transmission of nerve impulses to the brain. Others propose that migrating animals are guided by the effects of Earth's magnetic field on photoreceptors in the eye. The idea that animals "see" the magnetic field is supported by experiments showing that light of particular wavelengths must be present for birds to orient in a magnetic field during the day or night.

Behavioral Rhythms

Although the circadian clock plays a small but significant role in navigation by some migrating species, it has a major role in the daily activity of all animals. As discussed in Chapters 40 and 49, the output of the clock is a circadian rhythm, a daily cycle of rest and activity with far-reaching effects on behavioral physiology. The clock is normally synchronized with the light and dark cycles of the environment but can maintain rhythmic activity under constant environmental conditions, such as during hibernation.

Some behaviors, such as migration and reproduction, reflect biological rhythms with a longer cycle, or period, than the circadian rhythm. Behavioral rhythms linked to the yearly cycle of seasons are called *circannual rhythms*. Although migration and reproduction typically correlate with food availability, these behaviors are not a direct response to changes in food intake. Instead, circannual rhythms, like circadian rhythms, are influenced by the periods of daylight and darkness in the environment. For example, studies with several bird species have shown that an artificial environment with extended daylight can induce out-of-season migratory behavior.

Not all biological rhythms are linked to the light and dark cycles in the environment. Consider, for instance, the fiddler crab shown in Figure 51.1. The male's claw-waving courtship behavior is linked not to day length but to the timing of the new and full moon. Why? Fiddler crabs begin their lives as plankton, settling in the mudflats after several larval stages. By courting at the time of the new or full moon, crabs link their reproduction to the times of greatest tidal movement. The tides disperse larvae to deeper waters, where they complete early development in relative safety before returning to the tidal flats.

Animal Signals and Communication

Claw waving by fiddler crabs during courtship is an example of one animal (the male crab) generating the stimulus that guides the behavior of another animal (the female crab). A stimulus transmitted from one animal to another is called a **signal**. The transmission and reception of signals constitute animal **communication**, an essential element of interactions between individuals.

Forms of Animal Communication

Let's consider the courtship behavior of *Drosophila melanogaster*, the fruit fly (**Figure 51.4**), as an introduction to the four

Male visually recognizes female.

Female releases chemicals detected by the male's sense of smell.

(a) Orienting

Male taps female's abdomen with a foreleg.

(b) Tapping

Male extends and vibrates wing, producing a courtship song.

(c) "Singing"

▲ **Figure 51.4 Courtship behavior of the fruit fly.** Fruit fly courtship involves a fixed set of behaviors that follow one another in a fixed order.

common modes of animal communication: visual, chemical, tactile, and auditory.

Fruit fly courtship constitutes a *stimulus-response chain*, in which the response to each stimulus is itself the stimulus for the next behavior. In the first step, a male identifies a female of the same species and then orients his body toward hers. When the male sees and turns toward the female, he relies on *visual communication*. In addition, the male's sense of smell, or olfactory system, detects chemicals released into the air by the female. This is an example of *chemical communication*, the transmission and reception of signals in the form of specific molecules. Having recognized the female, the male approaches and taps the female with a foreleg. This touching, or *tactile communication*, alerts the female to the male's presence. In the process, chemicals on her abdomen are transferred to the male, providing further chemical confirmation of her species identity. In the third stage of courtship, the male extends and vibrates his wing, producing a specific courtship song. This singing, an example of *auditory communication*, informs the female that the male is of the same species. Only if all of these forms of communication are successful will a female allow the male to attempt copulation.

The information content of animal communication varies considerably. One of the most remarkable examples is the symbolic language of the European honeybee (*Apis mellifera*), discovered in the early 1900s by Austrian researcher Karl von Frisch. Using glass-walled observation hives, he and his students spent several decades observing these bees. Methodical recordings of bee movements enabled von Frisch to decipher a "dance language" that returning foragers use to inform other bees about the distance and direction of travel to food sources.

As illustrated in **Figure 51.5**, a returning bee quickly becomes the center of attention for other bees, called followers. If the food source is close to the hive (less than 50 m away), the returning bee moves in tight circles while waggling its abdomen from side to side. This behavior, called the "round dance," motivates the follower bees to leave the hive and search for nearby food.

When the food source is farther from the nest, the returning bee instead performs a "waggle dance." This dance, consisting of a half-circle swing in one direction, a straight run during which the bee waggles its abdomen, and a half-circle swing in the other direction, communicates to the follower bees both the direction and distance of the food source in relation to the hive. The angle of the straight run relative to the hive's vertical surface is the same as the horizontal angle of the food in relation to the sun. For example, if the returning bee runs at a 30° angle to the right of vertical, the follower bees leaving the hive fly 30° to the right of the horizontal direction of the sun. A dance with a longer straight run, and

(a) Worker bees cluster around a bee that recently returned from a foraging trip.

(b) The round dance indicates that food is near.

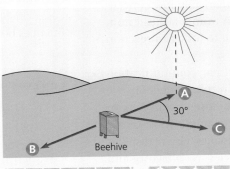

(c) The waggle dance, performed when food is distant, resembles a figure eight (below). Distance is indicated by the number of abdominal waggles performed in the straight-run part of the dance. Direction is indicated by the angle (in relation to the vertical surface of the hive) of the straight run.

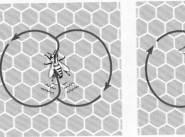

Location **A**: Food source is in same direction as sun.

Location **B**: Food source is in direction opposite sun.

Location **C**: Food source is 30° to right of sun.

▲ **Figure 51.5 Honeybee dance language.** Honeybees returning to the hive communicate the location of food sources through the symbolic language of a dance.

therefore more abdominal waggles per run, indicates a greater distance to the food source. As follower bees exit the hive, they fly almost directly to the area indicated by the waggle dance. By using flower odor and other clues, they locate the food source within this area.

Pheromones

Animals that communicate through odors or tastes emit chemical substances called **pheromones**. Pheromones are especially common among mammals and insects and often relate to reproductive behavior. For example, pheromones are the basis for the chemical communication in fruit fly courtship (see Figure 51.4). Pheromones are not limited to short-distance signaling, however. Male silkworm moths have receptors that can detect the pheromone from a female moth from several kilometers away. After the moths are together, pheromones also trigger specific courtship behaviors.

In a honeybee colony, pheromones produced by the queen and her daughters, the workers, maintain the hive's complex social order. One pheromone (once called the queen substance) has a particularly wide range of effects. It attracts workers to the queen, inhibits development of ovaries in workers, and attracts males (drones) to the queen during her mating flights out of the hive.

Pheromones can also serve as alarm signals. For example, when a minnow or catfish is injured, a substance released from the fish's skin disperses in the water, inducing a fright response in other fish. These nearby fish become more vigilant and often form tightly packed schools near the river or lake bottom, where they are safer from attack **(Figure 51.6)**. Pheromones can be very effective at remarkably low concentrations. For instance, just 1 cm^2 of skin from a fathead minnow contains sufficient alarm substance to induce a reaction in 58,000 L of water.

As we have seen, the forms of animal communication used to convey information are quite diverse. In general, the form of communication that evolves is closely related to an animal's lifestyle and environment. For example, most terrestrial mammals are nocturnal, which makes visual displays relatively ineffective. Instead, these species use olfactory and auditory signals, which work as well in the dark as in the light. In contrast, most birds are diurnal (active mainly in daytime) and communicate primarily by visual and auditory signals. Humans are also diurnal and, like birds, use primarily visual and auditory communication. We can thus detect and appreciate the songs and bright colors used by birds to communicate but miss many chemical cues on which other mammals base their behavior.

So far in this chapter, we have explored the types of stimuli that elicit behaviors—the first part of Tinbergen's first question. The second part of that question—the physiological mechanisms that mediate responses—was the focus of

(a) Minnows are widely dispersed in an aquarium before an alarm substance is introduced.

(b) Within seconds of the alarm substance being introduced, minnows aggregate near the bottom of the aquarium and reduce their movement.

▲ **Figure 51.6 Minnows responding to the presence of an alarm substance.**

Chapter 49. Stimuli activate sensory systems, are processed in the central nervous system, and result in motor outputs that constitute behavior. You may want to review those two chapters before proceeding to the next concept, which focuses on Tinbergen's second question—how experience influences behavior.

CONCEPT CHECK 51.1

1. If an egg rolls out of the nest, a mother graylag goose will retrieve it by nudging it with her beak and head. If researchers remove the egg or substitute a ball during this process, the goose continues to bob her beak and head while she moves back to the nest. Explain how and why this behavior occurs.
2. **MAKE CONNECTIONS** How is the seasonal timing of plant flowering similar in mechanism and function to the lunar-linked rhythm of fiddler crab courtship?
3. **WHAT IF?** Suppose you exposed various fish species to the alarm substance from minnows. Based on what you know about natural selection, suggest why some species might respond like minnows, some might increase activity, and some might show no change.

For suggested answers, see Appendix A.

CONCEPT 51.2

Learning establishes specific links between experience and behavior

For many behaviors—such as a fixed action pattern, a courtship stimulus-response chain, and pheromone signaling—nearly all individuals in a population exhibit virtually the same behavior, despite internal and environmental differences during development and throughout life. Behavior that is developmentally fixed in this way is known as **innate behavior**. In other cases, behavior is variable, depending on experience.

Experience and Behavior

Tinbergen's second question asks how an animal's experiences during growth and development influence the response to stimuli. How do researchers answer this question? One informative approach is a **cross-fostering study**, in which the young of one species are placed in the care of adults from another species. The extent to which the offspring's behavior changes in such a situation provides one measure of how the social and physical environment influences behavior.

The males of certain mouse species have behavioral differences that are well suited for cross-fostering experiments. Males of the species *Peromyscus californicus*, commonly called California mice, are highly aggressive toward other mice and provide extensive parental care. In contrast, male white-footed mice (*Peromyscus leucopus*) are less aggressive and engage in little parental care. When the pups of each species were placed in the nests of the other species, the cross-fostering altered some behaviors of both species **(Table 51.1)**. For instance, male California mice raised by white-footed mice were less aggressive toward intruders. Thus, experience during development can strongly influence aggressive behavior in these rodents.

Table 51.1 Influence of Cross-Fostering on Male Mice*

Species	Aggression Toward an Intruder	Aggression in Neutral Situation	Paternal Behavior
California mice fostered by white-footed mice	Reduced	No difference	Reduced
White-footed mice fostered by California mice	No difference	Increased	No difference

*Comparisons are with mice raised by parents of their own species.

One of the most important findings of the cross-fostering experiments with mice was that the influence of experience on behavior can be passed on to progeny: When the cross-fostered California mice became parents, they spent less time retrieving offspring who wandered off than did California mice raised by their own species. Thus, experience during development can modify physiology in a way that alters parental behavior, extending the influence of environment to a subsequent generation.

For humans, the influence of genetics and environment on behavior can be explored by a **twin study**, in which researchers compare the behavior of identical twins raised apart with the behavior of those raised in the same household. Twin studies have been instrumental in studying human behavioral disorders, such as schizophrenia, anxiety disorders, and alcoholism. As discussed in Chapter 49, these investigations have revealed that both genetics and environment (nature *and* nurture) contribute significantly to the behaviors that characterize these disorders in humans.

Learning

One of the most powerful ways that environmental conditions can influence behavior is through **learning**, the modification of behavior based on specific experiences. We will now consider a number of different types of learning, beginning with a form of learning first explored by Austrian biologist Konrad Lorenz.

Imprinting

A type of behavior that includes both learned and innate components is **imprinting**, the formation at a specific stage in life of a long-lasting behavioral response to a particular individual or object. Imprinting is distinguished from other types of learning by having a **sensitive period**, also called a critical period, a limited developmental phase when this type of learning can occur. During the sensitive period, the young imprint on their parent and learn the basic behaviors of their species, while the parent learns to recognize its offspring. Among gulls, for instance, the sensitive period for a parent to bond with its young lasts one to two days. If bonding does not occur, the parent will not care for the infant, leading to death for the offspring and a decrease in reproductive success for the parent.

But how do the young know on whom—or what—to imprint? For example, how do young birds know that they should follow their mother? The tendency to respond is innate in the birds; the outside world provides the *imprinting stimulus*, something to which the response will be directed. Experiments with many species of waterfowl indicate that they have no innate recognition of "mother." Rather, they identify with the first object they encounter that has certain key characteristics. In classic experiments done in the 1930s, Lorenz showed that the principal imprinting stimulus in graylag geese (*Anser anser*) is a nearby object that is moving away from the young. When incubator-hatched goslings spent their first few hours with Lorenz rather than with a goose, they imprinted on him and steadfastly followed him from then on **(Figure 51.7a)**. Furthermore, they showed no

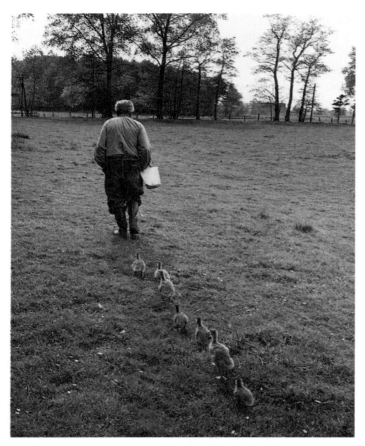

(a) These young greylag geese imprinted on ethologist Konrad Lorenz.

(b) A pilot wearing a crane suit and flying an ultralight plane acts as a surrogate parent to direct the migration of whooping cranes.

▲ **Figure 51.7 Imprinting.** Imprinting can be altered to **(a)** investigate animal behavior or **(b)** direct animal behavior.

WHAT IF? *Suppose the geese following Lorenz were bred to each other. How might their imprinting on Lorenz affect their offspring? Explain.*

recognition of their biological mother or other adults of their own species.

Imprinting has become an important component of efforts to save endangered species, such as the whooping crane (*Grus americana*). Scientists tried raising whooping cranes in captivity by using sandhill cranes (*Grus canadensis*) as foster parents. However, because the whooping cranes imprinted on their foster parents, none formed a *pair-bond* (strong attachment) with a whooping crane mate. To avoid such problems, captive breeding programs now isolate young cranes, exposing them to the sights and sounds of members of their own species.

Scientists have made further use of imprinting to teach cranes born in captivity to migrate along safe routes. Young whooping cranes are imprinted on humans in "crane suits" and then allowed to follow these "parents" as they fly ultralight aircraft along selected migration routes **(Figure 51.7b)**. Importantly, these cranes still form mating pair-bonds with other whooping cranes, indicating that the crane costumes have the features required to direct "normal" imprinting.

Spatial Learning and Cognitive Maps

Every natural environment has spatial variation, as in locations of nest sites, hazards, food, and prospective mates. Therefore, an organism's fitness may be enhanced by the capacity for **spatial learning**, the establishment of a memory that reflects the environment's spatial structure.

The idea of spatial learning intrigued Tinbergen while he was a graduate student in the Netherlands. At that time, he was studying the female digger wasp (*Philanthus triangulum*), which nests in small burrows dug into sand dunes. Tinbergen noticed that when a wasp left her nest to go hunting, she hid the entrance from potential intruders by covering it with sand. Upon her return, she flew directly to her hidden nest, despite the presence of hundreds of other burrows in the area. Tinbergen hypothesized that a wasp locates her nest by learning its position relative to visible landmarks, or location indicators. To test this hypothesis, he carried out an experiment in the wasps' natural habitat **(Figure 51.8)**. By manipulating objects around nest entrances, he demonstrated that digger wasps engage in spatial learning. This experiment was so simple and informative that it could be summarized very concisely. In fact, at 32 pages, Tinbergen's Ph.D. thesis from 1932 is still the shortest ever approved at Leiden University.

In many animal species, spatial learning can be quite sophisticated. Some animals guide their activity by a **cognitive map**, a representation in the nervous system of the spatial relationships between objects in an animal's surroundings. Rather than relying solely on moving from landmark to landmark, animals using cognitive maps can navigate more flexibly and efficiently by relating landmark positions to one another.

One striking example of cognitive mapping is found in the Clark's nutcracker (*Nucifraga columbiana*). Nutcrackers are corvids, the bird family that also includes ravens, crows, and jays. In the fall, a single nutcracker stores as many as 30,000 pine seeds in thousands of hiding places called caches, distributed over an area as large as 35 km². During the winter,

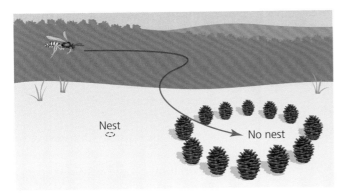
the birds relocate many of their caches. By experimentally varying the distance between landmarks, researchers demonstrated that birds could identify the halfway point between landmarks. This behavior suggests that nutcrackers employ an abstract geometric rule, which we can approximate as "Seed caches are found halfway between particular landmarks." Such rules, a fundamental property of cognitive maps, reduce the amount of detail required to remember an object's location. As we discussed in Chapter 49, corvids also display other forms of higher nervous system function.

Associative Learning

Learning often involves making associations between experiences. Consider, for example, a blue jay (*Cyanocitta cristata*) that ingests a brightly colored monarch butterfly (*Danaus plexippus*). Substances that the monarch accumulates from milkweed plants cause the blue jay to vomit almost immediately **(Figure 51.9)**. Following such experiences, blue jays avoid attacking monarchs and similar-looking butterflies. The ability to associate one environmental feature (such as a color) with another (such as a foul taste) is called **associative learning**.

Among animal behaviors, associative learning is particularly suited to laboratory studies because they typically involve either classical conditioning or operant conditioning. In *classical conditioning*, an arbitrary stimulus becomes associated with a particular outcome. Russian physiologist Ivan Pavlov carried out early experiments in classical conditioning, demonstrating that if he always rang a bell just before feeding a dog, the dog would eventually salivate when the bell sounded, anticipating food. In *operant conditioning*, also called trial-and-error learning, an animal first learns to associate one of its behaviors with a reward or punishment and then tends to repeat or avoid that behavior (see Figure 51.9). B. F. Skinner, an American pioneer in the study of operant conditioning, explored this process in the laboratory by, for example, having a rat learn through trial-and-error to obtain food by pressing a lever.

▲ **Figure 51.9 Associative learning.** Having ingested and vomited a monarch butterfly, a blue jay has probably learned to avoid this species.

Studies reveal that animals can learn to link many pairs of features of their environment, but not all. For example, pigeons can learn to associate danger with a sound but not with a color. However, they can learn to associate a color with food. What does this mean? The development and organization of the pigeon's nervous system apparently restrict the associations that can be formed. Moreover, such restrictions are not limited to birds. Rats, for example, can learn to avoid illness-inducing foods on the basis of smells, but not on the basis of sights or sounds.

If we take into account the evolution of behavior, the fact that some animals can't learn to make particular associations appears logical. The associations an animal can readily form typically reflect relationships likely to occur in nature. Conversely, associations that can't be formed are those unlikely to be of selective advantage in a native environment. In the case of a rat's diet in the wild, for example, a harmful food is far more likely to have a certain odor than to be associated with a particular sound.

Cognition and Problem Solving

The most complex forms of learning involve **cognition**—the process of knowing that involves awareness, reasoning, recollection, and judgment. Although it was once argued that only primates and certain marine mammals have high-level thought processes, many other groups of animals, including insects, appear to exhibit cognition in controlled laboratory studies. For example, an experiment using Y-shaped mazes tested whether honeybees can distinguish between "same" and "different." One maze had different colors, and one had different black-and-white striped patterns, either vertical or horizontal bars. Two groups of honeybees were trained in the color maze.

Upon entering, a bee would see a sample color and could then choose between an arm of the maze with the same color or an arm with a different color. Only one arm contained a food reward. The first group of bees were rewarded for flying into the arm with the *same* color as the sample **(Figure 51.10a)**; the second group were rewarded for choosing the arm with the *different* color. Next, they were tested in the bar maze, which had no food reward. After encountering a sample black-and-white pattern of bars, a bee could choose between an arm with the same pattern or an arm with a different pattern. The bees in the first group most often chose the arm with the same pattern **(Figure 51.10b)**, whereas those in the second group typically chose the arm with the different pattern.

The maze experiments provide strong experimental support for the hypothesis that honeybees can distinguish on the basis of "same" and "different." Remarkably, research published in 2010 indicates that honeybees can also learn to distinguish between human faces.

The information-processing ability of a nervous system can also be revealed in **problem solving**, the cognitive activity of devising a method to proceed from one state to another in the face of real or apparent obstacles. For example, if a chimpanzee is placed in a room with several boxes on the floor and a banana hung high out of reach, the chimp can assess the situation and stack the boxes, enabling it to reach the food. Such problem-solving behavior is highly developed in some mammals, especially primates and dolphins. Notable examples have also been observed in some bird species, especially corvids. In one study, ravens were confronted with food hanging from a branch by a string. After failing to grab the food in flight, one raven flew to the branch and alternately pulled up and stepped on the string until the food was within reach. A number of other ravens eventually arrived at similar solutions. Nevertheless, some ravens failed to solve the problem, indicating that problem-solving success in this species, as in others, varies with individual experience and abilities.

(a) Bees were trained in a color maze. As shown here, one group were rewarded for choosing the same color as the stimulus.

(b) Bees were tested in a pattern maze. If previously rewarded for choosing the same color, bees most often chose lines oriented the same way as the stimulus.

▲ **Figure 51.10 A maze test of abstract thinking by honeybees.** These mazes are designed to test whether honeybees can distinguish "same" from "different."

Development of Learned Behaviors

Most of the learned behaviors we have discussed develop over a relatively short time. Some behaviors develop more gradually. For example, some bird species learn songs in stages.

In the case of the white-crowned sparrow (*Zonotrichia leucophrys*), the first stage of song learning takes place early in life, when the fledgling sparrow first hears the song. If a fledgling is prevented from hearing real sparrows or recordings of sparrow songs during the first 50 days of its life, it fails to develop the adult song of its species. Although the young bird does not sing during the sensitive period, it memorizes the song of its species by listening to other white-crowned sparrows sing. During the sensitive period, fledglings chirp more in response to songs of their own species than to songs of other species. Thus, although young white-crowned sparrows learn the songs they will sing as adults, learning appears to be bounded by genetically controlled preferences.

The sensitive period when a white-crowned sparrow memorizes its species' song is followed by a second learning phase when the juvenile bird sings tentative notes called a subsong. The juvenile bird hears its own singing and compares it with the song memorized during the sensitive period. Once a sparrow's own song matches the one it memorized, the song "crystallizes" as the final song, and the bird sings only this adult song for the rest of its life.

The song-learning process is quite different for canaries than for white-crowned sparrows. Canaries, for example, do not have a single sensitive period for song learning. A young canary begins with a subsong, but the full song does not crystallize in the same way as in white-crowned sparrows. Between breeding seasons, the song becomes flexible again, and an adult male may learn new song "syllables" each year, adding to the song it already sings.

Song learning is one of many examples of how animals learn from other members of their species. In finishing our exploration of learning, we'll look at several more examples that reflect the more general phenomenon of social learning.

Social Learning

Many animals learn to solve problems by observing the behavior of other individuals. Young wild chimpanzees, for example, learn how to crack open oil palm nuts with two stones by copying experienced chimpanzees **(Figure 51.11)**. This type of learning through observing others is called **social learning**.

▲ **Figure 51.11 A young chimpanzee learning to crack oil palm nuts by observing an experienced elder.**

Another example of how social learning can modify behavior comes from studies of the vervet monkeys (*Cercopithecus aethiops*) in Amboseli National Park, Kenya. Vervet monkeys, which are about the size of a domestic cat, produce a complex set of alarm calls. Amboseli vervets give distinct alarm calls for leopards, eagles, or snakes, all of which prey on vervets. When a vervet sees a leopard, it gives a loud barking sound; when it sees an eagle, it gives a short double-syllable cough; and the snake alarm call is a "chutter." Upon hearing a particular alarm call, other vervets in the group behave in an appropriate way: They run up a tree on hearing the alarm for a leopard (vervets are nimbler than leopards in the trees); look up on hearing the alarm for an eagle; and look down on hearing the alarm for a snake **(Figure 51.12)**.

Infant vervet monkeys give alarm calls, but in a relatively undiscriminating way. For example, they give the "eagle" alarm on seeing any bird, including harmless birds such as bee-eaters. With age, the monkeys improve their accuracy. In fact, adult vervet monkeys give the eagle alarm only on seeing an eagle belonging to either of the two species that eat vervets. Infants probably learn how to give the right call by observing other members of the group and receiving social confirmation. For instance, if the infant gives the call on the right occasion— say, an eagle alarm when there is an eagle overhead—another member of the group will also give the eagle call. But if the infant gives the call when a bee-eater flies by, the adults in the group are silent. Thus, vervet monkeys have an initial, unlearned tendency to give calls upon seeing potentially threatening objects in the environment. Learning fine-tunes the call so that adult vervets give calls only in response to genuine danger and can fine-tune the alarm calls of the next generation.

▲ **Figure 51.12 Vervet monkeys learning correct use of alarm calls.** On seeing a python (foreground), vervet monkeys give a distinct "snake" alarm call (inset), and the members of the group stand upright and look down.

Social learning forms the roots of **culture**, which can be defined as a system of information transfer through social learning or teaching that influences the behavior of individuals in a population. Cultural transfer of information can alter behavioral phenotypes and thereby influence the fitness of individuals.

Changes in behavior that result from natural selection occur on a much longer time scale than does learning. In Concept 51.3, we'll examine the relationship between particular behaviors and the processes of selection related to survival and reproduction.

CONCEPT CHECK 51.2

1. How might associative learning explain why different species of distasteful or stinging insects have similar colors?
2. **WHAT IF?** How might you position and manipulate a few objects in a lab to test whether an animal can use a cognitive map to remember the location of a food source?
3. **MAKE CONNECTIONS** How can a learned behavior contribute to speciation? (See Concept 24.1, pp. 488–492.)

For suggested answers, see Appendix A.

CONCEPT 51.3

Selection for individual survival and reproductive success can explain most behaviors

We turn now from the physiology of behavior (how animals behave) to the benefits to a species from a particular behavior (why animals behave the way they do). In particular, we will address Tinbergen's third question—how behavior enhances survival and reproductive success in a population. We'll begin with an activity essential for both types of success: gathering food.

Foraging Behavior

Because adequate nutrition is essential to an animal's survival and reproductive success, we should expect natural selection to refine behaviors that enhance the efficiency of feeding. Food-obtaining behavior, or **foraging**, includes not only eating but also any activities an animal uses to search for, recognize, and capture food items.

Evolution of Foraging Behavior

The fruit fly (*Drosophila melanogaster*) has provided an opportunity to examine how foraging behavior might have evolved. Variation in a gene called *forager* (*for*) dictates the food-search behavior of fruit fly larvae. On average, larvae carrying the *for*^{R} ("Rover") allele travel nearly twice as far while feeding as do larvae with the *for*^{s} ("sitter") allele. Experiments have shown

that the enzyme encoded by the *forager* locus is more active in *for*^{R} larvae than in *for*^{s} larvae and has properties typical of an enzyme in a signal transduction pathway (see Chapter 45).

Both the *for*^{R} and *for*^{s} alleles are present in natural populations. What circumstances might favor one or the other allele? The answer became apparent in experiments when flies were kept for many generations at either low or high population densities. The larvae from the two samples clearly diverged in behavior, as measured by differences in average length of their foraging paths **(Figure 51.13)**. Larvae maintained for many generations at a low density foraged over shorter distances than those kept at high density. Furthermore, genetic tests indicated that the *for*^{s} allele had increased in frequency in the low-density populations, whereas the *for*^{R} allele had increased in frequency in the high-density group. These changes make sense. At low population density, short-distance foraging yields sufficient food, while long-distance foraging would result in unnecessary energy expenditure. Under crowded conditions, however, long-distance foraging could enable larvae to move beyond areas of food depletion. In summary, there was an observable and interpretable evolutionary change in behavior in the laboratory populations.

Optimal Foraging Model

To study the proximate and ultimate causation of diverse foraging strategies, biologists sometimes apply a type of cost-benefit analysis used in economics. This idea proposes that foraging behavior is a compromise between the benefits of nutrition and the costs of obtaining food. These costs might include the energy expenditure of foraging as well as the risk of being eaten while foraging. According to this **optimal foraging model**, natural selection should favor a foraging behavior that minimizes the costs of foraging and maximizes the benefits.

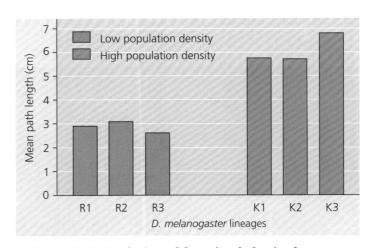

▲ **Figure 51.13 Evolution of foraging behavior by laboratory populations of *Drosophila melanogaster*.** After 74 generations of living at low population density, *D. melanogaster* larvae (populations R1–R3) followed foraging paths significantly shorter than those of *D. melanogaster* larvae that had lived at high density (populations K1–K3).

As an example of how the optimal foraging model can be applied, let's consider the feeding behavior of the Northwestern crow (*Corvus caurinus*). On islands off British Columbia, these crows search rocky tide pools for sea snails called whelks. After spotting a whelk, the crow picks the whelk up in its beak, flies upward, and drops the whelk onto the rocks. If the drop is successful, the shell breaks and the crow can dine on the whelk's soft parts. If not, the crow flies up and drops the whelk again and again until the shell breaks. What determines how high the crow flies? The higher the crow flies, the greater the force with which the whelk strikes the rocks, increasing the chance the shell will break. Flying higher, however, means consuming more energy.

If energetic considerations dominated selection for the crow's foraging behavior, the average drop height might reflect a trade-off between the cost of flying higher and the benefit of more frequent success. To test this idea, researchers dropped whelks from different heights and noted the number of drops required to break a shell. For each height, they calculated the average number of drops and the average *total flight height*, the drop height times the average number of drops **(Figure 51.14)**. A drop height of about 5 m turned out to be optimal, breaking the shells with the lowest total flight height—in other words, with the least work. The actual average flight height for crows in their whelk-eating behavior is 5.23 m, very close to the prediction based on an optimal trade-off between energy gained (food) and energy expended.

The close agreement between the predicted and actual flight heights suggests that the optimal foraging model reflects the selective forces shaping the evolution of this behavior. However, other models could explain the findings equally well. For example, the average flight height could minimize the average *time* necessary to break open a whelk. Further experiments are needed to evaluate these possibilities.

Balancing Risk and Reward

One of the most significant potential costs to a forager is risk of predation. Maximizing energy gain and minimizing energy costs are of little benefit if the behavior makes the forager a likely meal for a predator. It seems logical, therefore, that predation risk would influence foraging behavior. Such appears to be the case for the mule deer (*Odocoileus hemionus*), which lives in the mountains of western North America. Researchers found that the food available for mule deer was fairly uniform across the potential foraging areas, although somewhat lower in open, nonforested areas. In contrast, the risk of predation differed greatly; mountain lions (*Puma concolor*), the major predator, killed large numbers of mule deer at forest edges and only a small number in open areas and forest interiors.

How does mule deer foraging behavior reflect the differences in predation risk in particular areas? Mule deer feed predominantly in open areas. Thus, it appears that mule deer foraging behavior reflects the large variation in predation risk and not the smaller variation in food availability. This result underscores the point that behavior typically reflects a compromise between competing selective pressures.

Mating Behavior and Mate Choice

Just as foraging is crucial for individual survival, mating behavior and mate choice play a major role in determining reproductive success. These behaviors include seeking or attracting mates, choosing among potential mates, competing for mates, and caring for offspring. Although we tend to think of mating simply as the union of a male and female, the mating relationship between males and females varies greatly from species to species, defining a number of distinct mating systems.

Mating Systems and Sexual Dimorphism

Mating systems vary with regard to both the length and number of relationships. In many animal species, mating is **promiscuous**, with no strong pair-bonds. In species in which the mates remain together for a longer period, the relationship may be **monogamous** (one male mating with one female) or **polygamous** (an individual of one sex mating with several of the other). Polygamous relationships most often involve a single male and many females, a system called *polygyny*, though some species exhibit *polyandry*, in which a single female mates with several males.

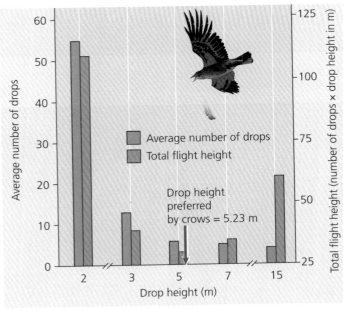

▲ **Figure 51.14 Energy costs and benefits in foraging behavior.** Experimental results indicate that dropping shells from a height of 5 m results in breakage with the least amount of work. The actual drop height preferred by crows corresponds almost exactly to the height that minimizes total flight height.

The extent to which males and females differ in appearance, a characteristic known as *sexual dimorphism*, typically varies with the type of mating system **(Figure 51.15)**. Among monogamous species, males and females are often so much alike morphologically that they may be difficult or impossible to distinguish based on external characteristics. In contrast, polygynous species are generally dimorphic, with males being showier and often larger than females. Polyandrous species are also dimorphic, but the females are generally more ornamented and larger than the males.

Mating Systems and Parental Care

The needs of the young are an important factor constraining the evolution of mating systems. Most newly hatched birds, for instance, cannot care for themselves. Rather, they require a large, continuous food supply, a need that is difficult for a single parent to meet. In such cases, a male that stays with and helps a single mate may ultimately have more viable offspring than it would by going off to seek additional mates. This may explain why most birds are monogamous. In contrast, for birds with young that can feed and care for themselves almost immediately after hatching, the males derive less benefit from staying with their partner. Males of these species, such as pheasants and quail, can maximize their reproductive success by seeking other mates, and polygyny is relatively common in such birds. In the case of mammals, the lactating female is often the only food source for the young; males usually play no role in raising the young. In mammalian species where males protect the females and young, such as lions, a male or small group of males typically takes care of a harem of many females at the same time.

Another factor influencing mating behavior and parental care is *certainty of paternity*. Young born to or eggs laid by a female definitely contain that female's genes. However, even within a normally monogamous relationship, a male other than the female's usual mate may have fathered that female's offspring. The certainty of paternity is relatively low in most species with internal fertilization because the acts of mating and birth (or mating and egg laying) are separated over time. This could explain why exclusively male parental care is rare in bird and mammal species. However, the males of many species with internal fertilization engage in behaviors that appear to increase their certainty of paternity. These behaviors include guarding females, removing any sperm from the female reproductive tract before copulation, and introducing large quantities of sperm that displace the sperm of other males.

Certainty of paternity is high when egg laying and mating occur together, as in external fertilization. This may explain why parental care in aquatic invertebrates, fishes, and amphibians, when it occurs at all, is at least as likely to be by males as

▼ **Figure 51.15 Relationship between mating system and male and female forms.**

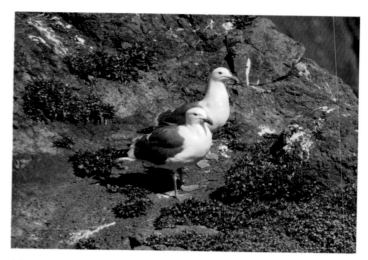

(a) In monogamous species, such as these western gulls, males and females are difficult to distinguish using external characteristics only.

(b) Among polygynous species, such as elk, the male (right) is often highly ornamented.

(c) In polyandrous species, such as these Wilson's phalaropes, females (top) are generally more ornamented than males.

▲ **Figure 51.16 Paternal care by a male jawfish.** The male jawfish, which lives in tropical marine environments, holds the eggs it has fertilized in its mouth, keeping them aerated and protecting them from egg predators until the young hatch.

▲ **Figure 51.17 Male stalk-eyed flies.** Male eye span plays a role in mate selection by females and, as shown here, in ritualized contests between males. In such contests, two males face off, with the male whose eye span is smaller very often retreating without any combat taking place.

by females (**Figure 51.16**; see also Figure 46.7). Among fishes and amphibians, parental care occurs in only 7% of species with internal fertilization but in 69% of species with external fertilization.

It is important to point out that certainty of paternity does not mean that animals are aware of those factors when they behave a certain way. Parental behavior correlated with certainty of paternity exists because it has been reinforced over generations by natural selection. Nevertheless, the relationship between certainty of paternity and male parental care remains an area of active research, enlivened by controversy.

Sexual Selection and Mate Choice

As you read in Chapter 23, the degree of sexual dimorphism within a species results from sexual selection, a form of natural selection in which differences in reproductive success among individuals are a consequence of differences in mating success. Recall from that chapter that sexual selection can take the form of *intersexual selection*, in which members of one sex choose mates on the basis of characteristics of the other sex, such as courtship songs, or *intrasexual selection*, which involves competition between members of one sex for mates. Let's look at some experimental evidence for sexual selection.

Mate Choice by Females Mate preferences of females may play a central role in the evolution of male behavior and anatomy through intersexual selection. As an example, let's consider the courtship behavior of stalk-eyed flies. The eyes of these insects are at the tips of stalks, which are longer in males than in females (**Figure 51.17**). During courtship, a male approaches the female headfirst. Researchers have shown that females are more likely to mate with males that have relatively long eyestalks. Why would females favor this seemingly arbitrary trait? As discussed in Chapter 23, ornaments such as long

eyestalks in these flies and bright coloration in male birds correlate in general with the male's health and vitality. A female whose mate choice is a healthy male is likely to produce more offspring that survive to reproduce.

Mate choice can also be influenced by imprinting, as revealed by experiments carried out with zebra finches. Both male and female zebra finches normally lack any feather crest on their head (**Figure 51.18**). To explore whether parental appearance affects mate preference in offspring independent of any genetic influence, researchers provided zebra finches with artificial ornamentation. A 2.5-cm-long red feather was taped to the forehead feathers of either or both zebra finch parents when their chicks were 8 days old, approximately 2 days before they opened their eyes. A control group of zebra finches were raised by unadorned parents. When the chicks matured,

▲ **Figure 51.18 Appearance of zebra finches in nature.** The male zebra finch (left) is more patterned and colorful than the female zebra finch.

they were presented with prospective mates that were either artificially ornamented with a red feather or non-ornamented (Figure 51.19). Males showed no preference. Females also showed no preference if they were raised by a male parent that was not ornamented. However, females raised by an ornamented male parent preferred ornamented males as their own mates. Thus, female finches apparently take cues from their fathers in choosing mates.

Mate-choice copying, a behavior in which individuals in a population copy the mate choice of others, has been studied in the guppy *Poecilia reticulata*. When a female guppy chooses between males with no other females present, the female almost always chooses the male with more orange coloration. To explore if the behavior of other females could influence this preference, an experiment was set up using both living females and artificial model females (Figure 51.20). If a female guppy observed the model "courting" a male with less extensive orange markings, she often copied the preference of the model female. That is, the female chose the male that had been presented in association with a model female rather than a more orange alternative. The exceptions were also informative. Mate-choice behavior typically did not change when the difference in coloration was particularly large. Mate-choice copying can thus mask genetically controlled female preference below a certain threshold of difference, in this case for male color.

Mate-choice copying, a form of social learning, has also been observed in several other fish and bird species. What is the selective pressure for such a mechanism? One possibility is that a female that mates with males that are attractive to other females increases the probability that her male offspring will also be attractive and have high reproductive success.

Male Competition for Mates The previous examples show how female choice can select for one best type of male in a given situation, resulting in low variation among males. Male competition for mates also can reduce variation among males.

▲ Figure 51.19 **Sexual selection influenced by imprinting.** Experiments demonstrated that female zebra finch chicks that had imprinted on artificially ornamented fathers preferred ornamented males as adult mates. For all experimental groups, male offspring showed no preference for either ornamented or non-ornamented female mates.

▶ Figure 51.20 **Mate choice copying by female guppies (*Poecilia reticulata*).** Female guppies generally choose the males with more orange coloration. But when males were matched for orange or differed in the amount of orange by 12% or 24%, the females in the experimental group chose the *less* orange male that was presented with a model female. Females ignored the apparent choice of the model female only where the alternative male had 40% more orange coloration.

Such competition may involve *agonistic behavior*, an often-ritualized contest that determines which competitor gains access to a resource, such as food or mates (**Figure 51.21**). The outcomes of such contests are often determined by strength or size, but the consequences may nevertheless be psychological rather than physical (see Figure 51.17).

Despite the potential for male competition to select for reduced variation, behavioral and morphological variation in males is extremely high in some vertebrate species, including species of fish and deer, as well as in a wide variety of invertebrates. In some species, sexual selection has led to the evolution of alternative male mating behavior and morphology. How do scientists analyze situations where more than one mating behavior can result in successful reproduction? One approach relies on the rules that govern games.

Applying Game Theory

Often, the fitness of a particular behavioral phenotype is influenced by other behavioral phenotypes in the population. In studying such situations, behavioral ecologists use a range of tools, including game theory. Developed by American mathematician John Nash and others to model human economic behavior, **game theory** evaluates alternative strategies in situations where the outcome depends on the strategies of all the individuals involved.

▲ **Figure 51.21 Agonistic interaction.** Male eastern grey kangaroos (*Macropus giganteus*) often "box" in contests that determine which male is most likely to mate with an available female. Typically, one male snorts loudly before striking the other around the head and throat with his forelimbs. Further snorting and cuffing, as well as grappling, often follow. If the male under attack does not retreat, the fight may escalate, with each male balancing on his tail while attempting to kick his rival with the sharp toenails of a hind leg.

▲ **Figure 51.22 Male polymorphism in the side-blotched lizard (*Uta stansburiana*).** An orange-throat male, left; a blue-throat male, center; a yellow-throat male, right.

As an example of applying game theory to mating behavior, let's consider the side-blotched lizard (*Uta stansburiana*) of California. Males can have orange, blue, or yellow throats (**Figure 51.22**). Each throat color is associated with a different pattern of behavior. Orange-throat males are the most aggressive and defend large territories that contain many females. Blue-throat males are also territorial but defend smaller territories and fewer females. Yellow-throats are nonterritorial males that mimic females and use "sneaky" tactics to gain the chance to mate.

Evidence indicates that the mating success of each male lizard type is influenced by the relative abundance of the other types, an example of frequency-dependent selection. In one study population, the most frequent throat coloration changed over a period of several years from blue to orange to yellow and back to blue.

By comparing the competition between side-blotched lizard males to the children's game of rock-paper-scissors, scientists devised an explanation for the cycles of variation in the lizard population. In the game, paper defeats rock, rock defeats scissors, and scissors defeats paper. Each hand symbol thus wins one matchup but loses the other. Similarly, each type of male lizard has an advantage over one of the other two types. When blue-throats are abundant, they can defend the few females in their territories from the advances of the sneaky yellow-throat males. However, blue-throats cannot defend their territories against the hyperaggressive orange-throats. Once the orange-throats become the most abundant, the larger number of females in each territory provides the opportunity for the yellow-throats to have greater mating success. The yellow-throats become more frequent, but then give way to the blue-throats, whose tactic of guarding small territories once again allows them the most success.

Game theory provides a way to think about complex evolutionary problems in which relative performance (reproductive success relative to other phenotypes), not absolute performance, is the key to understanding the evolution of behavior. This makes game theory an important tool because the relative performance of one phenotype compared with others is a measure of Darwinian fitness.

1. Why does the mode of fertilization correlate with the presence or absence of male parental care?
2. **MAKE CONNECTIONS** Balancing selection can maintain variation at a locus (see Concept 23.4, pp. 483–484). Based on the foraging experiments described in this chapter, devise a simple hypothesis to explain the presence of both for^R and for^s alleles in natural fly populations.
3. **WHAT IF?** Suppose an infection in a side-blotched lizard population killed many more males than females. What would be the immediate effect on male competition for reproductive success?

For suggested answers, see Appendix A.

CONCEPT **51.4**

Inclusive fitness can account for the evolution of behavior, including altruism

EVOLUTION We'll now explore issues related to the focus of Tinbergen's fourth question—the evolutionary history of behaviors. We will first look at examples that reveal the genetic underpinnings of behavior. Next, we will examine the genetic variation underlying the evolution of particular behaviors. Finally, we will see how expanding the definition of fitness beyond individual survival can help explain "selfless" behavior.

Genetic Basis of Behavior

In exploring the behavioral basis of behavior, we'll begin with the courtship behavior of the male fruit fly, diagrammed in Figure 51.4. During courtship, the male fly carries out a complex series of actions in response to multiple sensory stimuli. Genetic studies have revealed that a single gene called *fru* controls this entire courtship ritual. If the *fru* gene is mutated to an inactive form, males do not court or mate with females. (The name *fru* is short for *fruitless*, reflecting the absence of offspring from the mutant males.) Normal male and female flies express distinct forms of the *fru* gene. When females are genetically manipulated to express the male form of *fru*, they court other females, performing the role normally played by the male. How can a single gene control so many behaviors and actions? Experiments carried out cooperatively in several laboratories demonstrated that *fru* is a master regulatory gene that directs the expression and activity of many genes with narrower functions. Together, genes that are controlled by the *fru* gene bring about sex-specific development of the fly nervous system. In effect, *fru* programs the fly for male courtship behavior by overseeing a male-specific wiring of the central nervous system.

Researchers have also used insect courtship to explore genetic variation underlying differences in behavior. One well-studied example involves the courtship song of the green lacewing (Figure 51.23). Found throughout central to northern Eurasia and North America, these insects include at least

▼ Figure 51.23 | **INQUIRY**

Are the songs of green lacewing species under the control of multiple genes?

EXPERIMENT Charles Henry, Lucía Martínez, and Kent Holsinger crossed males and females of *Chrysoperla plorabunda* and *Chrysoperla johnsoni*, two morphologically identical species of lacewings that sing different courtship songs.

SOUND RECORDINGS

Chrysoperla plorabunda parent:

Standard repeating unit / Volley period / Vibration volleys

crossed with

Chrysoperla johnsoni parent:
Volley period

Standard repeating unit

The researchers compared the songs of the male and female parents with those of the hybrid offspring that had been raised in isolation from other lacewings.

RESULTS The F_1 hybrid offspring sang a song in which the length of the standard repeating unit was similar to that sung by the *Chrysoperla plorabunda* parent, but the volley period—the interval between vibration volleys—was more similar to that of the *Chrysoperla johnsoni* parent.

F_1 hybrids, typical phenotype:
Volley period

Standard repeating unit

CONCLUSION Since the song of the hybrid offspring has features of the songs of both parents, the results indicate that the songs sung by *Chrysoperla plorabunda* and *Chrysoperla johnsoni* are under the control of more than one gene.

SOURCE C. S. Henry et al., The inheritance of mating songs in two cryptic, sibling lacewing species, *Genetica* 116:269–289 (2002).

WHAT IF? Suppose the hybrids generated in this experiment were fertile. Would the appearance of the hybrid song shown in the figure be likely to lead to the formation of a new species? Explain your answer.

15 species, identical in appearance but having different courtship songs. When researchers at the University of Connecticut reared lacewings in isolation in the laboratory, they found that the lacewings performed the song specific to their species. Thus, they concluded, the courtship song must be genetically controlled. They then crossed different green lacewing species in the laboratory and analyzed the songs produced by the hybrid offspring. These experiments demonstrated that a different gene governs each component or property of the courtship song. Furthermore, the distinct courtship song of each green lacewing species reflects genetic differences at multiple, independent loci.

Whereas variation in multiple genes can bring about distinct behaviors, as is true for the lacewing courtship song, variation in a single locus is sometimes sufficient to bring about dramatic differences in behavior. One striking example is the behavior of two closely related species of voles, which are small, mouse-like rodents. Male meadow voles (*Microtus pennsylvanicus*) are solitary and do not form lasting relationships with mates. Following mating, they pay little attention to their pups. In contrast, male prairie voles (*Microtus ochrogaster*) form a pair-bond with a single female after they mate (Figure 51.24). Male prairie voles hover over their young pups, licking them and carrying them, while acting aggressively toward intruders.

Research suggested that a neurotransmitter released during mating is critical for the partnering and parental behavior of male voles. Known as ADH or vasopressin (see Chapter 44), this peptide binds to a specific receptor in the central nervous system. When male prairie voles are treated with a drug that inhibits the brain receptor for vasopressin, they fail to form pair-bonds after mating. Scientists have also observed that the vasopressin receptor gene of prairie voles is highly expressed in the brain, whereas that of meadow voles is not.

To test whether the amount of the vasopressin receptor present in the brain regulates the postmating behavior of voles, researchers inserted the vasopressin receptor gene from prairie voles into male meadow voles. The meadow voles carrying this gene not only developed brains with higher levels of the vasopressin receptor but also showed many of the same mating behaviors as male prairie voles, such as pair-bonding. Thus, although many genes influence pair-bond formation and parenting among voles, the level of the vasopressin receptor alone determines which behavioral pattern develops.

Genetic Variation and the Evolution of Behavior

Behavioral differences between closely related species, such as meadow and prairie voles, are common. Significant differences in behavior can also be found *within* a species but are often less obvious. When behavioral variation between populations of a species corresponds to variation in environmental conditions, it may be evidence of past evolution.

Case Study: Variation in Prey Selection

An example of genetically based behavioral variation within a species involves prey selection by the western garter snake (*Thamnophis elegans*). The natural diet of this species differs widely across its range in California. Coastal populations feed predominantly on banana slugs (*Ariolimus californicus*) (Figure 51.25). Inland populations feed on frogs, leeches, and fish, but not on banana slugs. In fact, banana slugs are rare or absent in the inland habitats.

◀ **Figure 51.24 A pair of prairie voles (*Microtus ochrogaster*) huddling.** Male North American prairie voles associate closely with their mates, as shown here, and contribute substantially to the care of young.

▲ **Figure 51.25 Western garter snake from a coastal habitat eating a banana slug.** Experiments indicate that the preference of these snakes for banana slugs may be influenced mainly by genetics rather than by environment.

When researchers offered banana slugs to snakes from each wild population, most coastal snakes readily ate them, whereas inland snakes tended to refuse. To what extent does genetic variation contribute to a snake's fondness for banana slugs? To answer this question, researchers collected pregnant snakes from each wild population and housed them in separate cages in the laboratory. While still very young, the offspring were offered a small piece of banana slug on each of ten days. More than 60% of the young snakes from coastal mothers ate banana slugs on eight or more of the ten days. In contrast, fewer than 20% of the young snakes from inland mothers ate a piece of banana slug even once. Perhaps not surprisingly, banana slugs thus appear to be a genetically acquired taste.

How did a genetically determined difference in feeding preference come to match the snakes' habitats so well? It turns out that the coastal and inland populations also vary with respect to their ability to recognize and respond to odor molecules produced by banana slugs. Researchers hypothesize that when inland snakes colonized coastal habitats more than 10,000 years ago, some of them could recognize banana slugs by scent. Because these snakes took advantage of this food source, they had higher fitness than snakes in the population that ignored the slugs. Over hundreds or thousands of generations, the capacity to recognize the slugs as prey increased in frequency in the coastal population. The marked variation in behavior observed today between the coastal and inland populations may be evidence of this past evolutionary change.

Case Study: Variation in Migratory Patterns

Another species suited to the study of behavioral variation is the blackcap (*Sylvia atricapilla*), a small migratory warbler. Blackcaps that breed in Germany generally migrate southwest to Spain and then south to Africa for the winter. In the 1950s, a few blackcaps began to spend their winters in Britain, and over time the population of blackcaps wintering in Britain grew to many thousands. Leg bands showed that some of these birds had migrated westward from central Germany. Why were there now two patterns of migration from Germany? To answer this question, researchers at the Max Planck Research Center in Radolfzell, Germany, devised a strategy to study migratory orientation in the laboratory (Figure 51.26). The results demonstrated that the two patterns of migration reflect genetic differences between the two populations.

The study of western European blackcaps indicated that the change in their migratory behavior occurred both recently and rapidly. Before the year 1950, there were no known westward-migrating blackcaps in Germany. By the 1990s, westward migrants made up 7–11% of the blackcap populations of Germany. Once westward migration began, it persisted and increased in frequency, perhaps due to the widespread use of winter bird feeders in Britain, as well as shorter migration distances.

▼ Figure 51.26

INQUIRY

Are differences in migratory orientation within a species genetically determined?

EXPERIMENT Peter Berthold and colleagues in southern Germany raised two sets of young birds for their study. One group consisted of the offspring of blackcaps captured while wintering in Britain and then bred in Germany in an outdoor cage. The other group consisted of young birds collected from nests near the laboratory and then raised in cages. In the autumn, Berthold's team placed the blackcaps captured in Britain and the young birds raised in cages in large, glass-covered funnel cages lined with carbon-coated paper for 1.5–2 hours. When the funnels were placed outside at night, the birds moved around, making marks on the paper that indicated the direction in which they were trying to "migrate."

Scratch marks

RESULTS The wintering adult birds captured in Britain and their laboratory-raised offspring both attempted to migrate to the west. In contrast, the young birds collected from nests in southern Germany attempted to migrate to the southwest.

CONCLUSION The young of the British blackcaps and the young birds from Germany (the control group) were raised under similar conditions but showed very different migratory orientations, indicating that migratory orientation has a genetic basis.

SOURCE P. Berthold et al., Rapid microevolution of migratory behavior in a wild bird species, *Nature* 360:668–690 (1992).

WHAT IF? Suppose the birds had not shown a difference in orientation in these experiments. Could you conclude that the behavior was not genetically based? Explain.

Altruism

Reconstructing the evolutionary basis of a behavior requires an understanding of the behavior's genetic basis and of the selective advantage conferred by the behavior. Typically, we assume that behaviors are selfish; that is, they benefit the individual at the expense of others, especially competitors. For example, superior foraging ability by one individual may leave less food for others. The problem comes, however, with "unselfish" behaviors. How can such behaviors arise through natural selection? To answer this question, let's look more closely at some examples of unselfish behavior and then consider how such behaviors might arise.

In discussing selflessness, we will use the term **altruism** to describe a behavior that reduces an animal's individual fitness but increases the fitness of other individuals in the population. Consider the Belding's ground squirrel, which lives in some mountainous regions of the western United States and is vulnerable to predators such as coyotes and hawks. A squirrel that sees a predator approach often gives a high-pitched alarm call that alerts unaware individuals to retreat to their burrows. Note that for the squirrel that warns others, the conspicuous alarm behavior increases the risk of being killed because it brings attention to the caller's location.

Another example of altruistic behavior occurs in honeybee societies, in which the workers are sterile. The workers themselves never reproduce, but they labor on behalf of a single fertile queen. Furthermore, the workers sting intruders, a behavior that helps defend the hive but results in the death of those workers.

Altruism is also observed in naked mole rats (*Heterocephalus glaber*), highly social rodents that live in underground chambers and tunnels in southern and northeastern Africa. The naked mole rat, which is almost hairless and nearly blind, lives in colonies of 75 to 250 or more individuals **(Figure 51.27)**. Each colony has only one reproducing female, the queen, who mates with one to three males, called kings. The rest of the colony consists of nonreproductive females and males who forage for underground roots and tubers and care for the queen, the kings, and new offspring. The nonreproductive individuals may sacrifice their own lives in trying to protect the queen or kings from snakes or other predators that invade the colony.

▲ **Figure 51.27 Naked mole rats, a species of colonial mammal that exhibits altruistic behavior.** Pictured here is a queen nursing offspring while surrounded by other members of the colony.

Inclusive Fitness

How can a Belding's ground squirrel, a worker honeybee, or a naked mole rat enhance its fitness by aiding members of the population that may be its closest competitors? How can altruistic behavior be maintained by evolution if it does not enhance the survival and reproductive success of the self-sacrificing individuals?

The selection for altruistic behavior is most readily apparent in the case of parents sacrificing for their offspring. When parents sacrifice their own well-being to produce and aid offspring, this actually increases the fitness of the parents because it maximizes their genetic representation in the population. However, individuals sometimes help others who are not their offspring.

Biologist William Hamilton proposed that an animal could increase its genetic representation in the next generation by "altruistically" helping close relatives other than its own offspring. Like parents and offspring, full siblings have half their genes in common. Therefore, selection might also favor helping siblings or helping one's parents produce more siblings. This idea led to Hamilton's idea of **inclusive fitness**, the total effect an individual has on proliferating its genes by producing its own offspring *and* by providing aid that enables other close relatives, who share many of those genes, to produce offspring.

Hamilton's Rule and Kin Selection

According to Hamilton, the three key variables in an act of altruism are the benefit to the recipient, the cost to the altruist, and the coefficient of relatedness. The benefit, B, is the average number of *extra* offspring that the beneficiary of an altruistic act produces. The cost, C, is how many *fewer* offspring the altruist produces. The **coefficient of relatedness**, r, equals the fraction of genes that, on average, are shared. Natural selection favors altruism when the benefit to the recipient multiplied by the coefficient of relatedness exceeds the cost to the altruist—in other words, when $rB > C$. This statement is called **Hamilton's rule**.

To better understand Hamilton's rule, let's apply it to a human population in which the average individual has two children. We'll imagine that a young man is close to drowning in heavy surf, and his sister risks her life to swim out and pull her sibling to safety. If the young man had drowned, his reproductive output would have been zero; but now, if we use the average, he can father two children. The benefit to the brother is thus two offspring ($B = 2$). What about the risk taken by his sister? Let's say that the sister has a 25% chance of drowning in attempting to rescue her brother. We can then calculate the cost of the altruistic act to the sister as 0.25 times 2, the number of offspring she would be expected to have if she had stayed on shore ($C = 0.25 \times 2 = 0.5$). Finally, we note that a brother and sister share half their genes on average ($r = 0.5$). One way to see this is in terms of the segregation of homologous chromosomes that occurs during meiosis of gametes (**Figure 51.28**; see also Chapter 13).

We can now use our values of B, C, and r to evaluate whether natural selection would favor the altruistic act in our imaginary scenario. For the surf rescue, $rB = 0.5 \times 2 = 1$, whereas $C = 0.5$. Because rB is greater than C, Hamilton's rule is satisfied; thus, natural selection would favor this altruistic act of the sister attempting to save her brother. Averaging over many individuals and generations, any particular gene in a sister faced with this situation will be passed on to more offspring if she risks the rescue than if she does not. Furthermore, among genes propagated in this way may be some that contribute to altruistic behavior. The natural selection that favors altruistic behavior by enhancing reproductive success of relatives is called **kin selection**.

Kin selection weakens with hereditary distance. Siblings have an r of 0.5, but between an aunt and her niece, $r = 0.25$ (¼), and between first cousins, $r = 0.125$ (⅛). Notice that as the degree of relatedness decreases, the rB term in the Hamilton inequality also decreases. Would natural selection favor rescuing a cousin? Not unless the surf were less treacherous. For the original conditions, $rB = 0.125 \times 2 = 0.25$, which is

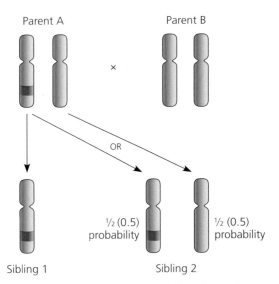

▲ Figure 51.28 The coefficient of relatedness between siblings. The red band indicates a particular allele (version of a gene) present on one chromosome, but not its homolog, in parent A. Sibling 1 has inherited the allele from parent A. There is a probability of ½ that sibling 2 will also inherit this allele from parent A. Any allele present on one chromosome of either parent will behave similarly. The coefficient of relatedness between the two siblings is thus ½, or 0.5.

WHAT IF? *The coefficient of relatedness of an individual to a full (nontwin) sibling or to either parent is the same, 0.5. Does this value also hold true in the cases of polyandry and polygyny?*

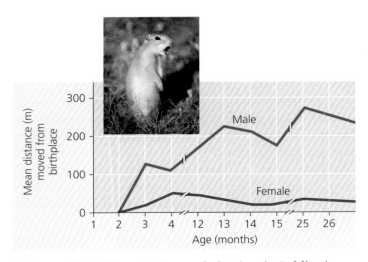

▲ Figure 51.29 Kin selection and altruism in Belding's ground squirrels. This graph helps explain the male-female difference in altruistic behavior of ground squirrels. Once weaned (pups are nursed for about one month), females are more likely than males to live near close relatives. Alarm calls that warn these relatives increase the inclusive fitness of the female altruist.

only half the value of C (0.5). British geneticist J. B. S. Haldane appears to have anticipated these ideas when he jokingly stated that he would not lay down his life for one brother, but would do so for two brothers or eight cousins.

If kin selection explains altruism, then the examples of unselfish behavior we observe among diverse animal species should involve close relatives. This is apparently the case, but often in complex ways. Like most mammals, female Belding's ground squirrels settle close to their site of birth, whereas males settle at distant sites (**Figure 51.29**). Since nearly all alarm calls are given by females, they are most likely aiding close relatives. In the case of worker bees, who are all sterile, anything they do to help the entire hive benefits the only permanent member who is reproductively active—the queen, who is their mother.

In the case of naked mole rats, DNA analyses have shown that all the individuals in a colony are closely related. Genetically, the queen appears to be a sibling, daughter, or mother of the kings, and the nonreproductive mole rats are the queen's direct descendants or her siblings. Therefore, when a nonreproductive individual enhances a queen's or king's chances of reproducing, the altruist increases the chance that some genes identical to its own will be passed to the next generation.

Reciprocal Altruism

Some animals occasionally behave altruistically toward others who are not relatives. A baboon may help an unrelated companion in a fight, or a wolf may offer food to another wolf even though they share no kinship. Such behavior can be adaptive if the aided individual returns the favor in the future. This sort of exchange of aid, called **reciprocal altruism**, is commonly invoked to explain altruism that occurs between unrelated humans. Reciprocal altruism is rare in other animals; it is limited largely to species (such as chimpanzees) with social groups stable enough that individuals have many chances to exchange aid. It is generally thought to occur when individuals are likely to meet again and when there would be negative consequences associated with not returning favors to individuals who had been helpful in the past, a pattern of behavior that behavioral ecologists refer to as "cheating."

Since cheating may benefit the cheater substantially, how could reciprocal altruism evolve? Game theory provides a possible answer in the form of a behavioral strategy called *tit for tat*. In the tit-for-tat strategy, an individual treats another in the same way it was treated the last time they met. Individuals adopting this behavior are always altruistic, or cooperative, on the first encounter with another individual and will remain so as long as their altruism is reciprocated. When their cooperation is not reciprocated, however, individuals employing tit for tat will retaliate immediately but return to cooperative behavior as soon as the other individual becomes cooperative. The tit-for-tat strategy has been used to explain the few apparently reciprocal altruistic interactions observed in animals—ranging from blood sharing between nonrelated vampire bats to social grooming in primates.

Evolution and Human Culture

Human culture is related to evolutionary theory in the discipline of **sociobiology**. The main premise of sociobiology is that certain behavioral characteristics exist because they are expressions of genes that have been perpetuated by natural selection. In his seminal 1975 book *Sociobiology: The New Synthesis*, E. O. Wilson speculated about the evolutionary basis of certain kinds of social behavior. By including a few examples from human culture, he sparked a debate that remains heated today.

The spectrum of human social behaviors may be influenced by our genetic makeup, but this is very different from saying that genes are rigid determinants of behavior. This distinction is at the core of the debate about evolutionary perspectives on human behavior. Skeptics fear that evolutionary interpretations of human behavior could be used to justify the status quo in human society, thus rationalizing current social injustices. Evolutionary biologists argue that this is a gross oversimplification and misunderstanding of what the data tell us about human biology. Evolutionary explanations of human behavior do not reduce us to robots stamped out of rigid genetic molds. Just as individuals vary extensively in anatomical features, we should expect inherent variations in behavior as well. Environment intervenes in the pathway from genotype to phenotype for physical traits and even more so for behavioral traits. And because of our capacity for learning and our versatility, human behavior is probably more plastic than that of any other animal. Over our recent evolutionary history, we have built up a diversity of structured societies with governments, laws, cultural values, and religions that define what is acceptable behavior and what is not, even when unacceptable behavior might enhance an individual's Darwinian fitness. Perhaps it is our social and cultural institutions that make us distinct and that provide those qualities in which there is the least continuum between humans and other animals.

CONCEPT CHECK 51.4

1. Explain why geographic variation in garter snake prey choice might indicate that the behavior evolved by natural selection.
2. **WHAT IF?** If an animal were unable to distinguish close from distant relatives, would the concept of inclusive fitness still be applicable? Explain.
3. **WHAT IF?** Suppose you applied Hamilton's logic to a situation in which one individual is past reproductive age. Could there still be a selection for an altruistic act?

For suggested answers, see Appendix A.

51 CHAPTER REVIEW

SUMMARY OF KEY CONCEPTS

CONCEPT 51.1

Discrete sensory inputs can stimulate both simple and complex behaviors (pp. 1118–1122)

- **Behavior** is the sum of responses to external and internal stimuli and includes muscular as well as nonmuscular activity. Tinbergen developed a set of questions that highlight the complementary nature of two perspectives. Proximate, or "how," questions focus on the environmental stimuli, if any, that trigger a behavior, as well as the genetic, physiological, and anatomical mechanisms underlying a behavioral act. Ultimate, or "why," questions address the evolutionary significance of a behavior.
- A **fixed action pattern** is a largely invariant behavior triggered by a simple cue known as a **sign stimulus**. Migratory movements involve navigation, which can be based on orientation relative to the sun, the stars, or Earth's magnetic field. Animal behavior is sometimes synchronized to the daily, or circadian, cycle of light and dark in the environment or to environmental cues that cycle over the seasons.

- The transmission and reception of signals constitute animal **communication**. Animals use visual, auditory, chemical (usually olfactory), and tactile signals, sometimes as part of a stimulus-response chain that governs a complex behavior. Chemical substances called pheromones transmit species-specific information through the environment in behaviors ranging from foraging to courtship.

? *How is migration based on circannual rhythms poorly suited for adaptation to global climate change?*

CONCEPT 51.2

Learning establishes specific links between experience and behavior (pp. 1123–1128)

- Cross-fostering studies can be used to measure the influence of social environment and experience on behavior.
- **Learning**, the modification of behavior based on experience, can take many forms:

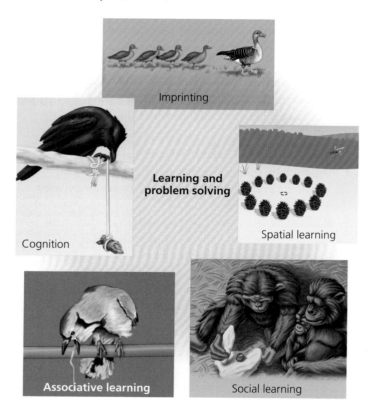

Imprinting

Learning and problem solving

Cognition

Spatial learning

Associative learning

Social learning

? *How do imprinting in geese and song development in sparrows differ with regard to the resulting behavior?*

CONCEPT 51.3

Selection for individual survival and reproductive success can explain most behaviors (pp. 1128–1134)

- An **optimal foraging model** is based on the idea that natural selection should favor foraging behavior that minimizes the costs of foraging and maximizes the benefits.
- Sexual dimorphism correlates with the type of mating relationship between males and females. These include **monogamous** and **polygamous** mating systems. Variation in mating system and variation in the mode of fertilization affect certainty of paternity, which in turn has a significant influence on mating behavior and parental care.

- Game theory provides a way of thinking about evolution in situations where the fitness of a particular behavioral phenotype is influenced by other behavioral phenotypes in the population.

? *In some spider species, the female eats the male immediately after copulation. How might you explain this behavior from an evolutionary perspective?*

CONCEPT 51.4

Inclusive fitness can account for the evolution of behavior, including altruism (pp. 1134–1139)

- Genetic studies in insects have revealed the existence of master regulatory genes that control complex behaviors. Within the underlying hierarchy, multiple genes influence specific behaviors, such as a courtship song. Research with two species of voles has revealed that variation in a single gene can determine differences in complex behaviors involved in both mating and parenting.
- When behavioral variation within a species corresponds to variation in environmental conditions, it may be evidence of past evolution. Field and laboratory studies have documented the genetic basis for a change in migratory behavior of certain birds and revealed behavioral differences in snakes that correlate with geographic variation in prey availability.
- On occasion, animals exhibit **altruism**. This behavior can be explained by the concept of **inclusive fitness**, the total effect an individual has on proliferating its genes by producing its own offspring *and* by providing aid that enables close relatives to produce offspring. **The coefficient of relatedness** and **Hamilton's rule** provide a way of measuring the strength of the selective forces favoring altruism against the potential cost of the "selfless" behavior. Kin selection favors altruistic behavior by enhancing the reproductive success of relatives. Altruistic behavior toward unrelated individuals can be adaptive if the aided individual returns the favor in the future, an exchange of aid called reciprocal altruism.

? *Suppose you studied the genetics of the lacewing courtship song, but not the effects of courtship mutations in flies or of variation in the vasopressin receptor gene of voles. What insight about the genetic basis of behavior would you likely have missed?*

TEST YOUR UNDERSTANDING

LEVEL 1: KNOWLEDGE/COMPREHENSION

1. Which of the following is true of innate behaviors?
   a. Their expression is only weakly influenced by genes.
   b. They occur with or without environmental stimuli.
   c. They are limited to invertebrate animals.
   d. They are expressed in most individuals in a population.
   e. They occur in invertebrates and some vertebrates but not mammals.

2. According to Hamilton's rule,
   a. natural selection does not favor altruistic behavior that causes the death of the altruist.
   b. natural selection favors altruistic acts when the resulting benefit to the beneficiary, corrected for relatedness, exceeds the cost to the altruist.
   c. natural selection is more likely to favor altruistic behavior that benefits an offspring than altruistic behavior that benefits a sibling.
   d. the effects of kin selection are larger than the effects of direct natural selection on individuals.
   e. altruism is always reciprocal.

3. Female spotted sandpipers aggressively court males and, after mating, leave the clutch of young for the male to incubate. This sequence may be repeated several times with different males until no available males remain, forcing the female to incubate her last clutch. Which of the following terms best describes this behavior?
   a. monogamy
   b. polygyny
   c. polyandry
   d. promiscuity
   e. certainty of paternity

LEVEL 2: APPLICATION/ANALYSIS

4. A region of the canary forebrain shrinks during the nonbreeding season and enlarges when breeding season begins. This change is probably associated with the annual
   a. addition of new syllables to a canary's song repertoire.
   b. crystallization of subsong into adult songs.
   c. sensitive period in which canary parents imprint on new offspring.
   d. renewal of mating and nest-building behaviors.
   e. elimination of the memorized template for songs sung the previous year.

5. Although many chimpanzees live in environments containing oil palm nuts, members of only a few populations use stones to crack open the nuts. The likely explanation is that
   a. the behavioral difference is caused by genetic differences between populations.
   b. members of different populations have different nutritional requirements.
   c. the cultural tradition of using stones to crack nuts has arisen in only some populations.
   d. members of different populations differ in learning ability.
   e. members of different populations differ in manual dexterity.

6. Which of the following is *not* required for a behavioral trait to evolve by natural selection?
   a. In each individual, the form of the behavior is determined entirely by genes.
   b. The behavior varies among individuals.
   c. An individual's reproductive success depends in part on how the behavior is performed.
   d. Some component of the behavior is genetically inherited.
   e. An individual's genotype influences its behavioral phenotype.

LEVEL 3: SYNTHESIS/EVALUATION

7. **DRAW IT** You are considering two optimal foraging models for the behavior of a mussel-feeding shorebird, the oystercatcher. In model A, the energetic reward increases solely with mussel size. In model B, you take into consideration that larger mussels are more difficult to open. Draw a graph of reward (energy benefit on a scale of 0–10) versus mussel length (scale of 0–70 mm) for each model. Assume that mussels under 10 mm provide no benefit and are ignored by the birds. Also assume that mussels start becoming difficult to open

when they reach 40 mm in length and impossible to open when 70 mm long. Considering the graphs you have drawn, how could you distinguish between the models by observation and measurement in the oystercatcher's habitat?

8. **EVOLUTION CONNECTION**
   We often explain our behavior in terms of subjective feelings, motives, or reasons, but evolutionary explanations are based on reproductive fitness. What is the relationship between the two kinds of explanation? For instance, is a human explanation for behavior, such as "falling in love," incompatible with an evolutionary explanation?

9. **SCIENTIFIC INQUIRY**
   Scientists studying scrub jays found that "helpers" often assist mated pairs of birds in raising their young. The helpers lack territories and mates of their own. Instead, they help the territory owners gather food for their offspring. Propose a hypothesis to explain what advantage there might be for the helpers to engage in this behavior instead of seeking their own territories and mates. How would you test your hypothesis? If it is correct, what results would you expect your tests to yield?

10. **SCIENCE, TECHNOLOGY, AND SOCIETY**
    Researchers are very interested in studying identical twins separated at birth and raised apart. So far, the data reveal that such twins frequently have similar personalities, mannerisms, habits, and interests. What general question do you think researchers hope to answer by studying such twins? Why do identical twins make good subjects for this research? What are the potential pitfalls of this research? What abuses might occur if the studies are not evaluated critically?

11. **WRITE ABOUT A THEME**
    The Genetic Basis of Life Learning is defined as a change in behavior based on experience. In a short essay (100–150 words), describe the role of heritable information in the acquisition of learning, using some examples from imprinting and associative learning.

For selected answers, see Appendix A.

MasteringBIOLOGY® www.masteringbiology.com

1. MasteringBiology® Assignments
Tutorial Animal Behavior and Learning
Activities Honeybee Waggle Dance Video • Homing Behavior in Digger Wasps
Questions Student Misconceptions • Reading Quiz • Multiple Choice • End-of-Chapter

2. eText
Read your book online, search, take notes, highlight text, and more.

3. The Study Area
Practice Tests • Cumulative Test • *BioFlix* 3-D Animations • MP3 Tutor Sessions • Videos • Activities • Investigations • Lab Media • Audio Glossary • Word Study Tools • Art

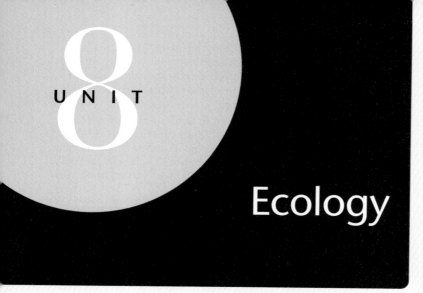

An Interview with
Camille Parmesan

Camille Parmesan planned to be a doctor when she first enrolled at the University of Texas in Austin in 1979. Three decades later, she's never regretted her decision to study butterflies around the world instead. Dr. Parmesan's research expertise is on the ecology, evolution, and behavior of butterflies and their plant hosts, particularly how climate change is affecting them today. As an expert on climate change, she has testified

before the U.S. Congress and been a lead author to the United Nations Intergovernmental Panel on Climate Change. She also advises many conservation groups, including The Nature Conservancy, World Wildlife Fund, and the National Wildlife Federation. Having earned both undergraduate and doctoral degrees from the University of Texas in Austin, she is currently an Associate Professor in the Section of Integrative Biology there.

What inspired you to go into science, and ecology in particular?
My mother had studied geology and botany, and as soon as I could walk, she started taking me on hikes through the forest or into the mountains and telling me what every rock and every plant and every bird was. She would have all her field guides with her, and if she didn't know something we would look it up together. So nature was always something that fascinated me. I loved being outdoors; I loved camping out; I loved hiking.

In high school, though, I felt that I really wanted to do something relevant for society, so I decided I wanted to be a medical doctor. I was premed throughout my undergraduate career until my last semester, and it was only because of some independent research projects that I changed my mind. I did one on honeybees, and I did one with primates. Then, the summer before graduation, I went out to the mountains of California and worked with butterflies for the summer. At that point, I asked myself, "Can I get paid to do this? I don't want to sit in an office or a hospital all day, every day, when I could be out here for three months of the year." So I switched my plans for my last semester. I wanted to do research in the mountains the rest of my life.

What did you do right out of college?
I took a break and worked as a research technician. It took me a couple of years before I was ready—refreshed enough—to enter grad school. As a technician, I was continuing to study the ecology and evolution of butterflies, following up on the research I did as an undergrad. But it can be frustrating to be doing this research and knowing it's not your own project; you're not really able to pursue what you're most interested in. I wanted to be working for excitement and satisfaction, not just for the pay.

What was your research in graduate school?
Ecology, evolution, and behavior. I started out working in the tropics, in Costa Rica, still studying interactions between butterflies and their host plants. So that theme was still there. But I was ready to learn a new system, and the tropics are absolutely amazing for a biologist. When you're working in the California mountains, you get to know the butterfly species in about 15 minutes because there are only about a dozen of them. Then you go to Costa Rica, and every single thing you see is a new species, and you're seeing dozens in a day. It was incredible. So I started a project down there and combined it with a study colony of butterflies I was growing back here in Texas as well. We had a little tropical greenhouse in the lab and a humidifier.

But you switched back to studying butterflies in temperate areas?
I absolutely loved the tropics, but I got very sick there, and so I went back to doing research in the temperate zone. When I started studying climate change, the need for really good historical records led me to study sites in Europe. Now I work in the European Alps and the Pyrenees, and I've gotten to know Sweden and Finland as well. My study site in the Alps is only a few hundred meters from the route taken by the Tour de France.

Why are butterflies useful for studying climate change?
Although I personally think butterflies are incredibly beautiful, and a lot of people agree with me, that is not the main reason we study them. The reason they are so important, especially to the study of climate change, is that they are extremely sensitive to very small variations in climate. Climate affects the development times of both the insects and their host plants, and changes in climate can alter how in sync the interacting species are. Species adjust their ranges so that they remain in a particular climate space, and thus act as indicators of change.

We don't know exactly what populations are responding to when they change their ranges. It's not just mean annual temperature. It's something much more complex, probably having to do with the timing of short bursts of heat, snowfalls, and other unusual events that affect how well butterfly populations do in any given year. If there are several years in a row with these kinds of extreme events, the populations could either boom, if they are good extreme events, or become extinct. We're just starting to understand how very tiny changes in the number of days in a row of, say, warm temperatures above a certain threshold can affect their survival.

One year when we arrived at our work site, we found that the snow pack was really light. Although the site was at an elevation of 8,000 feet, the snow melted in early April—really early—and the temperatures were unusually warm. The butterflies we were studying, called Edith's checkerspots (*Euphydryas editha*), started their flight season two months early, in April instead of in June. But the plants hadn't responded to the unusual weather and were still dormant. So when the butterflies came out, there was no nectar available for them, and they died. I remember going out to the hillside and seeing orange specks all over the hill. When I moved closer, I found that the specks were dead butterflies. They had emerged from their cocoons, but there was nothing for them to feed on.

So are butterflies a first warning signal for climate change?
Exactly, but you need a long record, over many years, to understand the signal. In Sweden, Finland, and Britain, for example, there are sites that have been monitored every year for 140 years. I have sites where either I or another butterfly researcher has been working nearly every year for the last 40 years. When Paul Ehrlich first started working with the Edith's checkerspot butterfly in the late 1950s, he reported how sensitive this species is to yearly climate variability, changes in temperature and rainfall. My husband, Mike Singer, studied the checkerspot for his dissertation under Ehrlich in the 1960s, and he found even more evidence for sensitivity to climate variability. This was long before any awareness of global warming. When I started studying the butterflies in the 1980s, I found the same thing, the most dramatic example being that horrible false spring when all the butterflies died. So the sensitivity of these butterflies to climate changes has been documented over 50 years of research. All butterflies are sensitive to climate change, but *Euphydryas editha* is especially so.

How did you first realize that your butterfly data suggested that climate change was already occurring?
In order to demonstrate the likelihood that climate change was affecting my butterfly, I was expecting to have to do a very complex analysis of my data, separating out all the different types of butterflies and their locations and figuring out what aspects of climate affected the butterflies each year. The dynamics of the coastal butterflies might be driven by winter precipitation, for example, in order for their host plants to grow. But when I put my data together, I said to my husband, "You know, I'm getting something really simple here. It looks like the butterflies in the south are going extinct, and the ones in the north are doing really well. Also, the ones at low elevation are going extinct, and the ones at high elevation are doing well. I think the butterfly is just shifting its range."

What kinds of species are most at risk from climate change and other environmental problems?
We're not too worried about the common species that live everywhere. It's the rarer ones with smaller distributions that are most at risk. Think about how many of our conservation programs are based on being able to preserve an area for habitat. As long as you keep invasive species and other threats out, you can usually maintain what the area was set up to protect. Climate change alters all of that. Suddenly your preserve is not climatically suitable. So a species may go extinct in your preserve, and yet outside of the preserve all you've got are cornfields and urban sprawl. Where are you going to put the species next?

Why is it important to study and maintain biodiversity on Earth?
For me, there are two reasons why biodiversity is important. First, there is what I call the spiritual component. Species are important because they give us a grounding in this world; they connect us to the rest of life. But biodiversity is also important because of the services that different species provide. Plants and microorganisms produce breathable air and purify our lakes and streams; wild animals and plants provide food and new genes for healthy crops. We are relying on lands outside of cities to provide us with those things.

> **"The sensitivity of these butterflies to climate changes has been documented over 50 years of research."**

What are some of the important, unanswered questions in ecology for climate change research?
I think that climate change in general is a field where we don't understand the responses well enough to know exactly where things are going. We're pretty sure of some processes occurring in the Arctic—the sea ice is melting, for instance. What we really don't understand is what's happening in the tropics. Will tropical rain forests expand as Earth warms, or are we going to be having extreme climates emerge at the equator like a few models project, even to the extent of the Amazon rain forest drying up? Will we have coral reefs in another hundred years? Or are they going to disappear as an entire ecosystem? We don't know at what point such processes may occur and be unstoppable.

What would you say to a student considering a career in ecology?
Many biology students entering college are interested in medicine or biotechnology. It's often not till their senior year that they realize that ecology is so interesting. In the career lecture I give in class, I tell students about all the different careers you can have with degrees in ecology and environmental sciences. Most students don't realize how many options there are. You can work for a large company or do consulting work. You can work for government agencies such as the Department of Agriculture, the Environmental Protection Agency, and the Fish and Wildlife Service. Every state has different natural resource agencies that need good biologists, too. You can also work internationally for groups such as the World Health Organization. There are so many useful opportunities beyond becoming a faculty member.

Why is ecology important for the general public?
An undergraduate working in my lab is a premed, yet this summer he's doing an ecological project on the Barton Springs salamander. I asked him if he could see links between human health and ecology, and he said, "Well, humans need clean water, and this salamander does too, so keeping the salamander healthy keeps us healthy." I was thrilled that a summer's field work has given someone in the health sciences the insight that for us to be healthy we need to have a healthy environment. Ecologists are one of the only groups of people who study how environmental health relates to climate change and nitrogen pollution from cars and other things that humans are doing that affect the environment. What specific impacts do those changes have? Ecologists are the scientists answering that important question.

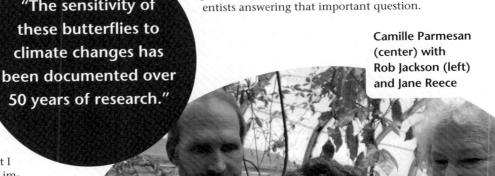

Camille Parmesan (center) with Rob Jackson (left) and Jane Reece

52

An Introduction to Ecology and the Biosphere

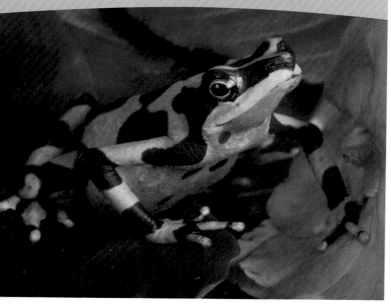

▲ **Figure 52.1 What threatens this amphibian's survival?**

KEY CONCEPTS

52.1 Earth's climate varies by latitude and season and is changing rapidly

52.2 The structure and distribution of terrestrial biomes are controlled by climate and disturbance

52.3 Aquatic biomes are diverse and dynamic systems that cover most of Earth

52.4 Interactions between organisms and the environment limit the distribution of species

OVERVIEW

Discovering Ecology

When University of Delaware undergraduate Justin Yeager spent his summer abroad in Costa Rica, all he wanted was to see the tropical rain forest and to practice his Spanish. Instead, he rediscovered the variable harlequin toad (*Atelopus varius*), a species thought to be extinct in the mountain slopes of Costa

Rica and Panama where it once lived (**Figure 52.1**). During the 1980s and 1990s, roughly two-thirds of the 82 known species of harlequin toads vanished. Scientists think that a disease-causing chytrid fungus, *Batrachochytrium dendrobatidis* (see Figure 31.26), contributed to many of these extinctions. Why was the fungus suddenly thriving in the rain forest? Cloudier days and warmer nights associated with global warming appear to have created an environment ideal for its success. As of 2009, the species that Yeager found was surviving as a single known population of fewer than 100 individuals.

What environmental factors limit the geographic distribution of harlequin toads? How do variations in their food supply or interactions with other species, such as pathogens, affect the size of their population? Questions like these are the subject of **ecology** (from the Greek *oikos*, home, and *logos*, study), the scientific study of the interactions between organisms and the environment. Ecological interactions occur at a hierarchy of scales that ecologists study, from single organisms to the globe (**Figure 52.2**).

Ecology's roots are in our basic human interest in observing other organisms. Naturalists, including Aristotle and Darwin, have long studied the living world and systematically recorded their observations. However, modern ecology involves more than observation. It is a rigorous experimental science that requires a breadth of biological knowledge. Ecologists generate hypotheses, manipulate environmental variables, and observe the outcome. In this unit, you will encounter many examples of ecological experiments, whose complex challenges have made ecologists innovators in experimental design and statistical inference.

In addition to providing a conceptual framework for understanding the field of ecology, Figure 52.2 provides the organizational framework for our final unit. In this chapter, we first describe Earth's climate and the importance of climate and other physical factors in determining the location of major life zones on land and in the oceans. We then examine how ecologists determine what controls the distribution and abundance of individual species. The next three chapters investigate population, community, and ecosystem ecology in detail, including approaches for restoring degraded ecosystems. The final chapter explores conservation biology and global ecology as we consider how ecologists apply biological knowledge to predict the global consequences of human activities and to conserve Earth's biodiversity.

CONCEPT 52.1

Earth's climate varies by latitude and season and is changing rapidly

The most significant influence on the distribution of organisms on land and in the oceans is **climate**, the long-term, prevailing weather conditions in a given area. Four physical

▼ Figure 52.2

Exploring The Scope of Ecological Research

Ecologists work at different levels of the biological hierarchy, from individual organisms to the planet. Here we present a sample research question for each level of the hierarchy.

Global Ecology

The **biosphere** is the global ecosystem—the sum of all the planet's ecosystems and landscapes. **Global ecology** examines how the regional exchange of energy and materials influences the functioning and distribution of organisms across the biosphere.

◀ How does ocean circulation affect the global distribution of crustaceans?

Landscape Ecology

A **landscape** (or seascape) is a mosaic of connected ecosystems. Research in **landscape ecology** focuses on the factors controlling exchanges of energy, materials, and organisms across multiple ecosystems.

◀ To what extent do the trees lining a river serve as corridors of dispersal for animals?

Ecosystem Ecology

An **ecosystem** is the community of organisms in an area and the physical factors with which those organisms interact. **Ecosystem ecology** emphasizes energy flow and chemical cycling between organisms and the environment.

◀ What factors control photosynthetic productivity in a temperate grassland ecosystem?

Community Ecology

A **community** is a group of populations of different species in an area. **Community ecology** examines how interactions between species, such as predation and competition, affect community structure and organization.

◀ What factors influence the diversity of species that make up a forest?

Population Ecology

A **population** is a group of individuals of the same species living in an area. **Population ecology** analyzes factors that affect population size and how and why it changes through time.

◀ What environmental factors affect the reproductive rate of locusts?

Organismal Ecology

Organismal ecology, which includes the subdisciplines of physiological, evolutionary, and behavioral ecology, is concerned with how an organism's structure, physiology, and behavior meet the challenges posed by its environment.

◀ How do hammerhead sharks select a mate?

Exploring Global Climate Patterns

Latitudinal Variation in Sunlight Intensity

Earth's curved shape causes latitudinal variation in the intensity of sunlight. Because sunlight strikes the **tropics** (those regions that lie between 23.5° north latitude and 23.5° south latitude) most directly, more heat and light per unit of surface area are delivered there. At higher latitudes, sunlight strikes Earth at an oblique angle, and thus the light energy is more diffuse on Earth's surface.

Global Air Circulation and Precipitation Patterns

Intense solar radiation near the equator initiates a global pattern of air circulation and precipitation. High temperatures in the tropics evaporate water from Earth's surface and cause warm, wet air masses to rise (blue arrows) and flow toward the poles. The rising air masses release much of their water content, creating abundant precipitation in tropical regions. The high-altitude air masses, now dry, descend (tan arrows) toward Earth around 30° north and south, absorbing moisture from the land and creating an arid climate conducive to the development of the deserts that are common at those latitudes. Some of the descending air then flows toward the poles. At latitudes around 60° north and south, the air masses again rise and release abundant precipitation (though less than in the tropics). Some of the cold, dry rising air then flows to the poles, where it descends and flows back toward the equator, absorbing moisture and creating the comparatively rainless and bitterly cold climates of the polar regions.

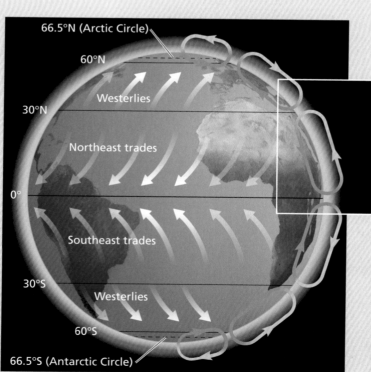

Air flowing close to Earth's surface creates predictable global wind patterns. As Earth rotates on its axis, land near the equator moves faster than that at the poles, deflecting the winds from the vertical paths shown above and creating the more easterly and westerly flows shown at left. Cooling trade winds blow from east to west in the tropics; prevailing westerlies blow from west to east in the temperate zones, defined as the regions between the Tropic of Cancer and the Arctic Circle and between the Tropic of Capricorn and the Antarctic Circle.

factors—temperature, precipitation, sunlight, and wind—are particularly important components of climate. In this section, we will describe climate patterns at two scales: **macroclimate**, patterns on the global, regional, and landscape level; and **microclimate**, very fine, localized patterns, such as those encountered by the community of organisms that live in the microhabitat beneath a fallen log. First let's examine Earth's macroclimate.

Global Climate Patterns

Global climate patterns are determined largely by the input of solar energy and Earth's movement in space. The sun warms the atmosphere, land, and water. This warming establishes the temperature variations, cycles of air and water movement, and evaporation of water that cause dramatic latitudinal variations in climate. **Figure 52.3** summarizes Earth's climate patterns and how they are formed.

Regional and Local Effects on Climate

Climate patterns can be modified by many factors, including seasonal variation in climate, large bodies of water, and mountain ranges. We will examine each of these factors in more detail.

Seasonality

As described in **Figure 52.4**, Earth's tilted axis of rotation and its annual passage around the sun cause strong seasonal cycles in middle to high latitudes. In addition to these global changes in day length, solar radiation, and temperature, the changing angle of the sun over the course of the year affects local environments. For example, the belts of wet and dry air on either side of the equator move slightly northward and southward with the changing angle of the sun, producing marked wet and dry seasons around 20° north and 20° south latitude, where many tropical deciduous forests grow. In addition, seasonal changes in wind patterns alter ocean currents, sometimes causing the upwelling of cold water from deep ocean layers. This nutrient-rich water stimulates the growth of surface-dwelling phytoplankton and the organisms that feed on them.

Bodies of Water

Ocean currents influence climate along the coasts of continents by heating or cooling overlying air masses that pass across the land. Coastal regions are also generally wetter than inland areas at the same latitude. The cool, misty climate produced by the cold California Current that flows southward

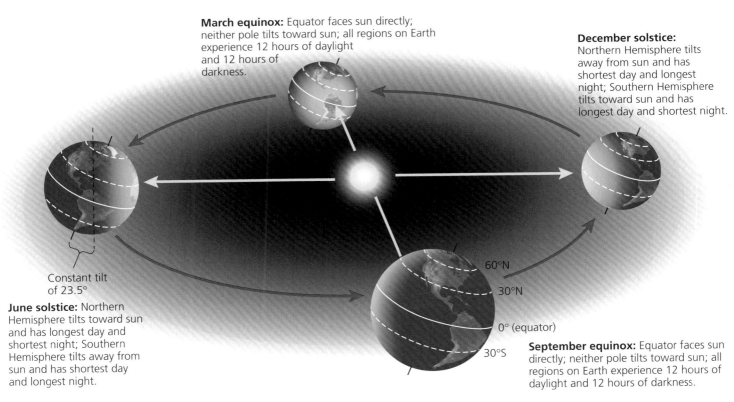

March equinox: Equator faces sun directly; neither pole tilts toward sun; all regions on Earth experience 12 hours of daylight and 12 hours of darkness.

December solstice: Northern Hemisphere tilts away from sun and has shortest day and longest night; Southern Hemisphere tilts toward sun and has longest day and shortest night.

Constant tilt of 23.5°

June solstice: Northern Hemisphere tilts toward sun and has longest day and shortest night; Southern Hemisphere tilts away from sun and has shortest day and longest night.

60°N
30°N
0° (equator)
30°S

September equinox: Equator faces sun directly; neither pole tilts toward sun; all regions on Earth experience 12 hours of daylight and 12 hours of darkness.

▲ **Figure 52.4 Seasonal variation in sunlight intensity.** Because Earth is tilted on its axis relative to its plane of orbit around the sun, the intensity of solar radiation varies seasonally. This variation is smallest in the tropics and increases toward the poles.

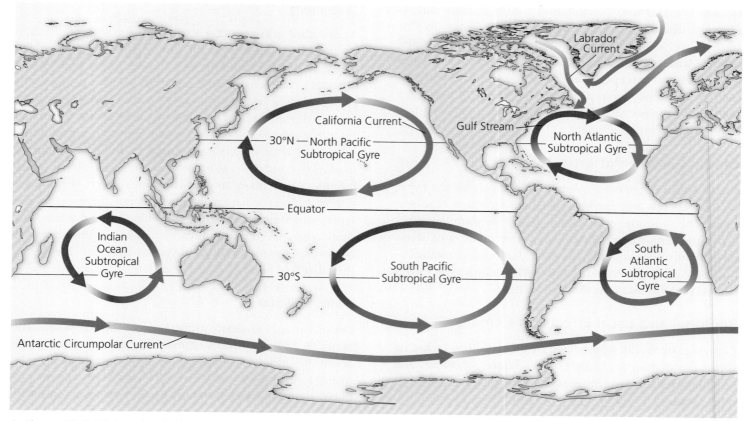

▲ **Figure 52.5 Global circulation of surface water in the oceans.** Water is warmed at the equator and flows north and south toward the poles, where it cools. Note the similarities between the direction of water circulation in the gyres and the direction of the trade winds in Figure 52.3.

along western North America supports a coniferous rain forest ecosystem along much of the continent's Pacific coast and large redwood groves farther south. Conversely, the west coast of northern Europe has a mild climate because the Gulf Stream carries warm water from the equator to the North Atlantic **(Figure 52.5)**. As a result, northwestern Europe is warmer during winter than southeastern Canada, which is farther south but is cooled by the Labrador Current flowing south from the coast of Greenland.

Because of the high specific heat of water (see Chapter 3), oceans and large lakes tend to moderate the climate of nearby land. During a hot day, when land is warmer than the water, air over the land heats up and rises, drawing a cool breeze from the water across the land **(Figure 52.6)**. In contrast, because temperatures drop more quickly over land than over water at night, air over the now warmer water rises, drawing cooler air from the land back out over the water and replacing it with warmer air from offshore. This local moderation of climate can be limited to the coast itself, however. In regions such as southern California and southwestern Australia, cool, dry ocean breezes in summer are warmed when they contact the land, absorbing moisture and creating a hot, arid climate just a few kilometers inland (see Figure 3.5). This

climate pattern also occurs around the Mediterranean Sea, which gives it the name *Mediterranean climate*.

Mountains

Like large bodies of water, mountains influence air flow over land. When warm, moist air approaches a mountain, the air rises and cools, releasing moisture on the windward side of the peak (see Figure 52.6). On the leeward side, cooler, dry air descends, absorbing moisture and producing a "rain shadow." This leeward rain shadow determines where many deserts are found, including the Great Basin and the Mojave Desert of western North America, the Gobi Desert of Asia, and the small deserts found in the southwest corners of some Caribbean islands.

Mountains also affect the amount of sunlight reaching an area and thus the local temperature and rainfall. South-facing slopes in the Northern Hemisphere receive more sunlight than north-facing slopes and are therefore warmer and drier. These physical differences influence species distributions locally. In many mountains of western North America, spruce and other conifers grow on the cooler north-facing slopes, but shrubby, drought-resistant plants inhabit the south-facing slopes. In addition, every 1,000-m increase in elevation

2 Air that encounters mountains flows upward, cools at higher altitudes, and releases water as rain and snow.

◄ **Figure 52.6 How large bodies of water and mountains affect climate.** This figure illustrates what can happen on a hot summer day.

1 Cool air flows inland from the water, moderating temperatures near the shore.

3 Less moisture is left in the air reaching the leeward side, which therefore has little precipitation. This rain shadow can create a desert on the back side of the mountain range.

Leeward side of mountains

Mountain range

Ocean

produces an average temperature drop of approximately 6°C, equivalent to that produced by an 880-km increase in latitude. This is one reason that high-elevation communities at one latitude can be similar to those at lower elevations much farther from the equator.

Microclimate

Many features in the environment influence microclimate by casting shade, altering evaporation from soil, or changing wind patterns. Forest trees often moderate the microclimate below them. Cleared areas therefore typically experience greater temperature extremes than the forest interior because of greater solar radiation and wind currents that arise from the rapid heating and cooling of open land. Within a forest, low-lying ground is usually wetter than higher ground and tends to be occupied by different tree species. A log or large stone can shelter organisms such as salamanders, worms, and insects, buffering them from the extremes of temperature and moisture. Every environment on Earth is characterized by a mosaic of small-scale differences in **abiotic**, or nonliving, factors, the chemical and physical attributes, such as temperature, light, water, and nutrients, that influence the distribution and abundance of organisms. Later in this chapter, we will also examine how all of the **biotic**, or living, factors—the other organisms that are part of an individual's environment—similarly influence the distribution and abundance of life on Earth.

Global Climate Change

Because climatic variables affect the geographic ranges of most plants and animals, any large-scale change in Earth's climate profoundly affects the biosphere. In fact, such a large-scale climate "experiment" is already under way. The burning of fossil fuels and deforestation are increasing the concentrations of carbon dioxide and other greenhouse gases in the atmosphere. As a result, Earth has warmed an average of 0.8°C (1.4°F) since 1900 and is projected to warm 1–6°C (2–11°F) more by the year 2100.

One way to predict the possible effects of future climate change on geographic ranges is to look back at the changes that have occurred in temperate regions since the last ice age ended. Until about 16,000 years ago, continental glaciers covered much of North America and Eurasia. As the climate warmed and the glaciers retreated, tree distributions expanded northward. A detailed record of these changes is captured in fossil pollen deposited in lakes and ponds. (Recall from Chapter 38 that wind and animals sometimes disperse pollen and seeds over great distances.) If researchers can determine the climatic limits of current distributions of organisms, they can make predictions about how those distributions may change with continued climatic warming.

A fundamental question when applying this approach to plants is whether seeds can disperse quickly enough to sustain the range shift of each species as climate changes. Fossil pollen shows that species with winged seeds that disperse relatively far from a parent tree, such as the sugar maple (*Acer saccharum*), expanded rapidly into the northeastern United States and Canada after the last ice age ended. In contrast, the northward range expansion of the eastern hemlock (*Tsuga canadensis*), whose seeds lack wings, was delayed nearly 2,500 years compared with the shift in suitable habitat.

Will plants and other species be able to keep up with the much more rapid warming projected for this century? Ecologists have attempted to answer this question for the American beech (*Fagus grandifolia*). Their models predict that the northern limit of the beech's range may move 700–900 km northward in the next century, and its southern range limit will

Current range
Predicted range
Overlap

(a) 4.5°C warming over next century

(b) 6.5°C warming over next century

▲ Figure 52.7 **Current range and predicted range for the American beech under two climate-change scenarios.**

? *The predicted range in each scenario is based on climate factors alone. What other factors might alter the distribution of this species?*

shift even more. The current and predicted geographic ranges of this species under two different climate-change scenarios are illustrated in **Figure 52.7**. If these predictions are even approximately correct, the beech's range must shift 7–9 km northward per year to keep pace with the warming climate. However, since the end of the last ice age, the beech has moved at a rate of only 0.2 km per year. Without human help in moving to new habitats, species such as the American beech may have much smaller ranges or even become extinct.

Changes in the distributions of species are already evident in many well-studied groups of terrestrial, marine, and freshwater organisms, consistent with the signature of a warmer world. Ecologist Camille Parmesan (see interview on pp. 1142–1143) has studied range changes in European butterfly species, including the silver-washed fritillary (*Argynnis paphia*; see **Figure 52.8**). Parmesan and her colleagues found that the

Sweden

Finland

Expanded range in 1997
Range in 1970

▲ Figure 52.8 **Northward range expansion of the silver-washed fritillary in Sweden and Finland.** This butterfly is one of many European species whose northern range limits have moved farther north in recent decades.

northern range limits of 22 of the 35 butterfly species studied had shifted farther north by 35–240 km over the time periods for which records exist, in some cases beginning in 1900. And other scientists have reported that a Pacific diatom species, *Neodenticula seminae*, recently has colonized the Atlantic Ocean for the first time in 800,000 years. As Arctic sea ice has receded in the past decade, the increased flow of water from the Pacific has swept these diatoms around Canada and into the Atlantic, where they quickly became established. The observation that many species are on the move in the face of climate change illustrates the importance of climate in determining species distributions, a topic we will explore further in the next section.

CONCEPT CHECK 52.1

1. Explain how the sun's unequal heating of Earth's surface leads to the development of deserts around 30° north and south of the equator.
2. What are some of the differences in microclimate between an unplanted agricultural field and a nearby stream corridor with trees?
3. **WHAT IF?** Changes in Earth's climate at the end of the last ice age happened gradually, taking centuries to thousands of years. If the current global warming happens very quickly, as predicted, how may this rapid climate change affect the ability of long-lived trees to evolve, compared with annual plants, which have much shorter generation times?
4. **MAKE CONNECTIONS** In Concept 10.4 (pp. 199–201), you learned about the important differences between C_3 and C_4 plants. Focusing just on the effects of temperature, would you expect the global distribution of C_4 plants to expand or contract as Earth becomes warmer? Why?

For suggested answers, see Appendix A.

CONCEPT 52.2

The structure and distribution of terrestrial biomes are controlled by climate and disturbance

Throughout this book, you have seen many examples of how climate and other factors influence where individual species are found on Earth (see Figure 30.5, for instance). We turn now to the role of climate in determining the nature and location of Earth's **biomes**, major life zones characterized by vegetation type (in terrestrial biomes) or by the physical environment (in aquatic biomes). We first examine the influence of climate on terrestrial biomes, surveying aquatic systems later in the chapter.

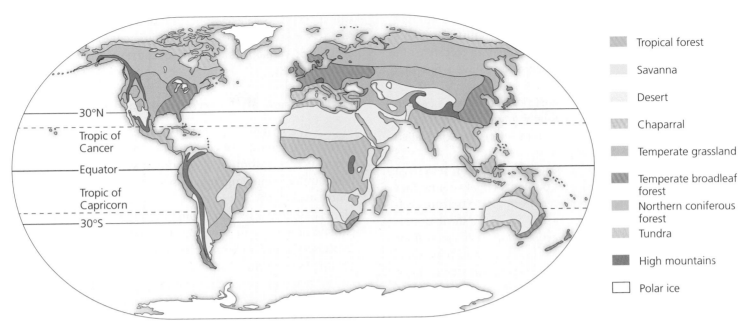

▲ **Figure 52.9 The distribution of major terrestrial biomes.** Although biomes are mapped here with sharp boundaries, biomes actually grade into one another, sometimes over large areas.

Climate and Terrestrial Biomes

Because of the latitudinal patterns of climate described in Figure 52.3, terrestrial biomes show strong latitudinal patterns in where they are found (**Figure 52.9**). One way to highlight the importance of climate on the distribution of biomes is to construct a **climograph**, a plot of the annual mean temperature and precipitation in a particular region. **Figure 52.10** is a climograph for some of the biomes found in North America. Notice, for instance, that the range of precipitation in northern coniferous and temperate forests is similar but that temperate forests are generally warmer. Grasslands are typically drier than either kind of forest, and deserts are drier still.

Factors other than mean temperature and precipitation also play a role in determining where biomes exist. For example, some areas in North America with a particular combination of temperature and precipitation support a temperate broadleaf forest, but other areas with similar values for these variables support a coniferous forest (see the overlap in Figure 52.10). How might we explain this variation? First, remember that the climograph is based on annual *averages*. Often, however, the *pattern* of climatic variation is as important as the average climate. Some areas may receive regular precipitation throughout the year, whereas other areas may have distinct wet and dry seasons. A similar phenomenon may occur for temperature. In addition, other abiotic characteristics, such as the type of bedrock in an area, may greatly affect mineral nutrient availability and soil structure, which in turn affect the kind of vegetation that can grow.

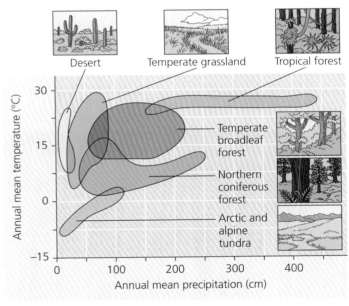

▲ **Figure 52.10 A climograph for some major types of biomes in North America.** The areas plotted here encompass the ranges of annual mean temperature and precipitation in the biomes.

General Features of Terrestrial Biomes

Most terrestrial biomes are named for major physical or climatic features and for their predominant vegetation. Temperate grasslands, for instance, are generally found in middle latitudes, where the climate is more moderate than in the tropics or polar regions, and are dominated by various grass species (see Figure 52.9). Each biome is also characterized by microorganisms, fungi, and animals adapted to that particular environment. Temperate grasslands are usually more likely than temperate forests to be populated by large grazing mammals and to have arbuscular mycorrhizal fungi.

Although Figure 52.9 shows distinct boundaries between the biomes, terrestrial biomes usually grade into each other without sharp boundaries. The area of intergradation, called an **ecotone**, may be wide or narrow.

Vertical layering is an important feature of terrestrial biomes, and the shapes and sizes of plants largely define that layering. In many forests, the layers from top to bottom consist of the upper **canopy**, the low-tree layer, the shrub understory, the ground layer of herbaceous plants, the forest floor (litter layer), and the root layer. Nonforest biomes have similar, though usually less pronounced, layers. Grasslands have an herbaceous layer of grasses and forbs (small broadleaf plants), a litter layer, and a root layer. Layering of vegetation provides many different habitats for animals, which sometimes exist in well-defined feeding groups, from the insectivorous birds and bats that feed above canopies to the small mammals, numerous worms, and arthropods that search for food in the litter and root layers below.

The species composition of each kind of biome varies from one location to another. For instance, in the northern coniferous forest (taiga) of North America, red spruce is common in the east but does not occur in most other areas, where black spruce and white spruce are abundant. As **Figure 52.11** shows, cacti living in deserts of North and South America appear very

similar to plants called euphorbs found in African deserts. But since cacti and euphorbs belong to different evolutionary lineages, their similarities are due to convergent evolution (see Concept 22.3).

Disturbance and Terrestrial Biomes

Biomes are dynamic, and disturbance rather than stability tends to be the rule. In ecological terms, **disturbance** is an event such as a storm, fire, or human activity that changes a community, removing organisms from it and altering resource availability. For instance, frequent fires can kill woody plants and keep a savanna from becoming the woodland that climate alone would support. Hurricanes and other storms create openings for new species in many tropical and temperate forests. Fires and outbreaks of pests, such as pine beetles and spruce budworms, produce gaps in northern coniferous forests that allow deciduous species, including aspen and birch, to grow. As a result of disturbances, biomes often exhibit extensive patchiness, with several different communities represented in a single area.

In many biomes, even the dominant plants depend on periodic disturbance. Natural wildfires are an integral component of grasslands, savannas, chaparral, and many coniferous forests. In North America, fires are no longer common across much of the Great Plains because tallgrass prairie ecosystems have been converted to agricultural fields that rarely burn. Before agricultural and urban development, much of the southeastern United States was dominated by a single conifer species, the longleaf pine. Without periodic burning, broadleaf trees tended to replace the pines. Forest managers now use fire as a tool to help maintain many coniferous forests.

Figure 52.12, on the next four pages, summarizes the major features of terrestrial biomes. As you read about the characteristics of each biome, remember that humans have altered much of Earth's surface, replacing natural communities with urban and agricultural ones. Most of the eastern United States, for example, is classified as temperate broadleaf forest, but little of that original forest remains.

▲ *Euphorbia canariensis*

◄ *Cereus peruvianus*

▲ **Figure 52.11 Convergent evolution in a cactus and a euphorb.** *Cereus peruvianus*, a cactus, is found in the Americas; *Euphorbia canariensis*, a euphorb, is native to the Canary Islands, off the northwest coast of Africa.

CONCEPT CHECK **52.2**

1. Based on the climograph in Figure 52.10, what mainly differentiates temperate grassland from temperate broadleaf forest?
2. Identify the natural biome in which you live, and summarize its abiotic and biotic characteristics. Do these reflect your actual surroundings? Explain.
3. **WHAT IF?** If global warming increases average temperatures on Earth by 4°C in this century, predict which biome is most likely to replace tundra in some locations as a result. Explain your answer.

For suggested answers, see Appendix A.

Exploring Terrestrial Biomes

Tropical Forest

Distribution Equatorial and subequatorial regions

Precipitation In **tropical rain forests**, rainfall is relatively constant, about 200–400 cm annually. In **tropical dry forests**, precipitation is highly seasonal, about 150–200 cm annually, with a six- to seven-month dry season.

Temperature High year-round, averaging 25–29°C with little seasonal variation

Plants Tropical forests are vertically layered, and competition for light is intense. Layers in rain forests include emergent trees that grow above a closed canopy, the canopy trees, one or two layers of subcanopy trees, and layers of shrubs and herbs (small, nonwoody plants). There are generally fewer layers in tropical dry forests. Broadleaf evergreen trees are dominant in tropical rain forests, whereas many tropical dry forest trees drop their leaves during the dry season.

Epiphytes such as bromeliads and orchids generally cover tropical forest trees but are less abundant in dry forests. Thorny shrubs and succulent plants are common in some tropical dry forests.

Animals Earth's tropical forests are home to millions of species, including an estimated 5–30 million still undescribed species of insects, spiders, and other arthropods. In fact, animal diversity is higher in tropical forests than in any other terrestrial biome. The animals, including amphibians, birds and other reptiles, mammals, and arthropods, are adapted to the vertically layered environment and are often inconspicuous.

Human Impact Humans long ago established thriving communities in tropical forests. Rapid population growth leading to agriculture and development is now destroying many tropical forests.

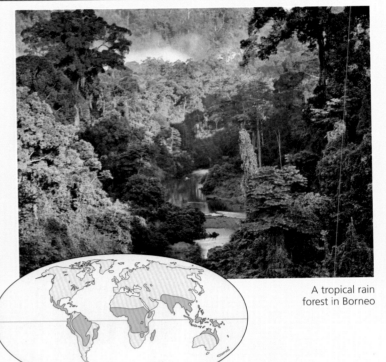

A tropical rain forest in Borneo

Desert

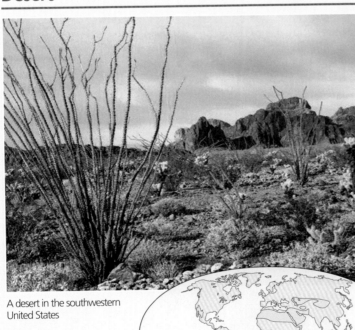

A desert in the southwestern United States

Distribution **Deserts** occur in bands near 30° north and south latitude or at other latitudes in the interior of continents (for instance, the Gobi Desert of north-central Asia).

Precipitation Precipitation is low and highly variable, generally less than 30 cm per year.

Temperature Temperature is variable seasonally and daily. Maximum air temperature in hot deserts may exceed 50°C; in cold deserts air temperature may fall below –30°C.

Plants Desert landscapes are dominated by low, widely scattered vegetation; the proportion of bare ground is high compared with other terrestrial biomes. The plants include succulents such as cacti or euphorbs, deeply rooted shrubs, and herbs that grow during the infrequent moist periods. Desert plant adaptations include heat and desiccation tolerance, water storage, and reduced leaf surface area. Physical defenses, such as spines, and chemical defenses, such as toxins in the leaves of shrubs, are common. Many of the plants exhibit C_4 or CAM photosynthesis (see Chapter 10).

Animals Common desert animals include snakes and lizards, scorpions, ants, beetles, migratory and resident birds, and seed-eating rodents. Many species are nocturnal. Water conservation is a common adaptation, with some species surviving solely on water from breaking down carbohydrates in seeds.

Human Impact Long-distance transport of water and deep groundwater wells have allowed humans to maintain substantial populations in deserts. Urbanization and conversion to irrigated agriculture have reduced the natural biodiversity of some deserts.

Exploring Terrestrial Biomes

Savanna

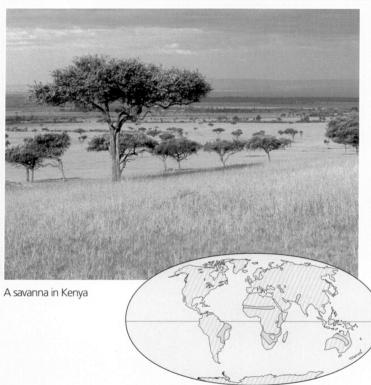

A savanna in Kenya

Distribution Equatorial and subequatorial regions

Precipitation Rainfall, which is seasonal, averages 30–50 cm per year. The dry season can last up to eight or nine months.

Temperature The **savanna** is warm year-round, averaging 24–29°C, but with somewhat more seasonal variation than in tropical forests.

Plants The scattered trees found at different densities in the savanna often are thorny and have small leaves, an apparent adaptation to the relatively dry conditions. Fires are common in the dry season, and the dominant plant species are fire-adapted and tolerant of seasonal drought. Grasses and small nonwoody plants called forbs, which make up most of the ground cover, grow rapidly in response to seasonal rains and are toler-ant of grazing by large mammals and other herbivores.

Animals Large plant-eating mammals, such as wildebeests and zebras, and predators, including lions and hyenas, are common inhabitants. However, the dominant herbivores are actually insects, especially termites. During seasonal droughts, grazing mammals often migrate to parts of the savanna with more forage and scattered watering holes.

Human Impact There is evidence that the earliest humans lived in savannas. Fires set by humans may help maintain this biome, though overly frequent fires reduce tree regeneration by killing the seedlings and saplings. Cattle ranching and overhunting have led to declines in large-mammal populations.

Chaparral

Distribution This biome occurs in midlatitude coastal regions on several continents, and its many names reflect its far-flung distribution: **chaparral** in North America, *matorral* in Spain and Chile, *garigue* and *maquis* in southern France, and *fynbos* in South Africa.

Precipitation Precipitation is highly seasonal, with rainy winters and dry summers. Annual precipitation generally falls within the range of 30–50 cm.

Temperature Fall, winter, and spring are cool, with average temperatures in the range of 10–12°C. Average summer temperature can reach 30°C, and daytime maximum temperature can exceed 40°C.

Plants Chaparral is dominated by shrubs and small trees, along with many kinds of grasses and herbs. Plant diversity is high, with many species confined to a specific, relatively small geo-graphic area. Adaptations to drought include the tough ever-green leaves of woody plants, which reduce water loss. Adaptations to fire are also prominent. Some of the shrubs produce seeds that will germinate only after a hot fire; food reserves stored in their fire-resistant roots enable them to resprout quickly and use nutrients released by the fire.

Animals Native mammals include browsers, such as deer and goats, that feed on twigs and buds of woody vegetation, and a high diversity of small mammals. Chaparral areas also support many species of amphibians, birds and other reptiles, and insects.

Human Impact Chaparral areas have been heavily settled and reduced through conversion to agriculture and urbanization. Humans contribute to the fires that sweep across the chaparral.

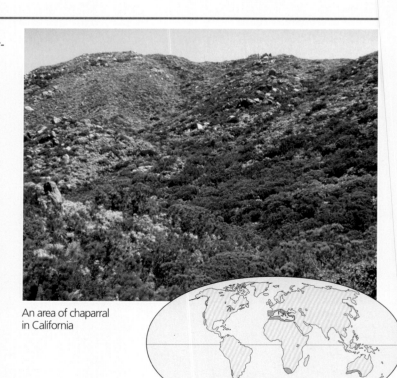

An area of chaparral in California

Temperate Grassland

Distribution The veldts of South Africa, the *puszta* of Hungary, the pampas of Argentina and Uruguay, the steppes of Russia, and the plains and prairies of central North America are examples of **temperate grasslands**.

Precipitation Precipitation is often highly seasonal, with relatively dry winters and wet summers. Annual precipitation generally averages between 30 and 100 cm. Periodic drought is common.

Temperature Winters are generally cold, with average temperatures frequently falling well below –10°C. Summers, with average temperatures often approaching 30°C, are hot.

Plants The dominant plants are grasses and forbs, which vary in height from a few centimeters to 2 m in tallgrass prairie. Many grassland plants have adaptations that help them survive periodic, protracted droughts and fire. For example, grasses can sprout quickly following fire. Grazing by large mammals helps prevent establishment of woody shrubs and trees.

Animals Native mammals include large grazers such as bison and wild horses. Temperate grasslands are also inhabited by a wide variety of burrowing mammals, such as prairie dogs in North America.

Human Impact Deep, fertile soils make temperate grasslands ideal places for agriculture, especially for growing grains. As a consequence, most grassland in North America and much of Eurasia has been converted to farmland. In some drier grasslands, cattle and other grazers have turned parts of the biome into desert.

Grasslands National Park, Saskatchewan

Northern Coniferous Forest

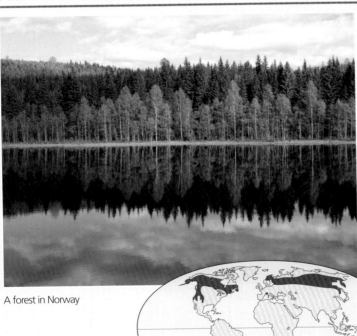

A forest in Norway

Distribution Extending in a broad band across northern North America and Eurasia to the edge of the arctic tundra, the **northern coniferous forest**, or *taiga*, is the largest terrestrial biome on Earth.

Precipitation Annual precipitation generally ranges from 30 to 70 cm, and periodic droughts are common. However, some coastal coniferous forests of the U.S. Pacific Northwest are temperate rain forests that may receive over 300 cm of annual precipitation.

Temperature Winters are usually cold; summers may be hot. Some areas of coniferous forest in Siberia typically range in temperature from –50°C in winter to over 20°C in summer.

Plants Northern coniferous forests are dominated by cone-bearing trees, such as pine, spruce, fir, and hemlock, some of which depend on fire to regenerate. The conical shape of many conifers prevents too much snow from accumulating and breaking their branches, and their needle- or scale-like leaves reduce water loss. The diversity of plants in the shrub and herb layers of these forests is lower than in temperate broadleaf forests.

Animals While many migratory birds nest in northern coniferous forests, other species reside there year-round. The mammals of this biome, which include moose, brown bears, and Siberian tigers, are diverse. Periodic outbreaks of insects that feed on the dominant trees can kill vast tracts of trees.

Human Impact Although they have not been heavily settled by human populations, northern coniferous forests are being logged at an alarming rate, and the old-growth stands of these trees may soon disappear.

Exploring Terrestrial Biomes

Temperate Broadleaf Forest

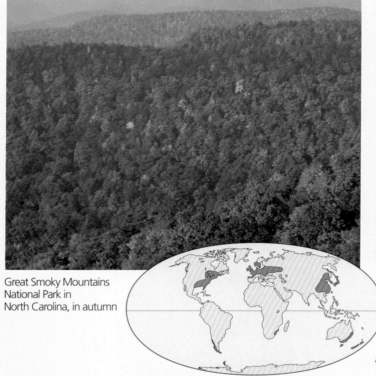

Great Smoky Mountains
National Park in
North Carolina, in autumn

Distribution Found mainly at midlatitudes in the Northern Hemisphere, with smaller areas in Chile, South Africa, Australia, and New Zealand

Precipitation Precipitation can average from about 70 to over 200 cm annually. Significant amounts fall during all seasons, including summer rain and, in some forests, winter snow.

Temperature Winter temperatures average around 0°C. Summers, with maximum temperatures near 35°C, are hot and humid.

Plants A mature **temperate broadleaf forest** has distinct vertical layers, including a closed canopy, one or two strata of understory trees, a shrub layer, and an herb layer. There are few epiphytes. The dominant plants in the Northern Hemisphere are deciduous trees, which drop their leaves before winter, when low temperatures would reduce photosynthesis and make water uptake from frozen soil difficult. In Australia, evergreen eucalyptus trees dominate these forests.

Animals In the Northern Hemisphere, many mammals hibernate in winter, while many bird species migrate to warmer climates. Mammals, birds, and insects make use of all the vertical layers of the forest.

Human Impact Temperate broadleaf forest has been heavily settled on all continents. Logging and land clearing for agriculture and urban development have destroyed virtually all the original deciduous forests in North America. However, owing to their capacity for recovery, these forests are returning over much of their former range.

Tundra

Distribution **Tundra** covers expansive areas of the Arctic, amounting to 20% of Earth's land surface. High winds and low temperatures produce similar plant communities, called *alpine tundra*, on very high mountaintops at all latitudes, including the tropics.

Precipitation Precipitation averages from 20 to 60 cm annually in arctic tundra but may exceed 100 cm in alpine tundra.

Temperature Winters are cold, with averages in some areas below –30°C. Summers temperatures generally average less than 10°C.

Plants The vegetation of tundra is mostly herbaceous, consisting of a mixture of mosses, grasses, and forbs, along with some dwarf shrubs and trees and lichens. A permanently frozen layer of soil called permafrost restricts the growth of plant roots.

Animals Large grazing musk oxen are resident, while caribou and reindeer are migratory. Predators include bears, wolves, and foxes. Many bird species migrate to the tundra for summer nesting.

Human Impact Tundra is sparsely settled but has become the focus of significant mineral and oil extraction in recent years.

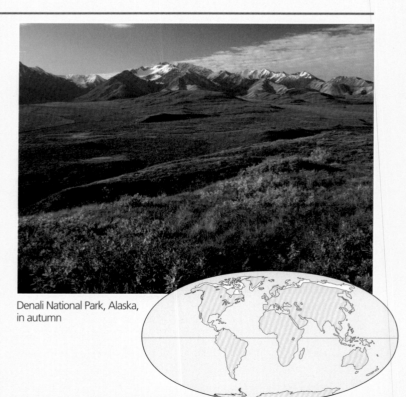

Denali National Park, Alaska, in autumn

CONCEPT 52.3

Aquatic biomes are diverse and dynamic systems that cover most of Earth

Now that we have examined terrestrial biomes, let's turn to aquatic biomes. Unlike terrestrial biomes, aquatic biomes are characterized primarily by their physical environment. They also show far less latitudinal variation, with all types found across the globe. Ecologists distinguish between freshwater and marine biomes on the basis of physical and chemical differences. Marine biomes generally have salt concentrations that average 3%, whereas freshwater biomes are usually characterized by a salt concentration of less than 0.1%.

The oceans make up the largest marine biome, covering about 75% of Earth's surface. Because of their vast size, they greatly impact the biosphere. Water evaporated from the oceans provides most of the planet's rainfall, and ocean temperatures have a major effect on global climate and wind patterns (see Figure 52.3). Marine algae and photosynthetic bacteria also supply a substantial portion of the world's oxygen and consume large amounts of atmospheric carbon dioxide.

Freshwater biomes are closely linked to the soils and biotic components of the surrounding terrestrial biome. The particular characteristics of a freshwater biome are also influenced by the patterns and speed of water flow and the climate to which the biome is exposed.

Zonation in Aquatic Biomes

Many aquatic biomes are physically and chemically stratified (layered), vertically and horizontally, as illustrated for both a lake and a marine environment in **Figure 52.13**. Light is absorbed by the water itself and by photosynthetic organisms, so its intensity decreases rapidly with depth. Ecologists distinguish between the upper **photic zone**, where there is sufficient light for photosynthesis, and the lower **aphotic zone**, where little light penetrates. The photic and aphotic zones together make up the **pelagic zone**. Deep in the aphotic zone lies the **abyssal zone**, the part of the ocean 2,000–6,000 m below the surface. At the bottom of all aquatic biomes, deep or shallow, is the **benthic zone**. Made up of sand and organic and inorganic sediments, the benthic zone is occupied by communities of organisms collectively called the **benthos**. A major source of food for many benthic species is dead organic matter called **detritus**, which "rains" down from the productive surface waters of the photic zone.

Thermal energy from sunlight warms surface waters to whatever depth the sunlight penetrates, but the deeper waters remain quite cold. In the ocean and in most lakes, a narrow layer of abrupt temperature change called a **thermocline**

(a) Zonation in a lake

The lake environment is generally classified on the basis of three physical criteria: light penetration (photic and aphotic zones), distance from shore and water depth (littoral and limnetic zones), and whether the environment is open water (pelagic zone) or bottom (benthic zone).

(b) Marine zonation

Like lakes, the marine environment is generally classified on the basis of light penetration (photic and aphotic zones), distance from shore and water depth (intertidal, neritic, and oceanic zones), and whether the environment is open water (pelagic zone) or bottom (benthic and abyssal zones).

separates the more uniformly warm upper layer from more uniformly cold deeper waters. Lakes tend to be particularly layered with respect to temperature, especially during summer and winter, but many temperate lakes undergo a semiannual mixing of their waters as a result of changing temperature

❶ In winter, the coldest water in the lake (0°C) lies just below the surface ice; water becomes progressively warmer at deeper levels of the lake, typically 4°C at the bottom.

❷ In spring, as the ice melts, the surface water warms to 4°C and mixes with the formerly cooler layers below, eliminating thermal stratification. Spring winds help mix the water, bringing oxygen to the bottom waters and nutrients to the surface.

❸ In summer, the lake regains a distinctive thermal profile, with warm surface water separated from cold bottom water by a narrow vertical zone of abrupt temperature change, called a thermocline.

❹ In autumn, as surface water cools rapidly, it sinks beneath the underlying layers, remixing the water until the surface begins to freeze and the winter temperature profile is reestablished.

▲ **Figure 52.14 Seasonal turnover in lakes with winter ice cover.** Because of the seasonal turnover shown here, lake waters are well oxygenated at all depths in spring and autumn; in winter and summer, when the lake is stratified by temperature, oxygen concentrations are lower in deeper waters and higher near the surface of the lake.

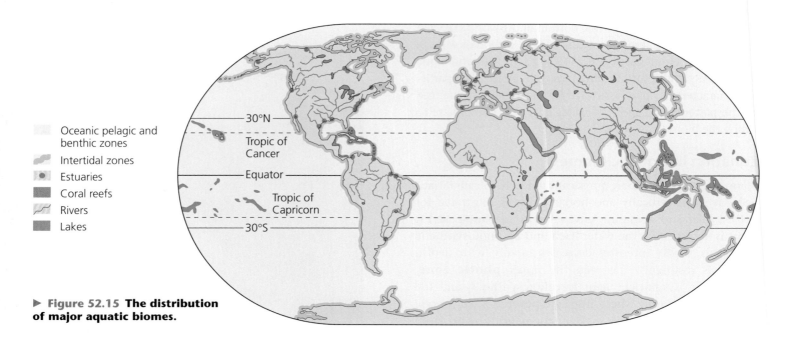

Oceanic pelagic and benthic zones
Intertidal zones
Estuaries
Coral reefs
Rivers
Lakes

▶ **Figure 52.15 The distribution of major aquatic biomes.**

profiles **(Figure 52.14)**. This **turnover**, as it is called, sends oxygenated water from a lake's surface to the bottom and brings nutrient-rich water from the bottom to the surface in both spring and autumn. These cyclic changes in the abiotic properties of lakes are essential for the survival and growth of organisms at all levels within this ecosystem.

In both freshwater and marine environments, communities are distributed according to water depth, degree of light penetration, distance from shore, and whether they are found in open water or near the bottom. Marine communities, in particular, illustrate the limitations on species

distribution that result from these abiotic factors. Plankton and many fish species occur in the relatively shallow photic zone (see Figure 52.13b). Because water absorbs light so well and the ocean is so deep, most of the ocean volume is virtually devoid of light (the aphotic zone) and harbors relatively little life, except for microorganisms and relatively sparse populations of fishes and invertebrates. Similar factors limit species distribution in deep lakes as well.

Figure 52.15 shows the locations of Earth's major aquatic biomes. **Figure 52.16**, on the next four pages, explores their main characteristics.

UNIVERSITY OF ALBERTA FACULTY BIO

David Schindler BSc Zoology (North Dakota State University) D. Phil. Rhodes Scholar (Oxford University)

Current Positions: Killam Memorial Chair and Professor of Ecology, Department of Biological Sciences. Officer of the Order of Canada; member of the Alberta Order of Excellence; Fellow of the Royal Societies of Canada and the U.K.; member of the US National Academy of Sciences.

I currently teach Biology 601, a graduate course in environmental policy decision making. I am a frequent guest lecturer in undergraduate ecology and limnology courses.

My academic career began in 1966 at Trent University. In 1968, I founded and became director of the Experimental Lakes Project in northwestern Ontario, a unique research facility focusing on interdisciplinary research on the effects of eutrophication, acid rain, radioactive elements and climate change on boreal ecosystems. In 1989 I came to Alberta as a Killam Memorial Chair and Professor of Ecology in the Department of Biological Sciences.

My research in whole lake experiments showed how eutrophication (over-fertilization with nutrients) and acid rain affect lakes and how that damage might be controlled. My research group has also studied the restoration of mountain lakes stocked with non-native fish species, the effects of climate warming on freshwater systems, and the impact of contaminants from the oil sands industry on the Athabasca River. My lab's research has been widely used in formulating ecologically sound management policy in Canada, USA and Europe.

Exploring Aquatic Biomes

Lakes

Physical Environment
Standing bodies of water range from ponds a few square meters in area to lakes covering thousands of square kilometers. Light decreases with depth, creating stratification (see Figure 52.13a). Temperate lakes may have a seasonal thermocline (see Figure 52.14); tropical lowland lakes have a thermocline year-round.

Chemical Environment The salinity, oxygen concentration, and nutrient content differ greatly among lakes and can vary with season. **Oligotrophic lakes** are nutrient-poor and generally oxygen-rich; **eutrophic lakes** are nutrient-rich and often depleted of oxygen in the deepest zone in summer and if covered with ice in winter. The amount of decomposable organic matter in bottom sediments is low in oligotrophic lakes and high in eutrophic lakes; high rates of decomposition in deeper layers of eutrophic lakes cause periodic oxygen depletion.

Geologic Features
Oligotrophic lakes may become more eutrophic over time as runoff adds sediments and nutrients. They tend to have less surface area relative to their depth than eutrophic lakes.

Photosynthetic Organisms Rooted and floating aquatic plants live in the **littoral zone**, the shallow, well-lit waters close to shore. Farther from shore, where water is too deep to support rooted aquatic plants, the **limnetic zone** is inhabited by a variety of phytoplankton, including cyanobacteria.

Heterotrophs In the limnetic zone, small drifting heterotrophs, or zooplankton, graze on the phytoplankton. The benthic zone is inhabited by assorted invertebrates whose species composition depends partly on oxygen levels. Fishes

An oligotrophic lake in Grand Teton National Park, Wyoming

A eutrophic lake in the Okavango Delta, Botswana

live in all zones with sufficient oxygen.

Human Impact Runoff from fertilized land and dumping of

wastes lead to nutrient enrichment, which can produce algal blooms, oxygen depletion, and fish kills.

Wetlands

Physical Environment A **wetland** is a habitat that is inundated by water at least some of the time and that supports plants adapted to water-saturated soil. Some wetlands are inundated at all times, whereas others flood infrequently.

Chemical Environment
Because of high organic production by plants and decomposition by microbes and other organisms, both the water and the soils are periodically low in dissolved oxygen. Wetlands have a high capacity to filter dissolved nutrients and chemical pollutants.

Geologic Features *Basin wetlands* develop in shallow basins, ranging from upland depressions to filled-in lakes and ponds. *Riverine wetlands* develop along shallow and periodically flooded banks of rivers and streams. *Fringe wetlands* occur along the coasts of large lakes and seas, where water flows back and forth because of rising lake levels or tidal action. Thus, fringe wetlands include both freshwater and marine biomes.

Photosynthetic Organisms
Wetlands are among the most productive biomes on Earth. Their water-saturated soils favor the growth of plants such as

floating pond lilies and emergent cattails, many sedges, tamarack, and black spruce, which have adaptations enabling them to grow in water or in soil that is periodically anaerobic owing to the presence of unaerated water. Woody plants dominate the vegetation of swamps, while bogs are dominated by sphagnum mosses.

Heterotrophs Wetlands are home to a diverse community of invertebrates, birds, and many other organisms. Herbivores, from crustaceans and aquatic insect larvae to muskrats, consume algae, detritus, and plants. Carnivores are also varied and may include dragonflies, otters, frogs, alligators, and herons.

Human Impact Draining and filling have destroyed up to 90% of wetlands, which help purify water and reduce peak flooding.

A basin wetland in the United Kingdom

Exploring Aquatic Biomes

Streams and Rivers

Physical Environment The most prominent physical characteristic of streams and rivers is their current. Headwater streams are generally cold, clear, turbulent, and swift. Farther downstream, where numerous tributaries may have joined, forming a river, the water is generally warmer and more turbid because of suspended sediment. Streams and rivers are stratified into vertical zones.

Chemical Environment The salt and nutrient content of streams and rivers increases from the headwaters to the mouth. Headwaters are generally rich in oxygen. Downstream water may also contain substantial oxygen, except where there has been organic enrichment. A large fraction of the organic matter in rivers consists of dissolved or highly fragmented material that is carried by the current from forested streams.

Geologic Features Headwater stream channels are often narrow, have a rocky bottom, and alternate between shallow sections and deeper pools. The downstream stretches of rivers are generally wide and meandering. River bottoms are often silty from sediments deposited over long periods of time.

Photosynthetic Organisms Headwater streams that flow through grasslands or deserts may be rich in phytoplankton or rooted aquatic plants.

Heterotrophs A great diversity of fishes and invertebrates inhabit unpolluted rivers and streams, distributed according to, and throughout, the vertical zones. In streams flowing through temperate or tropical forests, organic matter from terrestrial vegetation is the primary source of food for aquatic consumers.

Human Impact Municipal, agricultural, and industrial pollution degrade water quality and kill aquatic organisms. Damming and flood control impair the natural functioning of stream and river ecosystems and threaten migratory species such as salmon.

A headwater stream in the Great Smoky Mountains

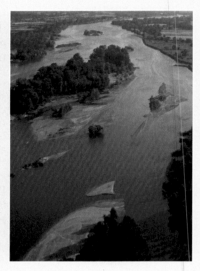

The Loire River (in France) far from its headwaters

Estuaries

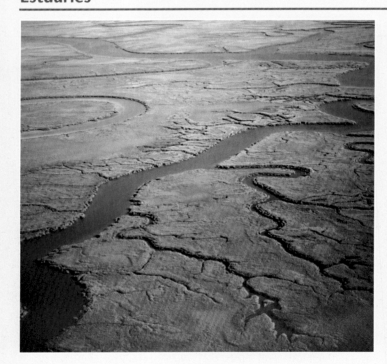

An estuary in the southeastern United States

Physical Environment An **estuary** is a transition area between river and sea. Seawater flows up the estuary channel during a rising tide and flows back down during the falling tide. Often, higher-density seawater occupies the bottom of the channel and mixes little with the lower-density river water at the surface.

Chemical Environment Salinity varies spatially within estuaries, from nearly that of fresh water to that of seawater. Salinity also varies with the rise and fall of the tides. Nutrients from the river make estuaries, like wetlands, among the most productive biomes.

Geologic Features Estuarine flow patterns combined with the sediments carried by river and tidal waters create a complex network of tidal channels, islands, natural levees, and mudflats.

Photosynthetic Organisms Saltmarsh grasses and algae, including phytoplankton, are the major producers in estuaries.

Heterotrophs Estuaries support an abundance of worms, oysters, crabs, and many fish species that humans consume. Many marine invertebrates and fishes use estuaries as a breeding ground or migrate through them to freshwater habitats upstream. Estuaries are also crucial feeding areas for waterfowl and some marine mammals.

Human Impact Filling, dredging, and pollution from upstream have disrupted estuaries worldwide.

Intertidal Zones

Physical Environment An **intertidal zone** is periodically submerged and exposed by the tides, twice daily on most marine shores. Upper zones experience longer exposures to air and greater variations in temperature and salinity. Changes in physical conditions from the upper to the lower intertidal zones limit the distributions of many organisms to particular strata, as shown in the photograph.

Chemical Environment Oxygen and nutrient levels are generally high and are renewed with each turn of the tides.

Geologic Features The substrates of intertidal zones, which are generally either rocky or sandy, select for particular behavior and anatomy among intertidal organisms. The configuration of bays or coastlines influences the magnitude of tides and the relative exposure of intertidal organisms to wave action.

Photosynthetic Organisms A high diversity and biomass of attached marine algae inhabit rocky intertidal zones, especially in the lower zone. Sandy intertidal zones exposed to vigorous wave action generally lack attached plants or algae, while sandy intertidal zones in protected bays or lagoons often support rich beds of sea grass and algae.

Heterotrophs Many of the animals in rocky intertidal environments have structural adaptations that enable them to attach to the hard substrate. The composition, density, and diversity of animals change markedly from the upper to the lower intertidal zones. Many of the animals in sandy or muddy intertidal zones, such as worms, clams, and predatory crustaceans, bury themselves and feed as the tides bring sources of food. Other common animals are sponges, sea anemones, echinoderms, and small fishes.

Human Impact Oil pollution has disrupted many intertidal areas. The construction of rock walls and barriers to reduce erosion from waves and storm surges has disrupted this zone in some locations.

Rocky intertidal zone on the Oregon coast

Oceanic Pelagic Zone

Physical Environment The **oceanic pelagic zone** is a vast realm of open blue water, constantly mixed by wind-driven oceanic currents. Because of higher water clarity, the photic zone extends to greater depths than in coastal marine waters.

Chemical Environment Oxygen levels are generally high. Nutrient concentrations are generally lower than in coastal waters. Because they are thermally stratified year-round, some tropical areas of the oceanic pelagic zone have lower nutrient concentrations than temperate oceans. Turnover between fall and spring renews nutrients in the photic zones of temperate and high-latitude ocean areas.

Geologic Features This biome covers approximately 70% of Earth's surface and has an average depth of nearly 4,000 m. The deepest point in the ocean is more than 10,000 m beneath the surface.

Photosynthetic Organisms The dominant photosynthetic organisms are phytoplankton, including photosynthetic bacteria, that drift with the oceanic currents. Spring turnover renews nutrients in temperate oceans producing a surge of phytoplankton growth. Because of the large extent of this biome, photosynthetic plankton account for about half of the photosynthetic activity on Earth.

Heterotrophs The most abundant heterotrophs in this biome are zooplankton. These protists, worms, copepods, shrimp-like krill, jellies, and small larvae of invertebrates and fishes graze on photosynthetic plankton. The oceanic pelagic zone also includes free-swimming animals, such as large squids, fishes, sea turtles, and marine mammals.

Human Impact Overfishing has depleted fish stocks in all Earth's oceans, which have also been polluted by waste dumping.

Open ocean off the island of Hawaii

Exploring Aquatic Biomes

Coral Reefs

Physical Environment **Coral reefs** are formed largely from the calcium carbonate skeletons of corals. Shallow reef-building corals live in the photic zone of relatively stable tropical marine environments with high water clarity, primarily on islands and along the edge of some continents. They are sensitive to temperatures below about 18–20°C and above 30°C. Deep-sea coral reefs, found between 200 and 1,500 m deep, are less known than their shallow counterparts but harbor as much diversity as many shallow reefs do.

Chemical Environment Corals require high oxygen levels and are excluded by high inputs of fresh water and nutrients.

Geologic Features Corals require a solid substrate for attachment. A typical coral reef begins as a *fringing reef* on a young, high island, forming an offshore *barrier reef* later in the history of the island and becoming a *coral atoll* as the older island submerges.

Photosynthetic Organisms Unicellular algae live within the tissues of the corals, forming a mutualistic relationship that provides the corals with organic molecules. Diverse multicellular red and green algae growing on the reef also contribute substantial amounts of photosynthesis.

Heterotrophs Corals, a diverse group of cnidarians (see Chapter 33), are themselves the predominant animals on coral reefs. However, fish and invertebrate diversity is exceptionally high. Overall animal diversity on coral reefs rivals that of tropical forests.

Human Impact Collecting of coral skeletons and overfishing have reduced populations of corals and reef fishes. Global warming and pollution may be contributing to large-scale coral death. Development of coastal mangroves for aquaculture has also reduced spawning grounds for many species of reef fishes.

A coral reef in the Red Sea

Marine Benthic Zone

A deep-sea hydrothermal vent community

Physical Environment The **marine benthic zone** consists of the seafloor below the surface waters of the coastal, or **neritic**, zone and the offshore, pelagic zone (see Figure 52.13b). Except for shallow, near-coastal areas, the marine benthic zone receives no sunlight. Water temperature declines with depth, while pressure increases. As a result, organisms in the very deep benthic, or abyssal, zone are adapted to continuous cold (about 3°C) and very high water pressure.

Chemical Environment Except in areas of organic enrichment, oxygen is usually present at sufficient concentrations to support diverse animal life.

Geologic Features Soft sediments cover most of the benthic zone. However, there are areas of rocky substrate on reefs, submarine mountains, and new oceanic crust.

Autotrophs Photosynthetic organisms, mainly seaweeds and filamentous algae, are limited to shallow benthic areas with sufficient light to support them. Unique assemblages of organisms, such as those shown in the photo, are found near **deep-sea hydrothermal vents** on mid-ocean ridges. In these dark, hot environments, the food producers are chemoautotrophic prokaryotes (see Chapter 27) that obtain energy by oxidizing H_2S formed by a reaction of the hot water with dissolved sulfate (SO_4^{2-}).

Heterotrophs Neritic benthic communities include numerous invertebrates and fishes. Beyond the photic zone, most consumers depend entirely on organic matter raining down from above. Among the animals of the deep-sea hydrothermal vent communities are giant tube worms (pictured at left), some more than 1 m long. They are nourished by chemoautotrophic prokaryotes that live as symbionts within their bodies. Many other invertebrates, including arthropods and echinoderms, are also abundant around the hydrothermal vents.

Human Impact Overfishing has decimated important benthic fish populations, such as the cod of the Grand Banks off Newfoundland. Dumping of organic wastes has created oxygen-deprived benthic areas.

The first two questions refer to Figure 52.16.

1. Why are phytoplankton, and not benthic algae or rooted aquatic plants, the dominant photosynthetic organisms of the oceanic pelagic zone?

2. **MAKE CONNECTIONS** Many organisms living in estuaries experience freshwater and saltwater conditions each day with the rising and falling of tides. Based on what you learned in Concept 44.1 (pp. 953–958), explain how these changing conditions challenge the survival of these organisms.

3. **WHAT IF?** Water leaving a reservoir behind a dam is often taken from deep layers of the reservoir. Would you expect fish found in a river below a dam in summer to be species that prefer colder or warmer water than fish found in an undammed river? Explain.

For suggested answers, see Appendix A.

CONCEPT **52.4**

Interactions between organisms and the environment limit the distribution of species

So far in this chapter we've examined Earth's climate and the characteristics of terrestrial and aquatic biomes. We've also introduced the range of biological levels at which ecologists work (see Figure 52.2). In this section, we will examine how ecologists determine what factors control the distribution of species, such as the harlequin toad shown in Figure 52.1.

Species distributions are a consequence of both ecological and evolutionary interactions through time. The differential survival and reproduction of individuals that lead to evolution occur in *ecological time*, the minute-to-minute time frame of interactions between organisms and the environment. Through natural selection, organisms adapt to their environment over the time frame of many generations, in *evolutionary time*. One example of how events in ecological time have led to evolution is the selection for beak depth in Galápagos finches (see Figures 23.1 and 23.2). On the island of Daphne Major, finches with larger, deeper beaks were better able to survive during a drought because they could eat the large, hard seeds that were available. Finches with shallower beaks, which required smaller, softer seeds that were in short supply, were less likely to survive and reproduce. Because beak depth is hereditary in this species, the generation of finches born after the drought had beaks that were deeper than those of previous generations.

Biologists have long recognized global and regional patterns in the distribution of organisms (see the discussion of biogeography in Chapter 22). Kangaroos, for instance, are found in Australia but nowhere else on Earth. Ecologists ask not only *where* species occur, but also *why* species occur where they do: What factors determine their distribution? In seeking to answer this question, ecologists focus on both biotic and abiotic factors that influence the distribution and abundance of organisms.

Figure 52.17 presents an example of how both kinds of factors might affect the distribution of a species, in this case the red kangaroo (*Macropus rufus*). As the figure shows, red kangaroos are most abundant in a few areas in the interior of Australia, where precipitation is relatively sparse and variable. They are not found around most of the periphery of the continent,

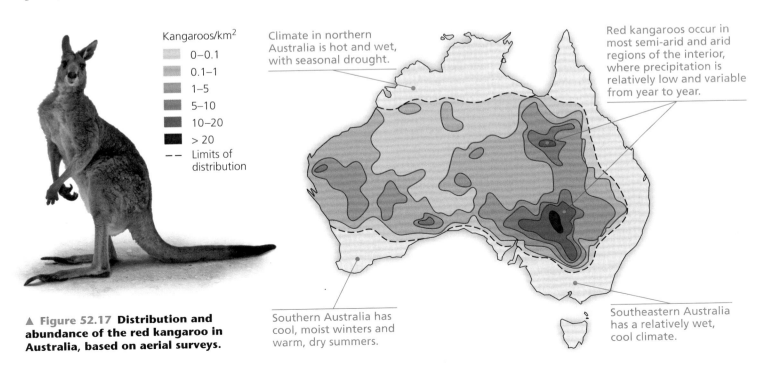

Kangaroos/km²

- 0–0.1
- 0.1–1
- 1–5
- 5–10
- 10–20
- \> 20
- – – Limits of distribution

Climate in northern Australia is hot and wet, with seasonal drought.

Red kangaroos occur in most semi-arid and arid regions of the interior, where precipitation is relatively low and variable from year to year.

Southern Australia has cool, moist winters and warm, dry summers.

Southeastern Australia has a relatively wet, cool climate.

▲ **Figure 52.17 Distribution and abundance of the red kangaroo in Australia, based on aerial surveys.**

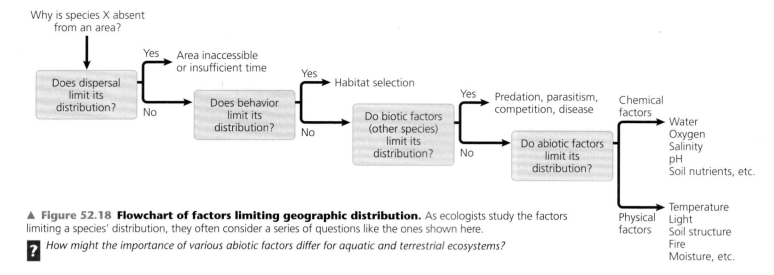

▲ Figure 52.18 Flowchart of factors limiting geographic distribution. As ecologists study the factors limiting a species' distribution, they often consider a series of questions like the ones shown here.

? *How might the importance of various abiotic factors differ for aquatic and terrestrial ecosystems?*

where the climate is wetter. At first glance, this distribution might suggest that an abiotic factor—the amount and variability of precipitation—directly determines where red kangaroos live. However, climate may also influence red kangaroo populations indirectly through biotic factors, such as pathogens, parasites, predators, competitors, and food availability. Ecologists generally need to consider multiple factors and alternative hypotheses when attempting to explain the distribution of species.

To see how ecologists might arrive at such an explanation, let's work our way through the series of questions in the flowchart in **Figure 52.18.**

Dispersal and Distribution

One factor that contributes greatly to the global distribution of organisms is **dispersal**, the movement of individuals or gametes away from their area of origin or from centers of high population density. A biogeographer who studies the distributions of species in the context of evolutionary theory might consider dispersal in hypothesizing why there are no kangaroos in North America: A barrier may have kept them from reaching the continent. While land-bound kangaroos have not reached North America under their own power, other organisms that disperse more readily, such as some birds, have. The dispersal of organisms is critical to understanding the role of geographic isolation in evolution (see Chapter 24) as well as the broad patterns of species distribution we see today, including that of the Pacific diatom discussed earlier in this chapter.

Natural Range Expansions and Adaptive Radiation

EVOLUTION The importance of dispersal is most evident when organisms reach an area where they did not exist previously. For instance, 200 years ago, the cattle egret (*Bubulcus ibis*) was found only in Africa and southwestern Europe. But in the late 1800s, some of these birds managed to cross the Atlantic Ocean and colonize northeastern South America.

From there, cattle egrets gradually spread southward and also northward through Central America and into North America, reaching Florida by 1960 **(Figure 52.19)**. Today they have breeding populations as far west as the Pacific coast of the United States and as far north as southern Canada.

In rare cases, such long-distance dispersal can lead to adaptive radiation, the rapid evolution of an ancestral species into new species that fill many ecological niches (see Chapter 25). The incredible diversity of Hawaiian silverswords is an example of adaptive radiation that was possible only with the long-distance dispersal of an ancestral tarweed from North America (see Figure 25.20).

► Figure 52.19 Dispersal of the cattle egret in the Americas. Native to Africa, cattle egrets were first reported in South America in 1877.

Natural range expansions clearly show the influence of dispersal on distribution. However, opportunities to observe such dispersal directly are rare, so ecologists often turn to experimental methods to better understand the role of dispersal in limiting the distribution of species.

Species Transplants

To determine if dispersal is a key factor limiting the distribution of a species, ecologists may observe the results of intentional or accidental transplants of the species to areas where it was previously absent. For a transplant to be considered successful, some of the organisms must not only survive in the new area but also reproduce there sustainably. If a transplant is successful, then we can conclude that the *potential* range of the species is larger than its *actual* range; in other words, the species *could* live in certain areas where it currently does not.

Species introduced to new geographic locations often disrupt the communities and ecosystems to which they have been introduced and spread far beyond the area of introduction. Consequently, ecologists rarely move species to new geographic regions. Instead, they document the outcome when a species has been transplanted for other purposes, such as to introduce game animals or predators of pest species, or when a species has been accidentally transplanted.

Behavior and Habitat Selection

As transplant experiments show, some organisms do not occupy all of their potential range, even though they may be physically able to disperse into the unoccupied areas. To follow our line of questioning from Figure 52.18, does behavior play a role in limiting distribution in such cases? When individuals seem to avoid certain habitats, even when the habitats are suitable, the organism's distribution may be limited by habitat selection behavior.

Although habitat selection is one of the least understood of all ecological processes, some instances in insects have been closely studied. Female insects often deposit eggs only in response to a very narrow set of stimuli, which may restrict distribution of the insects to certain host plants. Larvae of the European corn borer, for example, can feed on a wide variety of plants but are found almost exclusively on corn (maize) because egg-laying females are attracted by odors produced by the plant. Habitat selection behavior clearly restricts this insect to geographic locations where corn is found.

Biotic Factors

If behavior does not limit the distribution of a species, our next question is whether biotic factors—other species—are responsible. Often, negative interactions with predators (organisms that kill their prey) or herbivores (organisms that eat plants or algae) restrict the ability of a species to survive and reproduce. **Figure 52.20** describes a specific case of an herbivore, a sea urchin, limiting the distribution of a food species.

▼ **Figure 52.20**

INQUIRY

Does feeding by sea urchins limit seaweed distribution?

EXPERIMENT W. J. Fletcher, of the University of Sydney, Australia, reasoned that if sea urchins are a limiting biotic factor in a particular ecosystem, then more seaweeds should invade an area from which sea urchins have been removed. To isolate the effect of sea urchins from that of a seaweed-eating mollusc, the limpet, he removed only urchins, only limpets, or both from study areas adjacent to a control site.

RESULTS Fletcher observed a large difference in seaweed growth between areas with and without sea urchins.

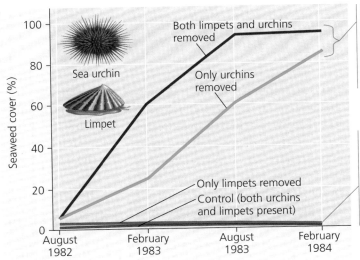

CONCLUSION Removing both limpets and urchins resulted in the greatest increase in seaweed cover, indicating that both species have some influence on seaweed distribution. But since removing only urchins greatly increased seaweed growth while removing only limpets had little effect, Fletcher concluded that sea urchins have a much greater effect than limpets in limiting seaweed distribution.

SOURCE W. J. Fletcher, Interactions among subtidal Australian sea urchins, gastropods, and algae: effects of experimental removals, *Ecological Monographs* 57:89–109 (1989).

WHAT IF? Seaweed cover increased the most when both urchins *and* limpets were removed. How might you explain this result?

In certain marine ecosystems, there is often an inverse relationship between the abundance of sea urchins and seaweeds (multicellular algae, such as kelp). Where urchins that graze on seaweeds and other algae are common, large stands of seaweeds do not become established. As described in Figure 52.20, Australian researchers have tested the hypothesis that sea urchins are a biotic factor limiting seaweed distribution. When sea urchins were removed from experimental plots, seaweed cover increased dramatically, showing that urchins limited the distribution of seaweeds.

In addition to predation and herbivory, the presence or absence of pollinators, food resources, parasites, pathogens, and competing organisms can act as a biotic limitation on species distribution. Some of the most striking cases of limitation occur when humans accidentally or intentionally introduce exotic predators or pathogens into new areas and wipe out native species.

Abiotic Factors

The last question in the flowchart in Figure 52.18 considers whether abiotic factors, such as temperature, water, oxygen, salinity, sunlight, or soil, might be limiting a species' distribution. If the physical conditions at a site do not allow a species to survive and reproduce, then the species will not be found there. Throughout this discussion, keep in mind that most abiotic factors vary substantially in space and time. Daily and annual fluctuations of abiotic factors may either blur or accentuate regional distinctions. Furthermore, organisms can avoid some stressful conditions temporarily through behaviors such as dormancy or hibernation.

Temperature

Environmental temperature is an important factor in the distribution of organisms because of its effect on biological processes. Cells may rupture if the water they contain freezes (at temperatures below 0°C), and the proteins of most organisms denature at temperatures above 45°C. Most organisms function best within a specific range of environmental temperature. Temperatures outside that range may force some animals to expend energy regulating their internal temperature, as mammals and birds do (see Chapter 40). Extraordinary adaptations enable certain organisms, such as thermophilic prokaryotes (see Chapter 27), to live outside the temperature range habitable by other life.

Water and Oxygen

The dramatic variation in water availability among habitats is another important factor in species distribution. Species living at the seashore or in tidal wetlands can desiccate (dry out) as the tide recedes. Terrestrial organisms face a nearly constant threat of desiccation, and the distribution of terrestrial species reflects their ability to obtain and conserve water. Many amphibians, such as the harlequin toad in Figure 52.1, are particularly vulnerable to drying because they use their moist, delicate skin for gas exchange. Desert organisms exhibit a variety of adaptations for acquiring and conserving water in dry environments, as described in Chapter 44.

Water affects oxygen availability in aquatic environments and in flooded soils. Because oxygen diffuses slowly in water, its concentration can be low in certain aquatic systems and soils, limiting cellular respiration and other physiological processes. Oxygen concentrations can be particularly low in both deep ocean and deep lake waters and sediments where organic matter is abundant. Flooded wetland soils may also have low oxygen content. Mangroves and other trees have specialized roots that project above the water and help the root system obtain oxygen (see Figure 35.4). Unlike many flooded wetlands, the surface waters of streams and rivers tend to be well oxygenated because of rapid exchange of gases with the atmosphere.

Salinity

As you learned in Chapter 7, the salt concentration of water in the environment affects the water balance of organisms through osmosis. Most aquatic organisms are restricted to either freshwater or saltwater habitats by their limited ability to osmoregulate (see Chapter 44). Although most terrestrial organisms can excrete excess salts from specialized glands or in feces or urine, salt flats and other high-salinity habitats typically have few species of plants or animals.

Salmon that migrate between freshwater streams and the ocean use both behavioral and physiological mechanisms to osmoregulate. They adjust the amount of water they drink to help balance their salt content, and their gills switch from taking up salt in fresh water to excreting salt in the ocean.

Sunlight

Sunlight absorbed by photosynthetic organisms provides the energy that drives most ecosystems, and too little sunlight can limit the distribution of photosynthetic species. In forests, shading by leaves in the treetops makes competition for light especially intense, particularly for seedlings growing on the forest floor. In aquatic environments, every meter of water depth selectively absorbs about 45% of the red light and about 2% of the blue light passing through it. As a result, most photosynthesis in aquatic environments occurs relatively near the surface.

▲ **Figure 52.21 Alpine tree line in Banff National Park, Canada.** Organisms living at high elevations are exposed not only to high levels of ultraviolet radiation but also to freezing temperatures, moisture deficits, and strong winds. Above the tree line, the combination of such factors restricts the growth and survival of trees.

Too much light can also limit the survival of organisms. In some ecosystems, such as deserts, high light levels can increase temperature stress if animals and plants are unable to avoid the light or to cool themselves through evaporation (see Chapter 40). At high elevations, the sun's rays are more likely to damage DNA and proteins because the atmosphere is thinner, absorbing less ultraviolet (UV) radiation. Damage from UV radiation, combined with other abiotic stresses, prevents trees from surviving above a certain elevation, resulting in the appearance of a tree line on mountain slopes **(Figure 52.21)**.

Rocks and Soil

In terrestrial environments, the pH, mineral composition, and physical structure of rocks and soil limit the distribution of plants and thus of the animals that feed on them, contributing to the patchiness of terrestrial ecosystems. The pH of soil can limit the distribution of organisms directly, through extreme acidic or basic conditions, or indirectly, by affecting the solubility of nutrients and toxins.

In a river, the composition of the rocks and soil that make up the substrate (riverbed) can affect water chemistry, which in turn influences the resident organisms. In freshwater and marine environments, the structure of the substrate determines the organisms that can attach to it or burrow into it.

Throughout this chapter, you have seen how the distributions of biomes and organisms depend on abiotic and biotic factors. In the next chapter, we continue to work our way through the hierarchy outlined in Figure 52.2, focusing on how abiotic and biotic factors influence the ecology of populations.

CONCEPT CHECK 52.4

1. Give examples of human actions that could expand a species' distribution by changing its (a) dispersal or (b) biotic interactions.
2. **WHAT IF?** You suspect that deer are restricting the distribution of a tree species by preferentially eating the seedlings of the tree. How might you test this hypothesis?
3. **MAKE CONNECTIONS** As you saw in Figure 25.20 (p. 525), Hawaiian silverswords underwent a remarkable adaptive radiation after their ancestor reached Hawaii, while the islands were still young. Would you expect the cattle egret to undergo a similar adaptive radiation in the Americas (see Figure 52.19)? Explain.

For suggested answers, see Appendix A.

52 CHAPTER REVIEW

SUMMARY OF KEY CONCEPTS

CONCEPT 52.1

Earth's climate varies by latitude and season and is changing rapidly (pp. 1144–1150)

- Global **climate** patterns are largely determined by the input of solar energy and Earth's revolution around the sun.
- The changing angle of the sun over the year, bodies of water, and mountains exert seasonal, regional, and local effects on **macroclimate**.
- Fine-scale differences in **abiotic** (nonliving) factors, such as sunlight and temperature, determine **microclimate**.
- Increasing greenhouse gas concentrations in the air are warming Earth and altering the distributions of many species. Some species will not be able to shift their ranges quickly enough to reach suitable habitat in the future.

? *Suppose global air circulation suddenly reversed, with most air ascending at 30° north and south latitude and descending at the equator. At what latitude would you most likely find deserts in this scenario?*

CONCEPT 52.2

The structure and distribution of terrestrial biomes are controlled by climate and disturbance (pp. 1150–1156)

- **Climographs** show that temperature and precipitation are correlated with **biomes**. Because other factors also play roles in biome location, biomes overlap.
- Terrestrial biomes are often named for major physical or climatic factors and for their predominant vegetation. Vertical layering is an important feature of terrestrial biomes.
- **Disturbance**, both natural and human-induced, influences the type of vegetation found in biomes. Humans have altered much of Earth's surface, replacing the natural terrestrial communities described and depicted in Figure 52.12 with urban and agricultural ones.

? *Some arctic tundra ecosystems receive as little rainfall as deserts but have much more dense vegetation. Based on Figure 52.10, what climatic factor might explain this difference? Explain.*

CONCEPT 52.3

Aquatic biomes are diverse and dynamic systems that cover most of Earth (pp. 1157–1163)

- Aquatic biomes are characterized primarily by their physical environment rather than by climate and are often layered with regard to light penetration, temperature, and community structure. Marine biomes have a higher salt concentration than freshwater biomes.
- In the ocean and in most lakes, an abrupt temperature change called a **thermocline** separates a more uniformly warm upper layer from more uniformly cold deeper waters.

? *In which aquatic biomes might you find an aphotic zone?*

CONCEPT 52.4

Interactions between organisms and the environment limit the distribution of species (pp. 1163–1167)

- Ecologists want to know not only *where* species occur but also *why* those species occur where they do.

- The distribution of species may be limited by **dispersal**, the movement of individuals away from their area of origin; behavior; **biotic** (living) factors; and abiotic factors, such as temperature extremes, salinity, and water availability.

? *If you were an ecologist studying the chemical and physical limits to the distributions of species, how might you rearrange the flow-chart preceding this question?*

TEST YOUR UNDERSTANDING

LEVEL 1: KNOWLEDGE/COMPREHENSION

1. Which of the following areas of study focuses on the exchange of energy, organisms, and materials between ecosystems?
   a. population ecology
   b. organismal ecology
   c. landscape ecology
   d. ecosystem ecology
   e. community ecology

2. Which lake zone would be absent in a very shallow lake?
   a. benthic zone
   b. aphotic zone
   c. pelagic zone
   d. littoral zone
   e. limnetic zone

3. Which of the following is true with respect to oligotrophic lakes and eutrophic lakes?
   a. Oligotrophic lakes are more subject to oxygen depletion.
   b. Rates of photosynthesis are lower in eutrophic lakes.
   c. Eutrophic lake water contains lower concentrations of nutrients.
   d. Eutrophic lakes are richer in nutrients.
   e. Sediments in oligotrophic lakes contain larger amounts of decomposable organic matter.

4. Which of the following biomes is correctly paired with the description of its climate?
   a. savanna—low temperature, precipitation uniform during the year
   b. tundra—long summers, mild winters
   c. temperate broadleaf forest—relatively short growing season, mild winters
   d. temperate grasslands—relatively warm winters, most rainfall in summer
   e. tropical forests—nearly constant day length and temperature

LEVEL 2: APPLICATION/ANALYSIS

5. Which of the following is characteristic of most terrestrial biomes?
   a. annual average rainfall in excess of 250 cm
   b. a distribution predicted almost entirely by rock and soil patterns
   c. clear boundaries between adjacent biomes
   d. vegetation demonstrating vertical layering
   e. cold winter months

6. The oceans affect the biosphere in all of the following ways *except*
   a. producing a substantial amount of the biosphere's oxygen.
   b. removing carbon dioxide from the atmosphere.
   c. moderating the climate of terrestrial biomes.
   d. regulating the pH of freshwater biomes and terrestrial groundwater.
   e. being the source of most of Earth's rainfall.

7. Which statement about dispersal is *false*?
   a. Dispersal is a common component of the life cycles of plants and animals.
   b. Colonization of devastated areas after floods or volcanic eruptions depends on dispersal.
   c. Dispersal occurs only on an evolutionary time scale.
   d. Seeds are important dispersal stages in the life cycles of most flowering plants.
   e. The ability to disperse can expand the geographic distribution of a species.

8. When climbing a mountain, we can observe transitions in biological communities that are analogous to the changes
   a. in biomes at different latitudes.
   b. at different depths in the ocean.
   c. in a community through different seasons.
   d. in an ecosystem as it evolves over time.
   e. across the United States from east to west.

9. Suppose that the number of bird species is determined mainly by the number of vertical strata found in the environment. If so, in which of the following biomes would you find the greatest number of bird species?
   a. tropical rain forest
   b. savanna
   c. desert
   d. temperate broadleaf forest
   e. temperate grassland

LEVEL 3: SYNTHESIS/EVALUATION

10. **WHAT IF?** If the direction of Earth's rotation reversed, the most predictable effect would be
    a. no more night and day.
    b. a big change in the length of the year.
    c. winds blowing from west to east along the equator.
    d. a loss of seasonal variation at high latitudes.
    e. the elimination of ocean currents.

11. **DRAW IT** After reading about the experiment of W. J. Fletcher described in Figure 52.20, you decide to study feeding relationships among sea otters, sea urchins, and kelp on your own. You know that sea otters prey on sea urchins and that urchins eat kelp. At four coastal sites, you measure kelp abundance. Then you spend one day at each site and mark whether otters are present or absent every 5 minutes during daylight hours. Make a graph that shows how otter density depends on kelp abundance, using the data shown below. Then formulate a hypothesis to explain the pattern you observed.

Site	Kelp Abundance (% cover)	Otter Density (# sightings per day)
1	75	98
2	15	18
3	60	85
4	25	36

12. **EVOLUTION CONNECTION**
    Discuss how the concept of time applies to ecological situations and evolutionary changes. Do ecological time and evolutionary time ever overlap? If so, what are some examples?

13. **SCIENTIFIC INQUIRY**
    Jens Clausen and colleagues, at the Carnegie Institution of Washington, studied how the size of yarrow plants (*Achillea lanulosa*) growing on the slopes of the Sierra Nevada varied with elevation. They found that plants from low elevations were generally taller than plants from high elevations, as shown below:

Source: J. Clausen et al., Experimental studies on the nature of species. III. Environmental responses of climatic races of *Achillea*, Carnegie Institution of Washington Publication No. 581 (1948).

Clausen and colleagues proposed two hypotheses to explain this variation within a species: (1) There are genetic differences between populations of plants found at different elevations. (2) The species has developmental flexibility and can assume tall or short growth forms, depending on local abiotic factors. If you had seeds from yarrow plants found at low and high elevations, what experiments would you perform to test these hypotheses?

14. **WRITE ABOUT A THEME**
    Feedback Regulation Global warming is occurring rapidly in Arctic marine and terrestrial ecosystems, including tundra and northern coniferous forests. In such locations, reflective white snow and ice cover are melting more quickly and extensively, uncovering darker-colored ocean water, plants, and rocks. In a short essay (100–150 words), explain how this process might represent a positive-feedback loop.

For selected answers, see Appendix A.

 www.masteringbiology.com

1. MasteringBiology® Assignments
Tutorial Aquatic Biomes
Activities Tropical Atmospheric Circulation • Terrestrial Biomes • Adaptations to Biotic and Abiotic Factors • Discovery Channel Video: Trees
Questions Student Misconceptions • Reading Quiz • Multiple Choice • End-of-Chapter

2. eText
Read your book online, search, take notes, highlight text, and more.

3. The Study Area
Practice Tests • Cumulative Test • *BioFlix* 3-D Animations • MP3 Tutor Sessions • Videos • Activities • Investigations • Lab Media • Audio Glossary • Word Study Tools • Art

Chapter 1

Figure Questions

Figure 1.7 The arrangement of fingers and opposable thumb in the human hand, combined with fingernails and a complex system of nerves and muscles, allows the hand to grasp and manipulate objects with great dexterity. **Figure 1.13** Substance B would be made continuously and would accumulate in large amounts. Neither C nor D would be made, so D would not be able to inhibit Enzyme 1 and regulate the pathway. **Figure 1.27** The percentage of brown artificial snakes attacked would probably be higher than the percentage of artificial kingsnakes attacked in all areas (whether or not inhabited by coral snakes).

Concept Check 1.1

1. Examples: A molecule consists of *atoms* bonded together. Each organelle has an orderly arrangement of *molecules*. Photosynthetic plant cells contain *organelles* called chloroplasts. A tissue consists of a group of similar *cells*. Organs such as the heart are constructed from several *tissues*. A complex multicellular organism, such as a plant, has several types of *organs*, such as leaves and roots. A population is a set of *organisms* of the same species. A community consists of *populations* of the various species inhabiting a specific area. An ecosystem consists of a biological *community* along with the nonliving factors important to life, such as air, soil, and water. The biosphere is made up of all of Earth's *ecosystems*. **2.** (a) Structure and function are correlated. (b) Cells are an organism's basic units, *and* the continuity of life is based on heritable information in the form of DNA. (c) Organisms interact with other organisms and with the physical environment, *and* life requires energy transfer and transformation. **3.** Some possible answers: *Emergent properties*: The ability of a human heart to pump blood requires an intact heart; it is not a capability of any of the heart's tissues or cells working alone. *Environmental interactions*: A mouse eats food, such as nuts or grasses, and deposits some of the food material as feces and urine. Construction of a nest rearranges the physical environment and may hasten degradation of some of its components. The mouse may also act as food for a predator. *Energy transfer*: A plant, such as a grass, absorbs energy from the sun and transforms it into molecules that act as stored fuel. Animals can eat part of the plant and use the food for energy to carry out their activities. *Structure and function*: The strong, sharp teeth of a wolf are well suited to grasping and dismembering its prey. *The cellular basis of life*: The digestion of food is made possible by chemicals (chiefly enzymes) made by cells of the digestive tract. *The genetic basis of life*: Human eye color is determined by the combination of genes inherited from the two parents. *Feedback regulation*: When your stomach is full, it signals your brain to decrease your appetite. *Evolution*: All plants have chloroplasts, indicating their descent from a common ancestor.

Concept Check 1.2

1. An address pinpoints a location by tracking from broader to narrower categories—a state, city, zip, street, and building number. This is analogous to the groups-subordinate-to-groups structure of biological taxonomy. **2.** The naturally occurring heritable variation in a population is "edited" by natural selection because individuals with heritable traits better suited to the environment survive and reproduce more successfully than others. Over time, better-suited individuals persist and their percentage in the population increases, while less suited individuals become less prevalent—a type of population editing.

3.

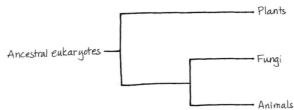

Concept Check 1.3

1. Inductive reasoning derives generalizations from specific cases; deductive reasoning predicts specific outcomes from general premises. **2.** The coloration pattern on the snakes **3.** Compared to a hypothesis, a scientific theory is usually more general and substantiated by a much greater amount of evidence. Natural selection is an explanatory idea that applies to all kinds of organisms and is supported by vast amounts of evidence of various kinds. **4.** Based on the results shown in Figure 1.27, you might predict that the colorful artificial snakes would be attacked more often than the brown ones, simply because they are easier to see. This prediction assumes that the area in Virginia where you are working has predators that attack snakes but no poisonous snakes that resemble the colorful artificial snakes.

Concept Check 1.4

1. Science aims to understand natural phenomena and how they work, while technology involves application of scientific discoveries for a particular purpose or to solve a specific problem. **2.** Natural selection could be operating. Malaria is present in sub-Saharan Africa, so there might be an advantage to people with the sickle-cell disease form of the gene that makes them more able to survive and

pass on their genes to offspring. Among those of African descent living in the United States, where malaria is absent, there would be no advantage, so they would be selected against more strongly, resulting in fewer individuals with the sickle-cell disease form of the gene.

Summary of Key Concepts Questions

1.1 Evolution explains the most fundamental aspects of all life on earth. It accounts for the common features shared by all forms of life due to descent from a common ancestor, while also providing an explanation for how the great diversity of living organisms on the planet has arisen. **1.2** Ancestors of this plant may have exhibited variation in how well their leaves conserved water. Because not much soil is present in the crevices where these plants are found, the variant plants that could conserve water may have survived better and been able to produce more offspring. Over time, a higher and higher proportion of individuals in the population would have had the adaptation of thick, water-conserving leaves. **1.3** Inductive reasoning is used in forming hypotheses, while deductive reasoning leads to predictions that are used to test hypotheses. **1.4** Different approaches taken by scientists studying natural phenomena at different levels complement each other, so more is learned about each problem being studied. A diversity of backgrounds among scientists may lead to fruitful ideas in the same way that important innovations have often arisen where a mix of cultures coexist.

Test Your Understanding

1. b **2.** d **3.** a **4.** c **5.** c **6.** c **7.** b **8.** c **9.** c **10.** d
11. Your figure should show: (1) For the biosphere, the Earth with an arrow coming out of a tropical ocean; (2) for the ecosystem, a distant view of a coral reef; (3) for the community, a collection of reef animals and algae, with corals, fishes, some seaweed, and any other organisms you can think of; (4) for the population, a group of fish of the same species; (5) for the organism, one fish from your population; (6) for the organ, the fish's stomach, and for the organ system, the whole digestive tract (see Chapter 41 for help); (7) for a tissue, a group of similar cells from the stomach; (8) for a cell, one cell from the tissue, showing its nucleus and a few other organelles; (9) for an organelle, the nucleus, where most of the cell's DNA is located; and (10) for a molecule, a DNA double helix. Your sketches can be very rough!

Chapter 2

Figure Questions

Figure 2.2 The most significant difference in the results would be that the two *Cedrela* saplings inside each garden would show similar amounts of dying leaf tissue because a poisonous chemical released from the *Duroia* trees would presumably reach the saplings via the air or soil and would not be blocked by the insect barrier. The *Cedrela* saplings planted outside the gardens would not show damage unless *Duroia* trees were nearby. Also, any ants present on the unprotected *Cedrela* saplings inside the gardens would probably not be observed making injections into the leaves. However, formic acid would likely still be found in the ants' glands, as it is for most species of ants. **Figure 2.9** Atomic number = 12; 12 protons, 12 electrons; 3 electron shells; 2 valence electrons **Figure 2.16** One possible answer:

Figure 2.19 The plant is submerged in water (H_2O), in which the CO_2 is dissolved. The sun's energy is used to make sugar, which is found in the plant and can act as food for the plant itself, as well as for animals that eat the plant. The oxygen (O_2) is present in the bubbles.

Concept Check 2.1

1. Table salt (sodium chloride) is made up of sodium and chlorine. We are able to eat the compound, showing that it has different properties from those of a metal (sodium) and a poisonous gas (chlorine). **2.** Yes, because an organism requires trace elements, even though only in small amounts **3.** A person with an iron deficiency will probably show fatigue and other effects of a low oxygen level in the blood. (The condition is called anemia and can also result from too few red blood cells or abnormal hemoglobin.) **4.** Variant ancestral plants that could tolerate the toxic elements could grow and reproduce in serpentine soils. (Plants that were well adapted to nonserpentine soils would not be expected to survive in serpentine areas.) The offspring of the variants would also vary, with those most capable of thriving under serpentine conditions growing best and reproducing most. Over many generations, this probably led to the serpentine-adapted species we see today.

Concept Check 2.2
1. 7 **2.** $^{15}_{7}$N **3.** 9 electrons; two electron shells; 1s, 2s, 2p (three orbitals); 1 electron is needed to fill the valence shell. **4.** The elements in a row all have the same number of electron shells. In a column, all the elements have the same number of electrons in their valence shells.

Concept Check 2.3
1. Each carbon atom has only three covalent bonds instead of the required four. **2.** The attraction between oppositely charged ions, forming ionic bonds **3.** If you could synthesize molecules that mimic these shapes, you might be able to treat diseases or conditions caused by the inability of affected individuals to synthesize such molecules.

Concept Check 2.4
1.

2. At equilibrium, the forward and reverse reactions occur at the same rate. **3.** $C_6H_{12}O_6 + 6 O_2 \rightarrow 6 CO_2 + 6 H_2O$ + Energy. Glucose and oxygen react to form carbon dioxide and water, releasing energy. We breathe in oxygen because we need it for this reaction to occur, and we breathe out carbon dioxide because it is a by-product of this reaction. (This reaction is called cellular respiration, and you will learn more about it in Chapter 9.)

Summary of Key Concepts Questions
2.1 Iodine (part of a thyroid hormone) and iron (part of hemoglobin in blood) are both trace elements, required in minute quantities. Calcium and phosphorus (components of bones and teeth) are needed by the body in much greater quantities.
2.2

Both neon and argon have completed valence shells, containing 8 electrons. They do not have unpaired electrons that could participate in chemical bonds. **2.3** Electrons are shared equally between the two atoms in a nonpolar covalent bond. In a polar covalent bond, the electrons are drawn closer to the more electronegative atom. In the formation of ions, an electron is completely transferred from one atom to a much more electronegative atom. **2.4** The concentration of products would increase as the added reactants were converted to products. Eventually, an equilibrium would again be reached in which the forward and reverse reactions were proceeding at the same rate and the relative concentrations of reactants and products returned to where they were before the addition of more reactants.

Test Your Understanding
1. a **2.** e **3.** b **4.** a **5.** d **6.** b **7.** c **8.** e

9. a. Ö::C:H This structure doesn't make sense because the valence shell of carbon is incomplete; carbon can form 4 bonds.

b. H:Ö:C:C::Ö This structure makes sense because all valence shells are complete, and all bonds have the correct number of electrons.

c. H:C:H.C::Ö This structure doesn't make sense because H has only 1 electron to share, so it cannot form bonds with 2 atoms.

d. This structure doesn't make sense for several reasons:
The valence shell of oxygen is incomplete; oxygen can form 2 bonds.
H:N..H H has only 1 electron to share, so it cannot form a double bond.
Nitrogen usually makes only 3 bonds. It does not have enough electrons to make 2 single bonds, make a double bond, and complete its valence shell.

Chapter 3

Figure Questions
Figure 3.2 One possible answer:

Figure 3.6 Without hydrogen bonds, water would behave like other small molecules, and the solid phase (ice) would be denser than liquid water. The ice would sink to the bottom and would no longer insulate the whole body of water, which would eventually freeze because the average annual temperature at the South Pole is –50°C. The krill could not survive. **Figure 3.7** Heating the solution would cause the water to evaporate faster than it is evaporating at room temperature. At a certain point, there wouldn't be enough water molecules to dissolve the salt ions. The salt would start coming out of solution and re-forming crystals. Eventually, all the water would evaporate, leaving behind a pile of salt like the original pile. **Figure 3.12** By causing the loss of coral reefs, a decrease in the ocean's carbonate concentration would have a ripple effect on noncalcifying organisms. Some of these organisms depend on the reef structure for protection, while others feed on species associated with reefs.

Concept Check 3.1
1. Electronegativity is the attraction of an atom for the electrons of a covalent bond. Because oxygen is more electronegative than hydrogen, the oxygen atom in H_2O pulls electrons toward itself, resulting in a partial negative charge on the oxygen atom and partial positive charges on the hydrogen atoms. Atoms in neighboring water molecules with opposite partial charges are attracted to each other, forming a hydrogen bond. **2.** The hydrogen atoms of one molecule, with their partial positive charges, would repel the hydrogen atoms of the adjacent molecule. **3.** The covalent bonds of water molecules would not be polar, and water molecules would not form hydrogen bonds with each other.

Concept Check 3.2
1. Hydrogen bonds hold neighboring water molecules together. This cohesion helps the chain of water molecules move upward against gravity in water-conducting cells as water evaporates from the leaves. Adhesion between water molecules and the walls of the water-conducting cells also helps counter gravity. **2.** High humidity hampers cooling by suppressing the evaporation of sweat. **3.** As water freezes, it expands because water molecules move farther apart in forming ice crystals. When there is water in a crevice of a boulder, expansion due to freezing may crack the boulder. **4.** A liter of blood would contain 7.8×10^{13} molecules of ghrelin (1.3×10^{-10} moles per liter × 6.02×10^{23} molecules per mole). **5.** The hydrophobic substance repels water, perhaps helping to keep the ends of the legs from becoming coated with water and breaking through the surface. If the legs were coated with a hydrophilic substance, water would be drawn up them, possibly making it more difficult for the water strider to walk on water.

Concept Check 3.3
1. 10^5, or 100,000 **2.** $[H^+] = 0.01 M = 10^{-2}M$, so pH = 2. **3.** $CH_3COOH \rightarrow CH_3COO^- + H^+$. CH_3COOH is the acid (the H^+ donor), and CH_3COO^- is the base (the H^+ acceptor). **4.** The pH of the water should decrease from 7 to about 2; the pH of the acetic acid solution will decrease only a small amount, because the reaction shown for question 3 will shift to the left, with CH_3COO^- accepting the influx of H^+ and becoming CH_3COOH molecules.

Summary of Key Concepts Questions
3.1

Each water molecule can make four hydrogen bonds with neighboring molecules. **3.2** Ions dissolve in water when polar water molecules form a hydration shell around them. Polar molecules dissolve as water molecules form hydrogen bonds with them and surround them. Solutions are homogeneous mixtures of solute and solvent. Colloids form when particles that are too large to dissolve remain suspended in a liquid. **3.3** CO_2 reacts with H_2O to form carbonic acid (H_2CO_3), which dissociates into H^+ and bicarbonate (HCO_3^-). Although the carbonic acid–bicarbonate reaction is a buffering system, adding CO_2 drives the reaction to the right, releasing more H^+ and lowering pH. The excess protons combine with CO_3^{2-} to form bicarbonate, lowering the concentration of carbonate available for the formation of calcium carbonate (calcification) by corals.

Test Your Understanding
1. d **2.** b **3.** c **4.** e **5.** c **6.** a **7.** e **8.** d
9.

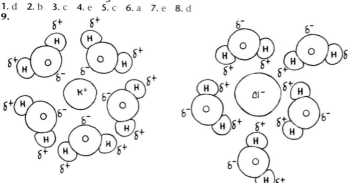

10. Both global warming and ocean acidification are caused by increasing levels of carbon dioxide in the atmosphere, the result of burning fossil fuels. **11.** Due to intermolecular hydrogen bonds, water has a high specific heat (the amount of heat required to increase the temperature of water by 1°C). When water is heated, much of the heat is absorbed in breaking hydrogen bonds before the water molecules increase their motion and the temperature increases. Conversely, when water is cooled, many H bonds are formed, which releases a significant amount of heat. This release of heat can provide some protection against freezing of the plants' leaves, thus protecting the cells from damage.

Chapter 4

Figure Questions
Figure 4.2 Because the concentration of the reactants influences the equilibrium (as discussed in Chapter 2), there might have been more HCN relative to CH_2O, since there would have been a higher concentration of the reactant gas containing nitrogen.
Figure 4.4

$$Na \cdot \qquad \cdot \ddot{P} \cdot \qquad \cdot \ddot{\underset{..}{S}} : \qquad \cdot \ddot{\underset{..}{C}} \ddot{l} :$$

Figure 4.6 The tails of fats contain only carbon-hydrogen bonds, which are relatively nonpolar. Because the tails occupy the bulk of a fat molecule, they make the molecule as a whole nonpolar and therefore incapable of forming hydrogen bonds with water.
Figure 4.7

$$
\begin{array}{c}
H \\
| \\
H-C-H \\
| \\
H \quad H \quad H \\
| \quad | \quad | \\
H-C-C-C-H \\
| \quad | \quad | \\
H \quad H \quad H \\
| \\
H-C-H \\
| \\
H
\end{array}
$$

Figure 4.9 Molecule b, because there are not only the two electronegative oxygens of the carboxyl group, but also an oxygen on the next (carbonyl) carbon. All of these oxygens help make the bond between the O and H of the —OH group more polar, thus making the dissociation of H^+ more likely.

Concept Check 4.1
1. Prior to Wöhler's experiment, the prevailing view was that only living organisms could synthesize "organic" compounds. Wöhler made urea, an organic compound, without the involvement of living organisms. **2.** The spark provided energy needed for the inorganic molecules in the atmosphere to react with each other. (You'll learn more about energy and chemical reactions in Chapter 8.)

Concept Check 4.2
1.

$$
\begin{array}{c}
H \qquad H \\
\diagdown \qquad \diagup \\
C=C \\
\diagup \qquad \diagdown \\
H \qquad H
\end{array}
$$

2. The forms of C_4H_{10} in (b) are structural isomers, as are the butenes in (c). **3.** Both consist largely of hydrocarbon chains. **4.** No. There is not enough diversity in the atoms. It can't form structural isomers because there is only one way for three carbons to attach to each other (in a line). There are no double bonds, so *cis-trans* isomers are not possible. Each carbon has at least two hydrogens attached to it, so the molecule is symmetrical and cannot have enantiomers.

Concept Check 4.3
1. It has both an amino group (—NH_2), which makes it an amine, and a carboxyl group (—COOH), which makes it a carboxylic acid. **2.** The ATP molecule loses a phosphate, becoming ADP. **3.** A chemical group that can act as a base has been replaced with a group that can act as an acid, increasing the acidic properties of the molecule. The shape of the molecule would also change, likely changing the molecules with which it can interact. The original cysteine molecule has an asymmetric carbon in the center. After replacement of the amino group with a carboxyl group, this carbon is no longer asymmetric.

$$
\begin{array}{c}
\quad \quad \quad H \\
O \quad \quad | \quad \quad O \\
\| \quad \quad \quad \quad \| \\
C-C-C \\
\diagup \quad | \quad \diagdown \\
HO \quad CH_2 \quad OH \\
\quad | \\
\quad SH
\end{array}
$$

Summary of Key Concepts Questions
4.1 Miller showed that organic molecules could form under the physical and chemical conditions believed to have been present on early Earth. This abiotic synthesis of organic molecules would have been a first step in the origin of life. **4.2** Acetone and propanal are structural isomers. Acetic acid and glycine have no asymmetric carbons, whereas glycerol phosphate has one. Therefore, glycerol phosphate can exist as forms that are enantiomers, but acetic acid and glycine cannot. **4.3** The methyl group is nonpolar and not reactive. The other six groups are called functional groups. They are each hydrophilic, increasing the solubility of organic compounds in water, and can participate in chemical reactions.

Test Your Understanding
1. b **2.** b **3.** d **4.** d **5.** a **6.** b **7.** a **8.** The molecule on the right; the middle carbon is asymmetric.
9. $\cdot \overset{\displaystyle \cdot}{\underset{\displaystyle \cdot}{Si}} \cdot$ Si has 4 valence electrons, the same number as carbon. Therefore, silicon would be able to form long chains, including branches, that could act as skeletons for large molecules. It would clearly do this much better than neon (with no valence electrons) or aluminum (with 3 valence electrons).

Chapter 5

Figure Questions
Figure 5.3 Glucose and fructose are structural isomers.
Figure 5.4

Linear form   Ring forming   Ring form

Note that the oxygen on carbon 5 lost its proton and that the oxygen on carbon 2, which used to be the carbonyl oxygen, gained a proton. Four carbons are in the fructose ring, and two are not. (The latter two carbons are attached to carbons 2 and 5, which are in the ring.) The fructose ring differs from the glucose ring, which has five carbons in the ring and one that is not. (Note that the orientation of this fructose molecule is flipped relative to that of the one in Figure 5.5b.)

Figure 5.5

Glucose Glucose → Maltose

Glucose Fructose → Sucrose

Figure 5.12

Figure 5.14

Figure 5.17

Peptide bond Carboxyl group Amino group

Figure 5.21 The R group on glutamic acid is acidic and hydrophilic, whereas that on valine is nonpolar and hydrophobic. Therefore, it is unlikely that valine can participate in the same intramolecular interactions that glutamic acid can. A change in these interactions causes a disruption of molecular structure.
Figure 5.24 The spirals are α helices.

Concept Check 5.1
1. The four main classes are proteins, carbohydrates, lipids, and nucleic acids. Lipids are not polymers.   2. Nine, with one water molecule required to hydrolyze each connected pair of monomers   3. The amino acids in the fish protein must be released in hydrolysis reactions and incorporated into other proteins in dehydration reactions.

Concept Check 5.2
1. $C_3H_6O_3$ 2. $C_{12}H_{22}O_{11}$ 3. The antibiotic treatment is likely to have killed the cellulose-digesting prokaryotes in the cow's stomach. The absence of these prokaryotes would hamper the cow's ability to obtain energy from food and could lead to weight loss and possibly death. Thus, prokaryotic species are reintroduced, in appropriate combinations, in the gut culture given to treated cows.

Concept Check 5.3
1. Both have a glycerol molecule attached to fatty acids. The glycerol of a fat has three fatty acids attached, whereas the glycerol of a phospholipid is attached to two fatty acids and one phosphate group.   2. Human sex hormones are steroids, a type of hydrophobic compound.   3. The oil droplet membrane could consist of

a single layer of phospholipids rather than a bilayer, because an arrangement in which the hydrophobic tails of the membrane phospholipids were in contact with the hydrocarbon regions of the oil molecules would be more stable.

Concept Check 5.4
1. The function of a protein is a consequence of its specific shape, which is lost when a protein becomes denatured.   2. Secondary structure involves hydrogen bonds between atoms of the polypeptide backbone. Tertiary structure involves interactions between atoms of the side chains of the amino acid subunits.   3. These are all nonpolar amino acids, so you would expect this region to be located in the interior of the folded polypeptide, where it would not contact the aqueous environment inside the cell.

Concept Check 5.5
1.

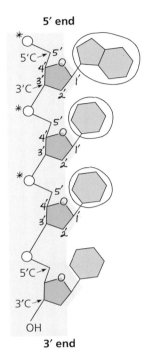

5' end

3' end

2. 5'–T A G G C C T–3'
    3'–A T C C G G A–5'

3. a.   Mismatch
    5'–T A A G C C T–3'
    3'–A T C C G G A–5'

   b. 3'–A T T C G G A–5'

Summary of Key Concepts Questions
Concept 5.1 The polymers of carbohydrates, proteins, and nucleic acids are built from three different types of monomers: monosaccharides, amino acids, and nucleotides, respectively.   **Concept 5.2** Both starch and cellulose are polymers of glucose, but the glucose monomers are in the α configuration in starch and the β configuration in cellulose. The glycosidic linkages thus have different geometries, giving the polymers different shapes and thus different properties. Starch is an energy-storage compound in plants; cellulose is a structural component of plant cell walls. Humans can hydrolyze starch to provide energy but cannot hydrolyze cellulose. Cellulose aids in the passage of food through the digestive tract.   **Concept 5.3** Lipids are not polymers because they do not exist as a chain of linked monomers. They are not considered macromolecules because they do not reach the giant size of many polysaccharides, proteins, and nucleic acids.   **Concept 5.4** A polypeptide, which may consist of hundreds of amino acids in a specific sequence (primary structure), has regions of coils and pleats (secondary structure), which are then folded into irregular contortions (tertiary structure) and may be noncovalently associated with other polypeptides (quaternary structure). The linear order of amino acids, with the varying properties of their side chains (R groups), determines what secondary and tertiary structures will form to produce a protein. The resulting unique three-dimensional shapes of proteins are key to their specific and diverse functions.   **Concept 5.5** The complementary base pairing of the two strands of DNA makes possible the precise replication of DNA every time a cell divides, ensuring that genetic information is faithfully transmitted. In some types of RNA, complementary base pairing enables

RNA molecules to assume specific three-dimensional shapes that facilitate diverse functions.

Test Your Understanding
1. d 2. a 3. b 4. a 5. b 6. c 7. d
8.

	Monomers or Components	Polymer or larger molecule	Type of linkage
Carbohydrates	Monosaccharides	Polysaccharides	Glycosidic linkages
Lipids	Fatty acids	Triacylglycerols	Ester linkages
Proteins	Amino acids	Polypeptides	Peptide bonds
Nucleic acids	Nucleotides	Polynucleotides	Phosphodiester linkages

9.

Original Strand   Complementary strand

Chapter 6

Figure Questions
Figure 6.6 A phospholipid is a lipid, consisting of a glycerol molecule joined to two fatty acids and one phosphate group. Together, the glycerol and phosphate end of the phospholipid form the "head," which is hydrophilic, while the hydrocarbon chains on the fatty acids form hydrophobic "tails." The presence in a single molecule of both a hydrophilic and a hydrophobic region makes the molecule ideal as the main building block of a membrane. **Figure 6.9** The DNA in a chromosome dictates synthesis of a messenger RNA (mRNA) molecule, which then moves out to the cytoplasm. There, the information is used for the production, on ribosomes, of proteins that carry out cellular functions. **Figure 6.10** Any of the bound ribosomes (attached to the endoplasmic reticulum) could be circled, because any could be making a protein that will be secreted. **Figure 6.22** Each centriole has 9 sets of 3 microtubules, so the entire centrosome (two centrioles) has 54 microtubules. Each microtubule consists of a helical array of tubulin dimers (as shown in Table 6.1).

Figure 6.24

Central pair of microtubules

They terminate here

The two central microtubules terminate above the basal body, so they aren't present at the level of the cross section through the basal body, indicated by the lower red rectangle in (a). **Figure 6.29** The microtubules would reorient, and based on the earlier results, the cellulose synthase proteins would also change their path, orienting along the repositioned microtubules. (This is, in fact, what was observed.)

Concept Check 6.1
1. Stains used for light microscopy are colored molecules that bind to cell components, affecting the light passing through, while stains used for electron microscopy involve heavy metals that affect the beams of electrons passing through. 2. (a) Light microscope, (b) scanning electron microscope

Concept Check 6.2
1. See Figure 6.8.
2.

This cell would have the same volume as the cells in columns 2 and 3 but proportionally more surface area than that in column 2 and less than that in column 3. Thus, the surface-to-volume ratio should be greater than 1.2 but less than 6. To obtain the surface area, you would add the area of the six sides (the top, bottom, sides, and ends): 125 + 125 + 125 + 125 + 1 + 1 = 502. The surface-to-volume ratio equals 502 divided by a volume of 125, or 4.0.

Concept Check 6.3
1. Ribosomes in the cytoplasm translate the genetic message, carried from the DNA in the nucleus by mRNA, into a polypeptide chain. 2. Nucleoli consist of DNA and the ribosomal RNA (rRNA) made according to its instructions, as well as proteins imported from the cytoplasm. Together, the rRNA and proteins are assembled into large and small ribosomal subunits. (These are exported through nuclear pores to the cytoplasm, where they will participate in polypeptide synthesis.) 3. No. Each chromosome is present whether its chromatin is relatively diffuse (when the cell is not dividing) or condensed (when the cell is dividing).

Concept Check 6.4
1. The primary distinction between rough and smooth ER is the presence of bound ribosomes on the rough ER. Both types of ER make phospholipids, but membrane proteins and secretory proteins are all produced on the ribosomes of the rough ER. The smooth ER also functions in detoxification, carbohydrate metabolism, and storage of calcium ions. 2. Transport vesicles move membranes and substances they enclose between other components of the endomembrane system. 3. The mRNA is synthesized in the nucleus and then passes out through a nuclear pore to be translated on a bound ribosome, attached to the rough ER. The protein is synthesized into the lumen of the ER and perhaps modified there. A transport vesicle carries the protein to the Golgi apparatus. After further modification in the Golgi, another transport vesicle carries it back to the ER, where it will perform its cellular function.

Concept Check 6.5
1. Both organelles are involved in energy transformation, mitochondria in cellular respiration and chloroplasts in photosynthesis. They both have multiple membranes that separate their interiors into compartments. In both organelles, the innermost membranes—cristae, or infoldings of the inner membrane, in mitochondria, and the thylakoid membranes in chloroplasts—have large surface areas with embedded enzymes that carry out their main functions. 2. Yes. Plant cells are able to make their own sugar by photosynthesis, but mitochondria in these eukaryotic cells are the organelles that are able to generate energy from sugars, a function required in all cells. 3. Mitochondria and chloroplasts are not derived from the ER, nor are they connected physically or via transport vesicles to organelles of the endomembrane system. Mitochondria and chloroplasts are structurally quite different from vesicles derived from the ER, which are bounded by a single membrane.

Concept Check 6.6
1. Both systems of movement involve long filaments that are moved in relation to each other by motor proteins that grip, release, and grip again adjacent polymers. 2. Dynein arms, powered by ATP, move neighboring doublets of microtubules relative to each other. Because they are anchored within the organelle and with respect to one another, the doublets bend instead of sliding past each other. Synchronized bending of the nine microtubule doublets brings about bending of both structures. 3. Such individuals have defects in the microtubule-based movement of cilia and flagella. Thus, the sperm can't move because of malfunctioning or nonexistent flagella, and the airways are compromised because cilia that line the trachea malfunction or don't exist, and so mucus cannot be cleared from the lungs.

Concept Check 6.7
1. The most obvious difference is the presence of direct cytoplasmic connections between cells of plants (plasmodesmata) and animals (gap junctions). These connections result in the cytoplasm being continuous between adjacent cells. 2. The cell would not be able to function properly and would probably soon die, as the cell wall or ECM must be permeable to allow the exchange of matter between the cell and its external environment. Molecules involved in energy production and use must be allowed entry, as well as those that provide information about the cell's environment. Other molecules, such as products synthesized by the cell for export and the by-products of cellular respiration, must be allowed to exit. 3. The parts of the protein that face aqueous regions would be expected to have polar or charged (hydrophilic) amino

acids, while the parts that go through the membrane would be expected to have nonpolar (hydrophobic) amino acids. You would predict polar or charged amino acids at each end (tail), in the region of the cytoplasmic loop, and in the regions of the two extracellular loops. You would predict nonpolar amino acids in the four regions that go through the membrane between the tails and loops.

Summary of Key Concepts Questions

6.1 Both light and electron microscopy allow cells to be studied visually, thus helping us understand internal cellular structure and the arrangement of cell components. Cell fractionation techniques separate out different groups of cell components, which can then be analyzed biochemically to determine their function. Performing microscopy on the same cell fraction helps to correlate the biochemical function of the cell with the cell component responsible. **6.2** The separation of different functions in different organelles has several advantages. Reactants and enzymes can be concentrated in one area instead of spread throughout the cell. Reactions that require specific conditions, such as a lower pH, can be compartmentalized. And enzymes for specific reactions are often embedded in the membranes that enclose or partition an organelle. **6.3** The nucleus contains the genetic material of the cell in the form of DNA, which codes for messenger RNA, which in turn provides instructions for the synthesis of proteins (including the proteins that make up part of the ribosomes). DNA also codes for ribosomal RNA, which is combined with proteins in the nucleolus into the subunits of ribosomes. Within the cytoplasm, ribosomes join with mRNA to build polypeptides, using the genetic information in the mRNA. **6.4** Transport vesicles move proteins and membranes synthesized by the rough ER to the Golgi for further processing and then to the plasma membrane, lysosomes, or other locations in the cell, including back to the ER. **6.5** According to the endosymbiont theory, mitochondria originated from an oxygen-using prokaryotic cell that was engulfed by an ancestral eukaryotic cell. Over time, the host and endosymbiont evolved into a single organism. Chloroplasts originated when at least one of these eukaryotic cells containing mitochondria engulfed and then retained a photosynthetic prokaryote. **6.6** Inside the cell, motor proteins interact with components of the cytoskeleton to move cellular parts. Motor proteins may "walk" vesicles along microtubules. The movement of cytoplasm within a cell involves interactions of the motor protein myosin and microfilaments (actin filaments). Whole cells can be moved by the rapid bending of flagella or cilia, which is caused by the motor-protein-powered sliding of microtubules within these structures. Cell movement can also occur when pseudopodia form at one end of a cell (caused by actin polymerization into a filamentous network), followed by contraction of the cell toward that end; this is powered by interactions of microfilaments with myosin. Interactions of motor proteins and microfilaments in muscle cells can propel whole organisms. **6.7** A plant cell wall is primarily composed of microfibrils of cellulose embedded in other polysaccharides and proteins. The ECM of animal cells is primarily composed of collagen and other glycoprotein fibers, such as fibronectins. These fibers are embedded in a network of carbohydrate-rich proteoglycans. A plant cell wall provides structural support for the cell and, collectively, for the plant body. In addition to giving support, the ECM of an animal cell allows for communication of environmental changes into the cell.

Test Your Understanding

1. b **2.** d **3.** b **4.** e **5.** a **6.** d **7.** c **8.** See Figure 6.8.

Chapter 7

Figure Questions
Figure 7.2

The hydrophilic portion is in contact with an aqueous environment (cytosol or extracellular fluid), and the hydrophobic portion is in contact with the hydrophobic portions of other phospholipids in the interior of the bilayer. **Figure 7.7** You couldn't rule out movement of proteins within membranes of the same species. You might propose that the membrane lipids and proteins from one species weren't able to mingle with those from the other species because of some incompatibility. **Figure 7.10** A transmembrane protein like the dimer in (f) might change its shape upon binding to a particular ECM molecule. The new shape might enable the interior portion of the protein to bind to a second, cytoplasmic protein that would relay the message to the inside of the cell, as shown in (c). **Figure 7.11** The shape of a protein on the HIV surface is likely to be complementary to the shape of the receptor (CD4) and also to that of the co-receptor (CCR5). A molecule that was a similar shape to the HIV surface protein could bind CCR5, blocking HIV binding. (Another alternative would be a molecule that bound to CCR5 and changed the shape of CCR5 so it could no longer bind HIV.)

Figure 7.12

The protein would contact the extracellular fluid. **Figure 7.14** The orange dye would be evenly distributed throughout the solution on both sides of the membrane. The solution levels would not be affected because the orange dye can diffuse through the membrane and equalize its concentration. Thus, no additional osmosis would take place in either direction. **Figure 7.19** The diamond solutes are moving into the cell (down), and the round solutes are moving out of the cell (up); both are moving against their concentration gradient.

Concept Check 7.1
1. They are on the inner side of the transport vesicle membrane. **2.** The grasses living in the cooler region would be expected to have more unsaturated fatty acids in their membranes because those fatty acids remain fluid at lower temperatures. The grasses living immediately adjacent to the hot springs would be expected to have more saturated fatty acids, which would allow the fatty acids to "stack" more closely, making the membranes less fluid and therefore helping them to stay intact at higher temperatures. (Cholesterol could not be used to moderate the effects of temperature on membrane fluidity because it is not found within plant cell membranes.)

Concept Check 7.2
1. O_2 and CO_2 are both nonpolar molecules that can easily pass through the hydrophobic interior of a membrane. **2.** Water is a polar molecule, so it cannot pass very rapidly through the hydrophobic region in the middle of a phospholipid bilayer. **3.** The hydronium ion is charged, while glycerol is not. Charge is probably more significant than size as a basis for exclusion by the aquaporin channel.

Concept Check 7.3
1. CO_2 is a nonpolar molecule that can diffuse through the plasma membrane. As long as it diffuses away so that the concentration remains low outside the cell, it will continue to exit the cell in this way. (This is the opposite of the case for O_2, described in this section.) **2.** The water is hypotonic to the plant cells, so the plant cells take up water. Thus, the cells of the vegetable remain turgid rather than plasmolyzing, and the vegetable (for example, lettuce or spinach) remains crisp and not wilted. **3.** The activity of *Paramecium caudatum*'s contractile vacuole will decrease. The vacuole pumps out excess water that accumulates in the cell; this accumulation occurs only in a hypotonic environment.

Concept Check 7.4
1. The pump uses ATP. To establish a voltage, ions have to be pumped against their gradients, which requires energy. **2.** Each ion is being transported against its electrochemical gradient. If either ion were transported down its electrochemical gradient, this *would* be considered cotransport. **3.** The internal environment of a lysosome is acidic, so it has a higher concentration of H^+ than does the cytoplasm. Therefore, you might expect the membrane of the lysosome to have a proton pump such as that shown in Figure 7.20 to pump H^+ into the lysosome.

Concept Check 7.5
1. Exocytosis. When a transport vesicle fuses with the plasma membrane, the vesicle membrane becomes part of the plasma membrane.
2.

3. The glycoprotein would be synthesized in the ER lumen, move through the Golgi apparatus, and then travel in a vesicle to the plasma membrane, where it would undergo exocytosis and become part of the ECM.

Summary of Key Concepts Questions

7.1 Plasma membranes define the cell by separating the cellular components from the external environment. This allows conditions inside cells to be controlled by membrane proteins, which regulate entry and exit of molecules and even cell function (see Figure 7.10). The processes of life can be carried out inside the controlled environment of the cell, so membranes are crucial. In eukaryotes, membranes also function to subdivide the cytoplasm into different compartments where distinct processes can occur, even under differing conditions such as pH. **7.2** Aquaporins are channel proteins that greatly increase the permeability of a membrane to water molecules, which are polar and therefore do not readily diffuse through the hydrophobic interior of the membrane. **7.3** There will be a net diffusion of water out of a cell into a hypertonic solution. The free water concentration is higher inside the cell than in the solution (where water molecules are not free, but are clustered around the higher concentration of solute particles). **7.4** One of the solutes moved by the cotransporter is actively transported against its concentration gradient. The energy for this transport comes from the concentration gradient of the other solute, which was established by an electrogenic pump that used energy to transport the other solute across the membrane. **7.5** In receptor-mediated endocytosis, specific molecules act as ligands when they bind to receptors on the plasma membrane. The cell can acquire bulk quantities of those molecules when a coated pit forms a vesicle and carries the bound molecules into the cell.

Test Your Understanding
1. b **2.** c **3.** a **4.** d **5.** b
6. (a)

(b) The solution outside is hypotonic. It has less sucrose, which is a nonpenetrating solute. (c) See answer for (a). (d) The artificial cell will become more turgid. (e) Eventually, the two solutions will have the same solute concentrations. Even though sucrose can't move through the membrane, water flow (osmosis) will lead to isotonic conditions.

Chapter 8

Figure Questions
Figure 8.12

Figure 8.20 Because the affinity of the caspase for the inhibitor is very low (as is expected of an allosterically inhibited enzyme), the inhibitor is likely to diffuse away. Because no additional source of the inhibitory compound is present and the concentration of inhibitor is very low, the inhibitor is unlikely to bind again to the allosteric binding site once the covalent linkage is broken. Therefore, the activity of the enzyme would most likely be normal. (In fact, this is what the researchers observed when they broke the disulfide linkage.)

Concept Check 8.1
1. The second law is the trend toward randomization, or increasing entropy. When the concentrations of a substance on both sides of a membrane are equal, the distribution is more random than when they are unequal. Diffusion of a substance to a region where it is initially less concentrated increases entropy, making it an energetically favorable (spontaneous) process as described by the second law. This explains the process seen in Figure 7.13. **2.** The apple has potential energy in its position hanging on the tree, and the sugars and other nutrients it contains have chemical energy. The apple has kinetic energy as it falls from the tree to the ground. Finally, when the apple is digested and its molecules broken down, some of the chemical energy is used to do work, and the rest is lost as thermal energy. **3.** The sugar crystals become less ordered (entropy increases) as they dissolve and become randomly spread out in the water. Over time, the water evaporates, and the crystals form again because the water volume is insufficient to keep them in solution. While the reappearance of sugar crystals may represent a "spontaneous" increase in order (decrease in entropy), it is balanced by the decrease in order (increase in entropy) of the water molecules, which changed from a relatively compact arrangement as liquid water to a much more dispersed and disordered form as water vapor.

Concept Check 8.2
1. Cellular respiration is a spontaneous and exergonic process. The energy released from glucose is used to do work in the cell or is lost as heat. **2.** When the H^+ concentrations are the same, the system is at equilibrium and can do no work. Hydrogen ions can perform work only if their concentrations on each side of a membrane differ—in other words, when a gradient is present. This is consistent with Figure 7.20, which shows that an energy input (provided by ATP hydrolysis) is required to establish the concentration gradient (the H^+ gradient) that can in turn perform work. **3.** The reaction is exergonic because it releases energy—in this case, in the form of light. (This is a nonbiological version of the bioluminescence seen in Figure 8.1.)

Concept Check 8.3
1. ATP usually transfers energy to endergonic processes by phosphorylating (adding phosphate groups to) other molecules. (Exergonic processes phosphorylate ADP to regenerate ATP.) **2.** A set of coupled reactions can transform the first combination into the second. Since this is an exergonic process overall, ΔG is negative and the first combination must have more free energy (see Figure 8.9). **3.** Active transport: The solute is being transported against its concentration gradient, which requires energy, provided by ATP hydrolysis.

Concept Check 8.4
1. A spontaneous reaction is a reaction that is exergonic. However, if it has a high activation energy that is rarely attained, the rate of the reaction may be low. **2.** Only the specific substrate(s) will fit properly into the active site of an enzyme, the part of the enzyme that carries out catalysis. **3.** In the presence of malonate, increase the concentration of the normal substrate (succinate) and see whether the rate of reaction increases. If it does, malonate is a competitive inhibitor. **4.** If lactose wasn't present in the environment as a source of food and the fucose-containing disaccharide was available, bacteria that could digest the latter would be better able to grow and multiply than those that could not.

Concept Check 8.5
1. The activator binds in such a way that it stabilizes the active form of an enzyme, whereas the inhibitor stabilizes the inactive form. **2.** An inhibitor that binds to the active site of the enzyme you want to inhibit could also bind to and block the enzymes with similar structures, causing significant side effects. For this reason, you would be better off choosing to screen chemical compounds that bind allosterically to the enzyme in question, because allosteric regulatory sites are less likely to share similarity with other enzymes.

Summary of Key Concepts Questions
8.1 The process of "ordering" a cell's structure is accompanied by an increase in the entropy or disorder of the universe. For example, an animal cell takes in highly ordered organic molecules as the source of matter and energy used to build and maintain its structures. In the same process, however, the cell releases heat and the simple molecules of carbon dioxide and water to the surroundings. The increase in entropy of the latter process offsets the entropy decrease in the former. **8.2** A spontaneous reaction has a negative ΔG and is exergonic. For a chemical reaction to proceed with a net release of free energy ($-\Delta G$), the enthalpy or total energy of the system must decrease ($-\Delta H$), and/or the entropy or disorder must increase (yielding a more negative term, $-T\Delta S$). Spontaneous reactions supply the energy to perform cellular work. **8.3** The free energy released from the hydrolysis of ATP may drive endergonic reactions through the transfer of a phosphate group to a reactant molecule, forming a more reactive phosphorylated intermediate. ATP hydrolysis also powers the mechanical and transport work of a cell, often by powering shape changes in the relevant motor proteins. Cellular respiration, the catabolic breakdown of glucose, provides the energy for the endergonic regeneration of ATP from ADP and $(P)_i$. **8.4** Activation energy barriers prevent the complex molecules of the cell, which are rich in free energy, from spontaneously breaking down to less ordered, more stable molecules. Enzymes permit a regulated metabolism by binding to specific substrates and forming enzyme-substrate complexes that selectively lower the E_A for the chemical reactions in a cell. **8.5** A cell tightly regulates its metabolic pathways in response to fluctuating needs for energy and materials. The binding of activators or inhibitors to regulatory sites on allosteric enzymes stabilizes either the active or inactive form of the subunits. For example, the binding of ATP to a catabolic enzyme in a cell with excess ATP would inhibit that pathway. Such types of feedback inhibition preserve chemical resources within a cell. If ATP supplies are depleted, binding of ADP to the regulatory site of catabolic enzymes would activate that pathway.

Test Your Understanding
1. b **2.** c **3.** b **4.** a **5.** c **6.** e **7.** c

9.

A. The substrate molecules are entering the cells, so no product is made yet.
B. There is sufficient substrate, so the reaction is proceeding at a maximum rate.
C. As the substrate is used up, the rate decreases (the slope is less steep).
D. The line is flat because no new substrate remains and thus no new product appears.

Chapter 9

Figure Questions

Figure 9.7 Because there is no external source of energy for the reaction, it must be exergonic, and the reactants must be at a higher energy level than the products. **Figure 9.9** The removal would probably stop glycolysis, or at least slow it down, since it would push the equilibrium for step 5 toward the left. If less (or no) glyceraldehyde 3-phosphate were available, step 6 would slow down (or be unable to occur). **Figure 9.15** At first, some ATP could be made, since electron transport could proceed as far as complex III, and a small H^+ gradient could be built up. Soon, however, no more electrons could be passed to complex III because it could not be reoxidized by passing its electrons to complex IV. **Figure 9.16** First, there are 2 NADH from the oxidation of pyruvate plus 6 NADH from the citric acid cycle (CAC); 8 NADH × 2.5 ATP/NADH = 20 ATP. Second, there are 2 $FADH_2$ from the CAC; 2 $FADH_2$ × 1.5 ATP/$FADH_2$ = 3 ATP. Third, the 2 NADH from glycolysis enter the mitochondrion through one of two types of shuttle. They pass their electrons either to 2 FAD, which become $FADH_2$ and result in 3 ATP, or to 2 NAD^+, which become NADH and result in 5 ATP. Thus, 20 + 3 + 3 = 26 ATP, or 20 + 3 + 5 = 28 ATP from all NADH and $FADH_2$.

Concept Check 9.1

1. Both processes include glycolysis, the citric acid cycle, and oxidative phosphorylation. In aerobic respiration, the final electron acceptor is molecular oxygen (O_2); in anaerobic respiration, the final electron acceptor is a different substance.
2. $C_4H_6O_5$ would be oxidized and NAD^+ would be reduced.

Concept Check 9.2

1. NAD^+ acts as the oxidizing agent in step 6, accepting electrons from glyceraldehyde 3-phosphate, which thus acts as the reducing agent. **2.** Since the overall process of glycolysis results in net production of ATP, it would make sense for the process to slow down when ATP levels have increased substantially. Thus, we would expect ATP to allosterically inhibit phosphofructokinase.

Concept Check 9.3

1. NADH and $FADH_2$; they will donate electrons to the electron transport chain.
2. CO_2 is released from the pyruvate that is the end product of glycolysis, and CO_2 is also released during the citric acid cycle. **3.** In both cases, the precursor molecule loses a CO_2 molecule and then donates electrons to an electron carrier in an oxidation step. Also, the product has been activated due to the attachment of a CoA group.

Concept Check 9.4

1. Oxidative phosphorylation would eventually stop entirely, resulting in no ATP production by this process. Without oxygen to "pull" electrons down the electron transport chain, H^+ would not be pumped into the mitochondrion's intermembrane space and chemiosmosis would not occur. **2.** Decreasing the pH means addition of H^+. This would establish a proton gradient even without the function of the electron transport chain, and we would expect ATP synthase to function and synthesize ATP. (In fact, it was experiments like this that provided support for chemiosmosis as an energy-coupling mechanism.) **3.** One of the components of the electron transport chain, ubiquinone (Q), must be able to diffuse within the membrane. It could not do so if the membrane were locked rigidly into place.

Concept Check 9.5

1. A derivative of pyruvate, such as acetaldehyde during alcohol fermentation, or pyruvate itself during lactic acid fermentation; oxygen **2.** The cell would need to consume glucose at a rate about 16 times the consumption rate in the aerobic environment (2 ATP are generated by fermentation versus up to 32 ATP by cellular respiration).

Concept Check 9.6

1. The fat is much more reduced; it has many —CH_2— units, and in all these bonds the electrons are equally shared. The electrons present in a carbohydrate molecule are already somewhat oxidized (shared unequally in bonds), as quite a few of them are bound to oxygen. **2.** When we consume more food than necessary for metabolic processes, our body synthesizes fat as a way of storing energy for later use. **3.** Glycogen is a storage polysaccharide in liver and muscle cells. When energy is needed, glucose units are hydrolyzed from glycogen. Glycolysis in the cytosol breaks down glucose to two pyruvate molecules, which are transported into the mitochondrion. Here they are further oxidized, ultimately producing the needed ATP. **4.** AMP will accumulate, stimulating phosphofructokinase, and thus increasing the rate of glycolysis. Since oxygen is not present, the cell will convert pyruvate to lactate in lactic acid fermentation, providing a supply of ATP. **5.** When oxygen is present, the fatty acid chains containing most of the energy of a fat are oxidized and fed into the citric acid cycle and the electron transport chain. During intense exercise, however, oxygen is scarce in muscle cells, so ATP must be generated by glycolysis alone. A very small part of the fat molecule, the glycerol backbone, can be oxidized via glycolysis, but the amount of energy released by this portion is insignificant compared to that released by the fatty acid chains. (This is why moderate exercise, staying below 70% maximum heart rate, is better for burning fat—because enough oxygen remains available to the muscles.)

Summary of Key Concepts Questions

9.1 Most of the ATP produced in cellular respiration comes from oxidative phosphorylation, in which the energy released from redox reactions in an electron transport chain is used to produce ATP. In substrate-level phosphorylation, an enzyme directly transfers a phosphate group to ADP from an intermediate substrate. All ATP production in glycolysis occurs by substrate-level phosphorylation; this form of ATP production also occurs at one step in the citric acid cycle. **9.2** The oxidation of the three-carbon sugar, glyceraldehyde 3-phosphate, yields energy. In this oxidation, electrons and H^+ are transferred to NAD^+, forming NADH, and a phosphate group is attached to the oxidized substrate. ATP is then formed by substrate-level phosphorylation when this phosphate group is transferred to ADP. **9.3** The release of six molecules of CO_2 represents the complete oxidation of glucose. During the processing of two pyruvates to acetyl CoA, the fully oxidized carboxyl group (—COO^-) is given off as CO_2. The remaining four carbons are released as CO_2 in the citric acid cycle as citrate is oxidized back to oxaloacetate. **9.4** The flow of H^+ through the ATP synthase complex causes the rotor and attached rod to rotate, exposing catalytic sites in the knob portion that produce ATP from ADP and $\textcircled{P}_i$. ATP synthases are found in the inner mitochondrial membrane, the plasma membrane of prokaryotes, and membranes within chloroplasts. **9.5** Anaerobic respiration yields more ATP. The 2 ATP produced by substrate-level phosphorylation in glycolysis represent the total energy yield of fermentation. NADH passes its "high-energy" electrons to pyruvate or a derivative of pyruvate, recycling NAD^+ and allowing glycolysis to continue. Anaerobic respiration uses an electron transport chain to capture the energy of the electrons in NADH via a series of redox reactions; ultimately, the electrons are transferred to an electronegative molecule other than oxygen. And additional molecules of NADH are produced in anaerobic respiration as pyruvate is oxidized. **9.6** The ATP produced by catabolic pathways is used to drive anabolic pathways. Also, many of the intermediates of glycolysis and the citric acid cycle are used in the biosynthesis of a cell's molecules.

Test Your Understanding

1. d **2.** c **3.** c **4.** a **5.** e **6.** a **7.** b
8.

Chapter 10

Figure Questions

Figure 10.3 Situating containers of algae near sources of CO_2 emissions makes sense because algae need CO_2 to carry out photosynthesis. The higher their rate of photosynthesis, the more plant oil they will produce. At the same time, algae would be absorbing the CO_2 emitted from industrial plants or from car engines, reducing the amount of CO_2 entering the atmosphere. **Figure 10.10** Red, but not violet-blue, wavelengths would pass through the filter, so the bacteria would not congregate where the violet-blue light normally comes through. Therefore, the left "peak" of bacteria would not be present, but the right peak would be observed because the red wavelengths passing through the filter would be used for photosynthesis. **Figure 10.12** In the leaf, most of the chlorophyll electrons excited by photon absorption are used to power the reactions of photosynthesis. **Figure 10.16** The person at the top of the photosystem I tower would not turn and throw his electron into the bucket. Instead, he would throw it onto the top of the ramp right next to the photosystem II tower. The electron would then roll down the ramp, get energized by a photon, and return to him. This cycle would continue as long as light was available. (This is why it's called cyclic electron flow.)
Figure 10.19

3 × 1 (=3)

3 × 6 (=18)

3 × 5 (=15)

6 × 3 (=18)

6 × 3 (=18)

5 × 3 (=15)

6 × 3 (=18)

1 × 3 (=3)

Three carbon atoms enter the cycle, one by one, as individual CO_2 molecules, and leave the cycle in one three-carbon molecule (G3P) per three turns of the cycle.
Figure 10.22

Chloroplast   Starch granules

Thylakoid membranes: Light reactions

Stroma: Calvin cycle

The photosystems that carry out the light reactions are embedded in the thylakoid membranes, and the ATP and NADPH that are formed are released into the stroma. There, they are used for the reactions of the Calvin cycle, which produces G3P. Excess sugar molecules that are not used by the plant can be converted to glucose, then stored in the form of starch.

Concept Check 10.1
1. CO_2 enters leaves via stomata, and water enters via roots and is carried to leaves through veins. 2. Using ^{18}O, a heavy isotope of oxygen, as a label, researchers were able to confirm van Niel's hypothesis that the oxygen produced during photosynthesis originates in water, not in carbon dioxide. 3. The light reactions could *not* keep producing NADPH and ATP without the $NADP^+$, ADP, and $\textcircled{P}_i$ that the Calvin cycle generates. The two cycles are interdependent.

Concept Check 10.2
1. Green, because green light is mostly transmitted and reflected—not absorbed—by photosynthetic pigments 2. In chloroplasts, light-excited electrons are trapped by a primary electron acceptor, which prevents them from dropping back to the ground state. In isolated chlorophyll, there is no electron acceptor, so the photoexcited electrons immediately drop back down to the ground state, with the emission of light and heat. 3. Water (H_2O) is the initial electron donor; $NADP^+$ accepts electrons at the end of the electron transport chain, becoming reduced to NADPH. 4. In this experiment, the rate of ATP synthesis would slow and eventually stop. Because the added compound would not allow a proton gradient to build up across the membrane, ATP synthase could not catalyze ATP production.

Concept Check 10.3
1. 6, 18, 12 2. The more potential energy a molecule stores, the more energy and reducing power is required for the formation of that molecule. Glucose is a valuable energy source because it is highly reduced, storing lots of potential energy in its electrons. To reduce CO_2 to glucose, much energy and reducing power are required in the form of large numbers of ATP and NADPH molecules, respectively. 3. The light reactions require ADP and $NADP^+$, which would not be formed in sufficient quantities from ATP and NADPH if the Calvin cycle stopped. 4. In glycolysis, G3P acts as an intermediate. The 6-carbon sugar fructose 1,6-bisphosphate is cleaved into two 3-carbon sugars, one of which is G3P. The other is an isomer called dihydroxyacetone phosphate, which can be converted to G3P by an isomerase. Because G3P is the substrate for the next enzyme, it is constantly removed, and the reaction equilibrium is pulled in the direction of conversion of dihydroxyacetone phosphate to more G3P. In the Calvin cycle, G3P acts as both an intermediate and a product. For every three CO_2 molecules that enter the cycle, six G3P molecules are formed, five of which must remain in the cycle and become rearranged to regenerate three 5-carbon RuBP molecules. The one remaining G3P is a product, which can be thought of as the result of "reducing" the three CO_2 molecules that entered the cycle into a 3-carbon sugar that can later be used to generate energy.

Concept Check 10.4
1. Photorespiration decreases photosynthetic output by adding oxygen, instead of carbon dioxide, to the Calvin cycle. As a result, no sugar is generated (no carbon is fixed), and O_2 is used rather than generated. 2. Without PS II, no O_2 is generated in bundle-sheath cells. This avoids the problem of O_2 competing with CO_2 for binding to rubisco in these cells. 3. Both problems are caused by a drastic change in Earth's atmosphere due to burning of fossil fuels. The increase in CO_2 concentration affects ocean chemistry by decreasing pH, thus affecting calcification by marine organisms. On land, CO_2 concentration and air temperature are conditions that plants have become adapted to, and changes in these characteristics have a strong effect on photosynthesis by plants. Thus, alteration of these two fundamental factors could have critical effects on organisms all around the planet, in all different habitats. 4. C_4 and CAM species would replace many of the C_3 species.

Summary of Key Concepts Questions
10.1 CO_2 and H_2O are the products of respiration; they are the reactants in photosynthesis. In respiration, glucose is oxidized to CO_2 as electrons are passed through an electron transfer chain from glucose to O_2, producing H_2O. In photosynthesis, H_2O is the source of electrons, which are energized by light, temporarily stored in NADPH, and used to reduce CO_2 to carbohydrate. **10.2** The action spectrum of photosynthesis shows that some wavelengths of light that are not absorbed by chlorophyll *a* are still effective at promoting photosynthesis. The light-harvesting complexes of photosystems contain accessory pigments such as chlorophyll *b* and carotenoids, which absorb different wavelengths and pass the energy to chlorophyll *a*, broadening the spectrum of light useful for photosynthesis.
10.3

In the reduction phase of the Calvin cycle, ATP phosphorylates a 3-carbon compound, and NADPH then reduces this compound to G3P. ATP is also used in the regeneration phase, when five molecules of G3P are converted to three molecules of the 5-carbon compound RuBP. Rubisco catalyzes the first step of carbon fixation—the addition of CO_2 to RuBP. **10.4** Both C_4 and CAM photosynthesis involve initial fixation of CO_2 to produce a 4-carbon compound (in mesophyll cells in C_4 plants and at night in CAM plants). These compounds are then broken down to release CO_2 (in the bundle-sheath cells in C_4 plants and during the day in CAM plants). ATP is required for recycling the molecule that is used initially to combine with CO_2. These pathways avoid the photorespiration that consumes ATP and reduces the photosynthetic output of C_3 plants when they close stomata on hot, dry, bright days. Thus, hot, arid climates would favor C_4 and CAM plants.

Test Your Understanding
1. d 2. b 3. c 4. d 5. c 6. b 7. d
9.

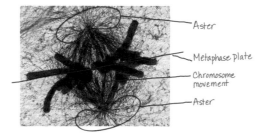

The ATP would end up outside the thylakoid. The thylakoids were able to make ATP in the dark because the researchers set up an artificial proton concentration gradient across the thylakoid membrane; thus, the light reactions were not necessary to establish the H^+ gradient required for ATP synthesis by ATP synthase.

Chapter 12

Figure Questions
Figure 12.4

One sister chromatid

Circling the other chromatid instead would also be correct. **Figure 12.5** The chromosome has four arms. **Figure 12.7** 12; 2; 2; 1
Figure 12.8

Aster
Metaphase plate
Chromosome movement
Aster

Figure 12.9 The mark would have moved toward the nearer pole. The lengths of fluorescent microtubules between that pole and the mark would have decreased, while the lengths between the chromosomes and the mark would have remained the same. **Figure 12.14** In both cases, the G_1 nucleus would have remained in G_1 until the time it normally would have entered the S phase. Chromosome condensation and spindle formation would not have occurred until the S and G_2 phases had been completed. **Figure 12.16** The cell would divide under conditions where it was inappropriate to do so. If the daughter cells and their descendants also ignored the checkpoint and divided, there would soon be an abnormal mass of cells. (This type of inappropriate cell division can contribute to the development of cancer.) **Figure 12.17** Passing the G_2 checkpoint in the diagram corresponds to the beginning of the "Time" axis of the graph, and entry into the mitotic phase (yellow background on the diagram) corresponds to the peaks of MPF activity and cyclin concentration on the graph (see the yellow M banner over the peaks). During G_1 and S phase in the diagram, Cdk is present without cyclin, so on the graph both cyclin concentration and MPF activity are low. The curved purple arrow in the diagram shows increasing cyclin concentration, seen on the graph during the end of S phase and throughout G_2 phase. Then the cell cycle begins again. **Figure 12.18** The cells in the vessel with PDGF would not be able to respond to the growth factor signal and thus would not divide. The culture would resemble that without the added PDGF. **Figure 12.21** The intracellular estrogen receptor, once activated, would be able to act as a transcription factor in the nucleus, turning on genes that may cause the cell to pass a checkpoint and divide. The HER2 receptor, when activated by a ligand, would form a dimer, and each subunit of the dimer would phosphorylate the other. This would lead to a series of signal transduction steps, ultimately turning on genes in the nucleus. As in the case of the estrogen receptor, the genes would code for proteins necessary to commit the cell to divide.

Concept Check 12.1
1. 2   **2.** 39; 39; 78

Concept Check 12.2
1. 6 chromosomes, duplicated; 12 chromatids   **2.** Following mitosis, cytokinesis results in two genetically identical daughter cells in both plant cells and animal cells. However, the mechanism of dividing the cytoplasm is different in animals and plants. In an animal cell, cytokinesis occurs by cleavage, which divides the parent cell in two with a contractile ring of actin filaments. In a plant cell, a cell plate forms in the middle of the cell and grows until its membrane fuses with the plasma membrane of the parent cell. A new cell wall grows inside the cell plate.   **3.** They elongate the cell during anaphase.   **4.** During eukaryotic cell division, tubulin is involved in spindle formation and chromosome movement, while actin functions during cytokinesis. In bacterial binary fission, it's the opposite: Tubulin-like molecules are thought to act in daughter cell separation, and actin-like molecules are thought to move the daughter bacterial chromosomes to opposite ends of the cell.   **5.** Microtubules made up of tubulin in the cell provide "rails" along which vesicles and other organelles can travel, based on interactions of motor proteins with tubulin in the microtubules. In muscle cells, actin in microfilaments interacts with myosin filaments to cause muscle contraction.   **6.** From the end of S phase in interphase through the end of metaphase in mitosis

Concept Check 12.3
1. The nucleus on the right was originally in the G_1 phase; therefore, it had not yet duplicated its chromosome. The nucleus on the left was in the M phase, so it had already duplicated its chromosome.   **2.** A sufficient amount of MPF has to exist for a cell to pass the G_2 checkpoint; this occurs through the accumulation of cyclin proteins, which combine with Cdk to form MPF.   **3.** Most body cells are in a nondividing state called G_0.   **4.** Both types of tumors consist of abnormal cells, but their characteristics are different. A benign tumor stays at the original site and can usually be surgically removed; the cells have some genetic and cellular changes from normal, non-tumor cells. Cancer cells from a malignant tumor have more significant genetic and cellular changes, can spread from the original site by metastasis, and may impair the functions of one or more organs.   **5.** The cells might divide even in the absence of PDGF. In addition, they would not stop when the surface of the culture vessel was covered; they would continue to divide, piling on top of one another.

Summary of Key Concepts Questions
12.1 The DNA of a eukaryotic cell is packaged into structures called *chromosomes*. Each chromosome is a long molecule of DNA, which carries hundreds to thousands of genes, with associated proteins that maintain chromosome structure and help control gene activity. This DNA-protein complex is called *chromatin*. The chromatin of each chromosome is long and thin when the cell is not dividing. Prior to cell division, each chromosome is duplicated, and the resulting sister *chromatids* are attached to each other by proteins at the centromeres and, for many species, all along their lengths (sister chromatid cohesion).   **12.2** Chromosomes exist as single DNA molecules in G_1 of interphase and in anaphase and telophase of mitosis. During S phase, DNA replication produces sister chromatids, which persist during G_2 of interphase and through prophase, prometaphase, and metaphase of mitosis.
12.3 Checkpoints allow cellular surveillance mechanisms to determine whether the cell is prepared to go to the next stage. Internal and external signals move a cell past these checkpoints. The G_1 checkpoint, called the "restriction point" in mammalian cells, determines whether a cell will complete the cell cycle and divide or switch into the G_0 phase. The signals to pass this checkpoint often are external—such as growth factors. Passing the G_2 checkpoint requires sufficient numbers of active MPF complexes, which in turn orchestrate several mitotic events. MPF also initiates degradation of its cyclin component, terminating the M phase. The M phase will not begin again until sufficient cyclin is produced during the next S and G_2 phases. The signal to pass the M phase checkpoint is not activated until all chromosomes are attached to kinetochore fibers and are aligned at the metaphase plate. Only then will sister chromatid separation occur.

Test Your Understanding
1. b   **2.** a   **3.** c   **4.** c   **5.** a   **6.** b
7. See Figure 12.7 for a description of major events.

Only one cell is indicated for each stage, but other correct answers are also present in this micrograph.
8. a   **9.** e
10.

Interphase   Prophase

Microtubules

Prometaphase   Metaphase   Anaphase

Nuclear envelope forming

Telophase and cytokinesis

Chapter 13

Figure Questions
Figure 13.4 The haploid number, *n*, is 3. A set is always haploid.
Figure 13.7

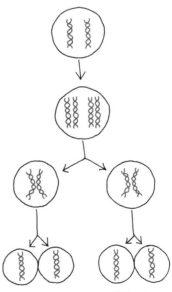

(A short strand of DNA is shown here for simplicity, but each chromosome or chromatid contains a very long coiled and folded DNA molecule.)
Figure 13.8 If the two cells in Figure 12.7 underwent another round of mitosis, each of the four resulting cells would have six chromosomes, while the four cells resulting from meiosis in Figure 13.8 each have three chromosomes. In mitosis, DNA replication (and thus chromosome duplication) precedes each prophase, ensuring that daughter cells have the same number of chromosomes as the parent cell. In meiosis, in contrast, DNA replication occurs only before prophase I (not prophase II). Thus, in two rounds of mitosis, the chromosomes duplicate twice and divide twice, while in meiosis, the chromosomes duplicate once and divide twice.   **Figure 13.9** Yes. Each of the six chromosomes (three per cell) shown in telophase I has one nonrecombinant chromatid and one recombinant chromatid. Therefore, eight possible sets of chromosomes can be generated for the cell on the left and eight for the cell on the right.

Concept Check 13.1
1. Parents pass genes to their offspring; the genes program cells to make specific enzymes and other proteins, whose cumulative action produces an individual's inherited traits.   **2.** Such organisms reproduce by mitosis, which generates offspring whose genomes are exact copies of the parent's genome (in the absence of mutation).   **3.** She should clone it. Cross-breeding it with another plant would generate offspring that have additional variation, which she no longer desires now that she has obtained her ideal orchid.

Concept Check 13.2
1. Each of the six chromosomes is duplicated, so each contains two DNA double helices. Therefore, there are 12 DNA molecules in the cell.   **2.** In meiosis, the chromosome count is reduced from diploid to haploid; the union of two haploid gametes in fertilization restores the diploid chromosome count.   **3.** The haploid number (n) is 7; the diploid number ($2n$) is 14.   **4.** This organism has the life cycle shown in Figure 13.6c. Therefore, it must be a fungus or a protist, perhaps an alga.

Concept Check 13.3
1. The chromosomes are similar in that each is composed of two sister chromatids, and the individual chromosomes are positioned similarly at the metaphase plate. The chromosomes differ in that in a mitotically dividing cell, sister chromatids of each chromosome are genetically identical, but in a meiotically dividing cell, sister chromatids are genetically distinct because of crossing over in meiosis I. Moreover, the chromosomes in metaphase of mitosis can be a diploid set or a haploid set, but the chromosomes in metaphase of meiosis II always consist of a haploid set.   **2.** If crossing over did not occur, the two homologs would not be associated in any way. This might result in incorrect arrangement of homologs during metaphase I and ultimately in formation of gametes with an abnormal number of chromosomes.

Concept Check 13.4
1. Mutations in a gene lead to the different versions (alleles) of that gene.
2. Without crossing over, independent assortment of chromosomes during meiosis I theoretically can generate 2^n possible haploid gametes, and random fertilization can produce $2^n \times 2^n$ possible diploid zygotes. Because the haploid number (n) of grasshoppers is 23 and that of fruit flies is 4, two grasshoppers would be expected to produce a greater variety of zygotes than would two fruit flies.   **3.** If the segments of the maternal and paternal chromatids that undergo crossing over are genetically identical and thus have the same two alleles for every gene, then the recombinant chromosomes will be genetically equivalent to the parental chromosomes. Crossing over contributes to genetic variation only when it involves the rearrangement of different alleles.

Summary of Key Concepts Questions
13.1 Genes program specific traits, and offspring inherit their genes from each parent, accounting for similarities in their appearance to one or the other parent. Humans reproduce sexually, which ensures new combinations of genes (and thus traits) in the offspring. Consequently, the offspring are not clones of their parents (which would be the case if humans reproduced asexually).   **13.2** Animals and plants both reproduce sexually, alternating meiosis with fertilization. Both have haploid gametes that unite to form a diploid zygote, which then goes on to divide mitotically, forming a diploid multicellular organism. In animals, haploid cells become gametes and don't undergo mitosis, while in plants, the haploid cells resulting from meiosis undergo mitosis to form a haploid multicellular organism, the gametophyte. This organism then goes on to generate haploid gametes. (In plants such as trees, the gametophyte is quite reduced in size and not obvious to the casual observer.)   **13.3** At the end of meiosis I, the two members of a homologous pair end up in different cells, so they cannot pair up and undergo crossing over.
13.4 First, during independent assortment in metaphase I, each pair of homologous chromosomes lines up independent of each other pair at the metaphase plate, so a daughter cell of meiosis I randomly inherits either a maternal or paternal chromosome. Second, due to crossing over, each chromosome is not exclusively maternal or paternal, but includes regions at the ends of the chromatid from a nonsister chromatid (a chromatid of the other homolog). (The nonsister segment can also be in an internal region of the chromatid if a second crossover occurs beyond the first one before the end of the chromatid.) This provides much additional diversity in the form of new combinations of alleles. Third, random fertilization ensures even more variation, since any sperm of a large number containing many possible genetic combinations can fertilize any egg of a similarly large number of possible combinations.

Test Your Understanding
1. a   2. d   3. b   4. a   5. d   6. c   7. d
8. (a)

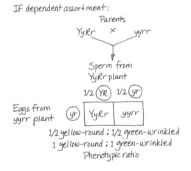

The chromosomes of one color make up a haploid set.
All red and blue chromosomes together make up a diploid set.

(b) The chromosomes of one color make up a haploid set. (In cases where crossovers have occurred, a haploid set of one color may include segments of chromatids of the other color.) All red and blue chromosomes together make up a diploid set.
(c) Metaphase I   **9.** This cell must be undergoing meiosis because homologous chromosomes are associated with each other at the metaphase plate; this does not occur in mitosis.

Chapter 14

Figure Questions
Figure 14.3 All offspring would have purple flowers. (The ratio would be one purple to zero white.) The P generation plants are true-breeding, so mating two purple-flowered plants produces the same result as self-pollination: All the offspring have the same trait.
Figure 14.8

If dependent assortment:

Parents
YyRr × yyrr

Sperm from
YyRr plant

1/2 (YR) 1/2 (yr)

Eggs from yyrr plant (yr) | YyRr | yyrr

1/2 yellow-round : 1/2 green-wrinkled
1 yellow-round : 1 green-wrinkled
Phenotypic ratio

If independent assortment:

Parents
YyRr × yyrr

Sperm from
YyRr plant

Eggs from yyrr plant 1/4 (YR) 1/4 (Yr) 1/4 (yR) 1/4 (yr)

(yr) | YyRr | Yyrr | yyRr | yyrr

1/4 yellow-round : 1/4 yellow-wrinkled:
1/4 green-round : 1/4 green-wrinkled
1 yellow-round : 1 yellow-wrinkled : 1 green-round : 1 green-wrinkled
Phenotypic ratio

Yes, this cross would also have allowed Mendel to make different predictions for the two hypotheses, thereby allowing him to distinguish the correct one. **Figure 14.10** Your classmate would probably point out that the F_1 generation hybrids show an intermediate phenotype between those of the homozygous parents, which supports the blending hypothesis. You could respond that crossing the F_1 hybrids results in the reappearance of the white phenotype, rather than identical pink offspring, which fails to support the idea of traits blending during inheritance. **Figure 14.11** Both the I^A and I^B alleles are dominant to the i allele, which results in no attached carbohydrate. The I^A and I^B alleles are codominant; both are expressed in the phenotype of I^AI^B heterozygotes, who have type AB blood. **Figure 14.13**

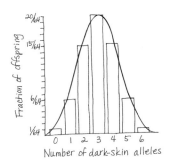

The majority of individuals have intermediate phenotypes (skin color in the middle range), while fewer individuals have phenotypes at either end (very dark or very light skin). (As you may know, this is called a "bell curve" and represents a "normal distribution.") **Figure 14.16** In the Punnett square, two of the three individuals with normal coloration are carriers, so the probability is ⅔. (Note that you must take into account everything you know when you calculate probability: You know she is not *aa*, so there are only three possible genotypes to consider.) **Figure 14.18** If one parent tests negative for the recessive allele, then the probability is zero that the offspring will have the disease and ½ that the offspring will be a carrier. If the first child is a carrier, the probability of the next child being a carrier is still ½ because the two births are independent events.

Concept Check 14.1
1. According to the law of independent assortment, 25 plants (1⁄16 of the offspring) are predicted to be *aatt*, or recessive for both characters. The actual result is likely to differ slightly from this value.

Parents
$AaTt$ × $AaTt$

Sperm from $AaTt$ plant

Eggs from $AaTt$ plant

	AT	At	aT	at
AT	AATT	AATt	AaTT	AaTt
At	AATt	AAtt	AaTt	Aatt
aT	AaTT	AaTt	aaTT	aaTt
at	AaTt	Aatt	aaTt	aatt

2. The plant could make eight different gametes (*YRI, YRi, YrI, Yri, yRI, yRi, yrI,* and *yri*). To fit all the possible gametes in a self-pollination, a Punnett square would need 8 rows and 8 columns. It would have spaces for the 64 possible unions of gametes in the offspring. 3. Self-pollination is sexual reproduction because meiosis is involved in forming gametes, which unite during fertilization. As a result, the offspring in self-pollination are genetically different from the parent. (As mentioned in the footnote on p. 263, we have simplified the explanation in referring to the single pea plant as a parent. Technically, the gametophytes in the flower are the two "parents.")

Concept Check 14.2
1. ½ homozygous dominant (*AA*), 0 homozygous recessive (*aa*), and ½ heterozygous (*Aa*) 2. ¼ *BBDD*; ¼ *BbDD*; ¼ *BBDd*; ¼ *BbDd* 3. The genotypes that fulfill this condition are *ppyyIi, ppYyii, Ppyyii, ppYYii,* and *ppyyii*. Use the multiplication rule to find the probability of getting each genotype, and then use the addition rule to find the overall probability of meeting the conditions of this problem:

$ppyyIi$ ½ (probability of pp) × ¼ (yy) × ½ (Ii) = $\frac{1}{16}$
$ppYyii$ ½ (pp) × ½ (Yy) × ½ (ii) = $\frac{2}{16}$
$Ppyyii$ ½ (Pp) × ¼ (yy) × ½ (ii) = $\frac{1}{16}$
$ppYYii$ ½ (pp) × ¼ (YY) × ½ (ii) = $\frac{1}{16}$
$ppyyii$ ½ (pp) × ¼ (yy) × ½ (ii) = $\frac{1}{16}$

Fraction predicted to have at least two recessive traits = $\frac{6}{16}$ or ⅜

Concept Check 14.3
1. Incomplete dominance describes the relationship between two alleles of a single gene, whereas epistasis relates to the genetic relationship between two genes (and the respective alleles of each). 2. Half of the children would be expected to have type A blood and half type B blood. 3. The black and white alleles are incompletely dominant, with heterozygotes being gray in color. A cross between a gray rooster and a black hen should yield approximately equal numbers of gray and black offspring.

Concept Check 14.4
1. ⅛ (Since cystic fibrosis is caused by a recessive allele, Beth and Tom's siblings who have CF must be homozygous recessive. Therefore, each parent must be a carrier of the recessive allele. Since neither Beth nor Tom has CF, this means they each have a ⅔ chance of being a carrier. If they are both carriers, there is a ¼ chance that they will have a child with CF. ⅔ × ⅔ × ¼ = ⅛); 0 (Both Beth and Tom would have to be carriers to produce a child with the disease.) 2. In normal hemoglobin, the sixth amino acid is glutamic acid (Glu), which is acidic (has a negative charge on its side chain). In sickle-cell hemoglobin, Glu is replaced by valine (Val), which is a nonpolar amino acid, very different from Glu. The primary structure of a protein (its amino acid sequence) ultimately determines the shape of the protein and thus its function. The substitution of Val for Glu enables the hemoglobin molecules to interact with each other and form long fibers, leading to the protein's deficient function and the deformation of the red blood cell. 3. Joan's genotype is *Dd*. Because the allele for polydactyly (*D*) is dominant to the allele for five digits per appendage (*d*), the trait is expressed in people with either the *DD* or *Dd* genotype. But because Joan's father does not have polydactyly, his genotype must be *dd*, which means that Joan inherited a *d* allele from him. Therefore Joan, who does have the trait, must be heterozygous. 4. In the monohybrid cross involving flower color, the ratio is 3.15 purple : 1 white, while in the human family in the pedigree, the ratio in the third generation is 1 free : 1 attached earlobe. The difference is due to the small sample size (two offspring) in the human family. If the second-generation couple in this pedigree were able to have 929 offspring as in the pea plant cross, the ratio would likely be closer to 3:1. (Note that none of the pea plant crosses in Table 14.1 yielded *exactly* a 3:1 ratio.)

Summary of Key Concepts Questions
14.1 Alternative versions of genes, called alleles, are passed from parent to offspring during sexual reproduction. In a cross between purple- and white-flowered homozygous parents, the F_1 offspring are all heterozygous, each inheriting a purple allele from one parent and a white allele from the other. Because the purple allele is dominant, it determines the phenotype of the F_1 offspring to be purple, and the expression of the white allele is masked. Only in the F_2 generation is it possible for a white allele to exist in a homozygous state, which causes the white trait to be expressed.

14.2

3/4 yellow × 3/4 round = 9/16 yellow-round
3/4 yellow × 1/4 wrinkled = 3/16 yellow-wrinkled
1/4 green × 3/4 round = 3/16 green-round
1/4 green × 1/4 wrinkled = 1/16 green-wrinkled

= 9 yellow-round : 3 yellow-wrinkled : 3 green-round : 1 green-wrinkled

14.3 The ABO blood group is an example of multiple alleles because this single gene has more than two alleles (I^A, I^B, and i). Two of the alleles, I^A and I^B, exhibit codominance, since both carbohydrates (A and B) are present when these two alleles exist together in a genotype. I^A and I^B each exhibit complete dominance over the i allele. This situation is not an example of incomplete dominance because each allele affects the phenotype in a distinguishable way, so the result is not intermediate between the two phenotypes. Because this situation involves a single gene, it is not an example of epistasis or polygenic inheritance. **14.4** The chance of the fourth child having cystic fibrosis is ¼, as it was for each of the other children, because each birth is an independent event. We already know both parents are carriers, so whether their first three children are carriers or not has no bearing on the probability that their next child will have the disease. The parents' genotypes provide the only relevant information.

Test Your Understanding
1. Gene, l. Allele, e. Character, g. Trait, b. Dominant allele, j. Recessive allele, a. Genotype, k. Phenotype, h. Homozygous, c. Heterozygous, f. Testcross, i. Monohybrid cross, d.
2.

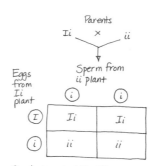

9 green-inflated : 3 green-constricted :
3 yellow-inflated : 1 yellow-constricted

3. Parental cross is $AAC^RC^R \times aaC^WC^W$. F_1 genotype is $AaC^R C^W$, phenotype is all axial-pink. F_2 genotypes are $1 AAC^RC^R : 2 AAC^RC^W : 1 AAC^WC^W : 2 AaC^RC^R :$ $4 AaC^RC^W : 2 AaC^WC^W : 1 aaC^RC^R : 2 aaC^RC^W : 1 aaC^WC^W$. F_2 phenotypes are 3 axial-red : 6 axial-pink : 3 axial-white : 1 terminal-red : 2 terminal-pink : 1 terminal-white. **4.** Man $I^A i$; woman $I^B i$; child ii. Genotypes for future children are predicted to be ¼ $I^A I^B$, ¼ $I^A i$, ¼ $I^B i$, ¼ ii. **5.** ½ **6.** A cross of $Ii \times ii$ would yield offspring with a genotypic ratio of $1 Ii : 1 ii$ (2:2 is an equivalent answer) and a phenotypic ratio of 1 inflated : 1 constricted (2:2 is equivalent).

Parents
Ii × ii

Sperm from
ii plant

Eggs
from
Ii
plant

	i	i
I	Ii	Ii
i	ii	ii

Genotypic ratio 1 Ii : 1 ii
(2:2 is equivalent)

Phenotypic ratio 1 inflated : 1 constricted
(2:2 is equivalent)

7. (a) ½₄; (b) ½₄; (c) ⅛; (d) ½₂ **8.** Albino (*b*) is a recessive trait; black (*B*) is dominant. First cross: parents $BB \times bb$; gametes *B* and *b*; offspring all *Bb* (black coat). The black guinea pig in the second cross is a heterozygote. Second cross: parents $Bb \times bb$; gametes ½ *B* and ½ *b* (heterozygous parent) and *b*; offspring ½ *Bb* and ½ *bb*. **9.** (a) $PPLl \times PPLl$, $PPLl \times PpLl$, or $PPLl \times ppLl$; (b) $ppLl \times ppLl$; (c) $PPLL \times$ any of the 9 possible genotypes or $PPll \times ppLl$; (d) $1 - \frac{9}{64} = \frac{3}{64}$; (c) ¼ × ¼ × ¼ = ½₄; (b) ½₆; (c) ½₅₆; (d) ½₄; (e) ½₂₈ **12.** (a) 1; (b) ½₂; (c) ⅛; (d) ½ **13.** ⅛ **14.** Matings of the original mutant cat with true-breeding noncurl cats will produce both curl and noncurl F_1 offspring if the curl allele is dominant, but only noncurl offspring if the curl allele is recessive. You would also obtain some true-breeding offspring homozygous for the curl allele from matings between the F_1 cats resulting from the original curl × noncurl crosses whether the curl trait is dominant or recessive. You know that cats are true-breeding when curl × curl matings produce only curl offspring. As it turns out, the allele that causes curled ears is dominant. **15.** ½₆ **16.** 25%, or ¼, will be cross-eyed; all (100%) of the cross-eyed offspring will also be white. **17.** The dominant allele *I* is epistatic to the *P/p* locus, and thus the genotypic ratio for the F_1 generation will be 9 $I\_P\_$ (colorless) : 3 I_pp (colorless) : 3 $iiP\_$ (purple) : 1 $iipp$ (red). Overall, the phenotypic ratio is 12 colorless : 3 purple : 1 red. **18.** Recessive. All affected individuals (Arlene, Tom, Wilma, and Carla) are

homozygous recessive *aa*. George is *Aa*, since some of his children with Arlene are affected. Sam, Ann, Daniel, and Alan are each *Aa*, since they are all unaffected children with one affected parent. Michael also is *Aa*, since he has an affected child (Carla) with his heterozygous wife Ann. Sandra, Tina, and Christopher can each have either the *AA* or *Aa* genotype. **19.** ½ **20.** 9 $B\_A\_$ (agouti) : 3 B_aa (black) : 3 $bbA\_$ (white) : 1 *bbaa* (white). Overall, 9 agouti : 3 black : 4 white.

Chapter 15

Figure Questions
Figure 15.2 The ratio would be 1 yellow-round : 1 green-round : 1 yellow-wrinkled : 1 green-wrinkled. **Figure 15.4** About ¾ of the F_2 offspring would have red eyes and about ¼ would have white eyes. About half of the white-eyed flies would be female and half would be male; similarly, about half of the red-eyed flies would be female and half would be male. **Figure 15.7** All the males would be color-blind, and all the females would be carriers. **Figure 15.9** The two largest classes would still be the parental-type offspring (offspring with the phenotypes of the true-breeding P generation flies), but now they would be gray-vestigial and black-normal because those were the specific allele combinations in the P generation. **Figure 15.10** The two chromosomes below, left, are like the two chromosomes inherited by the F_1 female, one from each P generation fly. They are passed by the F_1 female intact to the offspring and thus could be called "parental" chromosomes. The other two chromosomes result from crossing over during meiosis in the F_1 female. Because they have combinations of alleles not seen in either of the F_1 female's chromosomes, they can be called "recombinant" chromosomes. (Note that in this example, the alleles on the recombinant chromosomes, $b^+ vg^+$ and $b vg$, are the allele combinations that were on the parental chromosomes in the cross shown in Figures 15.9 and 15.10. The basis for calling them parental chromosomes is the combination of alleles that was present on the P generation chromosomes.)

Parental chromosomes   Recombinant chromosomes

Concept Check 15.1
1. The law of segregation relates to the inheritance of alleles for a single character. The law of independent assortment of alleles relates to the inheritance of alleles for two characters. **2.** The physical basis for the law of segregation is the separation of homologs in anaphase I. The physical basis for the law of independent assortment is the alternative arrangements of homologous chromosome pairs in metaphase I. **3.** To show the mutant phenotype, a male needs to possess only one mutant allele. If this gene had been on a pair of autosomes, *two* mutant alleles would have had to be present for an individual to show the recessive mutant phenotype, a much less probable situation.

Concept Check 15.2
1. Because the gene for this eye-color character is located on the X chromosome, all female offspring will be red-eyed and heterozygous ($X^{w^+} X^w$); all male offspring will inherit a Y chromosome from the father and be white-eyed ($X^w Y$). **2.** ¼ (½ chance that the child will inherit a Y chromosome from the father and be male × ½ chance that he will inherit the X carrying the disease allele from his mother) If the child is a boy, there is a ½ chance he will have the disease; a female would have zero chance (but ½ chance of being a carrier). **3.** With a disorder caused by a dominant allele, there is no such thing as a "carrier," since those with the allele have the disorder. Because the allele is dominant, the females lose any "advantage" in having two X chromosomes, since one disorder-associated allele is sufficient to result in the disorder. All fathers who have the dominant allele will pass it along to *all* their daughters, who will also have the disorder. A mother who has the allele (and thus the disorder) will pass it to half of her sons and half of her daughters.

Concept Check 15.3
1. Crossing over during meiosis I in the heterozygous parent produces some gametes with recombinant genotypes for the two genes. Offspring with a recombinant phenotype arise from fertilization of the recombinant gametes by homozygous recessive gametes from the double-mutant parent. **2.** In each case, the al-leles contributed by the female parent determine the phenotype of the offspring because the male in this cross contributes only recessive alleles. **3.** No. The order could be *A-C-B* or *C-A-B*. To determine which possibility is correct, you need to know the recombination frequency between *B* and *C*.

Concept Check 15.4
1. In meiosis, a combined 14-21 chromosome will behave as one chromosome. If a gamete receives the combined 14-21 chromosome and a normal copy of chromosome 21, trisomy 21 will result when this gamete combines with a normal gamete during fertilization. **2.** No. The child can be either $I^A I^A i$ or $I^A ii$. A sperm of genotype $I^A I^A$ could result from nondisjunction in the father during meiosis II, while an egg with the genotype *ii* could result from nondisjunction in the mother during either meiosis I or meiosis II. **3.** Activation of this gene could lead to the production of too much of this kinase. If the kinase is involved in a signaling

pathway that triggers cell division, too much of it could trigger unrestricted cell division, which in turn could contribute to the development of a cancer (in this case, a cancer of one type of white blood cell).

Concept Check 15.5
1. Inactivation of an X chromosome in females and genomic imprinting. Because of X inactivation, the effective dose of genes on the X chromosome is the same in males and females. As a result of genomic imprinting, only one allele of certain genes is phenotypically expressed.   2. The genes for leaf coloration are located in plastids within the cytoplasm. Normally, only the maternal parent transmits plastid genes to offspring. Since variegated offspring are produced only when the female parent is of the B variety, we can conclude that variety B contains both the wild-type and mutant alleles of pigment genes, producing variegated leaves. (Variety A contains only the wild-type allele of pigment genes.)   3. The situation is similar to that for chloroplasts. Each cell contains numerous mitochondria, and in affected individuals, most cells contain a variable mixture of normal and mutant mitochondria. The normal mitochondria carry out enough cellular respiration for survival.

Summary of Key Concepts Questions
15.1 Because the sex chromosomes are different from each other and because they determine the sex of the offspring, Morgan could use the sex of the offspring as a phenotypic characteristic to follow the parental chromosomes. (He could also have followed them under a microscope, as the X and Y chromosomes look different.) At the same time, he could record eye color to follow the eye-color alleles.   **15.2** Males have only one X chromosome, along with a Y chromosome, while females have two X chromosomes. The Y chromosome has very few genes on it, while the X has about 1,000. When a recessive X-linked allele that causes a disorder is inherited by a male on the X from his mother, there isn't a second allele present on the Y (males are hemizygous), so the male has the disorder. Because females have two X chromosomes, they must inherit two recessive alleles in order to have the disorder, a rarer occurrence.   **15.3** Crossing over results in new combinations of alleles. Crossing over is a random occurrence, and the more distance there is between two genes, the more chances there are for crossing over to occur, leading to a new allele combination. **15.4** In inversions and reciprocal translocations, the same genetic material is present in the same relative amount but just organized differently. In aneuploidy, duplications, deletions, and nonreciprocal translocations, the balance of genetic material is upset, as large segments are either missing or present in more than one copy. Apparently, this type of imbalance is very damaging to the organism. (Although it isn't lethal in the developing embryo, the reciprocal translocation that produces the Philadelphia chromosome can lead to a serious condition, cancer, by altering the expression of important genes.)   **15.5** In these cases, the sex of the parent contributing an allele affects the inheritance pattern. For imprinted genes, either the paternal or the maternal allele is expressed, depending on the imprint. For mitochondrial and chloroplast genes, only the maternal contribution will affect offspring phenotype because the offspring inherit these organelles from the mother, via the egg cytoplasm.

Test Your Understanding
1. 0; ½; 1/16   2. Recessive; if the disorder were dominant, it would affect at least one parent of a child born with the disorder. The disorder's inheritance is sex-linked because it is seen only in boys. For a girl to have the disorder, she would have to inherit recessive alleles from *both* parents. This would be very rare, since males with the recessive allele on their X chromosome die in their early teens.   3. 17%   4. The disorder would always be inherited from the mother.   5. Between *T* and *A*, 12%; between *A* and *S*, 5%   6. Between *T* and *S*, 18%; sequence of genes is *T–A–S*   7. ¼ for each daughter (½ chance that child will be female × ½ chance of a homozygous recessive genotype); ½ for first son.   8. 6%; wild-type heterozygous for normal wings and red eyes) × recessive homozygous for vestigial wings and purple eyes
9.

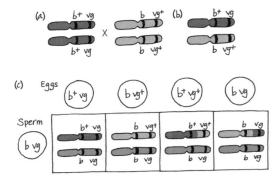

(d) 41.5% gray body, vestigial wings
    41.5% black body, normal wings
    8.5% gray body, normal wings
    8.5% black body, vestigial wings
10. The inactivation of two X chromosomes in XXX women would leave them with one genetically active X, as in women with the normal number of chromosomes. Microscopy should reveal two Barr bodies in XXX women.
11. *D–A–B–C*   12. Fifty percent of the offspring will show phenotypes resulting from crossovers. These results would be the same as those from a cross

where *A* and *B* were *not* on the same chromosome. Further crosses involving other genes on the same chromosome would reveal the genetic linkage and map distances.   **13.** 450 each of blue-oval and white-round (parentals) and 50 each of blue-round and white-oval (recombinants)   **14.** About one-third of the distance from the vestigial-wing locus to the brown-eye locus   **15.** Because bananas are triploid, homologous pairs cannot line up during meiosis. Therefore, it is not possible to generate gametes that can fuse to produce a zygote with the triploid number of chromosomes.

Chapter 16

Figure Questions
Figure 16.2 The living S cells found in the blood sample were able to reproduce to yield more S cells, indicating that the S trait is a permanent, heritable change, rather than just a one-time use of the dead S cells' capsules. **Figure 16.4** The radioactivity would have been found in the pellet when proteins were labeled (batch 1) because proteins would have had to enter the bacterial cells to program them with genetic instructions. It's hard for us to imagine now, but the DNA might have played a structural role that allowed some of the proteins to be injected while it remained outside the bacterial cell (thus no radioactivity in the pellet in batch 2). **Figure 16.11** The tube from the first replication would look the same, with a middle band of hybrid ^{15}N-^{14}N DNA, but the second tube would not have the upper band of two light blue strands. Instead it would have a bottom band of two dark blue strands, like the bottom band in the result predicted after one replication in the conservative model. **Figure 16.12** In the bubble at the top in (b), arrows should be drawn pointing left and right to indicate the two replication forks. **Figure 16.14** Looking at any of the DNA strands, we see that one end is called the 5′ end and the other the 3′ end. If we proceed from the 5′ end to the 3′ end on the left-most strand, for example, we list the components in this order: phosphate group → 5′ C of the sugar → 3′ C → phosphate → 5′ C → 3′ C. Going in the opposite direction on the same strand, the components proceed in the reverse order: 3′ C → 5′ C → phosphate. Thus, the two directions are distinguishable, which is what we mean when we say that the strands have directionality. (Review Figure 16.5 if necessary.)
Figure 16.17

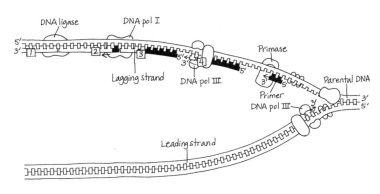

Figure 16.23 The two members of a homologous pair (which would be the same color) would be associated tightly together at the metaphase plate. In metaphase of mitosis, however, each chromosome would be lined up individually, so the two chromosomes of the same color would be in different places at the metaphase plate.

Concept Check 16.1
1. Chargaff's rule about base ratios states that in DNA, the percentages of A and T are essentially the same, as are those of G and C. The fly data are consistent with that rule. (Slight variations are most likely due to limitations of analytical technique.)   2. You can't tell which end is the 5′ end. You need to know which end has a phosphate group on the 5′ carbon (the 5′ end) or which end has an —OH group on the 3′ carbon (the 3′ end).   3. He was expecting that the mouse injected with the mixture of heat-killed S cells and living R cells would survive, since neither type of cell alone would kill the mouse.

Concept Check 16.2
1. Complementary base pairing ensures that the two daughter molecules are exact copies of the parental molecule. When the two strands of the parental molecule separate, each serves as a template on which nucleotides are arranged, by the base-pairing rules, into new complementary strands.

2.

Protein	Function
Helicase	Unwinds parental double helix at replication forks
Single-strand binding protein	Binds to and stabilizes single-stranded DNA until it can be used as a template
Topoisomerase	Relieves "overwinding" strain ahead of replication forks by breaking, swiveling, and rejoining DNA strands
Primase	Synthesizes an RNA primer at 5′ end of leading strand and at 5′ end of each Okazaki fragment of lagging strand
DNA pol III	Using parental DNA as a template, synthesizes new DNA strand by covalently adding nucleotides to 3′ end of a pre-existing DNA strand or RNA primer
DNA pol I	Removes RNA nucleotides of primer from 5′ end and replaces them with DNA nucleotides
DNA ligase	Joins 3′ end of DNA that replaces primer to rest of leading strand and joins Okazaki fragments of lagging strand

3. In the cell cycle, DNA synthesis occurs during the S phase, between the G_1 and G_2 phases of interphase. DNA replication is therefore complete before the mitotic phase begins.   **4.** Synthesis of the leading strand is initiated by an RNA primer, which must be removed and replaced with DNA, a task that could not be performed if the cell's DNA pol I were nonfunctional. In the overview box in Figure 16.17, just to the left of the top origin of replication, a functional DNA pol I would replace the RNA primer of the leading strand (shown in red) with DNA nucleotides (blue).

Concept Check 16.3
1. A nucleosome is made up of eight histone proteins, two each of four different types, around which DNA is wound. Linker DNA runs from one nucleosome to the next.   **2.** Euchromatin is chromatin that becomes less compacted during interphase and is accessible to the cellular machinery responsible for gene activity. Heterochromatin, on the other hand, remains quite condensed during interphase and contains genes that are largely inaccessible to this machinery.   **3.** The nuclear lamina is a netlike array of protein filaments that provides mechanical support just inside the nuclear envelope and thus maintains the shape of the nucleus. Considerable evidence also supports the existence of a nuclear matrix, a framework of protein fibers extending throughout the nuclear interior.

Summary of Key Concepts Questions
16.1 Each strand in the double helix has polarity, the end with a phosphate group on the 5′ carbon of the sugar being called the 5′ end, and the end with an —OH group on the 3′ carbon of the sugar being called the 3′ end. The two strands run in opposite directions, so each end of the molecule has both a 5′ and a 3′ end. This arrangement is called "antiparallel." If the strands were parallel, they would both run 5′ → 3′ in the same direction, so an end of the molecule would have either two 5′ ends or two 3′ ends.   **16.2** On both the leading and lagging strands, DNA polymerase adds onto the 3′ end of an RNA primer synthesized by primase, synthesizing DNA in the 5′ → 3′ direction. Because the parental strands are antiparallel, however, only on the leading strand does synthesis proceed continuously into the replication fork. The lagging strand is synthesized bit by bit in the direction away from the fork as a series of shorter Okazaki fragments, which are later joined together by DNA ligase. Each fragment is initiated by synthesis of an RNA primer by primase as soon as a given stretch of single-stranded template strand is opened up. Although both strands are synthesized at the same rate, synthesis of the lagging strand is delayed because initiation of each fragment begins only when sufficient template strand is available.   **16.3** Most of the chromatin in an interphase nucleus is uncondensed. Much is present as the 30-nm fiber, with some in the form of the 10-nm fiber and some as looped domains of the 30-nm fiber. (These different levels of chromatin packing may reflect differences in gene expression occurring in these regions.) Also, a small percentage of the chromatin, such as that at the centromeres and telomeres, is highly condensed heterochromatin.

Test Your Understanding
1. c   **2.** c   **3.** b   **4.** d   **5.** c   **6.** d   **7.** b   **8.** a
9. Like histones, the *E. coli* proteins would be expected to contain many basic (positively charged) amino acids, such as lysine and arginine, which can form weak bonds with the negatively charged phosphate groups on the sugar-phosphate backbone of the DNA molecule. **10.** Each species' DNA has a slightly different percentage of a given base. For example, the percentage of A ranges from 24.7% for *E. coli* to 32.8% for sea urchin. This illustrates Chargaff's rule that the DNA of different species varies in its base composition. Chargaff's other rule states

that in any given species, the percentage of A is roughly equal to that of T, and the percentage of C is roughly equal to that of G. For example, sea urchins have about 32–33% each of A and T and about 17% of G and C. (Your answer may use any similar examples from the table.)
12.

New DNA strand (olive)   Parental DNA strand (purple)

Sliding clamp   DNA pol III   Single-strand binding protein

Direction of replication

Chapter 17

Figure Questions
Figure 17.2 The previously presumed pathway would have been wrong. The new results would support this pathway: precursor → citrulline → ornithine → arginine. They would also indicate that class I mutants have a defect in the second step and class II mutants have a defect in the first step. **Figure 17.4** The mRNA sequence (5′-UGGUUUGGCUCA-3′) is the same as the nontemplate DNA strand sequence (5′-TGGTTTGGCTCA-3′), except there is U in the mRNA and T in the DNA. **Figure 17.7** The processes are similar in that polymerases form polynucleotides complementary to an antiparallel DNA template strand. In replication, however, both strands act as templates, whereas in transcription, only one DNA strand acts as a template. **Figure 17.8** The RNA polymerase would bind directly to the promoter, rather than depending on the previous binding of other factors. **Figure 17.25** The mRNA on the right (the longest one) started transcription first. The ribosome at the top, closest to the DNA, started translating first and thus has the longest polypeptide.

Concept Check 17.1
1. Recessive   **2.** A polypeptide made up of 10 Gly (glycine) amino acids
3. Template sequence
(from problem):   3′-TTCAGTCGT-5′

Nontemplate sequence: 5′-AAGTCAGCA-3′

mRNA sequence: 5′-AAGUCAGCA-3′

The nontemplate and mRNA nucleotide sequences are the same except that there is T in the nontemplate strand of DNA wherever there is U in the mRNA.

4. "Template sequence" (from nontemplate sequence in problem, written 3′ → 5′):   3′-ACGACTGAA-5′

mRNA sequence: 5′-UGCUGACUU-3′

Translated: Cys-STOP-Leu

(Remember that the mRNA is antiparallel to the DNA strand.) A protein translated from the nontemplate sequence would have a completely different amino acid sequence and would most likely be nonfunctional. (It would also be shorter because of the stop signal shown in the mRNA sequence above—and possibly others earlier in the mRNA sequence.)

Concept Check 17.2
1. Both assemble nucleic acid chains from monomer nucleotides whose order is determined by complementary base pairing to a template strand. Both synthesize in the 5′ → 3′ direction, antiparallel to the template. DNA polymerase requires a primer, but RNA polymerase can start a nucleotide chain from scratch. DNA polymerase uses nucleotides with the sugar deoxyribose and the base T, whereas RNA polymerase uses nucleotides with the sugar ribose and the base U.   **2.** The promoter is the region of DNA to which RNA polymerase binds to begin transcription, and it is at the upstream end of the gene (transcription unit).   **3.** In a bacterial cell, RNA polymerase recognizes the gene's promoter and binds to it. In a eukaryotic cell, transcription factors mediate the binding of RNA polymerase to the promoter. In both cases, sequences in the promoter bind precisely to the RNA polymerase, so the enzyme is in the right location and orientation.   **4.** The transcription factor that recognizes the TATA sequence would be unable to bind, so RNA polymerase could not bind and transcription of that gene probably would not occur.

Concept Check 17.3
1. Due to alternative splicing of exons, each gene can result in multiple different mRNAs and can thus direct synthesis of multiple different proteins.   **2.** In editing a video, segments are cut out and discarded (like introns), and the remaining segments are joined together (like exons) so that the regions of joining ("splicing") are not noticeable.   **3.** Once the mRNA has exited the nucleus, the cap

prevents it from being degraded by hydrolytic enzymes and facilitates its attachment to ribosomes. If the cap were removed from all mRNAs, the cell would no longer be able to synthesize any proteins and would probably die.

Concept Check 17.4
1. First, each aminoacyl-tRNA synthetase specifically recognizes a single amino acid and attaches it only to an appropriate tRNA. Second, a tRNA charged with its specific amino acid binds only to an mRNA codon for that amino acid.   **2.** The structure and function of the ribosome seem to depend more on the rRNAs than on the ribosomal proteins. Because it is single-stranded, an RNA molecule can hydrogen-bond with itself and with other RNA molecules. RNA molecules make up the interface between the two ribosomal subunits, so presumably RNA-RNA binding helps hold the ribosome together. The binding site for mRNA in the ribosome includes rRNA that can bind the mRNA. Also, complementary bonding within an RNA molecule allows it to assume a particular three-dimensional shape and, along with the RNA's functional groups, presumably enables rRNA to catalyze peptide bond formation during translation.   **3.** A signal peptide on the leading end of the polypeptide being synthesized is recognized by a signal-recognition particle that brings the ribosome to the ER membrane. There the ribosome attaches and continues to synthesize the polypeptide, depositing it in the ER lumen.   **4.** Because of wobble, the tRNA could bind to either 5'-GCA-3' or 5'-GCG-3', both of which code for alanine (Ala). Alanine would be attached to the tRNA.

Concept Check 17.5
1. In the mRNA, the reading frame downstream from the deletion is shifted, leading to a long string of incorrect amino acids in the polypeptide, and in most cases, a stop codon will arise, leading to premature termination. The polypeptide will most likely be nonfunctional.   **2.** Heterozygous individuals, said to have sickle-cell trait, have a copy each of the wild-type allele and the sickle-cell allele. Both alleles will be expressed, so these individuals will have both normal and sickle-cell hemoglobin molecules. Apparently, having a mix of the two forms of β-globin has no effect under most conditions, but during prolonged periods of low blood oxygen (such as at higher altitudes), these individuals can show some signs of sickle-cell disease.
3.

Normal DNA sequence
(template strand is on top): 3'-TACTTGTCCGATATC-5'
                                5'-ATGAACAGGCTATAG-3'

mRNA sequence: 5'-AUGAACAGGCUAUAG-3'

Amino acid Sequence: Met-Asn-Arg-Leu-STOP

Mutated DNA sequence
(template strand is on top): 3'-TACTTGTCCAATATC-5'
                                  5'-ATGAACAGGTTATAG-3'

mRNA sequence: 5'-AUGAACAGGUUAUAG-3'

Amino acid sequence: Met-Asn-Arg-Leu-STOP

No effect: The amino acid sequence is Met-Asn-Arg-Leu both before and after the mutation because the mRNA codons 5'-CUA-3' and 5'-UUA-3' both code for Leu. (The fifth codon is a stop codon.)

Concept Check 17.6
1. No, transcription and translation are separated in space and time in a eukaryotic cell, a result of the eukaryotic cell's nuclear compartment.   **2.** When one ribosome terminates translation and dissociates, the two subunits would be very close to the cap. This could facilitate their rebinding and initiating synthesis of a new polypeptide, thus increasing the efficiency of translation.

Summary of Key Concepts Questions
17.1 A gene contains genetic information in the form of a nucleotide sequence. The gene is first transcribed into an RNA molecule, and a messenger RNA molecule is ultimately translated into a polypeptide. The polypeptide makes up part or all of a protein, which performs a function in the cell and contributes to the phenotype of the organism.   **17.2** Both bacterial and eukaryotic genes have promoters, regions where RNA polymerase ultimately binds and begins transcription. In bacteria, RNA polymerase binds directly to the promoter; in eukaryotes, transcription factors bind first to the promoter, and then RNA polymerase binds to the transcription factors and promoter together.   **17.3** Both the 5' cap and the poly-A tail help the mRNA exit from the nucleus and then, in the cytoplasm, help ensure mRNA stability and allow it to bind to ribosomes.   **17.4** tRNAs function as translators between the nucleotide-based language of mRNA and the amino-acid-based language of polypeptides. A tRNA carries a specific amino acid, and the anticodon on the tRNA is complementary to the codon on the mRNA that codes for that amino acid. In the ribosome, the tRNA binds to the A site, where the polypeptide being synthesized is joined to the new amino acid, which becomes the new (C-terminal) end of the polypeptide. Next, the tRNA moves to the P site. When the next amino acid is added via transfer of the polypeptide to the new tRNA, the now empty tRNA moves to the E site, where it exits the ribosome.   **17.5** When a nucleotide base is altered chemically, its base-pairing characteristics may be changed. When that happens, an incorrect nucleotide is likely to be incorporated into the complementary strand during the next replication of the DNA, and successive rounds of replication will perpetuate the mutation. Once the gene is transcribed, the mutated codon may code for a different amino acid that inhibits or changes the function of a protein. If the chemical change in the base is detected and repaired by the DNA repair system before the next replication, no mutation will result.   **17.6** The presence of a nuclear envelope in eukaryotes means that transcription and translation are separated in space and therefore in time. This separation allows other processes (specifically, RNA processing) to occur and provides other steps at which gene expression can be regulated.

Test Your Understanding
1. b   **2.** d   **3.** a   **4.** a   **5.** b   **6.** d   **7.** e
8.

Type of RNA	Functions
Messenger RNA (mRNA)	Carries information specifying amino acid sequences of proteins from DNA to ribosomes
Transfer RNA (tRNA)	Serves as translator molecule in protein synthesis; translates mRNA codons into amino acids
Ribosomal RNA (rRNA)	Plays catalytic (ribozyme) roles and structural roles in ribosomes
Primary transcript	Is a precursor to mRNA, rRNA, or tRNA, before being processed; some intron RNA acts as a ribozyme, catalyzing its own splicing
Small nuclear RNA (snRNA)	Plays structural and catalytic roles in spliceosomes, the complexes of protein and RNA that splice pre-mRNA

Chapter 18

Figure Questions
Figure 18.3 As the concentration of tryptophan in the cell falls, eventually there will be none bound to repressor molecules. These will then take on their inactive shapes and dissociate from the operator, allowing transcription of the operon to resume. The enzymes for tryptophan synthesis will be made, and they will begin to synthesize tryptophan again in the cell. **Figure 18.11** The albumin gene enhancer has the three control elements colored yellow, gray, and red. The sequences in the liver and lens cells would be identical, since the cells are in the same organism. **Figure 18.18** Even if the mutant MyoD protein couldn't activate the *myoD* gene, it could still turn on genes for the other proteins in the pathway (other transcription factors, which would turn on the genes for muscle-specific proteins, for example). Therefore, some differentiation would occur. But unless there were other activators that could compensate for the loss of the MyoD protein's activation of the *myoD* gene, the cell would not be able to maintain its differentiated state. **Figure 18.22** Normal Bicoid protein would be made in the anterior end and compensate for the presence of mutant *bicoid* mRNA put into the egg by the mother. Development should be normal, with a head present. **Figure 18.24** The mutation is likely to be recessive because it is more likely to have an effect if both copies of the gene are mutated and code for nonfunctional proteins. If one normal copy of the gene is present, its product could inhibit the cell cycle. (However, there are also known cases of dominant *p53* mutations.)

Concept Check 18.1
1. Binding by the *trp* corepressor (tryptophan) activates the *trp* repressor, shutting off transcription of the *trp* operon; binding by the *lac* inducer (allolactose) inactivates the *lac* repressor, leading to transcription of the *lac* operon.   **2.** When glucose is scarce, cAMP is bound to CAP and CAP is bound to the promoter, favoring the binding of RNA polymerase. However, in the absence of lactose, the repressor is bound to the operator, blocking RNA polymerase binding to the promoter. Therefore, the operon genes are not transcribed.   **3.** The cell would continuously

produce β-galactosidase and the two other enzymes for lactose utilization, even in the absence of lactose, thus wasting cell resources.

Concept Check 18.2
1. Histone acetylation is generally associated with gene expression, while DNA methylation is generally associated with lack of expression. 2. General transcription factors function in assembling the transcription initiation complex at the promoters for all genes. Specific transcription factors bind to control elements associated with a particular gene and, once bound, either increase (activators) or decrease (repressors) transcription of that gene. 3. The three genes should have some similar or identical sequences in the control elements of their enhancers. Because of this similarity, the same specific transcription factors in muscle cells could bind to the enhancers of all three genes and stimulate their expression coordinately. 4. Degradation of the mRNA, regulation of translation, activation of the protein (by chemical modification, for example), and protein degradation 5. Expression of the gene encoding the yellow activator (YA) must be regulated at one of the steps shown in Figure 18.6. The YA gene might be transcribed only in liver cells because the necessary activators for the enhancer of the YA gene are found only in liver cells.

Concept Check 18.3
1. Both miRNAs and siRNAs are small, single-stranded RNAs that associate with a complex of proteins and then can base-pair with mRNAs that have a complementary sequence. This base pairing leads to either degradation of the mRNA or blockage of its translation. Some siRNAs, in association with other proteins, can bind back to the chromatin in a certain region, causing chromatin changes that affect transcription. Both miRNAs and siRNAs are processed from double-stranded RNA precursors by the enzyme Dicer. All miRNAs are specified by genes in the cell's genome, and the single transcript folds back on itself to form one or more double-stranded hairpins, each of which is processed into an miRNA. In contrast, siRNAs arise from a longer stretch of linear double-stranded RNA, which may be introduced into the cell by a virus or an experimenter. Alternatively, in some cases, a cellular gene specifies one RNA strand of the precursor molecule, and an enzyme then synthesizes the complementary strand. 2. The mRNA would persist and be translated into the cell division–promoting protein, and the cell would probably divide. If the intact miRNA is necessary for inhibition of cell division, then division of this cell might be inappropriate. Uncontrolled cell division could lead to formation of a mass of cells (tumor) that prevents proper functioning of the organism and could contribute to the development of cancer. 3. The *XIST* RNA is transcribed from the *XIST* gene on the X chromosome that will be inactivated. It then binds to that chromosome and induces heterochromatin formation. A likely model is that the *XIST* RNA somehow recruits chromatin modification enzymes that lead to formation of heterochromatin.

Concept Check 18.4
1. Cells undergo differentiation during embryonic development, becoming different from each other; in the adult organism, there are many highly specialized cell types. 2. By binding to a receptor on the receiving cell's surface and triggering a signal transduction pathway, involving intracellular molecules such as second messengers and transcription factors that affect gene expression 3. Because their products, made and deposited into the egg by the mother, determine the head and tail ends, as well as the back and belly, of the embryo (and eventually the adult fly) 4. The lower cell is synthesizing signaling molecules because the gene encoding them is activated, meaning that the appropriate specific transcription factors are binding to the gene's enhancer. The genes encoding these specific transcription factors are also being expressed in this cell because the transcriptional activators that can turn them on were expressed in the precursor to this cell. A similar explanation also applies to the cells expressing the receptor proteins. This scenario began with specific cytoplasmic determinants localized in specific regions of the egg. These cytoplasmic determinants were distributed unevenly to daughter cells, resulting in cells going down different developmental pathways.

Concept Check 18.5
1. Apoptosis is signaled by p53 protein when a cell has extensive DNA damage, so apoptosis plays a protective role in eliminating a cell that might contribute to cancer. If mutations in the genes in the apoptotic pathway blocked apoptosis, a cell with such damage could continue to divide and might lead to tumor formation. 2. When an individual has inherited an oncogene or a mutant allele of a tumor-suppressor gene 3. A cancer-causing mutation in a proto-oncogene usually makes the gene product overactive, whereas a cancer-causing mutation in a tumor-suppressor gene usually makes the gene product nonfunctional.

Summary of Key Concepts Questions
18.1 A corepressor and an inducer are both small molecules that bind to the repressor protein in an operon, causing the repressor to change shape. In the case of a corepressor (like tryptophan), this shape change allows the repressor to bind to the operator, blocking transcription. In contrast, an inducer causes the repressor to dissociate from the operator, allowing transcription to begin. 18.2 The chromatin must not be tightly condensed because it must be accessible to transcription factors. The appropriate specific transcription factors (activators) must bind to the control elements in the enhancer of the gene, while repressors must not be bound. The DNA must be bent by a bending protein so the activators can contact the mediator proteins and form a complex with general transcription factors at the promoter. Then RNA polymerase must bind and begin transcription. 18.3 miRNAs do not "code" for the amino acids of a protein—they are never translated. Each miRNA is cleaved from its hairpin RNA structure and then trimmed by Dicer. Next, one strand is degraded while

the other associates with a group of proteins to form a complex. Binding of the complex to an mRNA with a complementary sequence causes that mRNA to be degraded or blocks its translation. This is considered gene regulation because it controls the amount of a particular mRNA that can be translated into a functional protein. 18.4 The first process involves cytoplasmic determinants, including mRNAs and proteins, placed into specific locations in the egg by the mother. The cells that are formed from different regions in the egg during early cell divisions will have different proteins in them, which will direct different programs of gene expression. The second process involves the cell in question responding to signaling molecules secreted by neighboring cells. The signaling pathway in the responding cell also leads to a different pattern of gene expression. The coordination of these two processes results in each cell following a unique pathway in the developing embryo. 18.5 The protein product of a proto-oncogene is usually involved in a pathway that stimulates cell division. The protein product of a tumor-suppressor gene is usually involved in a pathway that inhibits cell division.

Test Your Understanding
1. d 2. a 3. a 4. a 5. c 6. d 7. c 8. e 9. b 10. b
11. a.

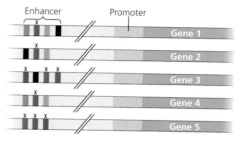

The purple, blue, and red activator proteins would be present.
b.

Only gene 4 would be transcribed.
c. In nerve cells, the orange, blue, green, and black activators would have to be present, thus activating transcription of genes 1, 2, and 4. In skin cells, the red, black, purple, and blue activators would have to be present, thus activating genes 3 and 5.

Chapter 19

Figure Questions
Figure 19.2 Beijerinck might have concluded that the agent was a toxin produced by the plant that was able to pass through a filter but that became more and more dilute. In this case, he would have concluded that the infectious agent could not replicate. **Figure 19.4** Top vertical arrow: Infection. Left upper arrow: Replication. Right upper arrow: Transcription. Right middle arrow: Translation. Lower left and right arrows: Self-assembly. Bottom middle arrow: Exit. **Figure 19.7** Any class V virus, including the viruses that cause influenza (flu), measles, and mumps **Figure 19.8** The main protein on the cell surface that HIV binds to is called CD4. However, HIV also requires a "co-receptor," which in many cases is a protein called CCR5. HIV binds to both of these proteins together and then is taken into the cell. Researchers discovered this requirement by studying individuals who seemed to be resistant to HIV infection, despite multiple exposures. These individuals turned out to have mutations in the gene that encodes CCR5 such that the protein apparently cannot act as a co-receptor, and so HIV can't enter and infect cells.

Concept Check 19.1
1. TMV consists of one molecule of RNA surrounded by a helical array of proteins. The influenza virus has eight molecules of RNA, each surrounded by a helical array of proteins, similar to the arrangement of the single RNA molecule in TMV. Another difference between the viruses is that the influenza virus has an outer envelope and TMV does not. 2. The T2 phages were an excellent choice for use in the Hershey-Chase experiment because they consist of only DNA surrounded by a protein coat, and DNA and protein were the two candidates for macromolecules that carried genetic information. Hershey and Chase were able to radioactively label each type of molecule alone and follow it during separate infections of *E. coli* cells with T2. Only the DNA entered the bacterial cell during infection, and only labeled DNA showed up in some of the progeny phage.

Hershey and Chase concluded that the DNA must carry the genetic information necessary for the phage to reprogram the cell and produce progeny phages.

Concept Check 19.2
1. Lytic phages can only carry out lysis of the host cell, whereas lysogenic phages may either lyse the host cell or integrate into the host chromosome. In the latter case, the viral DNA (prophage) is simply replicated along with the host chromosome. Under certain conditions, a prophage may exit the host chromosome and initiate a lytic cycle.   **2.** Both the viral RNA polymerase and the RNA polymerase in Figure 17.9 synthesize an RNA molecule complementary to a template strand. However, the RNA polymerase in Figure 17.9 uses one of the strands of the DNA double helix as a template, whereas the viral RNA polymerase uses the RNA of the viral genome as a template.   **3.** Because it synthesizes DNA from its RNA genome. This is the reverse ("retro") of the usual DNA → RNA information flow.   **4.** There are many steps that could be interfered with: binding of the virus to the cell, reverse transcriptase function, integration into the host cell chromosome, genome synthesis (in this case, transcription of RNA from the integrated provirus), assembly of the virus inside the cell, and budding of the virus. (Many of these, if not all, are targets of actual medical strategies to block progress of the infection in HIV-infected people.)

Concept Check 19.3
1. Mutations can lead to a new strain of a virus that can no longer be effectively fought by the immune system, even if an animal had been exposed to the original strain; a virus can jump from one species to a new host; and a rare virus can spread if a host population becomes less isolated.   **2.** In horizontal transmission, a plant is infected from an external source of virus, which could enter through a break in the plant's epidermis due to damage by herbivores. In vertical transmission, a plant inherits viruses from its parent either via infected seeds (sexual reproduction) or via an infected cutting (asexual reproduction).   **3.** Humans are not within the host range of TMV, so they can't be infected by the virus.

Summary of Key Concepts Questions
19.1 Viruses are generally considered nonliving, because they are not capable of replicating outside of a host cell. To replicate, they depend completely on host enzymes and resources.   **19.2** Single-stranded RNA viruses require an RNA polymerase that can make RNA using an RNA template. (Cellular RNA polymerases make RNA using a DNA template.) Retroviruses require reverse transcriptases to make DNA using an RNA template. (Once the first DNA strand has been made, the same enzyme can promote synthesis of the second DNA strand.)   **19.3** The mutation rate of RNA viruses is higher than that of DNA viruses because RNA polymerase has no proofreading function, so errors in replication are not corrected. Their higher mutation rate means that RNA viruses change faster than DNA viruses, leading to their being able to have an altered host range and to evade immune defenses in possible hosts.

Test Your Understanding
1. c **2.** d **3.** c **4.** d **5.** b
6. As shown below, the viral genome would be translated into capsid proteins and envelope glycoproteins directly, rather than after a complementary RNA copy was made. A complementary RNA strand would still be made, however, that could be used as a template for many new copies of the viral genome.

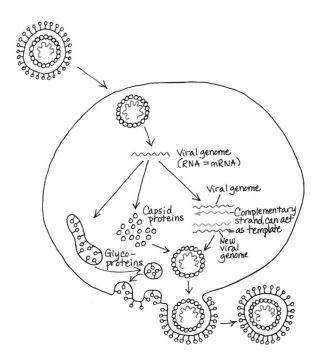

Chapter 20

Figure Questions
Figure 20.3

Figure 20.4 Cells containing no plasmid at all would be able to grow; these colonies would be white because they would lack functional *lacZ* genes. **Figure 20.10** Grow each clone of cells in culture. Isolate the plasmids from each and cut them with the restriction enzyme originally used to make the clone (see Figure 20.4). Run each sample on an electrophoretic gel, and recover the DNA of the insert from the gel band. **Figure 20.16** Crossing over, which causes recombination, is a random event. The chance of crossing over occurring between two loci increases as the distance between them increases. The SNP is located very close to an unknown disease-causing allele, and therefore crossing over rarely occurs between the SNP and the allele, so the SNP is a genetic marker indicating the presence of the particular allele. **Figure 20.18** None of the eggs with the transplanted nuclei from the four-cell embryo at the upper left would have developed into a tadpole. Also, the result might include only some of the tissues of a tadpole, which might differ, depending on which nucleus was transplanted. (This assumes that there was some way to tell the four cells apart, as one can in some frog species.) **Figure 20.22** Using converted iPS cells would not carry the same risk, which is its major advantage. Because the donor cells would come from the patient, they would be perfectly matched. The patient's immune system would recognize them as "self" cells and would not mount an attack (which is what leads to rejection).

Concept Check 20.1
1. The covalent sugar-phosphate bonds of the DNA strands   **2.** Yes, *Pvu*I will cut the molecule.

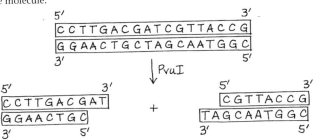

3. Some human genes are too large to be incorporated into bacterial plasmids. Bacterial cells lack the means to process RNA transcripts into mRNA, and even if the need for RNA processing is avoided by using cDNA, bacteria lack enzymes to catalyze the post-translational processing that many human proteins require to function properly.   **4.** During the replication of the ends of linear DNA molecules (see Figure 16.20), an RNA primer is used at the 5' end of each new strand. The RNA must be replaced by DNA nucleotides, but DNA polymerase is incapable of starting from scratch at the 5' end of a new DNA strand. During PCR, the primers are made of DNA nucleotides already, so they don't need to be replaced—they just remain as part of each new strand. Therefore, there is no problem with end replication during PCR, and the fragments don't shorten with each replication.

Concept Check 20.2
1. Any restriction enzyme will cut genomic DNA in many places, generating such a large number of fragments that they would appear as a smear rather than distinct bands when the gel is stained after electrophoresis.   **2.** In Southern blotting, Northern blotting, and microarray analysis, the labeled probe binds only to the specific target sequence owing to complementary nucleic acid hybridization (DNA-DNA hybridization in Southern blotting and microarray analysis, DNA-RNA hybridization in Northern blotting). In DNA sequencing, primers base-pair with the template, allowing DNA synthesis to start. In RT-PCR, the primers must base-pair with their target sequences in the DNA mixture.   **3.** A SNP is a single nucleotide that varies in the population, existing in two or more variations. A RFLP is a type of SNP that occurs in a restriction site, leading to a difference in restriction fragment length when cutting two variants with a restriction enzyme.   **4.** If a spot is green, the gene represented on that spot is expressed only in normal tissue. If red, the gene is expressed only in cancerous tissue. If yellow, the gene is expressed in both. And if black, the gene is expressed in neither type of tissue. As a researcher interested in cancer development, you would want to study genes represented by spots that are green or red because these are genes for which the expression level differs between the two types of tissues. Some of these genes may be expressed differently as a result of cancer, but others might play a role in causing cancer.

Concept Check 20.3
1. The state of chromatin modification in the nucleus from the intestinal cell was undoubtedly less similar to that of a nucleus from a fertilized egg, explaining why many fewer of these nuclei were able to be reprogrammed. In contrast, the chromatin in a nucleus from a cell at the four-cell stage would have been much more like that of a nucleus in a fertilized egg and therefore much more easily programmed to direct development.   **2.** No, primarily because of subtle (and perhaps not so subtle)

differences in their environments **3.** A technique would have to be worked out for turning a human iPS cell into a pancreatic cell (probably by inducing expression of pancreas-specific regulatory genes in the cell). **4.** The carrot cell has much more potential. The cloning experiment shows that an individual carrot cell can generate all the tissues of an adult plant. The muscle cell, on the other hand, will always remain a muscle cell because of its genetic program (it expresses the *myoD* gene, which ensures continued differentiation). The muscle cell is like other fully differentiated animal cells: It will remain fully differentiated on its own unless it is reprogrammed into an iPS cell using the new techniques described here. (This would be quite difficult to accomplish because a muscle cell has multiple nuclei.)

Concept Check 20.4
1. Stem cells continue to reproduce themselves. **2.** Herbicide resistance, pest resistance, disease resistance, salinity resistance, and delayed ripening **3.** Because hepatitis A is an RNA virus, you could isolate RNA from the blood and try to detect copies of hepatitis A RNA by one of three methods. First, you could run the RNA on a gel and then do a Northern blot using probes complementary to hepatitis A genome sequences. A second approach would be to use reverse transcriptase to make cDNA from the RNA in the blood, run the cDNA on a gel, and do a Southern blot using the same probe. However, neither of these methods would be as sensitive as RT-PCR, in which you would reverse-transcribe the blood RNA into cDNA and then use PCR to amplify the cDNA, using primers specific to hepatitis A sequences. If you then ran the products on an electrophoretic gel, the presence of a band would support your hypothesis.

Summary of Key Concepts Questions
20.1 A plasmid vector and a source of foreign DNA to be cloned are both cut with the same restriction enzyme, generating restriction fragments with sticky ends. These fragments are mixed together, ligated, and reintroduced into bacterial cells, which are then grown on the antibiotic ampicillin. The plasmid has two genes that allow selection of recombinant clones. The first is a gene for ampicillin resistance, which only allows cells to grow if they have taken up a plasmid. The second is a gene for β-galactosidase, which can generate a blue product if the gene is intact. The cloning site is within this gene, so only nonrecombinant colonies will be blue, and recombinant plasmids will be found in cells that are in white colonies. **20.2** Many techniques used to analyze genes and their expression involve nucleic acid hybridization: Southern and Northern blotting, DNA sequencing, PCR, *in situ* hybridization, and DNA microarray analysis. The base pairing between the two strands of a DNA molecule or between a DNA strand and an RNA strand is the key to finding specific nucleic acid sequences in all of these techniques. **20.3** Cloning a mouse involves transplanting a nucleus from a differentiated mouse cell into a mouse egg cell that has had its own nucleus removed. Fertilizing the egg cell and promoting its development into an embryo in a surrogate mother results in a mouse that is genetically identical to the mouse that donated the nucleus. In this case, the differentiated nucleus has been reprogrammed by factors in the egg cytoplasm. Mouse ES cells are generated from inner cells in mouse blastocysts, so in this case the cells are "naturally" reprogrammed by the process of reproduction and development. (Cloned mouse embryos can also be used as a source of ES cells.) iPS cells can be generated without the use of embryos from a differentiated adult mouse cell, by adding certain transcription factors into the cell. In this case, the transcription factors are reprogramming the cells to become pluripotent. **20.4** First, the disease must be caused by a single gene, and the molecular basis of the problem must be understood. Second, the cells that are going to be introduced into the patient must be cells that will integrate into body tissues and continue to multiply (and provide the needed gene product). Third, the gene must be able to be introduced into the cells in question in a safe way, as there have been instances of cancer resulting from some gene therapy trials. (Note that this will require testing the procedure in mice; moreover, the factors that determine a safe vector are not yet well understood. Maybe one of you will go on to solve this problem!)

Test Your Understanding
1. b **2.** c **3.** b **4.** c **5.** d **6.** b **7.** a **8.** c
9.

10. A cDNA library, made using mRNA from human lens cells, which would be expected to contain many copies of mRNA for the crystallin of interest

Chapter 21

Figure Questions
Figure 21.3 The fragments in stage 2 of this figure are like those in stage 2 of Figure 21.2, but in this figure their order relative to each other is not known and will be determined later by computer. The order of the fragments in Figure 21.2 is completely known before sequencing begins. (Determining the order takes longer but makes the eventual sequence assembly much easier.) **Figure 21.9** The transposon would be cut out of the DNA at the original site rather than copied, so the figure would show the original stretch of DNA without the transposon after the mobile transposon had been cut out. **Figure 21.11** The RNA transcripts extending from the DNA in each transcription unit are shorter on the left and longer on the right. This means that RNA polymerase must be starting on the left end of the unit and moving toward the right.
Figure 21.13

Crossover point

Figure 21.14 Pseudogenes are nonfunctional. They could have arisen by any mutations in the second copy that made the gene product unable to function. Examples would be base changes that introduce stop codons in the sequence, alter amino acids, or change a region of the gene promoter so that the gene can no longer be expressed. **Figure 21.15** Let's say a transposable element (TE) existed in the intron to the left of the indicated EGF exon in the EGF gene, and the same TE was present in the intron to the right of the indicated F exon in the fibronectin gene. During meiotic recombination, these TEs could cause nonsister chromatids on homologous chromosomes to pair up incorrectly, as seen in Figure 21.13. One gene might end up with an F exon next to an EGF exon. Further mistakes in pairing over many generations might result in these two exons being separated from the rest of the gene and placed next to a single or duplicated K exon. In general, the presence of repeated sequences in introns and between genes facilitates these processes because it allows incorrect pairing of nonsister chromatids, leading to novel exon combinations. **Figure 21.17** Since you know that chimpanzees do not speak but humans do, you'd probably want to know how many amino acid differences there are between the human wild-type FOXP2 protein and that of the chimpanzee and whether these changes affect the function of the protein. (As we explain later in the text, there are two amino acid differences.) You know that humans with mutations in this gene have severe language impairment. You would want to learn more about the human mutations by checking whether they affect the same amino acids in the gene product that the chimpanzee sequence differences affect. If so, those amino acids might play an important role in the function of the protein in language. Going further, you could analyze the differences between the chimpanzee and mouse FOXP2 proteins. You might ask: Are they more similar than the chimpanzee and human proteins? (It turns out that the chimpanzee and mouse proteins have only one amino acid difference and thus are more similar than the chimpanzee and human proteins, which have two differences, and more similar than the human and mouse proteins, which have three differences.)

Concept Check 21.1
1. In a linkage map, genes and other markers are ordered with respect to each other, but only the relative distances between them are known. In a physical map, the actual distances between markers, expressed in base pairs, are known. **2.** The three-stage approach employed in the Human Genome Project involves linkage mapping, physical mapping, and then sequencing of short, overlapping fragments that previously have been ordered relative to each other (see Figure 21.2). The whole-genome shotgun approach eliminates the linkage mapping and physical mapping stages; instead, short fragments generated by multiple restriction enzymes are sequenced and then ordered by computer programs that identify overlapping regions (see Figure 21.3).

Concept Check 21.2
1. The Internet allows centralization of databases such as GenBank and software resources such as BLAST, making them freely accessible. Having all the data in a central database, easily accessible on the Internet, minimizes the possibility of errors and of researchers working with different data. It streamlines the process of science, since all researchers are able to use the same software programs, rather than each having to obtain their own, possibly different, software. It speeds up dissemination of data and ensures as much as possible that errors are corrected in a timely fashion. These are just a few answers; you can probably think of more. **2.** Cancer is a disease caused by multiple factors. To focus on a single gene or a single defect would ignore other factors that may influence the behavior of the cancer and even the behavior of the single gene being studied. The systems approach, because it takes into account many factors at the same time, is more likely to lead to an understanding of the causes and most useful treatments for cancer. **3.** Some of the transcribed region is accounted for by introns. The rest is transcribed into noncoding RNAs, including small RNAs, such as microRNAs (miRNAs). These RNAs help regulate gene expression by blocking translation, causing degradation of mRNA, binding to the promoter and repressing transcription, or causing remodeling of chromatin structure.

The functions of the remainder are not yet known.   **4.** Genome-wide association studies use the systems biology approach in that they consider the correlation of many single nucleotide polymorphisms (SNPs) with particular diseases, such as heart disease and diabetes, in an attempt to find patterns of SNPs that correlate with each disease.

Concept Check 21.3
1. Alternative splicing of RNA transcripts from a gene and post-translational processing of polypeptides   **2.** The total number of completed genomes is found by clicking on "Published Complete Genomes." Add the figures for bacterial, archaeal, and eukaryotic "ongoing genomes" to get the number "in progress." Finally, look at the top of the Published Complete Genomes page to get numbers of completed genomes for each domain. (*Note:* You can click on the "Size" column and the table will be resorted by genome size. Scroll down to get an idea of relative sizes of genomes in the three domains. Remember, though, that most of the sequenced genomes are bacterial.)   **3.** Prokaryotes are generally smaller cells than eukaryotic cells, and they reproduce by binary fission. The evolutionary process involved is natural selection for more quickly reproducing cells: The faster they can replicate their DNA and divide, the more likely they will be able to dominate a population of prokaryotes. The less DNA they have to replicate, then, the faster they will reproduce.

Concept Check 21.4
1. The number of genes is higher in mammals, and the amount of noncoding DNA is greater. Also, the presence of introns in mammalian genes makes them larger, on average, than prokaryotic genes.   **2.** In the copy-and-paste transposon mechanism and in retrotransposition   **3.** In the rRNA gene family, identical transcription units for the three different RNA products are present in long, tandemly repeated arrays. The large number of copies of the rRNA genes enable organisms to produce the rRNA for enough ribosomes to carry out active protein synthesis, and the single transcription unit ensures that the relative amounts of the different rRNA molecules produced are correct. Each globin gene family consists of a relatively small number of nonidentical genes. The differences in the globin proteins encoded by these genes result in production of hemoglobin molecules adapted to particular developmental stages of the organism.   **4.** The exons would be classified as exons (1.5%); the enhancer region containing the distal control elements, the region closer to the promoter containing the proximal control elements, and the promoter itself would be classified as regulatory sequences (5%); and the introns would be classified as introns (20%).

Concept Check 21.5
1. If meiosis is faulty, two copies of the entire genome can end up in a single cell. Errors in crossing over during meiosis can lead to one segment being duplicated while another is deleted. During DNA replication, slippage backward along the template strand can result in segment duplication.   **2.** For either gene, a mistake in crossing over during meiosis could have occurred between the two copies of that gene, such that one ended up with a duplicated exon. This could have happened several times, resulting in the multiple copies of a particular exon in each gene.   **3.** Homologous transposable elements scattered throughout the genome provide sites where recombination can occur between different chromosomes. Movement of these elements into coding or regulatory sequences may change expression of genes. Transposable elements also can carry genes with them, leading to dispersion of genes and in some cases different patterns of expression. Transport of an exon during transposition and its insertion into a gene may add a new functional domain to the originally encoded protein, a type of exon shuffling. (For any of these changes to be heritable, they must happen in germ cells, cells that will give rise to gametes.)   **4.** Because more offspring are born to women who have this inversion, it must provide some advantage. It would be expected to persist and spread in the population. (In fact, evidence in the study allowed the researchers to conclude that it has been increasing in proportion in the population. You'll learn more about population genetics in the next unit.)

Concept Check 21.6
1. Because both humans and macaques are primates, their genomes are expected to be more similar than the macaque and mouse genomes are. The mouse lineage diverged from the primate lineage before the human and macaque lineages diverged.   **2.** Homeotic genes differ in their *non*homeobox sequences, which determine the interactions of homeotic gene products with other transcription factors and hence which genes are regulated by the homeotic genes. These nonhomeobox sequences differ in the two organisms, as do the expression patterns of the homeobox genes.   **3.** *Alu* elements must have undergone transposition more actively in the human genome for some reason. Their increased numbers may have then allowed more recombination errors in the human genome, resulting in more or different duplications. The divergence of the organization and content of the two genomes presumably made the chromosomes of each genome less homologous to those of the other, thus accelerating divergence of the two species by making matings less and less likely to result in fertile offspring.

Summary of Key Concepts Questions
21.1 Considering the sequencing of the human genome as an example, less time was required to sequence the first human genome using the whole-genome shotgun approach. Although this approach relied in part on data resulting from the three-stage approach used by the public consortium, the whole-genome shotgun approach was (and still is) faster and more efficient than the more labor-intensive three-stage process. The whole-genome shotgun approach was facilitated in large part by significant advances in computing power.   **21.2** The most significant finding was that more than 90% of the human genomic region studied was transcribed, which suggested that the transcribed RNA (and thus the DNA from which it was produced) was performing some unknown functions. The project has been expanded to include other species because to determine the functions of these transcribed DNA elements, it is necessary to carry out this type of analysis on the

genomes of species that can be used in laboratory experiments.   **21.3** (a) In general, bacteria and archaea have smaller genomes, lower numbers of genes, and higher gene density than eukaryotes. (b) Among eukaryotes, there is no apparent systematic relationship between genome size and phenotype. The number of genes is often lower than would be expected from the size of the genome—in other words, the gene density is often lower in larger genomes. (Humans are an example.)   **21.4** Transposable element-related sequences can move from place to place in the genome, and a subset of these sequences make a new copy of themselves when they do so. Thus, it is not surprising that they make up a significant percentage of the genome, and this percentage might be expected to increase over evolutionary time.   **21.5** Chromosomal rearrangements within a species lead to some individuals having different chromosomal arrangements. Each of these individuals could still undergo meiosis and produce gametes, and fertilization involving gametes with different chromosomal arrangements could result in viable offspring. However, during meiosis in the offspring, the maternal and paternal chromosomes might not be able to pair up, causing gametes with incomplete sets of chromosomes to form. Most often, when zygotes are produced from such gametes, they do not survive. Ultimately, a new species could form if two different chromosomal arrangements became prevalent within a population and individuals could mate successfully only with other individuals having the same arrangement.   **21.6** Comparing the genomes of two closely related species can reveal information about more recent evolutionary events, perhaps events that resulted in the distinguishing characteristics of the two species. Comparing the genomes of very distantly related species can tell us about evolutionary events that occurred a very long time ago. For example, genes that are shared between two distantly related species must have arisen before the two species diverged.

Test Your Understanding
1. c   **2.** a   **3.** a   **4.** c
5.

1. ATETI...PKSSD...TSSTT...NARRD
2. ATETI...PKSSE...TSSTT...NARRD
3. ATETI...PKSSD...TSSTT...NARRD
4. ATETI...PKSSD...TSSNT...SARRD
5. ATETI...PKSSD...TSSTT...NARRD
6. VTETI...PKSSD...TSSTT...NARRD

(a) Lines 1, 3, and 5 are the C, G, R species. (b) Line 4 is the human sequence. (c) Line 6 is the orangutan sequence. (d) There is one amino acid difference between the mouse (the E on line 2) and the C, G, R species (which have a D in that position). There are three amino acid differences between the mouse and the human. (The E, T, and N in the mouse sequence are instead D, N, and S, respectively, in the human sequence.) (e) Because only one amino acid difference arose during the 60–100 million years since the mouse and C, G, R species diverged, it is somewhat surprising that two additional amino acid differences resulted during the 6 million years since chimpanzees and humans diverged. This indicates that the *FOXP2* gene has been evolving faster in the human lineage than in the lineages of other primates.

Chapter 22

Figure Questions
Figure 22.6 The cactus-eater is more closely related to the seed-eater; Figure 1.22 shows that they share a more recent common ancestor (a seed-eater) than the cactus-eater shares with the insect-eater.   **Figure 22.8** More than 5.5 million years ago.   **Figure 22.12** The colors and body forms of these mantids allow them to blend into their surroundings, providing an example of how organisms are well matched to life in their environments. The mantids also share features with one another (and with all other mantids), such as six legs, grasping forelimbs, and large eyes. These shared features illustrate another key observation about life: the unity of life that results from descent from a common ancestor. Over time, as these mantids diverged from a common ancestor, they accumulated different adaptations that made them well suited for life in their different environments. Eventually, these differences became large enough that new species were formed, thus contributing to the great diversity of life.   **Figure 22.13** These results show that being reared from the egg stage on one plant species or the other did not result in the adult having a beak length appropriate for that host; instead, adult beak lengths were determined primarily by the population from which the eggs were obtained. Because an egg from a balloon vine population likely had long-beaked parents, while an egg from a goldenrain tree population likely had short-beaked parents, these results indicate that beak length is an inherited trait.   **Figure 22.14** Both strategies should increase the time it takes *S. aureus* to become resistant to a new drug. If a drug that harms *S. aureus* does not harm other bacteria, natural selection will not favor resistance to that drug in the other species. This would decrease the chance that *S. aureus* would acquire resistance genes from other bacteria—thus slowing the evolution of resistance. Similarly, selection for resistance to a drug that slows the growth but does not kill *S. aureus* is much weaker than selection for resistance to a drug the kills *S. aureus*—again slowing the evolution of resistance.   **Figure 22.17** Based on this evolutionary tree, crocodiles are more closely related to birds than to lizards because they share a more recent common

ancestor with birds (ancestor ⑤) than with lizards (ancestor ④). **Figure 22.20** Hind limb structure changed first. *Rodhocetus* lacked flukes, but its pelvic bones and hind limbs had changed substantially from how those bones were shaped and arranged in *Pakicetus*. For example, in *Rodhocetus*, the pelvis and hind limbs appear to be oriented for paddling, whereas they were oriented for walking in *Pakicetus*.

Concept Check 22.1

1. Hutton and Lyell proposed that events in the past were caused by the same processes operating today. This principle suggested that Earth must be much older than a few thousand years, the age that was widely accepted at that time. Hutton and Lyell also thought that geologic change occurs gradually, stimulating Darwin to reason that the slow accumulation of small changes could ultimately produce the profound changes documented in the fossil record. In this context, the age of Earth was important to Darwin, because unless Earth was very old, he could not envision how there would have been enough time for evolution to occur. **2.** By these criteria, Cuvier's explanation of the fossil record and Lamarck's hypothesis of evolution are both scientific. Cuvier thought that species did not evolve over time. He also suggested that catastrophes and the resulting extinctions were usually confined to local regions and that such regions were later repopulated by a different set of species that immigrated from other areas. These assertions can be tested against the fossil record, and his assertion that species do not evolve has been found to be false. With respect to Lamarck, his principle of use and disuse can be used to make testable predictions for fossils of groups such as whale ancestors as they adapted to a new habitat. Lamarck's principle of use and disuse and his associated principle of the inheritance of acquired characteristics can also be tested directly in living organisms (these principles have been found to be false).

Concept Check 22.2

1. Organisms share characteristics (the unity of life) because they share common ancestors; the great diversity of life occurs because new species have repeatedly formed when descendant organisms gradually adapted to different environments, becoming different from their ancestors. **2.** The fossil mammal species (or its ancestors) would most likely have colonized the Andes from within South America, whereas ancestors of mammals currently found in African mountains would most likely have colonized those mountains from other parts of Africa. As a result, the Andes fossil species would share a more recent common ancestor with South American mammals than with mammals in Africa. Thus, for many of its traits, the fossil mammal species would probably more closely resemble mammals that live in South American jungles than mammals that live on African mountains. It is also possible, however, that the fossil mammal species could resemble the African mountain mammals by convergent evolution (even though they were only distantly related to one another). **3.** As long as the white phenotype (encoded by the genotype *pp*) continues to be favored by natural selection, the frequency of the *p* allele will likely increase over time in the population. The explanation is that if the proportion of white individuals increases relative to purple individuals, the frequency of the recessive *p* allele will also increase relative to that of the *P* allele, which only appears in purple individuals (some of whom also carry a *p* allele).

Concept Check 22.3

1. An environmental factor such as a drug does not create new traits, such as drug resistance, but rather selects for traits among those that are already present in the population. **2.** (a) Despite their different functions, the forelimbs of different mammals are structurally similar because they all represent modifications of a structure found in the common ancestor. (b) Convergent evolution: The similarities between the sugar glider and flying squirrel indicate that similar environments selected for similar adaptations despite different ancestry. **3.** At the time that dinosaurs originated, Earth's landmasses formed a single large continent, Pangaea. Because many dinosaurs were large and mobile, it is likely that early members of these groups lived on many different parts of Pangaea. When Pangaea broke apart, fossils of these organisms would have moved with the rocks in which they were deposited. As a result, we would predict that fossils of early dinosaurs would have a broad geographic distribution (this prediction has been upheld).

Summary of Key Concepts Questions

Concept 22.1 Darwin thought that descent with modification occurred as a gradual, steplike process. The age of Earth was important to him because if Earth were only a few thousand years old (as conventional wisdom suggested), there wouldn't have been sufficient time for major evolutionary change. **Concept 22.2** All species have the potential to produce more offspring (overreproduce) than can be supported by the environment. This ensures that there will be what Darwin called a "struggle for existence" in which many of the offspring are eaten, starved, diseased, or unable to reproduce for a variety of other reasons. Members of a population exhibit a range of heritable variations, some of which make it likely that their bearers will leave more offspring than other individuals (for example, the bearer may escape predators more effectively or be more tolerant of the physical conditions of the environment). Over time, natural selection resulting from factors such as predators, lack of food, or the physical conditions of the environment can increase the proportion of individuals with favorable traits in a population (evolutionary adaptation). **Concept 22.3** The hypothesis that cetaceans originated from a terrestrial mammal and are closely related to even-toed ungulates is supported by several lines of evidence. For example, fossils document that early cetaceans had hind limbs, as expected for organisms that descended from a land mammal; these fossils also show that cetacean hind limbs became

reduced over time. Other fossils show that early cetaceans had a type of ankle bone that is otherwise found only in even-toed ungulates, providing strong evidence that even-toed ungulates are the land mammals to which cetaceans are most closely related. DNA sequence data also indicate that even-toed ungulates are the land mammals to which cetaceans are most closely related.

Test Your Understanding

1. b **2.** d **3.** d **4.** c **5.** a
7. (a)

(b) The rapid rise in the percentage of mosquitoes resistant to DDT was most likely caused by natural selection in which mosquitoes resistant to DDT could survive and reproduce while other mosquitoes could not. (c) In India—where DDT resistance first appeared—natural selection would have caused the frequency of resistant mosquitoes to increase over time. If resistant mosquitoes then migrated from India (for example, transported by wind or in planes, trains, or ships) to other parts of the world, the frequency of DDT resistance would increase there as well.

Chapter 23

Figure Questions

Figure 23.8 The predicted frequencies are 36% $C^R C^R$, 48% $C^R C^W$, and 16% $C^W C^W$. **Figure 23.12** Local survival should increase in both populations. The increase would probably occur more rapidly among birds born into the central population because gene flow from the mainland is higher in that population. **Figure 23.13** Directional selection. Goldenrain tree has smaller fruit than does the native host, balloon vine. Thus, in soapberry bug populations feeding on goldenrain tree, bugs with shorter beaks had an advantage, resulting in directional selection for shorter beak length. **Figure 23.16** Crossing a single female's eggs with both an SC and an LC male's sperm allowed the researchers to directly compare the effects of the males' contribution to the next generation, since both batches of offspring had the same maternal contribution. This isolation of the male's impact enabled researchers to draw conclusions about differences in genetic "quality" between the SC and LC males. **Figure 23.18** The researchers measured the percentages of successfully reproducing adults in the breeding adult population that had each phenotype. This approach of determining which phenotype was favored by selection assumes that reproduction was a sufficient indicator of relative fitness (as opposed to counting the number of eggs laid or offspring hatched, for example) and that mouth phenotype was the driving factor determining the fish's ability to reproduce.

Concept Check 23.1

1. (a) Within a population, genetic differences among individuals provide the raw material on which natural selection and other mechanisms can act. Without such differences, allele frequencies could not change over time—and hence the population could not evolve. (b) Genetic differences between separate populations can result from natural selection if different alleles are favored in different populations; this might occur, for example, if the different populations experienced different environmental conditions (as in Figure 23.4). Genetic differences between populations can also result from chance events (genetic drift) if the genetic changes have few or no phenotypic effects (as in Figure 23.3). **2.** Many mutations occur in somatic cells, which do not produce gametes and so are lost when the organism dies. Of mutations that do occur in cell lines that produce gametes, many do not have a phenotypic effect on which natural selection can act. Others have a harmful effect and are thus unlikely to increase in frequency because they decrease the reproductive success of their bearers. **3.** Its genetic variation (whether measured at the level of the gene or at the level of nucleotide sequences) would probably drop over time. During meiosis, crossing over and the independent assortment of chromosomes produce many new combinations of alleles. In addition, a population contains a vast number of possible mating combinations, and fertilization brings together the gametes of individuals with different genetic backgrounds. Thus, via crossing over, independent assortment of chromosomes, and fertilization, sexual reproduction reshuffles alleles into fresh combinations each generation. Without sexual reproduction, the rate of forming new combinations of alleles would be vastly reduced, causing the overall amount of genetic variation to drop.

Concept Check 23.2

1. 30,000. Half the loci (10,000) are fixed, meaning only one type of allele exists for each locus: $10,000 \times 1 = 10,000$. There are two types of alleles each for the other loci: $10,000 \times 2 = 20,000$. $10,000 + 20,000 = 30,000$. **2.** $p^2 + 2pq$; p^2 represents homozygotes with two *A* alleles, and *2pq* represents heterozygotes with one *A* allele. **3.** There are 120 individuals in the population, so there are 240 alleles. Of these, there are 124 *A* alleles—32 from the 16 *AA* individuals and 92 from the 92 *Aa* individuals. Thus, the frequency of the *A* allele is $p = 124/240 = 0.52$; hence, the frequency of the *a* allele is $q = 0.48$. Based on the Hardy-Weinberg equation, if the population were not evolving, the frequency of genotype *AA* should be $p^2 = 0.52 \times 0.52 = 0.27$; the frequency of genotype *Aa* should be $2pq = 2 \times 0.52 \times 0.48 = 0.5$; and the frequency of genotype *aa* should be $q^2 = 0.48 \times 0.48 = 0.23$. In a population of 120 individuals, these expected genotype frequencies lead us to predict that there would be 32 *AA* individuals (0.27×120), 60 *Aa* individuals (0.5×120), and 28 *aa* individuals (0.23×120). The actual numbers for the population (16 *AA*, 92 *Aa*, 12 *aa*) deviate from these expectations (fewer homozygotes and more heterozygotes than expected). This indicates that the population is not in Hardy-Weinberg equilibrium and hence may be evolving at this locus.

Concept Check 23.3

1. Natural selection is more "predictable" in that it alters allele frequencies in a nonrandom way: It tends to increase the frequency of alleles that increase the organism's reproductive success in its environment and decrease the frequency of alleles that decrease the organism's reproductive success. Alleles subject to genetic drift increase or decrease in frequency by chance alone, whether or not they are advantageous. **2.** Genetic drift results from chance events that cause allele frequencies to fluctuate at random from generation to generation; within a population, this process tends to decrease genetic variation over time. Gene flow is the exchange of alleles between populations, a process that can introduce new alleles to a population and hence may increase its genetic variation (albeit slightly, since rates of gene flow are often low). **3.** Selection is not important at this locus; furthermore, the populations are not small, and hence the effects of genetic drift should not be pronounced. Gene flow is occurring via the movement of pollen and seeds. Thus, allele and genotype frequencies in these populations should become more similar over time as a result of gene flow.

Concept Check 23.4

1. Zero, because fitness includes reproductive contribution to the next generation, and a sterile mule cannot produce offspring. **2.** Although both gene flow and genetic drift can increase the frequency of advantageous alleles in a population, they can also decrease the frequency of advantageous alleles or increase the frequency of harmful alleles. Only natural selection *consistently* results in an increase in the frequency of alleles that enhance survival or reproduction. Thus, natural selection is the only mechanism that consistently causes adaptive evolution. **3.** The three modes of natural selection (directional, stabilizing, and disruptive) are defined in terms of the selective advantage of different *phenotypes*, not different genotypes. Thus, the type of selection represented by heterozygote advantage depends on the phenotype of the heterozygotes. In this question, because heterozygous individuals have a more extreme phenotype than either homozygote, heterozygote advantage represents directional selection. **4.** Under prolonged low-oxygen conditions, some of the red blood cells of a heterozygote may sickle, leading to harmful effects (see Chapter 14). This does not occur in individuals with two normal hemoglobin alleles, suggesting that there may be selection against heterozygotes in malaria-free regions (where heterozygote advantage does not occur). However, since heterozygotes are healthy under most conditions, selection against them is unlikely to be strong.

Summary of Key Concepts Questions

23.1 One reason biologists estimate gene variability and nucleotide variability is to assess whether populations have enough genetic variation for evolution to occur. Gene variability indicates the extent to which individuals differ genetically at the whole-gene level. Nucleotide variability provides a measure of genetic variation at the DNA sequence level. **23.2** No, this is not an example of circular reasoning. Calculating *p* and *q* from observed genotype frequencies does not imply that those genotype frequencies must be in Hardy-Weinberg equilibrium. Consider a population that has 195 individuals of genotype *AA*, 10 of genotype *Aa*, and 195 of genotype *aa*. Calculating *p* and *q* from these values yields $p = q = 0.5$. Using the Hardy-Weinberg equation, the predicted equilibrium frequencies are $p^2 = 0.25$ for genotype *AA*, $2pq = 0.5$ for genotype *Aa*, and $q^2 = 0.25$ for genotype *aa*. Since there are 400 individuals in the population, these predicted genotype frequencies indicate there should be 100 *AA* individuals, 200 *Aa* individuals, and 100 *aa* individuals—numbers that differ greatly from the values that we used to calculate *p* and *q*. **23.3** It is unlikely that two such populations would evolve in similar ways. Since their environments are very different, the alleles favored by natural selection would probably differ between the two populations; although genetic drift may have important effects in each of these small populations, drift causes unpredictable changes in allele frequencies, so it is unlikely that drift would cause the populations to evolve in similar ways; both populations are geographically isolated, suggesting that little gene flow will occur between them (again making it less likely that they will evolve in similar ways). **23.4** Compared to males, it is likely that the females of such species would be larger, more colorful, endowed with more elaborate ornamentation (for example, a large morphological feature such as the peacock's tail), and more apt to engage in behaviors intended to attract mates or prevent other members of their sex from obtaining mates.

Test Your Understanding

1. e **2.** c **3.** e **4.** b **5.** a **6.** d

---

7. Although natural selection can improve the match between organisms and their environments, the evolutionary process can also lead to imperfections in organisms. A central reason for this is that evolution does not design organisms from scratch to match their environments and ways of life but works instead by a process of descent with modification: Organisms inherit a basic form from their ancestors, and that form is modified by natural selection over time. As a result, a flying mammal such as a bat has wings that are not perfectly designed, but rather represent modifications of forelimbs that bat ancestors used for walking. Imperfections in organisms result from a variety of other constraints, such as a lack of genetic variation for the trait in question, and the fact that adaptations often represent compromises (since organisms must do many different things, and a "perfect" design for one activity might impair the performance of another activity). **8.** The frequency of the *lap*^{94} allele forms a cline, decreasing as one moves from southwest to northeast across Long Island Sound.

A hypothesis that explains the cline and accounts for the observations stated in the question is that the cline is maintained by an interaction between selection and gene flow. Under this hypothesis, in the southwest portion of the Sound, salinity is relatively low, and selection against the *lap*^{94} allele is strong. Moving toward the northeast and into the open ocean, where salinity is relatively high, selection favors a high frequency of the *lap*^{94} allele. However, because mussel larvae disperse long distances, gene flow prevents the *lap*^{94} allele from becoming fixed in the open ocean or from declining to zero in the southwestern portion of Long Island Sound.

Chapter 24

Figure Questions

Figure 24.10 This was done to remove the possibility that the flies could differentiate among potential mates by detecting what those potential mates had eaten as larvae. If this had not been done, the strong preference of "starch flies" and "maltose flies" to mate with like-adapted flies could have occurred simply because the flies could detect (for example, by sense of smell) what their potential mates had eaten as larvae—and they preferred to mate with flies that had a similar smell to their own. **Figure 24.12** Such results would suggest that mate choice based on coloration does not provide a reproductive barrier between these two cichlid species. **Figure 24.13** The graph suggests there has been gene flow of some fire-bellied toad alleles into the range of the yellow-bellied toad. Otherwise, all individuals located to the left of the hybrid zone portion of the graph would have allele frequencies close to 1.0. **Figure 24.14** Because the populations had only just begun to diverge from one another at this point in the process, it is likely that any existing barriers to reproduction would weaken over time. **Figure 24.19** No. Over time, the chromosomes of the experimental hybrids came to resemble those of *H. anomalus*. This occurred even though conditions in the laboratory differed greatly from conditions in the field, where *H. anomalus* is found, suggesting that selection for laboratory conditions was not strong. Thus, it is unlikely that the observed rise in the fertility of the experimental hybrids was due to selection for life under laboratory conditions. **Figure 24.20** The presence of *M. cardinalis* plants that carry the *M. lewisii yup* allele would make it more likely that bumblebees would transfer pollen between the two monkey flower species. As a result, we would expect the number of hybrid offspring to increase.

Concept Check 24.1

1. (a) All except the biological species concept can be applied to both asexual and sexual species because they define species on the basis of characteristics other than ability to reproduce. In contrast, the biological species concept can be applied only to sexual species. (b) The easiest species concept to apply in the field would be the morphological species concept because it is based only on the appearance of the organism. Additional information about its ecological habits, evolutionary history, and reproduction are not required. **2.** Because these birds live in fairly similar environments and can breed successfully in captivity, the reproductive barrier in nature is probably prezygotic; given the species' differences in habitat preference, this barrier could result from habitat isolation.

Concept Check 24.2

1. In allopatric speciation, a new species forms while in geographic isolation from its parent species; in sympatric speciation, a new species forms in the absence of geographic isolation. Geographic isolation greatly reduces gene flow between populations, whereas ongoing gene flow is more likely in sympatric populations. As a result, sympatric speciation is less common than allopatric speciation. **2.** Gene flow between subsets of a population that live in the same area can be reduced in a variety of ways. In some species—especially plants—changes in chromosome number can block gene flow and establish reproductive isolation in a single generation. Gene flow can also be reduced in sympatric populations by habitat differentiation (as seen in the apple maggot fly, *Rhagoletis*) and sexual selection (as seen in Lake Victoria cichlids). **3.** Allopatric speciation would be less likely to occur on a nearby island than on an isolated island of the same size. The reason we expect this result is that continued gene flow between mainland populations and those on a nearby island reduces the chance that enough genetic divergence will take place for allopatric speciation to occur. **4.** If all of the homologs failed to separate during anaphase I of meiosis, some gametes would end up with an extra set of chromosomes (and others would end up with no chromosomes). If a gamete with an extra set of chromosomes fused with a normal gamete, a triploid would result; if two gametes with an extra set of chromosomes fused with each other, a tetraploid would result.

Concept Check 24.3

1. Hybrid zones are regions in which members of different species meet and mate, producing some offspring of mixed ancestry. Such regions can be viewed as "natural laboratories" in which to study speciation because scientists can directly observe factors that cause (or fail to cause) reproductive isolation. **2.** (a) If hybrids consistently survive and reproduce poorly compared to the offspring of intraspecific matings, reinforcement could occur. If it did, natural selection would cause prezygotic barriers to reproduction between the parent species to strengthen over time, decreasing the production of unfit hybrids and leading to a completion of the speciation process. (b) If hybrid offspring survived and reproduced as well as the offspring of intraspecific matings, indiscriminate mating between the parent species would lead to the production of large numbers of hybrid offspring. As these hybrids mated with each other and with members of both parent species, the gene pools of the parent species could fuse over time, reversing the speciation process.

Concept Check 24.4

1. The time between speciation events includes (1) the length of time that it takes for populations of a newly formed species to begin diverging reproductively from one another and (2) the time it takes for speciation to be complete once this divergence begins. Although speciation can occur rapidly once populations have begun to diverge from one another, it may take millions of years for that divergence to begin. **2.** Investigators transferred alleles at the *yup* locus (which influences flower color) from each parent species to the other. *M. lewisii* plants with an *M. cardinalis yup* allele received many more visits from hummingbirds than usual; hummingbirds usually pollinate *M. cardinalis* but avoid *M. lewisii*. Similarly, *M. cardinalis* plants with an *M. lewisii yup* allele received many more visits from bumblebees than usual; bumblebees usually pollinate *M. lewisii* and avoid *M. cardinalis*. Thus, alleles at the *yup* locus can influence pollinator choice, which in these species provides the primary barrier to interspecific mating. Nevertheless, the experiment does not prove that the *yup* locus alone controls barriers to reproduction between *M. lewisii* and *M. cardinalis*; other genes might enhance the effect of the *yup* locus (by modifying flower color) or cause entirely different barriers to reproduction (for example, gametic isolation or a postzygotic barrier). **3.** Crossing over. If crossing over did not occur, each chromosome in an experimental hybrid would remain as in the F_1 generation: composed entirely of DNA from one parent species or the other.

Summary of Key Concepts Questions

24.1 According to the biological species concept, a species is a group of populations whose members interbreed and produce viable, fertile offspring; thus, gene flow occurs between populations of a species. In contrast, members of different species do not interbreed and hence no gene flow occurs between their populations. Overall, then, in the biological species concept, species can be viewed as designated by the *absence* of gene flow—making gene flow of central importance to the biological species concept. **24.2** Sympatric speciation can be promoted by factors such as polyploidy, habitat shifts, and sexual selection, all of which can reduce gene flow between the subpopulations of a larger population. But such factors can also occur in allopatric populations and hence can also promote allopatric speciation. **24.3** If the hybrids are selected against, the hybrid zone could persist if individuals from the parent species regularly travel into the zone, where they mate to produce hybrid offspring. If hybrids are not selected against, there is no cost to the continued production of hybrids, and large numbers of hybrid offspring may be produced. However, natural selection for life in different environments may keep the gene pools of the two parent species distinct—thus preventing the loss (by fusion) of the parent species and once again causing the hybrid zone to be stable over time. **24.4** As the goatsbeard plant, Bahamas mosquitofish, and apple maggot fly examples illustrate, speciation continues to happen today. A new species can begin to form whenever gene flow is reduced between populations of the parent species. Such reductions in gene flow can occur in many ways: A new, geographically isolated population may be founded by a few colonists; some members of the parent species may begin to utilize new habitat; and sexual selection may isolate formerly connected populations or subpopulations. These and many other such events are happening today.

Test Your Understanding
1. b **2.** c **3.** c **4.** a **5.** e **6.** d **7.** e
10. Here is one possibility:

Chapter 25

Figure Questions

Figure 25.2 Proteins are almost always composed of the 20 amino acids shown in Figure 5.16. However, many other amino acids could potentially form in this or any other experiment. For example, any molecule that had a different R group than those listed in Figure 5.16 (yet still contained an α carbon, an amino group, and a carboxyl group) would be an amino acid—yet it would not be one of the 20 amino acids commonly found in nature. **Figure 25.5** Because uranium-238 has a half-life of 4.5 billion years, the x-axis would be relabeled (in billions of years) as 4.5, 9, 13.5, and 18. **Figure 25.10** You should have circled the node, shown in the tree diagram at approximately 580 million years ago (mya), that leads to the echinoderm/chordate lineage and to the lineage that gave rise to brachiopods, annelids, molluscs, and arthropods. Although the 580 mya date is estimated, this common ancestor must be at least as old as any of its descendants. Since fossil molluscs date to about 555 mya, the common ancestor represented by the circled branch point must be at least 555 million years old. **Figure 25.15** The blue curve is for marine animal families. Families often contain many species, so we would expect the percentage of families that became extinct to be lower than the percentage of species that became extinct. **Figure 25.25** The coding sequence of the *Pitx1* gene would differ between the marine and lake populations, but patterns of gene expression would not.

Concept Check 25.1

1. The hypothesis that conditions on early Earth could have permitted the synthesis of organic molecules from inorganic ingredients **2.** In contrast to random mingling of molecules in an open solution, segregation of molecular systems by membranes could concentrate organic molecules, assisting biochemical reactions. **3.** Today, genetic information usually flows from DNA to RNA, as when the DNA sequence of a gene is used as a template to synthesize the mRNA encoding a particular protein. However, the life cycle of retroviruses such as HIV shows that genetic information can flow in the reverse direction (from RNA to DNA). In these viruses, the enzyme reverse transcriptase uses RNA as a template for DNA synthesis, suggesting that a similar enzyme could have played a key role in the transition from an RNA world to a DNA world.

Concept Check 25.2

1. 22,920 years (four half-lives: $5,730 \times 4$) **2.** The fossil record shows that different groups of organisms dominated life on Earth at different points in time and that many organisms once alive are now extinct; specific examples of these points can be found in Figure 25.4. The fossil record also indicates that new groups of organisms can arise via the gradual modification of previously existing organisms, as illustrated by fossils that document the origin of mammals from their cynodont ancestors. **3.** The discovery of such a (hypothetical) fossil organism would indicate that aspects of our current understanding of the origin of mammals are not correct because mammals are thought to have originated much more recently (see Figure 25.6). For example, such a discovery could suggest that the dates of previous fossil discoveries are not correct or that the lineages shown in Figure 25.6 shared features with mammals but were not their direct ancestors. Such a discovery would also suggest that radical changes in multiple aspects of the skeletal structure of organisms could arise suddenly—an idea that is not supported by the known fossil record.

Concept Check 25.3

1. Free oxygen attacks chemical bonds and can inhibit enzymes and damage cells. As a result, prokaryotes that had thrived in anaerobic environments would have survived and reproduced poorly in oxygen-rich environments, driving many species to extinction. **2.** All eukaryotes have mitochondria or remnants of these organelles, but not all eukaryotes have plastids. **3.** A fossil record of life today

Appendix A Answers

A–23   APPENDIX A

would include many organisms with hard body parts (such as vertebrates and many marine invertebrates), but might not include some species we are very familiar with, such as those that have small geographic ranges and/or small population sizes (for example, endangered species such as the giant panda, tiger, and several rhinoceros species).

Concept Check 25.4

1. Continental drift alters the physical geography and climate of Earth, as well as the extent to which organisms are geographically isolated. Because these factors affect extinction and speciation rates, continental drift has a major impact on life on Earth.   2. Mass extinctions; major evolutionary innovations; the diversification of another group of organisms (which can provide new sources of food); migration to new locations where few competitor species exist   3. In principle, fossils of both common and rare species would be present right up to the time of the catastrophic event, then disappear. Reality is more complicated because the fossil record is not perfect. So the most recent fossil for a species might be a million years before the mass extinction—even though the species did not become extinct *until* the mass extinction. This complication is especially likely for rare species because few of their fossils will form and be discovered. Hence, for many rare species, the fossil record would not document that the species was alive immediately before the extinction (even if it was).

Concept Check 25.5

1. Heterochrony can cause a variety of morphological changes. For example, if the onset of sexual maturity changes, a retention of juvenile characteristics (paedomorphosis) may result. Paedomorphosis can be caused by small genetic changes that result in large changes in morphology, as seen in the axolotl salamander.   2. In animal embryos, *Hox* genes influence the development of structures such as limbs and feeding appendages. As a result, changes in these genes—or in the regulation of these genes—are likely to have major effects on morphology.   3. From genetics, we know that gene regulation is altered by how well transcription factors bind to noncoding DNA sequences called control elements. Thus, if changes in morphology are often caused by changes in gene regulation, portions of noncoding DNA that contain control elements are likely to be strongly affected by natural selection.

Concept Check 25.6

1. Complex structures do not evolve all at once, but in increments, with natural selection selecting for adaptive variants of the earlier versions.   2. Although the myxoma virus is highly lethal, initially some of the rabbits are resistant (0.2% of infected rabbits are not killed). Thus, assuming resistance is an inherited trait, we would expect the rabbit population to show a trend for increased resistance to the virus. We would also expect the virus to show an evolutionary trend toward reduced lethality. We would expect this trend because a rabbit infected with a less lethal virus would be more likely to live long enough for a mosquito to bite it and hence potentially transmit the virus to another rabbit. (A virus that kills its rabbit host before a mosquito transmits the virus to another rabbit dies with its host.)

Summary of Key Concepts Questions

Concept 25.1 Particles of montmorillonite clay may have provided surfaces on which organic molecules became concentrated and hence were more likely to react with one another. Montmorillonite clay particles may also have facilitated the transport of key molecules, such as short strands of RNA, into vesicles. These vesicles can form spontaneously from simple precursor molecules, "reproduce" and "grow" on their own, and maintain internal concentrations of molecules that differ from those in the surrounding environment. These features of vesicles represent key steps in the emergence of protocells and (ultimately) the first living cells.   **Concept 25.2** One challenge is that organisms do not use radioisotopes that have long half-lives to build their bones or shells. As a result, fossils older than 75,000 years cannot be dated directly. Fossils are often found in sedimentary rock, but those rocks typically contain sediments of different ages, again posing a challenge when trying to date old fossils. To circumvent these challenges, geologists date layers of volcanic rock that surround old fossils and that use radioisotopes with long half-lives. This approach provides minimum and maximum estimates for the ages of fossils sandwiched between two layers of volcanic rock.   **Concept 25.3** The "Cambrian explosion" refers to a relatively short interval of time (535–525 million years ago) during which large forms of many present-day animal phyla first appear in the fossil record. The evolutionary changes that occurred during this time, such as the appearance of large predators and well-defended prey, were important because they set the stage for many of the key events in the history of life over the last 500 million years.   **Concept 25.4** The broad evolutionary changes documented by the fossil record reflect the rise and fall of major groups of organisms. In turn, the rise or fall of any particular group results from a balance between speciation and extinction rates: A group increases in size when the rate at which its members produce new species is greater than the rate at which its member species are lost to extinction, while a group shrinks in size if extinction rates are greater than speciation rates.   **Concept 25.5** Yes. A change to the sequence or regulation of a developmental gene can produce major morphological changes. In some cases, such morphological changes may enable organisms to perform new functions or live in new environments—thus potentially leading to an adaptive radiation and the formation of a new group of organisms.   **Concept 25.6** Evolutionary change results from interactions between organisms and their current environments. No goal is involved in this process. As environments change over time, the features of organisms favored by natural selection may also change. When this happens, what once may have seemed like a "goal" of evolution (for example, improvements in the function of a feature previously favored by natural selection) may cease to be beneficial or may even be harmful.

Test Your Understanding
1. c   2. a   3. e   4. b   5. d
6.

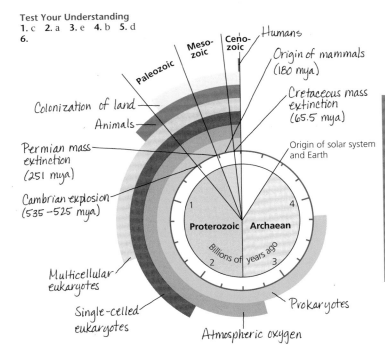

7. c   8. b

Chapter 26

Figure Questions

Figure 26.5 This new version does not alter any of the evolutionary relationships shown in Figure 26.5. For example, B and C remain sister taxa, taxon A is still as closely related to taxon B as it is to taxon C, and so on.

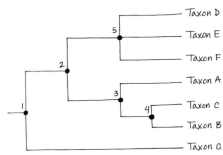

Figure 26.6 Unknown 1b (a portion of sample 1) and Unknowns 9–13 all would have to be located on the branch of the tree that currently leads to Minke (Southern Hemisphere) and Unknowns 1a and 2–8. **Figure 26.9** There are four possible bases (A, C, G, T) at each nucleotide position. If the base at each position depends on chance, not common descent, we would expect roughly one out of four (25%) of them to be the same. **Figure 26.11** You should have drawn a box around the frog, turtle, and leopard lineages, along with their most recent common ancestor. **Figure 26.12** The zebrafish lineage; of the five vertebrate lineages shown, its branch is the longest. **Figure 26.16** The lizard and snake lineage is the most basal taxon shown (closest to the root of the tree). Among the descendants of the common ancestor indicated by the blue dot, the crocodilian lineage is the most basal. **Figure 26.19** The molecular clock indicates that the divergence time is roughly 45–50 million years. **Figure 26.21** As shown in this diagram, Bacteria was the first to emerge and Archaea is the sister domain to Eukarya.

Concept Check 26.1

1. We are classified the same from the domain level to the class level; both the leopard and human are mammals. Leopards belong to order Carnivora, whereas humans do not.   2. The branching pattern of the tree indicates that the badger and the wolf share a common ancestor that is more recent than the ancestor that these two animals share with the leopard.   3. The tree in (c) shows a different pattern of evolutionary relationships. In (c), C and B are sister taxa, whereas C and D are sister taxa in (a) and (b).

4.

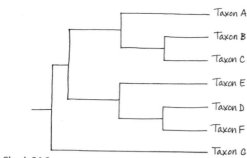

Taxon A
Taxon B
Taxon C
Taxon E
Taxon D
Taxon F
Taxon G

Concept Check 26.2

1. (a) Analogy, since porcupines and cacti are not closely related and since most other animals and plants do not have similar structures; (b) homology, since cats and humans are both mammals and have homologous forelimbs, of which the hand and paw are the lower part; (c) analogy, since owls and hornets are not closely related and since the structure of their wings is very different **2.** Species 2 and 3 are more likely to be closely related. Small genetic changes (as between species 2 and 3) can produce divergent physical appearances, but if many genes have diverged greatly (as in species 1 and 2), then the lineages have probably been separate for a long time.

Concept Check 26.3

1. No; when comparing groups of mammals, hair is a shared ancestral character common to all mammals and thus is not helpful in distinguishing different mammalian subgroups. **2.** The principle of maximum parsimony states that the hypothesis about nature we investigate first should be the simplest explanation found to be consistent with the facts. Actual evolutionary relationships may differ from those inferred by parsimony owing to complicating factors such as convergent evolution. **3.** The traditional classification provides a poor match to evolutionary history, thus violating the basic principle of cladistics—that classification should be based on common descent. Both birds and mammals originated from groups traditionally designated as reptiles, making reptiles (as traditionally delineated) a paraphyletic group. These problems can be addressed by removing *Dimetrodon* and cynodonts from the reptiles and by considering birds as a group of reptiles (specifically, as a group of dinosaurs).

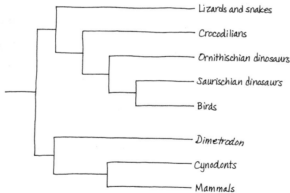

Lizards and snakes
Crocodilians
Ornithischian dinosaurs
Saurischian dinosaurs
Birds
Dimetrodon
Cynodonts
Mammals

Concept Check 26.4

1. Proteins are gene products. Their amino acid sequences are determined by the nucleotide sequences of the DNA that codes for them. Thus, differences between comparable proteins in two species reflect underlying genetic differences that have accumulated as the species diverged from one another. As a result, differences between the proteins can reflect the evolutionary history of the species. **2.** In RNA processing, the exons or coding regions of a gene can be spliced together in different ways, yielding different mRNAs and hence different protein products. As a result, different proteins could potentially be produced from the same gene in different tissues, thereby enabling the gene to perform different functions in these different tissues. **3.** These observations suggest that the evolutionary lineages leading to species 1 and species 2 diverged from one another before a gene duplication event in species 1 produced gene B from gene A.

Concept Check 26.5

1. A molecular clock is a method of estimating the actual time of evolutionary events based on numbers of base changes in orthologous genes. It is based on the assumption that the regions of genomes being compared evolve at constant rates. **2.** There are many portions of the genome that do not code for genes; many base changes in these regions could accumulate through drift without affecting an organism's fitness. Even in coding regions of the genome, some mutations may not have a critical effect on genes or proteins. **3.** The gene (or genes) used for the molecular clock may have evolved more slowly in these two taxa than in the species used to calibrate the clock; as a result, the clock would underestimate the time at which the taxa diverged from each other.

Concept Check 26.6

1. The kingdom Monera included bacteria and archaea, but we now know that these organisms are in separate domains. Kingdoms are subsets of domains, so a

single kingdom (like Monera) that includes taxa from different domains is not valid. **2.** Because of horizontal gene transfer, some genes in eukaryotes are more closely related to bacteria, while others are more closely related to archaea; thus, depending on which genes are used, phylogenetic trees constructed from DNA data can yield conflicting results.

3.

Archaea
Bacteria
Eukarya

Bacteria
Archaea
Eukarya

Eukarya
Bacteria
Archaea

The fossil record indicates that prokaryotes originated long before eukaryotes. This suggests that the third tree, in which the eukaryotic lineage diverged first, is not accurate and hence is not likely to receive support from genetic data.

Summary of Key Concepts Questions

26.1 The fact that humans and chimpanzees are sister species indicates that we share a more recent common ancestor with chimpanzees than we do with any other living primate species. But that does not mean that humans evolved from chimpanzees, or vice versa; instead, it indicates that both humans and chimpanzees are descendants of that common ancestor. **26.2** Homologous characters result from shared ancestry. As organisms diverge over time, some of their homologous characters will also diverge. The homologous characters of organisms that diverged long ago typically differ more than do the homologous characters of organisms that diverged more recently. As a result, differences in homologous characters can be used to infer phylogeny. In contrast, analogous characters result from convergent evolution, not shared ancestry, and hence can give misleading estimates of phylogeny. **26.3** All features of organisms arose at some point in the history of life. In the group in which a new feature first arises, that feature is a shared derived character that is unique to that clade. The group in which each shared derived character first appears can be determined, and the resulting nested pattern can be used to infer evolutionary history. **26.4** Orthologous genes should be used; for such genes, the homology results from speciation and hence reflects evolutionary history. **26.5** A key assumption of molecular clocks is that nucleotide substitutions occur at fixed rates and hence the number of nucleotide differences between two DNA sequences is proportional to the time since the sequences diverged from each other. Some limitations of molecular clocks: No gene marks time with complete precision; natural selection can favor certain DNA changes over others; nucleotide substitution rates can change over long periods of time (causing molecular clocks estimates of when events in the distant past occurred to be highly uncertain); and the same gene can evolve at different rates in different organisms **26.6** Genetic data indicated that many prokaryotes differed as much from each other as they did from eukaryotes. This indicated that organisms should be grouped into three "super-kingdoms," or domains (Archaea, Bacteria, Eukarya). These data also indicated that the previous kingdom Monera (which had contained all the prokaryotes) did not make biological sense and should be abandoned. Later genetic and morphological data also indicated that the former kingdom Protista (which had primarily contained single-celled organisms) should be abandoned because it was polyphyletic.

Test Your Understanding

1. b **2.** d **3.** a **4.** d **5.** d **6.** c **7.** d

9. (a)

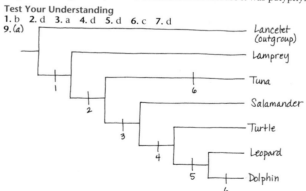

Lancelet (outgroup)
Lamprey
Tuna
Salamander
Turtle
Leopard
Dolphin

(b)

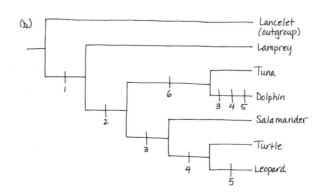

Lancelet (outgroup)
Lamprey
Tuna
Dolphin
Salamander
Turtle
Leopard

(c) The tree in (a) requires seven evolutionary changes, while the tree in (b) requires nine evolutionary changes. Thus, the tree in (a) is more parsimonious, since it requires fewer evolutionary changes.

Chapter 27

Figure Questions

Figure 27.10 It is likely that the expression or sequence of genes that affect glucose metabolism may have changed; genes for metabolic processes no longer needed by the cell also may have changed. **Figure 27.11** Transduction results in horizontal gene transfer when the host and recipient cells are members of different species. **Figure 27.16** Thermophiles live in very hot environments, so it is likely that their enzymes can continue to function normally at much higher temperatures than do the enzymes of other organisms. At low temperatures, however, the enzymes of thermophiles may not function as well as the enzymes of other organisms. **Figure 27.18** From the graph, plant uptake can be estimated as 0.7, 0.6, and 0.95 (mg K) for strains 1, 2, and 3, respectively. These values average to 0.75 mg K. If bacteria had no effect, the average plant uptake of potassium for strains 1, 2, and 3 should be close to 0.5 mg K, the value observed for plants grown in bacteria-free soil.

Concept Check 27.1

1. Adaptations include the capsule (shields prokaryotes from host's immune system) and endospores (enable cells to survive harsh conditions and to revive when the environment becomes favorable). **2.** Prokaryotic cells generally lack the internal compartmentalization of eukaryotic cells. Prokaryotic genomes have much less DNA than eukaryotic genomes, and most of this DNA is contained in a single ring-shaped chromosome located in the nucleoid rather than within a true membrane-bounded nucleus. In addition, many prokaryotes also have plasmids, small ring-shaped DNA molecules containing a few genes. **3.** Plastids such as chloroplasts are thought to have evolved from an endosymbiotic photosynthetic prokaryote. More specifically, the phylogenetic tree shown in Figure 26.21 indicates that plastids are closely related to cyanobacteria. Hence, we can hypothesize that the thylakoid membranes of chloroplasts resemble those of cyanobacteria because chloroplasts evolved from a cyanobacterium endosymbiont.

Concept Check 27.2

1. Prokaryotes have extremely large population sizes, in part because they have short generation times. The large number of individuals in prokaryotic populations makes it likely that in each generation there will be thousands of individuals that have new mutations at any particular gene, thereby adding considerable genetic diversity to the population. **2.** In transformation, naked, foreign DNA from the environment is taken up by a bacterial cell. In transduction, phages carry bacterial genes from one bacterial cell to another. In conjugation, a bacterial cell directly transfers plasmid or chromosomal DNA to another cell via a mating bridge that temporarily connects the two cells. **3.** The population that includes individuals capable of conjugation would probably be more successful, since some of its members could form recombinant cells whose new gene combinations might be advantageous in a novel environment. **4.** Yes. Genes for antibiotic resistance could be transferred (by transformation, transduction, or conjugation) from the nonpathogenic bacterium to a pathogenic bacterium; this could make the pathogen an even greater threat to human health. In general, transformation, transduction, and conjugation tend to increase the spread of resistance genes.

Concept Check 27.3

1. A phototroph derives its energy from light, while a chemotroph gets its energy from chemical sources. An autotroph derives its carbon from a form of CO_2, while a heterotroph gets its carbon from organic nutrients such as glucose. Thus, there are four nutritional modes: photoautotrophic, photoheterotrophic (unique to prokaryotes), chemoautotrophic (unique to prokaryotes), and chemoheterotrophic. **2.** Chemoheterotrophy; the bacterium must rely on chemical sources of energy, since it is not exposed to light, and it must be a heterotroph if it requires a source of carbon other than CO_2 (or a related compound, such as bicarbonate). **3.** If humans could fix nitrogen, we could build proteins using atmospheric N_2 and hence would not need to eat high-protein foods such as meat, fish, or soy. Our diet would, however, need to include a source of carbon, along with minerals and water. Thus, a typical meal might consist of carbohydrates as a carbon source, along with fruits and vegetables to provide essential minerals (and additional carbon).

Concept Check 27.4

1. Before molecular systematics, taxonomists classified prokaryotes according to phenotypic characters that did not clarify evolutionary relationships. Molecular comparisons—of DNA in particular—indicate key divergences in prokaryotic lineages. **2.** By not requiring that organisms be cultured in the laboratory, genetic prospecting has revealed an immense diversity of previously unknown prokaryotic species. Over time, the ongoing discovery of new species by genetic prospecting is likely to alter our understanding of prokaryotic phylogeny greatly. **3.** At present, all known methanogens are archaea in the clade Euryarchaeota; this suggests that this unique metabolic pathway probably arose in ancestral species within Euryarchaeota. Since Bacteria and Archaea have been separate evolutionary lineages for billions of years, the discovery of a methanogen from the domain Bacteria would suggest that adaptations that enabled the use of CO_2 to oxidize H_2 may have evolved twice—once in Archaea (within Euryarchaeota) and once in Bacteria. (It is also possible that a newly discovered bacterial methanogen could have acquired the genes for this metabolic pathway by horizontal gene transfer from a methanogen in domain Archaea. However, horizontal gene transfer is not a likely explanation because of the large number of genes involved and because gene transfers between species in different domains are rare.)

Concept Check 27.5

1. Although prokaryotes are small, their large numbers and metabolic abilities enable them to play key roles in ecosystems by decomposing wastes, recycling chemicals, and affecting the concentrations of nutrients available to other organisms. **2.** Cyanobacteria produce oxygen when water is split in the light reactions of photosynthesis. The Calvin cycle incorporates CO_2 from the air into organic molecules, which are then converted to sugars.

Concept Check 27.6

1. Sample answers: eating fermented foods such as yogurt, sourdough bread, or cheese; receiving clean water from sewage treatment; taking medicines produced by bacteria **2.** No. If the poison is secreted as an exotoxin, live bacteria could be transmitted to another person. But the same is true if the poison is an endotoxin—only in this case, the live bacteria that are transmitted may be descendants of the (now-dead) bacteria that produced the poison. **3.** Some of the many different species of prokaryotes that live in the human gut compete with one another for resources (in the food you eat). Because different prokaryotic species have different adaptations, a change in diet may alter which species can grow most rapidly, thus altering species abundance.

Summary of Key Concepts Questions

27.1. Prokaryotes are small, they have short generation times, and their populations can consist of trillions of individuals. As a result, populations of prokaryotes can evolve substantially in short periods of time, enabling them to adapt to a wide range of environments. Specific structural features that enable prokaryotes to thrive in diverse environments include their cell walls (which provide shape and protection), flagella (which function in directed movement), and ability to form endospores (which enable tolerance of harsh conditions). Prokaryotes also possess biochemical adaptations for growth in varied conditions, such as those that enable them to tolerate extremely hot or salty environments. **27.2** Prokaryotes reproduce extremely rapidly, and their populations can number in the trillions. As a result, even though mutations are rare, every day thousands of offspring are produced that have new mutations at particular gene loci. In addition, even though prokaryotes reproduce asexually and hence the vast majority of offspring are genetically identical to their parent, the genetic variation of their populations can be increased by transduction, transformation, and conjugation. Each of these (nonreproductive) processes can increase genetic variation by transferring DNA from one cell to another—even among cells that are of different species. **27.3** Prokaryotes have an exceptionally broad range of metabolic adaptations. As a group, prokaryotes perform all four modes of nutrition (photoautotrophy, chemoautotrophy, photoheterotrophy, and chemoheterotrophy), whereas eukaryotes perform only two of these (photoautotrophy and chemoheterotrophy). Prokaryotes are also able to metabolize nitrogen in a wide variety of forms (again unlike eukaryotes), and they frequently cooperate with other prokaryotic cells of the same or different species. **27.4** Phenotypic criteria such as shape, motility, and nutritional mode do not provide a clear picture of the evolutionary history of the prokaryotes. In contrast, molecular data have elucidated relationships among major groups of prokaryotes. Molecular data have also allowed researchers to sample genes directly from the environment; using such genes to construct phylogenies has led to the discovery of major new groups of prokaryotes. **27.5** Prokaryotes play key roles in the chemical cycles on which life depends. For example, prokaryotes are important decomposers, breaking down corpses and waste materials, thereby releasing nutrients to the environment where they can be used by other organisms. Prokaryotes also convert inorganic compounds to forms that other organisms can use. With respect to their ecological interactions, many prokaryotes form life-sustaining mutualisms with other species. In some cases, such as hydrothermal vent communities, the metabolic activities of prokaryotes provide an energy source on which hundreds of other species depend; in the absence of the prokaryotes, the community collapses. **27.6** Human well-being depends on our associations with mutualistic prokaryotes, such as the many species that live in our intestines and digest food that we cannot. Humans also can harness the remarkable metabolic capabilities of prokaryotes to produce a wide range of useful products. Negative effects of prokaryotes result primarily from bacterial pathogens that cause disease.

Test Your Understanding

1. e **2.** a **3.** d **4.** d **5.** b **6.** a
8. (a)

(b) Some *Rhizobium* strains are much more effective at promoting plant growth than other *Rhizobium* strains; the most ineffective strains have little positive effect (plant growth with these strains differs little from plant growth in the absence of *Rhizobium*). The ineffective strains may transfer relatively little nitrogen to their plant host, limiting plant growth.

Chapter 28

Figure Questions

Figure 28.10 Merozoites are produced by the asexual (mitotic) cell division of haploid sporozoites; similarly, gametocytes are produced by the asexual cell division of merozoites. Hence, it is likely that individuals in these three stages have the same complement of genes and that morphological differences between them result from changes in gene expression. **Figure 28.16** The sperm cells in the diagram are produced by the asexual (mitotic) division of cells in a single male gametophyte, which was itself produced by the asexual (mitotic) division of a single zoospore. Thus, the sperm cells are all derived from a single zoospore and so are genetically identical to one another. However, the male gametophyte that produced the sperm developed from one zoospore, while the female gametophyte that produced the egg developed from a different zoospore. Zoospores are produced by meiosis, so each zoospore differs genetically from the others. Hence, the sperm cells (which can be traced back to one zoospore) differ genetically from the egg cell (which can be traced back to another zoospore). **Figure 28.22** The following stage should be circled: step 6, where a mature cell undergoes mitosis and forms four or more daughter cells. In step 7, the zoospores eventually grow into mature haploid cells, but they do not produce new daughter cells. Likewise, in step 2, a mature cell develops into a gamete, but it does not produce new daughter cells. **Figure 28.23** If the assumption is correct, then their results indicate that the DHFR-TS gene fusion may be a derived trait shared by members of four supergroups of eukaryotes (Excavata, Chromalveolata, Rhizaria, and Archaeplastida). However, if the assumption is not correct, the presence or absence of the gene fusion may tell little about phylogenetic history. For example, if the genes fused multiple times, groups could share the trait because of convergent evolution rather than common descent. If the genes were secondarily split, a group with such a split could be placed (incorrectly) in Unikonta rather than its correct placement in one of the other four supergroups. **Figure 28.28** If diatom populations decrease in size as global temperatures warm, less carbon dioxide would be "pumped" from surface waters to the deep ocean floor. Atmospheric carbon dioxide levels might increase as a result, thereby potentially causing further warming. If this process continues, a positive-feedback loop would result in which warming causes diatom populations to drop, thereby causing additional warming, further drops in diatom populations, and so on.

Concept Check 28.1

1. Sample response: Protists include unicellular, colonial, and multicellular organisms; photoautotrophs, heterotrophs, and mixotrophs; species that reproduce asexually, sexually, or both ways; and organisms with diverse physical forms and adaptations.   2. Strong evidence shows that eukaryotes acquired mitochondria after an early eukaryote first engulfed and then formed an endosymbiotic association with an alpha proteobacterium. Similarly, chloroplasts in red and green algae appear to have descended from a photosynthetic cyanobacterium that was engulfed by an ancient heterotrophic eukaryote. Secondary endosymbiosis also played an important role: Various protist lineages acquired plastids by engulfing unicellular red or green algae.   3. The modified tree would look as follows:

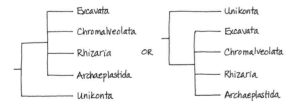

Concept Check 28.2

1. Their mitochondria do not have an electron transport chain and so cannot function in aerobic respiration.   2. Since the unknown protist is more closely related to diplomonads than to euglenids, it must have originated after the diplomonads and parabasalids diverged from the euglenozoans. In addition, since the unknown species has fully functional mitochondria—yet both diplomonads and parabasalids do not—it is likely that the unknown species originated *before* the last common ancestor of the diplomonads and parabasalids.

Concept Check 28.3

1. Some DNA data indicate that Chromalveolata is a monophyletic group, but other DNA data fail to support this result. In support of monophyly, for many species in the group, the structure of their plastids and the sequence of their plastid DNA suggest that the group originated by a secondary endosymbiosis event (in which a red alga was engulfed). However, other species in the group lack plastids entirely, making the secondary endosymbiosis hypothesis difficult to test.   2. The plastid DNA would likely be more similar to the chromosomal DNA of cyanobacteria based on the well-supported hypothesis that eukaryotic plastids (such as those found in the eukaryotic groups listed) originated by an endosymbiosis event in which a eukaryote engulfed a cyanobacterium. If the plastid is derived from the cyanobacterium, its DNA would be derived from the bacterial DNA.   3. Figure 13.6b. Algae and plants with alternation

of generations have a multicellular haploid stage *and* a multicellular diploid stage. In the other two life cycles, either the haploid stage or the diploid stage is unicellular.

Concept Check 28.4

1. Because foram tests are hardened with calcium carbonate, they form long-lasting fossils in marine sediments and sedimentary rocks.   2. Convergent evolution. The different organisms have come to display similar morphological adaptations over time owing to their similar lifestyles.   3. During photosynthesis, aerobic algae produce O_2 and use CO_2. O_2 is produced as a by-product of the light reactions, while CO_2 is used as an input to the Calvin cycle (the end products of which are sugars). Aerobic algae also perform cellular respiration, which uses O_2 as an input and produces CO_2 as a waste product.

Concept Check 28.5

1. Many red algae contain an accessory pigment called phycoerythrin, which gives them a reddish color and allows them to carry out photosynthesis in relatively deep coastal water. Also unlike brown algae, red algae have no flagellated stages in their life cycle and must depend on water currents to bring gametes together for fertilization.   2. *Ulva*'s thallus contains many cells and is differentiated into leaflike blades and a rootlike holdfast. *Caulerpa*'s thallus is composed of multinucleate filaments without cross-walls, so it is essentially one large cell.   3. Red algae have no flagellated stages in their life cycle and hence must depend on water currents to bring their gametes together. This feature of their biology might increase the difficulty of reproducing on land. In contrast, the gametes of green algae are flagellated, making it possible for them to swim in thin films of water. In addition, a variety of green algae contain compounds in their cytoplasm, cell wall, or zygote coat that protect against intense sunlight and other terrestrial conditions. Such compounds may have increased the chance that descendants of green algae could survive on land.

Concept Check 28.6

1. Amoebozoans have lobe-shaped pseudopodia, whereas forams have threadlike pseudopodia.   2. Slime molds are fungus-like in that they produce fruiting bodies that aid in the dispersal of spores, and they are animal-like in that they are motile and ingest food. However, slime molds are more closely related to gymnamoebas and entamoebas than to fungi or animals.   3. Support. Unikonts lack the unique cytoskeletal features shared by many excavates (see Concept 28.2). Thus, if the unikonts were the first group of eukaryotes to diverge from other eukaryotes (as shown in Figure 28.23), it would be unlikely that the eukaryote common ancestor had the cytoskeletal features found today in many excavates. Such a result would strengthen the case that many excavates share cytoskeletal features because they are members of a monophyletic group, the Excavata.

Concept Check 28.7

1. Because photosynthetic protists constitute the base of aquatic food webs, many aquatic organisms depend on them for food, either directly or indirectly. (In addition, a substantial percentage of the oxygen produced in photosynthesis on Earth is made by photosynthetic protists.)   2. Protists form mutualistic and parasitic associations with other organisms. Examples include photosynthetic dinoflagellates that form a mutualistic symbiosis with coral polyps, parabasalids that form a mutualistic symbiosis with termites, and the oomycete *Phytophthora ramorum*, a parasite of oak trees.   3. Corals depend on their dinoflagellate symbionts for nourishment, so coral bleaching would be expected to cause the corals to die. As the corals die, less food will be available for fishes and other species that eat coral. As a result, populations of these species may decline, and that, in turn, might cause populations of their predators to decline.

Summary of Key Concepts Questions

28.1 Sample response: Protists, plants, animals, and fungi are similar in that their cells have a nucleus and other membrane-bounded organelles, unlike the cells of prokaryotes. These membrane-bounded organelles make the cells of eukaryotes more complex than the cells of prokaryotes. With respect to differences between protists and other eukaryotes, most protists are unicellular, unlike animals, plants, and most fungi. Protists also have greater nutritional diversity than other eukaryotes. **28.2** Unique cytoskeletal features are shared by many excavates. In addition, some members of Excavata have an "excavated" feeding groove for which the group was named. DNA evidence does not strongly support or refute Excavata as a group. Overall, evidence for the group is relatively weak. **28.3** We can infer that the common ancestor of the group had a plastid, in this case of red algal origin. Thus, we would expect that members of Chromalveolata either would have plastids or would have lost their plastids over the course of evolution. **28.4** The main subgroups are the radiolarians, the forams, and the cercozoans. They are united as a clade by DNA similarities. **28.5** Red algae, green algae, and land plants are placed in the same supergroup because considerable evidence indicates that these organisms all descended from the same ancestor, an ancient heterotrophic protist that acquired a cyanobacterial endosymbiont. **28.6** The unikonts are a diverse group of eukaryotes that includes many protists, along with animals and fungi. Most of the protists in Unikonta are amoebozoans, a clade of amoebas that have lobe- or tube-shaped pseudopodia (as opposed to the threadlike pseudopodia of rhizarians). Other protists in Unikonta include several groups that are closely related to fungi and several other groups that are closely related to animals. **28.7** Sample response: Ecologically important protists include photosynthetic dinoflagellates that provide essential sources of energy to their symbiotic partners, the corals that build coral reefs. Other important protistan symbionts include those that enable termites to digest wood and *Plasmodium*, the pathogen that causes malaria. Photosynthetic protists such as diatoms are among the most important producers in aquatic communities; as such, many other species in aquatic environments depend on them for food.

Test Your Understanding

1. d **2.** b **3.** c **4.** e **5.** d **6.** d

7.

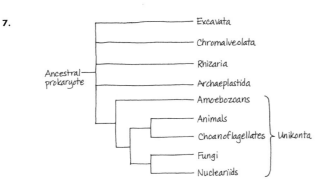

Pathogens that share a relatively recent common ancestor with humans should also share metabolic and structural characteristics with humans. Because drugs target the pathogen's metabolism or structure, developing drugs that harm the pathogen but not the patient should be most difficult for pathogens with whom we share the most recent evolutionary history. Working backward in time, we can use the phylogenetic tree to determine the order in which humans shared a common ancestor with pathogens in different taxa. This process leads to the prediction that it should be hardest to develop drugs to combat animal pathogens, followed by choanoflagellate pathogens, fungal and nucleariid pathogens, amoebozoans, other protists, and finally prokaryotes.

Chapter 29

Figure Questions
Figure 29.5 The life cycle in Figure 13.6b has alternation of generations; the others do not. Unlike the animal life cycle (Figure 13.6a), in alternation of generations, meiosis produces spores, not gametes. These spores then divide repeatedly by mitosis, ultimately forming a multicellular haploid individual that produces gametes. There is no multicellular haploid stage in the animal life cycle. An alternation of generations life cycle also has a multicellular diploid stage, whereas the life cycle shown in Figure 13.6c does not. **Figure 29.8** Yes. As shown in the diagram, the sperm cell and the egg cell that fuse each resulted from the mitotic division of spores produced by the same sporophyte. However, these spores would differ genetically from one another because they were produced by meiosis, a cell division process that generates genetic variation among the offspring cells. **Figure 29.10** Because the moss reduces nitrogen loss from the ecosystem, species that typically colonize the soils after the moss probably experience higher soil nitrogen levels than they otherwise would. The resulting increased availability of nitrogen may benefit these species because nitrogen is an essential nutrient that often is in short supply. **Figure 29.13** A fern that had wind-dispersed sperm would not require water for fertilization, thus removing a difficulty that ferns face when they live in arid environments. The fern would also be under strong selection to produce sperm above ground (as opposed to the current situation, where some fern gametophytes are located below ground). **Figure 29.16** When not reproducing, the lycophyte trees that dominate this forest would resemble poles covered by short leaves (microphylls). Since the trees would not have a branched canopy at their tops, the forest would be very open, and a considerable amount of light would reach the ground level.

Concept Check 29.1
1. Land plants share some key traits only with charophytes: rings of cellulose-synthesizing complexes, presence of peroxisome enzymes, similarity in sperm structure, and the formation of a phragmoplast in cell division. Comparisons of nuclear and chloroplast genes also point to a common ancestry. **2.** Spore walls toughened by sporopollenin (protects against harsh environmental conditions); multicellular, dependent embryos (provides nutrients and protection to the developing embryo); cuticle (reduces water loss) **3.** The multicellular diploid stage of the life cycle would not produce gametes. Instead, both males and females would produce haploid spores by meiosis. These spores would give rise to multicellular male and female haploid stages—a major change from the single-celled haploid stages (sperm and eggs) that we actually have. The multicellular haploid stages would produce gametes and reproduce sexually. An individual at the multicellular haploid stage of the human life cycle might look like us, or it might look completely different. **4.** Land plants, vascular plants, and seed plants are monophyletic because each of these groups includes the common ancestor of the group and all of the descendants of that common ancestor. The other two categories of plants, the nonvascular plants and the seedless vascular plants, are paraphyletic: These groups do not include all of the descendants of the group's most recent common ancestor.

Concept Check 29.2
1. Bryophytes do not have a vascular transport system, and their life cycle is dominated by gametophytes rather than sporophytes. **2.** Answers may include the following: Large surface area of protonema enhances absorption of water and minerals; the vase-shaped archegonia protect eggs during fertilization and transport nutrients to the embryos via placental transfer cells; the stalk-like seta conducts nutrients from the gametophyte to the capsule, where spores are produced; the peristome enables gradual spore discharge; stomata enable CO_2/O_2 exchange while minimizing water loss; lightweight spores are readily dispersed by wind.

3.

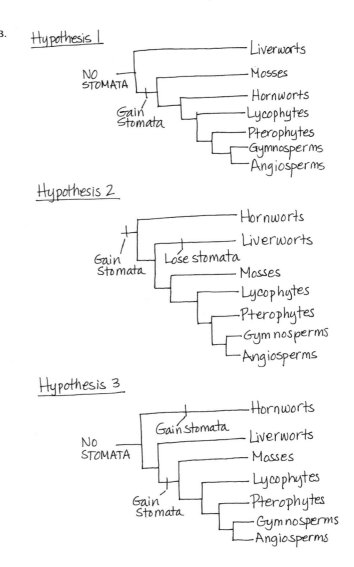

Concept Check 29.3
1. Lycophytes have microphylls, whereas seed plants and pterophytes (ferns and their relatives) have megaphylls. Pterophytes and seed plants also share other traits not found in lycophytes, such as overtopping growth and the initiation of new root branches at various points along the length of an existing root. **2.** Both seedless vascular plants and bryophytes have flagellated sperm that require moisture for fertilization; this shared similarity poses challenges for these species in arid regions. With respect to key differences, seedless vascular plants have lignified, well-developed vascular tissue, a trait that enables the sporophyte to grow tall and that has transformed life on Earth (via the formation of forests). Seedless vascular plants also have true leaves and roots, which, when compared with bryophytes, provide increased surface area for photosynthesis and improve their ability to extract nutrients from soil. **3.** If lycophytes and pterophytes formed a clade, the traits shared by pterophytes and seed plants might have been present in the common ancestor of all vascular plants, but lost in the lycophytes. Alternatively, the common ancestor of all vascular plants may have lacked the traits shared by pterophytes and seed plants; in this case, pterophytes and seed plants would share these traits as a result of convergent evolution. **4.** Three mechanisms contribute to the production of genetic variation in sexual reproduction: independent assortment of chromosomes, crossing over, and random fertilization. If fertilization were to occur between gametes from the same gametophyte, all of the offspring would be genetically identical. This would be the case because all of the cells produced by a gametophyte—including its sperm and egg cells—are the descendants of a single spore and hence are genetically identical. Genetic variation would continue to be generated by the first two mechanisms mentioned, but overall, the amount of genetic variation produced by sexual reproduction would drop.

Summary of Key Concepts Questions
29.1

29.2 Some mosses colonize bare, sandy soils, leading to the increased retention of nitrogen in these otherwise low-nitrogen environments. Other mosses harbor nitrogen-fixing cyanobacteria that increase the availability of nitrogen in the ecosystem. The moss *Sphagnum* is often a major component of deposits of peat (partially decayed organic material). Boggy regions with thick layers of peat, known as peatlands, cover broad geographic regions and contain large reservoirs of carbon. By storing large amounts of carbon—in effect, removing CO_2 from the atmosphere—peatlands affect the global climate, making them of considerable ecological importance.
29.3 Lignified vascular tissue provided the strength needed to support a tall plant against gravity, as well as a means to transport water and nutrients to plant parts located high above ground. Roots were another key trait, anchoring the plant to the ground and providing additional structural support for plants that grew tall. Tall plants could shade shorter plants, thereby outcompeting them for light. Because the spores of a tall plant disperse farther than the spores of a short plant, it is also likely that tall plants could colonize new habitats more rapidly than short plants.

Test Your Understanding
1. b **2.** e **3.** d **4.** c **5.** a **6.** a. diploid; b. haploid; c. haploid; d. diploid; e. haploid **7.** c
8. Based on our current understanding of the evolution of major plant groups, the phylogeny has the four branch points shown here:

Derived characters unique to the charophyte and land plant clade (indicated by branch point 1) include rings of cellulose-synthesizing complexes, peroxisome enzymes, flagellated sperm structure, and a phragmoplast. Derived characters unique to the land plant clade (branch point 2) include apical meristems, alternation of generations, walled spores produced in sporangia, and multicellular gametangia. Derived characters unique to the vascular plant clade (branch point 3) include life cycles with dominant sporophytes, complex vascular systems (xylem and phloem), and well-developed roots and leaves. Derived characters unique to the pterophyte and seed plant clade (branch point 4) include megaphylls and overtopping growth.
9. (a)

(b) In the first 40 years after a fire, nitrogen fixation rates were below 0.01 kg per ha per yr, which was less than 1% of the amount of nitrogen deposited from the atmosphere. Thus, in the initial decades after a fire, the moss *Pleurozium* and the nitrogen-fixing bacteria it harbors had relatively little effect on the amount of nitrogen added to the forest. With time, however, *Pleurozium* and its symbiotic, nitrogen-fixing bacteria became increasingly important. By 170 years after a fire, the percentage of the ground surface covered by the moss had increased to about 70%, leading to a corresponding increase in populations of the symbiotic bacteria. As would be predicted from this result, in older forests considerably more nitrogen (130–300%) was added by nitrogen fixation than was deposited from the atmosphere.

Chapter 30

Figure Questions
Figure 30.2 Retaining the gametophyte within the sporophyte shields the egg-containing gametophyte from UV radiation. UV radiation is a mutagen. Hence, we would expect fewer mutations to occur in the egg cells produced by a gametophyte retained within the body of a sporophyte. Most mutations are harmful. Thus, the fitness of embryos should increase because fewer embryos would carry harmful mutations. **Figure 30.3** Three generations: (1) the current sporophyte (cells of ploidy $2n$, found in the seed coat and in the megasporangium remnant that surrounds the spore wall); (2) the female gametophyte (cells of ploidy n, found in the food supply); and (3) the sporophyte of the next generation (cells of ploidy $2n$, found in the embryo) **Figure 30.6** Mitosis. A single haploid megaspore divides by mitosis to produce a multicellular, haploid female gametophyte. (Likewise, a single haploid microspore divides by mitosis to produce a multicellular male gametophyte.) **Figure 30.12** No. The branching order shown could still be correct if *Amborella* and other early angiosperms had originated prior to 150 million years ago, but angiosperm fossils of that age had not yet been discovered. In such a situation, the 140-million-year-old date for the origin of the angiosperms shown on the phylogeny would be incorrect. **Figure 30.16** Temperatures and the amount of sunlight striking the forest floor would both be likely to increase, whereas rainfall would likely decrease. Each of these changes could have dramatic effects on forest species that live near the edges of remaining forest fragments.

Concept Check 30.1
1. To reach the eggs, the flagellated sperm of seedless plants must swim through a film of water, usually over a distance of no more than a few centimeters. In contrast, the sperm of seed plants do not require water because they are produced within pollen grains that can be transported long distances by wind or by animal pollinators. Although flagellated in some species, the sperm of seed plants do not require mobility because pollen tubes convey them from the point at which the pollen grain is deposited (near the ovules) directly to the eggs. **2.** The reduced gametophytes of seed plants are nurtured by sporophytes and protected from stress, such as drought conditions and UV radiation. Pollen grains, with walls containing sporopollenin, provide protection during transport by wind or animals. Seeds have one or two layers of protective tissue, the seed coat, that improve survival by providing more protection from environmental stresses than do the walls of spores. Seeds also contain a stored supply of food, which provides nourishment for growth after dormancy is broken and the embryo emerges as a seedling. **3.** If a seed could not enter dormancy, the embryo would continue to grow after it was fertilized. As a result, the embryo might rapidly become too large to be dispersed, thus limiting its transport. The embryo's chance of survival might also be reduced because it could not delay growth until conditions become favorable.

Concept Check 30.2
1. Although gymnosperms are similar in not having their seeds enclosed in ovaries and fruits, their seed-bearing structures vary greatly. For instance, cycads have large cones, whereas some gymnosperms, such as *Ginkgo* and *Gnetum*, have small cones that look somewhat like berries, even though they are not fruits. Leaf shape also varies greatly, from the needles of many conifers to the palmlike leaves of cycads to *Gnetum* leaves that look like those of flowering plants. **2.** The pine life cycle illustrates heterospory, as ovulate cones produce megaspores and pollen cones produce microspores. The reduced gametophytes are evident in the form of the microscopic pollen grains that develop from microspores and the microscopic female gametophyte that develops from the megaspore. The egg is shown developing within an ovule, and a pollen tube is shown conveying the sperm. The figure also shows the protective and nutritive features of a seed. **3.** No. Fossil evidence indicates that gymnosperms originated at least 305 million years ago, but this does not mean that angiosperms are that old—only that the most recent common ancestor of gymnosperms and angiosperms must be that old.

Concept Check 30.3
1. In the oak's life cycle, the tree (the sporophyte) produces flowers, which contain gametophytes in pollen grains and ovules; the eggs in ovules are fertilized; the mature ovaries develop into dry fruits called acorns. We can view the oak's life cycle as starting when the acorn seeds germinate, resulting in embryos giving rise to seedlings and finally to mature trees, which produce flowers—and then more acorns. **2.** Pine cones and flowers both have sporophylls, modified leaves that produce spores. Pine trees have separate pollen cones (with pollen grains) and ovulate cones (with ovules inside cone scales). In flowers, pollen grains are produced by the anthers of stamens, and ovules are within the ovaries of carpels. Unlike pine cones, many flowers produce both pollen and ovules. **3.** The fact that the clade with bilaterally symmetrical flowers had more species establishes a correlation between flower shape and the rate of plant speciation. Flower shape is not necessarily responsible for the result because the shape (that is, bilateral or radial symmetry) may have been correlated with another

factor that was the actual cause of the observed result. Note, however, that flower shape was associated with increased speciation rates when averaged across 19 different pairs of plant lineages. Since these 19 lineage pairs were independent of one another, this association suggests—but does not establish—that differences in flower shape cause differences in speciation rates. In general, strong evidence for causation can come from controlled, manipulative experiments, but such experiments are usually not possible for studies of past evolutionary events.

Concept Check 30.4
1. Plant diversity can be considered a resource because plants provide many important benefits to humans; as a resource, plant diversity is nonrenewable because if a species is lost to extinction, that loss is permanent. **2.** A detailed phylogeny of the seed plants would identify many different monophyletic groups of seed plants. Using this phylogeny, researchers could look for clades that contained species in which medicinally useful compounds had already been discovered. Identification of such clades would allow researchers to concentrate their search for new medicinal compounds among clade members—as opposed to searching for new compounds in species that were selected at random from the more than 250,000 existing species of seed plants.

Summary of Key Concepts Questions
30.1 The integument of an ovule develops into the protective seed coat of a seed. The ovule's megaspore develops into a haploid female gametophyte, and two parts of the seed are related to that gametophyte: The food supply of the seed is derived from haploid gametophyte cells, and the embryo of the seed develops after the female gametophyte's egg cell is fertilized by a sperm cell. A remnant of the ovule's megasporangium surrounds the spore wall that encloses the seed's food supply and embryo. **30.2** Gymnosperms arose about 305 million years ago, making them a successful group in terms of their evolutionary longevity. Gymnosperms have the five derived traits common to all seed plants (reduced gametophytes, heterospory, ovules, pollen, and seeds), making them well adapted for life on land. Finally, because gymnosperms dominate immense geographic regions today, the group is also highly successful in geographic distribution. **30.3** The origin of flowering plants is puzzling because their distinctive features, flowers and fruits, bear little resemblance to structures in living gymnosperms. This makes it difficult to infer how flowers and fruits arose, leading Darwin to refer to the origin of flowering plants as an "abominable mystery." Progress has been made toward solving this mystery, particularly in our understanding of angiosperm phylogeny, but the mystery has yet to be solved. We still do not know, for example, which extinct group of seed plants is most closely related to flowering plants. **30.4** The loss of tropical forests could contribute to global warming (which would have negative effects on many human societies) and reduce agricultural production in some of the world's poorest regions. People also depend on Earth's biodiversity for many products and services and hence would be harmed by the loss of species that would occur if the world's remaining tropical forests were cut down. With respect to a possible mass extinction, tropical forests harbor at least 50% of the species on Earth. If the remaining tropical forests were destroyed, large numbers of these species could be driven to extinction, thus rivaling the losses that occurred in the five mass extinction events documented in the fossil record.

Test Your Understanding
1. d **2.** a **3.** b **4.** a **5.** d
6.

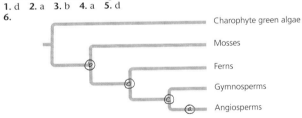

Charophyte green algae
Mosses
Ferns
Gymnosperms
Angiosperms

8. (a)

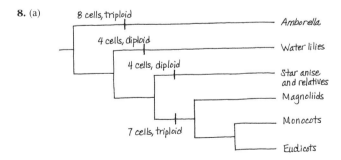

8 cells, triploid — Amborella
4 cells, diploid — Water lilies
4 cells, diploid — Star anise and relatives
— Magnoliids
— Monocots
7 cells, triploid — Eudicots

(b) The phylogeny indicates that basal angiosperms differed from other angiosperms in terms of the number of cells in female gametophytes and the ploidy of the endosperm. The ancestral state of the angiosperms cannot be determined from these data alone. It is possible that the common ancestor of angiosperms had seven-celled female gametophytes and triploid endosperm and hence that the eight-celled and four-celled conditions found in basal angiosperms represent derived traits for those lineages. Alternatively, either the eight-celled or four-celled condition may represent the ancestral state.

Chapter 31
Figure Questions
Figure 31.2 DNA from each of these mushrooms would be identical if each mushroom is part of a single hyphal network, as is likely. **Figure 31.16** One or both of the following would apply to each species: DNA analyses would reveal that it is a member of the ascomycete clade, or aspects of its sexual life cycle would indicate that it is an ascomycete (for example, it would produce asci and ascospores). **Figure 31.21** Two possible controls would be E−P− and E+P−. Results from an E−P− control could be compared with results from the E−P+ experiment, and results from an E+P− control could be compared with results from the E+P+ experiment. Together, these two comparisons would indicate whether the addition of the pathogen causes an increase in leaf mortality. Results from an E−P− experiment could also be compared with results from the second control (E+P−) to determine whether adding the endophytes has a negative effect on the plant. **Figure 31.26** The correspondence between when the chytrid fungi arrived to the region and when frog populations decreased greatly suggests that the chytrid was the cause of the decline, not just correlated to it. The fact that by 2009, the only surviving frogs were in the two lakes treated with fungicides provides additional support for causation.

Concept Check 31.1
1. Both a fungus and a human are heterotrophs. Many fungi digest their food externally by secreting enzymes into the food and then absorbing the small molecules that result from digestion. Other fungi absorb such small molecules directly from their environment. In contrast, humans (and most other animals) ingest relatively large pieces of food and digest the food within their bodies. **2.** The ancestors of such a mutualist most likely secreted powerful enzymes to digest the body of their insect host. Since such enzymes would harm a living host, it is likely that the mutualist would not produce such enzymes or would restrict their secretion and use. **3.** Carbon that enters the plant through stomata is fixed into sugar through photosynthesis. Some of these sugars are absorbed by the fungus that partners with the plant to form mycorrhizae; others are transported within the plant body and used in the plant. Thus, the carbon may be deposited in either the body of the plant or the body of the fungus.

Concept Check 31.2
1. The majority of the fungal life cycle is spent in the haploid stage, whereas the majority of the human life cycle is spent in the diploid stage. **2.** The two mushrooms might be reproductive structures of the same mycelium (the same organism). Or they might be parts of two separate organisms that have arisen from a single parent organism through asexual reproduction and thus carry the same genetic information.

Concept Check 31.3
1. DNA evidence indicates that fungi, animals, and their protistan relatives form a clade, the opisthokonts. Furthermore, an early-diverging fungal lineage, the chytrids, have posterior flagella, as do most other opisthokonts. This suggests that other fungal lineages lost their flagella after diverging from chytrids. **2.** This indicates that fungi had already established mutualistic relationships with plants by the date the fossils of the earliest vascular plants had formed. **3.** Fungi are heterotrophs. Prior to the colonization of land by plants, terrestrial fungi would have lived where other organisms (or their remains) were present and provided a source of food. Thus, if fungi had colonized land before plants, they could have fed on any prokaryotes or protists that lived on land or by the water's edge—but not on the plants or animals on which many fungi feed today.

Concept Check 31.4
1. Flagellated spores; molecular evidence also suggests that chytrids are an early-diverging fungal lineage. **2.** Possible answers include the following: In zygomycetes, the sturdy, thick-walled zygosporangium can withstand harsh conditions and then undergo karyogamy and meiosis when the environment is favorable for reproduction. In glomeromycetes, the hyphae have a specialized morphology that enables the fungi to form arbuscular mycorrhizae with plant roots. In ascomycetes, the asexual spores (conidia) are often produced in chains or clusters at the tips of conidiophores, where they are easily dispersed by wind. The often cup-shaped ascocarps house the sexual spore-forming asci. In basidiomycetes, the basidiocarp supports and protects a large surface area of basidia, from which spores are dispersed. **3.** Such a change to the life cycle of an ascomycete would reduce the number and genetic diversity of ascospores that result from a mating event. Ascospore number would drop because a mating event would lead to the formation of only one ascus. Ascospore genetic diversity would also drop because in ascomycetes, one mating event leads to the formation of asci by many different dikaryotic cells. As a result, genetic recombination and meiosis occur independently many different times—which could not happen if only a single ascus was formed. It is also likely that if such an ascomycete formed an ascocarp, the shape of the ascocarp would differ considerably from that found in its close relatives.

Concept Check 31.5
1. A suitable environment for growth, retention of water and minerals, protection from intense sunlight, and protection from being eaten. **2.** A hardy spore stage enables dispersal to host organisms through a variety of mechanisms; their ability to grow rapidly in a favorable new environment enables them to capitalize on the host's resources. **3.** Many different outcomes might have occurred. Organisms that currently form mutualisms with fungi might have gained the ability to perform the tasks currently done by their fungal partners, or they might have formed similar mutualisms with other organisms (such as bacteria). Alternatively, organisms that currently form mutualisms with fungi might be less effective at living in their present environments. For example, the colonization of land by plants might have been more difficult. And if plants did eventually colonize land without fungal mutualists, natural selection might have favored plants that formed more highly divided and extensive root systems (in part replacing mycorrhizae).

Summary of Key Concepts Questions

31.1 The body of a multicellular fungus typically consists of thin filaments called hyphae. These filaments form an interwoven mass (mycelium) that penetrates the substrate on which the fungus grows and feeds. Because the individual filaments are thin, the surface-to-volume ratio of the mycelium is maximized, making nutrient absorption highly efficient.
31.2

31.3 Phylogenetic analyses show that fungi and animals are more closely related to each other than either is to other multicellular eukaryotes (such as plants or multicellular algae). These analyses also show that fungi are more closely related to single-celled protists called nucleariids than they are to animals, whereas animals are more closely related to a different group of single-celled protists, the choanoflagellates, than they are to fungi. In combination, these results indicate that multicellularity evolved in fungi and animals independently, from different single-celled ancestors.
31.4

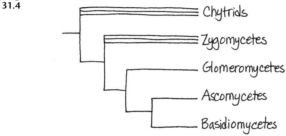

31.5 As decomposers, fungi break down the bodies of dead organisms, thereby recycling elements between the living and nonliving environments. Without the activities of fungi and bacterial decomposers, essential nutrients would remain tied up in organic matter, and life would cease. As an example of their key role as mutualists, fungi form mycorrhizal associations with plants. These associations improve the growth and survival of plants, thereby indirectly affecting the many other species (humans included) that depend on plants. As pathogens, fungi harm other species. In some cases, fungal pathogens have caused their host populations to decline across broad geographic regions, as seen for the American chestnut.

Test Your Understanding
1. b **2.** c **3.** d **4.** b **5.** a **6.** e
7.

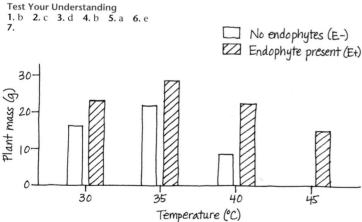

As indicated by the raw data and bar graph, grass plants with endophytes (E+) produced more new shoots and had greater biomass than did grass plants that lacked endophytes (E−). These differences were especially pronounced at the highest soil temperature, where E− grass plants produced no new shoots and had a biomass of zero (indicating they were dead).

Chapter 32

Figure Questions

Figure 32.3 As described in ❶ and ❷, choanoflagellates and a broad range of animals have collar cells. Since collar cells have never been observed in plants, fungi, or non-choanoflagellate protists, this suggests that choanoflagellates may be more closely related to animals than to other eukaryotes. If choanoflagellates are more closely related to animals than to any other group of eukaryotes, choanoflagellates and animals should share other traits that are not found in other eukaryotes. The data described in ❸ are consistent with this prediction. **Figure 32.6** The sea anemone embryos could be infused with a protein that can bind to β-catenin's DNA-binding site, thereby limiting the extent to which β-catenin activates the transcription of genes necessary for gastrulation. Such an experiment would provide an independent check of the results shown in step 4. **Figure 32.9** The cells of an early embryo with deuterostome development typically are not committed to a particular developmental fate, whereas the cells of an early embryo with protostome development typically are committed to a particular developmental fate. As a result, an embryo with deuterostome development would be more likely to contain stem cells that could give rise to cells of any type. **Figure 32.10** Ctenophora is the sister phylum in this figure, while Cnidaria is the sister phylum in Figure 32.11.

Concept Check 32.1

1. In most animals, the zygote undergoes cleavage, which leads to the formation of a blastula. Next, in gastrulation, one end of the embryo folds inward, producing layers of embryonic tissue. As the cells of these layers differentiate, a wide variety of animal forms result. Despite the diversity of animal forms, animal development is controlled by a similar set of *Hox* genes across a broad range of taxa. **2.** The imaginary plant would require tissues composed of cells that were analogous to the muscle and nerve cells found in animals: "Muscle" tissue would be necessary for the plant to chase prey, and "nerve" tissue would be required for the plant to coordinate its movements when chasing prey. To digest captured prey, the plant would need to either secrete enzymes into one or more digestive cavities (which could be modified leaves, as in a Venus flytrap) or secrete enzymes outside of its body and feed by absorption. To extract nutrients from the soil—yet be able to chase prey—the plant would need something other than fixed roots, perhaps retractable "roots" or a way to ingest soil. To conduct photosynthesis, the plant would require chloroplasts. Overall, such an imaginary plant would be very similar to an animal that had chloroplasts and retractable roots. **3.** As described in Chapter 18, miRNAs help regulate gene expression by binding to and hence blocking the translation of particular mRNA molecules, their "target mRNAs." Because each miRNA can bind to many target mRNAs, an increase in the number of miRNA molecules could potentially add many layers of control to the regulation of gene expression. As a result of a more varied and complex control of gene expression, the construction of a complex body form would be more likely in an organism with many miRNAs than in an organism with few miRNAs, even though both organisms had roughly the same total number of genes.

Concept Check 32.2

1. c, b, a, d **2.** We cannot infer whether animals originated before or after fungi. If correct, the date provided for the most recent common ancestor of fungi and animals would indicate that animals originated some time within the last billion years. The fossil record indicates that animals originated at least 565 million years ago. Thus, we could conclude only that animals originated sometime between 1 billion years ago and 565 million years ago.

Concept Check 32.3

1. Grade-level characteristics are those that multiple lineages share regardless of evolutionary history. Some grade-level characteristics may have evolved multiple times independently. Features that unite clades are derived characteristics that originated in a common ancestor and were passed on to the various descendants. **2.** A snail has a spiral and determinate cleavage pattern; a human has radial, indeterminate cleavage. In a snail, the coelomic cavity is formed by splitting of mesoderm masses; in a human, the coelom forms from folds of archenteron. In a snail, the mouth forms from the blastopore; in a human, the anus develops from the blastopore. **3.** Most coelomate triploblasts have two openings to their digestive tract, a mouth and an anus. As such, their bodies have a structure that is analogous to that of a doughnut: The digestive tract (the hole of the doughnut) runs from the mouth to the anus and is surrounded by various tissues (the solid part of the doughnut). The doughnut analogy is most obvious at early stages of development (see Figure 32.9c).

Concept Check 32.4

1. Cnidarians possess true tissues, while sponges do not. Also unlike sponges, cnidarians exhibit body symmetry, though it is radial and not bilateral as in other animal phyla. **2.** The morphology-based tree divides Bilateria into two major clades: Deuterostomia and Protostomia. The molecular-based tree recognizes three major clades: Deuterostomia, Ecdysozoa, and Lophotrochozoa. **3.** The phylogeny in Figure 32.11 indicates that molluscs are members of Lophotrochozoa, one the three main groups of bilaterians (the others being Deuterostomia and Ecdysozoa). As seen in Figure 25.10, the fossil record shows that molluscs were present tens of millions of years before the Cambrian explosion. Thus, long before the Cambrian explosion, the lophotrochoan clade had formed and was evolving independently of the evolutionary lineages leading to Deuterostomia and Ecdysozoa. Based on the phylogeny in Figure 32.11, we can also conclude that the lineages leading to Deuterostomia and Ecdysozoa were independent of one another before the Cambrian explosion. Since the lineages leading to the three main clades of bilaterians were evolving independently of one another prior to the Cambrian explosion, that explosion could be viewed as consisting of three "explosions," not one.

Summary of Key Concepts Questions

Concept 32.1 Unlike animals, which are heterotrophs that ingest their food, plants are autotrophs, and fungi are heterotrophs that grow on their food and feed by absorption. Animals lack cell walls, which are found in both plants and fungi. Animals also have muscle tissue and nerve tissue, which are not found in either plants or fungi. In addition, the sperm and egg cells of animals are produced by meiotic division, unlike what occurs in plants and fungi (where reproductive cells such as sperm and eggs are produced by mitotic division). Finally, animals regulate the development of body form with *Hox* genes, a unique group of genes that is not found in either plants or fungi. **Concept 32.2** Current hypotheses about the cause of the Cambrian explosion include new predator-prey relationships, an increase in atmospheric oxygen, and an increase in developmental flexibility provided by the origin of *Hox* genes and other genetic changes. **Concept 32.3** Body plans provide a helpful way to compare and contrast key features of organisms. However, phylogenetic analyses show that similar body plans have arisen independently in different groups of organisms. As such, similar body plans may have arisen by convergent evolution and hence may not be informative about evolutionary relationships. **Concept 32.4** To reconstruct the evolutionary history of animal life, researchers collect morphological and molecular data and use cladistic methods to analyze that data. In a cladistic approach, shared derived (morphological and molecular) characters are used to place organisms into a nested hierarchy of monophyletic clades.

Test Your Understanding
1. a **2.** d **3.** e **4.** c **5.** b
7.

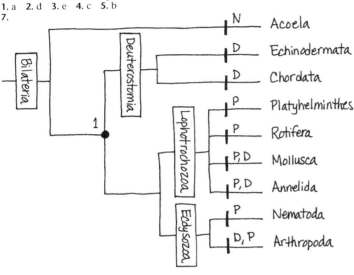

Based on the phylogeny, the ancestral condition in bilaterians may have been similar to that in Acoela, where the blastopore closes and the mouth forms elsewhere (N); however, it is also possible that blastopore fate in Acoela is a derived trait and hence is not informative about the ancestral condition. Although the phylogeny indicates that blastopore fate has changed multiple times over the course of evolution, a precise estimate cannot be made. For example, if we assume that the common ancestor of all non-Acoela bilaterians (marked with a 1 on the tree) exhibited protostomy, then blastopore fate has changed at least five times: once in common ancestor 1, once in Deuterostomia, at least once in Mollusca, at least once in Annelida, and at least once in Arthropoda. Other assumptions would lead to different estimates.

Chapter 33

Figure Questions
Figure 33.8 Within a reproductive polyp, a cell that gives rise to a medusa would have to divide by meiosis. A resulting haploid cell would then divide repeatedly (by mitosis), forming a haploid medusa. Later, cells in the medusa's gonads would divide by mitosis, forming the haploid eggs and sperm. **Figure 33.11** Adding fertilizer to the water supply would probably increase the abundance of algae, and that, in turn, would likely increase the abundance of snails (which eat algae). If the water was also contaminated with infected human feces, an increase in the number of snails would likely lead to an increase in the abundance of blood flukes (which require snails as an intermediate host). As a result, the occurrence of schistosomiasis might increase. **Figure 33.22** The extinctions of freshwater bivalves might lead to an increase in the abundance of photosynthetic protists and bacteria. Because these organisms are at the base of aquatic food webs, increases in their abundance could have major effects on aquatic communities (including both increases and decreases in the abundance of other species). **Figure 33.29** Such a result would be consistent with the *Ubx* and *abd-A Hox* genes having played a major role in the evolution of increased body segment diversity in arthropods. However, by itself, such a result would simply show that the presence of the *Ubx* and *abd-A Hox* genes was *correlated with* an increase in body segment diversity in arthropods; it would not provide direct experimental evidence that the acquisition of the *Ubx* and *adb-A* genes *caused* an increase in arthropod body segment diversity.

Concept Check 33.1
1. The flagella of choanocytes draw water through their collars, which trap food particles. The particles are engulfed by phagocytosis and digested, either by choanocytes or by amoebocytes. **2.** The collar cells of sponges (and some other animals—see Chapter 32) bear a striking resemblance to a choanoflagellate cell. This suggests that the last common ancestor of animals and their protist sister group may have resembled a choanoflagellate. Nevertheless, mesomycetozoans could still be the sister group of animals. If this is the case, the lack of collar cells in mesomyceto-

zoans would indicate that over time their structure evolved in ways that caused it to no longer resemble a choanoflagellate cell. It is also possible that choanoflagellates and sponges share similar-looking collar cells as a result of convergent evolution.

Concept Check 33.2
1. Both the polyp and the medusa are composed of an outer epidermis and an inner gastrodermis separated by a gelatinous layer, the mesoglea. The polyp is a cylindrical form that adheres to the substrate by its aboral end; the medusa is a flattened, mouth-down form that moves freely in the water. **2.** Cnidarian stinging cells (cnidocytes) function in defense and prey capture. They contain capsulelike organelles (cnidae), which in turn contain coiled threads. The threads either inject poison or stick to and entangle small prey. **3.** Evolution is not goal oriented; hence, it would not be correct to argue that cnidarians were not "highly evolved" simply because their form had changed relatively little over the past 560 million years. Instead, the fact that cnidarians have persisted for hundreds of millions of years indicates that the cnidarian body plan is a highly successful one.

Concept Check 33.3
1. Tapeworms can absorb food from their environment and release ammonia into their environment through their body surface because their body is very flat, due in part to the lack of a coelom. **2.** The inner tube is the alimentary canal, which runs the length of the body. The outer tube is the body wall. The two tubes are separated by the coelom. **3.** All molluscs have inherited a foot from their common ancestor. However, in different groups of molluscs, the structure of the foot has been modified over time (by natural selection) in ways that reflect how the foot is used in locomotion by members of each clade. In gastropods, the foot is used as a holdfast or to move slowly on the substrate. In cephalopods, the foot has been modified into part of the tentacles and into an excurrent siphon, through which water is propelled (resulting in movement in the opposite direction).

Concept Check 33.4
1. Nematodes lack body segments and a true coelom; annelids have both. **2.** The arthropod exoskeleton, which had already evolved in the ocean, allow terrestrial species to retain water and support their bodies on land. Wings allow them to disperse quickly to new habitats and to find food and mates. The tracheal system allows for efficient gas exchange despite the presence of an exoskeleton. **3.** Arthropod mouthparts are modified appendages, which are bilaterally paired. As a result, the mouthparts come into contact by moving laterally, not up and down. **4.** Yes. Under the traditional hypothesis, we would expect body segmentation to be controlled by similar *Hox* genes in annelids and arthropods. However, if annelids are in Lophotrochozoa and arthropods are in Ecdysozoa, body segmentation may have evolved independently in these two groups. In such a case, we might expect that different *Hox* genes would control the development of body segmentation in the two clades.

Concept Check 33.5
1. Each tube foot consists of an ampulla and a podium. When the ampulla squeezes, it forces water into the podium, which causes the podium to expand and contact the substrate. Adhesive chemicals are then secreted from the base of the podium, thereby attaching the podium to the substrate. **2.** Both insects and nematodes are members of Ecdysozoa, one of the three major clades of bilaterians. Therefore, a characteristic shared by *Drosophila* and *Caenorhabditis* may be informative for other members of their clade—but not necessarily for members of Deuterostomia. Instead, Figure 33.2 suggests that a species within Echinodermata or Chordata might be a more appropriate invertebrate model organism from which to draw inferences about humans and other vertebrates. **3.** Echinoderms include species with a wide range of body forms, some of which are shown in Figure 33.40. However, even echinoderms that look very different from one another, such as sea stars and sea cucumbers, share characteristics unique to their phylum, including a water vascular system and tube feet. The differences between echinoderm species illustrate the diversity of life, while the characteristics they share illustrate the unity of life. The match between organisms and their environments can be seen in such echinoderm features as the eversible stomachs of sea stars (enabling them to digest prey that are larger than their mouth) and the complex, jaw-like structure that sea urchins use to eat seaweed.

Summary of Key Concepts Questions
Concept 33.1 The sponge body consists of two layers of cells, both of which are in contact with water. As a result, gas exchange and waste removal occur as substances diffuse into and out of the cells of the body. Choanocytes and amoebocytes ingest food particles from the surrounding water. Choanocytes also release food particles to amoebocytes, which then digest the food particles and deliver nutrients to other cells. **Concept 33.2** The cnidarian body plan consists of a sac with a central digestive compartment, the gastrovascular cavity. The single opening to this compartment serves as both a mouth and an anus. The two main variations on this body plan are sessile polyps (which adhere to the substrate at the end of the body opposite to the mouth/anus) and motile medusae (which move freely through the water and resemble flattened, mouth-down versions of polyps). **Concept 33.3** No. Some lophotrochozoans have a crown of ciliated tentacles that function in feeding (called a lophophore), while others go through a distinctive developmental stage known as trochophore larvae. Many other lophotrochozoans do not have either of these features. As a result, the clade is defined primarily by DNA similarities, not morphological similarities. **Concept 33.4** Many nematode species live in soil and in sediments on the bottom of bodies of water. These free-living species play important roles in decomposition and nutrient cycling. Other nematodes are parasites, including many species that attack the roots of plants and some that attack animals (including humans). Arthropods have profound effects on all aspects of ecology. In aquatic

Appendix A Answers

ANSWERS **A–32**

environments, crustaceans play key roles as grazers (of algae), scavengers, and predators, and some species, such as krill, are important sources of food for whales and other vertebrates. On land, it is difficult to think of features of the natural world that are not affected in some way by insects and other arthropods, such as spiders and ticks. There are more than 1 million species of insects, many of which have enormous ecological effects as herbivores, predators, parasites, decomposers, and vectors of disease. Insects are also key sources of food for many organisms, including humans in some regions of the world.   **Concept 33.5** Echinoderms and chordates are both members of Deuterostomia, one of the three main clades of bilaterian animals. As such, chordates (including humans) are more closely related to echinoderms than we are to animals in any of the other phyla covered in this chapter. Nevertheless, echinoderms and chordates have evolved independently for over 500 million years. This statement does not contradict the close relationship of echinoderms and chordates, but it does make clear that "close" is a relative term indicating that these two phyla are more closely related to each other than either is to animal phyla not in Deuterostomia.

Test Your Understanding
1. a   **2.** d   **3.** b   **4.** e   **5.** c   **6.** d
7.

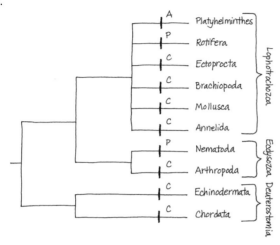

(a) Both phyla in Deuterostomia are coelomates, suggesting that their most recent common ancestor had a true coelom. Lophotrochozoa contains one phylum of acoelomates (Platyhelminthes), one phylum of pseudocoelomates (Rotifera), and four phyla of coelomates (Ectoprocta, Brachiopoda, Mollusca, Annelida); thus, we cannot, from this information alone, infer the condition of the most recent common ancestor shared by these phyla. Similarly, since Ecdysozoa contains one phylum of pseudocoelomates (Nematoda) and one phylum of coelomates (Arthropoda), we cannot infer whether their most recent common ancestor had a true coelom or not. (b) Depending on whether or not the last common ancestor of Bilateria had a true coelom, the presence of a true coelom has either been lost or gained multiple times during the evolutionary history of bilaterians. Thus, the presence of a true coelom appears to have changed over the course of evolution.

Chapter 34

Figure Questions

Figure 34.6 Results in these figures suggest that specific *Hox* genes, as well as the order in which they are expressed, have been highly conserved over the course of evolution. **Figure 34.20** *Tiktaalik* was a lobe-fin fish that had both fish and tetrapod characters. Like a fish, *Tiktaalik* had fins, scales, and gills. As described by Darwin's concept of descent with modification, such shared characters can be attributed to descent from ancestral species—in this case, *Tiktaalik*'s descent from fish ancestors. *Tiktaalik* also had traits that were unlike a fish, but like a tetrapod, including a flat skull, a neck, a full set of ribs, and the skeletal structure of its fin. These characters illustrate the second part of descent with modification, showing how ancestral features had become modified over time. **Figure 34.21** Sometime between 380 mya and 340 mya. We can infer this because amphibians must have originated after the most recent common ancestor of *Tulerpeton* and living tetrapods (and that ancestor originated 380 mya), but no later than the date of the earliest known fossils of amphibians (shown in the figure as 340 mya). **Figure 34.25** Crocodilians. Among extant amniotes, crocodilians are the sister group of birds. Hence, it is likely that DNA sequences in birds are more similar to those in crocodilians than they are to those of more distantly related amniotes. **Figure 34.37** In general, the process of exaptation occurs as a structure that had one function acquires a different function via a series of intermediate stages. Each of these intermediate stages typically has some function in the organism in which it is found. The incorporation of articular and quadrate bones into the mammalian ear illustrates exaptation because these bones originally evolved as part of the jaw, where they functioned as the jaw hinge, but over time they became co-opted for another function, namely the transmission of sound. **Figure 34.43** The phylogeny shows humans as the sister group to the lineage that contains chimpanzees and

bonobos. This relationship is not consistent with humans as having descended from either chimpanzees or bonobos. If humans had descended from chimpanzees, for example, the human lineage would be nested within the chimpanzee lineage, much as birds are nested within the reptile clade (see Figure 34.25). **Figure 34.50** No. The phylogeny shown in RESULTS does not include any information on when the branch points occurred, nor is it scaled by time. Thus, although the phylogeny shows the relative order in which lineages diverged, we cannot infer when those events took place.

Concept Check 34.1

1. The four characters are a notochord; a dorsal, hollow nerve chord; pharyngeal slits or clefts; and a muscular, post-anal tail.   **2.** In humans, these characters are present only in the embryo. The notochord becomes disks between the vertebrae, the tail is almost completely lost, and the pharyngeal clefts develop into various adult structures.   **3.** Not necessarily. It would be possible that the chordate common ancestor had this gene, which was then lost in the lancelet lineage and retained in other chordates. However, it would also be possible that the chordate common ancestor lacked this gene; this could occur if the gene originated after lancelets diverged from other chordates but before tunicates diverged from other chordates.

Concept Check 34.2

1. Hagfishes have a head and skull made of cartilage, plus a small brain, sensory organs, and tooth-like structures. They have a neural crest, gill slits, and more extensive organ systems. In addition, hagfishes have slime glands that ward off predators and may repel competing scavengers.   **2.** *Myllokunmingia*. Fossils of this organism provide evidence of ear capsules and eye capsules; these structures are part of the skull. Thus, *Myllokunmingia* is considered a craniate, as are humans. *Haikouella* did not have a skull.   **3.** Such a finding suggests that early organisms with a head were favored by natural selection in several different evolutionary lineages. However, while a logical argument can be made that having a head was advantageous, fossils alone do not constitute proof.

Concept Check 34.3

1. Lampreys have a round, rasping mouth, which they use to attach to fish. Conodonts had two sets of mineralized dental elements, which may have been used to impale prey and cut it into smaller pieces.   **2.** In armored jawless vertebrates, bone served as external armor that may have provided protection from predators. Some species also had mineralized mouthparts, which could be used for either predation or scavenging. Still others had mineralized fin rays, which may have enabled them to swim more rapidly and with greater steering control.

Concept Check 34.4

1. Both are gnathostomes and have jaws, four clusters of *Hox* genes, enlarged forebrains, and lateral line systems. Shark skeletons consist mainly of cartilage, whereas tuna have bony skeletons. Sharks also have a spiral valve. Tuna have an operculum and a swim bladder, as well as flexible rays supporting their fins. **2.** Aquatic gnathostomes have jaws (an adaptation for feeding) and paired fins and a tail (adaptations for swimming). Aquatic gnathostomes also typically have streamlined bodies for efficient swimming and swim bladders or other mechanisms (such as oil storage in sharks) for buoyancy.   **3.** Yes, that could have happened. The paired appendages of aquatic gnathostomes other than the lobe-fins could have served as a starting point for the evolution of limbs. The colonization of land by aquatic gnathostomes other than the lobe-fins might have been facilitated in lineages that possessed lungs, as that would have enabled those organisms to breathe air.

Concept Check 34.5

1. Tetrapods are thought to have originated about 365 million years ago when the fins of some lobe-fins evolved into the limbs of tetrapods. In addition to their four limbs with digits—a key derived trait for which the group is named—other derived traits of tetrapods include a neck (consisting of vertebrae that separate the head from the rest of the body), a pelvic girdle that is fused to the backbone, and a lack of gill slits.   **2.** Some fully aquatic species are paedomorphic, retaining larval features for life in water as adults. Species that live in dry environments may avoid dehydration by burrowing or living under moist leaves, and they protect their eggs with foam nests, viviparity, and other adaptations.   **3.** Many amphibians spend part of their life cycle in aquatic environments and part on land. Thus, they may be exposed to a wide range of environmental problems, including water and air pollution and the loss or degradation of aquatic and/or terrestrial habitats. In addition, amphibians have highly permeable skin, providing relatively little protection from external conditions, and their eggs do not have a protective shell.

Concept Check 34.6

1. The amniotic egg provides protection to the embryo and allows the embryo to develop on land, eliminating the necessity of a watery environment for reproduction. Another key adaptation is rib cage ventilation, which improves the efficiency of air intake and may have allowed early amniotes to dispense with breathing through their skin. Finally, not breathing through their skin allowed amniotes to develop relatively impermeable skin, thereby conserving water.   **2.** Yes. Although snakes lack limbs, they descended from lizards with legs. Some snakes retain vestigial pelvic and leg bones, providing evidence of their descent from an ancestor with legs.   **3.** Birds have weight-saving modifications, including the absence of teeth, a urinary bladder, and a second ovary in females. The wings and feathers are adaptations that facilitate flight, and so are efficient respiratory and circulatory systems that support a high metabolic rate.

4.

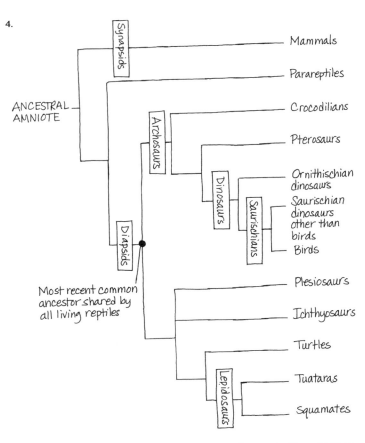

Synapsids — Mammals

Parareptiles

Archosaurs — Crocodilians

Pterosaurs

Dinosaurs — Ornithischian dinosaurs

Saurischians — Saurischian dinosaurs other than birds

Birds

ANCESTRAL AMNIOTE

Diapsids

Plesiosaurs

Ichthyosaurs

Turtles

Lepidosaurs — Tuataras

Squamates

Most recent common ancestor shared by all living reptiles

Under this convention, the reptiles would consist of all groups in Figure 34.25 except parareptiles and mammals.

Concept Check 34.7

1. Monotremes lay eggs. Marsupials give birth to very small live young that attach to a nipple in the mother's pouch, where they complete development. Eutherians give birth to more developed live young. **2.** Hands and feet adapted for grasping, flat nails, large brain, forward-looking eyes on a flat face, parental care, and movable big toe and thumb **3.** Mammals are endothermic, enabling them to live in a wide range of habitats. Milk provides young with a balanced set of nutrients, and hair and a layer of fat under the skin help mammals retain heat. Mammals have differentiated teeth, enabling them to eat many different kinds of food. Mammals also have relatively large brains, and many species are capable learners. Following the mass extinction at the end of the Cretaceous period, the absence of large terrestrial dinosaurs may have opened many new ecological niches to mammals, promoting their adaptive radiation. Continental drift also isolated many groups of mammals from one another, promoting the formation of many new species.

Concept Check 34.8

1. Hominins are a clade within the ape clade that includes humans and all species more closely related to humans than other apes. The derived characters of hominins include bipedal locomotion and relatively larger brains. **2.** In hominins, bipedal locomotion evolved long before large brain size. *Homo ergaster*, for example, was fully upright, bipedal, and as tall as modern humans, but its brain was significantly smaller than that of modern humans. **3.** Yes, both can be correct. *Homo sapiens* may have established populations outside of Africa as early as 115,000 years ago, as indicated by the fossil record. However, those populations may have left few or no descendants today. Instead, all living humans may have descended from Africans that spread from Africa roughly 50,000 years ago, as indicated by genetic data.

Summary of Key Concepts Questions

Concept 34.1 Lancelets are the most basal group of living chordates, and as adults they have key derived characters of chordates. This suggests that the chordate common ancestor may have resembled a lancelet in having an anterior end with a mouth along with the following four derived characters: a notochord; a dorsal, hollow nerve cord; pharyngeal slits or clefts; and a muscular, post-anal tail. **Concept 34.2** Craniates have a head and a more extensive muscular system than lancelets or tunicates. These features enable craniates to coordinate and perform more complex behaviors than found in lancelets and tunicates. Basal craniates (the hagfishes), for example, are scavengers that locate and feed on worms and dead or sick fishes. In contrast, lancelets and tunicates feed by filtering food items from the water. **Concept 34.3** Conodonts, among the earliest vertebrates in the fossil record, were very abundant for over 300 million years. While jawless, their well-developed teeth provide early signs of bone formation. Other species of jawless vertebrates developed armor on the outside of their bodies, which probably helped protect them from predators. Like lampreys, these species had paired fins for locomotion and an inner ear with semicircular canals that provided a

sense of balance. There were many species of these armored jawless vertebrates, but they all became extinct by the close of the Devonian period, 359 million years ago. **Concept 34.4** The origin of jaws altered how fossil gnathostomes obtained food, which in turn had large effects on ecological interactions. Predators could use their jaws to grab prey or remove chunks of flesh, stimulating the evolution of increasingly sophisticated means of defense in prey species. Evidence for these changes can be found in the fossil record, which includes fossils of 10-m-long predators with remarkably powerful jaws, as well as lineages of well-defended prey species whose bodies were covered by armored plates. **Concept 34.5** Amphibians require water for reproduction; their bodies can lose water rapidly through their moist, highly permeable skin; and amphibian eggs do not have a shell and hence are vulnerable to desiccation. **Concept 34.6** Birds are descended from theropod dinosaurs, and dinosaurs are nested within the archosaur lineage, one of the two main reptile lineages. Thus, the other living archosaur reptiles, the crocodilians, are more closely related to birds than they are to non-archosaur reptiles such as lizards. As a result, birds are considered reptiles. (Note that if reptiles were defined as excluding birds, the reptiles would not form a clade; instead, the reptiles would be a paraphyletic group.) **Concept 34.7** Mammals are members of a group of amniotes called synapsids. Early (nonmammalian) synapsids laid eggs and had a sprawling gait. Fossil evidence shows that mammalian features arose gradually over a period of more than 100 million years. For example, the jaw was modified over time in nonmammalian synapsids, eventually coming to resemble that of a mammal. By 180 million years ago, the first mammals had appeared. There were many species of early mammals, but most of them were small, and they were not abundant or dominant members of their community. Mammals did not rise to ecological dominance until after the extinction of the dinosaurs. **Concept 34.8** The fossil record shows that from 4.5 to 2.5 million years ago, a wide range of hominin species walked upright but had relatively small brain sizes. About 2.5 million years ago, the first members of genus *Homo* emerged. These species used tools and had larger brains than those of earlier hominins. Fossil evidence indicates that multiple members of our genus were alive at any given point in time. Furthermore, until about 1.3 million years ago, these various *Homo* species also coexisted with members of earlier hominin lineages, such as *Paranthropus*. The different hominins alive at the same periods of time varied in body size, body shape, brain size, dental morphology, and the capacity for tool use. Ultimately, except for *Homo sapiens*, all of these species became extinct. Thus, human evolution is viewed not as an evolutionary path leading to *H. sapiens*, but rather as an evolutionary tree with many branches—the only surviving lineage of which is our own.

Test Your Understanding

1. e **2.** c **3.** a **4.** b **5.** c **6.** c **8.** (a) Because brain size tends to increase consistently in such lineages, we can conclude that natural selection favored the evolution of larger brains and hence that the benefits outweighed the costs. (b) As long as the benefits of brains that are large relative to body size are greater than the costs, large brains can evolve. Natural selection might favor the evolution of brains that are large relative to body size because such brains confer an advantage in obtaining mates and/or an advantage in survival.

(c)

[Graph: y-axis "Mortality rate" from 0 to 1.0; x-axis "Deviation of brain size from expected" from -3 to 4]

Adult mortality tends to be lower in birds with larger brains.

Chapter 35

Figure Questions

Figure 35.9 The finding might suggest that the tan-colored trichomes deter the beetles by some means other than physically obstructing the beetles. Perhaps they contain a chemical that is harmful or distasteful to the beetles.

Concept Check 35.1

1. The vascular tissue system connects leaves and roots, allowing sugars to move from leaves to roots in the phloem and allowing water and minerals to move to the leaves in the xylem. **2.** (a) large axillary buds; (b) petioles; (c) a bulb, an underground shoot with a small stem and large storage leaves; (d) storage roots **3.** To get sufficient energy from photosynthesis, we would need lots of surface area exposed to the sun. This large surface-to-volume ratio, however, would create a new problem—evaporative water loss. We would have to be permanently connected to a water source—the soil, also our source of minerals. In short, we would probably look and behave very much like plants. **4.** As plant cells enlarge, they typically form a huge central vacuole that contains a dilute watery sap. Central vacuoles enable plant cells to become large with only a minimal investment of new cytoplasm. The orientation of the cellulose microfibrils in plant cell walls affects the growth pattern of cells.

Concept Check 35.2

1. Primary growth arises from apical meristems and involves production and elongation of organs. Secondary growth arises from lateral meristems and adds to the girth of roots and stems. **2.** Your dividing cells are normally limited in the types of cells they can form. In contrast, the products of cell division in a plant meristem can differentiate into all the types of plant cells. **3.** The largest, oldest leaves would be lowest on the shoot. Since they would probably be heavily shaded, they would not photosynthesize much regardless of their size. **4.** No, the carrot roots will probably be smaller at the end of the second year because the food stored in the root will be used to produce flowers, fruits, and seeds.

Summary of Key Concepts Questions

35.1 Here are a few examples: The cuticle of leaves and stems protects these structures from desiccation. Collenchyma and sclerenchyma cells have thick walls that provide support for plants. Strong, branching root systems help anchor the plant in the soil. **35.2** All plant organs and tissues are ultimately derived by meristematic activity.

Test Your Understanding

1. d **2.** c **3.** c **4.** a **5.** b **6.** e **7.** d
8.

Vessel element
Growth ring
Late wood
Early wood

Chapter 36

Figure Questions

Figure 36.3 The leaves are being produced in a counterclockwise spiral. **Figure 36.4** A higher leaf area index will not necessarily increase photosynthesis because of upper leaves shading lower leaves. **Figure 36.7** A proton pump inhibitor would depolarize the membrane potential because fewer H^+ ions would be pumped out across the plasma membrane. The immediate effect of an inhibitor of the H^+/sucrose transporter would be to hyperpolarize the membrane potential because fewer H^+ ions would be leaking back into the cell through these cotransporters. An inhibitor of the H^+/NO_3^- cotransporter would have no effect on the membrane potential because the simultaneous cotransport of a positively charged ion and a negatively charged ion has no net effect on charge difference across the membrane. An inhibitor of the K^+ ion channels would decrease the membrane potential because additional positively charged ions would not be accumulating outside the cell. **Figure 36.10** The Casparian strip blocks water and minerals from moving between endodermal cells or moving around an endodermal cell via the cell's wall. Therefore, water and minerals must pass through an endodermal cell's plasma membrane.

Concept Check 36.1

1. Vascular plants must transport minerals and water absorbed by the roots to all the other parts of the plant. They must also transport sugars from sites of production to sites of use. **2.** Many features of plant architecture affect self-shading, including leaf arrangement, leaf and stem orientation, and leaf area index. **3.** Increased stem elongation would raise the plant's upper leaves. Erect leaves and reduced lateral branching would make the plant less subject to shading by the encroaching neighbors. **4.** As discussed in Chapter 35 (p. 741), pruning shoot tips removes apical dominance, resulting in axillary buds growing into lateral shoots (branches). This branching produces a bushier plant with a higher leaf area index. **5.** Fungal hyphae are long, thin filaments that form a large interwoven network in the soil. Their high surface-to-volume ratio is an adaptation that enhances the absorption of materials from the soil.

Concept Check 36.2

1. The cell's ψ_P is 0.7 MPa. In a solution with a ψ of –0.4 MPa, the cell's ψ_P at equilibrium would be 0.3 MPa. **2.** The cells would still adjust to changes in their osmotic environment, but their responses would be slower. Although aquaporins do not affect the water potential gradient across membranes, they allow for more rapid osmotic adjustments. **3.** If tracheids and vessel elements were alive at maturity, their cytoplasm would impede water movement, preventing rapid long-distance transport. **4.** The protoplasts would burst. Because the cytoplasm has many dissolved solutes, water would enter the protoplast continuously without reaching equilibrium. (When present, the cell wall prevents rupturing by excessive expansion of the protoplast.)

Concept Check 36.3

1. Because water-conducting xylem cells are dead at maturity and form essentially hollow tubes, they offer little resistance to water flow, and their thick walls prevent the cells from collapsing under the negative pressure inside. **2.** At dawn, a drop is exuded because the xylem is under positive pressure due to root pressure. At noon, the xylem is under negative pressure tension when it is cut and the xylem sap is pulled away from the cut surface up into the stem. Root pressure cannot keep pace with the increased rate of transpiration at noon. **3.** The endodermis regulates the passage of water-soluble solutes by requiring all such molecules to cross a selectively permeable membrane. Presumably, the inhibitor never reaches the plant's photosynthetic cells. **4.** Perhaps greater root mass helps compensate for the lower water permeability of the plasma membranes. **5.** The Casparian strip and tight junctions both prevent movement of fluid between cells.

Concept Check 36.4

1. Stomatal opening at dawn is controlled mainly by light, CO_2 concentrations, and a circadian rhythm. Environmental stresses such as drought, high temperature, and wind can stimulate stomata to close during the day. Water deficiency can trigger release of the plant hormone abscisic acid, which signals guard cells to close stomata. **2.** The activation of the proton pump of stomatal cells would cause the guard cells to take up K^+. The increased turgor of the guard cells would lock the stomata open and lead to extreme evaporation from the leaf. **3.** After the flowers are cut, transpiration from any leaves and from the petals (which are modified leaves) will continue to draw water up the xylem. If cut flowers are transferred directly to a vase, air pockets in xylem vessels prevent delivery of water from the vase to the flowers. Cutting stems again underwater, a few centimeters from the original cut, will sever the xylem above the air pocket. The water droplets prevent another air pocket from forming while placing the flowers in a vase. **4.** Water molecules are in constant motion, traveling at different rates. The average speed of these particles depends on the water's temperature. If water molecules gain enough energy, the most energetic molecules near the liquid's surface will impart sufficient speed, and therefore sufficient kinetic energy, to cause water molecules to propel away from the liquid in the form of gaseous molecules or, more simply, as water vapor. As the particles with the highest kinetic energy levels evaporate, the average kinetic energy of the remaining liquid decreases. Because a liquid's temperature is directly related to the average kinetic energy of its molecules, the liquid cools as it evaporates.

Summary of Key Concepts Questions

36.1 Plants with tall shoots and elevated leaf canopies generally had an advantage over shorter competitors. A consequence of the selective pressure for tall shoots was the further separation of leaves from roots. This separation created problems for the transport of materials between root and shoot systems. Plants with xylem cells were more successful at supplying their shoot systems with soil resources (water and minerals). Similarly, those with phloem cells were more successful at supplying sugar sinks with carbohydrates. **36.2** Xylem sap is usually pulled up the plant by transpiration, much more often than it is pushed up the plant by root pressure. **36.3** Hydrogen bonds are necessary for the cohesion of water molecules to each other and for the adhesion of water to other materials, such as cell walls. Both adhesion and cohesion of water molecules are involved in the ascent of xylem sap under conditions of negative pressure. **36.4** Although stomata account for most of the water lost from plants, they are necessary for exchange of gases—for example, for the uptake of carbon dioxide needed for photosynthesis.

Test Your Understanding

1. c **2.** a **3.** b **4.** b **5.** c **6.** e **7.** c **8.** a **9.** d
10.

Apoplastic route
Symplastic route

Chapter 38

Figure Questions

Figure 38.4 Having a specific pollinator is more efficient because less pollen gets delivered to flowers of the wrong species. However, it is also a risky strategy: If the pollinator population suffers to an unusual degree from predation, disease, or climate change, then the plant may not be able to produce seeds. **Figure 38.8** In addition to having a single cotyledon, monocots have leaves with parallel leaf venation, scattered vascular bundles in their stems, a fibrous root system, floral parts in threes or multiples of threes, and pollen grains with only one opening. In contrast, dicots have two cotyledons, netlike leaf venation, vascular bundles in a ring, taproots, floral parts in fours or fives or multiples thereof, and pollen grains with three openings. **Figure 38.9** Beans use a hypocotyl hook to push through the soil. The delicate leaves and shoot apical meristem are also protected by being sandwiched between two large cotyledons. The coleoptile of maize seedlings helps protect the emerging leaves. **Figure 38.17** The crown gall bacterium (*Agrobacterium tumefaciens*) normally causes cancer-like growths in susceptible plants. *Agrobacterium* inserts its own genes into plant cells by means of plasmids. These plasmids have been genetically engineered to retain their ability to insert genes into plant cells without causing cancerous growth.

Concept Check 38.1
1. In angiosperms, pollination is the transfer of pollen from an anther to a stigma. Fertilization is the fusion of the egg and sperm to form the zygote; it cannot occur until after the growth of the pollen tube from the pollen grain. 2. Seed dormancy prevents the premature germination of seeds. A seed will germinate only when the environmental conditions are optimal for the survival of its embryo as a young seedling. 3. Long styles help to weed out pollen grains that are genetically inferior and not capable of successfully growing long pollen tubes. 4. No. The haploid (gametophyte) generation of plants is multicellular and arises from spores. The haploid phase of the animal life cycles is a single-celled gamete (egg or sperm) that arises directly from meiosis: There are no spores.

Concept Check 38.2
1. Asexually propagated crops lack genetic diversity. Genetically diverse populations are less likely to become extinct in the face of an epidemic because there is a greater likelihood that a few individuals in the population are resistant. 2. In the short term, selfing may be advantageous in a population that is so dispersed and sparse that pollen delivery is unreliable. In the long term, however, selfing is an evolutionary dead end because it leads to a loss of genetic diversity that may preclude adaptive evolution. 3. This might be possible, but satisfactory results would be very unlikely. Both tubers and fruits are tremendous energy sinks. Each plant has only a finite amount of energy to divide between sexual and asexual reproduction. Although a tomato-potato hybrid could, in theory, produce an offspring that makes fruits and tubers equally, these fruits and tubers would be of inferior quality or low yielding.

Concept Check 38.3
1. Traditional breeding and genetic engineering both involve artificial selection for desired traits. However, genetic engineering techniques facilitate faster gene transfer and are not limited to transferring genes between closely related varieties or species. 2. GM crops may be more nutritious and less susceptible to insect damage or pathogens that invade insect-damaged plants. They also may not require as much chemical spraying. However, unknown risks may include adverse effects on human health and nontarget organisms and the possibility of transgene escape. 3. *Bt* maize suffers less insect damage; therefore, *Bt* maize plants are less likely to be infected by fumonisin-producing fungi that infect plants through wounds. 4. In such species, engineering the transgene into the chloroplast DNA would not prevent its escape in pollen; such a method requires that the chloroplast DNA be found only in the egg. An entirely different method of preventing transgene escape would therefore be needed, such as male sterility, apomixis, or self-pollinating closed flowers.

Summary of Key Concepts Questions
38.1 After pollination, a flower typically changes into a fruit. The petals, sepals, and stamens typically fall off the flower. The stigma of the pistil withers and the ovary begins to swell. The ovules (embryonic seeds) inside the ovary begin to mature. **38.2** Asexual reproduction can be advantageous in a stable environment because individual plants that are well suited to that environment pass on all their genes to offspring. Also, asexual reproduction generally results in offspring that are less fragile than the seedlings produced by sexual reproduction. However, sexual reproduction offers the advantage of dispersal of tough seeds. Moreover, sexual reproduction produces genetic variety, which may be advantageous in an unstable environment. The likelihood is better that at least one offspring of sexual reproduction will survive in a changed environment. **38.3** "Golden Rice" has been engineered to produce more vitamin A, thereby raising the nutritional value of rice. A protoxin gene from a soil bacterium has been engineered into *Bt* maize. This protoxin is lethal to invertebrates but harmless to vertebrates. *Bt* crops require less pesticide spraying and have lower levels of fungal infection. The nutritional value of cassava is being increased in many ways by genetic engineering. Enriched levels of protein, iron, and beta-carotene (a vitamin A precursor) have been achieved, and cyanide-producing chemicals have been almost eliminated from the roots.

Test Your Understanding
1. c   2. a   3. c   4. e   5. c   6. c   7. d   8. c   9. d
10.

Chapter 40

Figure Questions
Figure 40.4 Such exchange surfaces are internal in the sense that they are inside the body. However, they are also continuous with openings on the external body surface that contact the environment. **Figure 40.8** The air conditioner would form a second control circuit, cooling the house when air temperature exceeded the set point. Such opposing, or antagonistic, pairs of control circuits increase the effectiveness of a homeostatic mechanism. **Figure 40.14** If a female Burmese python were not incubating eggs, her oxygen consumption would decrease with decreasing temperature, as for any other ectotherm. **Figure 40.17** The transport of nutrients across membranes and the synthesis of RNA and protein are coupled to ATP hydrolysis. These processes proceed spontaneously because there is an overall drop in free energy, with the excess energy given off as heat. Similarly, less than half of the free energy in glucose is captured in the coupled reactions of cellular respiration. The remainder of the energy is released as heat. **Figure 40.21** Nothing. Although genes that show a circadian variation in expression during euthermia exhibit constant RNA levels during hibernation, a gene that shows constant expression during hibernation might also show constant expression during euthermia.

Concept Check 40.1
1. All types of epithelia consist of cells that line a surface, are tightly packed, are situated on top of a basal lamina, and form an active and protective interface with the external environment. 2. By flattening its ears along its body, the jackrabbit can reduce the exposed surface area of its body and hence the amount of heat lost. However, by placing its ears flat, the jackrabbit reduces its ability to detect potential predators. 3. You need the nervous system to perceive the danger and provoke a split-second muscular response to keep from falling. The nervous system, however, does not make a direct connection with blood vessels or glucose-storing cells in the liver. Instead, the nervous system triggers the release of a hormone (called epinephrine, or adrenaline) by the endocrine system, bringing about a change in these tissues in just a few seconds.

Concept Check 40.2
1. In the enzyme-catalyzed biosynthetic process, the product of a pathway (in this case, isoleucine) inhibits the pathway that generated it. In thermoregulation, the product of the pathway (a change in temperature) decreases pathway activity by reducing the stimulus. 2. You would want to put the thermostat close to where you would be spending time, where it would be protected from environmental perturbations, such as direct sunshine, and not right in the path of the output of the heating system. Similarly, the sensors for homeostasis located in the human brain are separated from environmental influences and can monitor conditions in a vital and sensitive tissue. 3. In convergent evolution, the same biological trait arises independently in two or more species. Gene analysis can provide evidence for an independent origin. In particular, if the genes responsible for the trait in one species lack significant sequence similarity to the corresponding genes in another species, scientists conclude that there is a separate genetic basis for the trait in the two species and thus an independent origin. In the case of circadian rhythms, the clock genes in cyanobacteria appear unrelated to those in humans.

Concept Check 40.3
1. "Wind chill" involves heat loss through convection, as the moving air contributes to heat loss from the skin surface. 2. The hummingbird, being a very small endotherm, has a very high metabolic rate. If by absorbing sunlight certain flowers warm their nectar, a hummingbird feeding on these flowers is saved the metabolic expense of warming the nectar to its body temperature. 3. The ice water would cool tissues in your head, including blood that would then circulate throughout your body. This effect would accelerate the return to a normal body temperature. If, however, the ice water reached the eardrum and cooled the blood vessel that supplies the hypothalamus, the hypothalamic thermostat would respond by inhibiting sweating and constricting blood vessels in the skin, slowing cooling elsewhere in the body.

Concept Check 40.4
1. The mouse would consume oxygen at a higher rate because it is an endotherm, so its basal metabolic rate is higher than the ectothermic lizard's standard metabolic rate. 2. The house cat; smaller animals have a higher metabolic rate per unit body mass and a greater demand for food per unit body mass. 3. Although penguins do not grow as adults, they increase and decrease in size as they repeatedly form and use energy stores. A significant amount of energy might be stored in fat during part of the year but be used later in the year. Monitoring energy allocation only during the period when energy is stored in fat would lead to the erroneous conclusion that the penguin is growing.

Summary of Key Concepts Questions
40.1 Animals exchange materials with their environment across their body surface, and a spherical shape has the minimum surface area per unit volume. As body size increases, the ratio of surface area to body volume decreases. **40.2** No; even though an animal regulates some aspects of its internal environment, the internal environment fluctuates slightly around set points. Homeostasis is a dynamic state. Furthermore, there are sometimes programmed changes in set points, such as those resulting in radical increases in hormone levels at particular times in development. **40.3** Heat exchange across the skin is a primary mechanism for the regulation of body core temperature, with the result that the skin is cooler than the body core. **40.4** Because small animals have the highest ratio of BMR per unit mass, they have the greatest energetic savings per unit mass during hibernation. Consequently, the selective pressure favoring hibernation during evolution is especially strong for small animals.

Test Your Understanding
1. b **2.** c **3.** a **4.** b **5.** d **6.** c **7.** e
8.

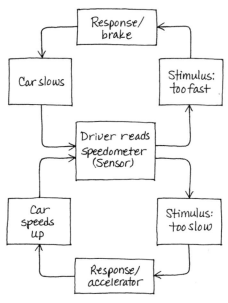

Test Your Understanding
1. a **2.** c **3.** c **4.** d **5.** d **6.** b
7.

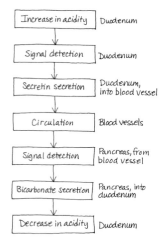

Chapter 41

Figure Questions

Figure 41.2 Just as penguin muscle protein provides amino acids for regrowth of large numbers of feathers, ovalbumin and casein provide amino acids for growth of a fertilized egg or nursing mammal. Thus, the common circumstance is a period of rapid developmental growth. **Figure 41.4** As in the described study, they needed a sample size large enough that they could expect a significant number of neural tube defects in the control group. The information needed to determine the appropriate sample size was the frequency of neural tube defects in first-time pregnancies in the general population.

Concept Check 41.1

1. The only essential amino acids are those that an animal cannot synthesize from other molecules. **2.** Many vitamins serve as enzyme cofactors, which, like enzymes themselves, are unchanged by the chemical reactions in which they participate. Therefore, only very small amounts of vitamins are needed. **3.** To identify the essential nutrient missing from an animal's diet, a researcher could supplement the diet with individual nutrients and determine which nutrient eliminates the signs of malnutrition.

Concept Check 41.2

1. A gastrovascular cavity is a digestive pouch with a single opening that functions in both ingestion and elimination; an alimentary canal is a digestive tube with a separate mouth and anus at opposite ends. **2.** As long as nutrients are within the cavity of the alimentary canal, they are in a compartment that is continuous with the outside environment via the mouth and anus and have not yet crossed a membrane to enter the body. **3.** Just as food remains outside the body in a digestive tract, gasoline moves from the fuel tank to the engine, and waste products exit through the exhaust without ever entering the passenger compartment of the automobile. In addition, gasoline, like food, is broken down in a specialized compartment, so that the rest of the automobile (or body) is protected from disassembly. In both cases, high-energy fuels are consumed, complex molecules are broken down into simpler ones, and waste products are eliminated.

Summary of Key Concepts Questions

41.1 Since collagen is found in all mammals, a likely explanation is that mammals other than primates and guinea pigs can synthesize vitamin C from other organic molecules. **41.2** A liquid diet containing glucose, amino acids, and other building blocks could be ingested and absorbed without the need for mechanical or chemical digestion.

Chapter 42

Figure Questions

Figure 42.2 Although gas exchange might be improved by a steady, one-way flow of fluid, there would likely be inadequate time for food to be digested and nutrients absorbed if fluid flowed through the cavity in this manner. **Figure 42.22** The three main lineages are Deuterostomia, Lophotrochozoa, and Ecdysozoa. All three are represented by the animals shown in Figure 42.22: Polychaetes (phylum Annelida) are lophotrochozoans, crayfish (phylum Arthropoda) are ecdysozoans, and sea stars (phylum Echinodermata) are deuterostomes. **Figure 42.26** The reduction in surface tension results from the presence of surfactant. Therefore, for all the infants that had died of RDS, you would expect the amount of surfactant to be near zero. For infants that had died of other causes, you would expect the amount of surfactant to be near zero for weights less than 1,200 g but much greater than zero for weights above 1,200 g.

Concept Check 42.1

1. In both an open circulatory system and a fountain, fluid is pumped through a tube and then returns to the pump after collecting in a pool. **2.** The ability to shut off blood supply to the lungs when the animal is submerged **3.** The O_2 content would be abnormally low because some oxygen-depleted blood returned to the right atrium from the systemic circuit would mix with the oxygen-rich blood in the left atrium.

Concept Check 42.5

1. Their interior position helps them stay moist. If the respiratory surfaces of lungs extended out into the terrestrial environment, they would quickly dry out, and diffusion of O_2 and CO_2 across these surfaces would stop. **2.** Earthworms need to keep their skin moist for gas exchange, but they need air outside this moist layer. If they stay in their waterlogged tunnels after a heavy rain, they will suffocate because they cannot get as much O_2 from water as from air. **3.** In the extremities of some vertebrates, blood flows in opposite directions in neighboring veins and arteries; this countercurrent arrangement maximizes the recapture of heat from blood leaving the body core in arteries, which is important for thermoregulation in cold environments. Similarly, in the gills of fish, water passes over the gills in the direction opposite to that of blood flowing through the gill capillaries, maximizing the extraction of oxygen from the water along the length of the exchange surface.

Summary of Key Concepts Questions

42.1 In a closed circulatory system, an ATP-driven muscular pump generally moves fluids in one direction on a scale of millimeters to meters. Exchange between cells and their environment relies on diffusion, which involves random movements of molecules. Concentration gradients of molecules across exchange surfaces can drive rapid net diffusion on a scale of 1 mm or less. **42.5.** Because CO_2 is such a small fraction of atmospheric gas (0.29 mm Hg/760 mm Hg, or less than 0.04%), the partial pressure gradient of CO_2 between the respiratory surface and the environment always strongly favors the release of CO_2 to the atmosphere.

Test Your Understanding
1. c 2. b 3. d 4. c 5. d 6. a 7. a 8. a
9.

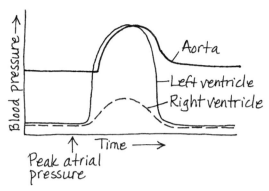

Chapter 44

Figure Questions
Figure 44.2 Aquaporins, which act as water channels.

Concept Check 44.1
1. Because the salt is moved against its concentration gradient, from low concentration (fresh water) to high concentration (blood)   2. A freshwater osmoconformer would have body fluids too dilute to carry out life's processes.   3. Without a layer of insulating fur, the camel must use the cooling effect of evaporative water loss to maintain body temperature, thus linking thermoregulation and osmoregulation.

Concept Check 44.2
1. Because uric acid is largely insoluble in water, it can be excreted as a semisolid paste, thereby reducing an animal's water loss.   2. Humans produce uric acid from purine breakdown, and reducing purines in the diet often lessens the severity of gout. Birds, however, produce uric acid as a waste product of general nitrogen metabolism. They would therefore need a diet low in all nitrogen-containing compounds, not just purines.

Concept Check 44.3
1. In flatworms, ciliated cells draw interstitial fluids containing waste products into protonephridia. In earthworms, waste products pass from interstitial fluids into the coelom. From there the cilia move the wastes into metanephridia via a funnel surrounding an internal opening to the metanephridia. In insects, the Malpighian tubules pump fluids from the hemolymph, which receives waste products during exchange with interstitial fluids in the course of circulation.   2. Filtration produces a fluid for exchange processes that is free of cells and large molecules, which are of benefit to the animal and could not readily be reabsorbed.   3. The presence of Na^+ and other ions (electrolytes) in the dialysate would limit the extent to which they would be removed from the filtrate during dialysis. Adjusting the electrolytes in the starting dialysate can thus lead to the restoration of proper electrolyte concentrations in the plasma. Similarly, the absence of urea and other waste products in the starting dialysate results in their efficient removal from the filtrate.

Summary of Key Concepts Questions
44.1 Water moves into a cell by osmosis when the fluid outside the cells is hypoosmotic (has a lower solute concentration than the cytosol).
44.2

Waste Attribute	Ammonia	Urea	Uric Acid
Toxicity	High	Very low	Low
Energy content	Low	Moderate	High
Water loss in excretion	High	Moderate	Low

44.3 Filtration retains large molecules that would be difficult to transport across membranes.

Test Your Understanding
1. d 2. a 3. c 4. e 5. d 6. b
7.

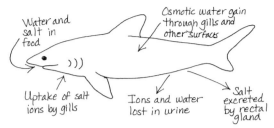

Chapter 46

Figure Questions
Figure 46.9 According to the graph, about one-third of the females rid themselves of all sperm from the first mating. Thus, two-thirds retain some sperm from the first mating. We would therefore predict that two-thirds of the females would have some offspring exhibiting the small-eye phenotype of the dominant mutation carried by the males with which the females mated first.

Concept Check 46.1
1. The offspring of sexual reproduction are more genetically diverse. However, asexual reproduction can produce more offspring over multiple generations.
2. Unlike other forms of asexual reproduction, parthenogenesis involves gamete production. By controlling whether or not haploid eggs are fertilized, species such as honeybees can readily switch between asexual and sexual reproduction.
3. No. Owing to random assortment of chromosomes during meiosis, the offspring may receive the same copy or different copies of a particular parental chromosome from the sperm and the egg. Furthermore, genetic recombination during meiosis will result in reassortment of genes between pairs of parental chromosomes.   4. Both fragmentation and budding in animals have direct counterparts in the asexual reproduction of plants.

Concept Check 46.2
1. Internal fertilization allows the sperm to reach the egg without either gamete drying out.   2. (a) Animals with external fertilization tend to release many gametes at once, resulting in the production of enormous numbers of zygotes. This increases the chances that some will survive to adulthood. (b) Animals with internal fertilization produce fewer offspring but generally exhibit greater care of the embryos and the young.   3. Like the uterus of an insect, the ovary of a plant is the site of fertilization. Unlike the plant ovary, the uterus is not the site of egg production, which occurs in the insect ovary. In addition, the fertilized insect egg is expelled from the uterus, whereas the plant embryo develops within a seed in the ovary.

Summary of Key Concepts Questions
46.1. No. Because parthenogenesis involves meiosis, the mother would pass on to each offspring a random and therefore typically distinct combination of the chromosomes she inherited from her mother and father.   **46.2.** None

Test Your Understanding
1. d 2. b 3. a 4. c 5. a 6. b 7. c 8. d
9.

(a)

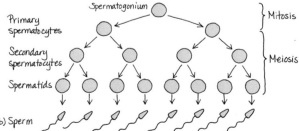

(b) Sperm

(c) The supply of stem cells would be used up and spermatogenesis would not be able to continue.

Chapter 47

Figure Questions

Figure 47.4 You could inject the compound into an unfertilized egg, expose the egg to sperm, and see whether the fertilization envelope forms. **Figure 47.21** The researchers allowed normal cortical rotation to occur, resulting in activation of the "back-forming" determinants. Then they forced the opposite rotation to occur, which established the back on the opposite side as well. Because the molecules on the normal side were already activated, forcing the opposite rotation apparently did not "cancel out" the establishment of the back side by the first rotation. **Figure 47.22** In Spemann's control, the two blastomeres were physically separated, and each grew into a whole embryo. In Roux's experiment, remnants of the dead blastomere were still contacting the live blastomere, which developed into a half-embryo. Therefore, molecules present in the dead cell's remnants may have been signaling to the live cell, inhibiting it from making all the embryonic structures. **Figure 47.23** You could inject the isolated protein or an mRNA encoding it into ventral cells of an earlier gastrula. If dorsal structures form on the ventral side, that would support the idea that the protein is the signaling molecule secreted or presented by the dorsal lip. You should also do a control experiment to make sure the injection process alone did not cause dorsal structures to form. **Figure 47.25** You could remove the AER and look for Sonic hedgehog mRNA or protein as a marker of the ZPA. If either was absent, that would support your hypothesis. You could also block FGF function and see whether the ZPA formed (by looking for Sonic hedgehog).

Concept Check 47.1

1. The fertilization envelope forms after cortical granules release their contents outside the egg, causing the vitelline membrane to rise and harden. The fertilization envelope serves as a barrier to fertilization by more than one sperm.
2. The increased Ca^{2+} concentration in the egg would cause the cortical granules to fuse with the plasma membrane, releasing their contents and causing a fertilization envelope to form, even though no sperm had entered. This would prevent fertilization. **3.** You would expect it to fluctuate. The fluctuation of MPF drives the transition between DNA replication (S phase) and mitosis (M phase), which is still required in the abbreviated cleavage cell cycle.

Concept Check 47.2

1. The cells of the notochord migrate toward the midline of the embryo (converge), rearranging themselves so there are fewer cells across the notochord, which thus becomes longer overall (extends; see Figure 47.16). **2.** Because microfilaments would not be able to contract and decrease the size of one end of the cell, both the inward bending in the middle of the neural tube and the outward bending of the hinge regions at the edges would be blocked. Therefore, the neural tube probably would not form. **3.** Dietary intake of the vitamin folic acid dramatically reduces the frequency of neural tube defects.

Concept Check 47.3

1. Axis formation establishes the location and polarity of the three axes that provide the coordinates for development. Pattern formation positions particular tissues and organs in the three-dimensional space defined by those coordinates.
2. Morphogen gradients act by specifying cell fates across a field of cells through variation in the level of a determinant. Morphogen gradients thus act more globally than cytoplasmic determinants or inductive interactions between pairs of cells. **3.** Yes, a second embryo could develop because inhibiting BMP-4 activity would have the same effect as transplanting an organizer. **4.** The limb that developed probably would have a mirror-image duplication, with the most posterior digits in the middle and the most anterior digits at either end.

Summary of Key Concepts Questions

47.1 The binding of a sperm to a receptor on the egg surface is very specific and likely would not occur if the two gametes were from different species. Without sperm binding, the sperm and egg membranes would not fuse. **47.2** The neural tube forms when the neural plate, a band of ectodermal tissue oriented along the anterior-posterior axis on the dorsal side of the embryo, rolls into a tube and pinches off from the rest of the ectoderm. Neural crest cells arise as groups of cells in the regions between the edges of the neural tube and the surrounding ectoderm migrate away from the neural tube. **47.3** Mutations that affected both limb and kidney development would be more likely to alter the function of monocilia because these organelles are important in several signaling pathways. Mutations that affected limb development but not kidney development would more likely alter a single pathway, such as Hedgehog signaling.

Test Your Understanding

1. a **2.** b **3.** e **4.** a **5.** d **6.** d **7.** b
8.

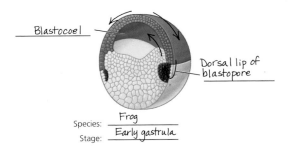

Blastocoel

Dorsal lip of blastopore

Species: _Frog_
Stage: _Early gastrula_

Chapter 49

Figure Questions

Figure 49.3 During swallowing, muscles along the esophagus alternately contract and relax, resulting in peristalsis. One model to explain this alternation is that each section of muscle receives nerve impulses that alternate between excitation and inhibition, just as the quadriceps and hamstring receive opposing signals in the knee-jerk reflex. **Figure 49.12** If the new mutation disrupted only pacemaker function, you should be able to restore rhythmic activity by removing the SCN and replacing it with an SCN transplant from either a wild-type or τ mutant hamster. Using the new mutant as the donor would not be as informative, since both failed transplants and successful ones would result in a lack of rhythmic activity.
Figure 49.14 Regions you would expect to be active regardless of the type of music played would include ones that are important for processing and interpreting sounds.

Concept Check 49.1

1. The sympathetic division would likely be activated. It mediates the "fight-or-flight" response in stressful situations. **2.** The preganglionic neurons use the same neurotransmitter and function similarly in each division (to stimulate postganglionic neurons). The postganglionic neurons use different neurotransmitters that generally bring about opposing functions in the same target tissues. **3.** Nerves contain bundles of axons, some that belong to motor neurons, which send signals outward from the CNS, and some that belong to sensory neurons, which bring signals into the CNS. Therefore, you would expect effects on both motor control and sensation. **4.** Neurosecretory cells of the adrenal medulla secrete the hormones epinephrine and norepinephrine in response to preganglionic input from sympathetic neurons. These hormones travel in the circulation throughout the body, triggering responses in many tissues.

Concept Check 49.2

1. The cerebral cortex on the left side of the brain initiates voluntary movement of the right side of the body. **2.** Alcohol diminishes function of the cerebellum. **3.** Paralysis reflects an inability to carry out motor commands transmitted from the cerebrum to the spinal cord. You would expect these patients to have injuries in the portion of the CNS extending from the spinal cord up to but not including the reticular formation. A coma reflects a disruption in the cycles of sleep and arousal regulated by communication between the reticular formation and the cerebrum. You would expect these patients to have injuries in the reticular formation or in the portion of the brain on the opposite side of the reticular formation from the spinal cord.

Summary of Key Concepts Questions

49.1 Because reflex circuits involve only a few neurons—the simplest consist of a sensory neuron and a motor neuron—the path for information transfer is short and simple, increasing the speed of the response. **49.2** The pons and medulla (the midbrain) coordinate visual reflexes; the cerebellum controls coordination of movement that depends on visual input; the thalamus serves as a routing center for visual information; and the cerebrum is essential for converting visual input to a visual image.

Test Your Understanding

1. c **2.** a **3.** d **4.** c **5.** d **6.** e
7.

(a)

Pain receptor in finger
Afferent sensory neuron from pain receptor in finger
Spinal cord
Pin pricks finger
Interneurons
Synapses in arm muscles
Hand pulls away
Efferent motor neurons to arm muscles

(b)

Pain perceived in somatosensory cortex of parietal lobe of cerebrum
Parietal lobe

Chapter 51

Figure Questions
Figure 51.2 The fixed action pattern based on the sign stimulus of a red belly ensures that the male will chase away any invading males of his species. By chasing away such males, the defender decreases the chance that another male will fertilize eggs laid in his nesting territory. **Figure 51.7** There should be no effect. Imprinting is an innate behavior that is carried out anew in each generation. Assuming the nest was not disturbed, the offspring of the Lorenz followers would imprint on the mother goose. **Figure 51.8** Perhaps the wasp doesn't use visual cues. It might also be that wasps recognize objects native to their environment, but not foreign objects, such as the pinecones. Tinbergen addressed these ideas before carrying out the pinecone study. When he swept away the pebbles and sticks around the nest, the wasps could no longer find their nests. If he shifted the natural objects in their natural arrangement, the shift in the landmarks caused a shift in the site to which the wasps returned. Finally, if natural objects around the nest site were replaced with pinecones while the wasp was in the burrow, the wasp nevertheless found her way back to the nest site. **Figure 51.23** Courtship song generation must be coupled to courtship song recognition. Unless the genes that control generation of particular song elements also control recognition, the hybrids might be unlikely to find mating partners, depending on what aspects of the songs are important for mate recognition and acceptance. **Figure 51.26** It might be that the birds require stimuli during flight to exhibit their migratory preference. If this were true, the birds would show the same orientation in the funnel experiment despite their distinct genetic programming. **Figure 51.28** It holds true for some, but not all individuals. If a parent has more than one reproductive partner, the offspring of different partners will have a coefficient of relatedness less than 0.5.

Concept Check 51.1
1. The proximate explanation for this fixed action pattern might be that nudging and rolling are released by the sign stimulus of an object outside the nest, and the behavior is carried to completion once initiated. The ultimate explanation might be that ensuring that eggs remain in the nest increases the chance of producing healthy offspring. **2.** In both cases, the detection of periodic variation in the environment results in a reproductive cycle timed to environmental conditions that optimize the opportunity for success. **3.** There might be selective pressure for other prey fish to detect an injured fish because the source of the injury might threaten them as well. Among predators, there might be selection for those that are attracted to the alarm substance because they would be more likely to encounter crippled prey. Fish with adequate defenses might show no change because they have a selective advantage if they do not waste energy responding to the alarm substance.

Concept Check 51.2
1. Natural selection would tend to favor convergence in color pattern because a predator learning to associate a pattern with a sting or bad taste would avoid all other individuals with that same color pattern, regardless of species. **2.** You might move objects around to establish an abstract rule, such as "past landmark A, the same distance as A is from the starting point," while maintaining a minimum of fixed metric relationships, that is, avoiding having the food directly adjacent to or a set distance from a landmark. As you might surmise, designing an informative experiment of this kind is not easy. **3.** Learned behavior, just like innate behavior, can contribute to reproductive isolation and thus to speciation. For example, learned bird songs contribute to species recognition during courtship, thereby helping ensure that only members of the same species mate.

Concept Check 51.3
1. Certainty of paternity is higher with external fertilization. **2.** Balancing selection could maintain the two alleles at the *forager* locus if population density fluctuated from one generation to another. At times of low population density, the energy-conserving sitter larvae (carrying the *for^s* allele) would be favored, while at higher population density, the more mobile Rover larvae (*for^R* allele) would have a selective advantage. **3.** Because females would now be present in much larger numbers than males, all three types of males should have some reproductive success. Nevertheless, since the advantage that the blue-throats rely on—a limited number of females in their territory—will be absent, the yellow-throats are likely to increase in frequency in the short term.

Concept Check 51.4
1. Because this geographic variation corresponds to differences in prey availability between two garter snake habitats, it seems likely that snakes with characteristics enabling them to feed on the abundant prey in their locale would have had increased survival and reproductive success. In this way, natural selection would have resulted in the divergent foraging behaviors. **2.** Yes. Kin selection does not require any recognition or awareness of relatedness. The older individual cannot be the beneficiary because he or she cannot have extra offspring. However, the cost is low for an older individual performing the altruistic act because that individual has already reproduced (but perhaps is still caring for a child or grandchild). There can therefore be selection for an altruistic act by a postreproductive individual that benefits a young relative.

Summary of Key Concepts Questions
51.1 Circannual rhythms are typically based on the cycles of light and dark in the environment. As the global climate changes, animals that migrate in response to these rhythms may shift to a location before or after local environmental conditions are optimal for reproduction and survival. **51.2** For the goose, all that is acquired is an object at which the behavior is directed. In the case of the sparrow, learning takes place that will give shape to the behavior itself. **51.3** Because feeding the female is likely to improve her reproductive success, the genes from the sacrificed male are likely to appear in a greater number of progeny. **51.4** You would likely have missed the idea that changes in a single gene can have large-scale effects on even complex behaviors.

Test Your Understanding
1. d **2.** b **3.** c **4.** a **5.** c **6.** a
7.

You could measure the size of mussels that oystercatchers successfully open and compare that with the size distribution in the habitat.

Chapter 52

Figure Questions
Figure 52.7 Dispersal limitations, the activities of people (such as a broad-scale conversion of forests to agriculture or selective harvesting), or many other factors, including those discussed later in the chapter (see Figure 52.18) **Figure 52.18** Some factors, such as fire, are relevant only for terrestrial systems. At first glance, water availability is primarily a terrestrial factor, too. However, species living along the intertidal zone of oceans or along the edge of lakes also suffer desiccation. Salinity stress is important for species in some aquatic and terrestrial systems. Oxygen availability is an important factor primarily for species in some aquatic systems and in soils and sediments. **Figure 52.20** When only urchins were removed, limpets may have increased in abundance and reduced seaweed cover somewhat (the difference between the purple and blue lines on the graph).

Concept Check 52.1
1. In the tropics, high temperatures evaporate water and cause warm, moist air to rise. The rising air cools and releases much of its water as rain over the tropics. The remaining dry air descends at approximately 30° north and south, causing deserts to occur in those regions. **2.** The microclimate around the stream will be cooler, moister, and shadier than that around the unplanted agricultural field. **3.** Trees that require a long time to reach reproductive age are likely to evolve more slowly than annual plants in response to climate change, constraining the potential ability of such trees to respond to rapid climate change. **4.** Plants with C_4 photosynthesis are likely to expand their range globally as Earth's climate warms. As described in Concept 10.4, C_4 photosynthesis minimizes photorespiration and enhances sugar production, an advantage that is especially useful in warmer regions where C_4 plants are found today.

Concept Check 52.2
1. Temperate broadleaf forests have higher mean annual precipitation. **2.** Answers will vary by location but should be based on the information and maps in Figure 52.12. How much your local area has been altered from its natural state will influence how much it reflects the expected characteristics of your biome, particularly the expected plants and animals. **3.** Northern coniferous forest is likely to replace tundra along the boundary between these biomes. To see why, note that northern coniferous forest is adjacent to tundra throughout North America, northern Europe, and Asia (see Figure 52.9) and that the temperature range for northern coniferous forest is just above that for tundra (see Figure 52.10).

Concept Check 52.3
1. In the oceanic pelagic zone, the ocean bottom lies below the photic zone, so there is too little light to support benthic algae or rooted plants. **2.** As explained in Concept 44.1, aquatic organisms either gain or lose water by osmosis if the osmolarity of their environment differs from their internal osmolarity. Water gain can cause cells to swell, and water loss can cause them to shrink. To avoid excessive changes in cell volume, organisms that live in estuaries must be able to compen-

sate for both water gain (under freshwater conditions) and water loss (under salt-water conditions). **3.** In a river below a dam, the fish are more likely to be species that prefer colder water. In summer, the deep layers of a reservoir are colder than the surface layers, so a river below a dam will be colder than an undammed river.

Concept Check 52.4

1. (a) Humans might transplant a species to a new area that it could not previously reach because of a geographic barrier. (b) Humans might eliminate a predator or herbivore species, such as sea urchins, from an area. **2.** One test would be to build a fence around a plot of land in an area that has trees of that species, excluding all deer from the plot. You could then compare the abundance of tree seedlings inside and outside the fenced plot over time. **3.** Because the ancestor of the silverswords reached isolated Hawaii early in the islands' existence, it likely faced little competition and was able to occupy many unfilled niches. The cattle egret, in contrast, arrived in the Americas only recently and has to compete with a well-established group of species. Thus, its opportunities for adaptive radiation have probably been much more limited.

Summary of Key Concepts Questions

52.1 Because dry air would descend at the equator instead of at 30° north and south latitude (where deserts exist today), deserts would be more likely to exist along the equator (see Figure 52.3). **52.2** Because tundra is much cooler than deserts (see Figure 52.10), less water evaporates during the growing season and the tundra stays more moist. **52.3** An aphotic zone is most likely to be found in the deep waters of a lake, the oceanic pelagic zone, or the marine benthic zone. **52.4** You could arrange a flowchart that begins with abiotic limitations—first determining the physical and chemical conditions under which a species could survive—and then moves through the other factors listed in the flowchart.

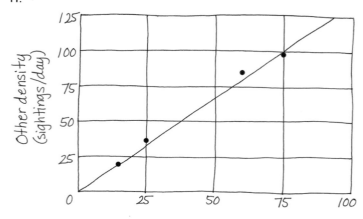

Based on what you learned from Figure 52.20 and on the positive relationship you observed in the field between kelp abundance and otter density, you could hypothesize that otters lower sea urchin density, reducing feeding of the urchins on kelp.

APPENDIX C The Metric System

Measurement	Unit and Abbreviation	Metric Equivalent	Metric-to-English Conversion Factor	English-to-Metric Conversion Factor
Length	1 kilometer (km)	$= 1{,}000 \ (10^3)$ meters	1 km = 0.62 mile	1 mile = 1.61 km
	1 meter (m)	$= 100 \ (10^2)$ centimeters	1 m = 1.09 yards	1 yard = 0.914 m
		= 1,000 millimeters	1 m = 3.28 feet	1 foot = 0.305 m
			1 m = 39.37 inches	
	1 centimeter (cm)	$= 0.01 \ (10^{-2})$ meter	1 cm = 0.394 inch	1 foot = 30.5 cm
				1 inch = 2.54 cm
	1 millimeter (mm)	$= 0.001 \ (10^{-3})$ meter	1 mm = 0.039 inch	
	1 micrometer (μm) (formerly micron, μ)	$= 10^{-6}$ meter $(10^{-3}$ mm)		
	1 nanometer (nm) (formerly millimicron, mμ)	$= 10^{-9}$ meter $(10^{-3}$ μm)		
	1 angstrom (Å)	$= 10^{-10}$ meter $(10^{-4}$ μm)		
Area	1 hectare (ha)	= 10,000 square meters	1 ha = 2.47 acres	1 acre = 0.405 ha
	1 square meter (m^2)	= 10,000 square centimeters	1 m^2 = 1.196 square yards	1 square yard = 0.8361 m^2
			1 m^2 = 10.764 square feet	1 square foot = 0.0929 m^2
	1 square centimeter (cm^2)	= 100 square millimeters	1 cm^2 = 0.155 square inch	1 square inch = 6.4516 cm^2
Mass	1 metric ton (t)	= 1,000 kilograms	1 t = 1.103 tons	1 ton = 0.907 t
	1 kilogram (kg)	= 1,000 grams	1 kg = 2.205 pounds	1 pound = 0.4536 kg
	1 gram (g)	= 1,000 milligrams	1 g = 0.0353 ounce	1 ounce = 28.35 g
			1 g = 15.432 grains	
	1 milligram (mg)	$= 10^{-3}$ gram	1 mg = approx. 0.015 grain	
	1 microgram (μg)	$= 10^{-6}$ gram		
Volume (solids)	1 cubic meter (m^3)	= 1,000,000 cubic centimeters	1 m^3 = 1.308 cubic yards	1 cubic yard = 0.7646 m^3
			1 m^3 = 35.315 cubic feet	1 cubic foot = 0.0283 m^3
	1 cubic centimeter (cm^3 or cc)	$= 10^{-6}$ cubic meter	1 cm^3 = 0.061 cubic inch	1 cubic inch = 16.387 cm^3
	1 cubic millimeter (mm^3)	$= 10^{-9}$ cubic meter $= 10^{-3}$ cubic centimeter		
Volume (liquids and gases)	1 kiloliter (kL or kl)	= 1,000 liters	1 kL = 264.17 gallons	
	1 liter (L or l)	= 1,000 milliliters	1 L = 0.264 gallons	1 gallon = 3.785 L
			1 L = 1.057 quarts	1 quart = 0.946 L
	1 milliliter (mL or ml)	$= 10^{-3}$ liter	1 mL = 0.034 fluid ounce	1 quart = 946 mL
		= 1 cubic centimeter	1 mL = approx. ¼ teaspoon	1 pint = 473 mL
			1 mL = approx. 15–16 drops (gtt.)	1 fluid ounce = 29.57 mL
				1 teaspoon = approx. 5 mL
	1 microliter (μL or μl)	$= 10^{-6}$ liter $(10^{-3}$ milliliters)		
Time	1 second (s or sec)	= ⅟₆₀ minute		
	1 millisecond (ms or msec)	$= 10^{-3}$ second		
Temperature	Degrees Celsius (°C) (Absolute zero, when all molecular motion ceases, is −273.15°C. The Kelvin [K] scale, which has the same size degrees as Celsius, has its zero point at absolute zero. Thus, 0 K = −273.15°C.)		°F = ⅘°C + 32	°C = ⅝ (°F − 32)

Appendix C The Metric System

APPENDIX **E** Classification of Life

This appendix presents a taxonomic classification for the major extant groups of organisms discussed in this text; not all phyla are included. The classification presented here is based on the three-domain system, which assigns the two major groups of prokaryotes, bacteria and archaea, to separate domains (with eukaryotes making up the third domain).

Various alternative classification schemes are discussed in Unit Five of the text. The taxonomic turmoil includes debates about the number and boundaries of kingdoms and about the alignment of the Linnaean classification hierarchy with the findings of modern cladistic analysis. In this review, asterisks (*) indicate currently recognized phyla thought by some systematists to be paraphyletic.

DOMAIN BACTERIA

- Proteobacteria
- Chlamydia
- Spirochetes
- Gram-positive Bacteria
- Cyanobacteria

DOMAIN ARCHAEA

- **Korarchaeota**
- **Euryarchaeota**
- **Crenarchaeota**
- **Nanoarchaeota**

DOMAIN EUKARYA

In the phylogenetic hypothesis we present in Chapter 28, major clades of eukaryotes are grouped together in the five "supergroups" listed below in blue type. Formerly, all the eukaryotes generally called protists were assigned to a single kingdom, Protista. However, advances in systematics have made it clear that Protista is in fact polyphyletic: Some protists are more closely related to plants, fungi, or animals than they are to other protists. As a result, the kingdom Protista has been abandoned.

Excavata
- Diplomonadida (diplomonads)
- Parabasala (parabasalids)
- Euglenozoa (euglenozoans)
  Kinetoplastida (kinetoplastids)
  Euglenophyta (euglenids)

Chromalveolata
- Alveolata (alveolates)
  Dinoflagellata (dinoflagellates)
  Apicomplexa (apicomplexans)
  Ciliophora (ciliates)
- Stramenopila (stramenopiles)
  Bacillariophyta (diatoms)
  Chrysophyta (golden algae)
  Phaeophyta (brown algae)
  Oomycota (water molds)

Archaeplastida
- Rhodophyta (red algae)
- Chlorophyta (green algae: chlorophytes)
- Charophyta (green algae: charophytes)
- Plantae
  Phylum Hepatophyta (liverworts) ⎫
  Phylum Bryophyta (mosses)   ⎬ Nonvascular
  Phylum Anthocerophyta (hornworts) ⎭ plants (bryophytes)
  Phylum Lycophyta (lycophytes)   ⎫ Seedless vascular
  Phylum Pterophyta (ferns, horsetails, ⎬ plants
    whisk ferns)   ⎭
  Phylum Ginkgophyta (ginkgo)   ⎫
  Phylum Cycadophyta (cycads)   ⎬ Gymnosperms ⎫
  Phylum Gnetophyta (gnetophytes) ⎪   ⎬ Seed
  Phylum Coniferophyta (conifers) ⎭   ⎪ plants
  Phylum Anthophyta (flowering   ⎱ Angiosperms ⎭
    plants)

Rhizaria
- Radiolaria (radiolarians)
- Foraminifera (forams)
- Cercozoa (cercozoans)

DOMAIN EUKARYA, continued

Unikonta
- Amoebozoa (amoebozoans)
    - Myxogastrida (plasmodial slime molds)
    - Dictyostelida (cellular slime molds)
    - Gymnamoeba (gymnamoebas)
    - Entamoeba (entamoebas)
- Nucleariida (nucleariids)
- Fungi
    - *Phylum Chytridiomycota (chytrids)
    - *Phylum Zygomycota (zygomycetes)
    - Phylum Glomeromycota (glomeromycetes)
    - Phylum Basidiomycota (club fungi)
    - Phylum Ascomycota (sac fungi)

- Choanoflagellata (choanoflagellates)
- Animalia
    - Phylum Porifera (sponges)
    - Phylum Ctenophora (comb jellies)
    - Phylum Cnidaria (cnidarians)
        - Hydrozoa (hydrozoans)
        - Scyphozoa (jellies)
        - Cubozoa (box jellies and sea wasps)
        - Anthozoa (sea anemones and most corals)
    - Phylum Acoela (acoel flatworms)
    - Phylum Placozoa (placozoans)
    - Lophotrochozoa (lophotrochozoans)
        - Phylum Kinorhyncha (kinorhynchs)
        - Phylum Platyhelminthes (flatworms)
            - Catenulida (chain worms)
            - Rhabditophora (planarians, flukes, tapeworms)
        - Phylum Nemertea (proboscis worms)
        - Phylum Ectoprocta (ectoprocts)
        - Phylum Brachiopoda (brachiopods)
        - Phylum Phoronida (phoronids)
        - Phylum Rotifera (rotifers)
        - Phylum Cycliophora (cycliophorans)
        - Phylum Mollusca (molluscs)
            - Polyplacophora (chitons)
            - Gastropoda (gastropods)
            - Bivalvia (bivalves)
            - Cephalopoda (cephalopods)
    - Phylum Annelida (segmented worms)
        - Polychaeta (polychaetes)
        - Oligochaeta (oligochaetes)
    - Phylum Acanthocephala (spiny-headed worms)
    - Ecdysozoa (ecdysozoans)
        - Phylum Loricifera (loriciferans)
        - Phylum Priapula (priapulans)
        - Phylum Nematoda (roundworms)
        - Phylum Arthropoda (This survey groups arthropods into a single phylum, but some zoologists now split the arthropods into multiple phyla.)
            - Subphylum Chelicerata (horseshoe crabs, arachnids)
            - Subphylum Myriapoda (millipedes, centipedes)
            - Subphylum Hexapoda (insects, springtails)
            - Subphylum Crustacea (crustaceans)
        - Phylum Tardigrada (tardigrades)
        - Phylum Onychophora (velvet worms)
    - Deuterostomia (deuterostomes)
        - Phylum Hemichordata (hemichordates)
        - Phylum Echinodermata (echinoderms)
            - Asteroidea (sea stars, sea daisies)
            - Ophiuroidea (brittle stars)
            - Echinoidea (sea urchins and sand dollars)
            - Crinoidea (sea lilies)
            - Holothuroidea (sea cucumbers)
        - Phylum Chordata (chordates)
            - Subphylum Cephalochordata (cephalochordates: lancelets)
            - Subphylum Urochrodata (urochordates: tunicates)
            - Subphylum Craniata (craniates)
                - Myxini (hagfishes)
                - Petromyzontida (lampreys)
                - Chondrichthyes (sharks, rays, chimaeras)
                - Actinopterygii (ray-finned fishes)
                - Actinistia (coelacanths)
                - Dipnoi (lungfishes) } Vertebrates
                - Amphibia (amphibians)
                - Reptilia (tuataras, lizards, snakes, turtles, crocodilians, birds)
                - Mammalia (mammals)

Credits

Chapter 8 8.1 Photoshot/NHPA; 8.2.2 Jupiter Images; 8.3.2 Robert N. Johnson/RnJ Photography; 8.3.3 Robert N. Johnson/RnJ Photography; 8.4.1 Brandon Blinkenberg/iStockphoto; 8.4.2 Bridget Lazenby/iStockphoto; 8.14.2 Thomas A. Steitz, Yale University; 8.14.3 Thomas A. Steitz, Yale University; 8.20.3 Scheer JM, Romanowski MJ, Wells JA. A common allosteric site and mechanism in caspases. *Proc Natl Acad Sci U S A.* 2006 May 16;103(20):7595–600; Fig. 4a; 8.22.2 Nicolae Simionescu.

Chapter 9 9.1 Anup Shah/Nature Picture Library.

Chapter 10 10.1 Bob Rowan, Progressive Image/Corbis; 10.2.2 Jean-Paul Nacivet/AGE Fotostock; 10.2.3 Lawrence Naylor/Photo Researchers; 10.2.4 M. I. Walker/Photo Researchers; 10.2.5 Susan M. Barns; 10.2.6 National Library of Medicine; 10.3 Robert Clark Photography, robertclark.com; 10.4.2 Image courtesy Andreas Holzenburg and Stanislav Vitha, Dept. of Biology and Microscopy & Imaging Center, Texas A&M University; 10.4.3 E.H Newcomb & WP Wergin/Biological Photo Service; 10.12.2 Christine L. Case, Skyline College; 10.13.2 From "Architecture of the photosynthetic oxygen-evolving center."; . . . K. N. Ferreira,T. M. Iverson, K. Maghlaoui, J. Barber, S. Iwata. *Science.* 2004 Mar 19;303(5665):1831–8. Epub 2004 Feb 5; 10.21.2 David Muench/Corbis; 10.21.3 Dave Bartruff/Corbis.

Chapter 12 12.1 Jan-Michael Peters/Silke Hauf; 12.2.2 Biophoto Associates/Photo Researchers; 12.2.3 C.R. Wyttenbach/Biological Photo Service; 12.2.4 Biophoto/Science Source/Photo Researchers; 12.3.2 John Murray; 12.4.2 Biophoto/Photo Researchers; 12.5.2 Biophoto/Photo Researchers; 12.7.2 Conly L. Rieder; 12.7.3 Conly L. Rieder; 12.7.4 Conly L. Rieder; 12.7.6 Conly L. Rieder; 12.7.7 Conly L. Rieder; 12.7.8 Conly L. Rieder; 12.8.2 J. Richard McIntosh, University of Colorado at Boulder; 12.8.3 Reproduced by permission from Matthew Schibler, from *Protoplasma* 137. Copyright © 1987: 29–44 by Springer-Verlag GmbH & Co KG; 12.10.2 Don W. Fawcett/Photo Researchers; 12.10.3 B. A. Palevitz, Courtesy of E. H. Newcomb, University of Wisconsin; 12.11.2 Elisabeth Pierson, FNWI-Radboud University Nijmegen, Pearson Science; 12.11.3 Elisabeth Pierson, FNWI-Radboud University Nijmegen, Pearson Science; 12.11.4 Elisabeth Pierson, FNWI-Radboud University Nijmegen, Pearson Science; 12.11.5 Elisabeth Pierson, FNWI-Radboud University Nijmegen, Pearson Science; 12.11.6 Elisabeth Pierson, FNWI-Radboud University Nijmegen, Pearson Science; 12.18.2 Guenter Albrecht-Buehler; 12.19.2 Lan Bo Chen; 12.19.3 Lan Bo Chen; 12.21 Anne Weston, LRI, CRUK, Wellcome Images; p. 245 USDA/ARS/Agricultural Research Service.

Chapter 13 13.1 Steve Granitz/WireImage/Getty Images; 13.2.2 Roland Birke/OKAPIA/Photo Researchers; 13.2.3 SuperStock; 13.3.2 Veronique Burger/Phanie Agency/Photo Researchers; 13.3.3 CNRI/Photo Researchers; 13.11.2 Mark Petronczki and Maria Siomos; 13.12.2 John Walsh, Micrographia.com.

Chapter 14 14.1 Mendel Museum, Augustinian Abbey, Brno; 14.14.2 Altrendo nature/Getty Images; 14.14.3 PictureNet Corporation/Corbis; 14.15.2 Photodisc/Getty Images; 14.15.3 Photodisc/Getty Images; 14.15.4 Anthony Loveday; 14.15.5 Anthony Loveday; 14.16.2 Rick Guidotti and Diane McLean/Positive Exposure; 14.17.2 Michael Ciesielski Photography; 14.18 Douglas C. Pizac/AP Images; 14.19.2 CNRI/Photo Researchers; p. 285 Norma Jubinville.

Chapter 15 15.1 David C. Ward; 15.3.2 From: "Learning to Fly: Phenotypic Markers in *Drosophila*." A poster of common phenotypic markers used in *Drosophila* genetics. Jennifer Childress, Richard Behringer, and Georg Halder. 2005. *Genesis* 43(1). Cover illustration; 15.3.3 From: "Learning to Fly: Phenotypic Markers in *Drosophila*." A poster of common phenotypic markers used in *Drosophila* genetics. Jennifer Childress, Richard Behringer, and Georg Halder. 2005. *Genesis* 43(1). Cover illustration; 15.5 Andrew Syred/Photo Researchers; 15.8.2 Dave King/Dorling Kindersley; 15.15.2 Lauren Shear/SPL/Photo Researchers; 15.15.3 CNRI/SPL/Photo Researchers; 15.18 Geoff Kidd/Photo Researchers; p. 304 James K. Adams, Biology, Dalton State College, Dalton, Georgia.

Chapter 16 16.1 National Institutes of Health; 16.3.2 Oliver Meckes/Photo Researchers; 16.6.2 Courtesy of the Library of Congress; 16.6.3 From "The Double Helix" by James D. Watson, Atheneum Press, N.Y., 1968, p. 215. © 1968. Courtesy CSHL Archive; 16.12.2 Jerome Vinograd; 16.12.3 From D. J. Burks and P. J. Stambrook, *The Journal of Cell Biology* 77 (1978). 762, fig. 6 by copyright permission of The Rockefeller University Press. Photo provided by P. J. Stambrook; 16.21 Peter Lansdorp; 16.22.2 S. C. Holt/Biological Photo Service; 16.22.3 Victoria E. Foe; 16.22.4 Barbara Hamkalo; 16.22.5 From J. R. Paulsen and U. K. Laemmli, *Cell* 12 (1977):817–828; 16.22.6 Biophoto/Photo Researchers; 16.23.2 From: Multicolor Spectral Karyotyping of Human Chromosomes. E. Schröck, S. du Manoir, T. Veldman, B. Schoell, J. Wienberg, M. A. Ferguson-Smith, Y. Ning, D. H. Ledbetter, I. Bar-Am, D. Soenksen, Y. Garini, T. Ried. *Science.* 1996 Jul 26;273(5274):494–7; 16.23.3 From: The new cytogenetics: blurring the boundaries with molecular biology; . . . M. R. Speicher, N. P. Carter. *Nat Rev Genet.* 2005 Oct;6(10):782–92; p. 324 Thomas A. Steitz, Yale University.

Chapter 17 17.1 Deutscher Fotodienst GmbH; 17.6.2 Keith V. Wood, University of California, San Diego; 17.6.3 AP Images; 17.16.2 Thomas Steitz; 17.17.2 Joachim Frank; 17.21.2 B. Hamkalo and O. Miller, Jr; 17.25.2 Reprinted with permission from O. L. Miller , Jr., B. A. Hamkalo, and C. A Thomas, Jr., *Science* 169 (1970):392. Copyright © 1970 American Association for the Advancement of Science.

Chapter 18 18.1 Reproduced by permission from Cook O, Biehs B, Bier E. Brinker and optomotor-blind act coordinately to initiate development of the L5 wing vein primordium in *Drosophila*. *Development.* 2004 May: 131(9):2113–24; 18.12.2 From: The new cytogenetics: blurring the boundaries with molecular biology; M. R. Speicher, N. P. Carter. *Nat Rev Genet.* 2005 Oct;6(10):782–92; 18.16.2 Mike Wu; 18.16.3 Hans Pfletschinger/Peter Arnold/PhotoLibrary; 18.20.2 F. R. Turner, Indiana University; 18.20.3 F. R. Turner, Indiana University; 18.21.2 Wolfgang Driever, University of Freiburg, Freiburg, Germany; 18.21.3 Wolfgang Driever, University of Freiburg, Freiburg, Germany; 18.22.2 Ruth Lehmann, The Whitehead Institution; 18.22.3 Ruth Lehmann, The Whitehead Institution; 18.26 Roy Kaltschmidt, Lawrence Berkeley National Laboratory.

Chapter 19 19.1 Science Picture Library/Photo Researchers; 19.2.2 Peter von Sengbusch/Botanik; 19.2.3 Peter von Sengbusch/Botanik; 19.2.4 Peter von Sengbusch/Botanik; 19.3.2 Robley C. Williams/Biological Photo Service; 19.3.3 R.C. Valentine and H.G. Pereira, "Antigens and Structure of the Adenovirus," *Journal of Molecular Biology* 13: 13–20 (1965); 19.3.4 Hazel Appleton, Health Protection Agency Centre for Infections/Photo Researchers; 19.3.5 Robley C. Williams/ Biological Photo Service; 19.8.2 C. Dauguet/Institute Pasteur/Photo Researchers; 19.8.3 C. Dauguet/Institute Pasteur/Photo Researchers; 19.8.4 C. Dauguet/Institute Pasteur/Photo Researchers; 19.8.5 C. Dauguet/Institute Pasteur/Photo Researchers; 19.8.6 C. Dauguet/Institute Pasteur/Photo Researchers; 19.9.2 NIBSC/Photo Researchers; 19.9.3 Seo Myung-gon/AP Images; 19.9.4 National Museum of Health and Medicine/Armed Forces Institute of Pathology; 19.10.2 Dennis E. Mayhew; 19.10.3 Thomas A. Zitter; 19.10.4 A. Vogler/Shutterstock.

Chapter 20 20.1 Reproduced with permission from R.F. Service, *Science* (1998) 282:396–3999. Copyright 1998 American Association for the Advancement of Science. Incyte Pharmaceuticals, Inc., Palo Alto, CA; 20.5.2 L. Brent Selinger, Pearson Science; 20.9.2 Repligen Corporation; 20.14 Ethan Bier; 20.15.2 Reproduced with permission from R.F. Service, *Science* (1998) 282:396–3999. Copyright 1998 American Association for the Advancement of Science. Incyte Pharmaceuticals, Inc., Palo Alto, CA; 20.20 Pat Sullivan/AP Images; 20.24.2 Brad DeCecco Photography; 20.24.3 Brad DeCecco Photography; 20.25.2 Steve Helber/AP Images.

Chapter 21 21.1 Karen Huntt/Corbis; 21.5.2 From "The genetic landscape of a cell." M. Costanzo, et al. *Science.* 2010 Jan 22;327(5964):425–31; 21.6 GeneChip Human Genome U133 Plus 2.0 Array, image courtesy of Affymetrix; 21.8.2 AP Images; 21.8.3 Courtesy of Virginia Walbot, Stanford University; 21.11.2 Courtesy of O. L. Miller Jr., Dept. of Biology, University of Virginia; 21.17.2 Shu W, Cho JY, Jiang Y, Zhang M, Weisz D, Elder GA, Schmeidler J, De Gasperi R, Sosa MA, Rabidou D, Santucci AC, Perl D, Morrisey E, Buxbaum JD. Altered ultrasonic vocalization in mice with a disruption in the *Foxp2* gene. : *Proc Natl Acad Sci U S A.* 2005 Jul 5; 102(27):9643–8; Fig. 3. Image supplied by Joseph Buxbaum; 21.17.3 Shu W, Cho JY, Jiang Y, Zhang M, Weisz D, Elder GA, Schmeidler J, De Gasperi R, Sosa MA, Rabidou D, Santucci AC, Perl D, Morrisey E, Buxbaum JD. Altered ultrasonic vocalization in mice with a disruption in the *Foxp2* gene. : *Proc Natl Acad Sci U S A.* 2005 Jul 5;102(27):9643–8; Fig. 3. Image supplied by Joseph Buxbaum; 21.17.4 Shu W, Cho JY, Jiang Y, Zhang M, Weisz D, Elder GA, Schmeidler J, De Gasperi R, Sosa MA, Rabidou D, Santucci AC, Perl D, Morrisey E, Buxbaum JD. Altered ultrasonic vocalization in mice with a disruption in the *Foxp2* gene. : *Proc Natl Acad Sci U S A.* 2005 Jul 5; 102(27):9643–8; Fig. 3. Image supplied by Joseph Buxbaum; 21.17.5 Joe McDonald/Corbis.

Chapter 22 22.1 Olivier Grunewald; 22.2.2 PD image: Skeleton of the "Rhinoceros unicorne de Java" in the Paris Museum of Natural History. From G. Cuvier, Recherches sur les ossemens fossiles, *Atlas*, pl. 17. 1836; 22.2.3 Eileen Tweedy/Picture Desk/Kobal Collection; 22.2.4 Wayne Lynch/AGE Fotostock; 22.2.5 Neg./Transparency no. 330300. Courtesy Dept. of Library Services, American Museum of Natural History; 22.4 Michael S. Yamashita/Corbis; 22.5.2 George Richmond/ARCHIV/Photo Researchers; 22.5.3 National Maritime Museum; 22.6.2 Michel Gunther/PhotoLibrary; 22.6.3 David Hosking/FLPA; 22.6.3 David Hosking/Alamy; 22.7 Darwin's Tree of life sketch, MS.DAR.121:p.36. Reproduced with the permission of the Cambridge University Library; 22.9.2 Gerard Schulz/Naturphoto; 22.9.3 Robert Sarno/iStockphoto; 22.9.4 Paul Rapson/Alamy; 22.9.5 Izaokas Sapiro/Shutterstock; 22.9.6 YinYang/iStockphoto; 22.9.7 floricela buzlea/iStockphoto; 22.10 Laura Jesse, Extension Entomologist, Iowa State University; 22.11.2 Richard Packwood/Oxford Scientific/Jupiter Images; 22.12.2 E. S. Ross, California Academy of Sciences; 22.12.3 Mark Taylor/Nature Picture Library; 22.13.1 Scott P. Carroll; 22.16.2 Dr. Keith Wheeler/Photo Researchers; 22.16.3 Lennart Nilsson/Scanpix; 22.18.2 Visible Earth (http://visibleearth.nasa.gov/), NASA; 22.19.2 Chris Linz, Thewissen lab, Northeastern Ohio Universities College of Medicine; 22.19.3 Chris Linz, Thewissen lab, Northeastern Ohio Universities College of Medicine; 22.19.4 Chris Linz, Thewissen lab, Northeastern Ohio Universities College of Medicine; 22.19.5 Chris Linz, Thewissen lab, Northeastern Ohio Universities College of Medicine.

Chapter 23 23.1 Rosemary B. Grant; 23.3.2 Erick Greene, University of Montana; 23.3.3 Erick Greene, University of Montana; 23.4.2 Janice Britton-Davidian, ISEM, UMR 5554 CNRS, Universite Montpellier II. Reprinted by permission from *Nature*, Vol. 403, 13 January 2000, p. 158. © 2000 Macmillan Magazines Ltd.; 23.4.3 Janice Britton-Davidian, ISEM, UMR 5554 CNRS, Universite Montpellier II. Reprinted by permission from *Nature*, Vol. 403, 13 January 2000, p. 158. © 2000 Macmillan Magazines Ltd.; 23.4.4 Steve Gorton/Dorling Kindersley; 23.5.2 New York State Department of Environmental Conservation; 23.6.2 Gary Schultz/Photoshot; 23.6.3 James L. Davis/ProWildlife; 23.11.2 William Ervin/SPL/Photo Researchers; 23.12.2 Jan Visser; 23.14.2 John Visser/Photoshot; 23.15 Dave Blackey/PhotoLibrary; 23.16.2 Allison M. Welch; 23.19 Merlin D. Tuttle, Bat Conservation International, www.batcon.org.

Chapter 24 24.1 Mark Jones/AGE Fotostock; 24.2.2 Malcolm Schuyl/Alamy; 24.2.3 Wave Rf/PhotoLibrary; 24.2.4 Robert Kneschke/iStockphoto; 24.2.5 Justin Horrocks/iStockphoto; 24.2.6 Photodisc/Getty Images; 24.2.7 Photodisc/Getty Images; 24.2.8 Photodisc/Getty Images; 24.2.9 Masterfile; 24.3.a2 Joe McDonald/Photoshot; 24.3.b2 Joe McDonald/Photoshot; 24.3.c2 USDA/APHIS/Animal and Plant Health Inspection Service; 24.3.d2 Stephen Krasemann/Photo Researchers; 24.3.e1 Michael Dietrich/imagebroker/Alamy; 24.3.f2 Takahito Asami; 24.3.g2 William E. Ferguson; 24.3.h2 Charles W. Brown; 24.3.i2 Photodisc/Getty Images; 24.3.j2 Corbis; 24.3.k2 DawnYL/Fotolia; 24.3.l2 Kazutoshi Okuno; 24.4.2 CLFProductions/Shutterstock; 24.4.3 Boris Karpinski/Alamy; 24.4.4 Troy Maben/AP Images; 24.6.2 John Shaw/Bruce Coleman/Photoshot; 24.6.3 Michael Fogden/Bruce Coleman/Photoshot; 24.6.4 Corbis; 24.7.2 From: Morphology, performance, fitness: functional insight into a post-Pleistocene radiation of mosquitofish. R. B. Langerhans. *Biology Letters* 2009;5(4):488–491; 24.7.3 From: Morphology, performance, fitness: functional insight into a post-Pleistocene radiation of mosquitofish. R. B. Langerhans. *Biology Letters* 2009;5(4):488–491; 24.8.2 Visible Earth (http://visibleearth.nasa.gov/), NASA; 24.8.3 Arthur Anker; 24.12 Ole Seehausen; 24.13.2 Jeroen Speybroeck, Research Institute for Nature and Forest, Belgium; 24.13.3 Jeroen Speybroeck, Research Institute for Nature and Forest, Belgium; 24.16.2 Ole Seehausen; 24.16.3 Ole Seehausen; 24.16.4 Ole Seehausen; 24.18 Jason Rick; 24.20.2 Reprinted by permission from *Nature* Bradshaw HD, Schemske DW. Allele substitution at a flower colour locus produces a pollinator shift in monkeyflowers. *Nature.* 2003 November 12;

426(6963):176–8 Copyright © 2003. Macmillan Magazines Limited; **24.20.3** Reprinted by permission from *Nature* Bradshaw HD, Schemske DW. Allele substitution at a flower colour locus produces a pollinator shift in monkeyflowers. *Nature.* 2003 November 12; 426(6963):176–8 Copyright © 2003. Macmillan Magazines Limited; **24.20.4** Reprinted by permission from *Nature* Bradshaw HD, Schemske DW. Allele substitution at a flower colour locus produces a pollinator shift in monkeyflowers. *Nature.* 2003 November 12; 426(6963):176–8 Copyright © 2003. Macmillan Magazines Limited; **24.20.5** Reprinted by permission from *Nature* Bradshaw HD, Schemske DW. Allele substitution at a flower colour locus produces a pollinator shift in monkeyflowers. *Nature.* 2003 November 12; 426(6963):176–8 Copyright © 2003. Macmillan Magazines Limited.

Chapter 25 **25.1** Gerhard Boeggemann; **p. 507.UN1** Rebecca Hunt; **25.2.2** UPI Photo/Landov; **25.3.2** Courtesy of F. M. Menger and Kurt Gabrielson, Emory University; **25.3.3** M. Hanczyc; **25.4.10** Specimen No 12478, Markus Moser, Staatliches Museum fur Naturkunde Stuttgart; **25.4.3** Sinclair Stammers/Photo Researchers; **25.4.4** Andrew H. Knoll, Harvard University; **25.4.5** Lisa-Ann Gershwin, University of California-Berkeley, Museum of Paleontology; **25.4.6** Chip Clark; **25.4.7** Ted Daeschler/Academy of Natural Sciences/ VIREO; **25.4.8** Roger Jones; **25.4.9** Seelevel.com; **25.11.2** Shuhai Xiao, Tulane University; **25.20.2** Gerald D. Carr; **25.20.3** Gerald D. Carr; **25.20.4** Gerald D. Carr; **25.20.5** Gerald D. Carr; **25.20.6** Gerald D. Carr; **25.20.7** Bruce G. Baldwin; **25.21.2** Jean Kern; **25.21.3** Jean Kern; **25.22** Juniors Bildarchiv/Alamy; **25.23** Reprinted from "The Origin of Form" by Sean B. Carroll, *Natural History*, November 2005. Burke, A.C. 2000, "*Hox*" Genes and the Global Patterning of the Somitic Mesoderm. In Somitogenesis. C. Ordahl (ed.) "Current Topics in Developmental Biology", Vo. 47. Academic Press; **25.25.1** Oxford Scientific/ PhotoLibrary; **25.25.3** Shapiro MD, Marks ME, Peichel CL, Blackman BK, Nereng KS, Jonsson B, Schluter D, Kingsley DM. Genetic and developmental basis of evolutionary pelvic reduction in threespine sticklebacks. *Nature.* Erratum. 2006 Feb 23;439(7079):1014; Fig. 1; **25.25.4** Shapiro MD, Marks ME, Peichel CL, Blackman BK, Nereng KS, Jonsson B, Schluter D, Kingsley DM. Genetic and developmental basis of evolutionary pelvic reduction in threespine sticklebacks. *Nature.* Erratum. 2006 Feb 23;439(7079):1014; Fig. 1.

Chapter 26 **26.1** Ken Griffiths/NHPA/Photoshot; **26.2.2** Ryan McVay/Photodisc/ Getty Images; **26.2.3** Neil Fletcher/Dorling Kindersley; **26.2.4** Dorling Kindersley; **26.17.2** Ed Heck; **26.17.3** Courtesy Dept. of Library Services, American Museum of Natural History.

Chapter 27 **27.1** Bonnie K. Baxter, Great Salt Lake Institute, Westminster College, Utah; **27.2.2** CDC; **27.2.3** Dr. Kari Lounatmaa/Photo Researchers; **27.2.4** Stem Jems/ Photo Researchers; **27.3.2** L. Brent Selinger, Pearson Science; **27.4.2** Dr. Immo Rantala/ Photo Researchers; **27.5.2** Kwangshin Kim/Photo Researchers; **27.6.2** Julius Adler; **27.7.2** S. W. Watson; **27.7.3** Norma J. Lang/Biological Photo Service; **27.8.2** Huntington Potter, Byrd Alzheimer's Institute and University of South Florida, David Dressler, Oxford University and Balliol College; **27.9.2** H.S. Pankratz, T.C. Beaman/ Biological Photo Service; **27.12.2** Charles C. Brinton, Jr., University of Pittsburgh; **27.14.2** Susan M. Barns; **27.16** Jack Dykinga/Stone/Getty Images; **27.17.3** L. Evans Roth/Biological Photo Service; **27.17.5** Yuichi Suwa; **27.17.7** National Library of Medicine; **27.17.9** From "Scanning electron microscopy of fruiting body formation by myxobacteria." P. L. Grilione and J. Pangborn. *J. Bacteriol.* 1975 December; 124(3): 1558–1565; **27.17.13** Photo Researchers; **27.17.15** Moredon Animal Health/SPL/Photo Researchers; **27.17.17** CNRI/SPL/Photo Researchers; **27.17.19** Culture Collection CCALA, Institute of Botany, Academy of Sciences Dukelska, Czech Republic; **27.17.21** Paul Hoskisson, Strathclyde Institute of Pharmacy and Biomedical Sciences, Glasgow, Scotland; **27.17.22** David M. Phillips/Photo Researchers; **27.18.2** Pascale Frey-Klett; **27.19** Ken Lucas/Biological Photo Service; **27.20.2** Scott Camazine/Photo Researchers; **27.20.3** David M. Phillips/Photo Researchers; **27.20.4** James Marshall/The Image Works; **27.21** Metabolix; **27.21.3** Courtesy of Exxon Mobil Corporation; **27.21.4** Seelevel.com.

Chapter 28 **28.1** Brian S. Leander; **28.3.3** Joel Mancuso, University of California, Berkeley; **28.3.5** M. I. Walker/NHPA/Photoshot; **28.3.7** Howard Spero, University of California-Davis; **28.3.8** NOAA; **28.3.10** Kim Taylor/Nature Picture Library; **28.3.11** David J. Patterson/micro*scope; **28.3.13** Tom Stack/PhotoLibrary; **28.4.2** David M. Phillips/The Population Council/Photo Researchers; **28.5.2** David J. Patterson; **28.6.2** Meckes/Ottawa/Photo Researchers; **28.7.2** D. J. Patterson, L. Amaral-Zettler, M. Peglar and T. Nerad, http://micro*scope.mbl.edu; **28.8.2** Guy Brugerolle, Universitad Clearmont, Ferrand; **28.9.2** Virginia Institute of Marine Science; **28.10.2** Masamichi Aikawa, Tokai University School of Medicine, Japan; **28.11.2** M. I. Walker/ Photo Researchers; **28.12.2** Centers for Disease Control & Prevention; **28.13.2** Steve Gschmeissner/Photo Researchers; **28.14.2** Stephen Durr; **28.15.2** Colin Bates; **28.16.2** J. Robert Waaland/Biological Photo Service; **28.17.2** Fred Rhoades; **28.18.2** Robert Brons/Biological Photo Service; **28.19.2** Eva Nowack; **28.20.2** D. P. Wilson, Eric & David Hosking/Photo Researchers; **28.20.3** Michael D. Guiry; **28.20.4** Biophoto Associates/Photo Researchers; **28.20.6** Michael Yamashita/IPN/Aurora Photos; **28.20.7** David Murray/Dorling Kindersley; **28.21.2** Laurie Campbell/NHPA; **28.21.3** Marine Sciences, University of Puerto Rico; **28.22.2** William L. Dentler; **28.24.2** George Barron; **28.24.3** Mikel Tapia (www.argazkik.com); **28.25.2** Robert Kay; **28.25.3** Robert Kay; **28.26.2** Kevin Carpenter and Patrick Keeling.

Chapter 29 **29.1** Martin Rugner/AGE Fotostock; **29.2.2** S. C. Mueller and R. M. Brown, Jr; **29.3.2** Natural Visions; **29.3.3** Linda Graham, University of Wisconsin-Madison; **29.5.1** Ed Reschke; **29.5.12** CDC; **29.5.3** Linda Graham, University of Wisconsin-Madison; **29.5.4** Karen S. Renzaglia; **29.5.6** Alan S. Heilman; **29.5.7** Michael Clayton, University of Wisconsin-Madison; **29.5.9** David John Jones (mybitoftheplanet.com); **29.6.2** Charles H. Wellman; **29.6.3** Charles H. Wellman; **29.8.2** Laurie Knight (www.laurieknight.net); **29.9.2** Linda Graham, University of Wisconsin-Madison; **29.9.3** Alvin E. Staffan/National Audubon Society/Photo Researchers; **29.9.4** Hidden Forest; **29.9.6** Hidden Forest; **29.9.8** Tony Wharton, Frank Lane Picture Agency/Corbis; **p. 609** From "Mosses and Other Bryophytes, an Illustrated Glossary" (2006) by Bill and Nancy Malcolm; **29.11.1** Brian Lightfoot/AGE Fotostock; **29.11.2** Chris Lisle/Corbis; **29.15.2** Jody Banks, Purdue University; **29.15.3** Murray Fagg, Australian National Botanic Gardens; **29.15.4** Helga & Kurt Rasbach; **29.15.6** Jon Meier/iStockphoto; **29.15.8** Milton Rand/Tom Stack & Associates; **29.15.9** Francisco Javier Yeste Garcia

(www.flickr.com/photos/fryega/); **29.15.10** Francisco Javier Yeste Garcia (www.flickr.com/photos/fryega/); **29.16.2** The Open University; **p. 616, top** Ed Reschke; **p. 616, bottom** Michael Clayton.

Chapter 30 **30.1** National Museum of Natural History, Smithsonian Institution; **30.5.1** Johannes Greyling/iStockphoto; **30.5.3** CC-BY-SA photo: Kurt Stueber (www.biolib.de); **30.5.4** Jeroen Peys/iStockphoto; **30.5.5** Michael Clayton; **30.5.6** Thomas Schoepke; **30.5.7** Bob Gibbons/FLPA; **30.5.8** Raymond Gehman/Corbis; **30.5.9** Adam Jones/Getty Images; **30.5.10** David Muench/Corbis; **30.5.11** Gunter Marx Photography/Corbis; **30.5.12** Royal Botanic Gardens Sydney; **30.5.13** Jaime Plaza/ AP Images; **30.5.14** Mario Verin/Photolibrary; **30.8.2** Dave King/ Dorling Kindersley; **30.8.3** Andy Crawford/Dorling Kindersley; **30.8.4** Dave King/ Dorling Kindersley; **30.8.5** Maria Dryfhout/iStockphoto; **30.8.6** Peter Rees/Getty Images; **30.9.2** PIXTAL/AGE Fotostock; **30.9.3** Hans Dieter Brandl, Frank Lane Picture Agency/Corbis; **30.9.4** Scott Camazine/Photo Researchers; **30.9.5** Derek Hall/ Dorling Kindersley; **30.11.2** David L. Dilcher; **30.13.1** Howard Rice/Dorling Kindersley; **30.13.2** Jack Scheper, Floridata.com; **30.13.3** Stephen McCabe; **30.13.4** Andrew Butler/Dorling Kindersley; **30.13.6** Eric Crichton/Dorling Kindersley; **30.13.7** John Dransfield; **30.13.8** Dorling Kindersley; **30.13.10** Terry W. Eggers/Corbis; **30.13.11** CC-BY-SA photo: Artslave; **30.13.12** Matthew Ward/Dorling Kindersley; **30.13.13** Tony Wharton, Frank Lane Picture Agency/Corbis; **30.13.14** Howard Rice/ Dorling Kindersley; **30.13.15** Gerald D. Carr; **30.14** kkaplin/Shutterstock; **30.15** D. Wilder; **30.16.2** NASA's Earth Observatory; **30.16.3** NASA's Earth Observatory.

Chapter 31 **31.1** Georg Müller; **31.2.2** Fred Rhoades/Mycena Consulting; **31.2.3** Hans Reinhard/Taxi/Getty Images; **31.2.4** George Barron, University of Guelph, Canada; **31.4.2** © N. Allin & G.L. Barron, University of Guelph/Biological Photo Service; **31.6.2** Biophoto Associates/Photo Researchers; **31.6.3** Popovaphoto/ dreamstime; **31.7.2** Stephen J. Kron; **31.9.2** Dirk Redecker, Robin Kodner, and Linda E. Graham. Glomalean Fungi from the Ordovician. *Science* 15 September 2000; 289: 1920–1921; **31.10.2** CDC; **31.11.2** John Taylor; **31.11.3** Ray Watson; **31.11.5** Reproduced by permission from Kiers ET, van der Heijden MG. Mutualistic stability in the arbuscular mycorrhizal symbiosis: exploring hypotheses of evolutionary cooperation. *Ecology.* 2006 July: 87(7):1627–36: Fig. 1a. Image by Marcel van der Heijden, Swiss Federal Research Station for Agroecology and Agriculture. Copyright © 2006, Ecological Society of America; **31.11.6** Frank Young/Papilio/Corbis; **31.11.7** Phil Dotson/Photo Researchers; **31.12.2** William E. Barstow; **31.13.2** Antonio D'Albore/ iStockphoto; **31.13.3** Alena Kubátová (http://botany.natur.cuni.cz/cs/sbirka-kultur-hub-ccf); **31.13.4** Ed Reschke/Peter Arnold/PhotoLibrary; **31.13.5** George Barron; **31.14.2** G.L. Barron/Biological Photo Service; **31.15.2** M. F. Brown/Biological Photo Service; **31.16.2** Viard/Jacana/Photo Researchers; **31.16.3** Douglas Adams/iStockphoto; **31.17.2** Fred Spiegel; **31.18.2** Fletcher and Baylis/Photo Researchers; **31.18.3** Michael Fogden/Photolibrary; **31.18.4** Frank Paul/Alamy; **31.19.2** Biophoto Associates/Photo Researchers; **31.20** University of Tennessee Entomology and Plant Pathology; **31.22** Mark Bowler/Photo Researchers; **31.23.2** Ralph Lee Hopkins/Getty Images; **31.23.3** Geoff Simpson/naturepl.com; **31.23.4** Wild-Worlders of Europe/ Benvie/naturepl.com; **31.24.2** Eye of Science/Photo Researchers; **31.25.2** Alamy; **31.25.3** Peter Chadwick/Dorling Kindersley; **31.25.4** Hecker-Sauer/AGE Fotostock; **31.26.2** Vance T. Vredenburg, San Francisco State University; **31.27.2** Christine Case.

Chapter 32 **32.1** Jeff Hunter/Image Bank/Getty Images; **p. 656** Biological Photo Service; **32.4.2** © The Museum Board of South Australia 2004 Photographer: Dr. J. Gehling; **32.4.3** © The Museum Board of South Australia 2004 Photographer: Dr. J. Gehling; **32.5** J. Sibbick/The Natural History Museum, London; **32.6.2** Wikramanayake AH, Hong M, Lee PN, Pang K, Byrum CA, Bince JM, Xu R, Martindale MQ. An ancient role for nuclear beta-catenin in the evolution of axial polarity and germ layer segregation. *Nature.* 2003 Nov 27;426(6965):446–50; Fig. 2, 3 and 4; **32.6.3** Wikramanayake AH, Hong M, Lee PN, Pang K, Byrum CA, Bince JM, Xu R, Martindale MQ. An ancient role for nuclear beta-catenin in the evolution of axial polarity and germ layer segregation. *Nature.* 2003 Nov 27;426(6965):446–50; Fig. 2, 3 and 4; **32.6.4** Wikramanayake AH, Hong M, Lee PN, Pang K, Byrum CA, Bince JM, Xu R, Martindale MQ. An ancient role for nuclear beta-catenin in the evolution of axial polarity and germ layer segregation. *Nature.* 2003 Nov 27;426(6965):446–50; Fig. 2, 3 and 4; **32.6.5** Wikramanayake AH, Hong M, Lee PN, Pang K, Byrum CA, Bince JM, Xu R, Martindale MQ. An ancient role for nuclear beta-catenin in the evolution of axial polarity and germ layer segregation. *Nature.* 2003 Nov 27; 426(6965):446–50; Fig. 2, 3 and 4; **32.12** Kent Wood/Photo Researchers; **32.13.2** Hecker/Sauer/AGE Fotostock.

Chapter 33 **33.1** C. Wolcott Henry III/National Geographic/Getty Images; **33.3.1** Andrew J. Martinez/Photo Researchers; **33.3.2** Robert Brons/Biological Photo Service; **33.3.3** Teresa (Zubi) Zuberbühler; **33.3.4** Stephen Dellaporta; **33.3.5** Gregory G. Dimijian/Photo Researchers; **33.3.6** Ed Robinson/Pacific Stock/Photolibrary; **33.3.7** Hecker/Sauer/AGE Fotostock; **33.3.8** W. I. Walker/Photo Researchers; **33.3.9** Kåre Telnes/Image Quest Marine; **33.3.10** PD image: Anilocra/Taken by Neil Campbell, University of Aberdeen, Scotland, UK; **33.3.11** Erling Svensen/UWPhoto ANS; **33.3.12** Peter Funch; **33.3.13** photonimo/iStockphoto; **33.3.14** Peter Batson/Image Quest Marine; **33.3.15** Reinhart Mobjerg Kristensen; **33.3.16** Erling Svensen/ UWPhoto ANS; **33.3.17** Andrew Syred/Photo Researchers; **33.3.18** Reproduced with permission from A. Eizinger and R. Sommer, Max Planck Institut fur entwicklungsbiologie, Tubingen. Copyright 2000 American Association for the Advancement of Science. Cover 278(5337) 17 Oct 97; **33.3.19** Thomas Stromberg; **33.3.20** Tim Flach/Stone/Getty Images; **33.3.21** Heather Angel/Natural Visions; **33.3.22** Robert Harding World Imagery/Alamy; **33.3.23** Robert Brons/Biological Photo Service; **33.4.2** Andrew J. Martinez/Photo Researchers; **33.7.2** Andrew J. Martinez/ Photo Researchers; **33.7.3** Robert Brons/Biological Photo Service; **33.7.4** Commonwealth of Australia (GBRMPA); **33.7.5** Neil G. McDaniel/Photo Researchers; **33.8.2** Robert Brons/Biological Photo Services; **33.9.2** Ed Robinson/Pacific Stock/PhotoLibrary; **33.11.2** CDC; **33.12.2** Eye of Science/Photo Researchers; **33.13.2** W. I. Walker/ Photo Researchers; **33.14.2** Hecker/Sauer/AGE Fotostock; **33.16** Jeff Foott/Tom Stack and Associates; **33.17.2** Amruta Bhelke/ Dreamstime.com; **33.17.3** Corbis; **33.19** H. W. Pratt/Biological Photo Service; **33.21.2** photonimo/iStockphoto; **33.21.3** Mark Conlin/Image Quest Marine; **33.21.4** Jonathan Blair/Corbis; **33.22.2** Photograph courtesy of the U.S. Bureau of

Fisheries (1919), and Illinois State Museum; **33.22.3** © Zoological Society of London (ZSL); **33.23.2** Peter Batson/Image Quest Marine; **33.24.2** A.N.T./NHPA/Photoshot; **33.25** Astrid & Hanns-Frieder Michler/Photo Researchers; **33.26.2** Reproduced with permission from A. Eizinger and R. Sommer, Max Planck Institut fur entwicklungsbiologie, Tubingen. Copyright 2000 American Association for the Advancement of Science. Cover 278(5337) 17 Oct 97; **33.27.2** SPL/Photo Researchers; **33.28** Collection of Dan Cooper; **33.29.2** Grenier JK, Garber TL, Warren R, Whitington PM, Carroll S. Evolution of the entire arthropod *Hox* gene set predated the origin and radiation of the onychophoran/arthropod clade. *Curr Biol.* 1997 Aug 1;7(8):547–53; Fig. 3c; **33.31** Mark Newman/FLPA; **33.32.2** Tim Flach/Stone/Getty Images; **33.32.3** Andrew Syred/Photo Researchers; **33.32.4** Eric Lawton/iStockphoto; **33.34.2** Premaphotos/Nature Picture Library; **33.34.3** Tom McHugh/Photo Researchers; **33.36** Meul/ARCO/Nature Picture Library; **33.37.2** John Shaw/Tom Stack and Associates; **33.37.3** John Shaw/Tom Stack and Associates; **33.37.4** John Shaw/Tom Stack and Associates; **33.37.5** John Shaw/Tom Stack and Associates; **33.38.2** Dr. John Brackenbury/Photo Researchers; **33.38.3** Perry Babin; **33.38.4** PREMAPHOTOS/Nature Picture Library; **33.38.5** Dante Fenolio/Photo Researchers; **33.38.6** John Cancalosi/Nature Picture Library; **33.38.7** Hans Christoph Kappel/Nature Picture Library; **33.38.8** Michael & Patricia Fogden/CORBIS; **33.38.9** CC-BY-SA photo: Bruce Marlin (www.cirrusimage.com/fly_whale-tail.htm); **33.39.2** Maximilian Weinzierl/Alamy; **33.39.3** Peter Herring/Image Quest Marine; **33.39.4** Peter Parks/Image Quest Marine; **33.40.2** Andrey Nekrasov/Image Quest Marine; **33.41** Daniel Janies; **33.42** Jeff Rotman/Photo Researchers; **33.43** Robert Harding World Imagery/Alamy; **33.44** Jurgen Freund/Nature Picture Library; **33.45** Hal Beral/Corbis.

Chapter 34 34.1 Xian-guang H, Aldridge RJ, Siveter DJ, Siveter DJ, Xiang-hong F. New evidence on the anatomy and phylogeny of the earliest vertebrates. *Proceedings of the Royal Society of London-B-Biological Sciences*, Sept. 22, 2002; 269 (1503) 1865–1869; Fig. 1c; **34.4.2** Oxford Scientific/PhotoLibrary; **34.5.2** Robert Brons/Biological Photo Service; **34.8.2** Nanjing Institute of Geology and Palaeontology; **34.9.2** Tom McHugh/Photo Researchers; **34.10.2** A Hartl/AGE Fotostock; **34.10.3** Marevision/AGE Fotostock; **34.14.2** The Field Museum, #GEO82014; **34.15.2** Carlos Villoch/Image Quest Marine; **34.15.3** Masa Ushioda/Image Quest Marine; **34.15.4** Andy Murch/V&W/Image Quest Marine; **34.17.2** James D. Watt/Image Quest Marine; **34.17.3** Jez Tryner/Image Quest Marine; **34.17.4** George Grall/Getty Images; **34.17.5** Fred McConnaughey/Photo Researchers; **34.18.2** From "The oldest - articulated osteichthyan reveals mosaic gnathostome characters." M. Zhu et al. *Nature*. 2009 Mar 26;458(7237):469–74; **34.19** Arnaz Mehta; **34.20.2** © Ted Daeschler/ Academy of Natural Sciences/VIREO; **34.20.3** © Ted Daeschler/Academy of Natural Sciences/VIREO; **34.20.4** © Kalliopi Monoyios; **34.22.2** Alberto Fernandez/AGE Fotostock America, Inc. **34.22.3** Michael Fogden/Bruce Coleman/Photoshot; **34.22.4** Michael Fogden/Bruce Coleman/Photoshot; **34.23.2** John Cancalosi/Peter Arnold/PhotoLibrary; **34.23.3** Stephen Dalton/Photo Researchers; **34.23.4** Hans Pfletschinger/Peter Arnold/PhotoLibrary; **34.24** Michael Fogden/OSF/PhotoLibrary; **34.27** Nobumichi Tamura; **34.28** Michael Fogden/OSF/PhotoLibrary; **34.29.2** Natural Visions/Alamy; **34.29.3** Matt T. Lee; **34.29.5** Medford Taylor/National Geographic Image Collection; **34.29.6** Carl & Ann Purcell/Corbis; **34.30.2** Visceralimage/dreamstime; **34.30.3** Janice Sheldon; **34.32** Russell Mountford/Alamy; **34.33** DLILLC/Corbis; **34.34** Yufeng Zhou/iStockphoto; **34.35.1** McPHOTO/AGE Fotostock; **34.35.2** paolo barbanera/AGE Fotostock; **34.36** Gianpiero Ferrari/FLPA; **34.36** Gianpiero Ferrari/FLPA; **34.38.2** D. Parer and E. Parer Cook/Auscape International Proprietary Ltd. **34.38.3** Mervyn Griffiths/Commonwealth Scientific and Industrial Research Organization; **34.39.2** John Cancalosi/Alamy; **34.39.3** Wells Bert & Babs/OSF/PhotoLibrary; **34.42** Frans Lanting/Corbis; **34.44.2** Kevin Schafer/AGE Fotostock America, Inc. **34.44.3** J & C Sohns/Morales/AGE Fotostock America, Inc. **34.45.3** Anup Shah/ImageState/Alamy Images; **34.45.4** T. J. Rick/Nature Picture Library; **34.45.5** E. A. Janes/AGE Fotostock America, Inc. **34.45.6** Frans Lanting/Corbis; **34.47** Fossilized bone, partial skeleton, of Ardipithecus ramidus, articulated, with bones laid in their approximate positions. Housed in National Museum of Ethiopia, Addis Ababa. Photo © T. White 2009, From "Ardipithecus ramidus and the Paleobiology of Early Hominids." T. White et al. *Science*. 2009 Oct 2;326(5949):75–86; **34.48.2** John Reader/SPL/Photo Researchers; **34.48.3** John Gurche Studios; **34.49.2** Alan Walker @ National Museums of Kenya. Printed with permission; **34.51** David L Brill/Brill Atlanta; **34.52** C. Henshilwood & F. d'Errico/Professor Chris Henshilwood.

Chapter 35 35.1 PD photo: John Walker (www.fourmilab.ch/); **35.3** Robert & Linda Mitchell; **35.4.2** CC-BY-SA photo: Forest & Kim Starr; **35.4.3** Rob Walls/Alamy; **35.4.4** YinYang/iStockphoto; **35.4.5** Robert Holmes/Corbis; **35.4.6** Geoff Tompkinson/Science Photo Library/Photo Researchers; **35.5.2** Donald Gregory Clever; **35.5.3** Gusto Productions/SPL/Photo Researchers; **35.5.4** Dorling Kindersley; **35.5.5** Aflo Foto Agency/Alamy; **35.7.2** Neil Cooper/Alamy; **35.7.3** Martin Ruegner/jupiterimages; **35.7.4** Mike Zens/Corbis; **35.7.5** Jerome Wexler/Photo Researchers; **35.7.6** Kathy Piper/iStockphoto; **35.9.2** Purdue Extension Entomology; **35.10.2** Brian Capon; **35.10.4** © Clouds Hill Imaging www.lastrefuge.co.uk; **35.10.6** Graham Kent, Pearson Science; **35.10.7.** Graham Kent, Pearson Science; **35.10.9** N.C. Brown Center for Ultrastructure Studies, SUNY-Environmental Science & Forestry, Syracuse, NY; **35.10.11** Graham Kent; **35.10.12** Reproduced with permission from "Plant Cell Biology on CD," by B E S Gunning, www.plantcellbiologyonCD.com; **35.10.13** Professor Ray E. Evert.

Chapter 36 36.1 Peggy Heard/FLPA/Alamy; **36.3.2** Rolf Rutishauser; **36.3.3** Rolf Rutishauser; **36.5.2** Dr. Jeremy Burgess/SPL/Photo Researchers; **p. 770, top** Nigel Cattlin/Holt Studios International/Photo Researchers; **p. 770, bottom** Nigel Cattlin/Holt Studios International/Photo Researchers; **36.11** Scott Camazine/Photo Researchers; **36.14.2** Graham Kent; **36.14.3** Graham Kent; **36.16.2** Mlane/Dreamstime.com; **36.16.3** Kate Shane, Southwest School of Botanical Medicine; **36.16.4** Frans Lanting/Corbis; **36.16.5** Natalie Bronstein; **36.16.6** Andrew de Lory/Dorling Kindersley; **36.16.7** Danita Delimont/Alamy.

Chapter 38 38.1 Pierre-Michel Blais; **38.3.2** Ed Reschke/Peter Arnold/PhotoLibrary; **38.3.3** Ed Reschke/Peter Arnold/PhotoLibrary; **38.3.4** David Scharf/Peter Arnold/PhotoLibrary; **38.4.2** Marianne Wiora; **38.4.3** Stephen Dalton/NHPA Limited/Photoshot; **38.4.4** Bjorn Rorslett Photographe; **38.4.5** Bjorn Rorslett Photographe; **38.4.7** Doug Backlund; **38.4.8** Martin Pieter Heigan; **38.4.9** Rolf Nussbaumer/Nature Picture Library; **38.4.10** Merlin D. Tuttle, Bat Conservation International, www.batcon.org; **38.5** Photo: © W. Barthlott/W. Rauh; **38.11.2** Kevin Schafer/Alamy; **38.11.3** Nature Production; **38.11.4** Brian Gordon Green/National Geographic Image Collection; **38.11.5** Steve Bloom Images/Alamy; **38.11.6** Aaron McCoy/Botanica/Photolibrary; **38.11.7** California Department of Food and Agriculture's Plant Health and Pest Prevention Services; **38.11.8** Kim A. Cabrera Photographer; **38.11.9** Steve Shattuck/CSIRO Entomology; **38.11.10** Alan Williams/ Alamy; **38.12.11** Dennis Frates/Alamy; **38.13.2** Marcel E. Dorken; **38.13.3** Marcel E. Dorken; **38.13.4** Nobumitsu Kawakubo, Gifu University, Japan; **38.14.2** Bruce Iverson, Photomicrography; **38.14.3** Bruce Iverson, Photomicrography; **38.14.4** Meriel G. Jones, University of Liverpool, UK; **38.15.2** Sinclair Stammers/Photo Researchers; **38.16.2** Andrew McRobb/Dorling Kindersley; **38.16.3** Andrew McRobb/Dorling Kindersley; **38.17** John Van Hasselt/Corbis.

Chapter 40 40.1 JOEL SARTORE/National Geographic Stock; **40.2.2** Brandon Cole/PhotoLibrary; **40.2.3** Duncan Usher/Alamy; **40.2.4** Frank Greenaway/Dorling Kindersley/Getty Images; **40.4.2** Susumu Nishinaga/Photo Researchers; **40.4.3** Eye of Science/Photo Researchers; **40.4.4** Susumu Nishinaga/Photo Researchers; **40.5.7** CNRI/SPL/Photo Researchers; **40.5.11** Dr. Gopal Murti/SPL/Photo Researchers; **40.5.13** Chuck Brown/Photo Researchers; **40.5.15** Nina Zanetti; **40.5.17** Nina Zanetti; **40.5.19** Nina Zanetti; **40.5.21** Alamy; **40.5.24** Nina Zanetti; **40.5.26** Ed Reschke/Peter Arnold Images/PhotoLibrary; **40.5.28** Manfred Kage/Peter Arnold/Photolibrary; **40.5.31** Ulrich Gartner; **40.5.33** Thomas Deerinck/National Center for Microscopy and Imaging Research, University of California, San Diego; **40.10.2** Patricio Robles Gil/naturepl.com; **40.10.3** Matt T. Lee; **40.13** Robert Ganz; **40.18** Jeff Rotman/Alamy.

Chapter 41 41.1 Michael deYoung/Corbis; **41.2** Roland Seitre/Peter Arnold/PhotoLibrary; **41.3** Stefan Huwiler/Rolf Nussbaumer Photography/Alamy; **41.5.2** cameilia/Shutterstock; **41.6.2** Hervey Bay Whale Watch (www.herveybaywhalewatch.com.au/); **41.6.4** Thomas Eisner; **41.6.5** Photo Lennart Nilsson/Scanpix; **41.6.6** Gunter Ziesler/Peter Arnold/PhotoLibrary.

Chapter 42 42.1 Stephen Dalton/Photo Researchers; **42.2.2** Reinhard dirscheri/PhotoLibrary; **42.2.3** Eric Grave/Photo Researchers; **42.22.2** Peter Batson/Image Quest Marine; **42.22.3** Olgysha/Shutterstock; **42.22.4** Jez Tryner/Image Quest Marine; **42.24.2** Prepared by Dr. Hong Y. Yan, University of Kentcky and Dr. Peng Chai, University of Texas; **42.25.2** Motta & Macchiarelli/Anatomy Dept., Univ. La Sapienza, Rome/Photo Researchers.

Chapter 44 44.1 David Wall/Alamy; **44.4** Mark Conlin/Image Quest Marine; **44.5.2** Dr. John Crowe, University of California, Davis; **44.5.3** Dr. John Crowe, University of California, Davis; **44.9** AFP/Getty Images; **44.14.5** Steve Gschmeissner/Photo Researchers.

Chapter 46 46.1 David Doubilet/Getty Images; **46.2** David Wrobel; **46.4** Chris Wallace Photography, photographersdirect.com; **46.5.2** P. de Vries, courtesy of David Crews; **46.6** Andy Sands/naturepl.com; **46.7** John Cancalosi/Peter Arnold/PhotoLibrary.

Chapter 47 47.1 Photo Lennart Nilsson/Scanpix; **47.4.2** Vacquier VD, Payne JE. Methods for quantitating sea urchin sperm-egg binding. *Exp Cell Res.* 1973 Nov;82(1):227–35; **47.4.3** Vacquier VD, Payne JE. Methods for quantitating sea urchin sperm-egg binding. *Exp Cell Res.* 1973 Nov;82(1):227–35; **47.4.4** Vacquier VD, Payne JE. Methods for quantitating sea urchin sperm-egg binding. *Exp Cell Res.* 1973 Nov;82(1):227–35; **47.4.5** Vacquier VD, Payne JE. Methods for quantitating sea urchin sperm-egg binding. *Exp Cell Res.* 1973 Nov;82(1):227–35; **47.4.7** Hafner, M., Petzelt, C., Nobiling, R., Pawley, J., Kramp, D. and G. Schatten. Wave of Free Calcium at Fertilization in the Sea Urchin Egg Visualized with Fura-2. *Cell Motil. Cytoskel.*, 9:271–277 (1988); **47.4.8** Hafner, M., Petzelt, C., Nobiling, R., Pawley, J., Kramp, D. and G. Schatten. Wave of Free Calcium at Fertilization in the Sea Urchin Egg Visualized with Fura-2. *Cell Motil. Cytoskel.*, 9:271–277 (1988); **47.4.9** Hafner, M., Petzelt, C., Nobiling, R., Pawley, J., Kramp, D. and G. Schatten. Wave of Free Calcium at Fertilization in the Sea Urchin Egg Visualized with Fura-2. *Cell Motil. Cytoskel.*, 9:271–277 (1988); **47.4.10** Hafner, M., Petzelt, C., Nobiling, R., Pawley, J., Kramp, D. and G. Schatten. Wave of Free Calcium at Fertilization in the Sea Urchin Egg Visualized with Fura-2. *Cell Motil. Cytoskel.*, 9:271–277 (1988); **47.6.2** George von Dassow; **47.6.3** George von Dassow; **47.6.4** George von Dassow; **47.6.5** George von Dassow; **47.7.2** Jürgen Berger/Max Planck Institute for Developmental Biology, Tübingen, Germany; **47.7.3** Andrew J. Ewald, Johns Hopkins Medical School; **47.9.2** Charles A. Ettensohn; **47.13.2** Huw Williams; **47.13.3** Thomas Poole, SUNY Health Science Center; **47.14.2** Dr. Keith Wheeler/Photo Researchers; **47.17.2** Hiroki Nishida, *Developmental Biology* 121 (1987): 526. Reprinted by permission of Academic Press; **47.17.3** Hiroki Nishida, *Developmental Biology* 121 (1987): 526. Reprinted by permission of Academic Press; **47.18.2** J. E. Sulston and H. R. Horvitz, *Dev. Biol.* 56 (1977):110–156; **47.19.2** Adapted from Strome (International Review of Cytology 114: 81–123, 1989); **47.20.2** Adapted from Strome (International Review of Cytology 114: 81–123, 1989); **47.20.3** Adapted from Strome (International Review of Cytology 114: 81–123, 1989); **47.20.4** Adapted from Strome (International Review of Cytology 114: 81–123, 1989); **47.20.5** Adapted from Strome (International Review of Cytology 114: 81–123, 1989); **47.24.2** Kathryn W. Tosney, University of Michigan; **47.25.2** Dennis Summerbell.

Chapter 49 49.1 Brainbow mouse cerebellum. Image by Tamily Weissman, Harvard University. The Brainbow mouse was produced by Livet J, Weissman TA, Kang H, Draft RW, Lu J, Bennis RA, Sanes JR, Lichtman JW. *Nature* (2007) 450:56–62; **49.6.2** N. Kedersha/Photo Researchers; **49.9** Larry Mulvehill/Corbis; **49.14.2** From "A functional MRI study of happy and sad affective states induced by classical music."; . . . M. T. Mitterschiffthaler et al. *Hum Brain Mapp.* 2007 Nov;28(11):1150–62.

Chapter 51 51.1 Michael Nichols/National Geographic/Getty Images; **51.3** Susan Lee Powell; **51.5.2** Kenneth Lorenzen, UC Davis; **51.7.2** Thomas McAvoy/Life Magazine/Getty Images; **51.7.3** Operation Migration Inc.; **51.9.2** Lincoln Brower, Sweet Briar College; **51.9.3** Lincoln Brower, Sweet Briar College; **51.9.4** Lincoln Brower, Sweet Briar College; **51.11** Clive Bromhall/OSF/PhotoLibrary; **51.12.2** Alissa Crandall/Corbis; **51.12.3** Richard Wrangham; **51.15.2** Matt T. Lee; **51.15.3**

David Osborn/Alamy; **51.15.4** Bill Schmoker; **51.16.2** James D Watt/Image Quest Marine; **51.17** Courtesy of Gerald S. Wilkinson; from G.S. Wilkinson and G. N. Dodson, in J. Choe and B. Crespi (eds)., "The Evolution of Mating Systems in Insects and Arachnids," Cambridge University Press, Cambridge (1997), pp. 310–328; **51.18** Cyril Laubscher/Dorling Kindersley; **51.21** Martin Harvey/Peter Arnold Images/PhotoLibrary; **51.22** Erik Svensson, Lund University, Sweden; **51.23.2** Robert Pickett/Corbis; **51.24** Lowell L. Getz and Lisa Davis; **51.25** Rory Doolin; **51.27** Jennifer Jarvis; **51.29.2** Stephen J. Krasemann/Peter Arnold/PhotoLibrary.

Chapter 52 52.1 Dr. Paul A. Zahl/Photo Researchers; **52.2.2** James D. Watt/Stephen Frink Collection/Alamy; **52.2.3** Gianni Tortoli/Photo Researchers; **52.2.4** Tom Bean/Corbis; **52.2.5** B. Tharp/Photo Researchers; **52.2.6** Yann Arthus-Bertrand/Corbis; **52.2.7** NASA/Goddard Space Flight Center; **52.11.1** JTB Photo Communications, Inc./Alamy; **52.11.2** imagebroker/Alamy; **52.12.2** Frans Lanting/Corbis; **52.12.4** Gordon Whitten/Corbis; **52.12.6** Wolfgang Kaehler/Corbis; **52.12.8** The California Chaparral Institute (http://californiachaparral.net). Photo supplied by Richard Halsey; **52.12.10** Tom Bean/Image Bank/ Getty Images; **52.12.12** Shutterstock; **52.12.14** Kennan Ward/Corbis; **52.12.16** Darrell Gulin/Corbis; **52.16.1** Allen Russell/PhotoLibrary; **52.16.2** AfriPics.com/Alamy; **52.16.3** David Tipling/Nature Picture Library; **52.16.4** Ron Watts/Corbis; **52.16.5** Photononstop/SuperStock; **52.16.6** James Randklev/Image Bank/Getty Images; **52.16.7** Stuart Westmorland/Corbis; **52.16.8** Stuart Westmorland/Corbis; **52.16.9** Digital Vision/Getty Images; **52.16.10** William Lange/Woods Hole Oceanographic Institution; **52.17.2** Geoff Dann/Dorling Kindersley; **52.19.2** Peter Llewellyn/Alamy; **52.21** Daniel Mosquin.

Chapter 53 53.1 Arpat Ozgul; **53.2** Todd Pusser/Naturepl.com; **53.4.2** Bernard Castelein/Nature Picture Library/Alamy; **53.4.3** Frans Lanting/Corbis; **53.4.4** Niall Benvie/Corbis; **53.8.2** Hansjoerg Richter/iStockphoto; **53.11** Photodisc/White/PhotoLibrary; **53.12** Tom Bean/Corbis; **53.13.2** H. Willcox/Wildlife Picture/Peter Arnold/Photolibrary; **53.14.2** Jean Louis Batt/Taxi/Getty Images; **53.14.3** Christine Osborne/ Corbis; **53.14.4** Edward Parker/Alamy; **53.17.2** fotoVoyager/iStockphoto; **53.17.3** Adrian Bailey/Aurora Photos; **53.17.4** Joe Raedle/Getty Images; **53.17.5** Patrick Clayton, www.fisheyeguyphotography.com; **53.17.6** JOZSEF SZENTPETERI/NGS Image Collection; **53.17.7** Andrew Syred/Photo Researchers; **53.17.8** Nicholas Bergkessel, Jr./ Photo Researchers; **53.19.2** Joe McDonald/Corbis; **53.20.2** Robert Kay; **53.21.2** Niclas Fritzén.

Illustration and Text Credits

4.6b, 9.9, 17.17b and **c** are adapted from C. K. Matthews and K. E. van Holde, *Biochemistry*, 2nd ed. Copyright © 1996 Pearson Education, Inc., publishing as Pearson Benjamin Cummings. **4.7, 6.6b, 17.11, 18.25, 20.8, 21.9, and 21.10** are adapted from W. M. Becker, J. B. Reece, and M. F. Poenie, *The World of the Cell*, 3rd ed. Copyright © 1996 Pearson Education, Inc., publishing as Pearson Benjamin Cummings. **Table 6.1a** Adapted from W. M. Becker, L. J. Kleinsmith, and J. Hardin, *The World of the Cell*, 4th ed. p. 753. Copyright © 2000 Pearson Education, Inc., publishing as Pearson Benjamin Cummings. **6.8** and cell organelle drawings in **6.11** and **6.12** are adapted from illustrations by Tomo Narashima in E. N. Marieb, *Human Anatomy and Physiology*, 5th ed. Copyright © 2001 Pearson Education, Inc., publishing as Pearson Benjamin Cummings. **6.9a** from *Human Anatomy and Physiology*, 5th ed. Copyright © 2001 Pearson Education, Inc., publishing as Pearson Benjamin Cummings. **30.4 and 30.13i** are adapted from M. W. Nabors, *Introduction to Botany*, Copyright © 2004 Pearson Education, Inc., publishing as Pearson Benjamin Cummings. **42.30a, 46.16, 49.8, and 49.10** are adapted from E. N. Marieb, *Human Anatomy and Physiology*, 4th ed. Copyright © 1998 Pearson Education, Inc., publishing as Pearson Benjamin Cummings. **42.30a** From Campbell et al., *Biology: Concepts and Connections*, 6th ed., fig. 22.10, p. 462. Copyright © 2009 Pearson Education, Inc., publishing as Pearson Benjamin Cummings. **44.8** and **51.8** are adapted from L. G. Mitchell, J. A. Mutchmor, and W. D. Dolphin. *Zoology*. Copyright © 1988 Pearson Education, Inc., publishing as Pearson Benjamin Cummings.

Chapter 1 1.25 Map provided courtesy of David W. Pfennig, University of North Carolina at Chapel Hill; **1.27** Data in bar graph based on D. W. Pfennig et al. 2001. Frequency-dependent Batesian mimicry. *Nature 410*:323.

Chapter 2 2.2 (bottom) Reprinted by permission of Macmillan Publishers Ltd. *Nature.* M.E. Frederickson et al. 'Devil's gardens' bedeviled by ants, *437*:495, 9/22/05. Copyright © 2005.

Chapter 3 3.8a Adapted from *Scientific American*, Nov. 1998, p.102.

Chapter 5 5.12 Adapted from *Biology: The Science of Life*, 3rd ed. by Robert Wallace et al. Copyright © 1991. Reprinted by permission of Pearson Education, Inc; **5.15 and 5.20F** PDB ID 1CGD: J. Bella, B. Brodsky, and H. M. Berman. 1995. Hydration structure of a collagen peptide. *Structure 3*: 893–906; **5.18** Adapted from D. W. Heinz et al. 1993. How amino-acid insertions are allowed in an alpha-helix of T4 lysozyme. *Nature 361*:561; **5.20D** PDB ID 3GS0: Palaninathan, S.K., Mohamedmohaideen, N.N., Orlandini, E., Ortore, G., Nencetti, S., Lapucci, A., Rossello, A., Freundlich, J.S., Sacchettini, J.C. 2009. Novel transthyretin amyloid fibril formation inhibitors: synthesis, biological evaluation, and X-ray structural analysis. *Public Library of Science One 4*: e6290–e6290; **5.20G, 21.10b, Un42.1** PDB ID 2HHB: G. Fermi, M. F. Perutz, B. Shaanan, R. Fourme. 1984. The crystal structure of human deoxyhaemoglobin at 1.74 A resolution. *J.Mol.Biol. 175*: 159–174.

Chapter 7 7.9 PDB ID 3HAO: N. H. Joh, A. Oberai, D. Yang, J. P. Whitelegge, J. U. Bowie. 2009. Similar energetic contributions of packing in the core of membrane and water-soluble proteins. *J. Am.Chem.Soc. 131*: 10846–10847.

Chapter 8 8.18 PDB ID 3e1f: D H. Juers, S. Rob, M. L. Dugdale, N. Rahimzadeh, C. Giang, M. Lee, B. W. Matthews, R.E. Huber. 2009. Direct and indirect roles of His-418 in metal binding and in the activity of beta-galactosidase (E. coli). *Protein Sci. 18*: 1281–1292; **8.19** PDB ID 1MDY: P. C. Ma, M.A. Rould, H. Weintraub, C.O. Pabo. 1994. Crystal structure of MyoD bHLH domain-DNA complex: perspectives on DNA recognition and implications for transcriptional activation. *Cell* (Cambridge, Mass.) *77*: 451–459; **8.20** Figures 4a and 4e from "A common allosteric site and mechanism in caspases" by J.M. Scheer et al., in *Proceedings of the National Academy of Sciences, 103*, no. 20: 7595–7600, May 16, 2006. Copyright © 2006 National Academy of Sciences, U.S.A. Used by permission.

Chapter 9 9.5 From *Molecular Biology of the Cell*, 4th edition, by Bruce Alberts et al., fig. 2.69, p. 92. Copyright © 2002 by Bruce Alberts, Alexander Johnson, Julian Lewis, Martin Raff, Keith Roberts, and Peter Walter. Used by permission.

Chapter 10 10.13b Figure 1a from "Architecture of the photosynthetic Oxygen-evolving center" by K.N. Ferreira et al., in *Science, 303*, No. 5665: 1831–1838, March 19, 2004. Copyright © 2004, The American Association for the Advancement of Science. Reprinted with permission from AAAS; **10.15** Adapted from Richard and David Walker. Energy, Plants, and Man, fig. 4.1, p. 69. Sheffield: University of Sheffield. Oxygraphics http://www.oxygraphics.co.uk. © Richard Walker. Used with permission.

Chapter 12 12.13 From *Molecular Biology of the Cell*, 4th edition, by Bruce Alberts et al., fig. 18.41, p. 1059. Copyright © 2002 by Bruce Alberts, Alexander Johnson, Julian Lewis, Martin Raff, Keith Roberts, and Peter Walter. Used by permission.

Chapter 17 17.13 Figure 10-45 from *Principles of Cell and Molecular Biology*, 2nd edition, by Valerie M. Kish and Lewis J. Kleinsmith. Copyright © 1995 HarperCollins College Publishers. Reprinted by permission of Pearson Education.

Chapter 18 18.15a Figure 1d from "An Abundant Class of Tiny RNAs with Probable Regulatory Roles in *Caenorhabditis elegans*" by N.C. Lau et al., in *Science, 294*, No. 5543: 858–862, Oct. 1, 2001. Copyright © 2001, The American Association for the Advancement of Science. Reprinted with permission from AAAS.

Chapter 20 20.10 Figure 15.24, p. 481, from *Genetics*, 5th ed., by Peter Russell. Copyright © 1998 Pearson Education, Inc., publishing as Pearson Benjamin Cummings. Used by permission of the publisher.

Chapter 21 21.2 Adapted from a figure by Chris A. Kaiser and Erica Beade; **21.5b** Figure 2B from "The Genetic Landscape of a Cell" by M. Costanzo et al., in *Science, 327*, No. 5964: 425–431, Jan. 22, 2010. Copyright © 2010, The American Association for the Advancement of Science. Reprinted with permission from AAAS; **21.17** Adapted from an illustration by William McGinnis in Peter Radetsky, "The homeobox: Something very precious that we share with flies, from egg to adult." Bethesda, MD: Howard Hughes Medical Institute, 1992, p. 92. Reprinted by permission of William McGinnis; **21.18** Adapted from M. Akam, "Hox genes and the evolution of diverse body plans," *Philosophical Transactions of the Royal Society B*, 1995, *349*: 313–319, fig. 3. © Royal Society of London. Reprinted by permission.

Chapter 22 22.8 © Utako Kikutani 2007. Used with permission; **22.13** Figure 4a from "Host Race Radiation in the Soapberry Bug: Natural History with the History" by S.P. Carroll and C. Boyd, in Evolution, Vol. 46 No. 4, p. 1060, Aug. 1992. Reproduced with permission of Blackwell Publishing Ltd.; **22.14** Reprinted from *Trends in Microbiology, 16*, Issue 8: 361–369. B.A. Diep and M. Otto, "The role of virulence determinants in community-associated MRSA pathogenesis," Copyright © 2008, with permission from Elsevier.

Chapter 23 23.5 Figure 3 from "Genetic mechanisms for adapting to a changing environment" by D.A. Powers et al., from *Annual Review of Genetics, 25*, Dec. 1991. Copyright © 1991 by Annual Reviews. Reprinted by permission; **23.11** Figure 20.6 (maps only) from *Discover Biology*, Second Edition by Michael L. Cain, Hans Damman, Robert A. Lue & Carol Kaesuk Loon, Editors. Copyright © 2002 by Sinauer Associates, Inc. Used by permission of W.W. Norton & Company, Inc.; **23.12** Reprinted by permission from Macmillan Publishers Ltd.: *Nature*. E. Postma and A. J. van Noordijk, Gene flow maintains a large genetic difference in clutch size at a small spatial scale, *433*, 1/6/05. Copyright © 2005; **23.14** Adapted from many sources including D. J. Futuyma. 2005. *Evolution*, fig. 11.3. Sunderland, MA: Sinauer Associates and from R. L. Carroll, 1988. *Vertebrate Paleontology and Evolution*. W.H. Freeman & Co.; **23.16** Adapted from A. M. Welch et al. 1998. Call duration as an indicator of genetic quality in male gray tree frogs. *Science* 280:1928–1930; **23.17** Adapted from A. C. Allison. 1961. Abnormal hemoglobin and erythrocyte enzyme-deficiency traits. In *Genetic Variation in Human Populations*, ed. G.A. Harrison. Oxford: Elsevier Science and from S. I. Hay et al., A world malaria map: *Plasmodium falciparum* endemicity in 2007. *PLoS Medicine 6*: fig. 3, p. 291; **23.18** Figure 2a from "Frequency-Dependent Natural Selection in the Handedness of Scale-Eating Cichlid Fish" by Michio Hori in *Science, 260*, No. 5105: 216–219, April 9, 1993. Copyright © 1993, The American Association for the Advancement of Science. Reprinted with permission from AAAS; **Un 23.2** Data from R. K. Koehn and T. J. Hilbish. 1987. The adaptive importance of genetic variation. *American Scientist* 75: 134–141.

Chapter 24 24.7 Figure 3 from "Ecological Speciation in *Gambusia* Fishes" by R.B. Langerhans et al., from *Evolution, 61*, No. 9, July 2007, published by The Society for the Study of Evolution. Copyright © 2007 R.B. Langerhans, M.E. Gifford, E.O. Joseph. Reprinted by permission; **24.9** From figure 2 in "Correspondence between sexual isolation and allozyme differentiation" *Proceedings of the National Academy of Science, 87*: 2715–2719, 1990, p. 2718. Copyright © 1990 Stephen G. Tilley, Paul A. Verrell, Steven J. Arnold. Used with permission; **24.10a** Adapted from D. M. B. Dodd, 1989. Reproductive isolation as a consequence of adaptive divergence in *Drosophila pseudoobscura. Evolution* 43: 1308–1311; **24.13** Hybrid Zone and the Evolutionary Process edited by R.G. Harrison (1993): Map of Bombina hybrid zone (p. 263) and figure 10.1 (p. 278) from chapter "Analysis of hybrid zones with bombina" by J. M. Szymura. By permission of Oxford University Press; **24.15** Reprinted by permission of Macmillan Publishers Ltd.: *Nature*. G. P. Saetre et al. A sexually selected character displacement in flycatchers reinforces premating isolation, *387*:589–591, fig. 2, 6/5/97. Copyright © 1997; **24.19b** From fig. 2 in L. H. Rieseberg et al. 1996. Role of Gene Interactions in Hybrid Speciation: Evidence from Ancient and Experimental Hybrids. *Science* 272: 741–745. Copyright © 1996. Reprinted with permission from AAAS.

Chapter 25 25.3a Graph from "Experimental Models of Primitive Cellular Compartments Encapsulation Growth and Division" by M.M. Hanczyc et al., in *Science, 302*, No. 5645: 618–622. Oct. 24, 2003. Copyright © 2003, The American Association for the Advancement of Science. Reprinted with permission from AAAS; **25.5** From Don L. Eicher, *Geologic Time*, 1st edition, © 1968. Printed and Electronically reproduced by permission of Pearson Education, Inc., Upper Saddle River, New Jersey; **25.6a–d** Adapted from many sources including D. J. Futuyma. 2005. *Evolution*, fig. 4.10. Sunderland, MA: Sinauer Associates and from R. L. Carroll, 1988. *Vertebrate Paleontology and Evolution*. W.H. Freeman & Co.; **25.6e** Adapted from Luo et al. 2001.

A new mammalia form from the Early Jurassic and evolution of mammalian characteristics. *Science* 292: 1535; **25.7** Adapted from D. J. Des Marais. September 8, 2000. When did photosynthesis emerge on Earth? *Science* 289: 1703–1705; **25.8** Reprinted by permission from Macmillan Publishers Ltd.: *Nature*. L. R. Kump. The rise of atmospheric oxygen, *451*:277–278, 1/17/08. Copyright © 2008; **25.13** Map adapted from http://gelology.er.usgs.gov/eastern/plates.html; **25.15** Graph created from D. M. Raup and J. J. Sepkoski, Jr. 1982. Mass extinctions in the marine fossil record. *Science*. 215: 1501–1503 and J. J. Sepkoski, Jr. 1984. A kinetic model of Phanerozoic taxonomic diversity. III. Post-Paleozoic families and mass extinctions. *Paleobiology*. Vol 10, No. 2, pp. 246–267 in D. J. Futuyma, fig. 7.3a, p. 143 and fig. 7.6, p. 145, Sunderland, MA: Sinauer Associates; **25.17** From Mayhew, P. J. et al. 2008. A long-term association between global temperature and biodiversity, origination and extinction in the fossil record. *Proceedings of the Royal Society B*, 275: 47–53, fig. 3b. Reprinted by permission; **25.18** Figure 3 from "Anatomical and ecological constraints on Phanerozoic animal diversity in the marine realm" by R.K. Bambach et al., in *Proceedings of the National Academy of Sciences, 99*, no. 10: 6854–6859, May 14, 2002. Copyright © 2002 National Academy of Sciences, U.S.A. Used by permission; **25.19** Adapted from Hickman, Roberts, and Larson.1997, *Zoology*, 10th ed, Wm. C. Brown, fig. 31.1; **25.24** Reprinted by permission from Macmillan Publishers Ltd: *Nature*. M. Ronshaugen et al. Hox protein mutation and macroevolution of the insect body plan, *415*:914–917, fig. 1a. Copyright © 2002; **25.26** Adapted from M. Strickberger, 1990. *Evolution*, Boston: Jones & Bartlett.

Chapter 26 26.6 Figure 1 from "Which Whales Are Hunted? A Molecular Genetic Approach to Monitoring Whaling" by C.S. Baker and S.R. Palumbi, in *Science, 265*, No. 5178:1538–1539, Sep. 9, 1994. Copyright © 1994, The American Association for the Advancement of Science. Reprinted with permission from AAAS; **26.12** With kind permission from Springer Science+Business Media: *Development Genes and Evolution*, "The evolution of the hedgehog gene family in chordates: insights from amphioxus hedgehog," vol. 209, 1999, pp. 40–47, Jan. 1999, S.M. Shimeld, fig. 3; **26.19** Figure 4.3c, p. 124 from *Molecular Markers, Natural History, and Evolution*, 2nd edition, by John Avise. Copyright © 2004 Sinauer Associates. Used by permission; **26.20** Figure from "Timing the Ancestor of the HIV-1 Pandemic Strains" by B. Korber et al., in *Science, 288*, No. 5472: 1789–1796, Jun 9, 2000. Copyright © 2000, The American Association for the Advancement of Science. Reprinted with permission from AAAS; **26.21** Figure 4.1, p. 45, "The three domains of life" by S.L. Baldauf et al., from *Assembling the Tree of Life*, edited by Joel Cracraft and Michael Donoghue. By permission of Oxford University Press, Inc. **26.22** Adapted from S. Blair Hedges. The origin and evolution of model organisms. *Nature Reviews Genetics 3*:838–848, fig. 1, p. 840.

Chapter 27 27.10 Reprinted by permission from Macmillan Publishers Ltd.: *Nature*. V.S. Cooper and R.E. Lenski. The population genetics of ecological specialization in evolving *E. coli* populations, *407*:736–739, fig. 1. Copyright © 2000; **27.18** Graph created from data in C. Calvaruso et al. 2006. Root-associated bacteria contribute to mineral weathering and to mineral nutrition in trees: A budgeting analysis. *Applied and Environmental Microbiology* 72: 1258–1266.

Chapter 28 28.2 Reprinted from *Trends in Genetics,18*, No. 11, J.M. Archibald and P.J. Keeling, "Recycled plastids: a 'green movement' in eukaryotic evolution," Copyright © 2002, with permission from Elsevier; **28.11** Figure 12.7, p. 350, from *Microbiology*, by R. W. Bauman. Copyright © 2004 Pearson Education, Inc., publishing as Benjamin Cummings; **28.23** Data from A. Stechman and T. Cavalier-Smith. 2002. Rooting the eukaryote tree by using a derived gene fusion, *Science* 297: 89–91; **28.28** Reprinted by permission from Macmillan Publishers Ltd.: *Nature*. M.J. Behrenfeld et al. Climate-driven trends in contemporary ocean productivity, *44*: 752–755, fig. 3. Copyright © 2006.

Chapter 29 29.10 Source: R. D. Bowden. 1991. Inputs, outputs and accumulation of nitrogen in an early successional moss *(Polytrichum)* ecosystem. *Ecological Monographs* 61: 207–223; **29.14** Adapted from Raven et al. *Biology of Plants*, 6th ed., fig. 19.7, W. H. Freeman & Co.

Chapter 30 30.12a From P. R. Crane. 1985. Phylogenetic analysis of seed plants and the origin of angiosperms. *Annals of the Missouri Botanical Garden*, *72*:716–793, fig. 11a, p. 738. Used by permission of Missouri Botanical Garden Press; **30.12b** Figure 2.3, p. 28, from *Phylogeny and Evolution of Angiosperms* by Douglas E. Soltis et al. Copyright © 2005 Sinauer Associates. Used by permission. **Table 30.1** Adapted from Randy Moore et al., *Botany*, 2nd ed. Dubuque, IA: Brown, 1998, Table 2.2, p. 37.

Chapter 31 31.21 Figures 4 and 5 from "Fungal endophytes limit pathogen damage in a tropical tree" by A.E. Arnold et al., in *Proceedings of the National Academy of Sciences, 100*, no. 26: 15652–15653, December 23, 2003. Copyright © 2003 National Academy of Sciences, U.S.A. Used by permission; **31.26** Figure 1 from "Reversing introduced species effects: Experimental removal of introduced fish leads to rapid recovery of a declining frog" by Vance T. Vredenburg from *Proceedings of the National Academy of Sciences 101*: 7646–7650. Copyright © 2004 National Academy of Sciences, U.S.A. Used by permission.

Chapter 33 33.22 C. Lydeard et al., The Global Decline of Nonmarine Mollusks, *BioScience*, Vol. 54, No. 4: 321–330. © 2004, American Institute of Biological Sciences. Used by permission. All rights reserved. (Updated data are from International Union for Conservation of Nature, 2008.); **33.29a** Reprinted from *Current Biology, 7*, Issue 8, J.K. Grenier, S. Carroll et al., "Evolution of the entire arthropod *Hox* gene set predated the origin and radiation of the onychophoran/arthropod clade," p. 551, fig. 2a, Copyright © 1987, with permission from Elsevier.

Chapter 34 34.8b From "Fossil sister group of craniates: Predicted and found" by J. Mallatt and J. Chen, from *Journal of Morphology, 258*, Issue 1, May 15, 2003. Copyright © 2003 Wiley-Liss, Inc. Reprinted with permission; **34.12** From *Vertebrates: Comparative Anatomy, Function, Evolution, 3/e* by Kenneth Kardong. © 2002 McGraw-Hill Science/Engineering/Mathematics. Reprinted by permission of The McGraw-Hill Companies, Inc. **34.18 (bottom)** Reprinted by permission of Macmillan Publishers Ltd.: *Nature*. M. Zhu et al. The oldest articulated osteichthyan reveals mosaic gnathostome characters, *458*:469–474. Copyright © 2009; **34.21 (left)** Reproduced by permission of the Royal Society of Edinburgh from Transactions of the Roya Society of Edinburgh: Earth Sciences, volume 87 (1996), pp. 363–421; **34.21 (right)** Reprinted by permission of Macmillan Publishers Ltd.: *Nature*.

N.H. Shubin et al. The pectoral fin of *Tiktaalik roseae* and the origin of the tetrapod limb, *440*:768, fig. 4. Copyright © 2006; **34.37a** Adapted from many sources including D. J. Futuyma. 2005. *Evolution*, 1/e, fig. 4.10. Sunderland, MA: Sinauer Associates and from R. L. Carroll, 1988. *Vertebrate Paleontology and Evolution*. W.H. Freeman & Co. **34.47** Drawn from many photos of fossils. Some sources are *O. tugenensis* photo in Michael Balter, Early hominid sows division, *ScienceNow*, Feb. 22, 2001, © 2001 American Association for the Advancement of Science. *A. garhi*, and *H. neanderthalensis* adapted from *The Human Evolution Coloring Book*. *K platyops* adapted from photo in Meave Leakey et al., New hominid genus from eastern Africa shows diverse middle Pliocene lineages, *Nature*, March 22, 2001, 410: 433. *P. boisei* drawn from a photo by David Bill. *H. ergaster* drawn from a photo at www.inhandmuseum.com. *S. tchadensis* drawn from a photo in Michel Brunet et al., A new hominid from the Upper Miocene of Chad, Central Africa, *Nature*, July 11, 2002, 418: 147, fig. 1b; **34.50 (a/b)** Reprinted by permission of Macmillan Publishers Ltd.: *Nature*. I.V. Ovchinnikov et al. Molecular analysis of Neanderthal DNA from the northern Caucasus, *404*: 492, fig.3a and b. Copyright © 2000.

Chapter 35 35.21 Figure 2b from "Mongolian Tree Rings and 20th-Century Warming" by G.C. Jacoby et al., in *Science, 273*, No. 5276: 771–773, Aug. 9, 1996. Copyright © 1996, The American Association for the Advancement of Science. Reprinted with permission from AAAS.

Chapter 40 40.14 Figure 2 from "Thermoregulation in a brooding female Indian python, Python molurus bivittatus" by V.H. Hutchison et al., in *Science, 151*, No. 3711: 694–695, Feb. 11, 1966. Copyright © 1966, The American Association for the Advancement of Science. Reprinted with permission from AAAS; **40.15** Figure 7 from "Thermoregulation in Endothermic Insects" by Bernd Heinrich, in *Science, 185*, No. 4153: 747–756, August 30, 1974. Copyright © 1974, The American Association for the Advancement of Science. Reprinted with permission from AAAS; **40.21** Adapted from figures 2b and 2c from "The circadian clock stops ticking during deep hibernation in the European hamster" by F.G. Revel et al., in *Proceedings of the National Academy of Sciences, 104*, no. 34: 13816–13820, Aug. 21, 2007. Copyright © 2007 National Academy of Sciences, U.S.A. Used by permission.

Chapter 41 41.9a Figure 23.1 from *Human Anatomy and Physiology*, 8e, by Elaine Marieb and Katja Hoehn. Copyright © 2010 Pearson Education, Inc., publishing as Pearson Benjamin Cummings. Used by permission of the publisher; **41.9b** Figure 2-1 from Rhoades, *Human Physiology*, 3e. © 1996 Brooks/Cole, a part of Cengage Learning, Inc. Reproduced by permission. www.cengage.com/permissions; **41.21** Figure "Appetite Controllers" from "Cellular Warriors at the Battle of the Bulge" by Jean Marx, from *Science, 299*: p. 86, Feb. 7, 2003. Illustration by Kathleen Sutliff. Copyright © 2003, The American Association for the Advancement of Science. Reprinted with permission from AAAS.

Chapter 42 42.20 Reprinted by permission from Macmillan Publishers Ltd.: *Nature*. D.J. Rader and A. Daugherty. Translating molecular discoveries into new therapies for atherosclerosis, *451*:904–913, fig. 1, 2/21/08. Copyright © 2008; **42.21** From J.C. Cohen et al., "Sequence variations in PCSK9, low LDL, and protection against coronary heart disease," *New England Journal of Medicine*. 2006 Mar 23; *354*:1264–72, fig. 1A. Copyright © 2006 Massachusetts Medical Society. Used by permission. All rights reserved; **42.26** Adapted from "Surface properties in relation to atelectasis and hyaline membrane disease" by M.E. Avery and J. Mead, from A.M.A. *American Journal of Diseases of Children 97*:517–523 (June 1959). Copyright © 1959 American Medical Association. Used by permission. All rights reserved.

Chapter 44 44.6 Kangaroo rat data adapted from K. B. Schmidt-Nielson. 1990. *Animal Physiology: Adaptation and Environment*, 4th ed., p. 339. Cambridge: Cambridge University Press; **44.7a** Adapted from K. B. Schmidt-Nielsen et al. 1958. Extrarenal salt excretion in birds. *American Journal of Physiology* 193: 101–107; **44.14B and 44.15** Figure 25.3b from *Human Anatomy and Physiology*, 8e, by Elaine Marieb and Katja Hoehn. Copyright © 2010 Pearson Education, Inc., publishing as Pearson Benjamin Cummings. Used by permission of the publisher; **44.21** Table 1 from "Requirement of human renal water channel aquaporin-2 for vasopressin-dependent concentration in urine" by P.M. Deen et al., in *Science, 264*, No. 5155: 92–95, April 1, 1994. Copyright © 1994, The American Association for the Advancement of Science. Reprinted with permission from AAAS; **44EOC** From W.S. Beck et al., *Life: An Introduction to Biology*, 3rd edition, copyright © 1991. Reprinted and electronically reproduced by permission of Pearson Education, Inc., Upper Saddle River, New Jersey.

Chapter 46 46.9 Reprinted by permission of Macmillan Publishers Ltd.: *Nature*. R.R. Snook and D.J. Hosken, "Sperm death and dumping in *Drosophila*," *428*:939–941, fig. 2. Copyright © 2004.

Chapter 47 47.16 Figures 1.10 and 8.25 from *Principles of Development* by Lewis Wolpert (1998). By permission of Oxford University Press, Inc. **47.17a** Figure 21-70 from *Molecular Biology of the Cell*, 4th ed, by Bruce Alberts, used with permission from Garland Science - Books, permission conveyed through Copyright Clearance Center, Inc. Adapted for use from "Cell commitment and gene expression in the axolotl embryo" by T.J. Mohun from *Cell 22*: 9–15 (1980), by permission of the author; **47.17b** Reprinted from *Developmental Biology, 121*, Issue 2, Hiroki Nishida, "Cell lineage analysis in ascidian embryos by intracellular injection of a tracer enzyme: III. Up to the tissue restricted stage," p. 526, Copyright © 1987, with permission from Elsevier; **47.18** From *Molecular Biology of the Cell*, 4th edition, by Bruce Alberts et al., fig. 21.17, p. 1172. Copyright © 2002 by Bruce Alberts, Alexander Johnson, Julian Lewis, Martin Raff, Keith Roberts, and Peter Walter. Used by permission; **47.23 (experiment, results left)** Figures 1.10 and 8.25 from *Principles of Development* by Lewis Wolpert (1998). By permission of Oxford University Press, Inc. **47.23 (results, right)** Figure 15.12, p. 604, from *Developmental Biology*, 5th edition, by Gilbert et al. Copyright © 1997 Sinauer Associates. Used by permission; **47.26** Figure 23.1 from *Human Anatomy and Physiology*, 8e, by Elaine Marieb and Katja Hoehn. Copyright © 2010 Pearson Education, Inc., publishing as Pearson Benjamin Cummings. Used by permission of the publisher.

Chapter 49 49.11 Adapted from L. M. Mukhametov. 1984. Sleep in marine mammals. In *Sleep Mechanisms*, by A. A. Borbély and J. L. Valatx (eds.). Munich: Springer-Verlag, pp 227–238; **49.12** Figure 2a from "Transplanted suprachiasmatic nucleus determines circadian period" by M.R. Ralph et al., in *Science, 247*, No. 4945: 975–978, Feb. 23,

1990. Copyright © 1990, The American Association for the Advancement of Science. Reprinted with permission from AAAS; **49.18** Adapted from E. D. Jarvis et al. 2005. Avian brains and a new understanding of vertebrate brain evolution. *Nature Reviews Neuroscience* 6: 151–159, fig. 1c; **49.22** Adapted from Gottesman, I. I. and Wolfgram, D. (1991). *Schizophrenia genesis: The origins of madness*, fig. 10, p. 96. New York: Freeman.

Chapter 51 **51.2b** Figure 20, p. 28, from *Study of Instinct* by N. Tinbergen (1989). By permission of Oxford University Press, Inc.; **51.4** Reprinted by permission from Macmillan Publishing Ltd.: *Nature Reviews: Genetics*: M.B. Sokolowski. Drosophila: Genetics meets behavior, 2:881, fig. 1. Copyright © 2001; **51.10** Figure 3a from "Prospective and retrospective learning in honeybees" by M. Biurfa and J. Benard, in *International Journal of Comparative Psychology, 19*, Issue 3: 358–367, 2006; Reprinted with permission; **51.13** Figure 2a from "Evolution of foraging behavior in Drosophila by density-dependent selection" by M.B. Sokolowski et al., in *Proceedings of the National Academy of Sciences, 94*, no. 14: 7373–7377, July 8, 1997. Copyright © 2007 National Academy of Sciences, U.S.A. Used by permission; **51.19** K. Witte and N. Sawka. 2003. Sexual imprinting on a novel trait in the dimorphic zebra finch: sexes differ. *Animal Behaviour* 65: 195–203. Art adapted from http://www.uni-bielefeld.de/biologue/vhf/KW/Forschungsprojekte2.html; **51.23 (left, bottom)** With kind permission from Springer Science+Business Media: *Genetica*, "The inheritance of mating songs in two cryptic, sibling lacewing species," vol. 116, 2002, pp. 269–289, C. S. Henry, fig. 2; **51.26 (top)** Adapted from a photograph by Jonathan Blair in Alcock, 2002. *Animal Behavior*, 7th ed. Sinauer Associates, Inc., Publiishers; **51.26 (bottom)** Reprinted by permission from Macmillan Publishers Ltd.: *Nature*. P. Berthold et al. Rapid microevolution of migratory behaviour in a wild bird species, *360*:668, fig. 1, 12/17/92. Copyright © 1992.

Chapter 52 **52.7** Adapted from L. Roberts. 1989. How fast can trees migrate? *Science* 243: 736, fig. 2. © 1989 by the American Association for the Advancement of Science; **52.8** Reprinted by permission from Macmillan Publishers Ltd.: *Nature*. C. Parmesan et al. Poleward shift of butterfly species' ranges associated with regional warming, *399*:579–583, fig. 3. Copyright © 1999; **52.9** Adapted from Heinrich Walter and Siegmar-Walter Breckle. 2003. *Walter's Vegetation of the Earth*, fig. 16, p. 36. Springer-Verlag, © 2003; **52.17** Figure 1.7, p. 9 from *Kangaroos, Their Ecology and Management in the Sheep Rangelands of Australia*, edited by Graeme Caughley, Neil Shepherd, Jeff Short. © Cambridge University Press 1987. Reprinted with the permission of Cambridge University Press; **52.19** Map adapted from R. L. Smith. 1974. *Ecology and Field Biology*, fig. 11.19, p. 353. Harper and Row Publishers. Map updated from D. A. Sibley. 2000. National Audubon Society *The Sibley Guide to Birds*, Alfred A. Knopf: New York; **52.20** Data from W. J. Fletcher. 1987. Interactions among subtidal Australian sea urchins, gastropods and algae: effects of experimental removals. *Ecological Monographs* 57: 89–109; **Un. 52.2** Data from J. Clausen, D. D. Keck, and W. M. Hiesey. 1948. Experimental studies on the nature of species. III. Environmental responses of climatic races of *Achillea*. Carnegie Institution of Washington Publication 581.

Glossary

5′ cap A modified form of guanine nucleotide added onto the 5′ end of a pre-mRNA molecule.

A site One of a ribosome's three binding sites for tRNA during translation. The A site holds the tRNA carrying the next amino acid to be added to the polypeptide chain. (A stands for aminoacyl tRNA.)

ABC hypothesis A model of flower formation identifying three classes of organ identity genes that direct formation of the four types of floral organs.

abiotic (ā′-bī-ot′-ik) Nonliving; referring to the physical and chemical properties of an environment.

abortion The termination of a pregnancy in progress.

abscisic acid (ABA) (ab-sis′-ik) A plant hormone that slows growth, often antagonizing the actions of growth hormones. Two of its many effects are to promote seed dormancy and facilitate drought tolerance.

absorption The third stage of food processing in animals: the uptake of small nutrient molecules by an organism's body.

absorption spectrum The range of a pigment's ability to absorb various wavelengths of light; also a graph of such a range.

abyssal zone (uh-bis′-ul) The part of the ocean's benthic zone between 2,000 and 6,000 m deep.

acanthodian (ak′-an-thō′-dē-un) Any of a group of ancient jawed aquatic vertebrates from the Silurian and Devonian periods.

accessory fruit A fruit, or assemblage of fruits, in which the fleshy parts are derived largely or entirely from tissues other than the ovary.

acclimatization (uh-klī′-muh-tī-zā′-shun) Physiological adjustment to a change in an environmental factor.

acetyl CoA Acetyl coenzyme A; the entry compound for the citric acid cycle in cellular respiration, formed from a fragment of pyruvate attached to a coenzyme.

acetylcholine (as′-uh-til-kō′-lēn) One of the most common neurotransmitters; functions by binding to receptors and altering the permeability of the postsynaptic membrane to specific ions, either depolarizing or hyperpolarizing the membrane.

acid A substance that increases the hydrogen ion concentration of a solution.

acid precipitation Rain, snow, or fog that is more acidic than pH 5.2.

acoelomate (uh-sē′-lō-māt) A solid-bodied animal lacking a cavity between the gut and outer body wall.

acrosomal reaction (ak′-ruh-sōm′-ul) The discharge of hydrolytic enzymes from the acrosome, a vesicle in the tip of a sperm, when the sperm approaches or contacts an egg.

acrosome (ak′-ruh-sōm) A vesicle in the tip of a sperm containing hydrolytic enzymes and other proteins that help the sperm reach the egg.

actin (ak′-tin) A globular protein that links into chains, two of which twist helically about each other, forming microfilaments (actin filaments) in muscle and other kinds of cells.

action potential An electrical signal that propagates (travels) along the membrane of a neuron or other excitable cell as a nongraded (all-or-none) depolarization.

action spectrum A graph that profiles the relative effectiveness of different wavelengths of radiation in driving a particular process.

activation energy The amount of energy that reactants must absorb before a chemical reaction will start; also called free energy of activation.

activator A protein that binds to DNA and stimulates gene transcription. In prokaryotes, activators bind in or near the promoter; in eukaryotes, activators generally bind to control elements in enhancers.

active immunity Long-lasting immunity conferred by the action of B cells and T cells and the resulting B and T memory cells specific for a pathogen. Active immunity can develop as a result of natural infection or immunization.

active site The specific region of an enzyme that binds the substrate and that forms the pocket in which catalysis occurs.

active transport The movement of a substance across a cell membrane against its concentration or electrochemical gradient, mediated by specific transport proteins and requiring an expenditure of energy.

adaptation Inherited characteristic of an organism that enhances its survival and reproduction in a specific environment.

adaptive immunity A vertebrate-specific defense that is mediated by B lymphocytes (B cells) and T lymphocytes (T cells). It exhibits specificity, memory, and self-nonself recognition. Also called acquired immunity.

adaptive radiation Period of evolutionary change in which groups of organisms form many new species whose adaptations allow them to fill different ecological roles in their communities.

addition rule A rule of probability stating that the probability of any one of two or more mutually exclusive events occurring can be determined by adding their individual probabilities.

adenosine triphosphate *See* ATP (adenosine triphosphate).

adenylyl cyclase (uh-den′-uh-lil) An enzyme that converts ATP to cyclic AMP in response to an extracellular signal.

adhesion The clinging of one substance to another, such as water to plant cell walls by means of hydrogen bonds.

adipose tissue A connective tissue that insulates the body and serves as a fuel reserve; contains fat-storing cells called adipose cells.

adrenal gland (uh-drē′-nul) One of two endocrine glands located adjacent to the kidneys in mammals. Endocrine cells in the outer portion (cortex) respond to adrenocorticotropic hormone (ACTH) by secreting steroid hormones that help maintain homeostasis during long-term stress. Neurosecretory cells in the central portion (medulla) secrete epinephrine and norepinephrine in response to nerve signals triggered by short-term stress.

adrenocorticotropic hormone (ACTH) A tropic hormone that is produced and secreted by the anterior pituitary and that stimulates the production and secretion of steroid hormones by the adrenal cortex.

aerobic respiration A catabolic pathway for organic molecules, using oxygen (O_2) as the final electron acceptor in an electron transport chain and ultimately producing ATP. This is the most efficient catabolic pathway and is carried out in most eukaryotic cells and many prokaryotic organisms.

age structure The relative number of individuals of each age in a population.

aggregate fruit A fruit derived from a single flower that has more than one carpel.

AIDS (acquired immunodeficiency syndrome) The symptoms and signs present during the late stages of HIV infection, defined by a specified reduction in the number of T cells and the appearance of characteristic secondary infections.

alcohol fermentation Glycolysis followed by the reduction of pyruvate to ethyl alcohol, regenerating NAD^+ and releasing carbon dioxide.

aldosterone (al-dos'-tuh-rōn) A steroid hormone that acts on tubules of the kidney to regulate the transport of sodium ions (Na^+) and potassium ions (K^+).

algae A diverse grade of photosynthetic protists, including unicellular and multicellular forms. Algal species are included in three of the five eukaryote supergroups (Chromalveolata, Rhizaria, and Archaeplastida).

alimentary canal (al'-uh-men'-tuh-rē) A complete digestive tract, consisting of a tube running between a mouth and an anus.

allele (uh-lē'-ul) Any of the alternative versions of a gene that may produce distinguishable phenotypic effects.

allergen An antigen that triggers an exaggerated immune response.

allopatric speciation (al'-uh-pat'-rik) The formation of new species in populations that are geographically isolated from one another.

allopolyploid (al'-ō-pol'-ē-ployd) A fertile individual that has more than two chromosome sets as a result of two different species interbreeding and combining their chromosomes.

allosteric regulation The binding of a regulatory molecule to a protein at one site that affects the function of the protein at a different site.

alpha (α) helix (al'-fuh hē'-liks) A coiled region constituting one form of the secondary structure of proteins, arising from a specific pattern of hydrogen bonding between atoms of the polypeptide backbone (not the side chains).

alternation of generations A life cycle in which there is both a multicellular diploid form, the sporophyte, and a multicellular haploid form, the gametophyte; characteristic of plants and some algae.

alternative RNA splicing A type of eukaryotic gene regulation at the RNA-processing level in which different mRNA molecules are produced from the same primary transcript, depending on which RNA segments are treated as exons and which as introns.

altruism (al'-trū-iz-um) Selflessness; behavior that reduces an individual's fitness while increasing the fitness of another individual.

alveolate (al-vē'-uh-let) A protist with membrane-bounded sacs (alveoli) located just under the plasma membrane.

alveolus (al-vē'-uh-lus) (plural, **alveoli**) One of the dead-end air sacs where gas exchange occurs in a mammalian lung.

Alzheimer's disease (alts'-hī-merz) An age-related dementia (mental deterioration) characterized by confusion and memory loss.

amacrine cell (am'-uh-krin) A neuron of the retina that helps integrate information before it is sent to the brain.

amino acid (uh-mēn'-ō) An organic molecule possessing both a carboxyl and an amino group. Amino acids serve as the monomers of polypeptides.

amino group A chemical group consisting of a nitrogen atom bonded to two hydrogen atoms; can act as a base in solution, accepting a hydrogen ion and acquiring a charge of 1+.

aminoacyl-tRNA synthetase An enzyme that joins each amino acid to the appropriate tRNA.

ammonia A small, toxic molecule (NH_3) produced by nitrogen fixation or as a metabolic waste product of protein and nucleic acid metabolism.

ammonite A member of a group of shelled cephalopods that were important marine predators for hundreds of millions of years until their extinction at the end of the Cretaceous period (65.5 million years ago).

amniocentesis (am'-nē-ō-sen-tē'-sis) A technique associated with prenatal diagnosis in which amniotic fluid is obtained by aspiration from a needle inserted into the uterus. The fluid and the fetal cells it contains are analyzed to detect certain genetic and congenital defects in the fetus.

amniote (am'-nē-ōt) Member of a clade of tetrapods named for a key derived character, the amniotic egg, which contains specialized membranes, including the fluid-filled amnion, that protect the embryo. Amniotes include mammals as well as birds and other reptiles.

amniotic egg An egg that contains specialized membranes that function in protection, nourishment, and gas exchange. The amniotic egg was a major evolutionary innovation, allowing embryos to develop on land in a fluid-filled sac, thus reducing the dependence of tetrapods on water for reproduction.

amoeba (uh-mē'-buh) A protist grade characterized by the presence of pseudopodia.

amoebocyte (uh-mē'-buh-sīt') An amoeba-like cell that moves by pseudopodia and is found in most animals. Depending on the species, it may digest and distribute food, dispose of wastes, form skeletal fibers, fight infections, or change into other cell types.

amoebozoan (uh-mē'-buh-zō'-an) A protist in a clade that includes many species with lobe- or tube-shaped pseudopodia.

amphibian Member of the tetrapod class Amphibia, including salamanders, frogs, and caecilians.

amphipathic (am'-fē-path'-ik) Having both a hydrophilic region and a hydrophobic region.

amplification The strengthening of stimulus energy during transduction.

amygdala (uh-mig'-duh-luh) A structure in the temporal lobe of the vertebrate brain that has a major role in the processing of emotions.

amylase (am'-uh-lās') An enzyme that hydrolyzes starch (a glucose polymer from plants) and glycogen (a glucose polymer from animals) into smaller polysaccharides and the disaccharide maltose.

anabolic pathway (an'-uh-bol'-ik) A metabolic pathway that consumes energy to synthesize a complex molecule from simpler molecules.

anaerobic respiration (an-er-ō'-bik) A catabolic pathway in which inorganic molecules other than oxygen accept electrons at the "downhill" end of electron transport chains.

analogous Having characteristics that are similar because of convergent evolution, not homology.

analogy (an-al'-uh-jē) Similarity between two species that is due to convergent evolution rather than to descent from a common ancestor with the same trait.

anaphase The fourth stage of mitosis, in which the chromatids of each chromosome have

separated and the daughter chromosomes are moving to the poles of the cell.

anatomy The structure of an organism.

anchorage dependence The requirement that a cell must be attached to a substratum in order to initiate cell division.

androgen (an'-drō-jen) Any steroid hormone, such as testosterone, that stimulates the development and maintenance of the male reproductive system and secondary sex characteristics.

aneuploidy (an'-yū-ploy'-dē) A chromosomal aberration in which one or more chromosomes are present in extra copies or are deficient in number.

angiosperm (an'-jē-ō-sperm) A flowering plant, which forms seeds inside a protective chamber called an ovary.

angiotensin II A peptide hormone that stimulates constriction of precapillary arterioles and increases reabsorption of NaCl and water by the proximal tubules of the kidney, increasing blood pressure and volume.

anhydrobiosis (an-hī'-drō-bī-ō'-sis) A dormant state involving loss of almost all body water.

animal pole The point at the end of an egg in the hemisphere where the least yolk is concentrated; opposite of vegetal pole.

anion (an'-ī-on) A negatively charged ion.

anterior Pertaining to the front, or head, of a bilaterally symmetrical animal.

anterior pituitary A portion of the pituitary that develops from nonneural tissue; consists of endocrine cells that synthesize and secrete several tropic and nontropic hormones.

anther In an angiosperm, the terminal pollen sac of a stamen, where pollen grains containing sperm-producing male gametophytes form.

antheridium (an-thuh-rid'-ē-um) (plural, **antheridia**) In plants, the male gametangium, a moist chamber in which gametes develop.

anthropoid (an'-thruh-poyd) Member of a primate group made up of the monkeys and the apes (gibbons, orangutans, gorillas, chimpanzees, bonobos, and humans).

antibody A protein secreted by plasma cells (differentiated B cells) that binds to a particular antigen; also called immunoglobulin. All antibodies have the same Y-shaped structure and in their monomer form consist of two identical heavy chains and two identical light chains.

anticodon (an'-tī-kō'-don) A nucleotide triplet at one end of a tRNA molecule that base-pairs with a particular complementary codon on an mRNA molecule.

antidiuretic hormone (ADH) (an'-tī-dī-yū-ret'-ik) A peptide hormone, also known as vasopressin, that promotes water retention by the kidneys. Produced in the hypothalamus and released from the posterior pituitary, ADH also functions in the brain.

antigen (an'-ti-jen) A substance that elicits an immune response by binding to receptors of B cells, antibodies, or of T cells.

antigen presentation The process by which an MHC molecule binds to a fragment of an intracellular protein antigen and carries it to the cell surface, where it is displayed and can be recognized by a T cell.

antigen receptor The general term for a surface protein, located on B cells and T cells, that binds to antigens, initiating adaptive immune responses. The antigen receptors on B cells are called B cell receptors, and the antigen receptors on T cells are called T cell receptors.

antigen-presenting cell A cell that upon ingesting pathogens or internalizing pathogen proteins generates peptide fragments that are bound by class II MHC molecules and subsequently displayed on the cell surface to T cells. Macrophages, dendritic cells, and B cells are the primary antigen-presenting cells.

antiparallel Referring to the arrangement of the sugar-phosphate backbones in a DNA double helix (they run in opposite $5' \rightarrow 3'$ directions).

aphotic zone (ā'-fō'-tik) The part of an ocean or lake beneath the photic zone, where light does not penetrate sufficiently for photosynthesis to occur.

apical bud (ā'-pik-ul) A bud at the tip of a plant stem; also called a terminal bud.

apical dominance (ā'-pik-ul) Tendency for growth to be concentrated at the tip of a plant shoot, because the apical bud partially inhibits axillary bud growth.

apical ectodermal ridge (AER) A thickened area of ectoderm at the tip of a limb bud that promotes outgrowth of the limb bud.

apical meristem (ā'-pik-ul mār'-uh-stem) Embryonic plant tissue in the tips of roots and buds of shoots. The dividing cells of an apical meristem enable the plant to grow in length.

apicomplexan (ap'-ē-kom-pleks'-un) A protist in a clade that includes many species that parasitize animals. Some apicomplexans cause human disease.

apomixis (ap'-uh-mik'-sis) The ability of some plant species to reproduce asexually through seeds without fertilization by a male gamete.

apoplast (ap'-ō-plast) Everything external to the plasma membrane of a plant cell, including cell walls, intercellular spaces, and the space within dead structures such as xylem vessels and tracheids.

apoptosis (ā-puh-tō'-sus) A type of programmed cell death, which is brought about by activation of enzymes that break down many chemical components in the cell.

aposematic coloration (ap'-ō-si-mat'-ik) The bright warning coloration of many animals with effective physical or chemical defenses.

appendix A small, finger-like extension of the vertebrate cecum; contains a mass of white blood cells that contribute to immunity.

aquaporin A channel protein in the plasma membrane of a plant, animal, or microorganism cell that specifically facilitates osmosis, the diffusion of free water across the membrane.

aqueous solution (ā'-kwē-us) A solution in which water is the solvent.

arachnid A member of a major arthropod group, the chelicerates. Arachnids include spiders, scorpions, ticks, and mites.

arbuscular mycorrhiza (ar-bus'-kyū-lur mī'-kō-rī'-zuh) Association of a fungus with a plant root system in which the fungus causes the invagination of the host (plant) cells' plasma membranes.

arbuscular mycorrhizal fungus A symbiotic fungus whose hyphae grow through the cell wall of plant roots and extend into the root cell (enclosed in tubes formed by invagination of the root cell plasma membrane).

Archaea (ar'-kē'-uh) One of two prokaryotic domains, the other being Bacteria.

Archaeplastida (ar'-kē-plas'-tid-uh) One of five supergroups of eukaryotes proposed in a current hypothesis of the evolutionary history of eukaryotes. This monophyletic group, which includes red algae, green algae, and land plants, descended from an ancient protist ancestor that engulfed a cyanobacterium. *See also* Excavata, Chromalveolata, Rhizaria, and Unikonta.

archegonium (ar-ki-gō'-nē-um) (plural, **archegonia**) In plants, the female gametangium, a moist chamber in which gametes develop.

archenteron (ar-ken'-tuh-ron) The endoderm-lined cavity, formed during gastrulation, that develops into the digestive tract of an animal.

archosaur (ar'-kō-sōr) Member of the reptilian group that includes crocodiles, alligators and dinosaurs, including birds.

arteriole (ar-ter'-ē-ōl) A vessel that conveys blood between an artery and a capillary bed.

artery A vessel that carries blood away from the heart to organs throughout the body.

arthropod A segmented ecdysozoan with a hard exoskeleton and jointed appendages. Familiar examples include insects, spiders, millipedes, and crabs.

artificial selection The selective breeding of domesticated plants and animals to encourage the occurrence of desirable traits.

ascocarp The fruiting body of a sac fungus (ascomycete).

ascomycete (as'-kuh-mī'-sēt) Member of the fungal phylum Ascomycota, commonly called sac fungus. The name comes from the saclike structure in which the spores develop.

ascus (plural, **asci**) A saclike spore capsule located at the tip of a dikaryotic hypha of a sac fungus.

asexual reproduction The generation of offspring from a single parent that occurs without the fusion of gametes (by budding, division of a single cell, or division of the entire organism into two or more parts). In most cases, the offspring are genetically identical to the parent.

assisted migration The translocation of a species to a favorable habitat beyond its native range for the purpose of protecting the species from human-caused threats.

assisted reproductive technology A fertilization procedure that generally involves surgically removing eggs (secondary oocytes) from a woman's ovaries after hormonal stimulation, fertilizing the eggs, and returning them to the woman's body.

associative learning The acquired ability to associate one environmental feature (such as a color) with another (such as danger).

aster A radial array of short microtubules that extends from each centrosome toward the plasma membrane in an animal cell undergoing mitosis.

astrocyte A glial cell with diverse functions, including providing structural support for neurons, regulating the interstitial environment, facilitating synaptic transmission, and assisting in regulating the blood supply to the brain.

atherosclerosis A cardiovascular disease in which fatty deposits called plaques develop in the inner walls of the arteries, obstructing the arteries and causing them to harden.

atom The smallest unit of matter that retains the properties of an element.

atomic mass The total mass of an atom, which is the mass in grams of 1 mole of the atom.

atomic nucleus An atom's dense central core, containing protons and neutrons.

atomic number The number of protons in the nucleus of an atom, unique for each element and designated by a subscript to the left of the elemental symbol.

ATP (adenosine triphosphate) (a-den'-ō-sēn trī-fos'-fāt) An adenine-containing nucleoside triphosphate that releases free energy when its phosphate bonds are hydrolyzed. This energy is used to drive endergonic reactions in cells.

ATP synthase A complex of several membrane proteins that functions in chemiosmosis with adjacent electron transport chains, using the energy of a hydrogen ion (proton) concentration gradient to make ATP. ATP synthases are found in the inner mitochondrial membranes of eukaryotic cells and in the plasma membranes of prokaryotes.

atrial natriuretic peptide (ANP) (ā'-trē-ul na'-trē-yū-ret'-ik) A peptide hormone secreted by cells of the atria of the heart in response to high blood pressure. ANP's effects on the kidney alter ion and water movement and reduce blood pressure.

atrioventricular (AV) node A region of specialized heart muscle tissue between the left and right atria where electrical impulses are delayed for about 0.1 second before spreading to both ventricles and causing them to contract.

atrioventricular (AV) valve A heart valve located between each atrium and ventricle that prevents a backflow of blood when the ventricle contracts.

atrium (ā'-trē-um) (plural, **atria**) A chamber of the vertebrate heart that receives blood from the veins and transfers blood to a ventricle.

autocrine Referring to a secreted molecule that acts on the cell that secreted it.

autoimmune disease An immunological disorder in which the immune system turns against self.

autonomic nervous system (ot'-ō-nom'-ik) An efferent branch of the vertebrate peripheral nervous system that regulates the internal environment; consists of the sympathetic, parasympathetic, and enteric divisions.

autopolyploid (ot'-ō-pol'-ē-ployd) An individual that has more than two chromosome sets that are all derived from a single species.

autosome (ot'-ō-sōm) A chromosome that is not directly involved in determining sex; not a sex chromosome.

autotroph (ot'-ō-trōf) An organism that obtains organic food molecules without eating other organisms or substances derived from other organisms. Autotrophs use energy from the sun or from oxidation of inorganic substances to make organic molecules from inorganic ones.

auxin (ôk'-sin) A term that primarily refers to indoleacetic acid (IAA), a natural plant hormone that has a variety of effects, including cell elongation, root formation, secondary growth, and fruit growth.

average heterozygosity (het'-er-ō-zī-gō'-si-tē) The percentage, on average, of a population's loci that are heterozygous in members of the population.

avirulent Describing a pathogen that can mildly harm, but not kill, the host.

axillary bud (ak'-sil-ār-ē) A structure that has the potential to form a lateral shoot, or branch. The bud appears in the angle formed between a leaf and a stem.

axon (ak'-son) A typically long extension, or process, of a neuron that carries nerve impulses away from the cell body toward target cells.

B cells The lymphocytes that complete their development in the bone marrow and become effector cells for the humoral immune response.

Bacteria One of two prokaryotic domains, the other being Archaea.

bacterial artificial chromosome (BAC) A large plasmid that acts as a bacterial chromosome and can carry inserts of 100,000 to 300,000 base pairs (100–300 kb).

bacteriophage (bak-tēr'-ē-ō-fāj) A virus that infects bacteria; also called a phage.

bacteroid A form of the bacterium *Rhizobium* contained within the vesicles formed by the root cells of a root nodule.

balancing selection Natural selection that maintains two or more phenotypic forms in a population.

bark All tissues external to the vascular cambium, consisting mainly of the secondary phloem and layers of periderm.

Barr body A dense object lying along the inside of the nuclear envelope in cells of female mammals, representing a highly condensed, inactivated X chromosome.

basal angiosperm A member of one of three clades of early-diverging lineages of flowering plants. Examples are *Amborella*, water lilies, and star anise and its relatives.

basal body (bā'-sul) A eukaryotic cell structure consisting of a "9 + 0" arrangement of microtubule triplets. The basal body may organize the microtubule assembly of a cilium or flagellum and is structurally very similar to a centriole.

basal metabolic rate (BMR) The metabolic rate of a resting, fasting, and nonstressed endotherm at a comfortable temperature.

basal taxon In a specified group of organisms, a taxon whose evolutionary lineage diverged early in the history of the group.

base A substance that reduces the hydrogen ion concentration of a solution.

basidiocarp Elaborate fruiting body of a dikaryotic mycelium of a club fungus.

basidiomycete (buh-sid'-ē-ō-mī'-sēt) Member of the fungal phylum Basidiomycota, commonly called club fungus. The name comes from the club-like shape of the basidium.

basidium (plural, **basidia**) (buh-sid'-ē-um, buh-sid'-ē-ah) A reproductive appendage that produces sexual spores on the gills of mushrooms (club fungi).

Batesian mimicry (bāt'-zē-un mim'-uh-krē) A type of mimicry in which a harmless species looks like a species that is poisonous or otherwise harmful to predators.

behavior Individually, an action carried out by muscles or glands under control of the nervous system in response to a stimulus; collectively, the sum of an animal's responses to external and internal stimuli.

behavioral ecology The study of the evolution of and ecological basis for animal behavior.

benign tumor A mass of abnormal cells with specific genetic and cellular changes such that the cells are not capable of surviving at a new site and generally remain at the site of the tumor's origin.

benthic zone The bottom surface of an aquatic environment.

benthos (ben'-thōz) The communities of organisms living in the benthic zone of an aquatic biome.

beta (β) pleated sheet One form of the secondary structure of proteins in which the polypeptide chain folds back and forth. Two regions of the chain lie parallel to each other and are held together by hydrogen bonds between atoms of the polypeptide backbone (not the side chains).

beta oxidation A metabolic sequence that breaks fatty acids down to two-carbon fragments that enter the citric acid cycle as acetyl CoA.

bicoid A maternal effect gene that codes for a protein responsible for specifying the anterior end in *Drosophila melanogaster*.

bilateral symmetry Body symmetry in which a central longitudinal plane divides the body into two equal but opposite halves.

bilaterian (bī'-luh-ter'-ē-uhn) Member of a clade of animals with bilateral symmetry and three germ layers.

bile A mixture of substances that is produced in the liver and stored in the gallbladder; enables formation of fat droplets in water as an aid in the digestion and absorption of fats.

binary fission A method of asexual reproduction by "division in half." In prokaryotes, binary fission does not involve mitosis, but in single-celled eukaryotes that undergo binary fission, mitosis is part of the process.

binomial The two-part, latinized format for naming a species, consisting of the genus and specific epithet; a binomen.

biodiversity hot spot A relatively small area with numerous endemic species and a large number of endangered and threatened species.

bioenergetics (1) The overall flow and transformation of energy in an organism. (2) The study of how energy flows through organisms.

biofilm A surface-coating colony of one or more species of prokaryotes that engage in metabolic cooperation.

biofuel A fuel produced from dry organic matter or combustible oils produced by plants.

biogenic amine A neurotransmitter derived from an amino acid.

biogeochemical cycle Any of the various chemical cycles, which involve both biotic and abiotic components of ecosystems.

biogeography The study of the past and present geographic distribution of species.

bioinformatics The use of computers, software, and mathematical models to process and integrate biological information from large data sets.

biological augmentation An approach to restoration ecology that uses organisms to add essential materials to a degraded ecosystem.

biological clock An internal timekeeper that controls an organism's biological rhythms. The biological clock marks time with or without environmental cues but often requires signals from the environment to remain tuned to an appropriate period. *See also* circadian rhythm.

biological magnification A process in which retained substances become more concentrated at each higher trophic level in a food chain.

biological species concept Definition of a species as a group of populations whose members have the potential to interbreed in nature and produce viable, fertile offspring, but do not produce viable, fertile offspring with members of other such groups.

biology The scientific study of life.

biomanipulation An approach that applies the top-down model of community organization to alter ecosystem characteristics. For example, ecologists can prevent algal blooms and eutrophication by altering the density of higher-level consumers in lakes instead of by using chemical treatments.

biomass The total mass of organic matter comprising a group of organisms in a particular habitat.

biome (bī'-ōm) Any of the world's major ecosystem types, often classified according to the predominant vegetation for terrestrial biomes and the physical environment for aquatic biomes and characterized by adaptations of organisms to that particular environment.

bioremediation The use of organisms to detoxify and restore polluted and degraded ecosystems.

biosphere The entire portion of Earth inhabited by life; the sum of all the planet's ecosystems.

biotechnology The manipulation of organisms or their components to produce useful products.

biotic (bī-ot'-ik) Pertaining to the living factors—the organisms—in an environment.

bipolar cell A neuron that relays information between photoreceptors and ganglion cells in the retina.

bipolar disorder A depressive mental illness characterized by swings of mood from high to low; also called manic-depressive disorder.

birth control pill A chemical contraceptive that inhibits ovulation, retards follicular development, or alters a woman's cervical mucus to prevent sperm from entering the uterus.

blade (1) A leaflike structure of a seaweed that provides most of the surface area for photosynthesis. (2) The flattened portion of a typical leaf.

blastocoel (blas'-tuh-sēl) The fluid-filled cavity that forms in the center of a blastula.

blastocyst (blas'-tuh-sist) The blastula stage of mammalian embryonic development, consisting of an inner cell mass, a cavity, and an outer layer, the trophoblast. In humans, the blastocyst forms 1 week after fertilization.

blastomere An early embryonic cell arising during the cleavage stage of an early embryo.

blastopore (blas'-tō-pōr) In a gastrula, the opening of the archenteron that typically develops into the anus in deuterostomes and the mouth in protostomes.

blastula (blas'-tyū-luh) A hollow ball of cells that marks the end of the cleavage stage during early embryonic development in animals.

blood A connective tissue with a fluid matrix called plasma in which red blood cells, white blood cells, and cell fragments called platelets are suspended.

blue-light photoreceptor A type of light receptor in plants that initiates a variety of responses, such as phototropism and slowing of hypocotyl elongation.

body cavity A fluid- or air-filled space between the digestive tract and the body wall.

body plan In animals, a set of morphological and developmental traits that are integrated into a functional whole—the living animal.

Bohr shift A lowering of the affinity of hemoglobin for oxygen, caused by a drop in pH. It facilitates the release of oxygen from hemoglobin in the vicinity of active tissues.

bolus A lubricated ball of chewed food.

bone A connective tissue consisting of living cells held in a rigid matrix of collagen fibers embedded in calcium salts.

book lung An organ of gas exchange in spiders, consisting of stacked plates contained in an internal chamber.

bottleneck effect Genetic drift that occurs when the size of a population is reduced, as by a natural disaster or human actions. Typically, the surviving population is no longer genetically representative of the original population.

bottom-up model A model of community organization in which mineral nutrients influence community organization by controlling plant or phytoplankton numbers, which in turn control herbivore numbers, which in turn control predator numbers.

Bowman's capsule (bō'-munz) A cup-shaped receptacle in the vertebrate kidney that is the initial, expanded segment of the nephron where filtrate enters from the blood.

brachiopod (bra'-kē- uh-pod') A marine lophophorate with a shell divided into dorsal and ventral halves. Brachiopods are also called lamp shells.

brain Organ of the central nervous system where information is processed and integrated.

brainstem A collection of structures in the vertebrate brain, including the midbrain, the pons, and the medulla oblongata; functions in homeostasis, coordination of movement, and conduction of information to higher brain centers.

branch point The representation on a phylogenetic tree of the divergence of two or more taxa from a common ancestor. A branch point is usually shown as a dichotomy in which a branch representing the ancestral lineage splits (at the branch point) into two branches, one for each of the two descendant lineages.

brassinosteroid A steroid hormone in plants that has a variety of effects, including inducing cell elongation, retarding leaf abscission, and promoting xylem differentiation.

breathing Ventilation of the lungs through alternating inhalation and exhalation.

bronchiole (brong'-kē-ōl') A fine branch of the bronchi that transports air to alveoli.

bronchus (brong'-kus) (plural, **bronchi**) One of a pair of breathing tubes that branch from the trachea into the lungs.

brown alga A multicellular, photosynthetic protist with a characteristic brown or olive color that results from carotenoids in its plastids. Most brown algae are marine, and some have a plantlike body (thallus).

bryophyte (brī'-uh-fīt) An informal name for a moss, liverwort, or hornwort; a nonvascular plant that lives on land but lacks some of the terrestrial adaptations of vascular plants.

budding Asexual reproduction in which outgrowths from the parent form and pinch off to live independently or else remain attached to eventually form extensive colonies.

buffer A solution that contains a weak acid and its corresponding base. A buffer minimizes changes in pH when acids or bases are added to the solution.

bulk feeder An animal that eats relatively large pieces of food.

bulk flow The movement of a fluid due to a difference in pressure between two locations.

bundle-sheath cell In C_4 plants, a type of photosynthetic cell arranged into tightly packed sheaths around the veins of a leaf.

C_3 plant A plant that uses the Calvin cycle for the initial steps that incorporate CO_2 into organic material, forming a three-carbon compound as the first stable intermediate.

C_4 plant A plant in which the Calvin cycle is preceded by reactions that incorporate CO_2 into a four-carbon compound, the end product of which supplies CO_2 for the Calvin cycle.

calcitonin (kal'-si-tō'-nin) A hormone secreted by the thyroid gland that lowers blood calcium levels by promoting calcium deposition in bone and calcium excretion from the kidneys; nonessential in adult humans.

callus A mass of dividing, undifferentiated cells growing in culture.

calorie (cal) The amount of heat energy required to raise the temperature of 1 g of water by 1°C; also the amount of heat energy that 1 g of water releases when it cools by 1°C. The Calorie (with a capital C), usually used to indicate the energy content of food, is a kilocalorie.

Calvin cycle The second of two major stages in photosynthesis (following the light reactions), involving fixation of atmospheric CO_2 and reduction of the fixed carbon into carbohydrate.

CAM plant A plant that uses crassulacean acid metabolism, an adaptation for photosynthesis in arid conditions. In this process, carbon dioxide entering open stomata during the night is converted to organic acids, which release CO_2 for the Calvin cycle during the day, when stomata are closed.

Cambrian explosion A relatively brief time in geologic history when many present-day phyla of animals first appeared in the fossil record. This burst of evolutionary change occurred about 535–525 million years ago and saw the emergence of the first large, hard-bodied animals.

cAMP *See* cyclic AMP (cAMP).

canopy The uppermost layer of vegetation in a terrestrial biome.

capillary (kap'-il-ār'-ē) A microscopic blood vessel that penetrates the tissues and consists of a single layer of endothelial cells that allows exchange between the blood and interstitial fluid.

capillary bed A network of capillaries in a tissue or organ.

capsid The protein shell that encloses a viral genome. It may be rod-shaped, polyhedral, or more complex in shape.

capsule (1) In many prokaryotes, a dense and well-defined layer of polysaccharide or protein that surrounds the cell wall and is sticky, protecting the cell and enabling it to adhere to substrates or other cells. (2) The sporangium of a bryophyte (moss, liverwort, or hornwort).

carbohydrate (kar'-bō-hī'-drāt) A sugar (monosaccharide) or one of its dimers (disaccharides) or polymers (polysaccharides).

carbon fixation The initial incorporation of carbon from CO_2 into an organic compound by an autotrophic organism (a plant, another photosynthetic organism, or a chemoautotrophic prokaryote).

carbonyl group (kar-buh-nēl') A chemical group present in aldehydes and ketones and consisting of a carbon atom double-bonded to an oxygen atom.

carboxyl group (kar-bok'-sil) A chemical group present in organic acids and consisting of a single carbon atom double-bonded to an oxygen atom and also bonded to a hydroxyl group.

cardiac cycle (kar'-dē-ak) The alternating contractions and relaxations of the heart.

cardiac muscle A type of striated muscle that forms the contractile wall of the heart. Its cells are joined by intercalated disks that relay the electrical signals underlying each heartbeat.

cardiac output The volume of blood pumped per minute by each ventricle of the heart.

cardiovascular system A closed circulatory system with a heart and branching network of arteries, capillaries, and veins. The system is characteristic of vertebrates.

carnivore An animal that mainly eats other animals.

carotenoid (kuh-rot'-uh-noyd' An accessory pigment, either yellow or orange, in the chloroplasts of plants and in some prokaryotes. By absorbing wavelengths of light that chlorophyll cannot, carotenoids broaden the spectrum of colors that can drive photosynthesis.

carpel (kar′-pul) The ovule-producing reproductive organ of a flower, consisting of the stigma, style, and ovary.

carrier In genetics, an individual who is heterozygous at a given genetic locus for a recessively inherited disorder. The heterozygote is generally phenotypically normal for the disorder but can pass on the recessive allele to offspring.

carrying capacity The maximum population size that can be supported by the available resources, symbolized as *K*.

cartilage (kar′-til-ij) A flexible connective tissue with an abundance of collagenous fibers embedded in chondroitin sulfate.

Casparian strip (ka-spar′-ē-un) A water-impermeable ring of wax in the endodermal cells of plants that blocks the passive flow of water and solutes into the stele by way of cell walls.

catabolic pathway (kat′-uh-bol′-ik) A metabolic pathway that releases energy by breaking down complex molecules to simpler molecules.

catalyst (kat′-uh-list) A chemical agent that selectively increases the rate of a reaction without being consumed by the reaction.

catastrophism (kuh-tas′-truh-fiz′-um) The principle that events in the past occurred suddenly and were caused by different mechanisms than those operating today. *See* uniformitarianism.

catecholamine (kat′-uh-kōl′-uh-mēn) Any of a class of neurotransmitters and hormones, including the hormones epinephrine and norepinephrine, that are synthesized from the amino acid tyrosine.

cation (cat′-ī-on) A positively charged ion.

cation exchange A process in which positively charged minerals are made available to a plant when hydrogen ions in the soil displace mineral ions from the clay particles.

cDNA library A gene library containing clones that carry complementary DNA (cDNA) inserts. The library includes only the genes that were transcribed in the cells whose mRNA was isolated to make the cDNA.

cecum (sē′-kum) (plural, **ceca**) The blind pouch forming one branch of the large intestine.

cell body The part of a neuron that houses the nucleus and most other organelles.

cell cycle An ordered sequence of events in the life of a cell, from its origin in the division of a parent cell until its own division into two. The eukaryotic cell cycle is composed of interphase (including G_1, S, and G_2 subphases) and M phase (including mitosis and cytokinesis).

cell cycle control system A cyclically operating set of molecules in the eukaryotic cell that both triggers and coordinates key events in the cell cycle.

cell division The reproduction of cells.

cell fractionation The disruption of a cell and separation of its parts by centrifugation at successively higher speeds.

cell plate A membrane-bounded, flattened sac located at the midline of a dividing plant cell, inside which the new cell wall forms during cytokinesis.

cell wall A protective layer external to the plasma membrane in the cells of plants, prokaryotes, fungi, and some protists. Polysaccharides such as cellulose (in plants and some protists), chitin (in fungi), and peptidoglycan (in bacteria) are important structural components of cell walls.

cell-mediated immune response The branch of adaptive immunity that involves the activation of cytotoxic T cells, which defend against infected cells.

cellular respiration The catabolic pathways of aerobic and anaerobic respiration, which break down organic molecules and use an electron transport chain for the production of ATP.

cellular slime mold A type of protist characterized by unicellular amoeboid cells and aggregated reproductive bodies in its life cycle.

cellulose (sel′-yū-lōs) A structural polysaccharide of plant cell walls, consisting of glucose monomers joined by β glycosidic linkages.

Celsius scale (sel′-sē-us) A temperature scale (°C) equal to $5/9(°F - 32)$ that measures the freezing point of water at 0°C and the boiling point of water at 100°C.

central canal The narrow cavity in the center of the spinal cord that is continuous with the fluid-filled ventricles of the brain.

central nervous system (CNS) The portion of the nervous system where signal integration occurs; in vertebrate animals, the brain and spinal cord.

central vacuole In a mature plant cell, a large membranous sac with diverse roles in growth, storage, and sequestration of toxic substances.

centriole (sen′-trē-ōl) A structure in the centrosome of an animal cell composed of a cylinder of microtubule triplets arranged in a 9 + 0 pattern. A centrosome has a pair of centrioles.

centromere (sen′-trō-mēr) In a duplicated chromosome, the region on each sister chromatid where they are most closely attached to each other by proteins that bind to specific DNA sequences; this close attachment causes a constriction in the condensed chromosome. (An uncondensed, unduplicated chromosome has a single centromere, identified by its DNA sequence.)

centrosome (sen′-trō-sōm) A structure present in the cytoplasm of animal cells that functions as a microtubule-organizing center and is important during cell division. A centrosome has two centrioles.

cephalization (sef′-uh-luh-zā′-shun) An evolutionary trend toward the concentration of sensory equipment at the anterior end of the body.

cercozoan An amoeboid or flagellated protist that feeds with threadlike pseudopodia.

cerebellum (sār′-ruh-bel′-um) Part of the vertebrate hindbrain located dorsally; functions in unconscious coordination of movement and balance.

cerebral cortex (suh-rē′-brul) The surface of the cerebrum; the largest and most complex part of the mammalian brain, containing nerve cell bodies of the cerebrum; the part of the vertebrate brain most changed through evolution.

cerebral hemisphere The right or left side of the cerebrum.

cerebrospinal fluid (suh-rē′-brō-spī′-nul) Blood-derived fluid that surrounds, protects against infection, nourishes, and cushions the brain and spinal cord.

cerebrum (suh-rē′-brum) The dorsal portion of the vertebrate forebrain, composed of right and left hemispheres; the integrating center for memory, learning, emotions, and other highly complex functions of the central nervous system.

cervix (ser′-viks) The neck of the uterus, which opens into the vagina.

chaparral A scrubland biome of dense, spiny evergreen shrubs found at midlatitudes along coasts where cold ocean currents circulate offshore; characterized by mild, rainy winters and long, hot, dry summers.

chaperonin (shap′-er-ō′-nin) A protein complex that assists in the proper folding of other proteins.

character An observable heritable feature that may vary among individuals.

character displacement The tendency for characteristics to be more divergent in sympatric populations of two species than in allopatric populations of the same two species.

checkpoint A control point in the cell cycle where stop and go-ahead signals can regulate the cycle.

chelicera (kē-lih′-suh-ruh) (plural, **chelicerae**) One of a pair of clawlike feeding appendages characteristic of chelicerates.

chelicerate (kē-lih-suh′-rāte) An arthropod that has chelicerae and a body divided into a cephalothorax and an abdomen. Living chelicerates include sea spiders, horseshoe crabs, scorpions, ticks, and spiders.

chemical bond An attraction between two atoms, resulting from a sharing of outer-shell electrons or the presence of opposite charges on the atoms. The bonded atoms gain complete outer electron shells.

chemical energy Energy available in molecules for release in a chemical reaction; a form of potential energy.

chemical equilibrium In a chemical reaction, the state in which the rate of the forward reaction equals the rate of the reverse reaction, so that the relative concentrations of the reactants and products do not change with time.

chemical reaction The making and breaking of chemical bonds, leading to changes in the composition of matter.

chemiosmosis (kem′-ē-oz-mō′-sis) An energy-coupling mechanism that uses energy stored in the form of a hydrogen ion gradient across a membrane to drive cellular work, such as the synthesis of ATP. Under aerobic conditions, most ATP synthesis in cells occurs by chemiosmosis.

chemoautotroph (kē′-mō-ot′-ō-trōf) An organism that obtains energy by oxidizing inorganic substances and needs only carbon dioxide as a carbon source.

chemoheterotroph (kē'-mō-het'-er-ō-trōf) An organism that requires organic molecules for both energy and carbon.

chemoreceptor A sensory receptor that responds to a chemical stimulus, such as a solute or an odorant.

chiasma (plural, **chiasmata**) (kī-az'-muh, kī-az'-muh-tuh) The X-shaped, microscopically visible region where crossing over has occurred earlier in prophase I between homologous nonsister chromatids. Chiasmata become visible after synapsis ends, with the two homologs remaining associated due to sister chromatid cohesion.

chitin (kī'-tin) A structural polysaccharide, consisting of amino sugar monomers, found in many fungal cell walls and in the exoskeletons of all arthropods.

chlorophyll (klōr'-ō-fil) A green pigment located in membranes within the chloroplasts of plants and algae and in the membranes of certain prokaryotes. Chlorophyll *a* participates directly in the light reactions, which convert solar energy to chemical energy.

chlorophyll *a* A photosynthetic pigment that participates directly in the light reactions, which convert solar energy to chemical energy.

chlorophyll *b* An accessory photosynthetic pigment that transfers energy to chlorophyll *a*.

chloroplast (klōr'-ō-plast) An organelle found in plants and photosynthetic protists that absorbs sunlight and uses it to drive the synthesis of organic compounds from carbon dioxide and water.

choanocyte (kō-an'-uh-sīt) A flagellated feeding cell found in sponges. Also called a collar cell, it has a collar-like ring that traps food particles around the base of its flagellum.

cholesterol (kō-les'-tuh-rol) A steroid that forms an essential component of animal cell membranes and acts as a precursor molecule for the synthesis of other biologically important steroids, such as many hormones.

chondrichthyan (kon-drik'-thē-an) Member of the class Chondrichthyes, vertebrates with skeletons made mostly of cartilage, such as sharks and rays.

chordate Member of the phylum Chordata, animals that at some point during their development have a notochord; a dorsal, hollow nerve cord; pharyngeal slits or clefts; and a muscular, post-anal tail.

chorionic villus sampling (CVS) (kōr'-ē-on'-ik vil'-us) A technique associated with prenatal diagnosis in which a small sample of the fetal portion of the placenta is removed for analysis to detect certain genetic and congenital defects in the fetus.

Chromalveolata One of five supergroups of eukaryotes proposed in a current hypothesis of the evolutionary history of eukaryotes. Chromalveolates may have originated by secondary endosymbiosis and include two large protist clades, the alveolates and the stramenopiles. *See also* Excavata, Rhizaria, Archaeplastida, and Unikonta.

chromatin (krō'-muh-tin) The complex of DNA and proteins that makes up eukaryotic chromosomes. When the cell is not dividing, chromatin exists in its dispersed form, as a mass of very long, thin fibers that are not visible with a light microscope.

chromosome (krō'-muh-sōm) A cellular structure carrying genetic material, found in the nucleus of eukaryotic cells. Each chromosome consists of one very long DNA molecule and associated proteins. (A bacterial chromosome usually consists of a single circular DNA molecule and associated proteins. It is found in the nucleoid region, which is not membrane bounded.) *See also* chromatin.

chromosome theory of inheritance A basic principle in biology stating that genes are located at specific positions (loci) on chromosomes and that the behavior of chromosomes during meiosis accounts for inheritance patterns.

chylomicron (kī'-lō-mī'-kron) A lipid transport globule composed of fats mixed with cholesterol and coated with proteins.

chyme (kīm) The mixture of partially digested food and digestive juices formed in the stomach.

chytrid (kī'-trid) Member of the fungal phylum Chytridiomycota, mostly aquatic fungi with flagellated zoospores that represent an early-diverging fungal lineage.

ciliate (sil'-ē-it) A type of protist that moves by means of cilia.

cilium (sil'-ē-um) (plural, **cilia**) A short appendage containing microtubules in eukaryotic cells. A motile cilium is specialized for locomotion or moving fluid past the cell; it is formed from a core of nine outer doublet microtubules and two inner single microtubules (the "9 + 2" arrangement) ensheathed in an extension of the plasma membrane. A primary cilium is usually nonmotile and plays a sensory and signaling role; it lacks the two inner microtubules (the "9 + 0" arrangement).

circadian rhythm (ser-kā'-dē-un) A physiological cycle of about 24 hours that persists even in the absence of external cues.

***cis-trans* isomer** One of several compounds that have the same molecular formula and covalent bonds between atoms but differ in the spatial arrangements of their atoms owing to the inflexibility of double bonds; formerly called a geometric isomer.

citric acid cycle A chemical cycle involving eight steps that completes the metabolic breakdown of glucose molecules begun in glycolysis by oxidizing acetyl CoA (derived from pyruvate) to carbon dioxide; occurs within the mitochondrion in eukaryotic cells and in the cytosol of prokaryotes; together with pyruvate oxidation, the second major stage in cellular respiration.

clade (klayd) A group of species that includes an ancestral species and all of its descendants.

cladistics (kluh-dis'-tiks) An approach to systematics in which organisms are placed into groups called clades based primarily on common descent.

class In Linnaean classification, the taxonomic category above the level of order.

cleavage (1) The process of cytokinesis in animal cells, characterized by pinching of the plasma membrane. (2) The succession of rapid cell divisions without significant growth during early embryonic development that converts the zygote to a ball of cells.

cleavage furrow The first sign of cleavage in an animal cell; a shallow groove around the cell in the cell surface near the old metaphase plate.

climate The long-term prevailing weather conditions at a given place.

climograph A plot of the temperature and precipitation in a particular region.

cline A graded change in a character along a geographic axis.

clitoris (klit'-uh-ris) An organ at the upper intersection of the labia minora that engorges with blood and becomes erect during sexual arousal.

cloaca (klō-ā'-kuh) A common opening for the digestive, urinary, and reproductive tracts found in many nonmammalian vertebrates but in few mammals.

clonal selection The process by which an antigen selectively binds to and activates only those lymphocytes bearing receptors specific for the antigen. The selected lymphocytes proliferate and differentiate into a clone of effector cells and a clone of memory cells specific for the stimulating antigen.

clone (1) A lineage of genetically identical individuals or cells. (2) In popular usage, an individual that is genetically identical to another individual. (3) As a verb, to make one or more genetic replicas of an individual or cell. *See also* gene cloning.

cloning vector In genetic engineering, a DNA molecule that can carry foreign DNA into a host cell and replicate there. Cloning vectors include plasmids and bacterial artificial chromosomes (BACs), which move recombinant DNA from a test tube back into a cell, and viruses that transfer recombinant DNA by infection.

closed circulatory system A circulatory system in which blood is confined to vessels and is kept separate from the interstitial fluid.

cnidocyte (nī'-duh-sīt) A specialized cell unique to the phylum Cnidaria; contains a capsule-like organelle housing a coiled thread that, when discharged, explodes outward and functions in prey capture or defense.

cochlea (kok'-lē-uh) The complex, coiled organ of hearing that contains the organ of Corti.

codominance The situation in which the phenotypes of both alleles are exhibited in the heterozygote because both alleles affect the phenotype in separate, distinguishable ways.

codon (kō'-don) A three-nucleotide sequence of DNA or mRNA that specifies a particular amino acid or termination signal; the basic unit of the genetic code.

coefficient of relatedness The fraction of genes that, on average, are shared by two individuals.

coelom (sē'-lōm) A body cavity lined by tissue derived only from mesoderm.

coelomate (sē'-lō-māt) An animal that possesses a true coelom (a body cavity lined by tissue completely derived from mesoderm).

coenocytic fungus (sē'-no-si'-tic) A fungus that lacks septa and hence whose body is made up of a continuous cytoplasmic mass that may contain hundreds or thousands of nuclei.

coenzyme (kō-en'-zīm) An organic molecule serving as a cofactor. Most vitamins function as coenzymes in metabolic reactions.

coevolution The joint evolution of two interacting species, each in response to selection imposed by the other.

cofactor Any nonprotein molecule or ion that is required for the proper functioning of an enzyme. Cofactors can be permanently bound to the active site or may bind loosely and reversibly, along with the substrate, during catalysis.

cognition The process of knowing that may include awareness, reasoning, recollection, and judgment.

cognitive map A neural representation of the abstract spatial relationships between objects in an animal's surroundings.

cohesion The linking together of like molecules, often by hydrogen bonds.

cohesion-tension hypothesis The leading explanation of the ascent of xylem sap. It states that transpiration exerts pull on xylem sap, putting the sap under negative pressure or tension, and that the cohesion of water molecules transmits this pull along the entire length of the xylem from shoots to roots.

cohort A group of individuals of the same age in a population.

coitus (kō'-uh-tus) The insertion of a penis into a vagina; also called sexual intercourse.

coleoptile (kō'-lē-op'-tul) The covering of the young shoot of the embryo of a grass seed.

coleorhiza (kō'-lē-uh-rī'-zuh) The covering of the young root of the embryo of a grass seed.

collagen A glycoprotein in the extracellular matrix of animal cells that forms strong fibers, found extensively in connective tissue and bone; the most abundant protein in the animal kingdom.

collecting duct The location in the kidney where processed filtrate, called urine, is collected from the renal tubules.

collenchyma cell (kō-len'-kim-uh) A flexible plant cell type that occurs in strands or cylinders that support young parts of the plant without restraining growth.

colloid A mixture made up of a liquid and particles that (because of their large size) remain suspended rather than dissolved in that liquid.

colon (kō'-len) The largest section of the vertebrate large intestine; functions in water absorption and formation of feces.

commensalism (kuh-men'-suh-lizm) A symbiotic relationship in which one organism benefits but the other is neither helped nor harmed.

communication In animal behavior, a process involving transmission of, reception of, and response to signals. The term is also used in connection with other organisms, as well as individual cells of multicellular organisms.

community All the organisms that inhabit a particular area; an assemblage of populations of different species living close enough together for potential interaction.

community ecology The study of how interactions between species affect community structure and organization.

companion cell A type of plant cell that is connected to a sieve-tube element by many plasmodesmata and whose nucleus and ribosomes may serve one or more adjacent sieve-tube elements.

competitive exclusion The concept that when populations of two similar species compete for the same limited resources, one population will use the resources more efficiently and have a reproductive advantage that will eventually lead to the elimination of the other population.

competitive inhibitor A substance that reduces the activity of an enzyme by entering the active site in place of the substrate, whose structure it mimics.

complement system A group of about 30 blood proteins that may amplify the inflammatory response, enhance phagocytosis, or directly lyse extracellular pathogens.

complementary DNA (cDNA) A double-stranded DNA molecule made *in vitro* using mRNA as a template and the enzymes reverse transcriptase and DNA polymerase. A cDNA molecule corresponds to the exons of a gene.

complete digestive tract A digestive tube that runs between a mouth and an anus; also called an alimentary canal.

complete dominance The situation in which the phenotypes of the heterozygote and dominant homozygote are indistinguishable.

complete flower A flower that has all four basic floral organs: sepals, petals, stamens, and carpels.

complete metamorphosis The transformation of a larva into an adult that looks very different, and often functions very differently in its environment, than the larva.

compound A substance consisting of two or more different elements combined in a fixed ratio.

compound eye A type of multifaceted eye in insects and crustaceans consisting of up to several thousand light-detecting, focusing ommatidia.

concentration gradient A region along which the density of a chemical substance increases or decreases.

conception The fertilization of an egg by a sperm in humans.

condom A thin, latex rubber or natural membrane sheath that fits over the penis to collect semen.

conduction The direct transfer of thermal motion (heat) between molecules of objects in direct contact with each other.

cone A cone-shaped cell in the retina of the vertebrate eye, sensitive to color.

conformer An animal for which an internal condition conforms to (changes in accordance with) changes in an environmental variable.

conidium (plural, **conidia**) A haploid spore produced at the tip of a specialized hypha in ascomycetes during asexual reproduction.

conifer Member of the largest gymnosperm phylum. Most conifers are cone-bearing trees, such as pines and firs.

conjugation (kon'-jū-gā'-shun) (1) In prokaryotes, the direct transfer of DNA between two cells that are temporarily joined. When the two cells are members of different species, conjugation results in horizontal gene transfer. (2) In ciliates, a sexual process in which two cells exchange haploid micronuclei but do not reproduce.

connective tissue Animal tissue that functions mainly to bind and support other tissues, having a sparse population of cells scattered through an extracellular matrix.

conodont An early, soft-bodied vertebrate with prominent eyes and dental elements.

conservation biology The integrated study of ecology, evolutionary biology, physiology, molecular biology, and genetics to sustain biological diversity at all levels.

contraception The deliberate prevention of pregnancy.

contractile vacuole A membranous sac that helps move excess water out of certain freshwater protists.

control element A segment of noncoding DNA that helps regulate transcription of a gene by serving as a binding site for a transcription factor. Multiple control elements are present in a eukaryotic gene's enhancer.

controlled experiment An experiment in which an experimental group is compared with a control group that varies only in the factor being tested.

convection The mass movement of warmed air or liquid to or from the surface of a body or object.

convergent evolution The evolution of similar features in independent evolutionary lineages.

convergent extension A process in which the cells of a tissue layer rearrange themselves in such a way that the sheet of cells becomes narrower (converges) and longer (extends).

cooperativity A kind of allosteric regulation whereby a shape change in one subunit of a protein caused by substrate binding is transmitted to all the other subunits, facilitating binding of additional substrate molecules to those subunits.

copepod (cō'-puh-pod) Any of a group of small crustaceans that are important members of marine and freshwater plankton communities.

coral reef Typically a warm-water, tropical ecosystem dominated by the hard skeletal structures secreted primarily by corals. Some coral reefs also exist in cold, deep waters.

corepressor A small molecule that binds to a bacterial repressor protein and changes the protein's shape, allowing it to bind to the operator and switch an operon off.

cork cambium (kam'-bē-um) A cylinder of meristematic tissue in woody plants that replaces the epidermis with thicker, tougher cork cells.

corpus callosum (kor'-pus kuh-lō'-sum) The thick band of nerve fibers that connects the right and left cerebral hemispheres in mammals, enabling the hemispheres to process information together.

corpus luteum (kor'-pus lū'-tē-um) A secreting tissue in the ovary that forms from the collapsed follicle after ovulation and produces progesterone.

cortex (1) The outer region of cytoplasm in a eukaryotic cell, lying just under the plasma membrane, that has a more gel-like consistency than the inner regions due to the presence of multiple microfilaments. (2) In plants, ground tissue that is between the vascular tissue and dermal tissue in a root or eudicot stem.

cortical nephron In mammals and birds, a nephron with a loop of Henle located almost entirely in the renal cortex.

corticosteroid Any steroid hormone produced and secreted by the adrenal cortex.

cotransport The coupling of the "downhill" diffusion of one substance to the "uphill" transport of another against its own concentration gradient.

cotyledon (kot'-uh-lē'-dun) A seed leaf of an angiosperm embryo. Some species have one cotyledon, others two.

countercurrent exchange The exchange of a substance or heat between two fluids flowing in opposite directions. For example, blood in a fish gill flows in the opposite direction of water passing over the gill, maximizing diffusion of oxygen into and carbon dioxide out of the blood.

countercurrent multiplier system A countercurrent system in which energy is expended in active transport to facilitate exchange of materials and generate concentration gradients.

covalent bond (kō-vā'-lent) A type of strong chemical bond in which two atoms share one or more pairs of valence electrons.

craniate A chordate with a head.

crassulacean acid metabolism (CAM) An adaptation for photosynthesis in arid conditions, first discovered in the family Crassulaceae. In this process, a plant takes up CO_2 and incorporates it into a variety of organic acids at night; during the day, CO_2 is released from organic acids for use in the Calvin cycle.

crista (plural, **cristae**) (kris'-tuh, kris'-tē) An infolding of the inner membrane of a mitochondrion. The inner membrane houses electron transport chains and molecules of the enzyme catalyzing the synthesis of ATP (ATP synthase).

critical load The amount of added nutrient, usually nitrogen or phosphorus, that can be absorbed by plants without damaging ecosystem integrity.

crop rotation The practice of planting nonlegumes one year and legumes in alternating years to restore concentrations of fixed nitrogen in the soil.

cross-fostering study A behavioral study in which the young of one species are placed in the care of adults from another species.

crossing over The reciprocal exchange of genetic material between nonsister chromatids during prophase I of meiosis.

cross-pollination In angiosperms, the transfer of pollen from an anther of a flower on one plant to the stigma of a flower on another plant of the same species.

crustacean (kruh-stā'-shun) A member of a subphylum of mostly aquatic arthropods that includes lobsters, crayfishes, crabs, shrimps, and barnacles.

cryptic coloration Camouflage that makes a potential prey difficult to spot against its background.

culture A system of information transfer through social learning or teaching that influences the behavior of individuals in a population.

cuticle (kyū'-tuh-kul) (1) A waxy covering on the surface of stems and leaves that prevents desiccation in terrestrial plants. (2) The exoskeleton of an arthropod, consisting of layers of protein and chitin that are variously modified for different functions. (3) A tough coat that covers the body of a nematode.

cyclic AMP (cAMP) Cyclic adenosine monophosphate, a ring-shaped molecule made from ATP that is a common intracellular signaling molecule (second messenger) in eukaryotic cells. It is also a regulator of some bacterial operons.

cyclic electron flow A route of electron flow during the light reactions of photosynthesis that involves only photosystem I and that produces ATP but not NADPH or O_2.

cyclin (sī'-klin) A cellular protein that occurs in a cyclically fluctuating concentration and that plays an important role in regulating the cell cycle.

cyclin-dependent kinase (Cdk) A protein kinase that is active only when attached to a particular cyclin.

cystic fibrosis (sis'-tik fī-brō'-sis) A human genetic disorder caused by a recessive allele for a chloride channel protein; characterized by an excessive secretion of mucus and consequent vulnerability to infection; fatal if untreated.

cytochrome (sī'-tō-krōm) An iron-containing protein that is a component of electron transport chains in the mitochondria and chloroplasts of eukaryotic cells and the plasma membranes of prokaryotic cells.

cytogenetic map A map of a chromosome that locates genes with respect to chromosomal features distinguishable in a microscope.

cytokine (sī'-tō-kīn') Any of a group of small proteins secreted by a number of cell types, including macrophages and helper T cells, that regulate the function of other cells.

cytokinesis (sī'-tō-kuh-nē'-sis) The division of the cytoplasm to form two separate daughter cells immediately after mitosis, meiosis I, or meiosis II.

cytokinin (sī'-tō-kī'-nin) Any of a class of related plant hormones that retard aging and act in concert with auxin to stimulate cell division, influence the pathway of differentiation, and control apical dominance.

cytoplasm (sī'-tō-plaz'-um) The contents of the cell bounded by the plasma membrane; in eukaryotes, the portion exclusive of the nucleus.

cytoplasmic determinant A maternal substance, such as a protein or RNA, that when placed into an egg influences the course of early development by regulating the expression of genes that affect the developmental fate of cells.

cytoplasmic streaming A circular flow of cytoplasm, involving interactions of myosin and actin filaments, that speeds the distribution of materials within cells.

cytoskeleton A network of microtubules, microfilaments, and intermediate filaments that extend throughout the cytoplasm and serve a variety of mechanical, transport, and signaling functions.

cytosol (sī'-tō-sol) The semifluid portion of the cytoplasm.

cytotoxic T cell A type of lymphocyte that, when activated, kills infected cells as well as certain cancer cells and transplanted cells.

dalton A measure of mass for atoms and subatomic particles; the same as the atomic mass unit, or amu.

data Recorded observations.

day-neutral plant A plant in which flower formation is not controlled by photoperiod or day length.

decapod A member of the group of crustaceans that includes lobsters, crayfishes, crabs, and shrimps.

decomposer An organism that absorbs nutrients from nonliving organic material such as corpses, fallen plant material, and the wastes of living organisms and converts them to inorganic forms; a detritivore.

deductive reasoning A type of logic in which specific results are predicted from a general premise.

deep-sea hydrothermal vent A dark, hot, oxygen-deficient environment associated with volcanic activity on or near the seafloor. The producers in a vent community are chemoautotrophic prokaryotes.

de-etiolation The changes a plant shoot undergoes in response to sunlight; also known informally as greening.

dehydration reaction A chemical reaction in which two molecules become covalently bonded to each other with the removal of a water molecule.

deletion (1) A deficiency in a chromosome resulting from the loss of a fragment through breakage. (2) A mutational loss of one or more nucleotide pairs from a gene.

demographic transition In a stable population, a shift from high birth and death rates to low birth and death rates.

demography The study of changes over time in the vital statistics of populations, especially birth rates and death rates.

denaturation (dē-nā'-chur-ā'-shun) In proteins, a process in which a protein loses its native shape due to the disruption of weak chemical bonds and interactions, thereby becoming biologically inactive; in DNA, the separation of the two strands of the double helix. Denaturation occurs under extreme (noncellular) conditions of pH, salt concentration, or temperature.

dendrite (den'-drīt) One of usually numerous, short, highly branched extensions of a neuron that receive signals from other neurons.

dendritic cell An antigen-presenting cell, located mainly in lymphatic tissues and skin, that is particularly efficient in presenting antigens to helper T cells, thereby initiating a primary immune response.

density The number of individuals per unit area or volume.

density dependent Referring to any characteristic that varies with population density.

density independent Referring to any characteristic that is not affected by population density.

density-dependent inhibition The phenomenon observed in normal animal cells that causes them to stop dividing when they come into contact with one another.

deoxyribonucleic acid (DNA) (dē-ok′-sē-rī′-bō-nū-klā′-ik) A nucleic acid molecule, usually a double-stranded helix, in which each polynucleotide strand consists of nucleotide monomers with a deoxyribose sugar and the nitrogenous bases adenine (A), cytosine (C), guanine (G), and thymine (T); capable of being replicated and determining the inherited structure of a cell's proteins.

deoxyribose (dē-ok′-si-rī′-bōs) The sugar component of DNA nucleotides, having one fewer hydroxyl group than ribose, the sugar component of RNA nucleotides.

depolarization A change in a cell's membrane potential such that the inside of the membrane is made less negative relative to the outside. For example, a neuron membrane is depolarized if a stimulus decreases its voltage from the resting potential of −70 mV in the direction of zero voltage.

dermal tissue system The outer protective covering of plants.

desert A terrestrial biome characterized by very low precipitation.

desmosome A type of intercellular junction in animal cells that functions as a rivet, fastening cells together.

determinate cleavage A type of embryonic development in protostomes that rigidly casts the developmental fate of each embryonic cell very early.

determinate growth A type of growth characteristic of most animals and some plant organs, in which growth stops after a certain size is reached.

determination The progressive restriction of developmental potential in which the possible fate of each cell becomes more limited as an embryo develops. At the end of determination, a cell is committed to its fate.

detritivore (deh-trī′-tuh-vōr) A consumer that derives its energy and nutrients from nonliving organic material such as corpses, fallen plant material, and the wastes of living organisms; a decomposer.

detritus (di-trī′-tus) Dead organic matter.

deuteromycete (dū′-tuh-rō-mī′-sēt) Traditional classification for a fungus with no known sexual stage.

deuterostome development (dū′-tuh-rō-stōm′) In animals, a developmental mode distinguished by the development of the anus from the blastopore; often also characterized by radial cleavage and by the body cavity forming as outpockets of mesodermal tissue.

development The events involved in an organism's changing gradually from a simple to a more complex or specialized form.

diabetes mellitus (dī′-uh-bē′-tis mel′-uh-tus) An endocrine disorder marked by an inability to maintain glucose homeostasis. The type 1 form results from autoimmune destruction of insulin-secreting cells; treatment usually requires daily insulin injections. The type 2 form most commonly results from reduced responsiveness of target cells to insulin; obesity and lack of exercise are risk factors.

diacylglycerol (DAG) (dī-a′-sil-glis′-er-ol) A second messenger produced by the cleavage of the phospholipid PIP$_2$ in the plasma membrane.

diaphragm (dī′-uh-fram′) (1) A sheet of muscle that forms the bottom wall of the thoracic cavity in mammals. Contraction of the diaphragm pulls air into the lungs. (2) A dome-shaped rubber cup fitted into the upper portion of the vagina before sexual intercourse. It serves as a physical barrier to the passage of sperm into the uterus.

diapsid (dī-ap′-sid) Member of an amniote clade distinguished by a pair of holes on each side of the skull. Diapsids include the lepidosaurs and archosaurs.

diastole (dī-as′-tō-lē) The stage of the cardiac cycle in which a heart chamber is relaxed and fills with blood.

diastolic pressure Blood pressure in the arteries when the ventricles are relaxed.

dicot A term traditionally used to refer to flowering plants that have two embryonic seed leaves, or cotyledons. Recent molecular evidence indicates that dicots do not form a clade; species once classified as dicots are now grouped into eudicots, magnoliids, and several lineages of basal angiosperms.

differential gene expression The expression of different sets of genes by cells with the same genome.

differentiation The process by which a cell or group of cells become specialized in structure and function.

diffusion The spontaneous movement of a substance down its concentration or electrochemical gradient, from a region where it is more concentrated to a region where it is less concentrated.

digestion The second stage of food processing in animals: the breaking down of food into molecules small enough for the body to absorb.

dihybrid (dī′-hī′-brid) An organism that is heterozygous with respect to two genes of interest. All the offspring from a cross between parents doubly homozygous for different alleles are dihybrids. For example, parents of genotypes *AABB* and *aabb* produce a dihybrid of genotype *AaBb*.

dihybrid cross A cross between two organisms that are each heterozygous for both of the characters being followed (or the self-pollination of a plant that is heterozygous for both characters).

dikaryotic (dī′-kār-ē-ot′-ik) Referring to a fungal mycelium with two haploid nuclei per cell, one from each parent.

dinoflagellate (dī′-nō-flaj′-uh-let) Member of a group of mostly unicellular photosynthetic algae with two flagella situated in perpendicular grooves in cellulose plates covering the cell.

dinosaur Member of an extremely diverse clade of reptiles varying in body shape, size, and habitat. Birds are the only extant dinosaurs.

dioecious (dī-ē′-shus) In plant biology, having the male and female reproductive parts on different individuals of the same species.

diploblastic Having two germ layers.

diploid cell (dip′-loyd) A cell containing two sets of chromosomes (2*n*), one set inherited from each parent.

diplomonad A protist that has modified mitochondria, two equal-sized nuclei, and multiple flagella.

directional selection Natural selection in which individuals at one end of the phenotypic range survive or reproduce more successfully than do other individuals.

disaccharide (dī-sak′-uh-rīd) A double sugar, consisting of two monosaccharides joined by a glycosidic linkage formed by a dehydration reaction.

dispersal The movement of individuals or gametes away from their parent location. This movement sometimes expands the geographic range of a population or species.

dispersion The pattern of spacing among individuals within the boundaries of a population.

disruptive selection Natural selection in which individuals on both extremes of a phenotypic range survive or reproduce more successfully than do individuals with intermediate phenotypes.

distal tubule In the vertebrate kidney, the portion of a nephron that helps refine filtrate and empties it into a collecting duct.

disturbance A natural or human-caused event that changes a biological community and usually removes organisms from it. Disturbances, such as fires and storms, play a pivotal role in structuring many communities.

disulfide bridge A strong covalent bond formed when the sulfur of one cysteine monomer bonds to the sulfur of another cysteine monomer.

DNA (deoxyribonucleic acid) (dē-ok′-sē-rī′-bō-nū-klā′-ik) A double-stranded, helical nucleic acid molecule, consisting of nucleotide monomers with a deoxyribose sugar and the nitrogenous bases adenine (A), cytosine (C), guanine (G), and thymine (T); capable of being replicated and determining the inherited structure of a cell's proteins.

DNA ligase (lī′-gās) A linking enzyme essential for DNA replication; catalyzes the covalent bonding of the 3′ end of one DNA fragment (such as an Okazaki fragment) to the 5′ end of another DNA fragment (such as a growing DNA chain).

DNA methylation The presence of methyl groups on the DNA bases (usually cytosine) of plants, animals, and fungi. (The term also refers to the process of adding methyl groups to DNA bases.)

DNA microarray assay A method to detect and measure the expression of thousands of genes at one time. Tiny amounts of a large number of single-stranded DNA fragments representing different genes are fixed to a glass slide and tested for hybridization with samples of labeled cDNA.

DNA polymerase (puh-lim′-er-ās) An enzyme that catalyzes the elongation of new DNA (for example, at a replication fork) by the addition of nucleotides to the 3′ end of an existing chain. There are several different DNA polymerases; DNA polymerase III and DNA polymerase I play major roles in DNA replication in *E. coli*.

DNA replication The process by which a DNA molecule is copied; also called DNA synthesis.

domain (1) A taxonomic category above the kingdom level. The three domains are Archaea, Bacteria, and Eukarya. (2) A discrete structural and functional region of a protein.

dominant allele An allele that is fully expressed in the phenotype of a heterozygote.

dominant species A species with substantially higher abundance or biomass than other species in a community. Dominant species exert a powerful control over the occurrence and distribution of other species.

dopamine A neurotransmitter that is a catecholamine, like epinephrine and norepinephrine.

dormancy A condition typified by extremely low metabolic rate and a suspension of growth and development.

dorsal Pertaining to the top of an animal with radial or bilateral symmetry.

dorsal lip The region above the blastopore on the dorsal side of the amphibian embryo.

double bond A double covalent bond; the sharing of two pairs of valence electrons by two atoms.

double circulation A circulatory system consisting of separate pulmonary and systemic circuits, in which blood passes through the heart after completing each circuit.

double fertilization A mechanism of fertilization in angiosperms in which two sperm cells unite with two cells in the female gametophyte (embryo sac) to form the zygote and endosperm.

double helix The form of native DNA, referring to its two adjacent antiparallel polynucleotide strands wound around an imaginary axis into a spiral shape.

Down syndrome A human genetic disease usually caused by the presence of an extra chromosome 21; characterized by developmental delays and heart and other defects that are generally treatable or non-life-threatening.

Duchenne muscular dystrophy (duh-shen′) A human genetic disease caused by a sex-linked recessive allele; characterized by progressive weakening and a loss of muscle tissue.

duodenum (dū′-uh-dēn′-um) The first section of the small intestine, where chyme from the stomach mixes with digestive juices from the pancreas, liver, and gallbladder as well as from gland cells of the intestinal wall.

duplication An aberration in chromosome structure due to fusion with a fragment from a homologous chromosome, such that a portion of a chromosome is duplicated.

dynamic stability hypothesis The concept that long food chains are less stable than short chains.

dynein (dī′-nē-un) In cilia and flagella, a large motor protein extending from one microtubule doublet to the adjacent doublet. ATP hydrolysis drives changes in dynein shape that lead to bending of cilia and flagella.

E site One of a ribosome's three binding sites for tRNA during translation. The E site is the place where discharged tRNAs leave the ribosome. (E stands for exit.)

ecdysozoan Member of a group of animal phyla identified as a clade by molecular evidence. Many ecdysozoans are molting animals.

ecdysteroid A steroid hormone, secreted by the prothoracic glands, that triggers molting in arthropods.

echinoderm (i-kī′-nō-derm) A slow-moving or sessile marine deuterostome with a water vascular system and, in larvae, bilateral symmetry. Echinoderms include sea stars, brittle stars, sea urchins, feather stars, and sea cucumbers.

ecological footprint The aggregate land and water area required by a person, city, or nation to produce all of the resources it consumes and to absorb all of the wastes it generates.

ecological niche (nich) The sum of a species' use of the biotic and abiotic resources in its environment.

ecological species concept A definition of species in terms of ecological niche, the sum of how members of the species interact with the nonliving and living parts of their environment.

ecological succession Transition in the species composition of a community following a disturbance; establishment of a community in an area virtually barren of life.

ecology The study of how organisms interact with each other and their environment.

ecosystem All the organisms in a given area as well as the abiotic factors with which they interact; one or more communities and the physical environment around them.

ecosystem ecology The study of energy flow and the cycling of chemicals among the various biotic and abiotic components in an ecosystem.

ecosystem engineer An organism that influences community structure by causing physical changes in the environment.

ecosystem service A function performed by an ecosystem that directly or indirectly benefits humans.

ecotone The transition from one type of habitat or ecosystem to another, such as the transition from a forest to a grassland.

ectoderm (ek′-tō-durm) The outermost of the three primary germ layers in animal embryos; gives rise to the outer covering and, in some phyla, the nervous system, inner ear, and lens of the eye.

ectomycorrhiza (ek′-tō-mī′-kō-rī′-zuh) Association of a fungus with a plant root system in which the fungus surrounds the roots but does not cause invagination of the host (plant) cells' plasma membranes.

ectomycorrhizal fungus A symbiotic fungus that forms sheaths of hyphae over the surface of plant roots and also grows into extracellular spaces of the root cortex.

ectoparasite A parasite that feeds on the external surface of a host.

ectopic Occurring in an abnormal location.

ectoproct A sessile, colonial lophophorate; also called a bryozoan.

ectothermic Referring to organisms for which external sources provide most of the heat for temperature regulation.

Ediacaran biota (ē′-dē-uh-keh′-run bī-ō′-tuh) An early group of soft-bodied, multicellular eukaryotes known from fossils that range in age from 565 million to 550 million years old.

effective population size An estimate of the size of a population based on the numbers of females and males that successfully breed; generally smaller than the total population.

effector cell (1) A muscle cell or gland cell that performs the body's response to stimuli as directed by signals from the brain or other processing center of the nervous system. (2) A lymphocyte that has undergone clonal selection and is capable of mediating an adaptive immune response.

egg The female gamete.

egg-polarity gene A gene that helps control the orientation (polarity) of the egg; also called a maternal effect gene.

ejaculation The propulsion of sperm from the epididymis through the muscular vas deferens, ejaculatory duct, and urethra.

ejaculatory duct In mammals, the short section of the ejaculatory route formed by the convergence of the vas deferens and a duct from the seminal vesicle. The ejaculatory duct transports sperm from the vas deferens to the urethra.

electrocardiogram (ECG or EKG) A record of the electrical impulses that travel through heart muscle during the cardiac cycle.

electrochemical gradient The diffusion gradient of an ion, which is affected by both the concentration difference of an ion across a membrane (a chemical force) and the ion's tendency to move relative to the membrane potential (an electrical force).

electrogenic pump An active transport protein that generates voltage across a membrane while pumping ions.

electromagnetic receptor A receptor of electromagnetic energy, such as visible light, electricity, or magnetism.

electromagnetic spectrum The entire spectrum of electromagnetic radiation, ranging in wavelength from less than a nanometer to more than a kilometer.

electron A subatomic particle with a single negative electrical charge and a mass about 1/2,000 that of a neutron or proton. One or more electrons move around the nucleus of an atom.

electron microscope (EM) A microscope that uses magnets to focus an electron beam on or through a specimen, resulting in a practical resolution of a hundredfold greater than that of a light microscope using standard techniques. A transmission electron microscope (TEM) is used to study the internal structure of thin sections of cells. A scanning electron microscope (SEM) is used to study the fine details of cell surfaces.

electron shell An energy level of electrons at a characteristic average distance from the nucleus of an atom.

electron transport chain A sequence of electron carrier molecules (membrane proteins) that shuttle electrons down a series of redox reactions that release energy used to make ATP.

electronegativity The attraction of a given atom for the electrons of a covalent bond.

electroporation A technique to introduce recombinant DNA into cells by applying a brief electrical pulse to a solution containing the cells. The pulse creates temporary holes in the cells' plasma membranes, through which DNA can enter.

element Any substance that cannot be broken down to any other substance by chemical reactions.

elimination The fourth and final stage of food processing in animals: the passing of undigested material out of the body.

embryo sac (em′-brē-ō) The female gametophyte of angiosperms, formed from the growth and division of the megaspore into a multicellular structure that typically has eight haploid nuclei.

embryonic lethal A mutation with a phenotype leading to death of an embryo or larva.

embryophyte Alternate name for land plants that refers to their shared derived trait of multicellular, dependent embryos.

emergent properties New properties that arise with each step upward in the hierarchy of life, owing to the arrangement and interactions of parts as complexity increases.

emigration The movement of individuals out of a population.

enantiomer (en-an′-tē-ō-mer) One of two compounds that are mirror images of each other and that differ in shape due to the presence of an asymmetric carbon.

endangered species A species that is in danger of extinction throughout all or a significant portion of its range.

endemic (en-dem′-ik) Referring to a species that is confined to a specific geographic area.

endergonic reaction (en′-der-gon′-ik) A nonspontaneous chemical reaction, in which free energy is absorbed from the surroundings.

endocrine gland (en′-dō-krin) A ductless gland that secretes hormones directly into the interstitial fluid, from which they diffuse into the bloodstream.

endocrine system The internal system of communication involving hormones, the ductless glands that secrete hormones, and the molecular receptors on or in target cells that respond to hormones; functions in concert with the nervous system to effect internal regulation and maintain homeostasis.

endocytosis (en′-dō-sī-tō′-sis) Cellular uptake of biological molecules and particulate matter via formation of vesicles from the plasma membrane.

endoderm (en′-dō-durm) The innermost of the three primary germ layers in animal embryos; lines the archenteron and gives rise to the liver, pancreas, lungs, and the lining of the digestive tract in species that have these structures.

endodermis In plant roots, the innermost layer of the cortex that surrounds the vascular cylinder.

endomembrane system The collection of membranes inside and surrounding a eukaryotic cell, related either through direct physical contact or by the transfer of membranous vesicles; includes the plasma membrane, the nuclear envelope, the smooth and rough endoplasmic reticulum, the Golgi apparatus, lysosomes, vesicles, and vacuoles.

endometriosis (en′-dō-mē-trē-ō′-sis) The condition resulting from the presence of endometrial tissue outside of the uterus.

endometrium (en′-dō-mē′-trē-um) The inner lining of the uterus, which is richly supplied with blood vessels.

endoparasite A parasite that lives within a host.

endophyte A fungus that lives inside a leaf or other plant part without causing harm to the plant.

endoplasmic reticulum (ER) (en′-dō-plaz′-mik ruh-tik′-yū-lum) An extensive membranous network in eukaryotic cells, continuous with the outer nuclear membrane and composed of ribosome-studded (rough) and ribosome-free (smooth) regions.

endorphin (en-dōr′-fin) Any of several hormones produced in the brain and anterior pituitary that inhibit pain perception.

endoskeleton A hard skeleton buried within the soft tissues of an animal.

endosperm In angiosperms, a nutrient-rich tissue formed by the union of a sperm with two polar nuclei during double fertilization. The endosperm provides nourishment to the developing embryo in angiosperm seeds.

endospore A thick-coated, resistant cell produced by some bacterial cells when they are exposed to harsh conditions.

endosymbiont theory The theory that mitochondria and plastids, including chloroplasts, originated as prokaryotic cells engulfed by an ancestral eukaryotic cell. The engulfed cell and its host cell then evolved into a single organism.

endosymbiosis A process in which a unicellular organism (the "host") engulfs another cell, which lives within the host cell and ultimately becomes an organelle in the host cell. *See also* endosymbiont theory.

endothelium (en′-dō-thē′-lē-um) The simple squamous layer of cells lining the lumen of blood vessels.

endothermic Referring to organisms that are warmed by heat generated by their own metabolism. This heat usually maintains a relatively stable body temperature higher than that of the external environment.

endotoxin A toxic component of the outer membrane of certain gram-negative bacteria that is released only when the bacteria die.

energetic hypothesis The concept that the length of a food chain is limited by the inefficiency of energy transfer along the chain.

energy The capacity to cause change, especially to do work (to move matter against an opposing force).

energy coupling In cellular metabolism, the use of energy released from an exergonic reaction to drive an endergonic reaction.

enhancer A segment of eukaryotic DNA containing multiple control elements, usually located far from the gene whose transcription it regulates.

enteric division One of three divisions of the autonomic nervous system; consists of networks of neurons in the digestive tract, pancreas, and gallbladder; normally regulated by the sympathetic and parasympathetic divisions of the autonomic nervous system.

entropy A measure of disorder, or randomness.

enzymatic hydrolysis The process in digestion that splits macromolecules from food by the enzymatic addition of water.

enzyme (en′-zīm) A macromolecule serving as a catalyst, a chemical agent that increases the rate of a reaction without being consumed by the reaction. Most enzymes are proteins.

enzyme-substrate complex A temporary complex formed when an enzyme binds to its substrate molecule(s).

epicotyl (ep′-uh-kot′-ul) In an angiosperm embryo, the embryonic axis above the point of attachment of the cotyledon(s) and below the first pair of miniature leaves.

epidemic A general outbreak of a disease.

epidermis (1) The dermal tissue system of nonwoody plants, usually consisting of a single layer of tightly packed cells. (2) The outermost layer of cells in an animal.

epididymis (ep′-uh-did′-uh-mus) A coiled tubule located adjacent to the mammalian testis where sperm are stored.

epigenetic inheritance Inheritance of traits transmitted by mechanisms not directly involving the nucleotide sequence of a genome.

epinephrine (ep′-i-nef′-rin) A catecholamine that, when secreted as a hormone by the adrenal medulla, mediates "fight-or-flight" responses to short-term stresses; also released by some neurons as a neurotransmitter; also known as adrenaline.

epiphyte (ep′-uh-fīt) A plant that nourishes itself but grows on the surface of another plant for support, usually on the branches or trunks of trees.

epistasis (ep′-i-stā′-sis) A type of gene interaction in which the phenotypic expression of one gene alters that of another independently inherited gene.

epithelial tissue (ep′-uh-thē′-lē-ul) Sheets of tightly packed cells that line organs and body cavities as well as external surfaces.

epithelium An epithelial tissue.

epitope A small, accessible region of an antigen to which an antigen receptor or antibody binds; also called an antigenic determinant.

EPSP *See* excitatory postsynaptic potential.

equilibrium potential (E_{ion}) The magnitude of a cell's membrane voltage at equilibrium; calculated using the Nernst equation.

erythrocyte (eh-rith'-ruh-sīt) A blood cell that contains hemoglobin, which transports oxygen; also called a red blood cell.

erythropoietin (EPO) (eh-rith'-rō-poy'-uh-tin) A hormone that stimulates the production of erythrocytes. It is secreted by the kidney when body tissues do not receive enough oxygen.

esophagus (eh-sof'-uh-gus) A muscular tube that conducts food, by peristalsis, from the pharynx to the stomach.

essential amino acid An amino acid that an animal cannot synthesize itself and must be obtained from food in prefabricated form.

essential element A chemical element required for an organism to survive, grow, and reproduce.

essential fatty acid An unsaturated fatty acid that an animal needs but cannot make.

essential nutrient A substance that an organism cannot synthesize from any other material and therefore must absorb in preassembled form.

estradiol (es'-truh-dī'-ol) A steroid hormone that stimulates the development and maintenance of the female reproductive system and secondary sex characteristics; the major estrogen in mammals.

estrogen (es'-trō-jen) Any steroid hormone, such as estradiol, that stimulates the development and maintenance of the female reproductive system and secondary sex characteristics.

estrous cycle (es'-trus) A reproductive cycle characteristic of female mammals except humans and certain other primates, in which the nonpregnant endometrium is reabsorbed rather than shed, and sexual response occurs only during mid-cycle at estrus.

estuary The area where a freshwater stream or river merges with the ocean.

ethylene (eth'-uh-lēn) A gaseous plant hormone involved in responses to mechanical stress, programmed cell death, leaf abscission, and fruit ripening.

etiolation Plant morphological adaptations for growing in darkness.

euchromatin (yū-krō'-muh-tin) The less condensed form of eukaryotic chromatin that is available for transcription.

eudicot (yū-dī'-kot) Member of a clade that contains the vast majority of flowering plants that have two embryonic seed leaves, or cotyledons.

euglenid (yū'-glen-id) A protist, such as *Euglena* or its relatives, characterized by an anterior pocket from which one or two flagella emerge.

euglenozoan Member of a diverse clade of flagellated protists that includes predatory heterotrophs, photosynthetic autotrophs, and pathogenic parasites.

Eukarya (yū-kar'-ē-uh) The domain that includes all eukaryotic organisms.

eukaryotic cell (yū'-ker-ē-ot'-ik) A type of cell with a membrane-enclosed nucleus and membrane-enclosed organelles. Organisms with eukaryotic cells (protists, plants, fungi, and animals) are called eukaryotes.

eumetazoan (yū'-met-uh-zō'-un) Member of a clade of animals with true tissues. All animals except sponges and a few other groups are eumetazoans.

eurypterid (yur-ip'-tuh-rid) An extinct carnivorous chelicerate; also called a water scorpion.

Eustachian tube (yū-stā'-shun) The tube that connects the middle ear to the pharynx.

eutherian (yū-thēr'-ē-un) Placental mammal; mammal whose young complete their embryonic development within the uterus, joined to the mother by the placenta.

eutrophic lake (yū-trōf'-ik) A lake that has a high rate of biological productivity supported by a high rate of nutrient cycling.

eutrophication A process by which nutrients, particularly phosphorus and nitrogen, become highly concentrated in a body of water, leading to increased growth of organisms such as algae or cyanobacteria.

evaporation The process by which a liquid changes to a gas.

evaporative cooling The process in which the surface of an object becomes cooler during evaporation, a result of the molecules with the greatest kinetic energy changing from the liquid to the gaseous state.

evapotranspiration The total evaporation of water from an ecosystem, including water transpired by plants and evaporated from a landscape, usually measured in millimeters and estimated for a year.

evo-devo Evolutionary developmental biology; a field of biology that compares developmental processes of different multicellular organisms to understand how these processes have evolved and how changes can modify existing organismal features or lead to new ones.

evolution Descent with modification; the idea that living species are descendants of ancestral species that were different from the present-day ones; also defined more narrowly as the change in the genetic composition of a population from generation to generation.

evolutionary tree A branching diagram that reflects a hypothesis about evolutionary relationships among groups of organisms.

Excavata One of five supergroups of eukaryotes proposed in a current hypothesis of the evolutionary history of eukaryotes. Excavates have unique cytoskeletal features, and some species have an "excavated" feeding groove on one side of the cell body. *See also* Chromalveolata, Rhizaria, Archaeplastida, and Unikonta.

excitatory postsynaptic potential (EPSP) An electrical change (depolarization) in the membrane of a postsynaptic cell caused by the binding of an excitatory neurotransmitter from a presynaptic cell to a postsynaptic receptor; makes it more likely for a postsynaptic cell to generate an action potential.

excretion The disposal of nitrogen-containing metabolites and other waste products.

exergonic reaction (ek'-ser-gon'-ik) A spontaneous chemical reaction, in which there is a net release of free energy.

exocytosis (ek'-sō-sī-tō'-sis) The cellular secretion of biological molecules by the fusion of vesicles containing them with the plasma membrane.

exon A sequence within a primary transcript that remains in the RNA after RNA processing; also refers to the region of DNA from which this sequence was transcribed.

exoskeleton A hard encasement on the surface of an animal, such as the shell of a mollusc or the cuticle of an arthropod, that provides protection and points of attachment for muscles.

exotoxin (ek'-sō-tok'-sin) A toxic protein that is secreted by a prokaryote or other pathogen and that produces specific symptoms, even if the pathogen is no longer present.

expansin Plant enzyme that breaks the cross-links (hydrogen bonds) between cellulose microfibrils and other cell wall constituents, loosening the wall's fabric.

exponential population growth Growth of a population in an ideal, unlimited environment, represented by a J-shaped curve when population size is plotted over time.

expression vector A cloning vector that contains a highly active bacterial promoter just upstream of a restriction site where a eukaryotic gene can be inserted, allowing the gene to be expressed in a bacterial cell. Expression vectors are also available that have been genetically engineered for use in specific types of eukaryotic cells.

external fertilization The fusion of gametes that parents have discharged into the environment.

extinction vortex A downward population spiral in which inbreeding and genetic drift combine to cause a small population to shrink and, unless the spiral is reversed, become extinct.

extracellular digestion The breakdown of food in compartments that are continuous with the outside of an animal's body.

extracellular matrix (ECM) The meshwork surrounding animal cells, consisting of glycoproteins, polysaccharides, and proteoglycans synthesized and secreted by the cells.

extraembryonic membrane One of four membranes (yolk sac, amnion, chorion, and allantois) located outside the embryo that support the developing embryo in reptiles and mammals.

extreme halophile An organism that lives in a highly saline environment, such as the Great Salt Lake or the Dead Sea.

extreme thermophile An organism that thrives in hot environments (often 60–80°C or hotter).

extremophile An organism that lives in environmental conditions so extreme that few other species can survive there. Extremophiles include extreme halophiles ("salt lovers") and extreme thermophiles ("heat lovers").

F factor In bacteria, the DNA segment that confers the ability to form pili for conjugation and associated functions required for the transfer of DNA from donor to recipient. The F factor may exist as a plasmid or be integrated into the bacterial chromosome.

F plasmid The plasmid form of the F factor.

F₁ generation The first filial, hybrid (heterozygous) offspring arising from a parental (P generation) cross.

F₂ generation The offspring resulting from interbreeding (or self-pollination) of the hybrid-F₁ generation.

facilitated diffusion The passage of molecules or ions down their electrochemical gradient across a biological membrane with the assistance of specific transmembrane transport proteins, requiring no energy expenditure.

facilitation An interaction in which one species has a positive effect on the survival and reproduction of another species without the intimate association of a symbiosis.

facultative anaerobe (fak′-ul-tā′-tiv an′-uh-rōb) An organism that makes ATP by aerobic respiration if oxygen is present but that switches to anaerobic respiration or fermentation if oxygen is not present.

family In Linnaean classification, the taxonomic category above genus.

fast block to polyspermy The depolarization of the egg plasma membrane that begins within 1–3 seconds after a sperm binds to an egg membrane protein. The depolarization lasts about 1 minute and prevents additional sperm from fusing with the egg during that time.

fast-twitch fiber A muscle fiber used for rapid, powerful contractions.

fat A lipid consisting of three fatty acids linked to one glycerol molecule; also called a triacylglycerol or triglyceride.

fate map A territorial diagram of embryonic development that displays the future derivatives of individual cells and tissues.

fatty acid A carboxylic acid with a long carbon chain. Fatty acids vary in length and in the number and location of double bonds; three fatty acids linked to a glycerol molecule form a fat molecule, also known as a triacylglycerol or triglyceride.

feces (fē′-sēz) The wastes of the digestive tract.

feedback inhibition A method of metabolic control in which the end product of a metabolic pathway acts as an inhibitor of an enzyme within that pathway.

fermentation A catabolic process that makes a limited amount of ATP from glucose (or other organic molecules) without an electron transport chain and that produces a characteristic end product, such as ethyl alcohol or lactic acid.

fertilization (1) The union of haploid gametes to produce a diploid zygote. (2) The addition of mineral nutrients to the soil.

fetus (fē′-tus) A developing mammal that has all the major structures of an adult. In humans, the fetal stage lasts from the 9th week of gestation until birth.

fiber A lignified cell type that reinforces the xylem of angiosperms and functions in mechanical support; a slender, tapered sclerenchyma cell that usually occurs in bundles.

fibroblast (fī′-brō-blast) A type of cell in loose connective tissue that secretes the protein ingredients of the extracellular fibers.

fibronectin An extracellular glycoprotein secreted by animal cells that helps them attach to the extracellular matrix.

filament In an angiosperm, the stalk portion of the stamen, the pollen-producing reproductive organ of a flower.

filtrate Cell-free fluid extracted from the body fluid by the excretory system.

filtration In excretory systems, the extraction of water and small solutes, including metabolic wastes, from the body fluid.

fimbria (plural, **fimbriae**) A short, hairlike appendage of a prokaryotic cell that helps it adhere to the substrate or to other cells.

first law of thermodynamics The principle of conservation of energy: Energy can be transferred and transformed, but it cannot be created or destroyed.

fission The separation of an organism into two or more individuals of approximately equal size.

fixed action pattern In animal behavior, a sequence of unlearned acts that is essentially unchangeable and, once initiated, usually carried to completion.

flaccid (flas′-id) Limp. Lacking turgor (stiffness or firmness), as in a plant cell in surroundings where there is a tendency for water to leave the cell. (A walled cell becomes flaccid if it has a higher water potential than its surroundings, resulting in the loss of water.)

flagellum (fluh-jel′-um) (plural, **flagella**) A long cellular appendage specialized for locomotion. Like motile cilia, eukaryotic flagella have a core with nine outer doublet microtubules and two inner single microtubules (the "9 + 2" arrangement) ensheathed in an extension of the plasma membrane. Prokaryotic flagella have a different structure.

florigen A flowering signal, probably a protein, that is made in leaves under certain conditions and that travels to the shoot apical meristems, inducing them to switch from vegetative to reproductive growth.

flower In an angiosperm, a specialized shoot with up to four sets of modified leaves, bearing structures that function in sexual reproduction.

fluid feeder An animal that lives by sucking nutrient-rich fluids from another living organism.

fluid mosaic model The currently accepted model of cell membrane structure, which envisions the membrane as a mosaic of protein molecules drifting laterally in a fluid bilayer of phospholipids.

follicle (fol′-uh-kul) A microscopic structure in the ovary that contains the developing oocyte and secretes estrogens.

follicle-stimulating hormone (FSH) A tropic hormone that is produced and secreted by the anterior pituitary and that stimulates the production of eggs by the ovaries and sperm by the testes.

follicular phase That part of the ovarian cycle during which follicles are growing and oocytes maturing.

food chain The pathway along which food energy is transferred from trophic level to trophic level, beginning with producers.

food vacuole A membranous sac formed by phagocytosis of microorganisms or particles to be used as food by the cell.

food web The interconnected feeding relationships in an ecosystem.

foot (1) The portion of a bryophyte sporophyte that gathers sugars, amino acids, water, and minerals from the parent gametophyte via transfer cells. (2) One of the three main parts of a mollusc; a muscular structure usually used for movement. *See also* mantle, visceral mass.

foraging The seeking and obtaining of food.

foram (foraminiferan) An aquatic protist that secretes a hardened shell containing calcium carbonate and extends pseudopodia through pores in the shell.

forebrain One of three ancestral and embryonic regions of the vertebrate brain; develops into the thalamus, hypothalamus, and cerebrum.

fossil A preserved remnant or impression of an organism that lived in the past.

founder effect Genetic drift that occurs when a few individuals become isolated from a larger population and form a new population whose gene pool composition is not reflective of that of the original population.

fovea (fō′-vē-uh) The place on the retina at the eye's center of focus, where cones are highly concentrated.

fragmentation A means of asexual reproduction whereby a single parent breaks into parts that regenerate into whole new individuals.

frameshift mutation A mutation occurring when nucleotides are inserted in or deleted from a gene and the number inserted or deleted is not a multiple of three, resulting in the improper grouping of the subsequent nucleotides into codons.

free energy The portion of a biological system's energy that can perform work when temperature and pressure are uniform throughout the system. The change in free energy of a system (ΔG) is calculated by the equation $\Delta G = \Delta H - T\Delta S$, where ΔH is the change in enthalpy (in biological systems, equivalent to total energy), T is the absolute temperature, and ΔS is the change in entropy.

frequency-dependent selection Selection in which the fitness of a phenotype depends on how common the phenotype is in a population.

fruit A mature ovary of a flower. The fruit protects dormant seeds and often aids in their dispersal.

functional group A specific configuration of atoms commonly attached to the carbon skeletons of organic molecules and involved in chemical reactions.

G protein A GTP-binding protein that relays signals from a plasma membrane signal receptor, known as a G protein-coupled receptor, to other signal transduction proteins inside the cell.

G protein-coupled receptor (GPCR) A signal receptor protein in the plasma membrane that responds to the binding of a signaling molecule by activating a G protein. Also called a G protein-linked receptor.

G₀ phase A nondividing state occupied by cells that have left the cell cycle, sometimes reversibly.

G₁ phase The first gap, or growth phase, of the cell cycle, consisting of the portion of interphase before DNA synthesis begins.

G₂ phase The second gap, or growth phase, of the cell cycle, consisting of the portion of interphase after DNA synthesis occurs.

gallbladder An organ that stores bile and releases it as needed into the small intestine.

game theory An approach to evaluating alternative strategies in situations where the outcome of a particular strategy depends on the strategies used by other individuals.

gametangium (gam'-uh-tan'-jē-um) (plural, **gametangia**) Multicellular plant structure in which gametes are formed. Female gametangia are called archegonia, and male gametangia are called antheridia.

gamete (gam'-ēt) A haploid reproductive cell, such as an egg or sperm. Gametes unite during sexual reproduction to produce a diploid zygote.

gametogenesis The process by which gametes are produced.

gametophore (guh-mē'-tō-fōr) The mature gamete-producing structure of a moss gametophyte.

gametophyte (guh-mē'-tō-fīt) In organisms (plants and some algae) that have alternation of generations, the multicellular haploid form that produces haploid gametes by mitosis. The haploid gametes unite and develop into sporophytes.

gamma-aminobutyric acid (GABA) An amino acid that functions as a CNS neurotransmitter in the central nervous system of vertebrates.

ganglia (gang'-glē-uh) (singular, **ganglion**) Clusters (functional groups) of nerve cell bodies in a centralized nervous system.

ganglion cell A type of neuron in the retina that synapses with bipolar cells and transmits action potentials to the brain via axons in the optic nerve.

gap junction A type of intercellular junction in animal cells, consisting of proteins surrounding a pore that allows the passage of materials between cells.

gas exchange The uptake of molecular oxygen from the environment and the discharge of carbon dioxide to the environment.

gastric juice A digestive fluid secreted by the stomach.

gastrovascular cavity A central cavity with a single opening in the body of certain animals, including cnidarians and flatworms, that functions in both the digestion and distribution of nutrients.

gastrula (gas'-trū-luh) An embryonic stage in animal development encompassing the formation of three layers: ectoderm, mesoderm, and endoderm.

gastrulation (gas'-trū-lā'-shun) In animal development, a series of cell and tissue movements in which the blastula-stage embryo folds inward, producing a three-layered embryo, the gastrula.

gated channel A transmembrane protein channel that opens or closes in response to a particular stimulus.

gated ion channel A gated channel for a specific ion. The opening or closing of such channels may alter a cell's membrane potential.

gel electrophoresis (ē-lek'-trō-fōr-ē'-sis) A technique for separating nucleic acids or proteins on the basis of their size and electrical charge, both of which affect their rate of movement through an electric field in a gel made of agarose or another polymer.

gene A discrete unit of hereditary information consisting of a specific nucleotide sequence in DNA (or RNA, in some viruses).

gene annotation Analysis of genomic sequences to identify protein-coding genes and determine the function of their products.

gene cloning The production of multiple copies of a gene.

gene expression The process by which information encoded in DNA directs the synthesis of proteins or, in some cases, RNAs that are not translated into proteins and instead function as RNAs.

gene flow The transfer of alleles from one population to another, resulting from the movement of fertile individuals or their gametes.

gene pool The aggregate of all copies of every type of allele at all loci in every individual in a population. The term is also used in a more restricted sense as the aggregate of alleles for just one or a few loci in a population.

gene therapy The introduction of genes into an afflicted individual for therapeutic purposes.

gene-for-gene recognition A widespread form of plant disease resistance involving recognition of pathogen-derived molecules by the protein products of specific plant disease resistance genes.

genetic drift A process in which chance events cause unpredictable fluctuations in allele frequencies from one generation to the next. Effects of genetic drift are most pronounced in small populations.

genetic engineering The direct manipulation of genes for practical purposes.

genetic map An ordered list of genetic loci (genes or other genetic markers) along a chromosome.

genetic profile An individual's unique set of genetic markers, detected most often today by PCR or, previously, by electrophoresis and nucleic acid probes.

genetic recombination General term for the production of offspring with combinations of traits that differ from those found in either parent.

genetic variation Differences among individuals in the composition of their genes or other DNA segments.

genetically modified (GM) organism An organism that has acquired one or more genes by artificial means; also known as a transgenic organism.

genetics The scientific study of heredity and hereditary variation.

genome (jē'-nōm) The genetic material of an organism or virus; the complete complement of an organism's or virus's genes along with its noncoding nucleic acid sequences.

genome-wide association study A large-scale analysis of the genomes of many people having a certain phenotype or disease, with the aim of finding genetic markers that correlate with that phenotype or disease.

genomic imprinting A phenomenon in which expression of an allele in offspring depends on whether the allele is inherited from the male or female parent.

genomic library A set of cell clones containing all the DNA segments from a genome, each within a plasmid, BAC, or other cloning vector.

genomics (juh-nō'-miks) The study of whole sets of genes and their interactions within a species, as well as genome comparisons between species.

genotype (jē'-nō-tīp) The genetic makeup, or set of alleles, of an organism.

genus (jē'-nus) (plural, **genera**) A taxonomic category above the species level, designated by the first word of a species' two-part scientific name.

geographic variation Differences between the gene pools of geographically separate populations or population subgroups.

geologic record The division of Earth's history into time periods, grouped into three eons—Archaean, Proterozoic, and Phanerozoic—and further subdivided into eras, periods, and epochs.

germ layer One of the three main layers in a gastrula that will form the various tissues and organs of an animal body.

gestation (jes-tā'-shun) Pregnancy; the state of carrying developing young within the female reproductive tract.

gibberellin (jib'-uh-rel'-in) Any of a class of related plant hormones that stimulate growth in the stem and leaves, trigger the germination of seeds and breaking of bud dormancy, and (with auxin) stimulate fruit development.

glans The rounded structure at the tip of the clitoris or penis that is involved in sexual arousal.

glia (glial cells) Cells of the nervous system that support, regulate, and augment the functions of neurons.

global climate change Increase in temperature and change in weather patterns all around the planet, due mostly to increasing atmospheric CO_2 levels from the burning of fossil fuels. The increase in temperature, called global warming, is a major aspect of global climate change.

global ecology The study of the functioning and distribution of organisms across the biosphere and how the regional exchange of energy and materials affects them.

glomeromycete (glō'-mer-ō-mī'-sēt) Member of the fungal phylum Glomeromycota, characterized by a distinct branching form of mycorrhizae called arbuscular mycorrhizae.

glomerulus (glō-mār'-yū-lus) A ball of capillaries surrounded by Bowman's capsule in the nephron and serving as the site of filtration in the vertebrate kidney.

glucagon (glū'-kuh-gon) A hormone secreted by pancreatic alpha cells that raises blood glucose levels. It promotes glycogen breakdown and release of glucose by the liver.

glucocorticoid A steroid hormone that is secreted by the adrenal cortex and that influences glucose metabolism and immune function.

glutamate An amino acid that functions as a neurotransmitter in the central nervous system.

glyceraldehyde 3-phosphate (G3P) (glis′-er-al′-de-hīd) A three-carbon carbohydrate that is the direct product of the Calvin cycle; it is also an intermediate in glycolysis.

glycogen (glī′-kō-jen) An extensively branched glucose storage polysaccharide found in the liver and muscle of animals; the animal equivalent of starch.

glycolipid A lipid with one or more covalently attached carbohydrates.

glycolysis (glī-kol′-uh-sis) A series of reactions that ultimately splits glucose into pyruvate. Glycolysis occurs in almost all living cells, serving as the starting point for fermentation or cellular respiration.

glycoprotein A protein with one or more covalently attached carbohydrates.

glycosidic linkage A covalent bond formed between two monosaccharides by a dehydration reaction.

gnathostome (na′-thu-stōm) Member of the vertebrate subgroup possessing jaws.

golden alga A biflagellated, photosynthetic protist named for its color, which results from its yellow and brown carotenoids.

Golgi apparatus (gol′-jē) An organelle in eukaryotic cells consisting of stacks of flat membranous sacs that modify, store, and route products of the endoplasmic reticulum and synthesize some products, notably noncellulose carbohydrates.

gonads (gō′-nadz) The male and female sex organs; the gamete-producing organs in most animals.

grade A group of organisms that share the same level of organizational complexity or share a key adaptation.

graded potential In a neuron, a shift in the membrane potential that has an amplitude proportional to signal strength and that decays as it spreads.

Gram stain A staining method that distinguishes between two different kinds of bacterial cell walls; may be used to help determine medical response to an infection.

gram-negative Describing the group of bacteria that have a cell wall that is structurally more complex and contains less peptidoglycan than the cell wall of gram-positive bacteria. Gram-negative bacteria are often more toxic than gram-positive bacteria.

gram-positive Describing the group of bacteria that have a cell wall that is structurally less complex and contains more peptidoglycan than the cell wall of gram-negative bacteria. Gram-positive bacteria are usually less toxic than gram-negative bacteria.

granum (gran′-um) (plural, **grana**) A stack of membrane-bounded thylakoids in the chloroplast. Grana function in the light reactions of photosynthesis.

gravitropism (grav′-uh-trō′-pizm) A response of a plant or animal to gravity.

gray matter Regions of dendrites and clustered neuron cell bodies within the CNS.

green alga A photosynthetic protist, named for green chloroplasts that are similar in structure and pigment composition to those of land plants. Green algae are a paraphyletic group, some of whose members are more closely related to land plants than they are to other green algae.

greenhouse effect The warming of Earth due to the atmospheric accumulation of carbon dioxide and certain other gases, which absorb reflected infrared radiation and reradiate some of it back toward Earth.

gross primary production (GPP) The total primary production of an ecosystem.

ground tissue system Plant tissues that are neither vascular nor dermal, fulfilling a variety of functions, such as storage, photosynthesis, and support.

growth An irreversible increase in size or biomass.

growth factor (1) A protein that must be present in the extracellular environment (culture medium or animal body) for the growth and normal development of certain types of cells. (2) A local regulator that acts on nearby cells to stimulate cell proliferation and differentiation.

growth hormone (GH) A hormone that is produced and secreted by the anterior pituitary and that has both direct (nontropic) and tropic effects on a wide variety of tissues.

guard cells The two cells that flank the stomatal pore and regulate the opening and closing of the pore.

gustation The sense of taste.

guttation The exudation of water droplets from leaves, caused by root pressure in certain plants.

gymnosperm (jim′-nō-sperm) A vascular plant that bears naked seeds—seeds not enclosed in protective chambers.

hair cell A mechanosensory cell that alters output to the nervous system when hairlike projections on the cell surface are displaced.

half-life The amount of time it takes for 50% of a sample of a radioactive isotope to decay.

Hamilton's rule The principle that for natural selection to favor an altruistic act, the benefit to the recipient, devalued by the coefficient of relatedness, must exceed the cost to the altruist.

haploid cell (hap′-loyd) A cell containing only one set of chromosomes (*n*).

Hardy-Weinberg principle The principle that frequencies of alleles and genotypes in a population remain constant from generation to generation, provided that only Mendelian segregation and recombination of alleles are at work.

haustorium (plural, **haustoria**) (ho-stor′-ē-um, ho-stor′-ē-uh) In certain symbiotic fungi, a specialized hypha that can penetrate the tissues of host organisms.

heart A muscular pump that uses metabolic energy to elevate the hydrostatic pressure of the circulatory fluid (blood or hemolymph). The fluid then flows down a pressure gradient through the body and eventually returns to the heart.

heart attack The damage or death of cardiac muscle tissue resulting from prolonged blockage of one or more coronary arteries.

heart murmur A hissing sound that most often results from blood squirting backward through a leaky valve in the heart.

heart rate The frequency of heart contraction (in beats per minute).

heat The total amount of kinetic energy due to the random motion of atoms or molecules in a body of matter; also called thermal energy. Heat is energy in its most random form.

heat of vaporization The quantity of heat a liquid must absorb for 1 g of it to be converted from the liquid to the gaseous state.

heat-shock protein A protein that helps protect other proteins during heat stress. Heat-shock proteins are found in plants, animals, and microorganisms.

heavy chain One of the two types of polypeptide chains that make up an antibody molecule and B cell receptor; consists of a variable region, which contributes to the antigen-binding site, and a constant region.

helicase An enzyme that untwists the double helix of DNA at replication forks, separating the two strands and making them available as template strands.

helper T cell A type of T cell that, when activated, secretes cytokines that promote the response of B cells (humoral response) and cytotoxic T cells (cell-mediated response) to antigens.

hemoglobin (hē′-mō-glō′-bin) An iron-containing protein in red blood cells that reversibly binds oxygen.

hemolymph (hē′-mō-limf′) In invertebrates with an open circulatory system, the body fluid that bathes tissues.

hemophilia (hē′-muh-fil′-ē-uh) A human genetic disease caused by a sex-linked recessive allele resulting in the absence of one or more blood-clotting proteins; characterized by excessive bleeding following injury.

hepatic portal vein A large vessel that conveys nutrient-laden blood from the small intestine to the liver, which regulates the blood's nutrient content.

herbivore (hur′-bi-vōr′) An animal that mainly eats plants or algae.

herbivory An interaction in which an organism eats parts of a plant or alga.

heredity The transmission of traits from one generation to the next.

hermaphrodite (hur-maf′-ruh-dīt′) An individual that functions as both male and female in sexual reproduction by producing both sperm and eggs.

hermaphroditism (hur-maf′-rō-dī-tizm) A condition in which an individual has both female and male gonads and functions as both a male and female in sexual reproduction by producing both sperm and eggs.

heterochromatin (het′-er-ō-krō′-muh-tin) Eukaryotic chromatin that remains highly compacted during interphase and is generally not transcribed.

heterochrony (het′-uh-rok′-ruh-nē) Evolutionary change in the timing or rate of an organism's development.

heterocyst (het′-er-ō-sist) A specialized cell that engages in nitrogen fixation in some filamentous cyanobacteria; also called a *heterocyte*.

heterokaryon (het'-er-ō-kār'-ē-un) A fungal mycelium that contains two or more haploid nuclei per cell.

heteromorphic (het'-er-ō-mōr'-fik) Referring to a condition in the life cycle of plants and certain algae in which the sporophyte and gametophyte generations differ in morphology.

heterosporous (het-er-os'-pōr-us) Referring to a plant species that has two kinds of spores: microspores, which develop into male gametophytes, and megaspores, which develop into female gametophytes.

heterotroph (het'-er-ō-trōf) An organism that obtains organic food molecules by eating other organisms or substances derived from them.

heterozygote advantage Greater reproductive success of heterozygous individuals compared with homozygotes; tends to preserve variation in a gene pool.

heterozygous (het'-er-ō-zī'-gus) Having two different alleles for a given gene.

hexapod An insect or closely related wingless, six-legged arthropod.

hibernation A long-term physiological state in which metabolism decreases, the heart and respiratory system slow down, and body temperature is maintained at a lower level than normal.

high-density lipoprotein (HDL) A particle in the blood made up of thousands of cholesterol molecules and other lipids bound to a protein. HDL scavenges excess cholesterol.

hindbrain One of three ancestral and embryonic regions of the vertebrate brain; develops into the medulla oblongata, pons, and cerebellum.

histamine (his'-tuh-mēn) A substance released by mast cells that causes blood vessels to dilate and become more permeable in inflammatory and allergic responses.

histone (his'-tōn) A small protein with a high proportion of positively charged amino acids that binds to the negatively charged DNA and plays a key role in chromatin structure.

histone acetylation The attachment of acetyl groups to certain amino acids of histone proteins.

HIV (human immunodeficiency virus) The infectious agent that causes AIDS. HIV is a retrovirus.

holdfast A rootlike structure that anchors a seaweed.

holoblastic (hō'-lō-blas'-tik) Referring to a type of cleavage in which there is complete division of the egg; occurs in eggs that have little yolk (such as those of the sea urchin) or a moderate amount of yolk (such as those of the frog).

homeobox (hō'-mē-ō-boks') A 180-nucleotide sequence within homeotic genes and some other developmental genes that is widely conserved in animals. Related sequences occur in plants and yeasts.

homeostasis (hō'-mē-ō-stā'-sis) The steady-state physiological condition of the body.

homeotic gene (hō-mē-o'-tik) Any of the master regulatory genes that control placement and spatial organization of body parts in animals, plants, and fungi by controlling the developmental fate of groups of cells.

hominin (hō'-mi-nin) A member of the human branch of the evolutionary tree. Hominins include *Homo sapiens* and our ancestors, a group of extinct species that are more closely related to us than to chimpanzees.

homologous chromosomes (hō-mol'-uh-gus) A pair of chromosomes of the same length, centromere position, and staining pattern that possess genes for the same characters at corresponding loci. One homologous chromosome is inherited from the organism's father, the other from the mother. Also called homologs, or a homologous pair.

homologous structures Structures in different species that are similar because of common ancestry.

homology (hō-mol'-ō-jē) Similarity in characteristics resulting from a shared ancestry.

homoplasy (hō'-muh-play'-zē) A similar (analogous) structure or molecular sequence that has evolved independently in two species.

homosporous (hō-mos'-puh-rus) Referring to a plant species that has a single kind of spore, which typically develops into a bisexual gametophyte.

homozygous (hō'-mō-zī'-gus) Having two identical alleles for a given gene.

horizontal cell A neuron of the retina that helps integrate the information that is sent to the brain.

horizontal gene transfer The transfer of genes from one genome to another through mechanisms such as transposable elements, plasmid exchange, viral activity, and perhaps fusions of different organisms.

hormone In multicellular organisms, one of many types of secreted chemicals that are formed in specialized cells, travel in body fluids, and act on specific target cells in other parts of the body, changing the target cells' functioning. Hormones are thus important in long-distance signaling.

hornwort A small, herbaceous, nonvascular plant that is a member of the phylum Anthocerophyta.

host The larger participant in a symbiotic relationship, often providing a home and food source for the smaller symbiont.

host range The limited number of species whose cells can be infected by a particular virus.

human chorionic gonadotropin (hCG) (kōr'-ē-on'-ik gō-na'-dō-trō'-pin) A hormone secreted by the chorion that maintains the corpus luteum of the ovary during the first three months of pregnancy.

Human Genome Project An international collaborative effort to map and sequence the DNA of the entire human genome.

humoral immune response (hyū'-mer-ul) The branch of adaptive immunity that involves the activation of B cells and that leads to the production of antibodies, which defend against bacteria and viruses in body fluids.

humus (hyū'-mus) Decomposing organic material that is a component of topsoil.

Huntington's disease A human genetic disease caused by a dominant allele; characterized by uncontrollable body movements and degeneration of the nervous system; usually fatal 10 to 20 years after the onset of symptoms.

hybrid Offspring that results from the mating of individuals from two different species or from two true-breeding varieties of the same species.

hybrid zone A geographic region in which members of different species meet and mate, producing at least some offspring of mixed ancestry.

hybridization In genetics, the mating, or crossing, of two true-breeding varieties.

hydration shell The sphere of water molecules around a dissolved ion.

hydrocarbon An organic molecule consisting only of carbon and hydrogen.

hydrogen bond A type of weak chemical bond that is formed when the slightly positive hydrogen atom of a polar covalent bond in one molecule is attracted to the slightly negative atom of a polar covalent bond in another molecule or in another region of the same molecule.

hydrogen ion A single proton with a charge of 1+. The dissociation of a water molecule (H_2O) leads to the generation of a hydroxide ion (OH^-) and a hydrogen ion (H^+); in water, H^+ is not found alone but associates with a water molecule to form a hydronium ion.

hydrolysis (hī-drol'-uh-sis) A chemical reaction that breaks bonds between two molecules by the addition of water; functions in disassembly of polymers to monomers.

hydronium ion A water molecule that has an extra proton bound to it; H_3O^+, commonly represented as H^+.

hydrophilic (hī'-drō-fil'-ik) Having an affinity for water.

hydrophobic (hī'-drō-fō'-bik) Having no affinity for water; tending to coalesce and form droplets in water.

hydrophobic interaction A type of weak chemical interaction caused when molecules that do not mix with water coalesce to exclude water.

hydroponic culture A method in which plants are grown in mineral solutions rather than in soil.

hydrostatic skeleton A skeletal system composed of fluid held under pressure in a closed body compartment; the main skeleton of most cnidarians, flatworms, nematodes, and annelids.

hydroxide ion A water molecule that has lost a proton; OH^-.

hydroxyl group (hī-drok'-sil) A chemical group consisting of an oxygen atom joined to a hydrogen atom. Molecules possessing this group are soluble in water and are called alcohols.

hymen A thin membrane that partly covers the vaginal opening in the human female. The hymen is ruptured by sexual intercourse or other vigorous activity.

hyperpolarization A change in a cell's membrane potential such that the inside of the membrane becomes more negative relative to the outside. Hyperpolarization reduces the chance that a neuron will transmit a nerve impulse.

hypersensitive response A plant's localized defense response to a pathogen, involving the death of cells around the site of infection.

hypertension A disorder in which blood pressure remains abnormally high.

hypertonic Referring to a solution that, when surrounding a cell, will cause the cell to lose water.

hypha (plural, **hyphae**) (hī′-fuh, hī′-fē) One of many connected filaments that collectively make up the mycelium of a fungus.

hypocotyl (hī′-puh-cot′-ul) In an angiosperm embryo, the embryonic axis below the point of attachment of the cotyledon(s) and above the radicle.

hypothalamus (hī′-pō-thal′-uh-mus) The ventral part of the vertebrate forebrain; functions in maintaining homeostasis, especially in coordinating the endocrine and nervous systems; secretes hormones of the posterior pituitary and releasing factors that regulate the anterior pituitary.

hypothesis (hī-poth′-uh-sis) A testable explanation for a set of observations based on the available data and guided by inductive reasoning. A hypothesis is narrower in scope than a theory.

hypotonic Referring to a solution that, when surrounding a cell, will cause the cell to take up water.

imbibition The physical adsorption of water onto the internal surfaces of structures.

immigration The influx of new individuals into a population from other areas.

immune system An animal body's system of defenses against agents that cause disease.

immunization The process of generating a state of immunity by artificial means. In active immunization, also called vaccination, an inactive or weakened form of a pathogen is administered, inducing B and T cell responses and immunological memory. In passive immunization, antibodies specific for a particular microbe are administered, conferring immediate but temporary protection.

immunodeficiency A disorder in which the ability of an immune system to protect against pathogens is defective or absent.

immunoglobulin (Ig) (im′-yū-nō-glob′-yū-lin) Any of the class of proteins that function as antibodies. Immunoglobulins are divided into five major classes that differ in their distribution in the body and antigen disposal activities.

imprinting In animal behavior, the formation at a specific stage in life of a long-lasting behavioral response to a specific individual or object. *See also* genomic imprinting.

***in situ* hybridization** A technique using nucleic acid hybridization with a labeled probe to detect the location of a specific mRNA in an intact organism.

***in vitro* fertilization (IVF)** (vē′-trō) Fertilization of oocytes in laboratory containers followed by artificial implantation of the early embryo in the mother's uterus.

***in vitro* mutagenesis** A technique used to discover the function of a gene by cloning it, introducing specific changes into the cloned gene's sequence, reinserting the mutated gene into a cell, and studying the phenotype of the mutant.

inclusive fitness The total effect an individual has on proliferating its genes by producing its own offspring and by providing aid that enables other close relatives to increase production of their offspring.

incomplete dominance The situation in which the phenotype of heterozygotes is intermediate between the phenotypes of individuals homozygous for either allele.

incomplete flower A flower in which one or more of the four basic floral organs (sepals, petals, stamens, or carpels) are either absent or nonfunctional.

incomplete metamorphosis A type of development in certain insects, such as grasshoppers, in which the young (called nymphs) resemble adults but are smaller and have different body proportions. The nymph goes through a series of molts, each time looking more like an adult, until it reaches full size.

indeterminate cleavage A type of embryonic development in deuterostomes in which each cell produced by early cleavage divisions retains the capacity to develop into a complete embryo.

indeterminate growth A type of growth characteristic of plants, in which the organism continues to grow as long as it lives.

induced fit Caused by entry of the substrate, the change in shape of the active site of an enzyme so that it binds more snugly to the substrate.

inducer A specific small molecule that binds to a bacterial repressor protein and changes the repressor's shape so that it cannot bind to an operator, thus switching an operon on.

induction The process in which one group of embryonic cells influences the development of another, usually by causing changes in gene expression.

inductive reasoning A type of logic in which generalizations are based on a large number of specific observations.

inflammatory response An innate immune defense triggered by physical injury or infection of tissue involving the release of substances that promote swelling, enhance the infiltration of white blood cells, and aid in tissue repair and destruction of invading pathogens.

inflorescence A group of flowers tightly clustered together.

ingestion The first stage of food processing in animals: the act of eating.

ingroup A species or group of species whose evolutionary relationships we seek to determine.

inhibin A hormone produced in the male and female gonads that functions in part by regulating the anterior pituitary by negative feedback.

inhibitory postsynaptic potential (IPSP) An electrical change (usually hyperpolarization) in the membrane of a postsynaptic neuron caused by the binding of an inhibitory neuro-

transmitter from a presynaptic cell to a postsynaptic receptor; makes it more difficult for a postsynaptic neuron to generate an action potential.

innate behavior Animal behavior that is developmentally fixed and under strong genetic control. Innate behavior is exhibited in virtually the same form by all individuals in a population despite internal and external environmental differences during development and throughout their lifetimes.

innate immunity A form of defense common to all animals that is active immediately upon exposure to pathogens and that is the same whether or not the pathogen has been encountered previously.

inner cell mass An inner cluster of cells at one end of a mammalian blastocyst that subsequently develops into the embryo proper and some of the extraembryonic membranes.

inner ear One of three main regions of the vertebrate ear; includes the cochlea (which in turn contains the organ of Corti) and the semicircular canals.

inositol trisphosphate (IP₃) (in-ō′-suh-tol) A second messenger that functions as an intermediate between certain signaling molecules and a subsequent second messenger, Ca^{2+}, by causing a rise in cytoplasmic Ca^{2+} concentration.

inquiry The search for information and explanation, often focusing on specific questions.

insertion A mutation involving the addition of one or more nucleotide pairs to a gene.

insulin (in′-suh-lin) A hormone secreted by pancreatic beta cells that lowers blood glucose levels. It promotes the uptake of glucose by most body cells and the synthesis and storage of glycogen in the liver and also stimulates protein and fat synthesis.

integral protein A transmembrane protein with hydrophobic regions that extend into and often completely span the hydrophobic interior of the membrane and with hydrophilic regions in contact with the aqueous solution on one or both sides of the membrane (or lining the channel in the case of a channel protein).

integrin In animal cells, a transmembrane receptor protein with two subunits that interconnects the extracellular matrix and the cytoskeleton.

integument (in-teg′-yū-ment) Layer of sporophyte tissue that contributes to the structure of an ovule of a seed plant.

integumentary system The outer covering of a mammal's body, including skin, hair, and nails, claws, or hooves.

intercalated disk (in-ter′-kuh-lā′-ted) A specialized junction between cardiac muscle cells that provides direct electrical coupling between the cells.

interferon (in′-ter-fēr′-on) A protein that has antiviral or immune regulatory functions. Interferon-α and interferon-β, secreted by virus-infected cells, help nearby cells resist viral infection; interferon-γ, secreted by T cells, helps activate macrophages.

intermediate disturbance hypothesis The concept that moderate levels of disturbance can foster greater species diversity than low or high levels of disturbance.

intermediate filament A component of the cytoskeleton that includes filaments intermediate in size between microtubules and microfilaments.

internal fertilization The fusion of eggs and sperm within the female reproductive tract. The sperm are typically deposited in or near the tract.

interneuron An association neuron; a nerve cell within the central nervous system that forms synapses with sensory and/or motor neurons and integrates sensory input and motor output.

internode A segment of a plant stem between the points where leaves are attached.

interphase The period in the cell cycle when the cell is not dividing. During interphase, cellular metabolic activity is high, chromosomes and organelles are duplicated, and cell size may increase. Interphase often accounts for about 90% of the cell cycle.

intersexual selection Selection whereby individuals of one sex (usually females) are choosy in selecting their mates from individuals of the other sex; also called mate choice.

interspecific competition Competition for resources between individuals of two or more species when resources are in short supply.

interspecific interaction A relationship between individuals of two or more species in a community.

interstitial fluid The fluid filling the spaces between cells in most animals.

intertidal zone The shallow zone of the ocean adjacent to land and between the high- and low-tide lines.

intracytoplasmic sperm injection (ICSI) The fertilization of an egg in the laboratory by the direct injection of a single sperm.

intrasexual selection Selection in which there is direct competition among individuals of one sex for mates of the opposite sex.

introduced species A species moved by humans, either intentionally or accidentally, from its native location to a new geographic region; also called non-native or exotic species.

intron (in′-tron) A noncoding, intervening sequence within a primary transcript that is removed from the transcript during RNA processing; also refers to the region of DNA from which this sequence was transcribed.

invasive species A species, often introduced by humans, that takes hold outside its native range.

inversion An aberration in chromosome structure resulting from reattachment of a chromosomal fragment in a reverse orientation to the chromosome from which it originated.

invertebrate An animal without a backbone. Invertebrates make up 95% of animal species.

ion (ī′-on) An atom or group of atoms that has gained or lost one or more electrons, thus acquiring a charge.

ion channel A transmembrane protein channel that allows a specific ion to diffuse across the membrane down its concentration or electrochemical gradient.

ionic bond (ī-on′-ik) A chemical bond resulting from the attraction between oppositely charged ions.

ionic compound A compound resulting from the formation of an ionic bond; also called a salt.

IPSP *See* inhibitory postsynaptic potential.

iris The colored part of the vertebrate eye, formed by the anterior portion of the choroid.

isomer (ī′-sō-mer) One of several compounds with the same molecular formula but different structures and therefore different properties. The three types of isomers are structural isomers, *cis-trans* isomers, and enantiomers.

isomorphic Referring to alternating generations in plants and certain algae in which the sporophytes and gametophytes look alike, although they differ in chromosome number.

isopod A member of one of the largest groups of crustaceans, which includes terrestrial, freshwater, and marine species. Among the terrestrial isopods are the pill bugs, or wood lice.

isotonic (ī-sō-ton′-ik) Referring to a solution that, when surrounding a cell, causes no net movement of water into or out of the cell.

isotope (ī′-sō-tōp′) One of several atomic forms of an element, each with the same number of protons but a different number of neutrons, thus differing in atomic mass.

iteroparity Reproduction in which adults produce offspring over many years; also known as repeated reproduction.

joule (J) A unit of energy: 1 J = 0.239 cal; 1 cal = 4.184 J.

juxtaglomerular apparatus (JGA) (juks′-tuh-gluh-mār′-yū-ler) A specialized tissue in nephrons that releases the enzyme renin in response to a drop in blood pressure or volume.

juxtamedullary nephron In mammals and birds, a nephron with a loop of Henle that extends far into the renal medulla.

karyogamy (kār′-ē-og′-uh-mē) In fungi, the fusion of haploid nuclei contributed by the two parents; occurs as one stage of sexual reproduction, preceded by plasmogamy.

karyotype (kār′-ē-ō-tīp) A display of the chromosome pairs of a cell arranged by size and shape.

keystone species A species that is not necessarily abundant in a community yet exerts strong control on community structure by the nature of its ecological role or niche.

kidney In vertebrates, one of a pair of excretory organs where blood filtrate is formed and processed into urine.

kilocalorie (kcal) A thousand calories; the amount of heat energy required to raise the temperature of 1 kg of water by 1°C.

kin selection Natural selection that favors altruistic behavior by enhancing the reproductive success of relatives.

kinetic energy (kuh-net′-ik) The energy associated with the relative motion of objects. Moving matter can perform work by imparting motion to other matter.

kinetochore (kuh-net′-uh-kōr) A structure of proteins attached to the centromere that links each sister chromatid to the mitotic spindle.

kinetoplastid A protist, such as a trypanosome, that has a single large mitochondrion that houses an organized mass of DNA.

kingdom A taxonomic category, the second broadest after domain.

K-selection Selection for life history traits that are sensitive to population density; also called density-dependent selection.

labia majora A pair of thick, fatty ridges that encloses and protects the rest of the vulva.

labia minora A pair of slender skin folds that surrounds the openings of the vagina and urethra.

labor A series of strong, rhythmic contractions of the uterus that expels a baby out of the uterus and vagina during childbirth.

lactation The continued production of milk from the mammary glands.

lacteal (lak′-tē-ul) A tiny lymph vessel extending into the core of an intestinal villus and serving as the destination for absorbed chylomicrons.

lactic acid fermentation Glycolysis followed by the reduction of pyruvate to lactate, regenerating NAD^+ with no release of carbon dioxide.

lagging strand A discontinuously synthesized DNA strand that elongates by means of Okazaki fragments, each synthesized in a $5' \rightarrow 3'$ direction away from the replication fork.

lancelet Member of the clade Cephalochordata, small blade-shaped marine chordates that lack a backbone.

landscape An area containing several different ecosystems linked by exchanges of energy, materials, and organisms.

landscape ecology The study of how the spatial arrangement of habitat types affects the distribution and abundance of organisms and ecosystem processes.

large intestine The portion of the vertebrate alimentary canal between the small intestine and the anus; functions mainly in water absorption and the formation of feces.

larva (lar′-vuh) (plural, **larvae**) A free-living, sexually immature form in some animal life cycles that may differ from the adult animal in morphology, nutrition, and habitat.

larynx (lār′-inks) The portion of the respiratory tract containing the vocal cords; also called the voice box.

lateral geniculate nucleus One of a pair of structures in the brain that are the destination for most of the ganglion cell axons that form the optic nerves.

lateral inhibition A process that sharpens the edges and enhances the contrast of a perceived image by inhibiting receptors lateral to those that have responded to light.

lateral line system A mechanoreceptor system consisting of a series of pores and receptor units along the sides of the body in fishes and aquatic amphibians; detects water movements made by the animal itself and by other moving objects.

lateral meristem (mār′-uh-stem) A meristem that thickens the roots and shoots of woody plants. The vascular cambium and cork cambium are lateral meristems.

lateral root A root that arises from the pericycle of an established root.

lateralization Segregation of functions in the cortex of the left and right cerebral hemispheres.

law of conservation of mass A physical law stating that matter can change form but cannot be created or destroyed. In a closed system, the mass of the system is constant.

law of independent assortment Mendel's second law, stating that each pair of alleles segregates, or assorts, independently of each other pair during gamete formation; applies when genes for two characters are located on different pairs of homologous chromosomes or when they are far enough apart on the same chromosome to behave as though they are on different chromosomes.

law of segregation Mendel's first law, stating that the two alleles in a pair segregate (separate from each other) into different gametes during gamete formation.

leading strand The new complementary DNA strand synthesized continuously along the template strand toward the replication fork in the mandatory $5' \rightarrow 3'$ direction.

leaf The main photosynthetic organ of vascular plants.

leaf primordium A finger-like projection along the flank of a shoot apical meristem, from which a leaf arises.

learning The modification of behavior based on specific experiences.

lens The structure in an eye that focuses light rays onto the photoreceptors.

lenticel (len'-ti-sel) A small raised area in the bark of stems and roots that enables gas exchange between living cells and the outside air.

lepidosaur (leh-pid'-uh-sōr) Member of the reptilian group that includes lizards, snakes, and two species of New Zealand animals called tuataras.

leptin A hormone produced by adipose (fat) cells that acts as a satiety factor in regulating appetite.

leukocyte (lū'-kō-sīt') A blood cell that functions in fighting infections; also called a white blood cell.

Leydig cell (lī'-dig) A cell that produces testosterone and other androgens and is located between the seminiferous tubules of the testes.

lichen The mutualistic association between a fungus and a photosynthetic alga or cyanobacterium.

life cycle The generation-to-generation sequence of stages in the reproductive history of an organism.

life history The traits that affect an organism's schedule of reproduction and survival.

life table An age-specific summary of the survival pattern of a population.

ligament A fibrous connective tissue that joins bones together at joints.

ligand (lig'-und) A molecule that binds specifically to another molecule, usually a larger one.

ligand-gated ion channel A transmembrane protein containing a pore that opens or closes as it changes shape in response to a signaling molecule (ligand), allowing or blocking the flow of specific ions; also called an ionotropic receptor.

light chain One of the two types of polypeptide chains that make up an antibody molecule and B cell receptor; consists of a variable region, which contributes to the antigen-binding site, and a constant region.

light microscope (LM) An optical instrument with lenses that refract (bend) visible light to magnify images of specimens.

light reactions The first of two major stages in photosynthesis (preceding the Calvin cycle). These reactions, which occur on the thylakoid membranes of the chloroplast or on membranes of certain prokaryotes, convert solar energy to the chemical energy of ATP and NADPH, releasing oxygen in the process.

light-harvesting complex A complex of proteins associated with pigment molecules (including chlorophyll *a*, chlorophyll *b*, and carotenoids) that captures light energy and transfers it to reaction-center pigments in a photosystem.

lignin (lig'-nin) A hard material embedded in the cellulose matrix of vascular plant cell walls that provides structural support in terrestrial species.

limiting nutrient An element that must be added for production to increase in a particular area.

limnetic zone In a lake, the well-lit, open surface waters far from shore.

linear electron flow A route of electron flow during the light reactions of photosynthesis that involves both photosystems (I and II) and produces ATP, NADPH, and O_2. The net electron flow is from H_2O to $NADP^+$.

linkage map A genetic map based on the frequencies of recombination between markers during crossing over of homologous chromosomes.

linked genes Genes located close enough together on a chromosome that they tend to be inherited together.

lipid (lip'-id) Any of a group of large biological molecules, including fats, phospholipids, and steroids, that mix poorly, if at all, with water.

littoral zone In a lake, the shallow, well-lit waters close to shore.

liver A large internal organ in vertebrates that performs diverse functions, such as producing bile, maintaining blood glucose level, and detoxifying poisonous chemicals in the blood.

liverwort A small, herbaceous, nonvascular plant that is a member of the phylum Hepatophyta.

loam The most fertile soil type, made up of roughly equal amounts of sand, silt, and clay.

lobe-fin Member of the vertebrate clade Sarcopterygii, osteichthyans with rod-shaped muscular fins, including coelacanths, lungfishes, and tetrapods.

local regulator A secreted molecule that influences cells near where it is secreted.

locomotion Active motion from place to place.

locus (lō'-kus) (plural, **loci**) A specific place along the length of a chromosome where a given gene is located.

logistic population growth Population growth that levels off as population size approaches carrying capacity.

long-day plant A plant that flowers (usually in late spring or early summer) only when the light period is longer than a critical length.

long-term memory The ability to hold, associate, and recall information over one's lifetime.

long-term potentiation (LTP) An enhanced responsiveness to an action potential (nerve signal) by a receiving neuron.

loop of Henle The hairpin turn, with a descending and ascending limb, between the proximal and distal tubules of the vertebrate kidney; functions in water and salt reabsorption.

lophophore (lof'-uh-fōr) In some lophotrochozoan animals, including brachiopods, a crown of ciliated tentacles that surround the mouth and function in feeding.

lophotrochozoan Member of a group of animal phyla identified as a clade by molecular evidence. Lophotrochozoans include organisms that have lophophores or trochophore larvae.

low-density lipoprotein (LDL) A particle in the blood made up of thousands of cholesterol molecules and other lipids bound to a protein. LDL transports cholesterol from the liver for incorporation into cell membranes.

lung An infolded respiratory surface of a terrestrial vertebrate, land snail, or spider that connects to the atmosphere by narrow tubes.

luteal phase That portion of the ovarian cycle during which endocrine cells of the corpus luteum secrete female hormones.

luteinizing hormone (LH) (lū'-tē-uh-nī'-zing) A tropic hormone that is produced and secreted by the anterior pituitary and that stimulates ovulation in females and androgen production in males.

lycophyte (lī'-kuh-fīt) An informal name for a member of the phylum Lycophyta, which includes club mosses, spike mosses, and quillworts.

lymph The colorless fluid, derived from interstitial fluid, in the lymphatic system of vertebrates.

lymph node An organ located along a lymph vessel. Lymph nodes filter lymph and contain cells that attack viruses and bacteria.

lymphatic system A system of vessels and nodes, separate from the circulatory system, that returns fluid, proteins, and cells to the blood.

lymphocyte A type of white blood cell that mediates immune responses. The two main classes are B cells and T cells.

lysogenic cycle (lī'-sō-jen'-ik) A type of phage replicative cycle in which the viral genome becomes incorporated into the bacterial host chromosome as a prophage, is replicated along with the chromosome, and does not kill the host.

lysosome (lī'-suh-sōm) A membrane-enclosed sac of hydrolytic enzymes found in the cytoplasm of animal cells and some protists.

lysozyme (lī'-sō-zīm) An enzyme that destroys bacterial cell walls; in mammals, found in sweat, tears, and saliva.

lytic cycle (lit'-ik) A type of phage replicative cycle resulting in the release of new phages by lysis (and death) of the host cell.

macroclimate Large-scale patterns in climate; the climate of an entire region.

macroevolution Evolutionary change above the species level. Examples of macroevolutionary change include the origin of a new group of organisms through a series of speciation events and the impact of mass extinctions on the diversity of life and its subsequent recovery.

macromolecule A giant molecule formed by the joining of smaller molecules, usually by a dehydration reaction. Polysaccharides, proteins, and nucleic acids are macromolecules.

macronutrient An essential element that an organism must obtain in relatively large amounts. *See also* micronutrient.

macrophage (mak'-rō-fāj) A phagocytic cell present in many tissues that functions in innate immunity by destroying microbes and in acquired immunity as an antigen-presenting cell.

magnoliid Member of the angiosperm clade that is most closely related to the combined eudicot and monocot clades. Extant examples are magnolias, laurels, and black pepper plants.

major depressive disorder A mood disorder characterized by feelings of sadness, lack of self-worth, emptiness, or loss of interest in nearly all things.

major histocompatibility complex (MHC) molecule A host protein that functions in antigen presentation. Foreign MHC molecules on transplanted tissue can trigger T cell responses that may lead to rejection of the transplant.

malignant tumor A cancerous tumor containing cells that have significant genetic and cellular changes and are capable of invading and surviving in new sites. Malignant tumors can impair the functions of one or more organs.

Malpighian tubule (mal-pig'-ē-un) A unique excretory organ of insects that empties into the digestive tract, removes nitrogenous wastes from the hemolymph, and functions in osmoregulation.

mammal Member of the class Mammalia, amniotes that have hair and mammary glands (glands that produce milk).

mammary gland An exocrine gland that secretes milk to nourish the young. Mammary glands are characteristic of mammals.

mandible One of a pair of jaw-like feeding appendages found in myriapods, hexapods, and crustaceans.

mantle One of the three main parts of a mollusc; a fold of tissue that drapes over the mollusc's visceral mass and may secrete a shell. *See also* foot, visceral mass.

mantle cavity A water-filled chamber that houses the gills, anus, and excretory pores of a mollusc.

map unit A unit of measurement of the distance between genes. One map unit is equivalent to a 1% recombination frequency.

marine benthic zone The ocean floor.

mark-recapture method A sampling technique used to estimate the size of animal populations.

marsupial (mar-sū'-pē-ul) A mammal, such as a koala, kangaroo, or opossum, whose young complete their embryonic development inside a maternal pouch called the marsupium.

mass extinction The elimination of a large number of species throughout Earth, the result of global environmental changes.

mass number The sum of the number of protons and neutrons in an atom's nucleus.

mast cell A vertebrate body cell that produces histamine and other molecules that trigger inflammation in response to infection and in allergic reactions.

mate-choice copying Behavior in which individuals in a population copy the mate choice of others, apparently as a result of social learning.

maternal effect gene A gene that, when mutant in the mother, results in a mutant phenotype in the offspring, regardless of the offspring's genotype. Maternal effect genes, also called egg-polarity genes, were first identified in *Drosophila melanogaster*.

matter Anything that takes up space and has mass.

maximum likelihood As applied to molecular systematics, a principle that states that when considering multiple phylogenetic hypotheses, one should take into account the hypothesis that reflects the most likely sequence of evolutionary events, given certain rules about how DNA changes over time.

maximum parsimony A principle that states that when considering multiple explanations for an observation, one should first investigate the simplest explanation that is consistent with the facts.

mechanoreceptor A sensory receptor that detects physical deformation in the body's environment associated with pressure, touch, stretch, motion, or sound.

medulla oblongata (meh-dul'-uh ōb'-long-go'-tuh) The lowest part of the vertebrate brain, commonly called the medulla; a swelling of the hindbrain anterior to the spinal cord that controls autonomic, homeostatic functions, including breathing, heart and blood vessel activity, swallowing, digestion, and vomiting.

Medusa (plural, **medusae**) (muh-dū'-suh) The floating, flattened, mouth-down version of the cnidarian body plan. The alternate form is the polyp.

megapascal (MPa) (meg'-uh-pas-kal') A unit of pressure equivalent to about 10 atmospheres of pressure.

megaphyll (meh'-guh-fil) A leaf with a highly branched vascular system, characteristic of the vast majority of vascular plants. *See* microphyll.

megaspore A spore from a heterosporous plant species that develops into a female gametophyte.

meiosis (mī-ō'-sis) A modified type of cell division in sexually reproducing organisms consisting of two rounds of cell division but only one round of DNA replication. It results in cells with half the number of chromosome sets as the original cell.

meiosis I The first division of a two-stage process of cell division in sexually reproducing organisms that results in cells with half the number of chromosome sets as the original cell.

meiosis II The second division of a two-stage process of cell division in sexually reproducing organisms that results in cells with half the number of chromosome sets as the original cell.

melanocyte-stimulating hormone (MSH) A hormone produced and secreted by the anterior pituitary with multiple activities, including regulating the behavior of pigment-containing cells in the skin of some vertebrates.

melatonin A hormone that is secreted by the pineal gland and that is involved in the regulation of biological rhythms and sleep.

membrane potential The difference in electrical charge (voltage) across a cell's plasma membrane due to the differential distribution of ions. Membrane potential affects the activity of excitable cells and the transmembrane movement of all charged substances.

memory cell One of a clone of long-lived lymphocytes, formed during the primary immune response, that remains in a lymphoid organ until activated by exposure to the same antigen that triggered its formation. Activated memory cells mount the secondary immune response.

menopause The cessation of ovulation and menstruation marking the end of a human female's reproductive years.

menstrual cycle (men'-strū-ul) In humans and certain other primates, a type of reproductive cycle in which the nonpregnant endometrium is shed through the cervix into the vagina; also called the uterine cycle.

menstrual flow phase That portion of the uterine (menstrual) cycle when menstrual bleeding occurs.

menstruation The shedding of portions of the endometrium during a uterine (menstrual) cycle.

meristem (mār'-uh-stem) Plant tissue that remains embryonic as long as the plant lives, allowing for indeterminate growth.

meristem identity gene A plant gene that promotes the switch from vegetative growth to flowering.

meroblastic (mār'-ō-blas'-tik) Referring to a type of cleavage in which there is incomplete division of a yolk-rich egg, characteristic of avian development.

mesoderm (mez'-ō-derm) The middle primary germ layer in a triploblastic animal embryo; develops into the notochord, the lining of the coelom, muscles, skeleton, gonads, kidneys, and most of the circulatory system in species that have these structures.

mesohyl (mez'-ō-hīl) A gelatinous region between the two layers of cells of a sponge.

mesophyll (mez'-ō-fil) Leaf cells specialized for photosynthesis. In C_3 and CAM plants, mesophyll cells are located between the upper and lower epidermis; in C_4 plants, they are located between the bundle-sheath cells and the epidermis.

messenger RNA (mRNA) A type of RNA, synthesized using a DNA template, that attaches to ribosomes in the cytoplasm and specifies the primary structure of a protein. (In eukaryotes, the primary RNA transcript must undergo RNA processing to become mRNA.)

metabolic pathway A series of chemical reactions that either builds a complex molecule (anabolic pathway) or breaks down a complex molecule to simpler molecules (catabolic pathway).

metabolic rate The total amount of energy an animal uses in a unit of time.

metabolism (muh-tab´-uh-lizm) The totality of an organism's chemical reactions, consisting of catabolic and anabolic pathways, which manage the material and energy resources of the organism.

metagenomics The collection and sequencing of DNA from a group of species, usually an environmental sample of microorganisms. Computer software sorts partial sequences and assembles them into genome sequences of individual species making up the sample.

metamorphosis (met´-uh-môr´-fuh-sis) A developmental transformation that turns an animal larva into either an adult or an adult-like stage that is not yet sexually mature.

metanephridium (met´-uh-nuh-frid´-ē-um) (plural, **metanephridia**) An excretory organ found in many invertebrates that typically consists of tubules connecting ciliated internal openings to external openings.

metaphase The third stage of mitosis, in which the spindle is complete and the chromosomes, attached to microtubules at their kinetochores, are all aligned at the metaphase plate.

metaphase plate An imaginary structure located at a plane midway between the two poles of a cell in metaphase on which the centromeres of all the duplicated chromosomes are located.

metapopulation A group of spatially separated populations of one species that interact through immigration and emigration.

metastasis (muh-tas´-tuh-sis) The spread of cancer cells to locations distant from their original site.

methanogen (meth-an´-ō-jen) An organism that produces methane as a waste product of the way it obtains energy. All known methanogens are in domain Archaea.

methyl group A chemical group consisting of a carbon bonded to three hydrogen atoms. The methyl group may be attached to a carbon or to a different atom.

microclimate Climate patterns on a very fine scale, such as the specific climatic conditions underneath a log.

microevolution Evolutionary change below the species level; change in the allele frequencies in a population over generations.

microfilament A cable composed of actin proteins in the cytoplasm of almost every eukaryotic cell, making up part of the cytoskeleton and acting alone or with myosin to cause cell contraction; also known as an actin filament.

micronutrient An essential element that an organism needs in very small amounts. *See also* macronutrient.

microphyll (mī´-krō-fil) In lycophytes, a small leaf with a single unbranched vein. *See* megaphyll.

micropyle A pore in the integuments of an ovule.

microRNA (miRNA) A small, single-stranded RNA molecule, generated from a hairpin structure on a precursor RNA transcribed from a particular gene. The miRNA associates with one or more proteins in a complex that can degrade or prevent translation of an mRNA with a complementary sequence.

microspore A spore from a heterosporous plant species that develops into a male gametophyte.

microtubule A hollow rod composed of tubulin proteins that makes up part of the cytoskeleton in all eukaryotic cells and is found in cilia and flagella.

microvillus (plural, **microvilli**) One of many fine, finger-like projections of the epithelial cells in the lumen of the small intestine that increase its surface area.

midbrain One of three ancestral and embryonic regions of the vertebrate brain; develops into sensory integrating and relay centers that send sensory information to the cerebrum.

middle ear One of three main regions of the vertebrate ear; in mammals, a chamber containing three small bones (the malleus, incus, and stapes) that convey vibrations from the eardrum to the oval window.

middle lamella (luh-mel´-uh) In plants, a thin layer of adhesive extracellular material, primarily pectins, found between the primary walls of adjacent young cells.

migration A regular, long-distance change in location.

mineral In nutrition, a simple nutrient that is inorganic and therefore cannot be synthesized in the body.

mineralocorticoid A steroid hormone secreted by the adrenal cortex that regulates salt and water homeostasis.

minimum viable population (MVP) The smallest population size at which a species is able to sustain its numbers and survive.

mismatch repair The cellular process that uses specific enzymes to remove and replace incorrectly paired nucleotides.

missense mutation A nucleotide-pair substitution that results in a codon that codes for a different amino acid.

mitochondrial matrix The compartment of the mitochondrion enclosed by the inner membrane and containing enzymes and substrates for the citric acid cycle, as well as ribosomes and DNA.

mitochondrion (mī´-tō-kon´-drē-un) (plural, **mitochondria**) An organelle in eukaryotic cells that serves as the site of cellular respiration; uses oxygen to break down organic molecules and synthesize ATP.

mitosis (mī-tō´-sis) A process of nuclear division in eukaryotic cells conventionally divided into five stages: prophase, prometaphase, metaphase, anaphase, and telophase. Mitosis conserves chromosome number by allocating replicated chromosomes equally to each of the daughter nuclei.

mitotic (M) phase The phase of the cell cycle that includes mitosis and cytokinesis.

mitotic spindle An assemblage of microtubules and associated proteins that is involved in the movement of chromosomes during mitosis.

mixotroph An organism that is capable of both photosynthesis and heterotrophy.

model organism A particular species chosen for research into broad biological principles because it is representative of a larger group and usually easy to grow in a lab.

molarity A common measure of solute concentration, referring to the number of moles of solute per liter of solution.

mold Informal term for a fungus that grows as a filamentous fungus, producing haploid spores by mitosis and forming a visible mycelium.

mole (mol) The number of grams of a substance that equals its molecular weight in daltons and contains Avogadro's number of molecules.

molecular clock A method for estimating the time required for a given amount of evolutionary change, based on the observation that some regions of genomes evolve at constant rates.

molecular mass The sum of the masses of all the atoms in a molecule; sometimes called molecular weight.

molecular systematics A scientific discipline that uses nucleic acids or other molecules to infer evolutionary relationships between different species.

molecule Two or more atoms held together by covalent bonds.

molting A process in ecdysozoans in which the exoskeleton is shed at intervals, allowing growth by the production of a larger exoskeleton.

monoclonal antibody (mon´-ō-klōn´-ul) Any of a preparation of antibodies that have been produced by a single clone of cultured cells and thus are all specific for the same epitope.

monocot Member of a clade consisting of flowering plants that have one embryonic seed leaf, or cotyledon.

monogamous (muh-nog´-uh-mus) Referring to a type of relationship in which one male mates with just one female.

monohybrid An organism that is heterozygous with respect to a single gene of interest. All the offspring from a cross between parents homozygous for different alleles are monohybrids. For example, parents of genotypes *AA* and *aa* produce a monohybrid of genotype *Aa*.

monohybrid cross A cross between two organisms that are heterozygous for the character being followed (or the self-pollination of a heterozygous plant).

monomer (mon´-uh-mer) The subunit that serves as the building block of a polymer.

monophyletic (mon'-ō-fī-let'-ik) Pertaining to a group of taxa that consists of a common ancestor and all of its descendants. A monophyletic taxon is equivalent to a clade.

monosaccharide (mon'-ō-sak'-uh-rīd) The simplest carbohydrate, active alone or serving as a monomer for disaccharides and polysaccharides. Also known as simple sugars, monosaccharides have molecular formulas that are generally some multiple of CH_2O.

monosomic Referring to a diploid cell that has only one copy of a particular chromosome instead of the normal two.

monotreme An egg-laying mammal, such as a platypus or echidna. Like all mammals, monotremes have hair and produce milk, but they lack nipples.

morphogen A substance, such as Bicoid protein in *Drosophila*, that provides positional information in the form of a concentration gradient along an embryonic axis.

morphogenesis (mōr'-fō-jen'-uh-sis) The cellular and tissue-based processes by which an animal body takes shape.

morphological species concept A definition of species in terms of measurable anatomical criteria.

moss A small, herbaceous, nonvascular plant that is a member of the phylum Bryophyta.

motor neuron A nerve cell that transmits signals from the brain or spinal cord to muscles or glands.

motor protein A protein that interacts with cytoskeletal elements and other cell components, producing movement of the whole cell or parts of the cell.

motor system An efferent branch of the vertebrate peripheral nervous system composed of motor neurons that carry signals to skeletal muscles in response to external stimuli.

motor unit A single motor neuron and all the muscle fibers it controls.

movement corridor A series of small clumps or a narrow strip of quality habitat (usable by organisms) that connects otherwise isolated patches of quality habitat.

MPF Maturation-promoting factor (or M-phase-promoting factor); a protein complex required for a cell to progress from late interphase to mitosis. The active form consists of cyclin and a protein kinase.

mucus A viscous and slippery mixture of glycoproteins, cells, salts, and water that moistens and protects the membranes lining body cavities that open to the exterior.

Müllerian mimicry (myū-lār'-ē-un) Reciprocal mimicry by two unpalatable species.

multifactorial Referring to a phenotypic character that is influenced by multiple genes and environmental factors.

multigene family A collection of genes with similar or identical sequences, presumably of common origin.

multiple fruit A fruit derived from an entire inflorescence.

multiplication rule A rule of probability stating that the probability of two or more independent

events occurring together can be determined by multiplying their individual probabilities.

muscle tissue Tissue consisting of long muscle cells that can contract, either on its own or when stimulated by nerve impulses.

mutagen (myū'-tuh-jen) A chemical or physical agent that interacts with DNA and can cause a mutation.

mutation (myū-tā'-shun) A change in the nucleotide sequence of an organism's DNA or in the DNA or RNA of a virus.

mutualism (myū'-chū-ul-izm) A symbiotic relationship in which both participants benefit.

mycelium (mī-sē'-lē-um) The densely branched network of hyphae in a fungus.

mycorrhiza (mī'-kō-rī'-zuh) (plural, **mycorrhizae**) A mutualistic association of plant roots and fungus.

mycosis (mī-kō'-sis) General term for a fungal infection.

myelin sheath (mī'-uh-lin) Wrapped around the axon of a neuron, an insulating coat of cell membranes from Schwann cells or oligodendrocytes. It is interrupted by nodes of Ranvier, where action potentials are generated.

myofibril (mī'-ō-fī'-bril) A longitudinal bundle in a muscle cell (fiber) that contains thin filaments of actin and regulatory proteins and thick filaments of myosin.

myoglobin (mī'-uh-glō'-bin) An oxygen-storing, pigmented protein in muscle cells.

myosin (mī'-uh-sin) A type of motor protein that associates into filaments that interact with actin filaments to cause cell contraction.

myotonia (mī'-uh-tō'-nī-uh) Increased muscle tension, characteristic of sexual arousal in certain human tissues.

myriapod (mir'-ē-uh-pod') A terrestrial arthropod with many body segments and one or two pairs of legs per segment. Millipedes and centipedes are the two major groups of living myriapods.

NAD⁺ Nicotinamide adenine dinucleotide, a coenzyme that cycles easily between oxidized (NAD^+) and reduced (NADH) states, thus acting as an electron carrier.

NADP⁺ Nicotinamide adenine dinucleotide phosphate, an electron acceptor that, as NADPH, temporarily stores energized electrons produced during the light reactions.

natural family planning A form of contraception that relies on refraining from sexual intercourse when conception is most likely to occur; also called the rhythm method.

natural killer cell A type of white blood cell that can kill tumor cells and virus-infected cells as part of innate immunity.

natural selection A process in which individuals that have certain inherited traits tend to survive and reproduce at higher rates than other individuals *because of* those traits.

negative feedback A form of regulation in which accumulation of an end product of a process slows the process; in physiology, a primary mechanism of homeostasis, whereby a change in a variable triggers a response that counteracts the initial change.

negative pressure breathing A breathing system in which air is pulled into the lungs.

nematocyst (nem'-uh-tuh-sist') In a cnidocyte of a cnidarian, a capsule-like organelle containing a coiled thread that when discharged can penetrate the body wall of the prey.

nephron (nef'-ron) The tubular excretory unit of the vertebrate kidney.

neritic zone The shallow region of the ocean overlying the continental shelf.

nerve A fiber composed primarily of the bundled axons of PNS neurons.

nerve net A weblike system of neurons, characteristic of radially symmetrical animals, such as hydras.

nervous system The fast-acting internal system of communication involving sensory receptors, networks of nerve cells, and connections to muscles and glands that respond to nerve signals; functions in concert with the endocrine system to effect internal regulation and maintain homeostasis.

nervous tissue Tissue made up of neurons and supportive cells.

net ecosystem production (NEP) The gross primary production of an ecosystem minus the energy used by all autotrophs and heterotrophs for respiration.

net primary production (NPP) The gross primary production of an ecosystem minus the energy used by the producers for respiration.

neural crest In vertebrates, a region located along the sides of the neural tube where it pinches off from the ectoderm. Neural crest cells migrate to various parts of the embryo and form pigment cells in the skin and parts of the skull, teeth, adrenal glands, and peripheral nervous system.

neural plasticity The capacity of a nervous system to change with experience.

neural tube A tube of infolded ectodermal cells that runs along the anterior-posterior axis of a vertebrate, just dorsal to the notochord. It will give rise to the central nervous system.

neurohormone A molecule that is secreted by a neuron, travels in body fluids, and acts on specific target cells, changing their functioning.

neuron (nyūr'-on) A nerve cell; the fundamental unit of the nervous system, having structure and properties that allow it to conduct signals by taking advantage of the electrical charge across its plasma membrane.

neuropeptide A relatively short chain of amino acids that serves as a neurotransmitter.

neurotransmitter A molecule that is released from the synaptic terminal of a neuron at a chemical synapse, diffuses across the synaptic cleft, and binds to the postsynaptic cell, triggering a response.

neutral theory The hypothesis that much evolutionary change in genes and proteins has no effect on fitness and therefore is not influenced by natural selection.

neutral variation Genetic variation that does not provide a selective advantage or disadvantage.

neutron A subatomic particle having no electrical charge (electrically neutral), with a mass of about 1.7×10^{-24} g, found in the nucleus of an atom.

neutrophil The most abundant type of white blood cell. Neutrophils are phagocytic and tend to self-destruct as they destroy foreign invaders, limiting their life span to a few days.

nitric oxide (NO) A gas produced by many types of cells that functions as a local regulator and as a neurotransmitter.

nitrogen cycle The natural process by which nitrogen, either from the atmosphere or from decomposed organic material, is converted by soil bacteria to compounds assimilated by plants. This incorporated nitrogen is then taken in by other organisms and subsequently released, acted on by bacteria, and made available again to the nonliving environment.

nitrogen fixation The conversion of atmospheric nitrogen (N_2) to ammonia (NH_3). Biological nitrogen fixation is carried out by certain prokaryotes, some of which have mutualistic relationships with plants.

nociceptor (nō′-si-sep′-tur) A sensory receptor that responds to noxious or painful stimuli; also called a pain receptor.

node A point along the stem of a plant at which leaves are attached.

node of Ranvier (ron′-vē-ā′) Gap in the myelin sheath of certain axons where an action potential may be generated. In saltatory conduction, an action potential is regenerated at each node, appearing to "jump" along the axon from node to node.

nodule A swelling on the root of a legume. Nodules are composed of plant cells that contain nitrogen-fixing bacteria of the genus *Rhizobium*.

noncompetitive inhibitor A substance that reduces the activity of an enzyme by binding to a location remote from the active site, changing the enzyme's shape so that the active site no longer effectively catalyzes the conversion of substrate to product.

nondisjunction An error in meiosis or mitosis in which members of a pair of homologous chromosomes or a pair of sister chromatids fail to separate properly from each other.

nonequilibrium model A model that maintains that communities change constantly after being buffeted by disturbances.

nonpolar covalent bond A type of covalent bond in which electrons are shared equally between two atoms of similar electronegativity.

nonsense mutation A mutation that changes an amino acid codon to one of the three stop codons, resulting in a shorter and usually nonfunctional protein.

norepinephrine A catecholamine that is chemically and functionally similar to epinephrine and acts as a hormone or neurotransmitter; also known as noradrenaline.

norm of reaction The range of phenotypes produced by a single genotype, due to environmental influences.

Northern blotting A technique that enables specific nucleotide sequences to be detected in samples of mRNA. It involves gel electrophoresis of RNA molecules and their transfer to a membrane (blotting), followed by nucleic acid hybridization with a labeled probe.

northern coniferous forest A terrestrial biome characterized by long, cold winters and dominated by cone-bearing trees.

no-till agriculture A plowing technique that minimally disturbs the soil, thereby reducing soil loss.

notochord (nō′-tuh-kord′) A longitudinal, flexible rod made of tightly packed mesodermal cells that runs along the anterior-posterior axis of a chordate in the dorsal part of the body.

nuclear envelope In a eukaryotic cell, the double membrane that surrounds the nucleus, perforated with pores that regulate traffic with the cytoplasm. The outer membrane is continuous with the endoplasmic reticulum.

nuclear lamina A netlike array of protein filaments that lines the inner surface of the nuclear envelope and helps maintain the shape of the nucleus.

nucleariid Member of a group of unicellular, amoeboid protists that are more closely related to fungi than they are to other protists.

nuclease An enzyme that cuts DNA or RNA, either removing one or a few bases or hydrolyzing the DNA or RNA completely into its component nucleotides.

nucleic acid (nū-klā′-ik) A polymer (polynucleotide) consisting of many nucleotide monomers; serves as a blueprint for proteins and, through the actions of proteins, for all cellular activities. The two types are DNA and RNA.

nucleic acid hybridization The process of base pairing between a gene and a complementary sequence on another nucleic acid molecule.

nucleic acid probe In DNA technology, a labeled single-stranded nucleic acid molecule used to locate a specific nucleotide sequence in a nucleic acid sample. Molecules of the probe hydrogen-bond to the complementary sequence wherever it occurs; radioactive, fluorescent, or other labeling of the probe allows its location to be detected.

nucleoid (nū′-klē-oyd) A non-membrane-bounded region in a prokaryotic cell where the DNA is concentrated.

nucleolus (nū-klē′-ō-lus) (plural, **nucleoli**) A specialized structure in the nucleus, consisting of chromosomal regions containing ribosomal RNA (rRNA) genes along with ribosomal proteins imported from the cytoplasm; site of rRNA synthesis and ribosomal subunit assembly. *See also* ribosome.

nucleosome (nū′-klē-ō-sōm′) The basic, bead-like unit of DNA packing in eukaryotes, consisting of a segment of DNA wound around a protein core composed of two copies of each of four types of histone.

nucleotide (nū′-klē-ō-tīd′) The building block of a nucleic acid, consisting of a five-carbon sugar covalently bonded to a nitrogenous base and one or more phosphate groups.

nucleotide excision repair A repair system that removes and then correctly replaces a damaged segment of DNA using the undamaged strand as a guide.

nucleotide-pair substitution A type of point mutation in which one nucleotide in a DNA strand and its partner in the complementary strand are replaced by another pair of nucleotides.

nucleus (1) An atom's central core, containing protons and neutrons. (2) The organelle of a eukaryotic cell that contains the genetic material in the form of chromosomes, made up of chromatin. (3) A cluster of neurons.

nutrition The process by which an organism takes in and makes use of food substances.

obligate aerobe (ob′-lig-et ār′-ōb) An organism that requires oxygen for cellular respiration and cannot live without it.

obligate anaerobe (ob′-lig-et an′-uh-rōb) An organism that only carries out fermentation or anaerobic respiration. Such organisms cannot use oxygen and in fact may be poisoned by it.

ocean acidification Decreasing pH of ocean waters due to absorption of excess atmospheric CO_2 from the burning of fossil fuels.

oceanic pelagic zone Most of the ocean's waters far from shore, constantly mixed by ocean currents.

odorant A molecule that can be detected by sensory receptors of the olfactory system.

Okazaki fragment (ō′-kah-zah′-kē) A short segment of DNA synthesized away from the replication fork on a template strand during DNA replication. Many such segments are joined together to make up the lagging strand of newly synthesized DNA.

olfaction The sense of smell.

oligodendrocyte A type of glial cell that forms insulating myelin sheaths around the axons of neurons in the central nervous system.

oligotrophic lake A nutrient-poor, clear lake with few phytoplankton.

ommatidium (ōm′-uh-tid′-ē-um) (plural, **ommatidia**) One of the facets of the compound eye of arthropods and some polychaete worms.

omnivore An animal that regularly eats animals as well as plants or algae.

oncogene (on′-kō-jēn) A gene found in viral or cellular genomes that is involved in triggering molecular events that can lead to cancer.

oocyte A cell in the female reproductive system that differentiates to form an egg.

oogenesis (ō′-uh-jen′-uh-sis) The process in the ovary that results in the production of female gametes.

oogonium (ō′-uh- gō′-nē-em) (plural, **oogonia**) A cell that divides mitotically to form oocytes.

oomycete (ō′-uh-mī′-sēt) A protist with flagellated cells, such as a water mold, white rust, or downy mildew, that acquires nutrition mainly as a decomposer or plant parasite.

open circulatory system A circulatory system in which fluid called hemolymph bathes the tissues and organs directly and there is no distinction between the circulating fluid and the interstitial fluid.

operator In bacterial and phage DNA, a sequence of nucleotides near the start of an operon to which an active repressor can attach. The binding of the repressor prevents RNA polymerase from attaching to the promoter and transcribing the genes of the operon.

operculum (ō-per'-kyuh-lum) In aquatic osteichthyans, a protective bony flap that covers and protects the gills.

operon (op'-er-on) A unit of genetic function found in bacteria and phages, consisting of a promoter, an operator, and a coordinately regulated cluster of genes whose products function in a common pathway.

opisthokont (uh-pis'-thuh-kont') Member of the diverse clade Opisthokonta, organisms that descended from an ancestor with a posterior flagellum, including fungi, animals, and certain protists.

opposable thumb A thumb that can touch the ventral surface of the fingertips of all four fingers.

opsin A membrane protein bound to a light-absorbing pigment molecule.

optic chiasm The place where the two optic nerves meet and axons representing distinct sides of the visual field are segregated from one another before reaching the brain.

optimal foraging model The basis for analyzing behavior as a compromise between feeding costs and feeding benefits.

oral cavity The mouth of an animal.

orbital The three-dimensional space where an electron is found 90% of the time.

order In Linnaean classification, the taxonomic category above the level of family.

organ A specialized center of body function composed of several different types of tissues.

organ identity gene A plant homeotic gene that uses positional information to determine which emerging leaves develop into which types of floral organs.

organ of Corti The actual hearing organ of the vertebrate ear, located in the floor of the cochlear duct in the inner ear; contains the receptor cells (hair cells) of the ear.

organ system A group of organs that work together in performing vital body functions.

organelle (ōr-guh-nel') Any of several membrane-enclosed structures with specialized functions, suspended in the cytosol of eukaryotic cells.

organic chemistry The study of carbon compounds (organic compounds).

organismal ecology The branch of ecology concerned with the morphological, physiological, and behavioral ways in which individual organisms meet the challenges posed by their biotic and abiotic environments.

organogenesis (ōr-gan'-ō-jen'-uh-sis) The process in which organ rudiments develop from the three germ layers after gastrulation.

orgasm Rhythmic, involuntary contractions of certain reproductive structures in both sexes during the human sexual response cycle.

origin of replication Site where the replication of a DNA molecule begins, consisting of a specific sequence of nucleotides.

orthologous genes Homologous genes that are found in different species because of speciation.

osculum (os'-kyuh-lum) A large opening in a sponge that connects the spongocoel to the environment.

osmoconformer An animal that is isoosmotic with its environment.

osmolarity (oz'-mō-lār'-uh-tē) Solute concentration expressed as molarity.

osmoregulation Regulation of solute concentrations and water balance by a cell or organism.

osmoregulator An animal that controls its internal osmolarity independent of the external environment.

osmosis (oz-mō'-sis) The diffusion of free water across a selectively permeable membrane.

osteichthyan (os'-tē-ik'-thē-an) Member of a vertebrate clade with jaws and mostly bony skeletons.

outer ear One of three main regions of the ear in reptiles (including birds) and mammals; made up of the auditory canal and, in many birds and mammals, the pinna.

outgroup A species or group of species from an evolutionary lineage that is known to have diverged before the lineage that contains the group of species being studied. An outgroup is selected so that its members are closely related to the group of species being studied, but not as closely related as any study-group members are to each other.

oval window In the vertebrate ear, a membrane-covered gap in the skull bone, through which sound waves pass from the middle ear to the inner ear.

ovarian cycle (ō-vār'-ē-un) The cyclic recurrence of the follicular phase, ovulation, and the luteal phase in the mammalian ovary, regulated by hormones.

ovary (ō'-vuh-rē) (1) In flowers, the portion of a carpel in which the egg-containing ovules develop. (2) In animals, the structure that produces female gametes and reproductive hormones.

oviduct (ō'-vuh-duct) A tube passing from the ovary to the vagina in invertebrates or to the uterus in vertebrates, where it is also known as a fallopian tube.

oviparous (ō-vip'-uh-rus) Referring to a type of development in which young hatch from eggs laid outside the mother's body.

ovoviviparous (ō'-vō-vī-vip'-uh-rus) Referring to a type of development in which young hatch from eggs that are retained in the mother's uterus.

ovulation The release of an egg from an ovary. In humans, an ovarian follicle releases an egg during each uterine (menstrual) cycle.

ovule (o'-vyūl) A structure that develops within the ovary of a seed plant and contains the female gametophyte.

oxidation The complete or partial loss of electrons from a substance involved in a redox reaction.

oxidative phosphorylation (fos'-fōr-uh-lā'-shun) The production of ATP using energy derived from the redox reactions of an electron transport chain; the third major stage of cellular respiration.

oxidizing agent The electron acceptor in a redox reaction.

oxytocin (ok'-si-tō'-sen) A hormone produced by the hypothalamus and released from the posterior pituitary. It induces contractions of the uterine muscles during labor and causes the mammary glands to eject milk during nursing.

P generation The true-breeding (homozygous) parent individuals from which F_1 hybrid offspring are derived in studies of inheritance; P stands for "parental."

P site One of a ribosome's three binding sites for tRNA during translation. The P site holds the tRNA carrying the growing polypeptide chain. (P stands for peptidyl tRNA.)

***p53* gene** A tumor-suppressor gene that codes for a specific transcription factor that promotes the synthesis of proteins that inhibit the cell cycle.

paedomorphosis (pē'-duh-mōr'-fuh-sis) The retention in an adult organism of the juvenile features of its evolutionary ancestors.

pain receptor A sensory receptor that responds to noxious or painful stimuli; also called a nociceptor.

paleoanthropology The study of human origins and evolution.

paleontology (pā'-lē-un-tol'-ō-jē) The scientific study of fossils.

pancreas (pan'-krē-us) A gland with exocrine and endocrine tissues. The exocrine portion functions in digestion, secreting enzymes and an alkaline solution into the small intestine via a duct; the ductless endocrine portion functions in homeostasis, secreting the hormones insulin and glucagon into the blood.

pandemic A global epidemic.

Pangaea (pan-jē'-uh) The supercontinent that formed near the end of the Paleozoic era, when plate movements brought all the landmasses of Earth together.

parabasalid A protist, such as a trichomonad, with modified mitochondria.

paracrine Referring to a secreted molecule that acts on a neighboring cell.

paralogous genes Homologous genes that are found in the same genome as a result of gene duplication.

paraphyletic (pār'-uh-fī-let'-ik) Pertaining to a group of taxa that consists of a common ancestor and some, but not all, of its descendants.

parareptile A basal group of reptiles, consisting mostly of large, stocky quadrupedal herbivores. Parareptiles died out in the late Triassic period.

parasite (pār'-uh-sīt) An organism that feeds on the cell contents, tissues, or body fluids of another species (the host) while in or on the host organism. Parasites harm but usually do not kill their host.

parasitism (pār'-uh-sit-izm) A symbiotic relationship in which one organism, the parasite, benefits at the expense of another, the host, by living either within or on the host.

parasympathetic division One of three divisions of the autonomic nervous system; generally enhances body activities that gain and conserve energy, such as digestion and reduced heart rate.

parathyroid gland One of four small endocrine glands, embedded in the surface of the thyroid gland, that secrete parathyroid hormone.

parathyroid hormone (PTH) A hormone secreted by the parathyroid glands that raises blood calcium level by promoting calcium release from bone and calcium retention by the kidneys.

parenchyma cell (puh-ren′-ki-muh) A relatively unspecialized plant cell type that carries out most of the metabolism, synthesizes and stores organic products, and develops into a more differentiated cell type.

parental type An offspring with a phenotype that matches one of the true-breeding parental (P generation) phenotypes; also refers to the phenotype itself.

Parkinson's disease A progressive brain disease characterized by difficulty in initiating movements, slowness of movement, and rigidity.

parthenogenesis (par′-thuh-nō′-jen′-uh-sis) A form of asexual reproduction in which females produce offspring from unfertilized eggs.

partial pressure The pressure exerted by a particular gas in a mixture of gases (for instance, the pressure exerted by oxygen in air).

passive immunity Short-term immunity conferred by the transfer of antibodies, as occurs in the transfer of maternal antibodies to a fetus or nursing infant.

passive transport The diffusion of a substance across a biological membrane with no expenditure of energy.

pathogen An organism, virus, viroid, or prion that causes disease.

pattern formation The development of a multicellular organism's spatial organization, the arrangement of organs and tissues in their characteristic places in three-dimensional space.

peat Extensive deposits of partially decayed organic material often formed primarily from the wetland moss *Sphagnum*.

pedigree A diagram of a family tree with conventional symbols, showing the occurrence of heritable characters in parents and offspring over multiple generations.

pelagic zone The open-water component of aquatic biomes.

penis The copulatory structure of male mammals.

PEP carboxylase An enzyme that adds CO_2 to phosphoenolpyruvate (PEP) to form oxaloacetate in mesophyll cells of C_4 plants. It acts prior to photosynthesis.

pepsin An enzyme present in gastric juice that begins the hydrolysis of proteins.

pepsinogen The inactive form of pepsin secreted by chief cells located in gastric pits of the stomach.

peptide bond The covalent bond between the carboxyl group on one amino acid and the amino group on another, formed by a dehydration reaction.

peptidoglycan (pep′-tid-ō-glī′-kan) A type of polymer in bacterial cell walls consisting of modified sugars cross-linked by short polypeptides.

perception The interpretation of sensory system input by the brain.

pericycle The outermost layer in the vascular cylinder, from which lateral roots arise.

periderm (pār′-uh-derm′) The protective coat that replaces the epidermis in woody plants during secondary growth, formed of the cork and cork cambium.

peripheral nervous system (PNS) The sensory and motor neurons that connect to the central nervous system.

peripheral protein A protein loosely bound to the surface of a membrane or to part of an integral protein and not embedded in the lipid bilayer.

peristalsis (par′-uh-stal′-sis) (1) Alternating waves of contraction and relaxation in the smooth muscles lining the alimentary canal that push food along the canal. (2) A type of movement on land produced by rhythmic waves of muscle contractions passing from front to back, as in many annelids.

peristome A ring of interlocking, tooth-like structures on the upper part of a moss capsule (sporangium), often specialized for gradual spore discharge.

peritubular capillary One of the tiny blood vessels that form a network surrounding the proximal and distal tubules in the kidney.

permafrost A permanently frozen soil layer.

peroxisome (puh-rok′-suh-sōm′) An organelle containing enzymes that transfer hydrogen atoms from various substrates to oxygen (O_2), producing and then degrading hydrogen peroxide (H_2O_2).

petal A modified leaf of a flowering plant. Petals are the often colorful parts of a flower that advertise it to insects and other pollinators.

petiole (pet′-ē-ōl) The stalk of a leaf, which joins the leaf to a node of the stem.

pH A measure of hydrogen ion concentration equal to $-\log [H^+]$ and ranging in value from 0 to 14.

phage (fāj) A virus that infects bacteria; also called a bacteriophage.

phagocytosis (fag′-ō-sī-tō′-sis) A type of endocytosis in which large particulate substances or small organisms are taken up by a cell. It is carried out by some protists and by certain immune cells of animals (in mammals, mainly macrophages, neutrophils, and dendritic cells).

pharyngeal cleft (fuh-rin′-jē-ul) In chordate embryos, one of the grooves that separate a series of pouches along the sides of the pharynx and may develop into a pharyngeal slit.

pharyngeal slit (fuh-rin′-jē-ul) In chordate embryos, one of the slits that form from the pharyngeal clefts and communicate to the outside, later developing into gill slits in many vertebrates.

pharynx (fār′-inks) (1) An area in the vertebrate throat where air and food passages cross. (2) In flatworms, the muscular tube that protrudes from the ventral side of the worm and ends in the mouth.

phase change A shift from one developmental phase to another.

phenotype (fē′-nō-tīp) The observable physical and physiological traits of an organism, which are determined by its genetic makeup.

pheromone (fār′-uh-mōn) In animals and fungi, a small molecule released into the environment that functions in communication between members of the same species. In animals, it acts much like a hormone in influencing physiology and behavior.

phloem (flō′-em) Vascular plant tissue consisting of living cells arranged into elongated tubes that transport sugar and other organic nutrients throughout the plant.

phloem sap The sugar-rich solution carried through a plant's sieve tubes.

phosphate group A chemical group consisting of a phosphorus atom bonded to four oxygen atoms; important in energy transfer.

phospholipid (fos′-fō-lip′-id) A lipid made up of glycerol joined to two fatty acids and a phosphate group. The hydrocarbon chains of the fatty acids act as nonpolar, hydrophobic tails, while the rest of the molecule acts as a polar, hydrophilic head. Phospholipids form bilayers that function as biological membranes.

phosphorylated intermediate A molecule (often a reactant) with a phosphate group covalently bound to it, making it more reactive (less stable) than the unphosphorylated molecule.

photic zone (fō′-tic) The narrow top layer of an ocean or lake, where light penetrates sufficiently for photosynthesis to occur.

photoautotroph (fō′-tō-ot′-ō-trōf) An organism that harnesses light energy to drive the synthesis of organic compounds from carbon dioxide.

photoheterotroph (fō′-tō-het′-er-ō-trōf) An organism that uses light to generate ATP but must obtain carbon in organic form.

photomorphogenesis Effects of light on plant morphology.

photon (fō′-ton) A quantum, or discrete quantity, of light energy that behaves as if it were a particle.

photoperiodism (fō′-tō-pēr′-ē-ō-dizm) A physiological response to photoperiod, the relative lengths of night and day. An example of photoperiodism is flowering.

photophosphorylation (fō′-tō-fos′-fōr-uh-lā′-shun) The process of generating ATP from ADP and phosphate by means of chemiosmosis, using a proton-motive force generated across the thylakoid membrane of the chloroplast or the membrane of certain prokaryotes during the light reactions of photosynthesis.

photoreceptor An electromagnetic receptor that detects the radiation known as visible light.

photorespiration A metabolic pathway that consumes oxygen and ATP, releases carbon dioxide, and decreases photosynthetic output. Photorespiration generally occurs on hot, dry, bright days, when stomata close and the O_2/CO_2 ratio in the leaf increases, favoring the binding of O_2 rather than CO_2 by rubisco.

photosynthesis (fō′-tō-sin′-thi-sis) The conversion of light energy to chemical energy that is stored in sugars or other organic compounds; occurs in plants, algae, and certain prokaryotes.

photosystem A light-capturing unit located in the thylakoid membrane of the chloroplast or in the membrane of some prokaryotes, consisting of a reaction-center complex surrounded by numerous light-harvesting complexes. There are two types of photosystems, I and II; they absorb light best at different wavelengths.

photosystem I (PS I) A light-capturing unit in a chloroplast's thylakoid membrane or in the membrane of some prokaryotes; it has two molecules of P700 chlorophyll *a* at its reaction center.

photosystem II (PS II) One of two light-capturing units in a chloroplast's thylakoid membrane or in the membrane of some prokaryotes; it has two molecules of P680 chlorophyll *a* at its reaction center.

phototropism (fō′-tō-trō′-pizm) Growth of a plant shoot toward or away from light.

phragmoplast (frag′-mō-plast′) An alignment of cytoskeletal elements and Golgi-derived vesicles that forms across the midline of a dividing plant cell.

phyllotaxy (fil′-uh-tak′-sē) The pattern of leaf attachment to the stem of a plant.

PhyloCode Proposed system of classification of organisms based on evolutionary relationships: Only groups that include a common ancestor and all of its descendants are named.

phylogenetic species concept A definition of species as the smallest group of individuals that share a common ancestor, forming one branch on the tree of life.

phylogenetic tree A branching diagram that represents a hypothesis about the evolutionary history of a group of organisms.

phylogeny (fī-loj′-uh-nē) The evolutionary history of a species or group of related species.

phylum (fī′-lum) (plural, **phyla**) In Linnaean classification, the taxonomic category above class.

physical map A genetic map in which the actual physical distances between genes or other genetic markers are expressed, usually as the number of base pairs along the DNA.

physiology The processes and functions of an organism.

phytochrome (fī′-tuh-krōm) A type of light receptor in plants that mostly absorbs red light and regulates many plant responses, such as seed germination and shade avoidance.

phytoremediation An emerging technology that seeks to reclaim contaminated areas by taking advantage of some plant species' ability to extract heavy metals and other pollutants from the soil and to concentrate them in easily harvested portions of the plant.

pilus (plural, **pili**) (pī′-lus, pī′-lī) In bacteria, a structure that links one cell to another at the start of conjugation; also known as a sex pilus or conjugation pilus.

pineal gland (pī′-nē-ul) A small gland on the dorsal surface of the vertebrate forebrain that secretes the hormone melatonin.

pinocytosis (pī′-nō-sī-tō′-sis) A type of endocytosis in which the cell ingests extracellular fluid and its dissolved solutes.

pistil A single carpel or a group of fused carpels.

pith Ground tissue that is internal to the vascular tissue in a stem; in many monocot roots,

parenchyma cells that form the central core of the vascular cylinder.

pituitary gland (puh-tū′-uh-tār′-ē) An endocrine gland at the base of the hypothalamus; consists of a posterior lobe, which stores and releases two hormones produced by the hypothalamus, and an anterior lobe, which produces and secretes many hormones that regulate diverse body functions.

placenta (pluh-sen′-tuh) A structure in the pregnant uterus for nourishing a viviparous fetus with the mother's blood supply; formed from the uterine lining and embryonic membranes.

placental transfer cell A plant cell that enhances the transfer of nutrients from parent to embryo.

placoderm A member of an extinct group of fishlike vertebrates that had jaws and were enclosed in a tough outer armor.

planarian A free-living flatworm found in ponds and streams.

plasma (plaz′-muh) The liquid matrix of blood in which the blood cells are suspended.

plasma cell The antibody-secreting effector cell of humoral immunity. Plasma cells arise from antigen-stimulated B cells.

plasma membrane The membrane at the boundary of every cell that acts as a selective barrier, regulating the cell's chemical composition.

plasmid (plaz′-mid) A small, circular, double-stranded DNA molecule that carries accessory genes separate from those of a bacterial chromosome; in DNA cloning, used as vectors carrying up to about 10,000 base pairs (10 kb) of DNA. Plasmids are also found in some eukaryotes, such as yeasts.

plasmodesma (plaz′-mō-dez′-muh) (plural, **plasmodesmata**) An open channel through the cell wall that connects the cytoplasm of adjacent plant cells, allowing water, small solutes, and some larger molecules to pass between the cells.

plasmodial slime mold (plaz-mō′-dē-ul) A type of protist that has amoeboid cells, flagellated cells, and a plasmodial feeding stage in its life cycle.

plasmodium A single mass of cytoplasm containing many diploid nuclei that forms during the life cycle of some slime molds.

plasmogamy (plaz-moh′-guh-mē) In fungi, the fusion of the cytoplasm of cells from two individuals; occurs as one stage of sexual reproduction, followed later by karyogamy.

plasmolysis (plaz-mol′-uh-sis) A phenomenon in walled cells in which the cytoplasm shrivels and the plasma membrane pulls away from the cell wall; occurs when the cell loses water to a hypertonic environment.

plastid One of a family of closely related organelles that includes chloroplasts, chromoplasts, and amyloplasts. Plastids are found in cells of photosynthetic eukaryotes.

plate tectonics The theory that the continents are part of great plates of Earth's crust that float on the hot, underlying portion of the mantle. Movements in the mantle cause the continents to move slowly over time.

platelet A pinched-off cytoplasmic fragment of a specialized bone marrow cell. Platelets circulate in the blood and are important in blood clotting.

pleiotropy (plī′-o-truh-pē) The ability of a single gene to have multiple effects.

pluripotent Describing a cell that can give rise to many, but not all, parts of an organism.

point mutation A change in a single nucleotide pair of a gene.

polar covalent bond A covalent bond between atoms that differ in electronegativity. The shared electrons are pulled closer to the more electronegative atom, making it slightly negative and the other atom slightly positive.

polar molecule A molecule (such as water) with an uneven distribution of charges in different regions of the molecule.

polarity A lack of symmetry; structural differences in opposite ends of an organism or structure, such as the root end and shoot end of a plant.

pollen grain In seed plants, a structure consisting of the male gametophyte enclosed within a pollen wall.

pollen tube A tube that forms after germination of the pollen grain and that functions in the delivery of sperm to the ovule.

pollination (pol′-uh-nā′-shun) The transfer of pollen to the part of a seed plant containing the ovules, a process required for fertilization.

poly-A tail A sequence of 50–250 adenine nucleotides added onto the 3′ end of a pre-mRNA molecule.

polygamous Referring to a type of relationship in which an individual of one sex mates with several of the other.

polygenic inheritance (pol′-ē-jen′-ik) An additive effect of two or more genes on a single phenotypic character.

polymer (pol′-uh-mer) A long molecule consisting of many similar or identical monomers linked together by covalent bonds.

polymerase chain reaction (PCR) (puh-lim′-uh-rās) A technique for amplifying DNA *in vitro* by incubating it with specific primers, a heat-resistant DNA polymerase, and nucleotides.

polynucleotide (pol′-ē-nū′-klē-ō-tīd) A polymer consisting of many nucleotide monomers in a chain. The nucleotides can be those of DNA or RNA.

polyp The sessile variant of the cnidarian body plan. The alternate form is the medusa.

polypeptide (pol′-ē-pep′-tīd) A polymer of many amino acids linked together by peptide bonds.

polyphyletic (pol′-ē-fī-let′-ik) Pertaining to a group of taxa derived from two or more different ancestors.

polyploidy (pol′-ē-ploy′-dē) A chromosomal alteration in which the organism possesses more than two complete chromosome sets. It is the result of an accident of cell division.

polyribosome (polysome) (pol′-ē-rī′-buh-sōm′) A group of several ribosomes attached to, and translating, the same messenger RNA molecule.

polysaccharide (pol′-ē-sak′-uh-rīd) A polymer of many monosaccharides, formed by dehydration reactions.

polytomy (puh-lit′-uh-mē) In a phylogenetic tree, a branch point from which more than two descendant taxa emerge. A polytomy indicates that the evolutionary relationships between the descendant taxa are not yet clear.

pons A portion of the brain that participates in certain automatic, homeostatic functions, such as regulating the breathing centers in the medulla.

population A group of individuals of the same species that live in the same area and interbreed, producing fertile offspring.

population dynamics The study of how complex interactions between biotic and abiotic factors influence variations in population size.

population ecology The study of populations in relation to their environment, including environmental influences on population density and distribution, age structure, and variations in population size.

positional information Molecular cues that control pattern formation in an animal or plant embryonic structure by indicating a cell's location relative to the organism's body axes. These cues elicit a response by genes that regulate development.

positive feedback A form of regulation in which an end product of a process speeds up that process; in physiology, a control mechanism in which a change in a variable triggers a response that reinforces or amplifies the change.

positive pressure breathing A breathing system in which air is forced into the lungs.

posterior Pertaining to the rear, or tail end, of a bilaterally symmetrical animal.

posterior pituitary An extension of the hypothalamus composed of nervous tissue that secretes oxytocin and antidiuretic hormone made in the hypothalamus; a temporary storage site for these hormones.

postzygotic barrier (pōst-zī-got′-ik) A reproductive barrier that prevents hybrid zygotes produced by two different species from developing into viable, fertile adults.

potential energy The energy that matter possesses as a result of its location or spatial arrangement (structure).

predation An interaction between species in which one species, the predator, eats the other, the prey.

pregnancy The condition of carrying one or more embryos in the uterus.

prepuce (prē′-pyūs) A fold of skin covering the head of the clitoris or penis.

pressure potential (Ψ_P) A component of water potential that consists of the physical pressure on a solution, which can be positive, zero, or negative.

prezygotic barrier (prē′-zī-got′-ik) A reproductive barrier that impedes mating between species or hinders fertilization if interspecific mating is attempted.

primary cell wall In plants, a relatively thin and flexible layer that surrounds the plasma membrane of a young cell.

primary consumer An herbivore; an organism that eats plants or other autotrophs.

primary electron acceptor In the thylakoid membrane of a chloroplast or in the membrane of some prokaryotes, a specialized molecule that shares the reaction-center complex with a pair of chlorophyll *a* molecules and that accepts an electron from them.

primary growth Growth produced by apical meristems, lengthening stems and roots.

primary immune response The initial adaptive immune response to an antigen, which appears after a lag of about 10 to 17 days.

primary oocyte (ō′-uh-sīt) An oocyte prior to completion of meiosis I.

primary producer An autotroph, usually a photosynthetic organism. Collectively, autotrophs make up the trophic level of an ecosystem that ultimately supports all other levels.

primary production The amount of light energy converted to chemical energy (organic compounds) by the autotrophs in an ecosystem during a given time period.

primary structure The level of protein structure referring to the specific linear sequence of amino acids.

primary succession A type of ecological succession that occurs in an area where there were originally no organisms present and where soil has not yet formed.

primary transcript An initial RNA transcript from any gene; also called pre-mRNA when transcribed from a protein-coding gene.

primary visual cortex The destination in the occipital lobe of the cerebrum for most of the axons from the lateral geniculate nuclei.

primase An enzyme that joins RNA nucleotides to make a primer during DNA replication, using the parental DNA strand as a template.

primer A short stretch of RNA with a free 3′ end, bound by complementary base pairing to the template strand and elongated with DNA nucleotides during DNA replication.

primitive streak A thickening along the future anterior-posterior axis on the surface of an early avian or mammalian embryo, caused by a piling up of cells as they congregate at the midline before moving into the embryo.

prion An infectious agent that is a misfolded version of a normal cellular protein. Prions appear to increase in number by converting correctly folded versions of the protein to more prions.

problem solving The cognitive activity of devising a method to proceed from one state to another in the face of real or apparent obstacles.

producer An organism that produces organic compounds from CO_2 by harnessing light energy (in photosynthesis) or by oxidizing inorganic chemicals (in chemosynthetic reactions carried out by some prokaryotes).

product A material resulting from a chemical reaction.

production efficiency The percentage of energy stored in assimilated food that is not used for respiration or eliminated as waste.

progesterone A steroid hormone that prepares the uterus for pregnancy; the major progestin in mammals.

progestin Any steroid hormone with progesterone-like activity.

progymnosperm (prō-jim′-nō-sperm) An extinct seedless vascular plant that may be ancestral to seed plants.

prokaryotic cell (prō′-kār-ē-ot′-ik) A type of cell lacking a membrane-enclosed nucleus and membrane-enclosed organelles. Organisms with prokaryotic cells (bacteria and archaea) are called prokaryotes.

prolactin A hormone produced and secreted by the anterior pituitary with a great diversity of effects in different vertebrate species. In mammals, it stimulates growth of and milk production by the mammary glands.

proliferative phase That portion of the uterine (menstrual) cycle when the endometrium regenerates and thickens.

prometaphase The second stage of mitosis, in which the nuclear envelope fragments and the spindle microtubules attach to the kinetochores of the chromosomes.

promiscuous Referring to a type of relationship in which mating occurs with no strong pair-bonds or lasting relationships.

promoter A specific nucleotide sequence in the DNA of a gene that binds RNA polymerase, positioning it to start transcribing RNA at the appropriate place.

prophage (prō′-fāj) A phage genome that has been inserted into a specific site on a bacterial chromosome.

prophase The first stage of mitosis, in which the chromatin condenses into discrete chromosomes visible with a light microscope, the mitotic spindle begins to form, and the nucleolus disappears but the nucleus remains intact.

prostaglandin (pros′-tuh-glan′-din) One of a group of modified fatty acids secreted by virtually all tissues and performing a wide variety of functions as local regulators.

prostate gland (pros′-tāt) A gland in human males that secretes an acid-neutralizing component of semen.

protease An enzyme that digests proteins by hydrolysis.

proteasome A giant protein complex that recognizes and destroys proteins tagged for elimination by the small protein ubiquitin.

protein (prō′-tēn) A biologically functional molecule consisting of one or more polypeptides folded and coiled into a specific three-dimensional structure.

protein kinase An enzyme that transfers phosphate groups from ATP to a protein, thus phosphorylating the protein.

protein phosphatase An enzyme that removes phosphate groups from (dephosphorylates) proteins, often functioning to reverse the effect of a protein kinase.

proteoglycan (prō′-tē-ō-glī′-kan) A large molecule consisting of a small core protein with many carbohydrate chains attached, found in the extracellular matrix of animal cells. A proteoglycan may consist of up to 95% carbohydrate.

proteomics (prō'-tē-ō'-miks) The systematic study of the full protein sets (proteomes) encoded by genomes.

protist An informal term applied to any eukaryote that is not a plant, animal, or fungus. Most protists are unicellular, though some are colonial or multicellular.

protocell An abiotic precursor of a living cell that had a membrane-like structure and that maintained an internal chemistry different from that of its surroundings.

proton (prō'-ton) A subatomic particle with a single positive electrical charge, with a mass of about 1.7×10^{-24} g, found in the nucleus of an atom.

proton pump An active transport protein in a cell membrane that uses ATP to transport hydrogen ions out of a cell against their concentration gradient, generating a membrane potential in the process.

protonema (plural, **protonemata**) A mass of green, branched, one-cell-thick filaments produced by germinating moss spores.

protonephridium (prō'-tō-nuh-frid'-ē-uhm) (plural, **protonephridia**) An excretory system, such as the flame bulb system of flatworms, consisting of a network of tubules lacking internal openings.

proton-motive force The potential energy stored in the form of a proton electrochemical gradient, generated by the pumping of hydrogen ions (H^+) across a biological membrane during chemiosmosis.

proto-oncogene (prō'-tō-on'-kō-jēn) A normal cellular gene that has the potential to become an oncogene.

protoplast The living part of a plant cell, which also includes the plasma membrane.

protoplast fusion The fusing of two protoplasts from different plant species that would otherwise be reproductively incompatible.

protostome development In animals, a developmental mode distinguished by the development of the mouth from the blastopore; often also characterized by spiral cleavage and by the body cavity forming when solid masses of mesoderm split.

provirus A viral genome that is permanently inserted into a host genome.

proximal tubule In the vertebrate kidney, the portion of a nephron immediately downstream from Bowman's capsule that conveys and helps refine filtrate.

pseudocoelomate (sū'-dō-sē'-lō-māt) An animal whose body cavity is lined by tissue derived from mesoderm and endoderm.

pseudogene (sū'-dō-jēn) A DNA segment very similar to a real gene but which does not yield a functional product; a DNA segment that formerly functioned as a gene but has become inactivated in a particular species because of mutation.

pseudopodium (sū'-dō-pō'-dē-um) (plural, **pseudopodia**) A cellular extension of amoeboid cells used in moving and feeding.

pterophyte (ter'-uh-fīt) An informal name for a member of the phylum Pterophyta, which includes ferns, horsetails, and whisk ferns and their relatives.

pterosaur Winged reptile that lived during the Mesozoic era.

pulmocutaneous circuit A branch of the circulatory system in many amphibians that supplies the lungs and skin.

pulmonary circuit The branch of the circulatory system that supplies the lungs.

pulse The rhythmic bulging of the artery walls with each heartbeat.

punctuated equilibria In the fossil record, long periods of apparent stasis, in which a species undergoes little or no morphological change, interrupted by relatively brief periods of sudden change.

Punnett square A diagram used in the study of inheritance to show the predicted genotypic results of random fertilization in genetic crosses between individuals of known genotype.

pupil The opening in the iris, which admits light into the interior of the vertebrate eye. Muscles in the iris regulate its size.

purine (pyū'-rēn) One of two types of nitrogenous bases found in nucleotides, characterized by a six-membered ring fused to a five-membered ring. Adenine (A) and guanine (G) are purines.

pyrimidine (puh-rim'-uh-dēn) One of two types of nitrogenous bases found in nucleotides, characterized by a six-membered ring. Cytosine (C), thymine (T), and uracil (U) are pyrimidines.

quantitative character A heritable feature that varies continuously over a range rather than in an either-or fashion.

quaternary structure (kwot-er-nār-ē) The particular shape of a complex, aggregate protein, defined by the characteristic three-dimensional arrangement of its constituent subunits, each a polypeptide.

R plasmid A bacterial plasmid carrying genes that confer resistance to certain antibiotics.

radial cleavage A type of embryonic development in deuterostomes in which the planes of cell division that transform the zygote into a ball of cells are either parallel or perpendicular to the vertical axis of the embryo, thereby aligning tiers of cells one above the other.

radial symmetry Symmetry in which the body is shaped like a pie or barrel (lacking a left side and a right side) and can be divided into mirror-imaged halves by any plane through its central axis.

radiation The emission of electromagnetic waves by all objects warmer than absolute zero.

radicle An embryonic root of a plant.

radioactive isotope An isotope (an atomic form of a chemical element) that is unstable; the nucleus decays spontaneously, giving off detectable particles and energy.

radiolarian A protist, usually marine, with a shell generally made of silica and pseudopodia that radiate from the central body.

radiometric dating A method for determining the absolute age of rocks and fossils, based on the half-life of radioactive isotopes.

radula A straplike scraping organ used by many molluscs during feeding.

***ras* gene** A gene that codes for Ras, a G protein that relays a growth signal from a growth factor receptor on the plasma membrane to a cascade of protein kinases, ultimately resulting in stimulation of the cell cycle.

ratite (rat'-īt) Member of the group of flightless birds.

ray-finned fish Member of the class Actinopterygii, aquatic osteichthyans with fins supported by long, flexible rays, including tuna, bass, and herring.

reabsorption In excretory systems, the recovery of solutes and water from filtrate.

reactant A starting material in a chemical reaction.

reaction-center complex A complex of proteins associated with a special pair of chlorophyll *a* molecules and a primary electron acceptor. Located centrally in a photosystem, this complex triggers the light reactions of photosynthesis. Excited by light energy, the pair of chlorophylls donates an electron to the primary electron acceptor, which passes an electron to an electron transport chain.

reading frame On an mRNA, the triplet grouping of ribonucleotides used by the translation machinery during polypeptide synthesis.

receptacle The base of a flower; the part of the stem that is the site of attachment of the floral organs.

receptor potential An initial response of a receptor cell to a stimulus, consisting of a change in voltage across the receptor membrane proportional to the stimulus strength.

receptor tyrosine kinase (RTK) A receptor protein spanning the plasma membrane, the cytoplasmic (intracellular) part of which can catalyze the transfer of a phosphate group from ATP to a tyrosine on another protein. Receptor tyrosine kinases often respond to the binding of a signaling molecule by dimerizing and then phosphorylating a tyrosine on the cytoplasmic portion of the other receptor in the dimer. The phosphorylated tyrosines on the receptors then activate other signal transduction proteins within the cell.

receptor-mediated endocytosis (en'-dō-sī-tō'-sis) The movement of specific molecules into a cell by the inward budding of vesicles containing proteins with receptor sites specific to the molecules being taken in; enables a cell to acquire bulk quantities of specific substances.

recessive allele An allele whose phenotypic effect is not observed in a heterozygote.

reciprocal altruism Altruistic behavior between unrelated individuals, whereby the altruistic individual benefits in the future when the beneficiary reciprocates.

recombinant chromosome A chromosome created when crossing over combines DNA from two parents into a single chromosome.

recombinant DNA A DNA molecule made *in vitro* with segments from different sources.

recombinant type (recombinant) An offspring whose phenotype differs from that of the true-breeding P generation parents; also refers to the phenotype itself.

rectum The terminal portion of the large intestine, where the feces are stored prior to elimination.

red alga A photosynthetic protist, named for its color, which results from a red pigment that masks the green of chlorophyll. Most red algae are multicellular and marine.

redox reaction (rē'-doks) A chemical reaction involving the complete or partial transfer of one or more electrons from one reactant to another; short for **red**uction-**ox**idation reaction.

reducing agent The electron donor in a redox reaction.

reduction The complete or partial addition of electrons to a substance involved in a redox reaction.

reflex An automatic reaction to a stimulus, mediated by the spinal cord or lower brain.

refractory period (rē-frakt'-ōr-ē) The short time immediately after an action potential in which the neuron cannot respond to another stimulus, owing to the inactivation of voltage-gated sodium channels.

regulator An animal for which mechanisms of homeostasis moderate internal changes in a particular variable in the face of external fluctuation of that variable.

regulatory gene A gene that codes for a protein, such as a repressor, that controls the transcription of another gene or group of genes.

reinforcement In evolutionary biology, a process in which a process in which natural selection strengthens prezygotic barriers to reproduction, thus reducing the chances of hybrid formation. Such a process is likely to occur only if hybrid offspring are less fit than members of the parent species.

relative abundance The proportional abundance of different species in a community.

relative fitness The contribution an individual makes to the gene pool of the next generation, relative to the contributions of other individuals in the population.

renal cortex The outer portion of the vertebrate kidney.

renal medulla The inner portion of the vertebrate kidney, beneath the renal cortex.

renal pelvis The funnel-shaped chamber that receives processed filtrate from the vertebrate kidney's collecting ducts and is drained by the ureter.

renin-angiotensin-aldosterone system (RAAS) A hormone cascade pathway that helps regulate blood pressure and blood volume.

repetitive DNA Nucleotide sequences, usually noncoding, that are present in many copies in a eukaryotic genome. The repeated units may be short and arranged tandemly (in series) or long and dispersed in the genome.

replication fork A Y-shaped region on a replicating DNA molecule where the parental strands are being unwound and new strands are being synthesized.

repressor A protein that inhibits gene transcription. In prokaryotes, repressors bind to the DNA in or near the promoter. In eukaryotes, repressors may bind to control elements within enhancers, to activators, or to other proteins in a way that blocks activators from binding to DNA.

reproductive isolation The existence of biological factors (barriers) that impede members of two species from producing viable, fertile offspring.

reproductive table An age-specific summary of the reproductive rates in a population.

reptile Member of the clade of amniotes that includes tuataras, lizards, snakes, turtles, crocodilians, and birds.

residual volume The amount of air that remains in the lungs after forceful exhalation.

resource partitioning The division of environmental resources by coexisting species such that the niche of each species differs by one or more significant factors from the niches of all coexisting species.

respiratory pigment A protein that transports oxygen in blood or hemolymph.

response (1) In cellular communication, the change in a specific cellular activity brought about by a transduced signal from outside the cell. (2) In feedback regulation, a physiological activity triggered by a change in a variable.

resting potential The membrane potential characteristic of a nonconducting excitable cell, with the inside of the cell more negative than the outside.

restriction enzyme An endonuclease (type of enzyme) that recognizes and cuts DNA molecules foreign to a bacterium (such as phage genomes). The enzyme cuts at specific nucleotide sequences (restriction sites).

restriction fragment A DNA segment that results from the cutting of DNA by a restriction enzyme.

restriction fragment length polymorphism (RFLP) A single nucleotide polymorphism (SNP) that exists in the restriction site for a particular enzyme, thus making the site unrecognizable by that enzyme and changing the lengths of the restriction fragments formed by digestion with that enzyme. A RFLP can be in coding or noncoding DNA.

restriction site A specific sequence on a DNA strand that is recognized and cut by a restriction enzyme.

reticular formation (re-tik'-yū-ler) A diffuse network of neurons in the core of the brainstem that filters information traveling to the cerebral cortex.

retina (ret'-i-nuh) The innermost layer of the vertebrate eye, containing photoreceptor cells (rods and cones) and neurons; transmits images formed by the lens to the brain via the optic nerve.

retinal The light-absorbing pigment in rods and cones of the vertebrate eye.

retrotransposon (re'-trō-trans-pō'-zon) A transposable element that moves within a genome by means of an RNA intermediate, a transcript of the retrotransposon DNA.

retrovirus (re'-trō-vī'-rus) An RNA virus that replicates by transcribing its RNA into DNA and then inserting the DNA into a cellular chromosome; an important class of cancer-causing viruses.

reverse transcriptase (tran-skrip'-tās) An enzyme encoded by certain viruses (retroviruses) that uses RNA as a template for DNA synthesis.

reverse transcriptase–polymerase chain reaction (RT-PCR) A technique for determining expression of a particular gene. It uses reverse transcriptase and DNA polymerase to synthesize cDNA from all the mRNA in a sample and then subjects the cDNA to PCR amplification using primers specific for the gene of interest.

Rhizaria (rī-za'-rē-uh) One of five supergroups of eukaryotes proposed in a current hypothesis of the evolutionary history of eukaryotes; a morphologically diverse protist clade that is defined by DNA similarities. *See also* Excavata, Chromalveolata, Archaeplastida, and Unikonta.

rhizobacterium A soil bacterium whose population size is much enhanced in the rhizosphere, the soil region close to a plant's roots.

rhizoid (rī'-zoyd) A long, tubular single cell or filament of cells that anchors bryophytes to the ground. Unlike roots, rhizoids are not composed of tissues, lack specialized conducting cells, and do not play a primary role in water and mineral absorption.

rhizosphere The soil region close to plant roots and characterized by a high level of microbiological activity.

rhodopsin (rō-dop'-sin) A visual pigment consisting of retinal and opsin. Upon absorbing light, the retinal changes shape and dissociates from the opsin.

rhythm method A form of contraception that relies on refraining from sexual intercourse when conception is most likely to occur; also called natural family planning.

ribonucleic acid (RNA) (rī'-bō-nū-klā'-ik) A type of nucleic acid consisting of a polynucleotide made up of nucleotide monomers with a ribose sugar and the nitrogenous bases adenine (A), cytosine (C), guanine (G), and uracil (U); usually single-stranded; functions in protein synthesis, gene regulation, and as the genome of some viruses.

ribose The sugar component of RNA nucleotides.

ribosomal RNA (rRNA) (rī'-buh-sō'-mul) RNA molecules that, together with proteins, make up ribosomes; the most abundant type of RNA.

ribosome (rī'-buh-sōm') A complex of rRNA and protein molecules that functions as a site of protein synthesis in the cytoplasm; consists of a large and a small subunit. In eukaryotic cells, each subunit is assembled in the nucleolus. *See also* nucleolus.

ribozyme (rī'-buh-zīm) An RNA molecule that functions as an enzyme, such as an intron that catalyzes its own removal during RNA splicing.

RNA interference (RNAi) A technique used to silence the expression of selected genes. RNAi uses synthetic double-stranded RNA molecules that match the sequence of a particular gene to trigger the breakdown of the gene's messenger RNA.

RNA polymerase An enzyme that links ribonucleotides into a growing RNA chain during transcription, based on complementary binding to nucleotides on a DNA template strand.

RNA processing Modification of RNA primary transcripts, including splicing out of introns, joining together of exons, and alteration of the 5' and 3' ends.

RNA splicing After synthesis of a eukaryotic primary RNA transcript, the removal of portions of the transcript (introns) that will not be included in the mRNA and the joining together of the remaining portions (exons).

rod A rodlike cell in the retina of the vertebrate eye, sensitive to low light intensity.

root An organ in vascular plants that anchors the plant and enables it to absorb water and minerals from the soil.

root cap A cone of cells at the tip of a plant root that protects the apical meristem.

root hair A tiny extension of a root epidermal cell, growing just behind the root tip and increasing surface area for absorption of water and minerals.

root pressure Pressure exerted in the roots of plants as the result of osmosis, causing exudation from cut stems and guttation of water from leaves.

root system All of a plant's roots, which anchor it in the soil, absorb and transport minerals and water, and store food.

rooted Describing a phylogenetic tree that contains a branch point (often, the one farthest to the left) representing the most recent common ancestor of all taxa in the tree.

rough ER That portion of the endoplasmic reticulum with ribosomes attached.

round window In the mammalian ear, the point of contact where vibrations of the stapes create a traveling series of pressure waves in the fluid of the cochlea.

r-selection Selection for life history traits that maximize reproductive success in uncrowded environments; also called density-independent selection.

rubisco (rū-bis'-kō) Ribulose bisphosphate (RuBP) carboxylase, the enzyme that catalyzes the first step of the Calvin cycle (the addition of CO_2 to RuBP).

ruminant (rū'-muh-nent) An animal, such as a cow or a sheep, with multiple stomach compartments specialized for an herbivorous diet.

S phase The synthesis phase of the cell cycle; the portion of interphase during which DNA is replicated.

saccule In the vertebrate ear, a chamber in the vestibule behind the oval window that participates in the sense of balance.

salicylic acid (sal'-i-sil'-ik) A signaling molecule in plants that may be partially responsible for activating systemic acquired resistance to pathogens.

salivary gland A gland associated with the oral cavity that secretes substances that lubricate food and begin the process of chemical digestion.

salt A compound resulting from the formation of an ionic bond; also called an ionic compound.

saltatory conduction (sol'-tuh-tōr'-ē) Rapid transmission of a nerve impulse along an axon, resulting from the action potential jumping from one node of Ranvier to another, skipping the myelin-sheathed regions of membrane.

sarcomere (sar'-kō-mēr) The fundamental, repeating unit of striated muscle, delimited by the Z lines.

sarcoplasmic reticulum (SR) (sar'-kō-plaz'-mik ruh-tik'-yū-lum) A specialized endoplasmic reticulum that regulates the calcium concentration in the cytosol of muscle cells.

saturated fatty acid A fatty acid in which all carbons in the hydrocarbon tail are connected by single bonds, thus maximizing the number of hydrogen atoms that are attached to the carbon skeleton.

savanna A tropical grassland biome with scattered individual trees and large herbivores and maintained by occasional fires and drought.

scaffolding protein A type of large relay protein to which several other relay proteins are simultaneously attached, increasing the efficiency of signal transduction.

scanning electron microscope (SEM) A microscope that uses an electron beam to scan the surface of a sample, coated with metal atoms, to study details of its topography.

schizophrenia (skit'-suh-frē'-nē-uh) A severe mental disturbance characterized by psychotic episodes in which patients have a distorted perception of reality.

Schwann cell A type of glial cell that forms insulating myelin sheaths around the axons of neurons in the peripheral nervous system.

science An approach to understanding the natural world.

scion (sī'-un) The twig grafted onto the stock when making a graft.

sclereid (sklār'-ē-id) A short, irregular sclerenchyma cell in nutshells and seed coats. Sclereids are scattered throughout the parenchyma of some plants.

sclerenchyma cell (skluh-ren'-kim-uh) A rigid, supportive plant cell type usually lacking a protoplast and possessing thick secondary walls strengthened by lignin at maturity.

scrotum A pouch of skin outside the abdomen that houses the testes; functions in maintaining the testes at the lower temperature required for spermatogenesis.

second law of thermodynamics The principle stating that every energy transfer or transformation increases the entropy of the universe. Usable forms of energy are at least partly converted to heat.

second messenger A small, nonprotein, water-soluble molecule or ion, such as a calcium ion (Ca^{2+}) or cyclic AMP, that relays a signal to a cell's interior in response to a signaling molecule bound by a signal receptor protein.

secondary cell wall In plant cells, a strong and durable matrix that is often deposited in several laminated layers around the plasma membrane and provides protection and support.

secondary consumer A carnivore that eats herbivores.

secondary endosymbiosis A process in eukaryotic evolution in which a heterotrophic eukaryotic cell engulfed a photosynthetic eukaryotic cell, which survived in a symbiotic relationship inside the heterotrophic cell.

secondary growth Growth produced by lateral meristems, thickening the roots and shoots of woody plants.

secondary immune response The adaptive immune response elicited on second or subsequent exposures to a particular antigen. The secondary immune response is more rapid, of greater magnitude, and of longer duration than the primary immune response.

secondary oocyte (ō'-uh-sīt) An oocyte that has completed the first of the two meiotic divisions.

secondary production The amount of chemical energy in consumers' food that is converted to their own new biomass during a given time period.

secondary structure Regions of repetitive coiling or folding of the polypeptide backbone of a protein due to hydrogen bonding between constituents of the backbone (not the side chains).

secondary succession A type of succession that occurs where an existing community has been cleared by some disturbance that leaves the soil or substrate intact.

secretion (1) The discharge of molecules synthesized by a cell. (2) The discharge of wastes from the body fluid into the filtrate.

secretory phase That portion of the uterine (menstrual) cycle when the endometrium continues to thicken, becomes more vascularized, and develops glands that secrete a fluid rich in glycogen.

seed An adaptation of some terrestrial plants consisting of an embryo packaged along with a store of food within a protective coat.

seed coat A tough outer covering of a seed, formed from the outer coat of an ovule. In a flowering plant, the seed coat encloses and protects the embryo and endosperm.

seedless vascular plant An informal name for a plant that has vascular tissue but lacks seeds. Seedless vascular plants form a paraphyletic group that includes the phyla Lycophyta (club mosses and their relatives) and Pterophyta (ferns and their relatives).

selective permeability A property of biological membranes that allows them to regulate the passage of substances across them.

self-incompatibility The ability of a seed plant to reject its own pollen and sometimes the pollen of closely related individuals.

semelparity Reproduction in which an organism produces all of its offspring in a single event; also known as big-bang reproduction.

semen (sē'-mun) The fluid that is ejaculated by the male during orgasm; contains sperm and secretions from several glands of the male reproductive tract.

semicircular canals A three-part chamber of the inner ear that functions in maintaining equilibrium.

semiconservative model Type of DNA replication in which the replicated double helix consists of one old strand, derived from the parental molecule, and one newly made strand.

semilunar valve A valve located at each exit of the heart, where the aorta leaves the left ventricle and the pulmonary artery leaves the right ventricle.

seminal vesicle (sem′-i-nul ves′-i-kul) A gland in males that secretes a fluid component of semen that lubricates and nourishes sperm.

seminiferous tubule (sem′-i-nif′-er-us) A highly coiled tube in the testis in which sperm are produced.

senescence (se-nes′-ens) The growth phase in a plant or plant part (as a leaf) from full maturity to death.

sensitive period A limited phase in an animal's development when learning of particular behaviors can take place; also called a critical period.

sensor In homeostasis, a receptor that detects a stimulus.

sensory adaptation The tendency of sensory neurons to become less sensitive when they are stimulated repeatedly.

sensory neuron A nerve cell that receives information from the internal or external environment and transmits signals to the central nervous system.

sensory reception The detection of a stimulus by sensory cells.

sensory receptor An organ, cell, or structure within a cell that responds to specific stimuli from an organism's external or internal environment.

sensory transduction The conversion of stimulus energy to a change in the membrane potential of a sensory receptor cell.

sepal (sē′-pul) A modified leaf in angiosperms that helps enclose and protect a flower bud before it opens.

septum (plural, **septa**) One of the cross-walls that divide a fungal hypha into cells. Septa generally have pores large enough to allow ribosomes, mitochondria, and even nuclei to flow from cell to cell.

serial endosymbiosis A hypothesis for the origin of eukaryotes consisting of a sequence of endosymbiotic events in which mitochondria, chloroplasts, and perhaps other cellular structures were derived from small prokaryotes that had been engulfed by larger cells.

serotonin (ser′-uh-tō′-nin) A neurotransmitter, synthesized from the amino acid tryptophan, that functions in the central nervous system.

set point In homeostasis in animals, a value maintained for a particular variable, such as body temperature or solute concentration.

seta (sē′-tuh) (plural, **setae**) The elongated stalk of a bryophyte sporophyte.

sex chromosome A chromosome responsible for determining the sex of an individual.

sex-linked gene A gene located on either sex chromosome. Most sex-linked genes are on the X chromosome and show distinctive patterns of inheritance; there are very few genes on the Y chromosome.

sexual dimorphism (dī-mor′-fizm) Differences between the secondary sex characteristics of males and females.

sexual reproduction A type of reproduction in which two parents give rise to offspring that have unique combinations of genes inherited from both parents via the gametes.

sexual selection A form of selection in which individuals with certain inherited characteristics are more likely than other individuals to obtain mates.

Shannon diversity An index of community diversity symbolized by H and represented by the equation $H = -(p_A \ln p_A + p_B \ln p_B + p_C \ln p_C + . . .)$, where A, B, C . . . are species, p is the relative abundance of each species, and ln is the natural logarithm.

shared ancestral character A character, shared by members of a particular clade, that originated in an ancestor that is not a member of that clade.

shared derived character An evolutionary novelty that is unique to a particular clade.

shoot system The aerial portion of a plant body, consisting of stems, leaves, and (in angiosperms) flowers.

short tandem repeat (STR) Simple sequence DNA containing multiple tandemly repeated units of two to five nucleotides. Variations in STRs act as genetic markers in STR analysis, used to prepare genetic profiles.

short-day plant A plant that flowers (usually in late summer, fall, or winter) only when the light period is shorter than a critical length.

short-term memory The ability to hold information, anticipations, or goals for a time and then release them if they become irrelevant.

sickle-cell disease A recessively inherited human blood disorder in which a single nucleotide change in the β-globin gene causes hemoglobin to aggregate, changing red blood cell shape and causing multiple symptoms in afflicted individuals.

sieve plate An end wall in a sieve-tube element, which facilitates the flow of phloem sap in angiosperm sieve tubes.

sieve-tube element A living cell that conducts sugars and other organic nutrients in the phloem of angiosperms; also called a sieve-tube member. Connected end to end, they form sieve tubes.

sign stimulus An external sensory cue that triggers a fixed action pattern by an animal.

signal In animal behavior, transmission of a stimulus from one animal to another. The term is also used in the context of communication in other kinds of organisms and in cell-to-cell communication in all multicellular organisms.

signal peptide A sequence of about 20 amino acids at or near the leading (amino) end of a polypeptide that targets it to the endoplasmic reticulum or other organelles in a eukaryotic cell.

signal transduction The linkage of a mechanical, chemical, or electromagnetic stimulus to a specific cellular response.

signal transduction pathway A series of steps linking a mechanical, chemical, or electrical stimulus to a specific cellular response.

signal-recognition particle (SRP) A protein-RNA complex that recognizes a signal peptide as it emerges from a ribosome and helps direct the ribosome to the endoplasmic reticulum (ER) by binding to a receptor protein on the ER.

silent mutation A nucleotide-pair substitution that has no observable effect on the phenotype; for example, within a gene, a mutation that results in a codon that codes for the same amino acid.

simple fruit A fruit derived from a single carpel or several fused carpels.

simple sequence DNA A DNA sequence that contains many copies of tandemly repeated short sequences.

single bond A single covalent bond; the sharing of a pair of valence electrons by two atoms.

single circulation A circulatory system consisting of a single pump and circuit, in which blood passes from the sites of gas exchange to the rest of the body before returning to the heart.

single nucleotide polymorphism (SNP) A single base-pair site in a genome where nucleotide variation is found in at least 1% of the population.

single-lens eye The camera-like eye found in some jellies, polychaete worms, spiders, and many molluscs.

single-strand binding protein A protein that binds to the unpaired DNA strands during DNA replication, stabilizing them and holding them apart while they serve as templates for the synthesis of complementary strands of DNA.

sinoatrial (SA) node A region in the right atrium of the heart that sets the rate and timing at which all cardiac muscle cells contract; the pacemaker.

sister chromatids Two copies of a duplicated chromosome attached to each other by proteins at the centromere and, sometimes, along the arms. While joined, two sister chromatids make up one chromosome. Chromatids are eventually separated during mitosis or meiosis II.

sister taxa Groups of organisms that share an immediate common ancestor and hence are each other's closest relatives.

skeletal muscle A type of striated muscle that is generally responsible for the voluntary movements of the body.

sliding-filament model The idea that muscle contraction is based on the movement of thin (actin) filaments along thick (myosin) filaments, shortening the sarcomere, the basic unit of muscle organization.

slow block to polyspermy The formation of the fertilization envelope and other changes in an egg's surface that prevent fusion of the egg with more than one sperm. The slow block begins about 1 minute after fertilization.

slow-twitch fiber A muscle fiber that can sustain long contractions.

small interfering RNA (siRNA) One of multiple small, single-stranded RNA molecules generated by cellular machinery from a long, linear, double-stranded RNA molecule. The siRNA associates with one or more proteins in a complex that can degrade or prevent translation of an mRNA with a complementary sequence. In some cases, siRNA can also block transcription by promoting chromatin modification.

small intestine The longest section of the alimentary canal, so named because of its small diameter compared with that of the large intestine; the principal site of the enzymatic hydrolysis of food macromolecules and the absorption of nutrients.

smooth ER That portion of the endoplasmic reticulum that is free of ribosomes.

smooth muscle A type of muscle lacking the striations of skeletal and cardiac muscle because of the uniform distribution of myosin filaments in the cells; responsible for involuntary body activities.

social learning Modification of behavior through the observation of other individuals.

sociobiology The study of social behavior based on evolutionary theory.

sodium-potassium pump A transport protein in the plasma membrane of animal cells that actively transports sodium out of the cell and potassium into the cell.

soil horizon A soil layer with physical characteristics that differ from those of the layers above or beneath.

solute (sol'-yūt) A substance that is dissolved in a solution.

solute potential (Ψ_S) A component of water potential that is proportional to the molarity of a solution and that measures the effect of solutes on the direction of water movement; also called osmotic potential, it can be either zero or negative.

solution A liquid that is a homogeneous mixture of two or more substances.

solvent The dissolving agent of a solution. Water is the most versatile solvent known.

somatic cell (sō-mat'-ik) Any cell in a multicellular organism except a sperm or egg or their precursors.

somite One of a series of blocks of mesoderm that exist in pairs just lateral to the notochord in a vertebrate embryo.

soredium (plural, **soredia**) In lichens, a small cluster of fungal hyphae with embedded algae.

sorus (plural, **sori**) A cluster of sporangia on a fern sporophyll. Sori may be arranged in various patterns, such as parallel lines or dots, which are useful in fern identification.

Southern blotting A technique that enables specific nucleotide sequences to be detected in samples of DNA. It involves gel electrophoresis of DNA molecules and their transfer to a membrane (blotting), followed by nucleic acid hybridization with a labeled probe.

spatial learning The establishment of a memory that reflects the environment's spatial structure.

spatial summation A phenomenon of neural integration in which the membrane potential of the postsynaptic cell is determined by the combined effect of EPSPs or IPSPs produced nearly simultaneously by different synapses.

speciation (spē'-sē-ā'-shun) An evolutionary process in which one species splits into two or more species.

species (spē'-sēz) A population or group of populations whose members have the potential to interbreed in nature and produce viable, fertile offspring, but do not produce viable, fertile offspring with members of other such groups.

species diversity The number and relative abundance of species in a biological community.

species richness The number of species in a biological community.

species-area curve The biodiversity pattern that shows that the larger the geographic area of a community is, the more species it has.

specific heat The amount of heat that must be absorbed or lost for 1 g of a substance to change its temperature by 1°C.

spectrophotometer An instrument that measures the proportions of light of different wavelengths absorbed and transmitted by a pigment solution.

sperm The male gamete.

spermatheca (sper'-muh-thē'-kuh) In many insects, a sac in the female reproductive system where sperm are stored.

spermatogenesis The continuous and prolific production of mature sperm cells in the testis.

spermatogonium (plural, **spermatogonia**) A cell that divides mitotically to form spermatocytes.

sphincter (sfink'-ter) A ringlike band of muscle fibers that controls the size of an opening in the body, such as the passage between the esophagus and the stomach.

spiral cleavage A type of embryonic development in protostomes in which the planes of cell division that transform the zygote into a ball of cells are diagonal to the vertical axis of the embryo. As a result, the cells of each tier sit in the grooves between cells of adjacent tiers.

spliceosome (splī'-sō-sōm) A large complex made up of proteins and RNA molecules that splices RNA by interacting with the ends of an RNA intron, releasing the intron and joining the two adjacent exons.

spongocoel (spon'-jō-sēl) The central cavity of a sponge.

spontaneous process A process that occurs without an overall input of energy; a process that is energetically favorable.

sporangium (spōr-an'-jē-um) (plural, **sporangia**) A multicellular organ in fungi and plants in which meiosis occurs and haploid cells develop.

spore (1) In the life cycle of a plant or alga undergoing alternation of generations, a haploid cell produced in the sporophyte by meiosis. A spore can divide by mitosis to develop into a multicellular haploid individual, the gametophyte, without fusing with another cell. (2) In fungi, a haploid cell, produced either sexually or asexually, that produces a mycelium after germination.

sporocyte A diploid cell, also known as a spore mother cell, that undergoes meiosis and generates haploid spores.

sporophyll (spō'-ruh-fil) A modified leaf that bears sporangia and hence is specialized for reproduction.

sporophyte (spō-ruh-fīt') In organisms (plants and some algae) that have alternation of generations, the multicellular diploid form that results from the union of gametes. The sporophyte produces haploid spores by meiosis that develop into gametophytes.

sporopollenin (spōr-uh-pol'-eh-nin) A durable polymer that covers exposed zygotes of charophyte algae and forms the walls of plant spores, preventing them from drying out.

stabilizing selection Natural selection in which intermediate phenotypes survive or reproduce more successfully than do extreme phenotypes.

stamen (stā'-men) The pollen-producing reproductive organ of a flower, consisting of an anther and a filament.

standard metabolic rate (SMR) Metabolic rate of a resting, fasting, and nonstressed ectotherm at a particular temperature.

starch A storage polysaccharide in plants, consisting entirely of glucose monomers joined by α glycosidic linkages.

start point In transcription, the nucleotide position on the promoter where RNA polymerase begins synthesis of RNA.

statocyst (stat'-uh-sist') A type of mechanoreceptor that functions in equilibrium in invertebrates by use of statoliths, which stimulate hair cells in relation to gravity.

statolith (stat'-uh-lith') (1) In plants, a specialized plastid that contains dense starch grains and may play a role in detecting gravity. (2) In invertebrates, a dense particle that settles in response to gravity and is found in sensory organs that function in equilibrium.

stele (stēl) The vascular tissue of a stem or root.

stem A vascular plant organ consisting of an alternating system of nodes and internodes that support the leaves and reproductive structures.

stem cell Any relatively unspecialized cell that can produce, during a single division, one identical daughter cell and one more specialized daughter cell that can undergo further differentiation.

steroid A type of lipid characterized by a carbon skeleton consisting of four fused rings with various chemical groups attached.

sticky end A single-stranded end of a double-stranded restriction fragment.

stigma (plural, **stigmata**) The sticky part of a flower's carpel, which receives pollen grains.

stimulus In feedback regulation, a fluctuation in a variable that triggers a response.

stipe A stemlike structure of a seaweed.

stock The plant that provides the root system when making a graft.

stoma (stō'-muh) (plural, **stomata**) A microscopic pore surrounded by guard cells in the epidermis of leaves and stems that allows gas exchange between the environment and the interior of the plant.

stomach An organ of the digestive system that stores food and performs preliminary steps of digestion.

stramenopile A protist in which a "hairy" flagellum (one covered with fine, hairlike projections) is paired with a shorter, smooth flagellum.

stratum (strah'-tum) (plural, **strata**) A rock layer formed when new layers of sediment cover older ones and compress them.

striated muscle Muscle in which the regular arrangement of filaments creates a pattern of light and dark bands.

strigolactones A class of plant hormone that inhibits shoot branching, triggers the germination of parasitic plant seeds, and stimulates the association of plant roots with mycorrhizal fungi.

strobilus (strō-bī'-lus) (plural, **strobili**) The technical term for a cluster of sporophylls known commonly as a cone, found in most gymnosperms and some seedless vascular plants.

stroke The death of nervous tissue in the brain, usually resulting from rupture or blockage of arteries in the head.

stroke volume The volume of blood pumped by a heart ventricle in a single contraction.

stroma (strō'-muh) The dense fluid within the chloroplast surrounding the thylakoid membrane and containing ribosomes and DNA; involved in the synthesis of organic molecules from carbon dioxide and water.

stromatolite Layered rock that results from the activities of prokaryotes that bind thin films of sediment together.

structural isomer One of several compounds that have the same molecular formula but differ in the covalent arrangements of their atoms.

style The stalk of a flower's carpel, with the ovary at the base and the stigma at the top.

substrate The reactant on which an enzyme works.

substrate feeder An animal that lives in or on its food source, eating its way through the food.

substrate-level phosphorylation The enzyme-catalyzed formation of ATP by direct transfer of a phosphate group to ADP from an intermediate substrate in catabolism.

sugar sink A plant organ that is a net consumer or storer of sugar. Growing roots, shoot tips, stems, and fruits are examples of sugar sinks supplied by phloem.

sugar source A plant organ in which sugar is being produced by either photosynthesis or the breakdown of starch. Mature leaves are the primary sugar sources of plants.

sulfhydryl group A chemical group consisting of a sulfur atom bonded to a hydrogen atom.

suprachiasmatic nucleus (SCN) A group of neurons in the hypothalamus of mammals that functions as a biological clock.

surface tension A measure of how difficult it is to stretch or break the surface of a liquid. Water has a high surface tension because of the hydrogen bonding of surface molecules.

surfactant A substance secreted by alveoli that decreases surface tension in the fluid that coats the alveoli.

survivorship curve A plot of the number of members of a cohort that are still alive at each age; one way to represent age-specific mortality.

suspension feeder An aquatic animal, such as a sponge, clam, or baleen whale, that feeds by sifting small organisms or food particles from the water.

sustainable agriculture Long-term productive farming methods that are environmentally safe.

sustainable development Development that meets the needs of people today without limiting the ability of future generations to meet their needs.

swim bladder In aquatic osteichthyans, an air sac that enables the animal to control its buoyancy in the water.

symbiont (sim'-bē-ont) The smaller participant in a symbiotic relationship, living in or on the host.

symbiosis An ecological relationship between organisms of two different species that live together in direct and intimate contact.

sympathetic division One of three divisions of the autonomic nervous system; generally increases energy expenditure and prepares the body for action.

sympatric speciation (sim-pat'-rik) The formation of new species in populations that live in the same geographic area.

symplast In plants, the continuum of cytoplasm connected by plasmodesmata between cells.

synapse (sin'-aps) The junction where a neuron communicates with another cell across a narrow gap via a neurotransmitter or an electrical coupling.

synapsid Member of an amniote clade distinguished by a single hole on each side of the skull. Synapsids include the mammals.

synapsis (si-nap'-sis) The pairing and physical connection of duplicated homologous chromosomes during prophase I of meiosis.

systematics A scientific discipline focused on classifying organisms and determining their evolutionary relationships.

systemic acquired resistance A defensive response in infected plants that helps protect healthy tissue from pathogenic invasion.

systemic circuit The branch of the circulatory system that supplies oxygenated blood to and carries deoxygenated blood away from organs and tissues throughout the body.

systems biology An approach to studying biology that aims to model the dynamic behavior of whole biological systems based on a study of the interactions among the system's parts.

systole (sis'-tō-lē) The stage of the cardiac cycle in which a heart chamber contracts and pumps blood.

systolic pressure Blood pressure in the arteries during contraction of the ventricles.

T cells The class of lymphocytes that mature in the thymus; they include both effector cells for the cell-mediated immune response and helper cells required for both branches of adaptive immunity.

taproot A main vertical root that develops from an embryonic root and gives rise to lateral (branch) roots.

tastant Any chemical that stimulates the sensory receptors in a taste bud.

taste bud A collection of modified epithelial cells on the tongue or in the mouth that are receptors for taste in mammals.

TATA box A DNA sequence in eukaryotic promoters crucial in forming the transcription initiation complex.

taxis (tak'-sis) An oriented movement toward or away from a stimulus.

taxon (plural, **taxa**) A named taxonomic unit at any given level of classification.

taxonomy (tak-son'-uh-mē) A scientific discipline concerned with naming and classifying the diverse forms of life.

Tay-Sachs disease A human genetic disease caused by a recessive allele for a dysfunctional enzyme, leading to accumulation of certain lipids in the brain. Seizures, blindness, and degeneration of motor and mental performance usually become manifest a few months after birth, followed by death within a few years.

technology The application of scientific knowledge for a specific purpose, often involving industry or commerce but also including uses in basic research.

telomerase An enzyme that catalyzes the lengthening of telomeres in eukaryotic germ cells.

telomere (tel'-uh-mēr) The tandemly repetitive DNA at the end of a eukaryotic chromosome's DNA molecule. Telomeres protect the organism's genes from being eroded during successive rounds of replication. *See also* repetitive DNA.

telophase The fifth and final stage of mitosis, in which daughter nuclei are forming and cytokinesis has typically begun.

temperate broadleaf forest A biome located throughout midlatitude regions where there is sufficient moisture to support the growth of large, broadleaf deciduous trees.

temperate grassland A terrestrial biome that exists at midlatitude regions and is dominated by grasses and forbs.

temperate phage A phage that is capable of replicating by either a lytic or lysogenic cycle.

temperature A measure of the intensity of heat in degrees, reflecting the average kinetic energy of the molecules.

template strand The DNA strand that provides the pattern, or template, for ordering, by complementary base pairing, the sequence of nucleotides in an RNA transcript.

temporal summation A phenomenon of neural integration in which the membrane potential of the postsynaptic cell in a chemical synapse is determined by the combined effect of EPSPs or IPSPs produced in rapid succession.

tendon A fibrous connective tissue that attaches muscle to bone.

terminator In bacteria, a sequence of nucleotides in DNA that marks the end of a gene and signals RNA polymerase to release the newly made RNA molecule and detach from the DNA.

territoriality A behavior in which an animal defends a bounded physical space against encroachment by other individuals, usually of its own species.

tertiary consumer (ter-shē-ār'-ē) A carnivore that eats other carnivores.

tertiary structure The overall shape of a protein molecule due to interactions of amino acid side chains, including hydrophobic interactions, ionic bonds, hydrogen bonds, and disulfide bridges.

testcross Breeding an organism of unknown genotype with a homozygous recessive individual to determine the unknown genotype. The ratio of phenotypes in the offspring reveals the unknown genotype.

testis (plural, **testes**) The male reproductive organ, or gonad, in which sperm and reproductive hormones are produced.

testosterone A steroid hormone required for development of the male reproductive system, spermatogenesis, and male secondary sex characteristics; the major androgen in mammals.

tetanus (tet'-uh-nus) The maximal, sustained contraction of a skeletal muscle, caused by a very high frequency of action potentials elicited by continual stimulation.

tetrapod A vertebrate clade whose members have limbs with digits. Tetrapods include mammals, amphibians, and birds and other reptiles.

thalamus (thal'-uh-mus) An integrating center of the vertebrate forebrain. Neurons with cell bodies in the thalamus relay neural input to specific areas in the cerebral cortex and regulate what information goes to the cerebral cortex.

thallus (plural, **thalli**) A seaweed body that is plantlike, consisting of a holdfast, stipe, and blades, yet lacks true roots, stems, and leaves.

theory An explanation that is broader in scope than a hypothesis, generates new hypotheses, and is supported by a large body of evidence.

thermal energy *See* heat.

thermocline A narrow stratum of abrupt temperature change in the ocean and in many temperate-zone lakes.

thermodynamics (ther'-mō-dī-nam'-iks) The study of energy transformations that occur in a collection of matter. *See* first law of thermodynamics; second law of thermodynamics.

thermoreceptor A receptor stimulated by either heat or cold.

thermoregulation The maintenance of internal body temperature within a tolerable range.

theropod Member of a group of dinosaurs that were bipedal carnivores.

thick filament A filament composed of staggered arrays of myosin molecules; a component of myofibrils in muscle fibers.

thigmomorphogenesis A response in plants to chronic mechanical stimulation, resulting from increased ethylene production. An example is thickening stems in response to strong winds.

thigmotropism (thig-mo'-truh-pizm) A directional growth of a plant in response to touch.

thin filament A filament consisting of two strands of actin and two strands of regulatory protein coiled around one another; a component of myofibrils in muscle fibers.

threatened species A species that is considered likely to become endangered in the foreseeable future.

threshold The potential that an excitable cell membrane must reach for an action potential to be initiated.

thrombus A fibrin-containing clot that forms in a blood vessel and blocks the flow of blood.

thylakoid (thī'-luh-koyd) A flattened, membranous sac inside a chloroplast. Thylakoids often exist in stacks called grana that are interconnected; their membranes contain molecular "machinery" used to convert light energy to chemical energy.

thymus (thī'-mus) A small organ in the thoracic cavity of vertebrates where maturation of T cells is completed.

thyroid gland An endocrine gland, located on the ventral surface of the trachea, that secretes two iodine-containing hormones, triiodothyronine (T_3) and thyroxine (T_4), as well as calcitonin.

thyroxine (T_4) One of two iodine-containing hormones that are secreted by the thyroid gland and that help regulate metabolism, development, and maturation in vertebrates.

Ti plasmid A plasmid of a tumor-inducing bacterium (the plant pathogen *Agrobacterium*) that integrates a segment of its DNA (T DNA) into a chromosome of a host plant. The Ti plasmid is frequently used as a vector for genetic engineering in plants.

tidal volume The volume of air a mammal inhales and exhales with each breath.

tight junction A type of intercellular junction between animal cells that prevents the leakage of material through the space between cells.

tissue An integrated group of cells with a common structure, function, or both.

tissue system One or more tissues organized into a functional unit connecting the organs of a plant.

Toll-like receptor (TLR) A membrane receptor on a phagocytic white blood cell that recognizes fragments of molecules common to a set of pathogens.

tonicity The ability of a solution surrounding a cell to cause that cell to gain or lose water.

top-down model A model of community organization in which predation influences community organization by controlling herbivore numbers, which in turn control plant or phytoplankton numbers, which in turn control nutrient levels; also called the trophic cascade model.

topoisomerase A protein that breaks, swivels, and rejoins DNA strands. During DNA replication, topoisomerase helps to relieve strain in the double helix ahead of the replication fork.

topsoil A mixture of particles derived from rock, living organisms, and decaying organic material (humus).

torpor A physiological state in which activity is low and metabolism decreases.

torsion In gastropods, a developmental process in which the visceral mass rotates up to 180°, causing the animal's anus and mantle cavity to be positioned above its head.

totipotent (tō'-tuh-pōt'-ent) Describing a cell that can give rise to all parts of the embryo and adult, as well as extraembryonic membranes in species that have them.

trace element An element indispensable for life but required in extremely minute amounts.

trachea (trā-kē-uh) The portion of the respiratory tract that passes from the larynx to the bronchi; also called the windpipe.

tracheal system In insects, a system of branched, air-filled tubes that extends throughout the body and carries oxygen directly to cells.

tracheid (trā'-kē-id) A long, tapered water-conducting cell found in the xylem of nearly all vascular plants. Functioning tracheids are no longer living.

trait One of two or more detectable variants in a genetic character.

trans fat An unsaturated fat, formed artificially during hydrogenation of oils, containing one or more *trans* double bonds.

transcription The synthesis of RNA using a DNA template.

transcription factor A regulatory protein that binds to DNA and affects transcription of specific genes.

transcription initiation complex The completed assembly of transcription factors and RNA polymerase bound to a promoter.

transcription unit A region of DNA that is transcribed into an RNA molecule.

transduction (1) A process in which phages (viruses) carry bacterial DNA from one bacterial cell to another. When these two cells are members of different species, transduction results in horizontal gene transfer. (2) In cellular communication, the conversion of a signal from outside the cell to a form that can bring about a specific cellular response; also called *signal transduction*.

transfer RNA (tRNA) An RNA molecule that functions as a translator between nucleic acid and protein languages by carrying specific amino acids to the ribosome, where they recognize the appropriate codons in the mRNA.

transformation (1) The conversion of a normal animal cell to a cancerous cell. (2) A change in genotype and phenotype due to the assimilation of external DNA by a cell. When the external DNA is from a member of a different species, transformation results in horizontal gene transfer.

transgenic Pertaining to an organism whose genome contains a gene introduced from another organism of the same or a different species.

translation The synthesis of a polypeptide using the genetic information encoded in an mRNA molecule. There is a change of "language" from nucleotides to amino acids.

translocation (1) An aberration in chromosome structure resulting from attachment of a chromosomal fragment to a nonhomologous chromosome. (2) During protein synthesis, the third stage in the elongation cycle, when the RNA carrying the growing polypeptide moves from the A site to the P site on the ribosome. (3) The transport of organic nutrients in the phloem of vascular plants.

transmission The passage of a nerve impulse along axons.

transmission electron microscope (TEM) A microscope that passes an electron beam through very thin sections stained with metal atoms and is primarily used to study the internal ultrastructure of cells.

transpiration The evaporative loss of water from a plant.

transport epithelium One or more layers of specialized epithelial cells that carry out and regulate solute movement.

transport protein A transmembrane protein that helps a certain substance or class of closely related substances to cross the membrane.

transport vesicle A small membranous sac in a eukaryotic cell's cytoplasm carrying molecules produced by the cell.

transposable element A segment of DNA that can move within the genome of a cell by means of a DNA or RNA intermediate; also called a transposable genetic element.

transposon A transposable element that moves within a genome by means of a DNA intermediate.

transverse (T) tubule An infolding of the plasma membrane of skeletal muscle cells.

triacylglycerol (trī-as′-ul-glis′-uh-rol) A lipid consisting of three fatty acids linked to one glycerol molecule; also called a fat or triglyceride.

triiodothyronine (T₃) (trī′-ī-ō′-dō-thī′-rō-nēn) One of two iodine-containing hormones that are secreted by the thyroid gland and that help regulate metabolism, development, and maturation in vertebrates.

trimester In human development, one of three 3-month-long periods of pregnancy.

triple response A plant growth maneuver in response to mechanical stress, involving slowing of stem elongation, thickening of the stem, and a curvature that causes the stem to start growing horizontally.

triplet code A genetic information system in which a set of three-nucleotide-long words specify the amino acids for polypeptide chains.

triploblastic Possessing three germ layers: the endoderm, mesoderm, and ectoderm. Most eumetazoans are triploblastic.

trisomic Referring to a diploid cell that has three copies of a particular chromosome instead of the normal two.

trochophore larva (trō′-kuh-fōr) Distinctive larval stage observed in some lophotrochozoan animals, including some annelids and molluscs.

trophic efficiency The percentage of production transferred from one trophic level to the next.

trophic structure The different feeding relationships in an ecosystem, which determine the route of energy flow and the pattern of chemical cycling.

trophoblast The outer epithelium of a mammalian blastocyst. It forms the fetal part of the placenta, supporting embryonic development but not forming part of the embryo proper.

tropic hormone A hormone that has an endocrine gland or cells as a target.

tropical dry forest A terrestrial biome characterized by relatively high temperatures and precipitation overall but with a pronounced dry season.

tropical rain forest A terrestrial biome characterized by relatively high precipitation and temperatures year-round.

tropics Latitudes between 23.5° north and south.

tropism A growth response that results in the curvature of whole plant organs toward or away from stimuli due to differential rates of cell elongation.

tropomyosin The regulatory protein that blocks the myosin-binding sites on actin molecules.

troponin complex The regulatory proteins that control the position of tropomyosin on the thin filament.

true-breeding Referring to organisms that produce offspring of the same variety over many generations of self-pollination.

tubal ligation A means of sterilization in which a woman's two oviducts (fallopian tubes) are tied closed to prevent eggs from reaching the uterus. A segment of each oviduct is removed.

tube foot One of numerous extensions of an echinoderm's water vascular system. Tube feet function in locomotion and feeding.

tumor-suppressor gene A gene whose protein product inhibits cell division, thereby preventing the uncontrolled cell growth that contributes to cancer.

tundra A terrestrial biome at the extreme limits of plant growth. At the northernmost limits, it is called arctic tundra, and at high altitudes, where plant forms are limited to low shrubby or matlike vegetation, it is called alpine tundra.

tunicate Member of the clade Urochordata, sessile marine chordates that lack a backbone.

turgid (ter′-jid) Swollen or distended, as in plant cells. (A walled cell becomes turgid if it has a lower water potential than its surroundings, resulting in entry of water.)

turgor pressure The force directed against a plant cell wall after the influx of water and swelling of the cell due to osmosis.

turnover The mixing of waters as a result of changing water-temperature profiles in a lake.

turnover time The time required to replace the standing crop of a population or group of populations (for example, of phytoplankton), calculated as the ratio of standing crop to production.

twin study A behavioral study in which researchers compare the behavior of identical twins raised apart with that of identical twins raised in the same household.

tympanic membrane Another name for the eardrum, the membrane between the outer and middle ear.

uniformitarianism The principle that mechanisms of change are constant over time. *See* catastrophism.

Unikonta (yū′-ni-kon′-tuh) One of five supergroups of eukaryotes proposed in a current hypothesis of the evolutionary history of eukaryotes. This clade, which is supported by studies of myosin proteins and DNA, consists of amoebozoans and opisthokonts. *See also* Excavata, Chromalveolata, Rhizaria, and Archaeplastida.

unsaturated fatty acid A fatty acid that has one or more double bonds between carbons in the hydrocarbon tail. Such bonding reduces the number of hydrogen atoms attached to the carbon skeleton.

urea A soluble nitrogenous waste produced in the liver by a metabolic cycle that combines ammonia with carbon dioxide.

ureter (yū-rē′-ter) A duct leading from the kidney to the urinary bladder.

urethra (yū-rē′-thruh) A tube that releases urine from the mammalian body near the vagina in females and through the penis in males; also serves in males as the exit tube for the reproductive system.

uric acid A product of protein and purine metabolism and the major nitrogenous waste product of insects, land snails, and many reptiles. Uric acid is relatively nontoxic and largely insoluble.

urinary bladder The pouch where urine is stored prior to elimination.

uterine cycle The changes that occur in the uterus during the reproductive cycle of the human female; also called the menstrual cycle.

uterus A female organ where eggs are fertilized and/or development of the young occurs.

utricle In the vertebrate ear, a chamber in the vestibule behind the oval window that opens into the three semicircular canals.

vaccination *See* immunization.

vaccine A harmless variant or derivative of a pathogen that stimulates a host's immune system to mount defenses against the pathogen.

vacuole (vak′-yū-ōl′) A membrane-bounded vesicle whose specialized function varies in different kinds of cells.

vagina Part of the female reproductive system between the uterus and the outside opening; the birth canal in mammals. During copulation, the vagina accommodates the male's penis and receives sperm.

valence The bonding capacity of a given atom; usually equals the number of unpaired electrons required to complete the atom's outermost (valence) shell.

valence electron An electron in the outermost electron shell.

valence shell The outermost energy shell of an atom, containing the valence electrons involved in the chemical reactions of that atom.

van der Waals interactions Weak attractions between molecules or parts of molecules that result from transient local partial charges.

variation Differences between members of the same species.

vas deferens In mammals, the tube in the male reproductive system in which sperm travel from the epididymis to the urethra.

vasa recta The capillary system in the kidney that serves the loop of Henle.

vascular cambium A cylinder of meristematic tissue in woody plants that adds layers of secondary vascular tissue called secondary xylem (wood) and secondary phloem.

vascular plant A plant with vascular tissue. Vascular plants include all living plant species except liverworts, mosses, and hornworts.

vascular tissue Plant tissue consisting of cells joined into tubes that transport water and nutrients throughout the plant body.

vascular tissue system A transport system formed by xylem and phloem throughout a vascular plant. Xylem transports water and minerals; phloem transports sugars, the products of photosynthesis.

vasectomy The cutting and sealing of each vas deferens to prevent sperm from entering the urethra.

vasocongestion The filling of a tissue with blood, caused by increased blood flow through the arteries of that tissue.

vasoconstriction A decrease in the diameter of blood vessels caused by contraction of smooth muscles in the vessel walls.

vasodilation An increase in the diameter of blood vessels caused by relaxation of smooth muscles in the vessel walls.

vector An organism that transmits pathogens from one host to another.

vegetal pole The point at the end of an egg in the hemisphere where most yolk is concentrated; opposite of animal pole.

vegetative reproduction Cloning of plants by asexual means.

vein (1) In animals, a vessel that carries blood toward the heart. (2) In plants, a vascular bundle in a leaf.

ventilation The flow of air or water over a respiratory surface.

ventral Pertaining to the underside, or bottom, of an animal with radial or bilateral symmetry.

ventricle (ven'-tri-kul) (1) A heart chamber that pumps blood out of the heart. (2) A space in the vertebrate brain, filled with cerebrospinal fluid.

venule (ven'-yūl) A vessel that conveys blood between a capillary bed and a vein.

vernalization The use of cold treatment to induce a plant to flower.

vertebrate A chordate animal with a backbone, including sharks and rays, ray-finned fishes, coelacanths, lungfishes, amphibians, reptiles, and mammals.

vesicle (ves'-i-kul) A membranous sac in the cytoplasm of a eukaryotic cell.

vessel A continuous water-conducting micropipe found in most angiosperms and a few nonflowering vascular plants.

vessel element A short, wide water-conducting cell found in the xylem of most angiosperms and a few nonflowering vascular plants. Dead at maturity, vessel elements are aligned end to end to form micropipes called vessels.

vestigial structure A feature of an organism that is a historical remnant of a structure that served a function in the organism's ancestors.

villus (plural, **villi**) (1) A finger-like projection of the inner surface of the small intestine. (2) A finger-like projection of the chorion of the mammalian placenta. Large numbers of villi increase the surface areas of these organs.

viral envelope A membrane, derived from membranes of the host cell, that cloaks the capsid, which in turn encloses a viral genome.

viroid (vī'-royd) A plant pathogen consisting of a molecule of naked, circular RNA a few hundred nucleotides long.

virulent Describing a pathogen against which an organism has little specific defense.

virulent phage A phage that replicates only by a lytic cycle.

virus An infectious particle incapable of replicating outside of a cell, consisting of an RNA or DNA genome surrounded by a protein coat (capsid) and, for some viruses, a membranous envelope.

visceral mass One of the three main parts of a mollusc; the part containing most of the internal organs. *See also* foot, mantle.

visible light That portion of the electromagnetic spectrum that can be detected as various colors by the human eye, ranging in wavelength from about 380 nm to about 750 nm.

vital capacity The maximum volume of air that a mammal can inhale and exhale with each breath.

vitamin An organic molecule required in the diet in very small amounts. Many vitamins serve as coenzymes or parts of coenzymes.

viviparous (vī-vip'-uh-rus) Referring to a type of development in which the young are born alive after having been nourished in the uterus by blood from the placenta.

voltage-gated ion channel A specialized ion channel that opens or closes in response to changes in membrane potential.

vulva Collective term for the female external genitalia.

water potential (Ψ) The physical property predicting the direction in which water will flow, governed by solute concentration and applied pressure.

water vascular system A network of hydraulic canals unique to echinoderms that branches into extensions called tube feet, which function in locomotion and feeding.

wavelength The distance between crests of waves, such as those of the electromagnetic spectrum.

wetland A habitat that is inundated by water at least some of the time and that supports plants adapted to water-saturated soil.

white matter Tracts of axons within the CNS.

wild type The phenotype most commonly observed in natural populations; also refers to the individual with that phenotype.

wilting The drooping of leaves and stems as a result of plant cells becoming flaccid.

wobble Flexibility in the base-pairing rules in which the nucleotide at the 5' end of a tRNA anticodon can form hydrogen bonds with more than one kind of base in the third position (3' end) of a codon.

xerophyte A plant adapted to an arid climate.

X-linked gene A gene located on the X chromosome; such genes show a distinctive pattern of inheritance.

X-ray crystallography A technique used to study the three-dimensional structure of molecules. It depends on the diffraction of an X-ray beam by the individual atoms of a crystallized molecule.

xylem (zī'-lum) Vascular plant tissue consisting mainly of tubular dead cells that conduct most of the water and minerals upward from the roots to the rest of the plant.

xylem sap The dilute solution of water and dissolved minerals carried through vessels and tracheids.

yeast Single-celled fungus that reproduces asexually by binary fission or by the pinching of small buds off a parent cell. Some species exhibit cell fusion between different mating types.

yolk Nutrients stored in an egg.

zero population growth (ZPG) A period of stability in population size, when additions to the population through births and immigration are balanced by subtractions through deaths and emigration.

zona pellucida The extracellular matrix surrounding a mammalian egg.

zone of polarizing activity (ZPA) A block of mesoderm located just under the ectoderm where the posterior side of a limb bud is attached to the body; required for proper pattern formation along the anterior-posterior axis of the limb.

zoned reserve An extensive region that includes areas relatively undisturbed by humans surrounded by areas that have been changed by human activity and are used for economic gain.

zoonotic pathogen A disease-causing agent that is transmitted to humans from other animals.

zoospore Flagellated spore found in chytrid fungi and some protists.

zygomycete (zī'-guh-mī'-sēt) Member of the fungal phylum Zygomycota, characterized by the formation of a sturdy structure called a zygosporangium during sexual reproduction.

zygosporangium (zī'-guh-spōr-an'-jē-um) In zygomycete fungi, a sturdy multinucleate structure in which karyogamy and meiosis occur.

zygote (zī'-gōt) The diploid cell produced by the union of haploid gametes during fertilization; a fertilized egg.

Index

Cotyledons, **628**, 807–8
Counseling, genetic, 279
Countercurrent exchange, **865**, **917**, 957–58
Countercurrent heat exchangers, 865
Countercurrent multiplier systems, **966**–67
Courtship rituals
    behavioral isolation and, 490*f*
    external fertilization and, 1000
    forms of animal communication in, 1120–21
    genetic basis of, 1134
    sexual selection and, 482–83
    sexual selection and female mate choice in,
        1131–32
Covalent bonds, **38**
    of disaccharides, 70
    in organic compounds, 60–61, 66
    protein tertiary structure and, 83*f*
Cowbirds, 1199
Coyotes, 890
Crabs, 691, 1194
Cranes, 1124
Craniates, **701**–3. *See also* Vertebrates
    derived characters of, 701–2
    hagfishes, 702
    origin of, 702
"Crank" drug, 63
Crassulacean acid metabolism (CAM) plants,
    201–**2**, 778
Crawling, 1111, 1113
Crayfish, 916*f*, 1090
C-reactive protein (CRP), 914, 915
Creatine phosphate, 1106
Crenarchaeota, 567, 570
Cretaceous mass extinction, 522
Creutzfeldt-Jakob disease, 393
Creuzot, John, 24*f*
Crick, Francis
    central dogma of, 328
    discovery of DNA molecular structure by, 3, 24, 305,
        308–10
    J. A. Steitz's work with, 246–47
    model of DNA replication of, 311–12
Crickets, 433, 690*f*
Cri du chat, 300
Crime scene investigation. *See* Forensic science
Crinoidea, 694
Cristae, **110**
Critical load, **1254**
Critical period, 1123
Crocodiles, 547, 717
Crop plants, 815–19. *See also* Angiosperms (Anthophyta);
    Plant(s)
    artificial selection and breeding of, 815–16
    biotechnology and genetic engineering of, 816–19
    debate over transgenic, 817–19
    domestication, artificial selection, and genetic
        engineering of, 801
    impact of oomycetes on, 588–89
    seed plants as, 633
    transgenic and genetically modified, 421–23
Crop rotation, **795**
Cross-fostering studies, **1123**
Crossing over, 254*f*, **294**
    gene duplication due to unequal, 439
    in meiosis, 254*f*
    in recombination of linked genes, 294–95*f*
    in sexual life cycles, 257, 258, 259*f*
Cross-pollination, **627**
    angiosperm, 627–28
    G. Mendel's techniques of, 263–64
    of plants, 815–16
Cross-talk, cell-signaling, 221–22
Crown gall disease, 736
Crows, 1129
Crustaceans, 446*f*, 527, 669*f*, **686**, 691–92
Crustose lichens, 649*f*

Cryolophosaurus, 507, 507*f*
Cryptic coloration, **1197**
Cryptochromes, 836
Crypts, 779*f*
Crystallin, 361*f*
Crystals, ice, 50*f*
Ctenophora, 667*f*
C-terminus, 80, 340
Cuboidal epithelium, 856*f*
Cubozoans (Cubozoa), 672
Cuckoo bee, 1197*f*
Culex pipiens (mosquito), 480
Culture, **1128**
    evolution of human social behavior and,
        1139
    social learning and, 1128
Cupula, 1094
Cuticle, **604**, **683**, 686, **742**
Cutthroat trout, 1183*f*
Cuttings, plant, 814, 829
Cuttlefish, 482
Cuvier, Georges, 453*f*, 454–55
Cyanide, 817*f*
Cyanobacteria
    as bacterial group, 569*f*
    blooms of, 1224
    bryophytes and, 608*f*, 609
    chemical recycling by, 570
    W. F. Doolittle's work on, 534–35
    endosymbiosis and, 576, 590
    fungi and, as lichens, 645, 649–50
    glycolysis and ancient, 179
    land colonization by, 518
    metabolic cooperation in, 565
    photosynthesis of, 195, 516
    terrestrial, 600
Cycadophyta, 622*f*
Cycads (Cycadophyta), 623*f*
Cyclic AMP (cyclic adenosine monophosphate, cAMP),
    216–17, **355**, 978, 1057
Cyclic electron flow, **195**
Cyclic GMP (cGMP), 217, 822–23
Cyclin, **239**–40
Cyclin-dependent kinases (cdks), **239**–40
Cycliophora, 668*f*
Cyclosporine, 651
Cynodonts, 513*f*
Cysteine, 65*f*, 79*f*
Cystic fibrosis, 273, **276**, 277
Cystic kidney disease, 1041
Cystinuria, 135
Cytochrome *c*, 224, 548
Cytochromes, **173**, 196
Cytogenetic maps, **296**–**97**, 427–28
Cytokines, **934**, 975, 979
Cytokinesis, **230**, 233*f*, 254*f*–55*f*
Cytokinins, 827*t*, **829**–30
Cytology, 97, 286
Cytoplasm, **98**
    cell cycle control signals in, 238
    cell-signaling responses in, 219–20
    cytokinesis and division of, 230
    of prokaryotic and eukaryotic cells, 98
Cytoplasmic determinants, **367**, 368*f*, 1036
Cytoplasmic genes, 300–301
Cytoplasmic responses, cell-signaling, 219–20
Cytoplasmic streaming, 117*f*–**18**, 589, 594
Cytosine, 87*f*–88, 308
Cytoskeletons, **112**–18
    actin microfilaments of, 116–18
    animal cell, 100*f*
    ATP mechanical work and, 151
    intermediate filaments of, 118
    membrane proteins and attachment to, 129*f*
    microtubules of, 113–16
    in morphogenesis, 1033–34

plant cell, 101*f*
support, motility, and regulation roles of,
    112–13
Cytosol, **98**
Cytosolic calcium, 822–23
Cytotoxic T cells, **941**–42

D

dalton (atomic mass unit), **33**, 52
Dalton, John, 33
Dance language, honeybee, 1121–22
Dandelions, 804*f*, 811*f*, 1181*f*
Danielli, James, 126
Danio rerio (zebrafish), 24
Daphnia, 998, 1179*f*
Darkness
    flowering in long-night plants and, 839–40
    plant etiolation response to, 821–22
Dark responses, rod cell, 1099*f*
D'Arrigo, Rosanne, 753*f*
Darwin, Charles
    barnacles and, 692
    Beagle voyage and field research of, on adaptations,
        455–57
    on earthworms, 682
    evidence supporting theory of, 460–67
    in flower pollination mutualism, 806
    on grandeur of evolutionary process, 467
    historical context of life and ideas of, 453–55
    on island species, 466
    on lung evolution from swim bladders, 707
    on mystery of speciation, 488
    on natural selection and differential reproductive
        success, 259–60
    on natural selection and inheritance, 469–70
    publication of *The Origin of Species* by, 452
    on speciation, 457–60
    on species diversity of tropics, 1211
    study by, of phototropism in grass coleoptiles, 825
    theory of descent with modification by, 14–16 (*see
        also* Descent with modification theory; Evolu-
        tion; Natural selection)
    timeline of work of, 453*f*
Darwin, Erasmus, 454
Darwin, Francis, 825
Darwinism, 14. *See also* Darwin, Charles; Descent
    with modification theory; Evolution; Natural
    selection
Data, **18**–19
Databases, genome-sequence, 429, 430*f*
Dating, fossil record, 512
dATP, 314
Daughter cells, 228, 229–30
Davidson, Norman, 850
Davson, Hugh, 126
Day-neutral plants, **839**
db gene, 893–94
DDT pesticide, 157, 1256
Dead zone, 1255
Death, cell. *See* Apoptosis
Deaths
    demographics and rates of, 1173–75
    high rates of, and reproductive rates, 1181
    population density and rates of, 1182
    population dynamics and, 1171*f*–72, 1175–76
    rate of human, 1188
Death signals, apoptosis, 224–25. *See also* Apoptosis
Decapods, **691**
December solstice, 1147*f*
Deciduous forest, nutrient cycling in, 1231
Declining-population approach, population conserva-
    tion, 1247–49
Decomposers, **570**, **1220**
    fungi as, 637, 639*f*, 642*f*, 645, 646, 648
    gymnamoebas, 596
    lichens as, 650

Signal transduction pathways, **207**
 coordinate control of, 362
 evolution of, 207
 general model for, in plants, 822*f*
 induction in differential gene expression and, 367, 368*f*
 integration of, in apoptosis, 223–25
 sensory amplification in, 1087–88
 in visual sensory transduction, 1098
Sign stimulus, **1119**
Silencing
 gene expression, 410–11
 transcription, 360, 366
Silent mutations, **344**, 345*f*, 470–71
Silk, 82*f*, 687
Silkworm moths, 1088–89*f*
Silverfish, 690*f*
Silverman, Mike, 92
Silversword plants, 540
Silver-washed fritillaries, 1149
Similarity, species and, 489*f*
Simple columnar epithelium, 856*f*
Simple fruits, **810**
Simple leaves, 741*f*
Simple sequence DNA, **436**–37
Simple squamous epithelium, 856*f*
Singer, S. J., 126
Singing, fruit fly, 1120*f*
Single bonds, **38**
Single-celled organisms
 eukaryotes and protists as, 575–76
 first, 514–17
Single circulation, **900**
Single-lens eyes, **1096**–97
Single nucleotide polymorphisms (SNPs), **411**–12, 417–18, 445
Single-strand binding proteins, **314**
Single-stranded DNA (ssDNA) viruses, 387*t*
Single-stranded RNA (ssRNA) viruses, 387*t*, 388*f*
Siphons, cone snail, 850
Sirenia, 725*f*
Sister cells, 228
Sister chromatid cohesion, 229, 253, 257
Sister chromatids, **229**–30, 251*f*, 255*f*, 257
Sister taxa, **538**–39
Sitis inversus, 1042
Size
 of genomes, 432–33
 locomotion costs and, 1115
 metabolic rate and animal body, 870
 prokaryote, 557–58
 of prokaryotic vs. eukaryotic cells, 8*f*, 98
 protist, 575
 of skeletons, 1112–13
Skeletal muscle, **858***f*, **1104**–9
 nervous system regulation of tension of, 1108–9*f*
 regulation of contraction of, 1106–7*f*
 sliding-filament model of muscle contraction and, 1104–6
 types of fibers in, 1109
Skeletal systems, 1110–13
 endoskeletons, 1112
 energy costs of locomotion in, 1114–15
 exoskeletons, 1111–12
 hydrostatic skeletons, 1111
 interaction of muscles and skeletons in locomotion in, 1110–11 (*see also* Locomotion)
 size and scale of skeletons in, 1112–13
 types of, 1111–13
Skeletons, carbon, 61–63
Skin
 cancer of, 28, 318, 1259
 human, 1088*f*
 mammalian, 864
 pigmentation of human, 274

Skinner, B. F., 1125
Skulls, human vs. chimpanzee, 525–26, 541
Skunks, 490*f*
Slash-and-burn agriculture, 634
Sleep, brain functions and, 1067–70
Sleeping sickness, 580–81, 691
Sliding-filament model, **1104**–6
Slime, hagfish, 702
Slime layer, 558
Slime molds, 594–96
Slow block to polyspermy, **1023**
Slow-twitch fibers, **1109**
Slugs, 677
Small interfering RNAs (siRNAs), **365**, 366
Small nuclear ribonucleoproteins (snRNPs), 247, 335
Small nuclear RNA (snRNA), 335–36
Smallpox, 391
Small-scale mutations, 344–46
Smithells, Richard, 879
Smithies, Oliver, 410
Smooth ER, 100*f*, 101*f*, 104*f*-**5**
Smooth muscle, **858***f*, **1110**
Smuts, 646
Snails, 490*f*, 503–4, 677, 680–81*f*
Snakes, 20–23, 482*f*, 716*f*, 717, 871, 1089*f*, 1135–36
Snapdragons, 271–72
Snapping shrimp, 494
Snook, Rhonda, 1002*f*
Snowball Earth hypothesis, 517–18
Snow geese, 1119*f*
Snow pea, 631*f*
Soapberry bugs, 461
Social behavior, 1139
Social learning, **1127**–28, 1132
Society
 plant biotechnology and, 819
 science, technology, and, 24–25
 science as social process, 23–24
Sociobiology, **1139**
Sociobiology: The New Synthesis (book), 1139
Sockeye salmon, 955*f*
Sodium, 32*t*, 877–78*t*
Sodium chloride, 31, 39–40
 dissolving of, in water, 50–51*f*
 elimination of excess, by marine birds, 957–58
 human diets and, 877–78*t*
 kidney processing of, 965–67
 in treating diarrhea, 137–38
Sodium-potassium pump, **136**
 as active transport, 136
 membrane proteins and, 137
Software, systems biology and, 430–32
Soil
 bacteria in, 568*f*, 570, 792–95
 bryophyte reduction of nitrogen leaching from, 609*f*
 plant resource acquisition from, 766–67
 species distributions and, 1167
Soil worm. *See Caenorhabditis elegans* (soil worm)
Solar energy. *See also* Energy
 in photosynthesis, 43, 184
 transfer and transformation of, as theme in biology, 6–7
Solid water. *See* Ice
Solomon, Susan, 28–29, 50
Solute potential, **769**
Solutes, **50**
 animal osmoregulation of, 953–58
 concentrations of, in aqueous solutions, 51–52
 diffusion of, 132–33
 effects of, on water potential, 769–70
 short-distance transport of, across plant plasma membranes, 768, 769*f*
Solutions, **50**
Solvents, **50**–52

Somatic cells, **229**–30, **249**
Somites, 700, **1032**–33
Songs
 courtship, 1134–35
 learning of, by birds, 1126–27
Sonic hedgehog growth factor, 1041
Soredia, **649**
Sori, **612**
Sound, 1088, 1090–94
Sour taste, 1101–2
South Atlantic Subtropical Gyre, 1148*f*
Southern, Edwin, 406
Southern blotting, **406**–7
South Pacific Subtropical Gyre, 1148*f*
Soybeans, 794–95, 993
Space-filling models, 38*f*, 41*f*, 60*f*, 76*f*, 81*f*, 309*f*
Spacek, Sissy, 248
Spanish flu, 391*f*, 392
Spatial learning, **1124**–25
Spatial summation, **1056**–57*f*
Spawning, 999–1000
Speciation, **488**–506. *See also* Evolution
 allopatric, 493–95
 allopatric vs. sympatric, 493*f*, 497–98
 as conception bridge between microevolution and macroevolution, 488
 C. Darwin on, 457–60
 differential, and species selection, 530
 genetics of, 503–4
 geographic separation and, 493–98
 hybrid zones, reproductive isolation, and, 498–501
 macroevolution and, 504
 morphological, ecological, and phylogenetic species concepts and, 492
 orthologous genes and, 548, 549*f*
 reproductive isolation and biological species concept, 488–92
 review of, 505
 sympatric, 495–98
 time course of, 501–3
Species, **489**
 adaptive radiations of, and tree of life, 16–17 (*see also* Phylogenetic trees)
 biological concept of, 488–92
 classification of, 12–14, 453–54, 537–38 (*see also* Taxonomy)
 communities and, 4*f* (*see also* Communities; Community ecology)
 comparing developmental processes of, 445–47
 comparing genomes of, 442–45
 with complete genome sequences available, 426, 432
 cross-species gene expression and evolutionary ancestry of, 403
 C. Darwin's theory of origin of, 14–16, 457–60 (*see also* Evolution; Natural selection)
 determining number of genes in, 432, 433*t*
 distributions of (*see* Species distributions)
 diversity of (*see* Biodiversity; Species diversity)
 endemic, 466
 extinction of mollusc, 680–81*f*
 extinctions of (*see* Extinctions; Mass extinctions)
 fusion of, 500–501*f*
 geographic distribution of, 466
 homologous genes in, 548, 549*f*
 identifying, of whale meat, 539*f*–40
 loss of amphibian, 712
 loss of seed plant, 633–34
 metagenomics and genome sequencing of groups of, 428–29
 morphological, ecological, and phylogenetic concepts of, 492
 morphology and, 488
 origin of (*see* Speciation)
 vertebrate, 697